Handbook of
PHARMACEUTICAL ADDITIVES

Handbook of
PHARMACEUTICAL ADDITIVES

An International Guide to More Than 6000 Products by Trade Name, Chemical, Function, and Manufacturer

Compiled by

Michael and Irene Ash

Gower

Published by
Gower Publishing Limited
Gower House
Croft Road
Aldershot
Hampshire GU11 3HR
England

Gower
Old Post Road
Brookfield
Vermont 05036
U.S.A.

British Library Cataloguing in Publication Data
Handbook of Pharmaceutical Additives: International Guide to More Than 6000 Products by Trade Name, Chemical, Function, and Manufacturer,
    I. Ash, Michael   II. Ash, Irene
    615.19

ISBN 0-566-07596-2

Library of Congress Cataloging-in-Publication Data
Handbook of pharmaceutical additives : an international guide to more than 6000 products by trade name, chemical, function,
    and manufacturer / compiled by Michael and Irene Ash.
        p. cm
    Includes bibliographical references
    ISBN 0-566-07596-2 (cloth)
    1. Excipients—Handbooks, manuals, etc. 2. Excipients—Directories.   I. Ash, Michael. II. Ash, Irene.
    [DNLM: 1. Adjuvants, Pharmaceutic—handbooks. 2. Excipients—handbooks. QV 39 H236416 1995]
    RS201.E87H355 1995
    615´1—dc20
    DNLM/DLC
    for Library of Congress

95-37911
CIP

Typeset in Arial Narrow by Synapse Information Resources, Inc.

Printed and bound in Great Britain by
Hartnolls Limited, Bodmin, Cornwall

iv

Contents

Preface

The **Handbook of Pharmaceutical Additives** describes approximately 3600 trade name products and 2500 chemicals that function as pharmaceutical additives. Pharmaceutical additives are defined in this reference as the secondary ingredients that are present in both prescription and over-the-counter drug formulations and function to enable or enhance the delivery of the drug or medicine in a variety of dosage forms (i.e., oral—tablets, capsules, and liquid; topicals—dermal, ophthalmic, and otic; suppositories; injectables; inhalants; etc.). This definition of pharmaceutical additives encompasses excipients, inert or inactive ingredients as well as synergists or chemicals that substantively contribute to the medicinal effects of the active ingredient. Therefore the range of functionality of the products and chemicals contained in this reference include: improvement in flow characteristics, product uniformity, stability, taste, and appearance; ease of handling and administration of the dose, convenience of use, and control of bioavailability. Some of the products contained in this reference are categorized in one pharmaceutical product as inactive and used in another product as an active or synergistic component. Entries for both trade names and chemicals contain extensive information gathered from world-wide manufacturers, distributors, trade journals, government documents, and other references.

Pharmaceutical production, marketing, and consumption is a $200 billion a year world-wide industry. Additive ingredients are an essential part of that industry and information about these chemicals is critical to the formulator, quality controller, pharmacist, physician, and consumer. Increased concern about toxicity and allergic adverse reactions to these ingredients has resulted in both governmental legislation and voluntary labeling on drug products sold, with standards set by pharmacopoeias and pharmaceutical associations.

This reference functions as a single source for information on both the trade name products and the generic chemicals that are used as pharmaceutical additives. Information on ingredients that are approved by the FDA or recommended by USP/NF, BP, and Eur. Ph is included in the individual entries and summarized in the Appendices. The products described in this Handbook are cross-referenced by chemical composition, function, CAS, EINECS, and FEMA numbers.

The book is divided into four sections:

Part I—*Trade Name Reference* contains almost 3500 alphabetical entries of trade name pharmaceutical additive products. Each entry provides information on its manufacturer, chemical composition, CAS and EINECS identifying numbers, general properties, applications and functions, toxicology, compliance, and regulatory information as provided by the manufacturer and other sources.

Part II—*Chemical Dictionary/Cross-Reference* contains an alphabetical listing of pharmaceutical chemicals. Each pharmaceutical chemical entry includes, wherever possible, its synonyms, CAS number, EINECS number, FEMA number, UN number, molecular and empirical formulas, chemical properties, functions and applications, toxicology, precautions, usage levels, and regulatory information, as well as some of the manufacturers of the chemical. The trade name products from Part I that are equivalent to the chemical or contain that chemical compound as the product's major chemical constituent are cross-referenced. Synonyms for these chemical entries are comprehensively cross-referenced back to the primary entry.

Part III—*Functional Cross-Reference* contains an alphabetical listing of major pharmaceutical additive functional categories. Over 75 categories are included, e.g., anticaking agents/glidants, base (ointment and suppository), colorants, denaturants, emulsifiers, encapsulants, fillers, flavors, protective agents, sweeteners, thickeners, etc. Each functional category entry is followed by an alphabetical listing of the trade name products and pharmaceutical chemicals that have that functional attribute.

Part IV—*Manufacturers Directory* contains detailed contact information on approximately 1500 manufacturers of the trade name products and chemicals referenced in this handbook. Wherever possible, telephone, telefax, and telex numbers, toll-free 800 numbers, and complete mailing addresses are included for each manufacturer.

The **Appendices** contain the following cross-references:

CAS Number-to-Trade Name Cross-Reference orders many trade names found in Part I by identifying CAS numbers; it should be noted that trade names contain more than one chemical component and the associated CAS numbers in this section refer to each trade name product's primary chemical component.

CAS Number-to-Chemical Cross-Reference orders chemicals found in Part II by CAS numbers.

EINECS Number-to-Trade Name Cross-Reference orders many trade names found in Part I by identifying EINECS numbers that refer to each trade name product's primary chemical component as well.

EINECS Number-to-Chemical Cross-Reference orders chemicals found in Part II by EINECS numbers.

FEMA Number-to-Chemical Cross-Reference orders chemicals that are found in Part II by the identifying numbers assigned to them by the Flavor and Extract Manufacturers Association.

Chemicals in Compliance with Pharmaceutical Standards are derived from the Inactive Ingredient Guide, the United States Pharmacopeia/National Formulary, British Pharmacopoeia, and European Pharmacopoeia. This section is meant to be used as a general guide. Local legislation should always be consulted regarding all pharmaceutical additive products as they vary from country to country.

This book is the culmination of many months of research, investigation of product sources, and sorting through a variety of technical data sheets and brochures acquired through personal contacts and correspondences with major chemical manufacturers world-wide as well as trade journals. We are especially grateful to Roberta Dakan for her skills in chemical information database management. Her tireless efforts have been instrumental in the production of this reference.

M. & I. Ash

NOTE:

The information contained in this reference is accurate to the best of our knowledge; however, no liability will be assumed by the publisher or the authors for the correctness or comprehensiveness of such information. The determination of the suitability of these products for prospective use is the responsibility of the user. It is herewith recommended that those who plan to use any of the products referenced seek the manufacturers instructions for the handling of that chemical.

Regulations and standards are complicated and are dependent on both the chemistry and the application involved. Variation in laws and standards exist from country to country. The ultimate decision on compliance must be made by the user with full understanding of the application as well as working with the producer or distributor of the ingredients used in the formulation.

Abbreviations

abs.	absolute
absorp.	absorption
ACGIH	American Conference of Governmental Industrial Hygienists
act.	active
ADI	acceptable daily intake (FAO/WHO)
ADR	adverse drug reactions
adsorp.	adsorption
alc.	alcohol
Am., Amer.	American
amts.	amounts
anhyd.	anhydrous
ANSI	American National Standards Institute
APHA	American Public Health Association
applic(s).	application(s)
aq.	aqueous
ASTM	American Society for Testing and Materials
at.wt.	atomic weight
autoignit.	autoignition
aux.	auxiliary
avail.	available
avg.	average
a.w.	atomic weight
b.p.	boiling point
BATF	U.S. Bureau of Alcohol, Tobacco, and Firearms
BGA	Federal Republic of Germany Health Dept. certification
BHA	butylated hydroxyanisole
BHT	butylated hydroxytoluene
biochem.	biochemical
biodeg.	biodegradable
blk.	black
BOD	biological oxygen demand
BP	British Pharmacopeia
br., brn.	brown
brnsh.	brownish
Btu	British thermal unit
byprod.	byproduct(s)
C	degrees Centigrade
CAS	Chemical Abstracts Service
CC	closed cup
cc	cubic centimeter(s)
CCl_4	carbon tetrachloride
CFR	Code of Federal Regulations (U.S.)
char.	characteristic
chel.	chelation
chem.	chemical
CI	Color Index
CIR	Cosmetic Ingredient Review
cks	centistoke(s)
CL	ceiling concentration
cm	centimeter(s)
cm^3	cubic centimeter(s)
CMC	carboxymethylcellulose
CNS	central nervous system
CO	carbon monoxide
COC	Cleveland Open Cup
coeff.	coefficient
compat.	compatible
compd(s).	compound(s)
compr.	compression
conc(s).	concentrated, concentration
contg.	containing

cosolv.	cosolvent
CP	Canadian Pharmacopeia
cp	centipoise(s)
cps	centipoise(s)
cryst.	crystalline, crystallization
cs or cSt	centistoke(s)
CTFA	Cosmetic, Toiletry and Fragrance Association
ctks	centistoke(s)
DAB	Deutsches Arzneibuch (German Pharmacopoeia)
DAC	Deutscher Arzneimittel Codex (German Pharmacopoeia Codex)
DAP	diallyl phthalate
DAP	diammonium phosphate
D&C	Drugs & Cosmetics
DE	dextrose equivalent
DEA	diethanolamide, diethanolamine
dec.	decomposes
decomp.	decomposition
deliq.	deliquescent
dens.	density
deriv.	derivative(s)
descrip.	description
diam.	diameter
dil.	dilute
disp.	dispersible, dispersion
dist.	distilled
distrib.	distributor
dk.	dark
DMF	Drug Master Files
DMSO	dimethyl sulfoxide
DOT	U.S. Department of Transportation
DTPA	diethylene triamine pentaacetic acid
DW	distilled water, deionized water
EC	European Community
EDTA	ethylenediamine tetraacetic acid
EEC	European Economic Community
e.g.	for example
EINECS	European Inventory of Existing Commercial Chemical Substances
elec.	electrical
EMA, E/MA	ethylene-methyl acrylate
EO	ethylene oxide
EP	European Pharmacopoeia
EPA	U.S. Environmental Protection Agency
EPDM	ethylene-propylene-diene rubber, ethylene-propylene terpolymer
equip.	equipment
esp.	especially
EU	European Union
Eur.Ph.	European Pharmacopoeia
EVA	ethylene vinyl acetate
exc.	excellent
F	degrees Fahrenheit
FCC	Food Chemicals Codex
FD&C	Foods, Drugs, and Cosmetics
FDA	Food and Drug Administration (U.S.)
FEMA	Flavor and Extract Manufacturers' Association (U.S.)
flamm.	flammable, flammability
f.p.	freezing point
ft	foot, feet
G	giga
g	gram(s)
G-H	Gardner-Holdt
gal	gallon(s)
GI	gastro-intestinal

glac.	glacial
GLY	glycine
GMP	good manufacturing practice
gr.	gravity
gran.	granules, granular
GRAS	generally regarded as safe
grn.	green
h	hour(s)
HC	hydrocarbon
HCl	hydrochloride, hydrochloric acid
HDPE	high-density polyethylene
HEDTA	hydroxyethylenediamine triacetic acid
Hg	mercury
HLB	hydrophilic lipophilic balance
hyd.	hydroxyl
hydrog.	hydrogenated
i.b.p.	initial boiling point
immisc.	immiscible
IM	intramuscular
in.	inch(es)
INCI	International Nomenclature Cosmetic Ingredient
incl.	including
incompat.	incompatible
ing.	ingestion
ingred(s).	ingredient(s)
inh.	inhalation
inj.	injection
inorg.	inorganic
insol.	insoluble
Int'l.	International
IP	intraperitoneal
IPA	isopropyl alcohol
IPM	isopropyl myristate
IPP	isopropyl palmitate
IU	International Unit
IV	intravenous
i.v.	iodine value
JCID	Japanese Cosmetic Ingredients Dictionary
JP	Japanese Pharmacopoeia
JSCI	Japanese Standard of Cosmetic Ingredients
k	kilo
kg	kilogram(s)
l	liter(s)
lb	pound(s)
LC50	lethal concentration 50%
LD0	lethal dose 0%
LD50	lethal dose 50%
lg.	large
liq.	liquid
lt.	light
Ltd.	Limited
M	mega
M	mole
m	milli or meter(s)
m-	meta
MA	maleic anhydride (INCI), methacrylic acid
manuf.	manufacturer
max.	maximum
mbar	millibar
MCT	medium chain triglycerides
MEA	monoethanolamine, monoethanolamide
mech.	mechanial
med.	medium

MEK	methyl ethyl ketone
mfg.	manufacture
mg	milligram(s)
MIBK	methyl isobutyl ketone
microcryst.	microcrystalline
microgran.	microgranules, microgranular
MID	Meat Inspection Division (USDA)
mil	1/1000th inch
min	minute(s)
min.	mineral, minimum
misc.	miscible, miscellaneous
mixt(s).	mixture(s)
ml	milliliter(s)
MLD	minimum lethal dose
mm	millimeter(s)
mN	millinewton(s)
mo, mos	month(s)
mod.	moderately
monocl.	monoclinic
m.p.	melting point
mPa•s	millipascal-second(s)
mus	mouse
m.w.	molecular weight
N	normal
n(20/D)	index of refraction for the sodium D line @ 20 C
nat.	natural
need.	needles
NF	National Formulary
nm	nanometer
no.	number
nonaq.	nonaqueous
nonbiodeg.	nonbiodegradable
nonflamm.	nonflammable
NSF	National Sanitation Foundation
NV	nonvolatiles
o-	ortho
OC	open cup
org.	organic
OSHA	Occupational Safety and Health Administration
OTC	over-the-counter
o/w	oil-in-water
oz	ounce
p-	para
Pa	Pascal
PA	polyamide
PABA	p-aminobenzoic acid
PCA	2-pyrrolidone-5-carboxylic acid
PE	polyethylene
PEG	polyethylene glycol
PEL	permissible exposure level
PET	polyethylene terephthalate
petrol.	petroleum
PG	propylene glycol
pH	hydrogen-ion concentration
Ph.	Pharmacopoeia
pharm.	pharmaceutical
Ph.Eur.	European Pharmacopoeia
pkg.	packaging
PM, P-M	Pensky-Martens
PMCC	Pensky-Martens closed cup
PMMA	polymethyl methacrylate
PMOC	Pensky-Martens open cup

PO	propylene oxide
POE	polyoxyethylene, polyoxyethylated
polyunsat.	polyunsaturated
powd.	powder
PP	polypropylene
ppb	parts per billion
PPG	polypropylene glycol
pph	parts per hundred (percent)
ppm	parts per million
pract.	practically
prep(s).	preparation(s)
prod.	product(s), production
props.	properties
ps	poise
pt.	point
Pt-Co	platinum-cobalt
PU	polyurethane
PVC	polyvinyl chloride
PVM	polyvinyl methyl ether
PVM/MA	polyvinyl methyl ether/maleic anhydride
PVP	polyvinylpyrrolidone
quat.	quaternary
RDA	recommended daily allowances
rdsh.	reddish
ref.	refractive
regs.	regulations
rep.	represents
resist.	resistance, resistant, resistivity
resp.	respectively
r.h.	relative humidity
R.T.	room temperature
s	second(s)
sapon.	saponification
sat.	saturated
S/B	styrene/butadiene
SC	subcutaneous
SD	specially denatured
SDA	specially denatured alcohol
SE	self-emulsifying
sec.	secondary
semicryst.	semicrystalline
semiliq.	semiliquid
semisyn.	semisynthetic
sl.	slight, slightly
sm.	small
soften.	softening
sol.	soluble, solubility
sol'n.	solution
solid.	solidification
solv(s).	solvent(s)
sp.	specific
spec.	specification, specialty
SPF	sun protection factor
spp.	non-specified species
SQ	subcutaneous
std.	standard
STEL	short term exposure limit
Stod.	Stoddard solvent
str.	strength
subcut.	subcutaneous
subl.	sublimes
surf.	surface

SUS	Saybolt Universal Seconds
susp.	suspension
syn.	synthetic
t-	tertiary
TAPPI	Technical Association of the Pulp & Paper Industry
TBHQ	tert-butyl hydroquinone
TCC	Tag closed cup
TDI	toluene diisocyanate
TEA	triethanolamine, triethanolamide
tech.	technical
temp.	temperature
tert	tertiary
THF	tetrahydrofuran
thru	through
TLV	Threshold Limit Value
TOC	Tag open cup
TSCA	Toxic Substances Control Act
TWA	time weighted average
typ.	typical
UN No.	United Nations Substance Identification Number (for transport purposes)
unsat.	unsaturated
USDA	U.S. Department of Agriculture
USP	Unites States Pharmacopeia
uv, UV	ultraviolet
V	volt
v/v	volume by volume
VA	vinyl acetate
veg.	vegetable
visc.	viscous, viscosity
VM&P	Varnish Makers and Painters
vol.	volume
wh.	white
WHO	World Health Organization (United Nations)
wks.	weeks
w/o	water-in-oil
wt.	weight
yel.	yellow
ylsh.	yellowish
yr	year
#	number
%	percent
<	less than
>	greater than
≤	less than or equal to
+	greater than or equal to
@	at
α	alpha
β	beta
δ, Δ	delta
ε	epsilon
γ	gamma
ω	omega
μ	micron, micrometer
μg	microgram
μm	micrometer
≈	approximately equal to

Part I
Trade Name Reference

A

A-641. [ICI Am.]
Chem. Descrip.: Sorbitol
CAS 50-70-4; EINECS 200-061-5
Uses: Humectant, nutritive sweetener, oleaginous vehicle, tablet diluent.

AA USP. [CasChem]
Chem. Descrip.: Castor oil
CAS 8001-79-4; EINECS 232-293-8
Uses: Emollient for pharmaceuticals; lubricant for protective coatings for vitamins, tableting
Regulatory: FDA approval
Properties: Sol. in alcohols, esters, ethers, ketone, and aromatic solvs.

AB®. [ANGUS]
Chem. Descrip.: 2-Amino-1-butanol
CAS 96-20-8; EINECS 202-488-2
Uses: Pharmaceutical intermediate for synthesis of ethambutol, an anti-tuberculosis drug
Properties: APHA 100 color; water-misc.; m.w. 89.1; dens. 7.86 lb/gal; m.p. -2 C; b.p. 178 C; flash pt. 193 F (TCC); pH 11.1 (0.1M aq.); 99% conc.
Toxicology: LD50 (oral, mus) 2.5 g/kg, (IP, mus) 0.48 g/kg; severe eye irritant; causes eye burns and skin irritation
Precaution: Combustible; keep away from heat and flame; corrosive to copper, brass, and aluminum.

Abil® EM-90. [Goldschmidt; Goldschmidt AG]
Chem. Descrip.: Cetyl dimethicone copolyol
Uses: Surfactant, emollient, conditioner, emulsifier for w/o type creams and lotions, skin protective treatments, suncare prods.
Properties: Liq.; HLB 4-6; 100% conc.; nonionic.

Abil® WE 09. [Goldschmidt AG]
Chem. Descrip.: Polyglyceryl-4 isostearate, cetyl dimethicone copolyol, hexyl laurate
Uses: Emulsifier for highly stable w/o creams and lotions; improves uv protection in sunscreens; for skin care treatment emulsions
Properties: Pale yel. liq.; sol. in veg. and min. oils; insol. in water; sp.gr. 0.89-0.93; HLB 5.0; 100% conc.; nonionic.

Abil®-Wax 2434. [Goldschmidt; Goldschmidt AG]
Chem. Descrip.: Stearoxy dimethicone
CAS 68554-53-0
Uses: Spreading agent, emollient for antiperspirants, sunscreens
Properties: Pale yel. liq. > 40 C, waxy < 10 C; sol. in cyclomethicone, min. oil, IPM, sunflower seed oil; sp.gr. 0.88 (35 C); m.p. 25 C; pour pt. 20-30 C; flash pt. > 100 C; 100% act.; nonionic.

Abil®-Wax 9801. [Goldschmidt; Goldschmidt AG]
Chem. Descrip.: Cetyl dimethicone
Uses: Wax providing emolliency and applic. benefits for antiperspirants; pigment solubilizer; spreading agent; esp. useful for sunscreen actives
Use level: 1-5%
Properties: Pale yel. liq. wax; sol. in cyclomethicone, min. oil, IPM, sunflower seed oil; sp.gr. 0.86; pour pt. 10 C; flash pt. 40 C; 100% act.; nonionic.

Abil®-Wax 9814. [Goldschmidt]
Chem. Descrip.: Cetyl dimethicone
Uses: Emollient, spreading agent, pigment grinding aid, dispersant used in sunscreens.

Ablunol S-20. [Taiwan Surf.]
Chem. Descrip.: Sorbitan laurate
CAS 1338-39-2
Uses: Emulsifier, emulsion stabilizer, thickener for pharmaceuticals
Properties: Oily liq.; oil-sol.; water-disp.; HLB 8.6; 100% act.; nonionic.

Ablunol S-40. [Taiwan Surf.]
Chem. Descrip.: Sorbitan palmitate
CAS 26266-57-9; EINECS 247-568-8
Uses: Emulsifier, emulsion stabilizer, thickener for pharmaceuticals
Properties: Waxy solid; oil-sol.; HLB 6.7; nonionic.

Ablunol S-60. [Taiwan Surf.]
Chem. Descrip.: Sorbitan stearate
CAS 1338-41-6; EINECS 215-664-9
Uses: Emulsifier, emulsion stabilizer, thickener for pharmaceuticals
Properties: Waxy flake; HLB 4.7; 100% act.; nonionic.

Ablunol S-80. [Taiwan Surf.]
Chem. Descrip.: Sorbitan oleate
CAS 1338-43-8; EINECS 215-665-4
Uses: Emulsifier, emulsion stabilizer, thickener for pharmaceuticals
Properties: Oily liq.; HLB 4.3; 100% act.; nonionic.

Ablunol S-85. [Taiwan Surf.]
Chem. Descrip.: Sorbitan trioleate
CAS 26266-58-0; EINECS 247-569-3
Uses: Emulsifier, emulsion stabilizer, thickener for pharmaceuticals

Properties: Oily liq.; HLB 1.8; 100% act.; nonionic.

Ablunol T-20. [Taiwan Surf.]
Chem. Descrip.: POE sorbitan laurate
Uses: O/w emulsifier for pharmaceuticals
Properties: Oily liq.; water-sol.; HLB 16.7; 100% solids; nonionic.

Ablunol T-40. [Taiwan Surf.]
Chem. Descrip.: POE sorbitan laurate
Uses: O/w emulsifier for pharmaceuticals
Properties: Oily liq.; water-sol.; HLB 15.6; 100% conc.; nonionic.

Ablunol T-60. [Taiwan Surf.]
Chem. Descrip.: POE sorbitan stearate
Uses: O/w emulsifier for pharmaceuticals
Properties: Oily liq.; water-sol.; HLB 14.9; 100% conc.; nonionic.

Ablunol T-80. [Taiwan Surf.]
Chem. Descrip.: POE sorbitan oleate
Uses: O/w emulsifier for pharmaceuticals
Properties: Oily liq.; water-sol.; HLB 15.0; 100% conc.; nonionic.

Abscents® Deodorizing Powd. [UOP]
Chem. Descrip.: Organophilic molecular sieve (sodium potassium aluminosilicate)
CAS 1318-02-1
Uses: Hypo-allergenic deodorizing powd. for odor control in unscented personal care prods. (feminine protection, diapers, deodorants, ostomy prods.); attracts odors and traps them tightly within its porous structure
Regulatory: Meets Codex requirements
Properties: Wh. free-flowing dry powd., odorless; 3-5 μ particle size; insol. in water or org. solvs.; sp.gr. 2.0; bulk dens. 33 lb/ft^3 (tapped); surf. area > 400 m^2/g; oil adsorp. 60 g/100 g; pH 5.0-6.5 (10% slurry); ref. index. 1.45-1.47
Toxicology: Low acute toxicity by ingestion, skin penetration, dust inhalation; sl. eye irritant; mild vaginal irritant; prolonged inh. may cause lung damage; avoid breathing dust
Precaution: Avoid sudden contact with high concs. of chems. having high heats of adsorption or reaction, e.g., olefins, HCl.

A-C® 7, 7A. [AlliedSignal/Perf. Addit.]
Chem. Descrip.: Polyethylene homopolymer wax
CAS 9002-88-4; EINECS 200-815-3
Uses: Thickener for pharmaceutical gels
Properties: Prills, powd.; sol. in hot min. oil and fatty esters; dens. 0.92 g/cc; visc. 450 cps (140 C); drop pt. 109 C; acid no. nil; hardness 2.5 dmm.

A-C® 617, 617A. [AlliedSignal/Perf. Addit.]
Chem. Descrip.: Polyethylene homopolymer
CAS 9002-88-4; EINECS 200-815-3
Uses: Thickener for pharmaceutical gels; increases permanency, emolliency, moisture retention, water resist., and thermal stability; film-former, oil or fragrance encapsulator, nonirritating abrasive
Properties: Wh. waxy prills, powd., char. waxy odor; sol. in hot min. oil and fatty esters; negligible sol. in water; dens. 0.91 g/cc; visc. 200 cps (140 C); drop pt. 101 C; acid no. nil; flash pt. > 231 C;

hardness 7.0 dmm
Toxicology: LD50 (oral, rat) > 2000 mg/kg; mild skin irritant; dust may cause mech. eye and respiratory tract irritation; OSHA TWA 5 mg/m^3 (respirable dust), 15 mg/m^3 (total dust) recommended
Precaution: Incompat. with strong oxidizing agents; hazardous decomp. prods.: oxides of carbon, various oxidized and nonoxidized hydrocarbons.

Accomid PK. [ABITEC]
Chem. Descrip.: Palm kernelamide DEA (1:1)
CAS 68155-12-2
Uses: Emulsifier, solubilizer, visc. builder, wetting agent for pharmaceutical dermatologicals, germicidal liq. soaps
Properties: Gardner 5 liq.; pH 9-11 (10% aq.); nonionic.

Acconon 200-MS. [ABITEC]
Chem. Descrip.: PEG-4 stearate
CAS 9004-99-3; EINECS 203-358-8
Uses: Surfactant used as emulsifier, dispersant, solubilizer, visc. control agent for pharmaceuticals
Properties: Gardner 4 max. solid; HLB 8; pH 5.5-6.5; nonionic
Custom product

Acconon 400-ML. [ABITEC]
Chem. Descrip.: PEG-8 laurate
CAS 9004-81-3; EINECS 253-458-0
Uses: Surfactant used as emulsifier, dispersant, solubilizer, visc. control agent for pharmaceuticals; nonionic.

Acconon 400-MO. [ABITEC]
Chem. Descrip.: PEG-8 oleate
CAS 9004-96-0
Uses: Emulsifier, dispersant, lubricant, chem. intermediate, solubilizer, visc. control agent for pharmaceuticals
Properties: Gardner 4 max. liq.; sol. in org. solv.; water-disp.; sp.gr. 1.01; dens. 8.4 lb/gal; m.p. < 10 C; HLB 12; pH 5.5-6.5; 99% act.; nonionic.

Acconon 400-MS. [ABITEC]
Chem. Descrip.: PEG-8 stearate
CAS 9004-99-3
Uses: Surfactant used as emulsifier, dispersant, solubilizer, visc. control agent for pharmaceuticals
Properties: Gardner 4 max. solid; HLB 12; pH 5.5-6.5; nonionic
Custom product

Acconon 1300 MS. [ABITEC]
Chem. Descrip.: PPG-3-laureth-9
CAS 9004-94-3
Uses: Surfactant used as emulsifier, visc. control agent for pharmaceutical dermatologicals
Properties: Gardner 3 max. liq.; sp.gr. 1.016-1.019; dens. 8.35-8.45 lb/gal; HLB 11; acid no. 1 max.; cloud pt. 135-145 F; pH 6.0-7.0 (5% aq.); 98.5% min. solids; nonionic.

Acconon CA-5. [ABITEC]
Chem. Descrip.: PEG-5 castor oil
CAS 61791-12-6

4

Uses: Surfactant used as emulsifier, dispersant, solubilizer, visc. control agent for pharmaceutical dermatologicals
Properties: Gardner 3 max. liq.; HLB 8.0; acid no. 2 max.; pH 6-7 (5% aq.); 98.5% min.solids; nonionic.

Acconon CA-8. [ABITEC]
Chem. Descrip.: PEG-8 castor oil
CAS 61791-12-6
Uses: Surfactant used as emulsifier, dispersant, solubilizer, visc. control agent for pharmaceuticals
Properties: Gardner 3 max. liq.; HLB 8; pH 6.0-7.0; nonionic
Unverified

Acconon CA-9. [ABITEC]
Chem. Descrip.: PEG-9 castor oil
CAS 61791-12-6
Uses: Surfactant used as emulsifier, dispersant, wetting agent for pharmaceutical dermatologicals
Properties: Gardner 3 max. liq.; water-disp.; HLB 12.0; acid no. 2 max.; pH 6-7 (5% aq.); 98.5% min. solids; nonionic.

Acconon CA-15. [ABITEC]
Chem. Descrip.: PEG-15 castor oil
CAS 61791-12-6
Uses: Surfactant used as emulsifier, dispersant, solubilizer, wetting agent for pharmaceutical dermatologicals
Properties: Gardner 3 max. liq.; water-disp.; HLB 16; acid no. 2 max.; pH 6.0-7.0 (5% aq.); nonionic.

Acconon CON. [ABITEC]
Chem. Descrip.: PEG-10 propylene glycol glyceryl laurate
Uses: Surfactant used as emulsifier, dispersant, solubilizer, visc. control agent for pharmaceuticals
Properties: Gardner 2 max. liq.; HLB 10; pH 6.0-7.0; nonionic
Custom product

Acconon E. [ABITEC]
Chem. Descrip.: PPG-15 stearyl ether
CAS 25231-21-4
Uses: Surfactant used as emulsifier, dispersant, solubilizer for pharmaceutical dermatologicals
Properties: Gardner 3 max. liq.; HLB 16; acid no. 1.5 max.; pH 4-6 (5% aq.); 98.55 min. solids; nonionic.

Acconon SA-2. [ABITEC]
Chem. Descrip.: Steareth-2
CAS 9005-00-9
Uses: Surfactant, emulsifier used for dermatologicals, lotions
Properties: Gardner 3 max. solid, low odor; HLB 5; acid no. 1 max.; pH 4-6 (5% aq.); 98.5% min. solids; nonionic.

Acconon TGH. [ABITEC]
Chem. Descrip.: PEG-10-PPG-10 glyceryl stearate
CAS 68783-63-1
Uses: Surfactant used as emulsifier, dispersant,

solubilizer, visc. control agent, wetting agent for pharmaceutical dermatologicals
Properties: Gardner 3 max. liq., mild odor; HLB 16; acid no. 2 max.; pH 6.0-7.0 (5% aq.); 98.5% min. solids; nonionic; biodeg.

Acconon W230. [ABITEC]
Chem. Descrip.: Ceteareth-20
CAS 68439-49-6
Uses: Surfactant used as emulsifier, dispersant, solubilizer, vehicle/carrier, wetting agent for pharmaceutical dermatologicals, medicated cleansing prods.
Properties: Gardner 3 max. solid, low odor; HLB 15; acid no. 1 max.; pH 5.5-7.0 (5% aq.); 98.5% min. solids; nonionic.

Ac-Di-Sol®. [FMC]
Chem. Descrip.: Crosslinked CMC
Uses: Tablet disintegrant
Properties: Bulk dens. 0.337 g/cc.

Acid Proof Caramel Powd. [MLG Enterprises Ltd.]
Chem. Descrip.: Double strength acid proof-type caramel
CAS 8028-89-5; EINECS 232-435-9
Uses: High intensity natural colorant for darkening pharmaceutical formulations
Properties: Free-flowing powd.; 100% min. thru 40 mesh, 90% min. thru 100 mesh; pH 3.0-4.0 (1%); 4% max. moisture
Storage: Unlimited shelf life under normal storage conditions.

Acritamer® 934. [R.I.T.A.]
Chem. Descrip.: Carbomer 934
Uses: Emulsifier, dispersing, suspending and visc. agent, gellant for use in systems where sparkling clarity is not essential; stabilizer for w/o and o/w emulsions; suitable for topical pharmaceuticals
Properties: Wh. fluffy hygroscopic powd.; water-disp.; m.w. 3,000,000; bulk dens. 15 lb/ft³; visc. 2000-5450 cps (0.2%), 26,000-39,500 cps (0.5%); pH 2.7-3.3 (0.5%)
Toxicology: Mildly irritating to eyes; nonirritating to skin, nonsensitizing.

Acritamer® 934P. [R.I.T.A.]
Chem. Descrip.: Carbomer 934 NF
Uses: Pharmaceutical grade emulsifier, dispersing, suspending and visc. agent and gellant for use in systems where sparkling clarity is not essential; stabilizer for w/o and o/w emulsions; for topicals and orals
Properties: Wh. fluffy hygroscopic powd.; bulk dens. 15 lb/ft³; visc. 2000-5450 cps (0.2%), 26,000-39,500 cps (0.5%); pH 2.7-3.3 (0.5%)
Toxicology: Mildly irritating to eyes; nonirritating to skin, nonsensitizing.

Acritamer® 940. [R.I.T.A.]
Chem. Descrip.: Carbomer 940
Uses: Emulsifier, dispersing, suspending and visc. agent, gellant for use in systems where sparkling clarity or a sharp visc. response is required; stabilizer for w/o and o/w emulsions; suitable for topical pharmaceuticals
Properties: Wh. fluffy hygroscopic powd.; m.w.

4,000,000; bulk dens. 15 lb/ft³; visc. 15,000-30,000 cps (0.2%), 45,000-70,000 cps (0.5%); pH 2.7-3.3 (0.5%)

Toxicology: Mildly irritating to eyes; nonirritating to skin, nonsensitizing.

Acritamer® 941. [R.I.T.A.]
Chem. Descrip.: Carbomer 941
Uses: Emulsifier, dispersing, suspending and visc. agent, gellant for use in systems where ionic strength interferes with proper gellation; stabilizer for w/o and o/w emulsions; suitable for topical pharmaceuticals
Properties: Wh. fluffy hygroscopic powd.; m.w. 1,250,000; bulk dens. 15 lb/ft³; visc. 2500-6400 cps (0.2%), 5400-11,400 cps (0.5%); pH 2.7-3.3 (0.5%)
Toxicology: Mildly irritating to eyes; nonirritating to skin, nonsensitizing.

Act II 500 USP. [Luzenac Am.]
Chem. Descrip.: Talc USP/FCC
CAS 14807-96-6; EINECS 238-877-9
Uses: Ultrafine high purity talc featuring softness, brightness; wh. extender and antitackifying agent; esp. for aerosol applics.
Regulatory: USP, CTFA, and FCC compliance
Properties: Powd.; 99.9% thru 400 mesh; median diam. 3.5 μ; tapped dens. 36 lb/ft³; pH 9 (10% slurry).

Activera™ 1-1FA (Filtered) [Active Organics]
Chem. Descrip.: Aloe vera gel
Uses: Pharmaceutical ingred. where consistent quality and color stability are important
Properties: Colorless cloudy liq.

Activera™ 1-200 A. [Active Organics]
Chem. Descrip.: Aloe vera gel
Uses: Used in pharmaceutical mfg.
Properties: Eggshell-wh. free-flowing powd.

Activera™ 104. [Active Organics]
Chem. Descrip.: Aloe vera gel
Uses: Pharmaceutical ingred. where clarity, color stability, purity, and batch-to-batch consistency are important
Properties: Colorless clear liq.

Acylan. [Croda Inc.; Croda Chem. Ltd.]
Chem. Descrip.: Acetylated lanolin
CAS 61788-48-5; EINECS 262-979-2
Uses: Lipid emollient for pharmaceutical prods.; forms water-repellent films
Properties: Gardner 11 soft solid; bland odor; sol. in min. oil and soft waxy hydrophobic films; m.p. 32-39 C; acid no. 2.0 max.; iodine no. 30 max.; sapon. no. 100-125; hyd. no. 12 max.; 100% act.

Adeka Propylene Glycol (P) [Asahi Denka Kogyo]
Chem. Descrip.: Propylene glycol
CAS 57-55-6; EINECS 200-338-0
Uses: Pharmaceutical grade solv., humectant, preservative, plasticizer
Properties: APHA > 10 color; sp.gr. 1.037-1.039.

Adinol CT95. [Croda Chem. Ltd.]
Chem. Descrip.: Sodium methyl cocoyl taurate
CAS 61791-42-2
Uses: Wetting, foaming, and dispersing agent for oral and topical pharmaceuticals; useful in germicidal scrubs; stable in presence of acid, alkali, and metal ions such as strontium
Use level: 0.5-10%
Properties: Wh. powd.; 95% min. conc.; anionic.

Admex® 760. [Hüls Am.]
Chem. Descrip.: Ultra high m.w. polymeric adipate polyester
Uses: High m.w. plasticizer with max. resist. to extraction, migration, and volatility; nonmigratory for skin patch drug delivery
Properties: Lt. colored clear bright fluid to visc. liq., mild ester odor; m.w. 13,500; sp.gr. 1.130; visc. 79,250 cps; pour pt. 35 F; acid no. 3; hyd. no. 2; flash pt. 575 F; ref. index 1.470.

Adol® 61 NF. [Procter & Gamble]
Chem. Descrip.: Stearyl alcohol
CAS 112-92-5; EINECS 204-017-6
Uses: Emollient, pharmaceutical raw material.

Adol® 90 NF. [Procter & Gamble]
Chem. Descrip.: Oleyl alcohol
CAS 143-28-2; EINECS 205-597-3
Uses: Pharmaceutical grade emollient imparting smoothness, freshness, and suppleness to the skin; used in lotions, creams; coupling agent; lubricant for aerosols; emulsion stabilizer
Properties: Lt. clear liq., low odor; sol. in ethanol, IPA, benzene, ethyl ether, acetone, turpentine, VM&P naphtha, kerosene, lt. min. oil; m.w. 268; sp.gr. 0.840; b.p. 282-349 C (760 mm, 90%); acid no. 0.5; iodine no. 90; sapon. no. 1.5; hyd. no. 210; cloud pt. 6 C; 100% conc.; nonionic.

AEPD®. [ANGUS]
Chem. Descrip.: 2-Amino-2-ethyl-1,3-propanediol
CAS 115-70-8; EINECS 204-101-2
Uses: Pharmaceutical intermediate
Properties: M.w. 119.2; water-sol.; m.p. 37.5 C; b.p. 152 C; flash pt. > 200 F (TCC); pH 10.8 (0.1M aq. sol'n.); 100% conc.; nonionic.

Aerosil® 200. [Degussa; Degussa AG]
Chem. Descrip.: Fumed silica USP/NF
CAS 112945-52-5; EINECS 231-545-4
Uses: Provides thickening and exc. storage stability to pharmaceutical creams, lotions, emulsions; free-flow and bulking agent for powds.; inert carrier for actives improving tableting chars., decreasing disintegration time, reducing coating time of pills
Regulatory: FDA 21CFR §133.146(b), 160.105(a) (d), 172.230(a), 172.480, 173.340(a), 175, 176, 177, 573.940; ≤ 3% for cosmetics, internal pharmaceuticals
Properties: Wh. fluffy powd.; 12 nm avg. particle size; sp.gr. 2.2; dens. ≈ 120 g/l (densed); surf. area 200 ± 25 m²/g; pH 3.6-4.3 (4% aq. susp.); > 99.8% assay
Toxicology: TLV 10 mg/m³ total dust; LD50 > 20,000 mg/kg; may cause eye, skin, or respiratory tract irritation on overexposure
Precaution: Incompat. with strong bases and hydrofluoric acid.

Aerosil® 300. [Degussa; Degussa AG]

Chem. Descrip.: Fumed silica
CAS 112945-52-5; EINECS 231-545-4
Uses: Processing aid, disintegrant, compatibilizer, visc. modifier, stabilizer for tablets, gelatin capsules, powds., toothpastes, ointments
Regulatory: FDA approved (≤ 3% for cosmetics)
Properties: Wh. fluffy powd.; 7 nm avg. particle size; sp.gr. 2.2; dens. ≈ 120 g/l (densed); surf. area 300 ± 30 m^2/g; pH 3.6-4.3 (4% aq. susp.); > 99.8% assay
Toxicology: TLV 10 mg/m^3 total dust; LD50 > 20,000 mg/kg; may cause eye, skin, or respiratory tract irritation on overexposure
Precaution: Incompat. with strong bases and hydrofluoric acid.

Aerosil® 380. [Degussa; Degussa AG]
Chem. Descrip.: Fumed silica
CAS 112945-52-5; EINECS 231-545-4
Uses: Processing aid, filler, disintegrant, compatibilizer, visc. modifier, stabilizer for tablets, gelatin capsules, powds., toothpastes, ointments
Regulatory: FDA 21CFR §133.146(b), 160.105(a)(d), 172.230(a), 172.480, 173.340(a), 175, 176, 177, 573.940
Properties: Wh. fluffy powd.; 7 nm avg. particle size; sp.gr. 2.2; dens. ≈ 120 g/l (densed); surf. area 380 ± 30 m^2/g; pH 3.6-4.3 (4% aq. susp.); > 99.8% assay
Toxicology: TLV 10 mg/m^3 total dust; LD50 > 20,000 mg/kg; may cause eye, skin, or respiratory tract irritation on overexposure
Precaution: Incompat. with strong bases and hydrofluoric acid.

Aerosil® COK 84. [Degussa]
Chem. Descrip.: Fumed silica and highly dispersed aluminum oxide (5:1)
Uses: Thickener for aq. systems; processing aid, disintegrant, compatibilizer, visc. modifier, stabilizer for tablets, gelatin capsules, powds., toothpastes, ointments
Properties: Wh. fluffy powd.; sp.gr. 2.2; dens. ≈ 50 g/l; surf. area 170 ± 30 m^2/g; pH 3.6-4.3 (4% aq. susp.); 82-86% SiO$_2$, 14-18% Al$_2$O$_3$.

Aerosil® R812. [Degussa]
Chem. Descrip.: Syn. amorphous fumed silica
CAS 68909-20-6; EINECS 231-545-4
Uses: Suspension and redispersability props. in pharmaceutical aerosols
Properties: Wh. fluffy powd.; 7 nm avg. particle size; sp.gr. 2.2; dens. ≈ 80 g/l (densed); surf. area 260 ± 30 m^2/g; pH 5.5-7.5 (in water:ethanol 1:3); > 99.8% assay.

Aerosil® R972. [Degussa; Degussa AG]
Chem. Descrip.: Syn. amorphous fumed silica
CAS 60842-32-2; EINECS 231-545-4
Uses: Free-flow aid for hydroscopic pharmaceuticals; renders caked material free-flowing with reduced tendency to absorb water
Regulatory: FDA approved (≤ 3% for cosmetics)
Properties: Fluffy wh. powd.; 16 nm avg. particle size; dens. ≈ 90 g/l (densed); surf. area 110 ± 20

m^2/g; pH 3.6-4.3 (in water:acetone or methanol 1:1); > 99.8% assay.

Aethoxal® B. [Henkel/Cospha; Henkel KGaA/Cospha]
Chem. Descrip.: PPG-5-laureth-5
CAS 68439-51-0
Uses: Superfatting agent, emollient for pharmaceuticals
Properties: Pale yel. oily liq.; forms spontaneous emulsion in warm water; oil-sol.; sp.gr. 0.9340-0.9370 (70 C); acid no. 0.5 max.; hyd. no. 84-92; pH 6.5-7.5 (5%); 99-100% conc.; nonionic; biodeg.

A.F.S. [United-Guardian]
Chem. Descrip.: Air-floated silica
EINECS 231-545-4
Uses: Viscosifier for liqs.; emulsion stabilizer; drier in underarm prods.; support agent and filler; for pharmaceutical, medical, health care fields
Custom product

Agar-Agar. [Commodity Services Int'l.]
Chem. Descrip.: Agar-agar, the extract of *Gracilaria* seaweeds
CAS 9002-18-0; EINECS 232-658-1
Uses: Controls water for pharmaceutical industry applics.; forms a rigid gel with water sol'ns. at a 1% conc.

Agar Agar NF Flake #1. [Meer]
Chem. Descrip.: Agar agar
CAS 9002-18-0; EINECS 232-658-1
Uses: Emulsifier, stabilizer, and gellant; for use in dental casts, as laxative, as suspending agent for barium sulfate in radiology, in suppositories, surgical lubricants, as carrier of topical medicaments
Properties: Water-sol.

Airaseptic Spray. [United-Guardian]
Uses: Antiseptic and deodorant spray to disinfect the air in operating rooms, sick rooms, hospitals, clinics, nursing homes; antimicrobial spray for surf. disinfection
Custom product

Akoext SB. [ABITEC]
Chem. Descrip.: Shea butter
CAS 977026-99-5
Uses: Bodying agent, emollient, lubricant, moisturizer, vehicle/carrier, visc. modifier for coating, dermatologicals, suppositories
Properties: Lovibond 2.5 max. color; m.p. 90-113 F; acid no. 15 max.; sapon. no. 178-190.

Akolizer C. [ABITEC]
Chem. Descrip.: Hydrog. cottonseed oil
CAS 68334-00-9; EINECS 269-804-9
Uses: Crystallization promoter, m.p. modifier, bodying agent, lubricant, and moisturizer for clinical nutrition, dermatologicals, encapsulation, soft gelatin capsules, suppositories, sustained release applics.
Properties: Lovibond 3R max. liq., flake, bead; drop pt. 142 F; acid no. 0.2 max.; iodine no. 1-5; sapon. no. 189-198.

Akolizer P. [ABITEC]
Chem. Descrip.: Hydrog. palm oil

7

CAS 68514-74-9

Uses: Crystallization promoter, m.p. modifier, bodying agent, lubricant, and moisturizer for clinical nutrition, dermatologicals, encapsulation, soft gelatin capsules, suppositories, sustained release applics.

Properties: Lovibond 3R max. liq., flake; drop pt. 140 F; acid no. .2 max.; iodine no. 1-5; sapon. no. 196-202.

Akolizer S. [ABITEC]
Chem. Descrip.: Hydrog. soybean oil
CAS 8016-70-4; EINECS 232-410-2

Uses: Crystallization promoter, m.p. modifier, bodying agent, lubricant, and moisturizer for cliical nutrition, dermatologicals, encapsulation, soft gelatin capsules, suppositories, sustained release applics.

Properties: Lovibond 3R max. liq., flake, bead; drop pt. 155 F; acid no. 0.2 max.; iodine no. 1-5; sapon. no. 189-197.

Akopol R. [ABITEC]
Chem. Descrip.: Partially hydrog. soybean and cottonseed oils

Uses: Fractionated nonlauric hard butter for use in pharmaceuticals

Properties: Lovibond 3.0 R max. liq./solid/flake; m.p. 97-101 F.

Akorex B. [ABITEC]
Chem. Descrip.: Partially hydrog. soybean and cottonseed oils

Uses: Diluent, lubricant, moisturizer for clinical nutrition, coating, delivery/absorp. enhancement, dermatologicals, microemulsions, soft gelatin capsules

Properties: Lovibond 4R max. color; m.p. 68-73 F; acid no. 0.1 max.; iodine no. 82-95.

Albagel Premium USP 4444. [Whittaker, Clark & Daniels]
Chem. Descrip.: Bentonite
CAS 1302-78-9; EINECS 215-108-5

Uses: Thickener, protective colloid, emulsifier, suspending agent.

Albone® 35 CG. [DuPont]
Chem. Descrip.: Hydrogen peroxide
CAS 7722-84-1; EINECS 231-765-0

Uses: Specially stabilized grade for prep. of stable dilute sol'ns. for consumer use in pharmaceutical applics.; meets USP specs. when properly diluted to 3%

Regulatory: FDA approved

Properties: Colorless clear liq., sl. pungent odor; sp.gr. 1.133 mg/m^3; dens. 9.45 lb/gal; m.p. -33 C; b.p. 108 C (760 mm Hg); pH 2.3-2.8; 35% hydrogen peroxide, 16.5% act. oxygen.

Albone® 50 CG. [DuPont]
Chem. Descrip.: Hydrogen peroxide
CAS 7722-84-1; EINECS 231-765-0

Uses: Specially stabilized grade for prep. of stable dilute sol'ns. for consumer use in pharmaceutical applics.; meets USP specs. when properly diluted to 3%

Regulatory: FDA approved

Properties: Colorless clear liq., sl. pungent odor; sp.gr. 1.196 mg/m^3; dens. 9.98 lb/gal; m.p. -52 C; b.p. 114 C (760 mm Hg); pH 1.5-2.0; 50% hydrogen peroxide, 23.5% act. oxygen.

Albone® 70CG. [DuPont]
Chem. Descrip.: Hydrogen peroxide
CAS 7722-84-1; EINECS 231-765-0

Uses: Specially stabilized grade for prep. of stable dilute sol'ns. for consumer use in pharmaceutical applics.; meets USP specs. when properly diluted to 3%

Regulatory: FDA approved

Properties: Colorless clear liq., sl. pungent odor; sp.gr. 1.3 mg/m^3; dens. 10.75 lb/gal; m.p. -40 C; b.p. 126 C (760 mm Hg); pH 0.4-0.8; 68% hydrogen peroxide, 32.9% act. oxygen.

Albrite® Diammonium Phosphate Food Grade. [Albright & Wilson UK]
Chem. Descrip.: Diammonium phosphate
CAS 7783-28-0; EINECS 231-987-8

Uses: Constituent of pharmaceutical preps.

Regulatory: FCC, UK compliance

Properties: Wh. crystals; sol. 69 g/100 g water @ 20 C; m.w. 132.06; bulk dens. 1.0 g/ml (loose); pH 8.0 (10 g/l sol'n.); 98% min. assay.

Albrite® Dicalcium Phosphate Anhyd. [Albright & Wilson UK]
Chem. Descrip.: Dicalcium phosphate food grade
CAS 7757-93-9; EINECS 231-826-1

Uses: Dispersant in tableting; source of calcium and phosphorus in foods for infants, invalids, and geriatric patients

Regulatory: EEC, UK compliance

Properties: Wh. impalpable powd., odorless, tasteless; m.w. 136.06; 39-42% calcium as CaO.

Storage: Protect packages from water and contamination.

Albrite® Monoammonium Phosphate Food Grade. [Albright & Wilson UK]
Chem. Descrip.: Ammonium phosphate
CAS 7722-76-1; EINECS 231-764-5

Uses: Mold culture nutrient in mfg. of pharmaceuticals

Regulatory: FCC, UK compliance

Properties: Wh. crystals; sol. 37 g/100 g water @ 20 C; m.w. 115.03; bulk dens. 1.05 g/ml (loose); pH 4.6 (10 g/l sol'n.); 98% min. assay.

Alcolan®. [Amerchol]
Chem. Descrip.: Petrolatum, sorbitan sesquioleate, and lanolin alcohol

Uses: W/o emulsifier, emollient base for pharmaceutical emulsions

Properties: Paste; 100% conc.; nonionic.

Alcolan® 36W. [Amerchol]
Chem. Descrip.: Lanolin, petrolatum, and sorbitan sesquioleate

Uses: Emulsifier, emollient for pharmaceutical emulsions

Properties: Paste; 100% conc.; nonionic.

Alcolan® 40. [Amerchol]
Chem. Descrip.: Petrolatum, lanolin, beeswax, sorbitan sesquioleate, and polysorbate 81

Uses: W/o emulsifier, emollient base for pharmaceutical emulsions
Properties: Paste; 100% conc.

Alcolec® Granules. [Am. Lecithin; Nattermann Phospholipid; Rhone-Poulenc Rorer]
Chem. Descrip.: Lecithin FCC
CAS 8002-43-5; EINECS 232-307-2
Uses: Wetting agent, release agent, o/w emulsifier, stabilizer, diet supplement in pharmaceuticals
Regulatory: FDA 21CFR §184.1400, GRAS; kosher approved
Properties: Lt. tan/yel. gran., bland odor and taste; sp.gr. 0.5; acid no. 36 max.; 97% act., 1% max. moisture; nonionic
Storage: Store below 25 C; 1 yr shelf life in original, unopened container.

Alcolec® Z-3. [Am. Lecithin; Nattermann Phospholipid; Rhone-Poulenc Rorer]
Chem. Descrip.: Hydroxylated lecithin
CAS 8029-76-3; EINECS 232-440-6
Uses: Wetting agent, emulsifier, solubilizer, dispersant for pharmaceuticals
Regulatory: FDA 21CFR §172.814, GRAS; kosher approved
Properties: Lt. amber liq.; sol. in most fat solv. except acetone; visc. 8000 cps; acid no. < 38; < 1.5% moisture, < 42% oil content; nonionic
Storage: 1 yr shelf life in original unopened container.

Aldo® MCT KFG. [Lonza]
Chem. Descrip.: Caprylic/capric triglyceride
CAS 73398-61-5; EINECS 265-724-3
Uses: Carrier or suspension medium for oil-sol. antibiotics and drugs; dietary supplements
Regulatory: Kosher
Properties: Clear liq., neutral odor and taste; acid no. 0.10 max.; iodine no. 1.0 max.; sapon. no. 335-360; hyd. no. 10 max.; 0.1% max. moisture.

Aldo® MLD. [Lonza]
Chem. Descrip.: Glyceryl laurate SE
CAS 27215-38-9
Uses: Emulsifier for pharmaceuticals
Properties: Cream soft solid; sol. in ethanol, ethyl acetate, toluol, naphtha, min. and veg. oils, disp. in water; sp.gr. 0.97; m.p. 21-26 C; HLB 6.8; sapon. no. 185-195; pH 7.5-8.5 (5% aq.); 100% conc.; nonionic.

Aldo® MO FG. [Lonza]
Chem. Descrip.: Glyceryl monooleate
CAS 25496-72-4
Uses: Emulsifier, solubilizer for pharmaceutical applics.
Regulatory: FDA 21CFR §184.1505, GRAS
Properties: Liq. with lt. haze, mild odor; HLB 3.0; acid no. 2 max.; sapon. no. 166-176; 42% min. alpha monoglyceride; nonionic
Storage: Store in cool, dry area.

Aldo® MR. [Lonza]
Chem. Descrip.: Glyceryl ricinoleate
CAS 141-08-2; EINECS 205-455-0
Uses: Emulsifier, solubilizer for pharmaceutical applics.

Properties: Yel. liq.; sol. in methanol, ethanol, ethyl acetate, toluol, veg. oil, disp. in water; sp.gr. 1.02; m.p. < -8 C; HLB 6.0; sapon. no. 66-69; pH 8.3-9.3; 100% conc.; nonionic.

Aldo® MS. [Lonza]
Chem. Descrip.: Glyceryl stearate
CAS 123-94-4
Uses: Emulsifier for pharmaceutical use
Properties: Wh. beads; sol. hot in methanol, ethanol, toluol, naphtha, min. and veg. oils, disp. in hot water; sp.gr. 0.97; m.p. 57-61 C; HLB 4.0; sapon. no. 158-165; pH 7.6-8.6 (3% aq.); 100% conc.; nonionic.

Aldo® MS-20 KFG. [Lonza]
Chem. Descrip.: PEG-20 glyceryl stearate
Uses: Emulsifier, solubilizer for pharmaceutical applics.
Properties: Solid; HLB 13.0; 100% conc.; nonionic.

Aldo® MSA. [Lonza]
Chem. Descrip.: Glyceryl stearate
CAS 123-94-4
Uses: Emulsifier for o/w pharmaceuticals
Properties: Wh. beads; sol. in ethanol, min. and veg. oil; disp. in water; HLB 11 ± 1; m.p. 56-60 C; sapon. no. 90-100; 100% conc., 17.5% min. mono content; nonionic.

Aldo® MSC. [Lonza]
Chem. Descrip.: Glyceryl stearate
CAS 31566-31-1
Uses: Emulsifier, surfactant for pharmaceuticals (OTC creams and lotions, skin and facial treatment prods.)
Properties: Lt. tan beads or flakes, mild fatty odor; sol. hot in methanol, ethanol, toluol, naphtha, min. and veg. oils, disp. in hot water; sp.gr. 0.97; m.p. 55-58 C; HLB 3.0; acid no. 6 max.; iodine no. 3 max.; sapon. no. 168-176; flash pt. (COC) 204 C; pH 6 (3%); 100% conc., 42-48% alpha mono; nonionic
Toxicology: LD50 (rat) > 5000 mg/kg; nonlethal, nontoxic; nonirritating to eyes and skin.

Aldo® MSD. [Lonza]
Chem. Descrip.: Glyceryl stearate SE
Uses: Emulsifier, solubilizer for pharmaceutical applics.
Properties: Wh. beads; sol. hot in methanol, ethanol, toluol, naphtha, min. and veg. oils, disp. in hot water; sp.gr. 0.97; m.p. 56-60 C; HLB 6.0; sapon. no. 140-150; pH 9.2-10.2 (3% aq.); 100% conc.; nonionic.

Aldo® PGHMS. [Lonza]
Chem. Descrip.: Propylene glycol monostearate
CAS 1323-39-3; EINECS 215-354-3
Uses: Emulsifier, stabilizer, solubilizer, emollient, lubricant, thickener, plasticizing agent, anti-irritant, and conditioner in pharmaceutical
Properties: Wh. flakes; sol. in ethanol, min. and veg. oils; insol. in water; HLB 3 ± 1; iodine no. 1.0 max.; sapon. no. 170-185; 100% conc.; nonionic.

Aldo® TC. [Lonza]
Chem. Descrip.: Caprylic/capric triglyceride; EINECS 265-724-3

Uses: Emollient in OTC creams and lotions; carrier for oil-sol. antibiotics

Properties: Lt. yel. clear liq.; bland; HLB 1.0; acid no. 1 max.; iodine no. 1 max.; sapon. no. 330-360; pH 4.5 (5%); 100% conc.; nonionic.

Aldosperse® MO-50 FG. [Lonza]
Chem. Descrip.: Mono- and diglycerides and 50% polysorbate 80
Uses: Solubilizer, dispersant for vitamin-mineral preps.
Regulatory: FDA 21CFR 712.840, 172.515, 184.1505 GRAS
Properties: Clear to sl. hazy semiliq.; HLB 9; acid no. 2 max.; iodine no. 45-55; sapon. no. 100-115; 15% alpha monoglyceride
Storage: Store in cool, dry area.

Aldosperse® O-20 KFG. [Lonza]
Chem. Descrip.: 80% Glyceryl stearate, 20% polysorbate 80
Uses: Emulsifier, solubilizer for pharmaceutical applics.
Regulatory: FDA 21CFR §172.840, 184.1505 (GRAS); kosher
Properties: Lt. tan beads, mild odor, bland taste; 100% thru 8 mesh, 5% max. thru 100 mesh; m.p. 50-65 C; HLB 5; acid no. 2 max.; sapon. no. 140-155; 100% conc.; nonionic
Storage: Store in cool, dry area below 35 C.

Alginic Acid FCC. [Meer]
Chem. Descrip.: Alginic acid FCC
CAS 9005-32-7; EINECS 232-680-1
Uses: Tablet binder for pharmaceutical and health food industries; holds tablet together during compression and disintegrates rapidly under acidic stomach conditions to allow active ingreds. to work faster
Properties: Wh. to off-wh. free-flowing powd.; ≥ 95% thru 80 mesh; visc. 5-50 cps (1%); pH 1.5-3.5 (1%).

Algon LA 40. [Auschem SpA]
Chem. Descrip.: PEG-4 laurate
CAS 9004-81-3
Uses: Emulsifier for pharmaceutical preps.
Properties: Liq.; HLB 12.2; 100% conc.; nonionic.

Algon LA 80. [Auschem SpA]
Chem. Descrip.: PEG-8 laurate
CAS 9004-81-3; EINECS 253-458-0
Uses: Emulsifier for pharmaceutical preps.
Properties: Liq.; HLB 13.0; 100% conc.; nonionic.

Algon OL 60. [Auschem SpA]
Chem. Descrip.: PEG-6 oleate
CAS 9004-96-0
Uses: Emulsifier for pharmaceutical preps.
Properties: Liq.; HLB 13.0; 100% conc.; nonionic.

Algon OL 70. [Auschem SpA]
Chem. Descrip.: PEG-7 oleate
CAS 9004-96-0
Uses: Emulsifier for pharmaceutical preps.
Properties: Liq.; HLB 10.4; 100% conc.; nonionic.

Algon ST 50. [Auschem SpA]
Chem. Descrip.: PEG-5 stearate
CAS 9004-99-3

Uses: Emulsifier for pharmaceutical preps.
Properties: Paste; HLB 9.0; 100% conc.; nonionic.

Algon ST 80. [Auschem SpA]
Chem. Descrip.: PEG-8 stearate
CAS 9004-99-3
Uses: Emulsifier for pharmaceutical preps.
Properties: Paste/solid; HLB 11.1; 100% conc.; nonionic.

Algon ST 100. [Auschem SpA]
Chem. Descrip.: PEG-10 stearate
CAS 9004-99-3
Uses: Emulsifier for pharmaceutical preps.
Properties: Solid; HLB 11.5; 100% conc.; nonionic.

Algon ST 200. [Auschem SpA]
Chem. Descrip.: PEG-20 stearate
CAS 9004-99-3
Uses: Emulsifier for pharmaceutical preps.
Properties: Solid; HLB 14.0; 100% conc.; nonionic.

Algon ST 400. [Auschem SpA]
Chem. Descrip.: PEG-40 stearate
CAS 9004-99-3
Uses: Emulsifier for pharmaceutical preps.
Properties: Flakes; HLB 16.9; 100% conc.; nonionic.

Algon ST 500. [Auschem SpA]
Chem. Descrip.: PEG-50 stearate
CAS 9004-99-3
Uses: Emulsifier for pharmaceutical preps.
Properties: Flakes; HLB 17.9; 100% conc.; nonionic.

Algon ST 1000. [Auschem SpA]
Chem. Descrip.: PEG-100 stearate
CAS 9004-99-3
Uses: Emulsifier for pharmaceutical preps.
Properties: Flakes; HLB 18.8; 100% conc.; nonionic.

Alkamuls® EL-620. [Rhone-Poulenc Surf. & Spec.]
Chem. Descrip.: PEG-30 castor oil
CAS 61791-12-6
Uses: Emulsifier, wetting agent, pigment dispersant, lubricant, solubilizer for pharmaceuticals
Regulatory: FDA, EPA compliance
Properties: Lt. brn. clear liq.; sol. in water, acetone, CCl_4, alcohols, veg. oil, ethers, toluene, xylene; sp.gr. 1.04-1.05; dens. 8.705 lb/gal; visc. 600-1000 cps; HLB 12.0; cloud pt. 42 C (1% aq.); flash pt. 291-295 C; surf. tens. 41 dynes/; 100% conc.; nonionic.

Alkamuls® EL-719. [Rhone-Poulenc Surf. & Spec.]
Chem. Descrip.: PEG-40 castor oil
CAS 61791-12-6
Uses: Emulsifier for vitamins and drugs
Regulatory: FDA, EPA compliance
Properties: Liq.; sol. in water, acetone, CCl4, alcohols, veg. oil, ether, toluene, xylene; sp.gr. 1.06-1.07; dens. 8.9-9.0 lb/gal; visc. 500-800 cps; HLB 13.6; cloud pt. 80 C (1% aq.); flash pt. 275-279 C; surf. tens. 38 dynes/cm (0.1%); 96% act.; nonionic.

Alkamuls® PSML-20. [Rhone-Poulenc Surf. & Spec.]
Chem. Descrip.: Polysorbate 20
CAS 9005-64-5

Uses: Emulsifier, solubilizer, visc. modifier, lubricant for pharmaceuticals

Regulatory: FDA approved as indirect additive

Properties: Yel. liq.; sol. in water, aromatic solv.; dens. 1.1 g/ml; HLB 16.7; sapon. no. 40-50; 97% act.; nonionic.

Alkamuls® PSMS-4. [Rhone-Poulenc Surf. & Spec.]
Chem. Descrip.: Polysorbate 61
CAS 9005-67-8
Uses: Emulsifier, lubricant used in suppositories in pharmaceutical indutry
Properties: Tan solid; typ. odor; water-disp.; dens. 1.1 g/ml; HLB 9.6; sapon. no. 98-113; 97% act.; nonionic.

Allantoin. [Sutton Labs]
Chem. Descrip.: Allantoin
CAS 97-59-6; EINECS 202-592-8
Uses: Skin protectant, anti-irritant for pharmaceutical creams and lotions; for minor cuts, burns, sunburn, chapped or windburned skin, fever blisters, diaper rash; orals, e.g., toothpaste, mouth rinses; germicidal creams/ointments; surgical scrubs
Use level: 0.5-2%
Regulatory: FDA approved as Category I (safe and effective) skin protectant
Properties: Wh. cryst. powd., odorless; sol. 0.5% in water; m.p. 225 C min. (dec.); 98-101.5% assay
Toxicology: Nontoxic, nonirritating, nonallergenic
Storage: Store in cool, dry area.

Aloe Con WG 40. [Florida Food Prods.]
Chem. Descrip.: Aloe vera whole gel
Uses: Used for therapeutic prods.
Properties: Dk. tan to brn., typ. aloe flavor; sp.gr. 1.1 ± 0.05; pH 3.5-5.0; 20 ± 1% solids
Storage: Store in container; protect from light; 6 mo shelf life.

Aloe Con WLG 200. [Florida Food Prods.]
Chem. Descrip.: Freeze-dried aloe vera whole leaf gel
Uses: Used for pharmaceuticals, health supplements
Properties: Sl. tan free-flowing powd.; pH 3.5-5.5 (1:199); < 7% moisture.

Aloe-Moist™. [Terry Labs]
Chem. Descrip.: Aloe vera gel, polyglyceryl methacrylate, and propylene glycol
Uses: Moisturizer with soothing, cooling effect used for OTC applics., first aid preps., acne and facial preps., suncare prods.; delayed evaporation chars.
Properties: Colorless clear to sl. hazy visc. gel; sol. in water; sp.gr. 1.1; visc. 75,000-150,000 cps; pH 5.0-5.6
Storage: Store at R.T.; protect from oxidation; may darken over time.

Aloe-Moist™ A. [Terry Labs]
Chem. Descrip.: Aloe vera gel, polyglyceryl methacrylate, propylene glycol, and stabilized β-carotene
Uses: Moisturizer with soothing, cooling effect used for OTC applics., topical analgesics/anesthetics, first aid preps., acne and facial preps., as a moisturizing base
Properties: Golden to orange clear to sl. hazy visc. gel; sol. in water; visc. 75,000-150,000 cps; pH 5.0-5.6
Storage: Store at R.T.; protect from oxidation; may darken over time.

Aloe Vera Gel 1X. [Terry Labs]
Chem. Descrip.: Aloe vera gel, food grade
Uses: Used in OTC pharmaceuticals (topical analgesics/anesthetics, hydrocortisone creams, first aid sprays/creams/gels, anti-acne preps., toothpaste, moisturizing base)
Properties: Yel.-grn. clear to sl. hazy liq., lt. veg. odor; sp.gr. 0.997-1.004; pH 3.5-5.0; 0.5% min. total solids
Storage: Store @ R.T.; protect from oxidation; may darken with age.

Aloe Vera Gel 10X. [Terry Labs]
Chem. Descrip.: Aloe vera gel, food grade
Uses: Used in OTC pharmaceuticals (topical analgesics/anesthetics, hydrocortisone creams, first aid sprays/creams/gels, anti-acne preps., toothpaste, moisturizing base)
Properties: Lt. amber clear to sl. hazy liq., mod. veg. odor; sp.gr. 1.022-1.032; pH 3.5-5.0; 5% min. total solids
Storage: Store @ R.T.; protect from oxidation; may darken with age.

Aloe Vera Gel 40X. [Terry Labs]
Chem. Descrip.: Aloe vera gel, food grade
Uses: Used in OTC pharmaceuticals (topical analgesics/anesthetics, hydrocortisone creams, first aid sprays/creams/gels, anti-acne preps., toothpaste, moisturizing base)
Properties: Amber clear to sl. hazy liq. with possible precipitate, strong veg. odor; sp.gr. 1.100-1.120; pH 3.5-5.0; 20% min. total solids
Storage: Store @ R.T.; protect from oxidation; may darken with age.

Aloe Vera Gel Decolorized 1X. [Terry Labs]
Chem. Descrip.: Aloe vera gel
Uses: Moisturizer with soothing props. used in OTC pharmaceuticals (topical analgesics/anesthetics, hydrocortisone creams, first aid sprays/creams/gels, anti-acne preps., bedsore preps., as a moisturizing base)
Properties: Colorless liq., sl. veg. odor; sp.gr. 0.997-1.004; pH 3.5-5.0; 0.5% min. total solids
Storage: Store @ R.T.; protect from oxidation; may darken with age.

Aloe Vera Gel Decolorized 10X. [Terry Labs]
Chem. Descrip.: Aloe vera gel
Uses: Moisturizer with soothing props. used in OTC pharmaceuticals (topical analgesics/anesthetics, hydrocortisone creams, first aid sprays/creams/gels, anti-acne preps., bedsore preps., as a moisturizing base)
Properties: Yel./grn. liq., lt. veg. odor; sp.gr. 1.022-1.032; pH 3.5-5.0; 5% min. total solids
Storage: Store @ R.T.; protect from oxidation; may darken with age.

Aloe Vera Gel Decolorized 40X. [Terry Labs]
Chem. Descrip.: Aloe vera gel
Uses: Moisturizer with soothing props. used in OTC pharmaceuticals (topical analgesics/anesthetics, hydrocortisone creams, first aid sprays/creams/gels, anti-acne preps., bedsore preps., as a moisturizing base)
Properties: Yel./amber liq., mod. veg. odor; sp.gr. 1.100-1.120; pH 3.5-5.0; 20% min. total solids
Storage: Store @ R.T.; protect from oxidation; may darken with age.

Aloe Vera Gel Thickened FG. [Terry Labs]
Chem. Descrip.: Aloe vera gel and carrageenan
Uses: Food grade aloe vera gel, visc. enhanced for internal or topical applics.
Properties: Yel.-grn. clear to sl. hazy gelatinous liq.; pH 3.5-5.0
Storage: Store @ R.T.; protect from heat and oxidation; may darken with age.

Aloe Vera Lipo-Quinone Extract™ Cosmetic Grade. [Terry Labs]
Chem. Descrip.: Aloe extract, mineral oil, coconut oil
Uses: Used in hydrophobic prods. or oil phases of formulations for OTC pharmaceuticals (topical analgesics/anesthetics, hydrocortisone creams, first aid creams, anti-acne preps., rubs, liniments, ointments)
Properties: Yel. oil, veg. odor; sp.gr. 0.870-0.884; acid no. 1.1 max.; sapon. no. 120-135
Storage: Store @ R.T.; do not store above 65 C for > 24 h; if stored below 25 C for prolonged periods, warm prod. to clarify.

Aloe Vera Lipo-Quinone Extract™ Food Grade. [Terry Labs]
Chem. Descrip.: Aloe extract, extracted onto soybean oil base
Uses: Used in internal/oral applics. and OTC pharmaceuticals (oral ointments, soft gel encapsulation, topical analgesics/anesthetics, hydrocortisone creams, first aid creams, anti-acne preps., rubs/liniments/ointments),
Properties: Yel. oil, veg. odor; sp.gr. 0.919-0.924; acid no. 1.1 max.; sapon. no. 185-200; < 10% moisture
Storage: Store at R.T.; do not store above 65 C for > 24 h; if stored below 25 C, heat prod. to clarify.

Aloe Vera Lipo-Quinone Extract™ Low Odor (CG) [Terry Labs]
Chem. Descrip.: Aloe extract, mineral oil, coconut oil
Uses: Used in hydrophobic prods. or oil phases of formulations for OTC pharmaceuticals (topical analgesics/anesthetics, hydrocortisone creams, first aid creams, anti-acne preps., rubs, liniments, ointments)
Properties: Lt. yel. oil, lt. veg. odor; sp.gr. 0.870-0.884; acid no. 1.1 max.; sapon. no. 120-135
Storage: Store @ R.T.; do not store above 65 C for > 24 h; if stored below 25 C for prolonged periods, warm prod. to clarify.

Aloe Vera Oil. [Agro-Mar; Tri-K Industries]
Chem. Descrip.: Aloe vera oil
Uses: Emollient leaving shiny, nongreasy film and soft feel on skin; vehicle for pigmented preps., blending agent and solubilizer for waxes and resins; ingred. for sun care prods., pharmaceuticals
Properties: Pale yel. clear to hazy oil, char. vegetable-type odor; sp.gr. 0.86 ± 0.04; b.p. 590 F; acid no. 3 max.; sapon. no. 10 max.
Toxicology: Nonhazardous.

Aloe Vera Powd. 200XXX Extract-Microfine. [Agro-Mar; Tri-K Industries]
Chem. Descrip.: Aloe vera gel
Uses: Rapidly dissolving ingred. for pharmaceutical industry
Properties: Off-wh. to lt. beige powd., mild vegetable odor; 100% water-sol.; pH 3.5-6.5 (0.5% aq.); 7.5-8.5% moisture
Toxicology: Dust may cause irritation on direct/prolonged contact with eyes or skin
Precaution: Material extremely slick when wet.

Alpha W6 HP 0.6. [Wacker-Chemie GmbH]
Chem. Descrip.: Hydroxypropyl-α-cyclodextrin CAS 99241-24-4
Uses: Complex hosting guest molecules; increases the sol. and bioavailability of other substances; masks flavor, odor, or coloration; stabilizes against light, oxidation, heat, and hydrolysis; turns liqs. or volatiles into stable solid powds.
Properties: M.w. 1184.

Alpha W6 M1.8. [Wacker-Chemie GmbH]
Chem. Descrip.: Methyl-α-cyclodextrin
Uses: Complex hosting guest molecules; increases the sol. and bioavailability of other substances; masks flavor, odor, or coloration; stabilizes against light, oxidation, heat, and hydrolysis; turns liqs. or volatiles into stable solid powds.
Properties: M.w. 1123.

Alpha W6 Pharma Grade. [Wacker-Chemie GmbH]
Chem. Descrip.: α-Cyclodextrin CAS 10016-20-3; EINECS 233-007-4
Uses: Complex hosting guest molecules; increases the sol. and bioavailability of other substances; masks flavor, odor, or coloration; stabilizes against light, oxidation, heat, and hydrolysis; turns liqs. or volatiles into stable solid powds.
Properties: Wh. cryst. powd.; sol. 14.5 g/100 ml in water; m.w. 972; > 98% act.
Toxicology: LD50 (acute IV, rat) 500-750 mg/kg; eye irritant but not corrosive; nonirritating to skin.

Alphadim® 90SBK. [Am. Ingreds.]
Chem. Descrip.: High-purity, molecularly dist. monoglyceride prepared from fully hardened soybean oil and glycerin
Uses: Pharmaceutical tableting aid
Regulatory: FDA GRAS; kosher
Properties: Wh. to cream fine bead; 99% thru 10 mesh; m.p. 70-75 C; iodine no. 3 max.; sapon. no. 150-165; HLB 3.5; 90% min. alpha monoester; nonionic
Storage: Indefinite storage life under proper cool, dry conditions.

Alphafil 500 USP. [Luzenac Am.]
Chem. Descrip.: Talc USP/FCC
CAS 14807-96-6; EINECS 238-877-9
Uses: High purity, extra-fine soft talc with very low abrasiveness, exc. color, brightness, and softness; glidant, lubricant, film enhancer, diluent, filler, antitackifying agent, opacifier, extender pigment for pharmaceuticals
Properties: Wh. powd.; 4 µ median particle size; 99.9% min. thru 400 mesh; bulk dens. 10-15 lb/ft^3 (loose), 39 lb/ft^3 (tapped); pH 9 (10% slurry).
Alpine Talc USP BC 127. [Whittaker, Clark & Daniels]
Chem. Descrip.: Talc
CAS 14807-96-6; EINECS 238-877-9
Uses: Glidant, anticaking agent, tablet lubricant, colorant.
Altalc 200 USP. [Luzenac Am.]
Chem. Descrip.: Talc USP/FCC
CAS 14807-96-6; EINECS 238-877-9
Uses: Pharmaceutical talc; detackifying and dusting, glidant, lubricant, diluent, filler, compression aid, tablet coating, excipient, opacifying extender pigments, film enhancement, aerosols, creams and lotions, medicated foot powds.
Properties: Wh. powd.; 9 µ median particle size; 98% min. thru 200 mesh; bulk dens. 24-28 lb/ft^3 (loose), 62 lb/ft^3 (tapped); brightness 85 min.; pH 8 (10% slurry).
Altalc 300 USP. [Luzenac Am.]
Chem. Descrip.: Talc USP/FCC
CAS 14807-96-6; EINECS 238-877-9
Uses: Pharmaceutical talc; exc. brightness; detackifying and dusting, glidant, lubricant, diluent, filler, compression aid, tablet coating, excipient, opacifying extender pigments, film enhancement, aerosols, creams and lotions
Properties: Wh. powd.; 6 µ median particle size; 98% min. thru 325 mesh; bulk dens. 15-19 lb/ft^3 (loose), 42 lb/ft^3 (tapped); brightness 86 min.; pH 9 (10% slurry).
Altalc 400 USP. [Luzenac Am.]
Chem. Descrip.: Talc USP/FCC
CAS 14807-96-6; EINECS 238-877-9
Uses: High purity exc. brightness talc for pharmaceuticals; glidant, lubricant, diluent, filler
Properties: Wh. powd.; 4 µ median particle size; 99.9% min. thru 325 mesh; bulk dens. 12-16 lb/ft^3 (loose), 41 lb/ft^3 (tapped); brightness 87 min.; pH 9 (10% slurry).
Altalc 500 USP. [Luzenac Am.]
Chem. Descrip.: Talc USP/FCC
CAS 14807-96-6; EINECS 238-877-9
Uses: High purity, ultrafine talc with very consistent particle size ideal for tableting applics.; diluent, glidant, antitackifying agent, TiO_2 extender pigment; suitable for aerosols
Properties: Wh. powd.; 4 µ median particle size; 99.9% thru 400 mesh; bulk dens. 11-15 lb/ft^3 (loose), 38 lb/ft^3 (tapped); pH 9 (10% slurry).
Amalty®. [Mitsubishi Int'l.; Towa Chem. Ind.]
Chem. Descrip.: Maltitol
CAS 585-88-6; EINECS 209-567-0
Uses: Mild sweetener with no aftertaste; does not cause tooth decay; heat-stable; humectant; for vitamin supplements, foods for diabetics, medicine (powd. medicine, lozenges, compresses)
Properties: Wh. powd. or gran.; m.p. 140 C $\geq$ 93.5% act.
Amaranth Oil. [Nu-World Amaranth]
Chem. Descrip.: Natural amaranth oil high in squalene
CAS 915-67-3; EINECS 213-022-2
Uses: Exc. natural source of omega acids, highly unsat.; free radical scavenger; aids temp. stability in pharmaceuticals
Properties: Light-colored clear oily liq., delicate agreeable odor and taste.
Amberlite® IRA-68. [Rohm & Haas]
Chem. Descrip.: Acrylic
Uses: Weakly basic anion exchange resin for pharmaceutical industry.
Amberlite® IRP-88. [Rohm & Haas]
Chem. Descrip.: Methacrylic acid DVB
Uses: Tablet disintegrant; bulk dens. 0.548 g/cc.
Amerchol® 400. [Amerchol; Amerchol Europe]
Chem. Descrip.: Petrolatum, lanolin alcohol, cetyl alcohol, lanolin, stearone
Uses: Aux. emulsifier, emulsion stabilizer for o/w and w/o pharmaceutical systems; moisturizing emollient with barrier props.
Properties: Lt. cream soft solid, pract. odorless; HLB 9.0; m.p. 49-50 C; acid no. 1.5; sapon. no. 8; 100% conc.; nonionic.
Amerchol® BL. [Amerchol; Amerchol Europe]
Chem. Descrip.: Lanolin, min. oil, and lanolin alcohol
Uses: Absorp. base, aux. emulsifier and stabilizer for o/w systems, w/o emollient, moisturizer for pharmaceuticals (lotions, ointments)
Properties: Yel.-amber semisolid, slight char. sterol odor; oil sol.; HLB 8.0; acid no. 2.0 max.; sapon. no. 60-70; 100% conc.; nonionic.
Amerchol® C. [Amerchol; Amerchol Europe]
Chem. Descrip.: Petrolatum, lanolin, lanolin alcohol
Uses: Absorp. base, aux. emulsifier and stabilizer for o/w systems, conditioner, emollient, moisturizer for pharmaceuticals (creams, ointments, dermatologicals, lotions)
Properties: Pale yel.-cream soft solid, slight, char. sterol odor; oil sol.; HLB 9.5; m.p. 40-46 C; acid no. 1.0 max.; sapon. no. 10-20; 100% conc.; nonionic.
Amerchol® CAB. [Amerchol; Amerchol Europe]
Chem. Descrip.: Petrolatum, lanolin alcohol
Uses: Emollient, w/o emulsifier, moisturizer, stabilizer, plasticizer for therapeutic ointments, burn preparations, dermatological prods., hypoallergenic preparations, pharmaceuticals, absorp. bases
Properties: Pale cream soft solid, faint, char. sterol odor; oil sol.; HLB 9.0; m.p. 40-46 C; acid no. 1 max.; sapon. no. 1.0 max.; 100% conc.; nonionic.
Amerchol® H-9. [Amerchol; Amerchol Europe]

Chem. Descrip.: Petrolatum, lanolin, lanolin alcohol

Uses: Emollient, w/o emulsifier, penetrant, stabilizer, absorp. base for pharmaceutical ointments, burn ointments, dermatologicals

Properties: Pale yel. soft solid, slight, char. sterol odor; oil sol.; HLB 9; m.p. 55-62 C; acid no. 1 max.; sapon. no. 15-27; 100% conc.; nonionic.

Amerchol L-101®. [Amerchol]

Chem. Descrip.: Min. oil, lanolin alcohol

Uses: Emollient, penetrant, w/o emulsifier, moisturizer, softener, stabilizer for pharmaceuticals

Properties: Pale yel. oily liq., faint char. sterol odor; oil sol.; sp.gr. 0.840-0.860; visc. 20-30 cps; HLB 8; acid no. 1 max.; sapon. no. 1 max.; 100% conc.; nonionic.

Amerchol® L-500. [Amerchol]

Chem. Descrip.: Min. oil, lanolin alcohol, octyldodecanol

Uses: Aux. w/o emulsifier, stabilizer, emollient, moisturizer, conditioner for pharmaceutical vehicles

Properties: Amber thick liq. to semisolid; oil-misc.; HLB 6; acid no. 2 max.; sapon. no. 5 max.; 100% conc.; nonionic.

Amerlate® P. [Amerchol; Amerchol Europe]

Chem. Descrip.: Isopropyl lanolate

CAS 63393-93-1; EINECS 264-119-1

Uses: Conditioner, penetrant, lubricant, moisturizer, emollient, w/o emulsifier, stabilizer, opacifier for pharmaceuticals

Properties: Yel. buttery solid, faint char. odor; HLB 9; acid no. 18 max.; sapon. no. 130-155; 100% act.; nonionic.

Amerlate® W. [Amerchol; Amerchol Europe]

Chem. Descrip.: Isopropyl lanolate

CAS 63393-93-1; EINECS 264-119-1

Uses: Dispersant/wetting agent for pigments in pharmaceuticals; emulsifier, softener, lubricant, emollient

Properties: Yel. buttery solid; faint char. odor; insol. in water; HLB 9; acid no. 18 max.; sapon. no. 135-165; hyd. no. 35-55; 100% act.; nonionic.

4-Aminobenzoic Acid, Pure, No. 102. [Rona; E. Merck]

Chem. Descrip.: PABA

CAS 150-13-0; EINECS 205-753-0

Uses: Pharmaceutical active.

Amino Gluten MG. [Croda Inc.]

Chem. Descrip.: Corn gluten amino acids, sodium chloride

Uses: Humecant for pharmaceuticals

Properties: Amber liq.; m.w. 150; water-sol.; 15% act. in water.

Aminoxid WS 35. [Goldschmidt; Goldschmidt AG]

Chem. Descrip.: Cocamidopropylamine oxide

CAS 68155-09-9; EINECS 268-938-5

Uses: Detergent, emulsifier, wetting agent, softener, foam stabilizer for pharmaceutical emulsions

Properties: Amber liq.; pH 5-7; 35% act.; nonionic.

Amonyl® 265 BA. [Seppic]

Chem. Descrip.: Coco-betaine

CAS 68424-94-2; EINECS 270-329-4

Uses: Surfactant, detergent, foamer, visc. modifier, conditioner, o/w emulsifier, substantivity agent for dermatological liq. cleansers

Properties: Liq.; sp.gr. 1.035 (20 C); cloud pt. < 0 C; pH 5-7.5 (5% aq.); 30% conc.; amphoteric.

Amonyl® 380 BA. [Seppic]

Chem. Descrip.: Cocamidopropyl betaine

Uses: Surfactant, detergent, foamer, visc. modifier, conditioner, o/w emulsifier, substantivity agent for dermatological liq. cleansers

Properties: Liq.; sp.gr. 1.050 (20 C); cloud pt. < 0 C; pH 5.5-7.0 (5% aq.); 30% act.; amphoteric.

Amonyl® 440 NI. [Seppic]

Chem. Descrip.: Cocamidopropyl betaine

Uses: Ultra mild surfactant, foamer for dermatological scrubs

Properties: Pract. colorless liq.; sp.gr. 1.050 (20 C); visc. ≈ 400 mPa•s (20 C); cloud pt. 0 C; pH 5.5-7.5 (10% aq.); 37% aq. sol'n.; amphoteric

Toxicology: Low skin irritation; eye irritant.

AMP. [ANGUS]

Chem. Descrip.: 2-Amino-2-methyl-1-propanol

CAS 124-68-5; EINECS 204-709-8

Uses: Buffer in pharmaceutical, diagnostic, and biochem. applics.

Regulatory: FDA 21CFR §175.105, 176.170, 176.180, 177.1210

Properties: APHA 20 solid; m.w. 89.14; sp.gr. 0.928 (40/40 C); dens. 7.78; visc. 102 cp (30 C); m.p. 30 C; b.p. 165 C; flash pt. (TCC) 172 F; 100% act.; nonionic; very low potential for accumulation or toxic effect in the environment

Toxicology: LD50 (oral, rat) 2.9 g/kg, (IP, mus) 0.32 g/kg; sl. toxic; severely irritating to skin and eyes; causes eye burns

Precaution: Combustible liq. and vapor; strongly alkaline; corrosive to copper, brass, and aluminum.

AMP-95. [ANGUS]

Chem. Descrip.: 2-Amino-2-methyl-1-propanol

CAS 124-68-5; EINECS 204-709-8

Uses: Buffer in pharmaceutical, diagnostic, and biochem. applics.

Regulatory: FDA 21CFR §175.105, 176.170, 176.180, 177.1210

Properties: Colorless liq.; m.w. 89.14; sp.gr. 0.928 (40/40 C); dens. 7.85; visc. 147 cp; f.p. -2 C; flash pt. (TCC) 182 F; surf. tens. 36-38 dynes/cm; 95% act. in water; nonionic; very low potential for accumulation or toxic effect in the environment

Toxicology: LD50 (oral, rat) 2.9 g/kg, (IP, mus) 0.32 g/kg; sl. toxic; severely irritating to skin and eyes; causes eye burns

Precaution: Combustible liq. and vapor; strongly alkaline; corrosive to copper, brase, and aluminum.

AMPD. [ANGUS]

Chem. Descrip.: 2-Amino-2-methyl-1,3-propanediol

CAS 115-69-5; EINECS 204-100-7

Uses: Pharmaceutical intermediate for prep. of chrysene derivs. used as anti-tumor agents; alkaline buffer for aq. systems; reagent chem. in biomedical and diagnostic applics.; raw material in hypoallergenic prods.
Regulatory: Approved in Japan (cosmetics)
Properties: Wh. cryst. solid, odorless; sol. 250 g/100 ml water; m.w. 105.14; m.p. 109-111 C; b.p. 151 C (10 mm); pH 10.8 (0.1M aq.); 99% conc.
Toxicology: LD50 (oral, mice) 3.5 g/kg, (IP, 0.41 g/kg); irritating to eyes, skin on prolonged contact
Storage: Store in cool, dry area; keep containers closed when not in use.

Amphisol®. [Givaudan-Roure; Bernel]
Chem. Descrip.: DEA-cetyl phosphate
CAS 61693-41-2
Uses: Skin-friendly emulsifier and emulsion stabilizer for pharmaceutical creams/lotions
Regulatory: FDA, EEC, and Japanese compliances
Properties: Wh. to off-wh. powd., pract. odorless to weakly fatty odor; sol. in water, oil; m.w. 427.6; acid no. 230-255; pH 6.0-7.5 (1% aq. disp.); anionic.

Amphisol® K. [Givaudan-Roure; Bernel]
Chem. Descrip.: Potassium cetyl phosphate
CAS 19035-79-1; EINECS 242-769-1
Uses: Emulsifier, stabilizer for pharmaceutical creams and lotions; stable over wide pH range
Regulatory: FDA, EEC, and Japanese compliances
Properties: Colorless solid; sol. in water, oil; anionic.

Anatone. [Am. Labs]
Chem. Descrip.: Peptic hydrolysate from pork tissue
Uses: Suitable for growth of anaerobic bacteria and prod. of toxins; used for testing disinfectants
Regulatory: USP compliance for peptone reagent stds.
Properties: Completely sol. in 2% sol'n.; pH 7 ± 0.1.

Anhydrous Emcompress®. [Mendell]
Chem. Descrip.: Dibasic calcium phosphate anhydrous USP/BP
CAS 7757-93-9; EINECS 231-826-1
Uses: For production of pharmaceutical tablets
Properties: Avg. particle size 136 μ; dens. (tapped) 0.7 g/cc.

Anhydrous Lanolin Grade 1. [Westbrook Lanolin]
Chem. Descrip.: Lanolin B.P./Ph.Eur. with 150 ppm BHT (as stabilizer)
CAS 8006-54-0; EINECS 232-348-6
Uses: Emulsifier, emollient, ointment base for pharmaceuticals
Properties: Lovibond 9-13Y/1.0-1.8R color; yel. soft grease, faint char. odor; sol. in oil; partly sol. in ethanol, min. oil, IPM; insol. in water; m.p. 38-44 C; acid no. 1 max.; sapon. no. 90-105; flash pt. > 100 C; substantially biodeg.
Toxicology: LD50 (oral, rat) > than max. pract. dose of 16 g/kg; nonirritating to skin and eyes; nonsensitizing
Precaution: Nonflamm., but will burn if strongly heated
Storage: Store in well-closed containers in cool place away from direct sunlight; avoid storage over 80 C, esp. for prolonged periods; 2 yrs storage life.

Anhydrous Lanolin Grade 2. [Westbrook Lanolin]
Chem. Descrip.: Lanolin B.P./Ph.Eur. with 150 ppm BHT (as stabilizer)
CAS 8006-54-0; EINECS 232-348-6
Uses: Emulsifier, emollient, ointment base for pharmaceuticals
Properties: Lovibond 14-20Y/1.5-3.0R color; yel. soft grease, faint char. odor; sol. in oil; partly sol. in ethanol, min. oil, IPM; insol. in water; m.p. 38-44 C; acid no. 1 max.; sapon. no. 90-105; flash pt. > 100 C; substantially biodeg.
Toxicology: LD50 (oral, rat) > than max. pract. dose of 16 g/kg; nonirritating to skin and eyes; nonsensitizing
Precaution: Nonflamm., but will burn if strongly heated
Storage: Store in well-closed containers in cool place away from direct sunlight; avoid storage over 80 C, esp. for prolonged periods; 2 yrs storage life.

Anhydrous Lanolin P.80. [Westbrook Lanolin]
Chem. Descrip.: Anhydrous lanolin, pesticide-reduced
CAS 8006-54-0; EINECS 232-348-6
Uses: Emulsifier, emollient, moisturizer for pharmaceuticals, sunscreen preps.
Properties: Lovibond 8-14Y/0.8-2.0R, yel. soft grease, faint char. odor; sol. in oil; insol. in water; m.p. 38-44 C; HLB 4.5; acid no. 1 max.; sapon. no. 90-105; flash pt. > 100 C; 100% conc.; nonionic; substantially biodeg.
Toxicology: Extremely low toxicity; LD50 (oral, rat) > max. pract. dose of 16 g/kg; nonirritating to skin and eyes
Precaution: Nonflamm., but will burn if strongly heated
Storage: Store in well-closed containers in cool place away from direct sunlight; avoid storage over 80 C, esp. for prolonged periods; 2 yrs storage life.

Anhydrous Lanolin P.95. [Westbrook Lanolin]
Chem. Descrip.: Anhydrous lanolin, pract. pesticide-free with 150 ppm BHT (as stabilizer)
CAS 8006-54-0; EINECS 232-348-6
Uses: Emulsifier, emollient, moisturizer for pharmaceuticals (ointments, sunscreen preps.)
Properties: Lovibond 8-14Y/0.8-2.0R color; yel. soft grease, faint char. odor; sol. in oil; insol. in water; m.p. 38-44 C; HLB 4.5; acid no. 1 max.; sapon. no. 90-105; flash pt. > 100 C; 100% conc.; nonionic; substantially biodeg.
Toxicology: Extremely low toxicity; LD50 (oral, rat) > max. pract. dose of 16 g/kg; nonirritating to skin and eyes
Precaution: Nonflamm., but will burn if strongly heated

Storage: Store in well-closed containers in cool place away from direct sunlight; avoid storage over 80 C, esp. for prolonged periods; 2 yrs storage life.

Anhydrous Lanolin Superfine. [Westbrook Lanolin]
Chem. Descrip.: Lanolin B.P./Ph.Eur. with 150 ppm BHT (as stabilizer)
CAS 8006-54-0; EINECS 232-348-6
Uses: Emulsifier, emollient, ointment base for pharmaceuticals
Properties: Lovibond 5-8Y/0.5-1.0R color; yel. soft grease, faint char. odor; sol. in oil; partly sol. in ethanol, min. oil, IPM; insol. in water; m.p. 38-44 C; acid no. 1 max.; sapon. no. 90-105; flash pt. > 100 C; substantially biodeg.
Toxicology: LD50 (oral, rat) > than max. pract. dose of 16 g/kg; nonirritating to skin and eyes; nonsensitizing
Precaution: Nonflamm., but will burn if strongly heated
Storage: Store in well-closed containers in cool place away from direct sunlight; avoid storage over 80 C, esp. for prolonged periods; 2 yrs storage life.

Anhydrous Lanolin USP. [Protameen]
Chem. Descrip.: Lanolin
CAS 8006-54-0; EINECS 232-348-6
Uses: Emollient.

Anhydrous Lanolin USP Cosmetic. [Fanning]
Chem. Descrip.: Lanolin
CAS 8006-54-0; EINECS 232-348-6
Uses: Emollient maintaining skin hydration; forms protective films on skin; for pharmaceutical ointments, protective creams and lotions, burn aids
Properties: Pale yel. tenacous, unctuous substance, faint char. odor; m.p. 36-42 C; iodine no. 18-36.

Anhydrous Lanolin USP Cosmetic AA. [Amerchol]
Chem. Descrip.: Lanolin
CAS 8006-54-0; EINECS 232-348-6
Uses: Emollient.

Anhydrous Lanolin USP Cosmetic Grade. [R.I.T.A.]
Chem. Descrip.: Lanolin USP
CAS 8006-54-0; EINECS 232-348-6
Uses: Provides emolliency, water absorp., emulsification, emulsion stabilization, and pigment dispersion to pharmaceuticals, topical formulations
Properties: Gardner 9+ max. color; m.p. 38-44 C; iodine no. 18-36; sapon. no. 93-107.

Anhydrous Lanolin USP Deodorized AAA. [Amerchol]
Chem. Descrip.: Lanolin
CAS 8006-54-0; EINECS 232-348-6
Uses: Emollient.

Anhydrous Lanolin USP Pharmaceutical. [Fanning]
Chem. Descrip.: Lanolin
CAS 8006-54-0; EINECS 232-348-6
Uses: Emollient maintaining skin hydration; forms protective films on skin; for pharmaceutical ointments, protective creams and lotions, burn aids
Properties: Pale yel. tenacous, unctuous substance, faint char. odor; m.p. 36-42 C; iodine no. 18-36.

Anhydrous Lanolin USP Pharmaceutical. [Amerchol]
Chem. Descrip.: Lanolin
CAS 8006-54-0; EINECS 232-348-6
Uses: Emollient.

Anhydrous Lanolin USP Pharmaceutical Grade. [R.I.T.A.]
Chem. Descrip.: Lanolin USP
CAS 8006-54-0; EINECS 232-348-6
Uses: Provides emolliency, water absorp., emulsification, emulsion stabilization, and pigment dispersion to pharmaceuticals, topical formulations
Properties: Gardner > 10+ color; m.p. 38-44 C; iodine no. 18-36; sapon. no. 93-107.

Anhydrous Lanolin USP Pharmaceutical Light Grade. [R.I.T.A.]
Chem. Descrip.: Lanolin USP
CAS 8006-54-0; EINECS 232-348-6
Uses: Provides emolliency, water absorp., emulsification, emulsion stabilization, and pigment dispersion to pharmaceuticals, topical formulations
Properties: Gardner 10+ max. color; m.p. 38-44 C; iodine no. 18-36; sapon. no. 93-107.

Anhydrous Lanolin USP Superfine [Fanning]
Chem. Descrip.: Lanolin
CAS 8006-54-0; EINECS 232-348-6
Uses: Emollient maintaining skin hydration; forms protective films on skin; for pharmaceutical ointments, protective creams and lotions, burn aids
Properties: Pale yel. tenacous, unctuous substance, faint char. odor; m.p. 36-42 C; iodine no. 18-36.

Anhydrous Lanolin USP Ultrafine. [Fanning]
Chem. Descrip.: Lanolin
CAS 8006-54-0; EINECS 232-348-6
Uses: Emollient maintaining skin hydration; forms protective films on skin; for pharmaceutical ointments, protective creams and lotions, burn aids
Properties: Pale yel. tenacous, unctuous substance, faint char. odor; m.p. 36-42 C; iodine no. 18-36.

Anhydrous Lanolin USP X-tra Deodorized. [R.I.T.A.]
Chem. Descrip.: Lanolin USP
CAS 8006-54-0; EINECS 232-348-6
Uses: Provides emolliency, water absorp., emulsification, emulsion stabilization, and pigment dispersion to pharmaceuticals, topical formulations
Properties: Gardner 8+ max. color; m.p. 38-44 C; iodine no. 18-36; sapon. no. 93-107.

Annatto OS #2894. [Crompton & Knowles/Ingred. Tech.]
Chem. Descrip.: Annatto seed extract in suspension with propylene glycol, refined edible vegetable oil, lecithin, and potassium hydroxide (as processing aid)
Uses: Color additive for pharmaceuticals
Regulatory: FDA 21CFR §73.30, 73.1030, 73.2030
Properties: Dk. reddish-brn. liq., bright yel. to yel.-orange when solubilized in fats/oils; sl. odor; sol. in fats and oils; sp.gr. 0.90 ± 0.10; 2.25% ± 0.15%

bixin content

Storage: 2 yrs shelf life stored in tight containers; avoid exposure to light and heat.

Annatto OS #2922. [Crompton & Knowles/Ingred. Tech.]

Chem. Descrip.: Annatto extract in suspension with propylene glycol, monoglycerides of refined vegetable oil, and potassium hydroxide (as processing aid)

Uses: Color additive for pharmaceuticals

Regulatory: FDA 21CFR §73.30, 73.1030, 73.2030

Properties: Dk. reddish-brn. liq., bright yel. to yel.-orange when disp. in water or oils; sl. odor; misc. in oil and water; sp.gr. 0.95 ± 0.10; 1.3 ± 0.2% bixin content

Storage: 2 yrs shelf life stored in tight containers; avoid exposure to light and heat.

Annatto OS #2923. [Crompton & Knowles/Ingred. Tech.]

Chem. Descrip.: Annatto extract in suspension with propylene glycol, monoglycerides of refined vegetable oil, and potassium hydroxide (as processing aid)

Uses: Color additive for pharmaceuticals

Regulatory: FDA 21CFR §73.30, 73.1030, 73.2030

Properties: Dk. reddish-brn. liq., bright yel. to yel.-orange when disp. in water or oils; sl. odor; misc. in oil and water; sp.gr. 0.95 ± 0.10; 1.75 ± 0.25% bixin content

Storage: 2 yrs shelf life stored in tight containers; avoid exposure to light and heat.

Annatto Liq. #3968, Acid Proof. [Crompton & Knowles/Ingred. Tech.]

Chem. Descrip.: Annatto extract in suspension with propylene glycol, and potassium hydroxide (as processing aid)

Uses: Color additive for pharmaceuticals

Regulatory: FDA 21CFR §73.30, 73.1030, 73.2030

Properties: Dk. reddish-brn. liq., bright yel. to yel.-orange when diluted with water; sl. odor; water-sol.; sp.gr. 0.95 ± 0.10; 3.25 ± 0.25% bixin content

Storage: 2 yrs shelf life stored in tight containers; avoid exposure to light and heat.

Annatto Powd. WS. [Crompton & Knowles]

Chem. Descrip.: Annatto powd.

CAS 1393-63-1; EINECS 215-735-4

Uses: Colorant for pharmaceuticals; exc. resist. to heat

Regulatory: FDA 21CFR §73.30, 73.1030, 73.2030

Properties: Orange-red free-flowing powd., sl. odor; 100% min. thru 80 mesh; sol. in water; insol. in alcohol, org. solvs., oils, fats

Storage: 1 yr shelf life stored in tight containers; avoid exposure to light, heat, and moisture.

Antarox® L-72. [Rhone-Poulenc Surf. & Spec.]

Chem. Descrip.: EO/PO block copolymer

Uses: Surfactant for pharmaceutical prods.

Properties: HLB 6.5; pour pt. -7 C; cloud pt. 25 C (1% aq.); nonionic.

Antarox® P-400. [Rhone-Poulenc Surf. & Spec.]

Chem. Descrip.: PPG

Uses: Solv. and cosolv. for pharmaceuticals

Properties: Liq.; pour pt. < -25 C; 100% conc.; nonionic.

Antarox® P-700. [Rhone-Poulenc Surf. & Spec.]

Chem. Descrip.: PPG

Uses: Solv. and cosolv. for pharmaceuticals

Properties: Liq.; pour pt. < -25 C; 100% conc.; nonionic.

Apifil®. [Gattefosse; Gattefosse SA]

Chem. Descrip.: PEG-8 beeswax

Uses: Structural self-emulsifying base for pharmaceutical o/w emulsions, creams; protects the drug, improves stability of the dosage form

Use level: 8-15%

Properties: Gardner < 8 waxy solid; weak odor; sol. @ 60 C in chloroform, methylene chloride; sl. sol. in veg. oils; insol. in water, ethanol; m.p. 60-65 C; HLB 5.0; acid no. < 5; iodine no. < 10; sapon. no. 70-90; 100% conc.; nonionic

Toxicology: LD0 (oral, rat) > 8.5 g/kg; sl. skin irritant, very sl. eye irritant.

Aquagel SP 399. [Marcel Trading]

Chem. Descrip.: Kappa carrageenan

CAS 9000-07-1; EINECS 232-524-2

Uses: Forms thermally reversible gels for pharmaceutical applics. that require a firm texture; gelation enhanced by addition of potassium salts

Properties: Wh. creamy free-flowing powd.; 96.9% thru 200 mesh; visc. 15-40 cps (1% aq., 75 C); pH 8-10 (1% aq., 30 C); 12% max. moisture.

Aqualon® Cellulose Gum. [Hercules/Aqualon]

Chem. Descrip.: Sodium carboxymethylcellulose, standard, food, and pharmaceutical grades

CAS 9004-32-4

Uses: Suspending agent, tableting binder, visc. increasing agent, excipient for pharmaceuticals; also therapeutic uses in bulk-forming laxatives

Regulatory: FDA 21CFR §182.1745, GRAS

Properties: Water-sol.

Toxicology: LD50 (oral, rat) 27 g/kg; sl. eye irritant; nonirritating to skin.

Aqualose L75. [Westbrook Lanolin]

Chem. Descrip.: PEG-75 lanolin USP

CAS 61790-81-6

Uses: Emollient, moisturizer, emulsifier, solubilizer

Properties: Wax; water-sol.; drop pt. 45-52 C; HLB 16.0; acid no. 5 max.; sapon. no. 10-26; cloud pt. 75-83 C (aq.); pH 3.5-7.0 (5% aq.); 100% conc.; nonionic.

Aqualose L75/50. [Westbrook Lanolin]

Chem. Descrip.: PEG-75 lanolin USP

CAS 61790-81-6

Uses: Emollient, emulsifier

Properties: Clear to sl. cloudy visc. liq. to soft gel; water-sol.; nonflamm.; 50% aq.; nonionic; substantially biodeg.; nonhazardous

Toxicology: Nontoxic.

Aquathik. [United-Guardian]

Uses: Gelling agent for aq. sol'ns. having a mildly acidic pH (down to 2.0); produces stable gels at levels of 2-3%; physiologically inert; for health care applics.

Argobase 125T. [Westbrook Lanolin]
Chem. Descrip.: Lanolin alcohol, min. oil, and octyldodecanol with 150 ppm BHT (antioxidant)
Uses: Liq. absorption base; enhances appearance and elegance of pharmaceutical preps.
Properties: Almost colorless to pale yel. clear oily liq., faint char. odor; sol. in min. oil, IPA, IPM; partly sol. in ethanol; insol. in water; sp.gr. 0.84-0.87; HLB 8.0; acid no. 1 max.; iodine no. 12 max.; sapon.no. 3 max.; hyd. no. 11-18; flash pt. > 100 C; ref. index 1.46-1.476; nonhazardous
Toxicology: Extremely low toxicity; LD50 (oral, rat) > max. pract. dose of 16 g/kg; nonirritating to eyes and skin
Precaution: Nonflamm., but will burn if strongly heated
Storage: 2 yrs shelf life when stored in well-closed containers under good conditions; avoid prolonged heating above 80 C; if cloudiness occurs, gently warm and stir.

Argobase EU. [Westbrook Lanolin]
Chem. Descrip.: Lanolin alcohol, min. oil, petrolatum, and paraffin
Uses: Emollient, emulsifier, stabilizer, absorp. base for pharmaceutical ointments or w/o emulsified creams; active therapeutic ingreds. may be dissolved in either the oil or water phase or physically dispersed as a suspension in the emulsion
Regulatory: Meets BP specs. for wool alcohols ointment
Properties: Pale yel. soft solid, pract. odorless; mostly sol. in min. oil, IPM; partly sol. in acetone, anhyd. ethanol and IPA; insol. in water; m.p. 39-45 C; HLB 4.0; acid no. 0.25 max.; flash pt. > 100 C; 6% conc.; nonionic; nonhazardous
Toxicology: BP GRAS for topical applic.
Precaution: Nonflamm., but will burn if strongly heated
Storage: Store in closed containers in cool place; avoid heating above 80 C; 2 yrs storage life under good conditions.

Argobase EUC 2. [Westbrook Lanolin]
Chem. Descrip.: Lanolin alcohol, cetearyl alcohol, ozokerite, min. oil, and petrolatum
Uses: W/o emulsifying absorp. base for pharmaceutical ointments, w/o creams; at low levels as HLB adjuster and stabilizer for o/w emulsions; emollient
Regulatory: Improved version of wool alcohols ointment for the German Pharmacopoeia
Properties: Creamy to pale yel. unctuous mass, almost odorless; mostly sol. in min. oil, IPM; partly sol. in acetone; sl. sol. in anhyd. ethanol and IPA; insol. in water; m.p. 35 C; acid no. 2 max.; sapon. no. 2 max.; flash pt. > 100 C; 12.5% act.; nonhazardous
Toxicology: Nontoxic
Precaution: Nonflamm., but will burn if strongly heated
Storage: 2 yrs storage life under good conditions; avoid overheating, esp. for prolonged periods.

Arlacel® 20. [ICI Spec. Chem.; ICI Surf. Am.; ICI Surf. Belgium]
Chem. Descrip.: Sorbitan laurate
Uses: Emulsifier for pharmaceuticals
Properties: Yel. amber liq.; sol. in methanol, ethanol, min., cottonseed and corn oils, ethylene glycol; sp.gr. 1.0; visc. 4250 cps; HLB 8.6; flash pt. > 300 F; 100% act.; nonionic.

Arlacel® 40. [ICI Spec. Chem.; ICI Surf. Am.; ICI Surf. Belgium]
Chem. Descrip.: Sorbitan palmitate
CAS 26266-57-9; EINECS 247-568-8
Uses: Emulsifier for pharmaceuticals
Properties: Cream beads; sol. in IPA; sp.gr. 1; HLB 6.7; pour pt. 48 C; flash pt. > 300 F; 100% act.; nonionic.

Arlacel® 60. [ICI Spec. Chem.; ICI Surf. Am.; ICI Surf. Belgium]
Chem. Descrip.: Sorbitan stearate
CAS 1338-41-6; EINECS 215-664-9
Uses: Emulsifier for pharmaceuticals
Properties: Cream-colored waxy beads, solid; sol. in IPA; HLB 4.7; flash pt. > 300 F; pour pt. 53 C; 100% act.; nonionic.

Arlacel® 80. [ICI Spec. Chem.; ICI Surf. Am.; ICI Surf. Belgium]
Chem. Descrip.: Sorbitan oleate
CAS 1338-43-8; EINECS 215-665-4
Uses: Emulsifier for pharmaceuticals
Properties: Yel. amber oil, liq.; sol. in IPA, min. and cottonseed oils; sp.gr. 1; visc. 1900 cps; HLB 4.3; flash pt. > 300 F; 100% act.; nonionic.

Arlacel® 83. [ICI Spec. Chem.; ICI Surf. Am.; ICI Surf. Belgium]
Chem. Descrip.: Sorbitan sesquioleate
CAS 8007-43-0; EINECS 232-360-1
Uses: Emulsifier for pharmaceuticals
Properties: Yel. clear oily liq.; sol. in min. and cottonseed oils, ethanol, IPA; sp.gr. 1; visc 1500 cps; HLB 3.7; flash pt. > 300 F; 100% act.; nonionic.

Arlacel® 85. [ICI Spec. Chem.; ICI Surf. Am.; ICI Surf. Belgium]
Chem. Descrip.: Sorbitan trioleate
CAS 26266-58-0; EINECS 247-569-3
Uses: Surfactant for pharmaceuticals
Properties: Yel. amber oily liq.; sol. in IPA, alcohol, min., cottonseed and corn oil; sp.gr. 0.95; visc. 250 cps; HLB 1.8; flash pt. > 300 F; 100% act.; nonionic.

Arlacel® 186. [ICI Spec. Chem.; ICI Surf. Am.; ICI Atkemix; ICI Surf. Belgium]
Chem. Descrip.: Glyceryl oleate, propylene glycol, 0.02% BHA and 0.01% citric acid as preservatives
Uses: Defoamer for oral pharmaceutical prods.
Properties: Pale yel. clear liq.; sol. in ethanol, IPA, cottonseed and min. oils; sp.gr. 1; visc. 150 cps; HLB 2.8; flash pt. > 300 F; 100% act.; nonionic.

Arlex. [ICI Surf. Am.]
Chem. Descrip.: Sorbitol
CAS 50-70-4; EINECS 200-061-5

Uses: Humectant, nutritive sweetener, oleaginous vehicle, tablet diluent.

Arlypon® F. [Henkel KGaA/Cospha]
Chem. Descrip.: Laureth-2
CAS 68439-50-9; EINECS 221-279-7
Uses: Thickener for pharmaceuticals
Use level: 1-3%
Properties: Colorless to ylsh. liq., mild odor; hyd. no. 182-188; cloud pt. 4-8 C; pH 5.5-8.0 (1%); 1% max. water
Storage: Store in sealed containers below 30 C; may become turbid after storage at 15 C, heat to 25 C to clear.

Armotan® MO. [Akzo Nobel bv]
Chem. Descrip.: Sorbitan oleate
CAS 1338-43-8; EINECS 215-665-4
Uses: W/o emulsifier for pharmaceutical preps.
Properties: Gardner 8 liq.; sp.gr. 1.01; visc. 9.5-11 poise; pour pt. -12 C; 100% conc.; nonionic.

Arquad® B-100. [Akzo Nobel]
Chem. Descrip.: Benzalkonium chloride, aq. IPA
CAS 68391-01-5
Uses: Antimicrobial for pharmaceuticals
Properties: Gardner 2 liq.; sol. in acetone, alcohol, most polar solvs., water; m.w. 380; sp.gr. 0.967; pour pt. 0 F; flash pt. (PMCC) 32 C; pH 7-8; 50% act. in aq. IPA; cationic.

Arquad® DM18B-90. [Akzo Nobel]
Chem. Descrip.: Octadecyl dimethylbenzyl ammonium chloride
CAS 122-19-0; EINECS 204-527-9
Uses: Conditioner, emulsifier for pharmaceuticals
Properties: Wh. powder; water sol.; pH 5-8 (1%); 90% min act.

Ascorbic Acid USP/FCC, 100 Mesh. [Int'l. Sourcing]
Chem. Descrip.: Ascorbic acid USP/FCC
CAS 50-81-7; EINECS 200-066-2
Uses: Vitamin, antioxidant
Properties: Translucent wh. to sl. yel. cryst. powd., pract. odorless, acidic taste; 95% min. thru 30 mesh, 50-65% thru 60 mesh; appreciable sol. in water; m.w. 176.13; sp.gr. 1.65; m.p. 375 F (dec.); pH 2.5-3.0; 99-100.5% assay
Toxicology: Possible skin and eye irritant from powd. contact; dust may irritant respiratory tract; heated to decomp., emits acrid smoke and irritating fumes
Storage: Store under cool, dry conditions free from metal contact; protect from light in well-closed containers.

Ascorbic Acid USP, FCC Fine Gran. No. 6045655. [Roche]
Chem. Descrip.: Ascorbic acid USP, FCC
CAS 50-81-7; EINECS 200-066-2
Uses: Source of vitamin C, antioxidant in pharmaceuticals (direct compression tablets, multivitamin tablets, dry preps.)
Regulatory: FDA GRAS
Properties: Wh. or sl. yel. cryst. powd., pract. odorless, pleasantly tart taste; sol. 1 g/3 ml water, 30 ml alcohol; m.w. 176.13; bulk dens. 0.8-1.1 (tapped); m.p. 190 C; pH 1.9-2.4 (10% aq.); 99-100.5% assay
Precaution: May deteriorate on exposure to atmospheric moisture, oxidizes readily in aq. sol'n.; avoid contact with iron, copper, or nickel salts
Storage: Store in tight, light-resist. containers, optimally @ ≤ 72 F; avoid exposure to moisture and excessive heat.

Ascorbic Acid USP, FCC Fine Powd. No. 6045652. [Roche]
Chem. Descrip.: Ascorbic acid
CAS 50-81-7; EINECS 200-066-2
Uses: Source of vitamin C, antioxidant in pharmaceutical prods. (vitamin C tablets, multivitamin capsules, chewable tablets)
Regulatory: FDA GRAS
Properties: Wh. or sl. yel. cryst. fine powd., pract. odorless, pleasantly tart taste; sol. 1 g/3 ml water, 30 ml alcohol; m.w. 176.13; bulk dens. 0.55-1.0 (tapped); m.p. 190 C; pH 1.9-2.4 (10% aq.); 99-100.5% assay
Precaution: May deteriorate on exposure to atmospheric moisture, oxidizes rapidly in aq. sol'n.; avoid contact with iron, copper, or nickel salts
Storage: Store in tight, light-resist. containers, optimally @ ≤ 72 F; avoid exposure to moisture and excessive heat.

Ascorbic Acid USP, FCC Gran. No. 6045654. [Roche]
Chem. Descrip.: Ascorbic acid USP, FCC
CAS 50-81-7; EINECS 200-066-2
Uses: Source of vitamin C and antioxidant in pharmaceutical prods. (direct compression tablets, multivitamin tablets, dry preps.)
Regulatory: FDA GRAS
Properties: Wh. or sl. yel. cryst. powd., pract. odorless, pleasantly tart taste; 100% thru 20 mesh, 20% max. thru 50 mesh; sol. 1 g/3 ml water, 30 ml alcohol; m.w. 176.13; bulk dens. 0.8-1.0 (tapped); m.p. 190 C; pH 1.9-2.4 (10% aq.); 99-100.5% assay
Precaution: May deteriorate on exposure to atmospheric moisture; oxidizes readily in aq. sol'n.; avoid contact with iron, copper, or nickel salts
Storage: Store in tight, light-resist. containers, optimally @ ≤ 72 F; avoid exposure to moisture and excessive heat.

Ascorbic Acid USP, FCC Type S No. 6045660. [Roche]
Chem. Descrip.: Ascorbic acid USP, FCC
CAS 50-81-7; EINECS 200-066-2
Uses: Source of vitamin C, antioxidant for pharmaceuticals (oral liq. prods., certain dry prods.)
Regulatory: FDA GRAS
Properties: Wh. or sl. yel. cryst. powd., pract. odorless, pleasantly tart taste; sol. 1 g/3 ml water, 30 ml alcohol; m.w. 176.13; bulk dens. 0.8-1.2 (tapped); m.p. 190 C; pH 1.9-2.4 (10% aq.); 99-100.5% assay
Precaution: May deteriorate on exposure to atmospheric moisture, oxidizes readily in aq. sol'n.; avoid contact with iron, copper, or nickel salts
Storage: Store in tight, light-resist. containers,

optimally @ ≤ 72 F; avoid exposure to moisture and excessive heat.

Ascorbic Acid USP, FCC Ultra-Fine Powd No. 6045653. [Roche]
Chem. Descrip.: Ascorbic acid USP, FCC
CAS 50-81-7; EINECS 200-066-2
Uses: Source of vitamin C and antioxidant in pharmaceutical prods. (vitamin C tablets, multivitamin tablets/capsules, chewable tablets; coating, dusting, layering of time-release prods.)
Regulatory: FDA GRAS
Properties: Wh. or sl. yel. cryst. powd., pract. odorless, pleasantly tart taste; 100% thru 100 mesh, 95% min. thru 200 mesh; sol. 1 g/3 ml water, 30 ml alcohol; m.w. 176.13; bulk dens. 0.8-1.1 (tapped); m.p. 190 C; pH 1.9-2.4 (10% aq.)
Precaution: May deteriorate on exposure to atmospheric moisture; oxidizes readily in aq. sol'n.; avoid contact with iron, copper, or nickel salts
Storage: Store in tight, light-resist. containers, optimally @ ≤ 72 F; avoid exposure to moisture and excessive heat.

Ascorbyl Palmitate NF, FCC No. 60412. [Roche]
Chem. Descrip.: Ascorbyl palmitate NF, FCC
CAS 137-66-6; EINECS 205-305-4
Uses: Fat-sol. form of ascorbic acid; antioxidant for pharmaceuticals; preservative for natural oils, oleates, fragrances, colors, vitamins, edible oils/waxes
Regulatory: FDA 21CFR §182.3149, GRAS
Properties: Wh. or ylsh. wh. cryst. powd., sl. odor; very sl. sol. in water and veg. oils; sol. 1 g/4.5 ml alcohol; m.w. 414.54; apparent dens. 8.7 lb/ft^3; m.p. 107-117 C; 95-100.5% assay
Storage: Store in tight containers in cool dry place @ 8-15 C; avoid exposure to light, moisture, excessive heat.

Asebiol®. [Laboratoires Sérobiologiques]
Chem. Descrip.: Amino acids, sulfur peptides, and vitamin B complex
Uses: Biotechnological active for oily skin care; regulates sebaceous secretions of acneic skin
Use level: 5-10%
Properties: Amber limpid liq.; water-sol.

Asol. [Lucas Meyer]
Chem. Descrip.: Lecithin fraction
CAS 8002-43-5; EINECS 232-307-2
Uses: Release agent, emulsifier for pharmaceuticals
Properties: Liq.; 40-100% conc.; nonionic.

ATBC. [Morflex]
Chem. Descrip.: Acetyltri-n-butyl citrate
CAS 77-90-7; EINECS 201-067-0
Uses: Plasticizer for aq. based pharmaceutical coatings; provides controlled sustained release of drugs; protects drugs from gastric juices but allows its release into the intestine
Regulatory: FDA 21CFR §172.515, 175.105, 175.300, 175.320, 175.380, 175.390, 176.170, 177.1210, 178.3910, 181.27
Properties: Insol. in water; m.w. 402.5; sp.gr. 1.045-1.055; dens. 8.74 lb/gal; visc. 32.7 cps; b.p. 173 C (1 mm); pour pt. -75 F; flash pt. (COC) 204 C; ref. index 1.4410-1.4425; 99% min. assay.

ATEC. [Morflex]
Chem. Descrip.: Acetyltriethyl citrate
CAS 77-89-4; EINECS 201-066-5
Uses: Plasticizer for aq. based pharmaceutical coatings; provides controlled sustained release of drugs; protects drugs from gastric juices but allows its release into the intestine
Regulatory: FDA 21CFR §175.105, 175.300, 175.320, 175.380, 176.170, 177.1210, 178.3910, 181.27
Properties: Sol. 0.72 g/100 ml water; m.w. 318.3; sp.gr. 1.135-1.139; dens. 9.47 lb/gal; visc. 53.7 cps; b.p. 132 C (1 mm); pour pt. -45 F; flash pt. (COC) 188 C; ref. index 1.432-1.441; 99% min. assay.

Avicel® PH-101. [FMC]
Chem. Descrip.: Microcryst. cellulose NF
CAS 9004-34-6
Uses: Binder, disintegrant, flow aid, and filler for pharmaceuticals and animal health prods.
Properties: Wh. powd., < 30% +200 mesh; odorless. but disp. in water; pH 5.5-7.0.

Avicel® PH-102. [FMC]
Chem. Descrip.: Microcryst. cellulose NF
CAS 9004-34-6
Uses: Binder, disintegrant, flow aid, and filler for pharmaceuticals and animal health prods.
Properties: Wh. powd., > 45% +200 mesh; odorless; insol. but disp. in water; pH 5.5-7.0.

Avicel® PH-103. [FMC]
Chem. Descrip.: Microcryst. cellulose NF
CAS 9004-34-6
Uses: Binder, disintegrant, flow aid, and filler for pharmaceuticals and animal health prods.
Properties: Wh. powd., < 30% +200 mesh; odorless; insol. but disp. in water; pH 5.5-7.0.

Avicel® PH-105. [FMC]
Chem. Descrip.: Microcryst. cellulose NF
CAS 9004-34-6
Uses: Binder, disintegrant, flow aid, and filler for pharmaceuticals and animal health prods.
Properties: Wh. fine powd., < 1% +400 mesh; insol. in water and org. solvs.; pH 5.0-7.0.

B

Baco AF. [BA Chem. Ltd.]
Chem. Descrip.: Alumina trihydate
CAS 21645-51-2
Uses: High purity grade for use in toothpaste, pharmaceuticals; stabilizes sol. of fluorine compds. in toothpaste
Unverified

Barquat® CT-29. [Lonza]
Chem. Descrip.: Cetrimonium chloride
CAS 112-02-7; EINECS 203-928-6
Uses: Coagulating agent in mfg. of antibiotics
Properties: Liq.; 29% act.

Basic Magnesium Carbonate USP Heavy. [Morton Int'l.]
Chem. Descrip.: Magnesium carbonate
Uses: Buffering agent in pharmaceuticals
Regulatory: USP, FCC compliance
Properties: Wh. powd.; 0.5% 325 mesh; bulk dens. 0.25 g/ml
Toxicology: Nontoxic to intact skin, may cause irritation to abraded skin.

Basic Magnesium Carbonate USP Heavy Low Moisture. [Morton Int'l.]
Chem. Descrip.: Magnesium carbonate USP
Uses: Antacid, fragrance carrier, colorant
Toxicology: Nontoxic to intact skin, may cause irritation to abraded skin.

Basic Magnesium Carbonate USP Light. [Morton Int'l.]
Chem. Descrip.: Magnesium carbonate
Uses: Buffering agent in pharmaceuticals
Regulatory: USP, FCC compliance
Properties: Wh. powd.; 0.5% 325 mesh; bulk dens. 0.15 g/ml
Toxicology: Nontoxic to intact skin, may cause irritation to abraded skin.

Basic Magnesium Carbonate USP Pregranular Heavy. [Morton Int'l.]
Chem. Descrip.: Magnesium carbonate USP
Uses: Antacid, fragrance carrier, colorant
Toxicology: Nontoxic to intact skin, may cause irritation to abraded skin.

Basic Magnesium Carbonate USP Pregranular Light. [Morton Int'l.]
Chem. Descrip.: Magnesium carbonate USP
Uses: Antacid, fragrance carrier, colorant
Toxicology: Nontoxic to intact skin, may cause irritation to abraded skin.

BBS. [ABITEC]
Chem. Descrip.: Partially hydrog. veg. oil (soybean and palm); nontropical version also avail.
Uses: Lubricant, moisturizer for clinical nutrition, coating, dermatologicals, encapsulation, soft gelatin capsules, sustained release applics.; USP/NF grades avail.
Properties: Lovibond 1.5R max. liq., plastic; m.p. 115-117 F; acid no. 0.1 max.

B&C Caramel Powd. [MLG Enterprises Ltd.]
Chem. Descrip.: Caramel color
CAS 8028-89-5; EINECS 232-435-9
Uses: Natural colorant for pharmaceuticals
Properties: Free-flowing powd.; 100% min. thru 40 mesh, 90% min. thru 100 mesh; pH 6.7-7.7 (1%); 4% max. moisture
Storage: Unlimited shelf life under normal storage conditions.

Benecel® Hydroxypropyl Methylcellulose. [Hercules/Aqualon]
Chem. Descrip.: Hydroxypropyl methylcellulose
CAS 9004-65-3
Uses: Protective colloid, suspending agent; tablet excipient.

Benecel® Methylcellulose. [Hercules/Aqualon]
Chem. Descrip.: Methyl cellulose
CAS 9004-67-5
Uses: Thickener, stabilizer, rheology control agent, film-former, suspending agent, water-retention aid, binder for pharmaceuticals
Properties: Water-sol.; visc. 10-12,000 mPa•s (2% aq.); nonionic.

Benol®. [Witco/Petroleum Spec.]
Chem. Descrip.: Wh. min. oil NF
Uses: Lubricant used in drug industry
Regulatory: FDA 21CFR §172.878, §178.3620a
Properties: Water wh., odorless, tasteless; sp.gr. 0.839-0.855; visc. 18-20 cSt (40 C); pour pt. -7 C; flash pt. 182 C.

Bentonite USP BC 670. [Whittaker, Clark & Daniels]
Chem. Descrip.: Bentonite
CAS 1302-78-9; EINECS 215-108-5
Uses: Thickener, protective colloid, emulsifier, suspending agent.

Benzoic Acid U.S.P./F.C.C. [Nipa Hardwicke]
Chem. Descrip.: Benzoic acid USP/FCC
CAS 65-85-0; EINECS 200-618-2
Uses: Preservative for pharmaceuticals, mouth-

washes

Regulatory: FDA 21CFR §184.1021, GRAS (to 0.1%)

Properties: Cryst., powd.; sol. 0.35 g/100 g water; m.w. 122.12; dens. 8.75 lb/gal; visc. 1.2 cps (130 C); vapor pressure 10 mm Hg (132 C); m.p. 122.4 C; b.p. 249 C; solid. pt. 121-123 C; flash pt. (TCC) 121 C; ref. index 1.504 (132 C); 99.5-100.5% assay

Toxicology: Relatively nontoxic; LD50 (oral, rat) 2530 mg/kg; may cause skin and eye irritation on direct contact.

Beta W7. [Wacker-Chemie GmbH]

Chem. Descrip.: β-Cyclodextrin

CAS 7585-39-9; EINECS 231-493-2

Uses: Complex hosting guest molecules; increases the sol. and bioavailability of other substances; masks flavor, odor, or coloration; stabilizes against light, oxidation, heat, and hydrolysis; turns liqs. or volatiles into stable solid powds.

Properties: Wh. cryst. powd.; sol. 1.85 g/100 ml in water; m.w. 1135

Toxicology: High dose levels may be hazardous; absorbed by intestinal walls, causes kidney damage; not degraded in the sm. intestines; high doses may cause gas generation and diarrhea.

Beta W7 HP 0.9. [Wacker-Chemie GmbH]

Chem. Descrip.: Hydroxypropyl-β-cyclodextrin

CAS 94035-02-6

Uses: Complex hosting guest molecules; increases the sol. and bioavailability of other substances; masks flavor, odor, or coloration; stabilizes against light, oxidation, heat, and hydrolysis; turns liqs. or volatiles into stable solid powds.

Properties: M.w. 1507.

Beta W7 M1.8. [Wacker-Chemie GmbH]

Chem. Descrip.: Methyl-β-cyclodextrin

Uses: Complex hosting guest molecules; increases the sol. and bioavailability of other substances; masks flavor, odor, or coloration; stabilizes against light, oxidation, heat, and hydrolysis; turns liqs. or volatiles into stable solid powds.

Properties: Sol. (g/100 ml): > 150 g water, 90 g methanol, 70 g $CHCl_3$, 65 g THF; m.w. 1311; not readily biodeg.

Toxicology: LD50 (oral, rat) > 8000 mg/kg; nonirritating to skin and eyes; even sm. amts. taken orally or repeated topical applic. can cause kidney damage.

Beta W7 P. [Wacker-Chemie GmbH]

Chem. Descrip.: β-Cyclodextrin polymer

CAS 7585-39-9; EINECS 231-493-2

Uses: Complex hosting guest molecules; increases the sol. and bioavailability of other substances; masks flavor, odor, or coloration; stabilizes against light, oxidation, heat, and hydrolysis; turns liqs. or volatiles into stable solid powds.

24% Beta Carotene HS-E in Veg. Oil No. 65671. [Roche]

Chem. Descrip.: β-Carotene FCC suspension in partially hydrogenated cottonseed oil and partially hydrogenated soybean oils, with 3.5% dl-α-

tocopherol, 1.5% ascorbyl palmitate, and citric acid as preservatives

Uses: Colorant and antioxidant for oil phases of prods., in pharmaceuticals

Regulatory: FDA 21CFR §73.95 (food use), 73.1095 (drug use), 73.2095 (cosmetic use), 182.1245, 182.5245 GRAS

Properties: Brick-red suspension, pourable fluid above 68 F, thick paste at refrigerated temps.; particle size ≥ 90% < 10 μ; sol. in all veg. oils and fats; 22% min. assay (β-carotene)

Storage: Store in tightly closed container in cool, dry place (59-86 F); stir well before use.

24% Beta Carotene Semi-Solid Suspension No. 65642. [Roche]

Chem. Descrip.: β-Carotene suspension with hydrog. coconut oil, 1% glyceryl stearate as stabilizer

Uses: Colorant for pharmaceuticals

Regulatory: FDA 21CFR §73.95 (food use), 73.1095 (drug use), 73.2095 (cosmetic use), 182.5245 GRAS

Properties: Brick-red homogeneous suspension, semisolid @ 70-90 F; particle size ≥ 90% < 10 μ; sol. in all veg. oils and fats; 24% min. assay (β-carotene)

Storage: Store in tightly closed container in cool, dry place.

30% Beta Carotene in Veg. Oil No. 65646. [Roche]

Chem. Descrip.: β-Carotene in food-grade veg. oils (partially hydrog. cottonseed oil and partially hydrogenated soybean oils)

Uses: Colorant, antioxidant for pharmaceuticals (soft gel capsules)

Regulatory: FDA 21CFR §73.95 (food use), 73.1095 (drug use), 73.2095 (cosmetic use), 182.5245 GRAS

Properties: Terra-cotta red suspension, fresh char. odor; crystal size 90% ≤ 10 μ; sol. 0.1% in all veg. oils and fats @ R.T.; 500,000 I.U. Vitamin A activity/g

Storage: Store in cool, dry place in tightly closed container; protect from freezing.

BFP 64 O. [Am. Ingreds.]

Chem. Descrip.: Mono- and diglycerides

Uses: Emulsifier for pharmaceuticals

Properties: Ivory wh. plastic; m.p. 102-106 F.

BFP 74E. [Am. Ingreds.]

Chem. Descrip.: Mono- and diglycerides with ≤ 0.01% citric acid and 0.02% BHT as preservatives

Uses: Emulsifier for topical ointments

Properties: Ivory wh. fine flakes; m.p. 135-145 F; iodine no. 3 max.; 40-46% alpha monoglycerides

Storage: Up to 6 mos storage life at temps. not to exceed 85 F.

Biodiastase 1000. [Mitsubishi Int'l.; Amano Enzyme USA; Unipex]

Chem. Descrip.: Fungal amylase from *Aspergillus oryzae*

CAS 9000-92-4; EINECS 232-567-7

Uses: Digestive enzyme for pharmaceutical use

Properties: Powd.

Biodiastase Conc. [Amano Enzyme USA; Unipex]
Chem. Descrip.: Amylase from *Aspergillus*
CAS 9000-92-4; EINECS 232-567-7
Uses: Enzyme for pharmaceutical use.

Biological Concentrate. [Am. Labs]
Chem. Descrip.: Conc. hydrolysate of beef tissues
Uses: For prep. of nutritive media; forms exc. medium for growth of either aerobic or anaerobic bacteria
Properties: Liq.; completely sol. in 2% sol'n.; pH 7-7.1; 50% min. solids
Storage: Store in original containers in cooler; remove to R.T. 24 h before use to facilitate handling.

Biophytex®. [Laboratoires Sérobiologiques]
Chem. Descrip.: Propylene glycol, butcherbroom extract, hydrocotyl extract, panthenol, hydrolyzed milk protein, calendula extract, hydrolyzed yeast protein, horse chestnut extract, and licorice extract
Uses: Soothing phytocomplex providing local anti-inflammatory and anti-irritant action in sun care prods.
Use level: 3-5%
Properties: Amber sl. syrupy liq.; water-sol.

Biopure® 100. [Nipa Hardwicke]
Chem. Descrip.: Imidazolidinyl urea
CAS 39236-46-9; EINECS 254-372-6
Uses: Preservative for dermopharmaceuticals
Properties: Wh. free-flowing fine powd., odorless; m.w. 406.3; pH 7.15 (1% aq.).

d-Biotin USP, FCC No. 63345. [Roche]
Chem. Descrip.: D-Biotin USP, FCC
CAS 58-85-5; EINECS 200-399-3
Uses: Component of enzyme systems involved in metabolism of fats and carbohydrates, in other biochemical processes; nutrient in pharmaceutical and special dietary prods. incl. multivitamins in liq., tablet, capsule or powd. forms
Properties: Pract. wh. cryst. powd.; 100% min. thru 80 mesh; sol. 1 g/5000 ml water, 1300 ml alcohol; more sol. in hot water, dil. alkali; insol. in other common org. solvs.; m.w. 244.31; m.p. 229-232 C; 97.5% min. assay
Precaution: Oxidized by hydrogen peroxide or potassium permanganate
Storage: Store @ 59-86 F.

Bitrit-1™ (1% Biotin Trituration No. 65324) [Roche]
Chem. Descrip.: Biotin FCC in dicalcium phosphate dihydrate carrier
Uses: Component of enzyme systems involved in metabolism of fats and carbohydrates, in other biochemical processes; nutrient in pharmaceutical and special dietary prods. incl. multivitamins in tablet, capsule or powd. forms
Properties: Wh. free-flowing powd.; 98% min. thru 80 mesh; insol. in water, org. solvs.; bulk dens. 50 lb/ft^3; 10 mg min. d-biotin/g
Storage: Store @ 59-86 F.

Bixin Crystal 95. [Helianthus SA]
Chem. Descrip.: Natural annatto pigment cis-bixin

CAS 8015-67-6
Uses: Natural orange color for pharmaceutical use
Regulatory: Complies with FDA 21CFR §73.30 for annatto color, exempt from U.S. certification
Properties: Reddish cryst. powd.; 95 ± 2% cis-bixin
Storage: Exceptionally stable; str. losses are limited to 3-5% annually at ambient temps. and are less under refrigerated conditions.

Blandol®. [Witco/Petroleum Spec.]
Chem. Descrip.: Wh. min. oil N.F.
Uses: Lubricant used in pharmaceutical ointments and creams
Regulatory: FDA 21CFR §172.878, §178.3620a
Properties: Water-wh., odorless, tasteless; sp.gr. 0.839-0.855; visc. 14-17 cSt (40 C); pour pt. -12 C; flash pt. 185 C.

BLO®. [ISP]
Chem. Descrip.: γ-Butyrolactone
CAS 96-48-0; EINECS 202-509-5
Uses: Solv.; stabilizer for aq. sol'ns. of drugs and vitamins; synthesis of vitamin B1, DL-methionine, DL-homoserine; intermediate for chlorophyll, vitamin E; CNS depressants, anesthetics, analgesics, analeptics; anti-cancer activity in mice
Properties: Liq.; misc. with water, methanol, acetone, benzene, CCl_4, ethyl ether, monochlorobenzene; insol. in aliphatic hydrocarbons; sp.gr. 1.12 (25/4 C); visc. 1.7 cP; m.p. -44 C; b.p. 204 C; flash pt. (OC) 98 C
Precaution: Noncorrosive; low fire hazard.

Bone Gelatin Type B 200 Bloom. [Hormel]
Chem. Descrip.: Gelatin
CAS 9000-70-8; EINECS 232-554-6
Uses: Stabilizer, gellant, protein used in pharmaceutical applics.
Properties: Beige, weak bouillon-like odor; 30 mesh; visc. 52 ± 4 mps; pH 4.5-5.8; 12% max. moisture
Storage: Stable for up to 1 yr when stored dry at ambient temps.; keep containers tightly closed.

Brij® 700. [ICI Spec. Chem.; ICI Surf. Am.; ICI Surf. Belgium]
Chem. Descrip.: Steareth-100
CAS 9005-00-9
Uses: Emulsifier, wetting agent for pharmaceuticals; oil solubilization
Properties: Pale yel. solid; sol. in water, alcohol; disp. in cottonseed oil; HLB 18.8; pour pt. 55 C; 100% conc.; nonionic.

Brillante. [Luzenac Am.]
Chem. Descrip.: Pure Italian talc USP
CAS 14807-96-6; EINECS 238-877-9
Uses: Specially treated for sheer, pearlescent appearance; used in creams, lotions
Properties: Powd.; 94% thru 200 mesh; median diam. 35 μ; tapped dens. 62 lb/ft^3; pH 9 (10% slurry).

Briquest® ADPA-60AW. [Albright & Wilson UK]
Chem. Descrip.: 1-Hydroxyethylidene-1,1-diphosphonic acid aq. sol'n.
Uses: Sequestrant for radioactive pharmaceuticals
Properties: APHA < 80 clear liq.; slight odor; m.w.

206; sp.gr. 1.46 (20 C); visc. 100 cP (20 C); pH 1.8 (1%); 60% act.

Britex C. [Auschem SpA]
Chem. Descrip.: Ceteth-2
CAS 9004-95-9
Uses: Emulsifier for pharmaceuticals
Properties: Waxy solid; HLB 5.3; 100% conc.; nonionic
Unverified

Britex C 100. [Auschem SpA]
Chem. Descrip.: Ceteth-10
CAS 9004-95-9
Uses: Emulsifier for pharmaceuticals
Properties: Solid; HLB 12.9; 100% conc.; nonionic.

Britex C 200. [Auschem SpA]
Chem. Descrip.: Ceteth-20
CAS 9004-95-9
Uses: Emulsifier for pharmaceuticals
Properties: Flakes; HLB 15.7; 100% conc.; nonionic.

Britex CO 220. [Auschem SpA]
Chem. Descrip.: Cetoleth-22
CAS 68920-66-1
Uses: Emulsifier for pharmaceuticals
Properties: Flakes; HLB 15.9; 100% conc.; nonionic
Unverified

Britex CS 110. [Auschem SpA]
Chem. Descrip.: Ceteareth-11
CAS 68439-49-6
Uses: Emulsifier for pharmaceuticals
Properties: Flakes; HLB 13.0; 100% conc.; nonionic.

Britex CS 200 B. [Auschem SpA]
Chem. Descrip.: Ceteareth-20 BP
CAS 68439-49-6
Uses: Emulsifier for pharmaceuticals
Properties: Flakes; HLB 15.5; 100% conc.; nonionic
Unverified

Britex CS 250. [Auschem SpA]
Chem. Descrip.: Ceteareth-25
CAS 68439-49-6
Uses: Emulsifier for pharmaceuticals
Properties: Flakes; HLB 16.5; 100% conc.; nonionic.

Britex L 20. [Auschem SpA]
Chem. Descrip.: Laureth-2
CAS 9002-92-0; EINECS 221-279-7
Uses: Emulsifier for pharmaceuticals
Properties: Liq.; HLB 6.5; 100% conc.; nonionic.

Britex L 40. [Auschem SpA]
Chem. Descrip.: Laureth-4
CAS 9002-92-0; EINECS 226-097-1
Uses: Emulsifier for pharmaceuticals
Properties: Liq.; HLB 9.7; 100% conc.; nonionic.

Britex L 100. [Auschem SpA]
Chem. Descrip.: Laureth-10
CAS 9002-92-0
Uses: Emulsifier for pharmaceuticals
Properties: Liq./paste; HLB 14.0; 100% conc.; nonionic.

Britex L 230. [Auschem SpA]
Chem. Descrip.: Laureth-23
CAS 9002-92-0
Uses: Emulsifier for pharmaceuticals
Properties: Solid; HLB 16.9; 100% conc.; nonionic.

Britex O 20. [Auschem SpA]
Chem. Descrip.: Oleth-2
CAS 9004-98-2
Uses: Emulsifier for pharmaceuticals
Properties: Liq.; HLB 4.9; 100% conc.; nonionic.

Britex O 100. [Auschem SpA]
Chem. Descrip.: Oleth-10
CAS 9004-98-2
Uses: Emulsifier for pharmaceuticals
Properties: Liq.; HLB 12.4; 100% conc.; nonionic.

Britex O 200. [Auschem SpA]
Chem. Descrip.: Oleth-20
CAS 9004-98-2
Uses: Emulsifier for pharmaceuticals
Properties: Paste/solid; HLB 15.3; 100% conc.; nonionic.

Britex S 20. [Auschem SpA]
Chem. Descrip.: Steareth-2
CAS 9005-00-9
Uses: Emulsifier for pharmaceuticals
Properties: Solid; HLB 4.9; 100% conc.; nonionic.

Britex S 100. [Auschem SpA]
Chem. Descrip.: Steareth-10
CAS 9005-00-9
Uses: Emulsifier for pharmaceuticals
Properties: Flakes; HLB 12.4; 100% conc.; nonionic.

Britex S 200. [Auschem SpA]
Chem. Descrip.: Steareth-20
CAS 9005-00-9
Uses: Emulsifier for pharmaceuticals
Properties: Flakes; HLB 15.3; 100% conc.; nonionic.

Britol®. [Witco/Petroleum Spec.]
Chem. Descrip.: Wh. min. oil USP
Uses: Emollient, lubricant, binder, carrier, moisture barrier, softener for pharmaceutical use
Regulatory: FDA 21CFR §172.878, §178.3620a
Properties: Water-wh., odorless, tasteless; sp.gr. 0.869-0.885; visc. 56-60 cSt (40 C); pour pt. -15 C; flash pt. 199 C.

Britol® 6NF. [Witco/Petroleum Spec.]
Chem. Descrip.: White min. oil NF
Uses: White oil functioning as binder, carrier, extender, lubricant, moisture barrier, protective agent, softener in pharmaceuticals
Properties: Sp.gr. 0.830-0.858; visc. 8.5-10.8 cst (40 C); pour pt. -24 C max.; flash pt. 166 C min.

Britol® 7NF. [Witco/Petroleum Spec.]
Chem. Descrip.: White min. oil NF
Uses: White oil functioning as binder, carrier, extender, lubricant, moisture barrier, protective agent, softener in pharmaceuticals
Properties: Sp.gr. 0.840-0.858; visc. 10.8-13.6 cst (40 C); pour pt. -18 C max.; flash pt. 171 C min.

Britol® 9NF. [Witco/Petroleum Spec.]
Chem. Descrip.: White min. oil NF

Uses: White oil functioning as binder, carrier, extender, lubricant, moisture barrier, protective agent, softener in pharmaceuticals
Properties: Sp.gr. 0.845-0.860; visc. 14.4-16.9 cst (40 C); pour pt. -18 C max.; flash pt. 171 C min.

Britol® 20USP. [Witco/Petroleum Spec.]
Chem. Descrip.: White min. oil USP
Uses: White oil functioning as binder, carrier, extender, lubricant, moisture barrier, protective agent, softener in pharmaceuticals
Properties: Sp.gr. 0.858-0.870; visc. 37.9-40.1 cst (40 C); pour pt. -18 C max.; flash pt. 193 C min.

Britol® 35USP. [Witco/Petroleum Spec.]
Chem. Descrip.: White min. oil USP
Uses: White oil functioning as binder, carrier, extender, lubricant, moisture barrier, protective agent, softener in pharmaceuticals
Properties: Sp.gr. 0.862-0.880; visc. 65.8-71.0 cst (40 C); pour pt. -15 C max.; flash pt. 216 C min.

Britol® 50USP. [Witco/Petroleum Spec.]
Chem. Descrip.: White min. oil USP
Uses: White oil functioning as binder, carrier, extender, lubricant, moisture barrier, protective agent, softener in pharmaceuticals
Properties: Sp.gr. 0.870-0.890; visc. 91-102.4 cst (40 C); pour pt. -12 C max.; flash pt. 249 C min.

Bromelain 1:10. [Solvay Enzymes]
Chem. Descrip.: Mixt. of proteases, standardized with lactose
CAS 9014-01-1; EINECS 232-752-2
Uses: Enzyme for hydrolysis of plant and animal proteins to peptides and amino acids; wound debriding agent in pharmaceuticals; also in certain blood typing studies
Properties: Tan to lt. brn. amorphous powd., free of offensive odor and taste; water-sol.

Bromelain Conc. [Solvay Enzymes]
Chem. Descrip.: Mixt. of proteases
CAS 9014-01-1; EINECS 232-752-2
Uses: Enzyme for hydrolysis of plant and animal proteins to peptides and amino acids; pharmaceuticals (wound debriding agent, blood typing studies)
Properties: Tan to lt. brn. amorphous powd., free of offensive odor and taste; water-sol.

Bronopol. [ANGUS; Boots Microcheck; Inolex; Tri-K Industries]
Chem. Descrip.: 2-Bromo-2-nitropropane-1,3-diol
CAS 52-51-7; EINECS 200-143-0
Uses: Antibacterial preservative for aq. systems, internal and topical formulations incl. antacids, suppositories, acne preps., creams and lotions
Use level: Up to 0.1% (CIR, cosmetic preservative)
Regulatory: FDA 21CFR §175.105, 176.300; EPA registered; JP, BP compliance
Properties: Wh. or almost wh. cryst. powd.; sol. in water, alcohol, glycols, and polyols; 99-100% purity
Toxicology: LD50 (acute oral, rat) 324 mg/kg; harmful or fatal if swallowed; eye irritant; not a primary skin irritant
Storage: Store in original container away from foodstuffs.

Bronopol-Boots® BP. [ANGUS; Boots Microcheck]
Chem. Descrip.: 2-Bromo-2-nitropropane-1,3-diol
CAS 52-51-7; EINECS 200-143-0
Uses: Long-term antibacterial preservative for pharmaceuticals, ophthalmic preps., medicated creams and lotions, anti-acne preps., antacid preps., toothpastes, oral prods., hypoallergenic prods.; wound irrigant sol'n. (Japan)
Regulatory: FDA 21CFR §175.105, 176.300; BP, EEC compliance; registered in France, Germany, India, Australia, Canada, Japan; food contact approved in U.S., France, Germany
Properties: Wh. or almost wh. cryst. powd.; sol. in water, alcohol, glycols, and polyols; m.w. 200; m.p. 130 C; 99% min. purity; rapidly biodeg.
Toxicology: Conc. sol'ns. are irritating to skin, eyes, respiratory system, harmful if swallowed; nonirritating to skin @ 0.01-0.1%; noncarcinogenic
Storage: 5 yr min. stability under good storage conditions; store in original container tightly closed.

Brookswax™ G. [Brooks Industries]
Chem. Descrip.: Stearyl alcohol and ceteareth-20
Uses: Emollient, pharmaceutical raw material.

Butyl Diglyme. [Ferro]
Chem. Descrip.: Diethylene glycol dibutyl ether
CAS 112-73-2; EINECS 204-001-9
Uses: Solv. for pharmaceuticals; drug carrier, stabilizer
Properties: Colorless clear liq.; mild nonresidual odor; sol. 0.3% in water; misc. with ethanol, acetone, benzene, diethyl ether, octane; m.w. 218.34; sp.gr. 0.8814; dens. 7.36 lb/gal; visc. 2.4 cP; f.p. -60.2 C; b.p. 256 C; flash pt. (CC) 118 C; ref. index 1.4235; pH neutral; surf. tens. 27 dynes/cm (20 C); sp. heat 0.495 cal/g/°C; 98.5% min. purity; LD50 3900 mg/kg; low to mod. acute toxicity; chronic exposure may cause reproductive effects
Precaution: Slowly biodeg.

Butyl Parasept® NF. [Nipa Hardwicke]
Chem. Descrip.: Butylparaben NF
CAS 94-26-8; EINECS 202-318-7
Uses: Preservative for pharmaceuticals, suppositories, eye washes, pills, anesthetics, syrups, injectable sol'ns., contraceptives, gelatin capsules, ointments, tinctures, OTC drugs; inactive ingred. in dentifrices, topical analgesics; active antimycotic
Properties: Wh. fine powd., pract. odorless and tasteless; sol. 240% in acetone, 210% in ethanol, 150% in ether, 110% in propylene glycol, 0.02% in water; m.w. 194.23; m.p. 68-72 C; nonhygroscopic; 99-100.5% assay
Toxicology: Avoid prolonged/repeated skin contact
Storage: Avoid exposure to high humidity and elevated temps. in storage.

Byco A. [Croda Colloids Ltd]
Chem. Descrip.: Hydrolyzed gelatin
CAS 68410-45-7; EINECS 270-082-2
Uses: Binder in pharmaceutical tableting, spray drying, wet/dry granulation, direct compr.; excipient,

film-former, coating agent; emulsion stabilizer; adjuvant protein in nutritional supplement; growth media; surgical dusting powd.
Use level: 2.5-5% (granulation)
Properties: Wh. to pale cream spray-dried powd., char. odor and taste; sol. in cold water; m.w. 2500-4000; bulk dens. 0.25-0.40 g/cc; pH 5.5-6.5 (10% aq.); 7% max. moisture
Storage: Store in cool dry conditions in sealed containers, away from odiferous materials; indefinitely stable.

Byco C. [Croda Colloids Ltd]
Chem. Descrip.: Hydrolyzed gelatin
CAS 68410-45-7; EINECS 270-082-2
Uses: Binder in pharmaceutical tableting, spray drying, wet/dry granulation, direct compr.; excipient, film-former, coating agent; emulsion stabilizer; adjuvant protein in nutritional supplement; growth media; surgical dusting powd.
Use level: 2.5-5% (granulation)
Properties: Wh. to pale cream spray-dried powd., char. odor and taste; sol. in water; m.w. 10,000-12,000; bulk dens. 0.15-0.30 g/cc; pH 5.5-6.5 (10% aq.); 7% max. moisture
Toxicology: LD50 (oral, rat) 5 g/kg
Storage: Store in cool dry conditions in sealed containers, away from odiferous materials; indefinitely stable.

Byco E. [Croda Colloids Ltd]
Chem. Descrip.: Hydrolyzed gelatin
CAS 68410-45-7; EINECS 270-082-2
Uses: Binder in pharmaceutical tableting, spray drying, wet/dry granulation, direct compr.; excipient, film-former, coating agent; emulsion stabilizer; adjuvant protein in nutritional supplement; growth media; surgical dusting powd.
Properties: Wh. to pale cream spray-dried powd., char. odor and taste; sol. in cold water; m.w. 10,000-12,000; bulk dens. 0.15-0.30 kg/l; visc. 35-45 mps (10%); pH 5.5-6.5 (10% aq.); 7% max. moisture
Storage: Store in cool dry conditions in sealed containers, away from odiferous materials; indefinitely stable.

Byco O. [Croda Colloids Ltd]
Chem. Descrip.: Hydrolyzed gelatin
CAS 68410-45-7; EINECS 270-082-2
Uses: Binder in pharmaceutical tableting, spray drying, wet/dry granulation, direct compr.; excipient, film-former, coating agent; emulsion stabilizer; adjuvant protein in nutritional supplement; growth media; surgical dusting powd.
Properties: Wh. to pale cream spray-dried powd., char. odor and taste; sol. in water; m.w. 1000-2000; bulk dens. 0.25-0.40 g/cc; pH 5.5-6.5 (10% aq.); 7% max. moisture
Toxicology: LD50 (oral, rat) 5 g/kg
Storage: Store in cool dry conditions in sealed containers, away from odiferous materials; indefinitely stable.

C

Cab-O-Sil® EH-5. [Cabot/Cab-O-Sil]
Chem. Descrip.: Fumed silica, undensed
CAS 112945-52-5; EINECS 231-545-4
Uses: Inert carrier, tablet binder/disintegrant, oil adsorbent, thermal stabilizer (suppositories), emulsifier, thickener, gellant, free-flow agent (foot and tooth powds., antiperspirants), suspending agent; in antacids, calamine, tranquilizer capsules
Properties: Wh. powd., odorless; 0.02% 325 mesh residue; sp.gr. 2.2; bulk dens. 2.5 lb/ft^3; surf. area 380 ± 30 m^2/g; ref. index 1.46; pH 3.7-4.3 (4% aq. slurry); > 99.8% assay
Toxicology: LD50 (oral, rat) > 5 g/kg; inert to mildly irritating to skin; inert to very mildly irritating to eyes
Storage: Store in dry environment away from chemical vapors.

Cab-O-Sil® H-5. [Cabot/Cab-O-Sil]
Chem. Descrip.: Fumed silica, undensed
CAS 112945-52-5; EINECS 231-545-4
Uses: Inert carrier, tablet binder/disintegrant, oil adsorbent, thermal stabilizer (suppositories), emulsifier, thickener, gellant, free-flow agent (foot and tooth powds., antiperspirants), suspending agent; in antacids, calamine, tranquilizer capsules
Properties: Wh. powd., odorless; 0.02% 325 mesh residue; sp.gr. 2.2; bulk dens. 2.5 lb/ft^3; surf. area 300 ± 25 m^2/g; ref. index 1.46; pH 3.7-4.3 (4% aq. slurry); > 99.8% assay
Toxicology: LD50 (oral, rat) > 5 g/kg; inert to mildly irritating to skin; inert to very mildly irritating to eyes
Storage: Store in dry environment away from chemical vapors.

Cab-O-Sil® HS-5. [Cabot/Cab-O-Sil]
Chem. Descrip.: Fumed silica, undensed
CAS 112945-52-5; EINECS 231-545-4
Uses: Rheology control and reinforcing agent for pharmaceuticals
Properties: 0.02% 325 mesh residue; bulk dens. 2.5 lb/ft^3; surf. area 325 ± 25 m^2/g; pH 3.7-4.3 (4% aq. slurry); > 99.8% assay
Toxicology: LD50 (oral, rat) > 5 g/kg; inert to mildly irritating to skin; inert to very mildly irritating to eyes
Storage: Store in dry environment away from

chemical vapors.

Cab-O-Sil® L-90. [Cabot/Cab-O-Sil]
Chem. Descrip.: Fumed silica, undensed
CAS 112945-52-5; EINECS 231-545-4
Uses: Inert carrier, tablet binder/disintegrant, oil adsorbent, thermal stabilizer (suppositories), emulsifier, thickener, gellant, free-flow agent (foot and tooth powds., antiperspirants), suspending agent; in antacids, calamine, tranquilizer capsules
Properties: Wh. powd., odorless; 0.02% 325 mesh residue; sp.gr. 2.2; bulk dens. 3 lb/ft^3; surf. area 100 ± 15 m^2/g; ref. index 1.46; pH 3.7-4.3 (4% aq. slurry); > 99.8% assay
Toxicology: LD50 (oral, rat) > 5 g/kg; inert to mildly irritating to skin; inert to very mildly irritating to eyes
Storage: Store in dry environment away from chemical vapors.

Cab-O-Sil® LM-150. [Cabot/Cab-O-Sil]
Chem. Descrip.: Fumed silica, undensed
CAS 112945-52-5; EINECS 231-545-4
Uses: Inert carrier, tablet binder/disintegrant, oil adsorbent, thermal stabilizer (suppositories), emulsifier, thickener, gellant, free-flow agent (foot and tooth powds., antiperspirants), suspending agent; in antacids, calamine, tranquilizer capsules
Properties: Wh. powd., odorless; 0.02% 325 mesh residue; sp.gr. 2.2; bulk dens. 2.5 lb/ft^3; surf. area 160 ± 15 m^2/g; ref. index 1.46; pH 3.7-4.3 (4% aq. slurry); > 99.8% assay
Toxicology: LD50 (oral, rat) > 5 g/kg; inert to mildly irritating to skin; inert to very mildly irritating to eyes
Storage: Store in dry environment away from chemical vapors.

Cab-O-Sil® M-5. [Cabot/Cab-O-Sil]
Chem. Descrip.: Fumed silica, undensed
CAS 112945-52-5; EINECS 231-545-4
Uses: Inert carrier, tablet binder/disintegrant, oil adsorbent, thermal stabilizer (suppositories), emulsifier, thickener, gellant, free-flow agent (foot and tooth powds., antiperspirants), suspending agent; in antacids, calamine, tranquilizer capsules
Properties: Wh. fine powd., odorless; 0.2-0.3 μ avg. particle size; 0.02% 325 mesh residue; insol.

in water; sp.gr. 2.2; dens. 18.3 lb/gal; bulk dens. 2.5 lb/ft^3; surf. area 200 ± 25 m^2/g; ref. index 1.46; pH 3.7-4.3 (40% aq. slurry); > 99.8% assay
Toxicology: LD50 (oral, rat) > 5 g/kg; nontoxic by ingestion; inert to mildly irritating to skin; inert to very mildly irritating to eyes
Storage: Store in dry environment away from chemical vapors.

Cab-O-Sil® MS-55. [Cabot/Cab-O-Sil]
Chem. Descrip.: Fumed silica, undensed
CAS 112945-52-5; EINECS 231-545-4
Uses: Inert carrier, tablet binder/disintegrant, oil adsorbent, thermal stabilizer (suppositories), emulsifier, thickener, gellant, free-flow agent (foot and tooth powds., antiperspirants), suspending agent; in antacids, calamine, tranquilizer capsules
Properties: Wh. powd., odorless; 0.02% 325 mesh residue; sp.gr. 2.2; bulk dens. 2.5 lb/ft^3; surf. area 255 ± 25 m^2/g; ref. index 1.46; pH 3.7-4.3 (4% aq. slurry); > 99.8% assay
Toxicology: LD50 (oral, rat) > 5 g/kg; inert to mildly irritating to skin; inert to very mildly irritating to eyes
Storage: Store in dry environment away from chemical vapors.

Cab-O-Sil® PTG. [Cabot/Cab-O-Sil]
Chem. Descrip.: Fumed silica, undensed
CAS 112945-52-5; EINECS 231-545-4
Uses: Rheology control and free-flow agent for pharmaceuticals
Properties: 0.02% 325 mesh residue; sp.gr. 2.2; bulk dens. 2.5 lb/ft^3; surf. area 200 ± 25 m^2/g; ref. index 1.46; pH 3.7-4.3 (4% aq. slurry); > 99.8% assay
Toxicology: LD50 (oral, rat) > 5 g/kg; inert to mildly irritating to skin; inert to very mildly irritating to eyes
Storage: Store in dry environment away from chemical vapors.

Cab-O-Sil® TS-530. [Cabot/Cab-O-Sil]
Chem. Descrip.: Fumed silica, hexamethyl-disilazane-surface treated (CAS 68909-20-6)
Uses: Rheology control agent; reinforcing filler for dental compds.
Properties: Wh. fluffy powd., odorless; 0.2-0.3 μ avg. particle size; insol. in water; sp.gr. 2.2; bulk dens. 3 lb/ft^3; surf. area 215 ± 30 m^2/g; pH 4.8-7.5 (4% aq. slurry); 4.2 ± 0.5% carbon content
Toxicology: LD50 (oral) > 5000 mg/kg; inh. may cause pulmonary inflammation; not considered a carcinogen
Precaution: Dry powds. can build static elec. charges subjected to friction; keep away from flamm. or explosive liqs.
Storage: Store in dry environment away from chemical vapors.

Cachalot® DE-10. [M. Michel]
Chem. Descrip.: Decyl alcohol
CAS 112-30-1; EINECS 203-956-9
Uses: Pharmaceutical raw material.

Cachalot® L-90. [M. Michel]

Chem. Descrip.: Lauryl alcohol
CAS 112-53-8; EINECS 203-982-0
Uses: Pharmaceutical raw material.

Cachalot® S-56. [M. Michel]
Chem. Descrip.: Stearyl alcohol USP
CAS 112-92-5; EINECS 204-017-6
Uses: Emollient
Properties: Hazen 20 color; sol. in acetone, alcohol, aromatic hydrocarbons, carbon disulfide, chloroform, glycol and diglycol ethers; m.w. 267-281; sp.gr. 0.815 (60 C); visc. 9 cps (70 C); m.p. 56-58 C; b.p. 330-350 C; acid no. 0.3 max.; iodine no. 1 max.; sapon no. 1 max.; hyd. no. 200-210; flash pt. 190 C; ref. index 1.4347-1.4349 (70 C).

Cachalot® Behenyl Alcohol BE-22. [M. Michel]
Chem. Descrip.: Behenyl alcohol
CAS 661-19-8; EINECS 211-546-6
Uses: Pharmaceutical raw material.

Cal-Carb® 4450. [Crompton & Knowles]
Chem. Descrip.: Food-grade calcium carbonate and maltodextrin NF
Uses: Carrier; economic direct compression vehicle for use in conventional pharmaceutical tablets, as well as calcium supplements and antacid tablets; exc. compr. props.
Properties: Wh. free-flowing gran.; 5% max. on 20 mesh, 25% max. thru 200 mesh; bulk dens. 1.00-1.30 g/ml (loose), 1.15-1.45 g/ml (tapped) ≥ 35.5% Ca.

Cal-Carb® 4450 PG. [Crompton & Knowles]
Chem. Descrip.: Calcium carbonate USP and maltodextrin NF
Uses: Carrier; economic direct compression vehicle for use in conventional pharmaceutical tablets, as well as calcium supplements and antacid tablets; exc. compr. props.
Properties: Wh. free-flowing gran.; 5% max. on 20 mesh, 25% max. thru 200 mesh; bulk dens. 1.00-1.30 g/ml (loose), 1.15-1.45 g/ml (tapped) ≥ 36% Ca.

Cal-Carb® 4457. [Crompton & Knowles]
Chem. Descrip.: Calcium carbonate USP and pregelatinized starch NF
Uses: Carrier; economic direct compression vehicle for use in conventional pharmaceutical tablets, as well as calcium supplements and antacid tablets; exc. compr. props.
Properties: Wh. free-flowing gran.; 5% max. on 20 mesh, 25% max. thru 200 mesh; bulk dens. 1.00-1.30 g/ml (loose), 1.15-1.45 g/ml (tapped) ≥ 36% Ca.

Cal-Carb® 4462. [Crompton & Knowles]
Chem. Descrip.: Precipitated calcium carbonate USP and pregelatinized starch NF
Uses: Carrier; direct compression vehicle for use in conventional pharmaceutical tablets, as well as calcium supplements and antacid tablets; exc. compr. and disintegration props.
Properties: Wh. free-flowing gran.; 5% max. on 20 mesh, 25% max. thru 200 mesh; bulk dens. 0.95 g/cc (loose), 1.05 g/cc (tapped) ≥ 36% Ca.

Calcium Ascorbate FCC No. 60475. [Roche]

Chem. Descrip.: Calcium ascorbate FCC
CAS 5743-27-1
Uses: Preservative, antioxidant, source of vitamin C for pharmaceuticals, esp. dry preps.
Regulatory: FDA GRAS
Properties: Wh. to sl. yel. powd., pract. odorless ; freely sol. in water; sl. sol. in alcohol; insol. in ether; m.w. 426.35; pH 6.8-7.4 (10% aq.) $\geq$ 98% assay
Storage: Store in tight light-resist. containers, optimally @ $\leq$ 72 F; avoid exposure to moisture, excessive heat.

Calcium Hydroxide USP 802. [Whittaker, Clark & Daniels]
Chem. Descrip.: Calcium hydroxide
CAS 1305-62-0; EINECS 215-137-3
Uses: Pharmaceutical ingred.

Calcium Pantothenate USP, FCC Type SD No. 63924. [Roche]
Chem. Descrip.: Calcium pantothenate USP FCC
CAS 137-08-6; EINECS 205-278-9
Uses: Source of pantothenic acid for solid dosage forms (tablets, capsules)
Properties: Wh. spray-dried, free-flowing powd., odorless, sl. hygroscopic; freely sol. in water (1 g/ 3 ml water); sol. in glycerin; pract. insol. in alcohol, chloroform, ether; m.w. 476.54; 90-110% assay
Precaution: Sl. sensitive to heat
Storage: Store in dry place @ 59-96 F.

Calfos. [Croda Colloids Ltd; O.C. Lugo]
Chem. Descrip.: Natural calcium phosphate from bovine sources
CAS 7758-87-4; EINECS 231-840-8
Uses: Calcium and phosphorus fortifier for pharmaceutical prods., tonics, health foods, geriatric prods., tablet supplements
Use level: 1% max. (anticaking agent)
Properties: Pale cream free-flowing powd., 50, 100, and 150 mesh grades; 29% min. Ca, 13.5% min. P
Storage: Store in dry conditions at ambient temps.

Calgene CC-22. [Calgene]
Chem. Descrip.: Propylene glycol dicaprylate/ dicaprate
Uses: Surfactant for pharmaceuticals; vehicle/ diluent/carrier for vitamins, drugs, flavors, color, fragrance
Regulatory: FDA compliance as food additive
Properties: Clear, almost colorless, tasteless, odorless liq.; sol. in ethanol, min. oil, acetone; sp.gr. 0.916; set pt. -20 C; iodine no. 0.5; sapon. no. 325; 100% conc.; nonionic.

Calgene CC-22-S. [Calgene]
Chem. Descrip.: Propylene glycol dicaprylate/ dicaprate
Uses: Surfactant for pharmaceuticals; vehicle/ diluent/carrier for vitamins, drugs, flavors, color, fragrance
Regulatory: FDA compliance as food additive
Properties: Clear, almost colorless, tasteless, odorless liq.; sol. in ethanol, min. oil acetone; sp.gr. 0.919; set pt. -20 C; iodine no. 0.5; sapon.

no. 325; 100% conc.; nonionic.

Calgene CC-33. [Calgene]
Chem. Descrip.: Caprylic/capric triglyceride
CAS 65381-09-1; EINECS 265-724-3
Uses: Surfactant for pharmaceuticals; vehicle/ diluent/carrier for vitamins, drugs, flavors, color, fragrance
Regulatory: GRAS
Properties: Clear, almost colorless, tasteless, odorless liq.; sol. in ethanol, min. oil, acetone; sp.gr. 0.945; set pt. -2 C; iodine no. 0.5; sapon. no. 340; 100% conc.; nonionic.

Calgene CC-33-F. [Calgene]
Chem. Descrip.: Caprylic/capric triglyceride
CAS 65381-09-1; EINECS 265-724-3
Uses: Surfactant for pharmaceuticals; vehicle/ diluent/carrier for vitamins, drugs, flavors, color, fragrance
Regulatory: GRAS
Properties: Clear, almost colorless, tasteless, odorless liq.; sol. in min. oil, acetone; sp.gr. 0.935; set pt. 5 C; iodine no. 8; sapon. no. 305; 100% conc.; nonionic.

Calgene CC-33-L. [Calgene]
Chem. Descrip.: Caprylic/capric triglyceride
CAS 65381-09-1; EINECS 265-724-3
Uses: Surfactant for pharmaceuticals; vehicle/ diluent/carrier for vitamins, drugs, flavors, color, fragrance
Regulatory: GRAS
Properties: Clear, almost colorless, tasteless, odorless liq.; sol. in min. oil, acetone; sp.gr. 0.938; set pt. 0 C; iodine no. 8; sapon. no. 308; 100% conc.; nonionic.

Calgene CC-33-S. [Calgene]
Chem. Descrip.: Caprylic/capric triglyceride
CAS 65381-09-1; EINECS 265-724-3
Uses: Surfactant for pharmaceuticals; vehicle/ diluent/carrier for vitamins, drugs, flavors, color, fragrance
Regulatory: GRAS
Properties: Clear, almost colorless, tasteless, odorless liq.; sol. in ethanol, min. oil, acetone; sp.gr. 0.945; set pt. -5 C; iodine no. 0.5; sapon. no. 347; 100% conc.; nonionic.

Calgon® Type 114A AWD. [Calgon Carbon]
Chem. Descrip.: Activated carbon
CAS 64365-11-3; EINECS 231-153-3
Uses: Used for pharmaceutical purification
Properties: Pulverized.

Calgon® Type ADP. [Calgon Carbon]
Chem. Descrip.: Activated carbon
CAS 64365-11-3; EINECS 231-153-3
Uses: Used for pharmaceutical purification
Regulatory: Certified to ANSI/NSF Std. 61
Properties: Pulverized, 80 x 325 sieve size; 65-80% on 325 mesh; iodine no. 1200 min.; 5% max. moisture.

Calgon® Type APA. [Calgon Carbon]
Chem. Descrip.: Activated carbon
CAS 64365-11-3; EINECS 231-153-3
Uses: Used for pharmaceutical purification, odor

control

Properties: 12 x 40 sieve size.

Calgon® Type BL®. [Calgon Carbon]
Chem. Descrip.: Activated carbon
CAS 64365-11-3; EINECS 231-153-3
Uses: Used for pharmaceutical purification
Properties: Pulverized; 65-75% -325 mesh; bulk dens. 0.59 g/cc (dense); surf. area 1000-1100 m^2/g; iodine no. 1000 min.; sp.heat 0.25 (100 C); 2% max. moisture.

Calgon® Type CAL®. [Calgon Carbon]
Chem. Descrip.: Activated carbon
CAS 64365-11-3; EINECS 231-153-3
Uses: Used for pharmaceutical purification
Properties: Gran.; 12 x 40 sieve size; 0.9-1.1 mm mean particle diam.; bulk dens. 0.49 g/cc (dense); surf. area 1000-1100 m^2/g; iodine no. 1000 min.; pH 7.5; sp.heat 0.25 (100 C); 2% max. moisture
Precaution: Wet activated carbon preferentially removes oxygen from air; oxygen depletion may reach hazardous levels.

Calgon® Type CPG®. [Calgon Carbon]
Chem. Descrip.: Activated carbon
CAS 64365-11-3; EINECS 231-153-3
Uses: Used for pharmaceutical and solv. purification
Properties: Gran.; 12 x 40 sieve size; 0.9-1.1 mm mean particle diam.; bulk dens. 0.50 g/cc (dense); surf. area 1000-1100 m^2/g; iodine no. 900 min.; pH 5-8; sp.heat 0.25 (100 C); 3% max. moisture
Precaution: Wet activated carbon preferentially removes oxygen from air; oxygen depletion may reach hazardous levels.

Calgon® Type CPG® LF. [Calgon Carbon]
Chem. Descrip.: Activated carbon
CAS 64365-11-3; EINECS 231-153-3
Uses: Used for pharmaceutical and solv. purification
Properties: 8 x 30, 12 x 40 sieve sizes.

Calgon® Type OL®. [Calgon Carbon]
Chem. Descrip.: Activated carbon
CAS 64365-11-3; EINECS 231-153-3
Uses: Used for pharmaceutical purification
Properties: Gran.; 20 x 50 sieve size; 3% > 20 mesh, 1% < 50 mesh; bulk dens. 0.48 g/cc (dense); surf. area 1000-1100 m^2/g; iodine no. 1050 min.; sp. heat 0.25 (100 C).

Calgon® Type PWA®. [Calgon Carbon]
Chem. Descrip.: Activated carbon
CAS 64365-11-3; EINECS 231-153-3
Uses: Used for pharmaceutical filtration and purification where low pH sol'ns. are encountered
Properties: Pulverized; 65-75% -325 mesh; bulk dens. 0.51 g/cc (dense); surf. area 900-1000 m^2/g; iodine no. 900 min.; pH 6-8; sp. heat 0.25 (100 C).

Calgon® Type RB®. [Calgon Carbon]
Chem. Descrip.: Activated carbon
CAS 64365-11-3; EINECS 231-153-3
Uses: Used for pharmaceutical purification
Properties: Pulverized; 60-75% -325 mesh; bulk dens. 0.48 g/cc (dense); surf. area 1100-1300 m^2/

g; iodine no. 1070 min.; sp.heat 0.25 (100 C); 2% max. moisture.

Calgon® Type RC®. [Calgon Carbon]
Chem. Descrip.: Activated carbon
CAS 64365-11-3; EINECS 231-153-3
Uses: Used for pharmaceutical purification
Properties: Pulverized; 60-75% -325 mesh; bulk dens. 0.48 g/cc (dense); surf. area 1050-1250 m^2/g; iodine no. 1020 min.; sp.heat 0.25 (100 C); 2% max. moisture.

Calgon® Type SGL®. [Calgon Carbon]
Chem. Descrip.: Activated carbon
CAS 64365-11-3; EINECS 231-153-3
Uses: Used for purification of pharmaceuticals
Properties: Gran.; 8 x 30 sieve size; 1.5-1.7 mm mean particle diam.; bulk dens. 0.52 g/cc (dense); surf. area 900-1000 m^2/g; iodine no. 900 min.; sp.heat 0.25 (100 C); 2% max. moisture
Precaution: Wet activated carbon preferentially removes oxygen from air; oxygen depletion may reach hazardous levels.

Cal-O-Vera 1:1. [Agro-Mar]
Chem. Descrip.: Aloe vera gel from *Aloe barbadensis miller* with sodium benzoate and citric acid preservatives
Uses: Used for health and pharmaceutical applics.
Properties: Opaque, translucent, colorless liq.; typ. veg. odor; slick, tangy taste; sp.gr. 1.004 ± 0.004; pH 3.5-5.5; 100% act.

Cal-O-Vera 10:1. [Agro-Mar]
Chem. Descrip.: Aloe vera gel with sodium benzoate and citric acid preservatives
Uses: Used for health and pharmaceutical applics.
Properties: Opaque liq.; typ. veg. odor; slick, tangy taste; sp.gr. 1.004 ± 0.004; pH 3.5-5.5.

Cal-O-Vera 40:1. [Agro-Mar]
Chem. Descrip.: Aloe vera gel from *Aloe barbadensis miller* with sodium benzoate and citric acid preservatives, and acidifier
Uses: Used for health and pharmaceutical applics.
Properties: Opaque tan liq.; typ. veg. odor; slick, tangy taste; sp.gr. 1.004 ± 0.004; pH 3.5-5.5.

Cal-O-Vera 200XXX Powd. [Agro-Mar]
Chem. Descrip.: Aloe vera gel from *Aloe barbadensis miller*
Uses: Used for health and pharmaceutical applics.; also avail. in rapidly dissolving, agglomerated, micro-fine form
Properties: Off-wh. to lt. beige powd.; pH 3.5-6.5 (reconstituted 200:1).

Cal-Tab®. [Crompton & Knowles]
Chem. Descrip.: Calcium sulfate dihydrate NF and acacia NF
Uses: Carrier; economical direct compression tableting vehicle for pharmaceuticals; exhibits exc. flow and compr. chars.
Properties: Wh. to off-wh. fine gran.; 5% max. on 20 mesh, 70% max. thru 200 mesh; bulk dens. 0.8 g/ml (loose), 1.0 g/ml (tapped); 93% min. calcium sulfate dihydrate.

Candex®. [Mendell]
Chem. Descrip.: Dextrose with small amounts of

higher glucose saccharides
CAS 50-99-7; EINECS 200-075-1
Uses: Offers sweet, nongritty taste and is easily blended with flavors, lubricants, and other dry additives; exc. flow and compaction props.; for use in chewable tablets, esp. those made by direct compression; cool refreshing mouthfeel
Properties: Wh. porous, spherical granules, sweet noncloying/nongritty taste; avg particle size 218 µ; 30% max. -100 mesh; very sol. in water; dens. (tapped) 0.77 g/ml; pH 3.5 min.

Candex® Plus. [Mendell]
Chem. Descrip.: Dextrates (CAS 50-99-7) with 0.3% max. magnesium stearate as anticaking agent
Uses: Vehicle for direct compression and wet granulation of pharmaceutical tablets, incl. chewable tablets
Properties: Wh. to very sl. off-wh. porous spherical granules, sweet noncloying/nongritty taste; avg. particle size 196 µ; 35% max. -100 mesh; dens. (tapped) 0.82 g/ml max.; pH 4.0-7.5.

Canthaxanthin Beadlets 10%. [Crompton & Knowles/ Ingred. Tech.]
Chem. Descrip.: Canthaxanthine in a matrix of gelatin, sucrose, food starch, vegetable oil with antioxidants, ascorbyl palmitate and dl-α-tocopherol
Uses: Color additive for drugs
Regulatory: FDA 21CFR §73.75, 73.1075
Properties: Purplish red free-flowing beadlets, sl. odor; disp. readily in warm water producing tomato-red hue; 100% min. thru mesh 20; 25% max. thru mesh 80; 10% canthaxanthine
Storage: Store in tight containers below 45 C; avoid exposure to heat, light, and moisture; 6 mos storage life.

CAO®-3. [PMC Specialties]
Chem. Descrip.: 2,6-Di-t-butyl-p-cresol (BHT)
CAS 128-37-0; EINECS 204-881-4
Uses: Food-grade antioxidant, stabilizer for pharmaceuticals
Regulatory: FDA 21CFR §137.350, 166.110, 172.115, 172.615, 172.878, 172.880, 172.882, 172.886, 173.340, 174, 175, 176, 177, 178, 181.24, 182.3173, 582.3173, GRAS, USDA; kosher
Properties: Wh. cryst., sl. odor; sol. (g/100 ml): 45-55 g aliphatic/aromatic solvs., 40-45 g animal fats, ketone, acetone, 25-30 g veg. oils; m.w. 220.36; sp.gr. 0.899 (80/4 C); bulk dens. 1.048; visc. 3.47 cst (80 C); f.p. 69.2 C min.; m.p. 157 F; b.p. 260-262 C (760 mm); flash pt. (COC) 275 C; ref. index 1.4859; 99% min. purity
Toxicology: ACGIH TLV-TWA 10 mg/m^3; may cause skin irritation, respiratory passage irritation, severe eye irritation/burns
Storage: Stable when stored below 77 F under dry conditions in unopened, original containers; may yel. sl. on aging.

CAO®-3/Blend 29. [PMC Specialties]
Chem. Descrip.: 98% BHT with 2% anticaking agent
CAS 128-37-0; EINECS 204-881-4
Uses: Antioxidant additive in animal feeds; retards oxidative deterioration in animal and veg. oils, fats, greases; protects potency of vitamins and pharmaceuticals used in animal feeds
Properties: Wh. powd., very faint odor; 90% thru 100 mesh, 80% thru 200 mesh; m.w. 220.36; bulk dens. 35 lb/ft^3; b.p. 260-262 C (760 mm); flash pt. (COC) 275 F.

Capcithin™. [Lucas Meyer]
Chem. Descrip.: Range of capsule grade fluid soy lecithin
CAS 8002-43-5; EINECS 232-307-2
Uses: Specially formulated for encapsulation; for health food industry, soft gel capsules, tonics.

C-A-P Enteric Coating Material. [Eastman]
Chem. Descrip.: Cellulose acetate phthalate USP/ NF
CAS 9004-38-0
Uses: Pharmaceutical excipient; enteric film-coating material for tablets or gran.; matrix binder for solid dosage forms; stable in strongly acid gastric fluids, but dissolves readily in mildly acidic to neutral environment of the sm. intestine
Properties: Wh. free-flowing powd.; visc. 68 cP (15% in acetone sol'n.); pH ≥ 6.2; 35% phthalyl, 24% acetyl
Storage: Store in cool, dry area; protect from moisture and humidity; bring drums to R.T. before opening to prevent moisture condensation on inside surfs.

Capmul® EMG. [ABITEC]
Chem. Descrip.: PEG-20 glyceryl stearate
Uses: O/w emulsifier, dispersant, emollient, solubilizer, wetting agent; for clinical nutrition, coating, delivery/absorp. enhancement, dermatologicals, microemulsions, suppositories
Regulatory: FDA 21CFR §172.834
Properties: Lovibond 4R max. solid; HLB 13.1; acid no. 2 max.; iodine no. 2 max.; sapon. no. 65-75; hyd. no. 65-80; 100% conc.; nonionic.

Capmul® GDL. [ABITEC]
Chem. Descrip.: Glyceryl dilaurate
CAS 27638-00-2; EINECS 248-586-9
Uses: Emulsifier, emollient, solubilizer; used for pharmaceuticals, clinical nutrition, coating, delivery/absorp. enhancement, dermatologicals, microemulsions
Properties: Lovibond 4R max. semisolid; m.p. 28-31 C; HLB 3-4; acid no. 3 max.; iodine no. 20 max.; sapon. no. 215-230; nonionic.

Capmul® GMO. [ABITEC]
Chem. Descrip.: Glyceryl oleate
CAS 25496-72-4
Uses: Emulsifier, emollient, solubilizer for pharmaceuticals, clinical nutrition, coating, delivery/ absorp. enhancement, dermatologicals, microemulsions
Regulatory: FDA 21CFR §184.1323
Properties: Lovibond 4R max. semisolid; sol. in org. solvs. and oils; m.p. 25 C max.; HLB 3-4; acid no.

3 max.; iodine no. 75 max.; sapon. no. 160-170; 40% min. mono; nonionic.

Capmul® GMS. [ABITEC]
Chem. Descrip.: Glyceryl stearate
CAS 31566-31-1
Uses: Bodying agent, emollient, emulsifier, lubricant, visc. modifier for clinical nutrition, coating, delivery/absorp. enhancement, dermatologicals, suppositories, tablets
Properties: Lovibond 4R max. beads; m.p. 57-62 C; HLB 3-4; acid no. 3 max.; iodine no. 5 max.; sapon. no. 155-165; 100% conc.; nonionic.

Capmul® MCM. [ABITEC]
Chem. Descrip.: Glyceryl caprylate/caprate
Uses: Solv., dispersant, emulsifier, solubilizer, vehicle/carrier, penetrant with bacteriostatic effects for pharmaceuticals, clinical nutrition, coating, delivery/absorp. enhancement, dermatologicals, microemulsions, suppositories
Properties: Lovibond 4R max. liq. to semisolid; sol. in oil and alcohol; HLB 5.5-6.0; acid no. 2.5 max.; iodine no. 2 max.; 55% min. alpha mono.

Capmul® MCM-90. [ABITEC]
Chem. Descrip.: Glyceryl caprylate/caprate
Uses: W/o emulsifier, solv. for pharmaceuticals
Properties: Liq.; acid no. 2.5 max.; iodine no. 2 max.; 80+% alpha mono.

Capmul® MCMC8. [ABITEC]
Chem. Descrip.: Glyceryl caprylate
CAS 26402-22-2; EINECS 247-668-1
Uses: Dispersant, emulsifier, solubilizer, vehicle/carrier, penetrant with bacteriostatic effects for delivery/absorp. enhancement, dermatologicals, microemulsions, suppositories
Properties: Lovibond 5R max. liq. to semisolid; acid no. 2.5 max.; iodine no. 2 max.; 55% min. alpha mono.

Capmul® POE-L. [ABITEC]
Chem. Descrip.: Polysorbate 20
CAS 9005-64-5
Uses: O/w emulsifier, solubilizer, dispersant, wetting agent for clinical nutrition, coating, delivery/absorp. enhancement, dermatologicals, microemulsions, suppositories
Properties: Gardner 3 max. semisolid; HLB 16.7; acid no. 2 max.; iodine no. 1 max.; sapon. no. 40-50; hyd. no. 96-108; 100% conc.; nonionic.

Capmul® POE-S. [ABITEC]
Chem. Descrip.: Polysorbate 60
CAS 9005-67-8
Uses: O/w emulsifier, solubilizer, dispersant, wetting agent; for clinical nutrition, coating, delivery/absorp. enhancement, dermatologicals, suppositories
Properties: Gardner 7 max. solid; HLB 15; acid no. 2 max.; iodine no. 2 max.; sapon. no. 45-55; hyd. no. 81-96; 100% conc.; nonionic.

Capmul® S. [ABITEC]
Chem. Descrip.: Sorbitan stearate
CAS 1338-41-6; EINECS 215-664-9
Uses: Bodying agent, emulsifier, visc. modifier for clinical nutrition, coating, delivery/absorp. en-

hancement, dermatologicals, suppositories, tablets
Properties: Gardner 6 max. bead; HLB 3.5-4.5; acid no. 10 max.; iodine no. 2 max.; sapon. no. 147-157; hyd. no. 235-260; 100% conc.; nonionic.

Caprol® 3GO. [ABITEC]
Chem. Descrip.: Polyglyceryl-3 oleate
CAS 9007-48-1
Uses: Dispersant, emollient, emulsifier, solubilizer, wetting agent for delivery/absorp. enhancer, dermatological emulsions, suppositories
Regulatory: FDA 21CFR §172.854
Properties: Gardner 7 max. liq.; sol. in org. solvs. and oils; HLB 6.5; acid no. 6 max.; iodine no. 78 max.; sapon. no. 125-150; 100% conc.; nonionic.

Caprol® 3GS. [ABITEC]
Chem. Descrip.: Polyglyceryl-3 stearate
CAS 37349-34-1; EINECS 248-403-2
Uses: Bodying agent, emulsifier, visc. modifier for delivery/absorp. enhancer, dermatological emulsions, suppositories
Regulatory: FDA 21CFR §172.854
Properties: Gardner 8 max. powd.; HLB 6.25; acid no. 6 max.; iodine no. 3 max.; sapon. no. 120-135; 100% conc.; nonionic.

Caprol® 6G2O. [ABITEC]
Chem. Descrip.: Polyglyceryl-6 dioleate
CAS 9007-48-1
Uses: Dispersant, emollient, emulsifier, solubilizer, coupling agent, humectant, wetting agent for delivery/absorp. enhancement, dermatological emulsions, suppositories
Regulatory: FDA 21CFR §172.854
Properties: Gardner 10 max. liq.; HLB 8.5; acid no. 6 max.; iodine no. 75 max.; sapon. no. 105-125; 100% conc.; nonionic.

Caprol® 6G2S. [ABITEC]
Chem. Descrip.: Polyglyceryl-6 distearate
CAS 61725-93-7
Uses: Coupling agent, bodying agent, hydrophilic o/w emulsifier, visc. modifier for delivery/absorp. enhancement, dermatological emulsions, suppositories
Regulatory: FDA 21CFR §172.854
Properties: Gardner 10 max. solid beads; HLB 8.5; acid no. 6 max.; iodine no. 3 max.; sapon. no. 105-125; 100% conc.; nonionic.

Caprol® 10G4O. [ABITEC]
Chem. Descrip.: Polyglyceryl-10 tetraoleate
CAS 34424-98-1; EINECS 252-011-7
Uses: Lipophilic w/o emulsifier, emollient, humectant, solubilizer, wetting agent for delivery/absorp. enhancement, dermatological emulsions, suppositories
Regulatory: FDA 21CFR §172.854
Properties: Gardner 7 max. liq.; HLB 6.2; acid no. 6 max.; iodine no. 60 max.; sapon. no. 125-150; 100% conc.; nonionic.

Caprol® 10G10O. [ABITEC]
Chem. Descrip.: Polyglyceryl-10 decaoleate
CAS 11094-60-3; EINECS 234-316-7
Uses: Dispersant, emollient, emulsifier, lubricant,

solubilizer for delivery/absorp. enhancement, dermatological emulsions, suppositories
Regulatory: FDA 21CFR §172.854
Properties: Gardner 9 max. liq.; sol. in oils and org. solvs.; HLB 3.5; acid no. 8 max.; iodine no. 85 max.; sapon. no. 155-185; 100% conc.; nonionic.

Caprol® ET. [ABITEC]
Chem. Descrip.: Polyglyceryl mixed veg. fatty acid esters; conforms to hydrog. veg. oil NF
CAS 67784-82-1; EINECS 269-820-6
Uses: Lubricant for suppositories, delivery/absorp. enhancement, dermatological emulsions; crystallization inhibitor
Regulatory: FDA 21CFR §172.854(c)
Properties: Gardner 8 max. semisolid; m.p. 37-39 C; HLB 2.5; acid no. 5 max.; iodine no. 25 max.; sapon. no. 176-198; 100% conc.; nonionic.

Caprol® PGE860. [ABITEC]
Chem. Descrip.: Decaglyceryl mono-, dioleate
CAS 9007-48-1
Uses: Clouding agent, dispersant, hydrophilic o/w emulsifier, solubilizer, visc. modifier, wetting agent for delivery/absorp. enhancement, dermatological emulsions, suppositories
Regulatory: FDA 21CFR §172.854
Properties: Gardner 10 max. visc. liq.; HLB 11.0; acid no. 6 max.; iodine no. 60 max.; sapon. no. 90-105; 100% conc.; nonionic.

Cap-Shure® FF-165-60. [Balchem]
Chem. Descrip.: Ferrous fumarate USP/FCC encapsulated with partially hydrog. soybean oil
Uses: Nutritive encapsulant for nutritional prods.; provides taste masking, enhanced flow props. temp./time release, and prevents reactivity with other ingreds.
Properties: Maroon free-flowing gran.; 2% max. on 20 mesh; coating m.p. 152-158 F; 60% ferrous fumarate, 40% hydrog. soybean oil
Storage: Store in cool, dry, odor-free environment @ 10-32 C.

Cap-Shure® KCL-140-50. [Balchem]
Chem. Descrip.: Potassium chloride USP/FCC encapsulated with partially hydrogenated cottonseed oil
Uses: Nutritive encapsulant for nutritional mixes and health foods; protective coating provides taste masking and delayed release
Properties: Wh. to off-wh. free-flowing gran.; 2% max. on 10 mesh; coating m.p. 141-147 F; 50% KCl; 50% hydrog. cottonseed oil
Storage: Store in cool, dry, odor-free environment @ 10-32 C.

Cap-Shure® KCL-165-70. [Balchem]
Chem. Descrip.: Potassium chloride USP/FCC encapsulated with partially hydrogenated soybean oil
Uses: Nutritive encapsulant for nutritional mixes and health foods; protective coating provides taste masking and delayed release
Properties: Wh. to off-wh. free-flowing gran.; 2% max. on 10 mesh; coating m.p. 152-158 F; 70% KCl, 30% hydrog. soybean oil.

Storage: Store in cool, dry, odor-free environment @ 10-32 C.

Capsulec 51-SB. [ADM Lecithin]
Chem. Descrip.: Capsule-grade lecithin
CAS 8002-43-5; EINECS 232-307-2
Uses: Emulsifier, binder for soft and hard gelatin encapsulation
Properties: Translucent fluid; visc. 10 stokes.

Capsulec 51-UB. [ADM Lecithin]
Chem. Descrip.: Capsule-grade lecithin
CAS 8002-43-5; EINECS 232-307-2
Uses: Emulsifier, binder for soft and hard gelatin encapsulation
Properties: Translucent fluid; visc. 10 stokes.

Capsulec 56-SB. [ADM Lecithin]
Chem. Descrip.: Capsule-grade lecithin
CAS 8002-43-5; EINECS 232-307-2
Uses: Emulsifier, binder for soft and hard gelatin encapsulation
Properties: Translucent fluid; visc. 20 stokes.

Capsulec 56-UB. [ADM Lecithin]
Chem. Descrip.: Capsule-grade lecithin
CAS 8002-43-5; EINECS 232-307-2
Uses: Emulsifier, binder for soft and hard gelatin encapsulation
Properties: Translucent fluid; visc. 20 stokes.

Capsulec 62-SB. [ADM Lecithin]
Chem. Descrip.: Capsule-grade lecithin
CAS 8002-43-5; EINECS 232-307-2
Uses: Emulsifier, binder for soft and hard gelatin encapsulation
Properties: Translucent fluid; visc. 60 stokes.

Capsulec 62-UB. [ADM Lecithin]
Chem. Descrip.: Capsule-grade lecithin
CAS 8002-43-5; EINECS 232-307-2
Uses: Emulsifier, binder for soft and hard gelatin encapsulation
Properties: Translucent fluid; visc. 60 stokes.

Captex® 200. [ABITEC]
Chem. Descrip.: Propylene glycol dicaprylate/dicaprate; conforms to hydrog. veg. oil NF
CAS 68583-51-7
Uses: Penetration aid, carrier, moisturizer, solubilizer, solv. for flavors, fragrance oil, sol. colorants, vitamins, medicinals; emollient for creams, lotions; for delivery/absorp. enhancement, dermatologicals, soft gelatin capsules, orals
Properties: APHA 100 liq.; sol. in alcohol, oils, hydrocarbons, ketones; visc. 7-13 mPa•s; acid no. 0.1 max.; iodine no. 1.0 max.; sapon. no. 315-335; cloud pt. < -20 C; ref. index 1.4393.

Captex® 200-E6. [ABITEC]
Chem. Descrip.: PEG-6 propylene glycol dicaprylate/dicaprate
Uses: Surfactant, emollient, emulsifier, moisturizer for dermatologicals, microemulsions; blooms in cold water
Properties: Gardner 4 liq.; HLB 12; acid no. 1 max.; pH 6.5-8.0 (5% aq.); 98.5% min. solids; nonionic.

Captex® 300. [ABITEC]
Chem. Descrip.: Caprylic/capric triglyceride

CAS 65381-09-1; EINECS 265-724-3
Uses: Diluent, emollient, lubricant, moisturizer, solubilizer, vehicle/carrier, visc. modifier for pharmaceuticals (clinical nutrition, delivery/absorp. enhancement, dermatologicals, soft gelatin capsules, orals); solv. for colors and perfumes
Properties: Gardner 2 max. liq., bland odor and flavor; sol. in alcohol, oils, hydrocarbons, ketones; visc. 24-30 mPa•s; acid no. 0.1 max.; iodine no. 0.5; sapon. no. 335-350; cloud pt. < -5 C; ref. index 1.4481.

Captex® 350. [ABITEC]
Chem. Descrip.: Caprylic/capric/lauric triglyceride; conforms to hydrog. veg. oil NF
CAS 68991-68-4
Uses: Diluent, emollient, moisturizer, solv., vehicle/carrier, fixative, and extender for pharmaceutical and nutritional applics. (clinical nutrition, delivery/absorp. enhancement, dermatologicals)
Properties: Gardner 2 max. liq., bland odor and flavor; visc. 36-42 mPa•s; acid no. 0.1 max.; iodine no. 1.52 max.; sapon. no. 290-310; cloud pt. 0 C max.; ref. index 1.4582.

Captex® 355. [ABITEC]
Chem. Descrip.: Caprylic/capric triglyceride
CAS 65381-09-1; EINECS 265-724-3
Uses: Diluent, emollient, lubricity vehicle, solubilizer, visc. modifier for pharmaceuticals (clinical nutrition, delivery/absorp. enhancement, dermatologicals, soft gelatin capsules, orals); carrier for essential oils, flavors, and fragrances
Properties: Lovibond R1.0 max. clear liq.; neutral odor; bland flavor; misc. with most org. solvs. incl. 95% ethanol; sp.gr. 0.92-0.96; visc. 26-32 mPa•s; acid no. 0.1 max.; iodine no. 0.5 max.; sapon. no. 325-345; cloud pt. < -5 C; ref. index 1.4486.

Captex® 800. [ABITEC]
Chem. Descrip.: Propylene glycol dioctanoate
CAS 56519-71-1
Uses: Emollient, moisturizer, nonoily lubricant imparting rich feel to skin in pharmaceuticals; penetration aid; carrier for essential oils, flavors; vehicle for vitamins, medicinals, nutritional prods.; for dermatologicals, suppositories
Properties: APHA 100 max. clear liq., neutral odor; bland flavor; misc. with most org. solvs. incl. 95% ethanol; visc. 9-13 mPa•s; acid no. 1.0 max.; iodine no. 1.0 max.; sapon. no. 320-340; cloud pt. < -20 C.

Captex® 810A. [ABITEC]
Chem. Descrip.: Caprylic/capric/linoleic triglyceride; conforms to hydrog. veg. oil NF
CAS 67701-28-4
Uses: Emollient, solv., vehicle/carrier, diluent, solubilizer in pharmaceutical and nutritional applics. (clinical nutrition, delivery/absorp. enhancement, dermatologicals; carrier for flavors/fragrances)
Properties: Gardner 2 max. liq.; acid no. 0.1 max.; iodine no. 25; sapon. no. 307-320.

Captex® 810D. [ABITEC]
Chem. Descrip.: Caprylic/capric/linoleic triglycer-

ide; conforms to hydrog. veg. oil NF
CAS 67701-28-4
Uses: Emollient, solv., vehicle/carrier, diluent, solubilizer in pharmaceutical and nutritional applics. (clinical nutrition, delivery/absorp. enhancement, dermatologicals; carrier for flavors/fragrances)
Properties: Gardner 2 max. liq.; acid no. 0.1 max.; iodine no. 85; sapon. no. 235-253.

Captex® 8000. [ABITEC]
Chem. Descrip.: Tricaprylin
CAS 538-23-8; EINECS 208-686-5
Uses: Nonoily lubricant imparting rich feel to the skin; for pharmaceuticals; carrier for essential oils, flavors; vehicle for vitamins, medicinals, nutritional prods.
Properties: APHA 150 max. clear liq.; neutral odor; bland flavor; misc. with most org. solvs. incl. 95% ethanol; visc. 20-28 mPa•s; acid no. 1.0 max.; iodine no. 1.0 max.; sapon. no. 350-365; cloud pt. < -5 C; ref. index 1.4469.

Captex® 8227. [ABITEC]
Chem. Descrip.: Triundecanoin
CAS 13552-80-2; EINECS 236-935-8
Uses: Emollient, lubricant, moisturizer, visc. modifier in pharmaceuticals (dermatological emulsions)
Properties: APHA 150 solid; acid no. 0.5 max.; iodine no. 5 max.; sapon. no. 270-290; cloud pt. 21 C.

Caramel Color Double Strength. [Crompton & Knowles/Ingred. Tech.]
Chem. Descrip.: Caramel
CAS 8028-89-5; EINECS 232-435-9
Uses: Color additive for drugs
Regulatory: FDA 21CFR §73.85, 73.1085, 73.2085
Properties: Dk. brn. visc. liq.; typ. odor; sol. in water; sp.gr. 1.2 ± 0.1; visc. 300 cps max.; pH 2.75 ± 0.5
Storage: 2 yrs shelf life stored in tight containers; avoid exposure to excessive heat, light, and moisture.

Caramel Color Single Strength. [Crompton & Knowles/Ingred. Tech.]
Chem. Descrip.: Caramel, acid proof
CAS 8028-89-5; EINECS 232-435-9
Uses: Color additive for drugs
Regulatory: FDA 21CFR §73.85, 73.1085, 73.2085
Properties: Dk. brn. visc. liq.; typ. odor; sol. in water; sp.gr. 1.3 ± 0.1; visc. 400 cps max.; pH 3.0 ± 0.3
Storage: 2 yr shelf life stored in tight containers; avoid exposure to excessive heat, light, and moisture.

Carbopol® 907. [BFGoodrich]
Chem. Descrip.: Polyacrylic acid
CAS 9003-01-4
Uses: Emulsifier, thickener, stabilizer, suspending agent, lubricant for topical pharmaceuticals
Regulatory: JSPI compliance; FDA 21CFR §175.105, 175.300, 175.320, 176.170, 176.180, 176.200, 177.1210, 177.2260; 40CFR § 180.1001
Properties: Wh. fluffy powd.; sol. in water, polar

solvs., many nonpolar solvs. blends; sp.gr. 1.41; bulk dens. 208 kg/m^3; visc. 0-3000 cps (4%); pH 2.5-3.0 (1% aq. disp.); 100% conc.; anionic; low aquatic toxicity; BOD=0, nonbiodeg.; removed with the biomass in typ. wastewater treatment
Storage: 2 yr min. shelf life stored in sealed containers, protected from moisture and extreme temps.; hygroscopic.

Carbopol® 910. [BFGoodrich]
Chem. Descrip.: Carbomer 910
Uses: Emulsifier, thickener, stabilizer, suspending agent, rheology agent for topical pharmaceuticals
Regulatory: NF, BP, JSPI compliance; FDA 21CFR §175.105, 175.300, 175.320, 176.170, 176.180, 176.200, 177.1210, 177.2260; 40CFR § 180.1001
Properties: Wh. fluffy powd.; sol. in water, polar solvs., many nonpolar solvs. blends; sp.gr. 1.41; bulk dens. 208 kg/m^3; visc. 3000-7000 cps (1%); pH 2.5-3.0 (1% aq. disp.); 100% conc.; anionic
Toxicology: LD50 (oral, rat) 10.25 g/kg, (dermal, rabbit) > 3 g/kg, (inh., rat) 1.71 mg/l; eye irritant; sl. skin irritant
Storage: 2 yr min. shelf life stored in sealed containers, protected from moisture and extreme temps.; hygroscopic.

Carbopol® 934. [BFGoodrich]
Chem. Descrip.: Carbomer 934
Uses: Rheology agent, emulsifier, thickener, stabilizer, suspending agent for stable topical pharmaceutical emulsions and suspensions, aq. and solv.-based gels
Regulatory: NF, BP, JSPI compliance; FDA 21CFR §175.105, 175.300, 175.320, 176.170, 176.180, 176.200, 177.1210, 177.2260; 40CFR § 180.1001
Properties: Wh. fluffy powd.; sol. in water, polar solvs., many nonpolar solvs. blends; sp.gr. 1.41; bulk dens. 208 kg/m^3; visc. 30,500-39,400 cps (0.5%); pH 2.5-3.0 (1% aq. disp.); 100% conc.; anionic; low aquatic toxicity; BOD=0, nonbiodeg.; removed with the biomass in typ. wastewater treatment
Toxicology: LD50 (oral) 2.5-40 g/kg, low acute toxicity; mild eye irritant; minimal skin irritant
Storage: 2 yr min. shelf life stored in sealed containers, protected from moisture and extreme temps.; hygroscopic.

Carbopol® 934P. [BFGoodrich]
Chem. Descrip.: Carbomer 934P
Uses: High purity grade for pharmaceuticals; thickener, suspending agent, emulsifier; for topicals, transdermals, sustained release tablets, oral suspensions, mucoadhesive applics.
Regulatory: NF, BP, IP, JSPI compliance; FDA 21CFR §175.105, 175.300, 175.320, 176.170, 176.180, 176.200, 177.1210, 177.2260; 40CFR §180.1001
Properties: Wh. fluffy powd., sl. acetic odor; m.w. ≈ 3,000,000; sol. in water, polar solvs., many nonpolar solvs. blends; sp.gr. 1.41; bulk dens. 208 kg/ m^3; visc. 2050-5450 cps (0.2%), 29,400-39,400

cps (0.5%); pH 2.5-3.0 (1% aq. disp.)
Toxicology: LD50 (oral) 2.5-40 g/kg, low acute toxicity; mild eye irritant; minimal skin irritant
Storage: 2 yr min. shelf life stored in sealed containers, protected from moisture and extreme temps.; hygroscopic.

Carbopol® 940. [BFGoodrich]
Chem. Descrip.: Carbomer 940
Uses: Emulsifier, thickener, stabilizer, suspending agent for topical pharmaceuticals, esp. sparkling clear water or hydroalcoholic topical gels; efficient solv. thickening with or without neutralizing; for aq. or solv. systems
Regulatory: NF, BP, JSPI compliance; FDA 21CFR §175.105, 175.300, 175.320, 176.170, 176.180, 176.200, 177.1210, 177.2260; 40CFR § 180.1001
Properties: Wh. fluffy powd.; sol. in water, polar solvs., many nonpolar solvs. blends; sp.gr. 1.41; bulk dens. 208 kg/m^3; visc. 40,000-60,000 cps (0.5%); pH 2.5-3.0 (1% aq. disp.); 100% conc.; anionic; low aquatic toxicity; BOD=0, nonbiodeg.; removed with the biomass in typ. wastewater treatment
Toxicology: Nonirritating to skin and eyes
Storage: 2 yr min. shelf life stored in sealed containers, protected from moisture and extreme temps.; hygroscopic.

Carbopol® 941. [BFGoodrich]
Chem. Descrip.: Carbomer 941
Uses: Emulsifier, thickener for low visc. sparkling clear topical pharmceutical gels, emulsion stabilization of topical lotions; effective in mod. ionic systems
Regulatory: NF, JSPI compliance; FDA 21CFR §175.105, 175.300, 175.320, 176.170, 176.180, 176.200, 177.1210, 177.2260; 40CFR § 180.1001
Properties: Wh. fluffy powd.; sol. in water, polar solvs., many nonpolar solvs. blends; sp.gr. 1.41; bulk dens. 208 kg/m^3; visc. 4000-11,000 cps (0.5%); pH 2.5-3.0 (1% aq. disp.); 100% conc.; anionic
Toxicology: LD50 (oral, rat) > 1 g/kg; nonirritating to eyes; low irritation potential on skin
Storage: 2 yr min. shelf life stored in sealed containers, protected from moisture and extreme temps.; hygroscopic.

Carbopol® 971P. [BFGoodrich]
Chem. Descrip.: Carbomer 941 (polymerized in ethyl acetate)
Uses: Emulsifier, thickener, stabilizer, suspending agent for pharmaceuticals, esp. oral and mucoadhesive applics., controlled-release tablets, oral suspensions, transdermals, low-visc. clear topical lotions and gels
Regulatory: USP/NF, BP, JSPI compliance; FDA 21CFR §175.105, 175.300, 175.320, 176.170, 176.180, 176.200, 177.1210, 177.2260; 40CFR §180.1001
Properties: Wh. fluffy powd., sl. acetic odor; 2-6 μ particle size; sp.gr. 1.41; bulk dens. 208 kg/m^3;

visc. 4000-11,000 cps (0.5%); acid no. 700-750; pH 2.5-3.0 (1% aq. disp.)

Toxicology: LD50 (dermal, rabbit) > 2.0 g/kg; nonirritating to eyes; nonsensitizing to human skin

Storage: 2 yr min. shelf life stored in sealed containers, protected from moisture and extreme temps.; hygroscopic.

Carbopol® 974P. [BFGoodrich]

Chem. Descrip.: Carbomer 934P (polymerized in ethyl acetate)

Uses: Emulsifier, thickener, stabilizer, suspending agent for pharmaceuticals, esp. oral and mucoadhesive applics., controlled-release tablets, oral suspensions, transdermals, topicals

Regulatory: NF, BP, JSPI compliance; FDA 21CFR §175.105, 175.300, 175.320, 176.170, 176.180, 176.200, 177.1210, 177.2260; 40CFR § 180.1001

Properties: Wh. fluffy powd.; sp.gr. 1.41; bulk dens. 208 kg/m^3; visc. 29,400-39,400 cps (0.5%); pH 2.5-3.0 (1% aq. disp.)

Toxicology: LD50 (dermal, rabbit) > 2.0 g/kg; nonirritating to eyes; nonsensitizing to human skin

Storage: 2 yr min. shelf life stored in sealed containers, protected from moisture and extreme temps.; hygroscopic.

Carbopol® 980. [BFGoodrich]

Chem. Descrip.: Carbomer 940

Uses: Efficient solv. thickener for pharmaceuticals, with or without neutralizing; for sparkling clear water or hydroalcoholic topical gels, aq. or solv. systems

Regulatory: NF, DAB, JSPI compliance; FDA 21CFR §175.105, 175.300, 175.320, 176.170, 176.180, 176.200, 177.1210, 177.2260; 40CFR §180.1001

Properties: Wh. fluffy powd.; sp.gr. 1.41; bulk dens. 208 kg/m^3; visc. 13,000-30,000 cps (0.2%), 40,000-60,000 cps (0.5%); ; pH 2.5-3.0 (1% aq. disp.)

Toxicology: Sl. irritating to skin; minimal eye irritant

Storage: 2 yr min. shelf life stored in sealed containers, protected from moisture and extreme temps.; hygroscopic.

Carbopol® 981. [BFGoodrich]

Chem. Descrip.: Carbomer 941

Uses: Emulsifier, thickener for low visc. sparkling clear pharmaceutical topical gels, emulsion stabilization of topical lotions; effective in mod. ionic systems

Regulatory: NF, JSPI compliance; FDA 21CFR §175.105, 175.300, 175.320, 176.170, 176.180, 176.200, 177.1210, 177.2260; 40CFR § 180.1001

Properties: Wh. fluffy powd.; sp.gr. 1.41; bulk dens. 208 kg/m^3; visc. 4000-10,000 cps (0.5%); pH 2.5-3.0 (1% aq. disp.)

Toxicology: Sl. irritating to skin; minimal eye irritant

Storage: 2 yr min. shelf life stored in sealed containers, protected from moisture and extreme temps.; hygroscopic.

Carbopol® 1342. [BFGoodrich]

Chem. Descrip.: Acrylates/C10-30 alkyl acrylate crosspolymer

Uses: Rheology agent, emulsifier, stabilizer, moisturizer, thickener, gellant for topical pharmaceuticals; emulsion stabilizer; for pourable prods. contg. suspended incompat. ingreds.; lt. gellant for water or hydroalcoholic systems

Regulatory: NF, JSCI compliance; FDA 21CFR §175.105, 175.300, 175.320, 176.170, 176.180, 176.200, 177.1210, 177.2260; 40CFR § 180.1001

Properties: Wh. fluffy powd., sl. acetic odor; sp.gr. 1.41; bulk dens. 208 kg/m^3; visc. 9500-26,500 cps (1%); pH 2.5-3.0 (1% aq. disp.)

Toxicology: LD50 (oral, rat) > 5 g/kg; nonirritating to skin; mod. eye irritant in conc. form, nonirritating @ 1%

Storage: 2 yr min. shelf life stored in sealed containers, protected from moisture and extreme temps.; hygroscopic.

Carbopol® 1382. [BFGoodrich]

Chem. Descrip.: Acrylates/C10-30 alkyl acrylate crosspolymer

Uses: Rheology agent, thickener, emulsion stabilizer for topical pharmaceuticals; formulation of pourable prods. contg. suspended incompat. ingreds.; light gellant for water or hydroalcoholic systems

Regulatory: JSCI compliance; FDA 21CFR §175.105, 175.300, 175.320, 176.170, 176.180, 176.200, 177.1210, 177.2260; 40CFR § 180.1001

Properties: Wh. fluffy powd.; sp.gr. 1.41; bulk dens. 208 kg/m^3; visc. 25,000-45,000 (1%); pH 2.5-3.0 (1% aq. disp.)

Toxicology: Sl. skin irritant; borderline eye irritant

Storage: 2 yr min. shelf life stored in sealed containers, protected from moisture and extreme temps.; hygroscopic.

Carbopol® 2984. [BFGoodrich]

Chem. Descrip.: Carbomer

Uses: Rheology agent, emulsifier, thickener, stabilizer, suspending agent used in topical pharmaceutical stable emulsions and suspensions, aq. and solv.-based gels

Regulatory: BP, JSPI compliance; FDA 21CFR §175.105, 175.300, 175.320, 176.170, 176.180, 176.200, 177.1210, 177.2260; 40CFR § 180.1001

Properties: Wh. fluffy powd.; sp.gr. 1.41; bulk dens. 208 kg/m^3; visc. 45,000-80,000 cps (0.5%); pH 2.5-3.0 (1% aq. disp.)

Storage: 2 yr min. shelf life stored in sealed containers, protected from moisture and extreme temps.; hygroscopic.

Carbopol® 5984. [BFGoodrich]

Chem. Descrip.: Carbomer

Uses: Rheology agent, emulsifier, thickener, stabilizer, suspending agent used in topical pharmaceutical stable emulsions and suspensions, aq.

and solv.-based gels

Regulatory: BP, JSPI compliance; FDA 21CFR §175.105, 175.300, 175.320, 176.170, 176.180, 176.200, 177.1210, 177.2260; 40CFR § 180.1001

Properties: Wh. fluffy powd.; sp.gr. 1.41; bulk dens. 208 kg/m³; visc. 25,000-45,000 cps (0.5%); pH 2.5-3.0 (1% aq. disp.)

Storage: 2 yr min. shelf life stored in sealed containers, protected from moisture and extreme temps.; hygroscopic.

Carbopol® ETD 2001. [BFGoodrich]

Chem. Descrip.: Crosslinked acrylic acid polymer with processing aid

Uses: Rheology agent, thickener, stabilizer, suspending agent for topical pharmaceutical aq. or solv. systems, sparkling clear water or hydroalcoholic topical gels; easier to disperse and mix

Regulatory: FDA 21CFR §175.105, 175.300, 175.320, 176.170, 176.180, 176.200, 177.1210, 177.2260; 40CFR §180.1001

Properties: Wh. fluffy powd.; sp.gr. 1.41; bulk dens. 208 kg/m³; visc. 45,000-65,000 cps (0.5%); pH 2.5-3.0 (1% aq. disp.)

Toxicology: Sl. skin irritant in conc. form, non to very sl. irritant @ 1%; sl. to mod. eye irritant (undiluted)

Storage: 2 yr min. shelf life stored in sealed containers, protected from moisture and extreme temps.; hygroscopic.

Carbopol® ETD 2020. [BFGoodrich]

Chem. Descrip.: Crosslinked acrylic acid polymer with processing aid

Uses: Thickener, emulsion stabilizer for topical pharmaceuticals; formulation of pourable prods. contg. suspended incompat. ingreds.; light gellant for water or hydroalcoholic systems; easier to disperse and mix

Regulatory: FDA 21CFR §175.105, 175.300, 175.320, 176.170, 176.180, 176.200, 177.1210, 177.2260; 40CFR §180.1001

Properties: Wh. fluffy powd.; sp.gr. 1.41; bulk dens. 208 kg/m³; visc. 32,000-77,000 cps (1%); pH 2.5-3.0 (1% aq. disp.)

Toxicology: Sl. skin irritant in conc. form, non to very sl. irritant @ 1%; sl. to mod. eye irritant (undiluted)

Storage: 2 yr min. shelf life stored in sealed containers, protected from moisture and extreme temps.; hygroscopic.

Carbopol® ETD 2050. [BFGoodrich]

Chem. Descrip.: Crosslinked acrylic acid polymer with processing aid

Uses: Emulsifier, thickener for low visc. sparkling clear pharmaceutical topical gels, emulsion stabilization of topical lotions; effective in mod. ionic systems; easier to disperse and mix

Regulatory: FDA 21CFR §175.105, 175.300, 175.320, 176.170, 176.180, 176.200, 177.1210, 177.2260; 40CFR §180.1001

Properties: Wh. fluffy powd.; sp.gr. 1.41; bulk dens. 208 kg/m³; visc. 8000-16,500 cps (0.5%); pH 2.5-

3.0 (1% aq. disp.)

Toxicology: Sl. skin irritant in conc. form, non to very sl. irritant @ 1%; sl. to mod. eye irritant (undiluted)

Storage: 2 yr min. shelf life stored in sealed containers, protected from moisture and extreme temps.; hygroscopic.

Carbowax® PEG 300. [Union Carbide]

Chem. Descrip.: PEG-6

CAS 25322-68-3; EINECS 220-045-1

Uses: Coupling agent, solv., vehicle, humectant, lubricant, binder, base; used in pharmaceuticals

Properties: Water-wh. visc. liq.; sol. in water, alcohols, glycerin, glycols; m.w. 285-315; sp.gr. 1.1250; dens. 9.38 lb/gal; visc. 5.8 cSt (99 C); f.p. -15 to -8 C; hyd. no. 356-394; flash pt. (PMCC) > 180 C; ref. index 1.463; pH 4.5-7.5 (5% aq.); surf. tens. 44.5 dynes/cm.

Carbowax® Sentry® PEG 300. [Union Carbide]

Chem. Descrip.: PEG-6, FCC grade

CAS 25322-68-3; EINECS 220-045-1

Uses: Coupling agent, solv., vehicle, humectant, lubricant, binder, base, bodying agent, dispersant for pharmaceuticals (coating, binder, plasticizer, and lubricant in tablets; antiperspirants; sunscreens), as glycerin replacement

Regulatory: FDA approved

Properties: Water-wh. visc. liq.; sol. in water, alcohols, glycerin, glycols; m.w. 285-315; sp.gr. 1.1250; dens. 9.38 lb/gal; visc. 5.8 cSt (99 C); f.p. -15 to -8 C; hyd. no. 356-394; flash pt. (PMCC) > 180 C; ref. index 1.463; pH 4.5-7.5 (5% aq.); surf. tens. 44.5 dynes/cm.

Carbowax® Sentry® PEG 400. [Union Carbide]

Chem. Descrip.: PEG-8, FCC grade

CAS 25322-68-3; EINECS 225-856-4

Uses: Coupling agent, solv., vehicle, humectant, lubricant, binder, base for pharmaceuticals (coating, binder, plasticizer, and lubricant in tablets; sunscreens; toothpaste)

Regulatory: FDA approved

Properties: Water-wh. visc. liq.; sol. in water, methanol, ethanol, acetone, trichloroethylene, Cellosolve®, Carbitol®, dibutyl phthalate, toluene; m.w. 380-420; sp.gr. 1.1254; dens. 9.39 lb/gal; visc. 7.3 cSt (99 C); f.p. 4-8 C; hyd. no. 267-295; flash pt. (PMCC) > 180 C; ref. index 1.465; pH 4.5-7.5 (5% aq.); surf. tens. 44.5 dynes/cm.

Carbowax® Sentry® PEG 540 Blend. [Union Carbide]

Chem. Descrip.: PEG-6 and PEG-32, FCC grade

Uses: Coupling agent, solv., vehicle, humectant, lubricant, binder, base for pharmaceuticals (coating, binder, plasticizer, and lubricant in tablets; ointments, antiperspirants, sunscreens)

Regulatory: FDA approved

Properties: Wh. soft waxy solid; sol. in methylene chloride, 73% in water, 50% in trichloroethylene, 48% in methanol; m.w. 500-600; sp.gr. 1.0930; dens. 9.17 lb/gal (55 C); visc. 15.1 cSt (99 C); m.p. 38-41 C; hyd. no. 187-224; flash pt. (PMCC) > 180 C; pH 4.5-7.5 (5% aq.).

Carbowax® Sentry® PEG 600. [Union Carbide]
Chem. Descrip.: PEG-12, FCC grade
CAS 25322-68-3; EINECS 229-859-1
Uses: Coupling agent, solv., vehicle, humectant, lubricant, binder, base for pharmaceuticals (coating, binder, plasticizer, and lubricant in tablets; antiperspirants; dentifrices; sunscreens)
Regulatory: FDA approved
Properties: Water-wh. visc. liq.; sol. in water, alcohols, glycols; m.w. 570-630; sp.gr. 1.1257; dens. 9.40 lb/gal; visc. 10.8 cSt (99 C); f.p. 20-25 C; hyd. no. 178-197; flash pt. (PMCC) > 180 C; ref. index 1.46; pH 4.5-7.5 (5% aq.); surf. tens. 44.5 dynes/cm.

Carbowax® Sentry® PEG 900. [Union Carbide]
Chem. Descrip.: PEG-20, FCC grade
CAS 25322-68-3
Uses: Coupling agent, solv., vehicle, humectant, lubricant, binder, base for pharmaceuticals (coating, binder, plasticizer, and lubricant in tablets; antiperspirants)
Regulatory: FDA approved
Properties: Wh. soft waxy solid; sol. 86% in water; m.w. 855-945; sp.gr. 1.0927 (60 C); dens. 9.16 lb/gal (55 C); visc. 15.3 cSt (99 C); m.p. 32-36 C; hyd. no. 119-131; flash pt. (PMCC) > 180 C; pH 4.5-7.5 (5% aq.).

Carbowax® Sentry® PEG 1000. [Union Carbide]
Chem. Descrip.: PEG-20, FCC grade
CAS 25322-68-3
Uses: Coupling agent, solv., vehicle, humectant, lubricant, binder, base for pharmaceuticals (coating, binder, plasticizer, and lubricant in tablets)
Regulatory: FDA approved
Properties: Wh. soft waxy solid; sol. 80% in water; m.w. 950-1050; sp.gr. 1.0926 (60 C); dens. 9.16 lb/gal (55 C); visc. 17.2 cSt (99 C); m.p. 37-40 C; hyd. no. 107-118; flash pt. (PMCC) > 180 C; pH 4.5-7.5 (5% aq.).

Carbowax® Sentry® PEG 1450. [Union Carbide]
Chem. Descrip.: PEG-32, FCC grade
CAS 25322-68-3
Uses: Coupling agent, solv., vehicle, humectant, lubricant, binder, base for pharmaceuticals (coating, binder, plasticizer, and lubricant in tablets)
Regulatory: FDA approved
Properties: Wh. soft waxy solid or flake; sol. 72% in water; m.w. 1300-1600; sp.gr. 1.0919 (60 C); dens. 9.17 lb/gal (55 C); bulk dens. 30 lb/ft^3 (flake); visc. 26.5 cSt (99 C); m.p. 43-46 C; hyd. no. 70-86; flash pt. (PMCC) > 180 C; pH 4.5-7.5 (5% aq.).

Carbowax® Sentry® PEG 3350. [Union Carbide]
Chem. Descrip.: PEG-75, FCC grade
CAS 25322-68-3
Uses: Coupling agent, solv., vehicle, humectant, lubricant, binder, base for pharmaceuticals (coating, binder, plasticizer, and lubricant in tablets)
Regulatory: FDA approved
Properties: Wh. hard waxy flake or powd.; sol. 67% in water; m.w. 3000-3700; sp.gr. 1.0926 (60 C); dens. 8.94 lb/gal (80 C); bulk dens. 30 lb/ft^3

(flake), 40 lb/ft^3 (powd.); visc. 90.8 cSt (99 C); m.p. 54-58 C; hyd. no. 30-37; flash pt. (PMCC) > 180 C; pH 4.5-7.5 (5% aq.).

Carbowax® Sentry® PEG 4600. [Union Carbide]
Chem. Descrip.: PEG-100, FCC grade
CAS 25322-68-3
Uses: Coupling agent, solv., vehicle, humectant, lubricant, binder, base for pharmaceuticals (coating, binder, plasticizer, and lubricant in tablets)
Regulatory: FDA approved
Properties: Wh. hard waxy flake or powd.; sol. 65% in water; m.w. 4400-4800; sp.gr. 1.0926 (60 C); dens. 8.95 lb/gal (80 C); bulk dens. 30 lb/ft^3 (flake), 40 lb/ft^3 (powd.); visc. 184 cSt (99 C); m.p. 57-61 C; hyd. no. 23-26; flash pt. PMCC) > 180 C; pH 4.5-7.5 (5% aq.).

Carbowax® Sentry® PEG 8000. [Union Carbide]
Chem. Descrip.: PEG-150, FCC grade
CAS 25322-68-3
Uses: Coupling agent, solv., vehicle, humectant, lubricant, binder, base for pharmaceuticals (coating, binder, plasticizer, and lubricant in tablets)
Regulatory: FDA approved
Properties: Wh. hard waxy flake or powd.; sol. 63% in water; m.w. 7000-9000; sp.gr. 1.0845 (60 C); dens. 8.96 lb/gal (80 C); bulk dens. 30 lb/ft^3 (flake), 40 lb/ft^3 (powd.); visc. 822 cSt (99 C); m.p. 60-63 C; hyd. no. 13-16; flash pt. (PMCC) > 180 C; pH 4.5-7.5 (5% aq.).

Carmacid R. [MLG Enterprises Ltd.]
Chem. Descrip.: Acid-stable ammonium carminate
Uses: Natural colorant producing red shades for pharmaceutical tableting; 7.5% carminic acid.

Carmacid Y. [MLG Enterprises Ltd.]
Chem. Descrip.: Carminic acid sprayed with maltodextrin
CAS 1390-65-4; EINECS 215-724-4
Uses: Natural colorant for pharmaceuticals producing yel.-orange shades
Properties: Powd.; 50% carminic acid.

Carmine AS. [Crompton & Knowles/Ingred. Tech.]
Chem. Descrip.: Carmine, acid stable, with proteins, citrates, aluminum salts, propylene glycol
Uses: Color additive for drugs; exc. coloring props. in acidic environments; exc. resist. to heat, light, and chems.
Regulatory: FDA 21CFR §73.100, 73.1100, 73.2087
Properties: Sl. visc. liq., bright red color when diluted in water; sl. odor; highly sol. in water and alcoholic beverages; pH 3.2 ± 0.2; 34 ± 1.7% solids, 2.5% min. carminic acid.
Storage: 1 yr shelf life stored in tight containers; avoid exposure to heat and light.

Carmine FG. [MLG Enterprises Ltd.]
Chem. Descrip.: Hydrated aluminum chelate of carminic acid, carmine lake-red powd.
CAS 1390-65-4; EINECS 215-724-4
Uses: Natural colorant producing red-blue shades for pharmaceuticals (tablet coatings, cough syrups)
Regulatory: FDA 21CFR §73.100, 73.1100,

73.2087; EEC E120
Properties: Sol. in alkaline media; insol. in water and alcohol; up to 60% carminic acid.
Storage: Keep in cool, dark place.
Carmine PG. [MLG Enterprises Ltd.]
Chem. Descrip.: Hydrated aluminum chelate of carminic acid, carmine lake-red powd.
CAS 1390-65-4; EINECS 215-724-4
Uses: Natural colorant producing purple shades; for pharmaceuticals (tablet coatings, cough syrups)
Regulatory: FDA 21CFR §73.100, 73.1100, 73.2087; EEC E120
Properties: Sol. in alkaline media; insol. in water and alcohol; up to 60% carminic acid.
Storage: Keep in cool, dark place.
Carmine Powd. 272010, 272015, 272020. [Crompton & Knowles/Ingred. Tech.]
Chem. Descrip.: Carmine
CAS 1390-65-4; EINECS 215-724-4
Uses: Color additive for drugs; exc. resist. to heat, light, and chems.
Regulatory: FDA 21CFR §73.100, 73.1100, 73.2087
Properties: Ylsh.-red to purple-red free-flowing powd., sl. odor; 100% min. thru 100 mesh; sol. in dil. alkali sol'n.; insol. in water, alcohol, org. solvs., oils, and fats; 50% min. carminic acid
Storage: 1 yr shelf life stored in tight containers; avoid exposure to heat, light, moisture.
Carmine Powd. WS. [Crompton & Knowles/Ingred. Tech.]
Chem. Descrip.: Carmine
CAS 1390-65-4; EINECS 215-724-4
Uses: Color additive for drugs; exc. resist. to heat, light, and chems.
Regulatory: FDA 21CFR §73.100, 73.1100, 73.2087
Properties: Free-flowing powd., bright red when diluted in water; sl. odor; 100% min. thru 100 mesh; highly sol. in water, alcoholic beverages; 50% min. carminic acid.
Storage: Store in tight containers; avoid exposure to heat, light, moisture; 6 mos storage life.
Carmine XY/UF. [MLG Enterprises Ltd.]
Chem. Descrip.: Hydrated aluminum chelate of carminic acid, carmine lake-red powd.
CAS 1390-65-4; EINECS 215-724-4
Uses: Natural colorant producing red-yel. shades, with high tinting str.; for pharmaceuticals (tablet coatings, cough syrups)
Regulatory: FDA 21CFR §73.100, 73.1100, 73.2087; EEC E120
Properties: Sol. in alkaline media; insol. in water and alcohol; up to 60% carminic acid.
Storage: Keep in cool, dark place.
Carminic Acid 90. [Helianthus SA]
Chem. Descrip.: Carminic acid
EINECS 215-724-4
Uses: Natural red color for pharmaceutical prods.; stable to oxidation, light, and temps. below 150 C
Properties: Brilliant red powd.; completely sol. in

water at pH > 4; 90% conc.
Precaution: Very reactive with calcium, magnesium, and other metallic salts.
Carmisol A. [MLG Enterprises Ltd.]
Chem. Descrip.: Ammonium salt of hydrated aluminum chelate of carminic acid
CAS 1390-65-4; EINECS 215-724-4
Uses: Natural colorant producing pink to magenta red shades for pharmaceuticals; for sol'ns. or dry blends
Regulatory: FDA 21CRR §73.100, 73.1100, 73.2087; EEC E120
Properties: Dk. red powd.; sol. in water; 50% carminic acid.
Storage: Keep in cool, dark place.
Carmisol NA. [MLG Enterprises Ltd.]
Chem. Descrip.: Sodium salt of hydrated aluminum chelate of carminic acid
CAS 1390-65-4; EINECS 215-724-4
Uses: Natural colorant producing pink to magenta red shades for pharmaceuticals (tablet coatings, cough syrups); may be used in dry blends
Regulatory: FDA 21CFR §73.100, 73.1100, 73.2087; EEC E120
Properties: Odorless; water-sol.; 50% carminic acid.
Storage: Keep in cool, dark place.
Carnation®. [Witco/Petroleum Spec.]
Chem. Descrip.: Wh. min. oil NF
Uses: Emollient and lubricant for pharmaceutical ointments and creams
Regulatory: FDA 21CFR §172.878, §178.3620a
Properties: Water-wh., odorless, tasteless; sp.gr. 0.829-0.845; visc. 11-14 cSt(40 C); pour pt. -12 C; flash pt. 185 C.
Carsoquat® CT-429. [Lonza]
Chem. Descrip.: Cetyl trimethyl ammonium chloride
CAS 112-02-7; EINECS 203-928-6
Uses: Coagulating agent in the mfg. of antibiotics and other pharmaceuticals
Properties: Clear to pale yel. liq.; water-sol.; m.w. 319; sp.gr. 0.968; dens. 8.1 lb/gal; pH 3.5-4.0 (2%); 29% act. in water; cationic.
Castor Oil USP. [United Catalysts]
Chem. Descrip.: Castor oil
CAS 8001-79-4; EINECS 232-293-8
Uses: Emollient.
Castorwax® MP-70. [CasChem]
Chem. Descrip.: Hydrog. castor oil
CAS 8001-78-3; EINECS 232-292-2
Uses: Wax for anhyd. pharmaceutical prods. requiring a soft creamy texture
Regulatory: FDA approval
Properties: M.p. 70 C; acid no. 2; iodine no. (Wijs) 38; sapon. no. 180; hyd. no. 158; penetration hardness 42.
Castorwax® NF. [CasChem]
Chem. Descrip.: Hydrog. castor oil NF
CAS 8001-78-3; EINECS 232-292-2
Uses: Wax for pharmaceutical applics.
Regulatory: FDA approval

Properties: Flake.
Catechol XP. [James River]
Chem. Descrip.: Pyrocatechol
CAS 120-80-9; EINECS 204-427-5
Uses: Pharmaceutical synthesis
Properties: M.p. 103.5 C min.; 99.5% min. act.
C-A-T Enteric Coating Polymer. [Eastman]
Chem. Descrip.: Cellulose acetate trimellitate
Uses: Pharmaceutical excipient; enteric film-coating material for tablets or gran.; matrix binder for solid dosage forms; stable in strongly acid gastric fluids, but dissolves readily in mildly acidic to neutral environment of the sm. intestine
Properties: Wh. free-flowing powd.; visc. 17.7 cS (5% in ethyl acetate/IPA/water sol'n.); pH ≥ 5.0; 29% trimellityl, 22% acetyl
Storage: Store in cool, dry area; protect from moisture and humidity; bring drums to R.T. before opening to prevent moisture condensation on inside surfs.
Catigene® DC 100. [Stepan Europe]
Chem. Descrip.: N-Alkyl (3% C12, 95% C14, 2% C16) dimethylbenzyl ammonium chloride
CAS 139-08-2; EINECS 205-352-0
Uses: Antimicrobial preservative for pharmaceuticals
Properties: Powd.; 100% act.; cationic.
Catinal MB-50A. [Toho Chem. Industry]
Chem. Descrip.: Dodecyl dimethyl benzyl ammonium chloride
CAS 139-07-1; EINECS 205-351-5
Uses: Germicide, disinfectant for medical/pharmaceutical industries
Properties: Liq.; cationic
Unverified
Cavitron Cyclo-dextrin.™ [Am. Maize Prods.]
Chem. Descrip.: Cyclodextrin
CAS 7585-39-9; EINECS 231-493-2
Uses: Molecular encapsulation; protects act. ingreds. against oxidation and decomp., eliminates/reduces undesired taste/odor, and contamination, stabilizes food flavors and fragrances, enhances solubility; avail. as α, β, γ, derivs., and polymers
Properties: Spherical beads; α: m.w. 973; sol. 12.7 g/100 ml in water; β: m.w. 1135; sol. 1.88 g/100 ml in water, > 41% in dimethyl sulfoxide, 28.3% dimethyl formamide, 7% ethylene glycol; γ: m.w. 1297; sol. 25.6 g/100 ml in water.
Cecavon MG 51. [Ceca SA]
Chem. Descrip.: Magnesium stearate
CAS 557-04-0; EINECS 209-150-3
Uses: Anticaking agent for pharmaceutical prods.
Properties: Powd.; dens. 0.20 max.; m.p. 140-145 C; 4.5-5.1% Mg.
Cecavon ZN 70. [Ceca SA]
Chem. Descrip.: Zinc stearate
CAS 557-05-1; EINECS 209-151-9
Uses: Waterproofing agent, lubricant, gellant, opacifier for pharmaceuticals
Properties: Powd.; dens. 0.20 max.; m.p. 125-130 C; 10.2-11% Zn.

Cecavon ZN 71. [Ceca SA]
Chem. Descrip.: Zinc stearate
CAS 557-05-1; EINECS 209-151-9
Uses: Waterproofing agent, lubricant, gellant, opacifier for pharmaceuticals
Properties: Powd.; dens. 0.20 max.; m.p. 125-130 C; 10.2-11% Zn.
Cecavon ZN 72. [Ceca SA]
Chem. Descrip.: Zinc stearate
CAS 557-05-1; EINECS 209-151-9
Uses: Waterproofing agent, lubricant, gellant, opacifier for pharmaceuticals
Properties: Powd.; dens. 0.20 max.; m.p. 125-130 C; 9.8-10.6% Zn.
Cecavon ZN 73. [Ceca SA]
Chem. Descrip.: Zinc stearate
CAS 557-05-1; EINECS 209-151-9
Uses: Waterproofing agent, lubricant, gellant, opacifier for pharmaceuticals
Properties: Powd.; dens. < 0.20; m.p. 125-130 C; 10.2-10.8% Zn.
Cecavon ZN 735. [Ceca SA]
Chem. Descrip.: Zinc stearate
CAS 557-05-1; EINECS 209-151-9
Uses: Waterproofing agent, lubricant, gellant, opacifier for pharmaceuticals
Properties: Liq.; sp.gr. 1 ± 0.10; visc. 50-200 mPa•s; 35 ± 2% dry content.
Cegesoft® C 17. [Henkel KGaA/Cospha]
Chem. Descrip.: Myristyl lactate
CAS 1323-03-1; EINECS 215-350-1
Uses: Pharmaceutical raw material; emollient; solubilizer for solid and oil-sol. pharmaceutical actives
Use level: 2-25% (lipstick), 2-15% (eye shadow), 2-5% (antiperspirant), 2-5% (bath oils), 2-5% (alcoholic sol'ns.)
Properties: Wh. to sl. ylsh. solid, faint intrinsic odor; sol. @ 5% in 70% ethanol; sol. with heat in 1,2-propylene glycol, IPA, oleyl alcohol, soy oil, paraffin oil; m.p. 29-34 C; acid no. 5 max.; sapon. no. 180-196
Storage: 6 mos max. storage stability in closed original containers under cool, dry condiitions.
Cegesoft® C 24. [Henkel KGaA/Cospha; Grünau GmbH]
Chem. Descrip.: Octyl palmitate
CAS 29806-73-3; EINECS 249-862-1
Uses: Spreading agent used in pharmaceutical skin care preps., sl. fatting emulsions and skin oils
Properties: Sl. ylsh. clear oil; m.w. 350; sp.gr. 0.855-0.865; visc. 10-15 mPa•s; acid no. 0.5 max.; sapon. no. 148-158; cloud pt. 2 C max.; ref. index 1.446-1.448
Storage: 1 yr min. storage life in original sealed containers in dry environment at temps. below 30 C.
Cekol® 30. [Metsä-Serla Oy]
Chem. Descrip.: Sodium CMC
CAS 9004-32-4
Uses: Binder, thickener, stabilizer and film-former for pharmaceutical applics., esp. tablet coating

Regulatory: USP/NF, Eur.Ph. and other compliances
Properties: Wh. to off-wh. fine powd. or gran., odorless; hygroscopic; sol. in water; dens. 1.6 g/cc (20 C); bulk dens. 400-800 kg/m³; visc. 10 mPa•s (1%); decomp. pt. 240 C; pH 6.5-8.0 (1%); biodeg.; BOD7 ≈ 50-100 gO₂/kg
Toxicology: LD50 (oral, rat) 27,000 mg/kg; powd. may dry the skin; dust may irritate eyes; inh. of dust may cause respiratory irritation
Storage: Store in cool, dry place; avoid dusting.
Cekol® 150. [Metsä-Serla Oy]
Chem. Descrip.: Sodium CMC
CAS 9004-32-4
Uses: Binder, thickener, stabilizer and film-former for pharmaceutical applics.; stabilizer, dispersant for o/w emulsions
Regulatory: USP/NF, Eur.Ph. and other compliances
Properties: Wh. to off-wh. fine powd. or gran., odorless; hygroscopic; sol. in water; dens. 1.6 g/cc (20 C); bulk dens. 400-800 kg/m³; visc. 20 mPa•s (1%); decomp. pt. 240 C; pH 6.5-8.0 (1%); biodeg.; BOD7 ≈ 50-100 gO₂/kg
Toxicology: LD50 (oral, rat) 27,000 mg/kg; powd. may dry the skin; dust may irritate eyes; inh. of dust may cause respiratory irritation
Storage: Store in cool, dry place; avoid dusting.
Cekol® 300. [Metsä-Serla Oy]
Chem. Descrip.: Sodium CMC
CAS 9004-32-4
Uses: Binder, thickener, stabilizer and film-former for pharmaceutical applics.
Regulatory: USP/NF, Eur.Ph. and other compliances
Properties: Wh. to off-wh. fine powd. or gran., odorless; hygroscopic; sol. in water; dens. 1.6 g/cc (20 C); bulk dens. 400-800 kg/m³; visc. 45 mPa•s (1%); decomp. pt. 240 C; pH 6.5-8.0 (1%); biodeg.; BOD7 ≈ 50-100 gO₂/kg
Toxicology: LD50 (oral, rat) 27,000 mg/kg; powd. may dry the skin; dust may irritate eyes; inh. of dust may cause respiratory irritation
Storage: Store in cool, dry place; avoid dusting.
Cekol® 700. [Metsä-Serla Oy]
Chem. Descrip.: Sodium CMC
CAS 9004-32-4
Uses: Binder, thickener, stabilizer and film-former for pharmaceutical applics., esp. nose-, eye-, and eardrops; stabilizer, dispersant for o/w emulsions
Regulatory: USP/NF, Eur.Ph. and other compliances
Properties: Wh. to off-wh. fine powd. or gran., odorless; hygroscopic; sol. in water; dens. 1.6 g/cc (20 C); bulk dens. 400-800 kg/m³; visc. 100 mPa•s (1%); decomp. pt. 240 C; pH 6.5-8.0 (1%); biodeg.; BOD7 ≈ 50-100 gO₂/kg
Toxicology: LD50 (oral, rat) 27,000 mg/kg; powd. may dry the skin; dust may irritate eyes; inh. of dust may cause respiratory irritation
Storage: Store in cool, dry place; avoid dusting.
Cekol® 2000. [Metsä-Serla Oy]

Chem. Descrip.: Sodium CMC
CAS 9004-32-4
Uses: Binder, thickener, stabilizer and film-former for pharmaceutical applics.
Regulatory: USP/NF, Eur.Ph. and other compliances
Properties: Wh. to off-wh. fine powd. or gran., odorless; hygroscopic; sol. in water; dens. 1.6 g/cc (20 C); bulk dens. 400-800 kg/m³; visc. 180 mPa•s (1%); decomp. pt. 240 C; pH 6.5-8.0 (1%); biodeg.; BOD7 ≈ 50-100 gO₂/kg
Toxicology: LD50 (oral, rat) 27,000 mg/kg; powd. may dry the skin; dust may irritate eyes; inh. of dust may cause respiratory irritation
Storage: Store in cool, dry place; avoid dusting.
Cekol® 4000. [Metsä-Serla Oy]
Chem. Descrip.: Sodium CMC
CAS 9004-32-4
Uses: Binder, thickener, stabilizer and film-former for pharmaceutical applics.
Regulatory: USP/NF, Eur.Ph. and other compliances
Properties: Wh. to off-wh. fine powd. or gran., odorless; hygroscopic; sol. in water; dens. 1.6 g/cc (20 C); bulk dens. 400-800 kg/m³; visc. 500 mPa•s (1%); decomp. pt. 240 C; pH 6.5-8.0 (1%); biodeg.; BOD7 ≈ 50-100 gO₂/kg
Toxicology: LD50 (oral, rat) 27,000 mg/kg; powd. may dry the skin; dust may irritate eyes; inh. of dust may cause respiratory irritation
Storage: Store in cool, dry place; avoid dusting.
Cekol® 10000. [Metsä-Serla Oy]
Chem. Descrip.: Sodium CMC
CAS 9004-32-4
Uses: Binder, thickener, stabilizer and film-former for pharmaceutical applics.; stabilizer, dispersant for suspensions
Regulatory: USP/NF, Eur.Ph. and other compliances
Properties: Wh. to off-wh. fine powd. or gran., odorless; hygroscopic; sol. in water; dens. 1.6 g/cc (20 C); bulk dens. 400-800 kg/m³; visc. 800 mPa•s (1%); decomp. pt. 240 C; pH 6.5-8.0 (1%); biodeg.; BOD7 ≈ 50-100 gO₂/kg
Toxicology: LD50 (oral, rat) 27,000 mg/kg; powd. may dry the skin; dust may irritate eyes; inh. of dust may cause respiratory irritation
Storage: Store in cool, dry place; avoid dusting.
Cekol® 30000. [Metsä-Serla Oy]
Chem. Descrip.: Sodium CMC
CAS 9004-32-4
Uses: Binder, thickener, stabilizer and film-former for pharmaceutical applics., esp. syrups, ointment bases
Regulatory: USP/NF, Eur.Ph. and other compliances
Properties: Wh. to off-wh. fine powd. or gran., odorless; hygroscopic; sol. in water; dens. 1.6 g/cc (20 C); bulk dens. 400-800 kg/m³; visc. 3500 mPa•s (1%); decomp. pt. 240 C; pH 6.5-8.0 (1%); biodeg.; BOD7 ≈ 50-100 gO₂/kg
Toxicology: LD50 (oral, rat) 27,000 mg/kg; powd.

may dry the skin; dust may irritate eyes; inh. of dust may cause respiratory irritation
Storage: Store in cool, dry place; avoid dusting.

Cekol® 50000. [Metsä-Serla Oy]
Chem. Descrip.: Sodium CMC
CAS 9004-32-4
Uses: Binder, thickener, stabilizer and film-former for pharmaceutical applics., esp. ointment bases
Regulatory: USP/NF, Eur.Ph. and other compliances
Properties: Wh. to off-wh. fine powd. or gran., odorless; hygroscopic; sol. in water; dens. 1.6 g/cc (20 C); bulk dens. 400-800 kg/m^3; visc. 6000 mPa•s (1%); decomp. pt. 240 C; pH 6.5-8.0 (1%); biodeg.; BOD7 ≈ 50-100 gO$_2$/kg
Toxicology: LD50 (oral, rat) 27,000 mg/kg; powd. may dry the skin; dust may irritate eyes; inh. of dust may cause respiratory irritation
Storage: Store in cool, dry place; avoid dusting.

Cellogen HP. [Dai-ichi Kogyo Seiyaku]
Chem. Descrip.: Carboxymethylcellulose sodium
CAS 9004-32-4; EINECS 265-995-8
Uses: Stabilizer and binder for pharmaceutical prods.
Properties: Powd.; 100% conc.; anionic.

Cellulase 4000. [Solvay Enzymes]
Chem. Descrip.: Fungal cellulase derived from *Aspergillus niger*, standardized with lactose
CAS 9012-54-8; EINECS 232-734-4
Uses: Enzyme for pharmaceuticals (aids digestion of cellulosics)
Properties: Wh. to lt. tan powd., free of offensive odor and taste; water-sol.

Cellulase AP 3. [Mitsubishi Int'l.; Amano Enzyme USA; Unipex]
Chem. Descrip.: Cellulase from *Aspergillus niger*
CAS 9102-54-8; EINECS 232-734-4
Uses: Digestive enzyme for pharmaceutical use
Properties: Powd.

Cellulase T-AP6. [Amano Enzyme USA; Unipex]
Chem. Descrip.: Cellulase from *Trichoderma*
CAS 9102-54-8; EINECS 232-734-4
Uses: Enzyme for pharmaceutical use
Properties: Powd.

Cellulase Tr Conc. [Solvay Enzymes]
Chem. Descrip.: Cellulase derived from *Trichoderma reesei*
CAS 9012-54-8; EINECS 232-734-4
Uses: Enzyme for pharmaceuticals (aids digestion of cellulosics)
Properties: Lt. tan to wh. powd., free of offensive odor and taste; water-sol.

Cellulase TRL. [Solvay Enzymes]
Chem. Descrip.: Cellulase
CAS 9012-54-8; EINECS 232-734-4
Uses: Enzyme for pharmaceuticals (aids digestion of cellulosics)
Properties: Liq.

Centrolex® F. [Central Soya]
Chem. Descrip.: Special grade lecithin
CAS 8002-43-5; EINECS 232-307-2
Uses: Crystallization control for pharmaceutical suppositories
Regulatory: FDA 21CFR §184.1400, GRAS; kosher approved
Properties: Lt. tan or yel. powd., bland odor and flavor; oil-sol., water-disp.; bulk dens. 0.45 g/cc; acid no. 36 max.; 1% max. moisture
Storage: Store in dry, closed, original container below 25 C; 1 yr shelf life in original unopened container.

Centrolex® P. [Central Soya]
Chem. Descrip.: Special grade lecithin
CAS 8002-43-5; EINECS 232-307-2
Uses: Emulsifier and suspending agent for pharmaceuticals; can be easily sterilized and filtered in solvs.; autoclavable in some applics.
Properties: Yel. gran., low flavor; oil-sol., water-disp.; bulk dens. 0.38 g/cc; acid no. 27; 0.7% moisture.

Ceraphyl® 28. [ISP Van Dyk]
Chem. Descrip.: Cetyl lactate
CAS 35274-05-6; EINECS 252-478-7
Uses: Lubricant and emollient for topical pharmaceuticals; reduces tack in deodorant sticks
Properties: Wh. solid, faint char. odor; sol. @ 5% in min. oil, peanut oil, IPM, oleyl alcohol, and 95% ethanol; partly sol. in water, propylene glycol; sp.gr. 0.893-0.905; HLB 13-15; acid no. 2 max.; sapon. no. 174-189
Toxicology: LD50 (oral, rat) > 20 ml/kg; nonirritating to eyes and skin.

Ceraphyl® 31. [ISP Van Dyk]
Chem. Descrip.: Lauryl lactate
CAS 6283-92-7; EINECS 228-504-8
Uses: Emollient, lubricant for topical pharmaceuticals; antitack agent in antiperspirants
Properties: Lt. yel. liq., faint char. odor; sol. in min. oil, peanut oil, 95% ethanol, propylene glycol, and IPM; partly sol. in 70% sorbitol; sp.gr. 0.910-0.922; HLB 10; acid no. 2 max.; sapon. no. 210-225; ref. index 1.4417-1.4456
Toxicology: LD50 (oral, rat) > 2 ml/kg; nonirritating to eyes; mild skin irritant.

Ceraphyl® 41. [ISP Van Dyk]
Chem. Descrip.: C12-15 alkyl lactate
Uses: Nongreasy emollient for topical pharmaceuticals, alcoholic and hydroalcoholic skin preps.; reduces tacky, greasy feel in formulations high in petrolatum or min. oil; antitack in antiperspirants
Properties: Clear to lt. yel. liq.; sol. in aerosol propellants, min. oil, 60% ethanol, propylene glycol, IPM, oleyl alcohol, methylene chloride; partly sol. in water, glycerin; sp.gr. 0.900-0.920; HLB 14; acid no. 2 max.; sapon. no. 195-210; ref. index 1.4430-1.4450
Toxicology: LD50 (oral, rat) 21 ± 9.2 ml/kg; moderate eye and skin irritant.

Ceraphyl® 45. [ISP Van Dyk]
Chem. Descrip.: Dioctyl malate
CAS 56235-92-8
Uses: Emollient for topical pharmaceuticals, hypoallergenic prods.; nongreasy skin feel; fragrance coupler; solubilizer for oxybenzone and other diffi-

cult-to-solubilize materials; antitack in antiperspirants, carbomer formulations

Properties: Colorless to pale yel. clear liq., char. mild odor; sol. @ 5% in cyclomethicone, min. oil, IPM, ethanol, dimethicone, hexylene glycol; disp. in propylene glycol; insol. in water; m.w. 358.52; sp.gr. 0.960-0.970; HLB 12; acid no. 5 max.; iodine no. 1 max.; sapon. no. 310 min.; ref. index 1.4480-1.4520

Toxicology: LD50 (oral, rat) > 5 g/kg; pract. nonirritating to eyes; not a primary skin irritant; noncomedogenic.

Ceraphyl® 50. [ISP Van Dyk]

Chem. Descrip.: Myristyl lactate

CAS 1323-03-1; EINECS 215-350-1

Uses: Lubricant, emollient for topical pharmaceuticals, medicated prods.; provides soft, silky, water-resist. film on the skin

Properties: Water-wh. to pale yel. liq. to soft solid; sol. in peanut oil, min. oil, ethanol, propylene glycol, IPM, oleyl alcohol; partly sol. in 70% sorbitol; insol. in water; sp.gr. 0.892-0.904; HLB 12; acid no. 2 max.; sapon. no. 166-181

Toxicology: LD50 (oral, rat) 20 ml/kg; nonirritating to skin.

Ceraphyl® 55. [ISP Van Dyk]

Chem. Descrip.: Tridecyl neopentanoate

CAS 106436-39-9

Uses: Emollient for topical pharmaceuticals; imparts nonoily, nonocclusive lubricity and elegant skin feel; improves gloss and spreading in pigmented prods.

Properties: Lt. yel. clear liq., char. mild odor; sol. @ 5% in corn oil, 95% ethanol, min. oil, IPM, cyclomethicone; insol. in water; m.w. 284; sp.gr. 0.850-0.860; acid no. 2 max.; sapon. no. 190 min.; ref. index 1.4345-1.4365

Toxicology: LD50 (oral, rat) > 5 g/kg; minimally irritating to eyes; mildly irritating to skin; noncomedogenic.

Ceraphyl® 140. [ISP Van Dyk]

Chem. Descrip.: Decyl oleate

CAS 59231-34-4; EINECS 222-981-6

Uses: Emollient, cosolv., slip agent, lubricant for topical pharmaceuticals, creams, lotions

Properties: Wh. to straw-colored liq., char. mild odor; sol. @ 5% in peanut oil, 95% ethanol, IPM, oleyl alcohol; insol. in water; sp.gr. 0.858-0.864; acid no. 5 max.; iodine no. 55-65; sapon. no. 130-145; ref. index 1.4540-1.4560; 100% act.; nonionic

Toxicology: LD50 (oral, rat) > 40 ml/kg; sl. eye irritant; very sl. skin irritant; nonsensitizing.

Ceraphyl® 140-A. [ISP Van Dyk]

Chem. Descrip.: Isodecyl oleate

CAS 59231-34-4; EINECS 261-673-6

Uses: Emollient, cosolv., and solubilizer for topical pharmaceuticals

Properties: Wh. to straw-colored liq., char. mild odor; sol. @ 5% in peanut oil, 95% ethanol, IPM, oleyl alcohol; insol. in water; sp.gr. 0.858-0.864; acid no. 5 max.; iodine no. 50-65; sapon.

no. 130-145; ref. index 1.4540-1.4560; 100% act.; nonionic

Toxicology: LD50 (oral, rat) > 40 ml/kg; nonirritating to eyes; mild skin irritant; nonsensitizing.

Ceraphyl® 230. [ISP Van Dyk]

Chem. Descrip.: Diisopropyl adipate

CAS 6938-94-9; EINECS 248-299-9

Uses: Emollient for topical pharmaceuticals; coupler for aq. alcoholic systems; reduces oiliness of min. oil prods.; fragrance solubilizer

Properties: Colorless clear liq.; sol. @ 5% in min. oil, 50% ethanol, propylene glycol, IPM, oleyl alcohol, 70% sorbitol; water-insol.; sp.gr. 0.950-0.962; acid no. 2 max.; sapon. no. 465-500; ref. index 1.4216-1.4245

Toxicology: LD50 (oral, rat) > 20 ± 3 ml/kg; nonirritatng to eyes and skin.

Ceraphyl® 368. [ISP Van Dyk]

Chem. Descrip.: Octyl palmitate

CAS 29806-73-3; EINECS 249-862-1

Uses: Nonoily, nonocclusive emollient for topical pharmaceuticals, sunscreens, emulsions, aerosol antiperspirants; antitack for antiperspirants; solubilizer for benzophenone-3

Properties: Water-wh. liq.; sol. @ 5% in min. oil, 95% ethanol, IPM, peanut oil, oleyl alcohol; insol. in water; sp.gr. 0.850-0.856; acid no. 3 max.; sapon. no. 146-156; ref. index 1.4445-1.4465

Toxicology: LD50 (oral, rat) > 40 ml/kg; nonirritating to eyes; mild primary skin irritant; nonsensitizing.

Ceraphyl® 375. [ISP Van Dyk]

Chem. Descrip.: Isostearyl neopentanoate

CAS 58958-60-4; EINECS 261-521-9

Uses: Mild emollient for topical pharmaceuticals; improves spreading in highly pigmented prods.; antitack for antiperspirants

Properties: Pale yel. clear liq.; sol. @ 5% in IPM, oleyl alcohol, 95% ethanol, peanut and min. oils; insol. in water; sp.gr. 0.850-0.870; acid no. 2 max.; sapon. no. 144-165; ref. index 1.4435-1.4475

Toxicology: LD50 (oral, rat) > 40 ml/kg; nonirritating to eyes and skin.

Ceraphyl® 424. [ISP Van Dyk]

Chem. Descrip.: Myristyl myristate

CAS 3234-85-3; EINECS 221-787-9

Uses: Emollient imparting rich, velvety skin feel to topical pharmaceutical emulsions, creams, lotions; increases visc. of creams and lotions at low concs.; reduces watery feel of low-oil emulsions; melts at body temp.

Properties: Wh. to sl. yel. waxy solid, bland char. odor; sol. @ 5% in peanut and min. oils, IPM, oleyl alcohol; insol. in water; m.p. 36-39 C; acid no. 3 max.; sapon. no. 120-130

Toxicology: LD50 (oral, rat) 8.6 g/kg; minimally irritating to eyes; mild skin irritant; nonsensitizing.

Ceraphyl® 494. [ISP Van Dyk]

Chem. Descrip.: Isocetyl stearate

CAS 25339-09-7; EINECS 246-868-6

Uses: Emollient, lubricant for topical pharmaceuticals, creams and lotions, skin care prods.; im-

Ceraphyl® 791

parts soft, elegant, nonoily feel
Properties: Wh. to lt. yel. liq., bland char. odor; sol. @ 5% in peanut oil, 95% ethanol, IPM, oleyl alcohol; insol. in water; sp.gr. 0.845-0.865; HLB 8; acid no. 5 max.; sapon. no. 95-110; ref. index 1.446-1.456
Toxicology: LD50 (oral, rabbit) > 5 g/kg; minimally irritating to eyes; nonirritating to skin.

Ceraphyl® 791. [ISP Van Dyk]
Chem. Descrip.: Isocetyl stearoyl stearate
CAS 97338-28-8
Uses: Pigment dispersant, emollient, lubricant, spreading agent for topical pharmaceuticals
Use level: 2-20%
Properties: Lt. to straw-colored liq., char. mild odor; sol. @ 5% in min. oil, IPP, IPM, oleyl alcohol, safflower oil; sp.gr. 0.865-0.885; acid no. 10 max.; sapon. no. 132-148; hyd. no. 15 max.; ref. index 1.4560-1.4590
Toxicology: Nonirritating, nonsensitizing.

Ceraphyl® 847. [ISP Van Dyk]
Chem. Descrip.: Octyldodecyl stearoyl stearate
CAS 90052-75-8; EINECS 289-991-0
Uses: Emollient for topical pharmaceuticals imparting lubricity and a rich, long-lasting, cushioned feel to the skin; reduces oily feel of other ingreds.
Properties: Lt. to straw-colored liq., char. mild odor; sol. in IPM, safflower oil, min. oil, oleyl alcohol, octyl palmitate; partly sol. in 95% ethanol, propylene glycol, 70% sorbitol; insol. in water; sp.gr. 0.860-0.880; HLB 6; acid no. 10 max.; sapon. no. 115-135; ref. index 1.447-1.467
Toxicology: LD50 (oral, rat) > 20 g/kg; nonirritating to eyes and skin.

Ceraphyl® GA-D. [ISP Van Dyk]
Chem. Descrip.: Maleated soybean oil, deodorized, 0.1% mixed tocopherols (antioxidant)
CAS 68648-66-8
Uses: Patented moisturizer and skin softener imparting a rich, nongreasy, nontacky, full-bodied, long-lasting feel to the skin; for creams, lotions, water-resist. sunscreens, topical pharmaceuticals
Properties: Amber-yel. visc. oily liq., mild char. odor; sol. @ 5% in dioctyl malate, castor oil, corn oil, IPM; insol. in water; acid no. 43-53; iodine no. 107 max.; sapon. no. 220-250; ref. index 1.4750-1.4850; 100% act.
Toxicology: LD50 (oral, rat) > 5 g/kg; nonirritating to eyes; mildly irritating to skin; nonsensitizing, noncomedogenic.

Ceraphyl® ICA. [ISP Van Dyk]
Chem. Descrip.: Isocetyl alcohol
CAS 36311-34-9; EINECS 252-964-9
Uses: Nongreasy emollient for topical pharmaceuticals, creams, lotions; carrier and extender for flavor and fragrances
Properties: Colorless clear liq., low odor; sol. @ 5% in peanut and min. oils, 95% ethanol, IPM, oleyl alcohol, castor oil, cyclomethicone; insol. in water; m.w. 242; sp.gr. 0.830-0.840; HLB 12-14; acid no. 5 max.; iodine no. 10 max.; sapon. no. 10

max.; hyd. no. 195-230
Toxicology: LD50 (oral, rat) > 5 g/kg; mild eye and skin irritant; noncomedogenic.

Cerasynt® 303. [ISP Van Dyk]
Chem. Descrip.: Diethylaminoethyl stearate
CAS 3179-81-5; EINECS 221-662-9
Uses: O/w emulsifier for topical pharmaceuticals; dispersant, wetting agent
Properties: Straw to amber liq. to semisolid, amine odor; sol. @ 5% in peanut oil, ethanol, IPM, oleyl alcohol; partly sol. in min. oil; gels in glycerin, 70% sorbitol; sp.gr. 0.860-0.880; acid no. 30-40; alkali no. 127-137; sapon. no. 150-160; pH 9.5-10.5 (3%); 100% conc.; cationic.

Cerasynt® 840. [ISP Van Dyk]
Chem. Descrip.: PEG-20 stearate
CAS 9004-99-3
Uses: Hydrophilic emulsifier, visc. builder, stabilizer for topical pharmaceutical o/w creams, lotions, medicated ointments
Properties: Solid; sol. @ 5% in ethanol; partly sol. in propylene glycol; forms liq. disp. in glycerin, solid disp. in peanut oil, IPM; m.p. 39.5-42.5 C; acid no. 5 max.; iodine no. 0.25 max.; sapon. no. 40-50; 100% conc.; nonionic.

Cerasynt® 945. [ISP Van Dyk]
Chem. Descrip.: Glyceryl stearate, laureth-23
Uses: Self-emulsifying acid-stable emulsifier, gellant, thickener for pharmaceutical creams and lotions, antiperspirants; electrolyte tolerant
Properties: Wh. to cream flakes; partly sol. @ 5% in water, oleyl alcohol; gels in peanut oil; insol. in ethanol, glycerin, propylene glycol, IPM; m.p. 53-55 C; HLB 7-8; acid no. 5 max.; iodine no. 0.5 max.; sapon. no. 142-152; 100% conc.; nonionic.

Cerasynt® D. [ISP Van Dyk]
Chem. Descrip.: Stearamide MEA-stearate
CAS 14351-40-7; EINECS 238-310-5
Uses: O/w emulsifier for topical pharmaceuticals
Properties: Cream flakes; insol. in water; gels in peanut oil, min. oil, IPM; m.p. 76-82 C; acid no. 10-20; iodine no. 0.5 max.; sapon. no. 97-107; 100% conc.; nonionic.

Cerasynt® GMS. [ISP Van Dyk]
Chem. Descrip.: Glyceryl stearate
Uses: Sec. o/w emulsifier for topical pharmaceuticals, creams, lotions; visc. builder for emulsions
Properties: Wh. to cream flakes; forms visc. disp. in peanut oil, min. oil; insol. in water, 95% ethanol, propylene glycol, IPM; m.p. 56-59 C; HLB 4.0; acid no. 3 max.; iodine no. 2 max.; sapon. no. 162-175; 100% conc.; nonionic.

Cerasynt® IP. [ISP Van Dyk]
Chem. Descrip.: Glycol stearate and other ingreds.
CAS 111-60-4; EINECS 203-886-9
Uses: O/w emulsifier for topical pharmaceuticals
Properties: Wh. to cream flake; partly sol. in peanut oil; water-insol.; m.p. 56.5-58.5 C; HLB 3.0; acid no. 5 max.; iodine no. 0.5 max.; sapon. no. 174-184; 100% conc.; nonionic
Toxicology: LD50 (oral, rat, 10% in corn oil) > 64 cc/kg; nonirritating to eyes and skin.

44

Cerasynt® M. [ISP Van Dyk]
Chem. Descrip.: Glycol stearate
CAS 111-60-4; EINECS 203-886-9
Uses: Sec. o/w emulsifier for topical pharmaceutical creams and lotions
Properties: Wh. to cream waxy flakes, mild char. odor; partly sol. in peanut oil; insol. in water, min. oil, glycerin, propylene glycol; m.p. 56-60 C; HLB 3.0; acid no. 5 max.; iodine no. 0.5 max.; sapon. no. 185-195; 100% conc.; nonionic.

Cerasynt® MN. [ISP Van Dyk]
Chem. Descrip.: Glycol stearate SE
CAS 86418-55-5
Uses: Primary o/w emulsifier in pharmaceutical creams and lotions; visc. builder for emulsions containing high percentage of water in aq. phase
Properties: Wh. to cream flakes; forms liq. disp. in water; insol. in min. oil, ethanol, glycerin, propylene glycol, IPM; m.p. 57-60 C; acid no. 5 max.; iodine no. 0.5 max.; sapon. no. 181-191; 100% conc.; anionic.

Cerasynt® PA. [ISP Van Dyk]
Chem. Descrip.: Propylene glycol stearate
CAS 1323-39-3; EINECS 215-354-3
Uses: Sec. o/w emulsifier for topical pharmaceuticals, lotions, soft creams; opacifier
Properties: Wh. to cream-colored flakes, bland char. odor; sol. @ 5% in peanut and min. oils, IPM, oleyl alcohol; water-insol.; m.p. 35-38 C; HLB 3.0; acid no. 5 max.; iodine no. 0.5 max.; sapon. no. 181-191; 100% conc.; nonionic
Toxicology: LD50 (oral, rat) 25.8 g/kg; minimally irritating to eyes; non or mildly irritating to skin.

Cerasynt® Q. [ISP Van Dyk]
Chem. Descrip.: Glyceryl stearate SE
Uses: O/w emulsifier for topical pharmaceuticals, creams, lotions
Properties: Wh. to cream flakes; sol. @ 5% in oleyl alcohol, partly sol. in water (pH 9), veg. oil, propylene glycol, IPM, 70% ethanol; disp. in min. oil, glycerin, 70% sorbitol; m.p. 57-59 C; acid no. 10 max.; iodine no. 1 max.; sapon. no. 150-160; 100% conc.; anionic.

Cerasynt® SD. [ISP Van Dyk]
Chem. Descrip.: Glyceryl stearate
Uses: Aux. o/w emulsifier in topical pharmaceutical emulsions; exc. color, odor, and heat stability
Properties: Wh. to cream-colored flakes, very mild char. odor; forms solid disp. @ 5% in peanut and min. oils; insol. in water, 70% ethanol, glycerin, propylene glycol; m.p. 55-57.5 C; HLB 4.0; acid no. 2 max.; iodine no. 0.5 max.; sapon. no. 165-177; 100% conc.; nonionic.

Cerasynt® WM. [ISP Van Dyk]
Chem. Descrip.: Glyceryl stearate, stearyl alcohol, and sodium lauryl sulfate
Uses: Acid-stable emulsifier for topical pharmaceutical o/w creams, lotions, ointments, antiperspirants; electrolyte tolerance and low pH stability
Properties: Wh. to cream flakes; forms liq. disp. @ 5% in IPM, solid disp. in water, peanut and min. oils, oelyl alcohol, 70% sorbitol; insol. in ethanol,

glycerin, propylene glycol; m.p. 55-57 C; acid no. 5 max.; iodine no. 0.5 max.; sapon. no. 140-150; 100% conc.; anionic.

Cerex ELS 50. [Auschem SpA]
Chem. Descrip.: PEG-5 hydrog. castor oil
CAS 61788-85-0
Uses: W/o emulsifier for pharmaceuticals
Properties: Liq.; HLB 4.9; nonionic
Unverified

Cerex ELS 250. [Auschem SpA]
Chem. Descrip.: PEG-25 hydrog. castor oil
CAS 61788-85-0
Uses: Solubilizer for pharmaceutical applics.
Properties: Liq.; HLB 10.8; nonionic.

Cerex ELS 400. [Auschem SpA]
Chem. Descrip.: PEG-40 hydrog. castor oil
CAS 61788-85-0
Uses: Solubilizer for pharmaceutical applics.
Properties: Liq.; HLB 14.0; nonionic.

Cerex ELS 450. [Auschem SpA]
Chem. Descrip.: PEG-45 hydrog. castor oil
CAS 61788-85-0
Uses: Solubilizer for pharmaceutical applics.
Properties: Liq.; HLB 14.4; nonionic.

Cetina. [Robeco]
Chem. Descrip.: Cetyl esters and stearamide DEA
Uses: Emulsifying wax, lubricant, emollient providing satiny feel for dermatologicals
Properties: Lt. colored flake, bland odor and taste; m.p. 43-50 C; acid no. 0-5; alkali no. 28 max.; sapon. no. 85-100; pH 8.5-10.0 (1%); 100% conc.; nonionic.

Cetiol®. [Henkel/Cospha; Henkel Canada; Henkel KGaA/Cospha]
Chem. Descrip.: Oleyl oleate with BHA (as antioxidant)
Uses: Emollient; oily component of strong greasy char., for pharmaceutical skin preps.; carrier for lipid sol. ingreds.
Properties: Pale yel. clear oil; m.w. 530; sp.gr. 0.861-0.880 (20 C); visc. 25-30 mPa•s; acid no. 1.0 max.; iodine no. 87-97; sapon. no. 100-110; hyd. no. 12 max.; cloud pt. < 15 C; ref. index 1.4640-1.4660 (20 C)
Storage: 1 yr storage life in original sealed containers at temps. below 30 C; protect from moisture.

Cetiol® 868. [Henkel/Cospha; Henkel Canada; Henkel KGaA/Cospha]
Chem. Descrip.: Octyl stearate
CAS 91031-48-0
Uses: Emollient; superfatting oil for o/w and w/o emulsions; for pharmaceutical skin care preps.
Properties: Pale yel. clear oily liq.; m.w. 390; sp.gr. 0.855-0.865; visc. 14-16 mPa•s; acid no. 0.5 max.; iodine no. 2; sapon. no. 140-150; cloud pt. < 8 C; ref. index 1.447-1.450; 100% act.
Storage: 1 yr storage life in sealed original containers at temps. below 30 C in dry environment.

Cetiol® A. [Henkel/Cospha; Henkel Canada; Henkel KGaA/Cospha]
Chem. Descrip.: Hexyl laurate
CAS 34316-64-8; EINECS 251-932-1

Uses: Vehicle for lipid-sol. topical act. ingreds. used in pharmaceuticals; mild emollient; good spreading props.; solubilizer for lipid-sol. compds.
Properties: Colorless clear oily liq., odorless; sol. @ 10% in min. and castor oil, IPM, oleyl alcohol, ethyl alcohol-SD 40 (95%), silicone fluid; sp.gr. 0.857-0.861; visc. 6 mPa•s; solid. pt. < 0 C; HLB 12; acid no. 0.2 max.; iodine no. 1; sapon. no. 190-205; hyd. no. 2 max.; cloud pt. < 5 C; flash pt. > 165 C; ref. index 1.438-1.441; 100% act.
Storage: 1 yr storage life in sealed containers below 30 C, protected against moisture.

Cetiol® B. [Henkel/Cospha; Henkel Canada; Henkel KGaA/Cospha]
Chem. Descrip.: Dibutyl adipate
CAS 105-99-7; EINECS 203-350-4
Uses: Emollient; oily component for skin oils, sun protection oils, pharmaceuticals
Properties: Colorless oily liq., faint intrinsic odor; sp.gr. 0.958-0.962; visc. 5-7 mPa•s; solid. pt. < -30 C; acid no. 0.5 max.; iodine no. 1 max.; sapon. no. 420-440; hyd. no. 1 max.; cloud pt. < -25 C; flash pt. 150 C min.; ref. index 1.434-1.437; 100% act.
Storage: 1 yr storage if in sealed original containers at temps. below 40 C, protected from moisture.

Cetiol® HE. [Henkel/Cospha; Henkel KGaA/Cospha]
Chem. Descrip.: PEG-7 glyceryl cocoate
Uses: Emollient oil, superfatting/refatting agent for pharmaceutical preps., esp. those with low alcohol content; solubilizer for lipoid-sol. actives
Properties: Clear low visc. oil; sol. @ 10%: sol. in water, castor oil, oleyl and ethyl alcohol-SD 40 (95%), ethyl alcohol 3A (70% aq.); dens. 1.050 g/ml; solid. pt. 0 C; cloud pt. < 0 C; acid no. 5 max.; iodine no. 5 max.; sapon. no. 90-100; ref. index 1.460; nonionic
Storage: 1 yr min. storage life in sealed containers at temps. below 30 C, protected against moisture; turbidity occurrng during storage at cooler temps. can be reversed by heating.

Cetiol® LC. [Henkel/Cospha; Henkel Canada; Henkel KGaA/Cospha]
Chem. Descrip.: Coco-caprylate/caprate
Uses: Very dry feeling, penetrating emollient used in pharmaceuticals; reduces oiliness in creams, lotions, and solid sticks; carrier for oil-sol. actives; superfatting agent
Properties: Sl. yel. clear oily liq., pract. odorless; sol. @ 10% in min. and castor oil, IPM, oleyl alcohol, silicone fluid; insol. in water; sp.gr. 0.855-0.860; visc. 9-12 mPa; solid. pt. < 13 C; HLB 9; acid no. 0.2 max.; iodine no. 1 max.; sapon. no. 165-173; hyd. no. 1 max.; cloud pt. 15 C max.; flash pt. > 180 C; ref. index 1.443-1.447
Storage: 1 yr min. storage if in sealed containers at temps. below 30 C, protected from moisture.

Cetiol® MM. [Henkel/Cospha; Henkel Canada; Henkel KGaA/Cospha]
Chem. Descrip.: Myristyl myristate
CAS 3234-85-3; EINECS 221-787-9
Uses: Emollient wax with superfatting props.; for

pharmaceutical skin care prods.
Properties: Wh. waxy solid, faint char. odor; misc. with oils and waxes; m.p. 38-42 C; acid no. 1 max.; iodine no. 1 max.; sapon. no. 120-135; hyd. no. 7 max.
Storage: 1 yr min. storage if stored in sealed original containers, protected from moisture.

Cetiol® OE. [Henkel/Cospha; Henkel KGaA/Cospha]
Chem. Descrip.: Dioctyl ether
CAS 629-82-3
Uses: Dry feel emollient for lt. pharmaceutical o/w and w/o emulsions; good spreading props.; resist. to hydrolysis
Properties: Clear liq.; sp.gr. 0.80; visc. 4 mPa•s; acid no. 0.5 max.; sapon. no. 0.1 max.; hyd. no. 0.5 max.; ref. index 1.430
Storage: 1 yr min. storage stability in sealed original containers in dry place at temps. below 40 C.

Cetiol® S. [Henkel/Cospha; Henkel Canada; Henkel KGaA/Cospha]
Chem. Descrip.: Dioctylcyclohexane
EINECS 283-854-9
Uses: Emollient, superfatting agent; used in pharmaceutical creams and emulsions
Properties: Colorless clear liq., faint odor; sp.gr. 0.825-0.835; visc. 25 mPa•s; acid no. 0.2 max.; iodine no. 0.5 max.; sapon. no. 0.5 max.; cloud pt. 0 C max.; ref. index 1.455-1.465; 100% act.
Storage: 1 yr min. storage life stored in sealed containers at temps. below 30 C, protected from humidity.

Cetiol® SB45. [Henkel/Cospha; Henkel Canada; Henkel KGaA/Cospha]
Chem. Descrip.: Shea butter
CAS 68424-60-2
Uses: Emollient, consistency giving agent for o/w and w/o creams and emulsions; native fatting agent for creams, lotions, sun protection preps., pharmaceutical preps.
Properties: Sl. ylsh. soft wax; misc. with fatty components; sp.gr. 0.89-0.92; m.p. 42-45 C; acid no. 0.2 max.; iodine no. 70-75; sapon. no. 175-185; 9-13% unsaponifiables
Storage: Store below 30 C in sealed containers impermeable to light and protected against humidity.

Cetiol® SN. [Henkel/Cospha; Henkel Canada; Henkel KGaA/Cospha]
Chem. Descrip.: Cetearyl isononanoate
Uses: Emollient for pharmaceutical skin care and sun protection preps.; oily component with expressed hydrophobic effect
Properties: Colorless to sl. yel. low visc. oily liq., faint intrinsic odor; sp.gr. 0.853-0.856; visc. 19-22 mPa•s; acid no. 0.2 max.; iodine no. 1 max.; sapon. no. 140-146; hyd. no. 1 max.; cloud pt. 15 C max.; ref. index 1.445-1.450
Storage: Protect from frost; 1 yr min. storage life in closed containers at temps. below 30 C.

Cetiol® V. [Henkel/Cospha; Henkel Canada; Henkel KGaA/Cospha]
Chem. Descrip.: Decyl oleate with antioxidant

(mixed tocopherols)
CAS 3687-46-5; EINECS 222-981-6
Uses: Penetrating emollient, carrier for lipid sol. substances used in pharmaceutical topical applics.
Regulatory: Austrian Pharmacopoeia
Properties: Yel. low visc. clear oily liq.; sol. @ 10%: sol. in min. and castor oil, IPM, oleyl alcohol; insol. in water; m.w. 415; dens. 0.86-0.87 g/cm^3; visc. 15-20 mPa•s (20 C); HLB 9; acid no. 1 max.; iodine no. 55-65; sapon. no. 130-140; solid. pt. < 0 C; cloud pt. < 5 C; ref. index 1.4555-1.4575 (20 C)
Storage: 1 yr min. storage stability in sealed original containers at temps. below 30 C in dry environment.

Cetomacrogol 1000 BP. [Croda Inc.; Croda Chem. Ltd.]
Chem. Descrip.: Ceteth-20 BP
CAS 9004-95-9
Uses: Emulsifier for o/w topical pharmaceutical creams and lotions
Use level: 0.5-5%
Regulatory: BP, NF compliance
Properties: Wh. to off-wh. solid; sol. in water, IPA, propylene glycol; m.w. 1000; HLB 15.7; 100% conc.; nonionic
Toxicology: LD50 (oral, rat) 3.6 g/kg; moderate skin irritant, severe eye irritant.

Cetostearyl Alcohol BP. [Croda Inc.]
Chem. Descrip.: Cetearyl alcohol BP
EINECS 267-008-6
Uses: Thickener, coemulsifier, stabilizer, opacifier for topical systems; forms dense pharmaceutical emulsions
Use level: 2-30%
Properties: Wh. to cream flakes; sol. in min. oil, IPA; sol. warm in propylene glycol; m.p. 45-53 C; acid no. 0.5 max.; iodine no. 3 max.; sapon. no. 1 max.; hyd. no. 208-228
Toxicology: LD50 (oral, rat) > 5 g/kg; mild skin and eye irritant.

Cetostearyl Alcohol NF. [Croda Inc.]
Chem. Descrip.: Cetearyl alcohol NF
EINECS 267-008-6
Uses: Thickener, coemulsifier, stabilizer, opacifier for topical systems; forms dense pharmaceutical emulsions
Use level: 2-30%
Properties: Wh. flakes; sol. in min. oil, IPA; sol. warm in propylene glycol
Toxicology: LD50 (oral, rat) > 5 g/kg; mild skin and eye irritant.

C-Flakes. [ABITEC]
Chem. Descrip.: Hydrog. cottonseed oil
CAS 68334-00-9; EINECS 269-804-9
Uses: Lubricant for pharmaceutical tablets
Properties: Lovibond R2.5 max.; m.p. 142-146 F; iodine no. 5 max.; sapon. no. 189-198.

Cheelox® 80. [Rhone-Poulenc Surf. & Spec.]
Chem. Descrip.: Pentasodium diethylenetriamine pentaacetate aq. sol'n.

CAS 140-01-2; EINECS 205-391-3
Uses: Chelating agent for antibiotic and pharmaceutical prod.
Properties: Pale straw clear aq. sol'n.; sp.gr. 1.30; dens. 10.8 lb/gal; chel. value 80 mg CaCO$_3$/g (@ pH 11); pH 11.5 (1% aq.); 40.2% min. act.

Ches® 500. [CasChem]
Chem. Descrip.: Nonfat drymilk, xanthan gum, propylene glycol, alginate, glyceryl stearate, sodium glyceryl oleate phosphate
Uses: Food grade stabilizer; cold mix emulsifier for pharmaceuticals; cold hot emulsion system; unique ambient temp. emulsifier which yields stable, aesthetic o/w emulsions
Properties: Powd.; 100% conc.

ChiroCLEC™-CR. [Altus Biologics]
Chem. Descrip.: Cross-linked enzyme crystals of *Candida rugosa* lipase
Uses: Stable catalyst for synthesis of optically pure drugs and peptides; stereoselective catalyst for the resolution of racemic esters, acids, and alcohols; also for regioselective and chemoselective acylations and deacylations
Properties: Insol. in water and org. solvs.

Chloracel® 40% Sol'n. [Reheis]
Chem. Descrip.: Sodium aluminum chlorhydroxy lactate complex
CAS 8038-93-5
Uses: Deodorant compat. with typical soap-based cologne sticks
Properties: Clear liq.; 40% act., 8% Al$_2$O$_3$, 3% Cl, 5.6% Na.

Chloracel® Solid. [Reheis]
Chem. Descrip.: Sodium aluminum chlorhydroxy lactate complex
CAS 8038-93-5
Uses: Deodorant compat. with typical soap-based cologne sticks
Properties: Wh. free-flowing powd.; 20% Al$_2$O$_3$, 7.5% Cl, 14% Na.

Chlorhydrol® 50% Sol'n. [Reheis]
Chem. Descrip.: Aluminum chlorohydrate
CAS 1327-41-9; EINECS 215-477-2
Uses: Antiperspirant active; 23.5% Al$_2$O$_3$, 8.2% Cl.

Chlorhydrol® Granular. [Reheis]
Chem. Descrip.: Aluminum chlorohydrate
CAS 1327-41-9; EINECS 215-477-2
Uses: Antiperspirant active
Properties: Gran.; 44.75 mm particle size; 90% min. thru 4 mesh; 47% Al$_2$O$_3$, 16.3% Cl.

Chlorhydrol®, Impalpable. [Reheis]
Chem. Descrip.: Aluminum chlorohydrate
CAS 1327-41-9; EINECS 215-477-2
Uses: Antiperspirant active.

Chlorhydrol® Powd. [Reheis]
Chem. Descrip.: Aluminum chlorohydrate
CAS 1327-41-9; EINECS 215-477-2
Uses: Antiperspirant active
Properties: Powd.; 150 µ particle size; 97% min. thru 100 mesh; 47% Al$_2$O$_3$, 16.3% Cl.

Cholesterol NF. [Croda Inc.; Croda Chem. Ltd.]
Chem. Descrip.: Cholesterol NF

CAS 57-88-5; EINECS 200-353-2
Uses: Emulsifier in w/o emulsions; coemulsifier/ stabilizer in o/w emulsions, absorption bases, ointments; useful in incorporating and emulsifying drug actives into oils and fats in the mfg. of hydrophilic petrolatum; for topicals
Use level: 0.1-1%
Properties: Wh. to pale yel. powd., almost odorless/ faint sterol odor; sol. in min. oil, sol. in 1% ethanol, turbid after 2 h; m.p. 147-150 C; HLB 1.0; 100% conc.; nonionic.
Cholesterol NF. [R.I.T.A.]
Chem. Descrip.: Cholesterol NF
CAS 57-88-5; EINECS 200-353-2
Uses: Emulsifier, emollient, conditioner, moisturizer, stabilizer, and solubilizer in ointments, sun preps., veterinary prods.
Properties: Wh. powd.
Chroma-GDF™. [Crompton & Knowles]
Chem. Descrip.: Color disp. incorporating pigment, glidant, and plasticizer
Uses: Pigment disp. for use with Eudragit RL-30D® to form complete one-step gastric disintegrating coating system for pharmaceuticals
Regulatory: GRAS; 30% aq. disp.
Storage: 1-3 yr shelf life (formula dependent); store in tightly sealed containers; avoid exposure to extreme heat; do not freeze.
Chroma-SRF™. [Crompton & Knowles]
Chem. Descrip.: Color disp. incorporating pigment, glidant, and plasticizer
Uses: Pigment disp. for use with Eudragit RL-30D® to form complete one-step gastric disintegrating coating system for pharmaceuticals
Regulatory: GRAS; 30% aq. disp.
Storage: 1-3 yr shelf life (formula dependent); store in tightly sealed containers; avoid exposure to extreme heat; do not freeze.
Chroma-Kote®. [Crompton & Knowles]
Chem. Descrip.: Pigment disp. avail. in an aq. base for aq. film or sugar coating or in a propylene glycol base for solv. coating
Uses: Pigment system used in conjunction with Dri-Klear as a complete coating system for pharmaceuticals; for coloring granulations, ointments, creams, and lotions; exc. dispersibility
Regulatory: GRAS
Storage: 1-2 yr shelf life (formula dependent); store in tightly sealed containers; avoid exposure to extreme heat; do not freeze.
Chroma-Seal™ 859027. [Crompton & Knowles]
Chem. Descrip.: Solv.-based ethylcellulose sol'n. (contg. IPA, SDA-3A alcohol, triacetin, magnesium stearate, acetylated monoglycerides, polyethylene glycol, oleic acid)
Uses: Seal coating system for pharmaceutical tablets; fast drying; applicable by std. or automated fluidized coating equip.; seals moisture-sensitive tablets prior to aq. film coating; provides protective coating and increased shelf life
Regulatory: GRAS
Properties: Opaque sol'n., typ. alcoholic odor;

sp.gr. 0.85 ± 0.05; visc. 280 cps; flash pt. (TCC) 60 F; ref. index 1.375 ± 0.015 (20 C)
Storage: 3 yr shelf life stored in tightly sealed metal containers in cool, dry location; protect from direct heat and flame; shake well prior to use.
Chroma-Seal™ 889031. [Crompton & Knowles]
Chem. Descrip.: Solv.-based ethylcellulose sol'n. (contg. IPA, SDA-3A alcohol, polyvinylpyrrolidone, triacetin, magnesium stearate, acetylated monoglycerides, oleic acid, polyethylene glycol)
Uses: Seal coating system for pharmaceutical tablets; fast drying; applicable by std. or automated fluidized coating equip.; seals moisture-sensitive tablets prior to aq. film coating; provides protective coating and increased shelf life
Regulatory: GRAS
Properties: Opaque sol'n., typ. alcoholic odor; sp.gr. 0.85 ± 0.05; visc. 280 cps; flash pt. (TCC) 60 F; ref. index 1.365 ± 0.015 (20 C)
Storage: 3 yr shelf life stored in tightly sealed metal containers in cool, dry location; protect from direct heat and flame; shake well prior to use.
Chroma-Teric™. [Crompton & Knowles]
Chem. Descrip.: Color disp. incorporating pigment, glidant, and plasticizer
Uses: Pigment disp. for use with Eudragit L-30D® or L100-55® to form complete one-step enteric coating system for pharmaceuticals; avail. as aq.-based disp. or in dry form; also avail. without plasticizer
Regulatory: GRAS; 30% aq. disp.
Storage: 1-3 yr shelf life (formula dependent); store in tightly sealed containers; avoid exposure to extreme heat; do not freeze.
Chroma-Tone™. [Crompton & Knowles]
Chem. Descrip.: Conc. dry pigment disp.
Uses: Pigment system used in conjunction with Dri-Klear as a complete coating system for aq. film coating of pharmaceuticals; for coloring granulations, dry blending applics.; exc. dispersibility
Regulatory: GRAS
Storage: 3 yr shelf life stored in tightly sealed containers in a dry location.
Chroma-Tone™ P. [Crompton & Knowles]
Chem. Descrip.: Dry pigment-polymer disp.
Uses: Complete coating system, without plasticizer, for aq. film coating of pharmaceuticals; exc. dispersibility
Regulatory: GRAS
Storage: 3 yr shelf life stored in tightly sealed containers in a dry location.
CI-90. [Carrageenan Co.]
Chem. Descrip.: Refined iota carrageenan stabilized with dextrose
Uses: Used in pharmaceutical ointments and formulations requiring high visc. with very low gel str. requirements; stable under freeze-thaw conditions
Properties: Wh. to cream powd.; > 95% thru 60 mesh; visc. 60-130 cps; pH 7-9.
CI-100. [Carrageenan Co.]
Chem. Descrip.: Iota carrageenan

CAS 9000-07-1; EINECS 232-524-2
Uses: Stabilizer; thickener for syrups and ointments; improves mouthfeel in tooth powds.
Use level: 0.6-1.0% (tooth powds.)
Properties: Wh. to cream powd.; > 95% thru 60 mesh; visc. 65-135 cps; pH 7-9.
Cire Lanol® CTO. [Seppic]
Chem. Descrip.: Ceteareth-33 and cetearyl alcohol
Uses: Self-emulsifying base for drug prods.; permits prep. of all emulsions, esp. fluid emulsions contg. oily phases
Regulatory: Complies with BP Cetomacrogol emulsifying wax
Properties: Wh. waxy flakes, pract. odorless; disp. in water; m.p. 50-53 C; acid no. 1 max.; hyd. no. 173-187; cloud pt. 60 C; pH 6.5-7.8 (10% aq.); 100% act.; nonionic.
Cithrol GML N/E. [Croda Universal Ltd.]
Chem. Descrip.: Glyceryl laurate
CAS 142-18-7; EINECS 205-526-6
Uses: Emulsifier, coemulsifier, stabilizer, wetting agent, lubricant for pharmaceutical applics.
Properties: Semisolid; HLB 4.9; 100% conc.; nonionic.
Cithrol GMO N/E. [Croda Chem. Ltd.]
Chem. Descrip.: Glyceryl oleate
CAS 111-03-5
Uses: Emulsifier, coemulsifier, stabilizer, wetting agent, lubricant for pharmaceutical applics.
Properties: Liq.; HLB 3.3; 100% conc.; nonionic.
Cithrol GMO S/E. [Croda Chem. Ltd.]
Chem. Descrip.: Glyceryl oleate SE
Uses: Emulsifier, coemulsifier, stabilizer, wetting agent, lubricant for pharmaceutical applics.
Properties: Liq.; HLB 4.1; 100% conc.; anionic.
Cithrol GMR N/E. [Croda Chem. Ltd.]
Chem. Descrip.: Glyceryl ricinoleate
CAS 141-08-2; EINECS 205-455-0
Uses: Emulsifier, coemulsifier, stabilizer, wetting agent, lubricant for pharmaceutical applics.
Properties: Liq.; HLB 2.7; 100% conc.; nonionic.
Cithrol GMR S/E. [Croda Universal Ltd.]
Chem. Descrip.: Glyceryl ricinoleate SE
Uses: Emulsifier, coemulsifier, stabilizer, wetting agent, lubricant for pharmaceutical applics.
Properties: Liq.; HLB 3.6; 100% conc.; anionic.
Cithrol GMS Acid Stable. [Croda Chem. Ltd.]
Chem. Descrip.: Glyceryl stearate SE
CAS 31566-31-1
Uses: Emulsifier, coemulsifier, stabilizer, wetting agent, lubricant for pharmaceutical applics.; base for creams and ointments
Properties: Solid; HLB 10.9; m.p. 52 C; sapon. no. 96; 100% conc.; nonionic.
Cithrol GMS N/E. [Croda Universal Ltd.]
Chem. Descrip.: Glyceryl stearate
CAS 31566-31-1
Uses: Emulsifier, coemulsifier, stabilizer, wetting agent, lubricant for pharmaceutical applics.
Properties: Solid; HLB 3.4; 100% conc.; nonionic.
Cithrol GMS S/E. [Croda Universal Ltd.]
Chem. Descrip.: Glyceryl stearate SE

CAS 31566-31-1
Uses: Emulsifier, coemulsifier, stabilizer, wetting agent, lubricant for pharmaceutical applics.
Properties: Solid; HLB 4.4; 100% conc.; anionic.
Cithrol PGML N/E. [Croda Universal Ltd.]
Chem. Descrip.: Propylene glycol laurate
CAS 142-55-2; EINECS 205-542-3
Uses: Emulsifier, coemulsifier, stabilizer, wetting agent, lubricant for pharmaceutical applics.
Properties: Liq.; HLB 2.7; 100% conc.; nonionic.
Cithrol PGMO N/E. [Croda Chem. Ltd.]
Chem. Descrip.: Propylene glycol oleate
CAS 1330-80-9; EINECS 215-549-3
Uses: Emulsifier, coemulsifier, stabilizer, wetting agent, lubricant for pharmaceutical applics.
Properties: Liq.; HLB 3.1; 100% conc.; nonionic.
Cithrol PGMR N/E. [Croda Universal Ltd.]
Chem. Descrip.: Propylene glycol ricinoleate
CAS 26402-31-3; EINECS 247-669-7
Uses: Emulsifier, coemulsifier, stabilizer, wetting agent, lubricant for pharmaceutical applics.
Properties: Liq.; HLB 2.7; 100% conc.; nonionic.
Cithrol PGMS N/E. [Croda Universal Ltd.]
Chem. Descrip.: Propylene glycol stearate
CAS 1323-39-3; EINECS 215-354-3
Uses: Emulsifier, coemulsifier, stabilizer, wetting agent, lubricant for pharmaceutical applics.
Properties: Solid; HLB 2.4; 100% conc.; nonionic.
Cithrol PGMS S/E. [Croda Universal Ltd.]
Chem. Descrip.: Propylene glycol stearate SE
Uses: Emulsifier, coemulsifier, stabilizer, wetting agent, lubricant for pharmaceutical applics.
Properties: Solid; HLB 3.2; 100% conc.; anionic.
Citric Acid Anhyd. USP/FCC. [PMC Specialties]
Chem. Descrip.: Citric acid USP/FCC
CAS 77-92-9; EINECS 201-069-1
Uses: Pharmaceutical additive
Regulatory: FDA compliance
Properties: Colorless or wh. free-flowing gran. and powd., odorless, tart taste; sol. (g/100 ml): 181 g in water, 59.1 g in alcohol; m.w. 192.13; 99.5-100.5% assay
Storage: Store in tightly sealed containers away from heat and humidity.
Citric Acid USP FCC Anhyd. Fine Gran. No. 69941. [Roche]
Chem. Descrip.: Citric acid USP, FCC
CAS 77-92-9; EINECS 201-069-1
Uses: Acidulant, flavor enhancer in solid/liq. pharmaceuticals and effervescent tablets
Regulatory: GRAS
Properties: Wh. cryst., pract. odorless, strong acid taste; 97% min. thru 30 mesh, 5% max. thru 100 mesh; sl. hygroscopic; very sol. in water (1 g/0.5 ml); freely sol. in alcohol (1 g/2 ml); sparingly sol. in ether (1 g/30 ml); m.w. 192.13; 99.5-100.5% assay
Storage: Store in dry place; avoid excessive exposure to heat and humidity.
Citric Acid USP FCC Anhyd. Gran. No. 69942. [Roche]
Chem. Descrip.: Citric acid USP, FCC

CAS 77-92-9; EINECS 201-069-1
Uses: Acidulant and flavor enhancer in solid/liq. pharmaceuticals, effervescent tablets; trace metal scavenger protecting labile substances
Regulatory: FDA GRAS
Properties: Wh. cryst., pract. odorless, strong acid taste; 98% min. thru 16 mesh, 10% max. thru 50 mesh; sl. hygroscopic; very sol. in water (1 g/0.5 ml); freely sol. in alcohol (1 g/2 ml); sparingly sol. in ether (1 g/30 ml); m.w. 192.13; 99.5-100.5% assay
Storage: Store in dry place; avoid exposure to heat and humidity.

Clarity. [ABITEC]
Chem. Descrip.: Fractionated partially hydrog. soybean oil
EINECS 232-410-2
Uses: Diluent, lubricant, moisturizer for clinical nutrition, coating, delivery/absorp. enhancement, dermatologicals, soft gelatin capsules
Properties: Lovibond 1.5R liq.; m.p. < 70 F; acid no. 0.1 max.; iodine no. 120 max.

Clearlan® 1650. [Henkel/Emery]
Chem. Descrip.: Lanolin anhydrous USP
CAS 8006-54-0; EINECS 232-348-6
Uses: Emollient
Properties: Lt. color.

Clintose® A. [ADM Corn Processing; MLG Enterprises Ltd.]
Chem. Descrip.: Dextrose
Uses: Sweetener used in tableting
Properties: Wh. cryst., odorless, bland sweet taste; 99% min. thru #16 screen; 99.7% act., 8.5% moisture.

Clintose® L. [ADM Corn Processing; MLG Enterprises Ltd.]
Chem. Descrip.: Enzyme converted ion exchange refined dextrose syrup
Uses: Sweetener used in tableting
Properties: Water-wh. syrup, char. odor, sweet taste; dens. 11.01 lb/gal (130 F); visc. 35 cps (120 F); pH 4.5; DE 99.5; 99.5% dextrose, 29.5% moisture
Storage: Store @ 130 F to avoid crystallization.

Cloisonné®. [Mearl]
Chem. Descrip.: Mica pigments coated with titanium dioxide and/or iron oxide with carmine, iron blue, etc.
Uses: Highly lustrous pigments with deep colors produced by combination of light interference and light absorption; for analgesic body lotions, sunscreens, toothpaste
Properties: Fine powds.

Cloronine. [United-Guardian]
Uses: Antiseptic, germicide, sanitizer for disinfecting medical/surgical instruments and equip., esp. where autoclaves are not avail.; purification of water supplies; oxidizing and deodorizing agent; releases hypochlorous acid when dissolved in water
Properties: Wh. powd.; rapidly sol. in water
Custom product

Clorpactin. [United-Guardian]
Uses: Broad-spectrum topical bactericide, fungicide, and virucide for treating localized infections; debriding agent for wounds; deodorizer for necrotizing conditions (diabetic gangrene); irrigation of sinus tracts; cleansing and antisepsis of bed-sores.

CM-80. [Carrageenan Co.]
Chem. Descrip.: Kappa carrageenan
CAS 9000-07-1; EINECS 232-524-2
Uses: High gel str. carrageenan producing max. visc. and gel str. when heated to 160-170 F then cooled to R.T.; for encapsulation
Use level: 0.5% (encapsulation)
Properties: Very lt. cream to wh. powd.; 99% thru 80 mesh; dissolves easily in water @ R.T.; completely sol. in water @ 80-85 C; pH 7-9 (1.5%, 30 C) ≤ 12% moisture.

CMC Daicel 1150. [Daicel USA]
Chem. Descrip.: Sodium carboxymethyl cellulose
CAS 9004-32-4
Uses: Thickener, binder, stabilizer, excipient, protective colloid, suspending agent for pharmaceutical ointments
Regulatory: FDA 21CFR §182.1745, GRAS
Properties: Wh. or lt. cream fine powd., odorless, tasteless; 95% min. thru 80 mesh; sol. in water; insol. in almost all org. solvs., oils, and fats; bulk dens. 0.6 g/ml; visc. 200-300 cps; 10% max. moisture
Storage: Hygroscopic-store unused portion in tightly closed containers.

CMC Daicel 1160. [Daicel USA]
Chem. Descrip.: Sodium carboxymethyl cellulose
CAS 9004-32-4
Uses: Thickener, binder, stabilizer, excipient, protective colloid, suspending agent for pharmaceutical tablets, granules
Regulatory: FDA 21CFR §182.1745, GRAS
Properties: Wh. or lt. cream fine powd., odorless, tasteless; 95% min. thru 80 mesh; sol. in water; insol. in almost all org. solvs., oils, and fats; bulk dens. 0.6 g/ml; visc. 300-500 cps; 10% max. moisture
Storage: Hygroscopic-store unused portion in tightly closed containers.

CMC Daicel 1220. [Daicel USA]
Chem. Descrip.: Sodium carboxymethyl cellulose
CAS 9004-32-4
Uses: Thickener, binder, stabilizer, excipient, protective colloid, suspending agent for x-ray contrast media
Regulatory: FDA 21CFR §182.1745, GRAS
Properties: Wh. to lt. cream fine powd., odorless, tasteless; 95% min. thru 80 mesh; sol. in water; insol. in almost all org. solvs., oils, and fats; bulk dens. 0.6 g/ml; visc. 10-20 cps; 10% max. moisture
Storage: Hygroscopic-store unused portion in tightly closed containers.

CMC Daicel 1260. [Daicel USA]
Chem. Descrip.: Sodium carboxymethyl cellulose

CAS 9004-32-4
Uses: Thickener, binder, stabilizer, excipient, protective colloid, suspending agent for toothpaste, syrupy medicines
Regulatory: FDA 21CFR §182.1745, GRAS
Properties: Wh. or lt. cream fine powd., odorless, tasteless; 95% min. thru 80 mesh; sol. in water; insol. in almost all org. solvs., oils, and fats; bulk dens. 0.6 g/ml; visc. 80-150 cps; 10% max. moisture
Storage: Hygroscopic; store unused portion in tightly closed containers.

Coated Ascorbic Acid 97.5% No. 60482. [Roche]
Chem. Descrip.: L-Ascorbic acid USP, FCC coated with ethylcellulose
Uses: Vitamin protected against reactive materials in pharmaceuticals (vitamin C tablets, esp. hard shell capsules/tablets contg. iron and/or antihistamines; aids compression in dry gran. methods)
Regulatory: FDA GRAS
Properties: Wh. to sl. off-wh. free-flowing fine gran. powd.; 100% thru 16 mesh, 35% max. thru 100 mesh; 97.5% min. assay
Storage: Store in tight, light-resist. containers, optimally @ ≤ 72 F; avoid exposure to moisture and excessive heat.

Cobee 76. [Stepan Food Ingreds.]
Chem. Descrip.: Refined, bleached, deodorized coconut oil
CAS 8001-31-8; EINECS 232-282-8
Uses: Emollient, superfatting agent, clouding agent used in pharmaceutical industry
Properties: Lovibond 20/2 soft solid; no odor or taste; m.p. 76-80 F
Unverified

Coconut Oil® 76. [Stepan Food Ingreds.]
Chem. Descrip.: Coconut oil, refined, bleached, deodorized
CAS 8001-31-8; EINECS 232-282-8
Uses: Pharmaceutical vehicle
Regulatory: FDA 21CFR §170.30 (GRAS); kosher grade avail.
Properties: Sl. yel. soft solid, mild fatty odor, bland taste; iodine no. 8.4; sapon. no. 256; 0.04% moisture
Toxicology: Low irritation potential
Storage: Avoid prolonged storage above 90 F.

Coconut Oil® 92. [Stepan Food Ingreds.]
Chem. Descrip.: Coconut oil, hydrog., refined, bleached, deodorized
CAS 8001-31-8; EINECS 232-282-8
Uses: Pharmaceutical vehicle
Regulatory: FDA 21CFR §170.30 (GRAS); kosher grade avail.
Properties: Cream-colored solid, mild fatty odor, bland taste; iodine no. 1.3; sapon. no. 255; 0.04% moisture
Toxicology: Low irritation potential
Storage: Avoid prolonged storage above 90 F.

Co-Grhetinol. [Maruzen Fine Chems.]
Chem. Descrip.: Stearyl glycyrrhetinate
CAS 13832-70-7

Uses: Anti-inflammatory, anti-allergenic for pharmaceuticals.

Collagenite. [United-Guardian]
Chem. Descrip.: Modified collagen
CAS 9007-34-5; EINECS 232-697-4
Uses: Intended to form tissue-compat. layers; gels as it cools; forms sheets or fibers for medical, health-care applics.
Properties: Sol. in hot water
Custom product

Colloid 488T. [TIC Gums]
Chem. Descrip.: Sodium alginate
CAS 9005-38-3
Uses: Gellant, film-former, emulsifier, suspending aid for pharmaceuticals (lotions, vitamin suspension)
Properties: Sol. in cold water.

Colloid 602. [TIC Gums]
Chem. Descrip.: Propylene glycol alginate
CAS 9005-37-2
Uses: Gellant, film-former, emulsifier, suspending aid for pharmaceuticals (lotions, vitamin suspension)
Properties: Sol. in cold water.

Colored Nu-Pareil® PG 14/18. [Crompton & Knowles]
Chem. Descrip.: Sucrose, starch NF, and FD&C or D&C colors
Uses: Carrier used in pharmaceutical industry for capsule or tablet identification
Properties: Wh. uniform, mostly spherical seeds; 1000-1400 µm; 100% thru 12 mesh, 75% min. thru 14 mesh; 62.5-91.5% sucrose, ≤ 4% moisture.

Colored Nu-Pareil® PG 16/20. [Crompton & Knowles]
Chem. Descrip.: Sucrose, starch NF, and FD&C or D&C colors
Uses: Carrier used in pharmaceutical industry for capsule or tablet identification
Properties: Wh. uniform, mostly spherical seeds; 850-1180 µm; 100% thru 14 mesh, 75% min. thru 16 mesh; 62.5-91.5% sucrose, ≤ 4% moisture.

Colored Nu-Pareil® PG 18/20. [Crompton & Knowles]
Chem. Descrip.: Sucrose, starch NF, and FD&C or D&C colors
Uses: Carrier used in pharmaceutical industry for capsule or tablet identification
Properties: Wh. uniform, mostly spherical seeds; 850-1000 µm; 100% thru 16 mesh, 75% min. thru 18 mesh; 62.5-91.5% sucrose, ≤ 4% moisture.

Colored Nu-Pareil® PG 20/25. [Crompton & Knowles]
Chem. Descrip.: Sucrose, starch NF, and FD&C or D&C colors
Uses: Carrier used in pharmaceutical industry for capsule or tablet identification
Properties: Wh. uniform, mostly spherical seeds; 710-850 µm; 100% thru 18 mesh, 75% min. thru 20 mesh; 62.5-91.5% sucrose, ≤ 4% moisture.

Colored Nu-Pareil® PG 25/30. [Crompton & Knowles]
Chem. Descrip.: Sucrose, starch NF, and FD&C or D&C colors
Uses: Carrier used in pharmaceutical industry for capsule or tablet identification

Properties: Wh. uniform, mostly spherical seeds; 610-710 μm; 100% thru 20 mesh, 75% min. thru 25 mesh; 62.5-91.5% sucrose, ≤ 4% moisture.

Colored Nu-Pareil® PG 30/35. [Crompton & Knowles]
Chem. Descrip.: Sucrose, starch NF, and FD&C or D&C colors
Uses: Carrier used in pharmaceutical industry for capsule or tablet identification
Properties: Wh. uniform, mostly spherical seeds; 500-600 μm; 100% thru 25 mesh, 75% min. thru 30 mesh; 62.5-91.5% sucrose, ≤ 4% moisture.

Compactrol®. [Mendell]
Chem. Descrip.: Calcium sulfate, dihydrate NF/FCC
CAS 10101-41-4; EINECS 231-900-3
Uses: Tablet and capsule filler for pharmaceutical tablets mfg. by direct compression
Regulatory: NF/FCC compliance
Properties: Wh. to sl. off-wh. free-flowing powd., odorless; avg. particle size 166 μ; 90% +140 mesh; dens. (tapped) 1.24 g/ml; 100% conc.

Comperlan® COD. [Henkel KGaA/Cospha; Pulcra SA]
Chem. Descrip.: Cocamide DEA
CAS 61791-31-9; EINECS 263-163-9
Uses: Foam and visc. increasing agent with emulsifying properties for pharmaceutical applics.; solv.
Properties: Yel. clear liq.; solid. pt. -5 to 5 C; pH 9.5-10.5 (2%); 85% conc.

Compritol 888. [Gattefosse]
Chem. Descrip.: Tribehenin
CAS 18641-57-1; EINECS 242-471-7
Uses: Pharmaceutical excipient, lubricant for tablets/capsules; protects the drug, improves stability of tablets, controls sustained release.

Compritol 888 ATO. [Gattefosse; Gattefosse SA]
Chem. Descrip.: Tribehenin
CAS 18641-57-1; EINECS 242-471-7
Uses: Formulation aid, excipient, lubricant, binding agent for tablet/capsule mfg.; improves compressibility; lipophilic agent for sustained release applics.
Use level: 0.5-4% (tablets, capsules); 10-30% (sustained-release formulations)
Regulatory: FDA 21CFR §184.1328 GRAS; USP and EP compliance
Properties: Off-wh. fine powd. (spherical particles), faint odor, tasteless; 85% thru 250 mesh; sol. hot in chloroform, methylene chloride; insol. in water, min. oil, ethanol; drop pt. 69-74 C; HLB 2.0; acid no. < 4; iodine no. < 3; sapon. no. 145-165; 100% conc.; nonionic
Toxicology: LD0 (oral, rat) > 5 g/kg
Storage: Preserve in orig. container; store below 35 C; prevent exposure to air, light, heat, and moisture.

Compritol HD5 ATO. [Gattefosse SA]
Chem. Descrip.: PEG-8 behenate and tribehenin
Uses: Tableting agent and lipophilic matrix
Properties: Drop pt. ≈ 62 C; HLB 5.0; acid no. < 4; iodine no. < 3; sapon. no. 105-125.

Controlled Particle Size KCl. [Reheis]
Chem. Descrip.: Potassium chloride USP/FCC, BP, EP
CAS 7447-40-7; EINECS 231-211-8
Uses: Functional additive for use in the pharmaceutical industry.

Copherol® 950LC. [Henkel/Cospha]
Chem. Descrip.: Tocopherol and coco-caprylate/caprate
Uses: Natural antioxidant and moisturizer for sun protection prods.
Properties: Amber clear visc. oil.

Copherol® 1250. [Henkel/Fine Chems.; Henkel Canada; Henkel KGaA/Cospha]
Chem. Descrip.: D-α-Tocopheryl acetate USP, FCC
CAS 58-95-7
Uses: Natural-source vitamin E, antioxidant, protectant, and moisturizer for sun protection, pharmaceuticals; stable to air, light, acid
Regulatory: USP, FCC compliance; kosher certified
Properties: Yel. clear visc. oil, nearly odorless; sol. in ethanol; misc. with acetone, ether, chloroform, veg. oils; insol. in water; m.w. 472.75; sp.gr. 0.94-0.96 g/cm^3; 1250 IU/g
Storage: Protect from heat, light, freezing; 1 yr shelf life stored cold in unopened original pkg.; unstable to alkalies and oxidizing agents.

Copherol® F-1300. [Henkel/Fine Chems.; Henkel Canada; Henkel KGaA/Cospha]
Chem. Descrip.: D-α-Tocopherol USP, FCC
CAS 59-02-9; EINECS 200-412-2
Uses: Natural-source vitamin E, antioxidant, protectant, and moisturizer for sun protection, pharmaceuticals
Regulatory: USP, FCC compliance; kosher certified
Properties: Amber clear visc. oil, mild to bland odor and taste; sol. in ethanol; misc. with acetone, ether, chloroform, veg. oils and fats; insol. in water; m.w. 430.69; sp.gr. 0.94-0.96 g/cm^3; 1300 IU/g
Precaution: Unstable to acid, light, alkali, and oxidizing agents
Storage: Store in tightly closed containers; protect from heat and light; use promptly once opened; 12 mos shelf life stored cold in original unopened containers.

Coriolus Mushroom Extract COREXT. [Garuda Int'l.]
Chem. Descrip.: Coriolus versicolor mushroom extract
Uses: Used in pharmaceutical prods.
Properties: Brn. fine powd.; 100% thru 80 mesh; 58.8% total polysaccharides, < 7% moisture
Storage: Store in cool room (5-10 C) in sealed polyethylene bag; 24 mos shelf life.

Coriolus Mycelia Extract CORMEXT. [Garuda Int'l.]
Chem. Descrip.: Coriolus versicolor mycelia extract
Uses: Used in pharmaceutical prods.
Properties: Brn. fine powd.; 100% thru 80 mesh;

30.2% total polysaccharides, < 7% moisture
Storage: Store in cool room (5-10 C) in sealed polyethylene bag; 24 mos shelf life.

Corn Po 4. [Tri-K Industries]
Chem. Descrip.: Phosphatized corn starch, a distarch phosphate, contg. < 0.1% P
CAS 55963-33-2
Uses: Production aid, filler, and carrier for pharmaceuticals; exc. sliding and adhesive props.
Properties: Wh. free-flowing powd., odorless; 20-30 μ particle size; insol. in water; sp.gr. 1.3; ignition temp. 540 C; pH 7-7.5
Toxicology: LD50 (oral) 4000 mg/kg; physiologically and toxicologically innocuous; nonsensitizing
Precaution: Possible dust explosion hazard if mixed with air in proper proportions
Storage: Store in dry place in well-closed bags; indefinitely stable under normal dry storage conditions.

Corn Po 4 Ster. [Tri-K Industries]
Chem. Descrip.: Phosphatized corn starch, a distarch phosphate, with 2% max. magnesium oxide
Uses: Sterilizable tissue-compat. glove powd.
Regulatory: Meets USP specs. for absorbable dusting powd. and BP specs. for sterilizable maize starch
Properties: Wh. free-flowing powd.; 20-30 μ particle size; pH 9.5-10.8 (10% susp.)
Toxicology: Physiologically and toxicologically innocuous.

CornSweet® Crystalline Fructose. [ADM Corn Processing; MLG Enterprises Ltd.]
Chem. Descrip.: Fructose FCC/USP
Uses: Sweetener offering intense sweetness, sweetness synergism, flavor enhancement, humectancy, low water activity, f.p. depression, high osmotic pressure
Properties: Wh. free-flowing cryst., odorless, clean very sweet taste; 1% max. on 16 mesh, 10% max. thru 100 mesh; bulk dens. 52 lb/ft³; m.p. 103 C; 99.9% act.
Storage: Store @ 25 C and 50% r.h.

42/43 Corn Syrup. [MLG Enterprises Ltd.]
Chem. Descrip.: Acid converted corn syrup
CAS 8029-43-4; EINECS 232-436-4
Uses: Sweetener used in pharmaceuticals
Properties: Water-wh. med. visc. liq., char. odor, sweet-bland taste; sp.gr. 1.4201 (100/60 F); dens. 11.84 lb/gal (100 F); visc. 1000 poises (80 F); pH 4.8; DE 42; Baumé 43 (100 F); 80.7% total solids, 19.3% moisture.

Corona PNL. [Croda Inc.]
Chem. Descrip.: Modified lanolin USP
EINECS 232-348-6
Uses: Superfatting emollient, emulsifier, moisturizer; may be used at 100% conc.; esp. for semisolid bases, orals, topicals, prods. for dry, itchy chapped skin, hemorrhoidal preps., suppositories, steroidal prods., acne prods., ophthalmics
Use level: 2-10%

Properties: Yel. soft solid; m.p. 38-44 C.

Corona Lanolin. [Croda Chem. Ltd.]
Chem. Descrip.: Anhyd. lanolin
CAS 8006-54-0; EINECS 232-348-6
Uses: Pharmaceutical base, emollient, moisturizing agent, cosolv., w/o emulsifier, superfatting agent, wetting/dispersing agent
Properties: Paste; oil-sol.; 100% conc.; nonionic.

Coronet Lanolin. [Croda Chem. Ltd.]
Chem. Descrip.: Super refined cosmetic grade lanolin
CAS 8006-54-0; EINECS 232-348-6
Uses: Pharmaceutical base, emollient, moisturizing agent, cosolv., w/o emulsifier, superfatting agent, wetting/dispersing agent; minimum odor, color, batch variation in this grade; sl. higher m.p. than USP and BP standards
Properties: Paste; 100% conc.; nonionic.

Cosmetic Lanolin. [Croda Inc.]
Chem. Descrip.: Lanolin USP
CAS 8006-54-0; EINECS 232-348-6
Uses: Superfatting emollient, emulsifier, moisturizer for topical pharmaceuticals, creams, lotions, sunscreen prods., ointments, diaper rash preps., hemorrhoidal preps., acne formulations
Properties: Lt. amber soft solid; partly sol. in min. oil; insol. in water, IPA, propylene glycol; m.p. 38-44 C
Toxicology: LD50 (oral, rat) > 20 g/kg; mild skin and eye irritant.

Cosmetic Lanolin Anhydrous USP. [Lanaetex Prods.]
Chem. Descrip.: Lanolin
CAS 8006-54-0; EINECS 232-348-6
Uses: Emollient.

Cosmetol® X. [CasChem]
Chem. Descrip.: Unrefined castor oil USP, with antioxidant
CAS 8001-79-4; EINECS 232-293-8
Uses: Deodorized specially refined grade of castor oil containing a food grade antioxidant; emollient, pigment wetter, cosolv., lubricant for antiperspirant sticks
Properties: Pour pt. -23 C; acid no. 2; iodine no. 86; sapon. no. 180; hyd. no. 164.

Cosmica®. [Mearl]
Uses: Pigment series where absorption colors are deposited directly on the mica, creating highly intense effects with minimal luster; suitable for analgesic body lotions, sunscreens, toothpaste.

Cosmowax. [Croda Inc.]
Chem. Descrip.: Stearyl alcohol, steareth-20, steareth-10
Uses: Self-emulsifying wax, emulsifier, stabilizer for pharmaceuticals, creams and lotions, antiperspirants
Properties: Creamy wh. waxy solid, low odor; m.p. 47-55 C; acid no. 0.5 max.; iodine no. 2 max.; sapon. no. 1 max.; 100% conc.; nonionic.

Cosmowax J. [Croda Inc.]
Chem. Descrip.: Cetearyl alcohol and ceteareth-20
Uses: O/w emulsifier and stabilizer with body,

opacity, and conditioning props. for pharmaceutical creams
Properties: Creamy wh. waxy solid; low odor; HLB 8.5; m.p. 47-55 C; acid no. 0.5 max.; iodine no. 2 max.; sapon. no. 1 max.; 100% conc.; nonionic.

Cosmowax K. [Croda Inc.]
Chem. Descrip.: Stearyl alcohol and ceteareth-20
Uses: Emulsifier, stabilizer with body, opacity and conditioning props. for pharmaceuticals
Properties: Creamy wh. waxy solid; low odor; HLB 8.0; m.p. 55-63 C; acid no. 0.5 max.; iodine no. 2 max.; sapon. no. 1 max.; 100% conc.; nonionic.

Cozeen®. [Zumbro; Garuda Int'l.]
Chem. Descrip.: Corn protein zein, special vegetable oils, glycerin
Uses: Natural nutritious edible coating to coat nutritional supplements and pharmaceutical tablets; provides aesthetic and barrier props.; filmformer, adhesive chars.
Properties: Sol. in alcohol; insol. in water
Storage: Store @ R.T. (18-24 C); stir before use.

CPC. [Zeeland]
Chem. Descrip.: Cetylpyridinium chloride
CAS 123-03-5; EINECS 204-593-9
Uses: Emulsifier; antibacterial, preservative for pharmaceuticals.

CPC Sumquat 6060. [Zeeland]
Chem. Descrip.: Cetylpyridinium chloride
CAS 123-03-5; EINECS 204-593-9
Uses: Emulsifier; antibacterial, preservative for pharmaceuticals.

Cracked Bleached Irish Moss. [Meer]
Chem. Descrip.: Irish moss
CAS 9000-07-1; EINECS 232-524-2
Uses: Bulk laxative in pharmaceuticals
Properties: Water-sol.

Creamjel. [United-Guardian]
Uses: Moisturizer, emulsifier for health-care use; combines a gel and cream in clear form; forms stable emulsions with a wide range of oils using no heat
Custom product

Cremba. [Croda Inc.]
Chem. Descrip.: Min. oil, petrolatum, lanolin alcohol, and lanolin
Uses: Emollient, moisturizer, aux. emulsifier for pharmaceuticals, detergent surgical scrubs; solubilizer for oil-sol. actives to yield w/o lotions or creams
Properties: Wh. to yel. soft solid; sol. in min. oil; m.p. 37-44 C; 100% conc.; nonionic
Toxicology: LD50 (oral, rat) > 5 g/kg; minimal skin and eye irritant
Custom product

Cremophor® A 11. [BASF AG]
Chem. Descrip.: Ceteareth-11
CAS 68439-49-6
Uses: Emulsifier for pharmaceutical preps.
Properties: Wh. wax; sol. in water, alcohol; sp.gr. 0.964-0.968 (60 C); drop pt. 34-38 C; HLB 12-14; acid no. < 1; iodine no. < 1; sapon. no. < 1; hyd. no. 70-80; pH 6-7; 100% act.; nonionic.

Cremophor® A 25. [BASF; BASF AG]
Chem. Descrip.: Ceteareth-25
CAS 68439-49-6
Uses: Emulsifier for pharmaceutical preps.
Properties: Wh. powd.; sol. in water, alcohol; sp.gr. 1.020-1.028 (60 C); drop pt. 44-48 C; HLB 15-17; acid no. < 1; iodine no. < 1; sapon. no. < 3; hyd. no. 35-45; pH 5-7; 100% act.; nonionic.

Cremophor® EL. [BASF; BASF AG]
Chem. Descrip.: PEG-35 castor oil
CAS 61791-12-6
Uses: Solubilizer, emulsifier used for essential oils, pharmaceuticals, veterinary medicine; solv. for steroids and fat-sol. vitamins; emulsifier for topical creams and parenterally administered cyclosporine
Properties: Pale yel. liq.; sol. in water, ethanol, propanol, ethyl acetate, chloroform, CCl_4, benzene, toluene, and xylene; sp.gr. 1.05-1.06; visc. 700-850 cps; HLB 12-14; acid no. < 2; sapon no. 65-70; ref. index 1.471; pH 6-8 (10% aq.); 100% act.; nonionic
Toxicology: May cause anaphylactic reactions.

Cremophor® RH 40. [BASF; BASF AG]
Chem. Descrip.: PEG-40 hydrog. castor oil
CAS 61788-85-0
Uses: Solubilizer, emulsifier for pharmaceuticals
Properties: Water-wh. visc. liq. or soft paste, very little odor or taste; sol. in water, ethanol, IPA, n-propanol, ethyl acetate, benzene, toluene, and xylene; HLB 14-16; acid no. ≤ 1; iodine no. ≤ 1; sapon. no. 50-60; hyd. no. 60-75; pH 6-7 (10% aq.); 100% act.; nonionic
Toxicology: LD50 (oral, rat) > 16 g/kg.

Cremophor® RH 410. [BASF AG]
Chem. Descrip.: PEG-40 hydrog. castor oil
CAS 61788-85-0
Uses: Solubilizer, emulsifier for pharmaceuticals
Properties: Sl. turbid visc. liq.; sol. in water, ethanol, IPA, n-propanol, ethyl acetate, benzene, toluene, and xylene; visc. ≤ 1800 mPa•s; HLB 14-16; acid no. ≤ 1; iodine no. ≤ 1; sapon. no. 45-55; pH 6-7 (10% aq.); 90% act.; nonionic.

Cremophor® RH 455. [BASF AG]
Chem. Descrip.: PEG-40 hydrog. castor oil and propylene glycol
Uses: Solubilizer, emulsifier for pharmaceuticals
Properties: Visc. liq.; sol. in water, ethanol, IPA, n-propanol, ethyl acetate, benzene, toluene, and xylene; visc. 1000-1500 cps; HLB 14-16; acid no. ≤ 1; iodine no. ≤ 1; sapon. no. 45-55; ref. index 1.459-1.464; pH 6-7 (10% aq.); 90% act.; nonionic.

Cremophor® S 9. [BASF; BASF AG]
Chem. Descrip.: PEG-8 stearate
CAS 9004-99-3
Uses: Emulsifier for o/w type, thickening agent; suspension stabilizer; lubricating and antitack effects; for pharmaceuticals
Properties: Ylsh. wh. visc. liq.; sol. in water, alcohols, acetone, ethyl acetate, chloroform, benzene, castor oil, and oleic acid; sp.gr. 0.97 (60 C);

HLB 12; acid no. 2; sapon. no. 88-98; 100% act.; nonionic.

Crill 1. [Croda Inc.; Croda Food Prods. Ltd.; Croda Surf. Ltd.]
Chem. Descrip.: Sorbitan laurate
CAS 1338-39-2
Uses: Emulsifier, pigment dispersant, cosolv., wetting agent, antifoam, visc. reducer, lubricant for pharmaceuticals
Regulatory: UK clearance
Properties: Pale yel. clear visc. liq.; sol. in ethanol, oleyl alcohol, min. oil; HLB 8.6; acid no. 4-7; sapon. no. 160-175; hyd. no. 330-358; 98% conc.; nonionic
Storage: Store under cool, dry conditions.

Crill 3. [Croda Inc.; Croda Food Prods. Ltd.; Croda Surf. Ltd.]
Chem. Descrip.: Sorbitan stearate NF
CAS 1338-41-6; EINECS 215-664-9
Uses: W/o emulsifier, lubricant; solubilizer for excipients and/or actives with low sol. in lipophilic bases; contributes to stability of o/w emulsions when used in combination with Crillets; for oral and topical pharmaceuticals
Use level: 0.5-5%
Regulatory: FDA 21CFR §172.836; UK clearance
Properties: Cream/yel. hard waxy solid; low odor; partially sol. in oleyl alcohol, olive oil, oleic acid; insol. in water; m.p. 54 C; HLB 4.7; acid no. 5-10; sapon. no. 146-157; hyd. no. 235-260; 98% conc.; nonionic
Toxicology: LD50 (oral, rat) > 31 g/kg; nonirritating to eyes
Storage: Store under cool, dry conditions.

Crill 4. [Croda Inc.; Croda Food Prods. Ltd.; Croda Surf. Ltd.]
Chem. Descrip.: Sorbitan oleate NF
CAS 1338-43-8; EINECS 215-665-4
Uses: W/o emulsifier, wetting agent, pigment dispersant, antifoam; solubilizer for excipients and/or actives with low sol. in lipophilic bases; aids stability of o/w emulsions when used in combination with Crillets; for oral and topical pharmaceuticals
Properties: Amber visc. liq.; sol. in ethyl, isopropyl, and oleyl alcohols, min. oil, IPM, olive oil, oleic acid; HLB 4.3; acid no. 5.5-7.5; sapon. no. 147-160; hyd. no. 193-209; 98% conc.; nonionic
Toxicology: LD50 (oral, rat) > 40 g/kg; nonirritating to eyes.

Crill 6. [Croda Inc.; Croda Surf. Ltd.]
Chem. Descrip.: Sorbitan isostearate
CAS 71902-01-7
Uses: W/o emulsifier; solubilizer for excipients and/or actives with low sol. in lipophilic bases; not prone to oxidation or declines in color and odor; for topical pharmaceuticals
Use level: 0.5-5%
Properties: Pale yel. clear visc. liq. to soft solid; sol. in min. oil, IPA, olive oil, partly sol. in oleyl alcohol, IPM; HLB 4.7; acid no. 8 max.; sapon. no. 143-153; hyd. no. 220-250; 98% conc.; nonionic

Toxicology: LD50 (oral, rat) > 16 g/kg (10% aq.); moderate skin irritant; nonirritating to eyes.

Crill 35. [Croda Inc.; Croda Surf. Ltd.]
Chem. Descrip.: Sorbitan tristearate
CAS 26658-19-5; EINECS 247-891-4
Uses: Emulsifier, lubricant for pharmaceutical applics.
Properties: Pale tan hard waxy solid; partly sol. in oleyl alcohol, min. and olive oil, IPM, oleic acid; m.p. 48 C; HLB 2.1; sapon. no. 176-188; 98% conc.; nonionic.

Crill 43. [Croda Inc.; Croda Surf. Ltd.]
Chem. Descrip.: Sorbitan sesquioleate
CAS 8007-43-0; EINECS 232-360-1
Uses: W/o emulsifier, wetting agent, pigment dispersant for pharmaceutical applics.
Properties: Amber visc. liq.; sol. in oleyl alcohol, min. and olive oil, oleic acid; HLB 3.7; sapon. no. 149-160; 98% conc.; nonionic.

Crill 45. [Croda Inc.; Croda Surf. Ltd.]
Chem. Descrip.: Sorbitan trioleate
CAS 26266-58-0; EINECS 247-569-3
Uses: W/o emulsifier, wetting agent, pigment dispersant for pharmaceutical applics.
Properties: Amber visc. liq.; sol. in oleyl alcohol, min. and olive oil, IPM, oleic acid; HLB 4.3; sapon. no. 172-186; 98% conc.; nonionic.

Crill 50. [Croda Surf. Ltd.]
Chem. Descrip.: Sorbitan oleate, tech.
CAS 1338-43-8; EINECS 215-665-4
Uses: Emulsifier, dispersant, wetting agent for pharmaceuticals
Properties: Liq.; 98% conc.; nonionic.

Crillet 1. [Croda Inc.; Croda Chem. Ltd.]
Chem. Descrip.: Polysorbate 20
CAS 9005-64-5
Uses: Solubilizer, emulsifier, dispersant, wetting agent; often combined with a member of the Crill range in emulsification systems; for pharmaceuticals
Properties: Clear, yel. clear liq.; low odor; sol. in water, ethyl and oleyl alcohol, oleic acid; HLB 16.7; sapon. no. 40-51; surf. tens. 38.5 dynes/cm (0.1%); 97% conc.; nonionic.

Crillet 2. [Croda Chem. Ltd.]
Chem. Descrip.: PEG-20 sorbitan palmitate
CAS 9005-66-7
Uses: Solubilizer, emulsifier, wetting agent for pharmaceutical applics.
Properties: Paste; HLB 15.6; 97% conc.; nonionic.

Crillet 3. [Croda Inc.; Croda Chem. Ltd.; Croda Food Prods. Ltd.]
Chem. Descrip.: Polysorbate 60 NF
CAS 9005-67-8
Uses: O/w emulsifier and wetting agent for oral, topical, ophthalmic, and parenteral pharmaceuticals; used with Crills to solubilize actives in syrups, in prep. of oral emulsions, as mild emulsifiers in ointments, creams, lotions
Use level: 0.5-5%
Regulatory: FDA 21CFR §172.836; UK clearance
Properties: Yel. liq. gels to soft solid on cooling;

sol. in ethyl, isopropyl, and oleyl alcohol, oleic acid; partly sol. in water; HLB 14.9; acid no. 2 max.; sapon. no. 45-55; hyd. no. 81-96; pH 5-7 (5%); surf. tens. 42.5 dynes/cm (0.1%); 97% conc.; nonionic
Toxicology: LD50 (oral, rat) > 38 g/kg; nonirritating to eyes
Storage: Store under cool, dry conditions.

Crillet 4. [Croda Inc.; Croda Chem. Ltd.; Croda Food Prods. Ltd.]
Chem. Descrip.: Polysorbate 80 NF
CAS 9005-65-6
Uses: O/w emulsifier and wetting agent for oral, topical, ophthalmic, and parenteral pharmaceuticals; used with Crills to solubilize actives in syrups, in prep. of oral emulsions, as mild emulsifiers in ointments, creams, lotions
Use level: 0.5-5%
Regulatory: FDA 21CFR §172.846; UK clearance
Properties: Yel. amber clear liq.; faint char. odor; sol. in water, ethyl, isopropyl, and oleyl alcohols, oleic acid; HLB 15.0; acid no. 2 max.; sapon. no. 45-55; hyd. no. 65-80; pH 6-7 (5%); surf. tens. 42.5 dynes/cm (0.1%); 97% conc.; nonionic
Toxicology: LD50 (oral, rat) > 38 g/kg; nonirritating to eyes
Storage: Store under cool, dry conditions.

Crillet 6. [Croda Inc.; Croda Chem. Ltd.]
Chem. Descrip.: PEG-20 sorbitan isostearate
CAS 66794-58-9
Uses: O/w emulsifier, solv., and wetting agent for topical pharmaceuticals; used with Crills; mild emulsifiers in ointments, creams, lotions
Use level: 0.5-5%
Properties: Clear yel. liq.; sol. in water, ethyl, isopropyl, and oleyl alcohols, oleic acid, xylene, trichlorethylene; HLB 14.9; acid no. 2 max.; sapon. no. 40-50; hyd. no. 65-85; surf. tens. 38.6 dynes/cm (0.1%); 97% conc.; nonionic.

Crillet 11. [Croda Chem. Ltd.]
Chem. Descrip.: PEG-4 sorbitan laurate
CAS 9005-64-5
Uses: Solubilizer, emulsifier, wetting agent for pharmaceutical applics.
Properties: Liq.; 97% conc.; nonionic.

Crillet 31. [Croda Chem. Ltd.]
Chem. Descrip.: Polysorbate 61
CAS 9005-67-8
Uses: Solubilizer, emulsifier, wetting agent for pharmaceutical applics.
Properties: Solid; 97% conc.; nonionic.

Crillet 35. [Croda Chem. Ltd.]
Chem. Descrip.: Polysorbate 65
CAS 9005-71-4
Uses: Solubilizer, emulsifier, wetting agent for pharmaceutical applics.
Properties: Cream/buff waxy solid; sol. in ethyl and oleyl alcohols, oleic acid, trichlorethylene, partly sol. in water; HLB 10.5; sapon. no. 88-98; surf. tens. 42.5 dynes/cm (0.1%); 97% conc.; nonionic.

Crillet 41. [Croda Chem. Ltd.]
Chem. Descrip.: PEG-5 sorbitan oleate

CAS 9005-65-6
Uses: Solubilizer, emulsifier, wetting agent for pharmaceutical applics.
Properties: Liq.; HLB 10.0; 97% conc.; nonionic.

Crillet 45. [Croda Chem. Ltd.]
Chem. Descrip.: Polysorbate 85
CAS 9005-70-3
Uses: Solubilizer, emulsifier, wetting agent for pharmaceutical applics.
Properties: Clear amber visc. liq.; sol. in ethyl and oleyl alcohols, IPM, oleic acid, kerosene, trichlorethylene, butyl stearate; HLB 11.0; sapon. no. 82-95; surf. tens. 41 dynes/cm (0.1%); 97% conc.; nonionic.

Croda 50 Bloom Gelatin. [Croda Colloids Ltd]
Chem. Descrip.: Gelatin BP, USP
CAS 9000-70-8; EINECS 232-554-6
Uses: Used in microencapsulation of vitamins A, D, and E for animal feed or human vitamin preps., esp. where cold water dispersible microcapsules are required
Properties: pH 5-6; 12% max. moisture
Toxicology: Nontoxic; nonirritating to eyes and skin
Precaution: Burns if ignited; potential fire or explosion hazard with prolonged accumulation of dust on very hot surfs.
Storage: Store in sealed containers in cool, dry conditions, away from odiferous materials; stable almost indefinitely, although 5 yr max. storage life is recommended.

Croda 60 Bloom Alkaline Processed Gelatin. [Croda Colloids Ltd]
Chem. Descrip.: Gelatin BP, USP
CAS 9000-70-8; EINECS 232-554-6
Uses: Used in hard shell gelatin capsules as a low bloom gelatin extender
Toxicology: Nontoxic; nonirritating to eyes and skin
Precaution: Burns if ignited; potential fire or explosion hazard with prolonged accumulation of dust on very hot surfs.
Storage: Store in sealed containers in cool, dry conditions, away from odiferous materials; stable almost indefinitely, although 5 yr max. storage life is recommended.

Croda 160 Bloom Limed Gelatin. [Croda Colloids Ltd]
Chem. Descrip.: Gelatin BP, USP
CAS 9000-70-8; EINECS 232-554-6
Uses: Used in soft shell gelatin capsules
Properties: Visc. 35-40 mps (6.6%, 60 C); pH 5-6; 12% max. moisture
Toxicology: Nontoxic; nonirritating to eyes and skin
Precaution: Burns if ignited; potential fire or explosion hazard with prolonged accumulation of dust on very hot surfs.
Storage: Store in sealed containers in cool, dry conditions, away from odiferous materials; stable almost indefinitely, although 5 yr max. storage life is recommended.

Croda 190 Bloom Acid Ossein Gelatin. [Croda Colloids Ltd]
Chem. Descrip.: Gelatin BP, USP

CAS 9000-70-8; EINECS 232-554-6
Uses: Used in soft shell gelatin capsules where the fills are water misc. (e.g., polyethylene glycol-based fills) or for very hygroscopic fills (e.g., chloralhydrate)
Properties: Visc. 27-32 mps (6.6%, 60 C); pH 5-6; 12% max. moisture
Toxicology: Nontoxic; nonirritating to eyes and skin
Precaution: Burns if ignited; potential fire or explosion hazard with prolonged accumulation of dust on very hot surfs.
Storage: Store in sealed containers in cool, dry conditions, away from odiferous materials; stable almost indefinitely, although 5 yr max. storage life is recommended.

Croda 250 Bloom Acid Ossein Gelatin. [Croda Colloids Ltd]
Chem. Descrip.: Gelatin BP, USP
CAS 9000-70-8; EINECS 232-554-6
Uses: Used in hard shell gelatin capsules; reduces capsule brittleness
Properties: Visc. 125-140 mps (12%, 60 C); pH 5-6; 12% max. moisture
Toxicology: Nontoxic; nonirritating to eyes and skin
Precaution: Burns if ignited; potential fire or explosion hazard with prolonged accumulation of dust on very hot surfs.
Storage: Store in sealed containers in cool, dry conditions, away from odiferous materials; stable almost indefinitely, although 5 yr max. storage life is recommended.

Crodacol C-95NF. [Croda Inc.]
Chem. Descrip.: Cetyl alcohol NF
CAS 36653-82-4; EINECS 253-149-0
Uses: Emulsion thickener, stabilizer, and coemulsifier for pharmaceutical suppositories, lotions, creams, and ointments; can be mixed with petrolatum to increase water-holding capacity
Use level: 2-30%
Properties: Wh. to cream flakes; sol. in IPA; sol. warm in min. oil, propylene glycol; m.p. 45-50 C; acid no. 0.3 max.; iodine no. 3 max.; sapon. no. 1 max.; hyd. no. 218-238; 95% conc.
Toxicology: LD50 (oral, rat) > 20 g/kg; mild eye and skin irritant.

Crodacol S-95NF. [Croda Inc.; Croda Chem. Ltd.]
Chem. Descrip.: Stearyl alcohol NF
CAS 112-92-5; EINECS 204-017-6
Uses: Emulsion thickener, stabilizer, and coemulsifier for pharmaceutical suppositories, lotions, creams, and ointments; can be mixed with petrolatum to increase water-holding capacity
Use level: 2-30%
Properties: Wh. flakes; sol. in IPA; sol. warm in min. oil, propylene glycol; insol. in water
Toxicology: LD50 (oral, rat) > 5 g/kg; nonirritating to skin; minimal eye irritant.

Crodafos N-3 Acid. [Croda Inc.; Croda Chem. Ltd.]
Chem. Descrip.: Oleth-3 phosphate
CAS 39464-69-2
Uses: Surfactant, conditioner, o/w emulsifier, gelling agent for pharmaceuticals; corrosion inhibitor and antigelling agent in aerosol antiperspirant systems
Use level: 0.5-5%
Properties: Amber visc. liq.; sol. in oil, water; acid no. 120-135; iodine no. 45-58; sapon. no. 125-145; pH 1-3 (2% aq.); 100% act.; anionic.

Crodalan 0477. [Croda Chem. Ltd.]
Chem. Descrip.: Lanolin alternative
Uses: Emollient, superfatting agent, w/o emulsifier for pharmaceuticals
Properties: Paste; 100% conc.; nonionic.

Crodalan AWS. [Croda Inc.; Croda Chem. Ltd.]
Chem. Descrip.: Polysorbate 80, cetyl acetate, acetylated lanolin alcohol
Uses: Emollient, superfatting agent, o/w emulsifier, dispersant, wetting agent, solubilizer used in pharmaceuticals
Use level: 1-5%
Properties: Golden liq.; faint fatty odor; sol. in alcohol, water; sp.gr. 1.02-1.08; acid no. 3 max.; hyd. no. 55-67; pH 5-7 (10% aq.); 100% act.; nonionic.

Crodalan LA. [Croda Inc.; Croda Chem. Ltd.]
Chem. Descrip.: Cetyl acetate and cetylated lanolin alcohol
Uses: Emollient, penetrant, wetting agent used in pharmaceuticals
Use level: 2-10%
Properties: Pale yel. clear, thin mobile liq.; odorless; sol. in min. oil, esters; cloud pt. 20 C; acid no. 2 max.; iodine no. 10 max.; sapon. no. 180-200; hyd. no. 8 max.; 100% act.; nonionic.

Crodamol CAP. [Croda Inc.; Croda Surf. Ltd]
Chem. Descrip.: Cetearyl octanoate and isopropyl myristate
Uses: Exc. solv. and nonoily emollient allowing easier emulsification of unctuous masses and improving emulsion stability in pharmaceuticals (burn creams, acne creams and lotions, antibiotic ointments); high water repellency; improves spreadability
Use level: 5-10%
Properties: Colorless clear liq., low odor; sol. in castor oil, corn oil, min. oil, oleyl alcohol, ethanol, IPA; sp.gr. 0.848-0.853; visc. 11.9 cst; cloud pt. 0 C
Toxicology: LD50 (oral, rat) 13.6 g/kg; moderate skin irritant; nonirritating to eyes.

Crodamol CP. [Croda Inc.; Croda Chem. Ltd.]
Chem. Descrip.: Cetyl palmitate
CAS 540-10-3; EINECS 208-736-6
Uses: Spermaceti wax replacement; lubricious emollient, plasticizer, stiffening agent for topical pharmaceuticals; improves body
Use level: 3-10%
Properties: Wh. flakes; oil-sol.; m.p. 50-54 C.

Crodamol CSP. [Croda Inc.]
Chem. Descrip.: Cetearyl palmitate
CAS 85341-79-3
Uses: Lubricious emollient, plasticizer, stiffener; improves feel and body of emulsions; replaces spermaceti wax and beeswax in topical pharma-

ceuticals
Use level: 3-10%
Properties: Gardner 3 max. wh. flakes; oil-sol.; m.p. 48-52 C; acid no. 1 max.; iodine no. 1 max.; sapon. no. 100-115.

Crodamol EO. [Croda Inc.]
Chem. Descrip.: Ethyl oleate NF
Uses: Vehicle for drug delivery systems; for parenteral and topical applics.
Properties: Pale yel. liq.

Crodamol GTCC. [Croda Inc.; Croda Surf. Ltd.]
Chem. Descrip.: Caprylic/capric triglyceride
EINECS 265-724-3
Uses: Nutritional source of lipid, solv., vehicle, stabilizer, emollient, spreading agent; nongreasy; exc. oxidative stability; for oral, parenteral, and topical pharmaceuticals; exc. dermatological props.
Use level: 2-15%
Properties: Colorless to pale straw clear liq.; sol. in castor oil, corn oil, min. oil, oleyl alcohol, ethanol; sp.gr. 0.950; visc. 30 cst.

Crodamol MM. [Croda Inc.; Croda Surf. Ltd.]
Chem. Descrip.: Myristyl myristate
CAS 3234-85-3; EINECS 221-787-9
Uses: Nongreasy emollient that modifies props. of hydrocarbon wax systems aiding feel in topical pharmaceutical lotions, creams, and ointments; liquefies at body temp.
Use level: 3-10%
Properties: Off-wh. waxy solid.; sol. in min. oil, IPM, IPA, oleyl alcohol; insol. in water; sp.gr. 0.832-0.837 (50 C); m.p. 36-39 C; acid no. 1 max.; sapon. no. 120-130
Toxicology: LD50 (oral, rat) > 5 g/kg; mild skin irritant, minimal eye irritant.

Crodamol PMP. [Croda Inc.; Croda Surf. Ltd]
Chem. Descrip.: PPG-2 myristyl ether propionate
Uses: Nonoily emollient with exc. solv. props.; improves spreadability, reduces tackiness in creams and ointments; allows easier emulsification of unctuous masses, improves emulsion stability; for burn creams, acne creams and lotions, antibiotic ointments
Use level: 5-20%
Properties: Gardner 1 max. colorless clear liq., very mild char. odor; sol. (1%) in min. oil, IPM, oleyl alcohol, ethanol/water, lanolin, cetyl alcohol; sp.gr. 0.870-0.880; visc. 8.9 cst; cloud pt. -5 C; acid no. 0.5 max.; iodine no. 1.0 max.; sapon. no. 140-155
Toxicology: LD50 (oral, rat) > 5 g/kg; minimal skin irritant, nonirritating to eyes; esp. low in comedogenic potential.

Crodamol PTC. [Croda Inc.; Croda Surf. Ltd]
Chem. Descrip.: Pentaerythrityl tetracaprylate/caprate
CAS 68441-68-9; EINECS 270-474-3
Uses: Lubricant, emollient for skin care prods., topical pharmaceuticals (burn creams, acne creams and lotions, antibiotic ointments)
Use level: 1-12%

Properties: Lt. yel. lipophilic visc. liq.; sol. in castor oil, corn oil, min. oil, oleyl alcohol, ethanol.; sp.gr. 0.945-0.955; visc. 50 cst; cloud pt. 10 C
Toxicology: LD50 (oral, rat) > 5 g/kg; minimal skin irritant, nonirritating to eyes; esp. low comedogenic potential.

Crodamol PTIS. [Croda Inc.; Croda Surf. Ltd]
Chem. Descrip.: Pentaerythrityl tetraisostearate
Uses: Lubricant, emollient for skin care prods., topical pharmaceuticals (burn creams, acne creams and lotions, antibiotic ointments)
Use level: 1-12%
Properties: Lt. amber visc. liq.; sol. in castor oil, corn oil, min. oil, oleyl alcohol; sp.gr. 0.915-0.930; visc. 298 cst; cloud pt. 0 C
Toxicology: LD50 (oral, rat) > 10 g/kg; minimal skin and eye irritant; esp. low in comedogenic potential.

Crodamol SS. [Croda Inc.; Croda Surf. Ltd]
Chem. Descrip.: Cetyl esters wax NF
EINECS 241-640-2
Uses: Syn. spermaceti NF; lubricous emollient, stiffening agent in emulsions where it imparts body and improves stability; for topical pharmaceuticals (burn creams, acne creams and lotions, antibiotic ointments)
Use level: 3-10%
Properties: Almost wh. cryst. solid, faint odor; sol. in min. oil; sol. warm in IPA; sp.gr. 0.82-0.84 (50 C); m.p. 43-47 C; acid no. 5 max.; iodine no. 1 max.; sapon. no. 109-120
Toxicology: LD50 (oral, rat) > 5 g/kg; nonirritating to skin, minimal eye irritant.

Crodamol W. [Croda Inc.; Croda Surf. Ltd]
Chem. Descrip.: Stearyl heptanoate
CAS 66009-41-4
Uses: Nongreasy emollient and water repellent for topical pharmaceuticals (burn creams, acne creams and lotions, antibiotic ointments, sunscreen preps., other topical prods.)
Use level: 2-20%
Properties: Wh. waxy solid; mild odor; sol. in castor oil, corn oil, min. oil, oleyl alcohol, ethanol, IPA; sp.gr. 0.850-0.855; m.p. 23-27 C
Toxicology: LD50 (oral, rat) > 16 g/kg; mild skin and eye irritant.

Crodarom Nut A. [Croda Inc.]
Chem. Descrip.: Propylene glycol, walnut extract
Uses: Botanical extract of *Juglans regia L.*; functional adjuvant for skin care prods.; helps relieve effects of eczema; suitable for suntan oils, foot care, antiperspirants
Properties: Dk. brn liq., char. odor; water-sol.; sp.gr. 1.039-1.055 (20 C); ref. index. 1.380-1.394 (20 C).

Crodarom Nut O. [Croda Inc.]
Chem. Descrip.: Peanut oil, min. oil, walnut extract
Uses: Botanical extract of *Juglans regia L.*; functional adjuvant for skin care prods.; helps relieve effects of eczema; suitable for suntan oils, foot care, antiperspirants
Properties: Dk. amber/brn. clear liq., char. odor; oil-

sol.; sp.gr. 0.867-0.868 (20 C); ref. index. 1.466-1.469 (20 C).

Crodasinic LS30. [Croda Chem. Ltd.]
Chem. Descrip.: Sodium N-lauroyl sarcosinate
CAS 137-16-6; EINECS 205-281-5
Uses: Mild surfactant, foaming, wetting agent, bacteriostat, enzyme inhibitor (hexokinase) for dental care preps., oral and topical pharmaceuticals, surgical scrubs
Use level: 1-3%
Properties: Clear to sl. turbid liq.; water-sol.; HLB 30; 30% act.; anionic.

Crodasinic LS35. [Croda Chem. Ltd.]
Chem. Descrip.: Sodium N-lauroyl sarcosinate
CAS 137-16-6; EINECS 205-281-5
Uses: Foaming agent, wetting agent, lubricant, bacteriostat, penetrant used in dental, pharmaceutical applics.
Properties: Clear liq.; water sol.; 35% act.; anionic; biodeg.

Croderol GA7000. [Croda Universal Ltd.]
Chem. Descrip.: Glycerin
CAS 56-81-5; EINECS 200-289-5
Uses: Conditioner, humectant, moisturizing agent in pharmaceuticals
Properties: Liq.

Crodesta F-10. [Croda Inc.; Croda Surf. Ltd.]
Chem. Descrip.: Sucrose distearate
CAS 27195-16-0; EINECS 248-317-5
Uses: Surfactant, wetting agent, dispersant, w/o emulsifier, component of coating systems; for oral and topical pharmaceuticals
Use level: 1-3%
Regulatory: FDA 21CFR 172.859
Properties: Off-wh. powd.; sol. in oil; insol. in water; HLB 3.0; m.p. 60-68 C; acid no. 5 max.; iodine no. 1 max.; sapon. no. 140-200; hyd. no. 80-130; 100% act.; nonionic.

Crodesta F-50. [Croda Inc.; Croda Surf. Ltd.]
Chem. Descrip.: Sucrose distearate
CAS 27195-16-0; EINECS 248-317-5
Uses: Wetting agent, dispersant, o/w emulsifier, component of coating systems; for topical and oral pharmaceuticals
Use level: 3-6%
Regulatory: FDA 21CFR 172.859
Properties: Off-wh. powd.; sol. in water; HLB 6.5; m.p. 74-78 C; acid no. 5 max.; iodine no. 1 max.; sapon. no. 93-153; hyd. no. 419-469; 100% act.; nonionic.

Crodesta F-110. [Croda Inc.; Croda Surf. Ltd.]
Chem. Descrip.: Sucrose distearate and sucrose stearate
Uses: Wetting agent, dispersant, o/w emulsifier, component of coating systems; for topical and oral pharmaceuticals
Use level: 3-6%
Regulatory: FDA 21CFR 172.859
Properties: Off-wh. powd.; water-sol.; HLB 12.0; m.p. 72-78 C; acid no. 5 max.; iodine no. 1 max.; sapon. no. 85-145; hyd. no. 475-525; 100% act.; nonionic.

Crodesta F-160. [Croda Inc.; Croda Surf. Ltd.]
Chem. Descrip.: Sucrose stearate
CAS 25168-73-4; EINECS 246-705-9
Uses: Wetting agent, dispersant, o/w emulsifier, component of coating systems; for topical and oral pharmaceuticals
Use level: 3-6%
Regulatory: FDA 21CFR 172.859
Properties: Wh. powd.; water-sol.; HLB 14.5; m.p. 70-74 C; acid no. 5 max.; iodine no. 1 max.; sapon. no. 75-153; hyd. no. 545-595; 100% act.; nonionic.

Crodesta SL-40. [Croda Inc.; Croda Surf. Ltd.]
Chem. Descrip.: Sucrose cocoate
CAS 91031-88-8
Uses: Mild high foaming agent, emollient for topical pharmaceuticals; useful in skin cleansers
Use level: 5-20%
Properties: Amber liq.; water-sol.; insol. in oil; HLB 15.0; acid no. 5 max.; iodine no. 1 max.; 100% conc.; nonionic.

Crodet L4. [Croda Chem. Ltd.]
Chem. Descrip.: PEG-4 laurate
CAS 9004-81-3
Uses: O/w emulsifier for pharmaceutical creams, lotions, and ointments; wetting agent, solubilizer for perfumes or aq. alcoholic preparations; dispersant
Properties: Pale straw liq.; sol. in ethyl, oleyl, and cetearyl alcohols, oleic acid; HLB 9.3; sapon. no. 138-150; 97% conc.; nonionic.

Crodet L8. [Croda Chem. Ltd.]
Chem. Descrip.: PEG-8 laurate
CAS 9004-81-3; EINECS 253-458-0
Uses: O/w emulsifier for pharmaceutical creams, lotions, and ointments; wetting agent, solubilizer for perfumes or aq. alcoholic preparations; dispersant
Properties: Pale straw liq.; sol. in ethyl, oleyl, and cetearyl alcohols, oleic acid; HLB 12.7; sapon. no. 95-106; 97% conc.; nonionic.

Crodet L12. [Croda Chem. Ltd.]
Chem. Descrip.: PEG-12 laurate
CAS 9004-81-3
Uses: O/w emulsifier for pharmaceutical creams, lotions, and ointments; wetting agent, solubilizer for perfumes or aq. alcoholic preparations; dispersant
Properties: Pale straw liq.; sol. in water, ethyl, oleyl, and cetearyl alcohols, oleic acid; HLB 14.5; sapon. no. 72-82; 97% conc.; nonionic.

Crodet L24. [Croda Chem. Ltd.]
Chem. Descrip.: PEG-24 laurate
CAS 9004-81-3
Uses: O/w emulsifier for pharmaceutical creams, lotions, and ointments; wetting agent, solubilizer for perfumes or aq. alcoholic preparations; dispersant
Properties: Off-wh. soft paste; sol. in water, ethyl and cetostearyl alcohol; HLB 16.8; sapon. no. 42-48; 97% conc.; nonionic.

Crodet L40. [Croda Chem. Ltd.]

Chem. Descrip.: PEG-40 laurate
CAS 9004-81-3
Uses: O/w emulsifier for pharmaceutical creams, lotions, and ointments; wetting agent, solubilizer for perfumes or aq. alcoholic preparations; dispersant
Properties: Off-wh. waxy solid; sol. in water, ethyl and cetostearyl alcohol; HLB 17.9; sapon. no. 26-31; 97% conc.; nonionic.

Crodet L100. [Croda Chem. Ltd.]
Chem. Descrip.: PEG-100 laurate
CAS 9004-81-3
Uses: O/w emulsifier for pharmaceutical creams, lotions, and ointments; wetting agent, solubilizer for perfumes or aq. alcoholic preparations; dispersant
Properties: Pale yel. waxy solid; sol. in water, ethyl and cetostearyl alcohol; HLB 19.1; sapon. no. 11-15; 97% conc.; nonionic.

Crodet S4. [Croda Chem. Ltd.]
Chem. Descrip.: PEG-4 stearate
CAS 9004-99-3; EINECS 203-358-8
Uses: O/w emulsifier for pharmaceutical creams, lotions, and ointments; wetting agent, solubilizer for perfumes or aq. alcoholic preparations; dispersant
Properties: Off-wh. soft paste; sol. in ethyl and oleyl alcohols, oleic acid, ceto stearyl alcohol, arachis oil and isoparaffinic solv.; HLB 7.7; sapon. no. 117-129; 97% conc.; nonionic.

Crodet S8. [Croda Chem. Ltd.]
Chem. Descrip.: PEG-8 stearate
CAS 9004-99-3
Uses: O/w emulsifier for pharmaceutical creams, lotions, and ointments; wetting agent, solubilizer for perfumes or aq. alcoholic preparations; dispersant
Properties: Off-wh. soft paste; sol. in ethyl and oleyl alcohols, oleic acid, ceto stearyl alcohol, arachis oil and isoparaffinic solv.; HLB 10.8; sapon. no. 84-94; 97% conc.; nonionic.

Crodet S12. [Croda Chem. Ltd.]
Chem. Descrip.: PEG-12 stearate
CAS 9004-99-3
Uses: O/w emulsifier for pharmaceutical creams, lotions, and ointments; wetting agent, solubilizer for perfumes or aq. alcoholic preparations; dispersant
Properties: Off-wh. waxy solid; sol. in ethyl, oleyl, and cetostearyl alcohol, water, oleic acide; HLB 13.4; sapon. no. 65-75; 97% conc.; nonionic.

Crodet S24. [Croda Chem. Ltd.]
Chem. Descrip.: PEG-24 stearate
CAS 9004-99-3
Uses: O/w emulsifier for pharmaceutical creams, lotions, and ointments; wetting agent, solubilizer for perfumes or aq. alcoholic preparations; dispersant
Properties: Off-wh. waxy solid; sol. in ethyl and cetostearyl alcohol, water; HLB 15.8; sapon. no. 38-47; 97% conc.; nonionic.

Crodet S40. [Croda Chem. Ltd.]

Chem. Descrip.: PEG-40 stearate
CAS 9004-99-3
Uses: O/w emulsifier for pharmaceutical creams, lotions, and ointments; wetting agent, solubilizer for perfumes or aq. alcoholic preparations; dispersant
Properties: Off-wh. waxy solid; sol. in ethyl and cetostearyl alcohol, water; HLB 16.7; sapon. no. 23-30; 97% conc.; nonionic.

Crodet S100. [Croda Chem. Ltd.]
Chem. Descrip.: PEG-100 stearate
CAS 9004-99-3
Uses: O/w emulsifier for pharmaceutical creams, lotions, and ointments; wetting agent, solubilizer for perfumes or aq. alcoholic preparations; dispersant
Properties: Off-wh. waxy solid; sol. in ethyl and cetostearyl alcohol, water; HLB 18.8; sapon. no. 10-14; 97% conc.; nonionic.

Crodex A. [Croda Chem. Ltd.]
Chem. Descrip.: Cetostearyl alcohol and sodium lauryl sulfate
Uses: Emulsifying wax BP for pharmaceuticals
Properties: Almost wh. waxy solid; faint char. odor; water-disp.; 100% conc.; anionic.

Crodex C. [Croda Chem. Ltd.]
Chem. Descrip.: Cetostearyl alcohol and Cetrimide BP
Uses: Emulsifying wax BPC, bactericides, for pharmaceuticals
Properties: Almost wh. waxy solid; faint char. odor; water-disp.; 100% conc.; cationic.

Crodex N. [Croda Chem. Ltd.]
Chem. Descrip.: Cetostearyl alcohol and ceteth-20
Uses: Emulsifying wax BP, wetting agent, penetrant, emulsifier for most emollient materials in pharmaceuticals
Properties: Almost wh. waxy solid; faint char. odor; water-disp.; 100% conc.; nonionic.

Croduret 50. [Croda Chem. Ltd.]
Chem. Descrip.: PEG-50 hydrog. castor oil
CAS 61788-85-0
Uses: Solubilizer and emulsifier for pharmaceutical applics.
Properties: Soft paste; water-sol.; 100% conc.; nonionic.

Crodyne BY-19. [Croda Inc.]
Chem. Descrip.: Pharmaceutical gelatin NF
CAS 9000-70-8; EINECS 232-554-6
Uses: Protective colloid for skin; tablet binder, excipient, film-former, coating agent; thickener, emulsion stabilizer; adjuvant protein in nutritional supplements
Use level: 1-5%
Properties: Buff cryst. powd., bland pleasant odor; water-sol.; m.w. 25,000; bulk dens. 0.6-0.7 g/cm^3; visc. 14-18 mps; pH 5.5-6.2 (10%); 85% act., 15.5-16.5% N
Toxicology: LD50 (oral, rat) > 5 g/kg; nonirritating to skin and eyes.

Cromul EM 0685. [Croda Chem. Ltd.]
Chem. Descrip.: Ceteth-5 and ceteareth-7

Uses: Emulsifier and opacifier for pharmaceutical creams and lotions
Properties: Soft waxy solid; 100% conc.; nonionic.

Crossential ALA. [Croda Inc.]
Chem. Descrip.: α-Linolenic acid
CAS 463-40-1; EINECS 207-334-8
Uses: Used in drug delivery for orals and topicals
Properties: Liq.; 75% purity.

Crossential GLA. [Croda Inc.]
Chem. Descrip.: γ-Linolenic acid
CAS 506-26-3
Uses: Used in drug delivery for orals and topicals
Properties: Liq.; 50% purity (as the ethyl ester).

Crossential LS. [Croda Inc.]
Chem. Descrip.: Linoleic acid
CAS 60-33-3; EINECS 200-470-9
Uses: Used in drug delivery for orals and topicals
Properties: Liq.; 99% purity.

Crossential Oleic. [Croda Inc.]
Chem. Descrip.: Oleic acid
CAS 112-80-1; EINECS 204-007-1
Uses: Emulsifier, solubilizer used in drug delivery for orals and topicals
Properties: Liq.; 99% purity.

Crovol A40. [Croda Inc.; Croda Chem. Ltd.]
Chem. Descrip.: PEG-20 almond glycerides
Uses: Emulsifier, wetting agent, plasticizer in aerosol systems, topicals; solubilizer and dispersant for fragrances and other lipophilic materials; emollient and solubilizer for hydroalcoholic systems, external analgesic prods.; esp. useful in cleansers
Use level: 1-10%
Properties: Yel. liq.; sol. in ethanol, oleyl alcohol, IPA; partly sol. in min. oil; disp. in water, propylene glycol; HLB 10.0; acid no. 2 max.; sapon. no. 90-100; hyd. no. 155-170; nonionic
Toxicology: Nonirritating to skin and eyes.

Crovol A70. [Croda Inc.; Croda Chem. Ltd.]
Chem. Descrip.: PEG-60 almond glycerides
Uses: Emulsifier reducing irritation potential of anionic/amphoteric systems, cleansing scrubs; solubilizer, dispersant for fragrances and other lipophilic materials; emollient, solubilizer for hydroalcoholic systems, external analgesic prods.
Use level: 1-10%
Properties: Yel. soft paste; sol. in water, ethanol, IPA, oleyl alcohol, maize oil; partly sol. in min. oil; HLB 15.0; acid no. 2 max.; sapon. no. 45-55; hyd. no. 70-90; nonionic
Toxicology: Nonirritating to skin and eyes.

Crovol M40. [Croda Inc.; Croda Chem. Ltd.]
Chem. Descrip.: PEG-20 corn glycerides
Uses: Emulsifier, wetting agent, plasticizer for aerosol systems; solubilizer/dispersant for lipophilic materials; emollient, solubilizer for hydroalcoholic systems, external analgesic prods.; protects against skin defatting in soap scrubs
Use level: 1-10%
Properties: Yel. liq.; sol. in ethanol, oleyl alcohol,

IPA; partly sol. in min. oil; disp. in water, propylene glycol; HLB 10.0; acid no. 2 max.; sapon. no. 90-100; hyd. no. 155-170; nonionic
Toxicology: Nonirritating to skin and eyes.

Crovol M70. [Croda Inc.; Croda Chem. Ltd.]
Chem. Descrip.: PEG-60 corn glycerides
Uses: Solubilizer/dispersant for lipophilic materials; emollient and solubilizer for hydroalcoholic systems, external analgesic prods.; protects against skin defatting in soaps and detergent scrubs; emulsifier, wetting agent, plasticizer in aerosol systems
Use level: 1-10%
Properties: Yel. liq. to paste; sol. in water, ethanol, oleyl alcohol, maize oil, IPA; partly sol. in min. oil; disp. in propylene glycol; HLB 15.0; acid no. 2 max.; sapon. no. 45-55; hyd. no. 70-85; nonionic
Toxicology: Nonirritating to eyes; minimal skin irritant.

Crystal® O. [CasChem]
Chem. Descrip.: Refined castor oil USP
CAS 8001-79-4; EINECS 232-293-8
Uses: Emollient, pigment wetter, cosolv., lubricant for antiperspirant sticks
Regulatory: FDA approval
Properties: Gardner 1-color; sp.gr. 0.959; visc. 7.5 stokes; pour pt. -23 C; acid no. 2; iodine no. 86; sapon. no. 180; hyd. no. 164.

Crystal® Crown. [CasChem]
Chem. Descrip.: Refined castor oil USP, with antioxidant
CAS 8001-79-4; EINECS 232-293-8
Uses: Emollient, pigment wetter, cosolv., lubricant for antiperspirant sticks
Regulatory: FDA approval
Properties: Gardner 1-color; sp.gr. 0.959; visc. 7.5 stokes; pour pt. -23 C; acid no. 2; iodine no. 86; sapon. no. 180; hyd. no. 164.

Crystal® Crown LP. [CasChem]
Chem. Descrip.: Castor oil USP
CAS 8001-79-4; EINECS 232-293-8
Uses: Highly refined cosmetic grade with antioxidant for formulations requiring low peroxide levels; pigment wetting and suspending agent for antiperspirants
Properties: M.p. -23 C; acid no. 2; iodine no. 86; sapon. no. 180; hyd. no. 164.

Crystosol USP 200. [Witco/H-I-P]
Chem. Descrip.: Min. oil
Uses: Lubricant.

Crystosol USP 240. [Witco/H-I-P]
Chem. Descrip.: Min. oil
Uses: Lubricant.

Crystosol USP 350. [Witco/H-I-P]
Chem. Descrip.: Min. oil
Uses: Lubricant.

Cumal. [Mitsubishi Gas]
Chem. Descrip.: P-Isopropylbenzaldehyde
CAS 122-03-2; EINECS 204-516-9
Uses: Intermediate for pharmaceuticals
Properties: Colorless liq., aromatic odor; sol. in ethanol, ether, toluene; insol. in water; m.w. 148.2;

sp.gr. 0.979; b.p. 235.5 C; acid no. 0.3; flash pt. (COC) 104 C; 98.5% purity

Toxicology: LD50 (oral, rat) 1390 mg/kg; eye and skin irritant

Storage: Store in cool, dry place

Unverified

Cutina® CP. [Henkel/Cospha; Henkel Canada; Henkel KGaA/Cospha]

Chem. Descrip.: Cetyl palmitate

CAS 540-10-3; EINECS 208-736-6

Uses: Syn. spermaceti; consistency factor for pharmaceutical creams, ointments, liq. emulsions

Properties: Wh. waxy coarse flakes; insol. in water; m.p. 50 C; HLB 9; acid no. 1 max.; iodine no. 1 max.; sapon. no. 112-123; ref. index 1.431-1.437

Storage: 1 yr min. storage life in original sealed containers at temps. below 30 C in a dry environment.

Cutina® FS 25 Flakes. [Henkel KGaA/Cospha]

Chem. Descrip.: Palmitic acid and stearic acid

Uses: Consistency factor after saponification; o/w emulsifier for cosmetic/pharmaceutical emulsions and ointments;

Properties: Almost wh. fine flakes, weak char. odor; solid. pt. 49-53 C; acid no. 211-215; iodine no. 1 max.

Storage: 1 yr min. shelf life in sealed original containers at temps. below 30 C.

Cutina® FS 45 Flakes. [Henkel KGaA/Cospha]

Chem. Descrip.: Palmitic acid and stearic acid

Uses: Consistency factor after saponification; o/w emulsifier used in pharmaceutical emulsions and ointments

Properties: Almost wh. fine flakes, weak char. odor; solid. pt. 51-55 C; acid no. 207-210; iodine no. 1 max.

Storage: 1 yr min. shelf life in sealed original containers at temps. below 30 C.

Cutina® GMS. [Henkel/Cospha; Henkel Canada; Henkel KGaA/Cospha]

Chem. Descrip.: Glyceryl stearate

CAS 67701-33-1

Uses: Hydrophilic nonself-emulsifying cream base for o/w and w/o emulsions; visc. agent for pharmaceutical ow/ emulsions, creams, ointments, sticks

Regulatory: JCID, Eu.Ph., DAB compliance

Properties: Wh. to sl. ylsh. waxy powd.; m.p. 58-60 C; acid no. 2 max.; iodine no. 0.5 max.; sapon. no. 167-175; 46-54% total monoesters, 2% max. water; nonionic

Storage: 1 yr min. storage life stored in original sealed container at temps. below 40 C in a dry environment.

Cutina® HR Powd. [Henkel/Cospha; Henkel Canada; Henkel KGaA/Cospha]

Chem. Descrip.: Hydrog. castor oil

CAS 8001-78-3; EINECS 232-292-2

Uses: Lubricant, tableting aid producing smooth, glossy surfs. on tablets; retardant at > 1%; suitable for separating incompat. medicaments and for embedding hygroscopic actives

Regulatory: JCID, NF, DAB compliance

Properties: Wh. to sl. yel. fine free-flowing powd.; particle size 30% < 10 µ; bulk dens. 350-410 g/l; m.p. 85-88 C; acid no. 3.1 max.; iodine no. 5 max.; sapon. no. 176-182; hyd. no. 154-162; 0.1% max. water

Storage: 1 yr storage life in sealed original containers protected against moisture and stored below 40 C.

Cutina® KD16. [Henkel Canada; Henkel/Cospha; Henkel KGaA/Cospha]

Chem. Descrip.: Glyceryl stearate SE with 9.5-10.5% potassium stearate

Uses: Base, emulsifier and fatting co-agent for o/w pharmaceutical ointments and creams

Properties: Wh. to sl. ylsh. waxy compd., faint odor; solid. pt. 55-60 C; acid no. 7 max.; sapon. no. 150-165; hyd. no. 190-220

Storage: Protect against frost; 1 yr storage life in sealed containers at temps. below 30 C.

Cutina® MD. [Henkel Canada; Henkel KGaA/Cospha]

Chem. Descrip.: Glyceryl stearate

Uses: Consistency factor, stabilizer for pharmaceutical ointments, creams, and liq. emulsions

Properties: Wh. to pale yel. waxy gran.; m.p. 53-57 C; acid no. 6 max.; sapon. no. 165-180; hyd. no. 210-250

Storage: 1 yr min. storage life in sealed containers at temps. below 30 C, protected from frost.

Cyanocobalamin USP Cryst. No. 69932. [Roche]

Chem. Descrip.: Cyanocobalamin USP

CAS 68-19-9; EINECS 200-680-0

Uses: Source of vitamin B12 in parenteral and oral liq. preps.; adaptable to solid dosage forms with special handling

Properties: Dk. red cryst. powd., pract. odorless; 100% thru 100 mesh; hygroscopic; sparingly sol. in water; m.w. 1355.38; pH neutral; 96-100.5% assay

Precaution: Loses activity in presence of alkalies or strong acids; in aq. sol'ns., deteriorates in presence of ascorbic acid, ferrous sulfate, and other reducing agents

Storage: Store in cool, dry place optimally @ 46-59 F; keep container tightly closed.

Cyclol SPS. [Witco/H-I-P]

Chem. Descrip.: Syn. spermaceti

Uses: Spermaceti substitute for pharmaceutical formulations

Properties: Wax; m.p. 42-50 C; 100% act.; nonionic.

D

DECMP. [Albright & Wilson Am.; Albright & Wilson UK]
Chem. Descrip.: Diethyl cyanomethylphosphonate
CAS 2537-48-6
Uses: Intermediate in mfg. of substituted nitriles via the Horner-Emmons reaction and their amide and heterocycle derivs.
Properties: M.w. 177; dens. 1.10 g/cm³; b.p. 132 C (1 mm); 98% min. assay.

Dehydag® Wax 14. [Henkel/Cospha]
Chem. Descrip.: Myristyl alcohol
CAS 112-72-1; EINECS 204-000-3
Uses: Consistency factor for pharmaceutical o/w and w/o creams, ointments, emulsions, liniments, and sticks
Properties: Flakes.

Dehydag® Wax 16. [Henkel/Cospha]
Chem. Descrip.: Cetyl alcohol
CAS 36653-82-4; EINECS 253-149-0
Uses: Consistency factor for pharmaceutical o/w and w/o creams, ointments, emulsions, liniments, and sticks
Properties: Flakes.

Dehydag® Wax 18. [Henkel/Cospha]
Chem. Descrip.: Stearyl alcohol
CAS 112-92-5; EINECS 204-017-6
Uses: Consistency factor for pharmaceutical o/w and w/o creams, ointments, emulsions, liniments, and sticks
Properties: Flakes.

Dehydag® Wax 22 (Lanette) [Henkel/Cospha]
Chem. Descrip.: Behenyl alcohol
CAS 661-19-8; EINECS 211-546-6
Uses: Consistency factor for pharmaceutical o/w and w/o creams, ointments, emulsions, liniments, and sticks
Properties: Fused/flakes.

Dehydag® Wax E. [Henkel Ltd]
Chem. Descrip.: Sodium cetearyl sulfate
CAS 68955-20-4
Uses: Emulsifier for pharmaceutical o/w creams and lotions
Properties: Wh. to sl. ylsh. powd., faint char. odor; water-sol.; dens. 0.180 g/ml; pH 6-8; 87% min. act.; anionic
Storage: 1 yr storage stability in sealed orig. containers at temps. below 30 C in dry environment.

Dehydag® Wax O. [Henkel/Cospha]

Chem. Descrip.: Cetearyl alcohol
EINECS 267-008-6
Uses: Consistency modifier used in pharmaceuticals
Properties: Wh. gran.; dens. 0.816 g/ml (60 C); solid. pt. 48-52 C; sapon. no. 1.0 max.; 100% conc.; nonionic.

Dehydol® LS 2 DEO. [Henkel Canada; Henkel KGaA/Cospha; Pulcra SA]
Chem. Descrip.: Laureth-2
CAS 68439-50-9; EINECS 221-279-7
Uses: Emulsifier, solubilizer for solvs., oils; raw material for pharmaceutical preps.
Properties: Water-wh. clear to sl. cloudy liq.; HLB 6.2; hyd. no. 196-204; cloud pt. 5-8 C; pH 6.0-7.5 (1%); 99-100% conc.; nonionic
Storage: 1 yr min. storage life in original sealed containers at temps. below 40 C; may become cloudy below 18 C; warm to 40 C and stir thoroughly to reverse.

Dehydol® LS 3 DEO. [Henkel; Henkel Canada; Henkel KGaA/Cospha]
Chem. Descrip.: Laureth-3
CAS 68439-50-9; EINECS 221-280-2
Uses: Emulsifier, solubilizer for solvs., oils; raw material for pharmaceutical preps.
Regulatory: Japanese compliance
Properties: Water-wh. to ylsh. clear to sl. cloudy liq., mild distinctive odor; dens. 0.880-0.8925 g/cm³ (70 C); cloud pt. 2-5 C; hyd. no. 171-178; pH 6.0-7.5 (1%); 0.3% max. water; nonionic
Storage: 1 yr min. storage life in original sealed containers at temps. below 40 C; may become cloudy below 18 C; warm to 40 C and stir thoroughly to reverse.

Dehydol® LS 4 DEO. [Henkel KGaA/Cospha]
Chem. Descrip.: Laureth-4
CAS 68439-50-9; EINECS 226-097-1
Uses: Emulsifier, solubilizer for solvs., oils; raw material for pharmaceutical preps.
Properties: Water-wh. clear to cloudy liq.; hyd. no. 150-158; cloud pt. 4-10 C; pH 6.0-7.5; 99-100% conc.; nonionic
Storage: 1 yr min. storage life in original sealed containers at temps. below 40 C; may become cloudy below 18 C; warm to 40 C and stir thoroughly to reverse.

Dehydol® PID 6. [Pulcra SA]

Chem. Descrip.: Laureth-6
CAS 3055-96-7; EINECS 221-282-3
Uses: Emulsifier, wetting agent for pharmaceutical applics.
Properties: Liq.; HLB 11.8; hyd. no. 178-182; pH 6.0-7.5 (1%); 100% conc.; nonionic.

Dehydol® PIT 6. [Pulcra SA]
Chem. Descrip.: Ethoxylated isotridecanol
CAS 24938-91-8
Uses: Emulsifier, wetting agent for pharmaceutical applics.
Properties: Liq.; HLB 11.7; 100% conc.; nonionic.

Dehymuls® E. [Henkel/Cospha; Henkel Canada; Henkel KGaA/Cospha]
Chem. Descrip.: Sorbitan sesquioleate, pentaerythritol cocoate, stearyl citrate, beeswax, and aluminum stearate
Uses: W/o emulsifier with high water absorbency and good resist. to temp. fluctuations; allows prod. of hydrocarbon-free pharmaceutical ointments; also for creams, anhyd. or hydrous preps.
Properties: Ylsh. waxy solid; drop pt. 45-60 C; HLB 6.0; iodine no. 20-30; sapon. no. 160-170; 100% conc.; anionic
Storage: 1 yr min. storage life in closed original containers at temps. below 30 C, protected from moisture.

Dehymuls® F. [Henkel Canada; Henkel KGaA/Cospha]
Chem. Descrip.: Dicocoyl pentaerythrityl distearyl citrate, microcrystalline wax, glyceryl oleate, aluminum stearate, propylene glycol
Uses: W/o emulsifier for pharmaceutical creams, emulsions, ointments
Properties: Wh. to sl. yel. wax, neutral odor; m.p. 60-75 C; acid no. 4-10; iodine no. 15-20; sapon. no. 120-140; 100% conc.; anionic
Toxicology: LD50 (oral, rat) 5 g/kg; compat. with eyes and skin
Storage: 3 yr min. storage life in closed containers at temps. below 30 C, protected from moisture.

Dehymuls® FCE. [Henkel KGaA/Cospha]
Chem. Descrip.: Dicocoyl pentaerythrityl distearyl citrate
Uses: Emulsifier for pharmaceutical w/o emulsions, esp. suited for use with high m.w. emollients and oils
Properties: Pale yel. flakes; m.p. 42-46 C; acid no. 7 max.; sapon. no. 215-230; hyd. no. 50-60; 100% conc.; nonionic
Toxicology: Nontoxic
Storage: 1 yr min storage stability in sealed original containers at temps. below 30 C, protected from moisture.

Dehymuls® HRE 7. [Henkel/Cospha; Henkel KGaA/Cospha]
Chem. Descrip.: PEG-7 hydrogenated castor oil
CAS 61788-85-0
Uses: Emulsifier for pharmaceutical w/o emulsions, esp. for low-visc. emulsions
Regulatory: DAC compliance
Properties: Pale yel. cloudy visc. liq., almost odor-

less; acid no. < 1; sapon. no. 125-140; hyd. no. 110-130; 100% conc.; nonionic
Storage: 1 yr min. storage life in sealed waterproof containers at temps. below 30 C.

Dehymuls® K. [Henkel KGaA/Cospha]
Chem. Descrip.: Petrolatum, decyl oleate, dicocoyl pentaerythrityl distearyl citrate, sorbitan sesquioleate, ceresin, min.oil, beeswax, aluminum stearate
Uses: SE base for mfg. of pharmaceutical w/o preps. incl. ointments, creams, and emulsions, and for anhyd. ground prods., esp. galenics
Properties: Wh. to sl. yel. soft waxy solid; solid. pt. 35-50 C; iodine no. 18-23; sapon. no. 75-85; 100% act.
Storage: 1 yr min. storage life in closed containers at temps. below 40 C, protected against moisture.

Dehymuls® SML. [Henkel KGaA/Cospha]
Chem. Descrip.: Sorbitan laurate NF/BP
Uses: W/o emulsifier and coemulsifier for pharmaceutical applics.
Properties: Yel. clear liq., pract. odorless; acid no. 4-7; sapon. no. 158-170; hyd. no. 330-358; nonionic
Toxicology: Nontoxic
Storage: 1 yr min. storage stability stored in sealed containers at temps. below 30 C, protected from frost.

Dehymuls® SMO. [Henkel KGaA/Cospha]
Chem. Descrip.: Sorbitan oleate NF/BP
CAS 1338-43-8; EINECS 215-665-4
Uses: Emulsifier and coemulsifier for w/o pharmaceutical ointments and creams
Properties: Yel.-brn. clear liq.; acid no. 5-8; iodine no. 62-76; sapon. no. 149-160; hyd. no. 193-209; nonionic
Toxicology: Nontoxic
Storage: 1 yr min. storage life when stored in sealed moisture-protected containers at temps. below 30 C.

Dehymuls® SMS. [Henkel KGaA/Cospha]
Chem. Descrip.: Sorbitan stearate NF/BP
CAS 1338-41-6; EINECS 215-664-9
Uses: W/o emulsifier for pharmaceutical industry
Properties: Wh. to ylsh. flakes; acid no. 5-10; sapon. no. 147-157; hyd. no. 235-260; nonionic
Toxicology: Nontoxic
Storage: 1 yr min. storage stability in sealed containers at temps. below 30 C, protected from moisture.

Dehymuls® SSO. [Henkel KGaA/Cospha]
Chem. Descrip.: Sorbitan sesquioleate
CAS 8007-43-0; EINECS 232-360-1
Uses: W/o emulsifier and coemulsifier for waxes and oils for pharmaceuticals
Properties: Yel.-brn. clear liq., pract. odorless; acid no. 12 max.; iodine no. 65-75; sapon. no. 150-165; hyd. no. 185-215; nonionic
Toxicology: Nontoxic.

Dehyton® AB-30. [Henkel Canada; Henkel KGaA/Cospha; Pulcra SA]
Chem. Descrip.: Coco-betaine

CAS 68424-94-2; EINECS 270-329-4
Uses: Surfactant for pharmaceutical preps.
Properties: Lt. yel. clear liq., mild inherent odor; pH 6.0-7.5; 29-31% act.; amphoteric
Storage: 1 yr storage stability in sealed original containers at 0-40 C; may cause corrosion in stainless steel tanks due to high salt content.

Dehyton® K. [Henkel KGaA/Cospha]
Chem. Descrip.: Cocamidopropyl betaine
CAS 61789-40-0
Uses: Raw material for mfg. of pharmaceutical surfactant preps.
Properties: Lt. yel. clear pumpable liq., mild inherent odor; pH 6.0-7.5; 29-32% act.; amphoteric
Storage: 1 yr min. storage stability in sealed original containers @ 0-40 C; may have corrosive effect on stainless steel tanks due to high salt content.

Dermajel. [United-Guardian]
Uses: Clear, ringing gel skin cleanser which has the pH of normal skin; cleanses, protects, and moisturizes the skin; for health-care prods.
Custom product

Descote® Ascorbic Acid 60%. [Particle Dynamics]
Chem. Descrip.: Encapsulated ascorbic acid USP; each gram of coated prod. contains 600 mg ascorbic acid in edible matrix
CAS 50-81-7; EINECS 200-066-2
Uses: Encapsulated ingreds. for nutritional supplements, pharmaceuticals; provides taste/odor masking, prevents interaction of actives; for chewable tablets, nutritional powd. mixes, weight loss supplements, health bars
Properties: Wh. to off-wh. relatively free-flowing material with some soft agglomerates, sl. char. odor, satisfactory taste; 95% min. thru 20 mesh, 20% max. thru 100 mesh; 58.8% min. assay
Storage: Physically/chemically stable when stored in cool, dry area, preferably @ 59-86 F.

Descote® Citric Acid 50%. [Particle Dynamics]
Chem. Descrip.: Encapsulated citric acid USP; each gram of coated prod. contains 500 mg of citric acid in an edible matrix
CAS 77-92-9; EINECS 201-069-1
Uses: Designed for incorporation into tablets and other dry dosage forms where it masks the char. citric acid taste and protects actives with inert coating
Properties: Wh. free-flowing material with some soft agglomerates, sl. char. odor; 98% min. thru 20 mesh, 30% max. thru 100 mesh; 49% min. assay
Storage: Store in cool, dry area, preferably @ 59-86 F.

Descote® Copper Gluconate 20%. [Particle Dynamics]
Chem. Descrip.: Encapsulated copper gluconate USP; each gram of coated prod. contains 200 mg copper gluconate in edible matrix
CAS 527-09-3; EINECS 204-408-2
Uses: Encapsulated ingreds. for use in tablets and other dry dosage forms; provides taste masking, prevents interaction of actives

Properties: Green to blue-green relatively free-flowing powd., sl. char odor, satisfactory taste; 98% min. thru 20 mesh, 20% max. thru 200 mesh; 19.6% min. assay
Storage: Physically/chemically stable when stored in cool, dry area @ 59-86 F.

Descote® Ferrous Fumarate 60%. [Particle Dynamics]
Chem. Descrip.: Encapsulated ferrous fumarate USP; each gram of coated prod. contains 600 mg ferrous fumarate in edible matrix
CAS 141-01-5; EINECS 205-447-7
Uses: Encapsulated ingreds. for use in tablets and other dry dosage forms; provides taste masking, prevents interaction of actives, good dissolution profile for iron
Properties: Reddish orange to reddish brn. relatively free-flowing powd., sl. char odor, satisfactory taste; 95% min. on 20 mesh, 30% max. on 200 mesh; 58.8% min. assay
Storage: Physically/chemically stable for 2 yrs when stored in cool, dry area @ 59-86 F.

Descote® Ferrous Sulfate 60%. [Particle Dynamics]
Chem. Descrip.: Encapsulated ferrous sulfate USP; each gram of coated prod. contains 600 mg ferrous sulfate in edible matrix
CAS 7720-78-7
Uses: Encapsulated ingreds. for use in tablets and other dry dosage forms; provides taste masking, prevents interaction of actives
Properties: Tan to cream relatively free-flowing powd., sl. char. odor, satisfactory taste; 95% min. thru 20 mesh, 30% max. thru 200 mesh; 58.8% min. assay
Storage: Physically/chemically stable when stored in cool, dry area, preferably @ 59-86 F.

Descote® Niacinamide 33$^1/_3$%. [Particle Dynamics]
Chem. Descrip.: Encapsulated niacinamide USP/FCC; each gram of coated prod. contains 333 mg niacinamide in edible coating of stearic acid with 1% silicon dioxide NF as flow agent
Uses: Encapsulated ingreds. for use in chewable multivitamin tablets and other dry dosage forms; provides taste/odor masking, prevents interaction of actives
Regulatory: Niacinamide is FDA GRAS as a nutrient; stearic acid is edible food grade
Properties: Pract. wh. relatively free-flowing powd., sl. char odor, satisfactory taste; 99% min. thru 20 mesh, 65% min. thru 60 mesh; 32.6% min. assay
Storage: Physically/chemically stable for 2 yrs when stored in cool, dry area @ 59-86 F.

Descote® Pyridoxine Hydrochloride 33$^1/_3$%. [Particle Dynamics]
Chem. Descrip.: Encapsulated pyridoxine hydrochloride; each gram of coated prod. contains 333 mg pyridoxine hydrochloride in edible coating of mono- and diglycerides
Uses: Encapsulated ingreds. for use in chewable multivitamin tablets and other dry dosage forms; provides taste/odor masking, prevents interac-

tion of actives

Regulatory: Pyridoxine HCl is FDA GRAS as a nutrient; coating materials are edible food grade prods.

Properties: Pract. wh. relatively free-flowing powd., sl. char odor, satisfactory taste; 99% min. thru 20 mesh, 80% min. thru 60 mesh; 32.6% min. assay

Storage: Physically/chemically stable when stored in cool, dry area @ 59-86 F.

Descote® Riboflavin 33¹/₃%. [Particle Dynamics]

Chem. Descrip.: Encapsulated riboflavin USP/FCC; each gram of coated prod. contains 333 mg ribovlavin in edible coating of mono- and diglycerides

Uses: Encapsulated ingreds. for use in chewable multivitamin tablets and other dry dosage forms; provides taste/odor masking, prevents interaction of actives, promotes bioavailability

Regulatory: Riboflavin is FDA GRAS as a nutrient; coating materials are edible food grade prods.

Properties: Orange-brn. relatively free-flowing powd., sl. char odor, satisfactory taste; 99% min. thru 20 mesh, 60% min. thru 60 mesh; 32.6% min. assay

Storage: Physically/chemically stable for 2 yrs when stored in cool, dry area @ 59-86 F.

Descote® Sodium Ascorbate 50%. [Particle Dynamics]

Chem. Descrip.: Encapsulated sodium ascorbate USP; each gram of coated prod. contains 500 mg sodium ascorbate in edible kosher matrix

CAS 134-03-2; EINECS 205-126-1

Uses: Encapsulated ingreds. for nutritional supplements, pharmaceuticals; provides taste/odor masking, prevents interaction of actives; for chewable tablets, nutritional powd. mixes, weight loss supplements, health bars

Properties: Lt. yel. to yel./tan free-flowing powd. with some soft agglomerates, sl. char. odor; 95% min. thru 20 mesh, 20% max. thru 200 mesh; 48.5% min. assay

Storage: 15 mos physical/chemical stability stored in cool, dry area, preferably @ 59-86 F.

Descote® Thiamine Mononitrate 33¹/₃%. [Particle Dynamics]

Chem. Descrip.: Encapsulated thiamine mononitrate USP/FCC; each gram of coated prod. contains 333 mg thiamine mononitrtate in edible coating of mono- and diglycerides

Uses: Encapsulated ingreds. for use in chewable multivitamin tablets and other dry dosage forms; provides taste/odor masking, prevents interaction of actives

Regulatory: Thiamine mononitrate is FDA GRAS as a nutrient; coating materials are edible food grade prods.

Properties: Pract. wh. relatively free-flowing powd., sl. char odor, satisfactory taste; 99% min. thru 20 mesh, 65% min. thru 60 mesh; 32.6% min. assay

Storage: Physically/chemically stable for 2 yrs when stored in cool, dry area @ 59-86 F.

Desiccated Beef Liver Granular Defatted. [Am. Labs]

Chem. Descrip.: Dried defatted granular form processed from beef livers

Uses: Nutritive food and pharmaceutical additive

Properties: Gran.

Desiccated Beef Liver Granular Undefatted. [Am. Labs]

Chem. Descrip.: Dried undefatted granular form processed from beef livers

Uses: Nutritive food and pharmaceutical additive

Properties: Gran.

Desiccated Beef Liver Powd. [Am. Labs]

Chem. Descrip.: Dried, undefatted powd. processed from beef livers

Uses: Nutritive food and pharmaceutical additive

Properties: Powd.

Desiccated Beef Liver Powd. Defatted. [Am. Labs]

Chem. Descrip.: Dried, defatted powd. processed from beef livers

Uses: Nutritive food and pharmaceutical additive

Properties: Powd.

Desiccated Hog Bile. [Am. Labs]

Chem. Descrip.: Vacuum-dried prod. from fresh hog bile contg. hyodeoxycholic acid, sodium glycohyodeoxycholate, sodium taurohydeoxycholate

Uses: Nutritive food and pharmaceutical additive

Storage: Preserve in tight containers with moisture-proof liners, in cool, dry place.

Desiccated Ox Bile. [Am. Labs]

Chem. Descrip.: Dried ox bile

Uses: Nutritive pharmaceutical additive

Properties: Powd.; pH 6.5-7.5

Storage: Preserve in tight containers with moisture-proof liners, in cool, dry place.

Desiccated Pork Liver Powd. [Am. Labs]

Chem. Descrip.: Dried, undefatted powd. processed from pork livers

Uses: Nutritive food and pharmaceutical additive

Properties: Powd.

Destab™. [Particle Dynamics]

Chem. Descrip.: Avail. in calcium carbonate, magnesium carbonate, magnesium oxide, calcium sulfates, ferrous fumarate, or oyster shell

Uses: Direct compression ingreds. for tableting of pharmaceutical and nutritional supplements; provides source of minerals, functions as antacid, buffer in buffered aspirin, or filler/binder excipient

Properties: Free-flowing gran.

Destab™ Calcium Carbonate 90. [Particle Dynamics]

Chem. Descrip.: 90% Calcium carbonate USP with 9% max. starch NF

Uses: Direct compression ingreds. for tablet and capsule formulations where optimum tableting and free-flowing chars. are desired

Properties: Wh. to off-wh. free-flowing powd.; 95% min. thru 20 mesh, 30% max. thru 200 mesh; bulk dens. 38-45 lb/ft³ (tapped); 2% max. moisture

Storage: Physically/chemically stable when stored in cool dry place @ 59-86 F.

Destab™ Calcium Carbonate 95. [Particle Dynamics]
Chem. Descrip.: 95% Calcium carbonate USP with 5% max. starch NF
Uses: Direct compression ingreds. for tablets and other dry dosage forms where optimum tableting and free-flowing chars. are desired
Properties: Wh. to off-wh. free-flowing powd.; ≤ 45% on 60 mesh, ≤ 25% thru 200 mesh; bulk dens. 38-45 lb/ft^3 (tapped); 2% max. moisture
Storage: Physically/chemically stable when stored in cool dry place @ 59-86 F.

Dexpanthenol USP, FCC No. 63909. [Roche]
Chem. Descrip.: Dexpanthenol
Uses: Moisturizer.

Diaion® WK10. [Mitsubishi Kasei]
Uses: Weakly acidic cation exchange resin (methacrylic type) for prep. of antibiotics, medicines
Unverified

Diamond Quality®. [CasChem]
Chem. Descrip.: Unrefined castor oil USP
CAS 8001-79-4; EINECS 232-293-8
Uses: Emollient, pigment wetter, cosolv., lubricant for antiperspirant sticks
Properties: Pour pt. -23 C; acid no. 2; iodine no. 86; sapon. no. 180; hyd. no. 164.

Diastase JP. [Amano Enzyme USA; Unipex]
Chem. Descrip.: Amylase of plant origin
CAS 9000-92-4; EINECS 232-567-7
Uses: Enzyme for pharmaceutical use.

Diglyme. [Ferro/Grant]
Chem. Descrip.: Diethylene glycol dimethyl ether
CAS 111-96-6; EINECS 203-924-4
Uses: Solv. for pharmaceutical applics.
Properties: Colorless clear; ethereal, nonresidual odor; water-sol.; misc. with ethanol, acetone, benzene, diethyl ether, octane; m.w. 134.17; sp.gr. 0.9451; dens. 7.88 lb/gal; visc. 2.0 cP; vapor pressure 2 mm Hg (20 C); f.p. -64 C; b.p. 162 C; flash pt. (CC) 57 C; ref. index 1.4078; pH neutral; surf. tens. 27 dynes/cm (20 C); sp. heat 0.403 cal/g/°C; 99.6% min. purity; slowly biodeg.
Toxicology: LD50 4670 mg/kg; low to mod. acute toxicity; avoid exposure to vapors, skin contact; TLV/8h TWA: 5 ppm; STEL 25 ppm; chronic exposure may cause reproductive effects.

Dimethicone L-45 Series. [Union Carbide]
Chem. Descrip.: Dimethylpolysiloxane polymers
Uses: Heat transfer fluid for drug mfg.; lubricant in antiperspirants/deodorants
Properties: Clear liq.; sol. in most nonpolar solvs.; visc. 10-100,000 cstk grades.

Dimodan PM. [Grindsted Prods.; Grindsted Prods. Denmark]
Chem. Descrip.: Dist. monoglyceride from edible refined hydrog. lard or tallow
Uses: Emulsifier for pharmaceuticals
Regulatory: EEC E471, FDA 21CFR §184.1505, 184.4505, GRAS
Properties: Beads; m.p. 70 C; iodine no. 2 max.; 90% min. monoester.; nonionic
Storage: Store in cool, dry area.

Dimodan PV. [Grindsted Prods.; Grindsted Prods. Denmark]
Chem. Descrip.: Hydrog. soybean oil dist. monoglyceride, unsat.
Uses: Emulsifier for pharmaceuticals
Regulatory: EEC, FDA §184.1505 (GRAS), 184.4505 (GRAS)
Properties: Beads, powd.; m.p. 72 C; iodine no. 2 max.; 90% min. monoester; nonionic.

DIPA Commercial Grade. [Dow]
Chem. Descrip.: Diisopropanolamine
CAS 110-97-4; EINECS 203-820-9
Uses: Emulsifier used to produce pharmaceuticals
Properties: Sp.gr. 0.992 (40/4 C); dens. 8.27 lb/gal (40 C); visc. 870 cps (30 C); f.p. 44 C; b.p. 249 C (760 mm Hg); flash pt. (Seta CC) 276 F; fire pt. 275 C; ref. index 1.4595 (30 C).

DIPA Low Freeze Grade 85. [Dow]
Chem. Descrip.: Diisopropanolamine
CAS 110-97-4; EINECS 203-820-9
Uses: Emulsifier used to produce pharmaceuticals
Properties: Sp.gr. 0.992 (40/4 C); dens. 8.27 lb/gal (40 C); visc. 870 cps (30 C); f.p. 44 C; b.p. 249 C (760 mm Hg); flash pt. (Seta CC) 276 F; fire pt. 275 C; ref. index 1.4595 (30 C); 15% water.

DIPA Low Freeze Grade 90. [Dow]
Chem. Descrip.: Diisopropanolamine
CAS 110-97-4; EINECS 203-820-9
Uses: Emulsifier used to produce pharmaceuticals
Properties: Sp.gr. 0.992 (40/4 C); dens. 8.27 lb/gal (40 C); visc. 870 cps (30 C); f.p. 44 C; b.p. 249 C (760 mm Hg); flash pt. (Seta CC) 276 F; fire pt. 275 C; ref. index 1.4595 (30 C); 10% water.

DIPA NF Grade. [Dow]
Chem. Descrip.: Diisopropanolamine
CAS 110-97-4; EINECS 203-820-9
Uses: Emulsifier used to produce pharmaceuticals
Properties: Sp.gr. 0.992 (40/4 C); dens. 8.27 lb/gal (40 C); visc. 870 cps (30 C); f.p. 44 C; b.p. 249 C (760 mm Hg); flash pt. (Seta CC) 276 F; fire pt. 275 C; ref. index 1.4595 (30 C).

Dipsal. [Scher]
Chem. Descrip.: Dipropylene glycol salicylate
CAS 7491-14-7
Uses: Emollient for pharmaceutical specialties; uv absorbent for sunscreens
Properties: Yel. clear liq., mild salicylate odor; sol. in most org. solvs.; water-insol.; m.w. 254; sp.gr. 1.165; dens. 9.66 lb/gal; f.p. < -5 C; acid no. 3 max.; iodine no. nil; sapon. no. 225-240; cloud pt. < -5 C; flash pt. (OC) > 160 C; ref. index 1.522.

Disodium Pamoate. [Cytec Industries]
Chem. Descrip.: Disodium pamoate
Uses: Used to produce pamoate salts of drug prods.; masks bitter taste in pharmaceutical prods.; permits slow release of active drugs
Properties: Pale yel. to tan powd.; m.w. 432.33 ≤ 5% moisture
Toxicology: Direct contact may cause severe eye or mild skin irritation; inh. of dust may cause respiratory tract irritation
Storage: Store in tightly closed containers at R.T.

in a contaminant-free area.

Distilled Lipolan. [Lipo]
Chem. Descrip.: Hydrog. lanolin
CAS 8031-44-5; EINECS 232-452-1
Uses: Emollient, lubricant, and conditioner used in topical pharmaceuticals
Properties: Wh./off-wh. paste; mild char. odor; insol. in water; m.p. 34-43 C; acid no. 1 max.; sapon. no. 3 max.

Distilled Whole Coconut Oil 6226 6222. [Dial]
Chem. Descrip.: Coconut oil fatty acid
EINECS 262-978-7
Uses: Emulsifier used in pharmaceuticals, chem. intermediates/derivs.
Properties: Acid no. 265-271; iodine no. 12 max.; 0.1% max. moisture.

DMP. [Shell]
Chem. Descrip.: 2,2-Dimethoxypropane
CAS 77-76-9; EINECS 201-056-0
Uses: Chemical intermediate for pharmaceuticals; 98% min. act.
Unverified

DMPA®. [IMC/Americhem]
Chem. Descrip.: Dimethylolpropionic acid
CAS 4767-03-7
Uses: In prep. of pharmaceuticals
Properties: Off-wh. free-flowing gran.; sol. in water, methanol; sl. sol. in acetone; insol. in benzene; m.w. 134; sp.gr. 1.355; m.p. 170-180 C
Toxicology: Essentially nontoxic; LD50 (mouse, oral) > 5000 mg/kg; sl. irritating to abraded skin; mod. eye irritant.

DMSO. [Elf Atochem N. Am.]
Chem. Descrip.: Dimethyl sulfoxide
CAS 67-68-5; EINECS 200-664-3
Uses: Protic solv. used as reaction medium in mfg. of pharmaceuticals.

Docusate Calcium USP in Corn Oil NF Sol'n. [Cytec Industries]
Chem. Descrip.: Docusate calcium USP in corn oil NF sol'n.
Uses: Pharmaceutical surfactant used in stool softeners, vitamin formulations, ear wax removal compds., as processing aids in tableting operations
Properties: Amber clear visc. liq.; acid no. 2 max.; 50% act.; ≤ 0.5% moisture.

Docusate Sodium USP. [Cytec Industries]
Chem. Descrip.: Dioctyl sodium sulfosuccinate USP
EINECS 209-406-4
Uses: Pharmaceutical surfactant, wetting agent, solubilizer, dispersant, emulsifier for tablets, tablet coating, treatment of constipation (alone or with other laxatives), topical creams, lotions, and ointments, vitamins, ear wax removal
Use level: 0.025-0.25% (wetting agent), 0.1-1% (tablets), 20% (tablet coating), 0.1-1% (solubilizer), 0.1-1% (anti-constipation)
Properties: Rolls of wh. wax-like plastic sheets, char. octyl alcohol odor; m.w. 444.57; 99-100.5% assay

Toxicology: LD50 (oral, rat) 1900-4000 mg/kg, (dermal, rabbit) > 10,000 mg/kg; ; prolonged eye or skin contact may cause irritation
Storage: Store in tightly closed containers below 24 C and 60% r.h.; higher temps. may cause prod. to fuse and discolor.

Docusate Sodium USP in Polyethylene Glycol 400 NF. [Cytec Industries]
Chem. Descrip.: Dioctyl sodium sulfosuccinate USP in PEG 400
Uses: Pharmaceutical surfactant used in stool softeners, vitamin formulations, ear wax removal compds., as processing aids in tableting operations
Properties: Wh. to yel. clear visc. liq.; sp.gr. 1.11-1.15 (25/15.5 C); acid no. 1 max.; 48.5-51.5% assay.

D'Oral. [United-Guardian]
Uses: Local anesthetic for applic. to the gums in cases of localized toothache or teething; for longer lasting action
Custom product

Double Strength Acid Proof Caramel Colour. [MLG Enterprises Ltd.]
Chem. Descrip.: Caramel color
CAS 8028-89-5; EINECS 232-435-9
Uses: Natural colorant for pharmaceuticals
Properties: Sp.gr. 1.266-1.277 (60 F); dens. 10.54-10.63 lb/gal (60 F); visc. 300 cps max. (68 F); pH 2.8-3.0
Storage: 2 yr min. shelf life.

Dover 50 A. [Luzenac Am.]
Chem. Descrip.: Platy talc USP
CAS 14807-96-6; EINECS 238-877-9
Uses: Extremely platy talc with exc. slip, high brightness and purity, and low oil absorp.; ideal for formulations with sensitive fragrances and pigments; for antiperspirants, creams, lotions
Properties: Powd.; 97% thru 200 mesh; 17 μ median diam.; oil absorp. 37; tapped dens. 65 lb/ft^3; pH 9 (10% slurry).

Dow E300 NF. [Dow]
Chem. Descrip.: PEG-6 NF
CAS 25322-68-3; EINECS 220-045-1
Uses: Used in pharmaceuticals (carrier for ointments for antiseptics and other medicaments, plasticizer in tablet film coatings, base for suppositories, carrier, solv., suspending agent in liq. preps., vehicle for actives in gelatin capsules)
Properties: Clear visc. liq.; sol. in water; m.w. 300; sp.gr. 1.125; dens. 9.36 lb/gal; f.p. -10 C; visc. 69 cSt; flash pt. (PMCC) > 400 F; ref. index 1.463; sp. heat 0.508 cal/g/°C
Toxicology: Extremely low acute oral toxicity; little or no irritation to eyes and skin; not recommended for use on abraded skin; may generate irritating vapors on decomp.

Dow E400 NF. [Dow]
Chem. Descrip.: PEG-8 NF
CAS 25322-68-3; EINECS 225-856-4
Uses: Used in pharmaceuticals (carrier for ointments for antiseptics and other medicaments,

plasticizer in tablet film coatings, base for suppositories, carrier, solv., suspending agent in liq. preps., vehicle for actives in gelatin capsules)
Properties: Clear visc. liq.; m.w. 400; sp.gr. 1.125; dens. 9.36 lb/gal; f.p. 6 C; visc. 90 cSt; flash pt. (PMCC) > 450 F; ref. index 1.465; sp. heat 0.498 cal/g/°C
Toxicology: Extremely low acute oral toxicity; little or no irritation to eyes and skin; not recommended for use on abraded skin; may generate irritating vapors on decomp.

Dow E600 NF. [Dow]
Chem. Descrip.: PEG-12 NF
CAS 25322-68-3; EINECS 229-859-1
Uses: Used in pharmaceuticals (carrier for ointments for antiseptics and other medicaments, plasticizer in tablet film coatings, base for suppositories, carrier, solv., suspending agent in liq. preps., vehicle for actives in gelatin capsules)
Properties: Clear visc. liq.; sol. in water, ethanol, cyclomethicone, sunscreens, lactic acid; m.w. 600; sp.gr. 1.126; dens. 9.37 lb/gal; f.p. 22 C; visc. 131 cSt; flash pt. (PMCC) > 450 F; ref. index 1.466; sp. heat 0.490 cal/g/°C
Toxicology: Extremely low acute oral toxicity; little or no irritation to eyes and skin; not recommended for use on abraded skin; may generate irritating vapors on decomp.

Dow E900 NF. [Dow]
Chem. Descrip.: PEG NF
CAS 25322-68-3
Uses: Used in pharmaceuticals (carrier for ointments for antiseptics and other medicaments, plasticizer in tablet film coatings, base for suppositories, carrier, solv., suspending agent in liq. preps., vehicle for actives in gelatin capsules)
Properties: Wh. waxy solid; m.w. 900; sp.gr. 1.204; f.p. 34 C; visc. 100 cSt (100 F); flash pt. (PMCC) > 450 F
Toxicology: Extremely low acute oral toxicity; little or no irritation to eyes and skin; not recommended for use on abraded skin; may generate irritating vapors on decomp.

Dow E1000 NF. [Dow]
Chem. Descrip.: PEG-20 NF
CAS 25322-68-3
Uses: Used in pharmaceuticals (carrier for ointments for antiseptics and other medicaments, plasticizer in tablet film coatings, base for suppositories, carrier, solv., suspending agent in liq. preps., vehicle for actives in gelatin capsules)
Properties: Wh. waxy solid; m.w. 1000; sp.gr. 1.214; f.p. 37 C; visc. 18 cSt (210 F); flash pt. (PMCC) > 450 F
Toxicology: Extremely low acute oral toxicity; little or no irritation to eyes and skin; not recommended for use on abraded skin; may generate irritating vapors on decomp.

Dow E1450 NF. [Dow]
Chem. Descrip.: PEG-32 NF
CAS 25322-68-3
Uses: Used in pharmaceuticals (carrier for oint-

ments for antiseptics and other medicaments, plasticizer in tablet film coatings, base for suppositories, carrier, solv., suspending agent in liq. preps., vehicle for actives in gelatin capsules)
Properties: Wh. waxy solid; m.w. 1450; sp.gr. 1.214; f.p. 44 C; visc. 29 cSt (210 F); flash pt. (PMCC) > 450 F
Toxicology: Extremely low acute oral toxicity; little or no irritation to eyes and skin; not recommended for use on abraded skin; may generate irritating vapors on decomp.

Dow E3350 NF. [Dow]
Chem. Descrip.: PEG-75 NF
CAS 25322-68-3
Uses: Used in pharmaceuticals (carrier for ointments for antiseptics and other medicaments, plasticizer in tablet film coatings, base for suppositories, carrier, solv., suspending agent in liq. preps., vehicle for actives in gelatin capsules)
Properties: Wh. waxy solid, pract. odorless; sol. > 100 g/100 g in water; m.w. 3350; sp.gr. 1.224; visc. 93 cSt (210 F); f.p. 54 C; b.p. dec.; flash pt. (PMCC) > 232 C; pH 4.5-7.5 (5% aq.)
Toxicology: Single dose oral toxicity believed to be very low; may cause sl. transient eye irritation; avoid prolonged/repeated contact with abraded skin
Precaution: Dusts may present explosive hazard; incompat. with oxidizers, conc. min. acids.

Dow E4500 NF. [Dow]
Chem. Descrip.: PEG-100 NF
CAS 25322-68-3
Uses: Used in pharmaceuticals (carrier for ointments for antiseptics and other medicaments, plasticizer in tablet film coatings, base for suppositories, carrier, solv., suspending agent in liq. preps., vehicle for actives in gelatin capsules)
Properties: Wh. waxy solid, sl. polyether odor; colorless visc. liq. above 136 F; sol. > 100 g/100 g in water; m.w. 4500; sp.gr. 1.224; visc. 180 cSt (210 F); f.p. 58 C; b.p. dec.; flash pt. (PMCC) > 232 C; pH 4.5-7.5 (5% aq.)
Toxicology: LD50 (oral, rat) > 50,000 mg/kg; extremely low oral toxicity; may cause sl. transient eye irritation; avoid prolonged/repeated exposure on abraded skin; contact with heated material may cause thermal burns
Precaution: Supports combustion; do not breathe smoke; incompat. with oxidizers and strong acids.

Dow E8000 NF. [Dow]
Chem. Descrip.: PEG-150 NF
CAS 25322-68-3
Uses: Used in pharmaceuticals (carrier for ointments for antiseptics and other medicaments, plasticizer in tablet film coatings, base for suppositories, carrier, solv., suspending agent in liq. preps., vehicle for actives in gelatin capsules)
Properties: Wh. waxy solid, clear liq. above 65 C, pract. odorless; sol. > 100 g/100 g in water; m.w. 8000; sp.gr. 1.224; f.p. 60 C; visc. 800 cSt (210 F); flash pt. (PMCC) > 260 C; pH 4.5-7.5 (5% aq.); >

99% act.

Toxicology: LD50 (oral, rat) > 50 g/kg (low oral toxicity); may cause sl. transient temporary eye irritation; avoid prolonged/repeated exposure on abraded skin

Precaution: Dusts may present explosive hazard; incompat. with oxidizers, conc. min. acids.

Dow Corning® 360 Medical Fluid (20 cs). [Dow Corning]

Chem. Descrip.: Dimethicone NF

Uses: Lubricant for plastic or rubber devices and instruments incl. hypodermic needles, rectoscopes; inert protective coating and water-repellent film on skin for barrier creams and sprays

Properties: Colorless clear liq.; sol. in aliphatic, aromatic, and chlorinated hydrocarbons, fluorocarbon; insol. in glycerin, ethylene glycol, methanol, ethanol, water; sp.gr. 0.949; dens. 8.0 lb/gal; visc. 20 cs; acid no. < 0.01; pour pt. -84 C; ref. index 1.400-1.405; surf. tens. 20.6 dynes/cm; dielec. str. 375 V/mil; vol. resist. 1 x 10^{15} ohm-cm

Storage: 36 mos shelf life when stored at or below 25 C.

Dow Corning® 360 Medical Fluid (100 cs). [Dow Corning]

Chem. Descrip.: Dimethicone NF

Uses: Lubricant for plastic or rubber devices and instruments incl. hypodermic needles, rectoscopes; inert protective coating and water-repellent film on skin for barrier creams and sprays

Properties: Colorless clear liq.; sol. in aliphatic, aromatic, and chlorinated hydrocarbons, fluorocarbon; insol. in glycerin, ethylene glycol, methanol, ethanol, water; sp.gr. 0.965; dens. 8.0 lb/gal; visc. 100 cs; acid no. < 0.01; pour pt. -65 C; ref. index 1.400-1.405; surf. tens. 20.9 dynes/cm; dielec. str. 400 V/mil; vol. resist. 1 x 10^{15} ohm-cm

Storage: 36 mos shelf life when stored at or below 25 C.

Dow Corning® 360 Medical Fluid (350 cs). [Dow Corning]

Chem. Descrip.: Dimethicone NF

Uses: Lubricant for plastic or rubber devices and instruments incl. hypodermic needles, rectoscopes; inert protective coating and water-repellent film on skin for barrier creams and sprays

Properties: Colorless clear liq.; sol. in aliphatic, aromatic, and chlorinated hydrocarbons, fluorocarbon; insol. in glycerin, ethylene glycol, methanol, ethanol, water; sp.gr. 0.970; dens. 8.1 lb/gal; visc. 350 cs; acid no. < 0.01; pour pt. -65 C; ref. index 1.400-1.405; surf. tens. 21.1 dynes/cm; dielec. str. 400 V/mil; vol. resist. 1 x 10^{15} ohm-cm

Storage: 36 mos shelf life when stored at or below 25 C.

Dow Corning® 360 Medical Fluid (1000 cs). [Dow Corning]

Chem. Descrip.: Dimethicone NF

Uses: Lubricant for plastic or rubber devices and instruments incl. hypodermic needles, rectoscopes; inert protective coating and water-repellent film on skin for barrier creams and sprays

Properties: Colorless clear liq.; sol. in aliphatic, aromatic, and chlorinated hydrocarbons, fluorocarbon; insol. in glycerin, ethylene glycol, methanol, ethanol, water; sp.gr. 0.970; dens. 8.1 lb/gal; visc. 1000 cs; acid no. < 0.01; pour pt. -50 C; ref. index 1.400-1.405; surf. tens. 21.2 dynes/cm; dielec. str. 400 V/mil; vol. resist. 1 x 10^{15} ohm-cm

Storage: 36 mos shelf life when stored at or below 25 C.

Dow Corning® 360 Medical Fluid (12,500 cs). [Dow Corning]

Chem. Descrip.: Dimethicone NF

Uses: Lubricant for plastic or rubber devices and instruments incl. hypodermic needles, rectoscopes; inert protective coating and water-repellent film on skin for barrier creams and sprays

Properties: Colorless clear liq.; sol. in aliphatic, aromatic, and chlorinated hydrocarbons, fluorocarbon; insol. in glycerin, ethylene glycol, methanol, ethanol, water; sp.gr. 0.970; dens. 8.1 lb/gal; visc. 12,500 cs; acid no. < 0.01; pour pt. -46 C; ref. index 1.400-1.405; surf. tens. 21.5 dynes/cm; dielec. str. 400 V/mil; vol. resist. 1 x 10^{15} ohm-cm

Storage: 36 mos shelf life when stored at or below 25 C.

Dow Corning® 365. [Dow Corning]

Chem. Descrip.: Dimethicone NF emulsion

Uses: Lubricant for rubber, metal, palstic, or glass biomedical articles; lubricant for parenteral drug pkg. components; surf. treatment; starch binder for latex gloves; good wetting and release chars.

Properties: Milk wh. liq.; water-dilutable; sp.gr. 0.99; pH 5.5; flash pt. none; 35% act.; nonionic

Storage: 36 mos shelf life when stored in original unopened containers between 5 and 40 C; avoid freezing.

Dow Corning® Q7-2243 LVA. [Dow Corning]

Chem. Descrip.: Simethicone USP

Uses: Antifoam for medical and pharmaceutical applics.; antiflatulent for treatment of intestinal gas and bloating; gas elimination during gastroscopic and x-ray exams; antacid prods.

Regulatory: FDA 21CFR §332.10, 173.340

Properties: Gray translucent visc. liq.; 100% act.

Storage: 18 mo shelf life stored in original unopened contaienrs at ambient temps.; avoid extreme temps.; settling may occur during storage; mix before use.

Dow Corning® Q7-2587. [Dow Corning]

Chem. Descrip.: Simethicone emulsion USP contg. simethicone USP, stearate emulsifiers, sorbic acid, benzoic acid, thickeners, and water

Uses: Antiflatulent for treatment of intestinal gas; gas elimination during gastroscopic and x-ray exams; antacid prods.; antifoam for pharmaceutical processes, e.g., fermentation, maceration, percolation, mixing, ampule/bottle filling applics.

Regulatory: Simethicone emulsion USP compliance; FDA 21CFR §332.10, 173.340

Properties: Wh. creamy flowable liq.; water-dilutable; pH 2.6; 30% act.; nonionic

Storage: 24 mos shelf life when stored between 5

and 32 C; stir gently before use; do not ship below 0 C; freeze/thaw cycling may break emulsion.

Dow Corning® Medical Antifoam AF Emulsion. [Dow Corning]
Chem. Descrip.: Simethicone USP emulsion with stearate emulsifiers, sorbic acid, and water
Uses: Defoamer and antifoam, esp. for aq. systems; suppressant for excessive GI gas; antiflatulent ingred. in antacids; adjunct to gastroscopic exams
Regulatory: FDA 21CFR§332.10 (OTC drug), 173.340 (to 33.3 ppm in foods)
Properties: Wh. creamy paste; water-dilutable; sp.gr. 1.0; pH 2.7; 30% act.; nonionic
Toxicology: Essentially no significant silicone absorption on ingestion
Storage: 12 mo shelf life stored in original unopened containers between 5 and 32 C; avoid freezing; freeze/thaw cycling may break emulsion.

DPCP. [Albright & Wilson Am.; Albright & Wilson UK]
Chem. Descrip.: Diphenyl chlorophosphate
CAS 2524-64-3
Uses: Intermediate in selective mfg. of phosphoric acid monoesters; protective agent for hydroxyl and ketone groups
Properties: M.w. 269; dens. 1.3 g/cm^3; b.p. 175 C (8 mm); 98% min. assay.

D.P.P.G. [Gattefosse SA]
Chem. Descrip.: Propylene glycol dipelargonate
CAS 41395-83-9; EINECS 255-350-9
Uses: Emollient and oily rancidless additive improving appearance for pharmaceutical preps., creams, lotions, alcoholic sol'ns., sunscreens
Properties: Gardner < 2 oily liq., faint odor; HLB 2.0; acid no. < 0.2; iodine no. < 1; sapon. no. 305-325
Toxicology: LD0 (oral, rat) > 16 g/kg; sl. irritating to eyes; nonirritating to skin.

Drakeol® 5. [Penreco]
Chem. Descrip.: Lt. min. oil NF
CAS 8042-47-5
Uses: Pharmaceutical ointments; lubricant for gelatin capsules
Regulatory: FDA 21CFR §172.878, 178.3620, 573.680
Properties: Water-wh. transparent liq., odorless; sol. in hydrocarbons; negligible sol. in water; sp.gr. 0.831-0.842; dens. 6.89-7.00 lb/gal; visc. 7.6-8.7 cSt (40 C); vapor pressure < 1 mm Hg (70 F); b.p. 320 F; pour pt. -9 C; flash pt. 154 C; ref. index 1.4600
Toxicology: Relatively nontoxic by ingestion unless aspiration occurs (which may cause pneumonitis and may be fatal); laxative props. may result in abdominal cramps, diarrhea; minimally irritating to eyes on direct contact; STEL 10 mg/m^3 (as oil mist)
Precaution: Combustion may produce dense smoke, CO, CO$_2$, other oxides; may react with strong oxidizing agents
Storage: Store in closed containers away from heat, sparks, open flame, oxidizers.

Drakeol® 6. [Penreco]
Chem. Descrip.: Lt. min. oil USP
CAS 8042-47-5
Uses: Base material
Regulatory: FDA compliance
Properties: Sp.gr. 0.827-0.836; dens. 6.94-7.02 lb/gal; visc. 9.2-10.6 cSt (40 C); pour pt. 15 F; flash pt. 320 F; ref. index 1.4613.

Drakeol® 7. [Penreco]
Chem. Descrip.: Lt. min. oil NF
CAS 8042-47-5
Uses: Carrier, base ingred. in topical ointments; lubricant for gelatine capsules
Regulatory: FDA 21CFR §172.878, 178.3620, 573.680
Properties: Sp.gr. 0.828-0.843; dens. 6.94-7.08 lb/gal; visc. 10.8-13.6 cSt (40 C); pour pt. -9 C; flash pt. 177 C; ref. index 1.4632.

Drakeol® 9. [Penreco]
Chem. Descrip.: Lt. min. oil NF
CAS 8042-47-5
Uses: Emulsified lubricant for laxatives, topical ointments
Regulatory: FDA 21CFR §172.878, 178.3620, 573.680
Properties: Sp.gr. 0.838-0.854; dens. 7.03-7.16 lb/gal; visc. 14.2-17.0 cSt (40 C); pour pt. 09 C; flash pt. 179 C; ref. index 1.4665.

Drakeol® 13. [Penreco]
Chem. Descrip.: Lt. min. oil NF
CAS 8042-47-5
Uses: Ingred. in pharmaceuticals (topical ointments)
Regulatory: FDA 21CFR §172.878, 178.3620, 573.680
Properties: Water-wh. transparent liq., odorless; sol. in hydrocarbons; sp.gr. 0.871 (60/60 F); dens. 7.11-7.27 lb/gal; visc. 24.2-26.3 cSt (40 C); vapor pressure < 1 mm Hg (70 F); i.b.p. 580 F; pour pt. -9 C; flash pt. 185 C; ref. index 1.4726
Toxicology: Relatively nontoxic by ingestion unless aspiration occurs (which may cause pneumonitis and may be fatal); laxative props. may result in abdominal cramps, diarrhea; minimally irritating to eyes on direct contact; STEL 10 mg/m^3 (as oil mist)
Precaution: Combustion may produce dense smoke, CO, CO$_2$, other oxides; may react with strong oxidizing agents
Storage: Store in closed containers away from heat, sparks, open flame, oxidizers.

Drakeol® 19. [Penreco]
Chem. Descrip.: Min. oil USP
CAS 8042-47-5
Uses: Ingred. in pharmaceuticals (laxatives, topical ointments)
Regulatory: FDA 21CFR §172.878, 178.3620, 573.680
Properties: Water-wh. transparent liq., odorless; sol. in hydrocarbons; sp.gr. 0.88 (60/60 F); dens. 7.14-7.31 lb/gal; visc. 34.9-37.3 cSt (40 C); vapor pressure < 1 mm Hg (70 F); b.p. 590 F; pour pt.

-12 C; flash pt. 188 C; ref. index 1.4725

Toxicology: Relatively nontoxic by ingestion unless aspiration occurs; laxative props. may result in abdominal cramps, diarrhea; minimally irritating to eyes on direct contact; STEL 10 mg/m^3 (as oil mist)

Precaution: Combustion may produce dense smoke, CO, CO_2, other oxides; may react with strong oxidizing agents

Storage: Store in closed containers away from heat, sparks, open flame, oxidizers.

Drakeol® 21. [Penreco]
Chem. Descrip.: Min. oil USP
CAS 8042-47-5
Uses: Ingred. in laxatives
Regulatory: FDA 21CFR §172.878, 178.3620, 573.680
Properties: Water-wh. transparent liq., odorless; sol. in hydrocarbons; sp.gr. 0.876 (60/60 F); dens. 7.15-7.32 lb/gal; visc. 38.4-41.5 cSt (40 C); vapor pressure < 1 mm Hg (70 F); b.p. 600 F; pour pt. -12 C; flash pt. 193 C; ref. index 1.4733
Toxicology: Relatively nontoxic by ingestion unless aspiration occurs; laxative props. may result in abdominal cramps, diarrhea; minimally irritating to eyes on direct contact; STEL 10 mg/m^3 (as oil mist)
Precaution: Combustion may produce dense smoke, CO, CO_2, other oxides; may react with strong oxidizing agents
Storage: Store in closed containers away from heat, sparks, open flame, oxidizers.

Drakeol® 32. [Penreco]
Chem. Descrip.: Min. oil USP
CAS 8042-47-5
Uses: Lubricant
Regulatory: FDA 21CFR §172.878, 178.3620, 573.680
Properties: Sp.gr. 0.856-0.876; dens. 7.18-7.35 lb/gal; visc. 60.0-63.3 cSt (40 C); pour pt. -12 C; flash pt. 213 C; ref. index 1.4770.

Drakeol® 34. [Penreco]
Chem. Descrip.: Min. oil USP
CAS 8042-47-5
Uses: Lubricant
Regulatory: FDA 21CFR §172.878, 178.3620, 573.680
Properties: Sp.gr. 0.858-0.872; dens. 7.19-7.31 lb/gal; visc. 72.0-79.5 cSt (40 C); pour pt. -9 C; flash pt. 238 C; ref. index 1.4760.

Drakeol® 35. [Penreco]
Chem. Descrip.: Min. oil USP
CAS 8042-47-5
Uses: Ingred. in laxatives
Regulatory: FDA 21CFR §172.878, 178.3620, 573.680
Properties: Water-wh. transparent liq., odorless; sol. in hydrocarbons; sp.gr. 0.882 (60/60 F); dens. 7.25-7.35 lb/gal; visc. 65.8-71.0 cSt (40 C); vapor pressure < 1 mm Hg (70 F); i.b.p. 650 f; pour pt. -15 C; flash pt. 216 C; ref. index 1.4785
Toxicology: Relatively nontoxic by ingestion un-

less aspiration occurs; laxative props. may result in abdominal cramps, diarrhea; minimally irritating to eyes on direct contact; STEL 10 mg/m^3 (as oil mist)
Precaution: Combustion may produce dense smoke, CO, CO_2, other oxides; may react with strong oxidizing agents
Storage: Store in closed containers away from heat, sparks, open flame, oxidizers.

Drewmulse® 3-1-O. [Stepan Food Ingreds.]
Chem. Descrip.: Triglyceryl oleate
CAS 9007-48-1
Uses: Emulsifier, solubilizer, dispersant for w/o and o/w emulsions, creams, lotions for internal and pharmaceutical use
Properties: Gardner 8 liq.; sol. in IPA, peanut oil, min. oil, water disp.; HLB 7.0; sapon. no. 125-150; nonionic
Unverified

Drewmulse® 3-1-S. [Stepan Food Ingreds.]
Chem. Descrip.: Triglyceryl stearate
CAS 37349-34-1; EINECS 248-403-2
Uses: Emulsifier, solubilizer, dispersant for w/o and o/w emulsions, creams, lotions for internal and pharmaceutical use
Properties: Gardner 10 liq.; disp. in water, IPA, peanut oil, min. oil, propylene glycol; HLB 7.0; sapon. no. 120-140; nonionic
Unverified

Drewmulse® 6-2-S. [Stepan Food Ingreds.]
Chem. Descrip.: Hexaglyceryl distearate
CAS 34424-97-0
Uses: Emulsifier, solubilizer, dispersant for w/o and o/w emulsions, creams, lotions for internal and pharmaceutical use
Properties: Gardner 13 solid; sol. in IPA, peanut oil, min. oil; HLB 8.0; sapon. 105-125; nonionic
Unverified

Drewmulse® 10-4-O. [Stepan Food Ingreds.]
Chem. Descrip.: Decaglyceryl tetraoleate
CAS 34424-98-1; EINECS 252-011-7
Uses: Emulsifier, solubilizer, dispersant for w/o and o/w emulsions, creams, lotions for internal and pharmaceutical use
Properties: Gardner 8 liq.; sol. in IPA, peanut oil, min. oil; water disp.; HLB 6.0; sapon. no. 125-145; nonionic
Unverified

Drewmulse® 10-8-O. [Stepan Food Ingreds.]
Chem. Descrip.: Decaglyceryl octaoleate
Uses: Emulsifier, solubilizer, dispersant for w/o and o/w emulsions, creams, lotions for internal and pharmaceutical use
Properties: Gardner 8 liq.; sol. in peanut oil, min. oil; HLB 4.0; sapon. no. 155-175; nonionic
Unverified

Drewmulse® 10-10-O. [Stepan Food Ingreds.; Stepan Europe]
Chem. Descrip.: Decaglyceryl decaoleate
CAS 11094-60-3; EINECS 234-316-7
Uses: Emulsifier, solubilizer, dispersant for w/o and o/w emulsions, creams, lotions for internal and

pharmaceutical use
Properties: Gardner 8 liq.; sol. in peanut oil, min. oil; HLB 3.0; sapon. no. 165-185; nonionic
Unverified

Drewmulse® 10-10-S. [Stepan Food Ingreds.]
Chem. Descrip.: Decaglyceryl decastearate
CAS 39529-26-5; EINECS 254-495-5
Uses: Emulsifier, solubilizer, dispersant for w/o and o/w emulsions, creams, lotions for internal and pharmaceutical use
Properties: Gardner 8 solid; sol. in peanut oil, min. oil; HLB 3.0; sapon. no. 160-180; nonionic
Unverified

Drewmulse® 10K. [Stepan Food Ingreds.]
Chem. Descrip.: Glyceryl mono-shortening from soya oil
CAS 1323-39-3
Uses: Lipophilic emulsifier used in pharmaceutical industry as dispersing aid, stabilizer; for o/w emulsion systems
Regulatory: FDA 21CFR §182.4505; kosher grade
Properties: Wh. soft solid, sl. fatty odor; m.p. 46 C; HLB 2.8; iodine no. 70; sapon. no. 170; 40% alpha monoester.
Storage: Avoid prolonged storage above 90 F.

Drewmulse® 85K. [Stepan Food Ingreds.]
Chem. Descrip.: Glyceryl oleate from tallow and soya
Uses: Emulsifier for pharmaceuticals (vitamins and minerals)
Properties: Lt. yel. semiliq.; HLB 3.4; sapon. no. 160-180; 40% alpha mono.

Drewmulse® 200K. [Stepan Food Ingreds.; Stepan Europe]
Chem. Descrip.: Glyceryl stearate
CAS 123-94-4
Uses: Emulsifier for pharmaceuticals (suppositories, cream bases)
Regulatory: FDA 21CFR §182.4505; kosher grade
Properties: Ivory wh. flakes, sl. fatty odor; m.p. 60 C; iodine no. 2; sapon. no. 175; 42% monoester; nonionic
Storage: Avoid prolonged storage above 90 F.

Drewmulse® 700K. [Stepan Food Ingreds.]
Chem. Descrip.: Glyceryl stearate, polysorbate 80
Uses: Emulsifier for pharmaceuticals
Regulatory: FDA 21CFR §182.4505; kosher grade
Properties: Cream-colored beads, mild fatty odor; sapon. no. 151; 0.8% moisture
Storage: Avoid prolonged storage above 90 F.

Drewmulse® 900K. [Stepan Food Ingreds.]
Chem. Descrip.: Glyceryl stearate
CAS 123-94-4
Uses: Emulsifier for pharmaceuticals (suppositories)
Regulatory: FDA 21CFR §182.4505; kosher grade
Properties: Off-wh. flakes; m.p. 63 C; HLB 3.2; iodine no. 2; sapon. 165; 50% alpha monoester; nonionic
Storage: Avoid prolonged storage above 90 F.

Drewmulse® 1128. [Stepan Food Ingreds.]
Chem. Descrip.: Glyceryl stearate, PEG-120 glyc-

eryl stearate, and PEG-120 propylene glycol stearate
Uses: Emulsifier, stabilizer, opacifier, and visc. builder in pharmaceuticals
Properties: Gardner 2 flake; HLB 8.4; 20% mono; nonionic
Unverified

Drewmulse® GMOK. [Stepan Food Ingreds.]
Chem. Descrip.: Glyceryl oleate
Uses: Emulsifier, stabilizer, opacifier, and visc. builder in pharmaceuticals (vitamin carrier, ointment and cream bases)
Properties: Gardner 6 liq.; HLB 3.4; 40-45% conc.; nonionic.

Drewmulse® HM-100. [Stepan Food Ingreds.]
Chem. Descrip.: Glyceryl stearate and PEG-40 stearate
Uses: Stabilizer and visc. builder in pharmaceuticals, opacifier; emulsifier for topical pharmaceuticals, ointments, creams, suppositories
Properties: Gardner 2 flake; HLB 8.4; 24% mono.

Drewmulse® POE-SML. [Stepan Food Ingreds.]
Chem. Descrip.: Polysorbate 20
CAS 9005-64-5
Uses: Solubilizer for fragrances, flavors, vitamins in aq. systems; w/o emulsifier for pharmaceuticals, emollient creams and lotions, topical ointments; anti-irritant
Properties: Liq., bland char. odor; HLB 15.1; acid no. 1; iodine no. 1; sapon. no. 47; hyd. no. 100; 2.5% moisture; nonionic.

Drewmulse® POE-SMO. [Stepan Food Ingreds.]
Chem. Descrip.: Polysorbate 80
CAS 9005-65-6
Uses: W/o emulsifier, solubilizer, dispersant, wetting agent, visc. control agent for pharmaceuticals; solubilizer, dispersant for vitamin/mineral preps.
Regulatory: FDA 21CFR §172.840; avail. in kosher grade
Properties: Amber visc. liq., mild odor; HLB 15.0; iodine no. 25; sapon. no. 50; hyd. no. 70; 2% moisture; nonionic
Storage: Avoid prolonged storage above 90 F.

Drewmulse® POE-SMS. [Stepan Food Ingreds.]
Chem. Descrip.: Polysorbate 60
CAS 9005-67-8
Uses: W/o emulsifier for pharmaceuticals; solubilizer, dispersant, wetting agent, visc. control agent
Properties: Solid; HLB 14.9; sapon. no. 45-55; nonionic.

Drewmulse® POE-STS. [Stepan Food Ingreds.]
Chem. Descrip.: Polysorbate 65
CAS 9005-71-4
Uses: W/o emulsifier for pharmaceuticals; solubilizer, dispersant, wetting agent, visc. control agent
Properties: Solid; HLB 10.5; sapon. no. 88-98; nonionic.

Drewmulse® SML. [Stepan Food Ingreds.]
Chem. Descrip.: Sorbitan laurate

CAS 1338-39-2

Uses: W/o emulsifier for pharmaceuticals; solubilizer, dispersant, wetting agent, visc. control agent

Properties: Liq.; HLB 8.6; sapon. no. 159-171; 100% conc.; nonionic.

Drewmulse® SMO. [Stepan Food Ingreds.]
Chem. Descrip.: Sorbitan oleate
CAS 1338-43-8; EINECS 215-665-4
Uses: W/o emulsifier, thickener, solubilizer, dispersant, wetting agent for pharmaceuticals
Properties: Liq.; HLB 4.7; iodine no. 69; sapon. no. 155; hyd. no. 196.8; 0.5% moisture; nonionic.

Drewmulse® SMS. [Stepan Food Ingreds.]
Chem. Descrip.: Sorbitan stearate
CAS 1338-41-6; EINECS 215-664-9
Uses: W/o emulsifier, solubilizer, dispersant, wetting agent, visc. control agent for pharmaceuticals; flavor and fragrance solubilizer; vitamins
Regulatory: Avail. in kosher grade (Drewsorb 60K)
Properties: Cream-colored beads, mild fatty odor; water-disp.; HLB 2.1; iodine no. 1; sapon. no. 150; hyd. no. 250; nonionic
Storage: Avoid prolonged storage above 90 F.

Drewmulse® STS. [Stepan Food Ingreds.]
Chem. Descrip.: Sorbitan tristearate
CAS 26658-19-5; EINECS 247-891-4
Uses: W/o emulsifier for pharmaceuticals; solubilizer, dispersant, wetting agent, visc. control agent
Properties: Solid; HLB 2.1; sapon. no. 170-190; nonionic.

Drewmulse® TP. [Stepan Food Ingreds.]
Chem. Descrip.: Glyceryl stearate
Uses: Emulsifier, stabilizer, opacifier, and visc. builder in pharmaceuticals
Properties: Gardner 4 flake; HLB 2.8; 40% mono; nonionic
Unverified

Drewmulse® V. [Stepan Food Ingreds.]
Chem. Descrip.: Glyceryl stearate (veg.)
Uses: Emulsifier, stabilizer, opacifier, and visc. builder in pharmaceuticals
Properties: Gardner 6 bead; HLB 3.8; 40% mono
Unverified

Drewmulse® V-SE. [Stepan Food Ingreds.]
Chem. Descrip.: Glyceryl stearate SE
Uses: Emulsifier, stabilizer, opacifier, and visc. builder in pharmaceuticals
Properties: Gardner 6 bead; HLB 8.4; 30% mono
Unverified

Drewpol® 3-1-O. [Stepan; Stepan Food Ingreds.]
Chem. Descrip.: Polyglyceryl-3 monooleate
CAS 9007-48-1
Uses: Emulsifier for pharmaceuticals
Properties: Amber clear liq.; HLB 7.0; acid no. 5.0 max.; nonionic.

Drewpol® 6-1-O. [Stepan; Stepan Canada]
Chem. Descrip.: Polyglyceryl-6 oleate
CAS 9007-48-1
Uses: Emulsifier for pharmaceuticals
Properties: Amber clear liq.; HLB 8.5; acid no. 6

max.

Drewpol® 10-4-O. [Stepan; Stepan Canada; Stepan Europe]
Chem. Descrip.: Polyglyceryl-10 tetraoleate
CAS 34424-98-1; EINECS 252-011-7
Uses: Emulsifier for pharmaceuticals; solubilizer for vitamins, flavors, medicaments
Properties: Amber clear liq.; HLB 6.0; acid no. 8.0 max.; 100% act.; nonionic.

Drewpol® 10-10-O. [Stepan; Stepan Canada; Stepan Europe]
Chem. Descrip.: Polyglyceryl-10 decaoleate
CAS 11094-60-3; EINECS 234-316-7
Uses: Emulsifier for pharmaceuticals; solubilizer for vitamins, flavors, medicaments
Properties: Amber clear liq.; HLB 3.0; acid no. 10.0 max.; nonionic.

Dri-Klear™. [Crompton & Knowles]
Chem. Descrip.: Cellulose polymer system with plasticizers
Uses: Coating system providing aq. film coating for pharmaceutical and vitamin tablets; rapid dissolution in water; min. foam generation; exc. substrate adhesion
Regulatory: GRAS
Properties: Wh. to off-wh. free-flowing powd., clear to opaque when solubilized (formula dependent)
Storage: 3 yr shelf life stored in tightly sealed containers in dry location.

Dry Beta Carotene Beadlets 10% CWS No. 65633. [Roche]
Chem. Descrip.: β-Carotene compded. with sucrose, fish gelatin, food starch, peanut oil, with antioxidants (ascorbyl palmitate, dl-α-tocopherol)
Uses: Source of vitamin A in pharmaceutical hard shell capsules
Regulatory: FDA 21CFR §73.95 (food use), 73.1095 (drug use), 73.2095 (cosmetic use), 182.5245 GRAS
Properties: Orange-red to dk. red beadlets; 100% thru 20 mesh, 20% max. thru 100 mesh; readily disp. in water with stirring; 167,000 IU provitamin A activity/g
Storage: Store in cool, dry place @ 46-59 F in tightly closed container; avoid moisture condensation.

Dry Beta Carotene Beadlets 10% No. 65661. [Roche]
Chem. Descrip.: β-Carotene compded. with gelatin, sucrose, food starch, peanut oil with antioxidants (ascorbyl palmitate, dl-α-tocopherol)
Uses: Vitamin A source in pharmaceutical hard shell capsules
Regulatory: FDA 21CFR §73.95 (food use), 73.1095 (drug use), 73.2095 (cosmetic use), 182.5245 GRAS
Properties: Orange-red to dk. red beadlets; 100% thru 20 mesh, 20% max. thru 100 mesh; readily disp. in warm water; 167,000 IU provitamin A/g
Storage: Store in cool, dry place @ 46-59 F in tightly closed containers; avoid moisture condensation.

Dry Phytonadione 1% SD No. 61748. [Roche]
Chem. Descrip.: Vitamin K₁ USP compded. with

dextrose, acacia, lactose, and 1% silicon dioxide
Uses: Component of enzyme systems associated with blood-clotting mechanism
Properties: Off-wh. to yel. free-flowing powd.; 98% min. thru 40 mesh, 50% min. thru 100 mesh; m.w. 450.68; 1% min. assay (phytonadione)
Storage: Store in cool, dry place protected from light; dec. on exposure to light.

Dry Vitamin A Palmitate Type 250-SD No. 65378. [Roche]
Chem. Descrip.: Vitamin A palmitate USP FCC compded. with modified food starch, lactose, fractionated coconut oil, and BHT, sodium benzoate, sorbic acid (preservatives), and silicon dioxide
Uses: For vitamin enrichment premixes
Properties: Lt. yel. to tan fine powd.; 98% min. thru 50 mesh, 80% min. thru 100 mesh; 250,000 IU/g assay
Toxicology: Vitamin A: sustained daily intakes exceeding 50,000 IU (adults), 20,000 IU (infants) may cause toxic effects (headache, vomiting, liver damage); US RDA 8000 IU (pregnant/lactating women)
Storage: Store in cool, dry place; avoid excessive heat and moisture; keep container tightly closed.

Dry Vitamin D₃ Beadlets Type 850 No. 652550401, 652550601. [Roche]
Chem. Descrip.: Cholecalciferol USP, FCC in gelatin matrix with food-grade modified starch, peanut oil, sucrose, and antioxidants (BHA, BHT)
Uses: Used in pharmaceuticals, dry preps., multivitamin tablets/capsules
Properties: Buff colored free-flowing spherical beadlets, sl. char. odor; 40 and 60 mesh resp.; 850,000 min. IU vitamin D/g
Toxicology: Vitamin D: potentially toxic esp. for young children; excessive ingestion may cause hypercalcemia, hypercalcuria
Storage: Store in cool, dry place, optimally @ 46-59 F; keep tightly closed.

Dry Vitamin D₃ Type 100 CWS No. 65242. [Roche]
Chem. Descrip.: Cholecalciferol compded. with edible fats finely dispersed in a starch-coated matrix of gelatin and sucrose; dl-α-tocopherol as antioxidant
Uses: Used in pharmaceuticals and prods. which are reconstituted with liqs., esp. effervescent tablets
Properties: Off-wh. to brnsh. fine gran. powd.; 100% thru 20 mesh, 16% max. thru 100 mesh; m.w. 384.64; 100,000 min. IU vitamin D/g
Toxicology: Vitamin D: potentially toxic esp. for young children; excessive ingestion may cause hypercalcemia, hypercalcuria
Storage: Store in cool, dry place in tightly closed container; sensitive to air, heat, light, and humidity.

Dry Vitamin E Acetate 50% SD No. 65356. [Roche]
Chem. Descrip.: Dl-α-Tocopheryl acetate USP, FCC compded. with hydrolyzed protein, 3% silicon dioxide

Uses: Vitamin E source for pharmaceuticals (multivitamin tablets, chewable or coated dietary supplements, hard shell capsules); esp. developed for direct compression tableting of chewable or coated tablets
Regulatory: FDA GRAS
Properties: Wh. to off-wh. free-flowing powd., acceptable odor and taste; 95% min. thru 20 mesh; sl. hygroscopic; disp. readily in cold or warm water; 50% min. dl-α-tocopheryl acetate
Storage: Store in dry place in tightly closed container; avoid excessive heat.

Dry Vitamin E Acetate 50% Type CWS/F No. 652530001. [Roche]
Chem. Descrip.: Dl-α-Tocopheryl acetate USP, FCC dispersed in a matrix of fish gelatin and maltodextrin
Uses: Vitamin E source for dry pharmaceutical prods. which are reconstituted with liqs.
Regulatory: FDA GRAS
Properties: Wh. to off-wh. spray-dried powd., acceptable odor and taste; 60% min. thru 80 mesh; sl. hygroscopic; disp. readily in cold or warm water; 50% min. dl-α-tocopheryl acetate
Storage: Store in dry place in tightly closed container; avoid excessive heat.

DSS Granular. [Cytec Industries]
Chem. Descrip.: Docusate sodium USP (85%) with sodium benzoate NF 15%
Uses: Pharmaceutical surfactant, solubilizer, wetting agent, dispersant for use as adjuvant in tablet formulations (aids granulation, improves tablet and dissolution chars., maintains tablet hardness); good stability; good compat. with many drug actives
Properties: Wh. cryst. powd.; anionic
Toxicology: Direct contact may cause eye or skin irritation
Storage: Store in tightly closed containers below 24 C with < 60% r.h.

DSS Tablet Grade. [Cytec Industries]
Chem. Descrip.: Docusate sodium USP (70%), colloidal silicon dioxide NF (27.5%), absorbable dusting powd. USP (0.5%), magnesium stearate NF (2%)
Uses: Pharmaceutical grade surfactant, solubilizer, wetting agent, dispersant for medicaments, as adjuvant to in tablet formulation (improves tablet and dissolution chars.); good stability, compat.; esp. for constipation treatments/preventives
Use level: 0.1-1% (adjuvant)
Properties: Wh. fine free-flowing powd.; 100% thru 20 mesh; 68-72% assay; anionic
Toxicology: Direct contact may cause eye or skin irritation
Storage: Store in tightly closed containers below 24 C and < 60% r.h.

Dulectin. [Solvay Duphar BV]
Chem. Descrip.: De-oiled soybean lecithin CAS 8002-43-5; EINECS 232-307-2
Uses: Surfactant, emulsifier, dispersant, and stabi-

lizer for pharmaceuticals
Properties: Powd.; 97% conc.; nonionic
Unverified

Duocrome®. [Mearl]
Chem. Descrip.: Titanium dioxide-coated mica and a thin layer of colored pigment (iron blue, carmine, and/or iron oxide)
Uses: Iridescent colors producing dual-color effects derived from light interference and light absorption; used in analgesic body lotions, sunscreens, toothpaste
Properties: Fine lustrous powd.; particle size 6-50 μm; sp.gr. ≈ 3.0.

Duratex. [Van Den Bergh Foods]
Chem. Descrip.: Partially hydrog. cottonseed oil NF
CAS 68334-00-9; EINECS 269-804-9
Uses: Lubricant for tablets; release agent
Regulatory: Kosher
Properties: Lovibond 5R max. powd.; m.p. 141-147 F; iodine no. 4 max.

Dur-Em® 117. [Van Den Bergh Foods]
Chem. Descrip.: Mono- and diglycerides with citric acid (preservative)
Uses: Emulsifier for pharmaceutical creams and lotions
Regulatory: FDA 21CFR §182.4505, GRAS; kosher
Properties: Wh. beads, flakes, typ. odor/flavor; m.p. 62-65 C; HLB 2.8; iodine no. 5 max.; flash pt. 300 F min.; 100% conc.; 40% min. alpha monoglyceride; nonionic
Storage: Store in cool, dry place away from odor-producing substances.

Dur-Em® 207-E. [Van Den Bergh Foods]
Chem. Descrip.: Mono- and diglcyerides with citric acid to help protect flavor
Uses: Emulsifier for pharmaceuticals
Regulatory: FDA 21CFR §182.4505, 136.110
Properties: Wh. free-flowing powd., bland odor/flavor; m.p. 140-146 F; HLB 4.2; iodine no. 5 max.; 100% act.; 50% min. alpha mono; nonionic
Storage: Store sealed in cool, dry area away from odor-producing substances; 90 days storage life @ 40-80 F.

Durkex 25BHA. [Van Den Bergh Foods]
Chem. Descrip.: Partially hydrog. soybean oil with polyglycerol esters of fatty acids and BHA to help protect flavor
Uses: Multipurpose shortening for pharmaceuticals; also avail. with BHT, TBHQ, lecithin, or no antioxidants
Regulatory: Kosher
Properties: Lovibond 2.0R max. liq.

Durkote Calcium Carbonate/Starch, Acacia Gum. [Van Den Bergh Foods]
Chem. Descrip.: Encapsulated ingred. (calcium chloride substrate with starch/acacia gum coating), USP/FCC
Uses: Highly conc., directly compressible form of calcium carbonate for use in direct compression tablets and food fortification; provides ease of tableting, improves flow, reduces dusting
Properties: Wh. to off-wh. free-flowing powd.

Durkote Ferrous Fumarate/Hydrog. Veg. Oil. [Van Den Bergh Foods]
Chem. Descrip.: Encapsulated ingred. (ferrous fumarate substrate with hydrog. veg. oil coating)
Uses: Fortification used in vitamin/mineral tablets and capsules where taste-masking, time-release, and controlled reactivity are desired; contains no sugar, starch, or free-flow agents
Properties: Maroon free-flowing gran.

Durkote Ferrous Sulfate/Hydrog. Veg. Oil. [Van Den Bergh Foods]
Chem. Descrip.: Encapsulated ingred. (ferrous sulfate substrate with hydrog. veg. oil coating)
Uses: Used for iron fortification, improved flow, taste-masking, time-release props., and preventing reaction with other ingreds.; useful in formulating nutritional prods., vitamin/mineral tablets and capsules
Properties: Tan free-flowing gran.

Durkote Malic Acid/Maltodextrin. [Van Den Bergh Foods]
Chem. Descrip.: Encapsulated ingred. (malic acid substrate with maltodextrin coating)
Uses: Acidification for tableted prods.; prevents hygroscopicity, color and flavor degradation, reduces dusting, controls pH, and prevents reactions with incompat. ingreds.
Properties: Wh. free-flowing gran.; water-sol.

Durkote Potassium Chloride/Hydrog. Veg. Oil. [Van Den Bergh Foods]
Chem. Descrip.: Encapsulated ingred. (potassium chloride substrate with hydrog. veg. oil coating)
Uses: Used in nutritional prods. and tablets for fortification where taste masking and reactivity control are desired
Properties: Wh. free-flowing gran.

Durkote Vitamin B-1/Hydrog. Veg. Oil. [Van Den Bergh Foods]
Chem. Descrip.: Encapsulated ingred. (vitamin B1 substrate with hydrog. veg. oil coating)
Uses: Used for fortified nutritional prods. and chewable tablets; provides taste masking, temp. and moisture protection, and a degree of time-release
Properties: Off-wh. to tan free-flowing powd.

Durkote Vitamin C/Hydrog. Veg. Oil. [Van Den Bergh Foods]
Chem. Descrip.: Encapsulated ingred. (vitamin C substrate with hydrog. veg. oil coating)
Uses: Used for vitamin/mineral tablets and capsules; provides exc. stability, temp. and moisture protection, taste masking, protection from reactivity and degradation, and time release props.
Properties: Tan or wh. to off-wh. free-flowing gran.

Dynacerin® 660. [Hüls Am.; Hüls AG]
Chem. Descrip.: Oleyl erucate
CAS 17673-56-2; EINECS 241-654-9
Uses: Emollient, lubricant, dispersant, solubilizer for pharmaceuticals; carrier/vehicle and solv. for topical ointments, creams, lotions; jojoba oil sub-

stitute; oxidation-stable

Properties: Ylsh. liq. wax; sol. in alcohol, min. oil, acetone; acid no. 1 max.; iodine no. 95 max.; sapon. no. 95-110; cloud pt. 15 C.

Dynasan® 112. [Hüls Am.; Hüls AG]

Chem. Descrip.: Trilaurin

CAS 538-24-9; EINECS 208-687-0

Uses: Consistency regulator for pharmaceutical creams, lotions; tablet lubricant, mold release agent, binder, retarding agent; powd. base

Properties: Wh. powd.; m.p. 43-47 C; clear pt. 45 C; acid no. 0.2 max.; iodine no. 1 max.; sapon. no. 257-266.

Dynasan® 114. [Hüls Am.; Hüls AG]

Chem. Descrip.: Trimyristin

CAS 555-45-3; EINECS 209-099-7

Uses: Consistency regulator for pharmaceutical creams, lotions; lubricant, binder, mold release agent, retarding agent for tablets; powd. base

Properties: Wh. powd./flakes; m.p. 55-58 C; clear pt. 57 C; acid no. 1.0 max.; iodine no. 1 max.;

sapon. no. 230-238.

Dynasan® 116. [Hüls Am.; Hüls AG]

Chem. Descrip.: Tripalmitin

CAS 555-44-2; EINECS 209-098-1

Uses: Lubricant, mold release, binder, retarding agent, flow and consistency regulator in prod. of pharmaceutical tablets

Properties: Wh. microcryst. powd.; sol. in ether and benzene; m.p. 61-65 C; clear pt. 63 C; acid no. 0.5 max.; iodine no. 1 max.; sapon. no. 205-215.

Dynasan® 118. [Hüls Am.; Hüls AG]

Chem. Descrip.: Tristearin

CAS 555-43-1; EINECS 209-097-6

Uses: Lubricant, mold release, binder, retarding agent, flow and consistency regulator in prod. of pharmaceutical tablets

Properties: Wh. microcryst. powd./flakes; sol. in ether and benzene; m.p. 69-73 C; clear pt. 71 C; acid no. 0.5 max.; iodine no. 1 max.; sapon. no. 186-192; nonionic.

E

Eastman® CA. [Eastman]
Chem. Descrip.: Cellulose acetate
CAS 9004-35-7
Uses: Excipient for formulation of microparticles for controlled-release pharmaceutical applics.

Eastman® CAB. [Eastman]
Chem. Descrip.: Cellulose acetate butyrate
CAS 9004-36-8
Uses: Excipient for formulation of drug-loaded microparticles.

Eastman® CAPr. [Eastman]
Chem. Descrip.: Cellulose acetate propionate
CAS 9004-39-1
Uses: Excipient for formulation of drug-loaded microparticles.

Eastman® OC [Eastman]
Chem. Descrip.: Oxidized cellulose
Uses: For controlled-release pharmaceutical applics.; hemostatic agent, bioabsorbable surgical thread, drug carrier, kidney dialyzer membrane, surgical lubricant, enzyme carrier, blood reducing agent.

Eastman® SAIB-SG. [Eastman]
Chem. Descrip.: Sucrose acetate isobutyrate, special grade
CAS 126-13-6; EINECS 204-771-6
Uses: Stabilizes o/w emulsions in pharmaceutical syrups and suspensions; clouding agent in clear liqs.; modifying extender for film-forming polymers (e.g., cellulose esters) in solid oral dosage forms; good thermal, uv, and hydrolytic stability
Regulatory: Kosher
Properties: Gardner < 1 visc. liq., low odor; sol. in most alcohols, veg. oils, flavoring oils, animal fats, veg.-based waxes; m.w. 832-856; sp.gr. 1.146; dens. 9.55 lb/gal; visc. 100,000 cP (30 C); dec. pt. 288 C; flash pt. (COC) 260 C; ref. index 1.454 (20 C)
Storage: Warm drum contents to 25-40 C for ease of handling.

Eastman® Triacetin. [Eastman]
Chem. Descrip.: Glyceryl triacetate USP
CAS 102-76-1; EINECS 203-051-9
Uses: Plasticizer for film coatings on pharmaceutical tablets, beads, and gran.; also in topical antifungal creams and ointments; compat. with cellulosics, methacrylic acid copolymers, and PVAP; high solv. power
Use level: 10-35% (tablet coatings)
Properties: Low color liq.; sol. 61.20 g/l in water (20 C); misc. with alcohol, ether, chloroform; m.w. 218.21; sp.gr. 1.1540; dens. 9.65 lb/gal (20 C); visc. 17.4 cP; f.p. 3.2 C; supercools to ≈ -70 C; m.p. -89 C; b.p. 258 C (760 mm); ref. index 1.4290.

Ebal. [Mitsubishi Gas]
Chem. Descrip.: p-Ethylbenzaldehyde
CAS 4748-78-1; EINECS 225-268-8
Uses: Pharmaceutical intermediate
Properties: Colorless liq., aromatic odor; sol. in ethanol, ether, toluene; insol. in water; m.w. 134.2; sp.gr. 1.000; b.p. 221 C; m.p. -33 C; acid no. 0.3; flash pt. (COC) 98 C; 97.5% purity
Toxicology: LD50 (oral, rat) 1700 mg/kg; eye and skin irritant
Unverified

Eccowet® W-50. [Eastern Color & Chem.]
Chem. Descrip.: Sodium aliphatic ester sulfonate
Uses: Wetting agent, penetrant, dispersant, solubilizer, emulsifier for topical pharmaceuticals
Properties: Colorless liq.; misc. with water; sol. in alcohol, glycols, acetones, dilute electrolyte sol'ns. (5%); visc. 55 cps; pH 8.0 ± 0.3 (1%); 50% conc.; anionic.

Eccowet® W-88. [Eastern Color & Chem.]
Chem. Descrip.: Sulfonated organic ester
Uses: Wetting agent, penetrant, dispersant, solubilizer, emulsifier for topical pharmaceuticals
Properties: Amber visc. liq.; pH 8.0 ± 0.3 (1%); 21% act.

Edible Beef Gelatin. [GMI Prods.]
Chem. Descrip.: Type B or calfskin gelatin
CAS 9000-70-8; EINECS 232-554-6
Uses: Edible protein for pharmaceuticals; carrier, base, stabilizer for capsules, enteric capsules, suppositories, topicals, adhesive substitute, binder/disintegrant in tablets, hemorrhage control agent; dusting powd. for surgical gloves; therapeutic use
Regulatory: GRAS
Properties: Pale yel. vitreous brittle solid, nearly odorless and tasteless; sol. in warm water; swells due to hydration in cold water; sp.gr. 1.2; dens. 1.3-1.4; b.p. > 100 C (dec.); pH 5.0-7.5; flash pt. nonflamm.; 9-13% moisture; biodeg.
Toxicology: Nuisance dust; contact with dust

causes mild eye irritation; inhaling dust may cause respiratory irritation
Storage: Store in airtight containers @ R.T.; avoid exposure to water or excessive heat.

Edicol®. [Indian Gum Industries; Commodity Services Int'l.]
Chem. Descrip.: Guar gum
CAS 9000-30-0; EINECS 232-536-8
Uses: Controls rheology by water-phase management; binder and disintegrant in tablets; controlled release agent in drug formulations; slimming and appetite control agent; diabetic formulations; antacids; suspensions; syrups; laxatives; toothpaste
Properties: Wh. to cream-wh. powd., sl. char. grassy or beany odor, neutral taste; sol. in hot and cold water; nonionic.

Edicol® P. [Indian Gum Industries; Commodity Services Int'l.]
Chem. Descrip.: Guar gum
CAS 9000-30-0; EINECS 232-536-8
Uses: Pharmaceutical grade for tablet binding, thickening toothpastes; nonionic.

Edicol® ULV Series. [Indian Gum Industries; Commodity Services Int'l.]
Chem. Descrip.: Ultra low visc. guar gum
CAS 9000-30-0; EINECS 232-536-8
Uses: Tablet disintegration bulking agent; in high solids/low visc. systems where specific rheological behavior and stability are required
Regulatory: EEC, FAO/WHO, FCC compliance
Properties: Cream-wh. powd.; > 90% thru 200 mesh; visc.: various grades from 30-1100 cps; pH 5.5-6.5; 13% max. moisture; nonionic
Storage: Store in cool, dry place out of the sun; 1 yr shelf life.

Elcema® F150. [Degussa]
Chem. Descrip.: Cellulose NF
CAS 9004-34-6; EINECS 232-674-9
Uses: Anticaking agent, tableting aid for prod. of tablets and pills in pharmaceutical industry; effective troubleshooter in solving capping problems
Properties: Fibrillated powd.

Elcema® G250. [Degussa]
Chem. Descrip.: Cellulose NF
CAS 9004-34-6; EINECS 232-674-9
Uses: Anticaking agent, tableting aid for prod. of tablets and pills in pharmaceutical industry; superior free-flow props. and faster disintegration
Properties: Wh. gran.

Elcema® P100. [Degussa]
Chem. Descrip.: Cellulose NF
CAS 9004-34-6; EINECS 232-674-9
Uses: Anticaking agent, tableting aid for prod. of tablets and pills in pharmaceutical industry; low friability, rapid disintegration
Properties: Wh. powd.

Elestab® HP 100. [Laboratoires Sérobiologiques]
Chem. Descrip.: Hexamidine diisethionate
CAS 659-40-5; EINECS 211-533-5
Uses: Broad-spectrum antimicrobial and preservative; cutaneous asepticizer; used for oily, acneic

skin care, antidandruff care; effective against Gram-positive and Gram-negative bacteria; good against yeasts, fungi
Use level: 0.03-0.10%
Properties: Wh. microcryst. powd.; water-sol.

Eltesol® PA 65. [Albright & Wilson France]
Chem. Descrip.: Phenol sulfonic acid, 65% aq.
CAS 74665-14-8; EINECS 277-962-5
Uses: Raw material for pharmaceutical chemicals
Properties: Clear red-brn. liq., phenolic odor; misc. with water; dens. 1.34 g/cm^3; visc. 100 cst max. (20 C); cryst. pt. 3 C; m.p. 0-10 C; b.p. > 100 C; 65% act.; readily biodeg., unlikely to accumulate in aquatic environment; discharge of lg. quantities may kill fish
Toxicology: Corrosive acid; may burn the mouth and upper digestive tract, may burn skin after prolonged contact; may cause severe, possibly permanent eye damage; spillages may be slippery
Precaution: May react with strong oxidizing agents; may react exothermically with bases; will react with metal containers with liberation of hydrogen (flamm.) gas
Storage: Store in tightly closed containers @ 5-40 C.

Eltesol® PSA 65. [Albright & Wilson UK]
Chem. Descrip.: Phenol sulfonic acid
CAS 1333-39-7
Uses: Raw material in pharmaceutical chemicals
Properties: Liq.; dens. 1.3 g/cm^3; visc. 50 cs; 65.0 ± 1.0% act. in water; anionic.

Eltesol® TSX. [Albright & Wilson France]
Chem. Descrip.: p-Toluene sulfonic acid monohydrate
CAS 104-15-4; EINECS 203-180-0
Uses: Raw material for pharmaceutical chemicals
Properties: Off-wh. cryst., faint odor; sol. 750 g/l water; readily sol. in lower alcohols; m.w. 190; dens. ≈ 0.5; m.p. 103 C; b.p. > 106 C; 96% conc.; anionic; readily biodeg., unlikely to accumulate in aquatic environment; discharge of lg. quantities may kill fish
Toxicology: LD50 (oral, rat) > 2000 mg/kg; corrosive acid; may irritate mouth and upper digestive tract; may significantly irritate skin on prolonged/repeated exposure, eyes, nose, upper respiratory tract
Precaution: May react with strong oxidants; may react exothermically with bases; will react with metal containers with liberation of hydrogen (flamm.) gas; combustion may produce fumes contg. CO_2, CO, SO_2; spillages may be slippery
Storage: Store in cool, dry area.

Eltesol® TSX/A. [Albright & Wilson Am.; Albright & Wilson UK]
Chem. Descrip.: p-Toluene sulfonic acid monohydrate
CAS 104-15-4; EINECS 203-180-0
Uses: In mfg. of pharmaceutical prods.
Properties: Wh. crystals; m.p. 103.5 C; 96% act.; anionic.

Eltesol® TSX/SF. [Albright & Wilson UK]
Chem. Descrip.: p-Toluene sulfonic acid mono-
hydrate
CAS 104-15-4; EINECS 203-180-0
Uses: In mfg. of pharmaceutical prods.
Properties: Wh. cryst.; m.p. 103.5 C; 98% act.;
anionic.
Emalex C-20. [Nihon Emulsion]
Chem. Descrip.: PEG-20 castor oil
CAS 61791-12-6
Uses: Emulsifier, solubilizer, dispersant in medical
pharmaceuticals
Regulatory: JSCI compliance
Properties: Pale yel. oil; HLB 9.
Emalex C-30. [Nihon Emulsion]
Chem. Descrip.: PEG-30 castor oil
CAS 61791-12-6
Uses: Emulsifier, solubilizer, dispersant in medical
pharmaceuticals
Regulatory: JSCI compliance
Properties: Pale yel. oil; HLB 11.
Emalex C-40. [Nihon Emulsion]
Chem. Descrip.: PEG-40 castor oil
CAS 61791-12-6
Uses: Emulsifier, solubilizer, dispersant in medical
pharmaceuticals
Regulatory: JSCI compliance
Properties: Pale yel. oil; HLB 13.
Emalex C-50. [Nihon Emulsion]
Chem. Descrip.: PEG-50 castor oil
CAS 61791-12-6
Uses: Emulsifier, solubilizer, dispersant in medical
pharmaceuticals
Regulatory: JSCI compliance
Properties: Pale yel. turbid oil; HLB 14.
Emalex ET-2020. [Nihon Emulsion]
Chem. Descrip.: Polysorbate 20
CAS 9005-64-5
Uses: Emulsifier, solubilizer in medical pharma-
ceuticals
Regulatory: JSCI compliance
Properties: Pale yel. oil; HLB 16; nonionic.
Emalex ET-8020. [Nihon Emulsion]
Chem. Descrip.: Polysorbate 80
CAS 9005-65-6
Uses: Emulsifier, solubilizer in medical pharma-
ceuticals
Regulatory: JSCI compliance
Properties: Pale yel. oil; HLB 14.
Emalex ET-8040. [Nihon Emulsion]
Chem. Descrip.: PEG-40 sorbitan oleate
Uses: Emulsifier, solubilizer in medical pharma-
ceuticals
Regulatory: JCID compliance
Properties: Pale yel. soft wax; HLB 18; nonionic.
Emalex GMS-10SE. [Nihon Emulsion]
Chem. Descrip.: Glyceryl monostearate, SE
Uses: Surfactant for medical pharmaceutical
applics.
Regulatory: JSCI compliance
Properties: Cream-colored wax; HLB 6.
Emalex GMS-15SE. [Nihon Emulsion]

Chem. Descrip.: Glyceryl monostearate, SE
Uses: Surfactant for medical pharmaceutical
applics.
Regulatory: JSCI compliance
Properties: Cream-colored soft wax; HLB 9.
Emalex GMS-20SE. [Nihon Emulsion]
Chem. Descrip.: Glyceryl monostearate, SE
Uses: Surfactant for medical pharmaceutical
applics.
Regulatory: JSCI compliance
Properties: Cream-colored wax; HLB 8.
Emalex GMS-25SE. [Nihon Emulsion]
Chem. Descrip.: Glyceryl monostearate, SE
Uses: Surfactant for medical pharmaceutical
applics.
Regulatory: JSCI compliance
Properties: Cream-colored soft wax; HLB 10.
Emalex GMS-45RT. [Nihon Emulsion]
Chem. Descrip.: Glyceryl monostearate, SE
Uses: Surfactant for medical pharmaceutical
applics.
Regulatory: JSCI compliance
Properties: Cream-colored wax; HLB 5.
Emalex GMS-50. [Nihon Emulsion]
Chem. Descrip.: Glyceryl monostearate, SE
Uses: Surfactant for medical pharmaceutical
applics.
Regulatory: JSCI compliance
Properties: Cream-colored wax; HLB 12.
Emalex GMS-55FD. [Nihon Emulsion]
Chem. Descrip.: Glyceryl monostearate, SE
Uses: Surfactant for medical pharmaceutical
applics.
Regulatory: JSCI compliance
Properties: Cream-colored wax; HLB 7.
Emalex GMS-195. [Nihon Emulsion]
Chem. Descrip.: Glyceryl monostearate, SE
Uses: Surfactant for medical pharmaceutical
applics.
Regulatory: JSCI compliance
Properties: Cream-colored wax; HLB 6.
Emalex GMS-A. [Nihon Emulsion]
Chem. Descrip.: Glyceryl monostearate
Uses: Surfactant for medical pharmaceutical
applics.
Regulatory: JSCI compliance
Properties: Cream-colored beads; HLB 3.
Emalex GMS-ASE. [Nihon Emulsion]
Chem. Descrip.: Glyceryl monostearate, SE
Uses: Surfactant for medical pharmaceutical
applics.
Regulatory: JSCI compliance
Properties: Cream-colored beads; HLB 7.
Emalex GMS-B. [Nihon Emulsion]
Chem. Descrip.: Glyceryl monostearate
Uses: Surfactant for medical pharmaceutical
applics.
Regulatory: JSCI compliance
Properties: Cream-colored beads; HLB 5.
Emalex GMS-P. [Nihon Emulsion]
Chem. Descrip.: Glyceryl monopalmitate
CAS 26657-96-5; EINECS 247-887-2

Uses: Surfactant for medical pharmaceutical applics.
Regulatory: JCID compliance
Properties: Cream-colored beads; HLB 4.

Emalex GWIS-100. [Nihon Emulsion]
Chem. Descrip.: Glyceryl monoisostearate
Uses: Surfactant for medical pharmaceutical applics.
Regulatory: JCID compliance
Properties: Pale yel. paste; HLB 5.

Emalex HC-40. [Nihon Emulsion]
Chem. Descrip.: PEG-40 hydrogenated castor oil
CAS 61788-85-0
Uses: Solubilizer for oily components and perfumes in alcoholic tonics, oil-sol. vitamins
Regulatory: JSCI compliance
Properties: Cream-colored soft paste; HLB 12; nonionic.

Emcocel® 50M. [Mendell]
Chem. Descrip.: Microcrystalline cellulose NF/BP
CAS 9004-34-6
Uses: Tablet binder for pharmaceuticals; features high binding capacity, tablet strength, ability to initiate disintegration, low friability, inherent lubricity.

Emcocel® 90M. [Mendell]
Chem. Descrip.: Microcryst. cellulose NF/BP
CAS 9004-34-6
Uses: Tablet binder, disintegrant for pharmaceuticals; features high binding capacity, tablet strength, ability to initiate disintegration, low friability, inherent lubricity, enhanced compression of other excipients
Properties: Avg. particle size 91 µ; 45% min +200 mesh; dens. (tapped) 0.40 g/ml max.; pH 5.5-7.0; 100% conc.

Emcocel® LM. [Mendell]
Chem. Descrip.: Microcrystalline cellulose NF
CAS 9004-34-6
Uses: Tablet binder for pharmaceuticals; features high binding capacity, tablet strength, ability to initiate disintegration, low friability, inherent lubricity, enhanced compression of other excipients
Regulatory: Conforms to FCC
Properties: Avg. particle size 51 µ; 30% max. +200 mesh; dens. (tapped) 0.40 g/ml max.; pH 5.5-7.0; 100% conc.

Emcompress®. [Mendell]
Chem. Descrip.: Dibasic calcium phosphate dihydrate USP/BP
CAS 7789-77-7; EINECS 231-826-1
Uses: Excipient, filler for prod. of pharmaceutical tablets by direct compression process
Regulatory: Conforms to USP, FCC, and BP
Properties: Wh. free-flowing powd.; avg. particle size 136 µ; 15% max. -200 mesh; readily sol. in dilute hydrochloric and nitric acids; relatively insol. in water and alcohol; dens. (tapped) 0.91 g/ml.

EmCon CO. [Fanning]
Chem. Descrip.: Castor oil USP

CAS 8001-79-4; EINECS 232-293-8
Uses: Skin conditioning agent, occlusive solv.
Properties: Gardner 1 oil; sp.gr. 0.957-0.961; acid no. 2 max.; iodine no. 83-88; sapon. no. 176-182; hyd. no. 160-168.

EmCon Limnanthes Alba. [Fanning]
Chem. Descrip.: Meadowfoam seed oil
Uses: Conditioner for pharmaceutical prods.
Regulatory: Japanese approvals
Properties: Gardner 6 max. color; sol. in castor and min. oils, ethyl acetate, IPM; sl. sol. in glycerin, ethanol; insol. in water; acid no. 0.1 max.; iodine no. 85-100; sapon. no. 165-185; cloud pt. 4.5 C.

EmCon Olive. [Fanning]
Chem. Descrip.: Olive oil USP
CAS 8001-25-0; EINECS 232-277-0
Uses: Conditioning agent, occlusive solv. for pharmaceutical ointments
Properties: Pale straw clear liq., bland odor; sp.gr. 0.910-0.915; acid no. 3.5 max.; iodine no. 79-88; sapon. no. 190-195.

EmCon Rice Bran. [Fanning]
Chem. Descrip.: Rice bran oil
CAS 68553-81-1; EINECS 271-397-8
Uses: Conditioning agent, occlusive solv. for pharmaceutical ointments
Properties: Sp.gr. 0.971-0.973; acid no. 0.10 max.; iodine no. 102-110; sapon. no. 185-195.

EmCon Tea Tree. [Fanning]
Chem. Descrip.: Tea tree oil distilled from leaves of *Melaleuca alternifolia*
CAS 68647-73-4
Uses: Antimicrobial in pharmaceutical ointments
Properties: Sp.gr. 0.920-0.930; ref. index 1.472-1.482.

EmCon W. [Fanning]
Chem. Descrip.: Wheat germ oil USP
CAS 8006-95-9
Uses: Lubricant for topical ointments
Properties: Gardner 10 max. oil; acid no. 0.5 max.; iodine no. 120-135; sapon. no. 180-195.

EmCon Walnut. [Fanning]
Chem. Descrip.: Walnut oil
CAS 8024-09-7
Uses: Lubricant for topical pharmaceuticals, ointments
Properties: Clear oil, sl. nutty odor; iodine no. 145-158; sapon. no. 180-200.

Emcosoy®. [Mendell]
Chem. Descrip.: Soy fiber
CAS 68513-95-1
Uses: Tablet disintegrant for direct compression prep.
Use level: 0.5-8% (tablets)
Regulatory: GRAS; kosher
Properties: Wh. to lt. tan gran. powd.; avg. particle size 50 µ; 90% -100 mesh; dens. (tapped) 0.54 g/ml max.; pH 6.5-7.5 (5% slurry); nonionic.

Emdex®. [Mendell]
Chem. Descrip.: Dextrates NF [dextrose (95%), isomaltose (2%), gentiobiose (2%), maltose (1%), maltotriose (< 0.1%), panose (< 0.5%)]

CAS 50-99-7; EINECS 200-075-1

Uses: Vehicle for direct compression of pharmaceutical tablets; also suitable for wet granulation procedures

Properties: Sweet taste; avg. particle size 211 µ; 25% max. -100 mesh; sol. 100 g/100 ml in water; insol. in alcohol and common org. solvs.; dens. (tapped) 0.77 g/ml; pH 3.8-5.8.

Emdex® Plus. [Mendell]
Chem. Descrip.: Dextrates NF (CAS 50-99-7) with 0.26% max. magnesium stearate as anticaking agent
Uses: Vehicle for direct compression of pharmaceutical tablets, incl. chewable tablets; offers flow, compressibility, lubricity, nonhygroscopicity, controlled particle size, rapid disintegration, sweet noncloying taste, cool soft mouthfeel
Properties: Free-flowing porous spheres, sweet noncloying taste; avg. particle size 211 µ; 30% max. -100 mesh; dens. (tapped) 0.90 g/ml max.; pH 4.5-7.5 (20% aq.).

Emerest® 2423. [Henkel/Cospha; Henkel Canada]
Chem. Descrip.: Triolein
CAS 122-32-7; EINECS 204-534-7
Uses: Lubricant, w/o emulsifier for pharmaceuticals
Properties: Gardner 3 liq.; sol. 5% in min. oil, xylene; dens. 7.6 lb/gal; visc. 43 cs; HLB 0.6; pour pt. 9 C; flash pt. 293 C; sapon no. 197; 100% act.; nonionic.

Emerest® 2715. [Henkel/Cospha; Henkel Canada]
Chem. Descrip.: PEG-40 stearate
CAS 9004-99-3
Uses: Emulsifier, stabilizer, antigellant, lubricant for pharmaceuticals
Properties: Wh. waxy solid or flake; sol. @ 5% in water, IPA; dens. 8.9 lb/gal (50 C); HLB 17.3; m.p. 50 C; acid no. 1 max.; sapon. no. 25-35; cloud pt. 75-81 C (5% saline); flash pt. 515 F; 100% conc.; nonionic.

Emersol® 6313 NF. [Henkel/Emery]
Chem. Descrip.: Low-titer oleic acid USP/NF
CAS 112-80-1; EINECS 204-007-1
Uses: Emulsifier, solubilizer for mfg. of ointments; pharmaceutic aid
Regulatory: FDA 21CFR §172.860; EPA-exempt
Properties: Lt. yel. clear liq., fatty acid odor; insol. in water; sp.gr. 0.891 (25/20 C); m.p. 14 C; b.p. 286 C (100 mm); acid no. 201-204; iodine no. 88-93; flash pt. (CC) 184-189 C
Toxicology: LD50 (oral, rat) > 21.5 ml/kg; mild eye and skin irritant
Storage: Store in closed containers away from heat and open flames; avoid contact with strong oxidizers, alkalies.

Emersol® 6321 NF. [Henkel/Emery]
Chem. Descrip.: Low-titer wh. oleic acid USP/NF
CAS 112-80-1; EINECS 204-007-1
Uses: Emulsifier, solubilizer for mfg. of ointments; pharmaceutic aid
Regulatory: FDA 21CFR §172.860; EPA-exempt
Properties: Lt. clear liq., fatty acid odor; insol. in water; sp.gr. 0.891 (25/20 C); m.p. 14 C; b.p. 286 C (100 mm); iodine no. 87-92; flash pt. (CC) 184-189 C
Toxicology: LD50 (oral, rat) > 21.5 ml/kg; mild eye, moderate skin irritant
Storage: Store in closed containers away from heat and open flames; avoid contact with strong oxidizers, alkalies.

Emersol® 6332 NF. [Henkel/Emery]
Chem. Descrip.: Stearic acid, triple pressed USP/NF
CAS 57-11-4; EINECS 200-313-4
Uses: Lubricant, emulsifier in suppositories, ointments
Regulatory: FDA 21CFR §172.860; EPA-exempt
Properties: Wh. waxy solid, fatty acid odor; insol. in water; sp.gr. 0.85 (75/20 C); m.p. 52-57 C; b.p. 383 C; acid no. 205-211; iodine no. 0.5 max.; flash pt. (COC) 185 C
Toxicology: LD50 (oral, rat) > 10 g/kg; mild eye and skin irritant
Storage: Store in closed containers away from heat and open flames; avoid contact with strong oxidizers, alkalies.

Emersol® 6333 NF. [Henkel/Emery]
Chem. Descrip.: Low-linoleic content oleic acid USP/NF
CAS 112-80-1; EINECS 204-007-1
Uses: Emulsifier, solubilizer for mfg. of ointments; pharmaceutic aid
Regulatory: FDA 21CFR §172.860; EPA-exempt
Properties: Lt. clear liq., fatty acid odor; insol. in water; sp.gr. 0.891 (25/20 C); m.p. 14 C; b.p. 286 C (100 mm); acid no. 200-204; iodine no. 86-91; flash pt. (CC) 184-189 C
Toxicology: LD50 (oral, rat) > 21.5 ml/kg; mild eye, moderate skin irritant
Storage: Store in closed containers away from heat and open flames; avoid contact with strong oxidizers, alkalies.

Emerwax® 1257. [Henkel/Cospha; Henkel Canada]
Chem. Descrip.: Emulsifying wax NF
CAS 97069-99-0
Uses: Emulsifier for pharmaceutical creams and lotions
Properties: Gardner < 2 wax; sol. @ 5% in triolein, IPA; disp. in water; dens. 8.1 lb/gal; m.p. 48-52 C; flash pt. 355 F; iodine no. 3.5 max.; sapon. no. 14 max.; 100% act.; nonionic.

Emerwax® 1266. [Henkel/Cospha; Henkel Canada]
Chem. Descrip.: Cetearyl alcohol and ceteareth-20
Uses: BP type self-emulsifying base; o/w emulsifier for pharmaceuticals, creams, lotions, antiperspirants
Properties: Wh. waxy solid; sol. in IPA; disp. in min. oil, triolein; dens. 8.0 lb/gal; m.p. 47-55 C; flash pt. 355 F; acid no. 1 max.; iodine no. 2 max.; sapon. no. 5 max.; 100% act.; nonionic.

Emery® 912. [Henkel/Emery]
Chem. Descrip.: Glycerin CP/USP
CAS 56-81-5; EINECS 200-289-5
Uses: Visc. modifier, flavor enhancer, moisturizer,

solv., humectant, thickener, and solubilizer in drug vehicles
Regulatory: EPA-exempt
Properties: Water-wh. visc. liq.; odorless; sol. in water; sp.gr. 1.2517; m.p. 18 C; b.p. 171 C; pour pt. 18 C; flash pt. (CC) 199 C; 96.0% min. glycerol.
Toxicology: TLV:TWA 10 mg/m³ (mist); LD50 (oral, rat) 12.6 g/kg; mild eye irritant, moderate skin irritant; inhalation of mist may cause respiratory irritation
Storage: Store in cool, dry area; avoid excessive heat, open flames; incompat. with strong acids and oxidizers.

Emery® 916. [Henkel/Emery]
Chem. Descrip.: Glycerin CP/USP
CAS 56-81-5; EINECS 200-289-5
Uses: Visc. modifier, flavor enhancer, moisturizer, solv., humectant, thickener, and solubilizer in drug vehicles
Regulatory: EPA-exempt
Properties: Water-wh. visc. liq.; odorless; sol. in water; sp.gr. 1.2607; m.p. 18 C; b.p. 171 C; pour pt. 18 C; flash pt. (CC) 199 C; 99.5% min. glycerol
Toxicology: TLV:TWA 10 mg/m³ (mist); LD50 (oral, rat) 12.6 g/kg; mild eye irritant, moderate skin irritant; inhalation of mist may cause respiratory irritation
Storage: Store in cool, dry area; avoid excessive heat, open flames; incompat. with strong acids and oxidizers.

Emery® 917. [Henkel/Emery]
Chem. Descrip.: Glycerin CP/USP kosher
CAS 56-81-5; EINECS 200-289-5
Uses: Visc. modifier, flavor enhancer, moisturizer, solv., humectant, thickener, and solubilizer in drug vehicles
Properties: Water-wh. liq.; sol. in water; sp.gr. 1.2607; m.p. 18 C; b.p. 171 C; flash pt. (CC) 199 C; 99.7% min. glycerol.
Toxicology: TLV:TWA 10 mg/m³ (mist); LD50 (oral, rat) 12.6 g/kg; mild eye irritant, moderate skin irritant; inhalation of mist may cause respiratory irritation
Storage: Store in cool, dry area; avoid excessive heat, open flames; incompat. with strong acids and oxidizers.

Emery® 918. [Henkel/Emery]
Chem. Descrip.: Glycerin CP/USP
CAS 56-81-5; EINECS 200-289-5
Uses: Visc. modifier, flavor enhancer, moisturizer, solv., humectant, thickener, and solubilizer in drug vehicles
Properties: Water-wh. liq.; sol. in water; sp.gr. 1.2612; m.p. 18 C; b.p. 171 C; flash pt. (CC) 199 C; 99.8% min. glycerol.
Toxicology: TLV:TWA 10 mg/m³ (mist); LD50 (oral, rat) 12.6 g/kg; mild eye irritant, moderate skin irritant; inhalation of mist may cause respiratory irritation
Storage: Store in cool, dry area; avoid excessive heat, open flames; incompat. with strong acids and oxidizers.

Emery® 1650. [Henkel/Cospha; Henkel Canada]
Chem. Descrip.: Anhyd. lanolin USP
CAS 8006-54-0; EINECS 232-348-6
Uses: Emulsifier, emollient, conditioner, lubricant
Properties: Yel. amber paste; sol. @ 5% in IPM; disp. in min. oil, triolein; HLB 10.0; dens. 7.9 lb/gal; m.p. 36-42 C; flash pt. 530 F; 100% conc.; nonionic.

Emery® 1656. [Henkel/Cospha; Henkel Canada]
Chem. Descrip.: Anhyd. lanolin USP
CAS 8006-54-0; EINECS 232-348-6
Uses: Emulsifier, emollient, conditioner, moisturizer, pigment dispersant for pharmaceutical ointments
Properties: Gardner < -12 paste; sol. in IPM; disp. in min. oil, triolein; dens. 7.9 lb/gal; m.p. 36-42 C; flash pt. 530 F.

Emery® 1660. [Henkel/Cospha; Henkel Canada]
Chem. Descrip.: Ultra anhyd. lanolin USP, cosmetic grade
CAS 8006-54-0; EINECS 232-348-6
Uses: Emulsifier, emollient, conditioner, lubricant, moisturizer, pigment dispersant
Properties: Yel. amber paste; sol. in IPM; disp. in min. oil, triolein; dens. 7.9 lb/gal; m.p. 38-44 C; flash pt. 460 F.

Emery® 1732. [Henkel/Cospha; Henkel Canada]
Chem. Descrip.: Min. oil and lanolin alcohol
Uses: Liq. absorption base; emollient, emulsion stabilizer, moisturizer, emulsifier for creams, lotions, topical pharmaceuticals
Properties: Yel. to straw colored liq.; sol. in min. oil, triolein, IPA, IPM; disp. in glycerin; dens. 7.2 lb/gal; visc. 15 cSt (100 F); pour pt. < 4 C; flash pt. 360 F.

Emery® 1740. [Henkel/Cospha; Henkel Canada]
Chem. Descrip.: Petrolatum, lanolin, lanolin oil, and min. oil
Uses: Absorption base; emulsifier for w/o systems, emollient, moisturizer for pharmaceutical ointments; very high water absorp.
Properties: Yel. to straw colored soft solid; sol. in min. oil, IPM; disp. in triolein; dens. 7.4 lb/gal; m.p. 40-46 C; flash pt. 450 F; 100% conc.; nonionic.

Emery® 1747. [Henkel/Cospha; Henkel Canada]
Chem. Descrip.: Lanolin/lanolin alcohol blend in petrolatum base
Uses: Primary w/o emulsifier, aux. o/w emulsifier; emollient, moisturizer for pharmaceutical ointments
Properties: Gardner < 6 solid; sol. in min. oil, IPM; disp. in triolein; dens. 7.4 lb/gal; m.p. 40-46 C; flash pt. 425 F.

Emery® HP-2050. [Henkel/Cospha; Henkel Canada; Henkel KGaA/Cospha]
Chem. Descrip.: High purity anhyd. lanolin USP, strongly pesticide minimized
CAS 8006-54-0; EINECS 232-348-6
Uses: W/o coemulsifier, emollient, conditioner, moisturizer, pigment dispersant for pharmaceuticals, creams, lotions
Regulatory: USP, BP, Ph.Eur., DAB compliance

Properties: Yel. amber paste, weak intrinsic odor; m.p. 38-44 C; acid no. 1 max.; iodine no. 18-36; sapon. no. 90-105

Storage: 1 yr storage stability when stored in unopened orig. container below 30 C protected from moisture.

Emery® HP-2060. [Henkel/Cospha; Henkel Canada]
Chem. Descrip.: High purity ultra anhyd. lanolin
CAS 8006-54-0; EINECS 232-348-6
Uses: Emulsifier, emollient, conditioner, moisturizer, pigment dispersant for pharmaceuticals
Properties: Pale yel. amber paste, low odor; m.p. 38-44.

Emery® Methyl Oleate. [Henkel/Emery]
Chem. Descrip.: Methyl oleate
Uses: Defoaming component in pharmaceutical fermentation
Properties: Acid no. 4 max.; iodine no. 85-91; sapon. no. 190-200.

Empicol® 0185. [Albright & Wilson UK]
Chem. Descrip.: Sodium lauryl sulfate
CAS 151-21-3; EINECS 205-788-1
Uses: Wetting/rewetting agent, emulsifier, dispersant, disintegrator; used in pharmaceuticals, dental care, medical preps.
Properties: Wh. powd.; dens. 0.35 g/cm^3; pH 9.5-10.5 (1% aq.); 94.0% min. act.; anionic.

Empicol® 0303. [Albright & Wilson France]
Chem. Descrip.: Sodium lauryl sulfate, narrow cut
CAS 68585-47-7; EINECS 271-557-7
Uses: Surfactant in toothpaste and pharmaceutical preps.
Regulatory: BP, NF compliance
Properties: Wh. fine powd., odorless; sol. 250 g/l in water; m.w. 296; dens. 0.35 g/cc; pH 9 ± 0.5 (1% aq.); 95% min. act.; anionic; readily biodeg., unlikely to accumulate in aquatic environment; discharge of lg. quantities may kill fish
Toxicology: LD50 (oral, rat) > 2000 mg/kg; irritant to mouth, upper digestive tract; significant irritant to skin on prolonged/repeated exposure, eyes, nose, upper respiratory tract; do not breathe dust
Precaution: May react exothermically with strong acids with liberation of sulfuric acid; may react with strong oxidants; may cause dust explosion; combustion may produce fumes contg. CO_2, CO, SO_2; spillages may be slippery
Storage: Hygroscopic; store in cool, dry area.

Empicol® 0303VA. [Albright & Wilson France]
Chem. Descrip.: Sodium lauryl sulfate, narrow cut
CAS 68585-47-7; EINECS 271-557-7
Uses: Surfactant in toothpaste and pharmaceutical preps.
Regulatory: BP, NF compliance
Properties: Wh./cream needles, odorless; sol. 250 g/l in water; dens. 0.5 g/cm^3; pH 9 ± 0.5 (1% aq.); 94% min. act.; anionic; readily biodeg., unlikely to accumulate in aquatic environment; discharge of lg. quantities may kill fish
Toxicology: LD50 (oral, rat) > 2000 mg/kg; irritant to mouth, upper digestive tract, nose, upper respiratory tract; significant irritant to skin on pro-

longed/repeated exposure, eyes; do not breathe dust
Precaution: May react exothermically with strong acids with liberation of sulfuric acid; may react with strong oxidants; may cause dust explosion; combustion may produce fumes contg. CO_2, CO, SO_2; spillages may be slippery
Storage: Hygroscopic; store in cool, dry area.

Empicol® LX. [Albright & Wilson Am.; Albright & Wilson UK]
Chem. Descrip.: Sodium lauryl sulfate
CAS 68585-47-7
Uses: Compounding aid for pharmaceutical creams
Properties: Wh. powd.; dens. 0.35 g/cc; pH 9.5-10.5 (1% aq.); 90% act.; anionic.

Empicol® LX100. [Albright & Wilson Am.; Albright & Wilson UK]
Chem. Descrip.: Sodium lauryl sulfate
CAS 151-21-3; EINECS 205-788-1
Uses: Surfactant in toothpaste, pharmaceutical preps.
Properties: Powd.; 97% act.; anionic.

Empicol® LXS95. [Albright & Wilson UK]
Chem. Descrip.: Sodium lauryl sulfate
CAS 151-21-3; EINECS 205-788-1
Uses: Foamer, emulsifier used in toothpaste, pharmaceuticals
Properties: Wh. powd.; dens 0.35 g/cc; pH 9.6-10.5 (1% aq.); 94.0% min. act.; anionic.

Empicol® LXV100. [Albright & Wilson Am.; Albright & Wilson UK]
Chem. Descrip.: Sodium lauryl sulfate
CAS 151-21-3; EINECS 205-788-1
Uses: Surfactant in toothpaste, pharmaceutical preps.
Properties: Needles; 95% act.; anionic.

Empicol® LXV/D. [Albright & Wilson UK]
Chem. Descrip.: Sodium lauryl sulfate USP, BP
CAS 151-21-3; EINECS 205-788-1
Uses: Surfactant in mfg. of toothpaste
Properties: Wh. needles; sp.gr. 0.5 g/cc; pH 9.5-10.5 (5% aq.); 90% act.; anionic.

Empicol® LZ. [Albright & Wilson UK]
Chem. Descrip.: Sodium lauryl sulfate
CAS 68955-19-1
Uses: Compounding aid for pharmaceutical creams
Properties: Wh. powd.; dens. 0.35 g/cc; pH 9.5-10.5 (1% aq.); 89.0% min. act.; anionic.

Empicol® LZ/D. [Albright & Wilson France]
Chem. Descrip.: Sodium lauryl sulfate, broad cut
CAS 68955-19-1; EINECS 273-257-1
Uses: Surfactant in toothpaste, pharmaceutical preps.
Regulatory: BP, EP, NF compliance
Properties: Wh. fine powd., mildly aggressive odor; sol. 250 g/l in water; dens. 0.3 g/cm^3; pH 9.5-10.5 (1% aq.); 90% min. act.; anionic; readily biodeg.; unlikely to accumulate in aquatic environment; discharge of lg. quantities may kill fish
Toxicology: LD50 (oral, rat) > 2000 mg/kg; irritant

to mouth, upper digestive tract, nose, upper respiratory tract; significant irritant to skin on prolonged/repeated exposure, eyes; do not breathe dust

Precaution: May react exothermically with strong acids with liberation of sulfuric acid; may react with strong oxidants; may cause dust explosion; combustion may produce fumes contg. CO_2, CO, SO_2; spillages may be slippery

Storage: Hygroscopic; store in cool, dry area.

Empicol® LZV/D. [Albright & Wilson France]
Chem. Descrip.: Sodium lauryl sulfate, broad cut
CAS 68955-19-1; EINECS 273-257-1
Uses: Surfactant in toothpaste, pharmaceutical preps.
Regulatory: BP, EP, NF compliance
Properties: Wh. to cream fine needles, odorless; sol. 250 g/l in water; dens. 0.5 g/cm³; pH 9.5-10.5 (1% aq.); 90% min. act.; anionic; readily biodeg.; unlikely to accumulate in aquatic environment; discharge of lg. quantities may kill fish
Toxicology: LD50 (oral, rat) > 2000 mg/kg; irritant to mouth, upper digestive tract, nose, upper respiratory tract; significant irritant to skin on prolonged/repeated exposure, eyes; do not breathe dust
Precaution: May react exothermically with strong acids with liberation of sulfuric acid; may react with strong oxidants; may cause dust explosion; combustion may produce fumes contg. CO_2, CO, SO_2; spillages may be slippery
Storage: Hygroscopic; store in cool, dry area.

Empigen® 5073. [Albright & Wilson UK]
Chem. Descrip.: Lauryl dimethylamine
CAS 67700-98-5; EINECS 266-922-2
Uses: Bactericide precursor for pharmaceutical applics.
Properties: Colorless liq., char. odor; sol. in ethanol; insol. in water; dens. 0.8; m.p. -4 C; b.p. > 200 C; flash pt. > 110 C; pH strongly alkaline; readily biodeg.; unlikely to accumulate in aquatic environment; discharge of lg. quantities may kill fish
Toxicology: Corrosive; harmful if swallowed; may burn mouth and upper digestive tract, skin; may cause severe, possibly permanent eye injury
Precaution: May react with strong oxidants; may react exothermically with acids; combustion may produce fumes contg. CO_2, CO, amine vapors, NO_x; spillages may be slippery
Storage: Store in tightly closed containers @ 5-40 C away from acids and strong oxidants.

Empigen® 5089. [Albright & Wilson UK]
Chem. Descrip.: Laurtrimonium chloride
CAS 112-00-5; EINECS 203-927-0
Uses: Bactericide for antiseptic detergents in pharmaceuticals
Properties: Pale yel. liq.; sp.gr. 0.97; pH 5.5-8.5; 34 ± 2% act. in water; cationic.

Empigen® BAC50. [Albright & Wilson UK]
Chem. Descrip.: Benzalkonium chloride NF
Uses: Bactericide for disinfectants, antiseptics in pharmaceuticals

Properties: Pale straw liq.; misc. with water, alcohol, acetone; sp.gr. 0.99; pH 7-9 (5%); 50% act.; cationic.

Empigen® BAC50/BP. [Albright & Wilson UK]
Chem. Descrip.: Benzalkonium chloride, 50% aq.
CAS 68989-00-4; EINECS 273-544-1
Uses: Bactericide for disinfectants, antiseptics in pharmaceuticals
Regulatory: BP, EP, NF compliance
Properties: Pale straw clear liq., char. odor; misc. with water; m.w. 354; dens. 0.99 g/cm³; visc. 120 mPa•s; m.p. < 0 C; b.p. 100 C; pH 5.25 ± 0.25 (5%); 50% act.; cationic; biodeg., unlikely to accumulate in aquatic environment; discharge of lg. quantities may kill fish
Toxicology: Corrosive; harmful if swallowed; may burn mouth, upper digestive tract, skin; may cause severe, possible permanent eye damage
Precaution: May react with strong oxidants; combustion may produce fumes contg. CO_2, CO, amine vapors, NO_x; spillages may be slippery
Storage: Store in tightly closed containers @ 5-40 C away from strong oxidants.

Empigen® BAC90. [Albright & Wilson UK]
Chem. Descrip.: Benzalkonium chloride
Uses: Bactericide for disinfectants, antiseptics in pharmaceuticals
Properties: Gel; 90% conc.; cationic.

Empigen® OB. [Albright & Wilson Am.; Albright & Wilson UK]
Chem. Descrip.: Lauramine oxide
CAS 1643-20-5; EINECS 216-700-6
Uses: Foaming agent for surgical scrubs
Properties: Pale straw liq.; dens. 0.98 g/cc; visc. 25 cs (20 C); pH 7.5 ± 0.5 (5% aq.); 30.0 ± 1.5% act.; nonionic.

Empilan® P7061. [Albright & Wilson Italy]
Chem. Descrip.: EO/PO block polymer
CAS 9003-11-6
Uses: Compounding aid for pharmaceuticals
Properties: Pract. colorless liq., char. odor; sol. > 100 g/l in water, ethanol; m.w. 2000; dens. 1.01 g/cm³; visc. 300 mPa•s; m.p. < -10 C; b.p. 145 C; hyd. no. 56.25; cloud pt. 39-43 C (10% in 25% BDG); pH 6.5 ± 1.5 (2.5%); surf. tens. 45.3 dynes/cm (0.1 g/l); 100% conc.; nonionic; discharge of lg quantities may kill fish
Toxicology: LD50 (oral, rat) > 2000 mg/kg; not classified hazardous; may cause irritation to mouth, upper digestive tract, skin on prolonged/repeated exposure, eye
Precaution: May react with strong oxidants; combustion may produce fumes contg. CO_2, CO; spillages may be slippery
Storage: Store in tightly closed containers @ 5-40 C away from strong oxidants.

Empilan® P7062. [Albright & Wilson Italy]
Chem. Descrip.: EO/PO block polymer
CAS 9003-11-6
Uses: Compounding aid for pharmaceuticals
Properties: Pract. colorless liq.; m.w. 2500; dens. 1.03 g/cm³; visc. 400 mPa•s; hyd. no. 45 ± 2;

cloud pt. 57-61 C (10% in 25% BDG); pH 6.25 ± 1.25 (2.5%); surf. tens. 45. 3 dynes/cm (0.1 g/l); 100% conc.; nonionic
Toxicology: Not classified hazardous.

Empilan® P7087. [Albright & Wilson Italy]
Chem. Descrip.: EO/PO block polymer
CAS 9003-11-6
Uses: Compounding aid for pharmaceuticals
Properties: Wh. flake; m.w. 7845 ± 1075; m.p. 50 C; hyd. no. 14.6; cloud pt. 66 C (0.5 g in 10% NaCl); pH 7.0 ± 1.0 (1%); 100% conc.; nonionic
Toxicology: Not classified hazardous.

Empiwax SK. [Albright & Wilson UK]
Chem. Descrip.: Cetearyl alcohol and sodium lauryl sulfate
Uses: SE wax as o/w emulsifier for pharmaceutical preps. and ointments
Properties: Wh. flake; 100% conc.

Empiwax SK/BP. [Albright & Wilson UK]
Chem. Descrip.: Cetearyl alcohol (CAS 67762-27-0/EINECS 267-008-6) and sodium lauryl sulfate (CAS 68955-19-1/EINECS 273-257-1)
Uses: SE wax as o/w emulsifier for pharmaceutical creams and lotions
Regulatory: Complies with BP specs. for emulsifying wax
Properties: Wh. waxy flake, mild char. odor; emulsifiable in water; bulk dens. 0.4 g/cm^3; m.p. 50 C; acid no. 0.2 max.; sapon. no. 2 max.; flash pt. > 150 C; 100% conc.; readily biodeg., unlikely to accumulate in aquatic environment; discharge of lg. quantities may kill fish
Toxicology: LD50 (oral, rat) > 2000 mg/kg; not classified hazardous; may cause irritation to mouth, upper digestive tract, skin on prolonged/repeated exposure, eyes
Precaution: May react exothermically with strong acids with liberation of sulfuric acid; may react with strong oxidants; combustion may produce fumes contg. CO_2, CO, SO_2; spillages may be slippery
Storage: Store @ 5-10 C above m.p. (liq. molten form); store in dry area below m.p. (solid form); store away from heat, humidity, strong oxidants.

Emulgade® 1000 NI. [Henkel/Cospha; Henkel Canada; Henkel KGaA/Cospha]
Chem. Descrip.: Cetearyl alcohol and ceteareth-20
Uses: SE raw material for prod. of liq. o/w emulsions and creams
Regulatory: BP compliance for cetomacrogol emulsifying wax
Properties: Wh. flakes, faint char. odor; solid. pt. 48-53 C; acid no. 0.5 max.; sapon. no. 1 max.; hyd. no. 175-190; ref. index 1.435-1.439 (60 C); pH 6-8 (1%); nonionic
Storage: 1 yr min. storage life in closed containers at temps. below 40 C, protected from moisture.

Emulgade® F. [Henkel/Cospha; Henkel Canada; Henkel KGaA/Cospha]
Chem. Descrip.: Cetearyl alcohol, PEG-40 castor oil, and sodium cetearyl sulfate
Uses: SE raw material for pharmaceutical creams, ointments, o/w emulsions
Properties: Wh. to sl. yel. gran.; sapon. no. 10-15; hyd. no. 160-175; pH 6.5-8.0 (1%); 95% fatty matter; anionic
Storage: 1 yr min. storage life in closed containers at temps. below 30 C, protected against moisture.

Emulgade® SE. [Henkel KGaA/Cospha]
Chem. Descrip.: Glyceryl stearate, ceteareth-20, ceteareth-12, cetearyl alcohol, and cetyl palmitate
Uses: Self-emulsifying wax mixt. with nonionic emulsifiers for mfg. of heat- and visc.-stable pharmaceutical o/w emulsions
Properties: Acid no. 1 max.; sapon. no. 90-100; hyd. no. 145-160
Storage: 1 yr storage stability in sealed original containers at temps. below 30 C.

Emulgator E 2149. [Goldschmidt; Goldschmidt AG]
Chem. Descrip.: Steareth-7, stearyl alcohol
Uses: Self-emulsifying emulsifier and stabilizer for pharmaceutical o/w emulsions; resist. to acid and alkaline substances
Properties: Wh.-ivory waxy solid; sol. warm in veg. and min. oils; disp. warm in water; m.p. 41-47 C; HLB 11.0; acid no. 2 max.; iodine no. 2 max.; sapon. no. 3 max.; 100% conc.; nonionic.

Emulgator E 2155. [Goldschmidt; Goldschmidt AG]
Chem. Descrip.: Stearyl alcohol, steareth-7, steareth-10
Uses: Self-emulsifying emulsifier and stabilizer for pharmaceutical o/w emulsions; resist. to acid and alkaline substances
Properties: Wh.-ivory waxy solid; sol. warm in veg. oils, sol. warm with sl. turbidity in min. oil; disp. warm in water; m.p. 49-55 C; HLB 11.0; acid no. 2 max.; iodine no. 2 max.; sapon. no. 3 max.; 100% conc.; nonionic.

Emulgator E 2568. [Goldschmidt; Goldschmidt AG]
Chem. Descrip.: Ceteareth-25
CAS 68439-49-6
Uses: Emulsifier and stabilizer for pharmaceutical o/w emulsions; resist. to acid and alkaline substances
Properties: Wh.-ivory waxy solid; sol. warm in water; disp. warm in veg. and min. oils; m.p. 43-49 C; HLB 16.0; acid no. 2 max.; iodine no. 1 max.; sapon. no. 3 max.; 100% conc.; nonionic.

Emulmetik™ 970. [Lucas Meyer]
Chem. Descrip.: Egg lecithin
CAS 8002-43-5; EINECS 232-307-2
Uses: Resorbable refatting agent, solubilizer, coemulsifier, nourishing and wetting agent for pharmaceutical preps., creams, lotions; prevents sedimentation; regulates water-binding capacity of the skin
Properties: Yel.-brn. paste; sol. in ether, ethanol, chlorinated hydrocarbons; sol. @ 50 C in fat, paraffin oil; disp. in water; acid no. 25 max.; iodine no. 80 max.

Emulsifier D-1. [Stepan Food Ingreds.]
Chem. Descrip.: Decaglyceryl hexaoleate
Uses: Emulsifier for pharmaceutical applics.

Properties: Amber clear to hazy liq.; acid no. 2; iodine no. 70; sapon. no. 152.5; hyd. no. 107; 0.1% moisture
Custom product

Emulsynt® 1055. [ISP Van Dyk]
Chem. Descrip.: Polyglyceryl-4 oleate, PEG-8 propylene glycol cocoate
Uses: Emulsifier for w/o creams and lotions, pharmaceutical ointments; stabilizer and aux. emulsifier for o/w systems
Properties: Lt. amber liq.; sol. @ 5% in peanut and min. oils, 95% ethanol, IPM, oleyl alcohol; gels in glycerin; insol. in water; sp.gr. 0.960-0.980; acid no. 5 max.; iodine no. 58-68; sapon. no. 142-152; 100% conc.; nonionic.

Emvelop®. [Mendell]
Chem. Descrip.: Hydrogenated veg. oil NF
CAS 68334-00-9; EINECS 269-804-9
Uses: Binder/vehicle for prod. of sustained-release tablet formulations by direct compression; also suitable for wet granulations
Properties: Fine powd.; 25% max. -200 mesh; dens. (tapped) 0.57 g/ml; m.p. 61-66 C; iodine no. 5 max.; sapon. no. 188-198
Storage: Stable when stored in tightly closed containers under ambient conditions.

Encapsin HPB. [Janssen Biotech NV]
Chem. Descrip.: Hydroxypropyl-β-cyclodextrin
CAS 94035-02-6
Uses: Drug delivery system for oral, parenteral, and local pharmaceuticals
Regulatory: Patented in Europe.

Encapsin HPG. [Janssen Biotech NV]
Chem. Descrip.: Hydroxypropyl-γ-cyclodextrin
CAS 99241-25-5
Uses: Drug delivery system for oral, parenteral, and local pharmaceuticals.

Epal® 16NF. [Albemarle]
Chem. Descrip.: Hexadecanol USP/NF
CAS 36653-82-4; EINECS 253-149-0
Uses: Emulsifier intermediate
Properties: Wh. waxy solid, mild char. odor; m.w. 242; sp.gr. 0.818 g/ml; dens. 6.83 lb/gal; f.p. 44 C; flash pt. (PMCC) 175 C; hyd. no. 232; 100% conc.
Toxicology: Temporary irritation on direct skin or eye contact
Storage: Protect against water contamination by blanketing with inert gas or dry air.

Epal® 18NF. [Albemarle]
Chem. Descrip.: Octadecanol USP/NF
CAS 112-92-5; EINECS 204-017-6
Uses: Emulsifier intermediate for deodorants
Properties: Wh. waxy solid, mild char. odor; m.w. 270; sp.gr. 0.812 g/ml; dens. 6.78 lb/gal; f.p. 54 C; flash pt. (PMCC) 191 C; hyd. no. 207; 100% conc.
Toxicology: Temporary irritation on direct skin or eye contact
Storage: Protect against water contamination by blanketing with inert gas or dry air.

Epikuron™ 145. [Lucas Meyer]
Chem. Descrip.: Phosphatidylcholine enriched fraction of soya phospholipids

Uses: Carrier, wetting agent, stabilizer, emulsifier, and choline enrichment for pharmaceutical applics.
Properties: 45% conc.

Epikuron™ 170. [Lucas Meyer]
Chem. Descrip.: Conc. phosphatidylcholine from soya
Uses: Carrier, emulsifier, choline enrichment for pharmaceuticals
Proprties: 70% conc.

Epikuron™ 200. [Lucas Meyer]
Chem. Descrip.: Isolated phosphatidylcholine from soya
Uses: Carrier, emulsifier, choline enrichment for pharmaceuticals and liposomes
Properties: 95% conc.

Epikuron™ H. [Lucas Meyer]
Chem. Descrip.: Range of soya phospholipids
Uses: Hydrophilic emulsifier, dispersant for pharmaceuticals and liposomes
Properties: Powd.

Eromenth®. [Commodity Services Int'l.]
Chem. Descrip.: Oil obtained from subspecies of *Mentha spicata* contg. no carvone or menthol; avail. as field mint oil or rectified oil
Uses: Peppermint-like oil without cooling and irritating effects of menthol; flavoring for pharmaceuticals, toothpaste, mouthwash
Properties: Colorless to pale yel. liq., aromatic odor of mint; sl. sol. in water; sp.gr. 0.894 g/cc; b.p. 209 C; flash pt. 67 C; ref. index 1.4552; biodeg.
Storage: Store in cool, well ventilated area, void of ignition sources.

Escalol® 507. [ISP Van Dyk]
Chem. Descrip.: Octyl dimethyl PABA
CAS 21245-02-3; EINECS 244-289-3
Uses: Nonstaining uv-B absorber for topical sunscreens
Properties: Pale yel. mobile liq., very mild char. odor; sol. in min. and peanut oil, ethanol, IPA; insol. in water; m.w. 277; sp.gr. 0.990-1.000; HLB 10-12; acid no. 1 max.; sapon. no. 195-215; ref. index 1.5390-1.5430; 98% min. purity
Toxicology: LD50 (oral, rat) 14.9 g/kg; pract. nonirritating to eyes; nonirritating, nonsensitizing to skin.

Escalol® 557. [ISP Van Dyk]
Chem. Descrip.: Octyl methoxycinnamate
CAS 5466-77-3; EINECS 226-775-7
Uses: Nonstaining uv-B absorber for sunscreens, esp. waterproof formulations; imparts emolliency to emulsions without being tacky or oily
Properties: Pale yel. liq. with slight odor; sol. in peanut oil, min. oil, ethanol (95%, 100%), oleyl alcohol, castor oil, IPM, cyclomethicone; m.w. 290.4; sp.gr. 1.005-1.013; HLB 6-8; acid no. 1 max.; sapon. no. 189 min.; ref. index 1.542-1.548; 98% min. purity
Toxicology: Minimally irritating to eyes; mildly irritating to skin.

Escalol® 567. [ISP Van Dyk]
Chem. Descrip.: Benzophenone-3
CAS 131-57-7; EINECS 205-031-5

Uses: Uv-A absorber for formulation of high-SPF sunscreens
Properties: Slightly ylsh. fine cryst. powd.; sol. in peanut oil, ethanol, oleyl alcohol, castor oil; m.w. 228.25; m.p. 62 C min.; 97% min. assay.

Escalol® 587. [ISP Van Dyk]
Chem. Descrip.: Octyl salicylate
CAS 118-60-5; EINECS 204-263-4
Uses: Uv-B sunscreen for high-SPF formulations; boosts efficacy of other sunscreen actives; solubilizer for benzophenone-3
Properties: Colorless to pale yel. liq., typ. bland odor; sol. in IPA, ethanol, min. oil, dimethicone, cyclomethicone, IPM, octyl palmitate; m.w. 250.34; sp.gr. 1.013-1.022; acid no. 2 max.; sapon. no. 200-230; ref. index 1.495-1.505
Toxicology: LD50 (oral, rat) < 5 g/kg; minimally irritating to eyes; mildly irritating to skin; nonsensitizing.

Escalol® 597. [ISP Van Dyk]
Chem. Descrip.: Octocrylene
CAS 6197-30-4; EINECS 228-250-8
Uses: Uv-B sunscreen used when high SPF values are required; esp. for water-resistant formulations
Properties: Yel. clear visc. liq., bland odor; sol. @ 5% in ethanol, castor oil, IPM, hexylene glycol, IPA; disp. in min. oil, dimethicone; insol. in water; m.w. 361; f.p. -10 C; 98% min. assay
Toxicology: LD50 (oral, rat) > 64 ml/kg; nonirritating to eyes; minimally irritating to skin.

Espholip. [Lucas Meyer]
Chem. Descrip.: Semisyn. phosphatidylcholine
Uses: Emulsifier, encapsulation aid for pharmaceuticals and liposomes.

Essential Aloe™ GII-1X. [Garuda Int'l.]
Chem. Descrip.: Aloe vera gel
Uses: Stabilized prod. for pharmaceutical industry; avail. in natural and purified grades.

Essential Aloe™ GII-10X. [Garuda Int'l.]
Chem. Descrip.: Aloe vera gel, ten-fold stabilized liq. conc.
Uses: Stabilized prod. for pharmaceutical industry; avail. in natural and purified grades.

Essential Aloe™ GII-40X. [Garuda Int'l.]
Chem. Descrip.: Aloe vera gel, forty-fold stabilized liq. conc.
Uses: Stabilized prod. for pharmaceutical industry; avail. in natural and purified grades.

Essential Aloe™ GII-100X. [Garuda Int'l.]
Chem. Descrip.: Aloe vera gel, hundred-fold powd. conc.
Uses: Stabilized prod. for pharmaceutical industry; avail. in natural and purified grades
Properties: Powd.

Essential Aloe™ GII-200X. [Garuda Int'l.]
Chem. Descrip.: Aloe vera gel, two hundred-fold powd. conc.
Uses: Stabilized prod. for pharmaceutical industry; avail. in natural and purified grades
Properties: Powd.

Estaram 299. [Unichema Int'l.; Unichema N. Am.]
Chem. Descrip.: Natural sat. fatty acid glycerides

Uses: Excipient, base for suppositories
Properties: Wh. to off-wh. flakes or pellets; m.p. 33.5-35.5 C; acid no. 0.2 max.; sapon. no. 240-255; hyd. no. 2 max.
Storage: Store @ R.T. in a dry atmosphere.

Estaram A. [Unichema Int'l.; Unichema N. Am.]
Chem. Descrip.: Natural sat. fatty acid glycerides
Uses: Excipient, base for suppositories
Properties: Wh. to off-wh. flakes or pellets; m.p. 33.0-35.0 C; acid no. 0.3 max.; sapon. no. 225-245; hyd. no. 35-45
Storage: Store @ R.T. in a dry atmosphere.

Estaram H5. [Unichema Int'l.; Unichema N. Am.]
Chem. Descrip.: Natural sat. fatty acid glycerides
Uses: Excipient, base for suppositories
Properties: Wh. to off-wh. flakes or pellets; m.p. 34-36 C; acid no. 0.2 max.; sapon. no. 235-245; hyd. no. 5 max.
Storage: Store @ R.T. in a dry atmosphere.

Estaram H15. [Unichema Int'l.; Unichema N. Am.]
Chem. Descrip.: Natural sat. fatty acid glycerides
Uses: Excipient, base for suppositories
Properties: Wh. to off-wh. flakes or pellets; m.p. 33.5-35.5 C; acid no. 0.2 max.; sapon. no. 230-240 ; hyd. no. 5-15
Storage: Store @ R.T. in a dry atmosphere.

Estaram H37. [Unichema Int'l.; Unichema N. Am.]
Chem. Descrip.: Natural sat. fatty acid glycerides
Uses: Excipient, base for suppositories
Properties: Wh. to off-wh. flakes or pellets; m.p. 36-38 C; acid no. 0.2 max.; sapon. no. 225-245; hyd. no. 3 max.
Storage: Store @ R.T. in a dry atmosphere.

Estaram S55. [Unichema Int'l.; Unichema N. Am.]
Chem. Descrip.: Natural sat. fatty acid glycerides
Uses: Excipient, base for suppositories
Properties: Wh. to off-wh. flakes or pellets; m.p. 33.5-35.5 C; acid no. 1.0 max.; sapon. no. 215-235; hyd. no. 50-65
Storage: Store @ R.T. in a dry atmosphere.

Estaram S58. [Unichema Int'l.; Unichema N. Am.]
Chem. Descrip.: Natural sat. fatty acid glycerides
Uses: Excipient, base for suppositories
Properties: Wh. to off-wh. flakes or pellets; m.p. 32-33.5 C; acid no. 1 max.; sapon. no. 215-225; hyd. no. 60-70
Storage: Store @ R.T. in a dry atmosphere.

Estaram W25. [Unichema Int'l.; Unichema N. Am.]
Chem. Descrip.: Natural sat. fatty acid glycerides
Uses: Excipient, base for suppositories
Properties: Wh. to off-wh. flakes or pellets; m.p. 33.5-35.5 C; acid no. 0.3 max.; sapon. no. 225-240; hyd. no. 20-30
Storage: Store @ R.T. in a dry atmosphere.

Estaram W45. [Unichema Int'l.; Unichema N. Am.]
Chem. Descrip.: Natural sat. fatty acid glycerides
Uses: Excipient, base for suppositories
Properties: Wh. to off-wh. flakes or pellets; m.p. 33.5-35.5 C; acid no. 0.3 max.; sapon. no. 225-235; hyd. no. 40-50
Storage: Store @ R.T. in a dry atmosphere.

Estasan GT 8-40 3578. [Unichema Int'l.; Unichema N.

Am.]

Chem. Descrip.: Caprylic/capric triglyceride (40% C8 + 60% C10)

CAS 65381-09-1; EINECS 265-724-3

Uses: Solv. and carrier for drugs, flavors, fragrances; fat source in dietetic prods., enteral and parenteral feeding formulae; spreading/penetrating aid; lubricant for mfg. of soft gelatin capsules; creams and lotions

Regulatory: BP, DAB compliance; Japan approval

Properties: Lovibond 5Y/0.5R oil, odorless, bland taste; visc. 29 mPa•s; acid no. 0.1 max.; iodine no. 2 max.; sapon. no. 300-315; hyd. no. 5 max.; cloud pt. 10 C; readily biodeg.

Storage: Store @ R.T. in dry atmosphere.

Estasan GT 8-60 3575. [Unichema Int'l.; Unichema N. Am.]

Chem. Descrip.: Caprylic/capric triglyceride (60% C8 + 40% C10)

CAS 65381-09-1; EINECS 265-724-3

Uses: Solv. and carrier for drugs, flavors, fragrances; fat source in dietetic prods., enteral and parenteral feeding formulae; spreading/penetrating aid; lubricant for mfg. of soft gelatin capsules; creams and lotions

Regulatory: BP, DAB compliance; Japan approval

Properties: Lovibond 5Y/0.5R oil, odorless, bland taste; visc. 23 mPa•s; acid no. 0.1 max.; iodine no. 0.5 max.; sapon. no. 325-345; hyd. no. 5 max.; cloud pt. -8 C; readily biodeg.

Storage: Store @ R.T. in dry atmosphere.

Estasan GT 8-60 3580. [Unichema Int'l.; Unichema N. Am.]

Chem. Descrip.: Caprylic/capric triglyceride (60% C8 + 40% C10)

CAS 65381-09-1; EINECS 265-724-3

Uses: Solv. and carrier for drugs, flavors, fragrances; fat source in dietetic prods., enteral and parenteral feeding formulae; spreading/penetrating aid; lubricant for mfg. of soft gelatin capsules; creams and lotions

Regulatory: BP, DAB compliance; Japan approval; kosher

Properties: Lovibond 5Y/0.5R oil, odorless, bland taste; visc. 23 mPa•s; acid no. 0.1 max.; iodine no. 0.5 max.; sapon. no. 325-345; hyd. no. 5 max.; cloud pt. -8 C; readily biodeg.

Storage: Store @ R.T. in dry atmosphere.

Estasan GT 8-65 3577. [Unichema Int'l.; Unichema N. Am.]

Chem. Descrip.: Caprylic/capric triglyceride (65% C8 + 35% C10)

CAS 65381-09-1; EINECS 265-724-3

Uses: Solv. and carrier for drugs, flavors, fragrances; fat source in dietetic prods., enteral and parenteral feeding formulae; spreading/penetrating aid; lubricant for mfg. of soft gelatin capsules; creams and lotions

Regulatory: BP, DAB compliance; Japan approval

Properties: Lovibond 5Y/0.5R oil, odorless, bland taste; visc. 23 mPa•s; acid no. 0.1 max.; iodine no. 0.5 max.; sapon. no. 325-360; hyd. no. 5 max.;

cloud pt. -5 C; readily biodeg.

Storage: Store @ R.T. in atmosphere.

Estasan GT 8-65 3581. [Unichema Int'l.; Unichema N. Am.]

Chem. Descrip.: Caprylic/capric triglyceride (65% C8 + 35% C10)

CAS 65381-09-1; EINECS 265-724-3

Uses: Solv. and carrier for drugs, flavors, fragrances; fat source in dietetic prods., enteral and parenteral feeding formulae; spreading/penetrating aid; lubricant for mfg. of soft gelatin capsules; creams and lotions

Regulatory: BP, DAB compliance; Japan approval; kosher

Properties: Lovibond 5Y/0.5R oil, odorless, bland taste; visc. 23 mPa•s; acid no. 0.1 max.; iodine no. 0.5 max.; sapon. no. 335-360; hyd. no. 5 max.; cloud pt. -5 C; readily biodeg.

Storage: Store @ R.T. in dry atmosphere.

Estasan GT 8-70 3579. [Unichema Int'l.; Unichema N. Am.]

Chem. Descrip.: Caprylic/capric triglyceride (70% C8 + 25-30% C10)

CAS 65381-09-1; EINECS 265-724-3

Uses: Solv. and carrier for drugs, flavors, fragrances; fat source in dietetic prods., enteral and parenteral feeding formulae; spreading/penetrating aid; lubricant for mfg. of soft gelatin capsules; creams and lotions

Regulatory: BP, DAB compliance; Japan approval; kosher

Properties: Lovibond 5Y/0.5R oil, odorless, bland taste; visc. 23 mPa•s; acid no. 0.1 max.; iodine no. 0.5 max.; sapon. no. 335-360; hyd. no. 5 max.; cloud pt. -12 C; readily biodeg.

Storage: Store @ R.T. in dry atmosphere.

Ethocel Medium Premium. [Dow]

Chem. Descrip.: Ethylcellulose NF

CAS 9004-57-3

Uses: Used for pharmaceutical tablet coating, granulation, controlled release applics.

Properties: Visc. avail. 50, 70, and 100 cps.

Ethocel Standard Premium. [Dow]

Chem. Descrip.: Ethylcellulose NF

CAS 9004-57-3

Uses: Binders for pharmaceutical tableting

Properties: Visc. avail. 4, 7, 10, 20, 45, and 100 cps.

Ethomeen® C/25. [Akzo Nobel; Akzo Nobel bv]

Chem. Descrip.: PEG-15 cocamine

CAS 61791-14-8

Uses: Emulsifier; used in topical pharmaceuticals

Regulatory: FDA approved for topicals

Properties: Gardner 12 max. clear liq.; sol. in acetone, IPA, CCl$_4$, Stod., benzene, water; sp.gr. 1.04; HLB 19.3; flash pt. (COC) 500 F; surf. tens. 41 dynes/cm (0.1%); 100% conc.; cationic.

Ethosperse® G-26. [Lonza]

Chem. Descrip.: Glycereth-26

CAS 31694-55-0

Uses: Emulsifier, humectant for pharmaceuticals

Properties: Pale straw clear liq.; sol. in water, methanol, ethanol, acetone, toluol; sp.gr. 1.12 (38 C); visc. 150 cps (38 C); HLB 18.0; acid no. 0.5

max.; hyd. no. 128-138; pH 6.0 (5%); 100% conc.; nonionic.

Ethosperse® LA-4. [Lonza]
Chem. Descrip.: Laureth-4
CAS 9002-92-0; EINECS 226-097-1
Uses: Emulsifier for pharmaceuticals
Properties: Water-wh. liq.; sol. in methanol, ethanol, acetone, toluol, min. oil, misc. with water, veg. oils; sp.gr. 0.95; visc. 30 cps; HLB 10.0; acid no. 0.3 max.; hyd. no. 145-160; 100% act.; nonionic.

Ethosperse® LA-12. [Lonza]
Chem. Descrip.: Laureth-12
CAS 9002-92-0; EINECS 221-286-5
Uses: Emulsifier for pharmacueticals; anti-irritant in deodorants and antiperspirants
Properties: Gardner 1 max. turbid liq.; sol. in methanol, ethanol, acetone, toluol, min. oil, misc. with water, veg. oils; sp.gr. 1.10; visc. 1000 cps; HLB 15.0; acid no. 2 max.; hyd. no. 72-82; pH 7 (5%); 100% act.; nonionic.

Ethosperse® LA-23. [Lonza]
Chem. Descrip.: Laureth-23
CAS 9002-92-0
Uses: O/w emulsifier, thickener, stabilizer for pharmaceuticals; anti-irritant in deodorants and antiperspirants
Properties: Wh. waxy solid; sol. in water, hot ethanol; m.p. 30-45 C; HLB 17.0; acid no. 0.3 max.; hyd. no. 45-52; 100% conc.; nonionic.

Ethosperse® SL-20. [Lonza]
Chem. Descrip.: Sorbeth-20
CAS 53694-15-8
Uses: Emulsifier, humectant for pharmaceuticals
Properties: Lt. yel. clear liq.; sol. in water, methanol, ethanol, acetone; sp.gr. 1.16; visc. 460 cps; HLB 17; acid no. 0.5 max.; hyd. no. 385-430; pH 7 (5%); 100% act.; nonionic.

Ethoxylan® 1685. [Henkel/Cospha; Henkel Canada]
Chem. Descrip.: PEG-75 lanolin
CAS 61790-81-6
Uses: Emollient, emulsifier, dispersant for antiperspirants, pharmaceutical vehicles
Properties: Dk. amber to brn. waxy solid; sol. @ 5% in water, IPA; dens. 9.6 lb/gal; m.p. 39 C; cloud pt. 85 C; flash pt. 530 F.

Ethoxylan® 1686. [Henkel/Cospha; Henkel Canada]
Chem. Descrip.: PEG-75 lanolin
CAS 61790-81-6
Uses: Emollient, emulsifier, dispersant for antiperspirants, pharmaceutical vehicles
Properties: Yel. to lt. amber liq.; sol. @ 5% in water, IPA; dens. 8.9 lb/gal; visc. 1767 cSt (100 F); pour pt. 1 C; cloud pt. 86 C; 50% aq. sol'n.

Ethylan® C160. [Akcros UK]
Chem. Descrip.: PEG ester of unsat. fatty acid
Uses: Oil emulsifier for pharmaceutical creams
Properties: Cream waxy solid, mild fatty odor; water-sol.; sp.gr. 1.080 (60 C); visc. 300 cs (60 C); HLB 17.6; pour pt. 39 C; cloud pt. > 100 C (1% aq.); flash pt. (COC) > 175 C; pH 7.0 (1% aq.); 100% act.; nonionic.

Ethylan® CF71. [Akcros UK]

Chem. Descrip.: Coconut fatty ester
Uses: Emulsifier for pharmaceuticals
Properties: Pale straw liq., mild fatty odor; sol. in water; sp.gr. 1.050; visc. 55 cs (40 C); HLB 14; pour pt. 14 C; cloud pt. 57 C (1% aq.); flash pt. (COC) > 175 C; pH 7.0 (1% aq.); 100% act.; nonionic.

Ethylan® GEO8. [Akcros UK]
Chem. Descrip.: Polysorbate 80
CAS 9005-65-6
Uses: Emulsifier for pharmaceuticals; solubilizer for perfume, flavors, essential oils
Properties: Amber clear liq., mild fatty odor; sol. in water, alcohols, hydrocarbons; sp.gr. 1.10; visc. 720 cs; HLB 15.0; pour pt. -20 C; flash pt. (PMCC) > 150 C; 97% act.; nonionic.

Ethylan® GL20. [Akcros UK]
Chem. Descrip.: Sorbitan laurate
CAS 1338-39-2
Uses: Emulsifier for pharmaceuticals
Properties: Amber visc. liq., mild odor; sol. in alcohols, hydrocarbons, natural and paraffinic oils; sp.gr. 1.04; visc. 5250 cs; HLB 8.0; pour pt. 15 C; flash pt. (PMCC) > 150 C; 100% act.; nonionic.

Ethylan® GO80. [Akcros UK]
Chem. Descrip.: Sorbitan oleate
CAS 1338-43-8; EINECS 215-665-4
Uses: Emulsifier for pharmaceuticals
Properties: Amber visc. liq., mild fatty odor; sol. in alcohols, hydrocarbons, natural and paraffinic oils; sp.gr. 1.00; visc. 1100 cs; HLB 4.3; pour pt. -20 C; flash pt. (PMCC) -5 C; 100% act.; nonionic.

Ethylan® GS60. [Akcros UK]
Chem. Descrip.: Sorbitan stearate
CAS 1338-41-6; EINECS 215-664-9
Uses: Emulsifier for pharmaceuticals
Properties: Tan waxy solid, mild odor; sol. in alcohols, hydrocarbons, natural and paraffinic oils; sp.gr. 0.98; HLB 4.7; pour pt. 50 C; flash pt. (PMCC) > 150 C; 100% act.; nonionic.

Ethylan® GT85. [Akcros UK]
Chem. Descrip.: Sorbitan trioleate
CAS 26266-58-0; EINECS 247-569-3
Uses: Emulsifier for pharmaceuticals
Properties: Amber visc. liq., mild fatty odor; sol. in alcohols, hydrocarbons, natural and paraffinic oils; sp.gr. 1.00; visc. 230 cs; HLB 1.5; pour pt. -10 C; flash pt. (PMCC) -10 C; 100% act.; nonionic.

Ethylan® L10. [Akcros UK]
Chem. Descrip.: PEG 1000 laurate
CAS 9004-81-3
Uses: Emulsifier for pharmaceuticals
Properties: Wh. solid; sp.gr. 1.056; visc. 76 cs (40 C); nonionic.

Ethyl Diglyme. [Ferro/Grant]
Chem. Descrip.: Diethylene glycol diethyl ether
CAS 112-73-2; EINECS 204-001-9
Uses: Solv. for pharmaceuticals
Properties: Colorless; mild, nonresidual odor; water-sol.; misc. with ethanol, acetone, benzene, diethyl ether, octane; m.w. 162.23; sp.gr. 0.9082;

dens. 7.56 lb/gal; visc. 1.4 cP; f.p. -44.3 C; b.p. 189 C; flash pt. (CC) 90 C; ref. index 1.4115; pH netural; surf. tens. 27.2 dynes/cm; 98.0% min. purity; slowly biodeg.

Toxicology: LD50 5000 mg/kg; low to mod. acute toxicity; chronic exposure may cause reproductive effects.

Ethyl Ether USP/ACS. [Quantum/USI]
Chem. Descrip.: Ethyl ether
CAS 60-29-7; EINECS 200-467-2
Uses: Surface antiseptic and cleaning agent, in liniments, as analgesic, expectorant.

Ethyl Parasept® NF. [Nipa Hardwicke]
Chem. Descrip.: Ethylparaben NF
CAS 120-47-8; EINECS 204-399-4
Uses: Preservative for pharmaceuticals, suppositories, eye washes, pills, anesthetics, syrups, injectable sol'ns., contraceptives, gelatin capsules, ointments, tinctures, OTC drugs; inactive ingred. in dentifrices, topical analgesics; active antimycotic
Properties: Wh. fine powd., pract. odorless and tasteless; sol. 115% in methanol, 84% in acetone, 70% in ethanol (100%), 43% in ether, 25% in propylene glycol (100%), 0.17% in water; m.w. 166.18; m.p. 115-118 C; nonhygroscipic; 99-100.5% assay
Toxicology: Avoid prolonged/repeated skin contact
Storage: Avoid exposure to high humidity and elevated temps. in storage.

Eudragit® L 100-55. [Röhm Pharma GmbH; Rohm Tech]
Chem. Descrip.: Methacrylic acid copolymer USP/NF
Uses: Aq. polymer disp. for prod. of enteric coated tablets; sol. in intestinal fluid above pH 5.5, but resist. to gastric fluids; masks unpleasant taste/odors of pharmaceutical ingreds.
Properties: Insol. in water, acids; anionic.

Eudragit® NE 30 D. [Röhm Pharma GmbH; Rohm Tech]
Chem. Descrip.: Ethyl acrylate/methyl methacrylate copolymer aq. disp.
Uses: For controlled-release permeable film coatings
Regulatory: Ph.Eur, DAB compliance.

Eudragit® RL 30 D. [Röhm Pharma GmbH; Rohm Tech]
Chem. Descrip.: Ammonio methacrylate copolymer, Type A, NF
Uses: High permeabilitly film coating for sustained release applics.
Regulatory: NF compliance.

Eudragit® RS 30 D. [Röhm Pharma GmbH; Rohm Tech]
Chem. Descrip.: Ammonio methacrylate copolymer, Type B, NF
Uses: Low permeabilitly film coating for sustained release applics.; gives pH-independent release of actives.

Eumulgin® B1. [Henkel/Cospha; Henkel Canada; Henkel KGaA/Cospha]

Chem. Descrip.: Ceteareth-12 JCID
CAS 68439-49-6
Uses: Emulsifier for pharmaceutical o/w emulsions; emollient, bodying agent, conditioner for ointments, creams
Properties: Waxy solid; sol. in alcohols, hydrocarbons, and most org. solvs.; sp.gr. 0.95; solid. pt. 50-68 F; HLB 12.0; hyd. no. 69-74; pH 6.0-7.5 (1%); 100% conc.; nonionic
Storage: 1 yr min. storage stability in sealed original containers at temps. below 30 C.

Eumulgin® B2. [Henkel/Cospha; Henkel Canada; Henkel KGaA/Cospha; Pulcra SA]
Chem. Descrip.: Ceteareth-20 NF/BP
CAS 68439-49-6
Uses: Emulsifier for pharmaceutical o/w emulsions; emollient, bodying agent, conditioner for ointments, creams
Regulatory: NF, BP, JCIC compliance
Properties: Wh. to sl. ylsh. waxy flakes; sol. in alcohols, hydrocarbons, and most org. solvs.; dens. 1.001-1.005 g/cm^3 (70 C); solid. pt. 39-42 C; HLB 15.5; acid no. 0.5 max.; sapon. no. 1 max.; hyd. no. 49-55; cloud pt. 90-94 C (1% in 5% NaCl); pH 6.0-7.5 (1%); 1% max. water; nonionic
Storage: 1 yr min. storage stability in sealed original containers at temps. below 40 C, under dry conditions.

Eumulgin® B3. [Henkel Canada; Henkel KGaA/Cospha; Pulcra SA]
Chem. Descrip.: Ceteareth-30
CAS 68439-49-6
Uses: Emulsifier for pharmaceutical w/o emulsions, transparent gels
Properties: Waxy solid; sp.gr. 0.95; solid. pt. 50-68 F; HLB 16.7; hyd. no. 35-40; cloud pt. 94-96 C; pH 6.0-7.5 (1%); 100% conc.; nonionic
Storage: 1 yr min. storage stability in closed original containers at temps. below 40 C, under dry conditions.

Eumulgin® HRE 40. [Henkel KGaA/Cospha]
Chem. Descrip.: PEG-40 hydrog. castor oil
CAS 61788-85-0
Uses: Solubilizer and o/w emulsifier for pharmaceutical preps.
Properties: Wh. wax; HLB 14-16; acid no. 1 max.; sapon. no. 50-60; hyd. no. 55-75; pH 6-7 (1%); 100% conc.; nonionic.

Eumulgin® HRE 60. [Henkel KGaA/Cospha]
Chem. Descrip.: PEG-60 hydrog. castor oil
CAS 61788-85-0
Uses: Solubilizer and o/w emulsifier for pharmaceutical preps.
Properties: Wax; HLB 15-17; acid no. < 1; sapon. no. 40-50; hyd. no. 50-70; pH 6-7 (1%); 100% conc.; nonionic.

Eumulgin® L. [Henkel/Cospha; Henkel KGaA/Cospha]
Chem. Descrip.: PPG-2-ceteareth-9
Uses: Solubilizer for pharmaceutical preps., esp. low alcohol content formulas
Properties: Lt. yel. clear free-flowing liq., faint char.

odor; sol. in alcohols, hydrocarbons, and most org. solvs.; acid no. 1 max.; hyd. no. 145-155; pH 6.0-7.5 (1%); 100% conc.; nonionic

Storage: 1 yr min. storage life in sealed containers @ R.T., protected from dampness and frost.

Eumulgin® O5. [Henkel/Cospha; Henkel Canada; Henkel KGaA/Cospha]
Chem. Descrip.: Oleth-5
CAS 9004-98-2
Uses: Emulsifier for prod. of pharmaceutical o/w emulsions, ointments
Properties: Bright yel. clear liq.; water-sol.; sp.gr. 0.912-0.9145 (70 C); HLB 12.0; hyd. no. 115-125; cloud pt. 16-22 C; pH 6.5-75 (1%); 100% conc.; nonionic
Storage: 1 yr min. storage life in closed original containers at temps. below 40 C, protected against moisture.

Eumulgin® O10. [Henkel/Cospha; Henkel Canada; Henkel KGaA/Cospha]
Chem. Descrip.: Oleth-10
CAS 9004-98-2
Uses: Emulsifier for prod. of pharmaceutical o/w emulsions, ointments
Properties: Ylsh. wh. soft waxy solid; sp.gr. 0.959-0.9615 (70 C); solid. pt. 50-68 F; HLB 12.0; hyd. no. 79-84; cloud pt. 26-30 C; pH 6.5-7.5 (1%); 100% conc.; nonionic
Storage: 1 yr min. storage life in closed original containers at temps. below 40 C, protected against moisture.

Eumulgin® PRT 36. [Pulcra SA]
Chem. Descrip.: PEG-36 castor oil
CAS 61791-12-6
Uses: Emulsifier, dispersant, solubilizer for pharmaceuticals
Properties: Liq.; HLB 12.7; sapon. no. 59-69; pH 6.0-7.5 (1%); 100% conc.; nonionic.

Eumulgin® PRT 56. [Pulcra SA]
Chem. Descrip.: PEG-56 castor oil
CAS 61791-12-6
Uses: Emulsifier, dispersant, solubilizer for pharmaceuticals
Properties: Paste; HLB 14.5; sapon. no. 45-55; pH 6.0-7.5 (1%); 100% conc.; nonionic.

Eumulgin® PRT 200. [Pulcra SA]
Chem. Descrip.: PEG-200 castor oil
CAS 61791-12-6
Uses: Emulsifier, dispersant, solubilizer for pharmaceuticals
Properties: Solid; HLB 18.1; sapon. no. 16-18; pH 5.0-6.5 (10%); 100% conc.; nonionic.

Eumulgin® RO 35. [Henkel KGaA/Cospha]
Chem. Descrip.: PEG-35 castor oil
CAS 61791-12-6
Uses: Emulsifier and solubilizer for fat-sol. vitamins and essential oils; yields o/w emulsions or clear to sl. opalescent liqs.
Regulatory: USP, NF compliance
Properties: Ylsh. liq., weak intrinsic odor; sp.gr. 1.014-1.018 (70 C); acid no. 2 max.; iodine no. 25-35; sapon. no. 63-73; hyd. no. 65-80; pH 6.5-7.5

(1%); 3% max. water; nonionic
Storage: 1 yr min. storage stability in sealed original containers below 30 C.

Eumulgin® SML 20. [Henkel KGaA/Cospha; Pulcra SA]
Chem. Descrip.: Polysorbate 20 NF/BP/DAB
CAS 9005-64-5
Uses: Solubilizer and emulsifier for pharmaceutical preps.
Properties: Lt. yel. liq.; HLB 16.7; acid no. 2 max.; iodine no. 5 max.; sapon. no. 40-50; hyd. no. 96-108; pH 7.5-8.0 (10%); 100% conc.; nonionic
Toxicology: Nontoxic
Storage: 1 yr min. storage stability in sealed original containers at temps. below 30 C, protected from humidity and frost.

Eumulgin® SMO 20. [Henkel KGaA/Cospha]
Chem. Descrip.: Polysorbate 80 BP, German pharmacopoeia
CAS 9005-65-6
Uses: Emulsifier, solubilizer for pharmaceutical creams, ointments, o/w emulsions
Properties: Ylsh. brn. visc. liq. to paste; acid no. 2 max.; iodine no. 18-24; sapon. no. 45-55; hyd. no. 65-80; nonionic
Toxicology: Nontoxic
Storage: 1 yr min. storage life in sealed, moisture-protected original containers at temps. below 30 C.

Eumulgin® SMS 20. [Henkel KGaA/Cospha]
Chem. Descrip.: Polysorbate 60 BP, NF, German pharmacopoeia
CAS 9005-67-8
Uses: Emulsifier, solubilizer for pharmaceutical creams, ointments, liq. o/w emulsions
Properties: Cloudy med.-visc. to pasty wax, almost odorless; acid no. 2 max.; iodine no. 5 max.; sapon. no. 45-55; hyd. no. 81-96; nonionic
Storage: 1 yr min. storage life in sealed moisture-protected original containers at temps. below 30 C.

Eutanol® G. [Henkel/Cospha; Henkel Canada; Henkel KGaA/Cospha]
Chem. Descrip.: Octyldodecanol
CAS 5333-42-6; EINECS 226-242-9
Uses: Lubricant, emollient with good spreadability for pharmaceutical skin care preps. (creams, lotions, antiperspirants); carrier for oil-sol. active ingreds.; pigment dispersant; stable to hydrolysis
Regulatory: NF, DAB, JCIC compliance
Properties: Lt. yel. clear oily liq., pract. odorless and tasteless; sol. in alcohols, esters, cosmetic oils, glycols, ketones, aromatics; insol. in water; m.w. 300; dens. 0.835-0.845 (20 C); visc. 58-64 mPa•s (20 C); acid no. 0.1 max.; iodine no. 8 max.; sapon. no. 5.0; hyd. no. 175-190; cloud pt. < -20 C; ref. index 1.4535-1.4555 (20 C); 90% min. conc.
Storage: 1 yr min. storage stability in original sealed containers at temps. below 30 C.

Eutanol® G16. [Henkel/Cospha; Henkel Canada; Henkel KGaA/Cospha]

Chem. Descrip.: Isocetyl alcohol
CAS 36311-34-9; EINECS 252-964-9
Uses: Emollient for pharmaceutical skin care prods.; carrier for oil-sol. active ingreds.; dispersant for pigments; spreading agent; stable to hydrolysis
Properties: Lt. yel. clear oily liq.; m.w. 250; sp.gr. 0.835-0.840; visc. 40-45 mPa•s; acid no. 0.5 max.; iodine no. 10 max.; sapon. no. 10 max.; hyd. no. 200-225; cloud pt. < -40 C; ref. index 1.4400-1.4600; 85% min. conc.
Storage: 1 yr min. storage stability in original sealed containers at temps. below 30 C; protect against humdity.

Explotab®. [Mendell]
Chem. Descrip.: Sodium starch glycolate NF/BP
CAS 9063-38-1
Uses: Tablet disintegrant for formulations prepared by direct compression or wet granulation techniques; rapid disintegration, enhanced dissolution
Use level: < 2.5% (tablets)
Regulatory: FDA registered
Properties: Wh. powd.; avg. particle size 42 µ; 100%-140 mesh; insol. in org. solvs.; disp. in cold water (2% aq.); m.w. 500,000-1,000,000; bulk dens. 0.780 g/cc; visc. 200 cps max. (4% disp.); m.p. chars at 200 C; pH 5.5-7.5
Storage: 4 yr shelf-life stability when stored in tightly closed containers at 75-80 F and 65-70% r.h.

Extract of Hog Bile. [Am. Labs]
Chem. Descrip.: Hog bile extract contg. hyodeoxycholic acid, sodium glycohyodeoxycholate, sodium taurohydeoxycholate
Uses: Nutritive pharmaceutical additive
Storage: Preserve in tight containers with moisture-proof liners, in cool, dry place.

Extract of Ox Bile NF XI. [Am. Labs]
Chem. Descrip.: Ox bile extract contg. 45-50% sodium taurocholate, 25% sodium glycocholate
Uses: Nutritive pharmaceutical additive
Properties: Lt. color; sol. in water, alcohol; pH 6.5-7.5
Storage: Preserve in tight containers with moisture-proof liners, in cool, dry place.

Extract of Whole Grapefruit. [Commodity Services Int'l.]
Chem. Descrip.: Oil derived from entire grapefruit, both fruit and peel, of *Citrus paradisi;* contains aldehydes, alcohols, esters, nookatone, other sesquiterpenes, ketones, etc.

Uses: Flavor ingred. where fresh, fruity grapefruit impact is desired; masks undesirable bitter taste in pharmaceuticals
Properties: Yel. oil, intense odor and taste of fresh grapefruit
Storage: 6 mos stability stored at 7 C in absence of light and air in sealed containers.

Extramalt 10. [Sandoz Nutrition]
Chem. Descrip.: 10% Nondiastatic dry malt extract with 90% corn syrup solids
Uses: Natural food ingred. imparting flavor, sweetness, color, nutrition (protein, vitamins, minerals), humectant props. to pharmaceuticals, health foods
Properties: Lt. tan powd., sweet taste, mild malt flavor; pH 5.0-5.8 (10%); 10% act.
Storage: 1 yr shelf life stored in cool, dry place (below 70 F) in sealed containers.

Extramalt 35. [Sandoz Nutrition]
Chem. Descrip.: 35% Nondiastatic dry malt extract with 65% corn syrup solids
Uses: Natural food ingred. imparting flavor, sweetness, color, nutrition (protein, vitamins, minerals), humectant props. to pharmaceuticals, health foods
Properties: Lt. brn color, moderate malt flavor, pleasant sweet taste; pH 5-6 (10%); 35% act.
Storage: 1 yr shelf life stored in cool, dry place (below 70 F) in sealed containers.

Extramalt Dark. [Sandoz Nutrition]
Chem. Descrip.: Nondiastatic dry malt extract
CAS 8002-48-0; EINECS 232-310-9
Uses: Natural food ingred. imparting flavor, sweetness, color, nutrition (protein, vitamins, minerals), humectant props. to pharmaceuticals, health foods
Properties: Dk. brn. with deep, rich malt flavor and aroma; pH 5.8-7.4 (10%); 100% act.
Storage: 1 yr shelf life stored in cool, dry place (below 70 F) in sealed containers.

Extramalt Light. [Sandoz Nutrition]
Chem. Descrip.: Nondiastatic dry malt and barley extract
Uses: Natural food ingred. imparting flavor, sweetness, color, nutrition (protein, vitamins, minerals), humectant props. to pharmaceuticals, health foods
Properties: Golden powd., char. malt flavor and aroma; pH 5-6 (10%); 100% act.
Storage: 1 yr shelf life stored in cool, dry place (below 70 F) in sealed containers.

F

F-500®. [Reheis]
Chem. Descrip.: Aluminum hydroxide
CAS 21645-51-2; EINECS 244-492-7
Uses: Antacid active for suspensions; when diluted to 4%, meets requirements for USP aluminum hydroxide suspensions which show little or no tendency to separate on standing
Properties: Wh. compressed gel; visc. 500 cps (@ 4% Al_2O_3); 8.9% min. Al_2O_3.

F-500® Low Sodium. [Reheis]
Chem. Descrip.: Aluminum hydroxide
CAS 21645-51-2; EINECS 244-492-7
Uses: Low sodium antacid active for suspensions; when diluted to 4%, meets requirements for USP aluminum hydroxide suspensions; exc. suspending chars.
Properties: Wh. compressed gel; apparent visc. 500 cps (@ 4% Al_2O_3); 8.9% min. Al_2O_3.

F-1000®. [Reheis]
Chem. Descrip.: Aluminum hydroxide USP
CAS 21645-51-2; EINECS 244-492-7
Uses: Antacid active for tablet and suspension use with good resuspending props.
Properties: Wh. amorphous powd., odorless; 44 µ min. particle size; 75% thru 325 mesh; apparent dens. 0.09-0.15 g/cc; apparent visc. 300 cps (@ 4% Al_2O_3).

F-1500™. [Reheis]
Chem. Descrip.: Aluminum hydroxide BP
CAS 21645-51-2; EINECS 244-492-7
Uses: Reactive dried gel antacid active for tablet and suspension use
Properties: Wh. amorphous powd., odorless; apparent dens. 0.25-0.35 g/cc; 47% min. Al_2O_3.

F-1500™ Reductionized. [Reheis]
Chem. Descrip.: Aluminum hydroxide BP
CAS 21645-51-2; EINECS 244-492-7
Uses: Reactive dried gel antacid active for tablet and suspension use with exc. resuspending chars.
Properties: Wh. amorphous powd., odorless; apparent dens. 0.10-0.16 g/cc; 47% min. Al_2O_3.

F-2000®. [Reheis]
Chem. Descrip.: Aluminum hydroxide USP
CAS 21645-51-2; EINECS 244-492-7
Uses: Antacid active used in tablet, powd., and suspension preps.
Properties: Wh. amorphous powd., odorless; 44 µ min. particle size; 85% thru 325 mesh; apparent dens. 0.10-0.18 g/cc; apparent visc. 150 cps (@ 4% Al_2O_3); 12.5% min. Al_2O_3.

F-2100®. [Reheis]
Chem. Descrip.: Aluminum hydroxide USP
CAS 21645-51-2; EINECS 244-492-7
Uses: Dried gel antacid active for tablet and suspension use
Properties: Wh. amorphous powd., odorless; 74 µ min. particle size; 85% thru 200 mesh; apparent dens. 0.30-0.40 g/cc.

F-2200®. [Reheis]
Chem. Descrip.: Aluminum hydroxide USP
CAS 21645-51-2; EINECS 244-492-7
Uses: Dried gel antacid active for tablet and suspension use offering min. dusting; used where tablet size is important
Properties: Wh. amorphous powd., odorless; 74 µ min. particle size; 50% thru 200 mesh; apparent dens. 0.35-0.45 g/cc.

F-2300™. [Reheis]
Chem. Descrip.: Aluminum hydroxide USP
CAS 21645-51-2; EINECS 244-492-7
Uses: Economical dried gel antacid active for tablet preps.
Properties: Wh. amorphous powd., odorless; 74 µ min. particle size; 50% thru 200 mesh; apparent dens. 0.20-0.40 g/cc.

F-3600™. [Reheis]
Uses: Direct compression antacid dried gel for tablet and suspension use; high dens., exc. free-flowing and nondusting chars.
Properties: Powd.; 98% min. thru 30 mesh; 10% max. thru 100 mesh; dens. 0.5 g/cc min. (tapped); 50% min. Al_2O_3.

F-4400™. [Reheis]
Chem. Descrip.: Aluminum hydroxide
CAS 21645-51-2; EINECS 244-492-7
Uses: Dried gel antacid active for tablet and suspension use, formulations of max. str., and for swallowable size antacid tablets
Properties: Wh. amorphous powd., odorless; apparent dens. 0.6-0.8 g/cc.

F-6000M™. [Reheis]
Chem. Descrip.: Aluminum hydroxide, magnesium hydroxide
Uses: Antacid active for formulating swallowable size and max. str. tablets

Properties: Powd.; apparent dens. 0.6 min. g/cc; 22.5% Al_2O_3, 26% MgO
Unverified

Fancol Acel. [Fanning]
Chem. Descrip.: Acetylated lanolin
CAS 61788-48-5; EINECS 262-979-2
Uses: Emollient, superfatting agent, lipophilic spreading agent for oils, creams, lotions, ointments, pharmaceuticals
Properties: Gardner 12 max. color; m.p. 30-40 C; acid no. 3 max.; sapon. no. 130 max.; hyd. no. 10 max.

Fancol ALA. [Fanning]
Chem. Descrip.: Cetyl acetate and acetylated lanolin alcohol
Uses: Lubricant for topical pharmaceutical ointments
Properties: Clear lt. oily liq.; acid no. 1 max.; iodine no. 12 max.; sapon. no. 200 max.; hyd. no. 8 max.

Fancol ALA-10. [Fanning]
Chem. Descrip.: Polysorbate 80, cetyl acetate, acetylated lanolin alcohol
Uses: Lubricant for topical pharmaceutical ointments
Properties: Amber to yel. liq., pract. odorless; acid no. 2 max.; sapon. no. 60-80; hyd. no. 55-70.

Fancol CAB. [Fanning]
Chem. Descrip.: Petrolatum, lanolin, lanolin alcohol
Uses: Lubricant, emollient, fatting agent for topical pharmaceuticals and tablets
Properties: Pale yel.-ivory soft solid, faint char. sterol odor; m.p. 40-46 C; acid no. 1 max.; sapon. no. 10-20.

Fancol CB. [Fanning]
Chem. Descrip.: Cocoa butter obtained from roasted seeds of Theobroma cacao
CAS 8002-31-1
Uses: Skin conditioner, occlusive solv., skin protectant for OTC drug prods.
Properties: Ylsh. wh. solid; iodine no. 35-40; sapon. no. 192-197; ref. index 1.4560-1.4580.

Fancol CB Extra. [Fanning]
Chem. Descrip.: Cocoa butter USP obtained from roasted seeds of Theobroma cacao
CAS 8002-31-1
Uses: Skin conditioner, occlusive solv., skin protectant for OTC drug prods.
Properties: Ylsh. wh. solid; iodine no. 35-43; sapon. no. 188-195; ref. index 1.4560-1.4580.

Fancol CH. [Fanning]
Chem. Descrip.: Cholesterol NF
CAS 57-88-5; EINECS 200-353-2
Uses: Film-former with lubricating, protective and anti-irritant props., aids cell regeneration, emulsifier for w/o formulations, precursor for prod. of vitamin D; for pharmaceuticals
Properties: Wh. gran.; sol. in acetone, chloroform, dioxane, ether, ethyl acetae, hexane, veg. oils; sl. sol. in alcohol; insol. in water; m.p. 147-150 C.

Fancol CO-30. [Fanning]
Chem. Descrip.: PEG-30 castor oil

CAS 61791-12-6
Uses: Surfactant, emulsifier for pharmaceutical ointments
Properties: Amber clear liq.; acid no. 2 max.; sapon. no. 70-80; hyd. no. 70-80.

Fancol HCO-25. [Fanning]
Chem. Descrip.: PEG-25 hydrog. castor oil
CAS 61788-85-0
Uses: Emulsifying agent for topical pharmaceutical ointments, tablets and salts
Properties: HLB 10.8; acid no. 2 max.; sapon. no. 80-90; pour pt. 4-8 C.

Fancol HL. [Fanning]
Chem. Descrip.: Hydrog. lanolin
CAS 8031-44-5; EINECS 232-452-1
Uses: Emollient, moisturizer, lubricant, plasticizer, chemical intermediate, humectant, mold release agent for pharmaceuticals
Properties: Wh. solid, trace odor; sol. in IPM, min. oil, castor oil, ethyl acetate, acetone (@ 75 C); insol. water; sp.gr. 0.855-0.865; m.p. 48-53 C; iodine no. 15 max.; sapon. no. 6 max.; ref. index 1.460-1.469 (50 C).

Fancol HL-20. [Fanning]
Chem. Descrip.: PEG-20 hydrog. lanolin
CAS 68648-27-1
Uses: Solubilizer, superfatting agent, gelling agent for pharmaceuticals, microemulsions
Properties: Pale cream soft waxy solid, very sl. odor; m.p. 40-50 C; sapon. no. 7 max.; hyd. no. 55 max.

Fancol HL-24. [Fanning]
Chem. Descrip.: PEG-24 hydrog. lanolin
CAS 68648-27-1
Uses: Solubilizer, superfatting agent for pharmaceutical creams and lotions, microemulsions; gelling agent for transparent gels
Properties: Pale cream soft waxy solid, very sl. odor; m.p. 40-50 C; sapon. no. 7 max.; hyd. no. 55 max.

Fancol Karite Extract. [Fanning]
Chem. Descrip.: Shea butter extract
CAS 68424-59-9
Uses: Emollient with exc. spreadability for suntan preps., ointments, suppositories
Properties: Gardner 3 max. color; sol. in castor oil; sl. sol. in min. oil, propylene glycol, glycerin, ethyl acetate, isopropyl lanolate; insol. in water; iodine no. 63-70.

Fancol LA. [Fanning]
Chem. Descrip.: Lanolin alcohol
CAS 8027-33-6; EINECS 232-430-1
Uses: Emollient, thickener, emulsifier, stabilizer, plasticizer, superfatting agent, dye dispersant, chemical intermediate, lubricant, humectant, mold release agent, conditioner for pharmaceuticals
Properties: Lt. amber to yel. wax-like solid, faint char. odor; sol. in CCl_4, chloroform, IPM (@ 75 C), min. oil (@ 75 C), oleyl alcohol; insol. water; m.p. 56 C; acid no. 3 max.; sapon. no. 12 max.; 100% act.; nonionic.

Fancol LA-15. [Fanning]
Chem. Descrip.: Laneth-15
CAS 61791-20-6
Uses: Emollient, emulsifier for stable o/w pharmaceutical emulsions and microemulsions
Properties: Yel. solid; HLB 12.7; acid no. 5 max.; hyd. no. 85; 100% act.; nonionic.

Fancol LAO. [Fanning]
Chem. Descrip.: Min. oil and lanolin alcohol
Uses: Conditioner, surfactant, stabilizer, moisturizer, humectant, penetrant, emollient, plasticizer, and primary emulsifier for use in pharmaceuticals
Properties: Yel. clear oily liq.; odorless; sol. in oils; insol. in water; sp.gr. 0.84-0.86; acid no. 1 max.; iodine no. 12 max.; sapon. no. 3.0 max.; hyd. no. 16 max.; 100% conc.; nonionic.

Fancol OA-95. [Fanning]
Chem. Descrip.: Oleyl alcohol
CAS 143-28-2; EINECS 205-597-3
Uses: Emulsion stabilizer, antifoam, coupling agent for pharmaceutical applics.
Properties: Liq.; sol. in IPA, acetone, lt. min. oil, trichloroethylene, kerosene, VMP naphtha, benzene, turpentine; acid no. 0.05 max.; iodine no. 90-96; sapon no. 1 max.; hyd. no. 200-212; cloud pt. 5 C max.; nonionic.

Fancol SORB. [Fanning]
Chem. Descrip.: Sorbitol
CAS 50-70-4; EINECS 200-061-5
Uses: Humectant, nutritive sweetener, oleaginous vehicle, tablet diluent.

Fancol VB. [Fanning]
Chem. Descrip.: Limnanthes alba and shea butter extract
Uses: Primary w/o emulsifier, sec. o/w emulsifier/stabilizer, moisturizer, humectant in pharmaceuticals
Properties: Gardner 3 max. color; sol. in castor oil, min. oil (70 visc.), ethyl acetate, IPM; insol. in propylene glycol, glycerin, water; acid no. 0.5 max.; iodine no. 85 max.; sapon. no. 165 max.; nonionic.

Fancor IPL. [Fanning]
Chem. Descrip.: Isopropyl lanolate
CAS 63393-93-1; EINECS 264-119-1
Uses: Hydrophilic emollient, moisturizer, w/o aux. emulsifier, stabilizer and opacifier, wetting and dispersing agent for pigments and talc, aids slip and gloss; superfatting agent
Properties: Buttery yel. solid; sol. @ 75 C in IPM, min. oil, castor oil; acid no. 18 max.; iodine no. 20 max.; sapon. no. 165 max.; hyd. no. 68 max.

Fancor ISO Cholesterol. [Fanning]
Uses: Pharmaceutical ingred.
Properties: M.p. 138-145 C; acid no. 0.5 max.

Fancor LFA. [Fanning]
Chem. Descrip.: Lanolin fatty acids
CAS 68424-43-1; EINECS 270-302-7
Uses: Emollient, stabilizer, emulsifier for pharmaceutical prods.
Properties: Wax-like solid; sol. in ethyl acetate; sl. sol. in IPM, min. oil; sol. @ 75 C in IPM, min. and

castor oil, acetone, ethyl acetate, ethyl alcohol; m.p. 57-65 C; acid no. 135-170; iodine no. 10 max.; sapon. no. 158-175; hyd. no. 50 max.; 100% conc.; nonionic.

Fancor Lanwax. [Fanning]
Chem. Descrip.: Natural lanolin wax ester
CAS 68201-49-0; EINECS 269-220-4
Uses: Water repellent, humectant, conditioner, corrosion inhibitor, emollient, lubricant for pharmaceuticals
Properties: Semisolid; m.p. 48-52 C; iodine no. 36 max.; sapon. no. 90-110; hyd. no. 35 max.

Fancorsil A. [Fanning]
Chem. Descrip.: Cyclomethicone and dimethicone
Uses: Emollient, solv. used in topical pharmaceutical ointments
Properties: Clear visc. liq.; sp.gr. 0.960; visc. 5000 cps min.; 100% solids.

Fancorsil HA Super. [Fanning]
Chem. Descrip.: Glycereth polyacrylate copolyol
Uses: Used in pharmaceuticals (topical ointments, emulsions)
Regulatory: Japanese approvals
Properties: Clear gel, odorless; sl. sol. in castor oil, glycerin, ethanol, dist. water; insol. in IPM, min. oil, propylene glycol; visc. $> 10^6$ cps; pH 4.5-5.5.

Fancorsil LIM 1. [Fanning]
Chem. Descrip.: Dimethicone copolyol eicosanate
CAS 157479-50-0
Uses: Softener and conditioner for topical pharmaceutical ointments
Properties: Yel. liq.; sol. in water; acid no. 8 max.

Fancorsil LIM 2. [Fanning]
Chem. Descrip.: Dimethicone copolyol eicosanate
CAS 157479-51-1
Uses: Softener and conditioner for topical pharmaceutical ointments
Properties: Sl. yel. wax; insol. in water; acid no. 5 max.

Fancorsil LIM 3. [Fanning]
Chem. Descrip.: Dimethicone copolyol eicosanate
CAS 157479-51-1
Uses: Softener and conditioner for topical pharmaceutical ointments
Properties: Yel. liq; disp. in water; acid no. 5 max.

Fancorsil P. [Fanning]
Chem. Descrip.: Cyclomethicone, dimethicone, and polyisobutene
Uses: Emollient, conditioner for pharmaceuticals
Properties: Clear liq.; sol. in ethyl acetate, IPM; sl. sol. in castor and min. oils, propylene glycol, glycerin; insol. in water; iodine no. 40-50; sapon. no. 80-90.

Fascat® 9100. [Elf Atochem N. Am.]
Uses: Esterification, transesterification, and polycondensation catalyst for mfg. of prods. intended for pharmaceutical applics. (e.g., coatings, epoxies, hybrid resins)
Regulatory: FDA 21CFR §175.105, 175.300, 176.170, 177.1210, 177.2420
Properties: Amorphous wh. powd.; insol. in water and org. solvs.; dissolves in acids with reaction;

sp.gr. 1.46; bulk dens. 0.84 g/cc; m.p. 300 C (dec.); 57% tin

Toxicology: Minimally irritating to eyes and skin.

Fascat® 9102. [Elf Atochem N. Am.]
Uses: Esterification, transesterification, and polycondensation catalyst for mfg. of prods. intended for pharmaceutical applics. (e.g., coatings, epoxies, hybrid resins)
Regulatory: FDA 21CFR §175.105, 175.300, 176.170, 177.1210, 177.2420
Properties: Pale yel. liq.; sol. in toluene, hydrocarbons, halocarbons, esters, etc.; insol. in water; sp.gr. 1.13; m.p. -18 C; 20% tin
Toxicology: May cause eye and skin irritation.

Fascat® 9201. [Elf Atochem N. Am.]
Chem. Descrip.: Organotin compd.
Uses: Esterification, transesterification, and polycondensation catalyst for mfg. of prods. intended for pharmaceutical applics. (e.g., coatings, epoxies, hybrid resins)
Regulatory: FDA 21CFR §175.105, 175.300, 176.170, 177.1210, 177.2420
Properties: Wh. powd.; insol. in water, org. solvs.; will dissolve in acids, alochols, esters with reaction; sp.gr. 1.62; bulk dens. 0.70 g/cc; m.p. > 290 C (dec.); 48% tin
Toxicology: Moderately toxic; may cause eye and skin burns on contact.

FC-24. [3M/Industrial Chem. Prods.]
Chem. Descrip.: Trifluoromethanesulfonic acid
CAS 1493-13-6; EINECS 216-087-5
Uses: In pharmaceuticals
Properties: Colorless liq.; sol. in polar org. solvs; misc. in water; m.w. 150.02; f.p. -40 C; b.p. 54 C (8 mm Hg); dens. 1.696 g/cc; visc. 2.87 cP; ref. index 1.325.

Filmex® A-2. [Quantum/USI]
Chem. Descrip.: 100 gal ethyl alcohol, 15.5 gal methyl alcohol, 1.05 gal MIBK
Uses: Solv. for pharmaceutical processing.

Filmex® B. [Quantum/USI]
Chem. Descrip.: 100 gal Ethyl alcohol, 10.25 gal methyl alcohol, 1.05 gal MIBK, 5.25 lb isobutyl alcohol (99%)
Uses: Solv. for pharmaceutical processing.

Filmex® C. [Quantum/USI]
Chem. Descrip.: 100 gal Ethyl alcohol, 5 gal methyl alcohol, 4.45 gal ethyl acetate (99%), 1.05 gal MIBK
Uses: Solv. for pharmaceutical processing.

Filmex® D-1. [Quantum/USI]
Chem. Descrip.: 100 gal Ethyl alcohol, 5 gal methyl alcohol, 1.05 gal MIBK, 15.75 lb isopropyl alcohol
Uses: Solv. for pharmaceutical processing.

Filmex® D-2. [Quantum/USI]
Chem. Descrip.: 100 gal Ethyl alcohol, 20.75 gal methyl alcohol, 1.05 gal MIBK
Uses: Solv. for pharmaceutical processing.

Finmalt L. [Xyrofin UK]
Chem. Descrip.: Maltitol syrup
CAS 585-88-6; EINECS 209-567-0
Uses: Sweetener for pharmaceuticals

Properties: Colorless liq., odorless, sweet taste; pH 4-6; 75% dry substance.
Storage: Store below 30 C; avoid temp. fluctuations, water condensation.

FK 500LS. [Degussa]
Chem. Descrip.: Amorphous precipitated silica
EINECS 215-683-2
Uses: Free-flow aid for hygroscopic materials with poor flow chars., e.g., vitamins; inert carrier for active substances
Regulatory: FDA approved
Properties: Powd.; 7 nm avg. particle size; dens 80 g/l (tapped); surf. area 450 m^2/g; pH 6.3 (5% aq. susp.); 98.5% assay.

Flamenco® Interference Color Powds. [Mearl]
Chem. Descrip.: Titanium dioxide coated mica
Uses: Pearlescent pigment for analgesic body lotions, sunscreens, toothpastes
Properties: Powd.

Flamenco® White Pearl Powds. [Mearl]
Chem. Descrip.: Titanium dioxide coated mica
Uses: Pearlescent pigment for analgesic body lotions, sunscreens, toothpastes
Properties: Powd.

Fluilan. [Croda Inc.; Croda Chem. Ltd.]
Chem. Descrip.: Lanolin oil
CAS 8006-54-0; EINECS 274-559-6
Uses: Emollient, penetrant, superfatting agent for topical pharmaceuticals, ointments, creams, and lotions
Use level: 2-10%
Properties: Pale yel. visc. liq., pleasant char. odor; sol. in min. oils, IPA, fatty alcohol, hydrocarbons, and aerosol propellents; cloud pt. 18 C max.; pour pt. 8 C max.; acid no. 2 max.; iodine no. 24-40; sapon. no. 80-100; 100% act.; nonionic
Toxicology: LD50 (oral, rat) > 20 g/kg; mild skin and eye irritant.

Fluilan AWS. [Croda Inc.]
Chem. Descrip.: PPG-12-PEG-65 lanolin oil
CAS 68458-58-8
Uses: Emollient, cleanser, and solubilizer for topical pharmaceuticals, cleansing wipe formulations, moisturizing creams and lotions; solubilizes actives into hydroalcoholic systems
Use level: 0.1-2%
Properties: Amber visc. liq., nearly odorless; sol. in water and alcohol; disp. in propylene glycol; acid no. 3 max.; iodine no. 7-15; sapon. no. 10-25; pH 5-7 (10%)
Toxicology: LD50 (oral, rat) > 5 g/kg; moderate skin irritant, minimal eye irritant.

Fluorad® FC-24. [3M/Industrial Chem. Prods.]
Chem. Descrip.: Trifluoromethanesulfonic acid
CAS 1493-13-6; EINECS 216-087-5
Uses: Used with nitric acid for higher yields of pharmaceuticals.

F-MA 11®. [Reheis]
Chem. Descrip.: Aluminum hydroxide, magnesium carbonate
Uses: Antacid which minimizes constipative or laxative effects; prompt and prolonged acid neu-

tralizing action

Properties: Dried gel; 44 μ min. particle size; 75% thru 325 mesh; apparent dens. 0.3-0.4 g/cc; 41.5% Al_2O_3, 7.5% MgO.

F-MA 11® HD. [Reheis]

Chem. Descrip.: Aluminum hydroxide, magnesium carbonate

Uses: Antacid which minimizes constipative or laxative effects; prompt and prolonged acid neutralizing action

Properties: Dried gel; apparent dens. 0.6-0.8 g/cc; 41.5% Al_2O_3, 7.5% MgO.

F-MA 11® Reductionized. [Reheis]

Chem. Descrip.: Aluminum hydroxide, magnesium carbonate

Uses: Antacid which minimizes constipative or laxative effects; prompt and prolonged acid neutralizing action

Properties: Dried gel; 44 μ min. particle size; 95% thru 325 mesh; apparent dens. 0.08-0.16 g/cc; 41.5% Al_2O_3, 7.5% MgO

Unverified

Foam Blast 5, 7. [Ross Chem.]

Chem. Descrip.: Silicone antifoam compd.

Uses: Food-grade antifoam for foam control in nonaq. systems, synthesis of pharmaceuticals; 100% act.

Foam Blast 10. [Ross Chem.]

Chem. Descrip.: Silicone antifoam compd.

Uses: Food-grade antifoam for foam control in nonaq. systems, synthesis of pharmaceuticals; more compat. and dispersible than Foam Blast 5, but less defoaming efficiency.

Foam Blast 100 Kosher. [Ross Chem.]

Chem. Descrip.: Silicone defoamer

Uses: Food-grade defoamer for starch and proteinaceous systems requiring an acid or alkaline tolerant defoamer

Regulatory: FDA §173.340, 100 ppm max., USDA, kosher compliance; exempt from labeling under 21CFR §101.100(a)(3)(ii)(c)

Properties: Wh. emulsion; disp. in water; dens. 8.50 lb/gal; visc. 1200-1600 cps; flash pt. (PMCC) none; pH 6.5-7.5; 10% act.; nonionic

Foam Blast 106. [Ross Chem.]

Chem. Descrip.: Silicone emulsion

Uses: Antifoam for hot and cold systems, in wide pH range; used in drug fermentations

Regulatory: FDA 21CFR §175.105, 175.210, 175.300, 176.170, 176.180, 176.200, 176.210, 178.3120

Properties: Milky wh. emulsion; disp. in water; sp.gr. 1.010; visc. 3200 cps; flash pt. (PMCC) none; pH 7.6; 10% act.; nonionic

Storage: Store at 60-90 F; exc. freeze/thaw stability; > 1 yr shelf life.

Foam Blast 150 Kosher. [Ross Chem.]

Chem. Descrip.: Silicone emulsion

Uses: Food-grade defoamer for starch and proteinaceous systems requiring an acid or alkaline tolerant defoamer

Regulatory: FDA §173.340, 33 ppm max., kosher

compliance

Properties: Wh. emulsion; disp. in water; dens. 8.30 lb/gal; visc. 2100 cps; flash pt. (PMCC) none; pH 7.0; 30% act.; nonionic.

Foamkill® 8G. [Crucible]

Chem. Descrip.: Silicone compd.

Uses: Defoamer for drug extraction and separation, drug processing, vitamins

Regulatory: FDA §173.340

Properties: Gray sl. hazy liq., bland odor; insol. in water; sp.gr. 1.020; b.p. > 300 F; flash pt. (TOC) > 300 F; 100% act.

Toxicology: May cause eye irritation, mild skin irritation on prolonged/repeated contact.

Foamkill® 30 Series. [Crucible]

Chem. Descrip.: Org. and organo-silicone conc.

Uses: Defoamer for pharmaceutical applics.

Foamkill® 618 Series. [Crucible]

Chem. Descrip.: Org. and organo-silicone conc.

Uses: Defoamer for pharmaceutical applics.

Foamkill® 634 Series. [Crucible]

Chem. Descrip.: Org. and organo-silicone conc.

Uses: Defoamer for pharmaceutical applics.

Foamkill® 810F. [Crucible]

Chem. Descrip.: Dimethicone emulsion

Uses: Defoamer for pharmaceutical applics. incl. general aq. systems

Regulatory: FDA §173.340, 176.210, 175.105, 175.320, 176.200

Properties: Wh. pourable visc. liq., bland odor; disp. in water; sp.gr. 1.000; dens. 8.3 lb/gal; visc. 300 cps; b.p. 212 F; flash pt. (TOC) > 212 F; pH 7.0; 10% act.; nonionic

Toxicology: May cause eye irritation, mild skin irritation on prolonged/repeated contact.

Foamkill® 830. [Crucible]

Chem. Descrip.: Organo-silicone emulsion

Uses: Defoamer for pharmaceutical applics.

Use level: 0.1-0.4%

Properties: Emulsion; very small particle size.

Foamkill® 830F. [Crucible]

Chem. Descrip.: Dimethicone

Uses: Defoamer for pharmaceutical applics. incl. general aq. systems

Regulatory: FDA §172.340, 173.340, 176.210, 175.105, 175.300, 176.200

Properties: Wh. pourable visc. liq., bland odor; disp. in water; sp.gr. 0.993; dens. 8.3 lb/gal; visc. 3500 cps; b.p. 212 F; flash pt. (TOC) > 212 F; pH 7.0; 30% act.; nonionic

Toxicology: May cause eye irritation, mild skin irritation on prolonged/repeated contact.

Foamkill® 836A. [Crucible]

Chem. Descrip.: Silicone emulsions

Uses: Defoamer for pharmaceutical applics.

Foamkill® MS Conc. [Crucible]

Chem. Descrip.: Silicone emulsion

Uses: Defoamer for pharmaceutical applics.

Folic Acid 10% Trituration No. 69997. [Roche]

Chem. Descrip.: Folic acid USP, FCC in calcium phosphate dibasic carrier

Uses: Vitamin essential for forming certain body

proteins and genetic materials for cell nucleus; for pharmaceutical formulations
Properties: Lt. yel. to ylsh. orange powd.; 100% thru 80 mesh; insol. in water and org. solvs.; m.w. 441.40; 10% min. assay
Precaution: Fairly stable in presence of air and heat, but destroyed by light and uv radiation
Storage: Store in tight, light-resist. containers; avoid exposure to moisture and excessive heat.

Folic Acid USP, FCC No. 20383. [Roche]
Chem. Descrip.: Folic acid USP, FCC
CAS 59-30-3; EINECS 200-419-0
Uses: Vitamin essential for forming certain body proteins and genetic materials for cell nucleus; for pharmaceutical formulations
Properties: Yel. to ylsh. orange cryst. powd., odorless; readily sol. in dil. alkali; sol. in sol'ns. of hot dil. acids; very sl. sol. in water; insol. in alcohol, acetone, ether, chloroform; m.w. 441.40; 87% min. assay (as is)
Precaution: Destroyed by lt. and uv radiation; unstable in sol'ns. with pH < 5
Storage: Store in tightly closed containers; protect from light.

Fonoline® White. [Witco/Petroleum Spec.]
Chem. Descrip.: Petrolatum USP
CAS 8027-32-5; EINECS 232-373-2
Uses: Soft, low m.p. for consumer use as petrol. jelly, ointments, in suncare prods., suppositories
Regulatory: FDA 21CFR §172.880
Properties: Wh., odorless; visc. 9-14 cSt (100 C); m.p. 53-58 C; pour pt. 20 F.

Fonoline® Yellow. [Witco/Petroleum Spec.]
Chem. Descrip.: Petrolatum USP
CAS 8027-32-5; EINECS 232-373-2
Uses: Soft, low m.p. for consumer use as petrol. jelly, ointments, in suncare prods., suppositories
Regulatory: FDA 21CFR §172.880
Properties: Yel., odorless; visc. 9-14 cSt (100 C); m.p. 53-58 C; pour pt. 20 F; 99% solids.

Forlan C-24. [R.I.T.A.]
Chem. Descrip.: Choleth-24 and ceteth-24
Uses: Emulsifier, emulsion stabilizer, emollient, moisturizer, solubilizer, visc. modifier, pigment dispersant, plasticizer for pharmaceuticals
Properties: Wh. flakes; sol. in alcohol, water; 100% conc.; nonionic.

Forlanit® E. [Henkel KGaA/Cospha]
Chem. Descrip.: Hydroxycetyl phosphate
Uses: O/w emulsifier for pharmaceutical emulsions
Properties: Flakes; 99% conc.

Free-flowing KCl. [Reheis]
Chem. Descrip.: Potassium chloride USP/FCC, BP, EP
CAS 7447-40-7; EINECS 231-211-8
Uses: Functional additive for pharmaceuticals; resists hardening and caking for up to 12 wks
Properties: Gran.; 20-60 mesh.

Freeze Dried Beef Liver Powd. [Am. Labs]
Chem. Descrip.: Dried powd. processed from beef livers
Uses: Nutritive pharmaceutical additive

Properties: Powd.
Freeze Dried Beef Liver Powd. Defatted. [Am. Labs]
Chem. Descrip.: Dried defatted powd. processed from beef livers
Uses: Nutritive pharmaceutical additive
Properties: Powd.
Storage: Store in cool, dry area.

Freeze Dried Pork Liver Powd. [Am. Labs]
Chem. Descrip.: Dried powd. processed from pork livers
Uses: Nutritive pharmaceutical additive
Properties: Powd.

Fructofin® C. [Xyrofin UK]
Chem. Descrip.: Fructose FCC/USP/NF
Uses: Food grade sweetener for pharmaceutical applics.; stable to air and heat
Properties: Wh. cryst. powd., pract. odorless, very sweet taste; very sol. in water ($\approx$ 3.5 g/ml); m.w. 180.16; pH 4.5-7 (0.1 g/ml aq.); 98% min. act.
Storage: 1 yr stability in original sealed pkg. stored below 25 C and < 60% r.h.; hygroscopic.

FruitSource® Granular. [LSI]
Chem. Descrip.: Prepared from grape juice conc. and whole rice syrup
Uses: Patented nutritive sweetener $1^1/_2$ times sweeter than sugar; for athletic foods/beverages, pharmaceutical tableting, throat lozenges, cough syrups; heat and cold stable
Regulatory: GRAS, kosher
Properties: Pale amber to off-wh. gran. powd., odorless, bland taste; avail. in 15 and 30 mesh; completely water-sol.; sp.gr. 0.8-0.9 g/cc; biodeg.
Precaution: Incompat. with powerful oxidizers
Storage: 1 yr stability in unopened container; store below 70 F, 50% r.h.

FruitSource® Liquid Sweetener. [LSI]
Chem. Descrip.: Prepared from grape juice conc. and whole rice syrup
Uses: Patented nutritive sweetener $1^1/_2$ times sweeter than sugar; for athletic foods/beverages, pharmaceutical tableting, throat lozenges, cough syrups; heat and cold stable
Regulatory: GRAS, kosher
Properties: Amber to dk. brn. liq., odorless, bland taste; completely water-sol.; dens. 11.8 lb/gal; visc. 92-95 cps; b.p. 220 F; biodeg.
Precaution: Incompat. with powerful oxidizers
Storage: 1 yr stability in unopened container, 2 wks in opened container; store below 80 F; darkening may occur.

FruitSource® Liquid Sweetener Plus. [LSI]
Chem. Descrip.: Prepared from grape juice conc. and whole rice syrup
Uses: Patented nutritive sweetener $1^1/_2$ times sweeter than sugar; for athletic foods/beverages, pharmaceutical tableting, throat lozenges, cough syrups; heat and cold stable
Regulatory: GRAS, kosher
Properties: Amber liq., bland very sweet taste; dens. 11.8 lb/gal; visc. 4000 cps
Storage: 1 yr stability in unopened container; store below 80 F; darkening may occur.

Fungal Lactase 100,000. [Solvay Enzymes]
Chem. Descrip.: Fungal lactase derived from *Aspergillus oryzae*
Uses: Food-grade enzyme for hydrolyzing lactose in pharmaceuticals (digestive aids, lactose intolerance prods.)
Properties: Lt. tan amorphous dry powd., free of offensive odor and taste; water-sol.
Storage: Activity loss ≤ 10% in 1 yr stored in sealed containers under cool dry conditions; 5 C storage extends life.

Fungal Protease 31,000. [Solvay Enzymes]
Chem. Descrip.: Protease derived from *Aspergillus oryzae var.*, maltodextrin diluent
CAS 9014-01-1; EINECS 232-752-2
Uses: Enzyme for hydrolysis of peptide bonds; pharmaceuticals (digestive aids)
Properties: Lt. tan to wh. powd., free of offensive odor and taste; water-sol.
Storage: Activity loss ≤ 10% in 1 yr stored in sealed containers under cool dry conditions; 5 C storage extends life.

Fungal Protease 60,000. [Solvay Enzymes]
Chem. Descrip.: Protease derived from *Aspergillus oryzae var.*, maltodextrin diluent
CAS 9014-01-1; EINECS 232-752-2
Uses: Enzyme for hydrolysis of peptide bonds; pharmaceuticals (digestive aids)

Properties: Lt. tan to wh. powd., free of offensive odor and taste; water-sol.
Storage: Activity loss ≤ 10% in 1 yr stored in sealed containers under cool dry conditions; 5 C storage extends life.

Fungal Protease 500,000. [Solvay Enzymes]
Chem. Descrip.: Protease derived from *Aspergillus oryzae var.*, maltodextrin diluent
CAS 9014-01-1; EINECS 232-752-2
Uses: Enzyme for hydrolysis of peptide bonds; pharmaceuticals (digestive aids)
Properties: Lt. tan to wh. powd., free of offensive odor and taste; water-sol.
Storage: Activity loss ≤ 10% in 1 yr stored in sealed containers under cool dry conditions; 5 C storage extends life.

Fungal Protease Conc. [Solvay Enzymes]
Chem. Descrip.: Protease derived from *Aspergillus oryzae var.*
CAS 9014-01-1; EINECS 232-752-2
Uses: Enzyme for hydrolysis of peptide bonds; pharmaceuticals (digestive aids)
Properties: Lt. tan to wh. dry powd., free of offensive odor and taste; water-sol.
Storage: Activity loss ≤ 10% in 1 yr stored in sealed containers under cool dry conditions; 5 C storage extends life.

G

G-1441. [ICI Surf. Am.]
Chem. Descrip.: PEG-40 sorbitan lanolate
CAS 8036-77-9
Uses: Emulsifier, surfactant for pharmaceuticals
Properties: Amber paste; sol. in water (hazy), IPA; sp.gr. 1; HLB 14; flash pt. > 300 F; pour pt. 33 C; 100% conc.; nonionic.

Galenol® 1618 AE. [Condea Chemie GmbH]
Chem. Descrip.: Cetearyl alcohol (80%) and ceteareth-20 (20%)
Uses: Self-emulsifying pharmaceutical raw material, o/w emulsion base for creams, ointments, liniments, and lotions
Properties: Flakes.

Galenol® 1618 CS. [Condea Chemie GmbH]
Chem. Descrip.: Cetearyl alcohol (90%) and sodium cetearyl sulfate (10%)
Uses: Self-emulsifying pharmaceutical raw material, o/w emulsion base for creams, ointments, liniments, and lotions
Properties: Flakes or pellets.

Galenol® 1618 DSN. [Condea Chemie GmbH]
Chem. Descrip.: Cetearyl alcohol (90%) and sodium lauryl sulfate (10%)
Uses: Self-emulsifying pharmaceutical raw material, o/w emulsion base for creams, ointments, liniments, and lotions
Properties: Flakes or pellets.

Galenol® 1618 KS. [Condea Chemie GmbH]
Chem. Descrip.: Cetearyl alcohol (90%) and sodium C12-C18 alkyl sulfate (10%)
Uses: Self-emulsifying pharmaceutical raw material, o/w emulsion base for creams, ointments, liniments, and lotions
Properties: Flakes or pellets.

Gamma W8. [Wacker-Chemie GmbH]
Chem. Descrip.: γ-Cyclodextrin
CAS 17465-86-0; EINECS 241-482-4
Uses: Complex hosting guest molecules; increases the sol. and bioavailability of other substances; masks flavor, odor, or coloration; stabilizes against light, oxidation, heat, and hydrolysis; turns liqs. or volatiles into stable solid powds.
Properties: Wh. cryst. powd.; sol. 23.2 g/100 ml in water; m.w. 1297
Toxicology: LD50 (acute IV, rat) > 3750 mg/kg; nonirritating to eye.

Gamma W8 HP0.6. [Wacker-Chemie GmbH]

Chem. Descrip.: Hydroxypropyl-γ-cyclodextrin
CAS 99241-25-5
Uses: Complex hosting guest molecules; increases the sol. and bioavailability of other substances; masks flavor, odor, or coloration; stabilizes against light, oxidation, heat, and hydrolysis; turns liqs. or volatiles into stable solid powds.
Properties: Wh. cryst. powd.; m.w. 1580.

Gamma W8 M1.8. [Wacker-Chemie GmbH]
Chem. Descrip.: Methyl-γ-cyclodextrin
Uses: Complex hosting guest molecules; increases the sol. and bioavailability of other substances; masks flavor, odor, or coloration; stabilizes against light, oxidation, heat, and hydrolysis; turns liqs. or volatiles into stable solid powds.
Properties: Wh. cryst. powd.; m.w. 1499.

Gamma Oryzanol. [Ikeda]
Chem. Descrip.: Oryzanol
CAS 11042-64-1
Uses: Uv absorbent and antioxidant for drugs, sunscreen creams and sticks
Properties: Wh. or pale yel. cryst. powd., odorless; 98% min. assay
Toxicology: LD50 (oral, mice) > 10,000 mg/kg.

Gantrez® AN-119. [ISP]
Chem. Descrip.: PVM/MA copolymer
CAS 52229-50-2
Uses: Dispersant, coupling agent, stabilizer; film-former in spray bandages; complexing agent for sustained-release iron preps.; ostomy adhesives; denture adhesives/stabilizers; dentifrices; thickener for aq. or org. solv. systems
Properties: Wh. fluffy powd.; sol. in water, alcohols, phenols, pyridine, aldehydes, ketones, acid, caustic, and org. solvs.; essentially insol. in aliphatic, aromatic, or halogenated hydrocabons, ethyl ether; m.w. 20,000; 100% conc.; anionic
Toxicology: LD50 8-9 g/kg (low toxicity).

Gantrez® AN-139. [ISP]
Chem. Descrip.: PVM/MA copolymer
CAS 9011-16-9
Uses: Dispersant, coupling agent, stabilizer; film-former in spray bandages; complexing agent for sustained-release iron preps.; ostomy adhesives; denture adhesives/stabilizers; dentifrices; thickener for aq. or org. solv. systems
Properties: Wh. fluffy powd.; sol. in water, alcohols, phenols, pyridine, aldehydes, ketones, acid,

caustic, and org. solvs.; essentially insol. in aliphatic, aromatic, or halogenated hydrocabons, ethyl ether; m.w. 41,000; 100% conc.; anionic.

Gantrez® AN-139 BF. [ISP]

Chem. Descrip.: PVM/MA copolymer
CAS 9011-16-9

Uses: Dispersant, coupling agent, stabilizer; filmformer in spray bandages; complexing agent for sustained-release iron preps.; ostomy adhesives; denture adhesives/stabilizers; dentifrices; thickener for aq. or org. solv. systems

Properties: Wh. free-flowing fluffy powd.; sol. in water, alcohols, phenols, pyridine, aldehydes, ketones, acid, caustic, and org. solvs.; essentially insol. in aliphatic, aromatic, or halogenated hydrocabons, ethyl ether; m.w. 41,000; flash pt. none; 98% min. act.; anionic

Toxicology: LD50 (oral, rat) 8000 mg/kg; minimal eye irritant; nonirritating to skin; contains 2% max. toluene, TLV/TWA 100 ppm, STEL 150 ppm; chronic exposure to toluene may cause liver, kidney, or lung damage; avoid breathing dust

Precaution: Incompat. with strong oxidizing or reducing agents.

Gantrez® AN-149. [ISP]

Chem. Descrip.: PVM/MA copolymer
CAS 52229-50-2

Uses: Dispersant, coupling agent, stabilizer; filmformer in spray bandages; complexing agent for sustained-release iron preps.; ostomy adhesives; denture adhesives/stabilizers; dentifrices; thickener for aq. or org. solv. systems

Properties: Wh. fluffy powd.; sol. in water, alcohols, phenols, pyridine, aldehydes, ketones, acid, caustic, and org. solvs.; essentially insol. in aliphatic, aromatic, or halogenated hydrocabons, ethyl ether; m.w. 50,000; 100% conc.; anionic.

Gantrez® AN-169. [ISP]

Chem. Descrip.: PVM/MA copolymer
CAS 52229-50-2

Uses: Dispersant, coupling agent, stabilizer; filmformer in spray bandages; complexing agent for sustained-release iron preps.; ostomy adhesives; denture adhesives/stabilizers; dentifrices; thickener for aq. or org. solv. systems

Properties: Wh. fluffy powd.; sol. in water, alcohols, phenols, pyridine, aldehydes, ketones, acid, caustic, and org. solvs.; essentially insol. in aliphatic, aromatic, or halogenated hydrocabons, ethyl ether; m.w. 67,000; 100% conc.; anionic.

Gantrez® ES-225. [ISP]

Chem. Descrip.: Ethyl ester of PVM/MA copolymer, ethanol

Uses: Dispersant, coupling agent, stabilizer; thickener for aq. or org. solv. systems; coating agent for enteric tablet coatings, sustained- or controlled-release coatings

Properties: Clear, visc. sol'n.; sol. [1 g resin (100% solids) in 9 g solv.] in ethanol, IPA, diethylene glycol, tetrahydrofuran, ethylene glycol monomethyl ether, butyl Carbitol, acetone, cyclohexanone, dioxane, water; sp.gr. 0.983; dens. 8.18

lb/gal; acid no. 275-300 (100% solids); 50% act. in ethanol; anionic

Toxicology: LD50 8-9 g/kg (low toxicity).

Gantrez® ES-335. [ISP]

Chem. Descrip.: Isopropyl ester of PVM/MA copolymer, IPA

Uses: Dispersant, coupling agent, stabilizer; thickener for aq. or org. solv. systems; coating agent for enteric tablet coatings, sustained- or controlled-release coatings

Properties: Clear, visc. sol'n.; sol. in alcohols, alkali, esters, ketones, and glycol ethers; sp.gr. 0.957; dens. 7.98 lg/gal; acid no. 250-280 (100% solids); 50% in IPA.; anionic.

Gantrez® ES-425. [ISP]

Chem. Descrip.: N-Butyl ester of PVM/MA copolymer, ethanol

Uses: Dispersant, coupling agent, stabilizer; thickener for aq. or org. solv. systems; coating agent for enteric tablet coatings, sustained- or controlled-release coatings

Properties: Clear, visc. sol'n.; sol. [1 g resin (100% solids) in 9 g solv.] in ethanol, IPA, diethylene glycol, tetrahydrofuran, ethylene glycol monomethyl ether, butyl Carbitol, ethyl acetate, acetone, cyclohexanone, dioxane, water; sp.gr. 0.977; dens. 8.13 lb/gal; acid no. 235-265 (100% solids); 50% solids in ethanol.; anionic.

Gantrez® ES-435. [ISP]

Chem. Descrip.: N-Butyl ester of PVM/MA copolymer, IPA

Uses: Dispersant, coupling agent, stabilizer; thickener for aq. or org. solv. systems; coating agent for enteric tablet coatings, sustained- or controlled-release coatings

Properties: Clear, visc. sol'n.; sol. in alcohols, alkali, esters, ketones, and glycol ethers; sp.gr. 0.962; dens. 8.02 lb/gal; acid no. 245-275 (100% solids); 50% in IPA.; anionic.

Gantrez® MS-955D. [ISP]

Chem. Descrip.: Calcium/sodium PVM/MA copolymer.
CAS 62386-95-2

Uses: Film-former in spray bandages; visc. modifier/stabilizer; enteric sustained-release tablet coating; bioadhesives; dentifrices

Properties: Wh. to off-wh.powd.; slowly sol. in water; bulk dens. > 0.7 g/cc (tapped); flash pt. none; pH 6-7 (1 g/100 ml water); 6-15% water

Toxicology: LD50 (oral, rat) 7000 mg/kg; sl. skin irritant; minimal eye irritant; nuisance dust: TLV/TWA 10 mg/m^3 total, 5 mg/m^3 respirable; avoid breathing dust

Precaution: Incompat. with strong oxidizing or reducing agents.

Gantrez® S-95. [ISP]

Chem. Descrip.: PVM/MA copolymer

Uses: Film-former in spray bandages; visc. modifier/stabilizer; enteric sustained-release tablet coating; bioadhesives; dentifrices

Properties: Powd.; rapid cold-water solubility over entire pH range; pH 2 (5% aq.); 100% conc.;

anionic.

Gantrez® S-97. [ISP]
Chem. Descrip.: PVM/MA copolymer
Uses: Film-former in spray bandages; visc. modi-fier/stabilizer; enteric sustained-release tablet coating; bioadhesives; dentifrices
Properties: Powd.; water-sol.; pH 2 (5% aq.).

Gardiquat 1450. [Albright & Wilson UK]
Chem. Descrip.: Benzalkonium chloride USP
Uses: Germicide, deodorant, algicide, slimicide
Properties: Almost water wh. clear liq.; cloud pt. 1 C; pH 7.0 ± 0.5 (1%); 50% act.
Precaution: Flamm.

Gardiquat 1480. [Albright & Wilson UK]
Chem. Descrip.: Benzalkonium chloride USP
Uses: Germicide, deodorant, algicide, slimicide
Properties: Almost water-wh. clear liq.; sp.gr. 0.945; cloud pt. 1 C max.; flash pt. (PMCC) 32 C; pH 7 ± 0.5 (1%); 80% act.

Gastric Mucin N.N.R. [Am. Labs]
Chem. Descrip.: Gastric mucin, the fraction precipi-tated by alcohol after pepsin-hydrochloric acid digestion of hog stomach linings
Uses: Protective emollient and lubricant used in treatment of peptic ulcer
Properties: Powd.; 99.6% thru 100 mesh; pH 4.2; 75% mucin.

Gelatin USP/NF, Type A. [Hormel]
Chem. Descrip.: Gelatin USP/NF, Type A, various bloom ranges 150-275
CAS 9000-70-8; EINECS 232-554-6
Uses: Gelatin capsule ingred., stabilizer, coatings, film-former, gellant, protein used in pharmaceuti-cal applics.
Regulatory: Kosher
Properties: Beige powd., weak bouillon-like odor; 6 mesh; pH 4.5-5.8; 12% max. moisture
Storage: Stable for up to 1 yr when stored dry at ambient temps.

Gelatin XF. [Hormel]
Chem. Descrip.: Gelatin USP/NF, Type A, 235 bloom
CAS 9000-70-8; EINECS 232-554-6
Uses: Hydrates rapidly; in pharmaceutical applics.
Regulatory: Kosher
Properties: Ivory fine powd., bland bouillon-like odor; 100 mesh; dens. 0.7-0.8 g/cc; visc. 40 ± 8 mps; pH 4.5-5.8; 8% max. moisture
Storage: Stable for at least 1 yr when stored dry at ambient temps.

Geleol. [Gattefosse; Gattefosse SA]
Chem. Descrip.: Glyceryl stearate
CAS 31566-31-1
Uses: Emulsifier, consistency enhancer, opacifier for food, veterinary, cosmetic, and pharmaceuti-cal prods.; thickener for pharmaceutical oint-ments, creams, and lotions
Properties: Gardner < 3 waxy solid, faint odor; m.p. 53-57 C; HLB 3.0; acid no. < 3; iodine no. < 3; sapon. no. 160-180; 100% conc.; nonionic
Toxicology: Sl. irritating to eyes, nonirritating to skin.

Gelot 64®. [Gattefosse; Gattefosse SA]
Chem. Descrip.: Glyceryl stearate and PEG-75 stearate
Uses: SE base for o/w pharmaceutical emulsions, creams; protects the drug, improves stability of the dosage form
Use level: 15-25%
Properties: Gardner < 5 waxy solid; weak odor; HLB 10; m.p. 59-65 C; acid no. < 6; iodine no. < 3; sapon. no. 105-125; 100% conc.; nonionic
Toxicology: LD50 (oral, rat) > 5 g/kg; nonirritating to skin and eyes.

GELRITE®. [Kelco]
Chem. Descrip.: Gellan gum
CAS 71010-52-1; EINECS 275-117-5
Uses: Gelling agent in microbiological media, plant tissue culture; immunological applics.; agar re-placer
Properties: Wh. to tan powd., sl. odor; water-sol.; bulk dens. $\approx$ 50 lb/ft^3; pH neutral (1%); readily biodeg.
Toxicology: LD50 (oral, rat) > 5000 mg/kg; exces-sive dust inhalation may cause respiratory irrita-tion; dry prod. may cause eye irritation
Precaution: Not flamm., but powd. will burn if involved in a fire; spills are slippery when wet; incompt. with strong oxidizers
Storage: Store in cool, dry place.

Gelucire 33/01. [Gattefosse SA]
Chem. Descrip.: Hemisynthetic glycerides
Uses: Excipient for hard gelatin capsules; protects the drug, improves stability of the dosage form
Properties: Drop pt. 33-38 C; HLB 1.0; acid no. < 2; iodine no. ≤ 3; sapon. no. 240-260
Toxicology: LD0 (oral, rat) > 20 g/kg.

Gelucire 35/10. [Gattefosse SA]
Chem. Descrip.: Saturated polyglycolized glycer-ides
Uses: Excipient for hard gelatin capsules; protects the drug, improves stability of the dosage form
Properties: Drop pt. 29-34 C; HLB 10.0; acid no. < 2; iodine no. < 2; sapon. no. 120-135
Toxicology: LD0 (oral, rat) > 20 g/kg.

Gelucire 37/02. [Gattefosse SA]
Chem. Descrip.: Saturated polyglycolized glycer-ides
Uses: Excipient for hard gelatin capsules; protects the drug, improves stability of the dosage form
Properties: Drop pt. 34.5-39.5 C; HLB 2.0; acid no. < 2; iodine no. < 2; sapon. no. 200-215
Toxicology: LD0 (oral, rat) > 20 g/kg.

Gelucire 42/12. [Gattefosse SA]
Chem. Descrip.: Saturated polyglycolized glycer-ides
Uses: Excipient for hard gelatin capsules; protects the drug, improves stability of the dosage form
Properties: Drop pt. 41.5-46.5 C; HLB 12.0; acid no. < 2; iodine no. < 2; sapon. no. 95-115
Toxicology: LD0 (oral, rat) > 20 g/kg.

Gelucire 44/14. [Gattefosse SA]
Chem. Descrip.: Saturated polyglycolized glycer-ides from hydrog. veg. oils

Uses: Excipient for semisolid formulations for hard gelatin capsules; provides fast release and bioavailability improvement of poor water sol. compds.

Regulatory: French pharmacopeia compliance

Properties: Gardner < 5 waxy solid, faint odor; sol. in chloroform, methylene chloride, ethanol; disp. in water; insol. in min. oil; drop pt. 42.5-47.5 C; HLB 14.0; acid no. < 2; iodine no. < 2; sapon. no. 79-93; hyd. no. 36-56

Toxicology: LD0 (oral, rat) > 20 g/kg; nontoxic

Storage: Store in orig. container, prevent exposure to air, light, heat, and moisture.

Gelucire 46/07. [Gattefosse SA]

Chem. Descrip.: Saturated polyglycolized glycerides

Uses: Excipient for hard gelatin capsules; protects the drug, improves stability of the dosage form

Properties: Drop pt. 47-52 C; HLB 7.0; acid no. < 2; iodine no. < 2; sapon. no. 125-140

Toxicology: LD0 (oral, rat) > 20 g/kg.

Gelucire 48/09. [Gattefosse SA]

Chem. Descrip.: Saturated polyglycolized glycerides

Uses: Excipient for hard gelatin capsules; protects the drug, improves stability of the dosage form

Properties: Drop pt. 46-51 C; HLB 9.0; acid no. < 2; iodine no. < 2; sapon. no. 105-125

Toxicology: LD0 (oral, rat) > 20 g/kg.

Gelucire 50/02. [Gattefosse SA]

Chem. Descrip.: Saturated polyglycolized glycerides

Uses: Excipient for semisolid formulations for hard gelatin capsules, sustained release applics.

Properties: Drop pt. 46.5-51.5 C; HLB 2.0; acid no. < 2; iodine no. < 2; sapon. no. 180-195

Toxicology: LD50 (oral, rat) > 18 ml/kg.

Gelucire 50/13. [Gattefosse SA]

Chem. Descrip.: Saturated polyglycolized glycerides

Uses: Excipient for hard gelatin capsules; protects the drug, improves stability of the dosage form

Properties: Drop pt. 46-51 C; HLB 13.0; acid no. < 2; iodine no. < 2; sapon. no. 65-80

Toxicology: LD0 (oral, rat) > 20 g/kg.

Gelucire 53/10. [Gattefosse SA]

Chem. Descrip.: Saturated polyglycolized glycerides

Uses: Excipient for hard gelatin capsules; protects the drug, improves stability of the dosage form

Properties: Drop pt. 47.5-52.5 C; HLB 10.0; acid no. < 2; iodine no. < 2; sapon. no. 95-115

Toxicology: LD0 (oral, rat) > 20 g/kg.

Gelucire 62/05. [Gattefosse SA]

Chem. Descrip.: Polyglycolized natural wax

Uses: Excipient for hard gelatin capsules; protects the drug, improves stability of the dosage form

Properties: Drop pt. 59-70 C; HLB 5.0; acid no. < 5; iodine no. < 10; sapon. no. 70-90

Toxicology: LD0 (oral, rat) > 8.5 g/kg; sl. irritating to skin and eyes.

Gemtone®. [Mearl]

Chem. Descrip.: Titanium dioxide-coated mica with iron oxides, iron blue, carmine, or chromium oxide

Uses: Rich, lustrous pigments deriving color from both light interference and light absorption; for analgesic body lotions, sunscreens, toothpaste

Properties: Powd.; avg. particle size 25 μ; sp.gr. 3.0.

Genu® HM USP 100. [Hercules]

Chem. Descrip.: Pectin, high-methoxyl, USP

CAS 9000-69-5; EINECS 232-553-0

Uses: Stabilizer, water binder, adhesive for pharmaceutical suspensions, emulsions, ostomy adhesives, wound care dressings

Use level: 0.2-0.6% (pharmaceutical)

Regulatory: FDA 21CFR §184.1588, GRAS.

Genu® HM USP L200. [Hercules]

Chem. Descrip.: Pectin, high-methoxyl, USP

CAS 9000-69-5; EINECS 232-553-0

Uses: Stabilizer, water binder, adhesive for pharmaceutical suspensions, emulsions, ostomy adhesives, wound care dressings

Use level: 1-20% (pharmaceutical)

Regulatory: FDA 21CFR §184.1588, GRAS.

Genu® Carrageenan. [Hercules/Aqualon]

Chem. Descrip.: Carrageenan

CAS 9000-07-1; EINECS 232-524-2

Uses: Gellant, thickener, stabilizer, and suspender used in pharmaceuticals; water binder.

Genugel® Series. [Hercules]

Chem. Descrip.: Carrageenan

CAS 9000-07-1; EINECS 232-524-2

Uses: Gellant, thickener, stabilizer, and suspender used in pharmaceuticals; water binder; imparts desirable body and mouthfeel.

Genu® Pectins. [Hercules/Aqualon]

Chem. Descrip.: Pectin; high-methoxyl and low-methoxyl purified natural hydrocolloid derived from citrus peels

CAS 9000-69-5; EINECS 232-553-0

Uses: Visc. builder, bodying agent, suspending agent, protective colloid, and stabilizer for pharmaceuticals; stabilizer, water binder, adhesive for pharmaceutical suspensions, emulsions, ostomy adhesives, wound care dressings

Regulatory: FDA 21CFR §184.1588, GRAS

Properties: Lt. cream to grayish powd.; no odor and flavor.

Genu® Pectin (citrus) type USP/100. [Copenhagen Pectin]

Chem. Descrip.: Pectin USP

CAS 9000-69-5; EINECS 232-553-0

Uses: Intended for use in ostomy bandages; thickener and stabilizer in pharmaceutical emulsions and suspensions

Regulatory: USP compliance

Properties: Wh. free-flowing gran., essentially odorless and flavorless; 100 mesh particle size; sol. in water; pH 3.6-4.1 (1% aq.)

Storage: 1 yr shelf life when kept under cool and dry conditions in unopened pkg.

Genu® Pectin (citrus) type USP/200. [Copenhagen Pectin]

Chem. Descrip.: Pectin USP
CAS 9000-69-5; EINECS 232-553-0
Uses: Intended for use in ostomy bandages; thickener and stabilizer in pharmaceutical emulsions and suspensions
Regulatory: USP compliance
Properties: Wh. free-flowing gran., essentially odorless and flavorless; 200 mesh particle size; sol. in water; pH 3.6-4.4 (1% aq.)
Storage: 1 yr shelf life when kept under cool and dry conditions in unopened pkg.

Genu® Pectin (citrus) type USP-H. [Copenhagen Pectin]
Chem. Descrip.: Pectin USP
CAS 9000-69-5; EINECS 232-553-0
Uses: Thickener and stabilizer in pharmaceutical emulsions and suspensions
Regulatory: USP compliance
Properties: Cream to lt. tan free-flowing gran., essentially odorless and flavorless; sol. in water; visc. 200-450 cP (2%); pH 3.6-4.4 (1% aq.)
Storage: 1 yr shelf life when kept under cool and dry conditions in unopened pkg.

Genu® Pectin (citrus) type USP-L/200. [Copenhagen Pectin]
Chem. Descrip.: Pectin USP
CAS 9000-69-5; EINECS 232-553-0
Uses: Thickener and stabilizer in pharmaceutical emulsions and suspensions
Regulatory: USP compliance
Properties: Cream to lt. tan free-flowing gran., essentially odorless and flavorless; sol. in water; visc. 80-180 cP (2%); pH 3.6-4.4 (1% aq.)
Storage: 1 yr shelf life when kept under cool and dry conditions in unopened pkg.

Genuvisco. [Hercules]
Chem. Descrip.: Carageenan
CAS 9000-07-1; EINECS 232-524-2
Uses: Gellant, thickener, stabilizer, and suspender used in pharmaceuticals; water binder; imparts desirable body and mouthfeel.

Germaben® II. [Sutton Labs]
Chem. Descrip.: Diazolidinyl urea (30%), propylene glycol (56%), methylparaben (11%), and propylparaben (3%)
Uses: Broad-spectrum antimicrobial preservative for pharmaceuticals, topicals, medicated shampoos, emulsion prods.; effective over wide pH range, against Gram-positive and -negative bacteria, yeast, molds; germicidal creams/ointments
Use level: 1% max.; 0.25-1% (medicated shampoos, emulsions), 1% (topicals)
Regulatory: USA and Europe approvals
Properties: Pale to lt. yel. clear visc. liq.; char. mild odor; sol. @ 1% in aq. sol'n. and oil-water emulsions; sp.gr. 1.1731-1.1839; vapor pressure 0.22 mm Hg (20 C); b.p. 187.2 C; flash pt. (TCC) > 93.3 C; 42.5-45.5% total solids; 5.8-6.4% N
Toxicology: LD50 (oral, rat) > 2000 mg/kg, (dermal, rabbit) > 2000 mg/kg; low acute oral toxicity; moderate skin irritant; severe eye irritant at full strength

Precaution: Explosive limits 2.6-12.5%
Storage: Keep container closed when not in use; store @ R.T.

Germall® 115. [Sutton Labs]
Chem. Descrip.: Imidazolidinyl urea USP/NF
CAS 39236-46-9; EINECS 254-372-6
Uses: Germicide, antimicrobial preservative for topical pharmaceuticals; active against bacteria, yeast, and mold; synergistic with other preservatives; for germicidal creams/ointments
Regulatory: EC approved
Properties: Wh. free-flowing fine powd., char. mild odor or odorless; hygroscopic; sol. (g/100 g): 200 g in water, 50 g in propylene glycol, 16 g in glycerin; m.w. 406.33; pH 6.0-7.5 (1% aq.); 26-28% N
Toxicology: LD50 (oral, rat) 5200 mg/kg, low acute oral toxicity; nonirritating to skin and eyes as aq. so'n.; mild transient eye irritant as powd.; inh. of powd. may cause respiratory irritation
Precaution: Conc. powd. in presence of ignition source may cause a dust explosion
Storage: Keep container closed when not in use; store in cool, dry location.

Germall® II. [Sutton Labs]
Chem. Descrip.: Diazolidinyl urea
CAS 78491-02-8; EINECS 278-928-2
Uses: Broad-spectrum antimicrobial preservative for topical pharmaceuticals; effective against Gram-negative and positive, and house isolate bacteria; effective at low conc. levels; germicidal creams/ointments
Regulatory: EC approved
Properties: Wh. free-flowing fine powd., char. mild odor or odorless; hygroscopic; very sol. in water, sol. in propylene glycol, glycerin; m.w. 278.23; 19-21% N; low avian toxicity; low toxicity to aquatic life
Toxicology: LD50 (oral, rat) 2570 mg/kg, (dermal, rabbit) > 2000 mg/kg; low acute oral toxicity; nonirritating to skin and eyes @ 5% aq. sol'n.; powd. may cause eye irritation; inh. of powd. may cause respiratory irritation
Precaution: Conc. powd. in presence of ignition source may cause a dust explosion
Storage: Keep container closed when not in use; store in cool, dry location.

Gloria®. [Witco/Petroleum Spec.]
Chem. Descrip.: Wh. min. oil USP
Uses: Emollient, lubricant for pharmaceuticals, ointments, creams, veterinary preps.
Regulatory: FDA 21CFR §172.878, §178.3620a
Properties: Water-wh., odorless, tasteless; sp.gr. 0.859-0.880; visc. 39-42 cSt (40 C); pour pt. -12 C; flash pt. 204 C.

Glucam® E-10. [Amerchol]
Chem. Descrip.: Methyl gluceth-10
CAS 68239-42-9
Uses: Solv. and solubilizer for topical pharmaceuticals
Properties: Pale yel. med. visc. syrup; pract. odorless; sol. in water, alcohol, hydroalcoholic sys-

tems; acid no. 1.5 max.; iodine no. 1 max.; sapon. no. 1.5 max; hyd. no. 350-370; 100% conc.; nonionic
Toxicology: LD50 (acute oral) > 5 ml/kg; nonirritating to eyes and skin.

Glucam® E-20. [Amerchol]
Chem. Descrip.: Methyl gluceth-20
CAS 68239-43-0
Uses: Solv. and solubilizer for topical pharmaceuticals, sunscreens
Properties: Pale yel. thin syrup; pract. odorless; sol. in water, alcohol, hydroalcoholic systems; acid no. 1.0 max.; iodine no. 1 max.; sapon. no. 1.0 max.; hyd. no. 205-225; 100% conc.
Toxicology: LD50 (acute oral) > 5 ml/kg; nonirritating to eyes and skin.

Glucam® E-20 Distearate. [Amerchol]
Chem. Descrip.: Methyl gluceth-20 distearate
CAS 98073-10-0
Uses: Aux. o/w emulsifier, moisturizer, emollient, conditioner, and lubricant for pharmaceuticals, deodorant sticks
Properties: Yel. semisolid; HLB 12.5; 100% conc.; nonionic
Toxicology: LD50 (acute oral) > 5 g/kg; pract. nonirritating to eyes; not a primary skin irritant.

Glucam® P-10. [Amerchol]
Chem. Descrip.: PPG-10 methyl glucose ether
CAS 61849-72-7
Uses: Solv. and solubilizer for topical pharmaceuticals
Properties: Pale yel. heavy visc. syrups; pract. odorless; sol. in water, alcohol, and hydroalcoholic systems, castor oil, IPM, IPP; visc. 8500 cps; acid no. 1.0 max.; iodine no. 1 max.; sapon. no. 1.0 max.; hyd. no. 285-305; 100% conc.; nonionic
Toxicology: LD50 (acute oral) > 5 ml/kg; nonirritating to skin; mild transient irritation to eyes.

Glucam® P-20. [Amerchol]
Chem. Descrip.: PPG-20 methyl glucose ether
CAS 61849-72-7
Uses: Solv. and solubilizer for topical pharmaceuticals
Properties: Pale yel. med. visc. syrup; pract. odorless; sol. in water, alcohol, and hydroalcoholic systems, castor oil, IPM, IPP; visc. 1700 cps; acid no. 1.0 max.; iodine no. 1 max.; sapon. no. 1.0 max.; hyd. no. 160-180; 100% conc.; nonionic
Toxicology: LD50 (acute oral) > 3 ml/kg; nonirritating to skin; mild transient irritation to eyes.

Glucam® P-20 Distearate. [Amerchol]
Chem. Descrip.: PPG-20 methyl glucose ether distearate
Uses: Skin moisturizer, conditioner, slip agent, and emollient for pharmaceuticals; barrier to reduce water loss from stratum corneum
Properties: Pale amber liq.; sol. in IPM, castor oil, corn oil, ethanol, hot min. oil; insol. in water, propylene glycol, aq. ethanol; acid no. 2.5 max.; sapon. no. 58-72; hyd. no. 50-70; flash pt. (COC) 545 F
Toxicology: LD50 (acute oral) > 5 g/kg; not a

primary skin irritant; pract. nonirritating to eyes.
Gluconal® CA A. [Akzo Nobel bv]
Chem. Descrip.: Calcium gluconate anhydrous
CAS 299-28-5; EINECS 206-075-8
Uses: Pharmaceutical/food grade mineral source for human and veterinary pharmaceutical preps., dietary supplements, fortified foods and animal feed
Properties: Wh. powd.; sol. 30 g/l water; m.w. 430.4; bulk dens. 250-350 kg/m³; pH 7.4 (1%); 95-100% act.
Toxicology: LD50 (oral, rat) > 5000 mg/kg.

Gluconal® CA M. [Akzo Nobel bv]
Chem. Descrip.: Calcium gluconate monohydrate
CAS 299-28-5; EINECS 206-075-8
Uses: Pharmaceutical/food grade mineral source for human and veterinary pharmaceutical preps., dietary supplements, fortified foods and animal feed
Properties: Wh. powd./gran.; sol. 40 g/l water; m.w. 448.4; bulk dens. 300-650 kg/m³; pH 7.5 (1%); 98.5-100% act.
Toxicology: LD50 (oral, rat) > 5000 mg/kg.

Gluconal® CA M B. [Akzo Nobel bv]
Chem. Descrip.: Calcium borogluconate
CAS 5743-34-0
Uses: Pharmaceutical/food grade mineral source for human and veterinary pharmaceutical preps., dietary supplements, fortified foods and animal feed
Properties: Wh. powd.; sol. 200 g/l water; m.w. 448.4 + 61.8; bulk dens. 550-650 kg/m³; pH 5.1 (1%); 82-89% act.
Toxicology: LD50 (oral, rat) > 2000 mg/kg.

Gluconal® CO. [Akzo Nobel bv]
Chem. Descrip.: Cobalt gluconate
CAS 71957-08-9
Uses: Pharmaceutical/food grade mineral source for human and veterinary pharmaceutical preps., dietary supplements, fortified foods and animal feed
Properties: Pink powd.; sol. 200 g/l water; m.w. 449.3; bulk dens. 450-550 kg/m³; pH 6.5 (1%); 88-100% act.
Toxicology: LD50 (oral, rat) 1420 mg/kg.

Gluconal® CU. [Akzo Nobel bv]
Chem. Descrip.: Copper gluconate
CAS 527-09-3; EINECS 208-408-2
Uses: Pharmaceutical/food grade mineral source for human and veterinary pharmaceutical preps., dietary supplements, fortified foods and animal feed
Properties: Lt. blue powd.; sol. 500 g/l water; m.w. 453.8; bulk dens. 450-550 kg/m³; pH 4.6 (1%); 98-100% act.
Toxicology: LD50 (oral, rat) 1710 mg/kg.

Gluconal® FE. [Akzo Nobel bv]
Chem. Descrip.: Ferrous gluconate
CAS 299-29-6; EINECS 206-076-3
Uses: Pharmaceutical/food grade mineral source for human and veterinary pharmaceutical preps., dietary supplements, fortified foods and animal

feed
Properties: Yel.-gray powd./gran.; sol. 100 g/l water; m.w. 446.1; bulk dens. 650-850 kg/m³; pH 4.5 (1%); 87.5-95% act.
Toxicology: LD50 (oral, rat) 4600 mg/kg.

Gluconal® K. [Akzo Nobel bv]
Chem. Descrip.: Potassium gluconate
CAS 299-27-4; EINECS 206-074-2
Uses: Pharmaceutical/food grade mineral source for human and veterinary pharmaceutical preps., dietary supplements, fortified foods and animal feed
Properties: Wh. powd./gran.; sol. 1000 g/l water; m.w. 234.3; bulk dens. 500-650 kg/m³; pH 7.1 (1%); 95-100% act.
Toxicology: LD50 (oral, rat) 6060 mg/kg.

Gluconal® MG. [Akzo Nobel bv]
Chem. Descrip.: Magnesium gluconate
CAS 3632-91-5; EINECS 222-848-2
Uses: Pharmaceutical/food grade mineral source for human and veterinary pharmaceutical preps., dietary supplements, fortified foods and animal feed
Properties: Wh. powd./gran.; sol. 160 g/l water; m.w. 414.6; bulk dens. 500-750 kg/m³; pH 7.3 (1%); 86-99% act.
Toxicology: LD50 (oral, rat) 9100 mg/kg.

Gluconal® MN. [Akzo Nobel bv]
Chem. Descrip.: Manganese gluconate
CAS 6485-39-8; EINECS 229-350-4
Uses: Pharmaceutical/food grade mineral source for human and veterinary pharmaceutical preps., dietary supplements, fortified foods and animal feed
Properties: Off-wh. powd.; sol. 110 g/l water; m.w. 445.2; bulk dens. 700-800 kg/m³; pH 6.4 (1%); 90.5-100% act.
Toxicology: LD50 (oral, rat) 5850 mg/kg.

Gluconal® NA. [Akzo Nobel bv]
Chem. Descrip.: Sodium gluconate
CAS 527-07-1; EINECS 208-407-7
Uses: Pharmaceutical/food grade mineral source for human and veterinary pharmaceutical preps., dietary supplements, fortified foods and animal feed
Properties: Wh. powd./gran.; sol. 600 g/l water; m.w. 218.1; bulk dens. 600-780 kg/m³; pH 6.9 (1%); 98-100% act.
Toxicology: LD50 (oral, rat) > 5000 mg/kg.

Gluconal® ZN. [Akzo Nobel bv]
Chem. Descrip.: Zinc gluconate
CAS 4468-02-4; EINECS 224-736-9
Uses: Pharmaceutical/food grade mineral source for human and veterinary pharmaceutical preps., dietary supplements, fortified foods and animal feed
Properties: Wh. powd./gran.; sol. 100 g/l water; m.w. 455.7; bulk dens. 600-800 kg/m³; pH 6.5 (1%); 85.5-100% act.
Toxicology: LD50 (oral, rat) > 5000 mg/kg.

Gluplex® AC. [Kelisema Srl]
Chem. Descrip.: Native wheat protein/cocoyl car-boxylate complex
Uses: Protein contributing mild detergency to medicinal soaps; protects against surfactant irritancy
Properties: Yel. clear to hazy liq, sl. char. odor; sol. in water @ pH 9-11; pH 9-10.

Glycerine (Pharmaceutical) [Asahi Denka Kogyo]
Chem. Descrip.: Glycerin
CAS 56-81-5; EINECS 200-289-5
Uses: Pharmaceutical grade for solvent, emollient, sweetener
Properties: Clear liq.; sp.gr. > 1.2598; > 98% purity.

Glycomul® L. [Lonza]
Chem. Descrip.: Sorbitan laurate
CAS 1338-39-2
Uses: Emulsifier for pharmaceutical uses
Properties: Amber clear liq.; sol. in methanol, ethanol, naphtha; disp. in water; sp.gr. 1.0; visc. 3100 cps (30 C); HLB 9; acid no. 7 max.; sapon. no. 158-170; hyd. no. 330-358; flash pt. 204 C; pH 6.5 (5%); 99% min. conc.; nonionic.

Glycomul® O. [Lonza]
Chem. Descrip.: Sorbitan oleate
CAS 1338-43-8; EINECS 215-665-4
Uses: Emulsifier for pharmaceutical uses
Properties: Amber clear liq.; sol. in ethyl acetate, min. and veg. oils, disp. in water; sp.gr. 1.0; visc. 1000 cps.; HLB 4.3; acid no. 7.5 max.; sapon. no. 143-160; hyd. no. 193-209; flash pt. 220 C; 100% conc.; nonionic.

Glycomul® P. [Lonza]
Chem. Descrip.: Sorbitan palmitate
CAS 26266-57-9; EINECS 247-568-8
Uses: Emulsifier for pharmaceutical uses
Properties: Cream beads; sol. in veg. and min. oil, ethyl acetate, ethanol, acetone, toluol; HLB 6.7; sapon. no. 139-150; 100% conc.; nonionic.

Glycomul® S. [Lonza]
Chem. Descrip.: Sorbitan stearate (also avail. in veg. and kosher grade)
CAS 1338-41-6; EINECS 215-664-9
Uses: Emulsifier for pharmaceutical uses
Properties: Lt. tan solid or beads; sol. in veg. oil; HLB 5.0; acid no. 5-10; sapon. no. 147-157; hyd. no. 235-260; 100% conc.; nonionic.

Glycomul® SOC. [Lonza]
Chem. Descrip.: Sorbitan sesquioleate
CAS 8007-43-0; EINECS 232-360-1
Uses: Emulsifier for pharmaceutical uses
Properties: Cream beads; sol. in methanol, ethanol, ethyl acetate; sp.gr. 1.0; visc. 1000 cps; HLB 4.0; sapon. no. 149-166; 100% conc.; nonionic.

Glycomul® TO. [Lonza]
Chem. Descrip.: Sorbitan trioleate
CAS 26266-58-0; EINECS 247-569-3
Uses: Emulsifier for pharmaceutical uses
Properties: Amber, oily liq.; sol. in ethyl acetate, toluol, naphtha, min. and veg. oils, disp. in water; sp.gr. 0.95; visc. 200 cps; HLB 1.8; sapon. no. 171-185; 100% conc.; nonionic.

Glycomul® TS. [Lonza]
Chem. Descrip.: Sorbitan tristearate

CAS 26658-19-5; EINECS 247-891-4
Uses: Emulsifier for pharmaceutical uses
Properties: Lt. tan beads; poorly sol. in ethyl acetate, toluol, disp. in acetone, naphtha, min. and veg. oils; HLB 2.1; sapon. no. 175-190; 100% conc.; nonionic.

Glycon® G 100. [Lonza]
Chem. Descrip.: Glycerin
CAS 56-81-5; EINECS 200-289-5
Uses: Humectant, bodying agent, moisture control agent for toothpaste
Properties: Sp.gr. 1.2607; 99.5% act.

Glycon® G-300. [Lonza]
Chem. Descrip.: Glycerin
CAS 56-81-5; EINECS 200-289-5
Uses: Humectant, bodying agent, moisture control agent for toothpaste
Properties: Sp.gr. 1.2517; 96% act.

Glycosperse® L-20. [Lonza]
Chem. Descrip.: Polysorbate 20
CAS 9005-64-5
Uses: Emulsifier for pharmaceuticals; flavor solubilizer and dispersant
Properties: Yel. clear liq.; sol. in water, alcohol, acetone; sp.gr. 1.1; visc. 400 cps; HLB 16.7; acid no. 2 max.; sapon. no. 40-50; hyd. no. 96-108; pH 7 (5%); 3% max. moisture; nonionic.

Glycosperse® O-5. [Lonza]
Chem. Descrip.: Polysorbate 81
CAS 9005-65-6
Uses: Emulsifier for pharmaceuticals; flavor solubilizer and dispersant
Properties: Amber liq.; sol. in alcohol, ethyl acetate, min. oil; disp. in water; sp.gr. 1.0; visc. 450 cps; HLB 10.0; sapon. no. 95-105; 100% conc.; nonionic.

Glycosperse® O-20. [Lonza]
Chem. Descrip.: Polysorbate 80
CAS 9005-65-6
Uses: Emulsifier for pharmaceuticals; flavor solubilizer and dispersant
Properties: Yel. liq.; sol. in water, alcohol, ethyl acetate, toluol, veg. oil; sp.gr. 1.0; visc. 400 cps; HLB 15; sapon. no. 44-56; 100% conc.; nonionic.

Glycosperse® O-20 FG. [Lonza]
Chem. Descrip.: Polysorbate 80 NF FCC
CAS 9005-65-6
Uses: Solubilizer, dispersant for vitamin-min. preps.
Regulatory: FDA 21CFR §172.515, 172.840
Properties: Amber clear liq., mild odor; HLB 15.0; acid no. 1 max.; iodine no. 19-22; sapon. no. 45-55; hyd. no. 65-80; 3% max. moisture; nonionic
Storage: Store in cool, dry area.

Glycosperse® O-20 KFG. [Lonza]
Chem. Descrip.: Polysorbate 80 NF FCC
CAS 9005-65-6
Uses: Solubilizer and dispersant for vitamin-min. preps.
Regulatory: FDA 21CFR §172.515, 172.840; kosher
Properties: Amber clear liq., mild odor; HLB 15.0;

acid no. 2 max.; sapon. no. 45-55; hyd. no. 65-80; 3% max. moisture; nonionic
Storage: Store in cool, dry area.

Glycosperse® P-20. [Lonza]
Chem. Descrip.: Polysorbate 40
CAS 9005-66-7
Uses: Emulsifier for pharmaceuticals; flavor solubilizer and dispersant
Properties: Yel. liq.; sol. in water, methanol, ethanol, acetone, ethyl acetate; sp.gr. 1.0; visc. 550 cps; HLB 15.6; sapon. no. 40-53; 100% conc.; nonionic.

Glycosperse® S-20. [Lonza]
Chem. Descrip.: Polysorbate 60
CAS 9005-67-8
Uses: Emulsifier for pharmaceuticals; flavor solubilizer and dispersant
Properties: Yel. liq.; sol. in water, ethyl acetate, toluol; sp.gr. 1.1; HLB 15.0; sapon. no. 44-56; 100% conc.; nonionic.

Glycosperse® TO-20. [Lonza]
Chem. Descrip.: Polysorbate 85
CAS 9005-70-3
Uses: Emulsifier for pharmaceuticals; flavor solubilizer and dispersant
Properties: Yel. liq., gels on standing; sol. in ethanol, methanol, ethyl acetate; water disp.; sp.gr. 1.0; visc. 300 cps; HLB 11.0; sapon. no. 82-95; 100% conc.; nonionic.

Glycosperse® TS-20. [Lonza]
Chem. Descrip.: Polysorbate 65
CAS 9005-71-4
Uses: Emulsifier for pharmaceuticals; flavor solubilizer and dispersant
Properties: Tan waxy solid; sol. in ethanol, methanol, acetone, ethyl acetate, naphtha, min. and veg. oils; disp. water, toluol; sp.gr. 1.05; HLB 11.0; sapon. no. 88-98; 100% conc.; nonionic.

Glycyrrhetinic Acid Phytosome®. [Indena SpA; Lipo]
Chem. Descrip.: Complex of 18β-glycyrrhetinic acid and soybean phospholipids
Uses: Skin protectant with smoothing, soothing, moisturizing props.; coadjuvant in treatment of wrinkles and stretch marks, treatment of sensitive, chapped, irritated skin, after-sun prods., dentifrices for sensitive gums, prods. for oral cavity protection
Properties: Lt. yel. amorphous powd.; water-disp.

GPC. [Rhone-Poulenc Rorer; Am. Lecithin]
Chem. Descrip.: Sn-Glycero(3)phosphocholine
CAS 28319-77-9
Uses: Natural raw material for pharmaceuticals
Properties: Cryst.

Granular Gum Arabic NF/FCC C-4010. [Meer]
Chem. Descrip.: Gum arabic
CAS 9000-01-5; EINECS 232-519-5
Uses: Protective colloid, stabilizer, thickener; pharmaceutical emulsions, antiseptics, to mask bitter or acid taste of medicaments, tablet binder, excipient
Properties: Colorless, odorless, and tasteless;

water-sol.

Granular Gum Arabic Type A-1 NF Premium.
[Gumix Int'l.]
Chem. Descrip.: Gum arabic
CAS 9000-01-5; EINECS 232-519-5
Uses: Protective colloid, stabilizer, suspending
agent, viscosifier for pharmaceuticals (suspen-
sions, emulsions, demulcent in cough drops/syr-
ups, tablet binder/adhesive)
Properties: Wh. gran., almost odorless and taste-
less; sol. in hot or cold water.

Granular Gum Arabic Type A-2 NF Premium.
[Gumix Int'l.]
Chem. Descrip.: Gum arabic
CAS 9000-01-5; EINECS 232-519-5
Uses: Protective colloid, stabilizer, suspending
agent, viscosifier for pharmaceuticals (suspen-
sions, emulsions, demulcent in cough drops/syr-
ups, tablet binder/adhesive)
Properties: Wh. gran., almost odorless and taste-
less; sol. in hot or cold water.

Granular Gum Ghatti #1. [Meer]
Chem. Descrip.: Gum ghatti
CAS 900-28-6
Uses: Stabilizer, binder, emulsifier forming o/w
emulsions; tablet binder and thick mucilage coat-
ings in pharmaceuticals
Properties: Water-sol.

Grape Skin Extract, 2X #3850. [Crompton & Knowles/
Ingred. Tech.]
Chem. Descrip.: Grape skin extract, dough
strength
Uses: Color additive for pharmaceuticals
Regulatory: FDA 21CFR §73.170
Properties: Deep purple-red sl. visc. liq., sl. odor;
sol. in water; sp.gr. 1.1 ± 0.1; pH 2.0 ± 0.1
Storage: 6 mos shelf life stored in tight containers
@ 5-15 C; avoid exposure to heat, light, moisture.

Grape Skin Extract, Double Strength. [Crompton &
Knowles/Ingred. Tech.]
Chem. Descrip.: Grape skin extract
Uses: Color additive for pharmaceuticals
Regulatory: FDA 21CFR §73.170
Properties: Deep purple-red sl. visc. liq., sl. odor;
sol. in water; sp.gr. 1.1 ± 0.1; pH 2.3 ± 0.1
Storage: 6 mos shelf life stored in tight containers
@ 5-15 C; avoid exposure to heat, light, moisture.

Grape Skin Extract, Powd. 282730. [Crompton &
Knowles/Ingred. Tech.]
Chem. Descrip.: Grape skin extract
Uses: Color additive for pharmaceuticals
Regulatory: FDA 21CFR §73.170
Properties: Deep purple free-flowing powd., sl.
odor; color hue in end-prod. depends on pH;
100% min. thru 100 mesh; sol. in water
Storage: 1 yr shelf life stored in tight containers;
avoid exposure to heat, light, moisture.

Grape Skin Extract, Single Strength. [Crompton &
Knowles/Ingred. Tech.]
Chem. Descrip.: Grape skin extract
Uses: Color additive for pharmaceuticals
Regulatory: FDA 21CFR §73.170

Properties: Deep purple-red sl. visc. liq., sl. odor;
sol. in water; sp.gr. 1.1 ± 0.1; pH 2.3 ± 0.1
Storage: 6 mos shelf life stored in tight containers
@ 5-15 C; avoid exposure to heat, light, moisture.

Grillocin® AT Basis. [Grillo-Werke AG; R.I.T.A.]
Chem. Descrip.: Zinc ricinoleate, propylene glycol,
disodium PEG-8 ricinosuccinate, PEG-7 glyceryl
cocoate, glycerin, triethanolamine
Uses: Deodorant for antiperspirants, esp. those
containing aluminum chlorhydrate
Properties: Ivory solid; dens. 1.04 g/cc; iodine no.
55 ± 7; sapon. no. 133 ± 7; pH 7.0 ± 0.5 (1% in
ethanol); 98% act.; 6.1 ± 0.2% zinc.
Toxicology: LD50 (oral, rat) > 5000 mg/kg; sl. skin
irritant; moderate eye irritant.

GTO 80. [SVO Enterprises]
Chem. Descrip.: Crude high oleic sunflower oil
CAS 8001-21-6; EINECS 232-273-9
Uses: Food grade environmentally friendly veg. oil
for use as feedstocks/raw materials in pharmaceuticals; oxidative and thermal stability; 77-82%
oleic acid; readily biodeg.

GTO 90. [SVO Enterprises]
Chem. Descrip.: Crude very high oleic sunflower oil
CAS 8001-21-6; EINECS 232-273-9
Uses: Food grade environmentally friendly veg. oil
for use as feedstocks/raw materials in pharmaceuticals; oxidative and thermal stability; 85%
min. oleic acid; readily biodeg.

GTO 90E. [SVO Enterprises]
Chem. Descrip.: Crude very high oleic sunflower oil
CAS 8001-21-6; EINECS 232-273-9
Uses: Food grade environmentally friendly veg. oil
for use as feedstocks/raw materials in pharmaceuticals; oxidative and thermal stability; 85%
min. oleic acid; readily biodeg.

Guardian Protective Skin Cream. [United-Guardian]
Uses: Antiseptic, moisturizer, skin protectant; intended for hospital personnel who frequently
change latex gloves where perspiration can build
up high germ counts
Properties: Clear gel
Custom product

Gum Arabic NF/FCC Clean Amber Sorts. [Meer]
Chem. Descrip.: Gum arabic
CAS 9000-01-5; EINECS 232-519-5
Uses: Protective colloid, stabilizer, thickener; pharmaceutical emulsions, antiseptics, to mask bitter
or acid taste of medicaments, tablet binder, excipient
Properties: Colorless, odorless, tasteless; water-
sol.

Gum Arabic NF, Tech. [Commodity Services Int'l.]
Chem. Descrip.: Gum arabic
CAS 9000-01-5; EINECS 232-519-5
Uses: Tableting agent and protective colloid in
pharmaceuticals.

Gum Arabic, Purified, Spray-Dried No. 1834. [MLG
Enterprises Ltd.]
Chem. Descrip.: Gum arabic
CAS 9000-01-5; EINECS 232-519-5
Uses: Thickener for pharmaceuticals; tableting aid

Properties: Wh. sl. ylsh. fine powd.; instantly water-sol.; visc. 28-35 cps (101%); pH 4.2-4.8 (10%); 5-6% moisture.

Gumixan K. [Gumix Int'l.]
Chem. Descrip.: Xanthan gum
CAS 11138-66-2; EINECS 234-394-2
Uses: Hydrophilic colloid, thickener, suspending agent, emulsion stabilizer for pharmaceuticals (syrups, emulsions, to suspend actives)
Use level: 0.1-0.5% (syrups, emulsions), 0.2-1% (suspending of actives); 1% (cosmetics)
Regulatory: FDA 21CFR §172.695; FCC; E-415; kosher
Properties: Cream to wh. powd., std. particle size; readily sol. in hot or cold water, common acidulants; sol. hot in glycerol, ethylene glycol.

Gumixan KF. [Gumix Int'l.]
Chem. Descrip.: Xanthan gum
CAS 11138-66-2; EINECS 234-394-2
Uses: Hydrophilic colloid, thickener, suspending agent, emulsion stabilizer for pharmaceuticals (syrups, emulsions, to suspend actives)
Use level: 0.1-0.5% (syrups, emulsions), 0.2-1% (suspending of actives); 1% (cosmetics)
Regulatory: FDA 21CFR §172.695; FCC; E-415; kosher
Properties: Cream to wh. fine powd.; readily sol. in hot or cold water, common acidulants; sol. hot in glycerol, ethylene glycol.

Gum Tragacanth Ribbons and Flakes. [Gumix Int'l.]
Chem. Descrip.: Tragacanth gum
CAS 9000-65-1; EINECS 232-552-5
Uses: Emulsifier, suspending agent, thickener, stabilizer, binder in pharmaceuticals (emulsions, jellies, creams, toothpastes)
Properties: Ylsh. wh. to tan powd., odorless, insipid taste; swells rapidly in hot or cold water; insol. in alcohol, other org. solvs.

H

Hamposyl® L-30. [Hampshire; Chemplex Chems.]
Chem. Descrip.: Sodium lauroyl sarcosinate
CAS 137-16-6; EINECS 205-281-5
Uses: Surfactant; in antidandruff shampoos, mouthwash, dentifrices, medicated cleansers; used in isolating agent for biotechnology prods.
Properties: Colorless liq.; misc. in water; m.w. 292; sp.gr. 1.02-1.03; visc. 30 cps; f.p. -1 C; HLB 30.0; pH 7.5-8.5 (10%); surf. tens. 30 dynes/cm; 30% act.; anionic.

Haro® Chem ALMD-2. [Akcros]
Chem. Descrip.: Aluminum distearate
CAS 300-92-5; EINECS 206-101-8
Uses: Metal soap stabilizer for pharmaceuticals
Properties: Solid.

Haro® Chem CPR-2. [Akcros]
Chem. Descrip.: Calcium stearate
CAS 1592-23-0; EINECS 216-472-8
Uses: Metal soap stabilizer for pharmaceuticals
Properties: Solid.
Unverified

Haro® Chem MF-2. [Akcros]
Chem. Descrip.: Magnesium stearate
CAS 557-04-0; EINECS 209-150-3
Uses: Stabilizer for pharmaceuticals
Properties: Solid.

Haro® Chem NG. [Akcros]
Chem. Descrip.: Sodium stearate
CAS 822-16-2; EINECS 212-490-5
Uses: Metal soap stabilizer for pharmaceuticals
Properties: Solid.
Unverified

Haro® Chem ZPR-2. [Akcros]
Chem. Descrip.: Zinc stearate
CAS 557-05-1; EINECS 209-151-9
Uses: Heat stabilizer for pharmaceuticals
Properties: Solid.

Hartolan. [Croda Inc.; Croda Chem. Ltd.]
Chem. Descrip.: Lanolin alcohols
CAS 8027-33-6; EINECS 232-430-1
Uses: Spreading agent, dispersant, stabilizer, plasticizer, w/o emulsifier, conditioner, superfatting agent, moisturizer, and emollient for pharmaceuticals
Properties: Brn. solid wax; sol. in oils, esters; m.p. 58 C; acid no. 2 max.; sapon. no. 5 mg max.; 100% conc.; nonionic.

Hectabrite® AW. [Am. Colloid]
Chem. Descrip.: Hectorite USP/NF
CAS 12173-47-6; EINECS 235-340-0
Uses: Emulsifier, thickener, suspension agent in pharmaceutical prods.; effective at low solids levels
Properties: Wh. soft flakes, 20-100 mesh particle size; pH 8.5-10.5 (2% disp.); dry brightness (GE) 78-85; 5-8% moisture.

Hectabrite® DP. [Am. Colloid]
Chem. Descrip.: Hectorite USP/NF
CAS 12173-47-6; EINECS 235-340-0
Uses: Very high visc., stabilizing and suspending agent; emulsifier and thickener for low solids formulations
Properties: Wh. powd.; 90% min. thru 200 mesh; visc. 3000 cps (4% disp.); pH 9.5-10.5 (2% disp.); dry brightness (GE) 82-86; 10% max. moisture.

Hectalite® 200. [Am. Colloid]
Chem. Descrip.: Sodium hectorite USP/NF
Uses: Viscosifier, suspension agent, binder for pharmaceutical prods. where color is important
Properties: Wh. fine powd.; 90% min. thru 200 mesh; visc. 2000 cps (5% disp.); pH 9.5-10.5 (2% disp.); 10% max. moisture.

Hemi-Cellulase Amano 90. [Mitsubishi Int'l.; Amano Enzyme USA]
Chem. Descrip.: Hemicellulase from *Aspergillus niger*
CAS 9025-56-3
Uses: Enzyme for pharmaceutical industry
Properties: Sl. ylsh. powd.; sol. in water; insol. in ethanol
Toxicology: Nontoxic, nonpathogenic; enzyme dust may cause sensitization when inhaled
Storage: Store in cool, dry place.

Hexetidine 90. [ANGUS]
Chem. Descrip.: Hexetidine
CAS 141-94-6; EINECS 205-513-5
Uses: Antimicrobial, antifungal agent for pharmaceuticals, oral hygiene, body cavity, and skin care prods. (ointments, vaginal gels, dentifrice, mouthwash)
Regulatory: EEC approved; complies with France and Germany pharmacopoeias
Properties: Clear ylsh. oily liq.; sol. in glycols, nonpolar solvs.; insol. in water; m.w. 339.6; sp.gr. 0.866; b.p. 172-176 C (1 mm Hg); ref. index 1.462-1.466; 90% act. min.

Toxicology: LD50 (oral, rat) 0.61 g/kg; toxic by intravenous route; corrosive to eyes, irritating to skin
Storage: Store @ 40-45 F.

Hexetidine 99. [ANGUS]
Chem. Descrip.: Hexetidine
CAS 141-94-6; EINECS 205-513-5
Uses: Antimicrobial, antifungal agent for pharmaceuticals, oral hygiene, body cavity, and skin care prods. (ointments, vaginal gels, dentifrice, mouthwash); disinfectants for skin, contact lens, wound dressings; dental plaque control
Regulatory: EEC approved; complies with EP, France and Germany pharmacopoeias
Properties: Clear ylsh. oily liq., amine odor; sol. in petrol. ether, methanol, benzene, glycols, nonpolar solvs.; insol. in water; m.w. 339.6; sp.gr. 0.866; b.p. 172-176 C (1 mm Hg); ref. index 1.463-1.467; 97% act. min.
Toxicology: LD50 (oral, rat) 0.61 g/kg; toxic by intravenous route; corrosive to eyes, irritating to skin
Storage: Store @ 40-45 F.

High Purity MTBE. [Arco]
Chem. Descrip.: Methyl t-butyl ether
CAS 1634-04-4; EINECS 216-653-1
Uses: Extraction solv., reaction medium in pharmaceuticals
Properties: Clear liq., terpene-like odor; sl. sol. in water; misc. with most org. solvs.; sp.gr. 0.737; f.p. -108 C; b.p. 55 C (760 mm Hg); ref. index 1.3694 (20 C); surf. tension 18.3 dynes/cm (32 C); visc. 0.350 cps (20 C); flash pt. -30 C; > 99.9% purity.

Hilton Davis Titanium Dioxide. [Hilton Davis]
Chem. Descrip.: Anatase titanium dioxide
CAS 13463-67-7; EINECS 236-675-5
Uses: Natural colorant, opacifier for drug use; excellent for use with FD&C lakes in panning or tablet coating; rutile forms avail. on request
Regulatory: FDA 21CFR 73.575 (foods), 73.1575 (drugs), 73.2572 (cosmetics)
Properties: Wh.

Hi-Sil® T-600. [PPG Industries]
Chem. Descrip.: Syn. silica, amorphous
EINECS 231-545-4
Uses: Thickener used to increase visc. and provide thixotropic action for liqs.; used in pharmaceuticals, toothpaste
Properties: Wh. powd., 0.021 μ particle size; 0.002% 325-mesh wet sieve residue; sp.gr. 2.1; dens. 17.5 lb/gal; dens. 2-4 lb/ft^3; ref. index 1.455; pH 6.5-7.3 (5%); 97.5% SiO$_2$
Unverified

Hodag 20-L. [Calgene]
Chem. Descrip.: PEG-4 laurate
CAS 9004-81-3
Uses: Emulsifier, wetting agent, plasticizer for pharmaceuticals
Properties: Liq.; HLB 10.0; 100% conc.; nonionic.

Hodag 22-L. [Calgene]
Chem. Descrip.: PEG-4 dilaurate

CAS 9005-02-1
Uses: Emulsifier, wetting agent, plasticizer for pharmaceuticals
Properties: Liq.; HLB 6.6; 100% conc.; nonionic.

Hodag 40-L. [Calgene]
Chem. Descrip.: PEG-8 laurate
CAS 9004-81-3; EINECS 253-458-0
Uses: Emulsifier, wetting agent, plasticizer for pharmaceuticals
Properties: Liq.; HLB 12.8; 100% conc.; nonionic.

Hodag 40-O. [Calgene]
Chem. Descrip.: PEG-8 oleate
CAS 9004-96-0
Uses: Emulsifier, wetting agent, plasticizer for pharmaceuticals
Properties: Liq.; HLB 11.4; 100% conc.; nonionic.

Hodag 40-R. [Calgene]
Chem. Descrip.: PEG-8 ricinoleate
CAS 9004-97-1
Uses: Emulsifier, wetting agent, plasticizer for pharmaceuticals
Properties: Liq.; HLB 11.6; 100% conc.; nonionic.

Hodag 40-S. [Calgene]
Chem. Descrip.: PEG-8 stearate
CAS 9004-99-3
Uses: Emulsifier, wetting agent, plasticizer for pharmaceuticals
Properties: Paste; HLB 11.1; 100% conc.; nonionic.

Hodag 42-L. [Calgene]
Chem. Descrip.: PEG-8 dilaurate
CAS 9005-02-1
Uses: Emulsifier, wetting agent, plasticizer for pharmaceuticals
Properties: Liq.; HLB 10.0; 100% conc.; nonionic.

Hodag 42-O. [Calgene]
Chem. Descrip.: PEG-8 dioleate
CAS 9005-07-6
Uses: Emulsifier, wetting agent, plasticizer for pharmaceuticals
Properties: Liq.; HLB 8.4; 100% conc.; nonionic.

Hodag 42-S. [Calgene]
Chem. Descrip.: PEG-8 distearate
CAS 9005-08-7
Uses: Emulsifier, wetting agent, plasticizer for pharmaceuticals
Properties: Paste; HLB 8.2; 100% conc.; nonionic.

Hodag 60-L. [Calgene]
Chem. Descrip.: PEG-12 laurate
CAS 9004-81-3
Uses: Emulsifier, wetting agent, plasticizer for pharmaceuticals
Properties: Liq.; HLB 14.8; 100% conc.; nonionic.

Hodag 60-S. [Calgene]
Chem. Descrip.: PEG-12 stearate
CAS 9004-99-3
Uses: Emulsifier, wetting agent, plasticizer for pharmaceuticals
Properties: Solid; HLB 13.6; 100% conc.; nonionic.

Hodag 62-O. [Calgene]
Chem. Descrip.: PEG-12 dioleate
CAS 9005-07-6; EINECS 288-459-5

Uses: Emulsifier, wetting agent, plasticizer for pharmaceuticals
Properties: Liq.; HLB 10.0; 100% conc.; nonionic.

Hodag 100-S. [Calgene]
Chem. Descrip.: PEG-20 stearate
CAS 9004-99-3
Uses: Emulsifier, wetting agent, plasticizer for pharmaceuticals
Properties: Solid; HLB 15.6; 100% conc.; nonionic.

Hodag 150-S. [Calgene]
Chem. Descrip.: PEG-6-32 stearate
CAS 9004-99-3
Uses: Emulsifier, wetting agent, plasticizer for pharmaceuticals
Properties: Solid; HLB 16.8; 100% conc.; nonionic.

Hodag GML. [Calgene]
Chem. Descrip.: Glyceryl laurate
CAS 142-18-7; EINECS 205-526-6
Uses: Emulsifier, opacifier, stabilizer for drug industry
Properties: Paste; HLB 3.0; 100% conc.; nonionic.

Hodag GMO. [Calgene]
Chem. Descrip.: Glyceryl oleate
CAS 25496-72-4
Uses: Emulsifier, opacifier, stabilizer for drug industry
Regulatory: FDA 21CFR §182.4505, Part 166
Properties: Yel. opaque liq., bland odor; insol. in water; sp.gr. 0.95; b.p. > 200 C (760 mm); HLB 2.7; flash pt. (COC) > 350 F; 100% conc.; nonionic
Toxicology: May cause eye irritation
Precaution: Avoid strong oxidizing agents
Storage: Store in well-ventilated areas @ 50-120 F; keep away from oxidizing agents, excessive heat, ignition sources.

Hodag GMO-D. [Calgene]
Chem. Descrip.: Glyceryl oleate
Uses: Emulsifier, opacifier, stabilizer for drug industry
Properties: Liq.; HLB 2.7; 100% conc.; anionic
Custom product

Hodag GMR. [Calgene]
Chem. Descrip.: Glyceryl ricinoleate
CAS 141-08-2; EINECS 205-455-0
Uses: Emulsifier, opacifier, stabilizer for drug industry
Properties: Amber liq.; nondispersible in water; sp.gr. 0.99; dens. 8.25 lb/gal; 100% conc.; nonionic.

Hodag GMR-D. [Calgene]
Chem. Descrip.: Glyceryl ricinoleate
CAS 141-08-2; EINECS 205-455-0
Uses: Emulsifier, opacifier, stabilizer for drug industry
Properties: Amber liq.; disp. in water; sp.gr. 1.00; dens. 8.25 lb/gal; 100% conc.; anionic.

Hodag GMS. [Calgene]
Chem. Descrip.: Glyceryl stearate
CAS 31566-31-1
Uses: Emulsifier, opacifier, stabilizer for drug industry
Regulatory: FDA 21CFR §172.854, 182.4505, Part

136
Properties: Wh. waxy solid, mild char. odor; insol. in water; sp.gr. 0.97; m.p. 58 C; b.p. > 200 C (760 mm); HLB 2.7; acid no. 5 max.; iodine no. 0.5; sapon. no. 160-175; flash pt. (COC > 175 C; pH 5.3 (5% in 25% IPA); 100% conc.; nonionic
Toxicology: May cause eye irritation
Precaution: Avoid strong oxidizing agents; dust is combustible
Storage: Store in well-ventilated areas @ 50-120 F; keep away from oxidizing agents, heat, ignition sources.

Hodag GMS-A. [Calgene]
Chem. Descrip.: Glyceryl stearate, PEG-100 stearate
Uses: Self-emulsifying, acid-stable prod. for use in neutral or sl. acidic pharmaceutical lotions or cream emulsions
Properties: Wh. flake; m.p. 50-60 C; acid no. 1 max.; sapon. no. 90-105; pH 6.0-8.5 (1% disp.); nonionic.

Hodag GTO. [Calgene]
Chem. Descrip.: Glyceryl trioleate
CAS 122-32-7; EINECS 204-534-7
Uses: Emulsifier, opacifier, stabilizer for drug industry
Properties: Liq.; HLB 1.0; 100% conc.; nonionic.

Hodag PE-1803. [Calgene]
Chem. Descrip.: Oleth-3 phosphate
CAS 39464-69-2
Uses: Emulsifier for pharmaceuticals
Properties: Lt. amber liq.; acid no. 125-145; 50% conc.
Toxicology: Relatively low skin irritation.

Hodag PE-1810. [Calgene]
Chem. Descrip.: Oleth-10 phosphate
CAS 39464-69-2
Uses: Emulsifier for pharmaceuticals
Properties: Cream paste; sol. in water, alcohol, fatty alcohols, min. oil, IPM, IPP; acid no. 80-100; 70% conc.
Toxicology: Relatively low skin irritation.

Hodag PE-1820. [Calgene]
Chem. Descrip.: Oleth-20 phosphate
CAS 39464-69-2
Uses: Surfactant for pharmaceutical use
Properties: Waxy solid; acid no. 60-80
Toxicology: Relatively low skin irritation.

Hodag PEG 200. [Calgene]
Chem. Descrip.: PEG-4
CAS 25322-68-3; EINECS 203-989-9
Uses: For pharmaceutical formulation
Properties: Clear liq.; water-sol.; m.w. 190-210; pH 4.5-7.5 (5%).

Hodag PEG 300. [Calgene]
Chem. Descrip.: PEG-6
CAS 25322-68-3; EINECS 220-045-1
Uses: For pharmaceutical formulation; plasticizer for spray-on bandages
Properties: Clear liq.; water-sol.; m.w. 285-315; visc. 5.4-6.4 cSt (210 F); pH 4.5-7.5 (5%).

Hodag PEG 400. [Calgene]

Chem. Descrip.: PEG-8
CAS 25322-68-3; EINECS 225-856-4
Uses: Pharmaceutical formulation
Properties: Clear liq.; water-sol.; m.w. 380-420; visc. 6.8-8.0 cSt (210 F); pH 4.5-7.5 (5%).

Hodag PEG 540. [Calgene]
Chem. Descrip.: PEG-6, PEG-32 (50/50 mixt.)
Uses: Pharmaceutical and suppository formulation
Properties: Wh. waxy solid; water-sol.; m.w. 500-600; visc. 26-33 cSt (210 F); f.p. 38-41 C; pH 4.5-7.5 (5%).

Hodag PEG 600. [Calgene]
Chem. Descrip.: PEG-12
CAS 25322-68-3; EINECS 229-859-1
Uses: Pharmaceutical formulation
Properties: Liq.; water-sol.; m.w. 570-630; visc. 9.9-11.3 cSt (210 F); pH 4.5-7.5 (5%).

Hodag PEG 1000. [Calgene]
Chem. Descrip.: PEG-20
CAS 25322-68-3
Uses: Pharmaceutical formulation
Properties: Wh. waxy solid; water-sol.; m.w. 950-1050; visc. 16-19 cSt (210 F); f.p. 37-40 C; pH 4.5-7.5 (5%).

Hodag PEG 1450. [Calgene]
Chem. Descrip.: PEG-32
CAS 25322-68-3
Uses: Pharmaceutical formulation
Properties: Wh. waxy solid; water-sol.; m.w. 1300-1600; visc. 25-32 Cst (210 F); f.p. 43-46 C; pH 4.5-7.5 (5%).

Hodag PEG 3350. [Calgene]
Chem. Descrip.: PEG-75
CAS 25322-68-3
Uses: Pharmaceutical formulation; tablet binder/lubricant
Properties: Wh. waxy solid; water-sol.; m.w. 3015-3685; visc. 76-110 cSt (210 F); f.p. 53-56 C; pH 4.5-7.5 (5%).

Hodag PEG 8000. [Calgene]
Chem. Descrip.: PEG-150
CAS 25322-68-3
Uses: Pharmaceutical formulation; tablet binder/lubricant
Properties: Wh. waxy solid; water-sol.; m.w. 7000-9000; visc. 470-900 cSt (210 F); f.p. 60-63 C; pH 4.5-7.5 (5%).

Hodag Antifoam CO-350. [Calgene]
Chem. Descrip.: Silicone antifoam
Uses: Antifoam for nonaq. foaming systems; for pharmaceuticals
Regulatory: FDA approved
Properties: Syrup-like fluid; sol. in amyl acetate, aromatic solvs., 2-ethylhexanol, kerosene; insol. in water, paraffin oil, glycols, ethanol, methanol, glycerin; sp.gr. 0.968; dens. 8.3 lb/gal; 100% act.

Hodag Antifoam F-1. [Calgene]
Chem. Descrip.: Simethicone
CAS 8050-81-5
Uses: Antifoam for aq. and nonaq. systems for pharmaceuticals
Regulatory: FDA approved, to 10 ppm max. in final prod.
Properties: Translucent syrup-like compd.; sol. in amyl acetate, aromatic solvs., 2-ethylhexanol, kerosene; insol. in water, paraffin oil, glycols, ethanol, methanol, glycerin; sp.gr. 0.990; dens. 8.3 lb/gal; 100% act.

Hodag Antifoam F-2. [Calgene]
Chem. Descrip.: Silicone antifoam
Uses: Antifoam for aq. and nonaq. systems for pharmaceuticals
Regulatory: FDA approved, 10 ppm max. in final prod.
Properties: Translucent syrup-like compd.; sol. in amyl acetate, aromatic solvs., 2-ethylhexanol, kerosene; sl. disp. in water; insol. in paraffin oil, glycols, ethanol, methanol, glycerin; sp.gr. 1.000; dens. 8.4 lb/gal; 100% act.

Hodag Antifoam FD-62. [Calgene]
Chem. Descrip.: Polymeric silicone emulsion
Uses: Antifoam for aq. systems for pharmaceuticals
Regulatory: FDA approved, 100 ppm max. in final prod.
Properties: Wh. creamy emulsion; disp. in water; 1.000; dens. 8.4 lb/gal; 10% act.

Hodag Antifoam FD-82. [Calgene]
Chem. Descrip.: Silicone emulsion
Uses: Antifoam for aq. foaming problems in pharmaceuticals
Regulatory: FDA approved, 30 ppm max. in final prod.
Properties: Wh. creamy emulsion; disp. in water; sp.gr. 0.970; dens. 8.1 lb/gal; 30% act.

Hoechst Wax E Pharma. [Hoechst AG]
Chem. Descrip.: Montan acid wax
CAS 68476-03-9; EINECS 270-664-6
Uses: Retarding agent for pharmaceutical use
Properties: Pale ylsh. fine powd. (< 125 µm); insol. in water; dens. 1.01-1.03 g/cc; visc. ≈ 30 mm^2/s (100 C); drop pt. 79-85 C; acid no. 15-20; sapon. no. 130-160.

Hony-Tab®. [Crompton & Knowles]
Chem. Descrip.: Dried honey with whole wheat flour and wheat bran
Uses: Directly compressible carrier for pharmaceuticals; enhances flavors or masks undesirable flavors; provides rich natural honey color to tablets
Properties: Golden yel. free-flowing gran.; 50% min. on 60 mesh, 25% max. thru 120 mesh; pH 5-6 (5%); 60% honey solids, ≤ 4% moisture.

HPMCP 50. [Eastman]
Chem. Descrip.: Hydroxypropyl methylcellulose phthalate USP/NF
Uses: Pharmaceutical excipient; enteric film-coating material or matrix binder for solid dosage forms; stable in strongly acid gastric fluids, but dissolves readily in mildly acidic to neutral environment of the sm. intestine
Properties: Wh. free-flowing powd.; bulk dens. 0.6 g/ml; pH ≥ 4.8; 24% phthalyl
Storage: Store in cool, dry area; protect from

moisture and humidity; bring drums to R.T. before opening to prevent moisture condensation on inside surfs.

HPMCP 55. [Eastman]
Chem. Descrip.: Hydroxypropyl methylcellulose phthalate USP/NF
Uses: Pharmaceutical excipient; enteric film-coating material or matrix binder for solid dosage forms; stable in strongly acid gastric fluids, but dissolves readily in mildly acidic to neutral environment of the sm. intestine
Properties: Wh. free-flowing powd.; bulk dens. 0.6 g/ml; pH ≥ 5.2; 33% phthalyl
Storage: Store in cool, dry area; protect from moisture and humidity; bring drums to R.T. before opening to prevent moisture condensation on inside surfs.

HPMCP 55S. [Eastman]
Chem. Descrip.: Hydroxypropyl methylcellulose phthalate USP/NF
Uses: Pharmaceutical excipient; enteric film-coating material for tablets or gran.; matrix binder for solid dosage forms; stable in strongly acid gastric fluids, but dissolves readily in mildly acidic to neutral environment of the sm. intestine
Properties: Wh.powd.; bulk dens. 0.5 g/ml; pH ≥ 5.2; 33% phthalyl
Storage: Store in cool, dry area; protect from moisture and humidity; bring drums to R.T. before opening to prevent moisture condensation on inside surfs.

HSC Aspartame. [Holland Sweetener N. Am.]
Chem. Descrip.: Aspartame FCC, USP-NF
CAS 22839-47-0; EINECS 245-261-3
Uses: Nutritive intense sweetener and flavor enhancer with sweetness ≈ 200 times that of sucrose; for pharmaceutical tablets, emulsions, sugar-free syrups
Regulatory: FDA 21CFR §172.804; JECFA compliance
Properties: Wh. cryst. powd., odorless, clean sweet taste without bitter or metallic aftertaste; sparinlgy sol. in water; sl. sol. in alcohol; m.w. 294.31; pH 4.5-6.0 (0.8% aq.); 98-102% assay
Toxicology: Nontoxic; ADI 50 mg/kg (FDA), 40 mg/kg (WHO); may be defatting to skin
Storage: Hygroscopic; 5 yr shelf life in tightly closed container with sealed inner bag under cool, dry conditions.

Hyaluronic Acid FCH. [Tri-k Industries]
Chem. Descrip.: Sodium hyaluronate
CAS 9067-32-7
Uses: Natural mucopolysaccharide, biological polymer, skin conditioning agent, visc. increasing agent
Properties: Wh. powd., odorless; sol. in water forming visc. sol'ns., paste at higher concs.; pH 6-7 (0.1%)
Toxicology: LD50 (oral, rat) > 1.5 g/kg, essentially nontoxic; may cause eye irritation; excessive inh. of dust can impede respiration due to hygroscopic props.

Precaution: Combustible dust; will burn in contact with flame, self-extinguishes when ignition source is removed; incompat. with strong oxidizing agents
Storage: Store in cool, dry place.

Hyamine® 10X. [Lonza]
Chem. Descrip.: Methylbenzethonium chloride
CAS 25155-18-4; EINECS 246-675-7
Uses: Germicide, disinfectant, sanitizer for pharmaceutical prods.
Properties: Wh. cryst.; dens. 27.5 lb/ft^3; surf. tens. 40 dynes/cm (0.01% aq.); 100% act.; cationic.

Hyamine® 1622 50%. [Lonza]
Chem. Descrip.: Benzethonium chloride
CAS 121-54-0; EINECS 204-479-9
Uses: Bactericide, deodorant, preservative for veterinary and pharmaceutical prods., topicals, surgical applics.
Properties: Lt. amber liq.; sol. in water, lower alcohols, glycols, ethoxyethanol, tetrachloroethane; misc. with ethylene dichloride, CCl$_4$; sp.gr. 1.03; dens. 8.56 lb/gal; pour pt. 25 F; flash pt. (Seta) 110 F; pH 8-10 (5%); surf. tens. 30 dynes/cm (0.1%); 50% act.; cationic
Toxicology: LD50 (oral, rat) 420 mg/kg, (dermal, rabbit) > 3 g/kg; may cause eye and skin irritation.

Hyamine® 1622 Crystals. [Lonza]
Chem. Descrip.: Benzethonium chloride
CAS 121-54-0; EINECS 204-479-9
Uses: Bactericide, deodorant, preservative for veterinary and pharmaceutical prods.
Properties: APHA 40 max. powd.; sol. in water, lower alcohols, glycols, ethoxyethanol, tetrachloroethane; misc. with ethylene dichloride, CCl$_4$; sp.gr. 0.44 g/cc; dens. 27.5 lb/ft^3; 100% act.

Hyamine® 3500 50%. [Lonza]
Chem. Descrip.: Benzalkonium chloride [n-Alkyl = 50% C14, 40% C12, 10% C16]
CAS 68424-85-1
Uses: Bactericide, disinfectant in pharmaceutical uses
Regulatory: FDA approved: sanitizer for food processing equip.
Properties: Pale yel. clear liq., mild odor; misc. with water, lower alcohols, ketones; m.w. 359.6; sp.gr. 0.96; dens. 8.0 lb/gal; visc. 42 cps; pour pt. 15 F; flash pt. (PM) 105 F; pH 7-9 (5%); surf. tens. 34 dynes/cm (0.1%); 50% act.; cationic
Toxicology: LD50 (oral, rat) 894 mg/kg; toxic to fish
Precaution: Do not mix with oxidizing/reducing agents.

Hydagen® B. [Henkel/Cospha; Henkel Canada]
Chem. Descrip.: α-Bisabolol
CAS 515-69-5; EINECS 208-205-9
Uses: Antiphlogistic active agent for emulsions, oils, lotions, and oral hygiene preps.
Properties: Liq.; sp.gr. 0.922-0.928; ref. index 1.492-1.498; 85% min. act.

Hydagen® C.A.T. [Henkel/Cospha; Henkel Canada; Henkel KGaA/Cospha]
Chem. Descrip.: Triethyl citrate USP/NF
CAS 77-93-0; EINECS 201-070-7

Uses: Nonmicrobiocidal deodorant active agent; stable in acid and neutral ranges
Use level: 1-5%
Properties: Pale yel. oily clear liq., pract. odorless; sp.gr. 1.135-1.139; acid no. 0.2 max.; sapon. no. 603-609; ref. index 1.439-1.441; 99% min. act.
Storage: 1 yr min. storage stability in sealed original containers at temps. below 30 C in a dry environment.

Hydagen® DEO. [Henkel/Cospha; Henkel Canada]
Chem. Descrip.: Triethyl citrate and BHT
Uses: Nonmicrobiocidal act. ingred. for deodorant systems
Properties: Pale yel. clear oily liq.; sol. in hydroalcoholic sol'ns.; sp.gr. 1.112-1.122; acid no. 0.2 max.; 99% act.

Hydex® 100 Coarse Powd. [Lonza]
Chem. Descrip.: Sorbitol NF/FCC
CAS 50-70-4; EINECS 200-061-5
Uses: Humectant, bodying agent, moisture control agent for toothpaste; binder and filler for pharmaceutical tablets
Properties: Wh. powd.; ≤ 5% +40 mesh, ≤ 10% -200 mesh; 100% act.

Hydex® 100 Coarse Powd. 35. [Lonza]
Chem. Descrip.: Sorbitol NF/FCC
CAS 50-70-4; EINECS 200-061-5
Uses: Humectant, bodying agent, moisture control agent for toothpaste; binder and filler for pharmaceutical tablets
Properties: Powd.; ≤ 5% +35 mesh, ≤ 10% -80 mesh; pH neutral.

Hydex® 100 Gran. 206. [Lonza]
Chem. Descrip.: Sorbitol NF/FCC
CAS 50-70-4; EINECS 200-061-5
Uses: Humectant, bodying agent, moisture control agent for toothpaste; binder and filler for pharmaceutical tablets
Properties: Wh. powd., 90% max. on 80 mesh screen; 100% act.

Hydex® 100 Powd. 60. [Lonza]
Chem. Descrip.: Sorbitol NF/FCC
CAS 50-70-4; EINECS 200-061-5
Uses: Humectant, bodying agent, moisture control agent for toothpaste; binder and filler for pharmaceutical tablets
Properties: Wh. powd.; ≤ 1% +60 mesh; 100% act.

Hydex® Tablet Grade. [Lonza]
Chem. Descrip.: Sorbitol
CAS 50-70-4; EINECS 200-061-5
Uses: Humectant, bodying agent, moisture control agent for toothpaste; binder and filler for pharmaceutical tablets
Properties: Wh. powd., 75% max. on 200 mesh screen; 100% act.

Hydral® 710. [Alcoa]
Chem. Descrip.: Hydrated alumina
CAS 21645-51-2
Uses: Polishing agent in dentifrices.

Hydrine. [Gattefosse; Gattefosse SA]
Chem. Descrip.: PEG-2 stearate
CAS 9004-99-3; 106-11-6; EINECS 203-363-5

Uses: Thickener, gellant, consistency stabilizer for pharmaceutical ointments, creams, lotions, emulsions
Properties: Gardner < 3 waxy solid, faint odor; drop pt. 45.5-48.5 C; HLB 5.0; acid no. < 6; iodine no. < 3; sapon. no. 150-160; 100% conc.
Toxicology: Nonirritating to skin and eyes.

Hydrobrite 200PO. [Witco/Petroleum Spec.]
Chem. Descrip.: Wh. min. oil USP
Uses: Binder, carrier, conditioner, dispersant, extender, lubricant, moisture barrier, protective agent
Regulatory: FDA 21CFR §172.878, 178.3620(a)
Properties: Odorless, tasteless; sp.gr. 0.845-0.885; visc. 33.5-46 cst (40 C); distill. pt. 243 C min. (10 mm, 2.5%); pour pt. 15 F max.

Hydrobrite 300PO. [Witco/Petroleum Spec.]
Chem. Descrip.: Wh. min. oil USP
Uses: Binder, carrier, conditioner, dispersant, extender, lubricant, moisture barrier, protective agent
Regulatory: FDA 21CFR §172.878, 178.3620(a)
Properties: Odorless, tasteless; sp.gr. 0.850-0.880; visc. 48-60 cSt (40 C); distill. pt. 260 C min. (10 mm, 2.5%); pour pt. 10 F.

Hydrobrite 380PO. [Witco/Petroleum Spec.]
Chem. Descrip.: Wh. min. oil USP
Uses: Binder, carrier, conditioner, dispersant, extender, lubricant, moisture barrier, protective agent
Regulatory: FDA 21CFR §172.878, 178.3620(a)
Properties: Odorless, tasteless; m.w. 485; sp.gr. 0.858-0.873; visc. 69-82 cSt (40 C); distill. pt. 280 C min. (10 mm, 2.5%); pour pt. 20 F max.; flash pt. (COC) 495 F.

Hydrobrite 550PO. [Witco/Petroleum Spec.]
Chem. Descrip.: Wh. min. oil USP
Uses: Binder, carrier, conditioner, dispersant, extender, lubricant, moisture barrier, protective agent
Regulatory: FDA 21CFR §172.878, 178.3620(a)
Properties: Odorless, tasteless; m.w. 540; sp.gr. 0.860-0.880; visc. 100-125 cSt (40 C); distill. pt. 295 C min. (10 mm, 2.5%); pour pt. 15 F max.; flash pt. (COC) 490 F min.; ref. index 1.470-1.478.

Hydrokote® 95. [ABITEC]
Chem. Descrip.: Hydrog. veg. oil
CAS 68334-28-1; EINECS 269-820-6
Uses: Specialty base used as replacement for cocoa butter in pharmaceutical applics. (suppositories, clinical nutrition, dermatologicals, soft gelatin capsules, sustained release)
Regulatory: FDA 21CFR §182.1 (GRAS)
Properties: M.p. 35.6-36.7 C; iodine no. 5 max.; sapon. no. 240-255.

Hydrokote® 97. [ABITEC]
Chem. Descrip.: Hydrog. veg. oil
CAS 68334-28-1; EINECS 269-820-6
Uses: Specialty base used as replacement for cocoa butter in pharmaceutical applics.
Regulatory: FDA 21CFR §182.1 (GRAS)
Properties: M.p. 36.1-37.2 C; iodine no. 5 max.;

sapon. no. 238-255.

Hydrokote® 102. [ABITEC]
Chem. Descrip.: Hydrog. veg. oil
CAS 68334-28-1; EINECS 269-820-6
Uses: Specialty base used as replacement for cocoa butter in pharmaceutical applics. (suppositories, clinical nutrition, dermatologicals, soft gelatin capsules, sustained release)
Regulatory: FDA 21CFR §182.1 (GRAS)
Properties: M.p. 38.3-39.4 C; iodine no. 5 max.; sapon. no. 230-250.

Hydrokote® 108. [ABITEC]
Chem. Descrip.: Hydrog. veg. oil
CAS 68334-28-1; EINECS 269-820-6
Uses: Specialty base used as replacement for cocoa butter in pharmaceutical applics. (suppositories, clinical nutrition, dermatologicals, soft gelatin capsules, sustained release)
Regulatory: FDA 21CFR §182.1 (GRAS)
Properties: M.p. 41.1-42.8 C; iodine no. 5 max.; sapon. no. 230-250.

Hydrokote® 112. [ABITEC]
Chem. Descrip.: Hydrog. veg. oil
CAS 68334-28-1; EINECS 269-820-6
Uses: Specialty base used as replacement for cocoa butter in pharmaceutical applics. (suppositories, clinical nutrition, dermatologicals, soft gelatin capsules, sustained release)
Regulatory: FDA 21CFR §182.1 (GRAS)
Properties: M.p. 45.6-47.8 C; iodine no. 5 max.; sapon. no. 225-245.

Hydrokote® 118. [ABITEC]
Chem. Descrip.: Hydrog. veg. oil
CAS 68334-28-1; EINECS 269-820-6
Uses: Specialty base used as replacement for cocoa butter in pharmaceutical applics. (suppositories, clinical nutrition, dermatologicals, soft gelatin capsules, sustained release)
Regulatory: FDA 21CFR §182.1 (GRAS)
Properties: M.p. 47.2-48.9 C; iodine no. 5 max.; sapon. no. 230-250.

Hydrokote® 175. [ABITEC]
Chem. Descrip.: Hard fat (fatty acid ester); conforms to hydrog. veg. oil NF
CAS 67701-26-2; EINECS 269-820-6
Uses: Emollient, bodying agent, lubricant, moisturizer, visc. modifier for clinical nutrition, suppositories, sustained release
Properties: M.p. 34.0-36.5 C; iodine no. 5 max.; sapon. no. 215-255.

Hydrokote® M. [ABITEC]
Chem. Descrip.: Hydrog. veg. oil
CAS 68334-28-1; EINECS 269-820-6
Uses: Emollient, bodying agent, lubricant, moisturizer, visc. modifier for clinical nutrition, dermatologicals, soft gelatin capsules, suppositories, sustained release
Properties: M.p. 36.1-37.2 C; iodine no. 5 max.; sapon. no. 238-255.

Hydrolactol 70. [Gattefosse]
Chem. Descrip.: Glyceryl stearate, propylene glycol stearate, glyceryl isostearate, propylene glycol isostearate, oleth-25, ceteth-25.
Uses: SE base for fluid, semifluid lotions and o/w creams, min. pigment formulations (sun filters)
Properties: Gardner < 6 waxy solid, faint odor; sol. in chloroform, methylene chloride; disp. in water; insol. in ethanol, min. oils; drop pt. 36-45 C; HLB 10.0; acid no. < 3; iodine no. < 5; sapon. no. 125-145; nonionic
Toxicology: Sl. irritating to skin, nonirritating to eyes.

Hydro-Magma. [Marine Magnesium]
Chem. Descrip.: Water and magnesium hydroxide
CAS 1309-42-8; EINECS 215-170-3
Uses: Used in mfg. of milk of magnesia and liq. antacids
Properties: Paste; 30% act.

Hydrophilol ISO. [Gattefosse SA]
Chem. Descrip.: Propylene glycol isostearate
CAS 68171-38-0; EINECS 269-027-5
Uses: Superfatting agent for pharmaceutical emulsions and microemulsions
Properties: Liq.; HLB 3-4; acid no. < 6; iodine no. < 15; sapon. no. 150-170
Toxicology: Sl. irritating to eyes, nonirritating to skin.

Hydrotalcite Powd. BP. [Reheis]
Chem. Descrip.: Hydrotalcite
Uses: Highly reactive, low sodium, dense, compressible antacid powd. for direct compression tablets and caplets; stabilizes intragastric pH @ 3-5
Properties: Free-flowing powd.; 40% MgO, 16.9% Al_2O_3, 0.1% Na.

Hydroxylan. [Fanning]
Chem. Descrip.: Hydroxylated lanolin
CAS 68424-66-8; EINECS 270-315-8
Uses: Emulsifier for w/o systems, stabilizer for o/w systems, wetting and dispersing agent, conditioner, emollient, tackifier; for pharmaceutical ointments
Properties: Yel. to lt. tan solid; m.p. 39-46 C; acid no. 10 max.; iodine no. 12-20; sapon. no. 95-110; hyd. no. 60-85; 100% conc.; nonionic.

Hyfatol 16-98. [Aarhus Oliefabrik A/S]
Chem. Descrip.: Cetyl alcohol
CAS 36653-82-4; EINECS 253-149-0
Uses: Emulsifier, emollient.

Hyfatol 18-95. [Aarhus Oliefabrik A/S]
Chem. Descrip.: Stearyl alcohol
CAS 112-92-5; EINECS 204-017-6
Uses: Emollient, pharmaceutical raw material.

Hyfatol 18-98. [Aarhus Oliefabrik A/S]
Chem. Descrip.: Stearyl alcohol
CAS 112-92-5; EINECS 204-017-6
Uses: Emollient, pharmaceutical raw material.

Hyflo Super-Cel. [Celite]
Chem. Descrip.: Diatomaceous earth
CAS 7631-86-9; EINECS 231-545-4
Uses: Filter aids for pharmaceuticals
Properties: Wh. powd.; 5% 150 mesh residue; sp.gr. 2.3; dens. 10 lb/ft³ (dry); pH 10.

Hypan® SA100H. [Kingston Tech.; Lipo]

Chem. Descrip.: Acrylic acid/acrylonitrogens copolymer
CAS 61788-40-7
Uses: Emulsifier and gellant for neutral pH; filmformer; able to form thixotropic gels, stable waterdilutable emulsions, conjugates with certain drugs for controlled delivery formulations, continuous oil film on drying
Properties: Semicryst. polymer.

Hypan® SR150H. [Kingston Tech.; Lipo]
Chem. Descrip.: Acrylic acid/acrylonitrogens copolymer
CAS 136505-00-5
Uses: Thickener and gellant for aq. formulations, esp. highly conc. salt sol'ns., surfactants and drugs; emulsifier of various oils to form stable multiple phase emulsions.

Hypol® 2002. [Hampshire]
Chem. Descrip.: PU prepolymer
Uses: Foamable hydrophilic prepolymer for medical, dental, and health care applics. (wound dressings, biocompatible coatings, drug delivery vehicles); produces foams with no extractable TDA, TDI, or other primary aromatic amines
Properties: Yel. to amber; dens. 1.19 g/ml; visc. 20,000 cps; 95.5% min. act.

Hystar® 3375. [Lonza]
Chem. Descrip.: Hydrog. starch hydrolysate
CAS 68425-17-2
Uses: Humectant, bodying agent, moisture control agent for toothpaste where sweet taste and low hygroscopicity are required
Regulatory: Kosher certification
Properties: Water-wh. clear liq.; sp.gr. 1.32; visc. 1500 cps (40 C); pH neutral; 75% act.

Hystar® 4075. [Lonza]
Chem. Descrip.: Hydrog. starch hydrolysate
CAS 68425-17-2
Uses: Humectant, bodying agent, moisture control agent for toothpaste where sweet taste and low hygroscopicity are required
Regulatory: Kosher certification
Properties: Water-wh. clear liq.; sp.gr. 1.33; visc. 1000 cps (40 C); pH neutral; 75% act.

Hystar® 5875. [Lonza]
Chem. Descrip.: Hydrog. starch hydrolysate
CAS 68425-17-2
Uses: Humectant, bodying agent, moisture control agent for toothpaste where texture and taste are important
Properties: Water-wh. clear liq.; sp.gr. 1.35; visc. 500 cps (40 C); pH neutral; 75% act.

Hystar® 6075. [Lonza]
Chem. Descrip.: Hydrog. starch hydrolysate
CAS 68425-17-2
Uses: Humectant, bodying agent, moisture control agent for toothpaste where very low hygroscopicity is required
Regulatory: Kosher certification
Properties: Water-wh. clear liq., bland taste; sp.gr. 1.35; visc. 2000 cps (40 C); pH neutral; 75% act.

Hystar® CG. [Lonza]

Chem. Descrip.: Hydrog. starch hydrolysate
CAS 68425-17-2
Uses: Lubricant, humectant for dentifrices
Properties: Water-wh. clear liq.; sp.gr. 1.30; visc. 380 cps; ref. index 1.46; pH neutral; 70% act.

Hystar® HM-75. [Lonza]
Chem. Descrip.: Hydrog. starch hydrolysate
CAS 68425-17-2
Uses: Humectant, bodying agent, moisture control agent for toothpaste where taste and texture are important
Regulatory: Kosher certification
Properties: Water-wh. clear liq.; sp.gr. 1.48; visc. 500 cps (40 C); pH neutral; 75% act.

Hystar® TPF. [Lonza]
Chem. Descrip.: Hydrog. starch hydrolysate
CAS 68425-17-2
Uses: Humectant, lubricant; maintains optimal moisture control in oral hygiene prods.
Regulatory: Kosher certification
Properties: Water-wh. clear liq.; sp.gr. 1.30; visc. 380 cps; pH neutral; 75% act. in water.

Hystrene® 1835. [Witco/H-I-P]
Chem. Descrip.: Mixt. tallow/coconut acid (CTFA)
Uses: Chemical intermediate, emulsifier for pharmaceuticals
Properties: Paste; solid. pt. 40 C max.; acid no. 214-222; iodine no. 36-42; sapon. no. 211-220.

Hystrene® 3022. [Witco/H-I-P]
Chem. Descrip.: Hydrog. menhaden acid
Uses: Chemical intermediate, emulsifier; used for pharmaceuticals
Properties: Solid; solid. pt. 50-54 C; acid no. 193-202; iodine no. 5; sapon. no. 193-202; 100% conc.

Hystrene® 4516. [Witco/H-I-P]
Chem. Descrip.: Stearic acid
CAS 57-11-4; EINECS 200-313-4
Uses: Lubricant, emulsifier; used in pharmaceuticals
Properties: Solid; acid no. 203-209; iodine no. 1 max.; sapon. no. 204-210; 100% conc.

Hystrene® 5012. [Witco/H-I-P]
Chem. Descrip.: Hydrog. stripped coconut acid
CAS 68938-15-8
Uses: Chemical intermediate, emulsifier; used for pharmaceuticals
Properties: Liq.; solid. pt. 24-33 C; acid no. 250-266; iodine no. 2 max.; sapon. no. 250-266; 100% conc.

Hystrene® 5016 NF. [Witco/H-I-P]
Chem. Descrip.: Stearic acid NF, triple pressed
CAS 57-11-4; EINECS 200-313-4
Uses: Stabilizer, lubricant, emulsifier; used in pharmaceuticals
Properties: Solid; acid no. 206-210; iodine no. 0.5 max.; sapon. no. 206-211; 100% conc.

Hystrene® 7022. [Witco/H-I-P]
Chem. Descrip.: Behenic fatty acid
CAS 112-85-6; EINECS 204-010-8
Uses: Lubricant, emulsifier; used in pharmaceuticals

Properties: Solid; acid no. 170-180; iodine no. 3.5; sapon. no. 170-181; 100% conc.

Hystrene® 9016. [Witco/H-I-P]
Chem. Descrip.: Palmitic acid (90%)
CAS 57-10-3; EINECS 200-312-9
Uses: Lubricant, emulsifier; used in pharmaceuticals
Properties: Solid; acid no. 216-220; iodine no. 0.5 max.; sapon. no. 216-221; 100% conc.

Hystrene® 9022. [Witco/H-I-P]
Chem. Descrip.: Behenic acid (90%)
CAS 112-85-6; EINECS 204-010-8
Uses: Lubricant, emulsifier; used in pharmaceuticals
Properties: Solid; acid no. 165-175; iodine no. 3;

sapon. no. 165-176; 100% conc.

Hystrene® 9512. [Witco/H-I-P]
Chem. Descrip.: Lauric acid (95%)
CAS 143-07-7; EINECS 205-582-1
Uses: Lubricant, emulsifier; used in pharmaceuticals
Properties: Solid; acid no. 276-281; iodine no. 0.5 max.; sapon. no. 276-282; 100% conc.

Hystrene® 9718 NF. [Witco/H-I-P]
Chem. Descrip.: Stearic acid NF(92%)
CAS 57-11-4; EINECS 200-313-4
Uses: Lubricant, emulsifier; used in pharmaceuticals
Properties: Solid; acid no. 196-201; iodine no. 0.8 max.; sapon. no. 196-202; 100% conc.

I

Ibbal. [Mitsubishi Gas]
Chem. Descrip.: P-Isobutylbenzaldehyde
Uses: Intermediate for pharmaceuticals
Properties: Colorless liq., aromatic odor; sol. in ethanol, ether, toluene; insol. in water; m.w. 162.2; sp.gr. 0.960; b.p. 240 C; acid no. 0.3; flash pt. (COC) 122 C; 98.5% purity
Toxicology: LD50 (oral, rat) 1000-5000 mg/kg; eye and skin irritant
Storage: Store in cool dry place
Unverified

Igepal® CO-630 Special. [Rhone-Poulenc Surf. & Spec.]
Chem. Descrip.: Nonoxynol-9 USP-NF
CAS 9016-45-9
Uses: GMP grade; used as spermicide, microbicide; emulsifier, solubilizer
Properties: Liq.; HLB 13.0; 100% act.; nonionic.

Imwitor® 191. [Hüls Am.; Hüls AG]
Chem. Descrip.: Glyceryl stearate
CAS 31566-31-1
Uses: Lubricant, binder, stabilizer, thickener, suspending agent, emulsifier for pharmaceuticals
Properties: Ylsh. powd.; sol. in oils, molten fats, acetone, ether; m.p. 66-71 C; solid. pt. 63-68 C; HLB 4.4; acid no. 3 max.; iodine no. 3 max.; sapon. no. 155-170; 90% monoglycerides; nonionic.

Imwitor® 308. [Hüls Am.]
Chem. Descrip.: Glyceryl caprylate
CAS 26402-26-6; EINECS 247-668-1
Uses: Solubilizer for pharmaceutical drugs; carrier/vehicle for drugs in capsules; coemulsifier for lipophilic materials; surfactant and bacteriostatic props.
Properties: Wh. cryst. solid, char. odor, bitter taste; sol. in ethanol, methylene chloride, acetone, ether, heptane; misc. with oils and fats; m.p. 30-34 C; HLB 6.0; acid no. 3 max.; iodine no. 1 max.; sapon. no. 245-265; 80% monoglycerides; nonionic.

Imwitor® 312. [Hüls Am.; Hüls AG]
Chem. Descrip.: Glyceryl laurate
CAS 142-18-7; EINECS 205-526-6
Uses: Coemulsifier for o/w emulsions; solubilizer, carrier for lipophilic drugs; bacteriostatic effect
Properties: Wh. cryst. solid; sol. in water/ethanol (50/50), acetone, ether, heptane; m.p. 56-60 C;

HLB 4.0; acid no. 3 max.; iodine no. 2 max.; sapon. no. 195-205; 90% min. monoglycerides; nonionic.

Imwitor® 370. [Hüls Am.; Hüls AG]
Chem. Descrip.: Glyceryl stearate citrate
CAS 39175-72-9
Uses: Food-grade emulsifier for polar oils and fats for oral pharmaceutical preps.; compat. to skin and mucous membranes; consistency regulator; solubilizer
Properties: Wh. to ivory powd., neutral odor and taste; m.p. 60 C; HLB 10-12; acid no. 15-25; iodine no. 3 max.; sapon. no. 230-260; 10-30% monoglycerides; anionic.

Imwitor® 375. [Hüls Am.; Hüls AG]
Chem. Descrip.: Glyceryl citrate/lactate/linoleate/oleate
CAS 9174-23-9
Uses: Food-grade emulsifier for polar fats and oils; for oral pharmaceuticals; compat. to skin and mucous membranes; optimizes skin feeling
Regulatory: E472b/E472c compliance
Properties: Yel. highly visc. liq., char. odor (similar to soya oil), neutral taste; sol. in acetone, MCT, fatty oils; water-disp.; HLB 11.0; acid no. 15 max.; iodine no. 90; sapon. no. 230-250; 10-30% monoglcyerides; nonionic.

Imwitor® 742. [Hüls Am.; Hüls AG]
Chem. Descrip.: Caprylic/capric glycerides
CAS 26402-26-6
Uses: Coemulsifier, solubilizer, carrier, solv. for lipophilic active substances; dispersant, absorp. promoter; filler for hard and soft gelatin capsules; enhances drug release and bioavailability; bacteriostatic effect
Regulatory: German pharmacopoeia compliance
Properties: Wh-ylsh. cryst. solid, sl. coconut odor, fatty bitter taste; sol. in ethanol, actone, ether, heptane, hexane; misc. with oils and fats; m.p. 25 C; HLB 3-4; acid no. 2 max.; iodine no. 1 max.; sapon. no. 250-280; 45% min. monoglycerides; nonionic
Toxicology: LD50 (oral, rat) > 5 g/kg; moderate skin irritant (undiluted).

Imwitor® 780 K. [Hüls Am.; Hüls AG]
Chem. Descrip.: Isostearyl diglyceryl succinate
CAS 66085-00-5
Uses: W/o emulsifier for highly polar oils and fats,

pharmaceutical preps.; produces very heat-stable emulsions with Miglyol Gel
Properties: Yel., med. visc. liq., sl. char. odor; sol. in chloroform, benzene, ethanol, oils; insol. in water; m.w. 580; sp.gr. 0.96-0.98; visc. 700-900 mPa•s; HLB 3.7; acid no. 3 max.; iodine no. 10 max.; sapon. no. 240-260; 100% conc.; nonionic
Toxicology: LD50 (oral, rat) > 5 g/kg (nontoxic); nonirritating to skin and eyes.

Imwitor® 900. [Hüls Am.; Hüls AG]
Chem. Descrip.: Glyceryl stearate
CAS 85666-92-8; EINECS 234-325-6
Uses: Lubricant, binder, retarding agent, suspending agent, stabilizer, thickener, emulsifier for pharmaceutical industry; consistency regulator, aux. dispersant for creams and lotions
Properties: Ylsh. powd.; sol. in fats, oils, waxes; m.p. 56-61 C; HLB 3.0; acid no. 3 max.; iodine no. 3 max.; sapon. no. 160-175; 40-50% monoglycerides; nonionic.

Imwitor® 928. [Hüls AG]
Chem. Descrip.: Glyceryl cocoate
CAS 61789-05-7; EINECS 263-027-9
Uses: Surfactant for pharmaceutical and nutritional fields; as emulsifier, solubilizer, dispersion aid, plasticizer, lubricant, consistency regulator, skin and mucous membrane protectant, refatting agent, penetrant, carrier, adsorp. promoter
Properties: Soft wh. substance; sol. in acetone, ether, water/ethanol; m.p. 33-37 C; acid no. 2 max.; iodine no. 3 max.; sapon. no. 200-220.

Imwitor® 960 Flakes. [Hüls Am.; Hüls AG]
Chem. Descrip.: Glyceryl stearate SE
CAS 85666-92-8
Uses: Emulsifier and ointment base for pharmaceutical o/w creams
Properties: Ylsh. flakes; typical odor; sol. in all fats, oils, waxes, in chloroform, benzene, ether, ethanol; m.p. 56-61 C; HLB 12.0; acid no. 6 max.; iodine no. 3 max.; sapon. no. 150-175; 30% min. monoglycerides; 100% conc.; anionic

Imwitor® 965. [Hüls Am.; Hüls AG]
Chem. Descrip.: Palm oil glycerides and potassium stearate
Uses: O/w emulsifier, cream base, suspending agent in pharmaceutical creams, lotions, emulsions
Properties: Wh. flakes, powd., faint fatty odor; sol. in fats, oils, waxes; disp. in hot water; m.p. 56-61 C; HLB 13.0; acid no. 6 max.; iodine no. 3 max.; sapon. no. 155-175; 30% min. monoglycerides, 100% conc.; anionic
Toxicology: Nontoxic.

Imwitor® 988. [Hüls AG]
Chem. Descrip.: Glyceryl caprylate
CAS 26402-26-6; EINECS 247-668-1
Uses: Surfactant for pharmaceutical and nutritional fields; as emulsifier, solubilizer, dispersion aid, plasticizer, lubricant, consistency regulator, skin and mucous membrane protectant, refatting agent, penetrant, carrier, adsorp. promoter
Properties: Almost colorless liq./semisolid; sol. in

water/ethanol (25/75), acetone, ether, heptane; acid no. 3 max.; iodine no. 3 max.; sapon. no. 275-300; 50% monoglycerides.

Incrocas 35. [Croda Inc.]
Chem. Descrip.: PEG-35 castor oil NF
CAS 61791-12-6
Uses: Surfactant, emulsifier, solv., wetting agent, emollient, lubricant for topical and parenteral pharmaceuticals
Use level: 0.5-5%
Properties: Pale yel. liq.; HLB 12.5; nonionic.

Incromega E. [Croda Inc.]
Chem. Descrip.: Omega 3 essential fatty acid ethyl ester
Uses: Used in oral and topical pharmaceuticals
Properties: Low color, low odor, bland taste.

Incromega F. [Croda Inc.]
Chem. Descrip.: Omega 3 essential fatty acid derived from marine oils, high in eicosapentaenoic acid and docosahexanoic acid
Uses: Used in oral and topical pharmaceuticals
Properties: Low color, low odor, bland taste.

Incromega T. [Croda Inc.]
Chem. Descrip.: Omega 3 essential fatty acid triglyceride
Uses: Used in oral and topical pharmaceuticals
Properties: Low color, low odor, bland taste.

Incropol CS-20. [Croda Inc.]
Chem. Descrip.: Ceteareth-20
CAS 68439-49-6
Uses: O/w emulsifier for topical pharmaceuticals; synergistic with Volpo series
Use level: 0.5-10%
Properties: Gardner 1 max. wh. solid; sol. in water, IPA; disp. in propylene glycol; insol. in min. oil; pH 5.5-7.5 (3%); HLB 15.5; 100% conc.; nonionic
Toxicology: LD50 (oral, rat) 2.1 g/kg; mild skin irritant; moderate eye irritant.

Incroquat B65C. [Croda Inc.]
Chem. Descrip.: Behenalkonium chloride, cetyl alcohol
Uses: Mild emulsifier for topical pharmaceutical creams and emulsions
Use level: 1-5%
Properties: Wh. flake; m.p. 80 C; 65% act.; cationic.

Incroquat Behenyl TMS. [Croda Inc.; Croda Surf. Ltd.]
Chem. Descrip.: Behentrimonium methosulfate, cetearyl alcohol
Uses: Self-emulsifying wax for topical pharmaceutical creams and emulsions; suspending structural agents; produces elegant cationic emulsions; capable of emulsifying silicone
Use level: 1-10%
Properties: Wh. flake, char. odor; m.p. 58-62 C; pH 6.0-7.0 (1%); 25% act.; cationic.

Industrene® 223. [Witco/H-I-P]
Chem. Descrip.: Hydrog. coconut acid
CAS 68938-15-8
Uses: Chemical intermediate, emulsifier; used in pharmaceuticals
Properties: Solid. pt. 23-26 C; acid no. 266-274; iodine no. 3 max.; sapon. no. 267-276.

Iodasept. [United-Guardian]
Chem. Descrip.: Povidone
CAS 9003-39-8; EINECS 201-800-4
Uses: Nonstaining iodine antiseptic for use as skin
scrub, in pre-operative preps., iodine lotion, stick
antiseptic for first aid kits
Custom product

Ionajel. [United-Guardian]
Uses: Health-care gel which holds α-hydroxy acids
and salicylic acid without adjusting the pH up-
wards; stable at pH levels below 3; exhibits increase in visc. after acidification
Properties: Clear gel
Custom product

Iron Bile Salts. [Am. Labs]
Chem. Descrip.: Blend of ox bile with a source of
ferric iron
Uses: Nutritive pharmaceutical additive
Properties: Brnsh.-yel. powd.; hygroscopic; pH 6.6.

Isatin. [BASF AG]
Uses: Intermediate for prod. of pharmaceuticals.

Isoamyl Alcohol 95%. [CPS]
Chem. Descrip.: Isoamyl alcohol
CAS 123-51-3; EINECS 204-633-5
Uses: Used for flavors, fragrances, fine chems.,
pharmaceuticals
Regulatory: FDA 21CFR §172.515
Properties: APHA 50 color; m.w. 88.15; sp.gr.
0.811 (20/20 C); distillation range 126-132 C (760
mm); flash pt. 47 C; 95% purity, 0.5% water.

Isoamyl Alcohol 99%. [CPS]
Chem. Descrip.: Isoamyl alcohol
CAS 123-51-3; EINECS 204-633-5
Uses: Used for flavors, fragrances, fine chems.,
pharmaceuticals
Regulatory: FDA 21CFR §172.515
Properties: APHA 20 color; m.w. 88.15; sp.gr.
0.811 (20/20 C); distillation range 128-132 C (760
mm); flash pt. 47 C; 99% purity, 0.2% water.

Isofol® 12. [Condea Chemie GmbH; Vista]
Chem. Descrip.: Butyl octanol
CAS 3913-02-8; EINECS 223-470-0
Uses: For pharmaceutical creams, ointments,
emulsions, sticks; solubilizer for lipid-sol. actives
Properties: Clear oily liq.; m.w. 186; sp.gr. 0.833;
visc. 23 mPa•s; m.p. < -30 C; b.p. 145-149 C (33
mbar); acid no. 0.1 max.; iodine no. 1.0 max.;
sapon. no. 1.0 max.; hyd. no. 296-305; flash pt.
120 C; ref. index 1.443; surf. tens. 28 mN/m; 95%
min. act.; biodeg.
Toxicology: Nontoxic; nonirritating to skin.

Isofol® 14T. [Condea Chemie GmbH; Vista]
Chem. Descrip.: C12-C16 Guerbet alcohol
Uses: For pharmaceutical creams, ointments,
emulsions, sticks; solubilizer for lipid-sol. actives
Properties: Clear oily liq.; m.w. 212-223; sp.gr.
0.835; visc. 32 mPa•s; m.p. < -25 C; b.p. 160-195
C (33 mbar); acid no. 0.1 max.; iodine no. 1.0
max.; sapon. no. 1.0 max.; hyd. no. 252-265; flash
pt. 139 C; ref. index 1.447; surf. tens. 30 mN/m;
95% min. act.; biodeg.
Toxicology: Nontoxic; nonirritating to skin.

Isofol® 16. [Condea Chemie GmbH; Vista]
Chem. Descrip.: Hexyl decanol
CAS 2425-77-6; EINECS 219-370-1
Uses: For pharmaceutical creams, ointments,
emulsions, sticks; solubilizer for lipid-sol. actives
Properties: Clear oily liq.; m.w. 242; sp.gr. 0.836;
visc. 38 mPa•s; m.p. -21 to -15 C; b.p. 193-197 C
(33 mbar); acid no. 0.1 max.; iodine no. 1.0 max.;
sapon. no. 1.0 max.; hyd. no. 225-235; flash pt.
156 C; ref. index 1.450; surf. tens. 30 mN/m; 97%
min. act.; biodeg.
Toxicology: Nontoxic; nonirritating to skin.

Isofol® 16 Caprylat. [Condea Chemie GmbH]
CAS 92777-70-9; EINECS 298-104-6
Uses: Oily components in pharmaceutical formulations incl. creams, lotions, deodorants, aerosol
and foam prods.
Properties: Clear oily liq.; m.w. 370; sp.gr. 0.855;
visc. 11 mPa•s; solid. pt. -48 C; acid no. 0.1 max.;
iodine no. 0.5 max.; sapon. no. 148-155; hyd. no.
0.1 max.; flash pt. 213 C; ref. index 1.446.

Isofol® 16 Laurat. [Condea Chemie GmbH]
CAS 34362-27-1; EINECS 251-959-9
Uses: Oily components in pharmaceutical formulations incl. creams, lotions, deodorants, aerosol
and foam prods.
Properties: Clear oily liq.; m.w. 426; sp.gr. 0.853;
visc. 16 mPa•s; solid. pt. -29 C; acid no. 0.1 max.;
iodine no. 0.5 max.; sapon. no. 129-136; hyd. no.
0.1 max.; flash pt. 225 C; ref. index 1.450.

Isofol® 16 Oleat. [Condea Chemie GmbH]
CAS 94278-07-6; EINECS 304-693-3
Uses: Oily components in pharmaceutical formulations incl. creams, lotions, deodorants, aerosol
and foam prods.
Properties: Clear oily liq.; m.w. 509; sp.gr. 0.861;
visc. 26 mPa•s; solid. pt. -40 C; acid no. 0.1 max.;
iodine no. 50-54; sapon. no. 108-114; hyd. no. 0.1
max.; flash pt. 260 C; ref. index 1.459.

Isofol® 16 Palmitat. [Condea Chemie GmbH]
CAS 69275-02-1; EINECS 273-942-5
Uses: Oily components in pharmaceutical formulations incl. creams, lotions, deodorants, aerosol
and foam prods.
Properties: Clear oily liq.; m.w. 482; sp.gr. 0.852;
visc. 24 mPa•s; solid. pt. -10 C; acid no. 0.1 max.;
iodine no. 0.5 max.; sapon. no. 114-120; hyd. no.
0.1 max.; flash pt. 237 C; ref. index 1.453.

Isofol® 18E. [Condea Chemie GmbH; Vista]
Chem. Descrip.: C16-C20 Guerbet alcohol
Uses: For pharmaceutical creams, ointments,
emulsions, sticks; solubilizer for lipid-sol. actives
Properties: Clear oily liq.; m.w. 269-279; sp.gr.
0.837; visc. 50 mPa•s; m.p. -10 to -6 C; b.p. 211-
218 C (33 mbar); acid no. 0.1 max.; iodine no. 1.0
max.; sapon. no. 1.0 max.; hyd. no. 201-209; flash
pt. 170 C; ref. index 1.452; surf. tens. 30 mN/m;
95% min. act.; biodeg.
Toxicology: Nontoxic; nonirritating to skin.

Isofol® 18T. [Condea Chemie GmbH; Vista]
Chem. Descrip.: C16-C20 Guerbet alcohol
Uses: For pharmaceutical creams, ointments,

emulsions, sticks; solubilizer for lipid-sol. actives
Properties: Clear oily liq.; m.w. 267-285; sp.gr. 0.837; visc. 50 mPa•s; m.p. -10 to -6 C; b.p. 207-236 C (33 mbar); acid no. 0.1 max.; iodine no. 1.0 max.; sapon. no. 1.0 max.; hyd. no. 197-210; flash pt. 170 C; ref. index 1.452; surf. tens. 30 mN/m; 95% min. act.; biodeg.
Toxicology: Nontoxic; nonirritating to skin.

Isofol® 20. [Condea Chemie GmbH; Vista]
Chem. Descrip.: Octyl dodecanol
CAS 5333-42-6; EINECS 226-242-9
Uses: For pharmaceutical creams, ointments, emulsions, sticks; solubilizer for lipid-sol. actives
Properties: Clear oily liq.; m.w. 298; sp.gr. 0.838; visc. 60 mPa•s; m.p. -1 to +1 C; b.p. 234-238 C (33 mbar); acid no. 0.1 max.; iodine no. 1.0 max.; sapon. no. 1.0 max.; hyd. no. 184-190; flash pt. 180 C; ref. index 1.454; surf. tens. 31 mN/m; 97% min. act.; biodeg.
Toxicology: Nontoxic; nonirritating to skin.

Isofol® 20 Myristat. [Condea Chemie GmbH]
CAS 22766-83-2; EINECS 245-205-8
Uses: Oily components in pharmaceutical formulations incl. creams, lotions, deodorants, aerosol and foam prods.
Properties: Clear oily liq.; m.w. 510; sp.gr. 0.851; visc. 27 mPa•s; solid. pt. -2 C; acid no. 0.1 max.; iodine no. 0.5 max.; sapon. no. 106-112; hyd. no. 0.1 max.; flash pt. 244 C; ref. index 1.457.

Isofol® 20 Oleat. [Condea Chemie GmbH]
CAS 22801-45-2; EINECS 245-228-3
Uses: Oily components in pharmaceutical formulations incl. creams, lotions, deodorants, aerosol and foam prods.
Properties: Clear oily liq.; m.w. 565; sp.gr. 0.860; visc. 32 mPa•s; solid. pt. -24 C; acid no. 0.1 max.; iodine no. 44-48; sapon. no. 92-98; hyd. no. 0.1 max.; flash pt. 272 C; ref. index 1.460.

Isofol® 24. [Condea Chemie GmbH; Vista]
Chem. Descrip.: Decyl dodecanol
Uses: For pharmaceutical creams, ointments, emulsions, sticks; solubilizer for lipid-sol. actives
Properties: Clear oily liq.; m.w. 354; sp.gr. 0.842; visc. 86 mPa•s; m.p. 17-20 C; b.p. 271-175 C (33 mbar); acid no. 0.1 max.; iodine no. 1.0 max.; sapon. no. 1.0 max.; hyd. no. 154-160; flash pt. 230 C; ref. index 1.457; surf. tens. 32 mN/m; 97%

min. act.; biodeg.
Toxicology: Nontoxic; nonirritating to skin.

Iso Isotearyle WL 3196. [Gattefosse SA]
Chem. Descrip.: Isostearyl isostearate
CAS 41669-30-1; EINECS 255-485-3
Uses: Superfatting agent for pharmaceutical emulsions and microemulsions
Properties: Liq.; HLB 1-2; acid no. < 6; iodine no. < 8; sapon. no. 90-110
Toxicology: LD0 (oral, rat) > 2 g/kg; sl. irritating to skin and eyes.

Isopropylmyristat. [Henkel KGaA/Cospha]
Chem. Descrip.: Isopropyl myristate BP/NF
CAS 110-27-0; EINECS 203-751-4
Uses: Spreading agent, dermatological carrier for pharmaceutical skin care preps.; good dissolution power for lipid-sol. actives
Regulatory: DAB, Ph.Eur., NF, JCIC compliance
Properties: Almost colorless oil, almost odorless; m.w. 270; dens. 0.850-0.855 g/cm^3 (20 C); visc. 5-6 mPa•s; acid no. 0.1 max.; sapon. no. 205-211; hyd. no. 2 max.; cloud pt. 2 C max.; ref. index 1.4335-1.4355 (20 C); 92% min. act.
Storage: 1 yr min. storage stability in sealed original containers at temps. below 30 C in a dry environment.

Isopropylpalmitat. [Henkel KGaA/Cospha]
Chem. Descrip.: Isopropyl palmitate DAB
CAS 142-91-6; EINECS 205-571-1
Uses: Dermatological carrier, solubilizer for lipid-sol. actives for pharmaceutical skin care preps., creams, emulsions, and ointments
Regulatory: DAB, Ph.Eur., JCIC compliance
Properties: Colorless clear fluid, odorless; misc. with oily components; m.w. 300; sp.gr. 0.852-0.854 (20 C); visc. 7-8 mPa•s (20 C); acid no. 0.5 max.; iodine no. 1 max.; sapon. no. 185-190; hyd. no. 2 max.; cloud pt. < 15 C; flash pt. 170 C min.; ref. index 1.438-1.439 (20 C); 90% min. act.
Storage: 1 yr min. storage life in sealed containers at temps. below 30 C, protected from moisture.

Ivarlan™ Light. [Brooks Industries]
Chem. Descrip.: Lanolin USP
CAS 8006-54-0; EINECS 232-348-6
Uses: Emollient
Properties: Lt. yel. unctuous soft solid, sl. char. odor; m.p. 40 C; 100% conc.

J

Jeffox PPG-400. [Huntsman]
Chem. Descrip.: PPG-400
Uses: Intermediate yielding esters; useful as defoaming agents in pharmaceuticals
Properties: Water-wh. visc. liq., faint ether-like odor; m.w. 400; dens. 8.40 lb/gal; visc. 150-175 SUS (100 F); flash pt. (PMCC) 320 F; pour pt. -35 F; pH 5-7.

Jeffox PPG-2000. [Huntsman]
Chem. Descrip.: PPG-2000
Uses: Intermediate yielding esters; useful as defoaming agents in pharmaceuticals
Properties: Water-wh. visc. liq., faint ether-like odor; m.w. 2000; dens. 8.37 lb/gal; flash pt. (PMCC) 370 F; pour pt. -25 F; pH 5-7.

Jerusalem Arthichoke Flour (JAF). [Zumbro; Garuda Int'l.]
Chem. Descrip.: Jerusalem artichoke flour
Uses: Bulking agent; nutraceutical ingred. stimulating friendly bifidobacteria and inhibiting undesirable bacteria associated with gastric upset, high blood pressure, elevated cholesterol levels; for health food tablets or capsules
Properties: Pale brn. flour, sl. sweet nutty flavor; 13.2% dietary fiber, 65.7% carbohydrates, 8.8% protein, 6% moisture
Storage: Store in cool dry area.

Jungbunzlauer GS 7097. [Jungbunzlauer Int'l. AG]
Chem. Descrip.: Glucose syrup derived from corn starch
CAS 8029-43-4; EINECS 232-436-4
Uses: Sweetener used in pharmaceuticals
Properties: PH 3.8-4.5; DE 96 min.; 94% min. glucose content.

Justfiber® CL-40-H. [Van Den Bergh Foods]
Chem. Descrip.: Cellulose fiber
CAS 9004-34-6; EINECS 232-674-9
Uses: Inert ingred. in pharmaceuticals
Regulatory: Kosher
Properties: Wh. powd.; avg. fiber length 40 μ; bulk dens. 3.2 cc/g; water absorp. 4.0-4.5 g H_2O/g.

Justfiber® CL-60-H. [Van Den Bergh Foods]
Chem. Descrip.: Cellulose fiber
EINECS 232-674-9
Uses: Tableting excipient for water binding in pharmaceuticals
Regulatory: Kosher
Properties: Wh. powd.; avg. fiber length 60 μ; bulk dens. 4.2 cc/g; water absorp. 5.5 g H_2O/g.

Justfiber® CL-80-H. [Van Den Bergh Foods]
Chem. Descrip.: Cellulose fiber
EINECS 232-674-9
Uses: Tableting excipient for water binding in pharmaceuticals
Regulatory: Kosher
Properties: Wh. powd.; avg. fiber length 80 μ; bulk dens. 4.4 cc/g; water absorp. 5.4-6.0 g H_2O/g.

K

Kallikrein. [Waitaki Int'l. Biosciences; Tri-K Industries]
Chem. Descrip.: Serine protease extracted from pancreas and urine
Uses: Skin rectifier; antihypertensive promoting vasodilation, cell renewal, wound healing, increased nutrient and oxygen uptake, and radiation protection in skin care prods. and pharmaceuticals
Properties: Powd. and sol'n.

Kaopolite® 1147. [Kaopolite]
Chem. Descrip.: Aluminum silicate, anhyd.
CAS 1327-36-2; EINECS 215-475-1
Uses: Abrasive for dentifrices
Properties: Powd.; 1.8 µ median particle size; 0.01% on 325 mesh; sp.gr. 2.62; dens. 21.91 lb/solid gal; bulking value 0.046 gal/lb; oil absorp. 65; brightness 93; ref. index 1.62; pH 5.5 (20% solids); hardness (Mohs) 5.

Kaopolite® SF. [Kaopolite]
Chem. Descrip.: Aluminum silicate, anhyd.
CAS 1327-36-2; EINECS 215-475-1
Uses: Gentle abrasive for dentifrices
Properties: Fine dry powd.; 0.7 µ median particle size; 0.01% on 325 mesh; sp.gr. 2.62; dens. 21.91 lb/solid gal; bulking value 0.046 gal/lb; oil absorp. 50; brightness 90; ref. index 1.62; pH 4.7 (20% solids); hardness (Mohs) 7.

Karajel. [Guardian Labs]
Chem. Descrip.: Glyceryl alginate
Uses: Moisturizer, carrier for other ingreds.; used in pharmaceuticals, medical applics., health-care prods.

Karaya Gum #1 FCC. [Meer]
Chem. Descrip.: Karaya gum
CAS 9000-36-6; EINECS 232-539-4
Uses: Stabilizer, water binder, emulsifier in pharmaceuticals (bulk laxatives, denture adhesives)
Properties: Water-sol.

Kaydol®. [Witco/Petroleum Spec.]
Chem. Descrip.: Wh. min. oil USP
Uses: Emollient, lubricant for pharmaceuticals, ointments, creams, veterinary preps.; internal lubricant for laxatives
Regulatory: FDA 21CFR §172.878, §178.3620a
Properties: Water-wh., odorless, tasteless; sp.gr. 0.869-0.885; visc. 64-70 cSt (40 C); pour pt. -23 C; flash pt. 216 C.

Kaydol® S. [Witco/Petroleum Spec.]

Chem. Descrip.: Wh. min. oil USP
Uses: Binder, carrier, conditioner, dispersant, extender, lubricant, moisture barrier, protective agent
Regulatory: FDA 21CFR §172.878, 178.3620(a)
Properties: Odorless, tasteless; sp.gr. 0.869-0.885; visc. 64.5-86 cSt (40 C); distill. pt. 243 C min. (10 mm, 2.5%); pour pt. 0 F; flash pt. (COC) 440 F.

KELACID®. [Kelco]
Chem. Descrip.: Alginic acid
CAS 9005-32-7; EINECS 232-680-1
Uses: Gelling agent, emulsifier, stabilizer for pharmaceuticals; tablet disintegrant, hemostatic agent, antacid tablets; primary reagent
Regulatory: FDA 21CFR §184.1011, GRAS; FCC/NF compliance; EEC E400 compliance
Properties: Wh. fibrous particles, sl. odor; 177 µ particle size; 80 mesh; sol. in alkaline sol'n.; swells in water; bulk dens. ≈ 50 lb/ft³; pH 2.9 (1% aq.); surf. tens. 53 dynes/cm; 7% moisture
Toxicology: LD50 (oral, rat) > 5000 mg/kg; excessive dust inhalation may cause respiratory irritation; dry powd. may cause eye irritation
Precaution: Not flamm., but powd. will burn if involved in fire; spills are slippery; incompat. with strong oxidizers
Storage: Store in cool, dry place.

KELCOLOID® D. [Kelco]
Chem. Descrip.: Propylene glycol alginate
CAS 9005-37-2
Uses: Emulsifier and stabilizer for pharmaceutical applics.
Regulatory: EEC E405 compliance
Properties: Cream fibrous particles; sp.gr. 1.46; dens. 33.71 lb/ft³; visc. 170 cps; ref. index 1.3343; pH 4.4; surf. tens. 58 dynes/cm; 13% max. moisture.

KELCOLOID® DH. [Kelco]
Chem. Descrip.: Propylene glycol alginate
CAS 9005-37-2
Uses: Emulsifier and stabilizer for pharmaceuticals, emulsions, low pH systems
Regulatory: FDA 21CFR §172.858, EEC E405 compliance
Properties: Cream agglomerated, sl. odor; 840 µ particle size; sol. in water; sp.gr. 1.46; dens. 33.71 lb/ft³; visc. 400 cps (1%), 7000 cps (2%); ref. index

1.3343; pH 3.7; surf. tens. 58 dynes/cm.
Toxicology: LD50 (oral, rat) > 5000 mg/kg; dry powd. may cause eye irritation
Precaution: Incompat. with strong oxidizers.

KELCOLOID® DSF. [Kelco]
Chem. Descrip.: Propylene glycol alginate
CAS 9005-37-2
Uses: Emulsifier and stabilizer for pharmaceuticals, emulsions, low pH systems
Regulatory: EEC E405 compliance
Properties: Cream agglomerated; sp.gr. 1.46; dens. 33.71 lb/ft³; visc. 20 cps; ref. index 1.3343; pH 4.0; surf. tens. 58 dynes/cm.

KELCOLOID® HVF. [Kelco]
Chem. Descrip.: Propylene glycol alginate
CAS 9005-37-2
Uses: Emulsifier and stabilizer for pharmaceuticals; thickener for low pH prods. such as cough syrups
Regulatory: FDA 21CFR §172.858, EEC E405 compliance
Properties: Cream fibrous particles, sl. odor; 175 μ particle size; 80 mesh; sol. in water; sp.gr. 1.46; dens. 33.71 lb/ft³; visc. 400 cps (1%), 7000 cps (2%); ref. index 1.3343; pH 3.7; surf. tens. 58 dynes/cm
Toxicology: LD50 (oral, rat) > 5000 mg/kg; dry powd. may cause eye irritation
Precaution: Incompat. with strong oxidizers.

KELCOLOID® LVF. [Kelco]
Chem. Descrip.: Propylene glycol alginate
CAS 9005-37-2
Uses: Emulsifier and stabilizer for pharmaceuticals, vitamin emulsions in low pH or neutral prods., oral min. oil emulsions
Regulatory: FDA 21CFR §172.858, EEC E405 compliance
Properties: Cream fibrous particles; 175 μ particle size; 80 mesh; sp.gr. 1.46; dens. 33.71 lb/ft³; visc. 120 cps (1%), 1200 cps (2%); ref. index 1.3343; pH 3.7; surf. tens. 58 dynes/cm
Toxicology: LD50 (oral, rat) > 5000 mg/kg; dry powd. may cause eye irritation
Precaution: Incompat. with strong oxidizers.

KELCOLOID® S. [Kelco]
Chem. Descrip.: Propylene glycol alginate
CAS 9005-37-2
Uses: Emulsifier and stabilizer for pharmaceuticals
Regulatory: FDA 21CFR §172.858, EEC E405 compliance
Properties: Cream fibrous particles; 175 μ particle size; sp.gr. 1.46; dens. 33.71 lb/ft³; visc. 20 cps (1%), 120 cps (2%); ref. index 1.3343; pH 4.1; surf. tens. 58 dynes/cm.
Toxicology: LD50 (oral, rat) > 5000 mg/kg; dry powd. may cause eye irritation
Precaution: Incompat. with strong oxidizers.

KELCOSOL®. [Kelco]
Chem. Descrip.: Algin
CAS 9005-38-3
Uses: High visc. gelling agent, thickener, and stabilizer in pharmaceutical applics., surgical jel-
lies; tablet binder; control agent in sustained release tablets
Regulatory: FDA 21CFR §184.1724, GRAS; EEC E401 compliance
Properties: Cream fibrous particles, sl. odor; 80 mesh; water-sol.; sp.gr. 1.64; dens. 43.38 lb/ft³; visc. 1300 cps (1%), 15,000 cps (2%); pH 7; surf. tens. 70 dynes/cm; 9% moisture
Toxicology: LD50 (oral, rat) > 5000 mg/kg; dry powd. may cause eye irritation
Precaution: Incompat. with strong oxidizers.

KELGIN® F. [Kelco]
Chem. Descrip.: Algin, refined
CAS 9005-38-3
Uses: Gelling agent, thickener, and stabilizer in pharmaceutical applics.
Regulatory: FDA 21CFR §184.1724, GRAS; EEC E401 compliance
Properties: Ivory gran., sl. odor; 80 mesh; water-sol.; sp.gr. 1.59; dens. 54.62 lb/ft³; visc. 300 cps (1%), 4000 cps (2%); ref. index 1.3343; pH 7; surf. tens. 62 dynes/cm; 13% moisture
Toxicology: LD50 (oral, rat) > 5000 mg/kg; dry powd. may cause eye irritation
Precaution: Incompat. with strong oxidizers.

KELGIN® HV. [Kelco]
Chem. Descrip.: Algin
CAS 9005-38-3
Uses: High visc. gelling agent, thickener, and stabilizer for pharmaceuticals, lotions, ointments; gelling agent for wound healing compositions
Regulatory: FDA 21CFR §184.1724, GRAS; EEC E401 compliance
Properties: Ivory gran., sl. odor; 30 mesh; water-sol.; sp.gr. 1.59; dens. 54.62 lb/ft³; visc. 800 cps (1%), 10,000 cps (2%); ref. index 1.3343; pH 7; surf. tens. 62 dynes/cm; 13% moisture
Toxicology: LD50 (oral, rat) > 5000 mg/kg; dry powd. may cause eye irritation
Precaution: Incompat. with strong oxidizers.

KELGIN® LV. [Kelco]
Chem. Descrip.: Algin
CAS 9005-38-3
Uses: Low-visc. gelling agent, thickener, and stabilizer for pharmaceutical applics., surgical jellies; gelling agent in wound healing films
Regulatory: FDA 21CFR §184.1724, GRAS; EEC E401 compliance
Properties: Ivory gran., sl. odor; 42 mesh; water-sol.; sp.gr. 1.59; dens. 54.62 lb/ft³; visc. 60 cps (1%), 500 cps (2%); ref. index 1.3343; pH 7; surf. tens. 62 dynes/cm; 13% moisture
Toxicology: LD50 (oral, rat) > 5000 mg/kg; dry powd. may cause eye irritation
Precaution: Incompat. with strong oxidizers.

KELGIN® MV. [Kelco]
Chem. Descrip.: Algin
CAS 9005-38-3
Uses: Med.-visc. gelling agent, thickener, and stabilizer for pharmaceutical applics., ointments, suppositories, lubricating/surgical jellies; bulk laxative

Regulatory: FDA 21CFR §184.1724, GRAS; EEC E401 compliance

Properties: Ivory gran., sl. odor; 30 mesh; water-sol.; sp.gr. 1.59; dens. 54.62 lb/ft^3; visc. 400 cps (1%), 6000 cps (2%); ref. index 1.3343; pH 7; surf. tens. 62 dynes/cm; 13% moisture

Toxicology: LD50 (oral, rat) > 5000 mg/kg; dry powd. may cause eye irritation

Precaution: Incompat. with strong oxidizers.

KELGIN® XL. [Kelco]

Chem. Descrip.: Refined sodium alginate
CAS 9005-38-3

Uses: Very low visc. gelling agent, thickener, and stabilizer for pharmaceuticals; film-former for clear sol. films (wound healing)

Regulatory: FDA 21CFR §184.1724, GRAS; EEC E401 compliance

Properties: Ivory gran., sl. odor; 42 mesh; water-sol.; sp.gr. 1.59; dens. 54.62 lb/ft^3; visc. 30 cps (1%), 160 cps (2%); ref. index 1.3343; pH 7; surf. tens. 62 dynes/cm; 13% moisture

Toxicology: LD50 (oral, rat) > 5000 mg/kg; dry powd. may cause eye irritation

Precaution: Incompat. with strong oxidizers.

Kelisema Bovine Natural Insoluble Elastin. [Kelisema Srl]

Chem. Descrip.: Elastin

Uses: Natural ingred. for pharmaceuticals, medicinal soaps

Properties: Straw-yel. powd., particle size < 0.1 mm; insol. in water.

Kelisema Collagen-CCK Complex. [Kelisema Srl]

Chem. Descrip.: Macromolecular soluble collagen and potassium cocoate

Uses: Mild ingred. for medicinal soaps.

Kelisema Natural Pure Shea Butter. [Kelisema Srl]

Chem. Descrip.: Shea butter
CAS 68424-60-2

Uses: Natural ingred. for skin-protecting treatments and in preps. against dry skin, dermatitis, dermatosis, eczema, solar erythema, burns, and gingivitis.

Kelisema Sodium Hyaluronate Bio. [Kelisema Srl]

Chem. Descrip.: Sodium hyaluronate
CAS 9067-32-7

Uses: Natural ingred. for pharmaceuticals.

KELMAR®. [Kelco]

Chem. Descrip.: Potassium alginate
CAS 9005-36-1

Uses: Gelling agent in dental impression compds.; suspending agent, thickener in low- or no-sodium formulations

Regulatory: FDA 21CFR §184.1610, GRAS; EEC E402 compliance

Properties: Cream gran., sl. odor; 100 mesh; water-sol.; bulk dens. ≈ 50 lb/ft^3; visc. 270 cps (1%), 3200 cps (2%); pH 7.0

Toxicology: LD50 (oral, rat) > 5000 mg/kg; excessive dust inhalation may cause respiratory irritation; dry powd. may cause eye irritation

Precaution: Not flamm., but powd. will burn if involved in a fire; spills may be slippery; incompat.

with strong oxidizers.

KELMAR® CR. [Kelco Int'l.]

Chem. Descrip.: Potassium alginate
CAS 9005-36-1

Uses: High-visc. thickener, suspending agent, and gellant for pharmaceutical sustained-release tablets

Regulatory: FDA 21CFR §184.1610, GRAS; EEC E402 compliance

Properties: Cream gran., sl. odor; 100 mesh; water-sol.; bulk dens. ≈ 50 lb/ft^3; visc. 270 cps (1%), 3200 cps (2%); pH 7.0

Toxicology: LD50 (oral, rat) > 5000 mg/kg; excessive dust inhalation may cause respiratory irritation; dry powd. may cause eye irritation

Precaution: Not flamm., but powd. will burn if involved in a fire; spills may be slippery; incompat. with strong oxidizers.

KELMAR® Improved. [Kelco]

Chem. Descrip.: Potassium alginate
CAS 9005-36-1

Uses: Gelling agent in dental impression compds.; suspending agent, thickener in low- or no-sodium formulations

Regulatory: FDA 21CFR §184.1610, GRAS; EEC E402 compliance

Properties: Cream gran., sl. odor; 80 mesh; water-sol.; bulk dens. ≈ 50 lb/ft^2; visc. 400 cps (1%), 4500 cps (2%); pH 7.0

Toxicology: LD50 (oral, rat) > 5000 mg/kg; excessive dust inhalation may cause respiratory irritation; dry powd. may cause eye irritation

Precaution: Not flamm., but powd. will burn if involved in a fire; spills may be slippery; incompat. with strong oxidizers.

KELSET®. [Kelco]

Chem. Descrip.: Sodium alginate
CAS 9005-38-3

Uses: Gelling agent and stabilizer for pharmaceutical applics., lotions, ointments

Regulatory: FDA 21CFR §184.1724, GRAS; EEC E401 compliance

Properties: Lt. ivory soft gel, sl. odor; 177 μ particle size; 80 mesh; water-sol.; bulk dens. ≈ 50 lb/ft^3; pH 7.0

Toxicology: LD50 (oral, rat) > 5000 mg/kg; dry powd. may cause eye irritation

Precaution: Incompat. with strong oxidizers.

KELTONE®. [Kelco]

Chem. Descrip.: Algin
CAS 9005-38-3

Uses: Gelling agent, emulsifier, and stabilizer for dental impression materials

Regulatory: FDA 21CFR §184.1724, GRAS; EEC E401 compliance.

KELTONE® HV. [Kelco]

Chem. Descrip.: Low calcium sodium alginate
CAS 9005-38-3

Uses: Med. visc. gelling agent, thickener, and stabilizer in pharmaceutical applics.; gellant in dental impression compds.; surgical jellies; denture adhesives; encapsulant for controlled-re-

lease drugs, enzyme immobilization
Regulatory: FDA 21CFR §184.1724, GRAS; EEC E401 compliance
Properties: Wh. to tan powd., sl. odor; 80 mesh; water-sol.; bulk dens. ≈ 50 lb/ft^3; visc. 400 cps (1%), 3500 cps (2%); pH 7
Toxicology: LD50 (oral, rat) > 5000 mg/kg; dry powd. may cause eye irritation
Precaution: Incompat. with strong oxidizers.

KELTONE® HVCR. [Kelco Int'l.]
Chem. Descrip.: Sodium alginate NF/PhEur
CAS 9005-38-3
Uses: High-visc. thickener, suspending agent, and gelling agent for pharmaceuticals, sustained-release tablets; for drugs with greater sol. in gastric than in intestinal fluid.

KELTONE® LV. [Kelco]
Chem. Descrip.: Low calcium sodium alginate
CAS 9005-38-3
Uses: Low-visc. gelling agent, thickener, and stabilizer for pharmaceutical applics.; encapsulating agent for cell entrapment, controlled-release drugs, enzyme immobilization; film-forming agent for clear sol. films (wound healing)
Regulatory: FDA 21CFR §184.1724, GRAS; EEC E401 compliance
Properties: Wh. to tan powd., sl. odor; 150 mesh; water-sol.; sp.gr. 1.64; bulk dens. ≈ 50 lb/ft^3; visc. 50 cps (1%), 250 cps (2%); pH 7; ref. index 1.3342
Toxicology: LD50 (oral, rat) > 5000 mg/kg; dry powd. may cause eye irritation
Precaution: Incompat. with strong oxidizers.

KELTONE® LVCR. [Kelco Int'l.]
Chem. Descrip.: Sodium alginate NF/PhEur
CAS 9005-38-3
Uses: Low-visc. thickener, suspending agent, and gelling agent for pharmaceuticals, sustained-release tablets where rapid release in intestinal fluid is desirable.

KELTOSE®. [Kelco]
Chem. Descrip.: Calcium alginate and ammonium alginate
Uses: Tablet binder and disintegrant for pharmaceuticals; bulk laxatives (contributes bulk and lubrication to the intestines)
Regulatory: FDA GRAS
Properties: Ivory gran., sl. odor; 177 μ particle size; 80 mesh; water-sol.; dens. ≈ 50 lb/ft^3; visc. 250 cps; pH 7.0; readily biodeg.
Toxicology: LD50 (oral, rat) > 5000 mg/kg; dry powd. may cause eye irritation, skin irritation on prolonged contact; excessive dust inhalation may cause respiratory irritation
Precaution: Not flamm., but powd. will burn if involved in a fire; spills may be slippery; incompat. with strong oxidizers, alkaline sol'ns.
Storage: Store in cool, dry place.

KELTROL®. [Kelco]
Chem. Descrip.: Food-grade xanthan gum
CAS 11138-66-2; EINECS 234-394-2
Uses: Thickener, emulsion stabilizer, suspending agent for creams, lotions, pharmaceuticals;

binder in toothpaste; stable in acid systems; salt compatibility
Regulatory: FDA 21CFR §172.695; EEC E415 compliance
Properties: Cream to wh. powd., sl. odor; ≥ 95% thru 80 mesh; sol. in hot and cold water; swells in glycerin and propylene glycol; sp.gr. 1.5; bulk dens. 52.2 lb/ft^3; visc. 1200-1600 cps (1% gum in 1% KCl sol'n.); pH 7.0; surf. tens. 75 dynes/cm; 11% moisture; readily biodeg.
Toxicology: LD50 (oral, rat) > 5000 mg/kg; excessive dust inhalation may cause respiratory irritation; dry powd. may cause eye irritation
Precaution: Not flamm., but powd. will burn if involved in a fire; spills are slippery; incompat. with strong oxidizers.

KELTROL® 1000. [Kelco]
Chem. Descrip.: Xanthan gum
CAS 11138-66-2; EINECS 234-394-2
Uses: High microbiological purity grade thickener, stabilizer for toothpaste, pharmaceuticals
Regulatory: FDA 21CFR §172.695; EEC E415 compliance
Properties: Wh. to tan powd., sl. odor; 175 μ particle size; water-sol.; bulk dens. ≈ 50 lb/ft^3; visc. 1400 cps (1%); pH 7.0; readily biodeg.
Toxicology: LD50 (oral, rat) > 5000 mg/kg; excessive dust inhalation may cause respiratory irritation; dry powd. may cause eye irritation
Precaution: Not flamm., but powd. will burn if involved in a fire; spills are slippery; incompat. with strong oxidizers.

KELTROL® BT. [Kelco]
Chem. Descrip.: Xanthan gum
CAS 11138-66-2; EINECS 234-394-2
Uses: Brine tolerant thickener, suspending agent, stabilizer for toothpaste, pharmaceuticals; excipient for OTC drugs; improved sol. in high salt systems
Regulatory: FDA 21CFR §172.695; FCC, NF, EEC E415 compliance; kosher
Properties: Cream to wh. gran. powd., sl. odor; ≥ 95% thru 80 mesh; sol. in hot or cold water; bulk dens. ≈ 50 lb/ft^3; visc. 1200-1600 cps (1% gum in 1% KCl sol'n.); pH 6.1-8.1 (1% aq.); 6-14% moisture; readily biodeg.
Toxicology: LD50 (oral, rat) > 5000 mg/kg; excessive dust inhalation may cause respiratory irritation; dry powd. may cause eye irritation
Precaution: Not flamm., but powd. will burn if involved in a fire; spills are slippery; incompat. with strong oxidizers.

KELTROL® CR. [Kelco]
Chem. Descrip.: Xanthan gum NF
CAS 11138-66-2; EINECS 234-394-2
Uses: Thickener, suspending and gelling agent for pharmacueticals, high dosage drugs, intermediate and low sol. drugs
Regulatory: FDA 21CFR §172.695; EEC E415 compliance
Properties: Wh. to tan powd., sl. odor; water-sol.; bulk dens. ≈ 50 lb/ft^3; pH neutral; readily biodeg.

Toxicology: LD50 (oral, rat) > 5000 mg/kg; excessive dust inhalation may cause respiratory irritation; dry powd. may cause eye irritation
Precaution: Not flamm., but powd. will burn if involved in a fire; spills are slippery; incompat. with strong oxidizers.

KELTROL® F. [Kelco]
Chem. Descrip.: Food-grade xanthan gum
CAS 11138-66-2; EINECS 234-394-2
Uses: Rapidly soluble stabilizer, thickener, emulsion stabilizer for creams, lotions, pharmaceuticals; binder in toothpaste; suspending agent
Regulatory: FDA 21CFR §172.695; EEC E415 compliance
Properties: Cream to wh. powd.; ≥ 92% thru 200 mesh; sol. in cold and hot water; swells in glycerin and propylene glycol; sp.gr. 1.5; bulk dens. 52.2 lb/ft^3; visc. 1200-1600 cps (1% gum in 1% KCl sol'n.); pH 7.0; surf. tens. 75 dynes/cm; 11% moisture; readily biodeg.
Toxicology: LD50 (oral, rat) > 5000 mg/kg; excessive dust inhalation may cause respiratory irritation; dry powd. may cause eye irritation
Precaution: Not flamm., but powd. will burn if involved in a fire; spills are slippery; incompat. with strong oxidizers.

KELTROL® GM. [Kelco]
Chem. Descrip.: Xanthan gum
CAS 11138-66-2; EINECS 234-394-2
Uses: Thickener, suspending agent, stabilizer for toothpaste, pharmaceuticals
Regulatory: FDA 21CFR §172.695; FCC, NF, EEC E415 compliance; kosher
Properties: Cream to wh. gran. powd., sl. odor; ≥ 95% thru 42 mesh, ≤ 25% thru 100 mesh; sol. in cold or hot water; bulk dens. ≈ 50 lb/ft^3; visc. 1200-1600 cps (1% gum in 1% KCl sol'n.); pH 6.1-8.0 (1% aq.); readily biodeg.
Toxicology: LD50 (oral, rat) > 5000 mg/kg; excessive dust inhalation may cause respiratory irritation; dry powd. may cause eye irritation
Precaution: Not flamm., but powd. will burn if involved in a fire; spills are slippery; incompat. with strong oxidizers.

KELTROL® RD. [Kelco]
Chem. Descrip.: Xanthan gum
CAS 11138-66-2; EINECS 234-394-2
Uses: Readily dispersible thickener, stabilizer used for toothpaste, pharmaceuticals
Regulatory: FDA 21CFR §172.695; EEC E415 compliance
Properties: Wh. to tan powd., sl. odor; 990 μ particle size; water-sol.; bulk dens. ≈ 50 lb/ft^3; visc. 1400 cps (1%); pH 7.0; readily biodeg.
Toxicology: LD50 (oral, rat) > 5000 mg/kg; excessive dust inhalation may cause respiratory irritation; dry powd. may cause eye irritation
Precaution: Not flamm., but powd. will burn if involved in a fire; spills are slippery; incompat. with strong oxidizers.

KELTROL® SF. [Kelco]
Chem. Descrip.: Xanthan gum

CAS 11138-66-2; EINECS 234-394-2
Uses: Altered rheology thickener, suspending agent, stabilizer for toothpaste, pharmaceuticals
Regulatory: FDA 21CFR §172.695; FCC, NF, EEC E415 compliance; kosher
Properties: Wh. to cream powd., sl. odor; ≥ 100% thru 60 mesh, ≥ 95% thru 80 mesh; sol. in cold or hot water; bulk dens. ≈ 50 lb/ft^3; visc. 800-1300 cps; pH 6.1-8.1; readily biodeg.
Toxicology: LD50 (oral, rat) > 5000 mg/kg; excessive dust inhalation may cause respiratory irritation; dry powd. may cause eye irritation
Precaution: Not flamm., but powd. will burn if involved in a fire; spills are slippery; incompat. with strong oxidizers.

KELTROL® T. [Kelco]
Chem. Descrip.: Xanthan gum
CAS 11138-66-2; EINECS 234-394-2
Uses: Thickener, suspending agent, flocculant, emulsion and foam stabilizer for pharmaceuticals, medicated syrups, elixirs, antacids, lotions, creams, toothpastes, oral min. oil emulsions; produces clear sol'ns.
Regulatory: FDA 21CFR §172.695; FCC, NF, EEC E415 compliance; kosher
Properties: Cream to wh. powd., sl. odor; 100% thru 60 mesh, ≥ 95% thru 80 mesh; sol. in hot or cold water; bulk dens. ≈ 50 lb/ft^3; visc. 1200-1600 cps (1% gum in 1% KCl sol'n.); pH 7.0 ± 1.0; readily biodeg.
Toxicology: LD50 (oral, rat) > 5000 mg/kg; excessive dust inhalation may cause respiratory irritation; dry powd. may cause eye irritation
Precaution: Not flamm., but powd. will burn if involved in a fire; spills are slippery; incompat. with strong oxidizers.

KELTROL® TF. [Kelco]
Chem. Descrip.: Xanthan gum
CAS 11138-66-2; EINECS 234-394-2
Uses: Rapidly soluble thickener, suspending agent, and emulsion and foam stabilizer for pharmaceuticals, medicated syrups, antacids, lotions, creams, toothpaste; suitable for clear systems
Regulatory: FDA 21CFR §172.695; FCC, NF, EEC E415 compliance; kosher
Properties: Cream to wh. powd., sl. odor; 100% thru 80 mesh, ≥ 92% thru 200 mesh; sol. in hot or cold water; bulk dens. ≈ 50 lb/ft^3; visc. 1200-1600 cps (1% gum in 1% KCl sol'n.); pH 7.0 ± 1.0; readily biodeg.
Toxicology: LD50 (oral, rat) > 5000 mg/kg; excessive dust inhalation may cause respiratory irritation; dry powd. may cause eye irritation
Precaution: Not flamm., but powd. will burn if involved in a fire; spills are slippery; incompat. with strong oxidizers.

KELVIS®. [Kelco]
Chem. Descrip.: Sodium alginate, refined
CAS 9005-38-3
Uses: Gellant, suspending agent, emulsifier, and stabilizer for pharmaceuticals, dental release agents; stabilizer for dentures and adhesive pads

Regulatory: FDA 21CFR §184.1724, GRAS; EEC E401 compliance
Properties: Ivory gran.; 150 mesh; water-sol.; sp.gr. 1.59; dens. 54.62 lb/ft³; visc. 760 cps (1%), 9000 cps (2%); ref. index 1.3343; pH 7; surf. tens. 62 dynes/cm; 13% moisture.

Kemester® 1418. [Witco/H-I-P]
Chem. Descrip.: Myristyl stearate
CAS 17661-50-6; EINECS 241-640-2
Uses: Emollient for pharmaceuticals.

Kemester® 5721. [Witco/H-I-P]
Chem. Descrip.: Tridecyl stearate
CAS 31556-45-3; EINECS 250-696-7
Uses: Emollient for pharmaceuticals
Properties: Gardner 1 max. color; m.p. 8 C; acid no. 2 max.; iodine no. 4 max.; sapon. no. 117-126.

Kemester® EGDL. [Witco/H-I-P]
Chem. Descrip.: Glycol dilaurate
CAS 624-04-4; EINECS 210-827-0
Uses: Emollient for pharmaceuticals.

Kemester® EGDS. [Witco/H-I-P]
Chem. Descrip.: Glycol distearate
CAS 627-83-8; EINECS 211-014-3
Uses: Opacifier, pearling additive, thickener for pharmaceuticals
Regulatory: FDA accepted
Properties: Gardner 2 max. solid; m.p. 60-63 C; acid no. 6 max.; iodine no. 1 max.; sapon. no. 190-200; 100% conc.

Kemester® EGMS. [Witco/H-I-P]
Chem. Descrip.: Glycol stearate
CAS 111-60-4; EINECS 203-886-9
Uses: Opacifier, pearling additive, thickener for pharmaceuticals
Properties: Gardner 1 solid; m.p. 56-60 C; acid no. 1; iodine no. 1 max.; sapon. no. 179-195.

Kemester® GDL. [Witco/H-I-P]
Chem. Descrip.: Glyceryl dilaurate
CAS 27638-00-2; EINECS 248-586-9
Uses: Emollient for pharmaceuticals.

Kemester® S20. [Witco/H-I-P]
Chem. Descrip.: Sorbitan laurate
Uses: For pharmaceuticals.

Kemester® S40. [Witco/H-I-P]
Chem. Descrip.: Sorbitan palmitate
CAS 26266-57-9; EINECS 247-568-8
Uses: Emulsifier for pharmaceuticals.

Kemester® S60. [Witco/H-I-P]
Chem. Descrip.: Sorbitan stearate
CAS 1338-41-6; EINECS 215-664-9
Uses: For pharmaceuticals.

Kemester® S65. [Witco/H-I-P]
Chem. Descrip.: Sorbitan tristearate
CAS 26658-19-5; EINECS 247-891-4
Uses: Emulsifier for pharmaceuticals.

Kemester® S80. [Witco/H-I-P]
Chem. Descrip.: Sorbitan oleate
CAS 1338-43-8; EINECS 215-665-4
Uses: For pharmaceuticals.

Kemester® S85. [Witco/H-I-P]
Chem. Descrip.: Sorbitan trioleate
CAS 26266-58-0; EINECS 247-569-3

Uses: For pharmaceuticals.

Kemstrene® 96.0% USP. [Witco/H-I-P]
Chem. Descrip.: Refined glycerin USP
CAS 56-81-5; EINECS 200-289-5
Uses: Humectant, solv.
Properties: Sp.gr. 1.25165 min; 96.0% purity.

Kemstrene® 99.0%. [Witco/H-I-P]
Chem. Descrip.: Refined glycerin USP
CAS 56-81-5; EINECS 200-289-5
Uses: Humectant, solv.
Properties: Sp.gr. 1.25945 min.; 99.0% purity.

Kemstrene® 99.7% USP. [Witco/H-I-P]
Chem. Descrip.: Refined glycerin USP
CAS 56-81-5; EINECS 200-289-5
Uses: Humectant, solv.
Properties: Sp.gr. 1.26124; 99.7% purity.

Kessco® 653. [Stepan; Stepan Canada]
Chem. Descrip.: Cetyl palmitate
CAS 540-10-3; EINECS 208-736-6
Uses: Syn. spermaceti wax, emollient, thickener, visc. booster for pharmaceutical creams and lotions; base material for stick prods.
Properties: Wh. flakes; sol. in boiling alcohol, ether, chloroform, other waxes, oils, hydrocarbons; insol. in water; m.p. 51-55 C; acid no. 2.0 max.; sapon. no. 109-117; nonionic.

Kessco CP. [Akzo Nobel bv]
Chem. Descrip.: Cetyl palmitate
CAS 540-10-3; EINECS 208-736-6
Uses: Replaces native spermaceti in pharmaceuticals
Properties: Flakes; nonionic.

Kessco® PEG 200 DL. [Stepan; Stepan Canada]
Chem. Descrip.: PEG-4 dilaurate
CAS 9005-02-1
Uses: Emulsifier, thickener, solubilizer, emollient, opacifier, spreading agent, wetting agent, dispersant for pharmaceuticals (ointments, suppositories), sunscreens
Properties: Lt. yel. liq.; sol. in IPA, acetone, CCl₄, ethyl acetate, toluol, IPM, wh. oil; water-disp.; sp.gr. 0.951; dens. 7.9 lb/gal; f.p. < 9C; HLB 5.9; acid no. 10.0 max.; iodine no. 9.0; sapon. no. 176-186; flash pt. (COC) 460 F; fire pt. 510 F; 100% act.

Kessco® PEG 200 DO. [Stepan; Stepan Canada]
Chem. Descrip.: PEG-4 dioleate
CAS 9005-07-6
Uses: Emulsifier, thickener, solubilizer, emollient, opacifier, spreading agent, wetting agent, dispersant for pharmaceuticals (ointments, suppositories), sunscreens
Properties: Lt. amber liq.; f.p. < -15 C; sol. in naptha, kerosene, IPA, acetone, CCl₄, ethyl acetate, toluol, IPM, peanut oil, wh. oil; water-disp.; sp.gr. 0.942; dens. 7.9 lb/gal; HLB 6.0; acid no. 10.0 max; sapon. no. 148-158; pH 5.0 (3%); flash pt. (COC) 545 F; nonionic.

Kessco® PEG 200 DS. [Stepan; Stepan Canada]
Chem. Descrip.: PEG-4 distearate
CAS 9005-08-7
Uses: Emulsifier, thickener, solubilizer, emollient,

opacifier, spreading agent, wetting agent, dispersant for pharmaceuticals (ointments, suppositories), sunscreens
Properties: Wh. to cream soft solid; sol. in naptha, kerosene, IPA, acetone, CCl_4, ethyl acetate, toluol, IPM, peanut oil, wh. oil; water-disp.; sp.gr. 0.9060 (65 C); HLB 5.0; m.p. 34 C; acid no. 10.0 max.; sapon. no. 153-162; pH 5.0 (3%); flash pt. (COC) 475 F; nonionic.

Kessco® PEG 200 ML. [Stepan; Stepan Canada]
Chem. Descrip.: PEG-4 laurate
CAS 9004-81-3
Uses: Emulsifier, thickener, solubilizer, emollient, opacifier, spreading agent, wetting agent, dispersant for pharmaceuticals (ointments, suppositories), sunscreens
Properties: Lt. yel. liq.; f.p. < 5 C; sol. in IPA, acetone, CCl_4, ethyl acetate, toluol, IPM, water-disp.; sp.gr. 0.985; dens. 8.2 lb/gal; HLB 9.8; acid no. 5.0 max.; sapon. no. 132-142; pH 4.5; flash pt. (COC) 385 F; nonionic.

Kessco® PEG 200 MO. [Stepan; Stepan Canada]
Chem. Descrip.: PEG-4 oleate
CAS 9004-96-0; EINECS 233-293-0
Uses: Emulsifier, thickener, solubilizer, emollient, opacifier, spreading agent, wetting agent, dispersant for pharmaceuticals (ointments, suppositories), sunscreens
Properties: Lt. amber liq.; f.p. < -15 C; sol. in IPA, acetone, CCl_4, ethyl acetate, toluol, water-disp.; sp.gr. 0.973; dens. 8.1 lb/gal; HLB 8.0; acid no. 5.0 max.; sapon. no. 115-124; pH 5.0; flash pt. (COC) 395 F; nonionic.

Kessco® PEG 200 MS. [Stepan; Stepan Canada]
Chem. Descrip.: PEG-4 stearate
CAS 9004-99-3; EINECS 203-358-8
Uses: Emulsifier, thickener, solubilizer, emollient, opacifier, spreading agent, wetting agent, dispersant for pharmaceuticals (ointments, suppositories), sunscreens
Properties: Wh. to cream soft solid; sol. in IPA, acetone, CCl_4, ethyl acetate, toluol, IPM, peanut oil; water-disp.; sp.gr. 0.9360 (65 C); HLB 7.9; m.p. 31 C; acid no. 5.0 max.; sapon. no. 120-129; flash pt. (COC) 410 F; nonionic.

Kessco® PEG 300 DL. [Stepan; Stepan Canada]
Chem. Descrip.: PEG-6 dilaurate
CAS 9005-02-1
Uses: Emulsifier, thickener, solubilizer, emollient, opacifier, spreading agent, wetting agent, dispersant for pharmaceuticals (ointments, suppositories), sunscreens
Properties: Lt. yel. liq.; f.p. < 13 C; sol. in naptha, IPA, acetone, toluol, IPM; water-disp.; sp.gr. 0.975; dens. 8.1 lb/gal; HLB 9.8; acid no. 10.0 max.; sapon. no. 148-158; flash pt. (COC) 475 F; nonionic.

Kessco® PEG 300 DO. [Stepan; Stepan Canada]
Chem. Descrip.: PEG-6 dioleate
CAS 9005-07-6
Uses: Emulsifier, thickener, solubilizer, emollient, opacifier, spreading agent, wetting agent, dis-

persant for pharmaceuticals (ointments, suppositories), sunscreens
Properties: Lt. amber liq.; f.p. < -5 C; sol. in IPA, acetone, CCl_4, ethyl acetate, toluol, IPM, peanut oil; water-disp.; sp.gr. 0.962; dens. 8.0 lb/gal; HLB 7.2; acid no. 10.0 max.; sapon. no. 128-137; pH 5.0; flash pt. (COC) 510 F; nonionic.

Kessco® PEG 300 DS. [Stepan; Stepan Canada]
Chem. Descrip.: PEG-6 distearate
CAS 9005-08-7
Uses: Emulsifier, thickener, solubilizer, emollient, opacifier, spreading agent, wetting agent, dispersant for pharmaceuticals (ointments, suppositories), sunscreens
Properties: Wh. to cream soft solid; sol. in naptha, kerosene, IPA, acetone, CCl_4, ethyl acetate, toluol, IPM, peanut oil, wh. oil; water-disp.; HLB 6.5; m.p. 32 C; acid no. 10.0 max.; sapon. no. 130-139; pH 5.0; nonionic.

Kessco® PEG 300 ML. [Stepan; Stepan Canada]
Chem. Descrip.: PEG-6 laurate
CAS 9004-81-3; EINECS 219-136-9
Uses: Emulsifier, thickener, solubilizer, emollient, opacifier, spreading agent, wetting agent, dispersant for pharmaceuticals (ointments, suppositories), sunscreens
Properties: Lt. yel. liq.; f.p. < 8 C; sol. in IPA, acetone, CCl_4, ethyl acetate, toluol; water-disp.; sp.gr. 1.011; dens. 8.4 lb/gal; HLB 11.4; acid no. 5.0 max.; sapon. no. 104-114; pH 4.5; flash pt. (COC) 445 F; nonionic.

Kessco® PEG 300 MO. [Stepan; Stepan Canada]
Chem. Descrip.: PEG-6 oleate
CAS 9004-96-0
Uses: Emulsifier, thickener, solubilizer, emollient, opacifier, spreading agent, wetting agent, dispersant for pharmaceuticals (ointments, suppositories), sunscreens
Properties: Lt. amber liq.; f.p. < -5 C; sol. in IPA, acetone, CCl_4, ethyl acetate, toluol; water-disp.; sp.gr. 0.998; dens. 8.3 lb/gal; HLB 9.6; acid no. 5.0 max.; sapon. no. 94-102; pH 5.0 (3% disp.); flash pt. (COC) 450 F; nonionic.

Kessco® PEG 300 MS. [Stepan; Stepan Canada]
Chem. Descrip.: PEG-6 stearate
CAS 9004-99-3
Uses: Emulsifier, thickener, solubilizer, emollient, opacifier, spreading agent, wetting agent, dispersant for pharmaceuticals (ointments, suppositories), sunscreens
Properties: Wh. to cream soft solid; sol. in IPA, acetone, CCl_4, ethyl acetate, toluol, IPM, peanut oil; water-disp.; sp.gr. 0.9660 (65 C); HLB 9.7; m.p. 28 C; acid no. 5.0 max.; sapon. no. 97-105; pH 5.0 (3% disp.); flash pt. (COC) 475 F; nonionic.

Kessco® PEG 400 DL. [Stepan; Stepan Canada]
Chem. Descrip.: PEG-8 dilaurate
CAS 9005-02-1
Uses: Emulsifier, thickener, solubilizer, emollient, opacifier, spreading agent, wetting agent, dispersant for pharmaceuticals (ointments, suppositories), sunscreens

Properties: Lt. yel. liq.; f.p. 18 C; sol. in naptha, IPA, acetone, CCl₄, ethyl acetate, toluol, IPM, peanut oil; water-disp.; sp.gr. 0.990; dens. 8.3 lb/gal; HLB 9.8; acid no. 10.0 max.; sapon. no. 127-137; flash pt. (COC) 480 F; nonionic.

Kessco® PEG 400 DO. [Stepan; Stepan Canada]
Chem. Descrip.: PEG-8 dioleate
CAS 9005-07-6
Uses: Emulsifier, thickener, solubilizer, emollient, opacifier, spreading agent, wetting agent, dispersant for pharmaceuticals (ointments, suppositories), sunscreens
Properties: Lt. amber liq.; f.p. < 7 C; sol. in naptha, IPA, acetone, CCl₄, ethyl acetate, toluol, IPM, peanut oil; water-disp.; sp.gr. 0.977; dens. 8.1 lb/gal; HLB 8.5; acid no. 10.0 max.; sapon. no. 113-122; pH 5.0; flash pt. (COC) 520 F; nonionic.

Kessco® PEG 400 DS. [Stepan; Stepan Canada]
Chem. Descrip.: PEG-8 distearate
CAS 9005-08-7
Uses: Emulsifier, thickener, solubilizer, emollient, opacifier, spreading agent, wetting agent, dispersant for pharmaceuticals (ointments, suppositories), sunscreens
Properties: Wh. to cream soft solid; sol. in naptha, IPA, acetone, CCl₄, ethyl acetate, toluol, IPM, peanut oil, wh. oil; water-disp; sp.gr. 0.9390 (65 C); HLB 8.5; m.p. 36 C; acid no. 10.0 max.; sapon. no. 115-124; pH 5.0 (3% disp.); flash pt. (COC) 500 F; 100% act.

Kessco® PEG 400 ML. [Stepan; Stepan Canada]
Chem. Descrip.: PEG-8 laurate
CAS 9004-81-3; EINECS 253-458-0
Uses: Emulsifier, thickener, solubilizer, emollient, opacifier, spreading agent, wetting agent, dispersant for pharmaceuticals (ointments, suppositories), sunscreens
Properties: Lt. yel. liq.; f.p. 12 C; sol. in water, IPA, acetone, CCl₄, ethyl acetate, toluol; sp.gr. 1.028; dens. 8.6 lb/gal; HLB 13.1; acid no. 5.0 max.; sapon. no. 86-96; flash pt. (COC) 475 F; nonionic.

Kessco® PEG 400 MO. [Stepan; Stepan Canada]
Chem. Descrip.: PEG-8 oleate
CAS 9004-96-0
Uses: Emulsifier, thickener, solubilizer, emollient, opacifier, spreading agent, wetting agent, dispersant for pharmaceuticals (ointments, suppositories), sunscreens
Properties: Lt. amber liq.; f.p. < 10 C; sol. in IPA, acetone, CCl₄, ethyl acetate, toluol; water-disp.; sp.gr. 1.013; dens. 8.4 lb/gal; HLB 11.4; acid no. 5.0 max.; sapon. no. 80-89; pH 5.0 (3% disp.); flash pt. (COC) 510 F; nonionic.

Kessco® PEG 400 MS. [Stepan; Stepan Canada]
Chem. Descrip.: PEG-8 stearate
CAS 9004-99-3
Uses: Emulsifier, thickener, solubilizer, emollient, opacifier, spreading agent, wetting agent, dispersant for pharmaceuticals (ointments, suppositories), sunscreens
Properties: Wh. to cream soft solid; sol. in IPA, acetone, CCl₄, ethyl acetate, toluol; water-disp.;

sp.gr. 0.9780 (65 C); HLB 11.6; m.p. 32 C; acid no. 5.0 max.; sapon. no. 83-92; pH 5.0 (3% disp.); flash pt. (COC) 480 F; nonionic.

Kessco® PEG 600 DL. [Stepan; Stepan Canada]
Chem. Descrip.: PEG-12 dilaurate
CAS 9005-02-1
Uses: Emulsifier, thickener, solubilizer, emollient, opacifier, spreading agent, wetting agent, dispersant for pharmaceuticals (ointments, suppositories), sunscreens
Properties: Liq.; sol. in IPA, acetone, CCl₄, ethyl acetate, toluol, IPM; water-disp.; sp.gr. 0.9820 (65 C); f.p. 24 C; HLB 11.7; acid no. 10.0 max.; sapon. no. 102-112; flash pt. (COC) 465 F; 100% act.

Kessco® PEG 600 DO. [Stepan; Stepan Canada]
Chem. Descrip.: PEG-12 dioleate
CAS 9005-07-6; EINECS 288-459-5
Uses: Emulsifier, thickener, solubilizer, emollient, opacifier, spreading agent, wetting agent, dispersant for pharmaceuticals (ointments, suppositories), sunscreens
Properties: Lt. amber liq.; f.p. 19 C; sol. in IPA, acetone, CCl₄, ethyl acetate, toluol, IPM, peanut oil; water-disp.; sp.gr. 1.001; dens. 8.3 lb/gal; HLB 10.5; acid no. 10.0 max.; sapon. no. 92-102; pH 5.0 (3% disp.); flash pt. (COC) 495 F; nonionic.

Kessco® PEG 600 DS. [Stepan; Stepan Canada]
Chem. Descrip.: PEG-12 distearate
CAS 9005-08-7
Uses: Emulsifier, thickener, solubilizer, emollient, opacifier, spreading agent, wetting agent, dispersant for pharmaceuticals (ointments, suppositories), sunscreens
Properties: Wh. to cream soft solid; sol. in IPA, acetone, CCl₄, ethyl acetate, toluol, IPM, peanut oil; water-disp.; sp.gr. 0.9670 (65 C); HLB 10.7; m.p. 39 C; acid no. 10.0 max.; sapon. no. 93-102; pH 5.0 (3% disp.); flash pt. (COC) 490 F; 100% act.

Kessco® PEG 600 ML. [Stepan; Stepan Canada]
Chem. Descrip.: PEG-12 laurate
CAS 9004-81-3
Uses: Emulsifier, thickener, solubilizer, emollient, opacifier, spreading agent, wetting agent, dispersant for pharmaceuticals (ointments, suppositories), sunscreens
Properties: Lt. yel. liq.; sol. in water, Na₂SO₄, IPA, acetone, CCl₄, ethyl acetate, toluol; sp.gr. 1.050; dens. 8.8 lb/gal; f.p. 23 C; HLB 14.6; acid no. 5.0 max.; sapon. no. 64-74; flash pt. (COC) 475 F; 100% act.

Kessco® PEG 600 MO. [Stepan; Stepan Canada]
Chem. Descrip.: PEG-12 oleate
CAS 9004-96-0
Uses: Emulsifier, thickener, solubilizer, emollient, opacifier, spreading agent, wetting agent, dispersant for pharmaceuticals (ointments, suppositories), sunscreens
Properties: Lt. amber liq.; f.p. 23 C; sol. in water, IPA, acetone, CCl₄, ethyl acetate, toluol; sp.gr. 1.037; dens. 8.7 lb/gal; HLB 13.5; acid no. 5.0

max.; sapon. no. 60-69; pH 5.0 (3% disp.); flash pt. (COC) 525 F; nonionic.

Kessco® PEG 600 MS. [Stepan; Stepan Canada]
Chem. Descrip.: PEG-12 stearate
CAS 9004-99-3
Uses: Emulsifier, thickener, solubilizer, emollient, opacifier, spreading agent, wetting agent, dispersant for pharmaceuticals (ointments, suppositories), sunscreens
Properties: Wh. to cream soft solid; sol. in water, IPA, acetone, CCl_4, ethyl acetate, toluol; sp.gr. 1.000 (65 C); HLB 13.6; m.p. 37 C; acid no. 5.0 max.; sapon. no. 61-70; pH 5.0 (3% disp.); flash pt. (COC) 480 F; nonionic.

Kessco® PEG 1000 DL. [Stepan; Stepan Canada]
Chem. Descrip.: PEG-20 dilaurate
CAS 9005-02-1
Uses: Emulsifier, thickener, solubilizer, emollient, opacifier, spreading agent, wetting agent, dispersant for pharmaceuticals (ointments, suppositories), sunscreens
Properties: Cream soft solid; f.p. 38 C; sol. in water, IPA, acetone, CCl_4, ethyl acetate; toluol, IPM; sp.gr. 1.015 (65 C); HLB 14.5; acid no. 10.0 max.; sapon. no. 68-78; flash pt. (COC) 475 F; nonionic.

Kessco® PEG 1000 DO. [Stepan; Stepan Canada]
Chem. Descrip.: PEG-20 dioleate
CAS 9005-07-6
Uses: Emulsifier, thickener, solubilizer, emollient, opacifier, spreading agent, wetting agent, dispersant for pharmaceuticals (ointments, suppositories), sunscreens
Properties: Cream soft solid; f.p. 37 C; sol. in water, IPA, acetone, CCl_4, ethyl acetate, toluol; sp.gr. 1.005 (65 C); HLB 13.1; acid no. 10.0 max.; sapon. no. 64-74; pH 5.0 (3% disp.); flash pt. (COC) 505 F; nonionic.

Kessco® PEG 1000 DS. [Stepan; Stepan Canada]
Chem. Descrip.: PEG-20 distearate
CAS 9005-08-7
Uses: Emulsifier, thickener, solubilizer, emollient, opacifier, spreading agent, wetting agent, dispersant for pharmaceuticals (ointments, suppositories), sunscreens
Properties: Cream wax; sol. in water, IPA, acetone, CCl_4, ethyl acetate, toluol; sp.gr. 1.005 (65 C); HLB 12.3; m.p. 40 C; acid no. 10.0 max.; sapon. no. 65-74; pH 5.0 (3% disp.); flash pt. (COC) 485 F; nonionic.

Kessco® PEG 1000 ML. [Stepan; Stepan Canada]
Chem. Descrip.: PEG-20 laurate
CAS 9004-81-3
Uses: Emulsifier, thickener, solubilizer, emollient, opacifier, spreading agent, wetting agent, dispersant for pharmaceuticals (ointments, suppositories), sunscreens
Properties: Cream soft solid; f.p. 40 C; sol. in water, propylene glycol (hot), Na_2SO_4, IPA, acetone, CCl_4, ethyl acetate, toluol; sp.gr. 1.035 (65 C); HLB 16.5; acid no. 5.0 max.; sapon. no. 41-51; flash pt. (COC) 490; nonionic.

Kessco® PEG 1000 MO. [Stepan; Stepan Canada]

Chem. Descrip.: PEG-20 oleate
CAS 9004-96-0
Uses: Emulsifier, thickener, solubilizer, emollient, opacifier, spreading agent, wetting agent, dispersant for pharmaceuticals (ointments, suppositories), sunscreens
Properties: Cream soft solid; f.p. 39 C; sol. in water, Na_2SO_4 (5%), IPA, acetone, CCl_4, ethyl acetate, toluol; sp.gr. 1.035 (65 C); HLB 15.4; acid no. 5.0 max.; sapon. no. 40-49; pH 5.0; flash pt. (COC) 515 F; nonionic.

Kessco® PEG 1000 MS. [Stepan; Stepan Canada]
Chem. Descrip.: PEG-20 stearate
CAS 9004-99-3
Uses: Emulsifier, thickener, solubilizer, emollient, opacifier, spreading agent, wetting agent, dispersant for pharmaceuticals (ointments, suppositories), sunscreens
Properties: Cream wax; sol. in water, Na_2SO_4 (5%), IPA, acetone, CCl_4, ethyl acetate, toluol; sp.gr. 1.030 (65 C); HLB 15.6; m.p. 41 C; acid no. 5.0 max.; sapon. no. 40-48; pH 5.0 (3% disp.); flash pt. (COC) 475 F; nonionic.

Kessco® PEG 1540 DL. [Stepan; Stepan Canada]
Chem. Descrip.: PEG-32 dilaurate
CAS 9005-02-1
Uses: Emulsifier, thickener, solubilizer, emollient, opacifier, spreading agent, wetting agent, dispersant for pharmaceuticals (ointments, suppositories), sunscreens
Properties: Cream wax; f.p. 42 C; sol. in water, Na_2SO_4 (5%); hot in propylene glycol, IPA, acetone, CCl_4, ethyl acetate, toluol; sp.gr. 1.04 (65 C); HLB 15.7; acid no. 10.0 max.; sapon. no. 48-56; pH 4.5 (3% disp.); flash pt. (COC) 450 F; nonionic.

Kessco® PEG 1540 DO. [Stepan; Stepan Canada]
Chem. Descrip.: PEG-32 dioleate
CAS 9005-07-6
Uses: Emulsifier, thickener, solubilizer, emollient, opacifier, spreading agent, wetting agent, dispersant for pharmaceuticals (ointments, suppositories), sunscreens
Properties: Cream wax; f.p. 44 C; sol. in water, propylene glycol, Na_2SO_4; hot in IPA, acetone, CCl_4, ethyl acetate, toluol; sp.gr. 1.025 (65 C); HLB 15.0; acid no. 10.0 max.; sapon. no. 45-55; pH 5.0 (3% disp.); flash pt. (COC) 480 F; nonionic.

Kessco® PEG 1540 DS. [Stepan; Stepan Canada]
Chem. Descrip.: PEG-32 distearate
CAS 9005-08-7
Uses: Emulsifier, thickener, solubilizer, emollient, opacifier, spreading agent, wetting agent, dispersant for pharmaceuticals (ointments, suppositories), sunscreens
Properties: Cream wax; sol. in water, IPA, acetone, CCl_4, ethyl acetate, toluol; sp.gr. 1.015 (65 C); HLB 14,8; m.p. 45 C; acid no. 10.0 max.; sapon. no. 49-58; pH 5.0; flash pt. (COC) 490 F; nonionic.

Kessco® PEG 1540 ML. [Stepan; Stepan Canada]
Chem. Descrip.: PEG-32 laurate
CAS 9004-81-3

Uses: Emulsifier, thickener, solubilizer, emollient, opacifier, spreading agent, wetting agent, dispersant for pharmaceuticals (ointments, suppositories), sunscreens

Properties: Cream wax; f.p. 46 C; sol. in water, Na_2SO_4 (5%); sol. hot in propylene glycol, IPA, acetone, CCl_4, ethyl acetate, toluol; sp.gr. 1.06 (65 C); HLB 17.6; acid no. 5.0 max.; sapon. no. 26-36; pH 4.5 (3% disp.); flash pt. (COC) 445 F; nonionic.

Kessco® PEG 1540 MO. [Stepan; Stepan Canada]
Chem. Descrip.: PEG-32 oleate
CAS 9004-96-0
Uses: Emulsifier, thickener, solubilizer, emollient, opacifier, spreading agent, wetting agent, dispersant for pharmaceuticals (ointments, suppositories), sunscreens
Properties: Cream wax; f.p. 45 C; sol. in water, propylene glycol, Na_2SO_4; sol. hot in IPA, acetone, CCl_4, ethyl acetate, toluol; sp.gr. 1.050 (65 C); HLB 17.0; f.p. 47 C; acid no. 5.0 max.; sapon. no. 28-37; pH 5.0 (3% disp.); flash pt. (COC) 520 F; nonionic.

Kessco® PEG 1540 MS. [Stepan; Stepan Canada]
Chem. Descrip.: PEG-32 stearate
CAS 9004-99-3
Uses: Emulsifier, thickener, solubilizer, emollient, opacifier, spreading agent, wetting agent, dispersant for pharmaceuticals (ointments, suppositories), sunscreens
Properties: Cream wax; sol. in water, Na_2SO_4 (5%), IPA, acetone, CCl_4, ethyl acetate, toluol; sp.gr. 1.050 (65 C); HLB 17.3; m.p. 47 C; acid no. 5.0 max.; sapon. no. 27-36; pH 5.0; flash pt. (COC) 495 F; nonionic.

Kessco® PEG 4000 DL. [Stepan; Stepan Canada]
Chem. Descrip.: PEG-75 dilaurate
CAS 9005-02-1
Uses: Emulsifier, thickener, solubilizer, emollient, opacifier, spreading agent, wetting agent, dispersant for pharmaceuticals (ointments, suppositories), sunscreens
Properties: Cream wax; f.p. 52 C; sol. in water, Na_2SO_4 (5%); sol. hot in propylene glycol, IPA, acetone, CCl_4, ethyl acetate, toluol; sp.gr. 1.065 (65 C); HLB 17.6; acid no. 5.0 max.; sapon. no. 20-30; pH 4.5 (3% disp.); flash pt. (COC) 495 F; nonionic.

Kessco® PEG 4000 DO. [Stepan; Stepan Canada]
Chem. Descrip.: PEG-75 dioleate
CAS 9005-07-6
Uses: Emulsifier, thickener, solubilizer, emollient, opacifier, spreading agent, wetting agent, dispersant for pharmaceuticals (ointments, suppositories), sunscreens
Properties: Cream wax; f.p. 49 C; sol. in water, propylene glycol, Na_2SO_4; sol. hot in IPA, acetone, CCl_4, ethyl acetate, toluol; sp.gr. 1.060 (65 C); HLB 17.8; acid no. 5.0 max.; sapon. no. 19-27; pH 5.0; flash pt. (COC) 500 F; nonionic.

Kessco® PEG 4000 DS. [Stepan; Stepan Canada]
Chem. Descrip.: PEG-75 distearate

CAS 9005-08-7
Uses: Emulsifier, thickener, solubilizer, emollient, opacifier, spreading agent, wetting agent, dispersant for pharmaceuticals (ointments, suppositories), sunscreens
Properties: Cream wax; sol. in water, Na_2SO_4 (5%), IPA, acetone, CCl_4, ethyl acetate, toluol; sp.gr. 1.060 (65 C); HLB 17.3; m.p. 51 C; acid no. 5.0 max.; sapon. no. 19-27; pH 5.0 (3% disp.); flash pt. (COC) 515 F; nonionic.

Kessco® PEG 4000 ML. [Stepan; Stepan Canada]
Chem. Descrip.: PEG-75 laurate
CAS 9004-81-3
Uses: Emulsifier, thickener, solubilizer, emollient, opacifier, spreading agent, wetting agent, dispersant for pharmaceuticals (ointments, suppositories), sunscreens
Properties: Cream wax; f.p. 55 C; sol. in water, Na_2SO_4 (5%); sol. hot in propylene glycol, IPA, acetone, CCl_4, ethyl acetate, toluol; sp.gr. 1.075 (65 C); HLB 18.8; acid no. 5.0 max.; sapon. no. 9-18; pH 4.5; flash pt. (COC) 515 F; nonionic.

Kessco® PEG 4000 MO. [Stepan; Stepan Canada]
Chem. Descrip.: PEG-75 oleate
CAS 9004-96-0
Uses: Emulsifier, thickener, solubilizer, emollient, opacifier, spreading agent, wetting agent, dispersant for pharmaceuticals (ointments, suppositories), sunscreens
Properties: Cream wax; f.p. 55 C; sol. in water, propylene glycol, Na_2SO_4; sol. hot in IPA, acetone, CCl_4, ethyl acetate, toluol; sp.gr. 1.075 (65 C); HLB 18.3; acid no. 5.0 max.; sapon. no. 10-18; pH 5.0; flash pt. (COC) 495 F; nonionic.

Kessco® PEG 4000 MS. [Stepan; Stepan Canada]
Chem. Descrip.: PEG-75 stearate
CAS 9004-99-3
Uses: Emulsifier, thickener, solubilizer, emollient, opacifier, spreading agent, wetting agent, dispersant for pharmaceuticals (ointments, suppositories), sunscreens
Properties: Cream wax; sol. in water, Na_2SO_4 (5%), IPA, acetone, CCl_4, ethyl acetate, toluol; sp.gr. 1.075 (64 C); HLB 18.6; m.p. 56 C; acid no. 5.0 max.; sapon. no. 10-18; pH 5.0; flash pt. (COC) 465 F; nonionic.

Kessco® PEG 6000 DL. [Stepan; Stepan Canada]
Chem. Descrip.: PEG-150 dilaurate
CAS 9005-02-1
Uses: Emulsifier, thickener, solubilizer, emollient, opacifier, spreading agent, wetting agent, dispersant for pharmaceuticals (ointments, suppositories), sunscreens
Properties: Cream wax; f.p. 57 C; sol. in water, Na_2SO_4 (5%); sol. hot in propylene glycol, IPA, acetone, CCl_4, ethyl acetate, toluol; sp.gr. 1.077 (65 C); HLB 18.7; m.p. 56 C; acid no. 9.0 max.; sapon. no. 12-20; pH 4.5 (3% disp.); flash pt. (COC) 435 F; nonionic.

Kessco® PEG 6000 DO. [Stepan; Stepan Canada]
Chem. Descrip.: PEG-150 dioleate
CAS 9005-07-6

Uses: Emulsifier, thickener, solubilizer, emollient, opacifier, spreading agent, wetting agent, dispersant for pharmaceuticals (ointments, suppositories), sunscreens

Properties: Cream wax; f.p. 56 C; sol. in water, propylene glycol, Na_2SO_4 (5%); sol. hot in IPA, acetone, CCl_4, ethyl acetate, toluol; sp.gr. 1.070 (65 C); HLB 18.3; acid no. 9.0 max.; sapon. no. 13-21; pH 5.0 (3% disp.); flash pt. 500 F; nonionic.

Kessco® PEG 6000 DS. [Stepan; Stepan Canada]
Chem. Descrip.: PEG-150 distearate
CAS 9005-08-7
Uses: Emulsifier, thickener, solubilizer, emollient, opacifier, spreading agent, wetting agent, dispersant for pharmaceuticals (ointments, suppositories), sunscreens
Properties: Cream wax; sol. in propylene glycol, Na_2SO_4 (5%), IPA, acetone, CCl_4, ethyl acetate, toluol; sp.gr. 1.075 (65 C); HLB 18.4; m.p. 55 C; acid no. 9.0 max.; sapon. no. 14-20; pH 5.0 (3% disp.); flash pt. (COC) 475 F; 100% act.

Kessco® PEG 6000 ML. [Stepan; Stepan Canada]
Chem. Descrip.: PEG-150 laurate
CAS 9004-81-3
Uses: Emulsifier, thickener, solubilizer, emollient, opacifier, spreading agent, wetting agent, dispersant for pharmaceuticals (ointments, suppositories), sunscreens
Properties: Cream wax; f.p. 61 C; sol. in water, Na_2SO_4 (5%); sol. hot in propylene glycol, IPA, acetone, CCl_4, ethyl acetate, toluol; sp.gr. 1.085 (65 C); HLB 19.2; acid no. 5.0 max.; sapon. no. 7-13; pH 4.5; nonionic.

Kessco® PEG 6000 MO. [Stepan; Stepan Canada]
Chem. Descrip.: PEG-150 oleate
CAS 9004-96-0
Uses: Emulsifier, thickener, solubilizer, emollient, opacifier, spreading agent, wetting agent, dispersant for pharmaceuticals (ointments, suppositories), sunscreens
Properties: Cream wax; f.p. 59 C; sol. in water, propylene glycol, Na_2SO_4 (5%); sol. hot in IPA, acetone, CCl_4, ethyl acetate, toluol; sp.gr. 1.085 (65 C); HLB 19.0; acid no. 5.0 max.; sapon. no. 7-13; pH 5.0; flash pt. 470 F; nonionic.

Kessco® PEG 6000 MS. [Stepan; Stepan Canada]
Chem. Descrip.: PEG-150 stearate
CAS 9004-99-3
Uses: Emulsifier, thickener, solubilizer, emollient, opacifier, spreading agent, wetting agent, dispersant for pharmaceuticals (ointments, suppositories), sunscreens
Properties: Cream wax; sol. in water, propylene glycol, Na_2SO_4 (5%), IPA, acetone, CCl_4, ethyl acetate, toluol; sp.gr. 1.080 (65 C); HLB 18.8; m.p. 61 C; acid no. 5.0 max.; sapon. no. 7-13; pH 5.0 (3% disp.); flash pt. (COC) 480 F; nonionic.

Kessco PGMS. [Stepan]
Chem. Descrip.: Propylene glycol stearate
CAS 1323-39-3; EINECS 215-354-3
Uses: Aux. emulsifier, opacifier; used in suppositories

Properties: Wh. to cream flake; m.p. 35 C; HLB 3.4; acid no. 3 max.

Kessco® Glycerol Distearate 386F. [Stepan Food Ingreds.]
Chem. Descrip.: Glyceryl distearate
CAS 1323-83-7; EINECS 215-359-0
Uses: Food-grade emulsifier for pharmaceutical use
Properties: Wh. to off-wh. waxy flake, typ. mild fatty odor; insol. in water; sol. in IPA, min. oil; partly sol. in peanut oil; m.p. 56-59 C; HLB 2.4; acid no. 5.0 max.; sapon. no. 182-188; flash pt. (COC) 450 F; 100% conc.

Kessco® Glyceryl Monostearate Pure. [Stepan; Stepan Canada]
Chem. Descrip.: Glyceryl stearate
Uses: Emollient, emulsifier, opacifier, bodying agent for pharmaceutical topical creams, lotions, and ointments, antiperspirants, sunscreens
Properties: Wh. flakes, typ. mild fatty odor; insol. in water; sol. in IPA, min. oil; partly sol. in peanut oil; m.p. 56.5-58.5 C; HLB 3.8; acid no. 3.0; iodine no. 0.5 max.; sapon. no. 168-176; flash pt. (COC) 410 F; 100% act.

Keycel®. [Protein Tech. Int'l.]
Chem. Descrip.: Powd. cellulose
CAS 9004-34-6; EINECS 232-674-9
Uses: Functional ingred. or noncaloric bulking agent for pharmaceutical applics.

Kimiloid HV. [Kimitsu Chem. Industries; Unipex]
Chem. Descrip.: Propylene glycol alginate
CAS 9005-37-2
Uses: Visc. promoter, shape-making agent, stabilizer for dentifrices
Regulatory: Meets official std. of Food Additives Regs., FCC, NF
Properties: Wh. or creamy powd.; 40 mesh pass; visc. 150 cp min.; pH 3.0-4.5; < 15% water.

Kimiloid NLS-K. [Kimitsu Chem. Industries; Unipex]
Chem. Descrip.: Propylene glycol alginate
CAS 9005-37-2
Uses: Visc. promoter, shape-making agent, stabilizer for pharmaceutical ointments
Regulatory: Meets official std. of Food Additives Regs., FCC, NF
Properties: Wh. or creamy powd.; 40 mesh pass; visc. 30-60 cp; pH 3.0-4.5; < 15% water.

Kimitsu Acid. [Kimitsu Chem. Industries; Unipex]
Chem. Descrip.: Alginic acid
CAS 9005-32-7; EINECS 232-680-1
Uses: Tablet disintegrant and for edible uses
Properties: Wh. powd., 80 mesh pass; pH 1.5-3.5; < 15% water.

Kimitsu Algin I-3. [Kimitsu Chem. Industries; Unipex]
Chem. Descrip.: Algin
CAS 9005-38-3
Uses: Visc. promoter, shape-making agent, stabilizer for pharmaceutical use (ointment base, dentifrice, substitute blood plasma)
Regulatory: Meets Japanese official std., FCC, NF
Properties: Wh. or creamy powd.; 80 mesh pass; visc. 320-380 cp; pH neutral; < 15% water.

Kimitsu Algin I-7. [Kimitsu Chem. Industries; Unipex]
Chem. Descrip.: Algin
CAS 9005-38-3
Uses: Visc. promoter, shape-making agent, stabilizer for pharmaceutical use (dental impressions)
Regulatory: Meets Japanese official std., FCC, NF
Properties: Wh. or creamy powd.; 80 mesh pass; visc. 650-750 cp; pH neutral; < 15% water.

Kimitsu Algin IS. [Kimitsu Chem. Industries; Unipex]
Chem. Descrip.: Algin
CAS 9005-38-3
Uses: Visc. promoter, shape-making agent, stabilizer for pharmaceutical use (dental impressions)
Regulatory: Meets Japanese official std., FCC, NF
Properties: Wh. or creamy powd.; 80 mesh pass; visc. 950-1100 cp; pH neutral; < 15% water.

Klearol®. [Witco/Petroleum Spec.]
Chem. Descrip.: Wh. min. oil NF
Uses: Emollient in pharmaceuticals
Regulatory: FDA 21CFR §172.878, §178.3620a
Properties: Water-wh., odorless, tasteless; sp.gr. 0.822-0.833; visc. 7-10 cSt (40 C); pour pt. -7 C; flash pt. 138 C.

Klucel® 'F' Grades. [Hercules/Aqualon]
Chem. Descrip.: Premium grades hydroxypropylcellulose NF; grades designated 'FF' also meet FCC specs.
CAS 9004-64-2
Uses: Surface-active thickener, stabilizer, filmformer, suspending agent, protective colloid; inert ingred. in drug prods.; film coating, binder for tablets; in medicinal elixirs, lotions, emulsions capsules, sustained-release dosage forms
Regulatory: FDA 21CFR §172.870
Properties: Off-wh. powd., tasteless; 85% min. thru 30 mesh, 99% min. thru 20 mesh; water-sol.; dissolves easily in many polar org. solvs.; soften. pt. 100-150 C; pH 5.0-8.5; surf. tens. 43.6 dynes/cm (0.1%); 5% max. moisture; nonionic
Toxicology: Nontoxic orally; nonirritating to skin; may cause transient eye irritation.

Kollidon®. [BASF AG]
Chem. Descrip.: PVP
CAS 9003-39-8; EINECS 201-800-4
Uses: Solubilizers, crystallization retarders, stabilizers for antibiotic suspensions, etc.; binders for tablets, dispersants.

Kollidon® 12PF, 17PF. [BASF]
Uses: Polymeric stabilizer for pharmaceutical injectables.

Kollidon® 25, 30, 90. [BASF]
Uses: Tablet coatings, binders, suspension stabilizers, thickening agents, and excipients for pharmaceutical use.

Kollidon® CL. [BASF; BASF AG]
Chem. Descrip.: Crospovidone
CAS 9003-39-8
Uses: Tablet-disintegrating agent, suspension stabilizer, excipient for pharmaceuticals; antidiarrheal agent
Properties: Insol. but swells in water; bulk dens. 0.363 g/cc.

Kollidon® CLM. [BASF]
Uses: Excipient and tablet disintegrant for pharmaceuticals.

Kollidon® USP. [BASF]
Chem. Descrip.: PVP
CAS 9003-39-8; EINECS 201-800-4
Uses: Stable, inert polymer used in tablet mfg., liq. dosages, ophthalmic preps., topical applics., diagnostic aids, dental adhesives, plaster casts, electrode gels, as plasma extender; tablet binder; granulating/coating agent; modifies visc.

Koraid PSM. [Kaopolite]
Chem. Descrip.: Alumino-silicate, modified
EINECS 231-545-4
Uses: Suspension aid for pigments and abrasive particles in water-based systems without increasing visc.; used for pharmaceuticals
Properties: Wh. microgran.; disp. in water with good shear; pH 9-10 (5%).

Korthix H-NF. [Kaopolite]
Chem. Descrip.: Bentonite
CAS 1302-78-9; EINECS 215-108-5
Uses: Thickener, protective colloid, emulsifier, suspending agent; bacteria-controlled grade for pharmaceutical use.

Koster Keunen Auto-Oxidized Beeswax. [Koster Keunen]
Chem. Descrip.: Oxidized beeswax
Uses: Esp. designed for depilatories
Properties: Wax; sp.gr. 0.950-0.980; m.p. 61-67 C; acid no. 25-35; iodine no. 1-10; sapon. no. 90-120; flash pt. > 250 C.

Koster Keunen Beeswax. [Koster Keunen]
Chem. Descrip.: Beeswax, white and yel.
Uses: Emulsifier, thickener, emollient for creams, lotions, salves, ointments; sustained release pharmaceuticals
Regulatory: FDA 21CFR §184.1973, 184.1975
Properties: Wax; sol. 24.2 g/100 ml in benzene; sp.gr. 0.950-0.960; m.p. 61-65 C; acid no. 17-24; iodine no. 8-11; cloud pt. < 65 C; flash pt. 242-250 C; ref. index 1.4398-1.4451; dielec. const. 3.1-3.3.

Koster Keunen Carnauba. [Koster Keunen]
Chem. Descrip.: Carnauba
CAS 8015-86-9; EINECS 232-399-4
Uses: Used for salves, creams, ointments; pill coatings
Regulatory: FDA 21CFR §182.1978
Properties: Wax; sol. (g/100 cc): 1.690 g chloroform, 0.610 g xylene, 0.518 g benzene, 0.440 g turpentine, 0.324 g acetone; sp.gr. 0.996-0.998; m.p. 82.5-86 C; acid no. 2-6; iodine no. 7-14; sapon. no. 78-88; flash pt. > 300 C; ref. index 1.463; dielec. const. 2.67-4.20.

Koster Keunen Carnauba, Powd. [Koster Keunen]
Chem. Descrip.: Carnauba
CAS 8015-86-9; EINECS 232-399-4
Uses: Used for tablets, coatings
Properties: Powd.; 120 mesh.

Koster Keunen Ceresine. [Koster Keunen]
Chem. Descrip.: Ceresine

CAS 8001-75-0; EINECS 232-290-1
Uses: Thickener used for creams, lotions, ointments, salves, pharmaceuticals
Regulatory: FDA §175.105
Properties: Wax; sp.gr. 0.88-0.92; m.p. various grades from 133-163 F; acid no. 0; sapon. no. < 1; ref. index 1.4416-1.4465; dielec. const. 2.15-2.33.

Koster Keunen Emulsifying Wax. [Koster Keunen]
Chem. Descrip.: Emulsifying wax prepared from cetearyl alcohol contg. a POE deriv. of a fatty acid ester of sorbitan
CAS 97069-99-0
Uses: Emulsifier, thickener used for topical pharmaceutical creams
Regulatory: FDA approved
Properties: Creamy-wh. solid, char. odor; sol. in hydrocarbons, ether, chloroform, alcohol; m.p. 48-52 C; acid no. < 2.5; iodine no. < 3.5; sapon. no. < 14; hyd. no. 178-192; pH 5.5-7.0 (3% disp.).

Koster Keunen Microcrystalline Waxes. [Koster Keunen]
Chem. Descrip.: Microcrystalline wax
CAS 64742-42-3; EINECS 264-038-1
Uses: Wax, coating agent used for pharmaceuticals
Regulatory: FDA §172.886, 178.3710
Properties: Wh. to amber wax; sp.gr. 0.90-0.94; visc. 50-100 (210 F); m.p. 140-190 F; acid no. 0-0.2; iodine no. 0.-1.5; sapon. no. 0-2; flash pt. > 425 F; fire pt. > 550 F.

Koster Keunen Ozokerite. [Koster Keunen]
Chem. Descrip.: Ozokerite
CAS 8021-55-4; EINECS 265-134-6
Uses: Thickener used for pharmaceutical ointments
Regulatory: FDA approved
Properties: Wax; sol. (g/100 g): 12.99 carbon bisulfide, 11.83 g petrol. ether (75 C), 6.06 g turpentine (160 C), 3.95 g xylene (137 C), 2.83 g toluene (109 C), 2.42 g chloroform; sp.gr. 0.85-0.95; m.p. various grades from 149-190 F; acid no. 0; iodine no. 7-9; sapon. no. 0; ref. index 1.440 (60 C); dielec. const. 2.37-2.55.

Koster Keunen Paraffin Wax. [Koster Keunen]
Chem. Descrip.: Paraffin
CAS 8002-74-2; EINECS 232-315-6
Uses: Wax used for pharmaceutical ointments and salves
Regulatory: FDA 21CFR §172.615, 175.250, 175.300
Properties: Wax; sol. (g/100 cc): 40 g benzene, 9 g min. oil, 3 g dichloroethane, 0.4 g IPA; m.p. various grades from 118-165 F; ref. index 1.4219-1.4357.

Koster Keunen Substitute Beeswax. [Koster Keunen]
Chem. Descrip.: Syn. beeswax
CAS 97026-94-0
Uses: Used where pure beeswax not required; for creams, lotions, ointments, salves; sustained release pharmaceuticals
Properties: Wax; m.p. 62-65 C; acid no. 17-24.

Koster Keunen Synthetic Japan Wax. [Koster Keunen]
Chem. Descrip.: Syn. Japan wax
CAS 67701-27-3
Uses: Used for pharmaceuticals
Properties: Wax; sol. in hot alcohol, carbon disulfide, chloroform, ether, benzene, petrol. ether, isopropyl ether, naphtha, pyridine, toluene, xylene, turpentine; insol. in water; sp.gr. 0.975-0.984; m.p. 50-56 C; acid no. 6-20; iodine no. 4-15; sapon. no. 210-237; flash pt. > 200 C; ref. index 1.450-1.4560 (60 C); dielec. const. 3.1-3.2.

Koster Keunen Synthetic Spermaceti. [Koster Keunen]
Chem. Descrip.: Syn. spermaceti (cetyl palmitate and other esters)
CAS 136097-97-7; EINECS 241-640-2
Uses: Emollient, moisturizer, thickener, gellant for mfg. of ointments, pharmaceuticals
Regulatory: FDA approved
Properties: Pastilles; sol. in boiling alcohol, chloroform, carbon disulfide, volatile oils; sp.gr. 0.940-0.946; visc. 6.7-7.4 (100 C); m.p. 45-49 C; acid no. 0-0.5; iodine no. < 3; sapon. no. 116-125; flash pt. > 240 C; ref. index 1.440 (60 C).

KS-2 Shiitake Mycelium Extract KS2EXT. [Garuda Int'l.]
Chem. Descrip.: Shiitake mycelium extract from *Lentinus edodes* with potency of 3.2% KS-2 polysaccharides
Uses: KS-2 peptidomannans, lentinan actives; used to formulate health food and pharmaceutical capsules, tablets
Properties: Whitish-brn. fine powd.; min. 20 mesh or finer; partly sol. in water
Storage: 24 mo shelf life.

L

Labrafac® CM10. [Gattefosse]
Chem. Descrip.: PEG-8 caprylic/capric glycerides
CAS 85536-08-9
Uses: Surfactant for oral SE drug delivery systems; bioavailability enhancer, emulsifier, solubilizer for pharmaceutical orals, topicals, vaginals, rectals, and nasals, soft or hard gelatin capsules
Properties: Gardner < 5 oily liq., faint odor; sol. in veg. oil, alcohol, chloroform, methylene chloride; partly sol. in propylene glycol; partly disp. in water; sp.gr. 1.000-1.040 (20 C); HLB 10; acid no. < 2; iodine no. < 2; sapon. no. 160-200; hyd. no. 115-155; ref. index 1.430-1.485 (20 C); nonionic
Toxicology: LD0 (oral, rat) > 2 g/kg
Storage: Preserve in orig. container; prevent exposure to air, light, heat, and moisture.

Labrafac® Hydro. [Gattefosse]
Chem. Descrip.: Caprylic/capric triglyceride PEG-4 complex
Uses: Hydrophilic rancidless oil, solv., bioavailability enhancer, emulsifier, solubilizer for pharmaceutical orals, topicals, vaginals, rectals, and nasals, creams, lotions, ointments
Properties: Gardner < 5 oily liq., faint odor; sol. in veg. oil, alcohol; partly disp. in water; HLB 4-5; acid no. < 2; iodine no. < 3; sapon. no. 265-285; nonionic
Toxicology: LD0 (oral, rat) > 20 ml/kg; sl. skin and eye irritant.

Labrafac® Hydro WL 1219. [Gattefosse; Gattefosse SA]
Chem. Descrip.: Caprylic/capric triglycerides PEG-4 esters
Uses: Hydrophilic oil for pharmaceutical formulations
Properties: Liq.; HLB 4.0; acid no. < 2; iodine no. < 2; sapon. no. 265-285; 100% conc.; nonionic
Toxicology: LD50 (oral, rat) > 20 ml/kg; sl. irritating to skin and eyes.

Labrafac® LIPO. [Gattefosse]
Chem. Descrip.: Caprylic/capric triglyceride
CAS 65381-09-1; EINECS 265-724-3
Uses: Non-rancidifying, temp. stable sat. lipophilic solv., superfatting agent for pharmaceutical and veterinary emulsions and microemulsions, aerosols, capsules, gels, creams, lotions, ointments
Properties: Gardner < 1 oily liq., odorless to faint odor; acid no. < 0.2; iodine no. < 2; sapon. no. 320-

340
Toxicology: LD50 (oral, rat) > 10 ml/kg; sl. eye irritant, nonirritating to skin.

Labrafac® Lipophile WL 1349. [Gattefosse]
Chem. Descrip.: Caprylic/capric triglyceride
CAS 65381-09-1; EINECS 265-724-3
Uses: Superfatting agent for pharmaceutical emulsions and microemulsions
Properties: Liq.
Toxicology: LD50 (oral, rat) > 10 ml/kg; sl. irritating to eyes; nonirritating to skin.

Labrafil® Isostearique. [Gattefosse]
Chem. Descrip.: Triisostearin PEG-6 esters
Uses: Solv., amphiphilic agent for improving drug delivery; nonrancidifying excipient for aerosols, nasal preps., creams
Properties: Gardner < 5 oily liq., faint odor; HLB 3-4; acid no. < 2; iodine no. < 15; sapon. no. 150-170; nonionic
Toxicology: LD50 (oral, rat) > 20 ml/kg; nonirritating to skin and eyes.

Labrafil® M 1944 CS. [Gattefosse; Gattefosse SA]
Chem. Descrip.: Apricot kernel oil PEG-6 esters
CAS 97488-91-0
Uses: Hydrophilic oil for topicals, injectables, orals, nasals, aerosols; bioavailability enhancer, emulsifier, excipient, solubilizer, vehicle; for oral liq. SE drug delivery systems, microemulsions, hard shell/soft gelatin capsules
Regulatory: U.S., Japan, Europe, French pharmacopeia compliance
Properties: Gardner < 5 oily liq. (40 C), faint odor; very sol. in chloroform, methylene chloride, min. oils; sol. in n-hexane; disp. in water; sp.gr. 0.935-0.955 (20 C); visc. 75-95 mPa•s (20 C); HLB 4.0; acid no. < 2; iodine no. 79-89; sapon. no. 155-169; hyd. no. 45-65; ref. index 1.465-1.475 (20 C); pH 4.5-6.0 (10% aq.); 100% conc.; nonionic
Toxicology: LD0 (oral, rat) > 20 ml/kg; nontoxic; nonirritating to skin
Storage: Store in orig. container; prevent exposure to air, light, heat, and moisture; if partial crystallization occurs, reheat to 45 C.

Labrafil® M 1966 CS. [Gattefosse]
Chem. Descrip.: Almond oil PEG-6 esters
Uses: Amphiphilic agent improving drug delivery; nonionic.

Labrafil® M 1969 CS. [Gattefosse; Gattefosse SA]

138

Chem. Descrip.: Peanut oil PEG-6 esters
Uses: Hydrophilic oil for pharmaceuticals; amphiphilic agent improving drug delivery
Properties: Liq.; HLB 4.0; acid no. ≤ 2; iodine no. 70-90; sapon. no. 150-165; 100% conc.; nonionic
Toxicology: LD0 (oral, rat) > 5 g/kg.

Labrafil® M 1980 CS. [Gattefosse; Gattefosse SA]
Chem. Descrip.: Olive oil PEG-6 esters
CAS 103819-46-1
Uses: Hydrophilic oil for pharmaceutical formulations; amphiphilic agent improving drug delivery
Properties: Liq.; HLB 4.0; acid no. ≤ 2; iodine no. 60-80; sapon. no. 50-170; 100% conc.; nonionic
Toxicology: LD0 (oral, rat) > 20 ml/kg.

Labrafil® M 2125 CS. [Gattefosse; Gattefosse SA]
Chem. Descrip.: Corn oil PEG-6 esters
CAS 85536-08-9
Uses: Hydrophilic oil for pharmaceuticals; amphiphilic agent improving drug delivery; solubilizer, cosurfactant, oily dispersions vehicle; for oral sol'ns., nasal sol'ns., creams, aerosols, emulsions, softgel capsules, hard shell capsules
Regulatory: U.S., Japan, Europe, French pharmacopeia compliance
Properties: Gardner < 5 oily liq. (45 C), faint odor; sol. in chloroform, methylene chloride, min. oils; disp. in water; insol. in ethanol; sp.gr. 0.935-0.955; visc. 70-90 mPa•s; HLB 4.0; acid no. < 2; iodine no. 100-110; sapon. no. 156-170; hyd. no. 45-65; ref. index 1.465-1.475; 100% conc.; nonionic
Toxicology: LD0 (oral, rat) > 20 ml/kg
Storage: Store in orig. container; prevent exposure to air, light, heat, and moisture; if partial crystallization occurs, reheat to 45 C.

Labrafil® M 2130 BS. [Gattefosse; Gattefosse SA]
Chem. Descrip.: Hydrog. palm/palm kernel oil PEG-6 esters
Uses: Hydrophilic wax for pharmaceutical formulations; amphiphilic agent for improving drug delivery
Properties: Solid; drop pt. 30.5-35.5 C; HLB 4.0; acid no. < 2; iodine no. < 2; sapon. no. 162-176; 100% conc.; nonionic
Toxicology: LD0 (oral, rat) > 20 ml/kg.

Labrafil® M 2130 CS. [Gattefosse; Gattefosse SA]
Chem. Descrip.: Palm kernel oil, palm oil, PEG-6, and hydrog. palm/palm kernel oil PEG-6 esters
Uses: Hydrophilic wax for pharmaceutical/veterinary formulations; bioavailability enhancer for oral use (hard shell capsule); cutaneous absorption enhancer for penetration of active drugs through the skin (lotions, creams), rectal and vaginal suppositories
Regulatory: French pharmacopeia compliance
Properties: Gardner < 5 doughy solid, faint odor; sol. in chloroform, methylene chloride; partly sol. in ethanol; disp. in water; insol. in min. oils; drop pt. 33-38 C; HLB 4.0; acid no. < 2; iodine no. < 2; sapon. no. 190-204; hyd. no. 65-85; 100% conc.; nonionic
Toxicology: LD0 (oral, rat) > 2 g/kg; nonirritating to skin and eyes.

Labrafil® M 2735 CS. [Gattefosse; Gattefosse SA]
Chem. Descrip.: Triolein PEG-6 esters
Uses: Hydrophilic hydrog. oil; excipient for pharmaceutical formulations
Properties: Liq.; HLB 4.0; acid no. ≤ 2; iodine no. 70-85; sapon. no. 150-170; 100% conc.; nonionic
Toxicology: LD0 (oral, rat) > 20 ml/kg; sl. irritating to skin and eyes.

Labrafil® WL 2609 BS. [Gattefosse]
Chem. Descrip.: Corn oil PEG-8 esters
Uses: Bioavailability enhancer, solubilizer, excipient, emulsifier for pharmaceutical liqs. and capsules; dissolves poorly water-sol. drugs
Properties: Oily liq.; sol. in veg. oil; partly sol. in propylene glycol, alcohol; partly disp. in water; HLB 6-7; nonionic.

Labrasol. [Gattefosse; Gattefosse SA]
Chem. Descrip.: PEG-8 caprylic/capric glycerides
CAS 85536-07-8
Uses: Hydrophilic oil, solv., excipient, solubilizer for pharmaceutical/veterinary preps.; surfactant for microemulsions; wetting agent; penetration enhancer; improves topical, rectal, and oral absorption; bioavailability enhancer for orals
Properties: Gardner < 5 oily liq., faint odor; sol. in water, veg. oil, propylene glycol; very sol. in ethanol, chloroform, methylene chloride; sp.gr. 1.060-1.070; visc. 80-110 mPa•s; HLB 14.0; acid no. < 1; iodine no. < 2; sapon. no. 85-105; ref. index 1.450-1.470; 100% conc.; nonionic
Toxicology: LD50 (oral, rat) 22 g/kg; sl. ocular irritant at 0.1 ml; nonirritating to skin
Storage: Preserve in org. container; prevent exposure to air, light, heat, and moisture.

Lactic Acid 88% USP/FCC. [Tri-K Industries]
Chem. Descrip.: Lactic acid USP/FCC
CAS 50-21-5
Uses: pH adjustor, humectant for pharmaceuticals; mild antiseptic props.
Regulatory: FDA 21CFR §184.1061, GRAS; kosher certified
Properties: Colorless to yel. liq., odorless; sol. in water; m.w. 90.1; sp.gr. 1.20; visc. 28.6 cps; pour pt. -10 C; b.p. dec.; pH 0; nonflamm.; 88-90% assay; hazardous waste; do not dump, spill or flush into sewers, public waterways, or the environment; dispose by neutralization or biodegradation
Toxicology: LD50 (oral, rat) 7600 mg/kg, pract. nontoxic, (dermal, rabbit) > 7940 mg/kg, pract. nontoxic; corrosive to eyes; severely irritating to skin and respiratory tract; ingestion can cause nausea, vomiting, vascular collapse; avoid breathing mist
Precaution: 50% lactic acid is corrosive to mild steel; combustion prods. incl. CO, CO_2, smoke
Storage: Keep container closed.

Lactitol MC. [Xyrofin UK]
Chem. Descrip.: Lactitol monohydrate, food grade
CAS 81025-04-9
Uses: Food grade sweetener for pharmaceutical

applics.; stable to air and heat

Properties: Wh. cryst. powd., odorless, mild sweet taste; sol. in water ($\approx$ 1.7 g/ml); m.w. 362.37; m.p. 95-105 C; pH 4.5-7 (0.1 g/ml aq.); 98% min. act.

Storage: 1 yr stability in original sealed pkg. stored below 25 C and < 65% r.h.; marginally hygroscopic.

Lafil WL 3254. [Gattefosse SA]

Chem. Descrip.: Polyglyceryl isostearostearate

Uses: Superfatting agent for pharmaceutical emulsions

Properties: Drop pt. 35.5-40.5 C; HLB 3.0; acid no. < 1; iodine no. $\leq$ 6; sapon. no. 155-175

Toxicology: LD0 (oral, rat) > 2 g/kg; sl. irritating to skin and eyes.

Lameform® TGI. [Henkel/Cospha; Henkel KGaA/ Cospha; Grünau GmbH]

Chem. Descrip.: Polyglyceryl-3 diisostearate

CAS 66082-42-6; EINECS 291-548-1

Uses: Emulsifier, emollient for pharmaceutical w/o emulsions and creams; good stability to oxidation

Regulatory: DAC compliance

Properties: Yel. visc. liq., sl. fatty odor; HLB 6.0; acid no. 3 max.; sapon. no. 140-160; hyd. no. 190-220; 100% conc.; nonionic

Storage: 1 yr min. storage life in sealed original containers under dry conditions; if cream is removed in portions and at low temps., care should be taken to ensure that the prod. is removed evenly.

Lamegin® EE Range. [Grünau GmbH]

Chem. Descrip.: Acetic acid esters of mono- and diglycerides of fatty acids

Uses: Coating agent, emulsifier for drug industry; nonionic.

Lamegin® GLP 10, 20. [Grünau GmbH]

Chem. Descrip.: Hydrog. tallow glyceride lactate

CAS 68990-06-7; EINECS 273-576-6

Uses: Emulsifier and plasticizer for drugs

Properties: Solid; 100% conc.; nonionic.

Lamegin® NSL. [Grünau GmbH]

Chem. Descrip.: Sodium stearoyl lactylate

CAS 25383-99-7; EINECS 246-929-7

Uses: Emulsifier for drugs

Properties: Powd.; 100% conc.; anionic

Unverified

Lanacet® 1705. [Henkel/Organic Prods.]

Chem. Descrip.: Acetylated lanolin USP

CAS 61788-48-5; EINECS 262-979-2

Uses: Emollient, superfatting agent

Properties: Solid; sol. in IPM, min. oil; 100% conc.; nonionic.

Lanaetex CO. [Lanaetex Prods.]

Chem. Descrip.: Castor oil USP

CAS 8001-79-4; EINECS 232-293-8

Uses: Emollient, lubricant, oleaginous vehicle.

Lan-Aqua-Sol 50. [Fanning]

Chem. Descrip.: PEG-75 lanolin

CAS 8039-09-6

Uses: Emulsifier for pharmaceutical emulsions; emollient, superfatting agent, conditioner for skin prods.; solubilizer, wetting agent, dispersing aid

Properties: Gardner 10 max. color, faint odor; sol. in ethanol, water; sl. sol. in glycerin, ethyl acetate; sp.gr. 1.00-1.04 (50/4 C); acid no. 3 max.; sapon. no. 9 max.; pH 5.5-7.0 (4% aq.); anionic.

Lan-Aqua-Sol 100. [Fanning]

Chem. Descrip.: PEG-75 lanolin

CAS 8039-09-6

Uses: Emulsifier for pharmaceutical emulsions; emollient, superfatting agent, conditioner for skin prods.; solubilizer, wetting agent, dispersing aid

Properties: Gardner 12 max. color, faint odor; sol. in ethanol, water; sl. sol. in ethyl acetate, glycerin; sp.gr. 1.02-1.07 (50/4 C); m.p. 45-51 C; acid no. 5 max.; sapon. no. 18 max.; pH 5.5-7.0 (4% aq.); anionic.

Lanbritol Wax N21. [Ronsheim & Moore]

Chem. Descrip.: Cetearyl alcohol, ceteth-12, and oleth-12

Uses: SE wax, emulsifier for pharmaceuticals

Properties: Wh. waxy solid; m.p. 45-53 C; 100% conc.; nonionic; biodeg.

Lanesta P. [Westbrook Lanolin]

Chem. Descrip.: Isopropyl lanolate with 15 ppm BHT (as stabilizer)

CAS 63393-93-1; EINECS 264-119-1

Uses: Nongreasy emollient, moisturizer; base and carrier for medical salves

Properties: Yel.-brn. soft buttery solid, faint char. odor; sol. in oil, IPM; mostly sol. in min. oil; partly sol. in acetone, anhyd. ethanol and IPA; insol. in water; m.p. 28-38 C; acid no. 4 max.; iodine no. 6-20; sapon. no. 125-155; flash pt. > 100 C; substantially biodeg.

Toxicology: Extremely low toxicity; LD50 (oral, rat) > max. pract. dose of 16 g/kg; nonirritating to skin and eyes

Precaution: Nonflamm., but will burn if strongly heated

Storage: Store in cool place; avoid heating above 80 C for prolonged periods; storage may produce separation-homogeneity restored on melting; 2 yrs storage life.

Lanesta SA-30. [Westbrook Lanolin]

Chem. Descrip.: Isopropyl lanolate with 150 ppm BHT (as stabilizer)

CAS 63393-93-1; EINECS 264-119-1

Uses: Nongreasy emollient, moisturizer; base and carrier for medical salves

Properties: Pale yel. soft buttery solid, faint char. odor; sol. in oil, IPM; mostly sol. in min. oil; partly sol. in acetone, anhyd. ethanol and IPA; insol. in water; m.p. 30-40 C; acid no. 18 max.; sapon. no. 140-160; hyd. no. 48-68; flash pt. > 100 C; substantially biodeg.

Toxicology: Extremely low toxicity; LD50 (oral, rat) > max. pract. dose of 16 g/kg; nonirritating to skin and eyes

Precaution: Nonflamm., but wil burn if strongly heated

Storage: Store in cool place; avoid heating above 80 C for prolonged periods; storage may produce separation-homogeneity restored on melting; 2

yrs storage life.

Laneto 50. [R.I.T.A.]
Chem. Descrip.: PEG-75 lanolin
CAS 8039-09-6
Uses: Emulsifier, emollient, conditioner, moisturizer, stabilizer, and solubilizer for ointments, sun preps., veterinary prods.
Properties: Amber liq., char. odor; water-sol.; sp.gr. 1.00-1.10; acid no. 1 max.; sapon. no. 10 max.; 50 ± 1% water; nonionic.

Laneto 100. [R.I.T.A.]
Chem. Descrip.: PEG-75 lanolin
CAS 61790-81-6
Uses: Emulsifier, emollient, conditioner, moisturizer, stabilizer, and solubilizer for ointments, sun preps., veterinary prods.
Properties: Amber solid; nonionic.

Laneto 100-Flaked. [R.I.T.A.]
Chem. Descrip.: PEG-75 lanolin
CAS 61790-81-6
Uses: Emollient, lubricant, solubilizer, emulsifier, plasticizer for pharmaceuticals, ointments, sun preps.; promotes emolliency and surface activity in aq. and hydroalcoholic systems
Properties: Yel. flakes, char. odor; water sol.; m.p. 45 C min.; acid no. 2 max.; iodine no. 8 max.; sapon. no. 20 max.; 100% conc.; nonionic.

Laneto AWS. [R.I.T.A.]
Chem. Descrip.: PPG-12-PEG-50 lanolin
CAS 68458-88-8
Uses: Emulsifier, emollient, conditioner, moisturizer, stabilizer, and solubilizer for ointments, sun preps., veterinary prods.
Properties: Amber liq.; sol. in water and alcohol; HLB 16.0; 100% conc.; nonionic.

Lanette® 14. [Henkel/Cospha; Henkel Canada; Henkel KGaA/Cospha]
Chem. Descrip.: Myristyl alcohol
CAS 112-72-1; EINECS 204-000-3
Uses: Emollient, consistency agent for pharmaceutical o/w and w/o creams, emulsions, sticks
Properties: Wh. flakes; sp.gr. 0.82-0.83 (40 C); m.p. 35-38 C; acid no. < 0.1; iodine no. < 0.3; sapon. no. < 0.3; hyd. no. 255-262; flash pt. 148 C; 100% conc.; nonionic
Storage: 3 yr min. storage life in original sealed containers at temps. below 40 C, protected from moisture.

Lanette® 16. [Henkel/Cospha; Henkel Canada; Henkel KGaA/Cospha]
Chem. Descrip.: Cetyl alcohol
CAS 36653-82-4; EINECS 253-149-0
Uses: Hydrophilic emollient, consistency agent, visc. regulator for pharmaceutical o/w creams, ointments, emulsions, sticks
Regulatory: Ph.Eur., NF, DAB compliance
Properties: Off-wh. flakes; sp.gr. 0.815-0.830 (40 C); m.p. 46-49 C; acid no. 0.1 max.; iodine no. < 0.5; sapon. no. < 0.5; hyd. no. 225-235; flash pt. 157 C; 0.1% max. water; nonionic
Toxicology: Toxicologically harmless; nonirritant to skin

Storage: 1 yr min. storage life in original sealed containers at temps. below 40 C, protected from moisture.

Lanette® 18. [Henkel/Cospha; Henkel KGaA/Cospha]
Chem. Descrip.: Stearyl alcohol
CAS 112-92-5; EINECS 204-017-6
Uses: Hydrophilic emollient, consistency agent, visc. regulator for pharmaceutical o/w creams, emulsions, sticks
Regulatory: Ph.Eur., NF, DAB, Italian Ph., French Ph., JSCI compliance
Properties: Off-wh. waxy flakes; m.p. 55-57.5 C; acid no. 0.1 max.; iodine no. 1 max.; sapon. no. 0.5 max.; hyd. no. 203-210; 100% conc.; nonionic
Storage: 1 yr min. storage life in original sealed containers at temps. below 40 C, protected from moisture.

Lanette® 18-22. [Henkel/Cospha]
Chem. Descrip.: C18-22 fatty alcohol
Uses: Emollient, consistency agent for pharmaceutical o/w and w/o creams, emulsions, sticks
Properties: Flakes; 100% conc.; nonionic.

Lanette® 18 DEO. [Henkel/Cospha; Henkel Canada]
Chem. Descrip.: Stearyl alcohol
CAS 112-92-5; EINECS 204-017-6
Uses: Emollient, consistency agent for pharmaceutical o/w and w/o creams, emulsions, sticks
Properties: Flakes; acid no. < 0.1; iodine no. < 1.0; sapon. no. < 0.5.

Lanette® 22 Flakes. [Henkel KGaA/Cospha]
Chem. Descrip.: Behenyl alcohol
CAS 661-19-8; EINECS 211-546-6
Uses: Emollient, consistency agent for pharmaceutical o/w and w/o creams, emulsions, sticks
Properties: Wh. to pale ylsh. hydrophilic waxy fused flakes; solid. pt. 64-67 C; acid no. 0.2 max.; iodine no. 1 max.; sapon. no. 0.5 max.; hyd. no. 170-180; 100% conc.; nonionic
Storage: 1 yr min. storage stability in sealed original containers at temps. below 40 C.

Lanette® E. [Henkel/Cospha; Henkel/Functional Prods; Henkel Canada; Henkel KGaA/Cospha]
Chem. Descrip.: Sodium cetearyl sulfate
CAS 68955-20-4
Uses: Emulsifier and wetting agent for pharmaceutical o/w emulsions, creams, and ointments
Regulatory: DAB, Austrian pharmacopoeia compliance
Properties: Wh. to lt. yel. powd., faint char. odor; dens. 150-250 g/l; pH 6.5-7.5 (1%); 90% min. act.; anionic
Storage: 1 yr storage stability in sealed orig. containers at temps. below 30 C in a dry envrionment.

Lanette® N. [Henkel/Cospha; Henkel Canada; Henkel KGaA/Cospha]
Chem. Descrip.: Cetearyl alcohol (90%) and sodium cetearyl sulfate (10%), stabilized with 0.12% phosphate buffer
Uses: Self-emulsifying base, consistency agent for pharmaceutical o/w creams, ointments, and liq. liniments

Regulatory: DAB, Austrian Ph., JCID compliance
Properties: Wh. flakes, faint char. odor; acid no. 1 max.; iodine no. 3 max.; hyd. no. 187-205; pH 6.5-8.0 (1%); 1.4% max. water; anionic
Storage: 1 yr storage stability in sealed orig. containers at temps. below 30 C in dry environment.

Lanette® O. [Henkel/Cospha; Henkel KGaA/Cospha]
Chem. Descrip.: Cetearyl alcohol USP/NF/EP/DAB/JSCI
CAS 67762-27-0; EINECS 267-008-6
Uses: Hydrophilic emollient, base, consistency factor, visc. regulator for pharmaceutical ointments, creams, o/w emulsions
Regulatory: NF, Ph.Eur., and DAB compliance
Properties: Wh. flakes; insol. in water; m.p. 49-56 C; acid no. 0.1 max.; iodine no. 0.5 max.; sapon. no. 1 max.; hyd. no. 215-225; 100% conc.; nonionic
Storage: 1 yr min. storage life in sealed containers at temps. below 40 C, protected against humidity.

Lanette® W. [Henkel/Cospha]
Chem. Descrip.: Cetearyl alcohol and sodium lauryl sulfate
Uses: SE base, consistency agent for mfg. of ointments, creams and liniments
Regulatory: BP compliance for emulsifying wax
Properties: Gran.; 100% conc.; anionic.

Lanette® Wax SX, SXBP. [Henkel/Cospha]
Chem. Descrip.: Cetearyl alcohol and sodium C12-15 alcohols sulfate (SXBP complies to B.P. specifications)
Uses: O/w emulsifier, SE wax for use in pharmaceutical preps., creams, ointments and lotions
Properties: Cream to pale yel. waxy flakes; faint char. odor; partially sol. in alcohol, almost insol. in water; m.p. 50 C; 100% conc.; anionic; biodeg.

Lanexol AWS. [Croda Inc.]
Chem. Descrip.: PPG-12-PEG-50 lanolin
CAS 68458-88-8
Uses: Emollient, conditioner, cleanser, superfatting agent, foam stabilizer, and lubricant for alcoholic and aq. compositions, topical pharmaceuticals
Use level: 1-5%
Properties: Amber visc. liq.; sol. in oil, water, ethanol and mixts.; disp. in propylene glycol; cloud pt. 65-80 C (1% aq.); pour pt. 13 C max.; acid no. 2 max.; iodine no. 10 max.; sapon. no. 10-20; pH 6.0-7.0 (1% aq.); 97% conc.; nonionic
Toxicology: LD50 (oral, rat) 32 g/kg; moderate skin irritant, minimal eye irritant.

Lanfrax® 1776. [Henkel/Cospha; Henkel Canada]
Chem. Descrip.: USP lanolin wax fraction
CAS 68201-49-0; EINECS 269-220-4
Uses: W/o emulsifier, emollient, crystallization inhibitor, and film-former for creams, lotions, suntan preps.
Properties: Lt. yel. waxy solid; 100% conc.; nonionic.

Lanfrax® 1779. [Henkel/Cospha; Henkel Canada]
Chem. Descrip.: Lanolin wax

CAS 68201-49-0; EINECS 269-220-4
Uses: W/o emulsifier, emollient, conditioner, moisturizer, film-former, stabilizer, crystallization inhibitor, pigment dispersant for pharmaceuticals (creams, lotions, suntan preps.)
Properties: Lt. yel. waxy solid, low odor; m.p. 49-52 C.

Lanogel® 21. [Amerchol]
Chem. Descrip.: PEG-27 lanolin
CAS 61790-81-6
Uses: Emollient, emulsifier, dispersant, wetting agent, solubilizer, foam stabilizer; used in pharmaceuticals, antiperspirants, germicidal hand soaps
Properties: ASTM 3 max. gel; HLB 15.0; 50% act.; nonionic.

Lanogel® 31. [Amerchol]
Chem. Descrip.: PEG-40 lanolin
CAS 61790-81-6
Uses: Emollient, emulsifier, dispersant, wetting agent, solubilizer, foam stabilizer; used in pharmaceuticals, antiperspirants, germicidal hand soaps
Properties: ASTM 3 max. gel; 50% act.; nonionic.

Lanogel® 41. [Amerchol]
Chem. Descrip.: PEG-75 lanolin
CAS 61790-81-6
Uses: Emollient, emulsifier, dispersant, wetting agent, solubilizer, foam stabilizer; used in pharmaceuticals, antiperspirants, germicidal hand soaps
Properties: ASTM 3 max. gel; HLB 15.0; 50% act.; nonionic.

Lanogel® 61. [Amerchol]
Chem. Descrip.: PEG-85 lanolin
CAS 61790-81-6
Uses: Emollient, emulsifier, dispersant, wetting agent, solubilizer, foam stabilizer; used in pharmaceuticals, antiperspirants, germicidal hand soaps
Properties: ASTM 3 max. gel; 50% act.; nonionic.

Lanolin Anhydrous USP. [Lanaetex Prods.]
Chem. Descrip.: Lanolin
CAS 8006-54-0; EINECS 232-348-6
Uses: Emollient.

Lanolin Anhydrous USP. [ChemMark Development]
Chem. Descrip.: Lanolin
CAS 8006-54-0; EINECS 232-348-6
Uses: Emollient.

Lanolin Pharmaceutical. [R.I.T.A.]
Chem. Descrip.: Lanolin
CAS 8006-54-0; EINECS 232-348-6
Uses: Epidermal moisturizer, lubricant, and emollient for personal care; stabilizer for emulsions, dispersions, and suspensions
Properties: Yel. grease.

Lanolin U.S.P. [Amerchol]
Chem. Descrip.: Lanolin USP
CAS 8006-54-0; EINECS 232-348-6
Uses: Emollient.

Lanolin USP. [R.I.T.A.]
Chem. Descrip.: Lanolin USP

CAS 8006-54-0; EINECS 232-348-6
Uses: Epidermal moisturizer, lubricant, and emollient for personal care; stabilizer for emulsions, dispersions, and suspensions
Properties: Yel. grease.
Lanotein AWS 30. [Fanning]
Chem. Descrip.: Propylene glycol, hydrolyzed collagen, PPG-12-PEG-65 lanolin oil
Uses: Conditioner, film-former, lubricant, humectant, and emollient for pharmaceuticals
Properties: Lt. amber liq.; bland odor; sol. in water; sl. sol. in glycerin @ 75 C; sp.gr. 1.05-1.08; pH 5.0-6.0.
Lantrol® 1673. [Henkel/Cospha; Henkel Canada]
Chem. Descrip.: Lanolin oil
EINECS 274-559-6
Uses: Emollient for medicinal preps., creams, lotions
Properties: Amber visc. liq.; sol. in min. oil, triolein, IPM; disp. in IPA; dens. 7.8 lb/gal; visc. 948 cSt (100 F); pour pt. 6 C; cloud pt. 18 C; flash pt. 525 F.
Lantrol® 1674. [Henkel/Cospha; Henkel Canada]
Chem. Descrip.: Lanolin oil
EINECS 274-559-6
Uses: Low odor version of Lantrol 1673; emollient for medicinal preps.
Properties: Amber visc. liq.; sol. in min. oil, castor oil, triolein, IPM; disp. in IPA; dens. 7.8 lb/gal; visc. 835 cSt (100 F); pour pt. 9 C; cloud pt. 20 C; flash pt. 525 F.
Lantrol® HP-2073. [Henkel/Cospha; Henkel Canada]
Chem. Descrip.: Lanolin oil
CAS 8006-54-0; EINECS 274-559-6
Uses: Lubricant, hydration agent, emulsifier, emollient for medicinal preps.
Properties: Amber visc. liq.; sol. in min. oil, IPM; disp. in IPA; insol. in water; iodine no. 18-36; no. 90-110; cloud pt. 18 C.
Lantrol® HP-2074. [Henkel/Cospha; Henkel Canada]
Chem. Descrip.: Lanolin oil
EINECS 274-559-6
Uses: Emulsifier, emollient, conditioner, moisturizer, pigment dispersant for pharmaceuticals
Properties: Gardner 9 liq.; cloud pt. 20 C.
Laponite® D. [LSI]
Chem. Descrip.: Sodium magnesium silicate
CAS 53320-86-8; EINECS 258-476-2
Uses: Used in conjunction with other thickeners for imparting a shear sensitive structure to clear gel and conventional toothpastes
Properties: Wh. free-flowing powd.; insol. in water but hydrates and swells to give clear and colorless colloidal disp. in water or aq. alcohol sol'ns.; bulk dens. 1000 kg/m^3; surf. area 370 m^2/g; pH 9.8 (2% susp.).
L.A.S. [Gattefosse SA]
Chem. Descrip.: PEG-8 caprylic/capric glycerides
CAS 85536-07-8
Uses: Excipient for creams, lotions; surfactant for microemulsions
Properties: Gardner < 5 oily liq., faint odor; sol. in

water; very sol. in ethanol, chloroform, methylene chloride; sp.gr. 1.060-1.070; visc. 80-110 mPa•s; HLB 14.0; acid no. < 1; iodine no. < 2; sapon. no. 85-105; ref. index 1.450-1.470; nonionic
Toxicology: LD0 (oral, rat) > 20 ml/kg, nontoxic; sl. ocular irritant at 0.1 ml; nonirritating to skin.
Laurex® CS [Albright & Wilson Am.; Albright & Wilson UK]
Chem. Descrip.: Cetearyl alcohol BP
EINECS 267-008-6
Uses: Raw material for pharmaceutical creams
Properties: Wh. waxy flake; dens. 0.4 g/cc; m.p. 48-53 C; acid no. 0.5 max.; sapon. no. 2.0 max.; flash pt. 150 C; 100% act.; nonionic.
Laurex® CS/D. [Albright & Wilson UK]
Chem. Descrip.: Cetearyl alcohol
CAS 67762-27-0; EINECS 267-008-6
Uses: Raw material for pharmaceutical creams
Regulatory: BP, EP compliance
Properties: Wh. waxy flakes, faint char. odor; sol. in ethanol, insol. in water; dens. 0.4 g/cm^3; m.p. 48-53 C; b.p. > 250 C; acid no. 1 max.; sapon. no. 2.0 max.; hyd. no. 218; flash pt. 150 C; 100% conc.; nonionic; readily biodeg., unlikely to accumulate in aquatic environments; discharge of lg. quantities may kill fish
Toxicology: LD50 (oral, rat) > 2000 mg/kg; not classified hazardous; may cause irritation to mouth, upper digestive tract, skin on prolonged/repeated exposure, eyes
Precaution: May react with strong oxidants; combustion may produce fumes contg. CO$_2$, CO; spillages may be slippery
Storage: Store @ 5-10 C above m.p. (liq. molten form); store well below m.p. (solid form); store away from heat, humidity, strong oxidizing agents.
Lauroglycol. [Gattefosse]
Chem. Descrip.: Propylene glycol laurate
CAS 142-55-2; EINECS 205-542-3
Uses: Excipient, permeation enhancer for topical and transdermal pharmaceutical formulations.
Lecigran™ 5750. [Riceland Foods]
Chem. Descrip.: Deoiled lecithin
CAS 8002-43-5; EINECS 232-307-2
Uses: Emulsifier, dry blending/instantizing agent for pharmaceuticals, dietary supplements; stabilizer, dispersant for color and flavor suspensions
Regulatory: FDA 21CFR §184.1400, GRAS
Properties: Fine powd., superior odor and flavor profile; 97% min. phospholipid.
Storage: Hygroscopic; store in sealed containers below 25 C; protect from light and moisture.
Lecigran™ 6750. [Riceland Foods]
Chem. Descrip.: Deoiled lecithin
CAS 8002-43-5; EINECS 232-307-2
Uses: Emulsifier, blending agent for pharmaceuticals, dietary supplements; stabilizer, dispersant for color and flavor suspensions
Properties: Extra fine powd.; 97% min. phospholipid.
Lecigran™ A. [Riceland Foods]

Chem. Descrip.: Deoiled lecithin with 1% flow agent to increase flowability
CAS 8002-43-5; EINECS 232-307-2
Uses: Emulsifier, blending agent for pharmaceuticals, dietary supplements; stabilizer, dispersant for color and flavor suspensions
Properties: Lt. tan to med. yel. fine gran., superior odor and flavor profiles; 97% min. phospholipid.
Storage: Hygroscopic; store in sealed containers below 25 C; protect from light and moisture.

Lecigran™ C. [Riceland Foods]
Chem. Descrip.: Deoiled lecithin with ≤ 2% tricalcium phosphate to enhance flowability
Uses: Emulsifier, blending agent for pharmaceuticals, dietary supplements; stabilizer, dispersant for color and flavor suspensions
Regulatory: FDA 21CFR §184.1400, GRAS
Properties: Lt. tan to med. yel. gran., superior odor and flavor profiles; 97% min. phospholipid.
Storage: Hygroscopic; store in sealed containers below 25 C; protect from light and moisture.

Lecigran™ F. [Riceland Foods]
Chem. Descrip.: Deoiled lecithin
CAS 8002-43-5; EINECS 232-307-2
Uses: Emulsifier, blending agent for pharmaceuticals, dietary supplements; stabilizer, dispersant for color and flavor suspensions
Regulatory: FDA 21CFR §184.1400, GRAS
Properties: Lt. tan to med. yel. fine gran., superior odor and flavor profiles; 97% min. phospholipid.
Storage: Hygroscopic; store in sealed containers below 25 C; protect from light and moisture.

Lecigran™ M. [Riceland Foods]
Chem. Descrip.: Deoiled lecithin
CAS 8002-43-5; EINECS 232-307-2
Uses: Emulsifier, blending agent for pharmaceuticals, dietary supplements; stabilizer, dispersant for color and flavor suspensions
Regulatory: FDA 21CFR §184.1400, GRAS
Properties: Lt. tan to med. yel. free-flowing gran., superior odor and flavor profile; 97% min. phospholipid.
Storage: Hygroscopic; store in sealed containers below 25 C; protect from light and moisture.

Lecigran™ Super A. [Riceland Foods]
Chem. Descrip.: Deoiled lecithin with calcium silicate as flow agent
Uses: Emulsifier, blending agent for pharmaceuticals, dietary supplements; specially formulated for direct compression tableting
Properties: Lt. tan to med. yel. free-flowing fine gran.; 94% min. phospholipid.
Storage: Hygroscopic; store in sealed containers below 25 C; protect from light and moisture.

Lecigran™ T. [Riceland Foods]
Chem. Descrip.: Deoiled lecithin with tricalcium phosphate to enhance flowability
Uses: Emulsifier, blending agent for pharmaceuticals, dietary supplements; stabilizer, dispersant for color and flavor suspensions
Properties: Powd.; 97% min. phospholipid.

LEM, Shiitake Mycelium Extract LEMEXT. [Garuda

Int'l.]
Chem. Descrip.: Shiitake mycelium extract from *Lentinus edodes* with 70% dextrose carrier
Uses: Polysaccharides, lignins actives; used to formulate health foods and pharmaceutical capsules, tablets, ampules
Properties: Brn. gran.; max. 20 mesh or finer; sol. in water
Storage: 24 mo shelf life.

Lexate® PX. [Inolex]
Chem. Descrip.: Petrolatum, lanolin alcohol
Uses: O/w and aux. emulsifier, emollient, surfactant, SE absorption base; vehicle for treatment and topical pharmaceuticals, creams, ointments
Properties: Faintly yel. semisolid, mild fatty char. odor; sol. in oils, insol. in water; m.p. 36-46 C; acid no. 0.3; sapon. no. 1.0; 100% solids
Storage: Store in tightly closed original containers at ambient temps. (13-30 C) to avoid deterioration or contamination.

Lexemul® 55G. [Inolex]
Chem. Descrip.: Glyceryl stearate
Uses: Surfactant, emulsifier, opacifier used in topical pharmaceuticals; improves lubricity, gloss in creams and lotions
Properties: Wh. flakes; mild fatty char. odor; m.p. 55-59 C; HLB 4.1; acid no. 2 max.; iodine no. 1 max.; sapon. no. 160-170; pH 5.5 (3% aq.); 100% conc.; nonionic.

Lexemul® 503. [Inolex]
Chem. Descrip.: Glyceryl stearate
Uses: Emulsifier, stabilizer, thickener, opacifier in emulsions, topical pharmaceuticals
Properties: Flakes, mild fatty char. odor; m.p. 57-60 C; HLB 3.2; acid no. 2 max.; iodine no. 3 max.; sapon. no. 158-168; pH 6.5 (3% aq. disp.); 100% conc.; nonionic
Storage: Store in tightly closed original containers between 13 and 30 C to avoid deterioration, contamination, or lumping.

Lexemul® 515. [Inolex]
Chem. Descrip.: Glyceryl stearate
Uses: Emulsifier, stabilizer, thickener, opacifier, emollient in emulsions, topical pharmaceuticals
Properties: Flakes, mild fatty char. odor; m.p. 60 C; HLB 3.8; acid no. 16-20; iodine no. 3 max.; sapon. no. 166-176; 100% conc.; nonionic
Storage: Store in tightly closed original containers between 13 and 30 C to avoid deterioration, contamination, or lumping.

Lexemul® AR. [Inolex]
Chem. Descrip.: Glyceryl stearate and stearamidoethyl diethylamine
Uses: Emulsifier, stabilizer, opacifier, and emollient for cationic systems in topical pharmaceuticals, deodorants, antiperspirants; self-emulsifying, acid-stable
Properties: Wh. to cream flakes, mild fatty odor; disp. in water (60 C); m.p. 60 C; HLB 4.1; acid no. 25-31; iodine no. 3 max.; sapon. no. 166-174; 100% conc.; cationic
Storage: Store in tightly closed original containers

between 13 and 30 C to avoid deterioration, contamination, or lumping.

Lexemul® AS. [Inolex]
Chem. Descrip.: Glyceryl stearate, sodium lauryl sulfate
Uses: SE acid-stable emulsifier, stabilizer, opacifier and emollient in topical pharmaceuticals
Properties: Wh to cream flakes; m.p. 60 C; HLB 4.9; acid no. 14-18; iodine no. 3 max.; sapon. no. 153-162; pH 5.5 (3% aq.); 100% conc.; anionic
Storage: Store in tightly closed original containers between 13 and 30 C to avoid deterioration, contamination, or lumping.

Lexemul® CS-20. [Inolex]
Chem. Descrip.: Cetearyl alcohol, ceteareth-20
Uses: Emulsifier, emollient used in antiperspirant creams and lotions, ointments, hydroquinone creams, topical pharmaceuticals
Properties: APHA 50 max. brittle flakes, mild fatty char. odor; m.p. 50 C; HLB 5.4; acid no. 1 max.; iodine no. 2 max.; sapon. no. 2 max.; pH 7.2 (3% aq. disp.); 100% conc.; nonionic.

Lexemul® EGMS. [Inolex]
Chem. Descrip.: Glycol stearate
CAS 111-60-4; EINECS 203-886-9
Uses: Emulsifier, bodying agent, stabilizer for creams, lotions, topical pharmaceuticals
Properties: Flakes, mild fatty char. odor; sol. in hot min. and veg. oils; water-insol.; m.p. 57 C; HLB 2.3; acid no. 2 max.; iodine no. 1 max.; sapon. no. 180-190; 100% conc.; nonionic
Storage: Store in tightly closed original containers between 13 and 30 C to avoid deterioration, contamination, or lumping.

Lexemul® PEG-200 DL. [Inolex]
Chem. Descrip.: PEG-4 dilaurate
CAS 9005-02-1
Uses: Emulsifier, emollient, lubricant for pharmaceuticals
Properties: Straw to yel. liq., typ. mild fatty odor; water-disp.; sp.gr. 0.954; m.p. 2-3 C; HLB 5.9; acid no. 5 max.; iodine no. 8 max.; sapon. no. 170-180; 100% conc.; nonionic
Storage: Store in tightly closed original containers below 32 C to avoid deterioration or contamination.

Lexgard® B. [Inolex]
Chem. Descrip.: Butylparaben USP
CAS 94-26-8; EINECS 202-318-7
Uses: Broad spectrum biostatic/biocidal preservative for topical pharmaceuticals
Properties: Wh. fine powd., odorless, tasteless; sol. in ethanol, propylene glycol; sol. 0.02 g/100 g in water; m.p. 68-72 C; 100% conc.
Toxicology: Nonirritating to skin, nonsensitizing
Storage: Store in tightly closed original containers below 38 C away from heat and moisture.

Lexgard® M. [Inolex]
Chem. Descrip.: Methylparaben USP
CAS 99-76-3; EINECS 202-785-7
Uses: Broad spectrum biostatic/biocidal preservative for topical pharmaceuticals

Use level: 0.1-1.0%
Regulatory: FDA 21CFR §150, 172.515, 184.1490, GRAS, Japan, Europe compliance
Properties: Wh. fine powd.; sol. in ethanol, propylene glycol; sol. 0.25 g/100 g in water; m.p. 125-128 C; 99% assay
Toxicology: Nontoxic
Storage: Store in tightly closed original containers below 38 C away from heat and moisture.

Lexgard® P. [Inolex]
Chem. Descrip.: Propylparaben USP
CAS 94-13-3; EINECS 202-307-7
Uses: Broad spectrum biostatic/biocidal preservative for topical pharmaceuticals
Regulatory: FDA 21CFR 150, 172.515, 184.1670, GRAS, Japan, Europe compliance
Properties: Wh. fine powd.; sol. in ethanol, propylene glycol; sol. 0.05 g/100 g in water; m.p. 95-98 C; 100% conc.
Storage: Store in tightly closed original containers below 38 C away from heat and moisture.

Lexol® 60. [Inolex]
Chem. Descrip.: IPP, IPM, and isopropyl stearate
Uses: Emollient for topical pharmaceuticals, aerosol antiperspirants, creams, and lotions
Properties: Colorless clear liq., odorless; sol. in acetone, benzene, CCl_4, castor oil, chloroform, ethanol, heptane, IPA; insol. in water; sp.gr. 0.848; dens. 7.1 lb/gal; visc. 7 cps; f.p. 8 C; acid no. 1 max.; iodine no. 1 max.; sapon. no. 190-198; flash pt. (PMCC) 165 C; ref. index 1.4358; 100% conc.; nonionic; biodeg.

Lexol® 3975. [Inolex]
Chem. Descrip.: Isopropyl palmitate, isopropyl myristate, isopropyl stearate
Uses: Emollient and solv. for topicals; oxidative resist.
Properties: Colorless liq., odorless; sol. in acetone, benzene, CCl_4, castor oil, chloroform, ethanol, heptane, IPA; insol. in water; sp.gr. 0.850-0.858; visc. 7 cps; f.p. 11 C; acid no. 1 max.; iodine no. 1 max.; sapon. no. 184-194; flash pt. (PMCC) 169 C; ref. index 1.4367; 100% conc.

Lexol® EHP. [Inolex]
Chem. Descrip.: Octyl palmitate
CAS 29806-73-3; EINECS 249-862-1
Uses: Emollient for topical pharmaceuticals, deodorants, nonocclusive creams and lotions, suncare prods.
Properties: Colorless clear liq., odorless; sol. in acetone, benzene, CCl_4, chloroform, ether, heptane, alcohol, veg. and min. oils; insol. in water; sp.gr. 0.858; visc. 13 cps; f.p. -2 C; acid no. 1 max.; iodine no. 1 max.; sapon. no. 145-155; flash pt. (PMCC) 206 C; ref. index 1.4460; 100% conc.
Storage: Store in tightly closed original containers @ 13-38 C to avoid deterioration or contamination; store bulk liq. under dry inert atmosphere in SS or aluminum vessels.

Lexol® GT-855. [Inolex]
Chem. Descrip.: Caprylic/capric triglyceride
CAS 65381-09-1; EINECS 265-724-3

Uses: Solv. for flavor ingreds.; vehicle for medicinals, antibiotics, vitamins; solubilizer; oxidative stability
Properties: APHA 100 max. clear liq., odorless; tasteless; alcohol-sol.; sp.gr. 0.943; visc. 27 cps; f.p. -19 C; acid no. 0.1 max.; iodine no. 1 max.; sapon. no. 325-355; flash pt. (PMCC) 224 C; ref. index 1.4479; 100% conc.

Lexol® GT-865. [Inolex]
Chem. Descrip.: Caprylic/capric triglyceride
CAS 65381-09-1; EINECS 265-724-3
Uses: Emollient, moisturizer for creams, lotions; vehicle for org. sunscreens and vitamins
Properties: APHA 100 max. clear liq., odorless, tasteless; sol. in alcohol; sp.gr. 0.947; visc. 25 cps; f.p. -19 C; acid no. 0.1 max.; iodine no. 1 max.; sapon. no. 335-355; flash pt. (PMCC) 233 C; ref. index 1.4471; 100% conc.

Lexol® IPP. [Inolex]
Chem. Descrip.: Isopropyl palmitate
CAS 142-91-6; EINECS 205-571-1
Uses: Emollient, solubilizer, carrier for topical pharmaceuticals
Properties: Colorless clear liq.; odorless; sol. in acetone, benzene, CCl_4, castor oil, chloroform, ethanol, heptane, IPA; insol. in water; m.w. 298; sp.gr. 0.850-0.855; dens. 7.1 lb/gal; visc. 7 cps; f.p. 11 C; acid no. 1 max.; iodine no. 1 max.; sapon. no. 182-191; flash pt. (PMCC) 170 C; ref. index 1.437; 100% conc.
Storage: Store in tightly closed original containers @ 13-38 C to avoid deterioration or contamination; store bulk liq. under dry inert atmosphere in SS or aluminum vessels.

Lexol® IPP-A. [Inolex]
Chem. Descrip.: Isopropyl palmitate
CAS 142-91-6; EINECS 205-571-1
Uses: Emollient, solubilizer, carrier for topical pharmaceuticals; oxidative stability
Properties: Colorless clear liq., odorless; sol. in acetone, benzene, CCl_4, castor oil, chloroform, ethanol, heptane, IPA, min. oil, dimethicone, cyclomethicone; insol. in water; visc. 7 cps; f.p. 11 C; HLB 13.5; acid no. 1 max.; iodine no. 1 max.; sapon. no. 182-191; flash pt. (PMCC) 170 C; ref. index 1.4370; 100% conc.
Storage: Store in tightly closed original containers @ 13-38 C to avoid deterioration or contamination; store bulk liq. under dry inert atmosphere in SS or aluminum vessels.

Lexol® IPP-NF. [Inolex]
Chem. Descrip.: Isopropyl palmitate NF
CAS 142-91-6; EINECS 205-571-1
Uses: Emollient, solubilizer, carrier for topical pharmaceuticals
Properties: APHA 20 max. clear liq., odorless; sol. in acetone, benzene, CCl_4, castor oil, chloroform, ethanol, heptane, IPA; insol. in water; sp.gr. 0.850-0.855; visc. 7 cps; f.p. 11 C; acid no. 1 max.; iodine no. 1 max.; sapon. no. 184-190; flash pt. (PMCC) 170 C; ref. index 1.4350-1.4380; 100% conc.

Storage: Store in tightly closed original containers @ 13-38 C to avoid deterioration or contamination; store bulk liq. under dry inert atmosphere in SS or aluminum vessels.

Lexol® PG-800. [Inolex]
Chem. Descrip.: Propylene glycol dioctanoate
CAS 56519-71-2
Uses: Emollient and moisturizer with nonoily feel, oxidation stability; for pharmaceutical creams, lotions, topicals; solv., carrier/vehicle for flavors, fragrances, vitamins, antibiotics, medicinals
Properties: Colorless clear liq., char. odor; sol. in alcohol, min. oil, acetone; sp.gr. 0.918; visc. 10 cps; f.p. -34 C; acid no. 1 max.; iodine no. 1 max.; sapon. no. 320-340; flash pt. (COC) 272 C; ref. index 1.4350; 100% conc.

Lexol® PG-865. [Inolex]
Chem. Descrip.: Propylene glycol dicaprylate/dicaprate
Uses: Solubilizer, solv., coupling agent, vehicle for flavors, fragrances, vitamins, antibiotics, medicinals
Properties: APHA 100 max. clear liq., odorless; sol. in alcohol, min. and veg. oil, acetone; sp.gr. 0.922; visc. 10 cps; f.p. -38 C; acid no. 0.1 max.; iodine no. 1 max.; sapon. no. 315-335; flash pt. (PMCC) 195 C; ref. index 1.4391; 100% conc.
Storage: Store in tightly closed original containers @ 13-38 C to avoid deterioration or contamination; store bulk liq. under dry inert atmosphere in SS or aluminum vessels.

Linalool 95. [SCM Glidco Organics]
Chem. Descrip.: Linalool
CAS 78-70-6; EINECS 201-134-4
Uses: Raw material in synthesis of isophytol and vitamin E
Regulatory: FDA 21CFR §182.60
Properties: Clear liq.; sol. 1 in 4 in 60% alcohol; m.w. 154.25; sp.gr. 0.861-0.870; dens. 7.20 lb/gal; b.p. 192.8 C; flash pt. (TCC) 80 C; ref. index 1.461-1.465 (20 C); 95% min. act.
Toxicology: LD50 (oral, rat) 2790 mg/kg, (dermal, rabbit) 5610 mg/kg; undiluted liq. may be irritating to skin and eyes.

Lipacide C8CO. [Seppic]
Chem. Descrip.: Capryloyl collagen amino acids
CAS 68989-52-6
Uses: Antimicrobial, antiseborrheic, antiacneic, antiseptic for dermal preps., esp. for prevention and treatment of skin prone to acne
Use level: 1-2% (antimicrobial/antiseborrheic in cosmetics, skin prods.); 2-4% (antiacneic in skin prods., makeup), 4-6% (antiseptics)
Properties: Dough-like appearance, char. odor; very sl. sol. in water (20 C); sol. in alcohols, polyols, acetone, ether, and surfactants; m.w. ≈ 240; acid no. 215-250
Toxicology: Nontoxic; nonirritating to eyes and skin; hypoallergenic
Storage: 3 yrs storage life stored away from heat.

Lipacide SH Co 90. [Seppic]
Chem. Descrip.: 18% Lipacide Cco (octanoyl

collagenic acid), 72% Cemulsol LA 90 (PEG lauryl alcohol), 10% water
CAS 82708-25-6
Uses: Surfactant with good wetting and foaming for shampoos; bacteriostatic and fungistatic props. for antidandruff shampoos
Use level: 10%
Properties: Yel. visc. liq., odorless to sl. odor; sol. in water; very sol. in acetone, ethanol, methanol; sol. cloudy in chloroform; visc. (kinematic) 110-140 mm^2/s (30 C); acid no. 35-55; pH 3-5; 8-12% water; biodeg.
Toxicology: LD50 (oral, mouse) 1.5 g/kg; nonirritating to skin; sl. eye irritant
Storage: 3 yrs shelf life; protect from light and heat; may become cloudy on storage-sl. heating will reclarify.

Lipacide SH K 90. [Seppic]
Chem. Descrip.: 18% Lipacide CK (octanoyl keratinic acid), 72% Cemulsol LA 90 (PEG lauryl alcohol), 10% water
CAS 82708-26-7
Uses: Surfactant with good wetting and foaming for shampoos; bacteriostatic and fungistatic props. for antidandruff shampoos
Use level: 10%
Properties: Yel. visc. liq., odorless to sl. odor; sol. in water; very sol. in acetone, ethanol, methanol; sol. cloudy in chloroform; visc. (kinematic) 120-150 mm^2/s (30 C); acid no. 35-55; pH 3-5; 8-12% water; biodeg.
Toxicology: LD50 (oral, rat) 2250 mg/kg; nonirritating to skin; sl. eye irritant
Storage: 3 yrs shelf life; protect from light and heat; may become cloudy on storage-sl. heating will reclarify.

Lipamine SPA. [Lipo]
Chem. Descrip.: Stearamidopropyl dimethylamine
CAS 7651-02-7; EINECS 231-609-1
Uses: Raw material for pharmaceuticals.

Lipase 8 Powd. [Am. Labs]
Chem. Descrip.: Lipase
CAS 9001-62-1; EINECS 232-619-9
Uses: Fat-splitting enzyme; ingred. for vitamin-mineral mixes
Properties: Sl. yel. or cream-colored powd., sl. nonoffensive odor
Storage: Preserve in tight containers in cool, dry place.

Lipase 16 Powd. [Am. Labs]
Chem. Descrip.: Lipase
CAS 9001-62-1; EINECS 232-619-9
Uses: Fat-splitting enzyme; ingred. for vitamin-mineral mixes
Properties: Sl. yel. or cream-colored powd., sl. nonoffensive odor
Storage: Preserve in tight containers in cool, dry place.

Lipase 24 Powd. [Am. Labs]
Chem. Descrip.: Lipase
CAS 9001-62-1; EINECS 232-619-9
Uses: Fat-splitting enzyme; ingred. for vitamin-

mineral mixes
Properties: Sl. yel. or cream-colored powd., sl. nonoffensive odor
Precaution: Preserve in tight containers in cool, dry place
Storage: Preserve in tight containers in cool, dry place.

Lipase 30 Powd. [Am. Labs]
Chem. Descrip.: Lipase
CAS 9001-62-1; EINECS 232-619-9
Uses: Fat-splitting enzyme; ingred. for vitamin-mineral mixes
Properties: Sl. yel. or cream-colored powd., sl. nonoffensive odor
Storage: Preserve in tight containers in cool, dry place.

Lipex 102. [ABITEC]
Chem. Descrip.: Shea butter
CAS 68424-60-2
Uses: Natural oil for pharmaceutical prods.
Properties: Lovibond R2.0 max.; m.p. 90-113 F; iodine no. 53-56; sapon. no. 178-190.

Lipex 104. [ABITEC]
Chem. Descrip.: Corn oil
CAS 8001-30-7; EINECS 232-281-2
Uses: Natural oil for pharmaceutical formulations
Properties: Gardner 2 max. liq.; acid no. 0.5 max.; iodine no. 115-130; sapon. no. 190; hyd. no. 3; cloud pt. -2 C.

Lipex 106. [ABITEC]
Chem. Descrip.: Illipe butter; oil of *Shorea stenoptera*
Uses: Natural oil for pharmaceutical formulations
Properties: Gardner 2 max. color; m.p. 81-95 F; acid no. 0.5 max.; iodine no. 30-35; sapon. no. 188-198; hyd. no. 6.

Lipex 109. [ABITEC]
Chem. Descrip.: Hydrog. cottonseed oil
CAS 68334-00-9; EINECS 269-804-9
Uses: Lubricant for pharmaceutical tablets.

Lipex 201. [ABITEC]
Chem. Descrip.: Rapeseed oil (canola)
Uses: Natural oil, lubricant for pharmaceutical formulations
Properties: Gardner 1.5 max. liq.; acid no. 0.5 max.; iodine no. 80-90; sapon. no. 185-195; hyd. no. 5; cloud pt. 6 C.

Lipex 202. [ABITEC]
Chem. Descrip.: Shea butter liq. fraction
CAS 68424-60-2
Uses: Natural oil for pharmaceutical formulations
Properties: Lovibond R 2.5 max.; iodine no. 63-67; sapon. no. 180-185.

Lipex 203. [ABITEC]
Chem. Descrip.: Fractionated mango kernel oil
Uses: Natural oil for pharmaceutical formulations
Properties: Gardner 4 max. liq.; acid no. 0.5 max.; iodine no. 55-65; sapon. no. 190; hyd. no. 9; cloud pt. 14 C.

Lipex 401. [ABITEC]
Chem. Descrip.: Hydrog. coconut oil
CAS 68334-28-1; EINECS 284-283-8

Uses: Natural oil for pharmaceutical formulations
Properties: Gardner 1.5 max. liq.; acid no. 0.5 max.; iodine no. < 3; sapon. no. 245-265; hyd. no. 2; cloud pt. 28 C.

Lipo 320. [Lipo]
Chem. Descrip.: Trilaurin
CAS 538-24-9; EINECS 208-687-0
Uses: Emollient for pharmaceuticals.

Lipo PE Base G-55. [Lipo]
Chem. Descrip.: Glycerin, diglycol/cyclohexanedimethanol/isophthalates/sulfoisophthalates copolymer
Uses: Raw material for pharmaceuticals.

Lipo PE Base GP-55. [Lipo]
Chem. Descrip.: Glycerin, diglycol/cyclohexanedimethanol/isophthalates/sulfoisophthalates copolymer, propylene glycol
Uses: Raw material for pharmaceuticals.

Lipobee 102. [Lipo]
Chem. Descrip.: Syn. beeswax
EINECS 275-286-5
Uses: Raw material for pharmaceuticals
Properties: Oil-misc.; water-insol.

Lipocare HA/EC. [Lipo]
Chem. Descrip.: Hyaluronic acid and echinacin
Uses: Raw material for pharmaceuticals.

Lipolan 31. [Lipo]
Chem. Descrip.: PEG-24 hydrog. lanolin
CAS 68648-27-1
Uses: O/w emulsifier, solubilizer, emollient, conditioner used in topical pharmaceuticals
Properties: Cream waxy solid; bland, char. odor; sol. in water and ethanol; acid no. 2 max.; sapon. no. 8; 100% act.; nonionic.

Lipolan 31-20. [Lipo]
Chem. Descrip.: PEG-20 hydrog. lanolin
CAS 68648-27-1
Uses: Emollient, emulsifier, solubilizer, stabilizer, conditioner, and moisturizer for pharmaceuticals, sun care, ointments, acne preps., veterinary prods.

Lipolan S. [Lipo]
Chem. Descrip.: Hydrog. lanolin
CAS 8031-44-5; EINECS 232-452-1
Uses: Emollient, lubricant, and conditioner for topical pharmaceuticals
Properties: Wh./off-wh. paste; mild char. odor; water-insol.; m.p. 45-53; acid no. 1 max.; sapon. no. 5 max.

Lipolan Distilled. [Lipo]
Chem. Descrip.: Dist. hydrog. lanolin
CAS 8031-44-5; EINECS 232-452-1
Uses: Emollient, emulsifier, solubilizer, stabilizer, conditioner, and moisturizer for pharmaceuticals, sun care, ointments, acne preps., veterinary prods.

Lipo Melanin. [Lipo]
Chem. Descrip.: Melanin
Uses: Raw material for pharmaceuticals.

Liponic 70-NC. [Lipo]
Chem. Descrip.: Sorbitol
CAS 50-70-4; EINECS 200-061-5

Uses: Humectant, plasticizer, softener, and lubricant; adds sweet taste and pleasant mouthfeel to oral hygiene prods. such as dentifrices and mouthwashes; oral dosage pharmaceuticals
Properties: Clear colorless sol'n.; water-sol.; sp.gr. 1.29-1.32; ref. index 1.455-1.470; pH neutral.

Liponic 76-NC. [Lipo]
Chem. Descrip.: Sorbitol
CAS 50-70-4; EINECS 200-061-5
Uses: Humectant, plasticizer, softener, and lubricant; adds sweet taste and pleasant mouthfeel to oral hygiene prods. such as dentifrices and mouthwashes; oral dosage pharmaceuticals
Properties: Colorless to pale yel. clear syrup; odorless; sp.gr. 1.32-1.35; ref. index. 1.468-1.475; 25% max. water.

Liponic 83-NC. [Lipo]
Chem. Descrip.: Sorbitol
CAS 50-70-4; EINECS 200-061-5
Uses: Humectant, plasticizer, softener, and lubricant; adds sweet taste and pleasant mouthfeel to oral hygiene prods. such as dentifrices and mouthwashes; oral dosage pharmaceuticals.

Liponic Sorbitol Sol'n. 70% USP. [Lipo]
Chem. Descrip.: Sorbitol
CAS 50-70-4; EINECS 200-061-5
Uses: Humectant which stabilizes moisture and helps prevent crystallization
Regulatory: FDA 21CFR §121.101; kosher grade avail.

Liposorb 70. [Lipo]
Chem. Descrip.: Sorbitol
CAS 50-70-4; EINECS 200-061-5
Uses: Humectant, nutritive sweetener, oleaginous vehicle, tablet diluent.

Lipovol P. [Lipo]
Chem. Descrip.: Apricot kernel oil
CAS 72869-69-3
Uses: Emollient used in pharmaceuticals; soft, nontacky afterfeel and high film gloss
Properties: Straw oily liq., bland char. fatty odor; sol. in min. oil and isopropyl esters; insol. in water; acid no. 1 max.; iodine no. 90-115; sapon. no. 185-195.

Lipovol SES. [Lipo]
Chem. Descrip.: Sesame oil
CAS 8008-74-0; EINECS 232-370-6
Uses: Emollient, solv., and vehicle used in pharmaceuticals; offers lt. nontacky feel and enhances gloss and spread of pigmented sticks
Properties: Yel. clear liq.; bland char. odor; sol. in isopropyl esters and min. oil; insol. in water; acid no. 0.2 max.; iodine no. 103-116; sapon. no. 188-195.

Lipovol SES-S. [Lipo]
Chem. Descrip.: Veg. oil, sesame oil
Uses: Emollient, solv., and vehicle used in pharmaceuticals; offers lt. nontacky feel and enhances gloss and spread of pigmented sticks
Properties: Yel. clear liq.; bland char. odor; acid no. 1.0 max.; sapon. no. 188-195.

Lipoxol® 200 MED. [Hüls Am.; Hüls AG]

Chem. Descrip.: PEG-4
CAS 25322-68-3; EINECS 203-989-9
Uses: Moisture and consistency regulators in creams, lotions, toothpastes, deodorant sticks
Regulatory: German pharmacopoeia compliance
Properties: Colorless clear liq.; water-sol.; visc. 60-70 mPa•s; solid. pt. -40 to -55 C; acid no. 0.2 max.; pH 4-7 (10% aq.).
Lipoxol® 300 MED. [Hüls Am.; Hüls AG]
Chem. Descrip.: PEG-6
CAS 25322-68-3; EINECS 220-045-1
Uses: Moisture and consistency regulators in creams, lotions, toothpastes, deodorant sticks
Regulatory: German pharmacopoeia compliance
Properties: Colorless clear liq.; water-sol.; visc. 85-95 mPa•s; solid. pt. -10 to -20 C; acid no. 0.2 max.; pH 4-7 (10% aq.).
Lipoxol® 400 MED. [Hüls Am.; Hüls AG]
Chem. Descrip.: PEG-8
CAS 25322-68-3; EINECS 225-856-4
Uses: Moisture and consistency regulators in creams, lotions, toothpastes, deodorant sticks
Regulatory: German pharmacopoeia compliance
Properties: Colorless clear liq.; water-sol.; visc. 105-140 mPa•s; solid. pt. 4-8 C; acid no. 0.2 max.; pH 4-7 (10% aq.).
Lipoxol® 550 MED. [Hüls Am.; Hüls AG]
Chem. Descrip.: PEG-6 and PEG-32
Uses: Moisture and consistency regulators in creams, lotions, toothpastes, deodorant sticks
Regulatory: German pharmacopoeia compliance
Properties: Wh. paste; water-sol.; visc. 22-26 mPa•s (50% aq.); solid. pt. 37-40 C; acid no. 0.2 max.; pH 4-7 (10% aq.).
Lipoxol® 600 MED. [Hüls Am.; Hüls AG]
Chem. Descrip.: PEG-12
CAS 25322-68-3; EINECS 229-859-1
Uses: Moisture and consistency regulators in creams, lotions, toothpastes, deodorant sticks
Regulatory: German pharmacopoeia compliance
Properties: Colorless to wh. liq./solid; water-sol.; visc. 15-20 mPa•s (50% aq.); solid. pt. 15-25 C; acid no. 0.2 max.; pH 4-7 (10% aq.).
Lipoxol® 800 MED. [Hüls Am.; Hüls AG]
Chem. Descrip.: PEG-16
CAS 25322-68-3
Uses: Moisture and consistency regulators in creams, lotions, toothpastes, deodorant sticks
Regulatory: German pharmacopoeia compliance
Properties: Wh. solid; water-sol.; visc. 20-25 mPa•s (50% aq.); solid. pt. 25-35 C; acid no. 0.2 max.; pH 4-7 (10% aq.).
Lipoxol® 1000 MED. [Hüls Am.; Hüls AG]
Chem. Descrip.: PEG-20
CAS 25322-68-3
Uses: Moisture and consistency regulators in creams, lotions, toothpastes, deodorant sticks
Regulatory: German pharmacopoeia compliance
Properties: Wh. solid; water-sol.; visc. 24-29 mPa•s (50% aq.); solid. pt. 30-40 C; acid no. 0.2 max.; pH 4-7 (10% aq.).
Lipoxol® 1550 MED. [Hüls Am.; Hüls AG]

Chem. Descrip.: PEG-32
CAS 25322-68-3
Uses: Moisture and consistency regulators in creams, lotions, toothpastes, deodorant sticks
Regulatory: German pharmacopoeia compliance
Properties: Wh. flakes; water-sol.; visc. 35-50 mPa•s (50% aq.); solid. pt. 40-50 C; acid no. 0.2 max.; pH 4-7 (10% aq.).
Lipoxol® 2000 MED. [Hüls Am.; Hüls AG]
Chem. Descrip.: PEG-40
CAS 25322-68-3
Uses: Moisture and consistency regulators in creams, lotions, toothpastes, deodorant sticks
Regulatory: German pharmacopoeia compliance
Properties: Wh. flakes; water-sol.; visc. 47-60 mPa•s (50% aq.); solid. pt. 47-52 C; acid no. 0.2 max.; pH 4-7 (10% aq.).
Lipoxol® 3000 MED. [Hüls Am.; Hüls AG]
Chem. Descrip.: PEG-60
CAS 25322-68-3
Uses: Moisture and consistency regulators in creams, lotions, toothpastes, deodorant sticks
Regulatory: German pharmacopoeia compliance
Properties: Wh. flakes; water-sol.; visc. 70-110 mPa•s (50% aq.); solid. pt. 50-56 C; acid no. 0.2 max.; pH 4-7 (10% aq.).
Lipoxol® 4000 MED. [Hüls Am.; Hüls AG]
Chem. Descrip.: PEG-75
CAS 25322-68-3
Uses: Moisture and consistency regulators in creams, lotions, toothpastes, deodorant sticks
Regulatory: German pharmacopoeia compliance
Properties: Wh. flakes/powd.; water-sol.; visc. 115-170 mPa•s (50% aq.); solid. pt. 50-58 C; acid no. 0.2 max.; pH 4-7 (10% aq.).
Lipoxol® 6000 MED. [Hüls Am.; Hüls AG]
Chem. Descrip.: PEG-150
CAS 25322-68-3
Uses: Moisture and consistency regulators in creams, lotions, toothpastes, deodorant sticks
Regulatory: German pharmacopoeia compliance
Properties: Wh. flakes/powd.; water-sol.; visc. 205-350 mPa•s (50% aq.); solid. pt. 55-62 C; acid no. 0.2 max.; pH 4-7 (10% aq.).
LiquaPar® Oil. [Sutton Labs]
Chem. Descrip.: 40% Isopropylparaben, 30% isobutylparaben, 30% n-butylparaben
Uses: Broad-spectrum preservative for topical pharmaceuticals; effective against Gram-positive and Gram-negative bacteria, yeast, and mold even at low concs.
Regulatory: USA, Japan (1% max. total parabens), and Europe (0.8% max.) approvals
Properties: Yel. clear visc. liq., mild char. odor; sol. in alcohol, propylene glycol; slightly sol. in water; sp.gr. 1.103; visc. 6450 cps; vapor pressure < 10 mm Hg; b.p. 268 C; acid no. 0.5 max.; sapon. no. 292-296; cloud pt. -12 C; flash pt. (PMCC) 118.3 C; ref. index 1.53; pH 5-8; 100% act.
Toxicology: LD50 (oral, rat) > 5000 mg/kg (pract. nontoxic); moderately irritating to skin; severe eye irritant; may irritate mucous membranes

Storage: Store container at R.T.; keep closed when not in use.

Liquid Absorption Base Type A. [Croda Inc.]
Chem. Descrip.: Min. oil, lanolin alcohol
Uses: Mild surfactant, emollient for facial cleansers, surgical scrubs, and baby wipe formulations; solubilizer for oil-sol. actives in pharmaceuticals; can absorb 20 times its wt. of water without separation on inversion
Properties: Clear yel. liq.; sol. in min. oil, IPA.

Liquid Absorption Base Type T. [Croda Inc.]
Chem. Descrip.: Min. oil, lanolin alcohol
Uses: Mild surfactant, emollient; primary oil phase ingred. in o/w emulsions; solubilizer for oil-sol. actives in pharmaceuticals
Properties: Clear yel. liq.

Liquid Base. [Croda Chem. Ltd.]
Chem. Descrip.: Lanolin-derived base
Uses: Emollient, moisturizer, emulsifier for pharmaceutical preps.
Properties: Liq.

Liquid Fish Gelatin Conc. [Croda Colloids Ltd; O.C. Lugo]
Chem. Descrip.: Gelatin from fish sources
CAS 9000-70-8; EINECS 232-554-6
Uses: Functional ingred. in pharmaceutical industry; emulsion stabilizer, protective colloid, film-former, adhesive agent, flocculant; controls crystal growth; inferior gelling chars. to mammalian gelatin
Properties: Pale amber clear visc. sol'n.; cold water sol. when dried as a film; visc. 60-85 mps; pH 4-6; 25% solids.

Liquid Vitamin D₃ No. 63643. [Roche]
Chem. Descrip.: Cholecalciferol with edible corn oil
Uses: Used in pharmaceuticals, oil dispersions, encapsulated prods.
Properties: Yel. clear liq., sl. char. odor, bland fatty taste; misc. with edible oils/fats; sol. in ether, hydrocarbons, chlorinated hydrocarbons; sl. sol. in alcohol; insol. in water; m.w. 384.64; sp.gr. 0.9-0.95; visc. 50-90 cps; 100,000 min. IU vitamin D/g
Toxicology: Vitamin D: potentially toxic esp. for young children; excessive ingestion may cause hypercalcemia, hypercalcuria
Storage: Store @ 70 F; refrigerate if stored for several mos, then hold @ 24 h before opening; close tightly.

Liquigel®. [Reheis]
Chem. Descrip.: Aluminum hydroxide
CAS 21645-51-2; EINECS 244-492-7
Uses: Pumpable low sodium antacid active for suspensions, liq. preps.
Properties: Fluid gel; 8.5% min. Al₂O₃.

Liquigel® AM. [Reheis]
Chem. Descrip.: Aluminum hydroxide, magnesium hydroxide
Uses: Pumpable low sodium antacid for suspensions
Properties: Fluid gel; 8.5% Al₂O₃, 5.1% MgO, 0.05% max. Na.

Liquigel® AMS. [Reheis]
Chem. Descrip.: Aluminum hydroxide, magnesium hydroxide
Uses: Low sodium antacid for suspensions
Properties: Fluid gel; 5.7% Al₂O₃, 7.7% MgO, 5% sorbitol, 0.05% max. Na.

Liquigel® D4. [Reheis]
Chem. Descrip.: Aluminum hydroxide
CAS 21645-51- 2; EINECS 244-492-7
Uses: Pumpable low sodium antacid active for suspensions
Properties: Fluid gel; 10% min. Al₂O₃.

Liquigel® HO. [Reheis]
Chem. Descrip.: Aluminum hydroxide
CAS 21645-51-2; EINECS 244-492-7
Uses: Pumpable low sodium antacid active for suspensions, liq. preps.
Properties: Fluid gel; 13% min. Al₂O₃.

Liver Conc. Paste. [Am. Labs]
Chem. Descrip.: Dried liver extract
Uses: Nutritive pharmaceutical additive
Properties: Lt. tan to dk. brn. powd. or paste, char. odor and taste; hygroscopic; partly sol. in water and alcohol
Storage: Store in tight containers in cool, dry place.

Locust Bean Gum Pharmaceutical Grade. [MLG Enterprises Ltd.]
Chem. Descrip.: Locust bean gum
CAS 9000-40-2; EINECS 232-541-5
Uses: Stabilizer and emulsifier for pharmaceuticals
Properties: Lt. cream to tan fine powd.; 98% thru 100 mesh BSS; visc. 1500-1800 cps (1%, 20 C, 24 h); pH 5.5-7 (1%).

Locust Bean Gum Speckless Type D-200. [Meer]
Chem. Descrip.: Locust bean gum
CAS 9000-40-2; EINECS 232-541-5
Uses: Excipient for pharmaceutical tablets; thickener for toothpaste; thickener, stabilizer for creams and lotions
Properties: Wh. to cream-wh. powd., nearly odorless; 97% thru 100 mesh, ≥ 25% thru 200 mesh; visc. ≥ 2800 cps (1%); pH 5.0-6.4.

Locust Bean Gum Type A-100. [Gumix Int'l.]
Chem. Descrip.: Locust bean gum
CAS 9000-40-2; EINECS 232-541-5
Uses: Thickener, visc. modifier, water-binder, suspending agent, stabilizer for pharmaceuticals (creams, lotions, toothpaste, tablet excipient)
Properties: Off-wh. to lt. tan powd.; disp. in water; insol. in most org. liqs.

Locust Bean Gum Type A-250. [Gumix Int'l.]
Chem. Descrip.: Locust bean gum
CAS 9000-40-2; EINECS 232-541-5
Uses: Thickener, visc. modifier, water-binder, suspending agent, stabilizer for pharmaceuticals (creams, lotions, toothpaste, tablet excipient)
Properties: Off-wh. to lt. tan powd.; disp. in water; insol. in most org. liqs.

Locust Bean Gum Type A-270. [Gumix Int'l.]
Chem. Descrip.: Locust bean gum
CAS 9000-40-2; EINECS 232-541-5
Uses: Thickener, visc. modifier, water-binder, sus-

pending agent, stabilizer for pharmaceuticals (creams, lotions, toothpaste, tablet excipient)
Properties: Off-wh. to lt. tan powd.; disp. in water; insol. in most org. liqs.

Loralan-CH. [Lanaetex Prods.]
Chem. Descrip.: Cholesterol USP
CAS 57-88-5; EINECS 200-353-2
Uses: Emulsifier, solubilizer.

Low I.V. Coconut Oil 6227, 6228. [Dial]
Chem. Descrip.: Coconut oil fatty acid
EINECS 262-978-7
Uses: Emulsifier used in pharmaceuticals, chem. intermediates/derivs.
Properties: Acid no. 265-271; iodine no. < 5; 0.1% max. moisture.

Lubragluv. [United-Guardian]
Uses: Autoclavable glove powd. for use as a glove lubricant in medical and health care fields
Properties: Powd.; water-sol.; water-absorbent
Custom product

Lubrajel® CG. [Guardian Labs; Amerchol]
Chem. Descrip.: Polyglycerylmethacrylate and propylene glycol
Uses: Autoclavable nondrying water-sol. lubricant, moisturizer for medical and surgical use, for pre-lubricating catheters, enema tips, thermometers; highest conc. grade
Properties: Clear, colorless visc. gel; sp.gr. 1.3 g/ml; visc. 300,000-400,000 cps; pH 5.0-6.0.

Lubrajel® DV. [Guardian Labs; Amerchol]
Chem. Descrip.: Polyglycerylmethacrylate and propylene glycol
Uses: Autoclavable nondrying water-sol. lubricant, moisturizer for medical and surgical use, for pre-lubricating catheters, enema tips, thermometers; highest visc. grade
Properties: Clear, colorless visc. gel; sp.gr. 1.3 g/ml; visc. 300,000-400,000 cps; pH 5.0-6.0.

Lubrajel® MS. [Guardian Labs; Amerchol]
Chem. Descrip.: Polyglycerylmethacrylate and propylene glycol
Uses: Autoclavable nondrying water-sol. lubricant, moisturizer for medical and surgical use, for pre-lubricating catheters, enema tips, thermometers; general purpose grade
Properties: Clear, colorless visc. gel; sp.gr. 1.3 g/ml; visc. 300,000-400,000 cps; pH 5.0-6.0.

Lubrajel® Oil. [Guardian Labs; Amerchol]
Chem. Descrip.: Polyglycerylmethacrylate
CAS 9003-01-4
Uses: Water-sol. lubricant, moisturizer for medical and surgical use, for pre-lubricating catheters, enema tips, thermometers; liq. form with visc. similar to min. oil
Properties: Liq.

Lubrajel® RR. [Guardian Labs]
Uses: γ radiation-resist. lubricating jelly for medical lubrication of catheters, as a sol. burn ointment on gauze pads (petrolatum replacement), as a soothing dressing.

Lubrajel® TW. [Guardian Labs; Amerchol]
Chem. Descrip.: Polyglycerylmethacrylate and

propylene glycol
Uses: Autoclavable nondrying water-sol. lubricant, moisturizer for medical and surgical use, for pre-lubricating catheters, enema tips, thermometers
Properties: Clear, colorless visc. gel; sp.gr. 1.3 g/ml; visc. 300,000-400,000 cps; pH 5.0-6.0.

Lubrajel® WA. [Guardian Labs; Amerchol]
Chem. Descrip.: Polyglycerylmethacrylate
CAS 9003-01-4
Uses: Water-sol. lubricant, moisturizer for medical and surgical use, for pre-lubricating catheters, enema tips, thermometers.

Lubraseptic Jelly. [United-Guardian]
Uses: Antibacterial and anesthetic jelly for use as a urethral anesthetic, for post-hemorrhoidec-tomies, and for endotracheal intubation; sterile lubricant on cystoscopes and proctoscopes in urological, rectal, and vaginal examinations
Properties: Water-sol.

Lubritab®. [Mendell]
Chem. Descrip.: Hydrogenated veg. oil NF
CAS 68334-00-9; EINECS 269-804-9
Uses: Lubricant for pharmaceutical tablets; aux. dry binder when tablets tend to cap or laminate
Use level: 0.5-2% (tablet lubricant); up to 5% (aux. dry binder in tablets)
Properties: Fine powd.; avg. particle size 104 μ; 25% -200 mesh; dens. (tapped) 0.57 g/ml; m.p. 61-66 C; acid no. 2 max.; sapon. no. 188-198.

Ludipress®. [BASF AG]
Chem. Descrip.: Based on lactose and Kollidon®
Uses: Direct tableting auxiliary for pharmaceuti-cals.

Lutrol® F 127. [BASF AG]
Chem. Descrip.: EO/PO block copolymer
CAS 106392-12-5
Uses: Thickening and gelling agent for pharmaceu-ticals
Properties: Microbeads; 100% conc.; nonionic.

Luviform® FA 119. [BASF AG]
Chem. Descrip.: PVM/MA copolymer
CAS 9011-16-9
Uses: Stabilizing and binding agent for tooth-pastes, denture retaining agents.

Luvitol® EHO. [BASF; BASF AG]
Chem. Descrip.: Cetearyl octanoate
Uses: Emollient oil component for pharmaceuticals
Properties: Liq.; 100% conc.; nonionic.

Lysidone®. [UCIB; Barnet Prods.]
Chem. Descrip.: Lysine PCA
CAS 30657-38-6
Uses: Moisturizer, cellular regenerative agent, antioxidant and free radical scavenger for phar-maceuticals, skin care, sun care; stable in aq. and hydroalcoholic phases
Properties: Yel. liq., odorless; sol. in water; pract. insol. in ethanol, ether, chloroform; m.w. 275.3; sp.gr. 1.10-1.14; visc. 16-20 cps; pH 6.5-8.0; 40% aq. sol'n.
Toxicology: LD50 (oral, rat) > 2000 mg/kg; nonirri-tating to skin, very sl. irritating to eyes.

M

Mackol 18. [McIntyre]
Chem. Descrip.: Stearyl alcohol
CAS 112-92-5; EINECS 204-017-6
Uses: Emollient, pharmaceutical raw material.
Macol® 1. [PPG/Specialty Chem.]
Chem. Descrip.: Poloxamer 181
CAS 9003-11-6
Uses: Defoamer, emulsifier, dispersant, gellant, solubilizer, wetting agent, lubricant base for medical and pharmaceutical applics.
Properties: APHA < 100 liq.; water-sol.; m.w. 2000; sp.gr. 1.015; dens. 8.5 lb/gal; visc. 285 cps; HLB 3.0; pour pt. -29 C; flash pt. (PMCC) 455 F; cloud pt. 24 C (1% aq.); ref. index 1.4520; Ross-Miles foam 10 mm (0.1%); 100% conc.; nonionic.
Macol® 2. [PPG/Specialty Chem.]
Chem. Descrip.: Poloxamer 182
CAS 9003-11-6
Uses: Emulsifier, wetting agent, dispersant, defoamer, gellant, solubilizer, lubricant base for medical and pharmaceutical applics.
Properties: Liq.; sol. in aromatic solvs.; m.w. 2500; sp.gr. 1.03; visc. 415 cps; HLB 7.0; pour pt. -4 C; cloud pt. 32 C (1% aq.); surf. tens. 42.8 dynes/cm (0.1%); Ross-Miles foam 35 mm (0.1%); 100% conc.; nonionic.
Macol® 2D. [PPG/Specialty Chem.]
Chem. Descrip.: EO/PO block copolymer
Uses: Wetting agent, dispersant, defoamer, gellant, solubilizer, lubricant base for medical and pharmaceutical applics.
Properties: Liq.; sol. in aromatic solvs.; m.w. 2360; sp.gr. 1.03; visc. 400 cps; HLB 7.6; pour pt. -1 C; cloud pt. 35 C (1% aq.); surf. tens. 43.0 dynes/cm (0.1%); Ross-Miles foam 15 mm (0.1%); 100% conc.; nonionic.
Macol® 2LF. [PPG/Specialty Chem.]
Chem. Descrip.: Block polymer
Uses: Wetting agent, dispersant, defoamer, gellant, solubilizer, lubricant base for medical and pharmaceutical applics.
Properties: Liq.; sol. in aromatic solvs.; m.w. 2300; sp.gr. 1.02; visc. 400 cps; HLB 6.6; pour pt. -7 C; cloud pt. 28 C (1% aq.); surf. tens. 41.2 dynes/cm (0.1%); Ross-Miles foam 26 mm (0.1%); 100% conc.; nonionic.
Macol® 4. [PPG/Specialty Chem.]
Chem. Descrip.: Poloxamer 184

CAS 9003-11-6
Uses: Foaming agent, emulsifier, wetting agent, dispersant, defoamer, gellant, solubilizer, lubricant base for medical and pharmaceutical applics.
Properties: Liq.; sol. in aromatic solvs.; m.w. 2900; sp.gr. 1.05; visc. 800 cps; HLB 15.0; pour pt. 16 C; cloud pt. 60 C (1% aq.); surf. tens. 43.2 dynes/cm (0.1%); Ross-Miles foam > 600 mm (0.1%); 100% conc.; nonionic.
Macol® 8. [PPG/Specialty Chem.]
Chem. Descrip.: Poloxamer 188
CAS 9003-11-6
Uses: Foaming agent, wetting agent, dispersant, gellant, solubilizer, lubricant base for medical and pharmaceutical applics.
Properties: Flake; sol. in aromatic solvs.; m.w. 8500; sp.gr. 1.06; visc. 1100 cps; HLB 29.0; pour pt. 52 C; cloud pt. > 100 C (1% aq.); surf. tens. 50.3 dynes/cm (0.1%); Ross-Miles foam > 600 mm (0.1%); 100% conc.; nonionic.
Macol® 10. [PPG/Specialty Chem.]
Chem. Descrip.: PO-EO block copolymers
Uses: Wetting agent, dispersant, defoamer, gellant, solubilizer, lubricant base for medical and pharmaceutical applics.
Properties: Liq.; sol. in aromatic solvs.; m.w. 3200; sp.gr. 1.04; visc. 660 cps; HLB 4.5; pour pt. -5 C; cloud pt. 32 C (1% aq.); surf. tens. 40.6 dynes/cm (0.1%); Ross-Miles foam 90 mm (0.1%); 100% conc.; nonionic.
Macol® 22. [PPG/Specialty Chem.]
Chem. Descrip.: Block polymer
Uses: Wetting agent, dispersant, defoamer, gellant, solubilizer, lubricant base for medical and pharmaceutical applics.
Properties: Liq.; sol. in aromatic solvs.; m.w. 2000; sp.gr. 1.01; visc. 520 cps; pour pt. -10 C; cloud pt. 17 C (1% aq.); 100% conc.; nonionic.
Macol® 27. [PPG/Specialty Chem.]
Chem. Descrip.: Poloxamer 407
CAS 9003-11-6
Uses: Emulsifier, wetting agent, dispersant, foamer, defoamer, gellant, solubilizer, lubricant base for medical and pharmaceutical applics.
Properties: Flake; sol. in aromatic solvs.; m.w. 12,500; sp.gr. 1.05 (77 C); visc. 3100 cps (77 C); HLB 2.2; m.p. 56 C; cloud pt. > 100 C (1% aq.);

surf. tens. 40.7 dynes/cm (0.1%); Ross-Miles foam > 600 mm (0.1%); 100% conc.; nonionic.

Macol® 33. [PPG/Specialty Chem.]
Chem. Descrip.: Meroxapol 311
CAS 9003-11-6
Uses: Wetting agent, dispersant, defoamer, gellant, solubilizer, lubricant base for medical and pharmaceutical applics.
Properties: APHA < 100 liq.; sol. in water, aromatic solvs.; m.w. 3200; sp.gr. 1.018; dens. 8.5 lb/gal; visc. 578 cps; HLB 4.0; pour pt. -25 C; cloud pt. 25 C (1% aq.); flash pt. (PMCC) < 450 F; ref. index 1.4522; surf. tens. 34.1 dynes/cm (0.1%); Ross-Miles foam < 5 mm (0.1%); 100% conc.; nonionic.

Macol® 40. [PPG/Specialty Chem.]
Chem. Descrip.: Meroxapol 252
CAS 9003-11-6
Uses: Wetting agent, dispersant, defoamer, gellant, solubilizer, lubricant base for medical and pharmaceutical applics.
Properties: Liq.; sol. in aromatic solvs.; m.w. 3100; sp.gr. 1.03; visc. 700 cps; pour pt. -5 C; cloud pt. 29 C (1% aq.); surf. tens. 37.5 dynes/cm (0.1%); Ross-Miles foam < 5 mm (0.1%); 100% conc.; nonionic.

Macol® 57. [PPG/Specialty Chem.]
Chem. Descrip.: PPG-10 butanediol
Uses: Nongreasy emollient for antiperspirants; good solv. for many sunscreen actives; crystal growth inhibitor
Properties: Water-wh. clear liq., mild char. odor; sol. in water, SD alcohol 40B, butylene glycol, IPM, benzyl laurate, almond oil; disp. in cyclomethicone, min. and jojoba oils; insol. in glycerin; sp.gr. 1.005; visc. < 100 cps; m.p. < -25 C; b.p. > 150 C; cloud pt. 42 C; flash pt. (CC) > 95 C; ref. index 1.450; pH 6.0
Toxicology: LD50 (oral) < 5 g/kg; nontoxic inhalation hazard; safe for external use.

Macol® 85. [PPG/Specialty Chem.]
Chem. Descrip.: Poloxamer 235
CAS 9003-11-6
Uses: Wetting agent, dispersant, defoamer, gellant, solubilizer, lubricant base for medical and pharmaceutical applics.
Properties: Paste; sol. in aromatic solvs.; m.w. 4600; sp.gr. 1.04 (60 C); visc. 320 cps (60 C); HLB 16.0; pour pt. 29 C; cloud pt. 85 C (1% aq.); surf. tens. 42.5 dynes/cm (0.1%); Ross-Miles foam > 600 mm (0.1%); 100% conc.; nonionic.

Macol® 124. [PPG/Specialty Chem.]
Chem. Descrip.: Cetearyl alcohol, ceteareth-20
Uses: Emulsifier for pharmaceutical applics.; recommended for very mild and hypo-allergenic skin care prods.
Properties: Flake; m.p. 52 C; acid no. 0.5; iodine no. 0.5; sapon. no. 2; flash pt. (PMCC) > 350 F; nonionic.

Macol® 125. [PPG/Specialty Chem.]
Chem. Descrip.: Stearyl alcohol, ceteareth-20
Uses: Emulsifier for pharmaceutical applics.; recommended for very mild and hypo-allergenic skin

care prods.
Properties: Flake; m.p. 60 C; acid no. 1; iodine no. 2.0; sapon. no. 2; flash pt. (PMCC) > 350 F; nonionic.

Macol® CA 30P. [PPG/Specialty Chem.]
Chem. Descrip.: PPG-30 cetyl ether
CAS 9035-85-2
Uses: Emollient, moisturizer for pharmaceutical formulations
Properties: Lt. yel. liq.; acid no. 1 max.; iodine no. 3 max.; hyd. no. 35-45; 0.5% max. water.

Macol® CPS. [PPG/Specialty Chem.]
Chem. Descrip.: Cetearyl alcohol, polysorbate 60, PEG-150 stearate, steareth-20
Uses: Emulsifier for pharmaceutical applics.; recommended for very mild and hypo-allergenic skin care prods.
Properties: Flake; m.p. 51 C; acid no. 1.5; iodine no. 2; sapon. no. 12; flash pt. (PMCC) > 350 F; nonionic.

Macol® E-200. [PPG/Specialty Chem.]
Chem. Descrip.: PEG-4
CAS 25322-68-3; EINECS 203-989-9
Uses: Component in pharmaceutical preps.; non-irritating humectant
Properties: Liq.; sol. @ 5% in water; m.w. 200; visc. 3 cst (210 F); flash pt. (PMCC) 300 F.

Macol® E-300. [PPG/Specialty Chem.]
Chem. Descrip.: PEG-6
CAS 25322-68-3; EINECS 220-045-1
Uses: Component in pharmaceutical preps.; non-irritating humectant
Properties: Liq.; water-sol.; visc. 6 cst (210 F).

Macol® E-400. [PPG/Specialty Chem.]
Chem. Descrip.: PEG-8
CAS 25322-68-3; EINECS 225-856-4
Uses: Component in pharmaceutical preps.; non-irritating humectant
Properties: Liq.; water-sol.; visc. 7.5 cst (210 F).

Macol® E-600. [PPG/Specialty Chem.]
Chem. Descrip.: PEG-12
CAS 25322-68-3; EINECS 229-859-1
Uses: Component in pharmaceutical preps.; non-irritating humectant
Properties: Solid; water-sol.; visc. 10.5 cSt (210 F).

Macrospherical® 95. [Reheis]
Chem. Descrip.: Aluminum chlorohydrate
CAS 1327-41-9; EINECS 215-477-2
Uses: Antiperspirant active for aerosols with controlled particle size; spray-dried to a relatively thick walled hollow sphere
Properties: Spherical powd., 90% min. > 10 μ particle size; 47% Al_2O_3, 16.3% Cl.

Magaldrate Fluid Gel. [Reheis]
Chem. Descrip.: Magaldrate
Uses: Low sodium extremely reactive antacid active esp. suitable for prod. of double-str. antacid preps.
Properties: Fluid gel; 21.5% magaldrate, 8% MgO, 5% Al_2O_3, 0.02% Na.

Magaldrate Powd. USP. [Reheis]
Chem. Descrip.: Magaldrate USP

Uses: Antacid active for tablet and suspension use; highly reactive, low sodium
Properties: Free-flowing powd.; > 85% magaldrate, 34.5% MgO, 22% Al_2O_3, 0.06% Na.

Magnabrite® F. [Am. Colloid]
Chem. Descrip.: Magnesium aluminum silicate USP/NF
CAS 12199-37-0; EINECS 235-374-6
Uses: Disintegrant, binder, stabilizing and suspending agent for pharmaceutical tablets, ointments, and pastes where dry blending is essential
Properties: Wh. fine powd.; 100% thru 325 mesh; insol. in water or alcohol; surf. area > 750 m^2/g; visc. 150-450 cps (5% solids); pH 9-10 (5% disp.); dry brightness (GE) 83-87; 8% max. moisture.

Magnabrite® FS. [Am. Colloid]
Chem. Descrip.: Magnesium aluminum silicate USP/NF
CAS 12199-37-0; EINECS 235-374-6
Uses: Disintegrant, binder, and suspension agent for tablets, ointments, and pastes where dry incorporation is essential
Properties: Wh. micronized powd.; 100% thru 325 mesh; insol. in water and alcohol; surf. area > 750 m^2/g; visc. 150-450 cps (5% solids); pH 9.0-10.0 (5% disp.); dry brightness (GE) 83-87; 8% max. moisture.

Magnabrite® HS. [Am. Colloid]
Chem. Descrip.: Magnesium aluminum silicate USP/NF
CAS 12199-37-0; EINECS 235-374-6
Uses: Suspending agent, gellant, and binder for use in pharmaceutical applics. where stability in acidic systems is essential
Properties: Wh. soft flakes, 20-100 mesh particle size; insol. in water and alcohol; surf. area > 750 m^2/g; visc. 40-200 cps (5% solids); pH 9.0-10.0 (5% disp.); dry brightness (GE) 70 min.; 8% max. moisture.

Magnabrite® HV. [Am. Colloid]
Chem. Descrip.: Magnesium aluminum silicate USP/NF
CAS 12199-37-0; EINECS 235-374-6
Uses: Emulsifying, thickening, stabilizing, and suspending agent for pharmaceutical formulations at low solids
Properties: Wh. soft flakes, 20-100 mesh particle size; insol. in water and alcohol; surf. area > 750 m^2/g; visc. 800-2200 cps (5% solids); pH 9-10 (5% disp.); dry brightness (GE) 83-87; 8% max. moisture.

Magnabrite® K. [Am. Colloid]
Chem. Descrip.: Magnesium aluminum silicate USP/NF, acid-stable
CAS 12199-37-0; EINECS 235-374-6
Uses: Stabilizing and suspending agent for acidic pharmaceutical preps.; controls flocculation
Properties: Wh. soft flakes.; 20-100 mesh particle size; insol. in water and alcohol; surf. area > 750 m^2/g; visc. 100-300 cps (5% solids); pH 9-10 (5% disp.); dry brightness (GE) 83-87; 8% max. moisture.

Magnabrite® S. [Am. Colloid]
Chem. Descrip.: Magnesium aluminum silicate USP/NF
CAS 12199-37-0; EINECS 235-374-6
Uses: Stabilizing and suspending agent for pharmaceuticals; used where good dispersibility, high visc., and wh. color are essential
Properties: Wh. soft flakes; 20-100 mesh particle size; insol. in water and alcohol; surf. area > 750 m^2/g; visc. 225-600 cps (5% solids); pH 9-10 (5% disp.); dry brightness (GE) 83-87; 8% max. moisture.

Magnasweet®. [Mafco Worldwide]
Chem. Descrip.: Monoammonium glycyrrhizinate
CAS 1407-03-0
Uses: Flavor enhancer, sweetness potentiator for artificial sweetener systems, syrups (cough/cold, oral antiseptics, antibiotics), chewables (antacids), lozenges, vitamins, powds.; masking agent for bitter aftertaste; synergist with natural sweeteners
Regulatory: FDA 21CFR §184.1408 GRAS
Properties: Powd. or presolubilized forms (glycerin or propylene glycol sol'ns.), intense lingering sweetness; hygroscopic; sol. in most solvs.
Storage: Exc. long-term shelf stability; avoid unwanted moisture accumulation.

Magnesium Hydroxide Fluid 25. [Reheis]
Chem. Descrip.: Magnesium hydroxide
CAS 1309-42-8; EINECS 215-170-3
Uses: Pumpable antacid active for combination antacid systems; stable; offers ease of handling and processing
Properties: Wh. fluid gel; 23-27% $Mg(OH)_2$.

Magnesium Hydroxide HD. [Reheis]
Chem. Descrip.: Magnesium hydroxide
CAS 1309-42-8; EINECS 215-170-3
Uses: Direct compression antacid dried gel for tablet and suspension use; high dens., exc. free-flow and nondusting chars.
Properties: Powd.; 98% min. thru 30 mesh, 15% max. thru 120 mesh; dens. 0.55 g/cc (tapped); 95-100.5% Mg(OH) 2.

Magnesium Hydroxide Paste. [Reheis]
Chem. Descrip.: Magnesium hydroxide
CAS 1309-42-8; EINECS 215-170-3
Uses: Antacid active which conforms to USP and BP specs. for magnesium hydroxide suspensions (milk of magnesia) when diluted to 7.75% Mg(OH) 2; also in combination with aluminum hydroxides for antacid preps.
Properties: Wh. smooth highly gelatinous paste; 29% Mg(OH) 2.

Magnesium Hydroxide Powd. [Reheis]
Chem. Descrip.: Magnesium hydroxide USP
CAS 1309-42-8; EINECS 215-170-3
Uses: Antacid active used in milk of magnesia and in combination with aluminum hydroxides for antacid preps.
Properties: Wh. finely divided free-flowing amorphous powd.; 95-100.5% assay
Unverified

Magnesium Hydroxide USP. [Morton Int'l.]
Chem. Descrip.: Magnesium hydroxide
CAS 1309-42-8; EINECS 215-170-3
Uses: Source of magnesium for vitamins, magnesium supplement in fortifiers, neutralizing agent, alkali in dentifrices and skin creams
Regulatory: USP, FCC compliance
Properties: Free-flowing powd.; 99% thru 325 mesh; bulk dens. 0.2 g/ml; 98.4% act.
Toxicology: Toxic when inhaled; harmless to skin.
Magnesium Hydroxide USP DC. [Morton Int'l.]
Chem. Descrip.: Magnesium hydroxide, dust-controlled form
CAS 1309-42-8; EINECS 215-170-3
Uses: Source of magnesium for vitamins, magnesium supplement in fortifiers, neutralizing agent; directly compressible; alkali in dentifrices and skin creams
Regulatory: USP, FCC compliance
Properties: Micro-pellets; 99% thru 20 mesh; bulk dens. 0.4 g/ml; 98.5% act.
Toxicology: Toxic when inhaled; harmless to skin.
Magnesium Oxide USP 30 Light. [Morton Int'l.]
Chem. Descrip.: Magnesium oxide
CAS 1309-48-4; EINECS 215-171-9
Uses: Antacid and mild laxative
Regulatory: USP, FCC compliance
Properties: Flat platelets; 3 µm avg. particle size; 99.5% min. thru 325 mesh; bulk dens. 0.1-0.2 g/ml; 98.4% act.
Magnesium Oxide USP 60 Light. [Morton Int'l.]
Chem. Descrip.: Magnesium oxide
CAS 1309-48-4; EINECS 215-171-9
Uses: Antacid and mild laxative
Regulatory: USP, FCC compliance
Properties: Flat platelets; 3 µm avg. particle size; 99.5% min. thru 325 mesh; bulk dens. 0.1-0.2 g/ml; 98.4% act.
Magnesium Oxide USP 90 Light. [Morton Int'l.]
Chem. Descrip.: Magnesium oxide
CAS 1309-48-4; EINECS 215-171-9
Uses: Antacid and mild laxative
Regulatory: USP, FCC compliance
Properties: Flat platelets; 3 µm avg. particle size; 99.5% min. thru 325 mesh; bulk dens. 0.1-0.2 g/ml; 98.4% act.
Magnesium Oxide USP Heavy. [Morton Int'l.]
Chem. Descrip.: Magnesium oxide
CAS 1309-48-4; EINECS 215-171-9
Uses: Antacid and mild laxative
Regulatory: USP, FCC compliance
Properties: Flat platelets; 3 µm avg. particle size; 99.5% min. thru 325 mesh; bulk dens. 0.2-0.3 g/ml; 98.4% act.
Maitake Mushroom Extract. [Garuda Int'l.]
Chem. Descrip.: Maitake mushroom extract from *Grifola frondosa* with 20% dextrose carrier
Uses: Used to formulate health foods and pharmaceuticals, capsules
Properties: Brn. fine powd.; min. 20 mesh or finer; partly sol. in water
Storage: 24 mo shelf life.

Maltrin® M040. [Grain Processing]
Chem. Descrip.: Maltodextrin
CAS 9050-36-6; EINECS 232-940-4
Uses: Nonsweet, nutritive polymer useful for wet binding and anticaking; film-former; adds visc. and mouthfeel, enhances color; nonirritating filler; humectant; inhibits crystal growth; for aq. film coating, creams and lotions, cleansers, wet granulation
Regulatory: 9CFR §318.7(c)(4), 319.140, 319.143, 319.182, 319.180, 319.181, 319.281, 319.300, 319.301, 319.306, 319.312, 381.147(f)(4), 381.159, 381.160; 21CFR §184.1444, GRAS
Properties: Wh. powd., bland flavor; can be dissolved up to 40% in water; bulk dens. 0.51 g/cc (packed); DE 5; pH 4-5; 6% max. moisture.
Maltrin® M050. [Grain Processing]
Chem. Descrip.: Maltodextrin
CAS 9050-36-6; EINECS 232-940-4
Uses: Nonsweet, nutritive film-forming polymer useful for adding visc., opacity, and mouthfeel to pharmaceuticals; for wet granulation
Regulatory: 9CFR §318.7(c)(4), 319.140, 319.143, 319.182, 319.180, 319.181, 319.281, 319.300, 319.301, 319.306, 319.312, 381.147(f)(4), 381.159, 381.160; 21CFR §184.1444, GRAS
Properties: Wh. powd.; can be dissolved up to 40% in water yielding opaque syrup; bulk dens. 0.56 g/cc (packed); DE 5; pH 4-5.
Maltrin® M100. [Grain Processing]
Chem. Descrip.: Maltodextrin
CAS 9050-36-6; EINECS 232-940-4
Uses: Nonsweet, nutritive polymer; inert carrier, filler, binder, extender, blending and bulking agent; exc. mouthfeel for chewable tablets; for film coating, spray drying, creams and lotions, dry/wet granulation, liq. preps., cleansers, throat lozenges
Regulatory: 9CFR §318.7(c)(4), 319.140, 319.143, 319.182, 319.180, 319.181, 319.281, 319.300, 319.301, 319.306, 319.312, 381.147(f)(4), 381.159, 381.160; 21CFR §184.1444, GRAS
Properties: Wh. powd., bland, low sweetness; disp. readily to produce clear sol'ns. at 30%; bulk dens. 0.56 g/cc (packed); DE 10; pH 4.0-4.7 (20%); 6% max. moisture.
Maltrin® M150. [Grain Processing]
Chem. Descrip.: Maltodextrin
CAS 9050-36-6; EINECS 232-940-4
Uses: Very sl. sweet nutritive polymer; bulking, bodying, binding agent; directly compressible; filler, humectant for creams/lotions; inert diluent for dry/wet granulation; visc. control in liqs.; medical nutrionals; cleansers; throat lozenges
Regulatory: 9CFR §318.7(c)(4), 319.140, 319.143, 319.182, 319.180, 319.181, 319.281, 319.300, 319.301, 319.306, 319.312, 381.147(f)(4), 381.159, 381.160; 21CFR §184.1444, GRAS
Properties: Wh. powd.; disp. to produce clear sol'n. at 50%; bulk dens. 0.61 g/cc (packed); DE 15; pH 4.0-4.7 (20%); 6% max. moisture.
Maltrin® M180. [Grain Processing]

Chem. Descrip.: Maltodextrin
CAS 9050-36-6; EINECS 232-940-4
Uses: Sl. sweet, nutritive polymer; directly compressible; bulking, bodying, and binding properties; film-former for aq. film coating; enhances color; for medical nutritionals, throat lozenges
Regulatory: 9CFR§318.7(c)(4), 319.140, 319.143, 319.182, 319.180, 319.181, 319.281, 319.300, 319.301, 319.306, 319.312, 381.147(f)(4), 381.159, 381.160; 21CFR §184.1444, GRAS
Properties: Wh. powd., bland; disp. easily to produce clear sol'ns. up to 60%; bulk dens. 0.63 g/cc (packed); DE 18; pH 4.0-4.7; 6% max. moisture.

Maltrin® M200. [Grain Processing]
Chem. Descrip.: Corn syrup solids
CAS 68131-37-3
Uses: Coating and binding agent; imparts smooth mouthfeel; directly compressible; visc. control in liqs.; regulates sweetness; inhibits crystal growth; medical nutritionals, dry granulation, tablets
Regulatory: FDA 21CFR §168.121, 184.1865, GRAS
Properties: Wh. powd.; disp. rapidly in cold or hot water to produce clear sol'n. at 60%; bulk dens. 0.64 g/cc (packed); DE 20; pH 4.0-4.7 (20%); 6% max. moisture.

Maltrin® M250. [Grain Processing]
Chem. Descrip.: Corn syrup solids
CAS 68131-37-3
Uses: Dried glucose syrup with good binding properties; imparts smooth mouthfeel; directly compressible; for spray drying applics.
Regulatory: FDA 21CFR §168.121, 184.1865, GRAS
Properties: Wh. powd., sl. sweet, no undesirable aftertaste; disp. rapidly in hot or cold water to produce clear sol'n. at 70%; bulk dens. 0.67 g/cc (packed); DE 25; pH 4.5-5.5; 6% max. moisture.

Maltrin® M510. [Grain Processing]
Chem. Descrip.: Agglomerated maltodextrin
CAS 9050-36-6; EINECS 232-940-4
Uses: Flowable form of Maltrin M100; exhibits exc. dispersibility and dissolution; directly compressible binder and inert diluent for pharmaceutical capsules, tablets; regulates sweetness; improves hardness, friability; low hygroscopicity
Regulatory: 9CFR§318.7(c)(4), 319.140, 319.143, 319.182, 319.180, 319.181, 319.281, 319.300, 319.301, 319.306, 319.312, 381.147(f)(4), 381.159, 381.160; 21CFR §184.1444, GRAS
Properties: Wh. free-flowing fine gran., bland; disp. easily to produce clear sol'ns. to 30%; bulk dens. 0.56 g/cc (packed); DE 10; pH 4.0-4.7.

Maltrin® M700. [Grain Processing]
Chem. Descrip.: Agglomerated maltodextrin NF
CAS 9050-36-6; EINECS 232-940-4
Uses: Agglomerated form of Maltrin M100; bulking/blending agent, inert carrier enhancing solubility and emulsification of absorbed components; exhibits exc. dissolution, neutral flavor
Regulatory: 9CFR§318.7(c)(4), 319.140, 319.143,

319.182, 319.180, 319.181, 319.281, 319.300, 319.301, 319.306, 319.312, 381.147(f)(4), 381.159, 381.160; 21CFR §184.1444, GRAS
Properties: Free-flowing gran.; disp. easily to clear sol'n. @ 30% solids, opaque sol'n. > 40% solids; bulk dens. 0.13 g/cc (packed); DE 9-12; pH 6.0-7.0 (20%); 6% max. moisture.

Maltrin® QD M440. [Grain Processing]
Chem. Descrip.: Agglomerated maltodextrin
CAS 9050-36-6; EINECS 232-940-4
Uses: Agglomerated form of Maltrin M040; exhibits exc. dispersibility and dissolution; for aq. film coating, bulk, blending, carrying, soaps and cleansers
Regulatory: 9CFR§318.7(c)(4), 319.140, 319.143, 319.182, 319.180, 319.181, 319.281, 319.300, 319.301, 319.306, 319.312, 381.147(f)(4), 381.159, 381.160; 21CFR §184.1444, GRAS
Properties: Wh. free-flowing gran. powd., bland; 90% min. on 200 mesh, 10% max. on 20 mesh; quickly dispersible at levels to 15% in water; bulk dens. 0.30 g/cc (packed); DE 4-7; pH 4.0-5.1 (20%); 6% max. moisture.

Maltrin® QD M500. [Grain Processing]
Chem. Descrip.: Agglomerated maltodextrin
CAS 9050-36-6; EINECS 232-940-4
Uses: Agglomerated form of Maltrin M100; exhibits exc. dispersibility and dissolution; directly compressible binder and good carrier; neutral flavor; inert diluent in capsules, tablets; regulates sweetness; improves hardness, friability; low hygroscopicity
Regulatory: 9CFR§318.7(c)(4), 319.140, 319.143, 319.182, 319.180, 319.181, 319.281, 319.300, 319.301, 319.306, 319.312, 381.147(f)(4), 381.159, 381.160; 21CFR §184.1444, GRAS
Properties: Wh. free-flowing gran., bland; 90% min. on 200 mesh, 10% min. on 20 mesh; quickly disp. in water to 30%; bulk dens. 0.34 g/cc (packed); DE 9-12; pH 4.0-5.1.

Maltrin® QD M550. [Grain Processing]
Chem. Descrip.: Agglomerated maltodextrin
CAS 9050-36-6; EINECS 232-940-4
Uses: Agglomerated form of Maltrin M150; exhibits exc. dispersibility and dissolution; directly compressible binder and good carrier for pharmaceuticals; for liq. preps., medical nutritionals, soaps and cleansers
Regulatory: 9CFR§318.7(c)(4), 319.140, 319.143, 319.182, 319.180, 319.181, 319.281, 319.300, 319.301, 319.306, 319.312, 381.147(f)(4), 381.159, 381.160; 21CFR §184.1444, GRAS
Properties: Wh. free-flowing gran.; 87% on 200 mesh, 4% on 20 mesh; quickly disp. up to 50% solids; bulk dens. 0.37 g/cc (packed); DE 13-17; pH 4.0-5.1; 6% max. moisture.

Maltrin® QD M580. [Grain Processing]
Chem. Descrip.: Agglomerated maltodextrin
CAS 9050-36-6; EINECS 232-940-4
Uses: Quickly disp. carbohydrate with high rate of sol'n., exc. particulate str.; for aq. film coating, medical nutritionals, tableting

Regulatory: 9CFR §318.7(c)(4), 319.140, 319.143, 319.182, 319.180, 319.181, 319.281, 319.300, 319.301, 319.306, 319.312, 381.147(f)(4), 381.159, 381.160; 21CFR §184.1444, GRAS
Properties: Wh. free-flowing gran., bland; 10% max. on 20 mesh, 85% min. on 200 mesh; quickly disp. in water to 60% conc.; absorbs up to 10-11% moisture remaining free-flowing; bulk dens. 0.40 g/cc (packed); DE 16.5-19.5; pH 4.0-5.1; 6% max. moisture.

Maltrin® QD M600. [Grain Processing]
Chem. Descrip.: Agglomerated corn syrup solids
CAS 68131-37-3
Uses: Agglomerated form of Maltrin M200; directly compressible binder and good carrier; bulking, blending agent; for capsules, medical nutritonals
Regulatory: FDA 21CFR §168.121, 184.1865, GRAS
Properties: Wh. free-flowing gran., bland, sl. sweet; 87% on 200 mesh, 4% on 20 mesh; quickly disp. in water to 60% conc.; bulk dens. 0.40 g/cc (packed); DE 20-23; pH 4.0-5.1 (20%); 6% max. moisture.

MANUCOL DM. [Kelco Int'l.]
Chem. Descrip.: Sodium alginate
CAS 9005-38-3
Uses: Gellant, suspending agent, thickener, stabilizer, film-former for pharmaceuticals
Regulatory: FDA 21CFR §184.1724, GRAS; EEC E401 compliance
Properties: Wh. to tan powd., sl. odor; 250 µ particle size; water-sol.; bulk dens. ≈ 50 lb/ft³; visc. 250 cps (1%), 5500 cps (2%); pH 6.0.
Toxicology: LD50 (oral, rat) > 5000 mg/kg; dry powd. may cause eye irritation
Precaution: Incompat. with strong oxidizers.

MANUCOL DMF. [Kelco Int'l.]
Chem. Descrip.: Sodium alginate
CAS 9005-38-3
Uses: Gellant, suspending agent, thickener, stabilizer, film-former for pharmaceuticals
Regulatory: FDA 21CFR §184.1724, GRAS; EEC E401 compliance
Properties: Wh. to tan powd., sl. odor; 105 µ particle size; water-sol.; bulk dens. ≈ 50 lb/ft³; visc. 300 cps (1%), 7000 cps (2%); pH 6.
Toxicology: LD50 (oral, rat) > 5000 mg/kg; dry powd. may cause eye irritation
Precaution: Incompat. with strong oxidizers.

MANUCOL LB. [Kelco Int'l.]
Chem. Descrip.: Algin
CAS 9005-38-3
Uses: Gellant, suspending agent, thickener, stabilizer, film-former for pharmaceuticals, liq. antacids
Regulatory: FDA 21CFR §184.1724, GRAS; EEC E401 compliance
Properties: Wh. to tan powd., sl. odor; 355 µ particle size; 40 mesh; water-sol.; bulk dens. ≈ 50 lb/ft³; visc. 150 cps (1%), 1500 cps (2%); pH 6
Toxicology: LD50 (oral, rat) > 5000 mg/kg; dry powd. may cause eye irritation

Precaution: Incompat. with strong oxidizers.
MANUCOL LKX. [Kelco Int'l.]
Chem. Descrip.: Sodium alginate
CAS 9005-38-3
Uses: Used in denture adhesives
Properties: 63 µ particle size; 250 mesh; visc. 4 cps (1%), 12 cps (2%).

Mapeg® 200 DL. [PPG/Specialty Chem.]
Chem. Descrip.: PEG-4 dilaurate
CAS 9005-02-1
Uses: Emulsifier, spreading agent, and dispersant used in pharmaceuticals
Properties: Yel. clear liq.; sol. in IPA, toluol, soybean and min. oil, water disp.; sp.gr. 0.95; m.p. 10 C; HLB 7.6; acid no. 10 max.; sapon. no. 176-192; flash pt. (PMCC) > 350 F; 100% conc.; nonionic.

Mapeg® 200 DO. [PPG/Specialty Chem.]
Chem. Descrip.: PEG-4 dioleate
CAS 9005-07-6
Uses: Emulsifier, emollient, and dispersant used in pharmaceuticals
Properties: Yel. clear liq.; sol. in IPA, toluol, soybean and min. oil, water disp.; sp.gr. 0.95; m.p. < -10 C; HLB 6.0; acid no. 10 max.; sapon. no. 148-158; flash pt. (PMCC) > 350 F; 100% conc.; nonionic.

Mapeg® 200 ML. [PPG/Specialty Chem.]
Chem. Descrip.: PEG-4 laurate
CAS 9004-81-3
Uses: Emulsifier, emollient, pigment dispersant used in pharmaceuticals
Properties: Yel. clear liq.; sol. in IPA, toluol, soybean and min. oil, water disp.; sp.gr. 0.991; m.p. 5 C; HLB 9.3; acid no. 5 max.; sapon. no. 139-159; flash pt. (PMCC) > 350 F; 100% conc.; nonionic.

Mapeg® 200 MO. [PPG/Specialty Chem.]
Chem. Descrip.: PEG-4 oleate
CAS 9004-96-0; EINECS 233-293-0
Uses: Emulsifier, dispersant used in pharmaceuticals
Properties: Yel. clear liq.; sol. in IPA, toluol, soybean oil; disp. hot in water; sp.gr. 0.97; m.p. < -10 C; HLB 8.3; acid no. 5 max.; sapon. no. 115-125; flash pt. (PMCC) > 350 F; 100% conc.; nonionic.

Mapeg® 400 DL. [PPG/Specialty Chem.]
Chem. Descrip.: PEG-8 dilaurate
CAS 9005-02-1
Uses: Emulsifier, dispersant used in pharmaceuticals
Properties: Lt. yel. liq.; sol. in IPA, toluol, soybean oil, water disp.; sp.gr. 0.98; m.p. 18 C; HLB 10.8; acid no. 10 max.; sapon. no. 130-140; flash pt. (PMCC) > 350 F; 100% conc.; nonionic.

Mapeg® 400 DO. [PPG/Specialty Chem.]
Chem. Descrip.: PEG-8 dioleate
CAS 9005-07-6
Uses: Emulsifier, emollient, and dispersant used in pharmaceuticals
Properties: Yel. liq.; sol. in IPA, toluol, soybean and min. oil, water disp.; sp.gr. 0.98; m.p. < 7 C; HLB 8.8; acid no. 10 max.; sapon. no. 114-122; flash pt. (PMCC) > 350 F; 100% conc.; nonionic.

Mapeg® 400 DOT. [PPG/Specialty Chem.]
Chem. Descrip.: PEG-8 ditallate
CAS 61791-01-3
Uses: Emulsifier, dispersant used in pharmaceuticals
Properties: Liq.; sol. @ 5% in IPA, min. spirits, toluene, min. oil; disp. in water; sp.gr. 0.98; HLB 8.8; acid no. 10 max.; sapon. no. 118; pour pt. 6 C; flash pt. (PMCC) > 350 F; 100% conc.; nonionic.

Mapeg® 400 DS. [PPG/Specialty Chem.]
Chem. Descrip.: PEG-8 distearate
CAS 9005-08-7
Uses: Emulsifier, dispersant used in pharmaceuticals
Properties: Wh. solid; sol. in IPA, toluol, soybean and min. oil, hot water disp.; m.p. 36 C; HLB 8.1; acid no. 10 max.; sapon. no. 116-125; flash pt. (PMCC) > 350 F; 100% conc.; nonionic.

Mapeg® 400 ML. [PPG/Specialty Chem.]
Chem. Descrip.: PEG-8 laurate
CAS 9004-81-3; EINECS 253-458-0
Uses: Emulsifier, dispersant used in pharmaceuticals
Properties: Lt. yel., liq.; sol. in IPA, toluol, water; disp. in min. spirits; sp.gr. 1.01; m.p. 12 C; HLB 13.2; acid no. 5 max.; sapon. no. 89-96; flash pt. (PMCC) > 350 F; 100% conc.; nonionic.

Mapeg® 400 MO. [PPG/Specialty Chem.]
Chem. Descrip.: PEG-8 oleate
CAS 9004-96-0
Uses: Emulsifier, spreading agent, dispersant used in pharmaceuticals
Properties: Yel. liq.; sol. in IPA, toluol, soybean oil, water disp.; sp.gr. 1.01; m.p. < 10 C; HLB 11.8; acid no. 5 max.; sapon. no. 80-88; flash pt. (PMCC) > 350 F; 100% conc.; nonionic.

Mapeg® 400 MOT. [PPG/Specialty Chem.]
Chem. Descrip.: PEG-8 tallate
CAS 61791-00-2
Uses: Emulsifier, dispersant used in pharmaceuticals
Properties: Liq.; sol. @ 5% in IPA, toluene; disp. in water, min. spirits, min. oil; sp.gr. 1.01; HLB 11.8; acid no. 5 max.; sapon. no. 84; pour pt. 5 C; flash pt. (PMCC) > 350 F; 100% conc.; nonionic.

Mapeg® 400 MS. [PPG/Specialty Chem.]
Chem. Descrip.: PEG-8 stearate
CAS 9004-99-3
Uses: Emulsifier, dispersant used in pharmaceuticals
Properties: Wh. solid; sol. in IPA, toluol, soybean oil, hot water disp.; m.p. 33 C; HLB 11.5; acid no. 5 max.; sapon. no. 84-93; flash pt. (PMCC) > 350 F; 100% conc.; nonionic.

Mapeg® 600 DO. [PPG/Specialty Chem.]
Chem. Descrip.: PEG-12 dioleate
CAS 9005-07-6; EINECS 288-459-5
Uses: Emulsifier, dispersant used in pharmaceuticals
Properties: Yel. liq.; sol. in IPA, toluol, soybean oil, water disp.; sp.gr. 1.00; m.p. 20 C; HLB 10.3; acid

no. 10 max.; sapon. no. 92-102; flash pt. (PMCC) > 350 F; 100% conc.; nonionic.

Mapeg® 600 DOT. [PPG/Specialty Chem.]
Chem. Descrip.: PEG-12 ditallate
CAS 61791-01-3
Uses: Emulsifier, dispersant used in pharmaceuticals
Properties: Amber liq.; sol. IPA, toluol, soybean oil; disp. water; sp.gr. 1.00; HLB 10.3; m.p. 15 C; acid no. 10 max.; sapon. no. 85-95; flash pt. (PMCC) > 350 F; 100% conc.; nonionic.

Mapeg® 600 DS. [PPG/Specialty Chem.]
Chem. Descrip.: PEG-12 distearate
CAS 9005-08-7
Uses: Emulsifier, dispersant used in pharmaceuticals
Properties: Wh. solid or flake; sol. in IPA, toluol, soybean oil, hot water disp.; m.p. 41 C; HLB 10.6; acid no. 10 max.; sapon. no. 94-104; flash pt. (PMCC) > 350 F; 100% conc.; nonionic.

Mapeg® 600 MOT. [PPG/Specialty Chem.]
Chem. Descrip.: PEG-12 tallate
CAS 61791-00-2
Uses: Emulsifier, dispersant used in pharmaceuticals
Properties: Visc. 175 cps; HLB 13.6; nonionic.

Mapeg® 600 MS. [PPG/Specialty Chem.]
Chem. Descrip.: PEG-12 stearate
CAS 9004-99-3
Uses: Emulsifier, dispersant used in pharmaceuticals
Properties: Wh. solid; sol. in IPA, toluol, soybean oil, water, propylene glycol; disp. hot in min. oil; m.p. 36 C; HLB 13.6; acid no. 5 max.; sapon. no. 62-70; flash pt. (PMCC) > 350 F; 100% conc.; nonionic.

Mapeg® 1000 MS. [PPG/Specialty Chem.]
Chem. Descrip.: PEG-20 stearate
CAS 9004-99-3
Uses: Emulsifier, dispersant used in pharmaceuticals
Properties: Wh. solid or flake; sol. in IPA, toluol, propylene glycol, water; m.p. 42 C; HLB 15.7; acid no. 5; sapon. no. 41-49; flash pt. (PMCC) > 350 F; 100% conc.; nonionic.

Mapeg® 6000 DS. [PPG/Specialty Chem.]
Chem. Descrip.: PEG-150 distearate
CAS 9005-08-7
Uses: Emulsifier, thickener, dispersant used in pharmaceuticals
Properties: Wh. solid or flake; sol. in IPA, toluol, propylene glycol, water; m.p. 55 C; HLB 18.4; acid no. 9 max.; sapon. no. 14-20; flash pt. (PMCC) > 350 F; 100% conc.; nonionic.

Mapeg® EGDS. [PPG/Specialty Chem.]
Chem. Descrip.: Glycol distearate
CAS 627-83-8; EINECS 211-014-3
Uses: Emulsifier, thickener, opacifier, pearling additive, and dispersant used in pharmaceuticals
Properties: Wh. solid or flake; sol. in IPA, toluol, soybean and min. oil; disp. in min. spirits; m.p. 63 C; HLB 1.4; acid no. 6 max.; sapon. no. 190-199;

flash pt. (PMCC) > 350 F; 100% conc.; nonionic.

Mapeg® EGMS. [PPG/Specialty Chem.]
Chem. Descrip.: Glycol stearate
CAS 111-60-4; EINECS 203-886-9
Uses: Emulsifier, thickener, opacifier, pearling additive, and dispersant used in pharmaceuticals
Properties: Wh. to cream solid or flake; sol. @ 5% in IPA, toluol, soybean and min. oil; disp. in min. spirits; m.p. 56 C; HLB 2.9; acid no. 4 max.; sapon. no. 180-188; flash pt. (PMCC) > 350 F; 100% conc.; nonionic.

Mapeg® S-40K. [PPG/Specialty Chem.]
Chem. Descrip.: PEG-40 stearate, kosher
CAS 9004-99-3
Uses: Emulsifier, dispersant for pharmaceuticals
Properties: Gardner 2 max. flake; sol. in IPA, toluol, propylene glycol, water; congeal pt. 37-47 C; HLB 17.2; acid no. 1 max.; sapon. no. 25-35; hyd. no. 27-40; flash pt. (PMCC) > 350 F; 100% conc.; nonionic.

Marinco® CH. [Marine Magnesium]
Chem. Descrip.: Magnesium carbonate USP, FCC
CAS 546-93-0; EINECS 208-915-9
Uses: Antacid, alkaline buffer, and min. supplement used in pharmaceuticals, dentifrices
Properties: Wh. free-flowing powd.; 100% thru 100 mesh, 97% min. thru 325 mesh; bulk dens. 10-14 lb/ft^3 (loose); 40-43.5% MgO
Storage: Store in dry environment in tightly sealed containers.

Marinco® CH-Granular. [Marine Magnesium]
Chem. Descrip.: Magnesium carbonate USP, FCC
EINECS 208-915-9
Uses: Antacid, alkaline buffer, mineral supplement
Properties: Wh. free-flowing gran.; 100% min. thru 20 mesh, 20% max. on 40 mesh; bulk dens. 35 lb/ft^3 min. (loose); 40-43.5% MgO
Storage: Store in dry environment in tightly sealed containers.

Marinco® CL. [Marine Magnesium]
Chem. Descrip.: Magnesium carbonate USP, FCC
EINECS 208-915-9
Uses: Antacid, alkaline buffer, ingred. used in pharmaceuticals, dentifrices; decolorizer, deodorizer in various processes
Properties: Wh. free-flowing powd.; 100% min. thru 100 mesh, 99% min. thru 325 mesh; bulk dens. 5-8 lb/ft^3 (loose); 40-43.5% MgO
Storage: Store in dry environment in tightly sealed containers.

Marinco H-USP. [Marine Magnesium]
Chem. Descrip.: Magnesium hydroxide USP, FCC
CAS 1309-42-8; EINECS 215-170-3
Uses: Antacid and alkaline buffer for milk of magnesia tablets and for making magnesium citrate
Properties: Wh. free-flowing powd.; 100% min. thru 100 mesh, 99% min. thru 325 mesh; bulk dens. 25-33 lb/ft^3; 95-100.5% MgOH
Storage: Store in dry environment in tightly sealed containers.

Marinco OH. [Marine Magnesium]
Chem. Descrip.: Magnesium oxide USP, FCC

CAS 1309-48-4; EINECS 215-171-9
Uses: Antacid, alkaline buffer, and mineral supplement
Properties: Wh. free-flowing powd.; 100% min. thru 100 mesh, 99.5% min. thru 325 mesh; bulk dens. 18-26 lb/ft^3 (loose); 96-100.5% MgO
Storage: Store in dry environment in tightly sealed containers.

Marinco OL. [Marine Magnesium]
Chem. Descrip.: Magnesium oxide USP/FCC
CAS 1309-48-4; EINECS 215-171-9
Uses: Antacid and alkaline buffer
Regulatory: FCC, USP compliance
Properties: Wh. free-flowing powd.; 100% min thru 100 mesh, 99.5% min. thru 325 mesh; bulk dens. 4-8 lb/ft^3; 96-100.5% MgO
Storage: Store in dry environment in tightly sealed containers.

Mark® 5095. [Witco/PAG]
Chem. Descrip.: Lauryl/stearyl thiodipropionate
Uses: Antioxidant for pharmaceuticals
Regulatory: FDA regulated
Properties: Wh. free-flowing powd.

Massa Estarinum® 299. [Hüls AG]
Uses: Suppository bases for pharmaceuticals
Properties: M.p. 33.5-35.5 C; solid. pt. 32-34.5 C; acid no. 0.3 max.; iodine no. 3 max.; sapon. no. 240-255; hyd. no. 2 max.

Massa Estarinum® A. [Hüls AG]
Uses: Suppository bases for pharmaceuticals
Properties: M.p. 33-35 C; solid. pt. 29-31 C; acid no. 0.5 max.; iodine no. 3 max.; sapon. no. 225-240; hyd. no. 35-45.

Massa Estarinum® AB. [Hüls AG]
Uses: Suppository bases for pharmaceuticals
Properties: M.p. 29-31 C; solid. pt. 26.5-28.5 C; acid no. 0.3 max.; iodine no. 3 max.; sapon. no. 235-245; hyd. no. 25-40.

Massa Estarinum® B. [Hüls AG]
Uses: Suppository bases for pharmaceuticals
Properties: M.p. 33.5-35.5 C; solid. pt. 31-33 C; acid no. 0.3 max.; iodine no. 3 max.; sapon. no. 225-240; hyd. no. 20-30.

Massa Estarinum® BB. [Hüls AG]
Uses: Suppository bases for pharmaceuticals
Properties: M.p. 33.5-35.5 C; solid. pt. 31.5-33.5 C; acid no. 0.3 max.; iodine no. 3 max.; sapon. no. 225-240; hyd. no. 18.5-28.5.

Massa Estarinum® BC. [Hüls AG]
Uses: Suppository bases for pharmaceuticals
Properties: M.p. 33.5-35.5 C; solid. pt. 30.5-32.5 C; acid no. 0.3 max.; iodine no. 3 max.; sapon. no. 225-240; hyd. no. 30-40.

Massa Estarinum® BCF. [Hüls AG]
Uses: Suppository bases for pharmaceuticals
Properties: M.p. 35-36.5 C; solid. pt. 33.5-35 C; acid no. 0.3 max.; iodine no. 3 max.; sapon. no. 225-240; hyd. no. 25-30.

Massa Estarinum® BD. [Hüls AG]
Uses: Suppository bases for pharmaceuticals
Properties: M.p. 33.5-35.5 C; solid. pt. 32-34 C; acid no. 0.3 max.; iodine no. 3 max.; sapon. no.

225-240; hyd. no. 15 max.

Massa Estarinum® C. [Hüls AG]
Uses: Suppository bases for pharmaceuticals
Properties: M.p. 36-38 C; solid. pt. 33-35 C; acid no. 0.3 max.; iodine no. 3 max.; sapon. no. 225-235; hyd. no. 20-30.

Massa Estarinum® D. [Hüls AG]
Uses: Suppository bases for pharmaceuticals
Properties: M.p. 40-42 C; solid. pt. 38-40 C; acid no. 0.3 max.; iodine no. 3 max.; sapon. no. 220-230; hyd. no. 30-40.

Massa Estarinum® E. [Hüls AG]
Uses: Suppository bases for pharmaceuticals
Properties: M.p. 34-36 C; solid. pt. 29-31 C; acid no. 1 max.; iodine no. 3 max.; sapon. no. 215-230; hyd. no. 45-60.

Mazamide® C-2. [PPG/Specialty Chem.]
Chem. Descrip.: PEG-3 cocamide MEA
Uses: Foam builder/stabilizer for pharmaceutical shampoos; solubilizer for coupling emollients and fragrances into high-foaming surfactant systems
Properties: Liq.; sp.gr. 0.95; flash pt. (PMCC) > 300 F; biodeg.

Mazamide® CMEA. [PPG/Specialty Chem.]
Chem. Descrip.: Cocamide MEA (1:1)
CAS 68140-00-1; EINECS 268-770-2
Uses: Foam booster/stabilizer, thickener, emulsifier for pharmaceutical shampoos
Properties: Flake; sp.gr. 0.93; flash pt. (PMCC) > 300 F; biodeg.

Mazamide® L-5. [PPG/Specialty Chem.]
Chem. Descrip.: PEG-6 lauramide DEA
Uses: Emulsifier, lubricant, foam builder, stabilizer for pharmaceutical creams, lotions; solubilizer for coupling emollients and fragrances into high-foaming systems
Properties: Solid; sp.gr. 1.05; flash pt. (PMCC) > 300 F; pH 9.5- 10.5; 100% conc.; nonionic; biodeg.

Mazawax® 163R. [PPG/Specialty Chem.]
Chem. Descrip.: Cetearyl alcohol and polysorbate 60
Uses: Emulsifier for pharmaceutical applics.; base; emollient, thickener
Properties: Wh. flake; m.p. 51 C; acid no. 1; iodine no. 0.5; sapon. no. 12; flash pt. (PMCC) > 350 F; 100% conc.; nonionic.

Mazawax® 163SS. [PPG/Specialty Chem.]
Chem. Descrip.: Cetearyl alcohol and polysorbate 60
Uses: Emulsifying wax for pharmaceutical creams; recommended for very mild and hypo-allergenic skin care prods.
Properties: Flake; m.p. 51 C; 100% conc.; nonionic.

Mazol® 159. [PPG/Specialty Chem.]
Chem. Descrip.: PEG-7 glyceryl cocoate
Uses: Emollient, solubilizer for pharmaceuticals
Properties: Amber liq.; sol. in water, min. oil; disp. in min. spirits, toluene, IPA; HLB 13.0; acid no. 5 max.; sapon. no. 82-98; flash pt. (PMCC) > 350 F.

Mazol® 165C. [PPG/Specialty Chem.]
Chem. Descrip.: Glyceryl stearate and PEG-100

stearate
Uses: Emulsifier blend, thickener, and opacifier for pharmaceutical o/w emulsions; acid-stable
Properties: Tan flake; sol. in IPA; disp. in water; sol. hot in min. oil, toluene; HLB 11.2; acid no. 2 max.; sapon. no. 90-100; flash pt. (PMCC) > 350 F; 100% conc.; nonionic.

Mazol® GMS-90. [PPG/Specialty Chem.]
Chem. Descrip.: Glyceryl stearate
Uses: Emulsifier for pharmaceuticals
Properties: Tan flake; sol. in IPA; sol. hot in min. oil, toluene; HLB 3.9; acid no. 2 max.

Mazol® GMS-D. [PPG/Specialty Chem.]
Chem. Descrip.: Glyceryl stearate SE
Uses: Emulsifier, emollient for pharmaceuticals
Properties: Tan flake; sol. in IPA; sol. hot in min. oil, toluene; disp. in water; HLB 6.0; acid no. 3.5 max.; sapon. no. 145-160; flash pt. (PMCC) > 350 F.

Mazol® GMS-K. [PPG/Specialty Chem.]
Chem. Descrip.: Glyceryl stearate
CAS 11099-07-3
Uses: Lubricant, emulsifier, plasticizer, and thickener for drug prods.
Regulatory: FDA 21CFR §184.4505, GRAS; kosher
Properties: Wh. to cream flakes, ester odor; sol. in IPA; sol. hot in min. oil, veg. oil, propylene glycol, toluene; disp. hot in ethanol; insol. in water; sp.gr. 0.908; m.p. 61 C; b.p. > 300 F; HLB 3.9; acid no. 3 max.; iodine no. 5 max.; sapon. no. 165-176; flash pt. (PMCC) > 350 F; 100% conc., 40% min. monoglyceride; nonionic
Toxicology: Nonirritating, noncomedogenic
Storage: Store in well-ventilated area below 120 F.

Mazol® PGO-31 K. [PPG/Specialty Chem.]
Chem. Descrip.: Triglyceryl oleate
CAS 9007-48-1
Uses: Emulsifier for pharmaceuticals; solubilizer for flavors and essential oils
Regulatory: FDA 21CFR §172.854, kosher
Properties: Gardner 8 max. liq.; sol. in min. oil, veg. oil, propylene glycol, toluene, IPA; disp. in ethanol, min. spirits; insol. in water; HLB 6.2; acid no. 3 max.; iodine no. 78; sapon. no. 140-150; 100% conc.; nonionic.

Mazol® PGO-104. [PPG/Specialty Chem.]
Chem. Descrip.: Decaglyceryl tetraoleate
CAS 34424-98-1; EINECS 252-011-7
Uses: Emulsifier for pharmaceuticals; solubilizer and carrier for flavors and essential oils
Regulatory: FDA 21CFR §172.854; kosher
Properties: Dk. liq.; sol. in IPA, min. oil, veg. oil, toluene; disp. in ethanol, propylene glycol, min. spirits; insol. in water; HLB 6.2; acid no. 8 max.; iodine no. 61; sapon. no. 125-145; flash pt. (PMCC) > 350 F.

Mazu® DF 200SP. [PPG/Specialty Chem.]
Chem. Descrip.: Simethicone
CAS 8050-81-5
Uses: Food grade defoamer formulated to meet the specific needs of the pharmaceutical industry
Regulatory: FDA compliance

Properties: Liq.; sp.gr. 0.99; dens. 8.3 lb/gal; visc. 1720 cSt; flash pt. (PMCC) > 350 F; 100% silicone.

MEA Commercial Grade. [Dow]
Chem. Descrip.: Monoethanolamine
CAS 141-43-5; EINECS 205-483-3
Uses: Emulsifier used in pharmaceuticals
Properties: Sp.gr. 1.0113 (25/4 C); dens. 8.45 lb/gal; visc. 18.9 cps; f.p. 10 C; b.p. 171 C (760 mm Hg); flash pt. (Seta CC) 201 F; fire pt. 200 F; ref. index 1.4525.

MEA Low Freeze Grade. [Dow]
Chem. Descrip.: Monoethanolamine
CAS 141-43-5; EINECS 205-483-3
Uses: Emulsifier used in pharmaceuticals
Properties: Sp.gr. 1.0113 (25/4 C); dens. 8.45 lb/gal; visc. 18.9 cps; f.p. 10 C; b.p. 171 C (760 mm Hg); flash pt. (Seta CC) 201 F; fire pt. 200 F; ref. index 1.4525.

MEA Low Iron Grade. [Dow]
Chem. Descrip.: Monoethanolamine
CAS 141-43-5; EINECS 205-483-3
Uses: Emulsifier used in pharmaceuticals
Properties: Sp.gr. 1.0113 (25/4 C); dens. 8.45 lb/gal; visc. 18.9 cps; f.p. 10 C; b.p. 171 C (760 mm Hg); flash pt. (Seta CC) 201 F; fire pt. 200 F; ref. index 1.4525.

MEA Low Iron-Low Freeze Grade. [Dow]
Chem. Descrip.: Monoethanolamine
CAS 141-43-5; EINECS 205-483-3
Uses: Emulsifier used in pharmaceuticals
Properties: Sp.gr. 1.0113 (25/4 C); dens. 8.45 lb/gal; visc. 18.9 cps; f.p. 10 C; b.p. 171 C (760 mm Hg); flash pt. (Seta CC) 201 F; fire pt. 200 F; ref. index 1.4525.

MEA NF Grade. [Dow]
Chem. Descrip.: Monoethanolamine NF
CAS 141-43-5; EINECS 205-483-3
Uses: Emulsifier used in pharmaceuticals
Properties: Sp.gr. 1.0113 (25/4 C); dens. 8.45 lb/gal; visc. 18.9 cps; f.p. 10 C; b.p. 171 C (760 mm Hg); flash pt. (Seta CC) 201 F; fire pt. 200 F; ref. index 1.4525.

Mearlmaid® AA. [Mearl]
Chem. Descrip.: Water, guanine, isopropyl alcohol, methylcellulose
Uses: Pearl colorant for analgesic body lotions, sunscreens
Properties: Paste.

Mearlmaid® TR. [Mearl]
Chem. Descrip.: Water, guanine, TEA-lauryl sulfate, isopropyl alcohol, methylcellulose
Uses: Natural pearl colorant for analgesic body lotions, sunscreens
Properties: Paste.

Medilan™ [Westbrook Lanolin]
Chem. Descrip.: Anhydrous lanolin USP/BP/Ph.Eur. with 150 ppm BHT (as stabilizer)
CAS 8006-54-0; EINECS 232-348-6
Uses: Medical grade hypoallergenic emollient, moisturizer, emulsifier for pharmaceuticals, sunscreen preps.; esp. for use on compromised skin

Properties: Lovibond 8-14Y/0.8-20.0R color; yel. soft grease, faint char. odor; sol. in oil; partly sol. in ethanol, min. oil, IPM; insol. in water; m.p. 38-44 C; HLB 4.5; acid no. 1 max.; sapon. no. 90-105; flash pt. > 100 C; 100% conc.; nonionic; substantially biodeg.
Toxicology: Extremely low toxicity; LD50 (oral, rat) > max. pract. dose of 16 g/kg; nonirritating to skin and eyes
Precaution: Nonflamm., but will burn if strongly heated
Storage: Store in well-closed containers in cool place away from direct sunlight; avoid storage over 80 C, esp. for prolonged periods; 2 yrs storage life.

Merecol® MS. [Meer]
Chem. Descrip.: Xanthan gum FCC standardized with veg. gums
CAS 11138-66-2; EINECS 234-394-2
Uses: Stabilizer for pharmaceutical applics.
Regulatory: FDA GRAS; kosher
Properties: Cream-colored powd.; ≥ 97% thru 80 mesh; readily sol. in hot and cold water; visc. ≥ 1200 cps (1%); pH 6.2-6.6 (1%).

Merezan® 8. [Meer]
Chem. Descrip.: Xanthan gum FCC from *Xanthomonas campestris*
CAS 11138-66-2; EINECS 234-394-2
Uses: High m.w. polysaccharide for the pharmaceutical industry
Properties: Cream-colored powd., ≥ 97% thru 80 mesh; readily sol. in hot and cold water; visc. ≥ 1200 cps (1%); pH 6.1-8.1 (1%)
Storage: Store in clean, cool, dry area; 1 yr min. shelf life.

Merezan® 20. [Meer]
Chem. Descrip.: Xanthan gum FCC from *Xanthomonas campestris*
CAS 11138-66-2; EINECS 234-394-2
Uses: High m.w. polysaccharide for the pharmaceutical industry
Properties: Cream-colored powd., ≥ 97% thru 200 mesh; readily sol. in hot and cold water; visc. ≥ 1200 cps (1%); pH 6.1-8.1
Storage: Store in clean, cool, dry area; 1 yr min. shelf life.

Methocel® A4C Premium. [Dow]
Chem. Descrip.: Methylcellulose
CAS 9004-67-5
Uses: Visc. control agent, gellant, lather enhancer/stabilizer, film-former, dispersant, lubricant, binder, emulsion stabilizer, and suspending agent
Regulatory: FDA GRAS 21CFR §182.1480, 9CFR 318.7, 381.147, FCC, USP, EP, JP, BP; kosher
Properties: Firm gel structure; water-sol.; visc. 400 mPa•s.

Methocel® A4M Premium. [Dow]
Chem. Descrip.: Methylcellulose
CAS 9004-67-5
Uses: Visc. control agent, gellant, lather enhancer/stabilizer, film-former, dispersant, lubricant,

binder, emulsion stabilizer, and suspending agent
Regulatory: FDA GRAS 21CFR §182.1480, 9CFR 318.7, 381.147, FCC, USP, EP, JP, BP; kosher
Properties: Firm gel structure; water-sol.; visc. 4000 mPa•s.

Methocel® A15C Premium. [Dow]
Chem. Descrip.: Methylcellulose
CAS 9004-67-5
Uses: Food gums used as thickener, stabilizer, emulsifier, and gellant
Regulatory: FDA GRAS 21CFR §182.1480, 9CFR 318.7, 381.147, FCC, USP, EP, JP, BP; kosher
Properties: Visc. 1500 cps.

Methocel® A15-LV. [Dow]
Chem. Descrip.: Methylcellulose
CAS 9004-67-5
Uses: Food gums used as thickener, stabilizer, emulsifier, and gellant; also for tablet coating applics.

Methocel® A15LV Premium. [Dow]
Chem. Descrip.: Methylcellulose
CAS 9004-67-5
Uses: Visc. control agent, gellant, lather enhancer/stabilizer, film-former, dispersant, lubricant, binder, emulsion stabilizer, and suspending agent for pharmaceutical tablet coating
Regulatory: FDA GRAS 21CFR §182.1480, 9CFR 318.7, 381.147, FCC, USP, EP, JP, BP; kosher
Properties: Wh./off-wh. powd.; visc. 15 mPa•s.

Methocel® A Premium. [Dow]
Chem. Descrip.: Methylcellulose USP
CAS 9004-67-5
Uses: Used for pharmaceutical tablet coating, granulation, controlled release applics.
Properties: Visc. avail. 15, 400, 1500, and 4000 cps.

Methocel® E3 Premium. [Dow]
Chem. Descrip.: Hydroxypropyl methylcellulose
CAS 9004-65-3
Uses: Visc. control agent, gellant, lather enhancer/stabilizer, film-former, dispersant, lubricant, binder, emulsion stabilizer, and suspending agent for pharmaceutical tablet coating
Regulatory: FDA 21CFR §172.874, USDA, FCC, USP, EP, JP, BP; kosher
Properties: Wh./off-wh. powd.; visc. 3 mPa•s.

Methocel® E4M Premium. [Dow]
Chem. Descrip.: Hydroxypropyl methylcellulose
CAS 9004-65-3
Uses: Visc. control agent, gellant, lather enhancer/stabilizer, film-former, dispersant, lubricant, binder, emulsion stabilizer, and suspending agent for suncare prods., controlled drug release
Regulatory: FDA 21CFR §172.874, USDA, FCC, USP, EP, JP, BP; kosher
Properties: Wh./off-wh. powd.; visc. 4000 mPa•s.

Methocel® E5P. [Dow]
Chem. Descrip.: Hydroxypropylmethylcellulose
CAS 9004-65-3
Uses: Used for pharmaceutical tablet coating
Properties: Wh./off-wh. powd.; visc. 4-6 mPa•s.

Methocel® E6 Premium. [Dow]
Chem. Descrip.: Hydroxypropyl methylcellulose
CAS 9004-65-3
Uses: Visc. control agent, gellant, lather enhancer/stabilizer, film-former, dispersant, lubricant, binder, emulsion stabilizer, and suspending agent for pharmaceutical tablet coating
Regulatory: FDA 21CFR §172.874, USDA, FCC, USP, EP, JP, BP; kosher
Properties: Wh./off-wh. powd.; visc. 6 mPa•s.

Methocel® E10MP CR. [Dow]
Chem. Descrip.: Hydroxypropylmethylcellulose
CAS 9004-65-3
Uses: Controlled-release grade for pharmaceutical release formulations
Properties: Wh./off-wh. powd.; visc. 10,000 mPa•s.

Methocel® E15LV Premium. [Dow]
Chem. Descrip.: Hydroxypropyl methylcellulose
CAS 9004-65-3
Uses: Visc. control agent, gellant, lather enhancer/stabilizer, film-former, dispersant, lubricant, binder, emulsion stabilizer, and suspending agent for pharmaceutical tablet coating
Regulatory: FDA 21CFR §172.874, USDA, FCC, USP, EP, JP, BP; kosher
Properties: Wh./off-wh. powd.; visc. 15 mPa•s.

Methocel® E50LV Premium. [Dow]
Chem. Descrip.: Hydroxypropyl methylcellulose
CAS 9004-65-3
Uses: Visc. control agent, gellant, lather enhancer/stabilizer, film-former, dispersant, lubricant, binder, emulsion stabilizer, and suspending agent
Regulatory: FDA 21CFR §172.874, USDA, FCC, USP, EP, JP, BP; kosher
Properties: Visc. 50 mPa•s.

Methocel® E50P. [Dow]
Chem. Descrip.: Hydroxypropyl methylcellulose
CAS 9004-65-3
Uses: Visc. control agent, gellant, lather enhancer/stabilizer, film-former, dispersant, lubricant, binder, emulsion stabilizer, and suspending agent for pharmaceutical tablet coating, mouthwashes
Properties: Wh./off-wh. powd.; visc. 40-60 mPa•s.

Methocel® E Premium. [Dow]
Chem. Descrip.: Hydroxypropyl methylcellulose USP
CAS 9004-65-3
Uses: Used for pharmaceutical tablet coating, granulation, controlled release applics.
Properties: Visc. avail. 3, 5, 6, 15, 50, 4000, and 10,000 cps.

Methocel® F4M Premium. [Dow]
Chem. Descrip.: Hydroxypropyl methylcellulose
CAS 9004-65-3
Uses: Thickener, stabilizer, emulsifier, gellant
Regulatory: FDA 21CFR §172.874, USDA, FCC, USP, EP, JP, BP; kosher
Properties: Vics. 4000 cps.

Methocel® F Premium. [Dow]
Chem. Descrip.: Hydroxypropyl methylcellulose

USP
CAS 9004-65-3
Uses: Used for pharmaceutical tablet coating, granulation, controlled release applics.
Properties: Visc. avail. 50 and 4000 cps.

Methocel® J Premium. [Dow]
Chem. Descrip.: Hydroxypropylmethylcellulose USP
CAS 9004-65-3
Uses: Used for pharmaceutical tablet coating, granulation, controlled release applics.
Properties: Visc. avail. 5, 15, 100, 4000, 15,000, and 100,000 cps.

Methocel® K3 Premium. [Dow]
Chem. Descrip.: Hydroxypropylmethylcellulose
CAS 9004-65-3
Uses: Used for pharmaceutical tablet coating; emulsion stabilizer, dispersant for flavor oil emulsions and encapsulation
Regulatory: FDA 21CFR §172.874, USDA, FCC, USP, EP, JP, BP; kosher
Properties: Wh./off-wh. powd.; visc. 3 mPa•s.

Methocel® K4M Premium. [Dow]
Chem. Descrip.: Hydroxypropyl methylcellulose
CAS 9004-65-3
Uses: Visc. control agent, gellant, lather enhancer/stabilizer, film-former, dispersant, lubricant, binder, emulsion stabilizer, and suspending agent for suncare prods., creams and lotions, controlled drug release
Regulatory: FDA 21CFR §172.874, USDA, FCC, USP, EP, JP, BP; kosher
Properties: Visc. 4000 mPa•s.

Methocel® K15M Premium. [Dow]
Chem. Descrip.: Hydroxypropyl methylcellulose
CAS 9004-65-3
Uses: Visc. control agent, gellant, lather enhancer/stabilizer, film-former, dispersant, lubricant, binder, emulsion stabilizer, and suspending agent for controlled drug release
Regulatory: FDA 21CFR §172.874, USDA, FCC, USP, EP, JP, BP; kosher
Properties: Wh./off-wh. powd.; visc. 15,000 mPa•s.

Methocel® K100LV Premium. [Dow]
Chem. Descrip.: Hydroxypropyl methylcellulose
CAS 9004-65-3
Uses: Visc. control agent, gellant, lather enhancer/stabilizer, film-former, dispersant, lubricant, binder, emulsion stabilizer, and suspending agent for controlled drug release
Regulatory: FDA 21CFR §172.874, USDA, FCC, USP, EP, JP, BP; kosher
Properties: Wh./off-wh. powd.; visc. 100 mPa•s.

Methocel® K100M Premium. [Dow]
Chem. Descrip.: Hydroxypropyl methylcellulose
CAS 9004-65-3
Uses: Visc. control agent, gellant, lather enhancer/stabilizer, film-former, dispersant, lubricant, binder, emulsion stabilizer, and suspending agent for toothpaste, controlled drug release
Regulatory: FDA 21CFR §172.874, USDA, FCC, USP, EP, JP, BP; kosher

Properties: Wh./off-wh. powd.; visc. 100,000 mPa•s.

Methocel® K Premium. [Dow]
Chem. Descrip.: Hydroxypropyl methylcellulose USP
CAS 9004-65-3
Uses: Used for pharmaceutical tablet coating, granulation, controlled release applics.
Properties: Visc. avail. 3, 100, 4000, 15,000, and 100,000 cps.

Methyl Parasept® NF/FCC. [Nipa Hardwicke]
Chem. Descrip.: Methylparaben NF/FCC
CAS 99-76-3; EINECS 202-785-7
Uses: Preservative for pharmaceuticals, suppositories, eye washes, pills, anesthetics, syrups, injectable sol'ns., contraceptives, gelatin capsules, ointments, tinctures, OTC drugs; inactive ingred. in dentifrices, topical analgesics; active antimycotic
Properties: Wh. fine powd., pract. odorless and tasteless; sol. 64% in acetone, 59% in methanol, 52% in ethanol (100%), 23% in ether, 22% in propylene glycol (100%), 0.25% in water; m.w. 152.15; m.p. 125-128 C; nonhygroscipic; 99-100.5% assay
Toxicology: Avoid prolonged/repeated skin contact
Storage: Avoid exposure to high humidity and elevated temps. in storage.

Mexpectin LA 100 Range. [Grindsted Prods.]
Chem. Descrip.: Amidated low-ester pectin
CAS 9000-69-5; EINECS 232-553-0
Uses: Gellant and mouthfeel modifier, protein stabilizer; suitable for pharmaceuticals
Regulatory: EEC, FDA §184.1588 (GRAS).

Mexpectin LC 700 Range. [Grindsted Prods.]
Chem. Descrip.: Low-ester pectin
CAS 9000-69-5; EINECS 232-553-0
Uses: Thickener and mouthfeel modifier, protein stabilizer; suitable for pharmaceuticals
Regulatory: EEC, FDA §184.1588 (GRAS).

Mexpectin XSS 100 Range. [Grindsted Prods.]
Chem. Descrip.: Pectin
CAS 9000-69-5; EINECS 232-553-0
Uses: Gellant and mouthfeel modifier; protein stabilizer; for pharmaceuticals; extra slow setting time, low setting temp.
Regulatory: EEC, FDA §184.1588 (GRAS).

Microbiotone. [Am. Labs]
Chem. Descrip.: Peptic hydrolysate of beef tissue
Uses: Pharmaceutical additive for bacteria work; medium for growth of aerobic and anaerobic bacteria
Regulatory: USP compliance
Properties: Gran.; completely sol. in 2% sol'n.; pH 6.8-7.2 (10%).

Micro-Cel® C. [Celite]
Chem. Descrip.: Syn. calcium silicate
CAS 1344-95-2; EINECS 215-710-8
Uses: Functional filler used to convert sticky, visc. liqs. to dry liqs. for use in pharmaceutical industry
Properties: Wh. fine powd.; 5% 325-mesh residue; sp.gr. 2.40; bulk dens. 8.5 lb/ft^3; surf. area 175

m^2/g; water absorp. 405%; oil absorp. 340%; ref. index 1.55; pH 10 (10% aq. slurry); 50% SiO_2, 29% CaO; 8% moisture.

Micro-Dry®. [Reheis]
Chem. Descrip.: Aluminum chlorohydrate
CAS 1327-41-9; EINECS 215-477-2
Uses: Antiperspirant active used where particle size and surface area are important factors; widely used for aerosols
Properties: Powd.; 44 µ particle size; 97% min. thru 325 mesh; 47% Al_2O_3, 16.3% Cl.

Micro-Dry® Superultrafine. [Reheis]
Chem. Descrip.: Aluminum chlorohydrate
CAS 1327-41-9; EINECS 215-477-2
Uses: Antiperspirant active with finer particle size; used in suspensoid type sticks, suspension and powder roll-ons
Properties: Powd.; 85% min. thru 10 µ; 47% Al_2O_3, 16.3% Cl.

Micro-Dry® Ultrafine. [Reheis]
Chem. Descrip.: Aluminum chlorohydrate
CAS 1327-41-9; EINECS 215-477-2
Uses: Antiperspirant active for use in suspensoid type sticks, suspension and powder roll-ons
Properties: Powd.; 38 µ particle size; 99% min. thru 400 mesh; 47% Al_2O_3, 16.3% Cl.

Micro-White® 10 Codex. [ECC Int'l.]
Chem. Descrip.: Calcium carbonate
CAS 1317-65-3; EINECS 207-439-9
Uses: Food-grade calcium supplement and extender
Regulatory: FCC, kosher
Properties: Wh. powd., odorless, tasteless; 1.0 µm mean particle size; trace retained on 325 mesh; negligible sol. in water; sp.gr. 2.71; pH 9-10; 97% $CaCO_3$
Toxicology: TLV-TWA 10 mg/m^3; considered nuisance dust; chronic exposure may cause respiratory problems; may cause skin irritation
Precaution: Nonflamm., nonexplosive; will react with acids to produce carbon dioxide.

Micro-White® 25 Codex. [ECC Int'l.]
Chem. Descrip.: Calcium carbonate
CAS 1317-65-3; EINECS 207-439-9
Uses: Food-grade calcium supplement and extender
Regulatory: FCC, kosher
Properties: Wh. powd., odorless, tasteless; 3 µm mean particle size; trace retained on 325 mesh; negligible sol. in water; sp.gr. 2.71; pH 9-10; 96.8% $CaCO_3$.
Toxicology: TLV-TWA 10 mg/m^3; considered nuisance dust; chronic exposure may cause respiratory problems; may cause skin irritation
Precaution: Nonflamm., nonexplosive; will react with acids to produce carbon dioxide.

Micro-White® 50 Codex. [ECC Int'l.]
Chem. Descrip.: Calcium carbonate
CAS 1317-65-3; EINECS 207-439-9
Uses: Food-grade calcium supplement and extender
Regulatory: FCC, kosher

Properties: Wh. powd., odorless, tasteless; 7 µm mean particle size; 0.35% retained on 325 mesh; negligible sol. in water; sp.gr. 2.71; pH 9-10; 95.5% $CaCO_3$.
Toxicology: TLV-TWA 10 mg/m^3; considered nuisance dust; chronic exposure may cause respiratory problems; may cause skin irritation
Precaution: Nonflamm., nonexplosive; will react with acids to produce carbon dioxide.

Micro-White® 100 Codex. [ECC Int'l.]
Chem. Descrip.: Calcium carbonate
CAS 1317-65-3; EINECS 207-439-9
Uses: Food-grade calcium supplement and extender
Regulatory: FCC, kosher
Properties: Wh. powd., odorless, tasteless; 17 µm mean particle size; 7% retained on 325 mesh; negligible sol. in water; sp.gr. 2.71; pH 9-10; 95% $CaCO_3$.
Toxicology: TLV-TWA 10 mg/m^3; considered nuisance dust; chronic exposure may cause respiratory problems; may cause skin irritation
Precaution: Nonflamm., nonexplosive; will react with acids to produce carbon dioxide.

Miglyol® 810. [Hüls Am.; Hüls AG]
Chem. Descrip.: Caprylic/capric triglyceride
CAS 65381-09-1; EINECS 265-724-3
Uses: Emollient, dispersant, lubricant, suspending agent, solubilizer; act. ingred. for pharmaceuticals; carrier/vehicle and solv. for inj. prods., topical ointments, creams, lotions, suppositories; penetrating and spreading props. on skin
Properties: Colorless liq., neutral odor; sol. in diethyl ether, petrol. ether, chloroform, IPA, toluene, alcohol, min. oil, acetone; sp.gr. 0.94-0.95; visc. 25-35 mPa•s; acid no. 0.1 max.; iodine no. 0.5 max.; sapon. no. 335-355; pH neutral; cloud pt. 0 C; nonionic.

Miglyol® 812. [Hüls Am.; Hüls AG]
Chem. Descrip.: Caprylic/capric triglyceride
CAS 65381-09-1; EINECS 265-724-3
Uses: Dispersant, lubricant, anticaking agent, carrier, solubilizer, suspending agent for pharmaceuticals (oral, external, suppositories); spreading and penetrating props. on skin; solv. for lipophilic drugs; carrier/filler in capsules; stable to oxidation
Properties: Colorless liq.; sol. in alcohol, min. oil, acetone; visc. 25-35 mPa•s; acid no. 0.1 max.; iodine no. 0.5 max.; sapon. no. 325-345; cloud pt. 10 C; 100% conc.; nonionic.

Miglyol® 818. [Hüls Am.; Hüls AG]
Chem. Descrip.: Caprylic/capric/linoleic triglyceride
CAS 67701-28-4
Uses: Emollient for topical creams, lotions, and oil formulations for pharmaceuticals; spreading and penetrating props. on skin
Properties: Virtually colorless liq.; visc. 30-35 mPa•s; acid no. 0.2 max.; iodine no. 10 max.; sapon. no. 315-335; cloud pt. 10 C.

Miglyol® 829. [Hüls Am.; Hüls AG]

Chem. Descrip.: Caprylic/capric/disuccinic triglyceride

Uses: Emollient, suspending agent for pharmaceutical topicals, cream and liq. emulsions, oral suspensions, and capsules

Properties: Ylsh. visc. liq.; sp.gr. 1.01; visc. 230-260 mPa•s; acid no. 1 max.; iodine no. 1 max.; sapon. no. 400-430; cloud pt. -30 C

Toxicology: Nontoxic.

Miglyol® 840. [Hüls Am.; Hüls AG]

Chem. Descrip.: Propylene glycol dicaprylate/dicaprate

Uses: Emollient, dispersant, lubricant, suspending agent, solubilizer; act. ingred. for pharmaceuticals; carrier/vehicle and solv. for inj. prods., topical ointments, creams, lotions, suppositories; oxidation-stable

Properties: Colorless liq.; sol. in alcohol, min. oil, acetone; visc. 8-14 mPa•s; acid no. 0.1 max.; iodine no. 0.5 max.; sapon. no. 320-340; cloud pt. -30 C.

Miglyol® 840 Gel B. [Hüls Am.; Hüls AG]

Chem. Descrip.: Propylene glycol dicaprylate/dicaprate, stearalkonium hectorite, propylene carbonate

Uses: Consistency regulator for creams; high temp. stabilizer esp. for w/o emulsions and anhyd. pharmaceuticals

Properties: Cream-colored paste; acid no. 0.5 max.; iodine no. 1 max.; sapon. no. 290-315

Toxicology: Nontoxic.

Miglyol® 8810. [Hüls Am.; Hüls AG]

Chem. Descrip.: Butylene glycol dicaprylate/caprate

Uses: Emollient, dispersant, lubricant, suspending agent; hypoallergenic; solubilizer; act. ingred. for pharmaceutical preps.; carrier/vehicle and solv. for inj. prods., topical ointments, creams, lotions; penetrating/spreading props. on skin

Properties: Colorless liq., neutral odor; sol. in alcohol, diethyl ether, n-hexane, fatty oils; insol. in water; visc. 8-13 mPa•s; acid no. 0.1 max.; iodine no. 1.0 max.; sapon. no. 295-315; hyd. no. 5 max.

Miglyol® Gel B. [Hüls Am.; Hüls AG]

Chem. Descrip.: Caprylic/capric triglyceride, stearalkonium hectorite, propylene carbonate

Uses: Pale oily gel with neutral props. for anhyd. formulations, ointments, w/o creams, topicals; consistency regulator in anhyd. and aq. pharmaceuticals; stabilizer for emulsions

Properties: Flesh-colored hard paste; acid no. 0.5 max.; sapon. no. 290-320

Toxicology: Nontoxic.

Miglyol® Gel T. [Hüls Am.; Hüls AG]

Chem. Descrip.: Caprylic/capric triglyceride, stearalkonium bentonite, propylene carbonate

Uses: Consistency regulator for creams; high temp. stabilizer esp. for w/o emulsions and anhyd. skin care formulations; pharmaceutical ointments and creams for topical use

Properties: Greenish hard paste; acid no. 0.5 max.; sapon. no. 290-315.

Milk Calcium ND (Food Grade) [Garuda Int'l.]

Chem. Descrip.: Natural calcium peptide source from cow's milk

Uses: Used to prepare nutritional supplement tablets or capsules for prevention of osteoporosis and to provide usable source of mineral calcium

Properties: Wh. to lt. cream free-flowing powd., neutral odor, mineral-salt flavor; 7% max. moisture

Storage: Store in cool, dry area; protect from moisture and strong odors; 1 yr min. shelf life.

Mineral Jelly No. 10. [Witco/Petroleum Spec.]

Chem. Descrip.: Petrolatum
EINECS 232-373-2

Uses: Used in pharmaceuticals (medicated ointments, suppositories, suncare prods.)

Regulatory: FDA 21CFR §172.880

Properties: Lovibond 1.0Y color; visc. 2.6-5.7 cSt (100 C); m.p. 38-43 C

Mineral Jelly No. 14. [Witco/Petroleum Spec.]

Chem. Descrip.: Petrolatum
CAS 8009-03-8; EINECS 232-373-2

Uses: Used in pharmaceuticals (medicated ointments, suppositories, suncare prods.)

Regulatory: FDA 21CFR §172.880

Properties: Lovibond 1.0Y color; visc. 2.6-5.7 cSt (100 C); m.p. 38-52 C.

Mineral Jelly No. 17. [Witco/Petroleum Spec.]

Chem. Descrip.: Petrolatum
CAS 8009-03-8; EINECS 232-373-2

Uses: Used in pharmaceuticals (medicated ointments, suppositories, suncare prods.)

Regulatory: FDA 21CFR §172.880

Properties: Lovibond 1.0Y color; visc. 2.6-5.7 cSt (100 C); m.p. 36-49 C.

Miranol® C2M Conc. NP. [Rhone-Poulenc Surf. & Spec.]

Chem. Descrip.: Disodium cocoamphodiacetate
CAS 68650-39-5; EINECS 272-043-5

Uses: Emulsifier, solubilizer, and stabilizer in pharmaceuticals

Properties: Clear, visc. liq.; sol. in water; pH 8.0-8.5 (20% aq.); 38% act.; amphoteric.

MOD. [Gattefosse]

Chem. Descrip.: 2-Octyldodecyl myristate

Uses: Emollient; rancidless additive improving appearance in pharmaceuticals; min. oil substitute

Properties: Oily liq., faint odor; acid no. < 7; iodine no. < 7; sapon. no. 95-115

Toxicology: LD0 (oral, rat) > 2 g/kg; nonirritating to skin; sl. eye irritant.

M.O.D. WL 2949. [Gattefosse]

Chem. Descrip.: Octyldodecyl myristate

Uses: Emollient; rancidless additive for pharmaceuticals

Properties: Oily liq.; HLB 1.0; acid no. ≤ 7; iodine no. ≤ 7; sapon. no. 90-110

Toxicology: LD50 (oral, rat) > 2 g/kg; sl. irritating to eyes; nonirritating to skin.

Modulan®. [Amerchol]

Chem. Descrip.: Acetylated lanolin

CAS 61788-48-5; EINECS 262-979-2
Uses: Conditioner, emollient, softener, lubricant for pharmaceutical prods.
Properties: Yel.-amber soft solid; faint, pleasant odor; sol. in min. oil; m.p. 30-40 C; acid no. 2.5 max.; sapon. no. 95-120; hyd. no. 10 max.

Mola-Tab®. [Crompton & Knowles]
Chem. Descrip.: Molasses, whole wheat flour, wheat bran
Uses: Pharmaceutical carrier; directly compressible form which maintains flavor and functional props. of molasses; enhances flavors or masks undesirable flavors; imparts rich natural molasses color to tablets
Properties: Dk. brn. free-flowing gran.; 50% min. on 60 mesh, 25% max. thru 120 mesh; pH 5-6 (5%); 60% act., ≤ 4% moisture.

Monawet MO-70R. [Mona Industries]
Chem. Descrip.: Dioctyl sodium sulfosuccinate, 15% water, 15% propylene glycol
Uses: Wetting, dispersing, emulsifying, penetrating and solubilizing agent for pharmaceuticals
Regulatory: EPA and FDA §175.105, 175.300, 175.320, 176.170, 176.210, 177.1200, 177.2800, 178.3400 compliance
Properties: Colorless clear liq.; sol. in polar and nonpolar solvs.; m.w. 444; sp.gr. 1.06; dens. 8.8 lb/gal; cloud pt. < -5 C; flash pt. (PMCC) 280 F; pH 6.0 (10%); surf. tens. 29 dynes/cm (0.1%); Ross-Miles foam 210 mm (0.1%); 70% act.; anionic.

Monoglyme. [Ferro/Grant]
Chem. Descrip.: Ethylene glycol dimethyl ether
CAS 110-71-4
Uses: Solv. vehicle for pharmaceuticals; reaction solv. for pharmaceutical mfg.
Properties: Colorless; ethereal, nonresidual odor; water-sol.; misc. with ethanol, acetone, benzene, diethyl ether, octane; m.w. 90.12; sp.gr. 0.8683 (20/20 C); dens. 7.24 lb/gal; visc. 1.1 cP (20 C); vapor pressure 54 mm Hg (20 C); f.p. -69 C; b.p. 85.2 C; flash pt. (CC) -6 C; ref. index 1.3792; pH neutral; surf. tens. 22.9 dynes/cm (20 C); sp. heat 0.438 cal/g/°C; 99.6% min. purity; slowly biodeg.
Toxicology: LD50 5370 mg/kg; low to mod. acute toxicity; avoid exposure to vapors, skin contact; TLV/8h TWA: 5 ppm; STEL 25 ppm; LD50 5100 mg/kg); chronic exposure may cause reproductive effects.

Monomuls® 60-10. [Grünau GmbH]
Chem. Descrip.: Pork lard mono- and diglycerides
Uses: Emulsifier, stabilizer, dispersant, opacifier for drugs
Regulatory: EEC E 471
Properties: Cream-colored lardy solid, neutral fatty odor/taste; sol. in warm xylene, ethanol, IPA; sol. cloudy in warm IPM, propylene glycol; disp. in warm water; m.p. 40-44 C; acid no. < 3; iodine no. 40-50; sapon. no. 165-175; pH 6-7 (1:10 in methanol/water); 57-62% monoglycerides; nonionic
Storage: 1 yr storage life.

Monomuls® 60-15. [Grünau GmbH]
Chem. Descrip.: Hydrog. lard mono-diglycerides

Uses: Emulsifier, stabilizer, dispersant, opacifier for drugs
Regulatory: EEC E 471
Properties: Ylsh.-wh. powd., neutral odor and taste; sol. in warm ethanol, IPA, xylene, soja oil; sol. cloudy in IPM; disp. in warm water; m.p. 60-64 C; acid no. < 3; iodine no. < 2; sapon. no. 165-175; pH 6-7 (1:10 in methanol/water); 57-62% monoglycerides; nonionic
Storage: 1 yr storage life.

Monomuls® 60-20. [Grünau GmbH]
Chem. Descrip.: Beef tallow mono- and diglycerides
CAS 67701-27-3
Uses: Emulsifier, stabilizer, dispersant, opacifier for drugs
Regulatory: EEC E 471
Properties: Cream-colored lardy solid, neutral fatty odor/taste; sol. in warm ethanol, IPA, IPM, xylene, paraffin oil; disp. in warm water; m.p. 48-52 C; acid no. < 3; iodine no. 32-42; sapon. no. 165-175; pH 6-7 (1:10 in methanol/water 1:1); 57-62% monoglycerides; nonionic
Storage: 1 yr storage life.

Monomuls® 60-25. [Grünau GmbH]
Chem. Descrip.: Hydrog. beef tallow glycerides
CAS 68308-54-3; EINECS 269-658-6
Uses: Emulsifier, stabilizer, dispersant, opacifier for drugs
Regulatory: EEC E 471
Properties: Ylsh.-wh. powd., neutral odor and taste; sol. in warm ethanol, IPA, IPM, xylene, soja oil; disp. in warm water; m.p. 60-64 C; acid no. < 3; iodine no. < 2; sapon. no. 165-175; pH 6-7 (1:10 in methanol/water 1:1); 57-62% monoglycerides; nonionic
Storage: 1 yr storage life.

Monomuls® 60-25/2. [Grünau GmbH]
Chem. Descrip.: Hydrog. beef tallow mono- and diglycerides with 2% sodium stearate
Uses: Emulsifier, stabilizer, dispersant, opacifier for drugs
Regulatory: EEC E 471
Properties: Cream-colored powd., neutral odor and taste; sol. in warm ethanol, IPA, xylene, paraffin oil, soja oil; disp. in warm water; m.p. 60-74 C; acid no. < 4; iodine no. < 2; sapon. no. 160-170; pH 8-9 (1:10 in methanol/water 1:1); 54-59% monoglycerides; nonionic
Storage: 1 yr storage life.

Monomuls® 60-30. [Grünau GmbH]
Chem. Descrip.: Palm oil mono-diglycerides
CAS 129521-59-1
Uses: Emulsifier, stabilizer, dispersant, opacifier for drugs
Regulatory: EEC E 471
Properties: Ylsh.-wh. lardy solid, sl. lardy odor/taste; sol. in warm ethanol, IPA, xylene, soya oil, cloudy in IPM; disp. in warm water; m.p. 38-42 C; acid no. < 3; iodine no. 40-50; sapon. no. 165-175; pH 6-7 (1:10 in methanol/water 1:1); 57-62% monoglycerides; anionic

Storage: 1 yr storage life.

Monomuls® 60-35. [Grünau GmbH]
Chem. Descrip.: Hydrog. palm oil glycerides
Uses: Emulsifier, stabilizer, dispersant, opacifier for drugs
Regulatory: EEC E 471
Properties: Ylsh.-wh. powd., neutral odor/taste; sol. in warm propylene glycol, ethanol, IPA, IPM, xylene; disp. in warm water; m.p. 58-62 C; acid no. < 3; iodine no. < 6; sapon. no. 165-175; pH 6-7 (1:10 in methanol/water 1:1); 57-62% monoglycerides; nonionic
Storage: 1 yr storage life.

Monomuls® 60-40. [Grünau GmbH]
Chem. Descrip.: Sunflower seed oil mono- and diglycerides
Uses: Emulsifier, stabilizer, dispersant, opacifier for drugs
Regulatory: EEC E 471
Properties: Ylsh.-wh. lardy soft solid, fatty odor and taste; sol. in warm ethanol, IPA, xylene, soja oil, cloudy in IPM; disp. in warm water; m.p. 28-32 C; acid no. < 3; iodine no. 100-120; sapon. no. 165-175; pH 6-7 (1:10 in methanol/water 1:1); 57-62% monoglycerides; nonionic
Storage: 1 yr storage life.

Monomuls® 60-45. [Grünau GmbH]
Chem. Descrip.: Hydrog. soybean oil mono- and diglycerides
CAS 68201-48-9
Uses: Emulsifier, stabilizer, dispersant, opacifier for drugs
Regulatory: EEC E 471
Properties: Ylsh.-wh. powd., neutral odor; sol. in warm ethanol, IPA, IPM, xylene; disp. in warm water; m.p. 62-66 C; acid no. < 3; iodine no. < 4; sapon. no. 165-175; pH 6-7 (1:10 in methanol/water 1:1); 57-62% monoglycerides; nonionic
Storage: 1 yr storage life.

Monomuls® 90-10. [Grünau GmbH]
Chem. Descrip.: Dist. pork lard glyceride
CAS 61789-10-4; EINECS 263-032-6
Uses: Emulsifier, stabilizer, dispersant, opacifier for drugs
Regulatory: EEC E 471
Properties: Lt cream-colored lardy solid, neutral lardy odor and taste; sol. in warm propylene glycol, ethanol, IPA, IPM, xylene, soja oil; insol. in water; m.p. 56-60 C; acid no. < 3; iodine no. 37-47; sapon. no. 155-165; pH 4-5 (1:10 in methanol/water 1:1); 90-95% monoglycerides; nonionic
Storage: 1 yr storage life.

Monomuls® 90-15. [Grünau GmbH]
Chem. Descrip.: Dist. hydrog. pork lard glyceride
CAS 8040-05-9
Uses: Emulsifier, stabilizer, dispersant, opacifier for drugs
Regulatory: EEC E 471
Properties: Wh. powd., neutral odor/taste; sol. in warm ethanol, IPA, IPM, xylene; disp. in warm water; m.p. 69-73 C; acid no. < 3; iodine no. < 2; sapon. no. 155-165; pH 4-5 (1:10 in methanol/

water 1:1); 90-95% monoglycerides; nonionic
Storage: 1 yr storage life.

Monomuls® 90-20. [Grünau GmbH]
Chem. Descrip.: Dist. beef tallow glyceride
CAS 61789-13-7; EINECS 263-035-2
Uses: Emulsifier, stabilizer, dispersant, opacifier for drugs
Regulatory: EEC E 471
Properties: Lt. cream-colored lardy solid, neutral fatty odor/taste; sol. in warm propylene glycol, ethanol, IPA, IPM, xylene, soja oil; insol. in water; m.p. 57-61 C; acid no. < 3; iodine no. 30-40; sapon. no. 155-165; pH 4-5 (1:10 in methanol/water 1:1); 90-95% monoglycerides; nonionic
Storage: 1 yr storage life.

Monomuls® 90-25. [Grünau GmbH]
Chem. Descrip.: Dist. hydrog. beef tallow glyceride
CAS 61789-09-1; EINECS 263-031-0
Uses: Nonself-emulsifying base and aux. material for mfg. of pharmaceuticals; emulsifier
Regulatory: EEC E 471
Properties: Wh. powd., neutral odor; sol. in warm ethanol, IPA, IPM, xylene; disp. in warm water; m.p. 68-72 C; HLB 3.8; acid no. < 3; iodine no. < 2; sapon. no. 155-165; pH 4-5 (1:10 methanol/water 1:1); 90-95% monoglycerides; nonionic
Storage: 1 yr min. storage life in sealed original containers at temps. below 40 C, protected from moisture.

Monomuls® 90-25/2. [Grünau GmbH]
Chem. Descrip.: Dist. hydrog. beef tallow glyceride with 2% sodium stearate
Uses: Emulsifier, stabilizer, dispersant, opacifier for drugs
Regulatory: EEC E 471
Properties: Lt. cream-colored powd., neutral odor and taste; sol. warm in ethanol, IPA, xylene, paraffin oil; disp. warm in water; m.p. 66-70 C; acid no. < 4; iodine no. < 2; sapon. no. 150-160; pH 8-9 (1:10 in methanol/water 1:1); 87-92% monoglycerides; anionic
Storage: 1 yr storage life.

Monomuls® 90-25/5. [Grünau GmbH]
Chem. Descrip.: Dist. hydrog. beef tallow glyceride, 5% sodium stearate
Uses: Emulsifier, stabilizer, dispersant, opacifier for drugs
Regulatory: EEC E 471
Properties: Lt. cream-colored powd., neutral odor and taste; sol. warm in ethanol, IPA, xylene, paraffin oil; disp. warm in water; m.p. 66-70 C; acid no. < 4; iodine no. < 2; sapon. no. 145-155; pH 8.5-9.5 (1:10 in methanol/water 1:1); 80-85% monoglycerides
Storage: 1 yr shelf life.

Monomuls® 90-30. [Grünau GmbH]
Chem. Descrip.: Dist. palm oil glyceride
Uses: Emulsifier, stabilizer, dispersant, opacifier for drugs
Regulatory: EEC E 471
Properties: Lt. cream-colored lardy solid, fatty odor and taste; sol. in warm propylene glycol, ethanol,

IPA, IPM, xylene, soja oil; insol. in water; m.p. 55-59 C; acid no. < 3; iodine no. 37-47; sapon. no. 155-165; pH 4-5 (1:10 in methanol/water 1:1); 90-95% monoglycerides; nonionic
Storage: 1 yr storage life.

Monomuls® 90-35. [Grünau GmbH]
Chem. Descrip.: Dist. hydrog. palm oil glyceride
CAS 67784-87-6
Uses: Emulsifier, stabilizer, dispersant, opacifier for drugs
Regulatory: EEC E 471
Properties: Wh. powd., neutral odor and taste; sol. in warm propylene glycol, ethanol, IPA, IPM, xylene; disp. in warm water; m.p. 64-68 C; acid no. < 3; iodine no. < 6; sapon. no. 155-165; pH 4-5 (1:10 in methanol/water 1:1); 90-95% monoglycerides; nonionic
Storage: 1 yr storage life.

Monomuls® 90-40. [Grünau GmbH]
Chem. Descrip.: Dist. sunflower seed oil glyceride
Uses: Emulsifier, stabilizer, dispersant, opacifier for drugs
Regulatory: EEC E 471
Properties: Wh. lardy soft solid, fatty odor and taste; sol. in warm propylene glycol, ethanol, IPA, IPM, xylene, soja oil; insol. in water; m.p. 29-33 C; acid no. < 3; iodine no. 100-120; sapon. no. 155-165; pH 4-5 (1:10 in methanol/water 1:1); 90-95% monoglycerides; nonionic
Storage: 1 yr storage life.

Monomuls® 90-45. [Grünau GmbH]
Chem. Descrip.: Dist. hydrog. soybean oil glyceride
Uses: Emulsifier, stabilizer, dispersant, opacifier for drugs
Regulatory: EEC E 471
Properties: Wh. powd., neutral odor and taste; sol. in warm ethanol, IPA, IPM, xylene, paraffin oil; disp. in warm water; m.p. 70-74 C; acid no. < 3; iodine no. < 4; sapon. no. 155-165; pH 4-5 (1:10 in methanol/water 1:1); 90-95% monoglycerides; nonionic
Storage: 1 yr storage life.

Monomuls® 90-O18. [Henkel/Cospha; Henkel KGaA/Cospha; Grünau GmbH]
Chem. Descrip.: Glyceryl oleate
CAS 111-03-5
Uses: W/o emulsifier, stabilizer, refatting agent, thickener for aq. pharmaceutical ointments, creams, and w/o emulsions
Use level: 1-5% (creams)
Regulatory: DAC compliance
Properties: Almost wh. paste, sl. fatty odor; HLB 3.4; acid no. 3 max.; iodine no. 67-80; sapon. no. 150-160; 100% conc.; nonionic
Toxicology: Up to 5% conc., toxicologically harmless with no irritating or sensitizing effects
Storage: 1 yr min. storage life in sealed original containers at temps. below 30 C, protected from moisture.

Monosteol. [Gattefosse SA; Gattefosse]
Chem. Descrip.: Propylene glycol palmitostearate

Uses: Emulsifier; stabilizer for pharmaceutical ointments, creams, lotions, emulsions
Properties: Gardner < 3 waxy solid, faint odor; drop pt. 33-36 C; HLB 4.0; acid no. < 6; iodine no. < 3; sapon. no. 165-175; 100% conc.; nonionic
Toxicology: Sl. irritating to skin and eyes.

Montane® 20. [Seppic]
Chem. Descrip.: Sorbitan laurate
CAS 1338-39-2; EINECS 215-663-3
Uses: Emulsifier for pharmaceutical formulations (pomatums, ointments, suppositories)
Regulatory: FCC, BP compliance
Properties: Liq., faint odor; sol. in ethanol; disp. in water, min. and veg. oils; visc. 4500 mPa•s; HLB 8.6; acid no. 6 max.; sapon. no. 158-170; hyd. no. 330-358; pH 7; 100% conc.; nonionic; biodeg.
Toxicology: Nonirritating to skin and eyes.

Montane® 40. [Seppic]
Chem. Descrip.: Sorbitan palmitate
CAS 26266-57-9; EINECS 247-568-8
Uses: O/w emulsifier for pharmaceutical formulations (pomatums, ointments, suppositories)
Regulatory: Approved for food use in U.S. and some European countries
Properties: Flakes, faint odor; sol. hot in ethanol, with turbidity in min. and veg. oils; gels in water; m.p. 49 C; HLB 6.7; acid no. 5 max.; sapon. no. 140-150; hyd. no. 275-305; pH 7; 100% conc.; nonionic; biodeg.
Toxicology: Nonirritating to skin and eyes.

Montane® 60. [Seppic]
Chem. Descrip.: Sorbitan stearate
CAS 1338-41-6; EINECS 215-664-9
Uses: O/w emulsifier for pharmaceutical formulations (pomatums, ointments, suppositories)
Regulatory: FCC, BP compliance; approved for food use in U.S. and some European countries
Properties: Flakes, faint odor; sol. hot in ethanol, veg. oil, turbid in min. oil; insol. in water; m.p. 55 C; HLB 4.7; acid no. 5-10; sapon. no. 147-157; hyd. no. 235-260; pH 7; 100% conc.; nonionic; biodeg.
Toxicology: Nonirritating to eyes, mildly irritating to skin.

Montane® 65. [Seppic]
Chem. Descrip.: Sorbitan tristearate
CAS 26658-19-5; EINECS 247-891-4
Uses: Emulsifier for pharmaceutical formulations (pomatums, ointments, suppositories)
Properties: Solid, faint odor; disp. in min. and veg. oils; insol. in water, ethanol; m.p. 54 C; acid no. 15 max.; sapon. no. 176-188; hyd. no. 66-80; HLB 2.1; pH 7; 100% conc.; nonionic; biodeg.
Toxicology: Nonirritating to skin and eyes.

Montane® 80. [Seppic]
Chem. Descrip.: Sorbitan oleate
CAS 1338-43-8; EINECS 215-665-4
Uses: Emulsifier for pharmaceutical formulations (pomatums, ointments, suppositories), esp. lipophilic anhyd. ointments
Regulatory: FCC, BP compliance
Properties: Liq., faint odor; sol. in ethanol, min. and

veg. oils; insol. in water; visc. 1000 mPa•s; HLB 4.3; acid no. 6 max.; iodine no. 62-76; sapon. no. 145-160; hyd. no. 193-209; pH 7; 100% conc.; nonionic; biodeg.
Toxicology: Nonirritating to skin and eyes.

Montane® 83. [Seppic]
Chem. Descrip.: Sorbitan sesquioleate
CAS 8007-43-0; EINECS 232-360-1
Uses: W/o emulsifier for pharmaceutical formulations (pomatums, ointments, suppositories), esp. absorption bases of lipophilic ointments or for w/o emulsions
Properties: Liq., faint odor; sol. in ethanol, min. and veg. oils; insol. in water; visc. 10,000 mPa•s; HLB 3.7; acid no. 6 max.; iodine no. 68-76; sapon. no. 150-166; hyd. no. 180-205; pH 7; 100% conc.; nonionic; biodeg.
Toxicology: Nonirritating to eyes.

Montane® 85. [Seppic]
Chem. Descrip.: Sorbitan trioleate
CAS 26266-58-0; EINECS 247-569-3
Uses: Emulsifier for pharmaceutical formulations (pomatums, ointments, suppositories), esp. lipophilic anhyd. ointments
Properties: Liq., faint odor; sol. in min. and veg. oils, sol. hot in ethanol; insol. in water; visc. 200 mPa•s; HLB 1.8; acid no. 15 max.; sapon. no. 170-190; hyd. no. 55-70; pH 7; 100% conc.; nonionic; biodeg.
Toxicology: Nonirritating to eyes, mildly irritating to skin.

Montane® 481. [Seppic]
Chem. Descrip.: Sorbitan oleate, beeswax, and stearic acid
Uses: W/o emulsifier for pharmaceutical formulations (pomatums, ointments, suppositories)
Properties: Soft waxy paste; sol. (hot, hazy) in min. oil; disp. in ethanol; insol. in water; m.p. 50-60 C; HLB 4.5; acid no. 14-22; sapon. no. 148-163; hyd. no. 136-170; 100% act.; nonionic; biodeg.
Toxicology: LD50 (oral, rat) > 10 g/kg; nonirritating to skin and eyes.

Montanol® 68. [Seppic]
Chem. Descrip.: Cetearyl glucoside
Uses: O/w emulsifier for dermopharmaceutical prods.; free of chem. impurities, solvs., ethylene oxide, and dioxane
Use level: 5%
Properties: Wh. flakes; m.p. ≈ 62 C; acid no. 0.5 max.; iodine no. 1 max.; sapon. no. 5 max.; hyd. no. 270-290; pH ≈ 6.5 (5%, 60 C); 100% conc.; nonionic.

Montanox® 20. [Seppic]
Chem. Descrip.: Polysorbate 20
CAS 9005-64-5
Uses: Hydrophilic emulsifier, solubilizer for pharmaceutical formulations (ointments, syrups, suspensions, suppositories) administered via oral or percutaneous routes
Properties: Liq.; sol. in water, ethanol; insol. in min. and veg. oils; visc. 400 mPa•s; HLB 16.7; acid no. 1 max.; iodine no. 5 max.; sapon. no. 40-50; hyd.

no. 96-108; cloud pt. 85-94 C; pH 6.0-7.5; nonionic
Toxicology: Nonirritating to skin and eyes.

Montanox® 20 DF. [Seppic]
Chem. Descrip.: Polysorbate 20, dioxane-free
CAS 9005-64-5
Uses: Hydrophilic emulsifier, solubilizer for pharmaceutical formulations (ointments, syrups, suspensions, suppositories) administered via oral or percutaneous routes
Properties: Liq.; HLB 16.7; 100% conc.; nonionic.

Montanox® 40. [Seppic]
Chem. Descrip.: Polysorbate 40
CAS 9005-66-7
Uses: Hydrophilic o/w emulsifier for pharmaceutical formulations (ointments, syrups, suspensions, suppositories)
Properties: Liq. to gel; sol. in water, ethanol; insol. in min. and veg. oils; HLB 15.6; acid no. 1 max.; sapon. no. 41-52; hyd. no. 89-105; pH 6.0-7.5; nonionic
Toxicology: Nonirritating to skin and eyes.

Montanox® 40 DF. [Seppic]
Chem. Descrip.: Polysorbate 40, dioxane-free
CAS 9005-66-7
Uses: Hydrophilic o/w emulsifier for pharmaceutical formulations (ointments, syrups, suspensions, suppositories)
Properties: Gel; HLB 15.6; 100% conc.; nonionic.

Montanox® 60. [Seppic]
Chem. Descrip.: Polysorbate 60
CAS 9005-67-8
Uses: Hydrophilic o/w emulsifier for pharmaceutical formulations (ointments, syrups, suspensions, suppositories)
Properties: Liq. to gel; sol. in water, ethanol; sol. hot with turbidity in min. oil; insol. in veg. oils; HLB 14.9; acid no. 1 max.; iodine no. 5 max.; sapon. no. 45-55; hyd. no. 81-96; cloud pt. 60-76 C; pH 6.0-7.5; nonionic
Toxicology: Nonirritating to skin and eyes.

Montanox® 60 DF. [Seppic]
Chem. Descrip.: Polysorbate 60, dioxane-free
CAS 9005-67-8
Uses: Hydrophilic o/w emulsifier for pharmaceutical formulations (ointments, syrups, suspensions, suppositories)
Properties: Gel; HLB 14.9; 100% conc.; nonionic.

Montanox® 65. [Seppic]
Chem. Descrip.: Polysorbate 65
CAS 9005-71-4
Uses: Hydrophilic emulsifier for pharmaceutical formulations (ointments, syrups, suspensions, suppositories)
Properties: Solid; sol. in ethanol, min. oil; disp. in water, veg. oil; HLB 10.5; acid no. 2 max.; sapon. no. 88-98; hyd. no. 44-60; pH 6.0-7.5; 100% conc.; nonionic
Toxicology: Nonirritating to skin and eyes.

Montanox® 80. [Seppic]
Chem. Descrip.: Polysorbate 80
CAS 9005-65-6

Uses: Hydrophilic emulsifier, solubilizer for pharmaceutical formulations (ointments, syrups, suspensions, suppositories) administered via oral or percutaneous routes
Properties: Liq.; sol. in water, ethanol; insol. in min. and veg. oils; visc. 500 mPa•s; HLB 15; acid no. 1 max.; iodine no.18-24; sapon. no. 45-55; hyd. no. 65-80; cloud pt. 57-63 C; pH 6.0-7.5; nonionic
Toxicology: Nonirritating to skin and eyes.

Montanox® 80 DF. [Seppic]
Chem. Descrip.: Polysorbate 80, dioxane-free
CAS 9005-65-6
Uses: Emulsifier for pharmaceutical ointments; solubilizer for oral or injectable pharmaceuticals
Properties: Liq.; HLB 15.0; 100% conc.; nonionic.

Montanox® 85. [Seppic]
Chem. Descrip.: Polysorbate 85
CAS 9005-70-3
Uses: W/o emulsifier, solubilizer for pharmaceutical formulations (ointments, syrups, suspensions, suppositories)
Properties: Liq.; sol. in ethanol, min. oil; sol. hot in veg. oil; disp. in water; visc. 200 mPa•s; HLB 11.0; acid no. 1 max.; iodine no. ≈ 44; sapon. no. 82-95; hyd. no. 39-52; pH 6.0-7.5; 100% conc.; nonionic
Toxicology: Nonirritating to skin and eyes.

Monteine PCO. [Seppic]
Chem. Descrip.: Palmitoyl collagen amino acids
Uses: Anti-inflammatory agent, waterproofing agent for suncare prods., ointments, dermatologicals, anti-acne creams; substantive to skin; improves spreadability on skin, nongreasy feel, storage stability
Use level: 2-10%
Properties: Wh. wax; sol. in dichloromethane/methanol mixts., oils
Toxicology: Nonirritating to skin and mucous membranes @ 10%.

Monthyle. [Gattefosse; Gattefosse SA]
Chem. Descrip.: Glycol stearate
CAS 111-60-4; EINECS 203-886-9
Uses: Emulsifier, consistency enhancer, stabilizer for pharmaceutical ointments, creams, lotions, emulsions
Properties: Gardner < 3 waxy solid, faint odor; drop pt. 55-58 C; HLB 3.0; acid no. < 6; iodine no. < 3; sapon. no. 170-180; 100% conc.; nonionic
Toxicology: Sl. irritating to eyes; nonirritating to skin.

Multiwax® 180-M. [Witco/Petroleum Spec.]
Chem. Descrip.: Microcryst. wax NF
CAS 63231-60-7; EINECS 264-038-1
Uses: Wax base, lubricant, protectant for pharmaceutical ointments; carrier for pigments and medication
Regulatory: FDA §172.886, 178.3710
Properties: Lt. yel.; misc. with petrol. prods., many essential oils, most animal and veg. fats, oils, and waxes; visc. 14.3-18.0 cSt (99 C); m.p. 82-88 C; flash pt. (COC) 277 C min.

Multiwax® ML-445. [Witco/Petroleum Spec.]
Chem. Descrip.: Microcryst. wax NF

CAS 63231-60-7; EINECS 264-038-1
Uses: Wax base, lubricant, protectant for pharmaceutical ointments, dental waxes; carrier for pigments and medication
Regulatory: FDA §172.886, 178.3710
Properties: Lt. yel.; misc. with petrol. prods., many essential oils, most animal and veg. fats, oils, and waxes; visc. 14.3-18.0 cSt (99 C); m.p. 77-82 C; flash pt. (COC) 274 C min.

Multiwax® W-445. [Witco/Petroleum Spec.]
Chem. Descrip.: Microcryst. wax NF
CAS 63231-60-7; EINECS 264-038-1
Uses: Wax base, lubricant, protectant used in pharmaceuticals, medicated creams and unguents, dental waxes; carrier for pigments and medication
Regulatory: FDA §172.886, 178.3710
Properties: Wh. wax; misc. with petrol. prods., many essential oils, most animal and veg. fats, oils, and waxes; visc. 14.3-18.0 cSt (99 C); m.p.77-82 C; flash pt. (COC) 274 C min.

Multiwax® W-835. [Witco/Petroleum Spec.]
Chem. Descrip.: Microcryst. wax
CAS 63231-60-7; EINECS 264-038-1
Uses: Wax base, lubricant, protectant for pharmaceutical ointments, dental prods.; carrier for pigments and medication
Regulatory: FDA §172.886, 178.3710
Properties: Wh.; visc. 14.3-18.0 cSt (99 C); m.p. 74-79 C; flash pt. (COC) 246 C min.

Multiwax® X-145A. [Witco/Petroleum Spec.]
Chem. Descrip.: Microcryst. wax NF
CAS 63231-60-7; EINECS 264-038-1
Uses: Wax base, lubricant, protectant for pharmaceutical ointments, dental prods.; carrier for pigments and medication
Regulatory: FDA §172.886, 178.3710
Properties: Lt. yel.; misc. with petrol. prods., many essential oils, most animal and veg. fats, oils, and waxes; visc. 14.3-18.0 cSt (99 C); m.p. 66-71 C; flash pt. (COC) 260 C min.

Mushroom Mycelia. [Garuda Int'l.]
Chem. Descrip.: Mushroom mycelia biomass from shiitake (*Lentinus edodes*) and reishi (*Ganoderma lucidum*) mushrooms
Uses: Used to formulate health food and pharmaceutical tablets, capsules
Properties: Dried fine powd.
Toxicology: Whole food, without toxicity or side effects.

Myacide® SP. [Inolex; Boots]
Chem. Descrip.: 2,4-Dichlorobenzyl alcohol
CAS 1777-82-8; EINECS 217-210-5
Uses: Antifungal agent, preservative for pharmaceutical formulations for areas where contamination by spoilage yeasts and molds is the problem; stable at pH 3-10 and to 100 C
Properties: Wh. to sl. yel. crystal; sol. (g/100 ml): 95 g in acetone, 80 g in methanol, 45 g in propylene glycol, 0.1 g in water; m.w. 177; m.p. 57-60 C; 98.5% min. act.

Myritol® 312. [Henkel KGaA/Cospha]

Chem. Descrip.: Caprylic/capric triglyceride
CAS 73398-61-5; EINECS 265-724-3
Uses: Spreading agent, med. fatting oil component of pharmaceutical skin care preps., w/o and o/w emulsions
Regulatory: JCIC, DAB, BP compliance
Properties: Sl. ylsh. clear oil, odorless; m.w. 500; dens. 0.943-0.950 g/cm^3 (20 C); visc. 28-32 mPa•s (20 C); acid no. 0.1 max.; iodine no. 0.5 max.; sapon. no. 330-340; hyd. no. 5 max.; cloud pt. < -5 C; ref. index 1.448-1.450 (20 C)
Storage: 1 yr storage stability in orig. unopened container at temps. below 30 C, protected from moisture.

Myritol® 318. [Henkel/Cospha; Henkel Canada; Henkel KGaA/Cospha]
Chem. Descrip.: Caprylic/capric triglyceride
CAS 73398-61-5; EINECS 265-724-3
Uses: Spreading agent, emollient for pharmaceutical skin care emulsions; oily component with solv. capacity; solubilizer; exc. oxidative stability
Regulatory: JCIC, DAB compliance
Properties: Sl. ylsh. clear low-visc. oily liq., odorless; m.w. 500; sp.gr. 0.945-0.949; visc. 27-33 mPa•s (20 C); acid no. 0.1 max.; iodine no. 0.5 max.; sapon. no. 335-350; hyd. no. 5 max.; cloud pt. < -5 C; ref. index 1.448-1.450 (20 C); 100% conc.; nonionic
Storage: 1 yr min. storage life in original containers at temps. below 30 C in a dry environment.

Myritol® PC. [Henkel/Cospha; Henkel KGaA/Cospha]
Chem. Descrip.: Propylene glycol dicaprylate/dicaprate
CAS 68583-51-7
Uses: Emollient with high spreadability for pharmaceutical skin care preps., antiperspirants; exc. solv. for active ingreds.
Regulatory: DAB, JCIC compliance
Properties: Colorless clear low visc. oil, faint char. odor; m.w. 340; sp.gr. 0.91-0.93 (20 C); visc. 9-12 mPa•s (20 C); acid no. 0.1 max.; iodine no. 0.5 max.; sapon. no. 325-335; hyd. no. 5 max.; cloud pt. < -20 C; ref. index 1.440-1.442 (20 C)
Storage: 1 yr min. storage stability in sealed original containers at temps. below 30 C in a dry environment.

Myrj® 45. [ICI Surf. Am.; ICI Surf. Belgium]
Chem. Descrip.: PEG-8 stearate
CAS 9004-99-3
Uses: General purpose o/w emulsifier for pharmaceuticals
Regulatory: Canada compliance
Properties: Wh. cream-colored soft waxy solid; sol. in alcohol, disp. in water; sp.gr. 1.0; HLB 11.1; pour pt. 28 C; sapon. no. 82-95; 100% conc.; nonionic.

Myrj® 49. [ICI Surf. Am.; ICI Surf. Belgium]
Chem. Descrip.: PEG-20 stearate
CAS 9004-99-3
Uses: O/w emulsifier for pharmaceutical applics.
Properties: Wh. cream solid; HLB 15.0; 100% conc.; nonionic.

Myrj® 51. [ICI Surf. Am.; ICI Surf. Belgium]
Chem. Descrip.: PEG-30 stearate
CAS 9004-99-3
Uses: O/w emulsifier for pharmaceutical applics.
Properties: Wh. cream solid; HLB 16.0; 100% conc.; nonionic.

Myrj® 52. [ICI Surf. Am.; ICI Surf. Belgium]
Chem. Descrip.: PEG-40 stearate NF
CAS 9004-99-3
Uses: O/w emulsifier for pharmaceutical applics.
Regulatory: FDA 21CFR §173.340
Properties: Ivory waxy solid or flake; sol. in water, acetone, ether, alcohol; sp.gr. 1.1; HLB 16.9; pour pt. 38 C; sapon. no. 25-35; 100% conc.; nonionic.

Myrj® 52S. [ICI Surf. Am.]
Chem. Descrip.: PEG-40 stearate NF
CAS 9004-99-3
Uses: O/w emulsifier for pharmaceutical applics.
Regulatory: FDA 21CFR §173.340
Properties: Wh. waxy granular solid; sol. in water, toluol, acetone, ether, Cellosolve, CCl$_4$, alcohol; sp.gr. 1.1; HLB 16.9; pour pt. 38 C; sapon. no. 25-35; 100% conc.; nonionic.

Myrj® 53. [ICI Surf. Am.; ICI Surf. Belgium]
Chem. Descrip.: PEG-50 stearate
CAS 9004-99-3
Uses: O/w emulsifier for pharmaceutical applics.
Properties: Wh. cream-colored solid; sol. in water, alcohol; HLB 17.9; pour pt. 42 C; sapon. no. 20-28; 100% conc.; nonionic.

Myrj® 59. [ICI Surf. Am.; ICI Surf. Belgium]
Chem. Descrip.: PEG-100 stearate
CAS 9004-99-3
Uses: O/w emulsifier for pharmaceutical applics.
Properties: Off-wh. to lt. tan solid; sol. in water, alcohol; HLB 18.8; pour pt. 46 C; 100% conc.; nonionic.

Myvacet® 5-07. [Eastman]
Chem. Descrip.: Acetylated hydrog. cottonseed glyceride
Uses: Plasticizer in solv. or aq. applied film coatings, esp. with cellulose esters, cellulose ethers, or acrylics; taste masking coatings; imparts glossy effect; sustained release in solid dosage forms
Regulatory: FDA 21CFR §172.828, EC E472a
Properties: Creamy wh. waxy solid; sol. in most common org. solvs.; immisc. with water; sp.gr. 0.94 (80 C); m.p. 41-46 C; HLB 3.8-4.0; acid no. 3 max.; iodine no. 5 max.; sapon. no. 279-292; hyd. no. 133-152; 48.5-51.5% acetylation; nonionic
Precaution: Plasticizes/softens some common plastics
Storage: 24 mo shelf life.

Myvacet® 7-07. [Eastman]
Chem. Descrip.: Acetylated hydrog. veg. oil monoglycerides
Uses: Plasticizer in solv. or aq. applied film coatings, esp. with cellulose esters, cellulose ethers, or acrylics; taste masking coatings; imparts glossy effect; sustained release in solid dosage

forms
Regulatory: FDA 21CFR §172.828, EC E472a
Properties: Creamy wh. waxy solid; sol. in most common org. solvs.; immisc. with water; sp.gr. 0.94 (80 C); m.p. 37-40 C; HLB 3.8-4.0; acid no. 3 max.; iodine no. 5 max.; sapon. no. 316-331; hyd. no. 80.5-95.0; 66.5-69.5% acetylation; nonionic
Precaution: Plasticizes/softens some common plastics
Storage: 24 mo shelf life.
Myvacet® 9-45. [Eastman]
Chem. Descrip.: Acetylated hydrog. soybean oil glycerides
Uses: Plasticizer in solv. or aq. applied film coatings, esp. with cellulose esters, cellulose ethers, or acrylics
Regulatory: FDA 21CFR §172.828, EC E472a
Properties: Clear liq.; sol. in all common org. solvs., 80% w/w aq. ethanol, veg. and min. oils; sp.gr. 0.94 (80 C); visc. 44.5 cP; m.p. 4-12 C; HLB 3.8-4.0; acid no. 3 max.; iodine no. 43-53; sapon. no. 370-382; hyd. no. 0-15; 96% min. acetylation
Precaution: Plasticizes/softens some common plastics
Storage: 12 mo shelf life.
Myvaplex® 600. [Eastman]
Chem. Descrip.: Glyceryl stearate from hydrog. soybean oil
Uses: Lubricant, glidant for tablet mfg.; for sustained-release tablets and gran.; high thermal stability
Regulatory: FDA 21CFR §184.1324, 184.1505, GRAS, EC E471
Properties: Small beads; sp.gr. 0.92 (80 C); m.p. 69 C; acid no. 3 max.; iodine no. 5 max.; 90% min. monoester
Storage: 24 mo shelf life.
Myvaplex® 600P NF. [Eastman]
Chem. Descrip.: Glyceryl monostearate (from hydrog. soybean oil)
Uses: Lubricant, glidant for tablet mfg.; matrix for sustained-release tablets and gran.; high thermal and good oxidative stability
Use level: 1-3% (tablet lubricant); 10-60% (matrix for sustained-release tablets)
Regulatory: FDA 21CFR §184.1324, 184.1505,

GRAS; NF compliance
Properties: Powd.; 100-180 µ particle size; sol. in warm ethanol, IPA and IPM; disp. in warm water; sp.gr. 0.92 (80 C); bulk dens. 0.48 g/ml; m.p. 69 C; acid no. 3 max.; iodine no. 5 max.; m.p. 69 C; 90% min. monoester.
Myvatex® TL. [Eastman]
Chem. Descrip.: Glyceryl stearate, propylene glycol stearate, sodium stearoyl lactylate, silicon dioxide
Uses: Pharmaceutical excipient; tableting lubricant which doesn't inhibit disintegration time; dispersing aid due to its ability to disperse in gastric fluid; reduces dustiness in actives
Regulatory: All components are either GRAS or permitted as direct food additives
Properties: Wh. powd.; 70% thru 100 mesh; disp. in water @ R.T.; sp.gr. 0.94 (80 C); m.p. 50-60 C; acid no. < 13; iodine no. < 5; 79% monoester; nonionic.
Myverol® 18-92. [Eastman]
Chem. Descrip.: Dist. glyceryl monolinoleate deriv. from sunflower oil
CAS 2277-28-3; EINECS 218-901-4
Uses: Matrix material for sustained release of solid drugs or medicaments insol. in the monoglyceride; for soft or hard gelatin capsules
Regulatory: FDA 21CFR §184.1505, GRAS; EC E471
Properties: Semiplastic; sp.gr. 0.90 (80 C); m.p. 41 C; HLB 3.8-4.0; acid no. 3 max.; iodine no. 105-115; 90% min. monoester; nonionic
Storage: 6 mo shelf life.
Myverol® 18-99. [Eastman]
Chem. Descrip.: Dist. glyceryl monoleate deriv. from refined low-erucic canola oil
Uses: Forms gelled cubic phase useful as a transdermal patch layer, for sustained release oral formulations and microspheres, topical permeation enhancement, solubilization of water-sol. drugs into an oil matrix
Regulatory: FDA 21CFR §184.1505, GRAS; EC E471
Properties: Semiplastic; sp.gr. 0.93 (80 C); m.p. 35 C; HLB 3.8-4.0; acid no. 3 max.; iodine no. 90-95; 90% min. monoester; nonionic
Storage: 6 mo shelf life.

N

Nacol® 4-99. [Condea Chemie GmbH; Vista]
Chem. Descrip.: 1-Butanol
CAS 71-36-3; EINECS 200-751-6
Uses: Pharmaceutical raw material
Properties: Hazen 5 max. color; m.w. 74; sp.gr.
0.809-0.812 (20/4 C); b.p. 116.5-118 C; acid no.
0.02 max.; iodine no. 0.05 max.; hyd. no. 753-760;
flash pt. (Abel-Pensky) 35 C; 99.6% min. act.

Nacol® 6-98. [Condea Chemie GmbH; Vista]
Chem. Descrip.: 1-Hexanol
CAS 111-27-3; EINECS 203-852-3
Uses: Pharmaceutical raw material
Properties: Hazen 10 max. color; m.w. 101-104;
sp.gr. 0.819 (20/4 C); pour pt. -52 C; b.p. 150-170
C; acid no. 0.02 max.; iodine no. 0.1 max.; hyd.
no. 540-555; flash pt. 58 C; 98% min. act.

Nacol® 8-97. [Condea Chemie GmbH; Vista]
Chem. Descrip.: 1-Octanol
CAS 111-87-5; EINECS 203-917-6
Uses: Pharmaceutical raw material
Properties: Hazen 10 max. color; m.w. 129-131;
sp.gr. 0.825 (20/4 C); pour pt. -16 C; b.p. 185-200
C; acid no. 0.05 max.; iodine no. 0.15 max.; hyd.
no. 428-435; flash pt. 82 C; 97.5% min. act.

Nacol® 8-99. [Condea Chemie GmbH; Vista]
Chem. Descrip.: 1-Octanol
CAS 111-87-5; EINECS 203-917-6
Uses: Pharmaceutical raw material
Properties: Hazen 10 max. color; m.w. 129-131;
sp.gr. 0.825 (20/4 C); pour pt. -14 C; b.p. 188-198
C; acid no. 0.03 max.; iodine no. 0.1 max.; hyd.
no. 428-435; flash pt. 82 C; 99.5% min. act.

Nacol® 10-97. [Condea Chemie GmbH; Vista]
Chem. Descrip.: 1-Decanol
CAS 112-30-1; EINECS 203-956-9
Uses: Pharmaceutical raw material
Properties: Hazen 10 max. color; m.w. 157-160;
sp.gr. 0.829 (20/4 C); pour pt. 6 C; b.p. 220-235 C;
acid no. 0.05 max.; iodine no. 0.2 max.; hyd. no.
350-357; flash pt. 95 C; 97.5% min. act.

Nacol® 10-99. [Condea Chemie GmbH; Vista]
Chem. Descrip.: 1-Decanol
CAS 112-30-1; EINECS 203-956-9
Uses: Pharmaceutical raw material
Properties: Hazen 10 max. color; m.w. 157-160;
sp.gr. 0.829 (20/4 C); pour pt. 6 C; b.p. 220-235 C;
acid no. 0.05 max.; iodine no. 0.1 max.; hyd. no.
350-357; flash pt. 95 C; 99% min. act.

Nacol® 12-96. [Condea Chemie GmbH; Vista]
Chem. Descrip.: 1-Dodecanol
CAS 112-53-8; EINECS 203-982-0
Uses: Pharmaceutical raw material
Properties: Hazen 10 max. color; m.w. 185-190;
sp.gr. 0.822 (40/4 C); solid. pt. 22-24 C; b.p. 255-
265 C; acid no. 0.05 max.; iodine no. 0.2 max.;
hyd. no. 295-305; flash pt. 116 C; 96.5% min. act.

Nacol® 12-99. [Condea Chemie GmbH; Vista]
Chem. Descrip.: 1-Dodecanol
CAS 112-53-8; EINECS 203-982-0
Uses: Pharmaceutical raw material
Properties: Hazen 10 max. color; m.w. 185-187;
sp.gr. 0.822 (40/4 C); solid. pt. 23-25 C; b.p. 258-
265 C; acid no. 0.03 max.; iodine no. 0.15 max.;
hyd. no. 299-304; flash pt. 119 C; 99% min. act.

Nacol® 14-95. [Condea Chemie GmbH; Vista]
Chem. Descrip.: 1-Tetradecanol
CAS 112-72-1; EINECS 204-000-3
Uses: Pharmaceutical raw material
Properties: Hazen 20 max. color; m.w. 212-219;
sp.gr. 0.809 (60/4 C); solid. pt. 36-38 C; b.p. 275-
290 C; acid no. 0.08 max.; iodine no. 0.3 max.;
hyd. no. 256-262; flash pt. 145 C; 95% min. act.

Nacol® 14-98. [Condea Chemie GmbH; Vista]
Chem. Descrip.: Myristyl alcohol
CAS 112-72-1; EINECS 204-000-3
Uses: Pharmaceutical raw material; emollient,
consistency giving factor for creams, ointments,
liniments, lotions, and sticks
Properties: Hazen 20 max. color; m.w. 212-216;
sp.gr. 0.809 (60/4 C); solid. pt. 37-39 C; b.p. 270-
290 C; acid no. 0.05 max.; iodine no. 0.25 max.;
hyd. no. 258-262; flash pt. 145 C; 98.5% min. act.

Nacol® 16-95. [Condea Chemie GmbH; Vista]
Chem. Descrip.: 1-Hexadecanol
CAS 36653-82-4; EINECS 253-149-0
Uses: Pharmaceutical raw material, emollient,
emulsifier
Properties: Hazen 20 max. color; m.w. 240-244;
sp.gr. 0.812 (60/4 C); solid. pt. 45-49 C; b.p. 300-
320 C; acid no. 0.1 max.; iodine no. 0.5 max.; hyd.
no. 226-235; flash pt. 150 C; 95% min. act.

Nacol® 16-98. [Condea Chemie GmbH; Vista]
Chem. Descrip.: Cetyl alcohol
CAS 36653-82-4; EINECS 253-149-0
Uses: Pharmaceutical raw material; emollient,
consistency giving factor for creams, ointments,

liniments, lotions, and sticks
Properties: Hazen 20 max. color; m.w. 240-244; sp.gr. 0.812 (60/4 C); solid. pt. 47-50 C; b.p. 305-320 C; acid no. 0.1 max.; iodine no. 0.4 max.; hyd. no. 226-235; flash pt. 155 C; 98% min. act.

Nacol® 18-94. [Condea Chemie GmbH; Vista]
Chem. Descrip.: 1-Octadecanol
CAS 112-92-5; EINECS 204-017-6
Uses: Pharmaceutical raw material
Properties: Hazen 40 max. color; m.w. 267-275; sp.gr. 0.815 (60/4 C); solid. pt. 55-58 C; b.p. 320-340 C; acid no. 0.2 max.; iodine no. 0.5 max.; hyd. no. 200-210; flash pt. 174 C; 94.5% min. act.

Nacol® 18-98. [Condea Chemie GmbH; Vista]
Chem. Descrip.: Stearyl alcohol
CAS 112-92-5; EINECS 204-017-6
Uses: Pharmaceutical raw material; emollient, consistency giving factor for creams, ointments, liniments, lotions, and sticks
Properties: Hazen 30 max. color; m.w. 267-275; sp.gr. 0.815 (60/4 C); solid. pt. 56-59 C; b.p. 325-340 C; acid no. 0.1 max.; iodine no. 0.5 max.; hyd. no. 200-210; flash pt. 174 C; 98% min. act.

Nacol® 20-95. [Condea Chemie GmbH; Vista]
Chem. Descrip.: Eicosanol
CAS 629-96-9; EINECS 211-119-4
Uses: Pharmaceutical raw material; emollient, consistency giving factor for creams, ointments, liniments, lotions, and sticks
Properties: Hazen 50 max. color; m.w. 298; sp.gr. 0.802 (80/4 C); solid. pt. 61-64 C; acid no. 0.3 max.; iodine no. 1 max.; hyd. no. 180-185; flash pt. 195 C; 95% min. act.

Nacol® 22-97. [Condea Chemie GmbH; Vista]
Chem. Descrip.: Docosanol
CAS 661-19-8; EINECS 211-546-6
Uses: Pharmaceutical raw material; emollient, consistency giving factor for creams, ointments, liniments, lotions, and sticks
Properties: Hazen 50 max. color; m.w. 326; sp.gr. 0.807 (80/4 C); solid. pt. 67-70 C; acid no. 0.1 max.; iodine no. 0.5 max.; hyd. no. 168-171; flash pt. 227 C; 97.5% min. act.

Nacolox®. [Condea Chemie GmbH]
Chem. Descrip.: Fatty alcohol ethoxylates
Uses: Pharmaceutical raw material; emollient, consistency giving factor for creams, ointments, liniments, lotions, and sticks.

Nafol® 1618 H. [Condea Chemie GmbH]
Chem. Descrip.: Cetearyl alcohol
EINECS 267-008-6
Uses: Pharmaceutical raw material.

Nafol® C14-C22. [Condea Chemie GmbH]
Chem. Descrip.: Fatty alcohol blend
Uses: Pharmaceutical raw material; emollient, consistency giving factor for creams, ointments, liniments, lotions, and sticks.

Narangrex Complex D. [MLG Enterprises Ltd.]
Chem. Descrip.: Citric conc. contg. conc. natural juices, deterpenated essential oils, syn. colorants, acidifiers, thickeners, and preservatives

Uses: Preformulated flavor base for pharmaceuticals.

Narangrex Complex G. [MLG Enterprises Ltd.]
Chem. Descrip.: Citric conc. contg. conc. natural juices, deterpenated essential oils, syn. colorants, acidifiers, thickeners, and preservatives
Uses: Preformulated flavor base for prod. of pharmaceuticals.

Nasojel. [United-Guardian]
Chem. Descrip.: Combination of Lubrajel derivs.
Uses: Moisturizer to keep tissue around the nose moisturized and less irritated during times of the common cold
Custom product

Natipide® II. [Am. Lecithin; Nattermann Phospholipid; Rhone-Poulenc Rorer]
Chem. Descrip.: Lecithin/water/ethanol liposome conc. containing 20% purified phospholipid fractions with high phosphatidylcholine content
Uses: Transparent gel containing empty liposomes ready to be loaded with actives; for dermatology; improves skin humidity and penetration
Use level: 10%
Properties: Transparent yel.-brn. semisolid vesicular gel, ethanolic odor; dilutable with water; sp.gr. 1.0 g/ml; visc. 5000 ± 2000 mPa•s (20 C); flash pt. 27.8 C; pH 6.5 ± 1.5; 16% ethanol; biodeg.
Toxicology: Harmless to eyes; nonirritating to skin
Storage: Store in clean, cool, dry place @ 10-25 C; protect from light.

Natipide® II PG. [Am. Lecithin; Nattermann Phospholipid; Rhone-Poulenc Rorer]
Chem. Descrip.: Water/lecithin/propylene glycol liposome
Uses: Alcohol-free version of Natipide II; easy loading of actives for dermatological prods.; moisturizer; reduces skin roughness
Properties: Transparent gel, odorless; dilutable with water; sp.gr. 1.0 g/ml; pH 6.5 ± 1.5; biodeg.
Toxicology: Harmless
Storage: Store below 20 C in closed containers; protect against freezing, light.

Natrosol® 250. [Aqualon]
Chem. Descrip.: Hydroxyethylcellulose
CAS 9004-62-0
Uses: Thickener, protective colloid, binder, stabilizer, suspending agent for pharmaceuticals
Regulatory: FDA 21CFR §175.105, 175.300, 176.170, 176.180, 177.1210, 182.99
Properties: Wh. to lt. tan gran. powd.; water-sol.; particle size 90% thru 40 mesh; water-sol.; avail. in various visc. grades; pH 6.0-8.5 (2%); nonionic
Unverified

Natrosol® Hydroxyethylcellulose. [Hercules/Aqualon]
Chem. Descrip.: Hydroxyethylcellulose
CAS 9004-62-0
Uses: Thickener, protective colloid, binder, stabilizer, suspending agent for pharmaceuticals
Properties: Sol. in hot and cold water, DMSO.

Natrosol® Plus CS, Grade 330. [Aqualon]

Chem. Descrip.: Cetyl hydroxyethylcellulose
Uses: Associative thickener providing visc. stability to aq. and surfactant pharmaceutical systems; binder, stabilizer, film-former, suspending agent
Properties: Wh. to off-wh. powd.; water-sol.; bulk dens. 0.75 g/ml; visc. 300 cps (1%); surf. tens. 62 dynes/cm; nonionic
Toxicology: LD50 > 5 g/kg (nontoxic); nonirritating to skin; mild ocular irritant.
Natural Arabic Type Gum Purified, Spray-Dried. [MLG Enterprises Ltd.]
Chem. Descrip.: Gum arabic
CAS 9000-01-5; EINECS 232-519-5
Uses: Pharmaceutical tableting
Properties: Lt. brn. fine powd.; instantly water-sol.; visc. 51 cps (10%); pH 5.6 (10%); 4.54% moisture.
Natural Glycerine USP 96%. [Dial]
Chem. Descrip.: Glycerin USP
CAS 56-81-5; EINECS 200-289-5
Uses: Used in toothpaste, external and internal pharmaceutical applics.
Properties: Colorless clear liq., char. odor; sp.gr. 1.2553 (15/15 C); pH neutral; 96% min. act.
Natural Glycerine USP 99%. [Dial]
Chem. Descrip.: Glycerin USP
CAS 56-81-5; EINECS 200-289-5
Uses: Used in toothpaste, external and internal pharmaceutical applics.
Properties: Colorless clear liq., char. odor; sp.gr. 1.2630 (15/15 C); pH neutral; 99% min. act.
Natural Glycerine USP 99.5%. [Dial]
Chem. Descrip.: Glycerin USP
CAS 56-81-5; EINECS 200-289-5
Uses: Used in toothpaste, external and internal pharmaceutical applics.
Properties: Colorless clear liq., char. odor; sp.gr. 1.2643 (15/15 C); pH neutral; 99.5% min. act.
Natural Liquid AP Carmine Colorant. [MLG Enterprises Ltd.]
Chem. Descrip.: Stabilized carminic acid aluminum-calcic lake ammonia sol'n.
CAS 1390-65-4; EINECS 215-724-4
Uses: Natural colorant for pharmaceuticals producing intense violet-red shades
Properties: Liq.; sol. in water and pH 3 acid sol'ns.; 3 ± 0.1% color (as carminic acid)
Storage: Store in tightly closed containers in fresh, dark rooms.
Natural Liquid Carmine Colorant (Type 100, 50, and Simple) [MLG Enterprises Ltd.]
Chem. Descrip.: Carminic acid aluminum-calcic lake hydroalcoholic ammoniacal sol'n.
CAS 1390-65-4; EINECS 215-724-4
Uses: Natural colorant for pharmaceuticals producing berry to strawberry red shades
Properties: Liq.; water-sol.; 3.0 ± 0.1% (100), 1.5 ± 0.05% (50), 0.65 ± 0.05% (simple), as carminic acid.
Storage: Store in fresh and dark rooms.
Natural Octacosanol GF. [Garuda Int'l.]
Chem. Descrip.: 8.1% Octacosanol, 9.9% natural

vegetable waxes, 82% corn syrup solids
Uses: Natural waxy alcohol blend to formulate health-food supplements and pharmaceuticals
Properties: Lt. yel. to brownish gran. powd.
Storage: 1 yr min. shelf life stored in cool, dry environment, protected from heat sources and sunlight.
Natural Prosweet™ Liq. #604. [Virginia Dare Extract]
Chem. Descrip.: Natural flavor
Uses: Multifunctional blend of flavor ingreds. to enhance flavor and reduce objectionable bitterness for pharmaceuticals, chewable tablets, cough drops, lozenges, mouthwashes and sprays, syrups and elixirs, toothpastes; prolongs flavor, enhances sweetness
Use level: 0.25-1.% (pharmaceutical)
Properties: Liq.
Natural Prosweet™ Powd. #875. [Virginia Dare Extract]
Chem. Descrip.: Natural flavor
Uses: Multifunctional blend of flavor ingreds. to enhance flavor and reduce objectionable bitterness for pharmaceuticals, chewable tablets, cough drops, lozenges, mouthwashes and sprays, syrups and elixirs, toothpastes; prolonges flavor, enhances sweetness
Use level: 0.25-1.% (pharmaceutical)
Properties: Liq.
Natural Red Beet Liq. 275280. [Crompton & Knowles]
Chem. Descrip.: Natural red beet liq. obtained by conc. the juice of selected beets, *Beta vulgaris*, pasteurized
CAS 7659-95-2
Uses: Color additive for pharmaceuticals; limited stability to heat, light, oxygen and SO_2
Regulatory: FDA 21CFR §73.40
Properties: Red-purple visc. liq., sl. odor; sol. in water and milk prods.; insol. in oils and fats; sp.gr. 1.35 ± 0.20; pH 4.55 ± 2.5; 0.335% betanin content
Storage: 6 mos shelf life stored in airtight containers in cool place; avoid exposure to heat, light, moisture.
Natural Red Beet Powd. 654200. [Crompton & Knowles]
Chem. Descrip.: Natural red beet powd. extracted from juice of *Beta vulgaris*, spray-dried using maltodextrin as a carrier
Uses: Color additive for pharmaceuticals; limited stability to heat, light, oxygen and SO_2
Regulatory: FDA 21CFR §73.40
Properties: Deep red-purple free-flowing fine powd., sl. odor; 100% min. thru 80 mesh; sol. in water and milk prods.; insol. in oils and fats; pH 5.0 ± 0.5; 0.335% betanin content
Storage: Very hygroscopic; 6 mos shelf life stored in airtight containers in cool place; avoid exposure to heat, light, moisture.
Natural Soluble Carmine Powd. [MLG Enterprises Ltd.]
Chem. Descrip.: Solubilized, spray-dried carminic acid aluminum-calcic lake

CAS 1390-65-4; EINECS 215-724-4
Uses: Natural colorant for pharmaceuticals producing red-violet shades
Properties: Impalpable powd.; 100% 80 mesh; water-sol.; 40 ± 1% (as carminic acid)
Storage: Keep in well closed containers, in fresh, dry room.

Natural Soluble Powder AP Carmine Colorant. [MLG Enterprises Ltd.]
Chem. Descrip.: Carminic acid aluminum-calcic lake, solubilized, stabilized, and spray-dried
CAS 1390-65-4; EINECS 215-724-4
Uses: Natural colorant for pharmaceuticals producing red to violaceous shades or stable cherry red @ pH 3
Properties: Impalpable powd.; 100% 80 mesh; sol. in water and pH 3 acid sol'ns.; 15 ± 0.5% color (as carminic acid)
Storage: Keep in tightly closed containers, in fresh, dry rooms.

Natural Yellow Colour Q-500, Q-1000, Q-2000. [MLG Enterprises Ltd.]
Chem. Descrip.: Annatto seed hydroalcoholic extract
CAS 8015-67-6
Uses: Natural colorant for pharmaceuticals producing pale yel. to orange shades
Properties: Liq.; sol. in water and ethyl alcohol; 0.25 ± 0.025% (Q-500), 0.5 ± 0.05% (Q-1000), 1.0 ± 0.1% (Q-2000), as norbixin.
Storage: Protect from light and heat; rotate stock every 3 mos.

Naxolate™ WA-97. [Ruetgers-Nease]
Chem. Descrip.: Sodium lauryl sulfate USP, BP
CAS 151-21-3; EINECS 205-788-1
Uses: Wetting agent, foamer, emulsifier for toothpaste
Properties: Wh. powd.; dens. 200 ± 50 g/l; 96-98% act.; anionic; biodeg.

Naxolate™ WAG. [Ruetgers-Nease]
Chem. Descrip.: Sodium lauryl sulfate USP, BP
CAS 151-21-3; EINECS 205-788-1
Uses: Wetting agent, foamer, emulsifier for toothpaste
Properties: Ivory wh. needles; dens. 500 ± 50 g/l; pH 7-10 (1% aq.); 89% act.; anionic; biodeg.

NCL-818. [United-Guardian]
Chem. Descrip.: Lubrajel prod.
Uses: Rapidly drying, nontacky moisturizer for medical and health-care fields; suitable for addition of fragrance and/or color
Custom product

NE™. [ANGUS]
Chem. Descrip.: Nitroethane
CAS 79-24-3; EINECS 201-188-9
Uses: Raw material for synthesis of act. pharmaceutical compds., for α-methyldopa, a hypertensive drug, and for phenylpropanolamine used in bronchial decongestants and wt. control agents
Properties: Liq.; sol. 4.6% in water (20 C); m.w. 75.1; dens. 1.051 g/ml (20 C), 8.75 lb/gal; visc. 0.677 cp (20 C); vapor pressure 20.93 mm Hg; f.p.

-89.52 C; b.p. 114 C; flash pt. (TCC) 87 F; ref. index 1.39193 (20 C); pH 6.0 (0.01M aq.); surf. tens. 32.66 dynes/cm (20 C); dielec. const. 28.06 (30 C); 98% min. purity; biodeg.; classified as solv. exempt under Rule 66
Toxicology: LD50 (oral, rat) 1625 ± 193 mg/kg; sl. toxic by ing.; nonirritating to eyes and skin; prolonged/repeated skin exposure may cause defatting; inh.: PEL/TWC 100 ppm, mild irritant, headache, nausea, vomiting; avoid prolonged breathing of vapors
Precaution: Flamm.; keep away from heat, sparks, flame
Storage: Keep container closed.

Neobee® 18. [Stepan Food Ingreds.; Stepan Europe]
Chem. Descrip.: Hybrid safflower oil, refined, deodorized
CAS 8001-23-8; EINECS 232-276-5
Uses: Emollient base for pharmaceuticals; solubilizer, solv., lubricant, nutritional fluid
Regulatory: FDA 21CFR §170.30, GRAS; avail. in kosher grade
Properties: Sl. yel. liq., sl. fatty odor, bland taste; sol. in alcohol, min. oil, acetone; sp.gr. 0.915; visc. 70 cps; iodine no. 90; sapon. no. 190; surf. tens. 31.6 dynes/cm.
Toxicology: Nonirritating
Storage: Avoid prolonged storage above 90 F.

Neobee® 1053. [Stepan Food Ingreds.]
Chem. Descrip.: Caprylic/capric triglyceride
CAS 65381-09-1; EINECS 265-724-3
Uses: Solubilizer, carrier for flavors, vitamins, antibiotics; diluent for injectables; nutritional supplement; emollient
Regulatory: FDA 21CFR §170.30, GRAS; avail. in kosher grade
Properties: Sl. yel. liq., bland odor, tasteless; sol. in min. oil, acetone, alcohol; sp.gr. 0.930-0.960; iodine no. 0.5; sapon. no. 333; hyd. no. 5; 0.05% moisture
Storage: Avoid prolonged storage above 90 F.

Neobee® 1054. [Stepan Food Ingreds.]
Chem. Descrip.: Propylene glycol dicaprylate/dicaprate
Uses: Cosolv. for pharmaceuticals; carrier for flavors and colors; solubilizer for antibiotics, medicinals; diluent; emollient for creams, lotions, ointments
Regulatory: FDA 21CFR §170.30, GRAS; avail. in kosher grade
Properties: Sl. yel. liq., bland odor; sol. in alcohol, min. oil, acetone; sp.gr. 0.910-0.923; iodine no. 0.1; sapon. no. 325; hyd. no. 1; 0.05% moisture
Storage: Avoid prolonged storage above 90 F.

Neobee® 1062. [Stepan Food Ingreds.]
Chem. Descrip.: Coconut oil-derived triglycerides
Uses: Cosolv., carrier for fat-sol. vitamins, medicinals, and ointments in pharmaceutical industry
Regulatory: FDA 21CFR §170.30, GRAS; avail. in kosher grade
Properties: Liq.; sol. in min. oil, acetone; sp.gr.

0.925-0.945; sapon. no. 295-315
Unverified

Neobee® M-5. [Stepan Food Ingreds.; Stepan Europe]
Chem. Descrip.: Caprylic/capric triglyceride
CAS 65381-09-1; EINECS 265-724-3
Uses: Diluent vehicle/carrier for vitamins, antibiotics, nutritional fluids, and medicinals; solubilizer, cosolv. for fragrance/flavoring, medicinals, food colors; source of nutritional MCT; emollient oil
Regulatory: FDA 21CFR §170.30, GRAS; avail. in kosher grade
Properties: Sl. yel. liq., bland odor, tasteless; sol. in alcohol, min. oil, acetone; sp.gr. 0.930-0.960; visc. 23 cps; acid no. 0.10 max.; iodine no. 1; sapon. no. 340; hyd. no. 5; surf. tens. 32.3 dynes/cm; 0.1% moisture
Storage: Avoid prolonged storage above 90 F.

Neobee® M-20. [Stepan Food Ingreds.; Stepan Europe]
Chem. Descrip.: Propylene glycol dicaprylate/dicaprate
CAS 68583-51-7
Uses: Solubilizer, vehicle for antibiotics, medicinals; diluent for essential oils, injectables
Regulatory: FDA 21CFR§170.30, 172.856; avail. in kosher grade
Properties: Pale yel. liq., bland odor; sol. in alcohol containing up to 20% water; iodine no. 1 max.; sapon. no. 326; hyd. no. 0.6; 0.04% moisture
Storage: Avoid prolonged storage above 90 F.

Neobee® O. [Stepan Food Ingreds.]
Chem. Descrip.: Caprylic/capric triglyceride
CAS 65381-09-1; EINECS 265-724-3
Uses: Solubilizer, cosolv., carrier for fat-sol. vitamins, flavors, medicinals, and ointments in pharmaceutical industry; diluent for injectables; source of nutritional MCT; spreading agent, penetrant
Regulatory: FDA 21CFR §170.30, GRAS; avail. in kosher grade
Properties: Sl. yel. liq., very sl. fatty odor; sol. in min. oil, acetone; sp.gr. 0.938; visc. 30 cps; iodine no. 4.2; sapon. no. 298; hyd. no. 5; surf. tens. 32 dynes/cm; 0.03% moisture
Storage: Avoid prolonged storage above 90 F.

Neobee® SL-110. [Stepan Food Ingreds.]
Chem. Descrip.: Interesterified MCT and soybean oil
CAS 8001-22-7; EINECS 232-274-4
Uses: Nutritional supplements
Properties: Yel. clear sl. visc. oil; iodine no. 23-33; sapon. no. 313-323; 0.1% max. moisture
Storage: Avoid prolonged storage above 90 F.

Neobee® SL-120. [Stepan Food Ingreds.]
Chem. Descrip.: Interesterified MCT and menhaden oil
CAS 8002-50-4; EINECS 232-311-4
Uses: Nutritional supplements
Properties: Yel. clear sl. visc. oil; iodine no. 36-44; sapon. no. 313-323; 0.1% max. moisture
Storage: Avoid prolonged storage above 90 F.

Neobee® SL-130. [Stepan Food Ingreds.]

Chem. Descrip.: Interesterified MCT and sunflower oils
CAS 8001-21-6; EINECS 232-273-9
Uses: Nutritional supplements
Properties: Yel. clear sl. visc. oil; iodine no. 49-59; sapon. no. 281-291; 0.1% max. moisture
Storage: Avoid prolonged storage above 90 F.

Neobee® SL-140. [Stepan Food Ingreds.]
Chem. Descrip.: Interesterified MCT, menhaden oil, soybean oil, and tributyrin
Uses: Nutritional supplements
Properties: Yel. clear sl. visc. oil; iodine no. 52-60; sapon. no. 340-350; 0.1% max. moisture
Storage: Avoid prolonged storage above 90 F.

NEPD. [ANGUS]
Chem. Descrip.: 2-Nitro-2-ethyl-1,3-propanediol
CAS 597-09-1
Uses: Pharmaceutical intermediate
Properties: M.w. 149.2; sol. 400 g/100 ml water; m.p. 56 C; b.p. decomposes; pH 5.5 (0.1 M aq. sol'n.).

Neustrene® 060. [Witco/H-I-P]
Chem. Descrip.: Refined hydrog. tallow glycerides
CAS 67701-27-3; EINECS 269-658-6
Uses: Pharmaceutical intermediate
Properties: Solid; acid no. 2.5 max.; iodine no. 1 max.; sapon. no. 193-205; 100% conc.

Neustrene® 064. [Witco/H-I-P]
Chem. Descrip.: Hydrog. soybean oil
CAS 68002-71-1; EINECS 232-410-2
Uses: Pharmaceutical intermediate
Properties: Solid; acid no. 4 max.; iodine no. 2 max.; sapon. no. 188-200; 100% conc.

Niacet Sodium Phenoxy Acetate. [Niacet]
Chem. Descrip.: Sodium phenoxy acetate
CAS 3598-16-1
Uses: For fermentation of penicillin V, esters of cortical hormones
Properties: Off-wh. powd.; sol. 21% in water, 6% in methanol, 0.5% in ethanol; m.w. 174.10; m.p. 270 C; pH 7.5-10.0 (10% aq.); 98% min. purity.

Niacin USP, FCC Fine Granular No. 69901. [Roche]
Chem. Descrip.: Nicotinic acid USP-FCC
CAS 59-67-6; EINECS 200-441-0
Uses: Vitamin, pellagra preventive; suitable for direct compression formulations; good hardness, low friability
Properties: Wh. fine gran. cryst. or cryst. powd., odorless; sol. 1 g/60 ml water; freely sol. in boiling alcohol, sol'ns. of alkali hydroxides and carbonates; pract. insol. in ether; m.w. 123.11; bulk dens. 0.56 g/ml (loose); m.p. 234-238 C; 99.5-101% assay
Toxicology: Ingestion may produce vascular dilation; high level intakes may produce severe liver damage
Storage: Store in tight, light-resist. containers; avoid exposure to moisture, excessive heat.

Niacin USP, FCC No. 69902. [Roche]
Chem. Descrip.: Nicotinic acid USP-FCC
CAS 59-67-6; EINECS 200-441-0
Uses: Vitamin, pellagra preventive in dietary

177

supplements
Properties: Wh. cryst. or cryst. powd., odorless or nearly odorless; sol. 1 g/60 ml water; freely sol. in boiling water and boiling alcohol, sol'ns. of alkali hydroxides and carbonates; pract. insol. in ether; m.w. 123.11; bulk dens. 0.36 g/cc; m.p. 234-238 C; 99.5-101% assay
Toxicology: Ingestion may produce vascular dilation; high level intakes may produce severe liver damage
Storage: Store in tight, light-resist. containers; avoid exposure to moisture, excessive heat.

Niacinamide Free Flowing No. 69914. [Roche]
Chem. Descrip.: Nicotinamide USP, FCC with 0.5% silicon dioxide (anticaking agent)
Uses: Essential nutrient for multivitamin preps.
Properties: Wh. cryst. powd., nearly odorless, bitter taste; 100% thru 30 mesh; sol. 1 g/1 ml water, 1.5 ml alcohol, 10 ml glycerin; m.w. 122.13; m.p. 128-131 C; 98.5-101% assay
Storage: Store in dry place @ 59-86 F.

Niacinamide USP, FCC No. 69905. [Roche]
Chem. Descrip.: Niacinamide
CAS 98-92-0; EINECS 202-713-4
Uses: Essential nutrient for solid and liq. multivitamin preps.
Properties: Wh. cryst. powd., pract. odorless, bitter taste; 90% min. thru 100 mesh; sol. 1 g/1 ml water, 1 g/1.5 ml alcohol, 1 g/10 ml glycerin; m.w. 122.13; m.p. 128-131 C; 98.5-101% assay
Storage: Store in dry place @ 59-86 F in tightly closed container; optimum storage temp. 46-59 F.

Niacinamide USP, FCC Fine Granular No. 69916. [Roche]
Chem. Descrip.: Niacinamide USP FCC
CAS 98-92-0; EINECS 202-713-4
Uses: Essential nutient for multivitamin preps.
Properties: Wh. free-flowing cryst. powd., nearly odorless, bitter taste; 70% min. thru 40 mesh, 5% min. thru 100 mesh; sol. 1 g/1 ml water, 1.5 ml alcohol, 10 ml glycerin; m.w. 122.13; m.p. 128-131 C; 98.5-101% assay
Storage: Store in dry place @ 59-86 F.

Niaproof® Anionic Surfactant 4. [Niacet]
Chem. Descrip.: Sodium tetradecyl sulfate
CAS 139-88-8; EINECS 214-737-2
Uses: Wetting agent, penetrant, emulsifier used in pharmaceuticals
Regulatory: FDA compliance
Properties: Colorless liq., mild char. odor; misc. with water; sp.gr. 1.031; dens. 8.58 lb/gal; b.p. 92 C; flash pt. (COC) none; pH 8.5 (0.1% aq.); surf. tens. 47 dynes/cm (0.1% aq.); Draves wetting 20 s (0.26%); Ross-Miles foam 10 mm; 27% act. in water; anionic
Toxicology: Moderate oral and skin toxicity; eye irritant; LD50 (oral, rats) 4.95 ml/kg
Precaution: Corrosive, slippery.

Niaproof® Anionic Surfactant 08. [Niacet]
Chem. Descrip.: Sodium 2-ethylhexyl sulfate
CAS 126-92-1; EINECS 204-812-8

Uses: Wetting agent, penetrant, emulsifier used in pharmaceuticals; stable to high concs. of electrolytes
Regulatory: FDA compliance
Properties: Colorless liq., mild char. odor; misc. with water; sp.gr. 1.109; dens. 9.23 lb/gal; b.p. 95 C; flash pt. (COC) none; pH 7.3 (0.1% aq.); surf. tens. 63 dynes/cm (0.1% aq.); Ross-Miles foam 10 mm (initial); 39% act.; anionic
Toxicology: Moderate oral and skin toxicity; eye irritant; LD50 (oral, rats) 7.27 ml/kg.

Nicopherol®. [Henkel/Fine Chems.]
Chem. Descrip.: D-α-Tocopheryl nicotinate
Uses: Used in pharmaceutical skin creams and lotions; for topical use only; stable to air and light
Properties: Lt. yel. waxy solid, bland odor; sol. in chloroform, acetone, ether, ethanol; poorly sol. in veg. oils; insol. in water; m.w. 535.82; dens. 0.94-0.97 g/cm^3; m.p. 42-48 C; 980 mg/g
Storage: Protect from heat; 1 yr shelf life stored cool in unopened original pkg.; unstable to alkali and acid.

Nikkol BC-5.5. [Nikko Chem. Co. Ltd.]
Chem. Descrip.: Ceteth-6
CAS 9004-95-9
Uses: Emulsifier for pharmaceuticals
Properties: Wh. solid; HLB 10.5; 100% conc.; nonionic.

Nikkol BC-7. [Nikko Chem. Co. Ltd.]
Chem. Descrip.: Ceteth-7
CAS 9004-95-9
Uses: Hydrophilic emulsifier for pharmaceuticals
Properties: Wh. solid; HLB 11.5; 100% conc.; nonionic.

Nikkol BC-10TX. [Nikko Chem. Co. Ltd.]
Chem. Descrip.: Ceteth-10
CAS 9004-95-9
Uses: Hydrophilic emulsifier for pharmaceuticals
Properties: Wh. solid; HLB 13.5; 100% conc.; nonionic.

Nikkol BC-15TX. [Nikko Chem. Co. Ltd.]
Chem. Descrip.: Ceteth-15
CAS 9004-95-9
Uses: Emulsifier for pharmaceuticals; used in refining techniques
Properties: Wh. solid; HLB 15.5; 100% conc.; nonionic.

Nikkol BC-20TX. [Nikko Chem. Co. Ltd.]
Chem. Descrip.: Ceteth-20
CAS 9004-95-9
Uses: Hydrophilic emulsifier for pharmaceuticals
Properties: Wh. solid; HLB 17.0; 100% conc.; nonionic.

Nikkol BC-23. [Nikko Chem. Co. Ltd.]
Chem. Descrip.: Ceteth-23
CAS 9004-95-9
Uses: Hydrophilic emulsifier, dispersant, solubilizer for o/w creams, lotions, medicated ointments
Properties: Solid; HLB 18.0; 100% conc.; nonionic.

Nikkol BC-25TX. [Nikko Chem. Co. Ltd.]
Chem. Descrip.: Ceteth-25
CAS 9004-95-9

Uses: Hydrophilic emulsifier, dispersant, and solubilizer for pharmaceuticals
Properties: Wh. solid; HLB 18.5; 100% conc.; nonionic.

Nikkol BC-30TX. [Nikko Chem. Co. Ltd.]
Chem. Descrip.: Ceteth-30
CAS 9004-95-9
Uses: Hydrophilic emulsifier, dispersant, and solubilizer for pharmaceuticals
Properties: Wh. solid; HLB 19.5; 100% conc.; nonionic.

Nikkol BC-40TX. [Nikko Chem. Co. Ltd.]
Chem. Descrip.: Ceteth-40
CAS 9004-95-9
Uses: Hydrophilic emulsifier, dispersant, and solubilizer for pharmaceuticals
Properties: Wh. solid; HLB 20.0; 100% conc.; nonionic.

Nikkol BEG-1630. [Nikko Chem. Co. Ltd.]
Chem. Descrip.: Isoceteth-30
Uses: Emulsifier and solubilizer used for pharmaceuticals
Properties: Solid; HLB 15.5; 100% conc.; nonionic
Unverified

Nikkol BPS-5. [Nikko Chem. Co. Ltd.]
Chem. Descrip.: PEG-5 phytosterol
Uses: Emulsifier for o/w and w/o compds., solubilizer, dispersant, emollient, foam stabilizer, visc. modifier, conditioner used in pharmaceuticals
Properties: Yel. paste; sol. in propylene glycol, ethanol; partly sol. in water; HLB 9.5; acid no. 0.25 max.; pH 4.8 (5%); 100% conc.; nonionic.

Nikkol CO-3. [Nikko Chem. Co. Ltd.]
Chem. Descrip.: PEG-3 castor oil
CAS 61791-12-6
Uses: Hydrotrope, w/o emulsifier used in pharmaceutical preps.
Properties: Pale yel. liq.; HLB 3.0; 100% conc.; nonionic.

Nikkol DDP-2. [Nikko Chem. Co. Ltd.]
Chem. Descrip.: Di-PEG-2 alkyl ether phosphate
Uses: Emulsifier, stabilizer, dispersant used in drugs
Properties: Yel. liq.; HLB 6.5; 100% conc.; anionic.

Nikkol DGDO. [Nikko Chem. Co. Ltd.]
Chem. Descrip.: Polyglyceryl-2 dioleate
Uses: W/o emulsifier for pharmaceuticals
Properties: Yel. liq.; HLB 7.0; 100% conc.; nonionic.

Nikkol DGMO-C. [Nikko Chem. Co. Ltd.]
Chem. Descrip.: Polyglyceryl-2 oleate
CAS 9007-48-1
Uses: W/o emulsifier for pharmaceuticals
Properties: Yel. liq.; HLB 5.5; 100% conc.; nonionic.

Nikkol DGMS. [Nikko Chem. Co. Ltd.]
Chem. Descrip.: Polyglyceryl-2 stearate
CAS 12694-22-3; EINECS 235-777-7
Uses: W/o emulsifier for pharmaceuticals
Properties: Pale yel. solid; HLB 5.0; 100% conc.; nonionic.

Nikkol DOP-8N. [Nikko Chem. Co. Ltd.]

Chem. Descrip.: Sodium dioleth-8 phosphate
Uses: Solubilizer for pharmaceutical applics.
Properties: Pale yel. liq.; 100% conc.; anionic.

Nikkol GBW-8. [Nikko Chem. Co. Ltd.]
Chem. Descrip.: PEG-8 sorbitan beeswax
Uses: Emulsifier for pharmaceuticals; nonionic.

Nikkol GBW-25. [Nikko Chem. Co. Ltd.]
Chem. Descrip.: PEG-6 sorbitan beeswax
CAS 8051-15-8
Uses: Emulsifier and emulsion stabilizer for pharmaceuticals
Properties: Yel. solid; HLB 7.5; 100% conc.; nonionic.

Nikkol GBW-125. [Nikko Chem. Co. Ltd.]
Chem. Descrip.: PEG-20 sorbitan beeswax
CAS 8051-73-8
Uses: Emulsifier and emulsion stabilizer for pharmaceuticals
Properties: Yel. solid; HLB 9.5; 100% conc.; nonionic.

Nikkol GO-430. [Nikko Chem. Co. Ltd.]
Chem. Descrip.: PEG-30 sorbitan tetraoleate
Uses: Emulsifier, solubilizer, superfatting agent used in drug industry
Properties: Pale yel. liq.; sol. in ethanol, ethyl acetate, xylene; partly sol. in water; sp.gr. 1.048; HLB 11.5; ref. index 1.4727; 100% conc.; nonionic.

Nikkol GO-440. [Nikko Chem. Co. Ltd.]
Chem. Descrip.: PEG-40 sorbitan tetraoleate
CAS 9003-11-6
Uses: Emulsifier, solubilizer, superfatting agent used in drug industry
Properties: Pale yel. liq.; sol. in ethanol, ethyl acetate, xylene; partly sol. in water, propylene glycol; sp.gr. 1.054; HLB 12.5; 100% conc.; nonionic.

Nikkol GO-460. [Nikko Chem. Co. Ltd.]
Chem. Descrip.: PEG-60 sorbitan tetraoleate
Uses: Emulsifier, solubilizer, superfatting agent used in drug industry
Properties: Pale yel. liq.; sol. in water, ethanol, ethyl acetate, xylene; partly sol. in propylene glycol; sp.gr. 1.060; HLB 14.0; 100% conc.; nonionic.

Nikkol HCO-5. [Nikko Chem. Co. Ltd.]
Chem. Descrip.: PEG-5 hydrog. castor oil
CAS 61788-85-0
Uses: Hydrotrope, w/o emulsifier used in pharmaceuticals
Properties: Pale yel. liq.; HLB 6.0; 100% conc.; nonionic.

Nikkol HCO-7.5. [Nikko Chem. Co. Ltd.]
Chem. Descrip.: PEG-7.5 hydrog. castor oil
CAS 61788-85-0
Uses: Hydrotrope, emulsifier used in pharmaceuticals
Properties: Liq.; HLB 6.0; 100% conc.; nonionic
Unverified

Nikkol HCO-10. [Nikko Chem. Co. Ltd.]
Chem. Descrip.: PEG-10 hydrog. castor oil
CAS 61788-85-0
Uses: Hydrotrope, emulsifier used in pharmaceu-

ticals
Properties: Pale yel. liq.; HLB 6.5; 100% conc.; nonionic.

Nikkol HCO-20. [Nikko Chem. Co. Ltd.]
Chem. Descrip.: PEG-20 hydrog. castor oil
CAS 61788-85-0
Uses: Hydrotrope, emulsifier used in pharmaceuticals
Properties: Pale yel. liq.; HLB 10.5; 100% conc.; nonionic.

Nikkol HCO-30. [Nikko Chem. Co. Ltd.]
Chem. Descrip.: PEG-30 hydrog. castor oil
CAS 61788-85-0
Uses: Hydrotrope, emulsifier used in pharmaceuticals
Properties: Pale yel. liq.; HLB 11.0; 100% conc.; nonionic.

Nikkol HCO-40. [Nikko Chem. Co. Ltd.]
Chem. Descrip.: PEG-40 hydrog. castor oil
CAS 61788-85-0
Uses: Hydrotrope, emulsifier used in pharmaceuticals
Properties: Pale yel. liq.; HLB 12.5; 100% conc.; nonionic.

Nikkol HCO-40 Pharm. [Nikko Chem. Co. Ltd.]
Chem. Descrip.: PEG-40 hydrog. castor oil
CAS 61788-85-0
Uses: Pharmaceutical grade emulsifier
Properties: Pale yel. liq.; high water sol.; nonionic.

Nikkol HCO-50. [Nikko Chem. Co. Ltd.]
Chem. Descrip.: PEG-50 hydrog. castor oil
CAS 61788-85-0
Uses: Hydrotrope, emulsifier used in pharmaceuticals
Properties: Wh. paste; HLB 13.5; 100% conc.; nonionic.

Nikkol HCO-50 Pharm. [Nikko Chem. Co. Ltd.]
Chem. Descrip.: PEG-50 hydrog. castor oil
CAS 61788-85-0
Uses: Pharmaceutical grade emulsifier
Properties: Wh. paste; high water sol.; nonionic.

Nikkol HCO-60. [Nikko Chem. Co. Ltd.]
Chem. Descrip.: PEG-60 hydrog. castor oil
CAS 61788-85-0
Uses: Hydrotrope, emulsifier used in pharmaceuticals
Properties: Wh. paste; HLB 14.5; 100% conc.; nonionic.

Nikkol HCO-60 Pharm. [Nikko Chem. Co. Ltd.]
Chem. Descrip.: PEG-60 hydrog. castor oil
CAS 61788-85-0
Uses: Pharmaceutical grade emulsifier
Properties: Wh. paste; high water sol.; nonionic.

Nikkol HCO-80. [Nikko Chem. Co. Ltd.]
Chem. Descrip.: PEG-80 hydrog. castor oil
CAS 61788-85-0
Uses: Hydrotrope, emulsifier used in pharmaceuticals
Properties: Pale yel. liq.; HLB 15.0; 100% conc.; nonionic.

Nikkol HCO-100. [Nikko Chem. Co. Ltd.]
Chem. Descrip.: PEG-100 hydrog. castor oil

CAS 61788-85-0
Uses: Hydrotrope, emulsifier used in pharmaceuticals
Properties: Wh. solid; HLB 16.5; 100% conc.; nonionic.

Nikkol MYS-1EX. [Nikko Chem. Co. Ltd.]
Chem. Descrip.: PEG-1 stearate
Uses: Pearling agent, emulsifier, or solubilizer for pharmaceuticals
Properties: Pale yel. solid; HLB 2.0; 100% conc.; nonionic.

Nikkol MYS-2. [Nikko Chem. Co. Ltd.]
Chem. Descrip.: PEG-2 stearate
CAS 106-11-6; EINECS 203-363-5
Uses: Emulsifier, solubilizer for pharmaceuticals
Properties: Pale yel. flake; HLB 4.0; 100% conc.; nonionic.

Nikkol MYS-4. [Nikko Chem. Co. Ltd.]
Chem. Descrip.: PEG-4 stearate
CAS 9004-99-3; EINECS 203-358-8
Uses: Emulsifier, solubilizer for pharmaceuticals
Properties: Pale yel. solid; HLB 6.5; 100% conc.; nonionic.

Nikkol MYS-10. [Nikko Chem. Co. Ltd.]
Chem. Descrip.: PEG-10 stearate
CAS 9004-99-3
Uses: Emulsifier, solubilizer for pharmaceuticals
Properties: Pale yel. solid; HLB 11.0; 100% conc.; nonionic.

Nikkol MYS-25. [Nikko Chem. Co. Ltd.]
Chem. Descrip.: PEG-25 stearate
CAS 9004-99-3
Uses: Emulsifier, solubilizer for pharmaceuticals
Properties: Pale yel. solid; HLB 15.0; 100% conc.; nonionic.

Nikkol MYS-40. [Nikko Chem. Co. Ltd.]
Chem. Descrip.: PEG-40 stearate
CAS 9004-99-3
Uses: Emulsifier, solubilizer for pharmaceuticals
Properties: Pale yel. solid; HLB 17.5; 100% conc.; nonionic.

Nikkol MYS-45. [Nikko Chem. Co. Ltd.]
Chem. Descrip.: PEG-45 stearate
CAS 9004-99-3
Uses: Emulsifier, solubilizer for pharmaceuticals
Properties: Pale yel. flake; HLB 18.0; 100% conc.; nonionic.

Nikkol MYS-55. [Nikko Chem. Co. Ltd.]
Chem. Descrip.: PEG-55 stearate
CAS 9004-99-3
Uses: Emulsifier, solubilizer for pharmaceuticals
Properties: Pale yel. flake; HLB 18.0; 100% conc.; nonionic.

Nikkol OTP-100S. [Nikko Chem. Co. Ltd.]
Chem. Descrip.: Sodium dioctyl sulfosuccinate USP
CAS 577-11-7; EINECS 209-406-4
Uses: Dispersant, wetting agent
Properties: Sponge-like solid; 98% conc.; anionic
Unverified

Nikkol PBC-31. [Nikko Chem. Co. Ltd.]
Chem. Descrip.: PPG-4-ceteth-1

Uses: Emulsifier, solubilizer, dispersant for pharmaceuticals
Properties: Colorless liq.; HLB 9.4; 100% conc.; nonionic.

Nikkol PMS-1C. [Nikko Chem. Co. Ltd.]
Chem. Descrip.: Propylene glycol stearate
CAS 1323-39-3; EINECS 215-354-3
Uses: Emulsifier, emulsion stabilizer, and dispersant for pharmaceuticals
Properties: Wh. solid; HLB 3.5; 100% conc.; nonionic.

Nikkol PMS-1CSE. [Nikko Chem. Co. Ltd.]
Chem. Descrip.: Propylene glycol stearate SE
Uses: Emulsifier, emulsion stabilizer, and dispersant for pharmaceuticals
Properties: Wh. solid; HLB 4.0; 100% conc.; nonionic.

Nikkol SI-10R. [Nikko Chem. Co. Ltd.]
Chem. Descrip.: Sorbitan isostearate
CAS 54392-26-6
Uses: W/o emulsifier for pharmaceuticals; refined grade (low color/odor)
Properties: Yel. liq.; HLB 5.0; 100% conc.; nonionic.

Nikkol SI-10T. [Nikko Chem. Co. Ltd.]
Chem. Descrip.: Sorbitan isostearate
CAS 54392-26-6
Uses: W/o emulsifier for pharmaceuticals
Properties: Liq.; HLB 5.0; 100% conc.; nonionic.

Nikkol SI-15R. [Nikko Chem. Co. Ltd.]
Chem. Descrip.: Sorbitan sesquiisostearate
Uses: W/o emulsifier for pharmaceuticals; refined grade (low color/odor)
Properties: Pale yel. visc. liq.; HLB 4.5; 100% conc.; nonionic.

Nikkol SI-15T. [Nikko Chem. Co. Ltd.]
Chem. Descrip.: Sorbitan isostearate
CAS 54392-26-6
Uses: W/o emulsifier for pharmaceuticals
Properties: Liq.; HLB 4.5; 100% conc.; nonionic
Unverified

Nikkol TDP-2. [Nikko Chem. Co. Ltd.]
Chem. Descrip.: C12-15 pareth-2 phosphate
Uses: Emulsifier and solubilizer for drugs
Properties: Yel. liq.; HLB 7.0; 100% conc.; anionic.

Nikkol TL-10, TL-10EX. [Nikko Chem. Co. Ltd.]
Chem. Descrip.: Polysorbate 20
CAS 9005-64-5
Uses: Hydrophilic emulsifier, solubilizer, and dispersant for pharmaceuticals
Properties: Pale yel. liq.; HLB 16.9; 100% conc.; nonionic.

Nikkol TO-10. [Nikko Chem. Co. Ltd.]
Chem. Descrip.: Polysorbate 80
CAS 9005-65-6
Uses: Hydrophilic emulsifier, solubilizer, and dispersant for pharmaceuticals
Properties: Yel. liq.; HLB 15.0; 100% conc.; nonionic.

Nikkol TO-30. [Nikko Chem. Co. Ltd.]
Chem. Descrip.: Polysorbate 85
CAS 9005-70-3

Uses: Hydrophilic emulsifier for pharmaceuticals
Properties: Yel. liq.; HLB 11.0; 100% conc.; nonionic.

Nikkol TO-106. [Nikko Chem. Co. Ltd.]
Chem. Descrip.: PEG-6 sorbitan oleate
CAS 9005-65-6
Uses: Hydrophilic emulsifier for pharmaceuticals
Properties: Yel. liq.; HLB 10.0; 100% conc.; nonionic.

Nikkol TS-10. [Nikko Chem. Co. Ltd.]
Chem. Descrip.: Polysorbate 60
CAS 9005-67-8
Uses: Emulsifier, solubilizer, and dispersant for o/w prods., pharmaceuticals
Properties: Yel. visc. liq.; sol. in water, ethanol, ethyl acetate, toluene; HLB 14.9; sapon. no. 43-49; pH 5.7-7.7 (5%); 100% conc.; nonionic.

Nikkol TS-30. [Nikko Chem. Co. Ltd.]
Chem. Descrip.: Polysorbate 65
CAS 9005-71-4
Uses: Emulsifier, solubilizer for o/w prods., pharmaceuticals
Properties: Yel. semisolid; HLB 11.0; 100% conc.; nonionic.

Nikkol TS-106. [Nikko Chem. Co. Ltd.]
Chem. Descrip.: PEG-6 sorbitan stearate
CAS 9005-67-8
Uses: Emulsifier, solubilizer for o/w prods., pharmaceuticals
Properties: Yel. paste; nonionic.

Nikkol Batyl Alcohol 100, EX. [Nikko Chem. Co. Ltd.]
Chem. Descrip.: Batyl alcohol
CAS 544-62-7; EINECS 208-874-7
Uses: Emollient, emulsifier, hydrotrope, emulsion thickener for pharmaceutical preparations
Properties: Wh. powd.; 100% conc.; nonionic.

Nikkol Behenyl Alcohol 65, 80. [Nikko Chem. Co. Ltd.]
Chem. Descrip.: Behenyl alcohol
CAS 661-19-8; EINECS 211-546-6
Uses: Emollient, emulsion stabilizer for pharmaceuticals
Properties: Wh. flake; sol. in warm ethanol, min. oil, 2-hexyldecanol, IPM; insol. in water.

Nikkol Chimyl Alcohol 100. [Nikko Chem. Co. Ltd.]
Chem. Descrip.: Cetyl glyceryl ether
Uses: Emulsifier, hydrotrope, emollient, emulsion thickener used for pharmaceutical prods.
Properties: Wh. powd.; 100% conc.; nonionic.

Nikkol Decaglyn 1-IS. [Nikko Chem. Co. Ltd.]
Chem. Descrip.: Polyglyceryl-10 isostearate
CAS 133738-23-5
Uses: Emulsifier, solubilizer, dispersant for pharmaceuticals
Properties: Pale yel. visc. liq.; HLB 12.5; 100% conc.; nonionic.

Nikkol Decaglyn 1-L. [Nikko Chem. Co. Ltd.]
Chem. Descrip.: Polyglyceryl-10 laurate
CAS 34406-66-1
Uses: Emulsifier, solubilizer, dispersant for pharmaceuticals
Properties: Pale yel. visc. liq.; HLB 17.0; 100%

conc.; nonionic.

Nikkol Decaglyn 1-LN. [Nikko Chem. Co. Ltd.]
Chem. Descrip.: Polyglyceryl-10 linoleate
Uses: Emulsifier, solubilizer, dispersant for pharmaceuticals
Properties: Pale yel. visc. liq.; HLB 12.0; 100% conc.; nonionic.

Nikkol Decaglyn 1-M. [Nikko Chem. Co. Ltd.]
Chem. Descrip.: Polyglyceryl-10 myristate
CAS 87390-32-7
Uses: Emulsifier, solubilizer, dispersant for pharmaceuticals
Properties: Pale yel. visc. liq.; HLB 14.5; 100% conc.; nonionic.

Nikkol Decaglyn 1-O. [Nikko Chem. Co. Ltd.]
Chem. Descrip.: Polyglyceryl-10 oleate
CAS 9007-48-1
Uses: Emulsifier, solubilizer, dispersant for pharmaceuticals
Properties: Pale yel. visc. liq.; HLB 13.5; 100% conc.; nonionic.

Nikkol Decaglyn 1-S. [Nikko Chem. Co. Ltd.]
Chem. Descrip.: Polyglyceryl-10 stearate
CAS 79777-30-3
Uses: Emulsifier, solubilizer, dispersant for pharmaceuticals
Properties: Pale yel. plate; HLB 12.5; 100% conc.; nonionic.

Nikkol Decaglyn 2-O. [Nikko Chem. Co. Ltd.]
Chem. Descrip.: Polyglyceryl-10 dioleate
CAS 33940-99-7
Uses: O/w emulsifier for pharmaceuticals
Properties: Pale yel. visc. liq.; HLB 10.0; 100% conc.; nonionic.

Nikkol Decaglyn 2-S. [Nikko Chem. Co. Ltd.]
Chem. Descrip.: Polyglyceryl-10 distearate
CAS 12764-60-2
Uses: O/w emulsifier for pharmaceuticals
Properties: Pale yel. plate; HLB 12.0; 100% conc.; nonionic.

Nikkol Dipotassium Glycyrrhizinate. [Nikko Chem. Co. Ltd.]
Chem. Descrip.: Dipotassium glycyrrhizinate
CAS 68797-35-3; EINECS 272-296-1
Uses: Anti-inflammatory, anti-allergenic surfactant for pharmaceuticals
Properties: Pale yel. cryst. powd.; water-sol.
Unverified

Nikkol Glycyrrhetinic Acid. [Nikko Chem. Co. Ltd.]
Chem. Descrip.: Glycyrrhetinic acid
CAS 471-53-4; EINECS 207-444-6
Uses: Anti-inflammatory, anti-allergenic for pharmaceuticals
Properties: Wh. cryst. powd.
Unverified

Nikkol Glycyrrhizic Acid. [Nikko Chem. Co. Ltd.]
Chem. Descrip.: Glycyrrhizic acid
CAS 1405-86-3; EINECS 215-785-7
Uses: Anti-inflammatory, anti-allergenic surfactant for pharmaceuticals
Properties: Wh. powd.; water-sol.
Unverified

Nikkol Stearyl Glycyrrhetinate. [Nikko Chem. Co. Ltd.]
Chem. Descrip.: Stearyl glycyrrhetinate
CAS 13832-70-7
Uses: Anti-inflammatory, anti-allergenic for pharmaceuticals
Properties: Wh. to pale yel. cryst. powd.; oil-sol.
Unverified

Nipa ISDN. [Nipa Hardwicke]
Chem. Descrip.: Isosorbide dinitrate
Uses: Preservative for pharmaceuticals.

Nipa Benzocaine. [Nipa Hardwicke]
Uses: Pharmaceutical preservative; topical anesthetic.

Nipabenzyl. [Nipa Hardwicke]
Chem. Descrip.: Benzylparaben
CAS 94-18-8; EINECS 202-311-9
Uses: Preservative, bactericide, fungicide for pharmaceuticals, topical, ophthalmic, oral, and injectable medicaments, ointments, creams, syrups, multi-dose injections, eye drops, vitamin sol'ns., vaccines
Regulatory: BP, NF, Eur.Ph., FCC compliance
Properties: Wh. fine cryst. powd., odorless, tasteless; sol. (g/100 g solv.) 102 g acetone, 79 g methanol, 72 g ethanol, 60 g lanolin, 42 g ether; m.w. 228.25; m.p. 110-112 C; 99% assay
Toxicology: LD50 (oral, rat) > 5 g/kg; nonirritating to skin, sl. harmful by ingestion, sl. irritating to eyes.

Nipabutyl. [Nipa Hardwicke]
Chem. Descrip.: Butylparaben NF, BP, FCC, Eur. Ph.
CAS 94-26-8; EINECS 202-318-7
Uses: Preservative, bactericide, fungicide for pharmaceuticals, topical, ophthalmic, oral, and injectable medicaments, ointments, creams, syrups, multi-dose injections, eye drops, vitamin sol'ns., vaccines
Regulatory: FDA GRAS; EC 0.4% max.; Japan 1%
Properties: Wh. cryst. powd., odorless or very faint aromatic odor, tasteless; sol. (g/100 g solv.) 240 g acetone, 220 g methanol, 208 g ethanol, > 200 g IPA, 150 g ether, > 100 g lanolin; m.w. 194.23; m.p. 68-69 C; > 99% act.
Toxicology: LD50 (oral, mouse) > 5 g/kg; nonirritating to skin; sl. irritating to eyes.

Nipabutyl Potassium. [Nipa Hardwicke; Nipa Laboratories Ltd]
Chem. Descrip.: Potassium butylparaben
CAS 38566-94-8
Uses: Preservative, bactericide, fungicide for pharmaceuticals, medicinal preps.
Properties: Wh. fine hygroscopic powd.; sol. in cold water; m.w. 232.32; pH 9.5-10.5 (0.1% aq.); > 99% act.
Toxicology: Nonirritating to skin; sl. irritating to eyes and nasal passages.

Nipabutyl Sodium. [Nipa Hardwicke; Nipa Laboratories Ltd]
Chem. Descrip.: Sodium butylparaben
CAS 36457-20-2

Uses: Preservative, bactericide, fungicide for pharmaceuticals, medicinal preps., soft gelatin capsules
Properties: Wh. fine hygroscopic powd.; sol. in cold water; m.w. 216.21; pH 9.5-10.5 (0.1% aq.); > 99% act.
Toxicology: LD50 (oral, mouse) > 2 g/kg; pure material irritating to skin; sl. irritating to eyes and nasal passages.

Nipacide® PX-R. [Nipa Hardwicke]
Chem. Descrip.: p-Chloro-m-xylenol
CAS 88-04-0; EINECS 201-793-8
Uses: Pharmaceutical grade antimicrobial agent used as an antiseptic base for OTC drug prods. incl. medicated powds., soaps, surgical scrubs, and antidandruff shampoos
Use level: 0.5-3.75%.

Nipacide® Potassium. [Nipa Hardwicke; Nipa Laboratories Ltd]
Uses: Preservative for aq. pharmaceuticals
Properties: Sol. in cold water.

Nipacide® Sodium. [Nipa Hardwicke; Nipa Laboratories Ltd]
Uses: Preservative for aq. pharmaceuticals
Properties: Sol. in cold water.

Nipacombin A. [Nipa Laboratories Ltd]
Chem. Descrip.: > 30% Sodium propylparaben, 15-30% sodium methylparaben, 15-30% sodium ethylparben, 5-15% sodium benzoate
Uses: Antimicrobial preservative for pharmaceuticals, esp. preservation of soft gelatin
Properties: Wh. fine cryst. powd.; sol. in cold water and in ethanol, diethyl ether; pH 9.5-10.5 (0.1% aq.); readily biodeg.; unlikely to accumulate in aquatic environment; discharge of lg. quantities may kill fish
Toxicology: LD50 (oral, rat) < 2000 mg/kg; harmful if swallowed; severe eye irritant; may cause irritation to mouth, upper digestive tract; prolonged/repeated exposure may cause skin irritation; inh. of dust may cause irritation to nose, upper respiratory tract
Precaution: May react with strong oxidants; may cause dust explosion; fire may produce fumes contg. CO and CO_2; spillages may be slippery
Storage: Store in cool, dry area away from strong oxidizing agents.

Nipacombin PK. [Nipa Hardwicke; Nipa Laboratories Ltd]
Uses: Preservative for aq. pharmaceuticals
Properties: Sol. in cold water.

Nipacombin SK. [Nipa Hardwicke; Nipa Laboratories Ltd]
Chem. Descrip.: Combination of sodium salts of Nipa esters
Uses: Antimicrobial preservative for oral pharmaceutials, liq. antacid suspensions and other alkaline sol'ns. (to pH 8.0-8.5)
Use level: 0.05-0.20%
Properties: Sol. in cold water.

Nipagin A. [Nipa Hardwicke; Nipa Laboratories Ltd]
Chem. Descrip.: Ethylparaben NF, BP, FCC,

Eur.Ph.
CAS 120-47-8; EINECS 204-399-4
Uses: Preservative, bactericide, fungicide for pharmaceuticals, topical, ophthalmic, oral, and injectable medicaments, ointments, creams, syrups, multi-dose injections, eye drops, vitamin sol'ns., vaccines
Regulatory: FDA GRAS; EC 0.4% max.; Japan 1%
Properties: Wh. fine cryst. powd., odorless or very faint aromatic odor, tasteless; sol. (g/100 g solv.) 84 g acetone, 81 g methanol, 70 g ethanol, 40 g ether, 30 g lanolin; m.w. 166.18; m.p. 115-117 C; pH 7; > 99% act.; not very resist. to microbial degradation
Toxicology: LD50 (oral, rat) > 8 g/kg; sl. poisonous if swallowed; nonirritating to skin; sl. irritating to eyes; produces a sl. burning sensation of mouth and tongue
Precaution: Dust in confined conditions can be a dangerous fire and explosion hazard; decomp. may produce acrid irritating thick black smoke.

Nipagin A Potassium. [Nipa Hardwicke; Nipa Laboratories Ltd]
Chem. Descrip.: Potassium ethylparaben
CAS 36457-19-9
Uses: Preservative, bactericide, fungicide for pharmaceuticals, medicinal preps.
Properties: Wh. fine hygroscopic powd., tasteless; sol. in cold water; m.w. 204.27; pH 9.5-10.5 (0.1% aq.); > 99% act.
Toxicology: Nonirritating to skin; sl. irritating to eyes and nasal passages.

Nipagin A Sodium. [Nipa Hardwicke; Nipa Laboratories Ltd]
Chem. Descrip.: Sodium ethylparaben
CAS 35285-68-8; EINECS 252-487-6
Uses: Antimicrobial preservative, bactericide, fungicide for pharmaceuticals, medicinal preps., soft gelatine capsules
Properties: Wh. fine powd., almost odorless, tasteless; hygroscopic; sol. in cold water; m.w. 188.16; pH 9.5-10.5 (0.1% aq.); > 99% act.; not very resist. to microbial degradation
Toxicology: LD50 (oral, mouse) 2.5 g/kg; sl. poisonous if swallowed; pure material irritating to skin; severe eye irritant; sl. irritating to nasal passages; produces sl. burning sensation of mouth and tongue
Precaution: Dust in confined conditions can be dangerous fire and explosion hazard; decomp. may produce acrid irritating thick black smoke.

Nipagin M. [Nipa Hardwicke]
Chem. Descrip.: Methylparaben NF, BP, FCC, Eur. Ph.
CAS 99-76-3; EINECS 202-785-7
Uses: Antimicrobial preservative, bactericide, fungicide for pharmaceuticals, topical, ophthalmic, oral, and injectable medicaments, ointments, creams, syrups, multi-dose injections, eye drops, vitamin sol'ns., vaccines
Regulatory: FDA GRAS; EC 0.4% max.; Japan 1%
Properties: Wh. fine cryst. powd., odorless or very

faint aromatic odor, tasteless; sol. (g/100 g solv.): 64 g acetone, 60 g IPA, 58 g methanol, 48 g ethanol, 35 g propylene glycol, 23 g ether; m.w. 152.15; m.p. 125-128 C; b.p. 298.6 C; pH ≤ 7; > 99% act.; not very resist. to microbial degradation

Toxicology: LD50 (oral, rat) > 8 g/kg; sl. poisonous if swallowed; sl. irritating to eyes; nonirritating to skin; produces sl. burning sensation of mouth and tongue

Precaution: Dust in confined conditions can be dangerous fire and explosion hazard; decomp. may produce acrid irritating thick black smoke.

Nipagin M Potassium. [Nipa Hardwicke; Nipa Laboratories Ltd]

Chem. Descrip.: Potassium methylparaben

CAS 26112-07-2; EINECS 247-464-2

Uses: Preservative, bactericide, fungicide for pharmaceuticals, medicinal preps.

Properties: Wh. fine hygroscopic powd., odorless or very faint aromatic odor, tasteless; sol. in cold water; m.w. 190.24; pH 9.5-10.5 (0.1% aq.); > 99% act.

Toxicology: LD50 (oral, rat) > 8 g/kg; nonirritating to skin; sl. irritating to eyes.

Nipagin M Sodium. [Nipa Hardwicke; Nipa Laboratories Ltd]

Chem. Descrip.: Sodium methylparaben

CAS 5026-62-0; EINECS 225-714-1

Uses: Preservative, bactericide, fungicide for pharmaceuticals, medicinal preps., soft gelatin capsules, cold-produced toothpaste

Properties: Wh. powd., almost odorless, tasteless; hygroscopic; sol. in cold water; m.w. 174.1; pH 9.5-10.5 (0.1%); > 99% act.; not very resist. to microbial degradation

Toxicology: LD50 (oral, mouse) 2.0 g/kg; poisonous of swallowed; severe eye irritant; sl. irritating to skin; sl. irritating to nasal passages; produces sl. burning sensation of mouth and tongue

Precaution: Dust in confined conditions can be dangerous fire and explosion hazard; decomp. may produce acrid irritating thick black smoke.

Nipaguard® BPX. [Nipa Hardwicke; Nipa Laboratories Ltd]

Chem. Descrip.: Phenoxyethanol, methylparaben, propylparaben, and bronopol

Uses: Broad-spectrum preservative system for use at pH 4.5-8.5 in oral/topical pharmaceuticals; readily incorporated in aq. phase; used in sunscreens

Regulatory: USA and Europe approvals

Properties: Sol. 0.5% in water; readily sol. in oil phases, many org. solvs.

Toxicology: Calculated LD50 (oral, rat) > 2000 mg/kg; low toxicity; nonirritating to skin, eyes, mucous membranes at normal use concs.

NiPar S-10™. [ANGUS]

Chem. Descrip.: 1-Nitropropane

CAS 108-03-2; EINECS 203-544-9

Uses: Pharmaceutical intermediate

Properties: Liq.; sol. 1.5% in water (20 C); m.w. 89.1; dens. 1.0 g/ml (20 C), 8.35 lb/gal; visc. 0.844

cp (20 C); vapor pressure 10.23 mm Hg; f.p. -104 C; b.p. 131 C; flash pt. (TCC) 96 F; ref. index 1.40160 (20 C); pH 6.0 (0.01M aq.); surf. tens. 30.64 dynes/cm (20 C); dielec. const. 23.24 (30 C); 98.5% min. purity

Toxicology: Harmful if inhaled; overexposure can cause liver damage and death; OSHA PEL 25 ppm; avoid breathing vapors

Precaution: Flamm.; keep away from heat, sparks, flame

Storage: Keep container closed.

NiPar S-20™. [ANGUS]

Chem. Descrip.: 2-Nitropropane

CAS 79-46-9; EINECS 201-209-1

Uses: Intermediate for synthesis of pharmaceuticals; used in beta blockers for treatment of cardiovascular disease and in anti-tumor drugs

Properties: APHA 20 max. color; sol. 1.7% in water; sol. in many nonaq. systems; m.w. 89.095; sp.gr. 0.988 (20 C); dens. 8.24 lb/gal; visc. 0.770 cp (20 C); vapor pressure 18 mm Hg; f.p. -91.3 C; b.p. 120 C; flash pt. (TOC) 100 F; ref. index 1.39439 (20 C); pH 6.2 (0.01M aq.); surf. tens. 29.87 dynes/cm (20 C); minimally photochemically reactive; Rule 66 exempt solv.

Toxicology: LD50 (oral, rat) 725 ± 160 mg/kg (sl. toxic); overexposure may cause liver damage, death; hazardous by inh. (mild respiratory tract irritant, headache, nausea, vomiting); OSHA PEL 10 ppm; liq. form nonirritating to eyes and skin; may be defatting

Precaution: Flamm.; keep away from heat, sparks, and flame; avoid contact with strong caustic or lye sol'ns. which may produce unstable alkali salts

Storage: Keep container closed.

Nipasept Potassium. [Nipa Hardwicke; Nipa Laboratories Ltd]

Uses: Preservative for aq. pharmaceuticals

Properties: Sol. in cold water.

Nipasept Sodium. [Nipa Hardwicke; Nipa Laboratories Ltd]

Chem. Descrip.: Sodium methylparaben, sodium propylparaben, and sodium ethylparaben

Uses: Preservative, bactericide, fungicide for pharmaceuticals, medicinal preps., syrups, sol'ns., suspensions, other oral medicines incl. alkaline preps. to pH 8.0-8.5

Properties: Sol. in cold water.

Nipasol M. [Nipa Hardwicke; Nipa Laboratories Ltd]

Chem. Descrip.: Propylparaben NF, BP, FCC, Eur.Ph.

CAS 94-13-3; EINECS 202-307-7

Uses: Preservative, bactericide, fungicide for pharmaceuticals, topical, ophthalmic, oral, and injectable medicaments, ointments, creams, syrups, multi-dose injections, eye drops, vitamin sol'ns., vaccines, paracetamol tablets

Use level: 0.1% (paracetamol tablets)

Regulatory: FDA GRAS; EC 0.4% max.; Japan 1%

Properties: Wh. fine cryst. powd., odorless or very faint aromatic odor, tasteless; sol. (g/100 g solv.): 105 g acetone, 100 g in methanol, ethanol, 88 g

IPA, 80 g lanolin, 50 g ether; m.w. 180.20; m.p. 95-98 C; > 99% act.

Toxicology: LD50 (oral, rat) > 8 g/kg (pract. nonharmful by ingestion); nonirritant to skin; sl. irritant to eyes.

Nipasol M Potassium. [Nipa Hardwicke; Nipa Laboratories Ltd]
Chem. Descrip.: Potassium propylparaben
CAS 84930-16-5
Uses: Preservative, bactericide, fungicide for pharmaceuticals, medicinal preps.
Properties: Wh. fine hygroscopic powd., odorless or very faint aromatic odor, tasteless; sol. in cold water; m.w. 218.29; pH 9.5-10.5 (0.1% aq.); > 99% act.
Toxicology: LD50 (oral, rat) > 8 g/kg (pract. nonharmful by ingestion); nonirritating to skin; sl. irritating to eyes.

Nipasol M Sodium. [Nipa Hardwicke; Nipa Laboratories Ltd]
Chem. Descrip.: Sodium propylparaben
CAS 35285-69-9; EINECS 252-488-1
Uses: Preservative, bactericide, fungicide for pharmaceuticals, medicinal preps.
Properties: Wh. hygroscopic powd.; sol. in cold water; m.w. 202.2; pH 9.5-10.5 (0.1%); > 99% act.
Toxicology: LD50 (oral, mouse) 3.7 g/kg (pract. nonharmful); nonirritating to skin; sl. irritating to eyes, nasal passages.

Nipastat. [Nipa Hardwicke]
Chem. Descrip.: Methylparaben (> 50%), butylparaben (> 20%), ethylparaben (<15%), and propylparaben (< 10%)
Uses: Preservative, bactericide, fungicide for pharmaceuticals, topical, ophthalmic, oral, and injectable medicaments, ointments, creams, syrups, multi-dose injections, eye drops, vitamin sol'ns., vaccines
Use level: 0.1-0.3% (pharmaceutical creams, lotions, ointments); 0.05-0.10% (with other preservatives in eye drops); 0.05-0.15% (oral medicines, vaccines)
Regulatory: USA and Europe approvals
Properties: Wh. fine cryst. powd., virtually odorless, tasteless; sol. 0.14% in water; m.p. 60-125 C; pH 7.0 (10% aq.)
Toxicology: Pract. nonharmful by ingestion; nonirritating to skin; sl. irritating to eyes.

Nissan Monogly M. [Nippon Oils & Fats]
Chem. Descrip.: Glyceryl stearate
Uses: Emulsifier for pharmaceuticals
Properties: Wh. flake; m.p. 53-61 C; HLB 3.0; 40% min. monoglyceride content; nonionic
Unverified

Nissan Nonion CP-08R. [Nippon Oils & Fats]
Chem. Descrip.: Sorbitan caprylate
Uses: Emulsifier for pharmaceuticals
Properties: Liq.; oil-sol.; HLB 7.3; 100% conc.; nonionic
Unverified

Nissan Nonion DN-202. [Nippon Oils & Fats]
Chem. Descrip.: POE lauryl ether

Uses: Emulsifier for pharmaceuticals
Properties: Liq.; oil-sol.; HLB 6.2; 100% conc.; nonionic
Unverified

Nissan Nonion DN-203. [Nippon Oils & Fats]
Chem. Descrip.: POE lauryl ether
Uses: Emulsifier for pharmaceuticals
Properties: Liq.; oil-sol.; HLB 7.9; 100% conc.; nonionic
Unverified

Nissan Nonion DN-209. [Nippon Oils & Fats]
Chem. Descrip.: POE lauryl ether
Uses: Emulsifier for pharmaceuticals
Properties: Liq.; oil-sol.; HLB 13.2; 100% conc.; nonionic
Unverified

Nissan Nonion LP-20R, LP-20RS. [Nippon Oils & Fats]
Chem. Descrip.: Sorbitan laurate
CAS 1338-39-2
Uses: Emulsifier for pharmaceuticals
Properties: Gardner 5 max. oily liq.; sol. in methanol, ethanol, acetone, xylene, ethyl ether, kerosene, disp. in water; HLB 8.6; 100% conc.; nonionic
Unverified

Nissan Nonion LT-221. [Nippon Oils & Fats]
Chem. Descrip.: Polysorbate 20
CAS 9005-64-5
Uses: Emulsifier for pharmaceuticals
Properties: Gardner 6 max. oily liq.; sol. in water, methanol, ethanol, acetone, xylene, ethyl ether, ethylene glycol, HLB 16.7; 100% conc.; nonionic
Unverified

Nissan Nonion MP-30R. [Nippon Oils & Fats]
Chem. Descrip.: Sorbitan myristate
Uses: Emulsifier for pharmaceuticals
Properties: Solid; oil-sol.; HLB 6.6; 100% conc.; nonionic
Unverified

Nissan Nonion OP-80R. [Nippon Oils & Fats]
Chem. Descrip.: Sorbitan oleate
CAS 1338-43-8; EINECS 215-665-4
Uses: Emulsifier for pharmaceuticals
Properties: Gardner 9 max. oily liq.; oil-sol.; HLB 4.3; 100% conc.; nonionic
Unverified

Nissan Nonion OP-83RAT. [Nippon Oils & Fats]
Chem. Descrip.: Sorbitan sesquioleate
CAS 8007-43-0; EINECS 232-360-1
Uses: Emulsifier for pharmaceuticals
Properties: Gardner 9 max. oily liq.; sol. in ethanol, acetone, xylene, ethyl ether, kerosene, methanol, warm in water; HLB 3.7; 100% conc.; nonionic
Unverified

Nissan Nonion OP-85R. [Nippon Oils & Fats]
Chem. Descrip.: Sorbitan trioleate
CAS 26266-58-0; EINECS 247-569-3
Uses: Emulsifier for pharmaceuticals
Properties: Gardner 9 max. oily liq.; oil-sol.; HLB 1.8; 100% conc.; nonionic
Unverified

Nissan Nonion OT-221. [Nippon Oils & Fats]
Chem. Descrip.: POE sorbitan monooleate
Uses: Emulsifier for pharmaceuticals
Properties: Gardner 6 max. oily liq.; sol. in water, ethanol, acetone, xylene, disp. in methanol; HLB 15.0; 100% conc.; nonionic
Unverified

Nissan Nonion PP-40R. [Nippon Oils & Fats]
Chem. Descrip.: Sorbitan palmitate
CAS 26266-57-9; EINECS 247-568-8
Uses: Emulsifier for pharmaceuticals
Properties: Gardner 7 max. waxy solid; oil-sol.; HLB 6.7; 100% conc.; nonionic
Unverified

Nissan Nonion PT-221. [Nippon Oils & Fats]
Chem. Descrip.: POE sorbitan monopalmitate
Uses: Emulsifier for pharmaceuticals
Properties: Gardner 8 max. oily liq.; sol. in water, methanol, ethanol, acetone, xylene, ethyl ether, ethylene glycol; HLB 15.3; 100% conc.; nonionic
Unverified

Nissan Nonion SP-60R. [Nippon Oils & Fats]
Chem. Descrip.: Sorbitan stearate
CAS 1338-41-6; EINECS 215-664-9
Uses: Emulsifier for pharmaceuticals
Properties: Gardner 5 max. waxy solid; sol. in methanol, ethanol, xylene, kerosene, ethyl ether, disp. in warm water; HLB 4.7; 100% conc.; nonionic
Unverified

Nissan Nonion ST-221. [Nippon Oils & Fats]
Chem. Descrip.: POE sorbitan monostearate
Uses: Emulsifier for pharmaceuticals
Properties: Gardner 5 max. oily liq.; sol. in water, methanol, ethanol, acetone, xylene, ethyl ether, kerosene; HLB 14.9; 100% conc.; nonionic
Unverified

Nissan Panacete 810. [Nippon Oils & Fats]
Chem. Descrip.: Med. chain triglyceride
Uses: Raw material for pharmaceuticals
Properties: Liq.; 100% conc.; nonionic
Unverified

NM™. [ANGUS]
Chem. Descrip.: Nitromethane
CAS 75-52-5; EINECS 200-876-6
Uses: Raw material for synthesis of act. pharmaceutical compds., e.g. for 1,1-bis(metylthio)-2-nitroethane used to mfg. ranitidine, an anti-ulcer drug, or serinol, a raw material for iopamidol, an injectable radio-opaque x-ray contrast medium
Properties: Sol. 10.5% in water (20 C); m.w. 61.0; sp.gr. 1.124-1.135; dens. 1.138 g/ml (20 C), 9.4 lb/gal; visc. 0.647 cp (20 C); vapor pressure 36.66 mm Hg; f.p. -28.55 C; b.p. 101 C; flash pt. (TCC) 96 F; ref. index 1.38188 (20 C); pH 6.4 (0.01M aq.); surf. tens. 37.48 dynes/cm (20 C); dielec. const. 35.87 (30 C); 98% min. purity; biodeg.; classified as solv. exempt under Rule 66
Toxicology: LD50 (oral, rat) 1210 ± 322 mg/kg; nonirritating to skin and eyes; prolonged/repeated skin contact may cause defatting; inh.: PEL/TWC 100 ppm; avoid prolonged breathing of vapors
Precaution: Flamm. liq. and vapor; keep away from heat, sparks, flame; forms shock-sensitive mixts. with amines; compds. formed with strong alkalies are explosive when dry; avoid mixing with amines or strong alkalies
Storage: Store in original container; do not clean drum with lye or caustic.

NMP. [ANGUS]
Chem. Descrip.: 2-Nitro-2-methyl-1-propanol
CAS 76-39-1
Uses: Pharmaceutical intermediate
Properties: M.w. 119.1; sol. 350 g/100 ml water; m.p. 90 C; b.p. 94 C; flash pt. 175 F (TCC); pH 5.1 (0.1 M aq. sol'n.).

Non-Diastatic Malt Syrup #40600. [MLG Enterprises Ltd.]
Chem. Descrip.: Liq. extract of corn and malted barley
CAS 8002-48-0; EINECS 232-310-9
Uses: Sweetener providing malt flavor; enriches color to a rich golden appearance; protein fortification; humectant increasing shelf life; enhances texture; for pharmaceuticals
Regulatory: Kosher
Properties: PH 4.3-5.5 (10%); 10-25% solids
Storage: Store @ 40-90 F; 6 mos max. shelf life.

Noramium MO 50. [Ceca SA]
Chem. Descrip.: Oleyl trimethyl ammonium chloride
Uses: Additive for antibiotics mfg.
Properties: Liq.; cationic
Unverified

Noramium MS 50. [Ceca SA]
Chem. Descrip.: Tallow trimethyl ammonium chloride
CAS 8030-78-2; EINECS 232-447-4
Uses: Emulsifier for pharmaceuticals
Properties: Liq.; 50% conc.; cationic
Unverified

Noramium MSH 50. [Ceca SA]
Chem. Descrip.: Hydrog. tallow trimethyl ammonium chloride
CAS 61788-78-1; EINECS 263-005-9
Uses: Additive for antibiotics mfg.
Properties: Liq.; 75% conc.; cationic
Unverified

Noramium S 75. [Ceca SA]
Chem. Descrip.: Tallow dimethyl benzyl ammonium chloride
CAS 61789-75-1; EINECS 263-085-5
Uses: Additive for antibiotics mfg.; cationic
Unverified

Norbixin 40. [Helianthus SA]
Chem. Descrip.: Norbixin; contains the alkaline hydrolysis prod. of the natural annatto pigment, bixin
CAS 8015-67-6
Uses: Natural orange color for pharmaceutical prods.
Regulatory: Complies with FDA 21CFR §73.30 for annatto color, exempt from U.S. certification

Properties: Brn. reddish powd.; readily sol. in mildly alkaline water giving clear cryst. sol'ns.; 35-40% norbixin

Precaution: Very reactive with calcium, magnesium, and other metallic salts

Storage: Refrigerated storage recommended to avoid pigment loss.

Norgel. [United-Guardian]
Chem. Descrip.: Nondrying high visc. aq. gel
Uses: Gel for medical field
Properties: Glass clear gel.; completely water-sol.

Novata® 299. [Henkel KGaA/Cospha]
Chem. Descrip.: Cocoglycerides
CAS 67701-26-2
Uses: Base for suppository and vaginal preps.; consistency giving agent for pharmaceutical ointments, creams, stick preps.
Regulatory: NF, DAB, Ph.Eur. compliance for hard fat
Properties: Wh. fatty fused, flakes, or pastille which melt to a colorless to sl. ylsh. liq. when heated; almost odorless and tasteless; dens. 0.955-0.975 (20 C); m.p. 33.5-35.5 C; solid. pt. 31.5-33.5 C; acid no. 0.3 max.; iodine no. 3 max.; sapon. no. 235-250; hyd. no. 5 max.; ref. index 1.4490 (40 C); 100% conc.; nonionic
Storage: 2 yr min. storage life in original containers at temps. below 30 C under dry conditions.

Novata® 3525. [Henkel KGaA/Cospha]
Chem. Descrip.: Sat. fatty acid triglycerides with mono- and diglycerides
Uses: Base for suppositories
Properties: Wh. brittle mass, almost tasteless, fatty to the touch; m.p. 35-36.5 C; acid no. < 0.5; iodine no. < 2; sapon. no. 230-240; hyd. no. 20-30
Storage: 1 yr min. storage life in sealed original containers at temps. below 30 C under dry conditions.

Novata® A. [Henkel KGaA/Cospha]
Chem. Descrip.: Cocoglycerides
CAS 67701-26-2
Uses: Base for suppositories produced on deepfreeze automatic devices; esp. suitable for extreme cooling
Regulatory: NF, DAB, Ph.Eur compliance for hard fat
Properties: Wh. fatty fused, flakes, or pastille which melt to a colorless to sl. ylsh. liq. when heated; almost odorless and tasteless; dens. 0.955-0.975 (20 C); m.p. 33.5-35.5 C; solid. pt. 29-31 C; acid no. 0.3 max.; iodine no. 3 max.; sapon. no. 225-240; hyd. no. 35-45; ref. index 1.4520 (40 C); 100% conc.; nonionic
Storage: 2 yr min. storage life in original containers at temps. below 30 C under dry conditions.

Novata® AB. [Henkel KGaA/Cospha]
Chem. Descrip.: Cocoglycerides
CAS 67701-26-2
Uses: Base for suppositories and vaginal globules; consistency giving agent for pharmaceutical ointments, creams, stick preps.; esp. useful during processing of very light and bulky substances

Regulatory: NF, DAB, Ph.Eur. compliance for hard fat
Properties: Wh. fatty fused, flakes, or pastille which melt to a colorless to sl. ylsh. liq. when heated; almost odorless and tasteless; dens. 0.955-0.975 (20 C); m.p. 29-31 C; solid. pt. 26.5-28.5 C; acid no. 0.3 max.; iodine no. 3 max.; sapon. no. 230-245; hyd. no. 25-40; ref. index 1.4530 (40 C); 100% conc.; nonionic
Storage: 2 yr min. storage life in original containers at temps. below 30 C under dry conditions.

Novata® B. [Henkel KGaA/Cospha]
Chem. Descrip.: Cocoglycerides
CAS 67701-26-2
Uses: Base for suppository and vaginal preps.; consistency giving agent for pharmaceutical ointments, creams, stick preps.
Properties: Wh. fatty fused, flakes, or pastille which melt to a colorless to sl. ylsh. liq. when heated; almost odorless and tasteless; dens. 0.955-0.975 (20 C); m.p. 33-35.5 C; solid. pt. 31-33 C; acid no. 0.3 max.; iodine no. 3 max.; sapon. no. 225-240; hyd. no. 20-30; ref. index 1.4530 (40 C); 100% conc.; nonionic
Storage: 2 yr min. storage life in original containers at temps. below 30 C under dry conditions.

Novata® BBC. [Henkel KGaA/Cospha]
Chem. Descrip.: Cocoglycerides
CAS 67701-26-2
Uses: Base for suppository and vaginal preps.; consistency giving agent for pharmaceutical ointments, creams, stick preps.
Properties: Wh. fatty fused, flakes, or pastille which melt to a colorless to sl. ylsh. liq. when heated; almost odorless and tasteless; dens. 0.955-0.975 (20 C); m.p. 34-36 C; solid. pt. 30.5-32.5 C; acid no. 0.3 max.; iodine no. 3 max.; sapon. no. 225-240; hyd. no. 20-30; ref. index 1.4530 (40 C); 100% conc.; nonionic
Storage: 2 yr min. storage life in original containers at temps. below 30 C under dry conditions.

Novata® BC. [Henkel KGaA/Cospha]
Chem. Descrip.: Cocoglycerides
CAS 67701-26-2
Uses: Base for suppository and vaginal preps.; consistency giving agent for pharmaceutical ointments, creams, stick preps.
Regulatory: NF, DAB, Ph.Eur. compliance for hard fat
Properties: Wh. fatty fused, flakes, or pastille which melt to a colorless to sl. ylsh. liq. when heated; almost odorless and tasteless; dens. 0.955-0.975 (20 C); m.p. 33-35.5 C; solid. pt. 30.5-32.5 C; acid no. 0.3 max.; iodine no. 3 max.; sapon. no. 225-240; hyd. no. 30-40; ref. index 1.4530 (40 C); 100% conc.; nonionic
Storage: 2 yr min. storage life in original containers at temps. below 30 C under dry conditions.

Novata® BCF. [Henkel KGaA/Cospha]
Chem. Descrip.: Cocoglycerides
CAS 67701-26-2
Uses: Base for suppository and vaginal preps.;

consistency giving agent for pharmaceutical ointments, creams, stick preps.
Regulatory: NF, DAB, Ph.Eur. compliance for hard fat
Properties: Wh. fatty fused, flakes, or pastille which melt to a colorless to sl. ylsh. liq. when heated; almost odorless and tasteless; dens. 0.955-0.975 (20 C); m.p. 35-37 C; solid. pt. 30-32 C; acid no. 1.0 max.; iodine no. 3 max.; sapon. no. 225-240; hyd. no. 20-30; ref. index 1.4500 (40 C); 100% conc.; nonionic
Storage: 2 yr min. storage life in original containers at temps. below 30 C under dry conditions.

Novata® BD. [Henkel KGaA/Cospha]
Chem. Descrip.: Cocoglycerides
CAS 67701-26-2
Uses: Base for suppository and vaginal preps., esp. where actives may react with hydroxyl groups; consistency giving agent for pharmaceutical ointments, creams, stick preps.
Regulatory: NF, DAB, Ph.Eur. compliance for hard fat
Properties: Wh. fatty fused, flakes, or pastille which melt to a colorless to sl. ylsh. liq. when heated; almost odorless and tasteless; dens. 0.955-0.975 (20 C); m.p. 33.5-35.5 C; solid. pt. 32-34 C; acid no. 0.3 max.; iodine no. 3 max.; sapon. no. 230-245; hyd. no. < 15; ref. index 1.4530 (40 C); 100% conc.; nonionic
Storage: 2 yr min. storage life in original containers at temps. below 30 C under dry conditions.

Novata® C. [Henkel KGaA/Cospha]
Chem. Descrip.: Cocoglycerides
CAS 67701-26-2
Uses: Base for suppository and vaginal preps.; consistency giving agent for pharmaceutical ointments, creams, stick preps.
Properties: Wh. fatty fused, flakes, or pastille which melt to a colorless to sl. ylsh. liq. when heated; almost odorless and tasteless; dens. 0.955-0.975 (20 C); m.p. 36-38 C; solid. pt. 33-35 C; acid no. 0.3 max.; iodine no. 3 max.; sapon. no. 220-235; hyd. no. 20-30; ref. index 1.4500 (40 C); 100% conc.; nonionic
Storage: 2 yr min. storage life in original containers at temps. below 30 C under dry conditions.

Novata® D. [Henkel KGaA/Cospha]
Chem. Descrip.: Cocoglycerides
CAS 67701-26-2
Uses: Base for suppository and vaginal preps.; consistency giving agent for pharmaceutical ointments, creams, stick preps.
Properties: Wh. fatty fused, flakes, or pastille which melt to a colorless to sl. ylsh. liq. when heated; almost odorless and tasteless; dens. 0.955-0.975 (20 C); m.p. 40-42 C; solid. pt. 38-40 C; acid no. 0.3 max.; iodine no. 3 max.; sapon. no. 220-235; hyd. no. 30-40; ref. index 1.4500 (45 C); 100% conc.; nonionic
Storage: 2 yr min. storage life in original containers at temps. below 30 C under dry conditions.

Novata® E. [Henkel KGaA/Cospha]

Chem. Descrip.: Cocoglycerides and other ingreds.
CAS 67701-26-2
Uses: SE base for emulsion suppository and vaginal preps.; consistency giving agent for pharmaceutical ointments, creams, stick preps.
Properties: Wh. fatty fused, flakes, or pastille which melt to a colorless to sl. ylsh. liq. when heated; almost odorless and tasteless; dens. 0.955-0.975 (20 C); m.p. 33.5-34.5 C; solid. pt. 29-31 C; acid no. 1.0 max.; iodine no. 3 max.; sapon. no. 215-230; hyd. no. 45-60; ref. index 1.4500 (40 C); 100% conc.; nonionic
Storage: 2 yr min. storage life in original containers at temps. below 30 C under dry conditions.

Novata® PK. [Henkel KGaA/Cospha]
Chem. Descrip.: Glyceryl tricocoate
Uses: Base for suppositories, esp. for active ingreds. capable of reacting with hydroxyl groups, and acetylsalicylic acid
Properties: Wh. fatty mass, almost odorless and tasteless; m.p. 32-35 C; acid no. 0.3 max.; iodine no. 3 max.; sapon. no. 240-250; hyd. no. 6 max.
Storage: 1 yr min. storage life in original containers at temps. below 30 C under dry conditions.

Noveon® AA-1. [BFGoodrich]
Chem. Descrip.: Polycarbophil
CAS 9003-01-4
Uses: Rheology control agent; exc. bioadhesive/mucoadhesive; controlled-release tablet binder; moisture enhancer; drug delivery matrix; used for formulation of topical, buccal, nasal, ophthalmic bioadhesive gels; reagent; complexing agent
Regulatory: USP compliance
Properties: Wh. powd.; sp.gr. 1.41; bulk dens. 208 kg/m^3; pH 4 max. (1% disp.).

Noveon® CA-1. [BFGoodrich]
Chem. Descrip.: Calcium polycarbophil; acrylic acid polymer calcium salt crosslinked with divinyl glycol
CAS 9003-97-8
Uses: Exc. water absorption; used for oral laxative, swallowable tablet form
Regulatory: USP compliance
Properties: Wh. to off-wh. coarse powd.; 30% max. thru 325 mesh, 99% min. thru 20 mesh; sp.gr. 1.41; bulk dens. 208 kg/m^3; pH 2.5-3.0 (1% aq. disp.).

Noveon® CA-2. [BFGoodrich]
Chem. Descrip.: Calcium polycarbophil; acrylic acid polymer calcium salt crosslinked with divinyl glycol
CAS 9003-97-8
Uses: Used for oral laxative, chewable/swallowable tablet form
Regulatory: USP compliance
Properties: Wh. to off-wh. fine powd.; 99% min. thru 100 mesh, typ. 80% < 25 µ; sp.gr. 1.41; bulk dens. 208 kg/m^3; pH 2.5-3.0 (1% aq. disp.).

Novol NF. [Croda Inc.; Croda Chem. Ltd.]
Chem. Descrip.: Super refined oleyl alcohol NF
CAS 143-28-2; EINECS 205-597-3

Uses: Emulsion stabilizer, modifier, solubilizer, superfatting agent, emollient, solv. and penetrant for topical and transdermal pharmaceuticals
Use level: 2-30%
Properties: Gardner 1 max. liq.; mild odor; sol. in min. oil, IPA, propylene glycol; misc. with fat, oil and wax mixts.; sp.gr. 0.845-0.855 (15 C); visc. 24-32 cps; acid no. 0.1 max.; sapon. no. 0.3 max.; hyd. no. 195-210
Toxicology: Mild skin irritant, nonirritating to eyes.
NS-20 [SVO Enterprises]
Chem. Descrip.: Sunflower oil, refined, bleached, winterized, deodorized
CAS 8001-21-6; EINECS 232-273-9
Uses: Food grade, environmentally friendly veg. oil for use as feedstocks/raw materials in pharmaceuticals; very high oxidative and thermal stability; readily biodeg.
Nu-Core® 35/45. [Crompton & Knowles]
Chem. Descrip.: Sucrose and starch NF
Uses: Carrier used in pharmaceutical industry for prod. of sustained or timed release dosage forms
Properties: Wh. uniform, mostly spherical seeds; 355-500 μm; 100% thru 30 mesh, 90% min. thru 35 mesh; 62.5-91.5% sucrose, ≤ 4% moisture.
Nu-Core® 40/50. [Crompton & Knowles]
Chem. Descrip.: Sucrose and starch NF
Uses: Carrier used in pharmaceutical industry for prod. of sustained or timed release dosage forms
Properties: Wh. uniform, mostly spherical seeds; 300-425 μm; 100% thru 35 mesh, 90% min. thru 40 mesh; 62.5-91.5% sucrose, ≤ 4% moisture.
Nu-Core® 45/60. [Crompton & Knowles]
Chem. Descrip.: Sucrose and starch NF
Uses: Carrier used in pharmaceutical industry for prod. of sustained or timed release dosage forms
Properties: Wh. uniform, mostly spherical seeds; 250-355 μm; 100% thru 40 mesh, 90% min. thru 45 mesh; 62.5-91.5% sucrose, ≤ 4% moisture.
Nu-Pareil® PG 14/18. [Crompton & Knowles]
Chem. Descrip.: Sucrose and starch NF
Uses: Carrier used in pharmaceutical industry in prod. of sustained or timed release dosage forms
Properties: Wh. uniform, mostly spherical seeds; 1000-1400 μm; 100% thru 12 mesh, 90% min. thru 14 mesh; 62.5-91.5% sucrose, ≤ 4% moisture.
Nu-Pareil® PG 16/20. [Crompton & Knowles]
Chem. Descrip.: Sucrose and starch NF
Uses: Carrier used in pharmaceutical industry in prod. of sustained or timed release dosage forms
Properties: Wh. uniform, mostly spherical seeds; 850-1180μm; 100% thru 14 mesh, 90% min. thru 16 mesh; 62.5-91.5% sucrose, ≤ 4% moisture.
Nu-Pareil® PG 18/20. [Crompton & Knowles]
Chem. Descrip.: Sucrose and starch NF
Uses: Carrier used in pharmaceutical industry in prod. of sustained or timed release dosage forms
Properties: Wh. uniform, mostly spherical seeds; 850-1000 μm; 100% thru 16 mesh, 90% min. thru 18 mesh; 62.5-91.5% sucrose, ≤ 4% moisture.
Nu-Pareil® PG 20/25. [Crompton & Knowles]

Chem. Descrip.: Sucrose and starch NF
Uses: Carrier used in pharmaceutical industry in prod. of sustained or timed release dosage forms
Properties: Wh. uniform, mostly spherical seeds; 710-850 μm; 100% thru 18 mesh, 90% min. thru 20 mesh; 62.5-91.5% sucrose, ≤ 4% moisture.
Nu-Pareil® PG 25/30. [Crompton & Knowles]
Chem. Descrip.: Sucrose and starch NF
Uses: Carrier used in pharmaceutical industry in prod. of sustained or timed release dosage forms
Properties: Wh. uniform, mostly spherical seeds; 610-710 μm; 100% thru 20 mesh, 90% min. thru 25 mesh; 62.5-91.5% sucrose, ≤ 4% moisture.
Nu-Pareil® PG 30/35. [Crompton & Knowles]
Chem. Descrip.: Sucrose and starch NF
Uses: Carrier used in pharmaceutical industry in prod. of sustained or timed release dosage forms
Properties: Wh. uniform, mostly spherical seeds; 500-600 μm; 100% thru 25 mesh, 90% min. thru 30 mesh; 62.5-91.5% sucrose, ≤ 4% moisture.
Nu-Tab®. [Crompton & Knowles]
Chem. Descrip.: Compressible sugar NF (sucrose, invert sugar, and a small amt. of magnesium stearate as manufacturing aid)
Uses: Carrier, vehicle; directly compressible diluent for most conventional tablets; effective in masking harsh flavors of many active ingreds.; compat. with flavorants and colorants; avail. in colors
Properties: Wh. free-flowing gran., sweet taste; 50% min. on 60 mesh, 10% max. thru 120 mesh; bulk dens. 0.69 g/ml (loose), 0.82 g/ml (tapped); 95-97% sucrose, 3-5% invert sugar, ≤ 0.5% magnesium stearate, ≤ 1% moisture.
Nymcel® ZSB-10. [Metsä-Serla Oy]
Chem. Descrip.: Sodium CMC
CAS 9004-32-4
Uses: Tablet disintegrant for pharmaceuticals
Use level: 1-3%
Properties: Wh. to off-wh. powd.or gran., odorless; hygroscopic; hydrophilic, but pract. insol. in water; dens. 1.6 g/cm^3 (20 C); bulk dens. 400-800 kg/m^3; visc. 2000 mPa•s min. (2% in 10% NaOH); decomp. pt. 240 C; pH 6.0-8.5 (1% susp.); 99.5% min. act.; biodeg.; BOD7 ≈ 50-100 g O$_2$/kg
Toxicology: LD50 (oral, rat) 27,000 mg/kg; powd. may dry the skin; dust may irritate the eyes; inh. of dust may cause respiratory irritation
Storage: Store in cool, dry place to avoid moisture absorp.; avoid dusting.
Nymcel® ZSB-16. [Metsä-Serla Oy]
Chem. Descrip.: Sodium CMC
CAS 9004-32-4
Uses: Tablet disintegrant for pharmaceuticals
Use level: 1-3%
Properties: Wh. to off-wh. powd. or gran., odorless; hygroscopic; hydrophilic, but pract. insol. in water; dens. 1.6 g/cm^3 (20 C); bulk dens. 400-800 kg/m^3; visc. 150 mPa•s min. (1% in 10% NaOH); decomp. pt. 240 C; pH 6.0-8.5 (1% susp.); 99.5% min. act.; biodeg.; BOD7 ≈ 50-100 g O$_2$/kg
Toxicology: LD50 (oral, rat) 27,000 mg/kg; powd.

may dry the skin; dust may irritate the eyes; inh. of dust may cause respiratory irritation

Storage: Store in cool, dry place to avoid moisture absorp.; avoid dusting.

Nymcel® ZSC. [Metsä-Serla Oy]

Chem. Descrip.: Carboxymethylcellulose calcium USP/NF

CAS 9050-04-8

Uses: Tablet disintegrant for pharmaceuticals; absorbs water very quickly assuring rapid disintegration and release of actives

Use level: 1-3%

Properties: Hydrophilic, water-insol.

Storage: Store in cool, dry place to avoid moisture absorp.

Nymcel® ZSD-16. [Metsä-Serla Oy]

Chem. Descrip.: Sodium CMC

CAS 9004-32-4

Uses: Tablet disintegrant for pharmaceuticals; somewhat densified version of Nymcel ZSB-16

Use level: 1-3%

Properties: Wh. to off-wh. powd. or gran., odorless; hygroscopic; hydrophilic, but pract. insol. in water; dens. 1.6 g/cm^3 (20 C); bulk dens. 400-800 kg/ m^3; visc. 150 mPa•s min. (1% in 10% NaOH); decomp. pt. 240 C; pH 6.0-8.5 (1% susp.); 99.5% min. act.; biodeg.; BOD7 ≈ 50-100 g O$_2$/kg

Toxicology: LD50 (oral, rat) 27,000 mg/kg; powd. may dry the skin; dust may irritate the eyes; inh. of dust may cause respiratory irritation

Storage: Store in cool, dry place to avoid moisture absorp.; avoid dusting.

Nymcel® ZSX. [Metsä-Serla Oy]

Chem. Descrip.: Croscarmellose sodium USP/NF

CAS 74811-65-7

Uses: Tablet disintegrant for pharmaceuticals

Use level: 1-3%

Properties: Wh. to off-wh. free-flowing powd. or gran., odorless; hygroscopic; water-insol.; dens. 1.6 g/cc (20 C); bulk dens. 400-800 kg/m^3; decomp. pt. 240 C; pH 5-7 (1% aq. susp.); biodeg.; BOD7 ≈ 50-100 g O$_2$/kg

Toxicology: LD50 (oral, rat) 27,000 mg/kg; powd. may dry the skin; dust may irritate the eyes; inh. of dust may cause respiratory irritation

Storage: Store in cool, dry place to avoid moisture absorp.

O

Octacosanol GF. [Garuda Int'l.]
Chem. Descrip.: Octacosanol in a base of maize syrup powd. (40 DE)
Uses: Natural waxy alcohol blend to formulate nutritional supplement tablets or capsules for dietetic and health food applics., e.g., sports endurance supplements, weight-loss prods., energy-boosting or stress-reducing supplements.

OHlan®. [Amerchol; Amerchol Europe]
Chem. Descrip.: Hydroxylated lanolin
CAS 68424-66-8; EINECS 270-315-8
Uses: Primary w/o emulsifier, aux. emulsifier and stabilizer, pigment wetting and dispersing agent, emollient and conditioner in absorp. bases, pharmaceuticals
Properties: Yel.-amber to lt. tan waxy solid; misc. with common oil phase ingredients, sol. at low levels in castor oil; oil-misc.; m.p. 39-46 C; HLB 4; acid no. 10 max.; sapon. no. 95-110; 100% conc.; nonionic.

Ointment Base No. 3. [Penreco]
Chem. Descrip.: Wh. petrolatum USP
CAS 8009-03-8; EINECS 232-373-2
Uses: Ointment base for eye and skin medications; carrier for medical materials; ophthalmic and topical ointments
Regulatory: FDA 21CFR 172.880, 178.3700, 573.720
Properties: Wh. semisolid, odorless; sol. in hydrocarbons; insol. in water; sp.gr. 0.8 (60/60 F); visc. 55-65 SUS (210 F); m.p. 118-125 F; congeal pt. 104-115 F; flash pt. (COC) 400 F
Precaution: Combustion may produce dense smoke, CO, CO_2, other oxides; may react with strong oxidizing agents
Storage: Store in closed containers away from heat, sparks, open flame, oxidizers.

Ointment Base No. 4. [Penreco]
Chem. Descrip.: Wh. petrolatum USP
CAS 8009-03-8; EINECS 232-373-2
Uses: Ointment base for eye and skin medications; carrier for medical materials; ophthalmic and topical ointments
Regulatory: FDA 21CFR 172.880, 178.3700, 573.720
Properties: Wh. semisolid, odorless; sol. in hydrocarbons; insol. in water; sp.gr. 0.8 (60/60 F); visc. 60-70 SUS (210 F); m.p. 118-125 F; congeal pt.

109-119 F; flash pt. (COC) 400 F
Toxicology: Pract. nontoxic by ingestion, but laxative props. may cause abdominal cramps, diarrhea; minimally irritating to eyes and skin on direct contact; STEL 10 mg/m^3 (as oil mist)
Precaution: Combustion may produce dense smoke, CO, CO_2, other oxides; may react with strong oxidizing agents
Storage: Store in closed containers away from heat, sparks, open flame, oxidizers.

Ointment Base No. 6. [Penreco]
Chem. Descrip.: Wh. petrolatum USP
CAS 8009-03-8; EINECS 232-373-2
Uses: Ointment base for eye and skin medications; carrier for medical materials; ophthalmic and topical ointments
Regulatory: FDA 21CFR 172.880, 178.3700, 573.720
Properties: Wh. semisolid, odorless; sol. in hydrocarbons; sp.gr. 0.864 (60/60 F); visc. 60-70 SUS (210 F); m.p. 122-133 F; congeal pt. 120-130 F; flash pt. (COC) 400 F
Precaution: Combustion may produce dense smoke, CO, CO_2, other oxides; may react with strong oxidizing agents
Storage: Store in closed containers away from heat, sparks, flame, oxidizers.

Olepal ISO. [Gattefosse SA]
Chem. Descrip.: PEG-6 isostearate
CAS 56002-14-3
Uses: Solvent and emulsifier for pharmaceutical emulsions and microemulsions
Properties: Liq.; HLB 12-13; acid no. < 6; iodine no. < 15; sapon. no. 95-125.

Opacode®. [Colorcon]
Chem. Descrip.: FDA-approved pigments and titanium dioxide in a solv. base
Uses: Finely dispersed edible monogramming ink for pharmaceuticals; exc. adhesion; provides sharp, clear monograms, minimal ink buildup on rollers.

Opacode® WB. [Colorcon]
Chem. Descrip.: FDA-approved pigments and titanium dioxide in a water base
Uses: Edible monogramming ink for pharmaceuticals; provides sharp, clear monograms
Properties: Minimal odor.

Opadry®. [Colorcon]

Opadry® Enteric

Chem. Descrip.: Coating system combining polymer, plasticizer and pigment in dry conc.

Uses: One-step colorant film coating system for aq. and org. solv. systems for pharmaceuticals.

Opadry® Enteric. [Colorcon]

Chem. Descrip.: Complete enteric film coating system combining polymer (PVAP), plasticizer and pigment in a dry conc.

Uses: One-step enteric film coating system for pharmaceutical org. solv. systems; provides targeted enteric drug release.

Opadry II®. [Colorcon]

Chem. Descrip.: Coating system combining polymer, plasticizer and pigment in dry conc.

Uses: One-step aq. colorant film coating system for pharmaceuticals; enhanced light stability.

Opaglos®. [Colorcon]

Chem. Descrip.: Coating sol'n. in a stabilized shellac base

Uses: Clear coating sol'n. for pharmaceutical tablet sealing and polishing applics.

Opalux®. [Colorcon]

Chem. Descrip.: Aq. color conc. of FDA-approved pigments and titanium dioxide in sugar syrup

Uses: Color conc. for sugar-coated tablets

Properties: Liq.

Opaseal®. [Colorcon]

Chem. Descrip.: Polyvinyl acetate phthalate alcoholic sol'n.

Uses: One-step system for core sealing or enteric coating applics.; provides targeted enteric drug release; good sol'n. shelf stability.

Opaspray®. [Colorcon]

Chem. Descrip.: Conc. of pigments and titanium dioxide

Uses: One-step preformulated liq. color conc. for pharmaceutical coating formulations sprayed from either org. solv. or aq. systems

Properties: Liq.

Opatint®. [Colorcon]

Chem. Descrip.: Conc. of approved pigments dispersed in selected vehicles (edible oil, glycerin, or sugar syrup)

Uses: Rapidly dispersible color conc. for pharmaceuticals; good heat and light stability

Properties: Liq.

Optigel CF, CG, CK, CL. [United Catalysts]

Chem. Descrip.: Smectite prod.

Uses: Emulsion stabilizer for pharmaceuticals.

Oramix® CG 110-60. [Seppic]

Chem. Descrip.: Caprylyl/capryl glucoside

CAS 68515-73-1

Uses: Foaming surfactant, solubilizer used in dermopharmaceutical prods.

Properties: Liq.; 60% conc.; nonionic.

Oramix® L30. [Seppic]

Chem. Descrip.: Sodium lauroyl sarcosinate

CAS 137-16-6; EINECS 205-281-5

Uses: Bacteriostatic props. in antidandruff shampoos, medicinal liq. soaps; solubilizer for antiseptic agents; anticaries agent in toothpaste

Use level: 1-5% (toothpaste), 1-5% (aerosols), 5-15% (shampoos), 10-50% (bath foams), 5-30% (medicinal liq. soap)

Properties: Liq.; sol. in water; pH 7.5-8.5 (10%); 28.5% min. act.; anionic

Toxicology: LD50 (oral) 2888 mg/kg; nontoxic by ing.; nonirritating to skin; irritating to eyes.

Oramix® NS 10. [Seppic]

Chem. Descrip.: Decyl glucoside

CAS 54549-25-6; EINECS 259-218-1

Uses: Foaming cosurfactant used in dermopharmaceutical prods.; maintains natural biological balance

Properties: Gardner 5 max. clear liq.; sp.gr. 1.07; visc. 2000 mPa•s; pH 3-5; 55% act. aq. sol'n.; nonionic; 100% biodeg.

Toxicology: LD50 (oral, rat) > 35,000 mg/kg; moderate eye irritant.

Orange Wax. [Koster Keunen]

Chem. Descrip.: Orange waxes

CAS 144514-51-2

Uses: Emollient, uv-A and -B absorber, natural antioxidant, anti-inflammatory, analgesic (on burns)

Use level: 1-5% (creams, lotions, makeup, shampoo, conditioners, shaving creams), 1-10% (anhyd. gels/lipsticks, soaps)

Properties: Lt. brn. to lt. orange semisolid, char. odor; very sl. sol. in water; sp.gr. 0.92-0.97; m.p. 45-57 C; congeal pt. 45-55 C; b.p. > 200 C; acid no. 8-20; sapon. no. 70-110; hyd. no. 20-50; flash pt. > 200 C

Toxicology: Virtually no irritation potential; molten wax may burn skin, cause mild upper respiratory irritation.

Orange Wax, Deodorized. [Koster Keunen]

Chem. Descrip.: Orange waxes

CAS 144514-51-2

Uses: Moisturizer, emollient, uv-A and -B absorber, antioxidant, wetting agent, mild antimicrobial, anti-inflammatory for creams, lotions, suncare, deodorants.

Orgasol 1002 D WHITE 5 COS. [Elf Atochem N. Am.]

Chem. Descrip.: Nylon 6

CAS 25038-54-4

Uses: Raw material for pharmaceuticals; absorbent, carrier used in personal hygiene prods.

Orgasol 2002 D NAT COS. [Elf Atochem N. Am.; Lipo]

Chem. Descrip.: Nylon 12

CAS 25038-74-8

Uses: Raw material for pharmaceuticals; absorbent, carrier used in personal hygiene prods.

Properties: Natural uncolored powd.; avg. particle size 20 μ.

Orgasol 2002 EX D NAT COS. [Elf Atochem N. Am.]

Chem. Descrip.: Nylon 12

CAS 25038-74-8

Uses: Raw material for pharmaceuticals; absorbent, carrier used in personal hygiene prods.

Properties: Natural uncolored extra-fine powd.; avg. particle size 10 μ.

Orgasol 2002 UD NAT COS. [Elf Atochem N. Am.; Lipo]

Chem. Descrip.: Nylon 12
CAS 25038-74-8
Uses: Raw material for pharmaceuticals; absorbent, carrier used in personal hygiene prods.
Properties: Natural uncolored ultra-fine powd.; avg. particle size 5 μ.

Orzol®. [Witco/Petroleum Spec.]
Chem. Descrip.: Wh. min. oil USP
Uses: Emollient, lubricant for drug industry
Regulatory: FDA 21CFR §172.878, 178.3620a
Properties: Water-wh.; sp.gr. 0.869-0.885; visc. 61-64 cSt (40 C); pour pt. -20 C; flash pt. 202 C.

Os-Tab™ 4455. [Crompton & Knowles]
Chem. Descrip.: Oyster shell powd., maltodextrin NF, acacia NF, microcrystalline cellulose NF
Uses: Direct compr. carrier for pharmaceutical tableting
Properties: Gran.; 5% max. on 20 mesh, 25% max. thru 200 mesh; bulk dens. 0.95-1.25 g/ml (loose), 1.15-1.45 g/ml (tapped) ≥ 36% Ca.

Ottasept®. [Nipa Hardwicke]
Chem. Descrip.: Chloroxylenol
CAS 88-04-0; EINECS 201-793-8
Uses: Broad spectrum antimicrobial for topical OTC applics.
Properties: Wh. cryst. powd.; sol. in most org. solvs.; insol. in water.

Ottasept® Extra. [Nipa Hardwicke]
Chem. Descrip.: 4-Chloro-3,5-xylenol
CAS 88-04-0; EINECS 201-793-8
Uses: Antimicrobial and preservative for pharmaceutical uses incl. medical powds., antiseptics; also disinfectant, sanitizing soap
Properties: Wh. cryst solid, faint odor; m.w. 156.6; sol. (g/100 ml solv.) 86.6 g in 95% ethanol, 50 g in IPA; dens. 5 lb/gal; m.p. 114 C; 99.4% act.

Ovothin™ 160. [Lucas Meyer]
Chem. Descrip.: Natural mixt. of egg phospholipids and egg oil
Uses: Emulsifier for pharmaceuticals, dietetic prods.

Ovothin™ 170. [Lucas Meyer]
Chem. Descrip.: Complex of egg yolk phospholipids
Uses: Emulsifier and dispersant for pharmaceuticals and liposomes.

Ovothin™ 180. [Lucas Meyer]
Chem. Descrip.: Isolated phosphatidylcholine from egg yolk
Uses: Emulsifier and dispersant for pharmaceuticals; 80% conc.

Ovothin™ 200. [Lucas Meyer]
Chem. Descrip.: Isolated phosphatidylcholine from egg yolk
Uses: Emulsifier and dispersant for pharmaceuticals and liposomes; 94% conc.

Ovucire WL 2558. [Gattefosse SA]
Chem. Descrip.: Hemisynthetic glycerides
Uses: Excipient for pharmaceutical pessaries/suppositories
Properties: Drop pt. 31-36 C; acid no. < 0.5; iodine no. ≤ 3; sapon. no. 240-260.

Ovucire WL 2944. [Gattefosse SA]
Chem. Descrip.: Hemisynthetic glycerides
Uses: Excipient for pharmaceutical pessaries/suppositories
Properties: Drop pt. 32.5-35.5 C; acid no. < 0.5; iodine no. < 3; sapon. no. 215-235
Toxicology: Nonirritating rectally.

Oxaban®-A. [ANGUS]
Chem. Descrip.: Dimethyl oxazolidine
CAS 51200-87-4; EINECS 257-048-2
Uses: Antimicrobial for pharmaceutical topical aq. systems; protects against bacterial growth
Regulatory: EEC approved
Properties: APHA 25 max. liq.; sol. in water, alcohols, glycols, and min. oil; sp.gr. 0.98-0.99; dens. 8.2 lb/gal; visc. ≈ 7.5 cp; f.p. < -20 F; flash pt. (TCC) 120 F; pH 10.5-11.5; 78% act. in water
Toxicology: LD50 (oral, rats) 950 mg/kg, (dermal, rabbits) 1400 mg/kg; can cause severe eye burns; harmful if swallowed
Precaution: Combustible liq.

Oxaban®-E. [ANGUS]
Chem. Descrip.: 7-Ethyl bicyclooxazolidine
CAS 7747-35-5; EINECS 231-810-4
Uses: Antibacterial for topical pharmaceuticals
Regulatory: EEC approved
Properties: Low odor; sol. in water, alcohols, glycols, min. oil, benzene, acetone, chlorinated hydrocarbons; sp.gr. 1.085 (30/20 C); f.p. 0 C; b.p. 71 C (15 mm Hg); flash pt. (TCC) 175 F; pH 8-9; surf. tens. 36.5 dynes/cm
Toxicology: LD50 (oral, male rat) 5250 mg/kg, (dermal, rabbits) 1948 mg/kg; severely irritating to skin and eyes.

Oxynex® 2004. [Rona; E. Merck]
Chem. Descrip.: BHT (20%), ascorbyl palmitate (10%), citric acid (10%), glyceryl stearate, propylene glycol
Uses: Antioxidant for pharmaceuticals
Regulatory: EC and US GRAS compliance
Properties: Unctuous mass, almost odorless, pract. tasteless; sol. in many org. solvs.; insol. in water.

Oxynex® K. [Rona; E. Merck]
Chem. Descrip.: PEG-8 (62%), tocopherol (30%), ascorbyl palmitate (5%), ascorbic acid (1%), and citric acid (1%)
Uses: Antioxidant, stabilizer for fats and oils; esp. for protection of sat. and unsat. components of the oil phase and for inhibition of formation of free radicals; used for pharmaceuticals
Regulatory: EC, GRAS compliance
Properties: Yel. to lt. brn. transparent liq., char. faint odor.

Oxynex® LM. [Rona; E. Merck]
Chem. Descrip.: Tocopherol (25%), lecithin (25%), ascorbyl palmitate (20%), glyceryl stearate, glyceryl oleate, citric acid (2.5%)
Uses: Antioxidant esp. suitable for high-grade veg. fats and fat-containing pharmaceutical preps.
Regulatory: German, EC, US GRAS compliances
Properties: Lt. brn. waxy solid; odorless and taste-

less in dilution; sol. in oils and fats.

Oyster Shell Powd. 4402. [Crompton & Knowles]
Chem. Descrip.: Oyster shell powd.
Uses: Premium carrier for pharmaceuticals; high

level of microbiological cleanliness
Properties: Powd.; 16 μ avg. particle size; 80% min. thru 325 mesh; 98% min. $CaCO_3$, 39% min. Ca.

P

P-4 Pharmaceutical Gelatin. [Hormel]
Chem. Descrip.: Gelatin USP, 150 bloom
CAS 9000-70-8; EINECS 232-554-6
Uses: Pharmaceutical gelatin with coarse mesh so it wets easily and melts slowly with min. amt. of entrapped air; used for soft capsule mfg. and microencapsulation
Properties: Coarse gran.; 70-80% on 20 mesh, 10-25% on 40 mesh; visc. 18-26 mps; pH 4.5-5.8; 12% max. moisture
Storage: 1 yr max. storage stability when kept dry at ambient temps.; keep containers tightly closed.

P-5 Pharmaceutical Gelatin. [Hormel]
Chem. Descrip.: Gelatin USP, 175 bloom
CAS 9000-70-8; EINECS 232-554-6
Uses: Pharmaceutical gelatin with coarse mesh so it wets easily and melts slowly with min. amt. of entrapped air; used for soft capsule mfg. and microencapsulation
Properties: Coarse gran.; 70-80% on 20 mesh, 10-25% on 40 mesh; visc. 26-30 mps; pH 4.5-5.8; 12% max. moisture
Storage: 1 yr max. storage stability when kept dry at ambient temps.; keep containers tightly closed.

P-6 Pharmaceutical Gelatin. [Hormel]
Chem. Descrip.: Gelatin USP, 200 bloom
CAS 9000-70-8; EINECS 232-554-6
Uses: Pharmaceutical gelatin with coarse mesh so it wets easily and melts slowly with min. amt. of entrapped air; used for soft capsule mfg. and microencapsulation
Properties: Coarse gran.; 70-80% on 20 mesh, 10-25% on 40 mesh; visc. 30-34 mps; pH 4.5-5.8; 12% max. moisture
Storage: 1 yr max. storage stability when kept dry at ambient temps.; keep containers tightly closed.

P-7 Pharmaceutical Gelatin. [Hormel]
Chem. Descrip.: Gelatin USP, 225 bloom
CAS 9000-70-8; EINECS 232-554-6
Uses: Pharmaceutical gelatin with coarse mesh so it wets easily and melts slowly with min. amt. of entrapped air; used for soft capsule mfg. and microencapsulation
Properties: Coarse gran.; 70-80% on 20 mesh, 10-25% on 40 mesh; visc. 34-39 mps; pH 4.5-5.8; 12% max. moisture
Storage: 1 yr max. storage stability when kept dry at ambient temps.; keep containers tightly closed.

P-8 Pharmaceutical Gelatin. [Hormel]
Chem. Descrip.: Gelatin USP, 250 bloom
CAS 9000-70-8; EINECS 232-554-6
Uses: Pharmaceutical gelatin with coarse mesh so it wets easily and melts slowly with min. amt. of entrapped air; used for soft capsule mfg. and microencapsulation
Properties: Coarse gran.; 70-80% on 20 mesh, 10-25% on 40 mesh; visc. 39-45 mps; pH 4.5-5.8; 12% max. moisture
Storage: 1 yr max. storage stability when kept dry at ambient temps.; keep containers tightly closed.

P-9 Pharmaceutical Gelatin. [Hormel]
Chem. Descrip.: Gelatin USP, 275 bloom
CAS 9000-70-8; EINECS 232-554-6
Uses: Pharmaceutical gelatin with coarse mesh so it wets easily and melts slowly with min. amt. of entrapped air; used for soft capsule mfg. and microencapsulation
Properties: Coarse gran.; 70-80% on 20 mesh, 10-25% on 40 mesh; visc. 47 ± 4 mps; pH 4.5-5.8; 12% max. moisture
Storage: 1 yr max. storage stability when kept dry at ambient temps.; keep containers tightly closed.

P-10 Pharmaceutical Gelatin. [Hormel]
Chem. Descrip.: Gelatin USP, 300 bloom
CAS 9000-70-8; EINECS 232-554-6
Uses: Pharmaceutical gelatin with coarse mesh so it wets easily and melts slowly with min. amt. of entrapped air; used for soft capsule mfg. and microencapsulation
Properties: Coarse gran.; 70-80% on 20 mesh, 10-25% on 40 mesh; visc. 54-58 mps; pH 4.5-5.8; 12% max. moisture
Storage: 1 yr max. storage stability when kept dry at ambient temps.; keep containers tightly closed.

PAG DLTDP. [Witco/PAG]
Chem. Descrip.: Dilauryl thiodipropionate
CAS 123-28-4; EINECS 204-614-1
Uses: Antioxidant for pharmaceuticals
Regulatory: FDA regulated
Properties: Wh. free-flowing powd.

PAG DSTDP. [Witco/PAG]
Chem. Descrip.: Distearyl thiodipropionate
CAS 693-36-7; EINECS 211-750-5
Uses: Antioxidant for pharmaceutical prods.
Regulatory: FDA regulated.

Palmabeads® Type 500 No. 65332. [Roche]

Chem. Descrip.: Vitamin A palmitate dispersed in gelatin matrix with sucrose, peanut oil, tricalcium phosphate, and BHA and BHT as antioxidants

Uses: For pharmaceutical formulations with high moisture content, prods. incl. min. salts, prods. not dispersed in cold water (e.g., compressed bars where high resist. to moisture and heat is required)

Properties: Yel. free-flowing spherical dry beadlets, bland typ. odor and taste; 95% max. thru 40 mesh, 15% max. thru 120 mesh; m.w. 524.9

Toxicology: Sustained daily intakes of vitamin A exceeding 50,000 IU (adults), 20,000 IU (infants) may cause toxic effects (headache, vomiting, liver damage); US RDA 8000 IU (pregnant/lactating women)

Storage: Store in cool, dry place in tightly closed containers @ 46-59 F.

Palma-Sperse® Type 250-S No. 65322. [Roche]

Chem. Descrip.: Vitamin A palmitate USP FCC compded. with gelatin, sorbitol, modified food starch, ascorbic acid, sodium citrate, sugar, caprylic/capric triglyceride, and BHT, BHA, dl-α-tocopherol (antioxidants)

Uses: Designed for pharmaceutical dry mix and fluid milk prods.

Regulatory: FDA GRAS

Properties: Yel. to tan sperhical dry free-flowing beadlets, sl. char. odor; 90% min. thru 30 mesh, 25% max. thru 80 mesh; disp. readily in water and milk at wide temp. range (40-200 F); m.w. 524.9; 250,000 IU/g assay

Toxicology: Sustained daily intakes of vitamin A exceeding 50,000 IU (adults), 20,000 IU (infants) may cause toxic effects (headache, vomiting, liver damage); US RDA 8000 IU (pregnant/lactating women)

Storage: Store in cool, dry place in tightly closed containers @ 46-59 F.

Palma-Sperse® Type 250A/50 D-S No. 65221. [Roche]

Chem. Descrip.: Vitamin A palmitate USP FCC, vitamin D_3 USP FCC compded. with gelatin, sorbitol, modified food starch, peanut oil, sodium citrate, sugar, caprylic/capric triglyceride, and ascorbic acid, BHT, BHA, dl-α-tocopherol (antioxidants)

Uses: Designed for dry mix and fluid milk prods.

Regulatory: FDA GRAS

Properties: Yel. spherical dry free-flowing beadlets, sl. typ. odor, satisfactory flavor; 90% min. thru 30 mesh, 25% max. thru 80 mesh; readily dispersible; 250,000 IU/g (vitamin A), 50,000 IU/g (vitamin D)

Toxicology: Vitamin A: sustained daily intakes exceeding 50,000 IU (adults), 20,000 IU (infants) may cause toxic effects (headache, vomiting, liver damage); US RDA 8000 IU (pregnant/lactating women); vitamin D: potentially toxic esp. in young children

Storage: Store in cool, dry place.

Pancreatic Lipase 250. [Solvay Enzymes]

Chem. Descrip.: Lipase

CAS 9001-62-1; EINECS 232-619-9

Uses: Enzyme for hydrolysis of triglycerides to glycerol and fatty acids; pharmaceuticals (digestive aids)

Properties: Cream-colored amorphous dry powd., free from offensive odor; water-sol.

Storage: Activity loss ≤ 10% in 1 yr stored in sealed containers under cool, dry conditions; 5 C storage extends life.

Pancreatin 3X USP Powd. [Am. Labs]

Chem. Descrip.: Lipase, amylase, and protease enzymes

Uses: Enzyme for pharmaceutical applics.

Properties: Powd.

Pancreatin 4X USP Powd. [Am. Labs]

Chem. Descrip.: Lipase, amylase, and protease enzymes

Uses: Enzyme for pharmaceutical applics.

Properties: Powd.

Pancreatin 5X USP Powd. [Am. Labs]

Chem. Descrip.: Lipase, amylase, and protease enzymes

Uses: Enzyme for pharmaceutical applics.

Properties: Powd.

Pancreatin 6X USP Powd. [Am. Labs]

Chem. Descrip.: Lipase, amylase, and protease enzymes

Uses: Enzyme for pharmaceutical applics.

Properties: Powd.

Pancreatin 8X USP Powd. [Am. Labs]

Chem. Descrip.: Lipase, amylase, and protease enzymes

Uses: Enzyme for pharmaceutical applics.

Properties: Powd.

Pancreatin USP Powd. [Am. Labs]

Chem. Descrip.: Lipase, amylase, and protease enzymes

Uses: Enzyme for pharmaceutical applics.

Properties: Powd.

Pancrelipase USP. [Am. Labs]

Chem. Descrip.: Lipase, amylase, and protease enzymes

Uses: Enzyme for pharmaceutical applics.

Properties: Powd.

d,l-Panthenol FCC Grade. [Tri-K Industries]

Chem. Descrip.: d,l-Panthenol

CAS 16485-10-2

Uses: Vitamin B additive for pharmaceutical applics.; converts to pantothenic acid in the organism, a component of coenzyme A with beneficial healing effect on skin ulcers, skin burns, cracked and hard skin

Properties: Cream to wh. powd., char. odor; sol. in water, ethanol, propylene glycol; m.w. 205.26; sp.gr. 1.2; f.p. dec. at 64-69 C; b.p. dec.; pH 9-10.5; 99% min. assay; do not flush into sewer or stream; dispose of in approved chemical waste landfill

Toxicology: Ingestion of large doses may produce gastrointestinal upset; skin contact may cause irritation; eye contact may cause irritation, redness, pain; chronic exposure may aggravate preexisting conditions (dermatitis, breathing difficulties, eye diseases)

Precaution: Possible fire hazard at elevated temps. or in contact with an ignition source; avoid extremes in temps. and high humidity

Storage: Store in cool, dry place in tightly closed containers in well ventilated area; protect from moisture.

DL-Panthenol USP, FCC No. 63915. [Roche]
Chem. Descrip.: DL-Panthenol
CAS 16485-10-2
Uses: Long-lasting moisturizer.

Papain 16,000. [Solvay Enzymes]
Chem. Descrip.: Protease
CAS 9014-01-1; EINECS 232-752-2
Uses: Enzyme for hydrolysis of proteins; pharmaceuticals (digestive aid)
Properties: Tan to lt. brn. amorphous dry powd., free of offensive odors and taste; water-sol.
Storage: Activity loss ≤ 10% in 1 yr stored in sealed containers under cool dry conditions; 5 C storage extends life.

Papain 30,000. [Solvay Enzymes]
Chem. Descrip.: Protease
CAS 9014-01-1; EINECS 232-752-2
Uses: Enzyme for hydrolysis of proteins; pharmaceuticals (digestive aid)
Properties: Tan to lt. brn. amorphous dry powd., free of offensive odors and taste; water-sol.
Storage: Activity loss ≤ 10% in 1 yr stored in sealed containers under cool dry conditions; 5 C storage extends life.

Papain Conc. [Solvay Enzymes]
Chem. Descrip.: Protease
CAS 9014-01-1; EINECS 232-752-2
Uses: Enzyme for hydrolysis of proteins; pharmaceuticals (digestive aid)
Properties: Tan to lt. brn. amorphous dry powd., free of offensive odors and taste; water-sol.
Storage: Activity loss ≤ 10% in 1 yr stored in sealed containers under cool dry conditions; 5 C storage extends life.

Paramount B. [Van Den Bergh Foods]
Chem. Descrip.: Partially hydrog. palm kernel oil
CAS 68990-82-9
Uses: Lauric fat for pharmaceutical applics.
Regulatory: Kosher
Properties: Solid; m.p. 93-96 F.

Paramount C. [Van Den Bergh Foods]
Chem. Descrip.: Partially hydrog. palm kernel oil, lecithin
Uses: Lauric fat for pharmaceutical applics.
Regulatory: Kosher
Properties: Flake; m.p. 101-104 F.

Paramount H. [Van Den Bergh Foods]
Chem. Descrip.: Partially hydrog. veg. oil (palm kernel, soybean, cottonseed)
EINECS 269-820-6
Uses: Lauric fat for pharmaceutical applics.
Regulatory: Kosher

Properties: Liq.; m.p. 107-109 F.

Paramount X. [Van Den Bergh Foods]
Chem. Descrip.: Partially hydrog. veg. oil (palm kernel, soybean, cottonseed)
EINECS 269-820-6
Uses: Lauric fat for pharmaceutical applics.
Regulatory: Kosher
Properties: Liq.; m.p. 107-109 F.

Paramount XX. [Van Den Bergh Foods]
Chem. Descrip.: Partially hydrog. veg. oil (palm kernel, soybean, cottonseed)
EINECS 269-820-6
Uses: Lauric fat for pharmaceutical applics.
Regulatory: Kosher
Properties: Flake; m.p. 117-119 F.

Patlac® LA USP. [R.I.T.A.]
Chem. Descrip.: Lactic acid
CAS 50-21-5; EINECS 200-018-0
Uses: Surfactant, humectant
Properties: Clear liq.; 88% act.; anionic
Toxicology: Irritant to eyes, skin, and mucous membranes in conc. form.

Patlac® NAL. [Am. Ingreds.; R.I.T.A.]
Chem. Descrip.: Sodium lactate
CAS 72-17-3; EINECS 200-772-0
Uses: PH buffer, humectant, stabilizer, component of stratum corneum; for pharmaceutical industry
Properties: Clear liq.; sp.gr. 1.31-1.34; pH 8-9; 60% conc.
Toxicology: Nontoxic if ingested; nonirritating to skin and eyes.

PD-23. [Witco/Petroleum Spec.]
Chem. Descrip.: Min. oil
Uses: Non-VOC solv. for pharmaceutical creams and lotions
Regulatory: FDA 21CFR §172.884, 178.3650
Properties: Colorless clear liq., nearly odorless; sp.gr. 0.800 (60/60 C); visc. 2.6 cSt (40 C); vapor pressure < 0.01 mm Hg (20 C); b.p. 452 F; pour pt. 0 F; flash pt. (COC) 230 F; ref. index 1.442.

PD-25. [Witco/Petroleum Spec.]
Chem. Descrip.: Petroleum distillate
Uses: Non-VOC solv. for pharmaceutical creams and lotions
Regulatory: FDA 21CFR §172.884, 178.3650
Properties: Colorless clear liq., nearly odorless; sp.gr. 0.810 (60/60 C); visc. 3.9 cSt (40 C); vapor pressure < 0.01 mm Hg (20 C); b.p. 510 F; pour pt. 20 F; flash pt. (COC) 260 F; ref. index 1.446.

PD-28. [Witco/Petroleum Spec.]
Chem. Descrip.: Petroleum distillate
Uses: Non-VOC solv. for pharmaceutical creams and lotions
Regulatory: FDA 21CFR §172.878, 178.3620a
Properties: Colorless liq., nearly odorless; sp.gr. 0.820 (60/60 C); visc. 4.6 cSt (40 C); vapor pressure < 0.01 mm Hg (20 C); b.p. 526 F; pour pt. 30 F; flash pt. (COC) 285 F; ref. index 1.450.

PDCP. [Albright & Wilson Am.; Albright & Wilson UK]
Chem. Descrip.: Phenyl dichlorophosphate
CAS 770-12-7
Uses: Intermediate in selective mfg. of phosphoric

acid diesters; protective agent for hydroxyl groups

Properties: M.w. 211; dens. 1.4 g/cm³; b.p. 241-243 C; 98% min. assay.

Pecogel® GC-310. [Phoenix]
Chem. Descrip.: PVP/dimethylaminoethylmethacrylate/polycarbamyl polyglycol ester
Uses: Polymeric hydrogel, film-former used in pharmaceutical topicals; water resist.
Properties: Lt. to dk. straw hazy visc. liq.; disp. in water; sp.gr. 1.016; visc. 3000-7000 cps; pH 8-9 (10%); nonflamm.; 10% aq. sol'n.; cationic
Toxicology: Nonirritating to skin, pract. nonirritating to eyes; LD50 (oral) > 5 g/kg, nontoxic orally; noncomedogenic; ingestion may cause nausea, vomiting, abdominal pain
Storage: Keep from freezing.

Pecogel® GC-1110. [Phoenix]
Chem. Descrip.: PVP/dimethylaminoethylmethacrylate/polycarbamyl polyglycol ester
Uses: Polymeric hydrogel used in pharmaceutical topicals; water resist.
Properties: Visc. liq.; disp. in water; sp.gr. 1.022; pH 8-9 (10%); nonflamm.; 10% aq. sol'n.; cationic
Toxicology: Nonirritating to skin; minimally irritating to eyes; LD50 (oral) > 5 g/kg, nontoxic orally; noncomedogenic; ingestion may cause nausea, vomiting, gastric disturbance; overexposure may cause dizziness, headache, nausea
Precaution: Hazardous ingreds.: 1.76% 1-methyl-2-pyrrolidone; hazardous decomp. prods.: combustion may produce CO, CO_2, NO_x
Storage: Protect from freezing.

Pecogel® H-12. [Phoenix]
Chem. Descrip.: PVP/polycarbamyl polyglycol ester
Uses: Polymeric hydrogel, film-former used in pharmaceutical topicals; water resist.
Properties: Off-wh. hazy visc. liq.; water-disp.; sp.gr. 0.954; visc. 3000-7000 cps; pH 8-9 (1%); nonflamm.; 12% aq. sol'n.; nonionic
Toxicology: Nonirritating to skin and eyes; LD50 (oral) > 5 g/kg, nontoxic orally; noncomedogenic; ingestion may cause nausea, vomiting, gastric disturbance; overexposure may cause dizziness, headache, nausea
Precaution: Hazardous decomp. prods.: combustion may produce CO, CO_2, NO_x
Storage: Protect from freezing.

Pecogel® H-115. [Phoenix]
Chem. Descrip.: PVP/polycarbamyl polyglycol ester
Uses: Polymeric hydrogel, film-former used in pharmaceutical topicals; water resist.
Properties: Off-wh. to yel. hazy visc. liq.; water-disp.; sp.gr. 1.027; visc. 4000-8000 cps; pH 8-9 (10%); nonflamm.; 15% aq. sol'n.; nonionic
Toxicology: Pract. nonirritating to eyes; nonirritating to skin; LD50 (oral) > 5 g/kg, nontoxic orally; noncomedogenic; ingestion may cause nausea, vomting, gastric disturbance; overexposure may cause dizziness, headache, nausea

Precaution: Hazardous ingreds.: 3.59% 1-methyl-2-pyrrolidone; hazardous decomp. prods.: combustion may produce CO, CO_2, NO_x
Storage: Protect from freezing.

Pecogel® H-1220. [Phoenix]
Chem. Descrip.: PVP/polycarbamyl polyglycol ester
Uses: Polymeric hydrogel, film-former used in pharmaceutical topicals; water resist.
Properties: Visc. liq.; disp. in water; sp.gr. 1.036; pH 8-9 (10%); nonflamm.; 20% aq. sol'n.; nonionic
Toxicology: Pract. nonirritating to eyes; nonirritating to skin; LD50 (oral) > 5 g/kg, nontoxic orally; noncomedogenic; ingestion may cause nausea, vomiting, gastric disturbance; overexposure may cause dizziness, headache, nausea
Precaution: Hazardous ingreds.: 4.73% 1-methyl-2-pyrrolidone; hazardous decomp. prods.: combustion may produce CO, CO_2, NO_x
Storage: Protect from freezing.

Pecogel® S-1120. [Phoenix]
Chem. Descrip.: PVP/dimethiconylacrylate/polycarbamyl polygycol ester
Uses: Polymeric hydrogel, film-former used in sunscreens, pharmaceutical topicals; water resist.
Properties: Wh. to lt. yel. hazy visc. liq., amine-like odor; water-disp.; dens. 8.6 lb/gal; visc. 500-3000 cps; pH 8-9 (10%); nonflamm.; 20% aq. sol'n.; nonionic
Toxicology: Nonirritating to eyes and skin; LD50 (oral) > 5 g/kg, nontoxic orally; noncomedogenic; inh. may irritate respiratory tract; contact may cause skin and eye irritation; ingestion may cause nausea, vomiting, gastric disturbance
Precaution: Hazardous ingreds.: 3.67% 1-methyl-2-pyrrolidone; incompat. with strong oxidizing or reducing agents; hazardous decomp. prods.: emits CO and NO_x fumes when heated to decomp.
Storage: Protect from freezing; do not leave containers open.

Pecosil® DCU. [Phoenix]
Chem. Descrip.: Dimethicone copolyol undecylenate
CAS 159100-33-1
Uses: Emollient used in sunscreens, pharmaceutical topicals; coupling agent, cosolv. for water and oil systems
Properties: Off-wh. to yel. clear to hazy liq.; sol. in water and castor oil; sp.gr. 1.01 g/ml; acid no. 15 max.; flash pt. (TCC) > 200 F; pH 5-7 (10%); 100% act.
Toxicology: Nonirritating to eyes; nonprimary skin irritant; nontoxic orally; noncomedogenic; skin exposure can cause irritation; ingestion may cause nausea, vomiting, abdominal pain
Precaution: Incompat. with strong oxidizers and reducers; hazardous decomp. prods.: thermal $(CO)_x$, $(SiO)_x$.

Pecosil® OS-100B. [Phoenix]
Chem. Descrip.: Dimethicone propylethylenedi-

amine behenate
CAS 133448-12-1
Uses: Hydrophobic film-former used in pharmaceutical topicals; humectant, protective barrier
Properties: Wh. to buff very visc. paste with opal-like appearance; insol. in water; sp.gr. 1.01 g/ml; pH 7 (10%); flash pt. (TCC) > 200 F; 100% act.; cationic
Toxicology: Nonirritating to skin and eyes; LD50 (oral) > 5 g/kg, nontoxic orally; noncomedogenic; skin exposure can cause irritation; ingestion may cause nausea, vomiting, abdominal pain
Precaution: Incompat. with strong oxidizers and reducers; hazardous decomp. prods.: thermal $(CO)_x$, $(SIO)_x$.

Pecosil® PS-100. [Phoenix]
Chem. Descrip.: Dimethicone copolyol phosphate
CAS 132207-31-9
Uses: Patented o/w emulsifier, pigment wetting and dispersing agent for topical pharmaceuticals, sunscreens
Properties: Clear to sl. hazy visc. liq.; water-sol.; sp.gr. 1.01 g/ml; acid no. 37-47; flash pt. (TCC) > 200 F; pH 2-4 (1%); 100% act.; anionic
Toxicology: Nonirritating to skin and eyes; nontoxic orally; noncomedogenic; skin exposure can cause irritation; ingestion may cause nausea, vomiting, abdominal pain
Precaution: Incompat. with strong oxidizers and reducers; hazardous decomp. prods.: thermal $(CO)_x$, $(SiO)_x$.

Pecosil® PS-100K. [Phoenix]
Chem. Descrip.: Potassium dimethicone copolyol phosphate
CAS 150522-09-1
Uses: O/w emulsifier for topical pharmaceuticals, sunscreen prods.
Properties: Yel. clear to sl. hazy liq.; sol. in water; sp.gr. 1.01 g/ml; acid no. 20 max.; pH 5-7 (10%); flash pt. (TCC) > 200 F; 55% aq. sol'n.
Toxicology: Nonprimary skin irritant; nonirritating to eyes; nontoxic orally; noncomedogenic; skin exposure can cause irritation; ingestion may cause nausea, vomiting, abdominal pain
Precaution: Incompat. with strong oxidizers and reducers; hazardous decomp. prods.: thermal $(CO)_x$.

Pecosil® SWP-83. [Phoenix]
Chem. Descrip.: Hydrolyzed wheat protein/dimethicone copolyol phosphate copolymer
Uses: Used in pharmaceutical topicals
Properties: Amber clear liq.; sol. in water; sp.gr. 1.01 g/ml; b.p. 100 C; flash pt. (TCC) > 200 F; pH 6-8 (10%); 35-38% act. in water
Toxicology: Nonirritating to eyes and skin; LD50 (oral) > 5 g/kg, nontoxic orally; noncomedogenic; skin exposure can cause irritation; ingestion may cause nausea, vomiting, abdominal pain
Precaution: Incompat. with strong oxidizers and reducers; hazardous decomp. prods.: thermal $(CO)_x$, $(SiO)_x$
Storage: 6 mos shelf life; store in cool, dry place.

Pecosil® WDS-100. [Phoenix]
Chem. Descrip.: Dimethicone copolyol phosphate
CAS 132207-31-9
Uses: O/w emulsifier, emollient for topical pharmaceuticals; pigment wetter and disperser
Properties: Clear to hazy liq.; water-disp.; sp.gr. 1.01 g/ml; acid no. 110 ± 8; flash pt. (TCC) > 200 F; pH 3-4 (10%); 100% act.; anionic
Toxicology: Nonirritating to eyes; nonprimary skin irritant; nontoxic orally; nocomedogenic; skin exposure can cause irritation; ingestion may cause nausea, vomiting, abdominal pain
Precaution: Incompat. with strong oxidizers and reducers; hazardous decomp. prods.: thermal $(CO)_x$ and $(SiO)_x$.

Peerless® No. 1. [R.T. Vanderbilt]
Chem. Descrip.: Sec. kaolin clay
CAS 1332-58-7; EINECS 296-473-8
Uses: Filler used in pharmaceuticals
Properties: Wh. particulate; particle size 1.2 μ, 99.8% thru -325-mesh screen; dens. 2.5 mg/m³, 16 lb/ft³; oil absorp. 27; pH 4.6 (10%); 44.29% SiO_2, 39.32% Al_2O_3.

Peerless® No. 2. [R.T. Vanderbilt]
Chem. Descrip.: Sec. kaolin clay
CAS 1332-58-7; EINECS 296-473-8
Uses: Filler used in pharmaceuticals
Properties: Lt. cream particulate; particle size 1.2 μ, 99.6% thru -325 mesh; dens. 2.5 mg/m³, 16 lb/ft³; oil absorp. 30; pH 4.8; 44.6% SiO_2, 39.5% Al_2O_3.

Peerless® No. 3. [R.T. Vanderbilt]
Chem. Descrip.: Sec. kaolin clay
CAS 1332-58-7; EINECS 296-473-8
Uses: Filler used in pharmaceuticals
Properties: Cream particulate; particle size 1.1 μ, 99.1% thru -325-mesh screen; dens. 2.5 mg/m³, 16 lb/ft³; oil absorp. 30; pH 4.9 (10%); 44.8% SiO_2, 39.2% Al_2O_3.

Peerless® No. 4. [R.T. Vanderbilt]
Chem. Descrip.: Sec. kaolin clay
CAS 1332-58-7; EINECS 296-473-8
Uses: Filler used in pharmaceuticals
Properties: Off-wh. particulate; particle size 1.5 μ; dens. 2.5 mg/m³; dens. 16 lb/ft³; oil absorp. 31; pH 4.5 (10%).

Pegosperse® 50 DS. [Lonza]
Chem. Descrip.: Glycol distearate
CAS 627-83-8; EINECS 211-014-3
Uses: Emollient, lubricant and pigment dispersant in pharmaceuticals
Properties: Wh. beads; sol. in ethanol, min. and veg. oil; insol. in water; HLB 1; m.p. 59 C; acid no. 6 max.; iodine no. < 1; sapon. no. 190-200; pH 5 (3%); 100% conc.; nonionic.

Pelemol® 89. [Phoenix]
Chem. Descrip.: Octyl isononanoate
CAS 71566-49-9; EINECS 275-637-2
Uses: Emollient used in pharmaceutical topicals; extremely dry and nonoily skin feel
Properties: Colorless to sl. yel. clear liq., sl. typ. odor; water-insol.; sp.gr. 0.855; b.p. > 175 C; acid

no. 1 max.; iodine no. 1 max.; sapon. no. 200-215; flash pt. (COC) > 150 C; 100% act.

Toxicology: Nonirritating to skin and eyes; nontoxic orally; noncomedogenic; skin exposure can cause irritation; ingestion may cause nausea, vomiting, abdominal pain; eye contact may cause irritation

Precaution: Hazardous decomp. prods.: burning may produce CO, CO_2.

Pelemol® BB. [Phoenix]
Chem. Descrip.: Behenyl behenate
CAS 17671-27-1; EINECS 241-646-5
Uses: Emollient, visc./body builder for topical pharmaceuticals
Properties: Off-wh. waxy flake; oil-sol.; water-insol.; m.p. 68 C; b.p. > 150 C; acid no. 3 max.; iodine no. 5 max.; sapon. no. 78-98; flash pt. (PMCC) > 150 C; pH ≈ 6
Toxicology: Nonirritating to eyes and skin; nontoxic orally; noncomedogenic; skin and eye exposure may cause irritation; ingestion may cause abdominal upset
Precaution: Incompat. with strong oxidizers and reducing agents; hazardous decomp. prods.: incomplete combustion produces CO
Storage: Avoid prolonged heated storage.

Pelemol® C-150. [Phoenix]
Chem. Descrip.: Trioctyldodecyl citrate dilinoleate
Uses: Used in pharmaceutical topicals
Properties: Clear oily liq.; insol. in water; sp.gr. 1.01 g/ml; flash pt. (TCC) > 200 F; pH 5-7 (10%)
Toxicology: Skin exposure can cause irritation; ingestion may cause nausea, vomiting, abdominal pain
Precaution: Incompat. with strong oxidizers and reducers; hazardous decomp. prods.: thermal (CO) x, (SiO) x
Storage: Protect from freezing and boiling (emulsion will break).

Pelemol® CA. [Phoenix]
Chem. Descrip.: Cetyl acetate
CAS 629-70-9; EINECS 211-103-7
Uses: Used in pharmaceutical topicals
Properties: Colorless clear liq. to yel. waxy solid; insol. in water; sp.gr. 0.85; m.p. 18 C; b.p. > 150 C; acid no. 1 max.; iodine no. 1 max.; sapon. no. 185-205; hyd. no. 8 max.; flash pt. (PMCC) > 150 C; pH ≈ 6 (10%)
Toxicology: Skin exposure may cause irritation; ingestion may cause abdominal upset; eye contact may cause irritation
Precaution: Incompat. with strong oxidizers and reducing agent; hazardous decomp. prods.: incomplete combustion produces CO
Storage: Avoid prolonged heated storage.

Pelemol® CCT. [Phoenix]
Chem. Descrip.: Caprylic capric triglyceride
CAS 977059-83-8; EINECS 265-724-3
Uses: Used in pharmaceutical topicals
Properties: Yel. clear oily liq., bland odor; insol. in water; sp.gr. 0.9; b.p. > 500 C; acid no. 1 max.; iodine no. 2 max.; sapon. no. 338-358; hyd. no. 10

max.; flash pt. (OP) 350 C; pH 5.5-7.0 (3% aq.); 0.2% max. moisture
Toxicology: Skin exposure can cause irritation; ingestion may cause nausea, vomiting, abdominal pain
Precaution: Incompat. with strong oxidizing agents; hazardous decomp. prods.: combustion produces oxides of carbon
Storage: Store in cool, dry location away from strong oxidizing agents; avoid excessive heat.

Pelemol® CL. [Phoenix]
Chem. Descrip.: Cetyl lactate
CAS 35274-05-6; EINECS 252-478-7
Uses: Emollient used in pharmaceutical topicals
Properties: Wh. clear liq. to solid, faint char. odor; insol. in water; sp.gr. 0.893-0.905; b.p. 342 C; acid no. 2 max.; sapon. no. 174-189; flash pt. (COC) > 202 C
Toxicology: LD50 (oral, rat) 20 ml/kg; nonirritating to eyes; nonprimary skin irritant; nonsensitizing
Precaution: Incompat. with strong oxidizers; hazardous decomp. prods.: CO, CO_2 when heated to decomp.

Pelemol® CP. [Phoenix]
Chem. Descrip.: Cetyl palmitate
CAS 540-10-3
Uses: Emollient, base, consistency factor used in pharmaceutical topicals
Properties: Wh. to tan flake, odorless; insol. in water; m.p. 51-55 C; b.p. > 100 C; acid no. 2 max.; sapon. no. 109-117; flash pt. (PM) 200 F
Toxicology: Prolonged skin and eye contact may cause mild irritation
Precaution: Incompat. with strong oxidizing agents; hazardous decomp. prods.: CO, CO_2
Storage: Store in cool, dry location; avoid excessive heat, strong oxidizing agents.

Pelemol® CR. [Phoenix]
Chem. Descrip.: Cetyl ricinoleate
CAS 10401-55-5; EINECS 233-864-4
Uses: Emollient for pharmaceutical topicals
Properties: Yel. liq. to cryst. semisolid; oil-sol.; insol. in water; sp.gr. 0.91 (30 C); m.p. 30 C; b.p. > 200 C; acid no. 5 max.; iodine no. 42-57; sapon. no. 95-110; hyd. no. 90-105; flash pt. (PMCC) > 150 C; pH ≈ 6 (10%); 0.5% max. moisture
Toxicology: Skin exposure can cause irritation; ingestion may cause nausea, vomiting, abdominal pain; eye contact may cause irritation
Precaution: Incompat. with strong oxidizing agents; hazardous decomp. prods.: incomplete combustion produces CO
Storage: Avoid prolonged heated storage.

Pelemol® DIPS. [Phoenix]
Chem. Descrip.: Diisopropyl sebacate
CAS 7491-02-3; EINECS 231-306-4
Uses: Emollient, solubilizer, coupling agent used in pharmaceutical topicals
Properties: Colorless clear liq., essentially odorless; oil-sol.; insol. in water; sp.gr. 0.93; b.p. 355 F; acid no. 1 max.; sapon. no. 380-400; flash pt. (COC) 350 F

Toxicology: Skin exposure can cause irritation; ingestion may cause nausea, vomiting, abdominal pain

Precaution: Burning may produce CO, CO_2.

Pelemol® DO. [Phoenix]

Chem. Descrip.: Decyl oleate

CAS 3687-46-5; EINECS 222-981-6

Uses: Emollient used in pharmaceutical topicals

Properties: Yel. clear liq., typ. bland odor; insol. in water; sp.gr. 0.86; b.p. > 200 C; acid no. 1 max.; iodine no. 65 max.; sapon. no. 130-145; flash pt. (COC) < 240 C

Precaution: Hazardous decomp. prods.: oxides of carbon

Storage: Store in cool, dry location away from strong oxidizing agents; avoid excessive heat, open flames, ignition sources.

Pelemol® EE. [Phoenix]

Chem. Descrip.: Eicosyl erucate

CAS 132208-25-4

Uses: Emollient for pharmaceutical topicals

Properties: Lt. yel. clear low-visc. liq.; oil-sol.; insol. in water; sp.gr. 0.86; b.p. > 200 C; acid no. 1 max.; flash pt. (COC) > 175 C; 100% vegetable derived; 100% act.

Toxicology: Nonirritating to eyes; nonprimary skin irritant; nontoxic orally; noncomedogenic; skin exposure can cause irritation; ingestion may cause nausea, vomiting, abdominal pain; may cause mucous membrane irritation if heated to produce vapors or as mist

Precaution: Combustible liq.; incompat. with strong oxidizers; hazardous decomp. prods.: combustion produces CO, CO_2, thick smoke

Storage: Store in closed containers below 120 F out of sun; do not store or use near heat, sparks, flame.

Pelemol® G7A. [Phoenix]

Chem. Descrip.: Glycereth-7 triacetate

CAS 57569-76-3

Uses: Humectant, emollient, coupling agent, solubilizer used in pharmaceutical topicals; solv. for sunscreen ingreds.

Properties: Sl. yel. clear visc. liq., bland odor; sol. in water, alcohol, hydro-alcoholic sol'ns.; sp.gr. ≈ 1.16; acid no. 7 max.; sapon. no. 305-330; hyd. no. 20 max.; flash pt. (PMCC) > 150 C; 100% act.

Toxicology: Nonirritating to eyes; nonprimary skin irritant; LD50 (oral) > 5 g/kg, nontoxic orally; noncomedogenic; skin exposure can cause irritation; ingestion may cause nausea, vomiting, abdominal pain

Precaution: Incompat. with oxidizing agents; hazardous decomp. prods.: may form oxides of carbon

Storage: Store in cool, dry place.

Pelemol® G7B. [Phoenix]

Chem. Descrip.: Glycereth-7 benzoate

CAS 12804-12-8

Uses: Lubricous emollient used in pharmaceutical topicals; blooms heavily in water

Properties: Colorless to sl. yel. clear visc. liq., mild odor; sol. in hydroalcoholic sol'ns., ethyl alcohol, propylene glycol, disp. in water; self-emulsifying; sp.gr. 1.16; vapor pressure < 0.1; b.p. > 185 C; acid no. 5 max.; sapon. no. 95-125; flash pt. (CCC) 100% act.

Toxicology: Nonirritating to skin and eyes; nontoxic orally; noncomedogenic; skin exposure can cause irritation; ingestion may cause nausea, vomiting, abdominal pain

Precaution: Hazardous decomp. prods.: may form CO, CO_2.

Pelemol® G45L. [Phoenix]

Chem. Descrip.: Glycereth-4.5 lactate

CAS 125804-28-6

Uses: Emollient, humectant for pharmaceutical topicals; useful in hydro/alcoholic formulations

Properties: Water-wh. to pale yel. clear visc. liq., mild typ. odor; sol. in water, methanol, IPA; insol. in min. oil; sp.gr. 0.858 ± 0.01 (20 C); b.p. dec. > 210 C; acid no. 5 max.; sapon. no. 165-185; flash pt. (COC) > 210 C; nonionic

Toxicology: Nonirritating to eyes and skin; nontoxic orally; skin exposure can cause irritation; ingestion may cause nausea, vomiting, abdominal pain

Precaution: Incompat. with strong oxidizing agents; hazardous decomp. prods.: CO, CO_2.

Pelemol® GTB. [Phoenix]

Chem. Descrip.: Glyceryl tribehenate

CAS 68334-28-1; EINECS 242-471-7

Uses: Emollient imparting body to pharmaceutical topicals

Properties: Off-wh. waxy solid, char. fatty odor; oil-sol.; insol. in water; sp.gr. 0.92; iodine no. 2 max.; flash pt. (COC) 315 C min.

Toxicology: Inh. hazard is negligible unless heated to produce vapors or as mist, which may cause mucous membrane irritation, dizziness, nausea; eye and prolonged/repeated skin contact may cause irritation; ingestion may irritate digestive tract

Precaution: Incompat. with strong oxidizing agents; hazardous decomp. prods.: combustion produces CO, CO_2, thick smoke

Storage: Store in closed containers below 120 F away from sun and oxidizing agents, excessive heat, ignition sources.

Pelemol® GTL. [Phoenix]

Chem. Descrip.: Glyceryl trilactate

Uses: Used in pharmaceutical topicals

Properties: Yel. oily visc. liq.; sol. in water; sp.gr. 0.96; b.p. > 200 C; acid no. 5 max.; sapon. no. 500-550; flash pt. (PMCC) > 150 C; pH ≈ 6 (10%); 0.5% max. moisture

Toxicology: Skin exposure may cause irritation; ingestion may cause abdominal upset; eye contact may cause irritation

Precaution: Incompat. with strong oxidizers and reducing agents; hazardous decomp. prods.: incomplete combustion produces CO

Storage: Avoid prolonged heated storage.

Pelemol® HAB. [Phoenix]

Chem. Descrip.: Dihydroabietyl behenate

CAS 127036-29-7
Uses: Emollient for pharmaceutical topicals, sunscreens
Properties: Amber soft solid; sol. in oil; insol. in water; sp.gr. 0.91 (40 C); m.p. 35 C; b.p. > 200 C; acid no. 10 max.; sapon. no. 75-95; flash pt. (TCC) > 150 C; pH ≈ 6
Toxicology: Nonirritating to skin and eyes; nontoxic orally; noncomedogenic; skin exposure may cause irritation; eye contact may cause irritation; ingestion may cause abdominal upset
Precaution: Incompat. with strong oxidizers and reducing agents; hazardous decomp. prods.: incomplete combustion produces CO
Storage: Avoid prolonged heated storage.

Pelemol® IBS. [Phoenix]
Chem. Descrip.: Isobutyl stearate
CAS 646-13-9
Uses: Lubricity and slip agent used in pharmaceutical topicals
Properties: Pale yel. clear liq., mild odor; negligible sol. in water; sp.gr. 0.85; vapor pressure negligible; f.p. 15 C; b.p. 185-222 C; acid no. 1 max.; iodine no. 0.5 max.; flash pt. (COC) 380 F
Toxicology: LD50 (oral, rat) > 5 cc/kg; mild irritant to skin and eyes on prolonged contact
Precaution: Incompat. with strong oxidizing agents; hazardous decomp. prods.: CO, CO_2
Storage: Store in cool, dry location away from strong oxidizing agents; avoid excessive heat.

Pelemol® ICB. [Phoenix]
Chem. Descrip.: Isocetyl behenate
CAS 94247-28-6; EINECS 304-205-9
Uses: Emollient for pharmaceutical topicals
Properties: Lt. yel. oily clear liq., mild char. odor; oil-sol.; insol. in water, alcohol; sp.gr. 0.91; f.p. 9 C; b.p. dec.; acid no. 3 max.; sapon. no. 70-95; flash pt. (COC) 345 F; 100% act.
Toxicology: Nonirritating to skin and eyes; nontoxic orally; noncomedogenic; skin exposure can cause irritation; ingestion may cause nausea, vomiting, abdominal pain
Precaution: Incompat. with strong oxidizing agents; hazardous decomp. prods.: oxides of carbon
Storage: Store in cool place away from strong oxidizing materials.

Pelemol® ICIS. [Phoenix]
Chem. Descrip.: Isocetyl isostearate
Uses: Emollient used in pharmaceutical topicals
Properties: Yel. liq.; insol. in water; sp.gr. 0.95; b.p. > 200 C; flash pt. (PMCC) > 150 C; pH ≈ 6 (10%)
Toxicology: Skin exposure can cause irritation; ingestion may cause abdominal upset; eye contact may cause irritation
Precaution: Incompat. with strong oxidizers and reducing agents; hazardous decomp. prods.: incomplete combustion produces CO
Storage: Avoid prolonged heated storage.

Pelemol® ICLA. [Phoenix]
Chem. Descrip.: Isocetyl laurate
CAS 20834-06-4

Uses: Used in pharmaceutical topicals
Properties: Pale yel. liq.; insol. in water; sp.gr. 0.95; b.p. > 200 C; flash pt. (PMCC) > 150 C; pH ≈ 6 (10%)
Toxicology: Skin exposure can cause irritation; ingestion may cause abdominal upset; eye contact may cause irritation
Precaution: Incompat. with strong oxidizers and reducing agents; hazardous decomp. prods.: incomplete combustion produces CO
Storage: Avoid prolonged heated storage.

Pelemol® ICO. [Phoenix]
Chem. Descrip.: Isocetyl octanoate
CAS 125804-19-5
Uses: Used in pharmaceutical topicals
Properties: Almost colorless liq., mild typ. odor; insol. in water; sp.gr. 0.89; b.p. > 200 C; flash pt. (COC) > 200 C
Toxicology: Skin exposure can cause irritation; ingestion may cause nausea, vomiting, abdominal pain
Precaution: Incompat. with strong oxidizing agents; hazardous decomp. prods.: CO, CO_2
Storage: Store in cool, dry location; avoid excessive heat.

Pelemol® ICS. [Phoenix]
Chem. Descrip.: Isocetyl stearate
CAS 25339-09-7; EINECS 246-868-6
Uses: Emollient for pharmaceutical topicals
Properties: Water-wh. liq., typ. mild odor; oil-sol.; insol. in water; sp.gr. 0.853-0.859; visc. 32 cps; f.p. 0 C; b.p. 149 C; acid no. 3 max.; iodine no. 5 max.; flash pt. (PMCC) > 200 F; ref. index 1.425
Precaution: Incompat. with strong oxidizing agents; hazardous decomp. prods.: combustion produces CO, CO_2
Storage: Store in cool, dry location; avoid excessive heat.

Pelemol® IDO. [Phoenix]
Chem. Descrip.: Isodecyl oleate
CAS 59231-34-4; EINECS 261-673-6
Uses: Emollient used in pharmaceutical topicals
Properties: Pale yel. med. visc. liq., typ. odor; sol. in peanut oil 95% ethanol, IPM, min. oil; insol. in water, 70% ethanol, glycerin, propylene glycol; sp.gr. 0.861; f.p. < 0 C; b.p. > 240 C; acid no. 1-5; iodine no. 45-50; sapon. no. 120-140; flash pt. (COC) 238 C; ref. index 1.455
Precaution: Incompat. with strong oxidizing agents; hazardous decomp. prods.: oxides of carbon
Storage: Store in cool, dry location away from strong oxidizing agents; avoid excessive heat, open flames, ignition sources.

Pelemol® IN-2. [Phoenix]
Chem. Descrip.: Isononyl isononanoate
CAS 42131-25-9
Uses: Emollient used in pharmaceutical topicals
Properties: Water-wh. clear mobile liq.; insol. in water; sp.gr. 0.85; b.p. > 150 C; acid no. 1 max.; sapon. no. 185-205; flash pt. (PMCC) > 150 C; pH ≈ 6 (10%); 0.5% max. moisture

Toxicology: Skin exposure may cause irritation; ingestion may cause abdominal upset; eye contact may cause irritation

Precaution: Incompat. with strong oxidizers and reducing agents; hazardous decomp. prods.: incomplete combustion produces CO

Storage: Avoid prolonged heated storage.

Pelemol® ISB. [Phoenix]
Chem. Descrip.: Isostearyl behenate
CAS 125804-16-2
Uses: Emollient, moisture barrier for pharmaceutical topicals
Properties: Wh. to off-wh. opaque soft paste, bland odor; oil-sol.; insol. in water; sp.gr. 0.985; m.p. 38-42 C; b.p. dec.; acid no. 3 max.; sapon. no. 80-100; flash pt. (COC) 350 F; 100% act.
Toxicology: Nonirritating to eyes; nonprimary skin irritant; LD50 (oral) > 5 g/kg, nontoxic orally; noncomedogenic; skin exposure can cause irritation; ingestion may cause nausea, vomiting, abdominal pain
Precaution: Hazardous decomp. prods.: may form toxic combustion prods.
Storage: Store in cool, dry place away from strong oxidizing agents; avoid excessive heat.

Pelemol® ISL. [Phoenix]
Chem. Descrip.: Isostearyl lactate
CAS 42131-28-2; EINECS 255-674-0
Uses: Emollient used in pharmaceutical topicals
Properties: Sl. yel. liq., mild typ. odor; oil-sol.; insol. in water; sp.gr. 0.808; b.p. > 175 C; acid no. 5 max.; sapon. no. 130-155; flash pt. (COC) > 175 C
Toxicology: Skin exposure can cause irritation; ingestion may cause nausea, vomiting, abdominal pain
Precaution: Incompat. with oxidizing agents; hazardous decomp. prods.: may form oxides of carbon
Storage: Store in cool, dry location away from strong oxidizing agents; avoid excessive heat.

Pelemol® L2A. [Phoenix]
Chem. Descrip.: Laureth-2 acetate
CAS 32289-26-2
Uses: Emollient for pharmaceutical topicals; coupler for hydro-alcoholic systems
Properties: Water-wh. to pale yel. clear liq., mild odor; sol. in hydro-alcoholic sol'ns., ethanol; disp. in water; sp.gr. 1.01 g/ml; b.p. < 300 C; acid no. 5 max.; sapon. no. 46-86; flash pt. (TCC) 480 F; 100% act.
Toxicology: Nonirritating to skin and eyes; nontoxic orally; skin exposure can cause irritation; ingestion may cause nausea, vomiting, abdominal pain
Precaution: Incompat. with strong oxidizers and reducers; hazardous decomp. prods.: thermal (CO)x; esters will hydrolyze at high and low pH.

Pelemol® LB. [Phoenix]
Chem. Descrip.: Lauryl behenate
CAS 42233-07-8
Uses: Used in pharmaceutical topicals
Properties: Off-wh. to yel. waxy solid; oil-sol.; insol.

in water; sp.gr. 0.90 (50 C); m.p. 46 C; b.p. > 200 C; acid no. 3 max.; sapon. no. 95-115; flash pt. (PMCC) > 150 C; pH ≈ 6 (10%); 0.5% max. moisture
Toxicology: Skin exposure can cause irritation; ingestion may cause abdominal upset; eye contact may cause irritation
Precaution: Incompat. with strong oxidizers and reducing agents; hazardous decomp. prods.: incomplete combustion produces CO
Storage: Avoid prolonged heated storage.

Pelemol® ML. [Phoenix]
Chem. Descrip.: Myristyl lactate
CAS 1323-03-1; EINECS 215-350-1
Uses: Emollient, moisture barrier used in pharmaceutical topicals
Properties: Water-wh. to lt. yel. clear oily liq. to soft solid, low odor; sol. in min. oil, alcohol, hydro/alcoholic systems; insol. in water; sp.gr. 0.85; f.p. 10-15 C; b.p. > 150 C; acid no. 3 max.; iodine no. nil; sapon. no. 175-195; flash pt. (PMCC) > 150 C; pH ≈ 6 (10%)
Toxicology: Skin exposure can cause irritation; ingestion may cause abdominal upset; eye contact may cause irritation
Precaution: Incompat. with strong oxidizers and reducing agents; hazardous decomp. prods.: incomplete combustion produces CO
Storage: Avoid prolonged heated storage.

Pelemol® MM. [Phoenix]
Chem. Descrip.: Myristyl myristate
CAS 3234-85-3; EINECS 221-787-9
Uses: Emollient used in pharmaceutical topicals
Properties: Wh. waxy flake; insol. in water; m.p. ≈ 40 C; b.p. > 150 C; acid no. 1 max.; iodine no. 2 max.; sapon. no. 120-130; flash pt. (PMCC) > 150 C; pH ≈ 6 (10%)
Toxicology: Skin exposure can cause irritation; ingestion may cause abdominal upset; eye contact may cause irritation
Precaution: Incompat. with strong oxidizers and reducing agents; hazardous decomp. prods.: incomplete combustion produces CO
Storage: Avoid prolonged heated storage.

Pelemol® MS. [Phoenix]
Chem. Descrip.: Myristyl stearate
CAS 17661-50-6; EINECS 241-640-2
Uses: Emollient, visc. builder for pharmaceutical topicals
Properties: Wh. to off-wh. cryst. waxy flake, mild fatty odor; insol. in water; sp.gr. 0.897 (55 C); m.p. ≈ 50 C; acid no. 5 max.; iodine no. 1 max.; sapon. no. 109-120; flash pt. (PMCC) > 200 C
Toxicology: May cause skin or eye irritation; ingestion may cause gastric upset
Precaution: Incompat. with strong oxidizing agents; hazardous decomp. prods.: may form CO
Storage: Store in cool, dry place.

Pelemol® ODM. [Phoenix]
Chem. Descrip.: Octyldodecyl myristate
CAS 22766-83-2
Uses: Emollient used in pharmaceutical topicals

Properties: Water-wh. to pale yel. liq., odorless; sol. in 3A alcohol, IPA, min. oil, veg. oil, benzaldehyde; insol. in water, propylene glycol, glycerine; sp.gr. < 1; vapor pressure < 1 mm Hg; b.p. dec.; acid no. 1 max.; sapon. no. 90-110; flash pt. (COC) 345 F; ref. index 1.455

Precaution: Incompat. with strong oxidizing agents; hazardous decomp. prods.: oxides of carbon

Storage: Store in cool, dry location away from strong oxidizing agents; avoid excessive heat.

Pelemol® OL. [Phoenix]
Chem. Descrip.: Oleyl lactate
CAS 42175-36-0
Uses: Softener, moisturizer for pharmaceutical topicals
Properties: Lt. amber visc. liq., mild fatty odor; sol. in alcohol, hydro/alcoholic sol'ns.; insol. in water; sp.gr. 0.90; vapor pressure negligible; b.p. > 207 C; acid no. 10 max.; flash pt. (COC) 157 C; 100% act.
Toxicology: Nonirritating to skin; pract. nonirritating to eyes; nontoxic orally; noncomedogenic
Precaution: Incompat. with strong oxidizing agents; avoid open flame, ignition sources; hazardous decomp. prods.: oxides of carbon
Storage: Store in cool, dry location; avoid excessive heat.

Pelemol® OP. [Phoenix]
Chem. Descrip.: Octyl palmitate
CAS 29806-73-3; EINECS 249-862-1
Uses: Emollient used in pharmaceutical topicals
Properties: Water-wh. clear liq., odorless; insol. in water; sp.gr. 0.854; f.p. 0 C; b.p. 150 C; acid no. 3 max.; sapon. no. 140-165; flash pt. (COC) > 395 F; 0.5% max. moisture
Toxicology: Skin exposure can cause irritation; ingestion may cause nausea, vomiting, abdominal pain
Precaution: Incompat. with strong oxidizing agents; hazardous decomp. prods.: combustion produces oxides of carbon
Storage: Store in cool, dry location away from strong oxidizing agents; avoid excessive heat.

Pelemol® PDD. [Phoenix]
Chem. Descrip.: Propylene glycol dicaprylate/dicaprate
Uses: Used in pharmaceutical topicals
Properties: APHA 50 max. color; dens. 7.5 lb/gal; b.p. > 300 F; iodine no. 1 max.; sapon. no. 315-335; hyd. no. 10 max.; flash pt. (PMCC) > 200 F; 0.1% max. moisture
Toxicology: Mist irritates nasal passages; nonprimary eye irritant, but contact may cause mild transient irritation; nonprimary skin irritant, but prolonged contact may cause mild, transient irritation
Precaution: Incompat. with strong alkali or caustic, strong oxidizing agents; avoid handling/storage near open flame; spillages may be slippery.

Pelemol® PTL. [Phoenix]
Chem. Descrip.: Pentaerythrityl tetralaurate

CAS 13057-50-6; EINECS 235-946-5
Uses: Hydrophobic oligomeric ester, emollient for pharmaceutical topicals, sunscreens
Properties: Yel. opalescent soft waxy paste, char. odor; oil-sol.; insol. in water; sp.gr. 0.85; m.p. 30 C; b.p. > 150 C; acid no. 6 max.; sapon. no. 190-210; flash pt. (PMCC) > 150 C; pH ≈ 6 (10%); 100% act.
Toxicology: Nonirritating to eyes; nonprimary skin irritant; nontoxic orally; noncomedogenic; skin exposure may cause irritation; ingestion may cause abdominal upset; eye contact may cause irritation
Precaution: Incompat. with strong oxidizers and reducing agents; hazardous decomp. prods.: incomplete combustion produces CO
Storage: Avoid prolonged heated storage.

Pelemol® TGC. [Phoenix]
Chem. Descrip.: Trioctyldodecyl citrate
CAS 126121-35-5
Uses: Emollient used in pharmaceutical topicals; wetting agent for pigments
Properties: Clear to sl. yel. sl. visc. oily liq., low odor; oil-sol.; insol. in water; sp.gr. 1.01 g/ml; acid no. 5 max.; sapon. no. 135-165; flash pt. (TCC) > 200 F
Toxicology: Nonirritating to skin and eyes; nontoxic orally; skin exposure can cause irritation; ingestion may cause nausea, vomiting, abdominal pain; inhalation in high concs. may cause coughing, headache, nausea
Precaution: Incompat. with strong oxidizers and reducers; hazardous decomp. prods.: (CO) x
Storage: Protect from freezing and boiling.

Pemulen® TR-1. [BFGoodrich]
Chem. Descrip.: Acrylates/C10-30 alkyl acrylate crosspolymer
Uses: O/w emulsifier for virtually all hydrophobic substances; for low-irritancy pharmaceutical creams, lotions, high-clarity topical gels, waterproof sunscreens, low or no alcohol fragrance prods.
Regulatory: USP/NF carbomer 1342 compliance; JSCI compliance
Properties: Wh. fluffy powd., sl. acetic odor; 2-6 μ particle size; sp.gr. 1.41; bulk dens. 176 kg/m^3; visc. 6500-15,500 cps; acid no. 700-750; pH 2.5-3.0 (1% aq. disp.); 100% conc.; anionic
Toxicology: Sl. skin irritant; borderline eye irritant
Storage: 2 yr min. shelf life stored in sealed containers, protected from moisture and extreme temps.; hygroscopic.

Pemulen® TR-2. [BFGoodrich]
Chem. Descrip.: Acrylates/C10-30 alkyl acrylate crosspolymer
Uses: O/w emulsifier for virtually all hydrophobic substances; for low-irritancy pharmaceutical creams, lotions, high-clarity topical gels, waterproof sunscreens, low or no alcohol fragrance prods.
Regulatory: USP/NF carbomer 1342 compliance; JSCI compliance

Properties: Wh. fluffy powd., sl. acetic odor; 2-6 µ particle size; sp.gr. 1.41; bulk dens. 176 kg/m³; visc. 1700-4500 cps; acid no. 700-750; pH 2.5-3.0 (1% aq. disp.); 100% conc.; anionic
Toxicology: Sl. skin irritant; borderline eye irritant
Storage: 2 yr min. shelf life stored in sealed containers, protected from moisture and extreme temps.; hygroscopic.

Penreco Amber. [Penreco]
Chem. Descrip.: Petrolatum USP
CAS 8009-03-8; EINECS 232-373-2
Uses: Emollient, base, lubricant, binder, protective coating, and carrier for pharmaceuticals
Regulatory: FDA 21CFR 172.880, 178.3700, 573.720
Properties: Yel. semisolid, odorless; sol. in hydrocarbons; sp.gr. 0.86 (60 F); visc. 68-82 SUS (210 F); m.p. 122-135 F; congeal pt. 123; solid. pt. 122 F; flash pt. (COC) 400 F
Toxicology: Pract. nontoxic by ingestion, but laxative props. may cause abdominal cramps, diarrhea; minimally irritating to eyes and skin on direct contact; STEL 10 mg/m³ (as oil mist)
Precaution: Combustion may produce dense smoke, CO, CO_2, other oxides; may react with strong oxidizing agents
Storage: Store in closed containers away from heat, sparks, open flame, oxidizers.

Penreco Blond. [Penreco]
Chem. Descrip.: Petrolatum USP
CAS 8009-03-8; EINECS 232-373-2
Uses: Emollient, base, lubricant, binder, protective coating, and carrier for pharmaceuticals
Regulatory: FDA 21CFR 172.880, 178.3700, 573.720
Properties: Yel. semisolid, odorless; sol. in hydrocarbons; sp.gr. 0.86 (60 F); visc. 68-82 SUS (210 F); m.p. 122-135 F; congeal pt. 123; solid. pt. 122 F; flash pt. (COC) 400 F
Toxicology: Pract. nontoxic by ingestion, but laxative props. may cause abdominal cramps, diarrhea; minimally irritating to eyes and skin on direct contact; STEL 10 mg/m³ (as oil mist)
Precaution: Combustion may produce dense smoke, CO, CO_2, other oxides; may react with strong oxidizing agents
Storage: Store in closed containers away from heat, sparks, open flame, oxidizers.

Penreco Cream. [Penreco]
Chem. Descrip.: Wh. petrolatum USP
CAS 8009-03-8; EINECS 232-373-2
Uses: Emollient, base, lubricant, binder, protective coating, and carrier for pharmaceuticals
Regulatory: FDA 21CFR 172.880, 178.3700, 573.720
Properties: Cream visc. semisolid, odorless; sol. in hydrocarbons; insol. in water; sp.gr. 0.87 (60/60 F); visc. 64-75 SUS (210 F); m.p. 122-125 F; b.p. 650 F; congeal pt. 125 F; solid. pt. 122 F; flash pt. (COC) 445 F
Toxicology: Pract. nontoxic by ingestion, but laxative props. may cause abdominal cramps, diar-

rhea; minimally irritating to eyes and skin on direct contact; STEL 10 mg/m³ (as oil mist)
Precaution: Combustion may produce dense smoke, CO, CO_2, other oxides; may react with strong oxidizing agents
Storage: Store in closed containers away from heat, sparks, open flame, oxidizers.

Penreco Lily. [Penreco]
Chem. Descrip.: Wh. petrolatum USP
CAS 8009-03-8; EINECS 232-373-2
Uses: Emollient, base, lubricant, binder, protective coating, and carrier for pharmaceuticals
Regulatory: FDA 21CFR 172.880, 178.3700, 573.720
Properties: Wh. visc. material, odorless; sol. in hydrocarbons; sp.gr. 0.86 (60/60 F); visc. 64-75 SUS (210 F); m.p. 122-135 F; b.p. 650 F; congeal pt. 124 F; solid. pt. 123 F; flash pt. (COC) 400 F
Toxicology: Pract. nontoxic by ingestion, but laxative props. may cause abdominal cramps, diarrhea; minimally irritating to eyes and skin on direct contact; STEL 10 mg/m³ (as oil mist)
Precaution: Combustion may produce dense smoke, CO, CO_2, other oxides; may react with strong oxidizing agents
Storage: Store in closed containers away from heat, sparks, open flame, oxidizers.

Penreco Regent. [Penreco]
Chem. Descrip.: Wh. petrolatum USP
CAS 8009-03-8; EINECS 232-373-2
Uses: Emollient, base, and carrier for pharmaceuticals (ophthalmic ointments, topical ointments, dental adhesives)
Regulatory: FDA 21CFR 172.880, 178.3700, 573.720
Properties: Wh. semisolid, odorless; sol. in hydrocarbons; sp.gr. 0.86 (60/60 F); visc. 57-70 SUS (210 F); m.p. 125-130 F; b.p. 650 F; congeal pt. 120 F; solid. pt. 119 F; flash pt. (COC) 400 F
Toxicology: Pract. nontoxic by ingestion, but laxative props. may cause abdominal cramps, diarrhea; minimally irritating to eyes and skin on direct contact; STEL 10 mg/m³ (as oil mist)
Precaution: Combustion may produce dense smoke, CO, CO_2, other oxides; may react with strong oxidizing agents
Storage: Store in closed containers away from heat, sparks, open flame, oxidizers.

Penreco Royal. [Penreco]
Chem. Descrip.: Petrolatum USP
CAS 8009-03-8; EINECS 232-373-2
Uses: Emollient, base, lubricant, binder, protective coating, and carrier for pharmaceuticals
Regulatory: FDA 21CFR 172.880, 178.3700, 573.720
Properties: Yel. semisolid, odorless; sol. in hydrocarbons; sp.gr. 0.86 (60 F); visc. 57-70 SUS (210 F); m.p. 118-130 F; congeal pt. 118 F; solid. pt. 115 F; flash pt. (COC) 400 F
Toxicology: Pract. nontoxic by ingestion, but laxative props. may cause abdominal cramps, diarrhea; minimally irritating to eyes and skin on direct

contact; STEL 10 mg/m^3 (as oil mist)

Precaution: Combustion may produce dense smoke, CO, CO_2, other oxides; may react with strong oxidizing agents

Storage: Store in closed containers away from heat, sparks, open flame, oxidizers.

Penreco Snow. [Penreco]
Chem. Descrip.: Wh. petrolatum USP
CAS 8009-03-8; EINECS 232-373-2
Uses: Emollient, base, solv., and carrier for pharmaceuticals (ophthalmic ointments, topical ointments, dental adhesives, petrolatum gauzes)
Regulatory: FDA 21CFR 172.880, 178.3700, 573.720
Properties: Wh. opaque semisolid, odorless; sol. in hydrocarbons; sp.gr. 0.86 (60/60 F); visc. 64-75 SUS (210 F); vapor pressure < 1 mm Hg (70 F); m.p. 122-135 F; b.p. 650 F; congeal pt. 123 F; solid. pt. 121 F; flash pt. (COC) 400 F
Toxicology: Pract. nontoxic by ingestion, but laxative props. may cause abdominal cramps, diarrhea; minimally irritating to eyes and skin on direct contact; STEL 10 mg/m^3 (as oil mist)
Precaution: Combustion may produce dense smoke, CO, CO_2, other oxides; may react with strong oxidizing agents
Storage: Store in closed containers away from heat, sparks, open flame, oxidizers.

Penreco Super. [Penreco]
Chem. Descrip.: Wh. petrolatum USP
CAS 8009-03-8; EINECS 232-373-2
Uses: Emollient, base, lubricant, binder, protective coating, and carrier for pharmaceuticals
Regulatory: FDA 21CFR 172.880, 178.3700, 573.720
Properties: Wh. opaque semisolid, odorless; sol. in hydrocarbons; sp.gr. 0.86 (60/60 F); visc. 60-75 SUS (210 F); m.p. 122-135 F; b.p. 650 F; congeal pt. 125 F; solid. pt. 124 F; flash pt. (COC) 400 F
Toxicology: Pract. nontoxic by ingestion, but laxative props. may cause abdominal cramps, diarrhea; minimally irritating to eyes and skin on direct contact; STEL 10 mg/m^3 (as oil mist)
Precaution: Combustion may produce dense smoke, CO, CO_2, other oxides; may react with strong oxidizing agents
Storage: Store in closed containers away from heat, sparks, open flame, oxidizers.

Penreco Ultima. [Penreco]
Chem. Descrip.: Wh. petrolatum USP
CAS 8009-03-8; EINECS 232-373-2
Uses: Emollient, base, and carrier for pharmaceuticals (ophthalmic ointments, topical ointments, dental adhesives, petrolatum gauzes)
Regulatory: FDA 21CFR 172.880, 178.3700, 573.720
Properties: Wh. opaque semisolid, odorless; sol. in hydrocarbons; sp.gr. 0.86 (60/60 F); visc. 60-70 SUS (210 F); m.p. 130-140 F; b.p. 650 F; congeal pt. 130 F; solid. pt. 128 F; flash pt. (COC) 400 F
Toxicology: Pract. nontoxic by ingestion, but laxative props. may cause abdominal cramps, diar-

rhea; minimally irritating to eyes and skin on direct contact; STEL 10 mg/m^3 (as oil mist)
Precaution: Combustion may produce dense smoke, CO, CO_2, other oxides; may react with strong oxidizing agents
Storage: Store in closed containers away from heat, sparks, open flame, oxidizers.

Pentonium 4Br40. [Pentagon Chems. Ltd]
Chem. Descrip.: Myrtrimonium bromide BP
CAS 1119-97-7; EINECS 214-291-9
Uses: Disinfectant, detergent sanitizer, antiseptic creams, purification of heparin
Regulatory: BP compliance
Properties: Colorless to pale yel. clear visc. liq.; 39-41% act.

Pentonium 24 BP. [Pentagon Chems. Ltd]
Chem. Descrip.: Alkyl (C12,C14) dimethyl benzyl ammonium chloride
Uses: Disinfectants, detergent sanitizers
Properties: PH 5.5-6.5 (2% aq.); 49-51% act.

Pepsin 1:3000 NF XII Powd. [Am. Labs]
Chem. Descrip.: Pepsin
CAS 9001-75-6; EINECS 232-629-3
Uses: Proteolytic enzyme for pharmaceutical applics.; digests coagulated egg albumen
Properties: Weak yel. to lt. brn. powd., nonoffensive char. odor, salty taste; freely sol. in water; pract. insol. in alcohol, chloroform, ether; pH 3-4 (2%)
Storage: Preserve in tight containers with moisture-proof liners, in cool, dry place.

Pepsin 1:10,000 Powd. or Gran. [Am. Labs]
Chem. Descrip.: Pepsin
CAS 9001-75-6; EINECS 232-629-3
Uses: Proteolytic enzyme for pharmaceutical applics.; digests coagulated egg albumen
Properties: Weak yel. to lt. brn. gran. or powd., nonoffensive char. odor, salty taste; freely sol. in water; pract. insol. in alcohol, chloroform, ether; pH 3-4 (2%)
Storage: Preserve in tight containers with moisture-proof liners, in cool, dry place.

Pepsin 1:15,000 Powd. [Am. Labs]
Chem. Descrip.: Pepsin
CAS 9001-75-6; EINECS 232-629-3
Uses: Proteolytic enzyme for pharmaceutical applics.; digests coagulated egg albumen
Properties: Weak yel. to lt. brn. powd., nonoffensive char. odor, salty taste; freely sol. in water; pract. insol. in alcohol, chloroform, ether; pH 3-4 (2%)
Storage: Preserve in tight containers with moisture-proof liners, in cool, dry place.

PeptiCLEC™-TR. [Altus Biologics]
Chem. Descrip.: Cross-linked enzyme crystals of thermolysin
Uses: Regio- and stereoselective catalyst for the synthesis of optically pure drugs and peptides, esp. aspartame precursor
Properties: Powd.; insol. in water.

Perfecta® USP. [Witco/Petroleum Spec.]
Chem. Descrip.: Petrolatum USP

CAS 8027-32-5; EINECS 232-373-2
Uses: Pharmaceutical grade with lightest color, med. consistency, high m.p.; as carrier, lubricant, moisture barrier, protective agent, softener for dental adhesives, medicated ointments, suncare prods.
Regulatory: FDA 21CFR §172.880
Properties: Lovibond 0.3Y color; visc. 9-14 cSt (100 C); m.p. 57-60 C.

Petrac® Magnesium Stearate MG-20 NF. [Syn. Prods.]
Chem. Descrip.: Magnesium stearate NF
CAS 557-04-0; EINECS 209-150-3
Uses: Dry lubricant and anticaking agent used in filling of pharmaceutical capsules; antistick props. in tableting; improves stability, smoothness, texture of emulsions, creams, ointments; improves water-repellency in medical powds.
Regulatory: FDA accepted
Properties: Wh. fluffy powd., 95% thru 200 mesh; 85% thru 325 mesh; dens. 22 lb/ft^3; soften. pt. 140 C.

Pharma-Carb®. [Crompton & Knowles]
Chem. Descrip.: Natural calcium carbonate USP
EINECS 207-439-9
Uses: Carrier for pharmaceuticals
Properties: Powd.; 12.5 µ avg. particle size; ≥ 100% thru 200 mesh; bulk dens. 75 lb/ft^3 (loose), 98 lb/ft^3 (packed); 98% min. assay.

Pharmaceutical Lanolin. [Croda Inc.]
Chem. Descrip.: Lanolin USP
CAS 8006-54-0; EINECS 232-348-6
Uses: Superfatting emollient, emulsifier, moisturizer for oral and topical pharmaceuticals, ointments, dressing creams, diaper rash and hemorrhoidal preps., acne preps., steroidal prods., ophthalmics
Properties: Lt. amber soft solid; partly sol. in min. oil; m.p. 38-44 C.

Pharma-Gel™. [Crompton & Knowles]
Chem. Descrip.: Pregelatinized corn starch NF
CAS 9005-25-8; EINECS 232-679-6
Uses: Carrier, binder in pharmaceutical wet granulating; tablet disintegrant and capsule filler
Properties: Bulk dens. 20 lb/ft^3 (loose), 34 lb/ft^3 (tapped); pH 5.75 ± 1.25.

Pharmasolve™. [ISP]
Chem. Descrip.: N-Methyl-2-pyrrolidone, GMP grade
CAS 872-50-4; EINECS 212-828-1
Uses: Solv. for pharmaceuticals; extraction solv.; increases water sol. of therapeutic compds.; nonaq. chem. reaction medium; synthesis of vitamin E precursor; solubilizer for topicals; bioadhesive; spray bandages; for transdermals, injectables
Properties: Clear liq., amine-like odor; misc. with water, most org. solvs. incl. alcohols, ketones, aromatic and chlorinated hydrocarbons; sp.gr. 1.027 (25/4 C); visc. 1.65 cp; vapor pressure 0.29 mm Hg (20 C); m.p. -24.4 C; b.p. 202 C; flash pt.(OC) 95 C; ref. index 1.465-1.470; pH sl. alka-

line; 99.85% min. purity; biodeg.
Toxicology: Low toxicity; LD50 (oral, rat) 4200 mg/kg, (dermal, rabbit) 8000 mg/kg; causes eye irritation; not a primary skin irritant; nonsensitizing; prolonged or repeated exposure causes severe skin irritation
Precaution: Combustible; flamm. limits 1.3-9.5%; noncorrosive; incompat. with strong oxidizing or reducing agents; heated to decomp., emits CO and NO$_x$ fumes
Storage: Keep container and vapors away from heat, spraks, flame; keep container closed.

Pharmasorb Colloidal Pharmaceutical Grade. [Engelhard]
Chem. Descrip.: Attapulgite clay
CAS 1337-76-4
Uses: Adsorbent for pharmaceuticals featuring superior adsorptive properties with effective acid adsorp.
Properties: Powd., particle size 2.9 and 0.14 µ resp., 0.10 and 0.30% resp.; cream and lt. cream resp.; sp.gr. 2.47 and 2.36 resp.; pH 7.5-9.5 resp.

Pharmatone. [Am. Labs]
Chem. Descrip.: High proteose peptone from pork tissues
Uses: Pharmaceutical additive for tonics and elixirs; high source of protein; useful in bacteriological media
Properties: 60 mesh powd.; completely sol. in 2% sol'n.; pH 5.5-6.5; 93.75% protein, 15% N.

Phenoleum. [United-Guardian]
Chem. Descrip.: Amyl:phenylphenol complex
Uses: Bactericide and fungicide for health-care disinfection
Properties: Water-sol.
Custom product

Phenonip. [Nipa Hardwicke]
Chem. Descrip.: Phenoxyethanol (> 70%), methylparaben > (15%), ethylparaben (< 5%), propylparaben (< 5%), butylparaben (< 10%)
Uses: Fully active liq. preservative system with low toxicity and wide spectrum activity, esp. against pseudomonads; for pharmaceuticals (proteinaceous prods., emulsions, skin antiseptics, deodorants)
Regulatory: USA, Japan, and Europe approvals
Properties: Pract. colorless visc. liq., faint aromatic odor; sol. 0.5% in water; misc. with ethanol, IPA, acetone, propylene glycol, IPM, ethyl acetate; sp.gr. 1.124; m.p. 13 C; b.p. 224-250 C (1013 m.bar); flash pt. (OC) 130 C; ref. index 1.5415; pH 7 (20 g/l water); 100% conc.
Toxicology: LD50 (oral, rat) 1.5 g/kg (sl. harmful); pure material irritating to skin, moderately irritating to eyes.

Phenosept. [Nipa Hardwicke]
Chem. Descrip.: Phenoxyisopropanol and p-chloro-m-xylenol
Uses: Antiseptic for skin care prods.

Phenoxetol. [Nipa Hardwicke]
Chem. Descrip.: Phenoxyethanol
CAS 122-99-6; EINECS 204-589-7

Uses: Broad-spectrum antimicrobial preservative for pharmaceuticals, e.g., antiseptic creams
Properties: Colorless sl. visc. liq., faint or pleasant odor; sol. 2.3% in water; misc. with acetone, ethanol, benzene, ether, propylene glycol, glycerin; m.w. 138.2; sp.gr. 1.1 (20/4 C); f.p. 11 C; b.p. 245.6 C; flash pt. (OC) 121 C; 99% min. assay
Toxicology: LD50 (oral, rat) 1.3 g/kg (sl. harmful); moderate eye irritant; pure material sl. irritating to skin.

Philacid 1200. [United Coconut Chem.]
Chem. Descrip.: Lauric acid (C12)
CAS 143-07-7; EINECS 205-582-1
Uses: Intermediate for mfg. of pharmaceuticals
Properties: Solid, flakes; acid no. 279-282; iodine no. 0.3 max.; sapon. no. 279-282.

Phloroglucinol. [Shell]
Chem. Descrip.: 1,3,5-Trihydroxybenzene
EINECS 203-611-2
Uses: Intermediate for pharmaceuticals
Unverified

Phosal® 50 PG. [Am. Lecithin; Nattermann Phospholipid; Rhone-Poulenc Rorer]
Chem. Descrip.: A preliposome system contg. 50% phosphatidylcholine in a propylene glycol/ethanol carrier
Uses: Dispersant, coemulsifier, solubilizer for pharmaceuticals creams and lotions; phospholipid sol'n. for emulsions and liposome preps. for dermatology
Properties: Honey yel. fluid, typ. odor, nut-like taste; dilutable with water; dens. 1.0-1.1 g/cm³ (20 C); visc. 5000 mPa•s max.; iodine no. ≈ 50; pH 5.5-7.5; 50% min. phosphatidylcholine; biodeg.
Toxicology: Harmless; edible; oral and topical applicable
Storage: Store in clean, cool, dry place @ 10-40 C; avoid large changes in temp., gross contamination with bacteria; protect from light.

Phosal® 50 SA. [Am. Lecithin; Nattermann Phospholipid; Rhone-Poulenc Rorer]
Chem. Descrip.: Safflower oil and lecithin
Uses: Improves skin humidity and penetration for dermatology; solubilizer for lipophilic substances; phosphatidylcholine source for nutritional supplements, esp. as capsule filling mass
Use level: 5-15% topical applic.
Properties: Honey yel. fluid, typ. odor; dilutable with water; dens. 1.0-1.1 g/cm³ (20 C); visc. 5000 mPa•s max.; pH 5.5-7.5; 53 ± 3% phosphatidylcholine.; biodeg.
Toxicology: Harmless; edible; oral and topical applicable
Storage: Store in clean, cool, dry place @ 15-20 C in well-closed containers; warming reverses sedimentation; protect from light, gross contamination with bacteria; use soon after opening.

Phosal® 53 MCT. [Am. Lecithin; Nattermann Phospholipid; Rhone-Poulenc Rorer]
Chem. Descrip.: Lecithin, caprylic/capric triglyceride, and alcohol (5% max.)
Uses: Solubilizer for lipophilic substances; prod. of liposomes; phosphatidylcholine source, esp. as filling mass for soft gelatin capsules
Use level: 5-15% topical applic.
Properties: Honey yel. fluid, typ. odor; dilutable with water; sp.gr. 1.0 g/ml; visc. 5000 mPa•s max.; flash pt. 30 C; 56 ± 3% phosphatidylcholine; 5% ethanol
Toxicology: Avoid eye contact and ingestion; harmless by inh. and skin contact
Storage: Store in clean, dry place @ R.T. in closed containers; warming reverses sedimentation; use immediately after opening; protect from light.

Phosal® 60 PG. [Am. Lecithin; Nattermann Phospholipid; Rhone-Poulenc Rorer]
Chem. Descrip.: A preliposome system containing 60% lecithin in propylene glycol
Uses: Prod. of emulsions and liposome preps. for dermatology; emulsifier for dermatology
Use level: 2-5% topical applic.
Properties: Semiliq., nut-like odor; dilutable with water; dens. 1.0-1.1 g/cm³; pH 4-5; 60% act.; biodeg.
Toxicology: Harmless; edible; oral and topical applicable
Storage: Store in clean, dry place @ 10-30 C closed containers; protect from light, gross contamination with bacteria.

Phosal® 75 SA. [Am. Lecithin; Nattermann Phospholipid; Rhone-Poulenc Rorer]
Chem. Descrip.: Lecithin, ethanol, and safflower oil
Uses: Solubilizer for lipophilic substances; phosphatidylcholine source for nutritional supplements; prod. of liposomes; improves skin humidity and penetration in dermatology
Use level: 3-10% topical applic.
Properties: Honey yel. fluid, nut-like odor; dilutable with water; dens. 1.0 g/cm³; visc. 5500 mPa•s max.; pH 6.2; 75 ± 3% phosphatidylcholine, 9% ethanol; biodeg.
Toxicology: Harmless; edible; oral and topical applicable
Storage: Store in clean, dry place @ 15-25 C in closed containers; warming reverses sedimentation; use soon after opening; protect from light, gross contamination with bacteria.

Phosal® NAT-50-PG. [Am. Lecithin; Nattermann Phospholipid; Rhone-Poulenc Rorer]
Chem. Descrip.: Lecithin, propylene glycol (< 25%)
Uses: An alcohol-free phospholipid system for mfg. of liposomes, micelles; emollient, emulsifier, stabilizer for pharmaceuticals
Properties: Yel. liq., acetic acid smell possible; dilutable with water; dens. 1.0 g/cm³; acid no. ≈ 25; pH 5.5-7.5; > 15% phosphatidylcholine, ≈ 15% oil; biodeg.
Toxicology: Harmless; edible; oral and topical applicable
Storage: 1 yr stability in unopened original container stored @ 20-25 C; protect from light, gross contamination with bacteria.

PhosPho F-97. [Fanning]
Chem. Descrip.: Lecithin

CAS 8002-43-5; EINECS 232-307-2
Uses: Used for topical pharmaceutical ointments
Properties: Lt. golden gran.; sol. in IPM, ethyl acetate, water; insol. in castor oil, propylene glycol, ethanol, min. oil, glycerol; HLB 7.0; acid no. 35 max.

PhosPho LCN-TS. [Fanning]
Chem. Descrip.: Lecithin
CAS 8002-43-5; EINECS 232-307-2
Uses: Phospholipid used as surfactant/emulsifier and skin conditioning agent for pharmaceuticals
Properties: Opaque appearance; sol. in IPM, castor oil, propylene glycol, ethyl acetate, min. oil, glycerol; insol. in water, ethanol; dens. 8.48 lb/gal (60 F); visc. 75 poises; HLB 4.0; acid no. 24; pH 5-7 (10% aq.).

PhosPho T-20. [Fanning]
Chem. Descrip.: Phospholipids
CAS 8002-43-5
Uses: Hydrophilic ingred. in topical pharmaceutical ointments
Properties: Gardner 14 max. translucent; sol. in IPM, castor oil, propylene glycol, ethyl acetate, water, min. oil, glycerol; insol. in ethanol; visc. 200 poises; HLB 12-13; acid no. 36 max.; pH 4-6 (10% aq.).

Phospholipid PTD. [Mona Industries]
Chem. Descrip.: Lauramidopropyl PEG-dimonium chloride phosphate
CAS 83682-78-4
Uses: Bactericidal, conditioner, foamer, emulsifier, solubilizer, dispersant, thickener and wetting agent for pharmaceuticals
Properties: Amber clear liq.; sp.gr. 1.05; dens. 8.7 lb/gal; pH 7.5 (10%); surf. tens. 43.1 dynes/cm (1%); 34% act.; cationic.

Phospholipid PTL. [Mona Industries]
Chem. Descrip.: Laurampho PEG-glycinate phosphate
Uses: Bactericidal, conditioner, foamer, emulsifier, solubilizer, dispersant, thickener and wetting agent for pharmaceuticals
Properties: Clear to opaque visc. liq.; sp.gr. 1.10; dens. 9.1 lb/gal; pH 7.5 (10%); surf. tens. 33.7 dynes/cm (1%); 30% act.; cationic.

Phospholipid PTZ. [Mona Industries]
Chem. Descrip.: Cocohydroxyethyl PEG-imidazolinium chloride phosphate
Uses: Bactericidal, conditioner, foamer, emulsifier, solubilizer, dispersant, thickener and wetting agent for pharmaceuticals
Properties: Amber clear liq.; sp.gr. 1.07; dens. 8.9 lb/gal; pH 7.0 (10%); surf. tens. 37.6 dynes/cm (1%); 30% act.; cationic.

Phospholipon® 80. [Am. Lecithin; Nattermann Phospholipid; Rhone-Poulenc Rorer]
Chem. Descrip.: Lecithin (soya 3-sn-phosphatidylcholine)
CAS 8002-43-5; EINECS 232-307-2
Uses: Pharmaceutical grade; emulsifier for pharmacy, dermatology; encapsulation of active compds.; min. 73% phosphatidylcholine for the mfg. of liposomes and mixed micelles
Use level: 1-3% (topicals)
Properties: Yel.-brn. waxy solid plastic, typ. odor; forms emulsions in water; dens. 1.0 g/cm³ (20 C); bulk dens. 400-500 kg/m³; acid no. 10 max.; pH 7 ± 1; 80% conc.; biodeg.; ecologically harmless; forms slippery surfs. with water; do not discharge into drains, surf. waters, groundwater
Toxicology: Harmless; edible; oral and topical applicable
Storage: Hygroscopic; store in clean, cool, dry place @ 5-20 C in tightly closed containers; protect from light.

Phospholipon® 80 H. [Am. Lecithin; Nattermann Phospholipid; Rhone-Poulenc Rorer]
Chem. Descrip.: Hydrog. lecithin
Uses: Prep. of liposomes for pharmaceuticals; increases skin humidity
Use level: 1-5% topical applic.
Properties: Wh. cryst.; iodine no. ≤ 30 ≥ 60% phosphatidylcholine
Storage: Store @ R.T., dry condition, sealed under inert gas.

Phospholipon® 90. [Am. Lecithin; Nattermann Phospholipid; Rhone-Poulenc Rorer]
Chem. Descrip.: Oil extracted lecithin fraction, 90% min. soya 3-sn-phosphatidylcholine
CAS 97281-47-5; EINECS 232-307-2
Uses: Pharmaceutical grade for encapsulation of active compds.; raw material for mfg. of liposomes and mixed micelles; solubilizer for parenteralia; emulsifier for pharmacy, dermatology
Use level: 1-10% topical applic.
Properties: Yel. waxy solid, typ. odor; dilutable with water; dens. 1.0 g/cm³ (20 C); acid no. 0.5 max.; pH 7 ± 1; 95% conc.; biodeg.; ecologically harmless; forms slippery surfs. with water; do not discharge into drains, surf. waters, groundwater
Toxicology: Harmless; edible; oral and topical applicable
Storage: Hygroscopic; store in clean, dry place @ 5-20 C in tightly closed containers; protect from light.

Phospholipon® 90 G. [Am. Lecithin; Nattermann Phospholipid; Rhone-Poulenc Rorer]
Chem. Descrip.: Lecithin, 90% min. soya 3-sn-phosphatidylcholine
CAS 97281-47-5; EINECS 232-307-2
Uses: Pharmaceutical grade for encapsulation of active compds.; raw material for mfg. of liposomes and mixed micelles; solubilizer for parenteralia; emulsifier for pharmacy, dermatology
Use level: 1-10% topical applic.
Properties: Lt. yel. solid or gran., typ. odor; dilutable with water; dens. 1.0 g/cm³ (20 C); bulk dens. 400-500 kg/m³; acid no. 0.5 max.; pH 7 ± 1; 95% conc.; biodeg.; ecologically harmless; forms slippery surfs. with water; do not discharge into drains, surf. waters, groundwater
Toxicology: Harmless; edible; oral and topical

applicable

Storage: Hygroscopic; store in clean, dry place @ 5-20 C in tightly closed containers, sealed under inert gas; protect from light.

Phospholipon® 90 H. [Am. Lecithin; Nattermann Phospholipid; Rhone-Poulenc Rorer]
Chem. Descrip.: Hydrog. soy lecithin
CAS 97281-48-6
Uses: Pharmaceutical grade for encapsulation of active compds.; min. 90% phosphatidylcholine for the mfg. of liposomes for drugs
Use level: 1-3% topical use
Properties: Wh. cryst. powd., odorless; forms emulsions in water; dens. 0.8 g/cm^3; bulk dens. 400-500 kg/m^3; acid no. 0.5 max.; iodine no. 1 max.; flash pt. > 220 C; pH 7 ± 1; 94% conc.; biodeg.; ecologically harmless; forms slippery surfs. with water; do not discharge into drains, surf. waters, groundwater
Toxicology: Harmless; edible; oral and topical applicable
Storage: Hygroscopic; store in clean, cool, dry place @ 5-20 C in tightly closed containers, sealed under inert gas; protect from light.

Phospholipon® 100, 100G. [Am. Lecithin; Nattermann Phospholipid; Rhone-Poulenc Rorer]
Chem. Descrip.: Lecithin (soya 3-sn-phosphatidylcholine)
CAS 97281-47-5; EINECS 232-307-2
Uses: Natural active ingred. for pharmaceuticals; raw material for mfg. of liposomes and mixed micelles; solubilizer for parenteralia; emulsifier for pharmacy, dermatology or transdermal delivery systems
Use level: 1-10% for topical applic.
Properties: Yel. solid or gran., typ. odor; dilutable in water; dens. 1.0 g/cm^3; acid no. 0.5 max.; pH 7 ± 1 ≥ 95% phosphatidylcholine; biodeg.
Toxicology: Harmless; edible, oral and topical applicable
Storage: Store @ 5-25 C, dry conditions, sealed under inert gas; protect from light.

Phospholipon® 100 H. [Am. Lecithin; Nattermann Phospholipid; Rhone-Poulenc Rorer]
Chem. Descrip.: Hydrog. lecithin (soya 3-sn-phosphatidylcholine)
CAS 97281-48-6; EINECS 306-549-5
Uses: Natural active ingred. for pharmaceuticals; prod. of liposomes
Properties: Cryst. powd., odorless; forms emulsions in water; dens. 0.8 g/cm^3; pH 7 ± 1; biodeg.; ecologically harmless; forms slippery surfs. with water; do not discharge into drains, surf. waters, groundwater
Toxicology: Harmless; edible; oral and topical applicable
Storage: Hygroscopic; store in clean, cool, dry place @ 5-20 C; protect from light.

Phospholipon® CC. [Am. Lecithin; Nattermann Phospholipid; Rhone-Poulenc Rorer]
Chem. Descrip.: 1,2-Dicaproyl-sn-glycero(3) phosphatidylcholine

CAS 3436-44-0
Uses: Emulsifier, solubilizer for dermatology; mfg. of liposomes and mixed micelles
Properties: Wh. cryst., typ. odor; dilutable with water; dens. 1.0 g/cm^3; pH 7 ± 1 (10 g/l water) ≥ 99% act.; biodeg.
Toxicology: Harmless; edible; oral and topical applicable
Storage: Store in clean, cool, dry place @ R.T.; protect from light.

Phospholipon® G. [Am. Lecithin; Nattermann Phospholipid; Rhone-Poulenc Rorer]
Chem. Descrip.: Soya 3-(3-sn-phosphatidyl) glycerol
Uses: Natural raw material for pharmaceuticals; mfg. of liposomes and mixed micelles
Properties: Cryst.

Phospholipon® GH. [Rhone-Poulenc Rorer; Am. Lecithin]
Chem. Descrip.: Hydrog. soya 3-(3-sn-phosphatidyl) glycerol
Uses: Natural raw material for pharmaceuticals
Properties: Cryst.

Phospholipon® LC. [Am. Lecithin; Nattermann Phospholipid; Rhone-Poulenc Rorer]
Chem. Descrip.: 1,2-Dilauroyl-sn-glycero(3) phosphocholine
CAS 18285-71-7
Uses: For mfg. of liposomes and mixed micelles
Properties: Powd.

Phospholipon® MC. [Am. Lecithin; Nattermann Phospholipid; Rhone-Poulenc Rorer]
Chem. Descrip.: 1,2-Dimyristoyl-sn-glycero(3) phosphatidylcholine
CAS 18194-24-6
Uses: Emulsifier, solubilizer for dermatology; mfg. of liposomes and mixed micelles
Properties: Wh. cryst., typ. odor; dilutable with water; dens. 1.0 g/cm^3 (20 C); pH 7 ± 1 ≥ 99% act.; biodeg.
Toxicology: Harmless; edible; oral and topical applicable
Storage: Store in clean, cool, dry place @ 5-20 C; protect from light.

Phospholipon® MG Na. [Am. Lecithin; Nattermann Phospholipid; Rhone-Poulenc Rorer]
Chem. Descrip.: 1,2-Dimyristoyl-sn-glycero(3) phosphatidylcholine sodium salt
CAS 116870-30-5
Uses: For mfg. of liposomes and mixed micelles
Properties: Wh. cryst., typ. odor; dilutable with water; dens. 1.0 g/cm^3 (20 C); pH 7 ± 1 ≥ 97% act.; biodeg.
Toxicology: Harmless; edible; oral and topical applicable
Storage: Store in clean, cool, dry place @ 5-20 C; protect from light.

Phospholipon® PC. [Am. Lecithin; Nattermann Phospholipid; Rhone-Poulenc Rorer]
Chem. Descrip.: 1,2-Dipalmitoyl-sn-glycero(3) phosphatidylcholine
CAS 2644-64-6

Uses: For mfg. of liposomes and mixed micelles
Properties: Wh. cryst., typ. odor; dilutable with water; dens. 1.0 g/cm³ (20 C); pH 7 ± 1 ≥ 99% act.; biodeg.
Toxicology: Harmless; edible; oral and topical applicable
Storage: Store in clean, cool, dry place @ 5-20 C; protect from light.

Phospholipon® PG Na. [Am. Lecithin; Nattermann Phospholipid; Rhone-Poulenc Rorer]
Chem. Descrip.: 1,2-Dipalmitoyl-sn-glycero(3) phosphatidylcholine sodium salt
CAS 116870-31-6
Uses: Emulsifier, solubilizer for dermatology; mfg. of liposomes and mixed micelles
Properties: Wh. cryst., typ. odor; dilutable with water; dens. 1.0 g/cm³ (20 C); pH 7 ± 1 ≥ 97% act.; biodeg.
Toxicology: Harmless; edible; oral and topical applicable
Storage: Store in clean, cool, dry place @ R.T.; protect from light.

Phospholipon® SC. [Am. Lecithin; Nattermann Phospholipid; Rhone-Poulenc Rorer]
Chem. Descrip.: 1,2-Distearoyl-sn-glycero(3) phosphatidylcholine
CAS 816-94-4
Uses: For mfg. of liposomes and mixed micelles
Properties: Wh. cryst., typ. odor; dilutable with water; dens. 1.0 g/cm³; pH 7 ± 1 (10 g/l water) ≥ 99% act.; biodeg.
Toxicology: Harmless; edible; oral and topical applicable
Storage: Store in clean, cool, dry place @ R.T.; protect from light.

Phospholipon® SG Na. [Am. Lecithin; Nattermann Phospholipid; Rhone-Poulenc Rorer]
Chem. Descrip.: 1,2-Distearoyl-sn-glycero(3) phosphatidylcholine sodium salt
Uses: Emulsifier, solubilizer for dermatology; mfg. of liposomes and mixed micelles
Properties: Wh. cryst., typ. odor; dilutable with water; dens. 1.0 g/cm³ (20 C); pH 7 ± 1 ≥ 97% act.; biodeg.
Toxicology: Harmless; edible; oral and topical applicable
Storage: Store in clean, cool, dry place @ R.T.; protect from light.

pHthalavin™. [Colorcon]
Chem. Descrip.: Polyvinyl acetate phthalate enteric polymer
Uses: Functional coating for targeted enteric drug release; good resist. to gastric fluid.

Phytonadione USP No. 61749. [Roche]
Chem. Descrip.: Vitamin K₁ USP
Uses: Component of enzyme systems associated with blood-clotting mechanism
Properties: Yel. to amber clear very visc. liq., odorless to sl. odor; sol. in dehydrated alcohol, benzene, chloroform, ether, veg. oils; sl. sol. in alcohol; insol. in water; m.w. 450.68; ref. index 1.5230-1.5260; 1% min. assay (phytonadione)

Precaution: Destroyed by sol'ns. of alkali hydroxides and by reducing agents; dec. on exposure to sunlight
Storage: Store in cool, dry place in tightly closed containers protected from light.

alpha-Pinene P&F, FCC. [SCM Glidco Organics]
Chem. Descrip.: α-Pinene with 500 ppm Tenox GT-1 (food-grade antioxidant)
CAS 7785-26-4; EINECS 232-077-3
Uses: Useful in flavor and fragrance applics. across a broad spectrum of prods.
Regulatory: FDA 21CFR §172.515
Properties: Colorless liq., warm resinous pine-like aroma, balsamic taste; sol. 1 in 15 in 80% alcohol; m.w. 136.24; sp.gr. 0.851-0.855; dens. 7.14 lb/gal; b.p. 156.7 C; flash pt. (TCC) 29.4 C; ref. index 1.464-1.468 (20 C); 99% min. act.
Toxicology: LD50 (oral, rat) > 5000 mg/kg, (dermal, rabbit) > 5000 mg/kg; mod. skin irritant; oxidized material produces some sensitization reactions.

beta-Pinene P&F. [SCM Glidco Organics]
Chem. Descrip.: β-Pinene with 500 ppm Tenox GT-1 (food-grade antioxidant)
CAS 18172-67-3; EINECS 242-060-2
Uses: Useful in flavor and fragrance applics. across a broad spectrum of prods.
Regulatory: FDA 21CFR §172.515
Properties: Clear appearance, dry woody or piney resinous odor; sol. 1 in 14 in 80% alcohol; m.w. 136.24; sp.gr. 0.864-0.872; dens. 7.24 lb/gal; b.p. 165 C; flash pt. (TCC) 35 C; ref. index 1.477-1.481 (20 C); 97% min. act.
Toxicology: LD50 (oral, rat) 4700 mg/kg, (dermal, rabbit) > 5000 mg/kg; mod. skin irritant; contact may cause skin and eye irritation.

Pionier® BS-WO II. [Hansen & Rosenthal]
Chem. Descrip.: Liq. paraffin, polyglycerin esters, waxes, stabilizers
Uses: Hydrophilic base for w/o ointments and creams
Properties: Ylsh. paste-like to liq.; drop pt. 63 C; acid no. 19.5; sapon. no. 64; hyd. no. 30.

Pionier® KWH-soft. [Hansen & Rosenthal]
Chem. Descrip.: Liq. paraffins, polyglycerin fatty acid ester, stabilizers, isopropyl palmitate
Uses: Hydrophilic base for cold processing of w/o ointments and creams
Properties: Opal gel-like; drop pt. 89 C; congeal pt. 74 C; acid no. 0.2; sapon. no. 30; hyd. no. 10; pH 7.0.

Pionier® MAA. [Hansen & Rosenthal]
Chem. Descrip.: Vaselinum album, cetyl-stearyl alcohol, wool wax alcohol
Uses: Hydrophilic base for w/o ointments and creams
Regulatory: Complies with DAP 9 wool wax alcohol ointment
Properties: Whitish vaseline-like; drop pt. 55 C; congeal pt. 53 C; acid no. 0.07; sapon. no. < 0.1; hyd. no. 12.

Pionier® NP 37. [Hansen & Rosenthal]
Chem. Descrip.: Acrylamide/sodium acrylate co-

polymer
CAS 25085-02-3
Uses: Neutralized hydrophilic thickener for cold processing of aq. pharmaceutical preps.; improves stability; for suncare preps., dentifrices, ointments
Properties: Wh. powd., pract. odorless; sol. in water, aq. alcoholic sol'ns.; dens. 0.23 g/cm^3; visc. 12,000-16,000 mPa•s (0.2% aq., 20 C)
Precaution: Incompat. with electrolytes (causes turbidity)
Storage: Sl. hygroscopic; store dry and hermetically sealed if possible.

Pionier® OEWA-II. [Hansen & Rosenthal]
Chem. Descrip.: Liq. paraffin, POE glyceryl stearate, wax, stearyl alcohol, glyceryl stearate, isopropyl palmitate
Uses: Hydrophilic base for o/w ointments and creams
Properties: Whitish paste-like to firm consistency; drop pt. 46 C; congeal pt. 41.5 C; acid no. 0.2; sapon. no. 83.1; hyd. no. ≈ 48.

Pionier® PLW. [Hansen & Rosenthal]
Chem. Descrip.: Polyethylene-white oil (paraffinum liquidum DAB9) gel
Uses: Hydrophobic base gel for cold processing of w/o emulsions (OTC medical preps., wound treatments, rheumatism/mucosa preps., medium for analgesics); better compat. than petrolatum; provides rapid liberation of active substances
Properties: Transparent.

Pionier® WWH-N. [Hansen & Rosenthal]
Chem. Descrip.: Liq. paraffins, waxes, isopropyl palmitate, polyglycerin fatty acid esters, stabilizers
Uses: Hydrophilic base for w/o ointments and creams
Properties: Ylsh. paste-like to liq.; drop pt. 92 C; congeal pt. 77 C; acid no. 0.4; sapon. no. 29; hyd. no. 34.7; pH 7.0.

Pionier® WWH-soft. [Hansen & Rosenthal]
Chem. Descrip.: Liq. paraffins, waxes, isopropyl palmitate, polyglycerin fatty acid esters, stabilizers
Uses: Hydrophilic base for w/o ointments and creams
Properties: Ylsh. paste-like to liq.; drop pt. 90.5 C; congeal pt. 75 C; acid no. 0.4; sapon. no. 29; hyd. no. 34.7; pH 7.0.

Plasdone® C-15. [ISP]
Chem. Descrip.: PVP (pyrogen-free Povidone USP K-17)
CAS 9003-39-8; EINECS 201-800-4
Uses: Solubilizer, stabilizer, protective colloid, suspending agent, dispersant, binder, filmformer; parenteral applics., antibiotics, antiseptics, steroid hormones, vitamins; bioadhesive; blood plasma expander; detoxicant; reduces irritation at inj. site
Regulatory: FDA 21CFR §173.55; USP, FCC, BP, German Ph., French Ph., Italian Ph. compliance
Properties: Wh. to creamy wh. powd, odorless,

tasteless; 50 μ mean particle size; hygroscopic; sol. in aq. and org. solv. systems; bulk dens. 0.1-0.25 g/cc; pH 3-7 (5% aq.); 5% max. moisture
Toxicology: Very low chronic oral toxicity
Storage: Prevent excessive moisture pickup.

Plasdone® C-30. [ISP]
Chem. Descrip.: PVP (Povidone USP)
CAS 9003-39-8; EINECS 201-800-4
Uses: Solubilizer, stabilizer, protective colloid, suspending agent, dispersant, binder, filmformer; parenteral applics., antibiotics, antiseptics, steroid hormones, vitamins; bioadhesive; blood plasma expander; detoxicant; reduces irritation at inj. site
Regulatory: FDA 21CFR §173.55; USP, FCC, BP, German Ph., French Ph., Italian Ph. compliance
Properties: Wh. to creamy wh. powd, odorless, tasteless; 30 μ mean particle size; hygroscopic; sol. in water, aq. and org. solv. systems; bulk dens. 0.25-0.4 g/cc; flash pt. none; pH 3-7 (5% aq.); 5% max. moisture
Toxicology: LD50 (oral, rat) > 100,000 mg/kg (very low toxicity); not absorbed topically; not a primary skin irritant; nonirritating to eyes; nonsensitizing; prolonged contact may cause dermatitis; nuisance dust: TLV/TWA 10 mg/m^3 total, 5 mg/m^3 respirable
Precaution: Incompat. with strong oxidizing or reducing agents; heated to decomp., emits toxic fumes of NO$_x$
Storage: Prevent excessive moisture pickup.

Plasdone® K-25. [ISP]
Chem. Descrip.: PVP (Povidone USP)
CAS 9003-39-8; EINECS 201-800-4
Uses: Gellant, tablet binder, coating agent; promotes pigment disp.; cohesive agent, stabilizer, protective colloid; detoxicant; drug vehicle/retardant; solubilizer, suspending agent in liqs.; filmformer in medicinal aerosols; for topicals, ophthalmics
Regulatory: FDA 21CFR §173.55; USP, FCC, BP, German Ph., French Ph., Italian Ph. compliance
Properties: Wh. or creamy wh. powd., odorless, tasteless; hygroscopic; sol. in aq. and org. solvs.; pH 3-7 (5% aq.); 5% max. moisture
Toxicology: Very low chronic oral toxicity
Storage: Prevent excessive moisture pickup.

Plasdone® K-29/32. [ISP]
Chem. Descrip.: PVP (Povidone USP)
CAS 9003-39-8; EINECS 201-800-4
Uses: Gellant, tablet binder, coating agent; promotes pigment disp.; cohesive agent, stabilizer, protective colloid; detoxicant; drug vehicle/retardant; solubilizer, suspending agent in liqs.; filmformer in medicinal aerosols; for topicals, ophthalmics
Regulatory: FDA 21CFR §173.55; USP, FCC, BP, German Ph., French Ph., Italian Ph. compliance
Properties: Wh. or creamy wh. powd., odorless, tasteless; hygroscopic; sol. in water, aq. and org. solvs.; flash pt. none; pH 3-7 (5% aq.); 5% max. moisture

Toxicology: LD50 (oral, rat) > 100,000 mg/kg; very low chronic oral toxicity; not absorbed topically; not a primary skin irritant; nonirritating to eyes; nuisance dust: TLV/TWA 10 mg/m³ total, 5 mg/m³ respirable

Precaution: Incompat. with strong oxidizing or reducing agents; heated to decomp., may emit toxic fumes of NOₓ

Storage: Prevent excessive moisture pickup.

Plasdone® K-90. [ISP]
Chem. Descrip.: PVP (Povidone USP)
CAS 9003-39-8; EINECS 201-800-4
Uses: Gellant, tablet binder, coating agent; promotes pigment disp.; cohesive agent, stabilizer, protective colloid; detoxicant; vehicle/retardant; solubilizer, suspending agent in liqs.; film-former in medicinal aerosols; for topicals, orals, ophthalmics
Regulatory: FDA 21CFR §173.55; USP, FCC, JP,BP, German Ph., French Ph., Italian Ph. compliance
Properties: Wh. or creamy wh. powd., odorless, tasteless; 10% max. < 75 µ particle size; hygroscopic; sol. in water, aq. and org. solvs.; bulk dens. 0.4-0.6 g/cc; pH 3-7 (5% aq.); 5% max. moisture
Toxicology: Very low chronic oral toxicity; essentially nontoxic by inh., IV, or other parenteral routes; not a primary skin irritant; nonsensitizing; nonirritating to eyes
Storage: Prevent excessive moisture pickup.

Plasdone® K-90D. [ISP]
Chem. Descrip.: PVP (Povidone USP), densified grade
CAS 9003-39-8; EINECS 201-800-4
Uses: Gellant, tablet binder, coating agent; promotes pigment disp.; cohesive agent, stabilizer, protective colloid; detoxicant; drug vehicle/retardant; solubilizer, suspending agent in liqs.; filmformer in medicinal aerosols; for topicals, ophthalmics
Properties: Wh. or creamy wh. powd., odorless, tasteless; 10% max. < 75 µ particle size; hygroscopic; sol. in aq. and org. solvs.; pH 3-7 (5% aq.); 5% max. moisture
Toxicology: Very low chronic oral toxicity
Storage: Prevent excessive moisture pickup.

Plasdone® K-90M. [ISP]
Chem. Descrip.: PVP (Povidone USP), micronized grade
CAS 9003-39-8; EINECS 201-800-4
Uses: Gellant, tablet binder, coating agent; promotes pigment disp.; cohesive agent, stabilizer, protective colloid; detoxicant; drug vehicle/retardant; solubilizer, suspending agent in liqs.; filmformer in medicinal aerosols; for topicals, ophthalmics
Properties: Wh. or creamy wh. powd., odorless, tasteless; 10% max. < 150 µ particle size; hygroscopic; sol. in aq. and org. solvs.; pH 3-7 (5% aq.); 5% max. moisture
Toxicology: Very low chronic oral toxicity

Storage: Prevent excessive moisture pickup.
Plasvita® TSM. [Hüls AG]
Chem. Descrip.: Methylene casein
Uses: Tablet disintegration agent for pharmaceuticals; high capillary activity, low swelling effect
Properties: Wh. powd., odorless, tasteless; insol. in water
Unverified

Pluracol® E400 NF. [BASF]
Chem. Descrip.: PEG-8
CAS 25322-68-3; EINECS 225-856-4
Uses: Excipient, carrier, solv., base, coupler for OTC pharmaceutical and oral care preps., e.g., mouthwashes, cough syrups
Properties: Liq.; m.w. 400; visc. 7.4 cs (99 C); pour pt. 5 C; flash pt. (COC) 182 C.

Pluracol® E600 NF. [BASF]
Chem. Descrip.: PEG-12
CAS 25322-68-3; EINECS 229-859-1
Uses: Excipient, carrier, solv., base, coupler for OTC pharmaceutical and oral care preps., e.g., mouthwashes, cough syrups
Properties: Liq.; m.w. 600; visc. 10.8 cs (99 C); pour pt. 20 C; flash pt. (COC) 249 C.

Pluracol® E1450 NF. [BASF]
Chem. Descrip.: PEG-32
CAS 25322-68-3
Uses: Excipient, carrier, solv., base, coupler for OTC pharmaceutical and oral care preps., e.g., mouthwashes, cough syrups
Properties: Solid; m.w. 600; visc. 28.5 cs (99 C); m.p. 45 C; flash pt. (COC) 255 C.

Plurol® Diisostearique. [Gattefosse SA]
Chem. Descrip.: Polyglyceryl-3 diisostearate
CAS 66082-42-6; EINECS 291-548-1
Uses: Cold process w/o emulsifier for pharmaceutical creams with exc. appearance, gloss, afterfeel, and stability at 50 C; for dry skin treatment, skin protection, dermatological suncare preps.
Use level: 5%
Properties: Pale yel. clear to sl. opalescent visc. liq., faint odor; sol. in min. and veg. oils; insol. in water, alcohols; acid no. < 5; iodine no. < 8; sapon. no. 128-148; ref. index 1.471-1.475; < 0.5% water content
Storage: Avoid moisture and air; storage below 18 C can lead to reversible opalescence.

Plurol® Isostearique. [Gattefosse SA]
Chem. Descrip.: Polyglyceryl-6 isostearate
CAS 126928-07-2
Uses: Emulsifier, cosurfactant for microemulsions
Properties: Gardner < 10 visc. liq., char. odor; sol. in chloroform, methylene chloride, veg. oils, ethanol; disp. in water; HLB 10.0; acid no. < 6; iodine no. < 10; sapon. no. 115-135; ref. index 1.470-1.480; 100% conc.; nonionic
Toxicology: Nonirritating to skin; sl. irritating to eyes.

Plurol® Oleique WL 1173. [Gattefosse SA]
Chem. Descrip.: Polyglyceryl-6 dioleate
CAS 76009-37-5

Uses: Emulsifier, cosurfactant for microemulsions; suspending agent for hard/soft gelatin capsules
Properties: Gardner < 10 visc. liq., char. odor; sol. in ethanol, chloroform, methylene chloride, veg. and min. oils; disp. in water; visc. 8-20 Pa•s; HLB 10.0; acid no. < 6; iodine no. 50-70; sapon. no. 110-140; pH 7.0-9.5 (10% aq.); ref. index 1.470-1.490; 100% conc.; nonionic
Toxicology: Sl. irritating to skin and eyes.

Pluronic® F68NF. [BASF]
Chem. Descrip.: Poloxamer 188 NF
CAS 9003-11-6
Uses: General pharmaceutical surfactant; emulsifier; solubilizer in topical and oral care prods.; protective gel coating in burn treatments; vehicles for ointments and fluoridated dentifrices
Properties: Solid; sol. in ethanol, water; m.w. 8350; sp.gr. 1.06 (77 C); dens. 8.8 lb/gal (77 C); visc. 1000 cps (77 C); m.p. 52 C; HLB 29.0; cloud pt. > 100 C (1% aq.); flash pt. (COC) 500 F; surf. tens. 50.3 dynes/cm (0.1%); Draves wetting > 360 s (0.1%); Ross-Miles foam 35 mm (0.1% aq., 50 C); 100% act.; nonionic
Toxicology: None to sl. eye and skin irritation.

Pluronic® F87NF. [BASF]
Chem. Descrip.: Poloxamer 237 NF
CAS 9003-11-6
Uses: General pharmaceutical surfactant; emulsifier; solubilizer in topical and oral care prods.; protective gel coating in burn treatments; vehicles for ointments and fluoridated dentifrices
Properties: Solid; sol. in ethanol, water, toluene; ; m.w. 7700; sp.gr. 1.04 (77 C); dens. 8.7 lb/gal (77 C); visc. 700 cps. (77 C); m.p. 49 C; HLB 24.0; cloud pt. > 100 C (1% aq.); flash pt. (COC) 472 F; surf. tens. 44.0 dynes/cm (0.1%); Draves wetting > 360 s (*0.1%); Ross-Miles foam 80 mm (0.1% aq., 50 C); 100% act.; nonionic
Toxicology: Non to sl. eye and skin irritation.

Pluronic® F108NF. [BASF]
Chem. Descrip.: Poloxamer 338 NF
CAS 9003-11-6
Uses: General pharmaceutical surfactant; emulsifier; solubilizer in topical and oral care prods.; protective gel coating in burn treatments; vehicles for ointments and fluoridated dentifrices
Properties: Prilled; sol. in ethanol, water; m.w. 14,000; sp.gr. 1.06 (77 C); dens. 8.8 lb/gal (77 C); visc. 8000 cps (77 C); m.p. 57 C; HLB 27.0; cloud pt. > 100 C (1% aq.); flash pt. (COC) 495 F; surf. tens. 41.2 dynes/cm (0.1%); Draves wetting > 360 s (0.1%); Ross-Miles foam 40 mm (0.1% aq., 50 C); 100% act.; nonionic
Toxicology: Non to sl. eye and skin irritation.

Pluronic® F127NF. [BASF]
Chem. Descrip.: Poloxamer 407 NF
CAS 9003-11-6
Uses: Gellant for pharmaceuticals; emulsifier; solubilizer in topical and oral care prods.; protective gel coating in burn treatments; vehicles for ointments and fluoridated dentifrices
Properties: Prilled; sol. in ethanol, water, toluene,

perchloroethylene; m.w. 12,500; sp.gr. 1.05 (77 C); dens. 8.8 lb/gal (77 C); visc. 3100 cps (77 C); m.p. 56 C; HLB 22.0; cloud pt. > 100 C (1% aq.); surf. tens. 40.6 dynes/cm (0.1%); Draves wetting > 360 s (0.1%); Ross-Miles foam 40 mm (0.1% aq., 50 C); 100% act.; nonionic
Toxicology: Non to sl. eye and skin irritation.

Pluronic® L44NF. [BASF]
Chem. Descrip.: Poloxamer 124 NF
CAS 9003-11-6
Uses: General pharmaceutical surfactant; emulsifier; solubilizer in topical and oral care prods.; protective gel coating in burn treatments; vehicles for ointments and fluoridated dentifrices
Properties: Liq.; m.w. 2200; sp.gr. 1.05; dens. 8.8 lb/gal; visc. 440 cps; HLB 16.0; pour pt. 16 C; cloud pt. 65 C (1% aq.); flash pt. (COC) 464 F; ref. index 1.4580; surf. tens. 45 dynes/cm (0.1%); Draves wetting > 360 s (0.1%); Ross-Miles foam 25 mm (0.1%, 50 C); 100% act.; nonionic
Toxicology: Non to sl. eye and skin irritation.

Polargel® HV. [Am. Colloid]
Chem. Descrip.: Bentonite USP/NF
CAS 1302-78-9; EINECS 215-108-5
Uses: High visc. wh. montmorillonite used as viscosifier, disintegrant, binder, suspension agent for pharmaceutical prods.
Properties: Wh. microfine powd.; 99% min. thru 200 mesh; vic. 800 cps min. (5% solids); pH 9.5-10.5 (2% disp.); dry brightness (GE) 83-87; 5-8% moisture.

Polargel® NF. [Am. Colloid]
Chem. Descrip.: Purified wh. bentonite USP/NF
CAS 1302-78-9; EINECS 215-108-5
Uses: Gellant, thickener, binder, and suspending agent for pharmaceuticals
Properties: Wh. fine powd.; 99% thru 200 mesh; visc. 40-200 cps (5% solids); pH 9.0-10.0 (5% disp.); dry brightness (GE) 85-90; 8% max. moisture.

Polargel® T. [Am. Colloid]
Chem. Descrip.: Bentonite USP/NF
CAS 1302-78-9; EINECS 215-108-5
Uses: Thickener, suspension agent, and binder for pharmaceutical prods.
Properties: Wh. fine powd.; 99% min. thru 200 mesh; visc. 200-500 cps (5% solids); pH 9.5-10.5 (2% disp.); dry brightness (GE) 83-87; 5-8% moisture.

Polawax®. [Croda Inc.; Croda Surf. Ltd.]
Chem. Descrip.: Emulsifying wax NF
CAS 97069-99-0
Uses: Emulsifier, thickener, opacifier, suspending agent; stabilizer for o/w emulsions; for topical pharmaceuticals, antibiotic creams and lotions, acne preps., analgesic rubs; pharmaceutical bases
Use level: 2-25%; 2-3% (fluid emulsions); 5-10% (thick visc. emulsions)
Properties: Creamy wh. flaked waxy solid, mild char. odor; sol. in alcohol; disp. in water, propylene glycol; m.p. 48-52 C; iodine no. 3.5 max.;

sapon. no. 14 max.; hyd. no. 178-192; pH 5.5-7.0 (3% aq.); 100% conc.; nonionic

Toxicology: LD50 (oral, rat) 16 g/kg; nonirritating to skin and eyes.

Polawax® A31. [Croda Inc.; Croda Surf. Ltd.]
Chem. Descrip.: Emulsifying wax NF
CAS 97069-99-0
Uses: O/w emulsifier and foaming agent used in quick-breaking foams, topical pharmaceuticals; optimized for hydroalcoholic systems; suitable for aerosols
Use level: 1-8%
Properties: Creamy wh. flakes, mild char. odor; sol. in alcohol and aerosol propellant, disp. in water, propylene glycol; m.p. 50-54 C; iodine no. 3.5 max.; sapon. no. 14 max.; hyd. no. 178-192; pH 5.5-7.0 (3% aq.); 100% conc.; nonionic
Toxicology: LD50 (oral, rat) > 5 g/kg; nonirritating to skin and eyes.

Polawax® GP200. [Croda Inc.; Croda Surf. Ltd.]
Chem. Descrip.: Self-emulsifying wax
Uses: Self-bodying emulsifier producing stable w/o emulsions for pharmaceuticals, lotions, creams, ointments; effective at high levels of electrolytes and active ingreds.; heat-stable; pharmaceutical bases
Properties: Wh. waxy solid; 97% conc.; nonionic.

Polyaldo® DGHO. [Lonza]
Chem. Descrip.: Polyglyceryl-10 hexaoleate
Uses: Emulsifier, emollient, lubricant for pharmaceuticals
Properties: Amber clear liq.; sol. in ethanol, min. and veg. oils; insol. in water; HLB 5 ± 1; sapon. no. 130-160; nonionic.

Polychol 5. [Croda Inc.; Croda Chem. Ltd.]
Chem. Descrip.: Laneth-5
CAS 61791-20-6
Uses: Coemulsifier in prod. of w/o emulsions and microemulsions for topical pharmaceuticals; solubilizer, gellant; cosolv. for nonmiscible oils; reduces greasy feeling of lanolin
Use level: 1-10%
Properties: Soft yel. wax; sol. in IPA, disp. in water, propylene glycol, min. oil; m.p. 35-48 C; HLB 7.5; acid no. 5 max.; hyd. no. 120-135; pH 4.5-6.0 (10% aq.); 100% conc.; nonionic
Toxicology: LD50 (oral, rat) 7.7 g/kg; mild skin irritant, nonirritating to eyes.

Polychol 10. [Croda Inc.; Croda Chem. Ltd.]
Chem. Descrip.: Laneth-10
CAS 61791-20-6
Uses: Mild emulsifier, thickener for pharmaceuticals
Properties: Soft golden yel. wax; sol. in IPA; disp. in water, min. oil; m.p. 35-43 C; HLB 10.7; acid no. 5 max.; hyd. no. 95-115; pH 4.5-6.0 (10% aq.); 97% conc.; nonionic
Toxicology: LD50 (oral, rat) > 5 g/kg; mild skin irritant, nonirritating to eyes
Custom product

Polychol 15. [Croda Inc.; Croda Chem. Ltd.]
Chem. Descrip.: Laneth-15

CAS 61791-20-6
Uses: Mild emulsifier, thickener for topical pharmaceuticals; solubilzer and gelling agent; cosolv. for nonmiscible oils; reduces greasy feeling of lanolin
Use level: 1-10%
Properties: Yel. soft wax; sol. in water, IPA, propylene glycol; disp. in min. oil; m.p. 34-42 C; HLB 12.7; acid no. 5 max.; hyd. no. 82-92; pH 3.5-5.5 (10% aq.); 100% conc.; nonionic
Toxicology: Nonirritating to skin and eyes.

Polychol 20. [Croda Inc.; Croda Chem. Ltd.]
Chem. Descrip.: Laneth-20
CAS 61791-20-6
Uses: Mild emulsifier, thickener for pharmaceuticals
Properties: Yel. semi-hard wax; almost totally water-sol.; sol. in IPA, propylene glycol; disp. in min. oil; m.p. 42-50 C; HLB 14.0; acid no. 5 max.; hyd. no. 50-70; pH 3.5-5.5 (10% aq.); 97% conc.; nonionic
Toxicology: LD50 (oral, rat) 9.2 g/kg; mild skin irritant, minimal eye irritant
Custom product

Polychol 40. [Croda Inc.; Croda Chem. Ltd.]
Chem. Descrip.: Laneth-40
CAS 61791-20-6
Uses: Mild emulsifier, thickener for pharmaceuticals
Properties: Yel. hard wax; sol. in water, IPA; disp. in min. oil, propylene glycol; m.w. 43-53 C; HLB 16.4; acid no. 5 max.; hyd. no. 35-50; pH 3.0-6.5 (10% aq.); 97% conc.; nonionic
Toxicology: LD50 (oral, rat) 10 g/kg; nonirritating to skin and eyes
Custom product

Poly-G® 200. [Olin]
Chem. Descrip.: PEG 200
CAS 25322-68-3; EINECS 203-989-9
Uses: Carrier for pharmaceuticals
Properties: APHA 25 max. liq.; m.w. 200; sol. in water, acetone, ethanol, ethyl acetate, toluene; sp.gr. 1.125; dens. 9.38 lb/gal; visc. 4.3 cs (99 C); flash pt. 171 C (COC)
Unverified

Polyjel. [United-Guardian]
Chem. Descrip.: Acid gel based on polyglcyeryl citrate
Uses: Base for pharmaceuticals; compat. with wide range of polar and nonpolar compds., e.g., potassium chloride, ethyl alcohol, lactic acid
Properties: Avail. in two visc. grades; pH 5-5.5
Custom product

Polyox® WSR 205. [Union Carbide]
Chem. Descrip.: PEG-14M
CAS 25322-68-3
Uses: Water-sol. coating for tablets; dispersant, antisettling agent in calamine lotion; lubricant, evaporation inhibitor for rubbing alc.; controlled-release drugs; contact lens fluid
Regulatory: EPA 40CFR §180.1001(d); FDA 21CFR §175.300, 175.380, 175.390, 176.170,

176.180, 177.1210, 177.1350

Properties: Wh. gran. powd., mild ammoniacal odor; 100% thru 10 mesh, 96% thru 20 mesh; sol. in water, some chlorinated solvs., alcohols, aromatic hydrocarbons, ketones; m.w. 600,000; sp.gr. 1.15-1.26; bulk dens. 19-37 lb/ft³; visc. 4500-8800 cps (5% aq.); m.p. 62-67 C; pH 8-10 (5% aq.); nonionic

Precaution: Slippery when wet

Storage: Store in sealed containers below 25 C, away from heat; avoid dust buildup.

Polyox® WSR 301. [Union Carbide]

Chem. Descrip.: PEG-90M

CAS 25322-68-3

Uses: Water-sol. coating for tablets; dispersant, antisettling agent in calamine lotion; lubricant, evaporation inhibitor for rubbing alc.; controlled-release drugs; contact lens fluid

Regulatory: EPA 40CFR §180.1001(d); FDA 21CFR §172.770, 175.300, 175.380, 175.390, 176.170, 176.180, 177.1210, 177.1350

Properties: Wh. gran. powd., mild ammoniacal odor; 100% thru 10 mesh, 96% thru 20 mesh; sol. in water, some chlorinated solvs., alcohols, aromatic hydrocarbons, ketones; m.w. 4,000,000; bulk dens. 19-37 lb/ft³; visc. 1650-5500 cps (1% aq.); m.p. 62-67 C; pH 8-10 (1% aq.); nonionic

Precaution: Slippery when wet

Storage: Store in sealed containers below 25 C, away from heat; avoid dust buildup.

Polyox® WSR 303. [Union Carbide]

Chem. Descrip.: Polyethylene oxide

CAS 25322-68-3

Uses: Water-sol. coating for tablets; dispersant, antisettling agent in calamine lotion; lubricant, evaporation inhibitor for rubbing alc.; controlled-release drugs; contact lens fluid

Regulatory: EPA 40CFR §180.1001(d); FDA 21CFR §172.770, 175.300, 175.380, 175.390, 176.170, 176.180, 177.1210, 177.1350

Properties: Wh. gran. powd., mild ammoniacal odor; 100% thru 10 mesh, 96% thru 20 mesh; sol. in water, some chlorinated solvs., alcohols, aromatic hydrocarbons, ketones; m.w. 7,000,000; bulk dens. 19-37 lb/ft³; visc. 7500-10,000 cps (1% aq.); m.p. 62-67 C; pH 8-10 (sol'n.); nonionic

Precaution: Slippery when wet

Storage: Store in sealed containers below 25 C, away from heat; avoid dust buildup.

Polyox® WSR 308. [Union Carbide]

Chem. Descrip.: Polyethylene oxide

CAS 25322-68-3

Uses: Water-sol. coating for tablets; dispersant, antisettling agent in calamine lotion; lubricant, evaporation inhibitor for rubbing alc.; controlled-release drugs; contact lens fluid

Regulatory: EPA 40CFR §180.1001(d); FDA 21CFR §172.770, 175.300, 175.380, 175.390, 176.170, 176.180, 177.1210, 177.1350

Properties: Wh. gran. powd., mild ammoniacal odor; 100% thru 10 mesh, 96% thru 20 mesh; sol. in water, some chlorinated solvs., alcohols, aro-

matic hydrocarbons, ketones; m.w. 8,000,000; sp.gr. 1.15-1.26; bulk dens. 19-37 lb/ft³; visc. 10,000-15,000 cps (1% aq.); m.p. 62-67 C; pH 8-10 (sol'n.); nonionic

Precaution: Slippery when wet

Storage: Store in sealed containers below 25 C, away from heat; avoid dust buildup.

Polyox® WSR 1105. [Union Carbide]

Chem. Descrip.: PEG-20M

CAS 25322-68-3

Uses: Water-sol. coating for tablets; dispersant, antisettling agent in calamine lotion; lubricant, evaporation inhibitor for rubbing alc.; controlled-release drugs; contact lens fluid

Regulatory: EPA 40CFR §180.1001(d); FDA 21CFR §175.300, 175.380, 175.390, 176.170, 176.180, 177.1210, 177.1350

Properties: Wh. gran. powd., mild ammoniacal odor; 100% thru 10 mesh, 96% thru 20 mesh; sol. in water, some chlorinated solvs., alcohols, aromatic hydrocarbons, ketones; m.w. 900,000; sp.gr. 1.15-1.26; bulk dens. 19-37 lb/ft³; visc. 8800-17,600 cps (5% aq.); m.p. 62-67 C; pH 8-10 (5% aq.); nonionic

Precaution: Slippery when wet

Storage: Store in sealed containers below 25 C, away from heat; avoid dust buildup.

Polyox® WSR 3333. [Union Carbide]

Chem. Descrip.: PEG-9M

CAS 25322-68-3

Uses: Water-sol. coating for tablets; dispersant, antisettling agent in calamine lotion; lubricant, evaporation inhibitor for rubbing alc.; controlled-release drugs; contact lens fluid

Regulatory: EPA 40CFR §180.1001(d); FDA 21CFR §175.300, 175.380, 175.390, 176.170, 176.180, 177.1210, 177.1350

Properties: Wh. gran. powd., mild ammoniacal odor; 100% thru 10 mesh, 96% thru 20 mesh; sol. in water, some chlorinated solvs., alcohols, aromatic hydrocarbons, ketones; m.w. 400,000; sp.gr. 1.15-1.26; bulk dens. 19-37 lb/ft³; visc. 2250-3350 cps (5% aq.); m.p. 62-67 C; pH 8-10 (5% aq.); nonionic

Precaution: Slippery when wet

Storage: Store in sealed containers below 25 C, away from heat; avoid dust buildup.

Polyox® WSR Coagulant. [Union Carbide]

Chem. Descrip.: PEG-115M

CAS 25322-68-3

Uses: Water-sol. coating for tablets; dispersant, antisettling agent in calamine lotion; lubricant, evaporation inhibitor for rubbing alc.; controlled-release drugs; contact lens fluid

Regulatory: EPA 40CFR §180.1001(d); FDA 21CFR §172.770, 175.300, 175.380, 175.390, 176.170, 176.180, 177.1210, 177.1350

Properties: Wh. gran. powd., mild ammoniacal odor; 100% thru 10 mesh, 96% thru 20 mesh; sol. in water, some chlorinated solvs., alcohols, aromatic hydrocarbons, ketones; m.w. 5,000,000; sp.gr. 1.15-1.26; bulk dens. 19-37 lb/ft³; visc.

5500-7500 cps (1% aq.); m.p. 62-67 C; pH 8-10 (sol'n.); nonionic
Precaution: Slippery when wet
Storage: Store in sealed containers below 25 C, away from heat; avoid dust buildup.

Polyox® WSR N-10. [Union Carbide]
Chem. Descrip.: PEG-2M
CAS 25322-68-3
Uses: Water-sol. coating for tablets; dispersant, antisettling agent in calamine lotion; lubricant, evaporation inhibitor for rubbing alc.; controlled-release drugs; contact lens fluid
Regulatory: EPA 40CFR §180.1001(d); FDA 21CFR §175.300, 175.380, 175.390, 176.170, 176.180, 177.1210, 177.1350
Properties: Wh. gran. powd., mild ammoniacal odor; 100% thru 10 mesh, 96% thru 20 mesh; sol. in water, some chlorinated solvs., alcohols, aromatic hydrocarbons, ketones; m.w. 100,000; sp.gr. 1.15-1.26; bulk dens. 19-37 lb/ft^3; visc. 12-50 cps (5% aq.); m.p. 62-67 C; pH 8-10 (5% aq.); nonionic
Precaution: Slippery when wet
Storage: Store in sealed containers below 25 C, away from heat; avoid dust buildup.

Polyox® WSR N-12K. [Union Carbide]
Chem. Descrip.: PEG-23M
CAS 25322-68-3
Uses: Water-sol. coating for tablets; dispersant, antisettling agent in calamine lotion; lubricant, evaporation inhibitor for rubbing alc.; controlled-release drugs; contact lens fluid
Regulatory: EPA 40CFR §180.1001(d); FDA 21CFR §175.300, 175.380, 175.390, 176.170, 176.180, 177.1210, 177.1350
Properties: Wh. gran. powd., mild ammoniacal odor; 100% thru 10 mesh, 96% thru 20 mesh; sol. in water, some chlorinated solvs., alcohols, aromatic hydrocarbons, ketones; m.w. 1,000,000; sp.gr. 1.15-1.26; bulk dens. 19-37 lb/ft^3; visc. 400-800 cps (2% aq.); m.p. 62-67 C; pH 8-10 (2% aq.); nonionic
Precaution: Slippery when wet
Storage: Store in sealed containers below 25 C, away from heat; avoid dust buildup.

Polyox® WSR N-60K. [Union Carbide]
Chem. Descrip.: PEG-45M
CAS 25322-68-3
Uses: Water-sol. coating for tablets; dispersant, antisettling agent in calamine lotion; lubricant, evaporation inhibitor for rubbing alc.; controlled-release drugs; contact lens fluid
Regulatory: EPA 40CFR §180.1001(d); FDA 21CFR §175.300, 175.380, 175.390, 176.170, 176.180, 177.1210, 177.1350
Properties: Wh. gran. powd., mild ammoniacal odor; 100% thru 10 mesh, 96% thru 20 mesh; sol. in water, some chlorinated solvs., alcohols, aromatic hydrocarbons, ketones; m.w. 2,000,000; sp.gr. 1.15-1.26; bulk dens. 19-37 lb/ft^3; visc. 2000-4000 cps (2% aq.); m.p. 62-67 C; pH 8-10 (2% aq.); nonionic

Precaution: Slippery when wet
Storage: Store in sealed containers below 25 C, away from heat; avoid dust buildup.

Polyox® WSR N-80. [Union Carbide]
Chem. Descrip.: PEG-5M
CAS 25322-68-3
Uses: Water-sol. coating for tablets; dispersant, antisettling agent in calamine lotion; lubricant, evaporation inhibitor for rubbing alc.; controlled-release drugs; contact lens fluid
Regulatory: EPA 40CFR §180.1001(d); FDA 21CFR §175.300, 175.380, 175.390, 176.170, 176.180, 177.1210, 177.1350
Properties: Wh. gran. powd., mild ammoniacal odor; 100% thru 10 mesh, 96% thru 20 mesh; sol. in water, some chlorinated solvs., alcohols, aromatic hydrocarbons, ketones; m.w. 200,000; sp.gr. 1.15-1.26; bulk dens. 19-37 lb/ft^3; visc. 65-115 cps (5% aq.); m.p. 62-67 C; pH 8-10 (5% aq.); nonionic
Precaution: Slippery when wet
Storage: Store in sealed containers below 25 C, away from heat; avoid dust buildup.

Polyox® WSR N-750. [Union Carbide]
Chem. Descrip.: PEG-7M
CAS 25322-68-3
Uses: Water-sol. coating for tablets; dispersant, antisettling agent in calamine lotion; lubricant, evaporation inhibitor for rubbing alc.; controlled-release drugs; contact lens fluid
Regulatory: EPA 40CFR §180.1001(d); FDA 21CFR §175.300, 175.380, 175.390, 176.170, 176.180, 177.1210, 177.1350
Properties: Wh. gran. powd., mild ammoniacal odor; 100% thru 10 mesh, 96% thru 20 mesh; sol. in water, some chlorinated solvs., alcohols, aromatic hydrocarbons, ketones; m.w. 300,000; sp.gr. 1.15-1.26; bulk dens. 19-37 lb/ft^3; visc. 600-1200 cps (5% aq.); m.p. 62-67 C; pH 8-10 (5% aq.); nonionic
Precaution: Slippery when wet
Storage: Store in sealed containers below 25 C, away from heat; avoid dust buildup.

Polyox® WSR N-3000. [Union Carbide]
Chem. Descrip.: PEG-14M
CAS 25322-68-3
Uses: Water-sol. coating for tablets; dispersant, antisettling agent in calamine lotion; lubricant, evaporation inhibitor for rubbing alc.; controlled-release drugs; contact lens fluid
Regulatory: EPA 40CFR §180.1001(d); FDA 21CFR §175.300, 175.380, 175.390, 176.170, 176.180, 177.1210, 177.1350
Properties: Wh. gran. powd., mild ammoniacal odor; 100% thru 10 mesh, 96% thru 20 mesh; sol. in water, some chlorinated solvs., alcohols, aromatic hydrocarbons, ketones; m.w. 400,000; sp.gr. 1.15-1.26; bulk dens. 19-37 lb/ft^3; visc. 2250-4500 cps (5% aq.); m.p. 62-67 C; pH 8-10 (5% aq.); nonionic
Precaution: Slippery when wet
Storage: Store in sealed containers below 25 C,

away from heat; avoid dust buildup.

Polyplasdone® INF-10. [ISP]
Chem. Descrip.: Crospovidone NF
CAS 9003-39-8
Uses: Treatment for intestinal disorders; protects intestinal mucosa; anti-inflammatory; detoxifier in antiphlogistic pastes to treat local injections; nutritional supplements anabolic regulator; anti-diarrheal treatments; in antibiotics
Properties: Wh. free-flowing powd., pract. odorless and tasteless; 100% < 30 μ particle size; insol. in water and all other common solvs.; pH 5-8 (1g/100 ml water); 5% max. moisture
Toxicology: Very low chronic toxicity; virtually unabsorbed in the gastrointestinal tract.

Polyplasdone® XL. [ISP]
Chem. Descrip.: Crospovidone NF
CAS 9003-39-8
Uses: Excipient; tablet binder/disintegrant/stabilizer; complexing agent for insol. polymeric iodine complexes; detoxifier; antidiarrhea agent; stabilizer for moisture-sensitive actives (vitamins, enzymes); in analgesics, antibiotics, transdermals
Properties: Off-wh. free-flowing powd., pract. odorless and tasteless; 0-400 μ particle size; insol. in water, acids, alkalies, all org. solvs.; m.w. > 10^6; dens. 1.22 g/cc; pH 5-8 (1g/100 ml water); 5% max. moisture
Toxicology: Very low chronic toxicity; virtually unabsorbed in the gastrointestinal tract.

Polyplasdone® XL-10. [ISP]
Chem. Descrip.: Crospovidone NF
CAS 9003-39-8
Uses: Excipient; tablet binder/disintegrant/stabilizer; complexing agent for insol. polymeric iodine complexes; detoxifier; antidiarrhea agent; stabilizer for moisture-sensitive actives (vitamins, enzymes); in analgesics, antibiotics, transdermals
Properties: Wh. to off-wh. free-flowing fine powd., pract. odorless and tasteless; 95% < 75 μ particle size; insol. in water and all other common solvs.; flash pt. none; pH 5-8 (1g/100 ml water); 5% max. moisture
Toxicology: LD50 (oral, rat) > 100,000 mg/kg; very low chronic toxicity; virtually unabsorbed topically and in the gastrointestinal tract; not a primary skin irritant; nonirritating to eyes; nuisance dust: TLV/TWA 10 mg/m^3 total, 5 mg/m^3 respirable
Precaution: Incompat. with strong oxidizing or reducing agents; heated to decomp., emits toxic fumes of NO$_x$.

Polypro 5000® Pharmaceutical Grade. [Hormel]
Chem. Descrip.: Hydrolyzed gelatin
CAS 68410-45-7; EINECS 270-082-2
Uses: Pharmaceutical-grade protein with coating and film forming, encapsulation, and moisturizing props.; can be used for applics. where complete sol. in cold water is needed; in meal supplement prods.
Regulatory: Kosher
Properties: Ivory to amber free-flowing powd., bland char. odor; cold water-sol.; m.w. 5000;

sp.gr. > 1; pH 5-6; 93-97% solids; biodeg.
Toxicology: Nontoxic by ingestion; avoid inhalation of dust
Storage: Store at ambient temps. below 80 F for up to 1 yr.

Polypro 15000® Pharmaceutical Grade. [Hormel]
Chem. Descrip.: Hydrolyzed gelatin
CAS 68410-45-7; EINECS 270-082-2
Uses: Pharmaceutical-grade protein with coating and film forming, encapsulation, and moisturizing props.; readily dissolvable films; in meal supplement prods. where protein fortification is needed
Regulatory: Kosher
Properties: Lt. ivory free-flowing powd., bland char. odor; nearly cold water-sol.; m.w. 15,000; pH 5-6 (10 g/50 ml water); 93-97% solids; biodeg.
Toxicology: Nontoxic by ingestion; avoid inhalation of dust
Storage: Store at ambient temps. below 80 F for up to 1 yr.

Polystep® B-3. [Stepan; Stepan Canada; Stepan Europe]
Chem. Descrip.: Sodium lauryl sulfate
CAS 151-21-3
Uses: Emulsifier
Regulatory: FDA 21CFR §175.105, 175.300, 176.170, 176.210, 177.1200, 177.1210, 177.2600, 177.2800, 178.3400; USP approved
Properties: Wh. powd.; 97.5% act.; anionic.

Pomelex Complex D. [MLG Enterprises Ltd.]
Chem. Descrip.: Citric conc. contg. conc. natural juices, deterpenated essential oils, syn. colorants, acidifiers, thickeners, and preservatives
Uses: Preformulated flavor base for prod. of pharmaceuticals.

Pomelex Complex G. [MLG Enterprises Ltd.]
Chem. Descrip.: Citric conc. contg. conc. natural juices, deterpenated essential oils, syn. colorants, acidifiers, thickeners, and preservatives
Uses: Preformulated flavor base for prod. of pharmaceuticals.

Potassium Sodium Copper Chlorophyllin 033280. [Crompton & Knowles/Ingred. Tech.]
Chem. Descrip.: Potassium sodium copper chlorophyllin
CAS 11006-31-1; EINECS 234-242-5
Uses: Blue-green colorant for dentifrices (0.1% max.)
Regulatory: FDA 21CFR §73.1125, 73.2125
Properties: Greenish-blk. powd., sl. odor; 99.5% min. thru 80 mesh; sol. in water; pH 10 ± 1 (10%); 75% min. total color
Storage: 6 mos shelf life stored in tight containers; avoid exposure to heat, light, moisture.

Powdered Agar Agar Bacteriological Grade. [Gumix Int'l.]
Chem. Descrip.: Agar agar
CAS 9002-18-0; EINECS 232-658-1
Uses: Gellant, suspending agent, emulsifier, bulking agent for slow-release capsules, supposito-

ries, surgical lubricants, emulsions; carrier for topical medicaments; excipient, disintegrant in tablets; laxatives; barium sulfate (radiology); dental use

Properties: Wh. to pale yel. powd., sl. char. odor, mucilaginous taste; insol. in cold water, slowly sol. in hot water, completely sol. in boiling water; insol. in alcohol and most org. solvs.

Powdered Agar Agar NF M-100 (Gracilaria) [Meer]
Chem. Descrip.: Agar agar
CAS 9002-18-0; EINECS 232-658-1
Uses: Emulsifier, stabilizer, gellant; in dental casts, as laxative, as suspending agent for barium sulfate in radiology, in suppositories, surgical lubricants, as carrier of topical medicaments
Properties: Water-sol.

Powdered Agar Agar NF MK-60. [Meer]
Chem. Descrip.: Agar agar
CAS 9002-18-0; EINECS 232-658-1
Uses: Emulsifier, stabilizer, gellant; in dental casts, as laxative, as suspending agent for barium sulfate in radiology, in suppositories, surgical lubricants, as carrier of topical medicaments
Properties: Water-sol.

Powdered Agar Agar NF MK-80-B. [Meer]
Chem. Descrip.: Agar agar
CAS 9002-18-0; EINECS 232-658-1
Uses: Emulsifier, stabilizer, gellant; in dental casts, as laxative, as suspending agent for barium sulfate in radiology, in suppositories, surgical lubricants, as carrier of topical medicaments
Properties: Water-sol.

Powdered Agar Agar NF MK-80 (Bacteriological) [Meer]
Chem. Descrip.: Agar agar
CAS 9002-18-0; EINECS 232-658-1
Uses: Emulsifier, stabilizer, gellant; in dental casts, as laxative, as suspending agent for barium sulfate in radiology, in suppositories, surgical lubricants, as carrier of topical medicaments
Properties: Water-sol.

Powdered Agar Agar NF S-100. [Meer]
Chem. Descrip.: Agar agar
CAS 9002-18-0; EINECS 232-658-1
Uses: Emulsifier, stabilizer, gellant; in dental casts, as laxative, as suspending agent for barium sulfate in radiology, in suppositories, surgical lubricants, as carrier of topical medicaments
Properties: Water-sol.

Powdered Agar Agar NF S-100-B. [Meer]
Chem. Descrip.: Agar agar
CAS 9002-18-0; EINECS 232-658-1
Uses: Emulsifier, stabilizer, gellant; in dental casts, as laxative, as suspending agent for barium sulfate in radiology, in suppositories, surgical lubricants, as carrier of topical medicaments
Properties: Water-sol.

Powdered Agar Agar NF S-150. [Meer]
Chem. Descrip.: Agar agar NF
CAS 9002-18-0; EINECS 232-658-1
Uses: Emulsifier, stabilizer, gellant; in dental casts, as laxative, as suspending agent for barium sul-

fate in radiology, in suppositories, surgical lubricants, as carrier of topical medicaments
Properties: Wh. to grayish wh. fine powd.; 100% thru 80 mesh, ≥ 90% thru 150 mesh; water-sol.

Powdered Agar Agar NF S-150-B. [Meer]
Chem. Descrip.: Agar agar
CAS 9002-18-0; EINECS 232-658-1
Uses: Emulsifier, stabilizer, gellant; in dental casts, as laxative, as suspending agent for barium sulfate in radiology, in suppositories, surgical lubricants, as carrier of topical medicaments
Properties: Water-sol.

Powdered Agar Agar Type K-60. [Gumix Int'l.]
Chem. Descrip.: Agar agar
CAS 9002-18-0; EINECS 232-658-1
Uses: Gellant, suspending agent, emulsifier, bulking agent for slow-release capsules, suppositories, surgical lubricants, emulsions; carrier for topical medicaments; excipient, disintegrant in tablets; laxatives; barium sulfate (radiology); dental use
Properties: Wh. to pale yel. powd., sl. char. odor, mucilaginous taste; insol. in cold water, slowly sol. in hot water, completely sol. in boiling water; insol. in alcohol and most org. solvs.

Powdered Agar Agar Type K-80. [Gumix Int'l.]
Chem. Descrip.: Agar agar
CAS 9002-18-0; EINECS 232-658-1
Uses: Gellant, suspending agent, emulsifier, bulking agent for slow-release capsules, suppositories, surgical lubricants, emulsions; carrier for topical medicaments; excipient, disintegrant in tablets; laxatives; barium sulfate (radiology); dental use
Properties: Wh. to pale yel. powd., sl. char. odor, mucilaginous taste; insol. in cold water, slowly sol. in hot water, completely sol. in boiling water; insol. in alcohol and most org. solvs.

Powdered Agar Agar Type K-100. [Gumix Int'l.]
Chem. Descrip.: Agar agar
CAS 9002-18-0; EINECS 232-658-1
Uses: Gellant, suspending agent, emulsifier, bulking agent for slow-release capsules, suppositories, surgical lubricants, emulsions; carrier for topical medicaments; excipient, disintegrant in tablets; laxatives; barium sulfate (radiology); dental use
Properties: Wh. to pale yel. powd., sl. char. odor, mucilaginous taste; insol. in cold water, slowly sol. in hot water, completely sol. in boiling water; insol. in alcohol and most org. solvs.

Powdered Agar Agar Type K-150. [Gumix Int'l.]
Chem. Descrip.: Agar agar
CAS 9002-18-0; EINECS 232-658-1
Uses: Gellant, suspending agent, emulsifier, bulking agent for slow-release capsules, suppositories, surgical lubricants, emulsions; carrier for topical medicaments; excipient, disintegrant in tablets; laxatives; barium sulfate (radiology); dental use
Properties: Wh. to pale yel. powd., sl. char. odor, mucilaginous taste; insol. in cold water, slowly

sol. in hot water, completely sol. in boiling water; insol. in alcohol and most org. solvs.

Powdered Aloe Vera (1:200) Food Grade. [Tri-K Industries]
Chem. Descrip.: Aloe vera gel
Uses: For suntan, sun treatment, burn gels, first aid creams, weight control prods.
Properties: Off-wh. to lt. beige powd., sl. vegetable odor to almost odorless, bland taste; pH 3.5-7.0 (0.5% aq.); 10% max. moisture
Storage: Store in tightly sealed container in cool, dry area below 120 F, protected from direct sunlight; hygroscopic.

Powdered Caramel Color 986010. [Crompton & Knowles/Ingred. Tech.]
Chem. Descrip.: Caramel powd.
CAS 8028-89-5; EINECS 232-435-9
Uses: Color additive for drugs; exc. resist. to heat and light
Regulatory: FDA 21CFR §73.85, 73.1085, 73.2085
Properties: Brn. free-flowing powd., typ. odor; 100% min. thru 80 mesh; sol. in water; pH 8.1 ± 0.5 (1%); 6% max. moisture
Storage: 2 yrs shelf life stored in tight containers; avoid exposure to excessive heat, light, and moisture.

Powdered Caramel Color, Acid Proof. [Crompton & Knowles/Ingred. Tech.]
Chem. Descrip.: Caramel powd.
CAS 8028-89-5; EINECS 232-435-9
Uses: Color additive for drugs
Regulatory: FDA 21CFR §73.85, 73.1085, 73.2085
Properties: Brn. free-flowing powd., typ. odor; 100% min. thru 80 mesh; sol. in water; pH 5.0 ± 0.5 (1%); 4% max. moisture
Storage: 2 yrs shelf life stored in tight containers; avoid exposure to excessive heat, light, and moisture.

Powdered Caramel Colour Non-Ammoniated-All Natural T-717. [MLG Enterprises Ltd.]
Chem. Descrip.: Caramel color
CAS 8028-89-5; EINECS 232-435-9
Uses: Natural colorant for pharmaceuticals
Regulatory: FDA 21CFR §73.85
Properties: 1% max. on 30 mesh, 58% max. on 200 mesh; pH 3.3 ± 0.3 (50%); 3.5 ± 0.3% moisture.

Powdered Guar Gum Type A. [Gumix Int'l.]
Chem. Descrip.: Guar gum
CAS 9000-30-0; EINECS 232-536-8
Uses: Thickener, visc. modifier, water-binder, stabilizer, lubricant for pharmaceuticals (appetite depressant, disintegrant and binder in compressed tablets)
Properties: Wh. to ylsh. powd., nearly odorless, bland taste; disp. in cold or hot water; insol. in org. solvs.

Powdered Guar Gum Type AA. [Gumix Int'l.]
Chem. Descrip.: Guar gum
CAS 9000-30-0; EINECS 232-536-8
Uses: Thickener, visc. modifier, water-binder, stabilizer, lubricant for pharmaceuticals (appetite depressant, disintegrant and binder in com-

pressed tablets)
Properties: Wh. to ylsh. powd., nearly odorless, bland taste; disp. in cold or hot water; insol. in org. solvs.

Powdered Guar Gum Type B. [Gumix Int'l.]
Chem. Descrip.: Guar gum
CAS 9000-30-0; EINECS 232-536-8
Uses: Thickener, visc. modifier, water-binder, stabilizer, lubricant for pharmaceuticals (appetite depressant, disintegrant and binder in compressed tablets)
Properties: Wh. to ylsh. powd., nearly odorless, bland taste; disp. in cold or hot water; insol. in org. solvs.

Powdered Guar Gum Type BB. [Gumix Int'l.]
Chem. Descrip.: Guar gum
CAS 9000-30-0; EINECS 232-536-8
Uses: Thickener, visc. modifier, water-binder, stabilizer, lubricant for pharmaceuticals (appetite depressant, disintegrant and binder in compressed tablets)
Properties: Wh. to ylsh. powd., nearly odorless, bland taste; disp. in cold or hot water; insol. in org. solvs.

Powdered Gum Arabic NF/FCC G-150. [Meer]
Chem. Descrip.: Gum arabic
CAS 9000-01-5; EINECS 232-519-5
Uses: Protective colloid, stabilizer, thickener, binder; pharmaceutical emulsions, antiseptics, to mask bitter or acid taste of medicaments, tablet binder, excipient
Properties: Colorless, odorless, tasteless; water-sol.

Powdered Gum Arabic NF/FCC Superselect Type NB-4. [Meer]
Chem. Descrip.: Gum arabic
CAS 9000-01-5; EINECS 232-519-5
Uses: Protective colloid, stabilizer, thickener, binder; pharmaceutical emulsions, antiseptics, to mask bitter or acid taste of medicaments, tablet binder, excipient
Properties: Colorless, odorless, tasteless; water-sol.

Powdered Gum Arabic Type B-100 NF Premium. [Gumix Int'l.]
Chem. Descrip.: Gum arabic
CAS 9000-01-5; EINECS 232-519-5
Uses: Protective colloid, stabilizer, suspending agent, viscosifier for pharmaceuticals (suspensions, emulsions, demulcent in cough drops/syrups, tablet binder/adhesive)
Properties: Powd., almost odorless and tasteless; sol. in hot or cold water.

Powdered Gum Arabic Type B-200 NF Premium. [Gumix Int'l.]
Chem. Descrip.: Gum arabic
CAS 9000-01-5; EINECS 232-519-5
Uses: Protective colloid, stabilizer, suspending agent, viscosifier for pharmaceuticals (suspensions, emulsions, demulcent in cough drops/syrups, tablet binder/adhesive)
Properties: Powd., almost odorless and tasteless;

sol. in hot or cold water.

Powdered Gum Ghatti #1. [Meer]
Chem. Descrip.: Gum ghatti
CAS 900-28-6
Uses: Stabilizer, binder, emulsifier forming o/w emulsions; tablet binder and thick mucilage coatings in pharmaceuticals
Properties: Off-wh. to lt. amber gum; 99% thru 80 mesh, ≥ 90% thru 100 mesh; visc. ≥ 100 cps (5%).

Powdered Gum Ghatti #2. [Meer]
Chem. Descrip.: Gum ghatti
CAS 900-28-6
Uses: Stabilizer, binder, emulsifier forming o/w emulsions; tablet binder and thick mucilage coatings in pharmaceuticals
Properties: Water-sol.

Powdered Gum Guar NF Type 80 Mesh B/T. [Meer]
Chem. Descrip.: Guar gum
CAS 9000-30-0; EINECS 232-536-8
Uses: Pharmaceutical tablet binder
Properties: Water-sol.

Powdered Gum Guar Type 140 Mesh B/T. [Meer]
Chem. Descrip.: Guar gum
CAS 9000-30-0; EINECS 232-536-8
Uses: Pharmaceutical tablet binder
Properties: Water-sol.

Powdered Gum Guar Type ECM. [Meer]
Chem. Descrip.: Guar gum
CAS 9000-30-0; EINECS 232-536-8
Uses: Pharmaceutical tablet binder
Properties: Water-sol.

Powdered Gum Guar Type M. [Meer]
Chem. Descrip.: Guar gum
CAS 9000-30-0; EINECS 232-536-8
Uses: Pharmaceutical tablet binder
Properties: Water-sol.

Powdered Gum Guar Type MM FCC. [Meer]
Chem. Descrip.: Guar gum
CAS 9000-30-0; EINECS 232-536-8
Uses: Pharmaceutical tablet binder
Properties: Wh. to cream-wh. fine powd., nearly odorless; 97% thru 140 mesh, ≥ 90% thru 200 mesh; visc. ≥ 3500 cps (1%); pH 5.0-6.4.

Powdered Gum Guar Type MM (HV) [Meer]
Chem. Descrip.: Guar gum
CAS 9000-30-0; EINECS 232-536-8
Uses: Pharmaceutical tablet binder
Properties: Water-sol.

Powdered Gum Guar Type MMM $^1/_2$. [Meer]
Chem. Descrip.: Guar gum
CAS 9000-30-0; EINECS 232-536-8
Uses: Pharmaceutical tablet binder
Properties: Water-sol.

Powdered Gum Guar Type MMW. [Meer]
Chem. Descrip.: Guar gum
CAS 9000-30-0; EINECS 232-536-8
Uses: Pharmaceutical tablet binder
Properties: Water-sol.

Powdered Gum Karaya Superfine #1 FCC. [Meer]
Chem. Descrip.: Karaya gum FCC
CAS 9000-36-6; EINECS 232-539-4
Uses: Stabilizer, water binder, emulsifier in phar-maceuticals (bulk laxatives, denture adhesives)
Properties: Water-sol.

Powdered Gum Karaya Superfine XXXX FCC. [Meer]
Chem. Descrip.: Karaya gum NF/FCC
CAS 9000-36-6; EINECS 232-539-4
Uses: Stabilizer, water binder, emulsifier in phar-maceuticals (bulk laxatives, denture adhesives)
Properties: Powd.; 100% thru 80 mesh, ≥ 60% thru 200 mesh; swells in water, insol. in alcohol; visc. ≥ 200 cps (1%); pH 4.4-4.8.

Powdered Gum Tragacanth BP. [Gumix Int'l.]
Chem. Descrip.: Tragacanth gum
CAS 9000-65-1; EINECS 232-552-5
Uses: Emulsifier, suspending agent, thickener, stabilizer, binder in pharmaceuticals (emulsions, jellies, creams, toothpastes)
Properties: Ylsh. wh. to tan powd., odorless, insipid taste; swells rapidly in hot or cold water; insol. in alcohol, other org. solvs.

Powdered Gum Tragacanth T-150. [Importers Service; Commodity Services Int'l.]
Chem. Descrip.: Gum tragacanth USP/NF/FCC
CAS 9000-65-1; EINECS 232-552-5
Uses: Emulsifier, thickener for pharmaceutical emulsions, ointments
Properties: Off-wh. free-flowing powd., bland mucilaginous odor and taste; 95% min. thru 140 mesh, 65% min. thru 200 mesh; visc. 1000 cps min. (1%); pH 5-6 (1%); 15% max. moisture.

Powdered Gum Tragacanth T-200. [Importers Service; Commodity Services Int'l.]
Chem. Descrip.: Gum tragacanth USP/NF/FCC
CAS 9000-65-1; EINECS 232-552-5
Uses: Emulsifier, thickener for pharmaceutical emulsions, ointments
Properties: Lt. cream to lt. yel. free-flowing powd., bland mucilaginous odor and taste; 95% min. thru 140 mesh, 65% min. thru 200 mesh; visc. 700 cps min. (1%); pH 5-6 (1%); 15% max. moisture.

Powdered Gum Tragacanth T-300. [Importers Service; Commodity Services Int'l.]
Chem. Descrip.: Gum tragacanth USP/NF/FCC
CAS 9000-65-1; EINECS 232-552-5
Uses: Emulsifier, thickener for pharmaceutical emulsions, ointments
Properties: Lt. cream to lt. yel. free-flowing powd., bland mucilaginous odor and taste; 95% min. thru 140 mesh, 65% min. thru 200 mesh; visc. 490 cps min. (1%); pH 5-6 (1%); 15% max. moisture.

Powdered Gum Tragacanth T-400. [Importers Service; Commodity Services Int'l.]
Chem. Descrip.: Gum tragacanth USP/NF/FCC
CAS 9000-65-1; EINECS 232-552-5
Uses: Emulsifier, thickener for pharmaceutical emulsions, ointments
Properties: Lt. cream to lt. yel. free-flowing powd., bland mucilaginous odor and taste; 95% min. thru 140 mesh, 65% min. thru 200 mesh; visc. 350 cps min. (1%); pH 5-6 (1%); 15% max. moisture.

Powdered Gum Tragacanth T-500. [Importers Service; Commodity Services Int'l.]

Chem. Descrip.: Gum tragacanth USP/NF/FCC
CAS 9000-65-1; EINECS 232-552-5
Uses: Emulsifier, thickener for pharmaceutical emulsions, ointments
Properties: Lt. cream to lt. yel. free-flowing powd., bland mucilaginous odor and taste; 95% min. thru 140 mesh, 65% min. thru 200 mesh; visc. 280 cps min. (1%); pH 5-6 (1%); 15% max. moisture.

Powdered Gum Tragacanth Type B-1 NF Premium. [Gumix Int'l.]
Chem. Descrip.: Tragacanth gum
CAS 9000-65-1; EINECS 232-552-5
Uses: Emulsifier, suspending agent, thickener, stabilizer, binder in pharmaceuticals (emulsions, jellies, creams, toothpastes)
Properties: Ylsh. wh. to tan powd., odorless, insipid taste; swells rapidly in hot or cold water; insol. in alcohol, other org. solvs.

Powdered Gum Tragacanth Type B-12 NF Premium. [Gumix Int'l.]
Chem. Descrip.: Tragacanth gum
CAS 9000-65-1; EINECS 232-552-5
Uses: Emulsifier, suspending agent, thickener, stabilizer, binder in pharmaceuticals (emulsions, jellies, creams, toothpastes)
Properties: Ylsh. wh. to tan powd., odorless, insipid taste; swells rapidly in hot or cold water; insol. in alcohol, other org. solvs.

Powdered Gum Tragacanth Type C-5 NF. [Gumix Int'l.]
Chem. Descrip.: Tragacanth gum
CAS 9000-65-1; EINECS 232-552-5
Uses: Emulsifier, suspending agent, thickener, stabilizer, binder in pharmaceuticals (emulsions, jellies, creams, toothpastes)
Properties: Ylsh. wh. to tan powd., odorless, insipid taste; swells rapidly in hot or cold water; insol. in alcohol, other org. solvs.

Powdered Gum Tragacanth Type G-1 NF Premium. [Gumix Int'l.]
Chem. Descrip.: Tragacanth gum
CAS 9000-65-1; EINECS 232-552-5
Uses: Emulsifier, suspending agent, thickener, stabilizer, binder in pharmaceuticals (emulsions, jellies, creams, toothpastes)
Properties: Ylsh. wh. to tan powd., odorless, insipid taste; swells rapidly in hot or cold water; insol. in alcohol, other org. solvs.

Powdered Gum Tragacanth Type G-2 NF Premium. [Gumix Int'l.]
Chem. Descrip.: Tragacanth gum
CAS 9000-65-1; EINECS 232-552-5
Uses: Emulsifier, suspending agent, thickener, stabilizer, binder in pharmaceuticals (emulsions, jellies, creams, toothpastes)
Properties: Ylsh. wh. to tan powd., odorless, insipid taste; swells rapidly in hot or cold water; insol. in alcohol, other org. solvs.

Powdered Gum Tragacanth Type G-2S NF Premium. [Gumix Int'l.]
Chem. Descrip.: Tragacanth gum
CAS 9000-65-1; EINECS 232-552-5

Uses: Emulsifier, suspending agent, thickener, stabilizer, binder in pharmaceuticals (emulsions, jellies, creams, toothpastes)
Properties: Ylsh. wh. to tan powd., odorless, insipid taste; swells rapidly in hot or cold water; insol. in alcohol, other org. solvs.

Powdered Gum Tragacanth Type M-3 NF Premium. [Gumix Int'l.]
Chem. Descrip.: Tragacanth gum
CAS 9000-65-1; EINECS 232-552-5
Uses: Emulsifier, suspending agent, thickener, stabilizer, binder in pharmaceuticals (emulsions, jellies, creams, toothpastes)
Properties: Ylsh. wh. to tan powd., odorless, insipid taste; swells rapidly in hot or cold water; insol. in alcohol, other org. solvs.

Powdered Locust Bean Gum Type D-200. [Meer]
Chem. Descrip.: Locust bean gum FCC
CAS 9000-40-2; EINECS 232-541-5
Uses: Excipient for pharmaceutical tablets; thickener for tooth paste
Properties: Water-sol.

Powdered Locust Bean Gum Type D-300. [Meer]
Chem. Descrip.: Locust bean gum FCC
CAS 9000-40-2; EINECS 232-541-5
Uses: Excipient for pharmaceutical tablets; thickener for tooth paste
Properties: Water-sol.

Powdered Locust Bean Gum Type P-100. [Meer]
Chem. Descrip.: Locust bean gum FCC
CAS 9000-40-2; EINECS 232-541-5
Uses: Excipient for pharmaceutical tablets; thickener for tooth paste
Properties: Water-sol.

Powdered Locust Bean Gum Type PP-100. [Meer]
Chem. Descrip.: Locust bean gum FCC
CAS 9000-40-2; EINECS 232-541-5
Uses: Excipient for pharmaceutical tablets; thickener for tooth paste
Properties: Water-sol.

Powdered Tragacanth Gum Type A/10. [Meer]
Chem. Descrip.: Tragacanth gum
CAS 9000-65-1; EINECS 232-552-5
Uses: Thickener, water binder, suspending agent, emulsifier for medicinal emulsions, pharmaceutical jellies and creams
Properties: Water-sol.

Powdered Tragacanth Gum Type E-1. [Meer]
Chem. Descrip.: Tragacanth gum
CAS 9000-65-1; EINECS 232-552-5
Uses: Thickener, water binder, suspending agent, emulsifier for medicinal emulsions, pharmaceutical jellies and creams
Properties: Water-sol.

Powdered Tragacanth Gum Type G-3. [Meer]
Chem. Descrip.: Tragacanth gum
CAS 9000-65-1; EINECS 232-552-5
Uses: Thickener, water binder, suspending agent, emulsifier for medicinal emulsions, pharmaceutical jellies and creams
Properties: Water-sol.

Powdered Tragacanth Gum Type L. [Meer]

Chem. Descrip.: Tragacanth gum
CAS 9000-65-1; EINECS 232-552-5
Uses: Thickener, water binder, suspending agent,
emulsifier for medicinal emulsions, pharmaceutical jellies and creams
Properties: Water-sol.

Powdered Tragacanth Gum Type W. [Meer]
Chem. Descrip.: Tragacanth gum NF
CAS 9000-65-1; EINECS 232-552-5
Uses: Thickener, water binder, suspending agent,
emulsifier for medicinal emulsions, pharmaceutical jellies and creams
Properties: Wh. to cream-wh. fine powd.; 100%
thru 80 mesh, ≥ 45% thru 200 mesh; visc. 420-520 cps (1%); pH 4.8-5.8.

PPA. [Hoechst AG; Hoechst Celanese/Fine Chems.]
Chem. Descrip.: Propane phosphonic acid anhydride, 50% sol'n. in ethyl acetate or DMF
Uses: Coupling reagent for peptide/amide synthesis for pharmaceuticals; > 90% purity
Storage: Unlimited shelf life stored tightly closed in a cool, dry place in original container.

Precifac ATO. [Gattefosse SA]
Chem. Descrip.: Cetyl palmitate
CAS 540-10-3; EINECS 208-736-6
Uses: Tableting agent and lipophilic matrix for pharmaceuticals
Properties: Drop pt. 48-52 C; HLB 2.0; acid no. < 6; iodine no. < 3; sapon. no. 95-120
Toxicology: LD0 (oral, rat) > 5 mg/kg.

Precirol ATO 5. [Gattefosse SA]
Chem. Descrip.: Tripalmitin and tristearin
Uses: Lipophilic agent, excipient, tableting agent,
binder, lubricant for solid/semisolid formulations,
sustained release; protects the drug, improves
stability of the dosage form
Properties: Solid; drop pt. 53-57 C; HLB 2.0; acid
no. < 6; iodine no. < 3; sapon. no. 175-195; 100%
conc.; nonionic
Toxicology: LD0 (oral, rat) > 6 g/kg.

Precirol WL 2155 ATO. [Gattefosse; Gattefosse SA]
Chem. Descrip.: Glyceryl ditristearate
CAS 8067-32-1
Uses: Additive for tablets mfg.
Properties: Solid; drop pt. 63.5-67.5 C; HLB 2.0;
acid no. < 6; iodine no. < 3; sapon. no. 180-190;
100% conc.; nonionic
Toxicology: LD0 (oral, rat) > 6 g/kg.

Pre-Gel Amaranth Powd. [Nu-World Amaranth]
Chem. Descrip.: Natural amaranth powd.
CAS 915-67-3; EINECS 213-022-2
Uses: Absorbent, diluent, disintegration agent,
nutrition, compression agent
Properties: Off-wh. free-flowing powd.; 4.5-6.0%
moisture.

Premium Powdered Gum Ghatti G-1. [Importers
Service; Commodity Services Int'l.]
Chem. Descrip.: Gum ghatti
CAS 900-28-6
Uses: Emulsifier, stabilizer for pharmaceuticals
Properties: Lt. brn. free-flowing powd., odorless;
99.9% min. thru 80 mesh, 98% min. thru 140

mesh; visc. 200 cps min. (5%); pH 4.5-5.2 (5%);
15% max. moisture.

Premium Powdered Gum Karaya No. 1. [Importers
Service; Commodity Services Int'l.]
Chem. Descrip.: Karaya gum
CAS 9000-36-6; EINECS 232-539-4
Uses: Used in pharmaceuticals
Properties: Buff to lt. tan free-flowing powd., faint
acetic acid-like odor; 99% min. thru 80 mesh; visc.
300 cps min. (1%), 7000 cps min. (2%); pH 4.3-5.0
(1%); 19% max. moisture.

Premium Powdered Gum Karaya No. 1 Special.
[Importers Service; Commodity Services Int'l.]
Chem. Descrip.: Karaya gum
CAS 9000-36-6; EINECS 232-539-4
Uses: Used in pharmaceuticals
Properties: Wh. to buff free-flowing powd., faint
acetic acid-like odor; 99% min. thru 80 mesh; visc.
400 cps min. (1%), 8000 cps min. (2%); pH 4.3-5.0
(1%); 20% max. moisture.

Premium Spray Dried Gum Arabic. [Importers Service; Commodity Services Int'l.]
Chem. Descrip.: Gum arabic
CAS 9000-01-5; EINECS 232-519-5
Uses: Emulsifier and tablet binder particularly well
suited for slugging operations
Properties: Wh. to cream free-flowing powd., odorless, tasteless; 99% min. thru 60 mesh, 80% min.
thru 140 mesh; visc. 150 cps max. (20%); pH 4.0-4.8 (20%); 12% max. moisture.

Pricerine 9088. [Unichema Int'l.; Unichema N. Am.]
Chem. Descrip.: Glycerin USP
CAS 56-81-5; EINECS 200-289-5
Uses: Tonicity agent, emollient, humectant for
pharmaceuticals
Properties: APHA 10 max. color, char. odor; sp.gr.
1.2608 min.; 99.5% min. act.

Primojel®. [Generichem]
Chem. Descrip.: Sodium starch glycolate
CAS 9063-38-1
Uses: Tablet disintegrant
Properties: Bulk dens. 0.769 g/cc.

Prolase® 300. [Gist-brocades]
Chem. Descrip.: Protease (papain)
CAS 9014-01-1; EINECS 232-752-2
Uses: Pharmaceutical grade enzyme; protein digestive aid; also for removal of protein from soft
contact lenses
Properties: Powd.

Promulgen® D. [Amerchol]
Chem. Descrip.: Cetearyl alcohol and ceteareth-20
Uses: Gellant, o/w emulsifier, emollient, and stabilizer for pharmaceuticals; highly resist. to acidic
and alkaline conditions
Properties: Wh. waxy solid; odorless; m.p. 47-55 C;
acid no. 1 max.; sapon. no. 2 max.; 100% conc.;
nonionic.

Promulgen® G. [Amerchol]
Chem. Descrip.: Stearyl alcohol and ceteareth-20
Uses: Gellant, o/w emulsifier, emollient, and stabilizer for pharmaceuticals; highly resist. to acidic
and alkaline conditions

Properties: Yel. liq.; sp.gr. 0.848; visc. 35 cps; m.p. 55-63 C; acid no. 1 max.; sapon. no. 2 max.; 100% act.; nonionic.

Pronova™. [Pronova Biopolymer]
Chem. Descrip.: Sodium hyaluronate
CAS 9067-32-7
Uses: Polysaccharides used for medical, pharmaceutical, veterinary, botanical, microbiological uses.

Pronova™ LVG. [Pronova Biopolymer]
Chem. Descrip.: Sodium alginate
CAS 9005-38-3
Uses: Low visc. grade.

Pronova™ LVM [Pronova Biopolymer]
Chem. Descrip.: Sodium alginate
CAS 9005-38-3
Uses: Low visc. grade.

Pronova™ MVG. [Pronova Biopolymer]
Chem. Descrip.: Sodium alginate
CAS 9005-38-3
Uses: Med. visc. grade.

Pronova™ MVM. [Pronova Biopolymer]
Chem. Descrip.: Sodium alginate
CAS 9005-38-3
Uses: Med. visc. grade.

Pronova™ P LVG. [Pronova Biopolymer]
Chem. Descrip.: Sodium alginate
CAS 9005-38-3
Uses: Endotoxin spec. (< 10,000 EU/g).

Pronova™ P MVG. [Pronova Biopolymer]
Chem. Descrip.: Sodium alginate
CAS 9005-38-3
Uses: Endotoxin spec. (< 10,000 EU/g).

Pronova™ UP MVG. [Pronova Biopolymer]
Chem. Descrip.: Sodium alginate
CAS 9005-38-3
Uses: Highest avail. purity; recommended for *in vivo* uses; very low endotoxin content (< 1500 EU/g).

Propylene Glycol USP/FCC Ultra Grade. [Eastman]
Chem. Descrip.: Propylene glycol USP/FCC
CAS 57-55-6; EINECS 200-338-0
Uses: Solv. for org. chems. for medicinal purposes, some water-sol. vitamins, dyes, perfumes; softening agent, spreader, emollient, humectant and preservative for pharmaceuticals; vehicle for drugs, ointments
Regulatory: FDA 21CFR §184.1666, GRAS; EPA exempt from pesticide tolerances; USDA accepted; kosher
Properties: Colorless clear visc. liq., essentially odorless, sl. char. taste; misc. with water, acetone, chloroform; sp.gr. 1.0351-1.0364; i.b.p. 186 C min.; 99.5% min. purity
Storage: Hygroscopic; storage in lined steel tank recommended; becomes quite visc. at low temps.

Propylene Phenoxetol. [Nipa Hardwicke]
Chem. Descrip.: Phenoxyisopropanol
CAS 4169-04-4; EINECS 224-027-4
Uses: Antiseptic for skin care prods.
Properties: Colorless sl. visc. liq., faint pleasant odor; sl. sol. in water; misc. with ethanol and acetone; dens. 1.062 g/ml (20 C); flash pt. (OC) 121 C
Toxicology: LD50 (oral, rat) 2.4 ml/kg, sl. harmful by ing.; produces local anesthetic effect on lips, tongue, mucous membranes; pure material is mod. irritating to skin and eyes; nonirritating to skin @ 5%; nonirritating to eyes @ 1%
Precaution: Very sl. fire risk; no explosion hazard
Storage: Store in orig. container under normal indoor storage conditions; material may solidify at low temps.

Propyl Parasept® NF/FCC. [Nipa Hardwicke]
Chem. Descrip.: Propylparaben NF/FCC
CAS 94-13-3; EINECS 202-307-7
Uses: Preservative for pharmaceuticals, suppositories, eye washes, pills, anesthetics, syrups, injectable sol'ns., contraceptives, gelatin capsules, ointments, tinctures, OTC drugs; inactive ingred. in dentifrices, topical analgesics; active antimycotic
Properties: Wh. fine powd., pract. odorless and tasteless; sol. 124% in methanol, 95% in ethanol (100%), 84% in acetone, 50% in ether, 26% in propylene glycol (100%), 0.02% in water; m.w. 180.20; m.p. 95-98 C; nonhygroscipic; 99-100.5% assay
Toxicology: Avoid prolonged/repeated skin contact
Storage: Avoid exposure to high humidity and elevated temps. in storage.

Prosweet™ Liq. [Virginia Dare Extract]
Chem. Descrip.: Natural and artificial flavor
Uses: Multifunctional blend of flavor ingreds. to enhance flavor and reduce objectionable bitterness for pharmaceuticals, chewable tablets, cough drops, lozenges, mouthwashes and sprays, syrups and elixirs, toothpastes; prolonges flavor, enhances sweetness
Use level: 0.25-1.% (pharmaceutical)
Properties: Liq.

Prosweet™ Powd. [Virginia Dare Extract]
Chem. Descrip.: Natural and artificial flavor
Uses: Multifunctional blend of flavor ingreds. to enhance flavor and reduce objectionable bitterness for pharmaceuticals, chewable tablets, cough drops, lozenges, mouthwashes and sprays, syrups and elixirs, toothpastes; prolonges flavor, enhances sweetness
Use level: 0.25-1.% (pharmaceutical)
Properties: Powd.

Protacid F 120. [Pronova Biopolymer]
Chem. Descrip.: Alginic acid
CAS 9005-32-7; EINECS 232-680-1
Uses: Disintegrant and gel former useful for sustained-release suppositories, in treatment of esophageal reflux
Properties: Wh. to tan powd., sl. odor; 120 mesh (BS); sol. in alkali; insol. in water; $BOD_5 \approx 300$ mg O_2/g; $COD \approx 660$ mg O_2/g
Toxicology: TLV 10 mg/m^3 total dust (nuisance dust); LD50 (oral, rat) > 5 g/kg, essentially nontoxic; may cause eye irritation; excessive inh. of dust can impede respiration

Precaution: Combustible dust; will burn in contact with flame and self-extinguish when ignition source is removed; incompat. with strong oxidizing agents; spillages may be slippery
Storage: Store in cool, dry place.

Protanal KF 200. [Pronova Biopolymer]
Chem. Descrip.: Potassium alginate
CAS 9005-36-1
Uses: Gellant for dental impression materials
Properties: Wh. to tan powd., sl. odor; 200 mesh (BS); water-sol.; visc. 200-400 mPa•s (1%); BOD$_5$ ≈ 300 mg O$_2$/g; COD ≈ 660 mg O$_2$/g
Toxicology: TLV 10 mg/m^3 total dust (nuisance dust); LD50 (oral, rat) > 5 g/kg, essentially non-toxic; may cause eye irritation; excessive inh. of dust can impede respiration
Precaution: Combustible dust; will burn in contact with flame, self-extinguishes when ignition source is removed; incompat. with strong oxidizing agents; spillages may be slippery
Storage: Store in cool, dry place.

Protanal KF 200 RBS. [Pronova Biopolymer]
Chem. Descrip.: Potassium alginate
CAS 9005-36-1
Uses: Gellant for dental impression materials
Properties: Wh. to tan powd., sl. odor; 200 mesh (BS); water-sol.; visc. 200-400 mPa•s (1%); BOD$_5$ ≈ 300 mg O$_2$/g; COD ≈ 660 mg O$_2$/g
Toxicology: TLV 10 mg/m^3 total dust (nuisance dust); LD50 (oral, rat) > 5 g/kg, essentially non-toxic; may cause eye irritation; excessive inh. of dust can impede respiration
Precaution: Combustible dust; will burn in contact with flame, self-extinguishes when ignition source is removed; incompat. with strong oxidizing agents; spillages may be slippery
Storage: Store in cool, dry place.

Protanal KF 200 S. [Pronova Biopolymer]
Chem. Descrip.: Potassium alginate
CAS 9005-36-1
Uses: Gellant for dental impression materials
Properties: Wh. to tan powd., sl. odor; 200 mesh (BS); water-sol.; visc. 200-400 mPa•s (1%); BOD$_5$ ≈ 300 mg O$_2$/g; COD ≈ 660 mg O$_2$/g
Toxicology: TLV 10 mg/m^3 total dust (nuisance dust); LD50 (oral, rat) > 5 g/kg, essentially non-toxic; may cause eye irritation; excessive inh. of dust can impede respiration
Precaution: Combustible dust; will burn in contact with flame, self-extinguishes when ignition source is removed; incompat. with strong oxidizing agents; spillages may be slippery
Storage: Store in cool, dry place.

Protanal LF 5/60. [Pronova Biopolymer]
Chem. Descrip.: Sodium alginate
CAS 9005-38-3
Uses: Useful in pharmaceuticals in treatment of esophageal reflux
Properties: Wh. to tan powd., sl. odor; 60 mesh (BS); water-sol.; visc. 10-40 mPa•s (1%); BOD$_5$ ≈ 300 mg O$_2$/g; COD ≈ 660 mg O$_2$/g
Toxicology: TLV 10 mg/m^3 total dust (nuisance

dust); LD50 (oral, rat) > 5 g/kg, essentially nontoxic; may cause eye irritation; excessive inh. of dust can impede respiration
Precaution: Combustible dust; will burn in contact with flame, self-extinguishes when ignition source is removed; incompat. with strong oxidizing agents; spillages may be slippery
Storage: Store in cool, dry place.

Protanal LF 10/40. [Pronova Biopolymer]
Chem. Descrip.: Sodium alginate
CAS 9005-38-3
Uses: Forms gels useful in dermatology and wound healing
Properties: Wh. to tan powd., sl. odor; 40 mesh (BS); water-sol.; visc. 10-40 mPa•s (1%); BOD$_5$ ≈ 300 mg O$_2$/g; COD ≈ 660 mg O$_2$/g
Toxicology: TLV 10 mg/m^3 total dust (nuisance dust); LD50 (oral, rat) > 5 g/kg, essentially non-toxic; may cause eye irritation; excessive inh. of dust can impede respiration
Precaution: Combustible dust; will burn in contact with flame, self-extinguishes when ignition source is removed; incompat. with strong oxidizing agents; spillages may be slippery
Storage: Store in cool, dry place.

Protanal LF 10/60. [Pronova Biopolymer]
Chem. Descrip.: Sodium alginate
CAS 9005-38-3
Uses: Pharmaceutical excipient; tablet binding agent; thickener, stabilizing agent; in larger amts. in sustained-release dosages; forms gels useful in dermatology and wound healing
Properties: Wh. to tan powd., sl. odor; 60 mesh (BS); water-sol.; visc. 40-70 mPa•s (1%); BOD$_5$ ≈ 300 mg O$_2$/g; COD ≈ 660 mg O$_2$/g
Toxicology: TLV 10 mg/m^3 total dust (nuisance dust); LD50 (oral, rat) > 5 g/kg, essentially non-toxic; may cause eye irritation; excessive inh. of dust can impede respiration
Precaution: Combustible dust; will burn in contact with flame, self-extinguishes when ignition source is removed; incompat. with strong oxidizing agents; spillages may be slippery
Storage: Store in cool, dry place.

Protanal LF 20/200. [Pronova Biopolymer]
Chem. Descrip.: Sodium alginate
CAS 9005-38-3
Uses: Pharmaceutical excipient; tablet binding agent; thickener, stabilizing agent; gellant for sustained-release pharmaceutical tablets, microencapsulation, oral suspensions
Properties: Wh. to tan powd., sl. odor; 200 mesh (BS); water-sol.; visc. 100-200 mPa•s (1%); BOD$_5$ ≈ 300 mg O$_2$/g; COD ≈ 660 mg O$_2$/g
Toxicology: TLV 10 mg/m^3 total dust (nuisance dust); LD50 (oral, rat) > 5 g/kg, essentially non-toxic; may cause eye irritation; excessive inh. of dust can impede respiration
Precaution: Combustible dust; will burn in contact with flame, self-extinguishes when ignition source is removed; incompat. with strong oxidizing agents; spillages may be slippery

Storage: Store in cool, dry place.

Protanal LF 120 M. [Pronova Biopolymer]
Chem. Descrip.: Sodium alginate
CAS 9005-38-3
Uses: Gellant for sustained-release pharmaceutical tablets, microencapsulation, oral suspensions; forms gels useful in dermatology and wound healing
Properties: Wh. to tan powd., sl. odor; 120 mesh (BS); water-sol.; visc. 70-150 mPa•s (1%); BOD_5 ≈ 300 mg O_2/g; COD ≈ 660 mg O_2/g
Toxicology: TLV 10 mg/m^3 total dust (nuisance dust); LD50 (oral, rat) > 5 g/kg, essentially nontoxic; may cause eye irritation; excessive inh. of dust can impede respiration
Precaution: Combustible dust; will burn in contact with flame, self-extinguishes when ignition source is removed; incompat. with strong oxidizing agents; spillages may be slippery
Storage: Store in cool, dry place.

Protanal LF 200. [Pronova Biopolymer]
Chem. Descrip.: Sodium alginate
CAS 9005-38-3
Uses: Pharmaceutical excipient; tablet binding agent; thickener, stabilizing agent; in larger amts. in sustained-release dosages; gellant for dental impression materials
Properties: Wh. to tan powd., sl. odor; 200 mesh (BS); water-sol.; visc. 200-400 mPa•s (1%); BOD_5 ≈ 300 mg O_2/g; COD ≈ 660 mg O_2/g
Toxicology: TLV 10 mg/m^3 total dust (nuisance dust); LD50 (oral, rat) > 5 g/kg, essentially nontoxic; may cause eye irritation; excessive inh. of dust can impede respiration
Precaution: Combustible dust; will burn in contact with flame, self-extinguishes when ignition source is removed; incompat. with strong oxidizing agents; spillages may be slippery
Storage: Store in cool, dry place.

Protanal LF 200 M. [Pronova Biopolymer]
Chem. Descrip.: Sodium alginate
CAS 9005-38-3
Uses: Gellant for sustained-release pharmaceutical tablets, microencapsulation, oral suspensions; dental impression materials
Properties: Wh. to tan powd., sl. odor; 200 mesh (BS); water-sol.; visc. 70-150 mPa•s (1%); BOD_5 ≈ 300 mg O_2/g; COD ≈ 660 mg O_2/g
Toxicology: TLV 10 mg/m^3 total dust (nuisance dust); LD50 (oral, rat) > 5 g/kg, essentially nontoxic; may cause eye irritation; excessive inh. of dust can impede respiration
Precaution: Combustible dust; will burn in contact with flame, self-extinguishes when ignition source is removed; incompat. with strong oxidizing agents; spillages may be slippery
Storage: Store in cool, dry place.

Protanal LF 200 RB. [Pronova Biopolymer]
Chem. Descrip.: Sodium alginate
CAS 9005-38-3
Uses: Gellant for sustained-release pharmaceutical tablets, microencapsulation, oral suspen-

sions
Properties: Wh. to tan powd., sl. odor; 200 mesh (BS); water-sol.; visc. 200-400 mPa•s (1%); BOD_5 ≈ 300 mg O_2/g; COD ≈ 660 mg O_2/g
Toxicology: TLV 10 mg/m^3 total dust (nuisance dust); LD50 (oral, rat) > 5 g/kg, essentially nontoxic; may cause eye irritation; excessive inh. of dust can impede respiration
Precaution: Combustible dust; will burn in contact with flame, self-extinguishes when ignition source is removed; incompat. with strong oxidizing agents; spillages may be slippery
Storage: Store in cool, dry place.

Protanal LF 200 S. [Pronova Biopolymer]
Chem. Descrip.: Sodium alginate
CAS 9005-38-3
Uses: Gellant for dental impression materials
Properties: Wh. to tan powd., sl. odor; 200 mesh (BS); water-sol.; visc. 200-400 mPa•s (1%); BOD_5 ≈ 300 mg O_2/g; COD ≈ 660 mg O_2/g
Toxicology: TLV 10 mg/m^3 total dust (nuisance dust); LD50 (oral, rat) > 5 g/kg, essentially nontoxic; may cause eye irritation; excessive inh. of dust can impede respiration
Precaution: Combustible dust; will burn in contact with flame, self-extinguishes when ignition source is removed; incompat. with strong oxidizing agents; spillages may be slippery
Storage: Store in cool, dry place.

Protanal LFMg 5/60. [Pronova Biopolymer]
Chem. Descrip.: Magnesium alginate
Uses: Useful in pharmaceuticals in treatment of esophageal reflux
Properties: Powd.; 60 mesh (BS); visc. 10-40 mPa•s (1%).

Protanal LFR 5/60. [Pronova Biopolymer]
Chem. Descrip.: Sodium alginate
CAS 9005-38-3
Uses: Useful in treatment of esophageal reflux
Properties: Wh. to tan powd., sl. odor; 60 mesh (BS); water-sol.; visc. < 10 mPa•s (1%); BOD_5 ≈ 300 mg O_2/g; COD ≈ 660 mg O_2/g
Toxicology: TLV 10 mg/m^3 total dust (nuisance dust); LD50 (oral, rat) > 5 g/kg, essentially nontoxic; may cause eye irritation; excessive inh. of dust can impede respiration
Precaution: Combustible dust; will burn in contact with flame, self-extinguishes when ignition source is removed; incompat. with strong oxidizing agents; spillages may be slippery
Storage: Store in cool, dry place.

Protanal SF. [Pronova Biopolymer]
Chem. Descrip.: Sodium alginate
CAS 9005-38-3
Uses: Pharmaceutical excipient; tablet binding agent; thickener, stabilizing agent; in larger amts. in sustained-release dosages
Properties: Wh. to tan powd., sl. odor; 16 mesh (BS); water-sol.; visc. 400-600 mPa•s (1%); BOD_5 ≈ 300 mg O_2/g; COD ≈ 660 mg O_2/g
Toxicology: TLV 10 mg/m^3 total dust (nuisance dust); LD50 (oral, rat) > 5 g/kg, essentially non-

toxic; may cause eye irritation; excessive inh. of dust can impede respiration

Precaution: Combustible dust; will burn in contact with flame, self-extinguishes when ignition source is removed; incompat. with strong oxidizing agents; spillages may be slippery

Storage: Store in cool, dry place.

Protanal SF 120. [Pronova Biopolymer]

Chem. Descrip.: Sodium alginate

CAS 9005-38-3

Uses: Pharmaceutical excipient; tablet binding agent; thickener, stabilizing agent; in larger amts. in sustained-release dosages

Properties: Wh. to tan powd., sl. odor; 120 mesh (BS); water-sol.; visc. 400-600 mPa•s (1%); BOD_5 ≈ 300 mg O_2/g; COD ≈ 660 mg O_2/g

Toxicology: TLV 10 mg/m^3 total dust (nuisance dust); LD50 (oral, rat) > 5 g/kg, essentially nontoxic; may cause eye irritation; excessive inh. of dust can impede respiration

Precaution: Combustible dust; will burn in contact with flame, self-extinguishes when ignition source is removed; incompat. with strong oxidizing agents; spillages may be slippery

Storage: Store in cool, dry place.

Protanal SF 120 RB. [Pronova Biopolymer]

Chem. Descrip.: Sodium alginate

CAS 9005-38-3

Uses: Gellant for sustained-release pharmaceutical tablets, microencapsulation, oral suspensions

Properties: Wh. to tan powd., sl. odor; 120 mesh (BS); water-sol.; visc. 400-600 mPa•s (1%); BOD_5 ≈ 300 mg O_2/g; COD ≈ 660 mg O_2/g

Toxicology: TLV 10 mg/m^3 total dust (nuisance dust); LD50 (oral, rat) > 5 g/kg, essentially nontoxic; may cause eye irritation; excessive inh. of dust can impede respiration

Precaution: Combustible dust; will burn in contact with flame, self-extinguishes when ignition source is removed; incompat. with strong oxidizing agents; spillages may be slippery

Storage: Store in cool, dry place.

Protanal TA 250. [Pronova Biopolymer]

Chem. Descrip.: Triethanolamine alginate

Uses: Gellant for dental impression materials

Properties: Powd.; 200 mesh (BS); visc. 200-300 mPa•s (1%).

Protanal TA 375. [Pronova Biopolymer]

Chem. Descrip.: Triethanolamine alginate

Uses: Gellant for dental impression materials

Properties: Powd.; 200 mesh (BS); visc. 400-500 mPa•s (1%).

Protanal TFX 200. [Pronova Biopolymer]

Chem. Descrip.: Calcium alginate

CAS 9005-35-0

Uses: Gellant for sustained-release pharmaceutical oral suspensions; forms gels useful in dermatology and wound healing

Properties: Wh. to tan powd., sl. odor; 200 mesh (BS); insol. in water; visc. 100-400 mPa•s (1%); BOD_5 ≈ 300 mg O_2/g; COD ≈ 660 mg O_2/g

Toxicology: TLV 10 mg/m^3 total dust (nuisance dust); LD50 (oral, rat) > 5 g/kg, essentially nontoxic; may cause eye irritation; excessive inh. of dust can impede respiration

Precaution: Combustible dust; will burn in contact with flame, self-extinguishes when ignition source is removed; incompat. with strong oxidizing agents; spillages may be slippery

Storage: Store in cool, dry place.

Protegin®. [Goldschmidt; Goldschmidt AG]

Chem. Descrip.: Min. oil, petrolatum, ozokerite, glyceryl oleate, lanolin alcohol

Uses: Emollient, emulsifier; absorption base for w/ o pharmaceutical emulsions

Properties: lovry soft waxy solid; sol. warm in min. oil, sol. warm with sl. turbidity in veg. oils; insol. in water; m.p. 58-65 C; HLB 3.0; acid no. 1 max.; sapon. no. 8-12; hyd. no. 18-30; 100% conc.; nonionic.

Protegin® W. [Goldschmidt; Goldschmidt AG]

Chem. Descrip.: Petrolatum, ozokerite, hydrog. castor oil, glyceryl isostearate, polyglyceryl-3 oleate

Uses: SE w/o emulsifier, emollient, absorp. base for pharmaceuticals

Properties: Ivory waxy solid; sol. warm in veg. and min. oils; disp. warm in water; m.p. 75-82 C; HLB 3.0; acid no. 1 max.; sapon. no. 18-28; hyd. no. 18-28; 100% conc.; nonionic.

Protegin® WX. [Goldschmidt; Goldschmidt AG]

Chem. Descrip.: Petrolatum, ozokerite, hydrog. castor oil, glyceryl isostearate, polyglyceryl-3 oleate

Uses: SE w/o emulsifier, emollient, absorp. base for pharmaceuticals

Properties: Ivory waxy solid; sol. warm in veg. and min. oils; disp. warm in water; m.p. 76-83 C; HLB 3.5; acid no. 1 max.; sapon. no. 27-37; hyd. no. 32-42; 100% conc.; nonionic.

Protegin® X. [Goldschmidt; Goldschmidt AG]

Chem. Descrip.: Min. oil, petrolatum, ozokerite, glyceryl oleate, lanolin alcohol

Uses: SE w/o emulsifier, emollient, absorp. base for pharmaceuticals

Properties: Ivory waxy paste; sol. warm in min. oil, sol. warm with sl. turbidity in veg. oils; insol. in water; m.p. 58-65 C; HLB 3.5; acid no. 1 max.; sapon. no. 10-16; hyd. no. 25-38; 100% conc.; nonionic.

Proteol UCO. [Seppic]

Chem. Descrip.: Sodium-TEA undecylenoyl collagen amino acids

Uses: Foaming lipoprotein, fungistat for antidandruff shampoos

Use level: 5-20% (dermatological soap), 515% (antidandruff shampoos), 3-10% (foaming formulations)

Properties: Brn. liq.; dens. 1.045-1.055; visc. 5-15 mm^2/s (30 C); pH 6.8-7.2; anionic; 90% min. biodeg.

Toxicology: Nontoxic; nonirritating to skin; eye irritant

Storage: 3 yrs storage life; may become cloudy during storage-warming reclarifies.

Protol®. [Witco/Petroleum Spec.]
Chem. Descrip.: Wh. min. oil USP
Uses: Emollient, lubricant in pharmaceutical creams and lotions
Regulatory: FDA 21CFR §172.878, §178.3620a
Properties: Water-wh., odorless, tasteless; sp.gr. 0.859-0.875; visc. 35-37 cSt (40 C); pour pt. -12 C; flash pt. 188 C.

Protopet® Alba. [Witco/Petroleum Spec.]
Chem. Descrip.: Petrolatum USP
CAS 8027-32-5; EINECS 232-373-2
Uses: Med. consistency and m.p. petrolatum functioning as carrier, lubricant, emollient, moisture barrier, protective agent, softener for pharmaceutical ointments, suncare prods.
Regulatory: FDA 21CFR §172.880
Properties: Lovibond 1.0Y color, odorless; visc. 10-16 cSt (100 C); m.p. 54-60 C.

Protopet® White 1S. [Witco/Petroleum Spec.]
Chem. Descrip.: Petrolatum USP
CAS 8027-32-5; EINECS 232-373-2
Uses: Med. consistency and m.p. petrolatum functioning as carrier, lubricant, emollient, moisture barrier, protective agent, softener for pharmaceutical ointments, suppositories, dental adhesives, suncare prods.
Regulatory: FDA 21CFR §172.880
Properties: Lovibond 1.5Y color, odorless; visc. 10-16 cSt (100 C); m.p. 54-60 C.

Protopet® White 2L. [Witco/Petroleum Spec.]
Chem. Descrip.: Petrolatum USP
CAS 8027-32-5; EINECS 232-373-2
Uses: Med. consistency and m.p. petrolatum functioning as carrier, lubricant, emollient, moisture barrier, protective agent, softener for pharmaceutical ointments
Regulatory: FDA 21CFR §172.880
Properties: Lovibond 8Y0.6R color, odorless; visc. 10-16 cSt (100 C); m.p. 54-60 C.

Protopet® White 3C. [Witco/Petroleum Spec.]
Chem. Descrip.: Petrolatum USP
CAS 8027-32-5; EINECS 232-373-2
Uses: Med. consistency and m.p. petrolatum functioning as carrier, lubricant, emollient, moisture barrier, protective agent, softener for pharmaceutical ointments
Regulatory: FDA 21CFR §172.880
Properties: Lovibond 25Y1.0R color, odorless; visc. 10-16 cSt (100 C); m.p. 54-60 C.

Protopet® Yellow 2A. [Witco/Petroleum Spec.]
Chem. Descrip.: Petrolatum USP
CAS 8027-32-5; EINECS 232-373-2
Uses: Med. consistency and m.p. petrolatum functioning as carrier, lubricant, emollient, moisture barrier, protective agent, softener for pharmaceutical ointments, suppositories, suncare prods.
Regulatory: FDA 21CFR §172.880
Properties: Lovibond 30Y/2.5R color, odorless; visc. 10-16 cSt (100 C); m.p. 54-60 C.

Protopet® Yellow 3C. [Witco/Petroleum Spec.]

Chem. Descrip.: Petrolatum USP
CAS 8027-32-5; EINECS 232-373-2
Uses: Ingred. in ointments; lubricant in pharmaceutical mfg.
Properties: Amber or yel.; visc. 50-60 SUS (210 F); m.p. 52-60 C.

Protopet® Yellow A. [Witco/Petroleum Spec.]
Chem. Descrip.: Wh. petrolatum USP
CAS 8027-32-5; EINECS 232-373-2
Uses: Ingred. in ointments; lubricant in pharmaceutical mfg.
Properties: Wh.; visc. 50-60 SUS (210 F); m.p. 52-60 C.

Prox-onic EP 1090-1. [Protex]
Chem. Descrip.: Difunctional block polymer ending in primary hydroxyl groups
Uses: Defoamer for pharmaceuticals
Properties: Liq.; m.w. 2000; HLB 3.0; cloud pt. 24 C (1% aq.); 100% act.; nonionic
Unverified

Prox-onic L 081-05. [Protex]
Chem. Descrip.: POE (5) linear alcohol ether
Uses: Low foam wetting agent, emulsifier, coupling agent, solubilizer for pharmaceutical emulsions, antiperspirants; biodeg.
Unverified

Prox-onic L 101-05. [Protex]
Chem. Descrip.: POE (5) linear alcohol ether
Uses: Low foam wetting agent, emulsifier, coupling agent, solubilizer for pharmaceutical emulsions, antiperspirants; biodeg.
Unverified

Prox-onic L 102-02. [Protex]
Chem. Descrip.: POE (2) linear alcohol ether
Uses: Low foam wetting agent, emulsifier, coupling agent, solubilizer for pharmaceutical emulsions, antiperspirants; biodeg.
Unverified

Prox-onic L 121-09. [Protex]
Chem. Descrip.: POE (9) linear alcohol ether
Uses: Low foam wetting agent, emulsifier, coupling agent, solubilizer for pharmaceutical emulsions, antiperspirants; biodeg.
Unverified

Prox-onic L 161-05. [Protex]
Chem. Descrip.: POE (5) linear alcohol ether
Uses: Low foam wetting agent, emulsifier, coupling agent, solubilizer for pharmaceutical emulsions, antiperspirants; biodeg.
Unverified

Prox-onic L 181-05. [Protex]
Chem. Descrip.: POE (5) linear alcohol ether
Uses: Low foam wetting agent, emulsifier, coupling agent, solubilizer for pharmaceutical emulsions, antiperspirants; biodeg.
Unverified

Prox-onic L 201-02. [Protex]
Chem. Descrip.: POE (2.5) linear alcohol ether
Uses: Low foam wetting agent, emulsifier, coupling agent, solubilizer for pharmaceutical emulsions, antiperspirants; biodeg.
Unverified

Prox-onic OA-1/020. [Protex]
Chem. Descrip.: Oleth-20
CAS 9004-98-2
Uses: Solubilizer/emulsifier for essential oils, pharmaceuticals
Properties: Solid; HLB 15.3; cloud pt. > 100 C (1% aq.); nonionic
Unverified

Prox-onic OA-2/020. [Protex]
Chem. Descrip.: Oleth-20
CAS 9004-98-2
Uses: Solubilizer/emulsifier for essential oils, pharmaceuticals
Properties: Liq.; HLB 15.3; cloud pt. > 100 C (1% aq.); nonionic
Unverified

Prox-onic PEG-2000. [Protex]
Chem. Descrip.: PEG-2M
CAS 25322-68-3
Uses: Low foam wetting agent, emulsifier in pharmaceutical emulsions
Properties: M.w. 2000; solid. pt. 48-52 C; hyd. no. 51-62
Unverified

Prox-onic PEG-10,000. [Protex]
Chem. Descrip.: PEG-10M
CAS 25322-68-3
Uses: Low foam wetting agent, emulsifier in pharmaceutical emulsions
Properties: M.w. 10,000; solid. pt. 55-60 C; hyd. no. 9-12
Unverified

Prox-onic PEG-20,000. [Protex]
Chem. Descrip.: PEG-20M
CAS 25322-68-3
Uses: Low foam wetting agent, emulsifier in pharmaceutical emulsions
Properties: M.w. 20,000; solid. pt. 60 C; hyd. no. 7-11
Unverified

Prox-onic PEG-35,000. [Protex]
Chem. Descrip.: PEG-35M
CAS 25322-68-3
Uses: Low foam wetting agent, emulsifier in pharmaceutical emulsions
Properties: M.w. 35,000; solid. pt. 60 C; hyd. no. < 7
Unverified

Pruv™. [Mendell]
Chem. Descrip.: Sodium stearyl fumarate NF/FCC
CAS 4070-80-8
Uses: Lubricant for pharmaceutical tablets
Properties: Wh. fine powd. with agglomerates of flat, circular shaped particles ≤ 8 µm; sol. 20 g/100 ml of water (90 C); dens. (tapped) 0.3-0.5 g/cm; m.p. 224-245 C with decomp.; sapon. no. 142-146; 100% conc.

PTAL. [Mitsubishi Gas]
Chem. Descrip.: p-Tolualdehyde
CAS 104-87-0; EINECS 203-246-9
Uses: Intermediate for pharmaceuticals
Properties: Colorless liq., aromatic odor; sol.
0.27% in water @ 40 C; m.w. 120.2; b.p. 205.9 C; m.p. -5.6 C; acid no. 0.2; flash pt. (COC) 88 C; 96.4% purity
Toxicology: LD50 (oral, rat) 1000 mg/kg; eye and skin irritant
Unverified

Punctilious® SDA 1-1. [Quantum/USI]
Chem. Descrip.: Specially denatured ethanol
CAS 64-17-5; EINECS 200-578-6
Uses: Solv. or thinner; used in external pharmaceuticals
Properties: Sol. in methanol; misc. in ether, water, chloroform.

Purac® PH 88. [Purac Am.]
Chem. Descrip.: Lactic acid, pharmaceutical grade
CAS 50-21-5
Uses: Humectant, preservative, pharmaceutical intermediate
Regulatory: EP, BP, JP, and DAB compliance
Properties: APHA 10 max. liq., bland acid taste; m.w. 90; sp.gr. 1.21-1.22; 87.5-88.5% assay.

Purac® USP 88. [Purac Am.]
Chem. Descrip.: Lactic acid USP
CAS 50-21-5
Uses: Acidulant, preservative, flavoring
Regulatory: FDA GRAS; FCC, JSFA, USP, EEC E 270 compliance
Properties: APHA 50 max. liq., bland acid taste; m.w. 90; sp.gr. 1.21-1.22 (20 C); 87.5-88.5% assay.

Puracal® PG. [Purac Am.]
Chem. Descrip.: Calcium lactate pentahydrate
CAS 814-80-2; EINECS 212-406-7
Uses: Nutrient supplement in pharmaceuticals
Regulatory: USA GRAS, FCC, USP, EP, DAB, EEC E327 compliances
Properties: Wh. gran.; nonhygroscopic; sol. 9 g/100 ml in water; pH 6.0-8.5 (10%); 98% min. assay.

Puracal® PP. [Purac Am.]
Chem. Descrip.: Calcium lactate pentahydrate
CAS 814-80-2; EINECS 212-406-7
Uses: Nutrient supplement in pharmaceuticals
Regulatory: USA GRAS, FCC, USP, EP, DAB, JSFA compliance
Properties: Wh. powd./chips; sol. 9 g/100 ml in water; m.w. 218 (anhyd.); pH 6.0-8.5 (10% aq.); 98% min. assay.

Puracal® TG. [Purac Am.]
Chem. Descrip.: Calcium lactate trihydrate
CAS 814-80-2; EINECS 212-406-7
Uses: Nutrient supplement in pharmaceuticals
Regulatory: USA GRAS, FCC, USP, EP, DAB, EEC E327 compliance
Properties: Wh. gran.; sol. 9 g/100 ml in water; m.w. 218 (anhyd.); pH 6.0-8.5 (10%); 98% min. assay.

Puramex® AL. [Purac Am.]
Chem. Descrip.: Aluminum lactate
CAS 18917-91-4
Uses: Dietary supplement in pharmaceuticals
Properties: Wh. powd.; sol. 26 g/100 ml in water; m.w. 294; pH 3-4 (4%); 99% min. assay.

Puramex® FE. [Purac Am.]
Chem. Descrip.: Ferrous lactate
CAS 5905-52-2; EINECS 227-608-0
Uses: Nutrient supplement in pharmaceuticals
Regulatory: FDA GRAS; EEC E585 compliance
Properties: Powd.; sol. 2.2 g/100 ml in water; m.w. 234 (anhyd.); pH 4.5-6.0 (2% aq.); 98% min. assay.

Puramex® MG. [Purac Am.]
Chem. Descrip.: Magnesium lactate
CAS 18917-93-6
Uses: Nutrient supplement in pharmaceuticals
Properties: Wh. powd.; sol. 5.2 g/100 ml in water; m.w. 202 (anhyd.); pH 5.0-7.0 (5% aq.); 98% min. assay.

Puramex® MN. [Purac Am.]
Chem. Descrip.: Manganese lactate
CAS 16039-56-8
Uses: Nutrient supplement in pharmaceuticals
Properties: Pink powd.; sol. 10 g/100 ml in water; m.w. 233 (anhyd.); pH 5.0-7.0 (5% aq.); 98% min. assay.

Puramex® ZN. [Purac Am.]
Chem. Descrip.: Zinc lactate
CAS 16039-53-5
Uses: Dietary supplement in pharmaceuticals
Properties: Wh. powd.; sol. 5 g/100 ml in water; m.w. 243; 98% min. assay.

Purasal® NH 70. [Purac Am.]
Chem. Descrip.: Ammonium lactate
CAS 515-98-0
Uses: Pharmaceutical intermediate
Properties: APHA 60 max. liq.; m.w. 107; sp.gr. 1.16-1.19 (20 C); ref. index 1.42-1.45; pH 4-5 (10% sol'n.); 69-71% assay.

Purasal® P/HQ 60. [Purac Am.]
Chem. Descrip.: Potassium lactate
CAS 996-31-6; EINECS 213-631-3
Uses: Humectant and antimicrobial preservative for pharmaceuticals
Regulatory: FDA GRAS; EEC E326 compliance
Properties: APHA 100 max. liq., mildly saline taste; m.w. 128 (anhyd.); sp.gr. 1.32-1.35 g/ml (20 C); ref. index 1.415-1.422; pH 5.5-7.5 (10% aq.); 58-62% assay.

Purasal® P/USP 60. [Purac Am.]
Chem. Descrip.: Potassium lactate
CAS 996-31-6; EINECS 213-631-3
Uses: Antimicrobial; extends shelf life, enhances flavor, controls pathogens
Regulatory: FDA GRAS, USDA 9CFR §319.180
Properties: APHA 100 max. liq., mildly saline taste; m.w. 128 (anhyd.); sp.gr. 1.32-1.35 g/ml (20 C); ref. index 1.415-1.422; pH 6.5-8.5; 58-62% assay.

Purasal® S/HQ 60. [Purac Am.]
Chem. Descrip.: Sodium lactate
CAS 72-17-3; EINECS 200-77-20
Uses: Humectant, antimicrobial preservative for pharmaceutical applics.
Regulatory: FDA GRAS; JSFA, EEC E325 compliance

Properties: APHA 100 max. liq., mildly saline taste; m.w. 112 (anhyd.); sp.gr. 1.32-1.34 g/ml (20 C); ref. index 1.422-1.425; pH 6.5-8.5 (10% aq.); 59-61% assay.

Purasal® S/PF 60. [Purac Am.]
Chem. Descrip.: Sodium lactate
CAS 72-17-3; EINECS 200-77-20
Uses: Pharmaceutical intermediate
Regulatory: FDA GRAS; USP, EEC E325 compliance
Properties: APHA 50 max. liq.; m.w. 112 (anhyd.); sp.gr. 1.32-1.34 g/ml (20 C); ref. index 1.422-1.425; pH 6.5-8.5 (10% aq.); 59-61% assay.

Purasal® S Powd. [Purac Am.]
Chem. Descrip.: Sodium lactate
CAS 72-17-3; EINECS 200-77-20
Uses: Intermediate, raw material in pharmaceuticals
Regulatory: FDA GRAS
Properties: Wh. powd.; 94% min. assay.

Purasolv® BL. [Purac Am.]
Chem. Descrip.: Butyl lactate
CAS 138-22-7
Uses: Pharmaceutical intermediate
Regulatory: FDA GRAS flavor
Properties: Colorless clear liq., char. odor; partly misc. with water and most org. solvs.; m.w. 146; sp.gr. 0.975-0.985 (20 C); b.p. 180-195 C; flash pt. (CC) 79 C; ref. index 1.418-1.422; 97% min. assay.

Pureco® 76. [ABITEC]
Chem. Descrip.: Coconut oil
CAS 8001-31-8; EINECS 232-282-8
Uses: Diluent, emollient, lubricant, and vehicle/carrier used in clinical nutrition, delivery/absorp. enhancement, microemulsions, soft gelatin capsules
Properties: Lovibond R1.5 max. liq.; m.p. 76 F; iodine no. 12 max.; sapon. no. 248-264.

Pureco® 100. [ABITEC]
Chem. Descrip.: Partially hydrog. coconut oil
CAS 68334-28-1; EINECS 284-283-8
Uses: Lubricant, moisturizer for clinical nutrition, coating, dermatologicals, soft gelatin capsules, suppositories; base for liq. and solid medicated soaps and skin prods.
Properties: Lovibond 1R max. liq. plastic; m.p. 96-101 F; acid no. 5 max.; iodine no. 0-4; sapon. no. 246-264.

Pure-Dent® B700. [Grain Processing]
Chem. Descrip.: Unmodified corn starch USP, NF
CAS 9005-25-8; EINECS 232-679-6
Uses: Binder and diluent for granulations and tablets when used wet or dry; disintegrant, lubricant, dusting starch
Properties: Off-wh. powd., no odor, bland flavor; pH 5.5-6.5; 9-12.5% moisture.

Pure-Dent® B810. [Grain Processing]
Chem. Descrip.: Corn starch FCC, NF
CAS 9005-25-8; EINECS 232-679-6
Uses: Binder, diluent, absorbent, and disintegrant for wh. pharmaceutical tablets

Regulatory: FDA 21CFR §172.892
Properties: Wh. powd., no odor, bland flavor; pH 4.5-7.0; 8-11% moisture.
Pure-Dent® B812. [Grain Processing]
Chem. Descrip.: Corn starch USP
CAS 9005-25-8; EINECS 232-679-6
Uses: For topical applics.
Regulatory: FDA 21CFR §172.892
Properties: Wh. powd., odorless, bland flavor; pH 6.0; 11% moisture.
Pure-Dent® B815. [Grain Processing]
Chem. Descrip.: Corn starch NF
CAS 9005-25-8; EINECS 232-679-6
Uses: Tableting aid for pharmaceutical use
Regulatory: FDA 21CFR §172.892
Properties: Wh. fine powd., odorless, bland flavor; pH 4.5-7.0; 8-11% moisture.
Pure-Dent® B816. [Grain Processing]
Chem. Descrip.: Topical corn starch USP
CAS 9005-25-8; EINECS 232-679-6
Uses: For pharmaceutical use
Regulatory: FDA 21CFR §172.892
Properties: Wh. powd., odorless, bland flavor; pH 6.0; 11% moisture.
Pure-Dent® B851. [Grain Processing]
Chem. Descrip.: Modified corn starch USP contg. magnesium oxide
Uses: Absorbable dusting powd. for use as lubricant for surgical and examination gloves; may be sterilized by autoclaving, ethylene oxide, or irradiation; not suitable for ingestion
Properties: Wh. flowable powd., odorless; 1.5% max. on 200 mesh, 10% max. on 325 mesh; pH 10-10.8; 8-11% moisture.
Pure-Dent® B852. [Grain Processing]
Chem. Descrip.: Modified corn starch USP
CAS 9005-25-8; EINECS 232-679-6
Uses: Absorbable dusting powd. for use as lubricant for examination gloves and other nonsurgical uses; not suitable for ingestion
Properties: Wh. powd.
Pure-Dent® B880. [Grain Processing]
Chem. Descrip.: Corn starch NF
CAS 9005-25-8; EINECS 232-679-6
Uses: Pharmaceutical starch for use as binder, diluent, absorbent, and disintegrant in tablets
Regulatory: FDA 21CFR §172.892
Properties: Wh. powd., odorless, bland flavor; pH 6.0; 11% moisture.
Pure-Dent® B890. [Grain Processing]
Chem. Descrip.: Food starch modified NF
CAS 53124-00-8
Uses: Pharmaceutical starch for use as binder, diluent, absorbent, and disintegrant in tablets and granulations
Regulatory: FDA 21CFR §172.892
Properties: Wh. powd., odorless, bland flavor; pH 6.0; 11% moisture.
Pure Food Starch Bleached 142-A. [ADM Corn Processing]
Chem. Descrip.: Corn starch
CAS 9005-25-8; EINECS 232-679-6

Uses: For aspirin, pharmaceuticals
Properties: Wh. (bleach) powd.; 98+% thru 200 mesh; pH 5.5; 10% moisture, 0.3% protein.
Pure Malt Colorant A6000. [MLG Enterprises Ltd.]
Chem. Descrip.: Nondiastatic extract of malted barley
CAS 8002-48-0; EINECS 232-310-9
Uses: Natural colorant providing rich deep reddish-brn., fortification to pharmaceuticals
Regulatory: Kosher
Properties: Black liq.; pH 4.5-5.5 (10%); 79-80% solids
Storage: Store in clean, dry area @ 40-65 F; avoid direct sunlight; 6 mos max. shelf life.
Pure Malt Colorant A6001. [MLG Enterprises Ltd.]
Chem. Descrip.: Nondiastatic extract of malted barley
CAS 8002-48-0; EINECS 232-310-9
Uses: Natural colorant providing rich deep reddish-brn., fortification to pharmaceuticals
Regulatory: Kosher
Properties: Dk. red to black free-flowing powd.; hygroscopic; pH 4.5-5.5 (10%); 4% moisture
Storage: Store in clean, dry area @ 40-65 F; 6 mos max. shelf life.
Purity® 21. [Nat'l. Starch & Chem.]
Chem. Descrip.: Corn starch NF
CAS 9005-25-8; EINECS 232-679-6
Uses: Binder, filler and disintegrant for pharmaceutical formulations, foot powds.
Properties: Wh. free-flowing powd.; disp. in water; 12% volatiles.
Purtalc USP. [Charles B. Chrystal]
Chem. Descrip.: Talc
CAS 14807-96-6; EINECS 238-877-9
Uses: Glidant, anticaking agent, tablet lubricant, colorant.
PVP-Iodine 17/12, 30/06. [BASF; BASF AG]
Chem. Descrip.: PVP-iodine
CAS 25655-41-8
Uses: Broad spectrum microbicide for pharmaceuticals.
PVP/VA E-335. [ISP]
Chem. Descrip.: PVP/VA copolymer with 30/70 mole ratio in ethanol sol'n.
Uses: Film-former for antiseptic/anesthetic spray bandages, antibiotic aerosol bandages, spray or rub-on gloves and protective masks
Properties: Liq.; sol. in aq. and most common org. solvs.; 50% act. in ethanol
Toxicology: Very low chronic oral toxicity; safe in contact with skin.
PVP/VA E-535. [ISP]
Chem. Descrip.: PVP/VA copolymer with 50/50 mole ratio in ethanol sol'n.
Uses: Film-former for antiseptic/anesthetic spray bandages, antibiotic aerosol bandages, spray or rub-on gloves and protective masks; solubilizer, visc. modifier/stabilizer; granulation binder
Properties: Liq.; sol. in aq. and most common org. solvs.; 50% act. in ethanol
Toxicology: Very low chronic oral toxicity; safe in

contact with skin.

PVP/VA E-635. [ISP]
Chem. Descrip.: PVP/VA copolymer with 60/40 mole ratio in ethanol sol'n.
Uses: Film-former for antiseptic/anesthetic spray bandages, antibiotic aerosol bandages, spray or rub-on gloves and protective masks; solubilizer, visc. modifier/stabilizer; granulation binder
Properties: Liq.; sol. in aq. and most common org. solvs.; 50% act. in ethanol
Toxicology: Very low chronic oral toxicity; safe in contact with skin.

PVP/VA E-735. [ISP]
Chem. Descrip.: PVP/VA copolymer with 70/30 mole ratio in ethanol sol'n.
Uses: Film-former for antiseptic/anesthetic spray bandages, antibiotic aerosol bandages, spray or rub-on gloves and protective masks; solubilizer, visc. modifier/stabilizer; granulation binder
Properties: Liq.; sol. in aq. and most common org. solvs.; 50% act. in ethanol
Toxicology: Very low chronic oral toxicity; safe in contact with skin.

PVP/VA I-235. [ISP]
Chem. Descrip.: PVP/VA copolymer with 20/80 mole ratios in IPA sol'n.
Uses: Film-former for antiseptic/anesthetic spray bandages, antibiotic aerosol bandages, spray or rub-on gloves and protective masks; solubilizer, visc. modifier/stabilizer; granulation binder
Properties: Liq.; sol. in aq. and most common org.solvs.; 50% act. in IPA
Toxicology: Very low chronic oral toxicity; safe in contact with skin.

PVP/VA I-335. [ISP]
Chem. Descrip.: PVP/VA copolymer with 30/70 mole ratios in IPA sol'n.
Uses: Film-former for antiseptic/anesthetic spray bandages, antibiotic aerosol bandages, spray or rub-on gloves and protective masks; solubilizer, visc. modifier/stabilizer; granulation binder
Properties: Liq.; sol. in aq. and most common org.solvs.; 50% act. in IPA
Toxicology: Very low chronic oral toxicity; safe in contact with skin.

PVP/VA I-535. [ISP]
Chem. Descrip.: PVP/VA copolymer with 50/50 mole ratios in IPA sol'n.
Uses: Film-former for antiseptic/anesthetic spray bandages, antibiotic aerosol bandages, spray or rub-on gloves and protective masks; solubilizer, visc. modifier/stabilizer; granulation binder
Properties: Liq.; sol. in aq. and most common org.solvs.; 50% act. in IPA
Toxicology: Very low chronic oral toxicity; safe in contact with skin.

PVP/VA I-735. [ISP]
Chem. Descrip.: PVP/VA copolymer with 70/30 mole ratios in IPA sol'n.
Uses: Film-former for antiseptic/anesthetic spray bandages, antibiotic aerosol bandages, spray or rub-on gloves and protective masks; solubilizer,

visc. modifier/stabilizer; granulation binder
Properties: Liq.; sol. in aq. and most common org.solvs.; 50% act. in IPA
Toxicology: Very low chronic oral toxicity; safe in contact with skin.

PVP/VA S-630. [ISP]
Chem. Descrip.: PVP/VA copolymer (60/40 mole ratio)
CAS 25086-89-9
Uses: Film-former for antiseptic/anesthetic spray bandages, antibiotic aerosol bandages, spray or rub-on gloves and protective masks; solubilizer, visc. modifier/stabilizer; tablet binder and coating agent for film coating of tablets
Properties: Solid; sol. in aq. and most common org. solvs.; 100% act.

Pyrax® ABB. [R.T. Vanderbilt]
Chem. Descrip.: Pyrophyllite (hydrated aluminum silicate)
CAS 12269-78-2
Uses: Diluent, carrier used in pharmaceuticals; color additive for drugs
Properties: Variable powd., 11 μ diam.; pH 6.5 (10% solids).

Pyrax® B. [R.T. Vanderbilt]
Chem. Descrip.: Pyrophyllite (hydrated aluminum silicate)
CAS 12269-78-2
Uses: Diluent, carrier used in pharmaceuticals; color additive for drugs
Properties: Wh. powd.; 10 μ median particle size; 95% thru 325 mesh; dens. 2.80 mg/m^3; bulk dens. 52 lb/ft^3 (compacted); oil absorp. 26; brightness 80; ; pH 6.9 (10% aq. slurry).

Pyridine 1°. [Nepera]
Chem. Descrip.: Pyridine
CAS 110-86-1; EINECS 203-809-9
Uses: Chem. intermediate; can undergo electrophilic and nucleophilic substitution, act as an acid scavenger, catalyze reactions; used in pharmaceuticals
Properties: Water-wh. liq., char. odor; > 99.5% assay
Unverified

Pyridoxine Hydrochloride USP. [Roche]
Chem. Descrip.: Vitamin B$_6$
Uses: Oil control agent for skin care prods.

Pyridoxine Hydrochloride USP, FCC Fine Powd. No. 60650. [Roche]
Chem. Descrip.: Vitamin B$_6$
CAS 58-56-0; EINECS 200-386-2
Uses: Dietary supplement for mfg. of dry and liq. pharmaceuticals
Regulatory: FDA 21CFR §182.5676, GRAS
Properties: Wh. cryst. powd., odorless; 95% min. thru 100 mesh; freely sol. in water (1 g/5ml); sl. sol. in alcohol (1 g/100 ml); insol. in ether; m.w. 205.64; m.p. 202-206 C; pH 2-4 (10% aq.); 98% min. assay
Toxicology: Ingestion of 500 mg or more daily for 6 mos may cause ataxia and severe neuropathy
Precaution: Avoid exposure to excessive heat,

alkali, light

Storage: Store in tightly closed containers away from light, moisture, excessive heat @ optimum temp. < 72 F.

2-Pyrol®. [ISP]

Chem. Descrip.: 2-Pyrrolidone

CAS 616-45-5; EINECS 204-648-7

Uses: Solv., solubilizer; synthesis of piracetam; treatment of cerebral distress; intermediate for N-phenyl amidines (diuretic, muscle relaxant, anti-inflammatory props.), γ-aminobutyric acid derivs.; injectables; tetracycline veterinary parenterals

Properties: Liq.; solidfies below 25 C; misc. with water, ethanol, ethyl ether, chloroform, benzene, ethyl acetate, CS_2; insol. in aliphatic hydrocarbons; sp.gr. 0.11 (25/4 C); visc. 13.3 cp; m.p. 25 C; b.p. 245 C; flash pt. (OC) 130 C

Precaution: Noncorrosive; low fire hazard.

Q

QO® Furan. [Great Lakes]
  Chem. Descrip.: Furan
  Uses: Chemical intermediate in mfg. of pharma-ceuticals
  Properties: Colorless; sol. in most org. liqs.
Quadrol®. [BASF]
  Chem. Descrip.: Tetra (2-hydroxypropyl) ethylene-diamine
  CAS 102-60-3; EINECS 203-041-4
  Uses: Intermediate used in pharmaceuticals
  Properties: Liq.; m.w. 292; sol. in water, ethyl alcohol, toluene, ethylene glycol, perchloroethyl-ene; sp.gr. 1.03; ref. index 1.478; 99.2% tert.

amine.
Quataphen. [United-Guardian]
  Chem. Descrip.: Alkyl quat. ammonium compd. complexed with a strongly antimicrobial arylphenol in the presence of a catalyst
  Uses: Conc. germicide and disinfectant for medical and health-care use
  Custom product
Querton 246. [Berol Nobel AB]
  Chem. Descrip.: Alkyl dimethylbenzyl ammonium chloride
  CAS 68424-85-1; EINECS 270-325-2
  Uses: Bactericide, fungicide for medical care.

R

R-1000™. [Reheis]
Chem. Descrip.: Aluminum hydroxide
CAS 21645-51-2; EINECS 244-492-7
Uses: Low sodium antacid active for suspensions; when diluted to 4% Al_2O_3, meets requirements for USP aluminum hydroxide suspensions
Properties: Wh. compressed gel; apparent visc. 140 cps (@ 4% Al_2O_3); 10% min. Al_2O_3
Unverified

Reach® 101. [Reheis]
Chem. Descrip.: Aluminum chlorohydrate
CAS 1327-41-9; EINECS 215-477-2
Uses: Antiperspirant for increased wetness protection, esp. for aerosols
Properties: Powd.; 97% thru 325 mesh; pH 4.0-4.4 (15% aq.); 46-48.5% Al_2O_3, 15.8-17.5% Cl.

Reach® 103. [Reheis]
Chem. Descrip.: Aluminum chlorohydrate
CAS 1327-41-9; EINECS 215-477-2
Uses: Antiperspirant for increased wetness protection, esp. for aerosols
Properties: Powd.; 47.3% Al_2O_3, 16.6% Cl.

Reach® 301 [Reheis]
Chem. Descrip.: Aluminum chlorohydrate
CAS 1327-41-9; EINECS 215-477-2
Uses: Antiperspirant for increased wetness protection, esp. for aerosols; useful in both hydro-alcoholic and aq. based systems incl. pump systems and compressed air systems
Properties: Powd.; 46.3% Al_2O_3, 19.7% Cl.

Reach® 301 Sol'n. [Reheis]
Chem. Descrip.: Aluminum chlorohydrate
CAS 1327-41-9; EINECS 215-477-2
Uses: Antiperspirant for increased wetness protection, esp. for aerosols; useful in both hydro-alcoholic and aq. based systems incl. pump systems and compressed air systems
Properties: Powd.; 23.1% Al_2O_3, 9.8% Cl.

Reach® 501. [Reheis]
Chem. Descrip.: Aluminum chlorohydrate
CAS 1327-41-9; EINECS 215-477-2
Uses: Antiperspirant for increased wetness protection, esp. for aerosols; useful in both hydro-alcoholic and aq. based systems incl. pump systems and compressed air systems
Properties: Powd.; 97% thru 325 mesh; pH 4.0-4.4 (15% aq.); 47.0% Al_2O_3, 16.3% Cl.

Reach® 501 Sol'n. [Reheis]
Chem. Descrip.: Aluminum chlorohydrate
CAS 1327-41-9; EINECS 215-477-2
Uses: Antiperspirant for increased wetness protection, esp. for aerosols; useful in both hydro-alcoholic and aq. based systems incl. pump systems and compressed air systems
Properties: Powd.; 23.5% Al_2O_3, 8.2% Cl.

Reach® AZO. [Reheis]
Chem. Descrip.: Aluminum zirconium octachlorohydrex GLY
Uses: Antiperspirant active.

Reach® AZP-701. [Reheis]
Chem. Descrip.: Aluminum zirconium tetrachlorohydrex glycine
Uses: Enhanced efficacy antiperspirant for nonaq. systems, sticks, roll-ons; 15% Al, 14.2% Zr, 17.8% Cl, 12% Gly.

Reach® AZP-855. [Reheis]
Chem. Descrip.: Aluminum zirconium tetrachlorohydrex glycine
Uses: Enhanced efficacy antiperspirant for nonaq. systems, sticks, roll-ons; 16% Al, 10.0% Zr, 18.6% Cl, 12% Gly.

Reach® AZP-902. [Reheis]
Chem. Descrip.: Aluminum zirconium tetrachlorohydrex glycine
Uses: Enhanced efficacy antiperspirant for nonaq. systems, sticks, roll-ons; 15% Al, 14.2% Zr, 17.8% Cl, 12% Gly.

Reach® AZP-908. [Reheis]
Chem. Descrip.: Aluminum zirconium tetrachlorohydrex glycine
Uses: Enhanced efficacy antiperspirant for nonaq. systems, sticks, roll-ons; 15% Al, 14.2% Zr, 17.8% Cl, 12% Gly.

Reach® AZP-908PG. [Reheis]
Chem. Descrip.: Aluminum zirconium tetrachlorohydrex glycine/propylene glycol complex
Uses: Antiperspirant active for clear and low-residue systems; 12% Al, 11.6% Zr, 23.2% propylene glycol.

Reach® AZZ-855. [Reheis]
Chem. Descrip.: Aluminum zirconium trichlorohydrex GLY
Uses: Antiperspirant active; 16.0% Al, 10.7% Zr, 15.2% Cl, 15% Gly.

Reach® AZZ-902. [Reheis]
Chem. Descrip.: Aluminum zirconium trichloro-

hydrex GLY
Uses: Antiperspirant active; 15.2% Al, 14.8% Zr, 15.7% Cl, 15% Gly.

Reach® AZZ-908PG. [Reheis]
Chem. Descrip.: Aluminum zirconium trichloro-hydrex GLY/propylene glycol complex
Uses: Antiperspirant active for clear and low-residue systems; 11.7% Al, 12.3% Zr, 22.6% propylene glycol.

Rederm® Gel. [Reheis]
Chem. Descrip.: Aluminum hydroxide
CAS 21645-51-2; EINECS 244-492-7
Uses: Adsorbent gel with astringent props.; protein binder; antimicrobial; for OTC topical prods., e.g., hand creams, acne preps., astringent lotions, etc.
Properties: Almost translucent gel; 9% Al_2O_3.

Rederm® Powd. [Reheis]
Chem. Descrip.: Aluminum hydroxide
CAS 21645-51-2; EINECS 244-492-7
Uses: Adsorbent with astringent props.; protein binder; antimicrobial; for OTC topical prods., e.g., hand creams, acne preps., astringent lotions, etc.; 59% Al_2O_3.

Red Reishi Mushroom Extract RREXTR. [Garuda Int'l.]
Chem. Descrip.: Reishi mushroom extract from *Ganoderma lucidum* with potency fo 4% min. triterpenes, 12.5% polysaccharides
Uses: Triterpenes, polysaccharides actives; used to formulate health food and pharmaceutical capsules and tablets
Properties: Brn. fine powd.; min. 20 mesh or finer; partly sol. in water
Storage: 24 mo shelf life.

Red Soluble Powd. Natural Colorant. [MLG Enterprises Ltd.]
Chem. Descrip.: Blend of solubilized carminic acid aluminum lake with norbixin
Uses: Natural colorant for pharmaceuticals producing berry red shades
Properties: Impalpable powd.; 100% 80 mesh; water-sol.; 32 ± 0.7% (as carminic acid)
Storage: Keep in tightly closed containers away from light and in dry and preferably refrigerated room.

Rehydragel® CG. [Reheis]
Chem. Descrip.: Aluminum hydroxide
CAS 21645-51-2; EINECS 244-492-7
Uses: Adsorbent gel for pharmaceuticals (enhances suspensions, builds visc.); carrier for antitoxins in veterinary vaccines
Properties: Translucent compressed gel; 9% Al_2O_3.

Rehydragel® HPA. [Reheis]
Chem. Descrip.: Aluminum hydroxide
CAS 21645-51-2; EINECS 244-492-7
Uses: Adsorbent, protein binder for biological materials in human and veterinary vaccines
Properties: Sterile thixotropic submicron fluid gel; 2% Al_2O_3.

Rehydragel® LV. [Reheis]
Chem. Descrip.: Aluminum hydroxide

CAS 21645-51-2; EINECS 244-492-7
Uses: Adsorbent gel and protein binder for use as a fluid adjuvant in the prep. of parenteral sol'ns.
Properties: Low visc. gel; 2% Al_2O_3.

Rehydragel® T. [Reheis]
Chem. Descrip.: Aluminum hydroxide
CAS 21645-51-2; EINECS 244-492-7
Uses: Adsorbent, protein binder for biological materials
Properties: Wh. opaque thixotropic gel; 2% Al_2O_3.

Rehydrol® II. [Reheis]
Chem. Descrip.: Aluminum chlorohydrex PG
Uses: Antiperspirant active for pumps, roll-ons and alcoholic sticks
Properties: Solid; sol. 50% max. in alcohol and water; 36% min. Al_2O_3, 12.5% min. Cl, 22% min. propylene glycol.

Reishi Extract. [Garuda Int'l.]
Chem. Descrip.: Reishi mushroom extract from *Ganoderma lucidum* with potency of 4% triterpenoids and 12.5% β-glucan polysaccharides
Uses: Used to formulate health foods and pharmaceuticals; may provide neurological and cardiovascular benefits, anti-inflammatory effect, immunopotentiator effect in cancer treatment
Properties: Dried powd.

Reishi Mycelium Biomass REIMYC. [Garuda Int'l.]
Chem. Descrip.: Reishi mycelium biomass from *Ganoderma lucidum*
Uses: Polysaccharides and peptidomannans actives; used to formulate health food and pharmaceutical capsules and tablets
Properties: Lt. reddsh.-brn. powd.; insol. in water
Storage: 24 mo shelf life.

Reishi Mycelium Extract REMEXT. [Garuda Int'l.]
Chem. Descrip.: Reishi mycelium extract from *Ganoderma lucidum* with 70% dextrose carrier
Uses: Polysaccharides and lignins actives; used to formulate health foods and pharmaceuticals tablets, capsules, ampules
Properties: Brownish-red gran.; min. 20 mesh or finer; sol. in water
Storage: 24 mo shelf life.

Renex® 759. [ICI Surf. Am.; ICI Surf. UK]
Chem. Descrip.: Octoxynol-9 USP/NF
CAS 9002-93-1
Uses: Emulsifier, solubilizer
Properties: Pale yel. liq.; HLB 13.0.

Renex® PEG 300. [ICI Surf. Am.; ICI Surf. UK]
Chem. Descrip.: PEG-6 USP/NF
CAS 25322-68-3; EINECS 220-045-1
Uses: Surfactant
Properties: Colorless liq.

Renex® PEG 400. [ICI Surf. Am.; ICI Surf. UK]
Chem. Descrip.: PEG-8 USP/NF
CAS 25322-68-3; EINECS 225-856-4
Uses: Surfactant
Properties: Colorless liq.

Renex® PEG 600. [ICI Surf. Am.; ICI Surf. UK]
Chem. Descrip.: PEG-12 USP/NF
CAS 25322-68-3; EINECS 229-859-1

Uses: Surfactant
Properties: Wh. paste.
Renex® PEG 1000. [ICI Surf. Am.; ICI Surf. UK]
Chem. Descrip.: PEG-20 USP/NF
CAS 25322-68-3
Uses: Surfactant
Properties: Wh. solid.
Renex® PEG 1500FL. [ICI Surf. Am.; ICI Surf. UK]
Chem. Descrip.: PEG-32 USP/NF
CAS 25322-68-3
Uses: Surfactant
Properties: Wh. solid.
Renex® PEG 4000FL. [ICI Surf. Am.; ICI Surf. UK]
Chem. Descrip.: PEG-75 USP/NF
CAS 25322-68-3
Uses: Surfactant
Properties: Wh. solid.
Renex® PEG 6000FL. [ICI Surf. Am.; ICI Surf. UK]
Chem. Descrip.: PEG-150 USP/NF
CAS 25322-68-3
Uses: Surfactant
Properties: Wh. solid.
Renex® PEG 8000FL. [ICI Surf. Am.; ICI Surf. UK]
Chem. Descrip.: PEG USP/NF
Uses: Surfactant
Properties: Wh. solid.
Rewopal® CSF 11. [Rewo GmbH]
Chem. Descrip.: Ceteareth-11
CAS 68439-49-6
Uses: Solubilizer, emulsifier for pharmaceutical preps.
Properties: Flake; 100% conc.; nonionic
Unverified
Rezal® 33GP. [Reheis]
Chem. Descrip.: Aluminum zirconium trichloro-hydrex-glycine
Uses: Antiperspirant active for suspension roll-ons and suspensoid sticks
Properties: Powd.; 53 μ particle size; 95% min. thru 270 mesh; 14.6% Al, 14.9% Zr, 15% glycine.
Rezal® 36. [Reheis]
Chem. Descrip.: Aluminum zirconium tetrachloro-hydrex-glycine
Uses: Antiperspirant active for high alcohol content antiperspirants
Properties: Liq.; 45% total solids.
Rezal® 36G. [Reheis]
Chem. Descrip.: Aluminum zirconium tetrachloro-hydrex-glycine
Uses: Antiperspirant active for aq. nonaerosol systems, roll-ons, creams
Properties: Liq.; 35% act.
Rezal® 36G Conc. [Reheis]
Chem. Descrip.: Aluminum zirconium tetrachloro-hydrex-glycine
Uses: Antiperspirant active for nonaerosol systems
Properties: Liq.; 46% act.
Rezal® 36GP. [Reheis]
Chem. Descrip.: Aluminum zirconium tetrachloro-hydrex-glycine
Uses: Antiperspirant active for suspension roll-ons and suspensoid type sticks

Properties: Powd.; 98.5% min. thru 325 mesh.
Rezal® 36GPG. [Reheis]
Chem. Descrip.: Aluminum zirconium tetrachloro-hydrex-glycine and propylene glycol complex
Uses: Antiperspirant active for low residue and clear antiperspirant sticks
Properties: Powd.; sol. in polyols such as proplene glycol and glycerin; also avail. as propylene glycol sol'n.; 11.7% Al, 11.5% Zr, 9.5% glycine, 21% propylene glycol.
Rezal® 36GP Superultrafine. [Reheis]
Chem. Descrip.: Aluminum zirconium tetrachloro-hydrex-glycine
Uses: Antiperspirant active for suspension roll-ons and suspensoid sticks; fine particle size results in improved aesthetics
Properties: Powd.; 85% min. thru 10 μ.
Rezal® 67. [Reheis]
Chem. Descrip.: Aluminum zirconium pentachloro-hydrate
Uses: Antiperspirant active for hydroalcoholic and aq. systems such as clear and emulsified roll-ons and creams
Properties: Liq.; 40% act.; 8% Al, 4% Zr.
Rezal® 67P. [Reheis]
Chem. Descrip.: Aluminum zirconium pentachloro-hydrate
Uses: Antiperspirant active for use in suspensoid sticks and suspension roll-ons
Properties: Powd., 97% thru 325 mesh; 20% Al, 10% Zr.
Rheodol AO-10. [Kao Corp. SA]
Chem. Descrip.: Sorbitan oleate
CAS 1338-43-8; EINECS 215-665-4
Uses: Emulsifier for pharmaceuticals
Properties: Liq.; HLB 4.3; 100% conc.; nonionic
Unverified
Rheodol AO-15. [Kao Corp. SA]
Chem. Descrip.: Sorbitan sesquioleate
CAS 8007-43-0; EINECS 232-360-1
Uses: Emulsifier for pharmaceuticals
Properties: Liq.; HLB 3.7; 100% conc.; nonionic
Unverified
Rheodol AS-10. [Kao Corp. SA]
Chem. Descrip.: Sorbitan stearate
CAS 1338-41-6; EINECS 215-664-9
Uses: Emulsifier for pharmaceuticals
Properties: Solid; HLB 4.7; 100% conc.; nonionic
Unverified
Rheodol MO-60. [Kao Corp. SA]
Chem. Descrip.: Glyceryl oleate
Uses: Emulsifier for pharmaceuticals
Properties: Liq.; HLB 2.8; 100% conc.; nonionic
Unverified
Rheodol MS-50, MS-60, SEM. [Kao Corp. SA]
Chem. Descrip.: Glyceryl stearate
Uses: Emulsifier for pharmaceuticals
Properties: Powd.; HLB 2.8, 3.5, and 11.0 resp.; 100% conc.; nonionic
Unverified
Rheodol TW-L106, -L120. [Kao Corp. SA]
Chem. Descrip.: POE sorbitan laurate

Uses: Emulsifier for pharmaceuticals
Properties: Liq.; HLB 13.3 and 16.7 resp.; 100% conc.; nonionic
Unverified

Rhodasurf® E-15. [Rhone-Poulenc Surf. & Spec.]
Chem. Descrip.: Ceteareth-30
CAS 68439-49-6
Uses: Emulsifier
Properties: Wax; HLB 16.7; cloud pt. > 95 C (1%); pH 6.5 (1%); 100% act.; nonionic.

Rhodasurf® L-4. [Rhone-Poulenc Surf. & Spec.]
Chem. Descrip.: Laureth-4
CAS 68002-97-1; EINECS 226-097-1
Uses: Emollient for pharmaceuticals
Properties: Liq.; HLB 9.7; cloud pt. 0-5; pH 6.5 (1%); 100% conc.; nonionic.

Rhodasurf® L-25. [Rhone-Poulenc Surf. & Spec.]
Chem. Descrip.: Laureth-23
CAS 9002-92-0
Uses: Emollient for pharmaceuticals
Properties: Wax; HLB 16.9; cloud pt. > 95 C (1%); pH 6.5 (1%); 100% act.; nonionic.

Rhodasurf® LA-12. [Rhone-Poulenc Surf. & Spec.]
Chem. Descrip.: C12-15 pareth-12
CAS 68131-39-5
Uses: Emollient for pharmaceuticals
Properties: Wh. paste, low odor; water-sol.; sp.gr. 1.0; HLB 14.4; 100% act.; nonionic.

Rhodasurf® ON-870. [Rhone-Poulenc Surf. & Spec.]
Chem. Descrip.: Oleth-20
CAS 9004-98-2
Uses: High foaming emulsifier, stabilizer, dispersant, wetting agent, solubilizer for pharmaceutical industry
Regulatory: FDA, EPA compliance
Properties: Wh. solid wax; sol. in water, xylene, ethanol, ethylene glycol, butyl Cellosolve; sp.gr. 1.04; HLB 15.4; pour pt. 46 C; cloud pt. < 100 C (1% aq.); flash pt. (PMCC) 93 C; surf. tens. 37 dynes/cm (0.1%); 100% act.; nonionic.

Rhodasurf® ON-877. [Rhone-Poulenc Surf. & Spec.]
Chem. Descrip.: Oleth-20
CAS 9004-98-2
Uses: Solubilizer and emulsifier for essential oils and pharmaceuticals
Properties: Liq.; HLB 15.4; cloud pt. < 100 C (1% aq.); 70% conc.; nonionic.

Rhodasurf® PEG 300. [Rhone-Poulenc Surf. & Spec.]
Chem. Descrip.: PEG-6
CAS 25322-68-3; EINECS 220-045-1
Uses: Binder/lubricant in pharmaceuticals
Properties: Liq.; m.w. 285-315; water-sol.; dens. 1.13 g/ml; pH 5-8 (5% DW); 100% conc.

Rhodasurf® PEG 600. [Rhone-Poulenc Surf. & Spec.]
Chem. Descrip.: PEG-14
CAS 25322-68-3
Uses: Lubricant, binder for pharmaceuticals
Properties: Wh. liq.; m.w. 570-630; water sol.; sp.gr. 1.13 (30/15.5 C); f.p. 20-25 C; pH 5-8; 100% conc.

Rhodigel®. [Rhone-Poulenc Food Ingreds.; R.T. Vanderbilt]
Chem. Descrip.: Xanthan gum
CAS 11138-66-2; EINECS 234-394-2
Uses: Emulsion stabilizer, suspending agent, thickener for pharmaceutical applics.
Regulatory: Kosher
Properties: Fine gran.; sol. in cold water.

Rhodigel® 23. [Rhone-Poulenc Food Ingreds.]
Chem. Descrip.: Xanthan gum
CAS 11138-66-2; EINECS 234-394-2
Uses: Pharmaceutical grade thickener, stabilizer, and suspending agent.

Rhodigel® 200. [Rhone-Poulenc Food Ingreds.; R.T. Vanderbilt]
Chem. Descrip.: Xanthan gum
CAS 11138-66-2; EINECS 234-394-2
Uses: Used in pharmaceuticals to suspend insol. additives; exc. pseudo plastic props.
Regulatory: Kosher
Properties: Very fine gran.; sol. in cold water.

Riboflavin USP, FCC 184045. [Crompton & Knowles/ Ingred. Tech.]
Chem. Descrip.: Riboflavin USP, FCC
CAS 83-88-5; EINECS 201-507-1
Uses: Color additive for dry drug formulations, tablets, coatings and capsules
Regulatory: FDA 21CFR §73.450
Properties: Yel. to orange-yel. free-flowing cryst. powd., sl. odor, char. bitter taste; 100% min. thru 100 mesh; very sol. in dil. alkaline sol'ns.; sl. sol. in water (0.12 mg/mL); 100% assay
Storage: 6 mos shelf life stored in tight containers @ 72 ± 12 F whenever possible; avoid exposure to heat, light, moisture.

Riboflavin USP, FCC No. 602940002. [Roche]
Chem. Descrip.: Riboflavin USP, FCC
CAS 83-88-5; EINECS 201-507-1
Uses: Source of vitamin B_2 in liq. and solid pharmaceutical preps.
Properties: Orange-yel. cryst. powd., sl. odor, char. bitter taste; < 20 μ particle size; very sol. in dil. alkalies; very sl. sol. in water, alcohol, isotonic sodium chloride sol'n.; insol. in ether, chloroform; m.w. 376.37; m.p. 280 C; 98-102% assay
Storage: Store in dry place @ 59-86 F in tight, light-resist. containers; avoid excessive heat.

Riboflavin USP, FCC Type S. [Roche]
Chem. Descrip.: Vitamin B_2
CAS 83-88-5; EINECS 201-507-1
Uses: Colorant.

Riboflavin-5´-Phosphate Sodium USP, FCC No. 60296. [Roche]
Chem. Descrip.: Riboflavin-5´-phosphate sodium USP, FCC
CAS 130-40-5; EINECS 204-988-6
Uses: Source of riboflavin in pharmaceutical liqs., parenteral sol'ns., B-complex syrups, certain solid dosage forms
Properties: Orange-yel. fine cryst., sl. odor, bitter taste; sol. 4.3 g/100 ml @ pH 3.8, 11.2 g/100 ml water @ pH 7; m.w. 514.37; pH 5-6.5 (1:100 aq.); 73-79% assay (riboflavin)
Precaution: Incompat. with sol'ns. contg. calcium

or metallic salts which form insoluble phosphates

Storage: Store in dry place @ 59-86 F in tight, light-resist. containers; avoid heat and prolonged exposure to light.

Ricinion. [Gattefosse]
Chem. Descrip.: PEG-33 castor oil
CAS 61791-12-6
Uses: Solv., emulsifier for pharmaceutical emulsions
Properties: Liq.; HLB 12-13; acid no. 30-40; sapon. no. 60-80
Toxicology: LD0 (oral, rat) > 10 ml/kg; nonirritating to skin and eyes.

Rilanit GMRO. [Henkel KGaA]
Chem. Descrip.: Glyceryl ricinoleate
CAS 141-08-2; EINECS 205-455-0
Uses: Improves compat., delays resorption in suppositories to mitigate irritation of rectal mucous membranes
Properties: Semiliq.

Ringwell. [United-Guardian]
Chem. Descrip.: Surfactant sol'n. contg. 3% hydrogen peroxide
CAS 7722-84-1; EINECS 231-765-0
Uses: Antiseptic, oxidizing agent; 'fizzes' on contact with the skin; for pharmaceutical and healthcare fields
Properties: 'ringing gel' @ R.T.; liquefies in the cold, but reverts to gel form @ R.T.; 3% act. Custom product

RITA IPM. [R.I.T.A.]
Chem. Descrip.: Isopropyl myristate
CAS 110-27-0; EINECS 203-751-4
Uses: Emollient, spreading agent, solubilizer for pharmaceuticals
Properties: Liq.

RITA IPP. [R.I.T.A.]
Chem. Descrip.: Isopropyl palmitate
CAS 142-91-6; EINECS 205-571-1
Uses: Emollient, spreading agent, solubilizer for pharmaceuticals
Properties: Liq.

Ritaceti. [R.I.T.A.]
Chem. Descrip.: Cetyl esters
EINECS 241-640-2
Uses: Raw material for pharmaceuticals
Properties: Wh. flakes.

Ritacetyl®. [R.I.T.A.]
Chem. Descrip.: Acetylated lanolin
CAS 61788-48-5; EINECS 262-979-2
Uses: Superfatting agent, emollient, spreading agent, film-former for ointments, sun preps.
Properties: Yel./amber soft waxy semisolid, bland odor; oil-sol.; m.p. 30-40 C; acid no. 3 max.; sapon. no. 125 max.; hyd. no. 10 max.; 100% conc.; nonionic.

Ritachlor 50%. [R.I.T.A.]
Chem. Descrip.: Aluminum chlorohydrate
CAS 1327-41-9; EINECS 215-477-2
Uses: Antiperspirant
Properties: Aq. sol'n.

Ritachol®. [R.I.T.A.]
Chem. Descrip.: Min. oil and lanolin alcohol
Uses: Absorp. base, primary or aux. emulsifier used in pharmaceuticals; stabilizer for emulsions, dispersions, and suspensions; epidermal moisturizer, lubricant, and emollient
Properties: Pale straw liq.; faint sterol-type odor; misc. with min. oil, esters, and glycerides; sp.gr. 0.84-0.86; HLB 8; acid no. 1 max.; iodine no. 12 max.; sapon. no. 2 max.; 100% act.; nonionic
Toxicology: Nontoxic; nonirritating to skin and eyes; nonsensitizing.

Ritachol® 1000. [R.I.T.A.]
Chem. Descrip.: Cetearyl alcohol, polysorbate 60, PEG-150 stearate, steareth-20
Uses: Emulsifier for pharmaceuticals, skin treatment creams/lotions, antiperspirants
Properties: Wh. waxy flakes, low odor; m.p. 48-52 C; acid no. 1.5 max.; iodine no. 3.5 max.; sapon. no. 9-14; hyd. no. 178-192; pH 5.5-7.0 (3% aq.); 100% conc.; nonionic
Toxicology: Nonirritating.

Ritachol® 2000. [R.I.T.A.]
Chem. Descrip.: Cetearyl alcohol and polysorbate 60
Uses: Emulsifier, conditioner for pharmaceuticals; used in powd. suspension formulas; stable over wide pH and temp. range
Properties: Wh. waxy flakes; m.p. 48-52 C; acid no. 0.1-1.0; iodine no. 3.5 max.; sapon. no. 9-14; hyd. no. 178-192; pH 5.5-7.0 (3% aq.); 100% conc.; nonionic
Toxicology: Nonirritating.

Ritachol® 3000. [R.I.T.A.]
Chem. Descrip.: Cetearyl alcohol, polysorbate 60, PEG-150 stearate, steareth-20, cetyl alcohol, laneth-16, PEG-60 lanolin
Uses: Emulsifying wax for pharmaceutical prods., antiperspirants, germicides; high electrolyte tolerance
Properties: Ylsh. waxy flake; acid no. 2 max.; iodine no. 6 max.; sapon. no. 14 max.; hyd. no. 168-186; pH 5.3-6.8 (3% aq.); 100% conc.; nonionic
Toxicology: Nonirritating.

Ritachol® 4000. [R.I.T.A.]
Chem. Descrip.: Cetyl alcohol, steareth-20, PEG-60 lanolin
Uses: Emulsifying wax, emollient, and thickener for pharmaceuticals
Properties: Ylsh. waxy flake; acid no. 1 max.; sapon. no. 5 max.; hyd. no. 160-180; 100% conc.; nonionic
Toxicology: Nonirritating.

Ritachol® SS. [R.I.T.A.]
Chem. Descrip.: Stearyl stearate
CAS 2778-96-3; EINECS 220-476-5
Uses: Raw material for pharmaceuticals
Properties: Wh. flakes.

Ritahydrox. [R.I.T.A.]
Chem. Descrip.: Hydroxylated lanolin
CAS 68424-66-8; EINECS 270-315-8
Uses: W/o emulsifier, hypoallergenic emollient, superfatting agent, pigment dispersant, emulsion

stabilizer, thickener with high water absorp., skin wetting; for ointments, sun preps.
Properties: Yel. paste; HLB 4.0; m.p. 39-46 C; acid no. 10 max.; iodine no. 15-23; sapon. no. 95-110; hyd. no. 60-85; 100% conc.; nonionic.

Ritalan®. [R.I.T.A.]
Chem. Descrip.: Lanolin oil USP
EINECS 274-559-6
Uses: Moisturizer, plasticizer, penetrant, emollient with high spreading coefficient; hypoallergenic nonsensitizing skin lubricant; prevents defatting; for topicals, sunscreens
Properties: Amber clear liq., sl. odor; sol. in lipids, min. oil; insol. in water; acid no. 2 max.; iodine no. 18-36; cloud pt. 18 C; 100% conc.; nonionic.

Ritalan® AWS. [R.I.T.A.]
Chem. Descrip.: PPG-12-PEG-65 lanolin oil
CAS 68458-58-8
Uses: Aux. emulsifier, moisturizer, emollient for ointments, sun preps.
Properties: Lt. amber liq., odorless; sol. in water and alcohol; HLB 18.0; acid no. 3 max.; iodine no. 10 max.; sapon. no. 10-25; hyd. no. 50 max.; pH 5-7 (10%); 100% act.; nonionic.

RITA Lanolin. [R.I.T.A.]
Chem. Descrip.: Lanolin
CAS 8006-54-0; EINECS 232-348-6
Uses: Emollient, emulsifier, penetrant, moisturizer with good skin feel, adhesive/cohesive and tackifying props. for pharmaceutical formulations, sun care prods.
Properties: Ointment-like material, sl. char. odor; sol. in chloroform, ether; partly sol. in alcohol; insol. in water, min. oil.

Ritapan D. [R.I.T.A.]
Chem. Descrip.: D-panthenol
CAS 81-13-0; EINECS 201-327-3
Uses: Nutrient, humectant for skin care formulations; soothing to skin irritated by minor wounds, sun, insect bites, and allergic reactions
Properties: Clear visc. liq.

Ritapan DL. [R.I.T.A.]
Chem. Descrip.: DL-panthenol
CAS 16485-10-2
Uses: Nutrient, humectant for skin care formulations; soothing to skin irritated by minor wounds, sun, insect bites, and allergic reactions
Properties: Wh. powd.

Ritapan TA. [R.I.T.A.]
Chem. Descrip.: Panthenyl triacetate
CAS 98133-47-2
Uses: Nutrient, humectant for skin care formulations; soothing to skin irritated by minor wounds, sun, insect bites, and allergic reactions
Properties: Clear visc. liq.

Ritasol. [R.I.T.A.]
Chem. Descrip.: Isopropyl lanolate
CAS 63393-93-1; EINECS 264-119-1
Uses: Emollient, spreading agent, water-resistant film-former for ointments, sun preps.
Properties: Yel. paste; 100% conc.; nonionic.

Ritawax. [R.I.T.A.]

Chem. Descrip.: Lanolin alcohol
CAS 8027-33-6; EINECS 232-430-1
Uses: Emulsifier, emollient, stabilizer, and thickener for pharmaceuticals, sunscreens; strong water absorp. props.; hardener for wax systems
Properties: Amber firm waxy solid, char. odor; sol. in alcohol, IPM, other oils; m.p. 53-61 C; acid no. 2 max.; sapon. no. 10 max.; hyd. no. 118-160; 100% conc.; nonionic.

Ritawax AEO. [R.I.T.A.]
Chem. Descrip.: Polysorbate 80, acetylated lanolin alcohol, cetyl acetate
Uses: Emollient, lubricant, moisturizer, penetrant, solubilizer, dispersant, plasticizer, cosolv., emulsifier for personal care prods.; vehicle for medicaments
Properties: Lemon yel. to straw-colored clear oily liq., char. bland odor; sol. in water, IPA, castor oil, min. oil, veg. oil; acid no. 2 max.; sapon. no. 65-80; hyd. no. 60-70; 100% conc.; nonionic.

Ritawax ALA. [R.I.T.A.]
Chem. Descrip.: Cetyl acetate and acetylated lanolin alcohol
Uses: Emollient, lubricant, moisturizer, penetrant, plasticizer, cosolv., solubilizer, emulsifier for personal care prods.; vehicle for medicaments
Properties: Lemon yel. to straw-colored oily liq., char. bland odor; sol. in min. oil, castor oil, veg. oil, alcohol; acid no. 1 max.; iodine no. 10 max.; sapon. no. 180-200; hyd. no. 8 max.; 100% conc.; nonionic.

Ritawax Super. [R.I.T.A.]
Chem. Descrip.: Lanolin alcohol
CAS 8027-33-6; EINECS 232-430-1
Uses: Emulsifier, emollient, conditioner, moisturizer, stabilizer, and solubilizer in ointments, sun preps., veterinary prods.
Properties: Amber solid.

R-MA 11®. [Reheis]
Chem. Descrip.: Aluminum hydroxide, magnesium carbonate
Uses: Antacid which minimizes constipative or laxative effects; prompt and prolonged acid neutralizing action
Properties: Dried gel; 74 µ min. particle size; 80% thru 200 mesh; apparent dens. 0.27-0.33 g/cc; 41.5% Al_2O_3, 8% MgO.

R-MA 11™ HD (Low Sodium). [Reheis]
Uses: Direct compression antacid dried gel for tablet and suspension use; high dens., exc. free-flow and nondusting chars.
Properties: Powd.; 98% min. thru 30 mesh, 15% max. thru 120 mesh; dens. 0.55 g/cc (tapped); 41.8% Al_2O_3, 8.5% MgO.

R-MA 40®. [Reheis]
Chem. Descrip.: Aluminum hydroxide, magnesium carbonate
Uses: Antacid which minimizes constipative or laxative effects; prompt and prolonged acid neutralizing action
Properties: Dried gel; 74 µ min. particle size; 75% thru 325 mesh; apparent dens. 0.25-0.35 g/cc;

39.7% Al_2O_3, 15.7% MgO.

Robane®. [Robeco]
Chem. Descrip.: Squalane NF
CAS 111-01-3; EINECS 203-825-6
Uses: Liq. vehicle natural to skin and sebum; moisturizer, emollient, lubricant, humectant; aids spread of topical agents over the skin, increases skin respiration, prevents insensible water loss, imparts suppleness to skin without greasy feel
Properties: Colorless liq. oil, odorless, tasteless; misc. with veg. and min. oils, org. solvs., lipophilic substances, and human sebum; m.w. 422.83; sp.gr. 0.807-0.810; visc. 32-34 cps; f.p. -38 C; b.p. 350 C; acid no. 0.2 max.; iodine no. 4 max.; sapon. no. 2 max.; flash pt. 230 C; ref. index 1.4510-1.4525
Toxicology: Nontoxic, nonirritating
Precaution: Keep away from open flame.

Rocoat® Niacinamide 33$^1/_3$% No. 69907. [Roche]
Chem. Descrip.: Niacinamide USP FCC coated with mono and diglycerides of edible fatty acids and ≤ 1.5% silicon dioxide
Uses: Incorporated into chewable multivitamin tablets and other dry dosage forms; provides taste-free and odorless form and protects the vitamin
Regulatory: FDA GRAS
Properties: Wh. relatively free-flowing powd. with some soft agglomerates, sl. char. odor, satisfactory taste; 99% min. thru 20 mesh, 50% max. thru 200 mesh; 32.6-35.3% assay (niacinamide)
Storage: Store below 72 F.

Rocoat® Niacinamide 33$^1/_3$% Type S No. 69909. [Roche]
Chem. Descrip.: Niacinamide USP FCC in inert coating of food-grade stearic acid with ≈ 1% silicon dioxide (flow agent)
Uses: Incorporated into chewable multivitamin tablets and other dry dosage forms; provides taste-free and odorless form and protects the vitamin
Regulatory: FDA GRAS
Properties: Wh. relatively free-flowing powd. with some soft agglomerates, sl. char. odor, satisfactory taste; 99% min. thru 30 mesh, 65% min. thru 60 mesh; 32.6-35.3% assay (niacinamide)
Storage: Store below 72 F.

Rocoat® Pyridoxine Hydrochloride 33$^1/_3$% No. 60688. [Roche]
Chem. Descrip.: Pyridoxine hydrochloride USP FCC in inert coating of mono- and diglycerides of edible fatty acids
Uses: Incorporated into chewable multivitamin tablets and other dry dosage forms; provides taste-free and odorless form and protects vitamin
Regulatory: FDA GRAS
Properties: Wh. to off-wh. relatively free-flowing powd. with some soft agglomerates, odorless to sl. odor, satisfactory taste; 99% min. thru 20 mesh, 50% max. thru 200 mesh; 32.6-35.3% assay (pyridoxine HCl)
Storage: Store below 72 F.

Rocoat® Riboflavin 25% No. 60289. [Roche]
Chem. Descrip.: Riboflavin USP-FCC in an inert coating of mono- and diglycerides of edible fatty acids and starch
Uses: Nutrient incorporated into chewable multivitamin tablets and other dry dosage forms; provides taste-free and odor-free form of vitamin B_2, protects the vitamin, provides uniform distribution
Regulatory: FDA GRAS
Properties: Orange relatively free-flowing powd. with some soft agglomerates, sl. char. odor, satisfactory taste; 99% min. thru 20 mesh, 50% max. thru 200 mesh; 24-5.28.8% assay
Storage: Store below 72 F.

Rocoat® Riboflavin 33$^1/_3$ No. 60288. [Roche]
Chem. Descrip.: Riboflavin USP-FCC and cornstarch in an inert coating of mono- and diglycerides of edible fatty acids
Uses: Nutrient incorporated into chewable multivitamin tablets and other dry dosage forms; provides taste-free and odor-free form of vitamin B_2, protects the vitamin
Regulatory: FDA GRAS
Properties: Orange relatively free-flowing powd. with some soft agglomerates, sl. char. odor, satisfactory taste; 99% min. thru 20 mesh, 50% max. thru 200 mesh; 32.6-35.3% assay
Storage: Store below 72 F.

Rocoat® Thiamine Mononitrate 33$^1/_3$% No. 60188. [Roche]
Chem. Descrip.: Thiamine nitrate USP/FCC in inert coating of mono- and diglycerides of edible fatty acids
Uses: Nutrient incorporated into chewable multivitamin tablets and other dry dosage forms; provides taste-free and odor-free form of vitamin B_1, protects the vitamin
Regulatory: FDA GRAS
Properties: Wh. to off-wh. relatively free-flowing powd. with some soft agglomerates, sl. odor, satisfactory taste; 99% min. thru 30 mesh, 50% max. thru 200 mesh; 32.6-35.3% assay
Storage: Store in a dry place @ 46-59 F.

Ross Beeswax. [Frank B. Ross]
Chem. Descrip.: Beeswax
Uses: Used in medicinal ointments/salves
Regulatory: FDA 21CFR §184.1973, 184.1975
Properties: Lt. taffy to deep brn. wax, char. honey odor; m.p. 62-65 C; acid no. 17-24; cloud pt. -65 C max.

Ross Beeswax Substitute. [Frank B. Ross]
Chem. Descrip.: Beeswax substitutes
Uses: For use where pure beeswax is not required in medicinals (ointments, salves)
Properties: Avail. in various grades: yel. or wh.; m.p. from 130-160 F; acid no. from nil to 27; sapon. no. from nil to 103.

Ross Beeswax Substitute 628/5. [Frank B. Ross]
Chem. Descrip.: Paraffin, candelilla wax, hydrog. tallow glycerides, stearic acid, and cetyl alcohol
Uses: For use where pure beeswax is not required in medicinals (ointments, salves)

241

Properties: M.p. 140-150 F; acid no. 17-27; sapon. no. 60-80.

Ross Carnauba Wax. [Frank B. Ross]
Chem. Descrip.: Carnauba wax
CAS 8015-86-9; EINECS 232-399-4
Uses: Used for medicinal ointments and salves
Regulatory: FDA 21CFR §182.1978
Properties: Flakes or powd.; sp.gr. 0.996-0.998; m.p. 181.4 F min.; acid no. 2-10; iodine no. 7-14; sapon. no. 78-95; flash pt. 570 F min.; ref. index 1.4540.

Ross Castor Wax. [Frank B. Ross]
Chem. Descrip.: Hydrog. castor oil
CAS 8001-78-3; EINECS 232-292-2
Uses: Wax for pharmaceuticals.

Ross Ceresine Wax. [Frank B. Ross]
Chem. Descrip.: Ceresine wax
CAS 8001-75-0; EINECS 232-290-1
Uses: Thickener used in medicinal ointments and slaves
Regulatory: FDA 21CFR §175.105
Properties: Wh., yel., tan, or orange grades; sp.gr. 0.880-0.935; m.p. 53.3-87.8 C; acid no. nil; sapon. no. 2 max.; ref. index 1.425-1.435.

Ross Japan Wax. [Frank B. Ross]
Chem. Descrip.: Japan wax
CAS 8001-39-6
Uses: Wax used in pharmaceuticals
Regulatory: FDA 21CFR §175.105, 175.300, 175.350, 176.170, 182.10
Properties: Pale cream colored wax, gummy feel; sp.gr. 0.975-0.984; m.p. 46.5-51.5 C; acid no. 6-30; iodine no. 4-15; sapon. no. 200-225; flash pt. 385 F min.; ref. index 1.4550.

Ross Japan Wax Substitute 525. [Frank B. Ross]
Chem. Descrip.: Fish glycerides, tallow glycerides, oleostearine, microcryst. wax
Uses: Wax used in pharmaceuticals
Properties: M.p. 53-56 C; acid no. 4; sapon. no. 185-195.

Ross Japan Wax Substitute 966. [Frank B. Ross]
Chem. Descrip.: Hydrog. soybean oil, paraffin
Uses: Wax used in pharmaceuticals
Properties: M.w. 51-55 C; acid no. 5; sapon. no. 185-195.

Ross Spermaceti Wax Substitute 573. [Frank B. Ross]
Chem. Descrip.: Cetyl esters
EINECS 241-640-2
Uses: Emollient, thickener for medicinal ointments and salves
Properties: Sp.gr. 0.940-0.946; m.p. 42-50 C; acid no. 2-8; iodine no. 3 max.; sapon. no. 117-148; flash pt. 470 F min.

RSP 50-5 BZK. [Crystal]
Chem. Descrip.: Benzalkonium chloride NF
Uses: Preservative in OTC drug prods.
Properties: Clear straw to lt. amber liq., mild odor; freely sol. in water, lower alcohols, ketones, glycols; m.w. 350.4; sp.gr. 0.96-0.98; pH 6-8 (10% in dist. water); 50% act.; cationic
Storage: Cryst. may occur after prolonged storage at low temps.; warming returns to homogeneous liq. state.

RSP 451-5 BZK. [Crystal]
Chem. Descrip.: Benzalkonium chloride NF
Uses: Preservative in OTC drug prods.
Properties: Clear straw to lt. abmer liq., mild odor; freely sol. in water, lower alcohols, ketones, glycols; sp.gr. 0.96-0.98; pH 6-8 (10% in dist. water); 50% act.; cationic
Storage: Cryst. may occur after prolonged storage at low temps.; warming returns to homogeneous liq. state.

Ryoto Sugar Ester B-370. [Mitsubishi Kasei Foods]
Chem. Descrip.: Sucrose tribehenate
Uses: Emulsifier; solubilizer, stabilizer for fat-sol. vitamins and antibiotics; tablet lubricant, disintegrator, binder, and filler
Properties: Powd.; partly sol. in propylene glycol, glycerin, liq. paraffin, soybean oil, cottonseed oil, water; m.p. 53-63 C; decomp. pt. 241 C; HLB 3.

Ryoto Sugar Ester L-195. [Mitsubishi Kasei Foods]
Chem. Descrip.: Sucrose polylaurate
Uses: Emulsifier for pharmaceuticals
Properties: HLB 1.

Ryoto Sugar Ester L-595. [Mitsubishi Kasei Foods]
Chem. Descrip.: Sucrose dilaurate
Uses: Emulsifier; solubilizer, stabilizer for fat-sol. vitamins and antibiotics; tablet lubricant, disintegrator, binder, and filler
Properties: Pellet; sol. in water, ethanol; partly sol. in glycerin; HLB 5.

Ryoto Sugar Ester L-1570. [Mitsubishi Kasei Foods]
Chem. Descrip.: Sucrose laurate
CAS 25339-99-5; EINECS 246-873-3
Uses: Emulsifier; solubilizer, stabilizer for fat-sol. vitamins and antibiotics; tablet lubricant, disintegrator, binder, and filler
Properties: Surf. tens. 31.7 dynes/cm (0.1% aq.); Ross-Miles foam 177 mm (0.25% aq., initial).

Ryoto Sugar Ester L-1695. [Mitsubishi Kasei Foods]
Chem. Descrip.: Sucrose laurate
CAS 25339-99-5; EINECS 246-873-3
Uses: Emulsifier; solubilizer, stabilizer for fat-sol. vitamins and antibiotics; tablet lubricant, disintegrator, binder, and filler
Properties: Pellet; sol. in water, ethanol; partly sol. in glycerin; m.p. 35-47 C; decomp. pt. 235 C; HLB 16; surf. tens. 31.6 dynes/cm (0.1% aq.).

Ryoto Sugar Ester LN-195. [Mitsubishi Kasei Foods]
Chem. Descrip.: Sucrose polylinoleate
Uses: Emulsifier.

Ryoto Sugar Ester LWA-1570. [Mitsubishi Kasei Foods]
Chem. Descrip.: Sucrose laurate
CAS 25339-99-5; EINECS 246-873-3
Uses: Emulsifier; solubilizer, stabilizer for fat-sol. vitamins and antibiotics; tablet lubricant, disintegrator, binder, and filler
Properties: Paste; HLB 15.0; 40% conc.; nonionic.

Ryoto Sugar Ester M-1695. [Mitsubishi Kasei Foods]
Chem. Descrip.: Sucrose myristate
Uses: Emulsifier; solubilizer, stabilizer for fat-sol.

vitamins and antibiotics; tablet lubricant, disintegrator, binder, and filler
Properties: Pellet; sol. in water, propylene glycol, ethanol; partly sol. in glycerin; m.p. 27-40 C; decomp. pt. 243 C; HLB 16.

Ryoto Sugar Ester O-170. [Mitsubishi Kasei Foods]
Chem. Descrip.: Sucrose polyoleate
Uses: Emulsifier
Properties: HLB 1.

Ryoto Sugar Ester O-1570. [Mitsubishi Kasei Foods]
Chem. Descrip.: Sucrose oleate
Uses: Emulsifier; solubilizer, stabilizer for fat-sol. vitamins and antibiotics; tablet lubricant, disintegrator, binder, and filler
Properties: Pellet; sol. in water, ethanol; partly sol. in glycerin; m.p. 27-43 C; decomp. pt. 227 C; HLB 15; surf. tens. 34.5 dynes/cm (0.1% aq.); Ross-Miles foam 14 mm (0.25% aq., initial).

Ryoto Sugar Ester OWA-1570. [Mitsubishi Kasei Foods]
Chem. Descrip.: Sucrose oleate
Uses: Emulsifier; solubilizer, stabilizer for fat-sol. vitamins and antibiotics; tablet lubricant, disintegrator, binder, and filler
Properties: Paste; HLB 15.0; 40% conc.; nonionic.

Ryoto Sugar Ester P-1570. [Mitsubishi Kasei Foods]
Chem. Descrip.: Sucrose palmitate
CAS 26446-38-8; EINECS 247-706-7
Uses: Emulsifier; solubilizer, stabilizer for fat-sol. vitamins and antibiotics; tablet lubricant, disintegrator, binder, and filler
Properties: Powd.; partly sol. in water, propylene glycol, glycerin, liq. paraffin, soybean and cottonseed oils; m.p. 47-54 C; decomp. pt. 237 C; HLB 15.0; surf. tens. 35.4 dynes/cm (0.1% aq.); Ross-Miles foam 15 mm (0.25% aq., initial); 100% conc.; nonionic.

Ryoto Sugar Ester P-1570S. [Mitsubishi Kasei Foods]
Chem. Descrip.: Sucrose palmitate, high ignition residue
CAS 26446-38-8; EINECS 247-706-7
Uses: Emulsifier; solubilizer, stabilizer for fat-sol. vitamins and antibiotics; tablet lubricant, disintegrator, binder, and filler
Properties: Powd.; sol. in water; partly sol. in propylene glycol, glycerin, liq. paraffin, soybean and cottonseed oils; HLB 15; nonionic.

Ryoto Sugar Ester P-1670. [Mitsubishi Kasei Foods]
Chem. Descrip.: Sucrose palmitate
CAS 26446-38-8; EINECS 247-706-7
Uses: Emulsifier; solubilizer, stabilizer for fat-sol. vitamins and antibiotics; tablet lubricant, disintegrator, binder, and filler
Properties: Powd.; sol. in water; partly sol. in propylene glycol, glycerin, liq. paraffin, soybean and cottonseed oils; m.p. 40-48 C; decomp. pt. 235 C; HLB 16; surf. tens. 34.5 dynes/cm (0.1% aq.); Ross-Miles foam 24 mm (0.25% aq., initial); nonionic.

Ryoto Sugar Ester S-070. [Mitsubishi Kasei Foods]
Chem. Descrip.: Sucrose polystearate

Uses: O/w and w/o emulsifier for pharmaceuticals
Properties: Powd.; 100% conc.; nonionic.

Ryoto Sugar Ester S-170. [Mitsubishi Kasei Foods]
Chem. Descrip.: Sucrose di, tristearate
Uses: Emulsifier; solubilizer, stabilizer for fat-sol. vitamins and antibiotics; tablet lubricant, disintegrator, binder, and filler
Properties: Powd.; partly sol. in propylene glycol, glycerin, liq. paraffin, soybean and cottonseed oils; insol. in water; m.p. 51-61 C; decomp. pt. 260 C; HLB 1.0; 100% conc.; nonionic.

Ryoto Sugar Ester S-170 Ac. [Mitsubishi Kasei]
Chem. Descrip.: Sucrose tetrastearate triacetate
Uses: Emulsifier.

Ryoto Sugar Ester S-270. [Mitsubishi Kasei Foods]
Chem. Descrip.: Sucrose di, tristearate
Uses: Emulsifier; solubilizer, stabilizer for fat-sol. vitamins and antibiotics; tablet lubricant, disintegrator, binder, and filler
Properties: Powd.; partly sol. in propylene glycol, glycerin, liq. paraffin, soybean and cottonseed oils; insol. in water; m.p. 52-61 C; decomp. pt. 253 C; HLB 2.0; 100% conc.; nonionic.

Ryoto Sugar Ester S-370. [Mitsubishi Kasei Foods]
Chem. Descrip.: Sucrose tristearate
Uses: Emulsifier; solubilizer, stabilizer for fat-sol. vitamins and antibiotics; tablet lubricant, disintegrator, binder, and filler
Properties: Powd.; partly sol. in propylene glycol, glycerin, liq. paraffin, soybean and cottonseed oils; insol. in water; m.p. 51-58 C; decomp. pt. 238 C; HLB 3; 100% conc.; nonionic.

Ryoto Sugar Ester S-370F. [Mitsubishi Kasei Foods]
Chem. Descrip.: Sucrose tristearate
Uses: Emulsifier; solubilizer, stabilizer for fat-sol. vitamins and antibiotics; tablet lubricant, disintegrator, binder, and filler
Properties: Fine powd.; HLB 3; nonionic.

Ryoto Sugar Ester S-570. [Mitsubishi Kasei Foods]
Chem. Descrip.: Sucrose distearate
CAS 27195-16-0; EINECS 248-317-5
Uses: Emulsifier; solubilizer, stabilizer for fat-sol. vitamins and antibiotics; tablet lubricant, disintegrator, binder, and filler
Properties: Powd.; partly sol. in propylene glycol, glycerin, liq. paraffin, soybean and cottonseed oils; insol. in water; m.p. 50-57 C; decomp. pt. 231 C; HLB 5.0; surf. tens. 38.1 dynes/cm (0.1% aq.); 100% conc.; nonionic.

Ryoto Sugar Ester S-770. [Mitsubishi Kasei Foods]
Chem. Descrip.: Sucrose distearate
CAS 27195-16-0; EINECS 248-317-5
Uses: Emulsifier; solubilizer, stabilizer for fat-sol. vitamins and antibiotics; tablet lubricant, disintegrator, binder, and filler
Properties: Powd.; partly sol. in propylene glycol, glycerin, liq. paraffin, soybean and cottonseed oils, water; m.p. 49-60 C; decomp. pt. 233 C; HLB 7.0; surf. tens. 37.4 dynes/cm (0.1% aq.).

Ryoto Sugar Ester S-970. [Mitsubishi Kasei Foods]
Chem. Descrip.: Sucrose mono, distearate
CAS 27195-16-0; EINECS 248-317-5

Uses: Emulsifier; solubilizer, stabilizer for fat-sol. vitamins and antibiotics; tablet lubricant, disintegrator, binder, and filler
Properties: Powd.; partly sol. in propylene glycol, glycerin, liq. paraffin, soybean and cottonseed oils, water; m.p. 49-56 C; decomp. pt. 234 C; HLB 9.0; surf. tens. 35.8 dynes/cm (0.1% aq.); 100% conc.; nonionic.

Ryoto Sugar Ester S-1170. [Mitsubishi Kasei Foods]
Chem. Descrip.: Sucrose stearate
CAS 25168-73-4; EINECS 246-705-9
Uses: Emulsifier; solubilizer, stabilizer for fat-sol. vitamins and antibiotics; tablet lubricant, disintegrator, binder, and filler
Properties: Powd.; partly sol. in propylene glycol, glycerin, liq. paraffin, soybean and cottonseed oils, water; m.p. 49-55 C; decomp. pt. 234 C; HLB 11; surf. tens. 34.8 dynes/cm (0.1% aq.); 100% conc.; nonionic.

Ryoto Sugar Ester S-1170S. [Mitsubishi Kasei Foods]
Chem. Descrip.: Sucrose stearate, high ignition residue
CAS 25168-73-4; EINECS 246-705-9
Uses: Emulsifier; solubilizer, stabilizer for fat-sol. vitamins and antibiotics; tablet lubricant, disintegrator, binder, and filler
Properties: Powd.; sol. in water; partly sol. in propylene glycol, glycerin, liq. paraffinn, soybean and cottonseed oils; HLB 11; nonionic.

Ryoto Sugar Ester S-1570. [Mitsubishi Kasei Foods]
Chem. Descrip.: Sucrose stearate
CAS 25168-73-4; EINECS 246-705-9

Uses: Emulsifier; solubilizer, stabilizer for fat-sol. vitamins and antibiotics; tablet lubricant, disintegrator, binder, and filler
Properties: Powd.; sol. in water; partly sol. in propylene glycol, glycerin, liq. paraffin, soybean and cottonseed oils; m.p. 49-55 C; decomp. pt. 234 C; HLB 15.0; surf. tens. 34.7 dynes/cm (0.1% aq.); Ross-Miles foam 11 mm (0.25% aq., initial); 100% conc.; nonionic.

Ryoto Sugar Ester S-1670. [Mitsubishi Kasei Foods]
Chem. Descrip.: Sucrose stearate
CAS 25168-73-4; EINECS 246-705-9
Uses: Emulsifier; solubilizer, stabilizer for fat-sol. vitamins and antibiotics; tablet lubricant, disintegrator, binder, and filler
Properties: Powd.; sol. in water; partly sol. in propylene glycol, glycerin, liq. paraffin, soybean and cottonseed oils; m.p. 49-56 C; decomp. pt. 237 C; HLB 16; surf. tens. 34.7 dynes/cm (0.1% aq.); Ross-Miles foam 12 mm (0.25% aq., initial); nonionic.

Ryoto Sugar Ester S-1670S. [Mitsubishi Kasei Foods]
Chem. Descrip.: Sucrose stearate, high ignition residue
CAS 25168-73-4; EINECS 246-705-9
Uses: Emulsifier; solubilizer, stabilizer for fat-sol. vitamins and antibiotics; tablet lubricant, disintegrator, binder, and filler
Properties: Powd.; sol. in water; partly sol. in propylene glycol, glycerin, liq. paraffin, soybean and cottonseed oils; HLB 16; nonionic.

S

Safester A-75. [Induchem AG; Lipo]
Chem. Descrip.: Ethyl linoleate
CAS 544-35-4; EINECS 208-868-4
Uses: Vitamin deriv. for pharmaceuticals
Use level: 0.5-3%
Regulatory: EEC, USA permitted
Properties: Yel. liq.; oil-sol.

Safester A 75 WS. [Induchem AG]
Chem. Descrip.: Solubilized ethyl linoleate with PEG-12 glyceryl laurate and PEG-36 castor oil
Uses: Vitamin deriv. for pharmaceuticals
Use level: 2-5%
Regulatory: EEC and USA permitted
Properties: Ylsh. liq.; water-sol.

Sandopan® DTC-Acid. [Sandoz]
Chem. Descrip.: Trideceth-7 carboxylic acid
Uses: Detergent, wetting agent for medicated liq. and bar soaps
Properties: Clear liq.; sol. in oils, solvs.; HLB 13.0 (@ pH 2.5); pH 2.5 (10%); surf. tens. 31.6 dynes/cm (0.01%); Ross-Miles foam 145 mm (0.1%, 40 C, initial); 90% conc.; anionic.

Sandopan® LA-8-HC. [Sandoz]
Chem. Descrip.: Sodium laureth-5 carboxylic acid
CAS 33939-64-9
Uses: Mild surfactant for medicated soaps and shampoos
Properties: Clear liq.; pH 2.5 (10%); surf. tens. 38.6 dynes/cm (0.01%); Ross-Miles foam 155 mm (initial); 91% act.; anionic.

Sanisol C. [Kao Corp. SA]
Chem. Descrip.: Benzalkonium chloride
Uses: Disinfectant, sanitizer for pharmaceuticals
Properties: Liq.
Unverified

Sanisol CPR, CR, CR-80%. [Kao Corp. SA]
Chem. Descrip.: Benzalkonium chloride
Uses: Disinfectant, sanitizer for pharmaceuticals
Properties: Liq., liq., paste resp.; 75, 50, and 80% conc.; cationic
Unverified

Sanisol HTPR. [Kao Corp. SA]
Chem. Descrip.: Benzalkonium chloride
Uses: Disinfectant, sanitizer for pharmaceuticals
Properties: Liq./paste; 75% conc.; cationic
Unverified

Sanisol OPR, TPR. [Kao Corp. SA]
Chem. Descrip.: Benzalkonium chloride

Uses: Disinfectant, sanitizer for pharmaceuticals
Properties: Liq.; 75% conc.; cationic
Unverified

Saponated Benzyl Benzoate. [Pentagon Chems. Ltd]
Chem. Descrip.: Saponated benzyl benzoate NF
Uses: Acaricide in treatment of scabies
Properties: Amber oily liq.; sp.gr. 1.098-1.106 (20 C)
Storage: Storage below 20 C may cause turbidity and separation; gently warm above 20 C and agitate to restore to clear original form; 12 mos storage at 50 C causes no deterioration apart from darkening.

Sarkosyl® L. [Ciba-Geigy AG]
Chem. Descrip.: Lauroyl sarcosine
CAS 97-78-9; EINECS 202-608-3
Uses: Foam booster/stabilizer, wetting agent, lubricant, emulsifier used in dentifrices, pharmaceuticals
Properties: Powd.; m.w. 264-285; sol. in org. solvs.; insol. in water; sp.gr. 0.969; m.p. 35-37 C; 94% min. purity; anionic
Unverified

Sarkosyl® LC. [Ciba-Geigy AG]
Chem. Descrip.: Cocoyl sarcosine
CAS 68411-97-2; EINECS 270-156-4
Uses: Foam booster/stabilizer, wetting agent, lubricant, emulsifier used in dentifrices, pharmaceuticals
Properties: Powd.; m.w. 285-300; sol. in org. solvs.; insol. in water; sp.gr. 0.969; m.p. 23-28 C; 94% min. purity
Unverified

Satialgine™ H8. [Mendell]
Chem. Descrip.: Alginic acid NF/FCC
CAS 9005-32-7; EINECS 232-680-1
Uses: Tablet disintegrant for pharmaceutical compressed tablets in wet or dry granulations; offers rapid swelling in aq. media
Use level: 1-5% (tablets)
Properties: Wh. to ylsh. wh. fibrous powd.; 75% max. -325 mesh; acid no. ≥ 230; pH 1.5-3.5 (3% aq.).

Saytex® VBR. [Albemarle]
Chem. Descrip.: Monomeric vinyl bromide
CAS 593-60-2
Uses: Intermediate in mfg. of pharmaceuticals
Properties: Off-wh. low-boiling liq., char. pungent

odor; m.w. 106.96; f.p. -139.2 C; b.p. 15.8 C (760 mm Hg); dens. 12.7 lb/gal (20 C); flash pt. (COC) none; 99.8% vinyl bromide; 74.5% Br.

SB-30. [J.M. Huber/Engineered Mins.]
Chem. Descrip.: Alumina trihydrate
CAS 21645-51-2
Uses: Filler used in pharmaceuticals
Properties: Off-wh. unground particulate; 50 µ median particle diam.; 10% on 100 mesh, 95% on 325 mesh; sp.gr. 2.42; bulk dens. 1.2 g/cc (loose); surf. area 0.1 m^2/g; brightness (TAPPI) 80; ref. index 1.57; hardness (Moh) 2.5-3.5; 64.9% Al$_2$O$_3$.

Seagel L. [Marine Colloids]
Chem. Descrip.: Locust bean gum
CAS 9000-40-2; EINECS 232-541-5
Uses: Stabilizer, thickener, emulsifier for pharmaceuticals.

Sebase. [Westbrook Lanolin]
Chem. Descrip.: PEG-30 lanolin, cetearyl alcohol, min. oil, and p-chloro-m-cresol with 150 ppm BHT (antioxidant)
Uses: Complete self-emulsifying base for pharmaceuticals; emollient, moisturizer, emulsifier, lubricant, visc. stabilizer; elegant carrier for therapeutically active substances for hospital/pharmacy use
Properties: Pale yel. pearly unctuous soft wax, faint char. odor; partly sol. in water, ethanol, anhyd. IPA, min. oil, IPM; drop pt. 30-38 C; HLB 8.0; acid no. 1.5 max.; sapon. no. 6-24; hyd. no. 9-16; flash pt. > 100 C; 100% conc.; nonionic; nonhazardous
Toxicology: Extremely low toxicity
Precaution: Nonflamm., but will burn if strongly heated
Storage: Store in cool place; if contents of container are melted but not all use, mix remainder before use; 2 yrs storage life under good conditions.

Sedefos 75®. [Gattefosse; Gattefosse SA]
Chem. Descrip.: Glycol stearate, PEG-2 stearate, and trilaneth-4 phosphate
Uses: SE base for pharmaceuticals, esp. acidic prods. and anhyd. cream formulations
Use level: 15-20%
Properties: Gardner < 5 waxy solid; weak odor; HLB 10-11; m.p. 43-48 C; acid no. < 6; iodine no. < 3; sapon. no. 105-120; 100% conc.; anionic
Toxicology: Sl. irritating to skin, nonirritating to eyes.

Sellig R 3395. [Ceca SA]
Chem. Descrip.: PEG-33 castor oil
CAS 61791-12-6
Uses: Surfactant, emulsifier for pharmaceuticals, veterinary applics.; solubilizer for essential oils
Properties: Pale yel. visc. liq.; sp.gr. 1.08 ± 0.06; HLB 12.0; iodine no. 33 ± 4; sapon. no. 67 ± 4; pH 7 ± 0.5 (10%); 95% conc.; nonionic.

Sepigel 305. [Seppic]
Chem. Descrip.: Polyacrylamide, C13-14 isoparaffin, laureth-7
Uses: Thickener for aq. gels and emulsions; provides instantaneous gelling on addition of water; emulsifier, stabilizer; for anti-lice conditioners,

antibiotic gels
Regulatory: Japan approved for cosmetics
Properties: Fluid emulsion; visc. 60,000-90,000 mPa•s (2%); pH ≈ 6; 50% act.
Toxicology: Nonirritating to skin and eyes.

Sequestrene® NA2. [Ciba-Geigy/Dyestuffs]
Chem. Descrip.: Disodium EDTA dihydrate
CAS 139-33-3; EINECS 205-358-3
Uses: Chelating agent for control of trace metal contamination in pharmaceutical prods.
Properties: Wh. cryst. powd.; odorless; water-sol.; pH 6.0 (5%); 99% act.

Sequestrene® NA2Ca. [Ciba-Geigy/Dyestuffs]
Chem. Descrip.: Disodium-calcium EDTA dihydrate
Uses: Chelating agent for control of trace metal contamination in pharmaceutical prods.
Properties: Wh. cryst. powd.; odorless; 97-102% act.

Servirox OEG 45. [Servo Delden BV]
Chem. Descrip.: PEG-17 castor oil
CAS 61791-12-6
Uses: Used in phytopharmaceutical applics.
Properties: Liq.; 100% conc.; nonionic
Unverified

Servirox OEG 55. [Servo Delden BV]
Chem. Descrip.: PEG-26 castor oil
CAS 61791-12-6
Uses: Used in phytopharmaceutical applics.
Properties: Liq.; 100% conc.; nonionic
Unverified

Servirox OEG 65. [Servo Delden BV]
Chem. Descrip.: PEG-32 castor oil
CAS 61791-12-6
Uses: Used in phytopharmaceutical applics.
Properties: Liq.; 100% conc.; nonionic
Unverified

Servirox OEG 90/50. [Servo Delden BV]
Chem. Descrip.: PEG-180 castor oil
CAS 61791-12-6
Uses: Used in phytopharmaceutical applics.
Properties: Liq.; 50% conc.; nonionic
Unverified

Sesame Oil USP/NF 16. [Natural Oils Int'l.; Tri-K Industries]
Chem. Descrip.: Sesame oil
CAS 8008-74-0; EINECS 232-370-6
Uses: Solv., vehicle
Properties: Pale straw clear oil, bland odor and taste; insol. in water; sp.gr. 0.916-0.921; iodine no. 103-116; sapon. no. 188-195; flash pt. (OC) 640 F
Toxicology: Nonhazardous
Storage: Preserve in tight, light-resist. containers; avoid exposure to excessive heat.

Sheerskin. [United-Guardian]
Chem. Descrip.: Polymer
Uses: Film-former which dries to a clear water-insol. film that is degradable and sol. in soap and water; used for coating the skin, forming water-repellent films on the skin; for medical, health-care applics.

Custom product

Shiitake KS-2. [Garuda Int'l.]
Chem. Descrip.: Shiitake mushroom extract from *Lentinus edodes* mycelium with potency of 3.2% KS-2 polysaccharides
Uses: Used to formulate health foods and pharmaceuticals, tablets, capsules; possible anti-tumor, immune potentiating, interferon-stimulating, cholesterol-reducing activity; rich in vitamins and enzymes
Properties: Dried powd.
Toxicology: LD50 > 12,500 mg/kg; conutrient food, without toxicity or side effects.

Shiitake Mushroom Extract SHIEXT. [Garuda Int'l.]
Chem. Descrip.: Shiitake mushroom extract from *Lentinus edodes* with 20% dextrose carrier
Uses: Polysaccharides, lentinan actives; used to formulate health foods and pharmaceutical capsules, nutritional supplements
Properties: Brn. fine powd.; min. 20 mesh or finer; sol. in water
Storage: 24 mo shelf life.

Shiitake Mycelium Biomass SHIMYC. [Garuda Int'l.]
Chem. Descrip.: Shiitake mycelium biomass from *Lentinus edodes*
Uses: Polysaccharides, peptidomannans, lentinan actives; used to formulate health food and pharmaceutical capsules, tablets
Properties: Lt. brn. powd.; insol. in water
Storage: 24 mo shelf life.

Sicopharm®. [BASF AG]
Uses: Sol. dyes and pigments for coloring pharmaceuticals.
Unverified

Sicopharm® Iron Oxides. [Colorcon]
Chem. Descrip.: Syn. color pigments
Uses: High purity colorants for pharmaceutical applics.
Properties: Avail. in red, yel., brn., and blk.

Sident® 15. [Degussa]
Chem. Descrip.: Silica
EINECS 231-545-4
Uses: Abrasiveness and thickening agent for toothpastes.

Sident® 22LS. [Degussa]
Chem. Descrip.: Silica
EINECS 231-545-4
Uses: Nonabrasive thickening agent for toothpastes; allows prod. of pastes and transparent gels of high brilliance.

Sident® 22S. [Degussa]
Chem. Descrip.: Syn. amorphous precipitated silica
CAS 112926-00-8; EINECS 231-545-4
Uses: Nonabrasive thickening agent for toothpastes; allows prod. of pastes and transparent gels of high brilliance
Regulatory: FDA compliance
Properties: Wh. loose powd.; tapped dens. 90 g/l; surf. area 190 m^2/g; pH 6.2 (5%); 100% act.

Silvercide. [United-Guardian]
Chem. Descrip.: Suspension of silver sulfadiazine in Lubrajel
Uses: Provides exc. nondrying water-sol. jelly with long-acting bactericidal activity; for use on burns and abrasions
Custom product

Silwet® L-77. [OSi Specialties]
Chem. Descrip.: Polyalkylene oxide-modified polymethylsiloxane
CAS 27306-78-1
Uses: Surfactant, flow/leveling agent, dispersant, wetting agent, spreading agent for pharmaceuticals
Properties: Pale amber clear liq.; sol. in methanol, IPA, acetone, xylene, methylene chloride; disp. in water; m.w. 600; sp.gr. 1.007; dens. 8.37 lb/gal; visc. 20 cSt; HLB 5-8; cloud pt. < 10 C (0.1%); flash pt. (PMCC) 116 C; pour pt. 2 C; surf. tens. 20.5 dyne/cm (0.1%); Draves wetting 8 s (0.1%); Ross-Miles foam 33 mm (0.1%, initial); 100% act.; nonionic.

Silwet® L-720. [OSi Specialties]
Chem. Descrip.: Dimethicone copolyol
CAS 68554-65-4
Uses: Surfactant for pharmaceutical use
Regulatory: FDA approved
Properties: Colorless clear liq.; sol. in water, methanol, IPA, acetone, xylene, methylene chloride; m.w. 12,000; sp.gr. 1.036; dens. 8.61 lb/gal; visc. 1100 cSt; HLB 9-12; cloud pt. 42 C (1%); flash pt. (PMCC) 96 C; pour pt. -34 C; surf. tens. 29.3 dyne/cm (0.1% aq.); Draves wetting > 300 s (0.1%); Ross-Miles foam 43 mm (0.1%, initial); 50% act.; nonionic.

Silwet® L-7500. [OSi Specialties]
Chem. Descrip.: Dimethicone copolyol
CAS 68440-66-4
Uses: Surfactant, antifoam, dispersant, emulsifier, leveling/flow control agent, lubricant for pharmaceuticals
Properties: Lt. yel. clear liq.; sol. in methanol, IPA, acetone, xylene, hexanes, methylene chloride; insol. in water; m.w. 3000; sp.gr. 0.982; dens. 8.16 lb/gal; visc.140 cSt; HLB 5-8; pour pt. -43 C; flash pt. (PMCC) 121 C; 100% act.; nonionic.

Silwet® L-7602. [OSi Specialties]
Chem. Descrip.: Dimethicone copolyol
CAS 68938-54-5
Uses: Surfactant, defoamer, dispersant, emulsifier, leveling/flow control agent for pharmaceuticals
Properties: Pale yel. clear liq.; sol. in methanol, IPA, acetone, xylene, methylene chloride; disp. in water; m.w. 3000; sp.gr. 1.027; dens. 8.54 lb/gal; visc. 100 cSt; HLB 5-8; flash pt. (PMCC) 127 C; pour pt. -15 C; surf. tens. 26.6 dyne/cm (1.1% aq.); 100% act; nonionic.

Simchin® Natural. [R.I.T.A.]
Chem. Descrip.: Jojoba oil
CAS 61789-91-1
Uses: Coating material and carrier for pharmaceuticals and topicals
Properties: Yel. liq.; sp.gr. 0.863-0.864; f.p. 7-10.6

C; m.p. 6.8-7 C; acid no. 2 max.; iodine no. 82-93; sapon. no. 92-95.6; ref. index 1.4650-1.4665
Toxicology: Nontoxic.

Simchin® Refined. [R.I.T.A.]
Chem. Descrip.: Jojoba oil
CAS 61789-91-1
Uses: Coating material and carrier for pharmaceuticals and topicals
Properties: Gardner 1 liq. wax, almost odorless; sp.gr. 0.863-0.864; f.p. 7-10.6 C; m.p. 6.8-7 C; acid no. 2 max.; iodine no. 82-93; sapon. no. 92-95.6; ref. index 1.4650-1.4665; 100% conc.
Toxicology: Nontoxic, nonirritating.

Simulsol® 58. [Seppic]
Chem. Descrip.: Ceteth-20
CAS 9004-95-9
Uses: O/w emulsifier, gellant, stabilizer, wetting agent, detergent, dispersant, solubilizer for pharmaceutical actives and essential oils for creams and ointments
Regulatory: BP compliance
Properties: Flakes; sol. @ 10% in water, ethanol 95 C; sol. hot in propylene glycol; insol. in vaseline oil; m.p. 40 C; HLB 15.7; acid no. 0.5 max.; hyd. no. 50-58; cloud pt. 91 C; pH 6.5-7.5 (10% aq.); 100% conc.; nonionic
Toxicology: LD50 (oral, rat) 2.5 g/kg; nonirritating to skin, mildly irritating to eyes.

Simulsol® 78. [Seppic]
Chem. Descrip.: Steareth-20
CAS 9005-00-9
Uses: Emulsifier, gellant, stabilizer, wetting agent, detergent, dispersant, solubilizer for pharmaceuticals (creams, ointments)
Properties: Wax; sol. @ 10% in 95 C ethanol, propylene glycol; insol. in water, vaseline oil; HLB 15.3; m.p. 44 C; acid no. 1 max.; hyd. no. 45-60; cloud pt. 90 C; pH 6.5-7.5 (10% aq.); 100% conc.; nonionic
Toxicology: LD50 (oral, rat) > 4 g/kg.

Simulsol® 98. [Seppic]
Chem. Descrip.: Oleth-20
CAS 9004-98-2
Uses: Emulsifier, gellant, stabilizer, wetting agent, detergent, dispersant, solubilizer for pharmaceutical formulations (creams, ointments); solubilizer for min. oil, veg. oil, lanolin
Properties: Soft wax; sol. @ 10% in water, 95 C ethanol; disp. in propylene glycol; insol. in vaseline oil; m.p. 25 C; HLB 15.3; acid no. 1 max.; hyd. no. 50-60; cloud pt. 88 C; pH 6.5-7.5 (10% aq.); 100% conc.; nonionic
Toxicology: LD50 (oral, rat) 2.5 g/kg.

Simulsol® 165. [Seppic]
Chem. Descrip.: PEG-100 stearate, glyceryl stearate; free of dioxane and other impurities
Uses: SE acid-stable o/w emulsifier, opacifier, gellant for pharmaceuticals, esp. hydrophilic anhyd. ointments; stabilizer for other emulsifying systems
Properties: Gardner 1 max. flakes; m.p. 55-59 C; acid no. 1 max.; sapon. no. 90-97; hyd. no. 110-

130; pH 6.0-7.5 (10% aq.); 100% act.; nonionic
Toxicology: Nontoxic; well tolerated by skin.

Simulsol® 989. [Seppic]
Chem. Descrip.: PEG-7 hydrog. castor oil
CAS 61788-85-0
Uses: Lipophilic w/o emulsifier for pharmaceutical fluid and semifluid emulsions
Properties: Gardner 4 max. liq.; acid no. 1.5 max.; sapon. no. 120-140; hyd. no. 115-135; pH 6.0-7.5 (5% aq.); 100% act.; nonionic
Toxicology: LD50 (oral, rat) > 30 g/kg; very good safety for skin and mucous membranes.

Simulsol® 1292. [Seppic]
Chem. Descrip.: PEG-25 hydrog. castor oil
CAS 61788-85-0
Uses: Emulsifier, solubilizer for pharmaceutical formulations
Properties: Liq.; 100% act.

Simulsol® 1293. [Seppic]
Chem. Descrip.: PEG-40 hydrog. castor oil
CAS 61788-85-0
Uses: Emulsifier, solubilizer for pharmaceutical formulations
Properties: Paste; 100% act.

Simulsol® 5719. [Seppic]
Chem. Descrip.: Ethoxydiglycol, ceteareth-16, nonoxynol-8
Uses: Emulsifier, solubilizer for pharmaceutical formulations
Properties: Liq.; 100% act.

Simulsol® 5817. [Seppic]
Chem. Descrip.: PEG-35 castor oil
CAS 61791-12-6
Uses: Emulsifier, solubilizer for pharmaceutical formulations.

Simulsol® CS. [Seppic]
Chem. Descrip.: Ceteareth-33
CAS 68439-49-6
Uses: Emulsifier, gellant, stabilizer, wetting agent, detergent, dispersant, solubilizer for pharmaceuticals (creams, ointments)
Properties: Flakes; sol. @ 10% in 95 C ethanol, propylene glycol; disp. in vaseline oil; insol. in water; m.p. 47-52 C; HLB 18.0; acid no. 1 max.; hyd. no. 32-39; 100% act.
Toxicology: LD50 (oral, rat) > 15 g/kg; nonirritating to skin and eyes.

Simulsol® M 52. [Seppic]
Chem. Descrip.: PEG-40 stearate
CAS 9004-99-3
Uses: O/w emulsifier for pharmaceutical formulations, esp. hydrophilic anhyd. ointments
Regulatory: USP compliance
Properties: Flakes; sol. @ 10% in water, ethanol; insol.in vaseline oil; m.p. 47 C; HLB 16.9; acid no. 1 max.; sapon. no. 25-35; hyd. no. 27-40; pH 6.0-7.5 (10% aq.); 100% conc.; nonionic
Toxicology: LD50 (oral, rat) > 16 g/kg; nonirritating to skin and eyes.

Simulsol® OL 50. [Seppic]
Chem. Descrip.: PEG-40 castor oil
CAS 61791-12-6

Uses: Emulsifier, solubilizer for pharmaceutical formulations.

Simulsol® P4. [Seppic]
Chem. Descrip.: Laureth-4
CAS 5274-68-0; EINECS 226-097-1
Uses: O/w emulsifier, gellant, stabilizer, wetting agent, detergent, dispersant, solubilizer for pharmaceuticals (creams, ointments)
Properties: Liq.; sol. @ 10% in 95 C ethanol, vaseline oil, propylene glycol; disp. in water; HLB 9.7; acid no. 2 max.; hyd. no. 145-165; cloud pt. 64-69 C; pH 6.5-7.5 (10% aq.); 100% conc.; nonionic
Toxicology: LD50 (oral, rat) 9 g/kg; mildly skin irritant.

Simulsol® P23. [Seppic]
Chem. Descrip.: Laureth-23
CAS 9002-92-0
Uses: O/w emulsifier, gellant, stabilizer, wetting agent, detergent, dispersant, solubilizer for pharmaceuticals (creams, ointments)
Properties: Wax; sol. @ 10% in water, 95 C ethanol, propylene glycol; insol. in vaseline oil; m.p. 41 C; HLB 16.9; acid no. 2 max.; hyd. no. 40-60; cloud pt. 95 C; pH 6.5-7.5 (10% aq.); 100% act.; nonionic
Toxicology: LD50 (oral, rat) 9 g/kg; nonirritating to skin.

Simulsol® PS20. [Seppic]
Chem. Descrip.: PEG-25 propylene glycol stearate
Uses: Emollient, visc. regulator for pharmaceutical formulations, esp. hydrophilic anhyd. ointments.

Single Strength Acid Proof Caramel Colour. [MLG Enterprises Ltd.]
Chem. Descrip.: Caramel color
CAS 8028-89-5; EINECS 232-435-9
Uses: Natural colorant for pharmaceuticals
Properties: Sp.gr. 1.315-1.325 (60 F); dens. 10.95-11.03 lb/gal (60 F); visc. 400 cps max. (68 F); pH 2.7-3.0
Storage: 2 yr min. shelf life.

Sipernat® 22LS. [Degussa]
Chem. Descrip.: Precipitated silica
EINECS 215-683-2
Uses: Thickener for pharmaceuticals; free-flow aid for hygroscopic materials with poor flow chars., e.g., vitamins; inert carrier for actives
Regulatory: FDA approved
Properties: Tapped dens. 80 g/l; surf. area 190 m²/g; pH 6.2; 98% SiO_2.

Sipernat® 22S. [Degussa]
Chem. Descrip.: Syn. amorphous precipitated silica
CAS 112926-00-8; EINECS 215-683-2
Uses: Free-flow aid for hygroscopic materials with poor flow chars., e.g., vitamins; inert carrier for actives
Regulatory: 21CFR §172.480, 173.340, 175.105, 175.300, 176.200, 176.210, 177.1200, 177.2600, 178.3210
Properties: Wh. loose powd.; 18 nm avg. particle size; dens. 120 g/l (tapped); surf. area 190 m²/g;

pH 6.3 (5% aq. susp.); 98% assay.

Skin-Lite. [United-Guardian]
Chem. Descrip.: 70% Isopropyl alcohol sol'n. of a polymer
Uses: Film-former providing a flexible, stretchable film on the skin which breathes but is water repellent; film is removable by soap and water; for medical, health-care fields
Custom product

S-Maz® 60K. [PPG/Specialty Chem.]
Chem. Descrip.: Sorbitan stearate
CAS 1338-41-6; EINECS 215-664-9
Uses: Emulsifier and coupling agent for pharmaceuticals, creams and lotions
Regulatory: FDA 21CFR §172.515, 172.842, 173.340, 573.960; kosher
Properties: Wh. to cream flakes, ester odor; sol. in ethanol; disp. in water; sp.gr. 0.954 (70 C); m.p. 52 C; b.p. > 300 F; HLB 4.7; acid no. 10 max.; sapon. no. 147-157; hyd. no. 235-260; flash pt. (PMCC) > 350 F; nonionic
Toxicology: LD50 (oral, rat) > 32 g/kg; nonirritating
Storage: Store in well-ventilated area below 120 F.

Snowite® Oat Fiber. [Canadian Harvest USA]
Chem. Descrip.: Oat hull-based fiber
Uses: Natural fiber for boosting dietary fiber levels without masking delicate flavors; used in supplements, pharmaceuticals
Regulatory: GRAS; USDA approval
Properties: Avail. in granulations from med. to micro-fine, coarse avail. on request; creamy-wh. color, neutral odor, bland flavor; 90% total dietary fiber; pH 5.5-6.5; 5% max. moisture.

Soageena®. [Mitsubishi Int'l.]
Chem. Descrip.: Carrageenan
CAS 9000-07-1; EINECS 232-524-2
Uses: Thickener, gellant, suspending agent, foam stabilizer, binder for pharmaceuticals, lotions, creams, toothpaste
Regulatory: Japan, FAO/WHO 8.355, FDA 21CFR §172.620, 172.626, 182.7255, EEC E407 compliances.

Soageena® LX7. [Mitsubishi Int'l.]
Chem. Descrip.: Carrageenan
CAS 9000-07-1; EINECS 232-524-2
Uses: Smooth bodying agent for toothpaste
Use level: 0.2-0.4% (toothpaste)
Properties: PH 6.5-9.5 (0.5%).

Soageena® LX26. [Mitsubishi Int'l.]
Chem. Descrip.: Carrageenan
CAS 9000-07-1; EINECS 232-524-2
Uses: Gel binding agent for pharmaceuticals
Use level: 2-3%
Properties: PH 6.5-9.5 (0.5%).

Soageena® WX87. [Mitsubishi Int'l.]
Chem. Descrip.: Carrageenan
CAS 9000-07-1; EINECS 232-524-2
Uses: Provides slow release for pharmaceutical tablets
Properties: PH 6.5-9.5 (0.5%).

Sobalg FD 000 Range. [Grindsted Prods.]
Chem. Descrip.: Alginic acid

CAS 9005-32-7; EINECS 232-680-1
Uses: Provides solubility and gelation control in pharmaceuticals
Regulatory: EEC, FDA §184.1011 (GRAS).

Sobalg FD 100 Range. [Grindsted Prods.]
Chem. Descrip.: Sodium alginate
CAS 9005-38-3
Uses: Stabilizer, gellant, film-former for pharmaceuticals
Regulatory: EEC E 401, FDA §184.1724, GRAS
Properties: Off-wh. to ylsh. powd.; sol. in water; visc. < 50 to > 950 cP; pH 5.5-7.5 (1%); 90.8-106% assay
Storage: 12 mos storage under cool, dry conditions.

Sobalg FD 200 Range. [Grindsted Prods.]
Chem. Descrip.: Potassium alginate
CAS 9005-36-1
Uses: Gellant for pharmaceuticals, dental applics.
Regulatory: EEC, FDA §184.1610 (GRAS)
Properties: Off-wh. to ylsh. powd.; sol. in water; visc. 300-650 cP; pH 5.5-7.5 (1%); 89.2-105.5% assay
Storage: 6 mo storage under cool, dry conditions.

Sobalg FD 300 Range. [Grindsted Prods.]
Chem. Descrip.: Ammonium alginate
CAS 9005-34-9
Uses: Gellant for pharmaceuticals
Regulatory: EEC, FDA §184.1133 (GRAS)
Properties: Off-wh. to ylsh. powd.; sol. in water; visc. 125-850 cP; pH 5.5-7.5 (1%); 88.7-103.6% assay
Storage: 6 mo storage under cool, dry conditions.

Sobalg FD 460. [Grindsted Prods.]
Chem. Descrip.: Calcium alginate
CAS 9005-35-0
Uses: Gellant for pharmaceuticals
Regulatory: EEC, FDA §184.1187 (GRAS)
Properties: Off-wh. to ylsh. powd.; 98% min. thru 100 mesh (French); insol. in water; 89.6-104.5% assay
Storage: 12 mo storage under cool, dry conditions.

Sobalg FD 900 Range. [Grindsted Prods.]
Chem. Descrip.: Special alginate blend
Uses: Provides solubility and gelation control in pharmaceuticals.

Socci 7340. [Morton Int'l./Plastics Additives]
Uses: Antimicrobial for pharmaceutical deodorants.

Sodium Ascorbate USP, FCC Fine Gran. No. 6047709. [Roche]
Chem. Descrip.: Sodium ascorbate USP, FCC
CAS 134-03-2; EINECS 205-126-1
Uses: Preservative, antioxidant, and vitamin C source in pharmaceuticals, esp. where neutral pH and less acid taste are important, and where free-flowing gran. prod. is required
Regulatory: FDA GRAS
Properties: Wh. to ylsh. cryst. powd., pract. odorless, pleasantly saline taste with tart overtone; 100% thru 30 mesh, 15% max. thru 100 mesh; sol. 1 g/2 ml water; m.w. 198.11; bulk dens. 0.8-1.1

(tapped); pH 7-8 (10% aq.); 99-101% assay
Precaution: Oxidizes readily in sol'n.; exposure to light or atmospheric moisture may darken prod.; avoid contact with iron, copper, or nickel salts
Storage: Store in tight, light-resist. containers, optimally @ ≤ 72 F; avoid exposure to moisture and excessive heat.

Sodium Ascorbate USP, FCC Fine Powd. No. 6047708. [Roche]
Chem. Descrip.: Sodium ascorbate USP, FCC
CAS 134-03-2; EINECS 205-126-1
Uses: Preservative, antioxidant, and vitamin C source in pharmaceuticals, esp. where rapid sol., neutral pH, and less acid taste is important
Regulatory: FDA GRAS
Properties: Wh. to ylsh. powd. or cryst., pract. odorless, pleasantly saline taste with tart overtone; 98% min. thru 80 mesh; sol. 1 g/2 ml water; m.w. 198.11; bulk dens. 0.6-1.1 (tapped); pH 7-8 (10% aq.); 99-101% assay
Precaution: Oxidizes readily in sol'n.; exposure to light or atmospheric moisture may darken prod.; avoid contact with iron, copper, or nickel salts
Storage: Store in tight, light-resist. containers, optimally @ ≤ 72 F; avoid exposure to moisture and excessive heat.

Sodium Ascorbate USP, FCC Type AG No. 6047710. [Roche]
Chem. Descrip.: Sodium ascorbate USP, FCC
CAS 134-03-2; EINECS 205-126-1
Uses: Preservative, antioxidant, and vitamin C source in foods and pharmaceuticals, esp. where neutral pH and less acid taste are important; may be used in direct compression formulations, multivitamin mixts. to improve flow, chewable vitamin C tablets
Regulatory: FDA GRAS
Properties: Wh. to ylsh. cryst. powd., pract. odorless, pleasantly saline taste with tart overtone; 99.5% thru 40 mesh, 7% max. thru 140 mesh; sol. 1 g/2 ml water; m.w. 198.11; bulk dens. 0.6-0.8(tapped); pH 7-8 (10% aq.); 99-101% assay
Precaution: Oxidizes readily in sol'n.; exposure to light or atmospheric moisture may darken prod.; avoid contact with iron, copper, or nickel salts
Storage: Store in tight, light-resist. containers, optimally @ ≤ 72 F; avoid exposure to moisture and excessive heat.

Sodium Benzoate BP88. [Pentagon Chems. Ltd; Unipex]
Chem. Descrip.: Sodium benzoate BP, EP
CAS 532-32-1; EINECS 208-534-8
Uses: Preservative for pharmaceutical and dental formulations; tableting lubricant for pharmaceuticals; liver function test reagent; treatment of rheumatoid arthritis, cystitis, acute tonsilitis
Properties: Wh. gran. or flaky powd.; 99% min. assay.

Sodium Bicarbonate USP No. 1 Powd. [Rhone-Poulenc Food Ingreds.]
Chem. Descrip.: Sodium bicarbonate USP
CAS 144-55-8; EINECS 205-633-8

Uses: Used for pharmaceuticals (antibiotic mfg.)
Properties: Wh. free-flowing cryst., odorless; 2% min. on 80 mesh, 20% max. on 200 mesh; bulk dens. 60 lb/ft^3; 99% min. assay.

Sodium Bicarbonate USP No. 2 Fine Gran. [Rhone-Poulenc Food Ingreds.]
Chem. Descrip.: Sodium bicarbonate USP
CAS 144-55-8; EINECS 205-633-8
Uses: Mild buffering agent
Properties: Wh. free-flowing cryst., odorless; 2% min. on 80 mesh, 70% max. on 200 mesh; bulk dens. 65 lb/ft^3; 99% min. assay.

Sodium Bicarbonate USP No. 3 Extra Fine Powd. [Rhone-Poulenc Food Ingreds.]
Chem. Descrip.: Sodium bicarbonate USP
CAS 144-55-8; EINECS 205-633-8
Uses: Used for pharmaceuticals, deodorant powds.
Properties: Wh. free-flowing cryst., odorless; 40% min. on 60 mesh, 5% max. on 200 mesh; bulk dens. 42 lb/ft^3; 99% min. assay.

Sodium Bicarbonate USP No. 5 Coarse Gran. [Rhone-Poulenc Food Ingreds.]
Chem. Descrip.: Sodium bicarbonate USP
CAS 144-55-8; EINECS 205-633-8
Uses: Used for pharmaceuticals (antacid preps., effervescent salts, dentifrices)
Properties: Wh. free-flowing cryst., odorless; 50% max. on 80 mesh, 90% max. 170 mesh; bulk dens. 62 lb/ft^3; 99% min. assay.

Sodium Citrate USP, FCC Dihydrate Gran. No. 69976. [Roche]
Chem. Descrip.: Sodium citrate dihydrate USP FCC
Uses: PH control agent
Regulatory: FDA GRAS
Properties: Colorless cryst. or wh. cryst. powd., pract. odorless, saline taste; 3% max. on 16 mesh, 3% max. thru 140 mesh; sl. deliq. in moist air; sol. 65 g/100 ml water; insol. in alcohol; m.w. 294.10; 99-100.5% assay
Storage: 12 mos storage life in original, unopened containers at temps. below 25 C.

Sodium Citrate USP, FCC Dihydrate Fine Gran. No. 69975. [Roche]
Chem. Descrip.: Sodium citrate USP, FCC
CAS 68-04-2; EINECS 200-675-3
Uses: PH adjustor, buffering agent
Regulatory: FDA GRAS
Properties: Colorless cryst. or wh. cryst. powd., pract. odorless, saline taste; 1% max. on 3 mesh, 10% max. thru 100 mesh; sl. deliq. in moist air; sol. 65 g/100 ml water; insol. in alcohol; m.w. 294.10; 99-100.5% assay
Storage: 12 mos storage life in original unopened pkgs. at temps. below 25 C.

Softigen® 701. [Hüls Am.; Hüls AG]
Chem. Descrip.: Glyceryl ricinoleate
CAS 141-08-2; EINECS 205-455-0
Uses: Emollient, refatting and skin protecting agent for pharmaceuticals (creams, ointments, soaps, mucosal protective in rectal and vaginal supposi-

tories), sunscreens; good adhesion to mucosae
Properties: Ylsh.-wh. paste/clear oily liq. @ 30-35 C, char. odor; sol. in ether, benzene, toluene, xylene, chloroform, and dichlorethylene; misc. with fats, oils; sp.gr. 0.979-0.981; visc. 500-600 mPa•s (30 C); acid no. 3 max.; iodine no. 70-80; sapon. no. 155-170; 100% conc.; nonionic.

Softigen® 767. [Hüls Am.; Hüls AG]
Chem. Descrip.: PEG-6 caprylic/capric glycerides
CAS 52504-24-2
Uses: Superfatting and wetting agent; solubilizer for volatile and fixed oils; emollient used in pharmaceuticals, esp. for treatment of psoriatic conditions
Properties: Ylsh. visc. oily liq., faint char. odor; sol. in water @ 1.3%; sol. in acetone, ethyl and butyl acetate, castor oil, IPA; dens. 1.080 g/ml; visc. 160 mPa•s; HLB 19; acid no. 1 max.; iodine no. 1 max.; sapon. no. 90-110; surf. tens. 29.7 dynes/cm (1%); 100% act.; nonionic
Toxicology: LD50 (oral, rat) > 5 g/kg (pract. nontoxic); nonirritating to skin and eyes.

Softisan® 100. [Hüls Am.; Hüls AG]
Chem. Descrip.: Hydrog. coco-glycerides
Uses: Consistency regulator, emollient, ointment base for pharmaceutical industry; cocoa butter substitute; assists penetration of skin by active ingreds.
Properties: Wh. pastilles; neutral odor and taste; sol. in benzene, ether, xylene, toluene, chloroform, CCl$_4$, dioxane; sp.gr. 0.950-0.980; visc. 30 cps (40 C); m.p. 33-36 C; solid. pt. 29-33 C; acid no. 0.2 max.; iodine no. 3 max.; sapon. no. 230-250; hyd. no. 15 max.; ref. index 1.4490-1.4510 (40 C); nonionic
Toxicology: Nontoxic.

Softisan® 133. [Hüls Am.; Hüls AG]
Chem. Descrip.: Hydrog. coco-glycerides
Uses: Fat component and consistency regulator in pharmaceutical creams, ointments; assists penetration of skin by active ingreds.
Properties: Wh. pastilles; neutral odor and taste; sol. in benzene, toluene, acetone, chloroform, petrol. spirit; insol. in water; m.p. 32-34 C; solid. pt. 29-32 C; acid no. 0.2 max.; iodine no. 3 max.; sapon. no. 235-255; hyd. no. 15 max.; ref. index 1.445-1.449 (50 C).

Softisan® 134. [Hüls Am.; Hüls AG]
Chem. Descrip.: Hydrog. coco-glycerides
Uses: Fat component and consistency regulator in pharmaceutical creams, ointments; assists penetration of skin by active ingreds.
Properties: Wh. pastilles; neutral odor and taste; sol. in benzene, toluene, acetone, chloroform, petrol. spirit; insol. in water; m.p. 33-36 C; solid. pt. 27-32 C; acid no. 0.3 max.; iodine no. 3 max.; sapon. no. 220-235; hyd. no. 40-50; ref. index 1.445-1.449 (50 C).

Softisan® 138. [Hüls Am.; Hüls AG]
Chem. Descrip.: Hydrog. coco-glycerides
Uses: Fat component and consistency regulator in pharmaceutical creams, ointments; assists pen-

etration of skin by active ingreds.
Properties: Wh. blocks; neutral odor and taste; sol. in benzene, toluene, acetone, chloroform, petrol. spirit; insol. in water; m.p. 37-40 C; solid. pt. 32-36 C; acid no. 1.5 max.; iodine no. 3 max.; sapon. no. 215-235; hyd. no. 15 max.; ref. index 1.445-1.449 (50 C).

Softisan® 142. [Hüls Am.; Hüls AG]
Chem. Descrip.: Hydrog. coco-glycerides
Uses: Fat component and consistency regulator in pharmaceutical creams, ointments; assists penetration of skin by active ingreds.
Properties: Wh. pastilles; neutral odor and taste; sol. in benzene, toluene, acetone, chloroform, petrol. spirit; insol. in water; m.p. 42-44 C; solid. pt. 37-42 C; acid no. 0.3 max.; iodine no. 3 max.; sapon. no. 215-235; hyd. no. 15 max.; ref. index 1.445-1.449 (50 C).

Softisan® 154. [Hüls Am.; Hüls AG]
Chem. Descrip.: Hydrog. palm oil
Uses: Fat component and consistency regulator in pharmaceutical creams, ointments; assists penetration of skin by active ingreds.
Properties: Wh. flakes; neutral odor and taste; sol. in benzene, toluene, acetone, chloroform, petrol. spirit; insol. in water; m.p. 53-58 C; solid. pt. 48-53 C; acid no. 1 max.; iodine no. 3 max.; sapon. no. 195-210; hyd. no. 10 max.; ref. index 1.445-1.460 (50 C).

Softisan® 378. [Hüls Am.]
Chem. Descrip.: Caprylic/capric/stearic triglyceride
Uses: Absorption-promoting fat base for pharmaceutical creams and ointments, emollient, moisturizer, stabilizer; good skin compatibility and resorption chars. for the prep. of nonaq. ointments and creams; filler/carrier for hard and soft gelatin capsules
Properties: Off-wh. to ylsh. pasty wax; m.p. 37-40 C; acid no. 1 max.; iodine no. 1 max.; sapon no. 245-260; hyd. no. 20 max.; 100% act.; nonionic.

Softisan® 601. [Hüls Am.; Hüls AG]
Chem. Descrip.: Glyceryl cocoate, hydrog. coconut oil, and ceteareth-25
Uses: Emollient; pharmaceutical self-emulsifying base for o/w or anhyd. prods.; water absorption to 65%; for washable o/w creams, wound and skin healing creams, hemorrhoidal ointments, steroid ointments, rheumatism creams
Properties: Wh.-ylsh. pellets; sp.gr. 0.97 (60 C); m.p. 40-45 C; acid no. 1 max.; iodine no. 5 max.; sapon. no. 120-140; hyd. no. 230-270; 100% conc.; nonionic.

Softisan® 649. [Hüls Am.; Hüls AG]
Chem. Descrip.: Bis diglyceryl caprylate/caprate/isostearate/stearate/hydroxystearate adipate
Uses: Emollient, ointment base, stabilizer for pharmaceutical creams, ointments, and emulsions; lanolin substitute; good adhesion to skin, high waterbinding power; for skin care prods., hemorrhoidal creams, absorp. basic creams
Properties: Ylsh. paste; almost odorless; sol. in

ether, chloroform; misc. with fats, oils; acid no. 2 max.; iodine no. 3 max.; sapon. no. 270-290; hyd. no. 55-85.

Solan. [Croda Inc.]
Chem. Descrip.: PEG-60 lanolin
CAS 61790-81-6
Uses: Solubilizer, superfatting agent, visc. enhancer, plasticizer in topical pharmaceutical aq. systems; provides emolliency and cleansing action in cleansing wipe formulations
Use level: 1-10%
Properties: Yel. wax; sol. in water, propylene glycol; sol. warm in IPA; m.p. 46-54 C; acid no. 2 max.; iodine no. 10 max.; sapon. no. 8-16; pH 5.5-7.0 (1% aq.); 100% act.; nonionic
Toxicology: LD50 (oral, rat) > 5 g/kg; nonirritating to skin.

Solan 50. [Croda Inc.]
Chem. Descrip.: PEG-60 lanolin
CAS 61790-81-6
Uses: Hydrophilic surfactant, emollient, conditioner, thickener, superfatting agent, foam stabilizer, humectant for pharmaceuticals
Properties: Gardner 11 max. visc. liq.; water-sol.; acid no. 2 max.; iodine no. 6 max.; sapon. no. 8 max.; pH 5.5-7.0 (1% aq.); 50% act.; nonionic.

Solimate. [United-Guardian]
Uses: Mutual solv. and solubilizing agent esp. suited for solubilizing vitamins A, D, E; physiologically inert to tissue; can solubilize many org. substances to make clear aq. sol'ns.; for pharmaceutical, medical, health-care fields
Custom product

Solka-Floc®. [Protein Tech. Int'l.]
Chem. Descrip.: Powd. cellulose
CAS 9004-34-6; EINECS 232-674-9
Uses: Functional ingred. or noncaloric bulking agent for pharmaceutical applics.

Solka-Floc® BW-40. [Mendell]
Chem. Descrip.: Cellulose NF
CAS 9004-34-6; EINECS 232-674-9
Uses: Binder, diluent, disintegrant, stabilizer, absorption aid, stabilizer, tablet filler for pharmaceutical formulations; moisture absorp. and retention props.
Properties: Avg. particle size 60 µ; 82-95% thru 100 mesh; dens. (tapped) 0.35 g/ml; pH 5.0-7.5.

Solka-Floc® BW-100. [Mendell]
Chem. Descrip.: Cellulose NF
CAS 9004-34-6; EINECS 232-674-9
Uses: Binder, diluent, disintegrant, stabilizer, absorption aid, stabilizer, tablet filler for pharmaceutical formulations; recommended for direct compression and wet granulations
Properties: Avg. particle size 40 µ; 95% min. thru 60 mesh; dens. (tapped) 0.46 g/ml; pH 5.0-7.5.

Solka-Floc® BW-200. [Mendell]
Chem. Descrip.: Cellulose NF
CAS 9004-34-6; EINECS 232-674-9
Uses: Binder, diluent, disintegrant, stabilizer, absorption aid, tablet filler for pharmaceutical formulations

Properties: Avg. particle size 35 µ; 98% min. thru 60 mesh; dens. (tapped) 0.46 g/ml; pH 5.0-7.5.

Solka-Floc® BW-2030. [Mendell]
Chem. Descrip.: Cellulose NF
CAS 9004-34-6; EINECS 232-674-9
Uses: Binder, diluent, disintegrant, stabilizer, absorption aid, tablet filler for pharmaceutical formulations
Properties: Avg. particle size 35 µ; 80% min. thru 100 mesh; dens. (tapped) 0.45 g/ml; pH 5.0-7.5.

Solka-Floc® Fine Granular. [Mendell]
Chem. Descrip.: Cellulose NF
CAS 9004-34-6; EINECS 232-674-9
Uses: Binder, diluent, disintegrant, stabilizer, absorption aid, tablet filler for pharmaceutical formulations; exc. flow and improved compressibility
Properties: 15% max. thru 200 mesh; dens. (tapped) 0.68 g/ml; pH 5.0-7.5.

Solubilisant γ 2420. [Gattefosse]
Chem. Descrip.: Octoxynol-11, polysorbate 20
Uses: Solubilizer for perfumes and essential oils for use in pharmaceutical/veterinary aq. sol'ns., lotions
Properties: Very pale yel. visc. transparent liq., faint odor; nonionic
Toxicology: Mild sensitizer to eyes; nonirritating to skin.

Solubilisant γ 2428. [Gattefosse]
Chem. Descrip.: PEG-40 hydrog. castor oil, polysorbate 20, octoxynol-11
Uses: Solubilizer for perfumes and essential oils for use in pharmaceutical/veterinary aq. sol'ns., lotions
Properties: Yel. visc. liq. with possible sl. turbidity, faint odor; nonionic
Toxicology: Sl. irritating to skin and eyes.

Soluble Liver Powd. [Am. Labs]
Chem. Descrip.: Enzymatic digest of liver
Uses: Nutritional supplement for tablets and capsules; also for pharmaceutical and veterinary preps.
Properties: Brn. powd., char. odor; hygroscopic; completely sol. in water; pH 4.8 (2%)
Storage: Store in cool, dry area.

Soluble Trachea CS 16 Substance. [Am. Labs]
Chem. Descrip.: Defatted powd. processed from beef trachea contg. 16-17% chondroitin sulfate
CAS 9007-28-7
Uses: Nutritive additive
Properties: Cream-colored amorphous powd., char. odor; sol. > 50 g/100 ml in water; 87% protein, 13% N
Precaution: Dust-air mixts. may be explosive
Storage: Hygroscopic; preserve in tight containers in cool, dry place.

Solulan® 25. [Amerchol; Amerchol Europe]
Chem. Descrip.: Laneth-25, ceteth-25, oleth-25 and steareth-25
Uses: O/w emulsifier, dispersant, lubricant, solubilizer for pharmaceuticals
Properties: Yel. waxy solid; faint pleasant odor; sol. @ 5% in water, 30% ethanol; HLB 16; cloud pt. 85-92 C; acid no. 3 max.; sapon. no. 8 max.; pH 4.5-7.5 (10% aq.); 100% conc.; nonionic.

Solulan® 97. [Amerchol; Amerchol Europe]
Chem. Descrip.: Polysorbate 80 acetate, cetyl acetate and acetylated lanolin alcohol
Uses: Dispersant, lubricant, emollient, conditioner for pharmaceuticals
Properties: Lt. amber visc. liq.; faint pleasant odor; sol. @ 5% in water, ethanol; HLB 15; acid no. 3 max.; sapon. no. 110-130; pH 4.5-7.5 (10% aq.); 100% conc.; nonionic.

Solulan® 98. [Amerchol; Amerchol Europe]
Chem. Descrip.: Polysorbate 80, cetyl acetate, acetylated lanolin alcohol
Uses: Dispersant, lubricant, emollient, conditioner for pharmaceuticals; also aids pearling of stearic acid emulsions
Properties: Lt. amber visc. liq.; faint pleasant odor; sol. @ 5% in water, ethanol; HLB 13; acid no. 3 max.; sapon. no. 65-75; pH 4.5-7.5 (10% aq.); 100% conc.; nonionic.

Solulan® PB-2. [Amerchol; Amerchol Europe]
Chem. Descrip.: PPG-2 lanolin alcohol ether
CAS 68439-53-2
Uses: Spreading agent, dispersant, plasticizer; emollient and conditioner for pharmaceuticals
Properties: Amber semisolid, liq.; sol. in castor oil, IPM, IPP, anhyd. ethanol; HLB 8.0; acid no. 3 max.; sapon. no. 7 max.; 100% conc.; nonionic.

Solulan® PB-5. [Amerchol; Amerchol Europe]
Chem. Descrip.: PPG-5 lanolin alcohol ether
CAS 68439-53-2
Uses: Spreading agent, dispersant, plasticizer; emollient and conditioner for pharmaceuticals
Properties: Lt. amber clear visc. liq.; sol. in castor oil, IPM, IPP, anhyd. ethanol; HLB 10.0; acid no. 2 max.; sapon. no. 6 max.; 100% conc.; nonionic.

Solulan® PB-10. [Amerchol; Amerchol Europe]
Chem. Descrip.: PPG-10 lanolin alcohol ether
CAS 68439-53-2
Uses: Spreading agent, dispersant, plasticizer; emollient and conditioner for pharmaceuticals
Properties: Straw clear heavy-visc. liq.; sol. in castor oil, IPM, IPP, anhyd. ethanol; HLB 12.0; acid no. 1 max.; sapon. no. 4 max.; 100% conc.; nonionic.

Solulan® PB-20. [Amerchol; Amerchol Europe]
Chem. Descrip.: PPG-20 lanolin alcohol ether
CAS 68439-53-2
Uses: Spreading agent, dispersant, plasticizer; emollient and conditioner for pharmaceuticals
Properties: Lt. straw clear med-visc. liq.; sol. in castor oil, IPM, IPP, anhyd. ethanol; HLB 14.0; acid no. 0.75 max.; sapon. no. 3 max.; 100% conc.; nonionic.

Soluphor® P. [BASF; BASF AG]
Chem. Descrip.: Pyrrolidone-2
Uses: Solv. for pharmaceutical injectables, veterinary medicine.

Sol-U-Tein EA. [Fanning]
Chem. Descrip.: Albumen
CAS 9006-50-2; EINECS 232-936-2

Uses: Binder, coagulant, film-former, skin conditioning agent for pharmaceutical prods.
Properties: Yel. powd.; 100% thru 80 mesh; 90% thru 100 mesh; bland odor; pH 6.5-8.0; 75% ovalbumin, ovoconalbumin, ovomucoid, ovomucin, ovoglobulin, lysozyme, and avidin.

Soluwax. [United-Guardian]
Chem. Descrip.: Water-sol. 'wax' deriv. from polyalkylene glycols
Uses: Environmentally harmless lubricant and body thickener for lotions and creams in pharmaceutical, medical, health-care fields
Properties: Water-sol.
Custom product

Sonojell® No. 4. [Witco/Petroleum Spec.]
Chem. Descrip.: Petrolatum
EINECS 232-373-2
Uses: Emollient base for pharmaceuticals (medicated ointments, suppositories, suncare prods.)
Regulatory: FDA 21CFR §172.880
Properties: Lovibond 0.5Y color; visc. 2.6-5.7 cSt (100 C); m.p. 38-52 C.

Sonojell® No. 9. [Witco/Petroleum Spec.]
Chem. Descrip.: Petrolatum
EINECS 232-373-2
Uses: Emollient base for pharmaceuticals (medicated ointments, suppositories, suncare prods.)
Regulatory: FDA 21CFR §172.880
Properties: Lovibond color 0.5Y; visc. 2.6-5.7 Cst (100 C); m.p. 42-49 C.

Sorba. [Croda Chem. Ltd.]
Chem. Descrip.: Lanolin
CAS 8006-54-0; EINECS 232-348-6
Uses: Emollient for pharmaceutical applics.

Sorbelite™ C. [Mendell]
Chem. Descrip.: Crystalline γ-sorbitol NF
CAS 50-70-4; EINECS 200-061-5
Uses: Excipient providing sweetness and cooling mouthfeel to direct compression tablet mfg.; improved flowability, exc. cohesion
Properties: Coarse powd.; avg. particle size 403 µ; 5% -100 mesh; very highly sol. in water; dens. (tapped) 0.64 g/ml max.; 91-100.5% assay.

Sorbelite™ FG. [Mendell]
Chem. Descrip.: Crystalline γ-sorbitol NF
CAS 50-70-4; EINECS 200-061-5
Uses: Excipient for direct compression of pharmaceutical tablets where added sweetness and cooling mouthfeel are desired
Properties: Wh. fine gran.; avg. particle size 124 µ; 65% -100 mesh; very highly sol. in water; dens. (tapped) 0.85 g/ml; 91-100.5% assay.

Sorbilene ISM. [Auschem SpA]
Chem. Descrip.: PEG-20 sorbitan isostearate
CAS 66794-58-9
Uses: Emulsifier for pharmaceuticals
Properties: Liq.; HLB 15.0; 100% conc.; nonionic.

Sorbilene L. [Auschem SpA]
Chem. Descrip.: Polysorbate 20
CAS 9005-64-5
Uses: Emulsifier, solubilizer for pharmaceuticals
Properties: Liq.; HLB 16.7; 100% conc.; nonionic.

Sorbilene L 4. [Auschem SpA]
Chem. Descrip.: Polysorbate 21
CAS 9005-64-5
Uses: Emulsifier for pharmaceuticals
Properties: Liq.; HLB 13.3; 100% conc.; nonionic.

Sorbilene LH. [Auschem SpA]
Chem. Descrip.: Polysorbate 20, low dioxane
CAS 9005-64-5
Uses: Emulsifier for pharmaceuticals
Properties: Liq.; HLB 16.7; 100% conc.; nonionic
Unverified

Sorbilene O. [Auschem SpA]
Chem. Descrip.: Polysorbate 80
CAS 9005-65-6
Uses: Emulsifier, solubilizer for pharmaceuticals, emulsifiable concs.
Properties: Liq.; HLB 15.0; 100% conc.; nonionic.

Sorbilene O 5. [Auschem SpA]
Chem. Descrip.: Polysorbate 81
CAS 9005-65-6
Uses: Emulsifier for pharmaceuticals
Properties: Liq.; HLB 10.0; 100% conc.; nonionic.

Sorbilene P. [Auschem SpA]
Chem. Descrip.: Polysorbate 40
CAS 9005-66-7
Uses: Emulsifier for pharmaceuticals
Properties: Liq./paste; HLB 15.7; 100% conc.; nonionic.

Sorbilene S. [Auschem SpA]
Chem. Descrip.: Polysorbate 60
CAS 9005-67-8
Uses: Emulsifier for pharmaceuticals
Properties: Liq./paste; HLB 14.8; 100% conc.; nonionic.

Sorbilene S 4. [Auschem SpA]
Chem. Descrip.: Polysorbate 61
CAS 9005-67-8
Uses: Emulsifier for pharmaceuticals
Properties: Solid; HLB 9.6; 100% conc.; nonionic.

Sorbilene TO. [Auschem SpA]
Chem. Descrip.: Polysorbate 85
CAS 9005-70-3
Uses: Emulsifier for pharmaceuticals
Properties: Liq.; HLB 11.0; 100% conc.; nonionic.

Sorbilene TS. [Auschem SpA]
Chem. Descrip.: Polysorbate 65
CAS 9005-71-4
Uses: Emulsifier for pharmaceuticals
Properties: Solid; HLB 10.5; 100% conc.; nonionic.

Sorbirol ISM. [Auschem SpA]
Chem. Descrip.: Sorbitan isostearate
CAS 54392-26-6
Uses: Emulsifier for pharmaceuticals
Properties: Liq.; HLB 4.3; 100% conc.; nonionic
Unverified

Sorbirol O. [Auschem SpA]
Chem. Descrip.: Sorbitan oleate
CAS 1338-43-8; EINECS 215-665-4
Uses: Emulsifier for pharmaceuticals
Properties: Liq.; HLB 4.3; 100% conc.; nonionic.

Sorbirol P. [Auschem SpA]
Chem. Descrip.: Sorbitan palmitate

CAS 26266-57-9; EINECS 247-568-8
Uses: Emulsifier for pharmaceuticals
Properties: Solid; HLB 6.7; 100% conc.; nonionic.
Sorbirol S. [Auschem SpA]
Chem. Descrip.: Sorbitan stearate
CAS 1338-41-6; EINECS 215-664-9
Uses: Emulsifier for pharmaceuticals
Properties: Flakes; HLB 4.7; 100% conc.; nonionic.
Sorbirol SQ. [Auschem SpA]
Chem. Descrip.: Sorbitan sesquioleate
CAS 8007-43-0; EINECS 232-360-1
Uses: Emulsifier for pharmaceuticals
Properties: Liq.; HLB 3.7; 100% conc.; nonionic.
Sorbirol TO. [Auschem SpA]
Chem. Descrip.: Sorbitan trioleate
CAS 26266-58-0; EINECS 247-569-3
Uses: Emulsifier for pharmaceuticals
Properties: Liq.; HLB 1.8; 100% conc.; nonionic.
Sorbirol TS. [Auschem SpA]
Chem. Descrip.: Sorbitan tristearate
CAS 26658-19-5; EINECS 247-891-4
Uses: Emulsifier for pharmaceuticals
Properties: Solid; HLB 2.1; 100% conc.; nonionic.
Sorbitol L. [Auschem SpA]
Chem. Descrip.: Sorbitan laurate
CAS 1338-39-2
Uses: Emulsifier for pharmaceuticals
Properties: Liq.; HLB 8.6; 100% conc.; nonionic
Unverified
Sorgen 30. [Dai-ichi Kogyo Seiyaku]
Chem. Descrip.: Sorbitan sesquioleate
CAS 8007-43-0; EINECS 232-360-1
Uses: Antifoamer and emulsifier for pharmaceutical prods.
Properties: Liq.; HLB 3.7; 100% conc.; nonionic.
Sorgen 40. [Dai-ichi Kogyo Seiyaku]
Chem. Descrip.: Sorbitan oleate
CAS 1338-43-8; EINECS 215-665-4
Uses: Antifoamer and emulsifier for pharmaceutical prods.
Properties: Liq.; HLB 4.3; 100% conc.; nonionic.
Sorgen 50. [Dai-ichi Kogyo Seiyaku]
Chem. Descrip.: Sorbitan stearate
CAS 1338-41-6; EINECS 215-664-9
Uses: Antifoamer and emulsifier for pharmaceutical prods.
Properties: Pellet; HLB 4.7; 100% conc.; nonionic.
Sorgen 90. [Dai-ichi Kogyo Seiyaku]
Chem. Descrip.: Sorbitan laurate
CAS 1338-39-2; EINECS 215-663-3
Uses: Antifoamer and emulsifier for pharmaceutical prods.
Properties: Liq.; HLB 8.6; 100% conc.; nonionic.
Sorgen TW80. [Dai-ichi Kogyo Seiyaku]
Chem. Descrip.: POE sorbitan monooleate
CAS 9005-65-6; EINECS 215-665-4
Uses: Solubilizer and emulsifier for pharmaceutical prods.
Properties: Liq.; water-sol.; HLB 15.0; 100% conc.; nonionic.
Span® 20. [ICI Surf. Am.; ICI Surf. Belgium]
Chem. Descrip.: Sorbitan laurate NF

CAS 1338-39-2
Uses: Emulsifier, stabilizer, thickener, lubricant, softener for pharmaceuticals
Properties: Amber liq.; sol. (@ 1%) in IPA, perchloroethylene, xylene, cottonseed oil, min. oil; sol. (hazy) in propylene glycol; visc. 4250 cps; HLB 8.6; 100% act.; nonionic.
Span® 40. [ICI Surf. Am.; ICI Surf. Belgium]
Chem. Descrip.: Sorbitan palmitate NF
CAS 26266-57-9; EINECS 247-568-8
Uses: Emulsifier, stabilizer, thickener, lubricant, softener for pharmaceuticals
Properties: Tan solid; sol. (@ 1%) in IPA, xylene; sol. (hazy) in perchloroethylene; HLB 6.7; pour pt. 48 C; 100% act.; nonionic.
Span® 60. [ICI Surf. Am.]
Chem. Descrip.: Sorbitan stearate NF
CAS 1338-41-6; EINECS 215-664-9
Uses: Emulsifier, stabilizer, thickener, lubricant, softener for pharmaceuticals
Regulatory: FDA 21CFR §172.515, 172.842, 173.340; Canada compliance
Properties: Tan beads; sol. (@1%): sol. in IPA; sol. (hazy) in perchloroethylene, xylene; insol. in water, cottonseed oil; HLB 4.7; pour pt. 127 F; nonionic.
Span® 60K. [ICI Surf. Am.; ICI Surf. Belgium]
Chem. Descrip.: Sorbitan stearate NF
CAS 1338-41-6; EINECS 215-664-9
Uses: Emulsifier, stabilizer, thickener, lubricant, softener for pharmaceuticals
Regulatory: FDA 21CFR §172.842
Properties: Pale cream beads; sol. (@1%): sol. in IPA; sol. (hazy) in perchloroethylene, xylene; HLB 4.7; pour pt. 53 C; 100% act.; nonionic.
Span® 60 VS. [ICI Surf. Am.]
Chem. Descrip.: Sorbitan stearate
CAS 1338-41-6; EINECS 215-664-9
Uses: Emulsifier, solubilizer for pharmaceuticals
Properties: Beads; HLB 4.7; 100% conc.
Unverified
Span® 65. [ICI Surf. Am.; ICI Surf. Belgium]
Chem. Descrip.: Sorbitan tristearate
CAS 26658-19-5; EINECS 247-891-4
Uses: Emulsifier, stabilizer, thickener, lubricant, softener for pharmaceuticals
Regulatory: Canada compliance
Properties: Cream solid; sol. (@ 1%) in IPA, perchloroethylene, xylene; HLB 2.1; pour pt. 53 C; 100% act.; nonionic.
Span® 65K. [ICI Surf. Am.]
Chem. Descrip.: Sorbitan tristearate
CAS 26658-19-5; EINECS 247-891-4
Uses: Emulsifier, stabilizer, thickener, lubricant, softener for pharmaceuticals
Regulatory: Kosher
Properties: Tan waxy bead; HLB 2.1; pour pt. 53 C; nonionic.
Span® 85. [ICI Surf. Am.; ICI Surf. Belgium]
Chem. Descrip.: Sorbitan trioleate
CAS 26266-58-0; EINECS 247-569-3
Uses: Emulsifier, stabilizer, thickener, lubricant, soft-

enerfor pharmaceuticals
Regulatory: Canada compliance
Properties: Amber liq.; sol. (@ 1%) in IPA, perchloroethylene, xylene, cottonseed and min. oils; visc. 210 cps; HLB 1.8; 100% act.; nonionic.

Special Fat 42/44. [Hüls Am.]
Chem. Descrip.: Hydrog. coconut oil
CAS 68334-28-1; EINECS 284-283-8
Uses: Raw material for pharmaceutical industry.

Special Fat 168T. [Hüls Am.; Hüls AG]
Chem. Descrip.: Hydrog. tallow
CAS 8030-12-4; EINECS 232-442-7
Uses: Raw material for pharmaceutical industry; hydrophobing agent for powd. preps.
Properties: Powd., flakes; m.p. 56-60 C; acid no. 5 max.; iodine no. 3 max.; sapon. no. 190-210.

Spectradyne® G. [Lonza]
Chem. Descrip.: Chlorhexidine gluconate BP
CAS 18472-51-0; EINECS 242-354-0
Uses: Antimicrobial for pharmaceuticals, veterinary prods., anti-plaque dental prods.
Properties: Liq.; 20% act.

Spectra-Sorb® UV 9. [Am. Cyanamid]
Chem. Descrip.: Benzophenone-3
CAS 131-57-7; EINECS 205-031-5
Uses: Uv lt. absorber used in sunscreens, pharmaceutical formulations
Properties: Pale cream to off-wh. powd.; m.w. 228.25; sol. (g/100 ml solv.): 100 g propylene glycol monostearate, 57 g in ethoxyethyl alcohol, 47 g in diglycol stearate, 15 g in IPM, 11.3 g in soybean oil, 0 g in water; sp.gr. 1.324; m.p. 63.0-64.5 C; 100% assay.

Spermwax®. [Robeco]
Chem. Descrip.: Cetyl esters wax NF
CAS 17661-50-6; EINECS 241-640-2
Uses: Syn. spermaceti used in dermatologicals as stiffening agent, slip and visc. aid; provides smoothness and rigidity
Properties: Solid; m.p. 43-47 C; HLB 8.4-9.4; acid no. 5 max.; iodine no. 1 max.; sapon. no. 109-120.

Spinomar NaSS. [Tosoh]
Chem. Descrip.: Sodium p-styrenesulfonate
CAS 2695-37-6; EINECS 220-266-3
Uses: In pharmaceuticals
Properties: Wh. powd., nil odor; sol. in water; insol. in aliphatic, halogenated, or high alcohol solvs.; m.w. 206.20; apparent sp. dens. 0.5; decomp. pt. 330 C; flash pt. nil; 81.5% act.
Toxicology: LD 50 (oral, mouse) 16 g/kg (as 40% olive oil susp.)
Storage: Store in air-tight containers in dark place; if dried, subject to slow oxidation and/or polymerization.

SPL Heparin Ammonium. [Scientific Protein Labs]
Chem. Descrip.: Heparin ammonium
CAS 60800-63-7; EINECS 232-681-7
Uses: Anticoagulant; used in medical devices and in vitro laboratory applics. for coatings and as a reagent
Properties: Off-wh. amorphous powd.; hygroscopic; sol. in water
Storage: Preserve in tight containers in cool, dry place.

SPL Heparin Lithium. [Scientific Protein Labs]
Chem. Descrip.: Heparin lithium
CAS 9045-22-1; EINECS 232-681-7
Uses: Anticoagulant; used in medical devices and in vitro laboratory applics. for coatings and as a reagent
Properties: Off-wh. amorphous powd.; hygroscopic; sol. in water
Storage: Preserve in tight containers in cool, dry place.

SPL Heparin Sodium USP. [Scientific Protein Labs]
Chem. Descrip.: Heparin sodium USP
CAS 9041-08-1; EINECS 232-681-7
Uses: Anticoagulant, pharmaceutical aid; coating agent to prevent coagulation in laboratory applics.
Properties: Wh. amorphous powd.; hygroscopic; sol. in water; pH 5.0-7.5 (1%)
Storage: Preserve in tight containers in cool, dry place.

SPL High Lipase Pancreatic Enzyme Conc. (PEC) [Scientific Protein Labs]
Chem. Descrip.: Enzymes, principally lipase, proteases, amylase
Uses: Used for treatment of pancreatic insufficiency esp. where digestion of lipids is of paramount importance
Properties: Cream-colored amorphous powd., faint char. but not offensive odor; partly sol. in water; insol. in alcohol ≤ 5% moisture
Storage: Store in tight containers in cool, dry place.

Split Coconut Oil 6254, 6255. [Dial]
Chem. Descrip.: Coconut oil fatty acid
EINECS 262-978-7
Uses: Emulsifier used in pharmaceuticals, chem. intermediates/derivs.
Properties: Acid no. 265-271; iodine no. 8-12; 0.5% max. moisture.

SPL Pancreatin 3X USP. [Scientific Protein Labs]
Chem. Descrip.: Enzymes, principally proteases, amylase, lipase
Uses: Used for treatment of pancreatic insufficiency; hydrolyzes fats to glycerol and fatty acids, changes protein into proteoses and derived substances, converts starch to dextrins and sugars
Properties: Cream-colored amorphous powd., faint char. but not offensive odor; partly sol. in water; insol. in alcohol
Storage: Store in tight containers in cool, dry place.

SPL Pancreatin 4X USP. [Scientific Protein Labs]
Chem. Descrip.: Enzymes, principally proteases, amylase, lipase
Uses: Used for treatment of pancreatic insufficiency; hydrolyzes fats to glycerol and fatty acids, changes protein into proteoses and derived substances, converts starch to dextrins and sugars
Properties: Cream-colored amorphous powd., faint char. but not offensive odor; partly sol. in water; insol. in alcohol
Storage: Store in tight containers in cool, dry place.

SPL Pancreatin 5X USP. [Scientific Protein Labs]

Chem. Descrip.: Enzymes, principally proteases, amylase, lipase

Uses: Used for treatment of pancreatic insufficiency; hydrolyzes fats to glycerol and fatty acids, changes protein into proteoses and derived substances, converts starch to dextrins and sugars

Properties: Cream-colored amorphous powd., faint char. but not offensive odor; partly sol. in water; insol. in alcohol

Storage: Store in tight containers in cool, dry place.

SPL Pancreatin 6X USP. [Scientific Protein Labs]

Chem. Descrip.: Enzymes, principally proteases, amylase, lipase

Uses: Used for treatment of pancreatic insufficiency; hydrolyzes fats to glycerol and fatty acids, changes protein into proteoses and derived substances, converts starch to dextrins and sugars

Properties: Cream-colored amorphous powd., faint char. but not offensive odor; partly sol. in water; insol. in alcohol

Storage: Store in tight containers in cool, dry place.

SPL Pancreatin 7X USP. [Scientific Protein Labs]

Chem. Descrip.: Enzymes, principally proteases, amylase, lipase

Uses: Used for treatment of pancreatic insufficiency; hydrolyzes fats to glycerol and fatty acids, changes protein into proteoses and derived substances, converts starch to dextrins and sugars

Properties: Cream-colored amorphous powd., faint char. but not offensive odor; partly sol. in water; insol. in alcohol

Storage: Store in tight containers in cool, dry place.

SPL Pancreatin 8X USP. [Scientific Protein Labs]

Chem. Descrip.: Enzymes, principally proteases, amylase, lipase

Uses: Used for treatment of pancreatic insufficiency; hydrolyzes fats to glycerol and fatty acids, changes protein into proteoses and derived substances, converts starch to dextrins and sugars

Properties: Cream-colored amorphous powd., faint char. but not offensive odor; partly sol. in water; insol. in alcohol

Storage: Store in tight containers in cool, dry place.

SPL Pancreatin USP. [Scientific Protein Labs]

Chem. Descrip.: Pancreatin USP contg. enzymes, principally proteases, amylase, lipase

Uses: Used for treatment of pancreatic insufficiency; hydrolyzes fats to glycerol and fatty acids, changes protein into proteoses and derived substances, converts starch to dextrins and sugars

Properties: Cream-colored amorphous powd., faint char. but not offensive odor; partly sol. in water; insol. in alcohol

Storage: Store in tight containers in cool, dry place.

SPL Pancrelipase USP. [Scientific Protein Labs]

Chem. Descrip.: Enzymes, principally lipase, amylase, protease

Uses: Used for treatment of pancreatic insufficiency; hydrolyzes fats to glycerol and fatty acids, changes protein into proteoses and derived substances, converts starch to dextrins and sugars

Properties: Cream-colored amorphous powd., faint

char. but not offensive odor; partly sol. in water; insol. in alcohol

Storage: Store in tight containers in cool, dry place.

SPL Undiluted Pancreatic Enzyme Conc. (PEC) [Scientific Protein Labs]

Chem. Descrip.: Enzymes, principally proteases, amylase, lipase

Uses: Used for treatment of pancreatic insufficiency; hydrolyzes fats to glycerol and fatty acids, changes protein into proteoses and derived substances, converts starch to dextrins and sugars

Properties: Cream-colored amorphous powd., faint char. but not offensive odor; partly sol. in water; insol. in alcohol

Storage: Store in tight containers in cool, dry place.

Spray Dried Fish Gelatin. [Croda Colloids Ltd; O.C. Lugo]

Chem. Descrip.: Gelatin from fish sources

CAS 9000-70-8; EINECS 232-554-6

Uses: Emulsion stabilizer, protective colloid, film-former, adhesive agent, flocculant; controls crystal growth; inferior gelling chars. to mammalian gelatin

Properties: Spray-dried powd.; dissolves in cold water; visc. 60-85 mps; pH 5.0-6.5 (10%); 7% max. moisture.

Spray Dried Fish Gelatin/Maltodextrin. [Croda Colloids Ltd; O.C. Lugo]

Chem. Descrip.: 50% Gelatin from fish sources, 50% maltodextrin

Uses: Emulsion stabilizer, protective colloid, film-former, adhesive agent, flocculant; controls crystal growth; inferior gelling chars. to mammalian gelatin

Properties: Spray-dried powd.; dissolves readily in cold water; pH 5.0-6.5 (10%); 5% max. moisture.

Spray Dried Gum Arabic NF/FCC CM. [Meer]

Chem. Descrip.: Gum arabic

CAS 9000-01-5; EINECS 232-519-5

Uses: Protective colloid, stabilizer, thickener, binder for pharmaceutical emulsions, antiseptics, to mask bitter or acid taste of medicaments, tablet binder, excipient

Properties: Colorless, odorless, tasteless; water-sol.

Spray Dried Gum Arabic NF/FCC CS (Low Bacteria) [Meer]

Chem. Descrip.: Gum arabic

CAS 9000-01-5; EINECS 232-519-5

Uses: Protective colloid, stabilizer, thickener, binder for pharmaceutical emulsions, antiseptics, to mask bitter or acid taste of medicaments, tablet binder, excipient

Properties: Colorless, odorless, tasteless; water-sol.

Spray Dried Gum Arabic NF/FCC CS-R. [Meer]

Chem. Descrip.: Gum arabic

CAS 9000-01-5; EINECS 232-519-5

Uses: Protective colloid, stabilizer, thickener, binder for pharmaceutical emulsions, antiseptics, to mask bitter or acid taste of medicaments, tablet binder, excipient

Properties: Colorless, odorless, tasteless; water-sol.

Spray Dried Gum Arabic NF Type CSP. [Meer]
Chem. Descrip.: Gum arabic NF from *Acacia senegal*
CAS 9000-01-5; EINECS 232-519-5
Uses: Binder used in pharmaceutical tableting industry
Properties: Creamy wh. powd., 98% thru 120 mesh; sol. 1 g/2 ml of water yielding lt. amber sol'n.; pH 4.0-4.5.

Spray Dried Gum Arabic Type A-180 NF Premium. [Gumix Int'l.]
Chem. Descrip.: Gum arabic
CAS 9000-01-5; EINECS 232-519-5
Uses: Protective colloid, stabilizer, suspending agent, viscosifier for pharmaceuticals (suspensions, emulsions, demulcent in cough drops/syrups, tablet binder/adhesive)
Properties: Powd., almost odorless and tasteless; sol. in hot or cold water.

Spray Dried Gum Arabic Type A-230 NF Extra. [Gumix Int'l.]
Chem. Descrip.: Gum arabic
CAS 9000-01-5; EINECS 232-519-5
Uses: Protective colloid, stabilizer, suspending agent, viscosifier for pharmaceuticals (suspensions, emulsions, demulcent in cough drops/syrups, tablet binder/adhesive)
Properties: Powd., almost odorless and tasteless; sol. in hot or cold water.

Spray Dried Gum Talha (Acacia). [Commodity Services Int'l.]
Chem. Descrip.: Acacia gum
CAS 9000-01-5; EINECS 232-519-5
Uses: Used in pharmaceuticals
Properties: Tan to brn. powd., odorless, tasteless; 99% min. thru 60 mesh, 80% min. thru 140 mesh; visc. 150 cps max. (20%); pH 4.0-4.8 (20%); 12% max. moisture.

Spray Dried Gum Talha (Acacia) Special. [Commodity Services Int'l.]
Chem. Descrip.: Acacia gum
CAS 9000-01-5; EINECS 232-519-5
Uses: Used in pharmaceuticals
Properties: Cream to lt. tan powd., odorless, tasteless; 99% min. thru 60 mesh, 80% min. thru 140 mesh; visc. 150 cps max. (20%); pH 4.0-4.8 (20%); 12% max. moisture.

Spray Dried Hydrolysed Fish Gelatin. [Croda Colloids Ltd; O.C. Lugo]
Chem. Descrip.: Gelatin from fish sources
CAS 9000-70-8; EINECS 232-554-6
Uses: Source of high m.w. film-forming protein; emulsion stabilizer, protective colloid, filmformer, adhesive agent, flocculant; controls crystal growth; inferior gelling chars. to mammalian gelatin
Properties: Spray-dried powd.; dissolves readily in cold water; visc. 30-45 mps (10%); pH 5.0-6.5 (10%); 5% max. moisture.

Spray Dried Kordofan Gum Arabic. [MLG Enterprises Ltd.]
Chem. Descrip.: Gum arabic

CAS 9000-01-5; EINECS 232-519-5
Uses: Emulsifier, stabilizer for pharmaceutical tableting
Regulatory: BP, EP, USP, DAB compliance; 10% max. moisture.

Stabilized Micro-Lite Corn Bran. [Canadian Harvest USA]
Chem. Descrip.: Corn bran
Uses: Natural fiber for high-fiber formulations, pharmaceuticals
Properties: Avail. in fine and ultrafine granulations, med. avail. on request; lt. yel. color, bland flavor; 82% total dietary fiber; 10% max. moisture.

Stabilized Red Wheat Bran. [Canadian Harvest USA]
Chem. Descrip.: Wheat bran
Uses: Natural fiber stabilized to protect against flavor degradation and to provide crispness and mouthfeel; for pharmaceuticals
Properties: Avail. in coarse, med., and fine granulations; red brn. color, nutty flavor; 42% total dietary fiber; 10% max. moisture.

Stabilized White Wheat Bran. [Canadian Harvest USA]
Chem. Descrip.: Wheat bran
Uses: Fiber used in supplements, pharmaceuticals; softer texture and milder flavor than Stabilized Red Wheat Bran
Properties: Avail. in coarse, med., and fine granulations; tan color, nutty flavor; 38% total dietary fiber; 10% max. moisture.

Staform P. [Meer]
Chem. Descrip.: Gum ghatti
CAS 900-28-6
Uses: Tablet binder and thick mucilage coatings in pharmaceuticals
Properties: Water-sol.

Stamere® CK-S. [Meer]
Chem. Descrip.: Carrageenan
CAS 9000-07-1; EINECS 232-524-2
Uses: Lubricant, emollient for pharmaceutical jellies, laxatives; tablet binder
Properties: Water-sol.

Stamere® N-325. [Meer]
Chem. Descrip.: Carrageenan
CAS 9000-07-1; EINECS 232-524-2
Uses: Lubricant, emollient for pharmaceutical jellies, laxatives; tablet binder
Properties: Water-sol.

Stamere® N-350. [Meer]
Chem. Descrip.: Carrageenan
CAS 9000-07-1; EINECS 232-524-2
Uses: Lubricant, emollient for pharmaceutical jellies, laxatives; tablet binder
Properties: Water-sol.

Stamere® N-350 S. [Meer]
Chem. Descrip.: Carrageenan
CAS 9000-07-1; EINECS 232-524-2
Uses: Lubricant, emollient for pharmaceutical jellies, laxatives; tablet binder
Properties: Water-sol.

Stamere® NI. [Meer]
Chem. Descrip.: Carrageenan

CAS 9000-07-1; EINECS 232-524-2

Uses: Lubricant, emollient for pharmaceutical jellies, laxatives; tablet binder.

Standamul® 302. [Henkel/Cospha]

Chem. Descrip.: Propylene glycol dicaprylate/dicaprate

Uses: Base, emollient used in pharmaceutical prods.

Properties: Clear visc. oily liq.; char. odor; sol. in min. and castor oil, IPM, oleyl alcohol, anhyd. ethanol, and silicone fluid; sp.gr. 0.921; HLB 9; acid no. 0.5 max.; sapon. no. 315-335; 100% conc.

Standamul® 318. [Henkel/Organic Prods.]

Chem. Descrip.: Caprylic/capric triglyceride

CAS 65381-09-1; EINECS 265-724-3

Uses: Base, emollient, carrier used in pharmaceutical prods.

Properties: Clear visc. oily liq.; odorless; sol. in min. and castor oil, IPM, oleyl alcohol and anhyd. ethanol; sp.gr. 0.950; visc. 25 cps; HLB 12; cloud pt. -5 C max.; acid no. 0.5 max.; sapon. no. 340-350; 100% conc.

Standamul® 1414-E. [Henkel/Cospha]

Chem. Descrip.: Myreth-3 myristate

CAS 59686-68-9

Uses: Carrier, SE base, emulsifier, coupler, emollient and moisturizer used in pharmaceutical prods.

Properties: Clear visc. oily liq.; sol. in min. and castor oil, IPM, oleyl alcohol, anhyd. ethanol; HLB 12; cloud pt. 25 C max.; sapon. no. 90-100; 100% conc.

Standamul® 1616. [Henkel/Cospha]

Chem. Descrip.: Cetyl palmitate

CAS 540-10-3; EINECS 208-736-6

Uses: Spermaceti replacement, consistency giving agent used in pharmaceutical prods.

Properties: Wh. waxy solid; faint char. odor; sol. in min. and castor oil, IPM, oleyl alcohol; m.p. 45-55 C; HLB 9; sapon. no. 115-130; 100% conc.

Standamul® 7061. [Henkel/Cospha]

Chem. Descrip.: Isocetyl stearate

CAS 25339-09-7; EINECS 246-868-6

Uses: Base, emollient used in pharmaceutical prods.

Properties: Clear visc. oil; faint char. odor; sol. in min. and castor oil, IPM, oleyl alcohol; sp.gr. 0.865; visc. 25 cps; HLB 8; cloud pt. 0 C max.; acid no. 0.5 max.; sapon. no. 105-115; 100% conc.

Standamul® 7063. [Henkel/Cospha]

Chem. Descrip.: Octyl dodecyl stearate

CAS 22766-82-1; EINECS 245-204-2

Uses: Base, emollient used in pharmaceutical prods.

Properties: Clear visc. oil; faint char. odor; sol. in min. and castor oil, IPM, oleyl alcohol; sp.gr. 0.865; visc. 100 cps; HLB 8; cloud pt. 0 C max.; acid no. 0.5 max.; sapon. no. 90-105; 100% conc.

Standamul® 7105. [Henkel/Cospha]

Chem. Descrip.: Caprylic/capric triglyceride

CAS 65381-09-1; EINECS 265-724-3

Uses: Base used in pharmaceutical prods.

Properties: Clear visc. oil; faint char. odor; sol. in min. and castor oil, IPM, oleyl alcohol and anhyd. ethanol; sp.gr. 1.064; visc. 100 cps max.; HLB 12; cloud pt. -5 C max.; sapon. no. 340-350; 100% conc.

Standamul® CTA. [Henkel/Cospha]

Chem. Descrip.: Hexyl laurate

CAS 34316-64-8; EINECS 251-932-1

Uses: Emollient, spreading agent, carrier, base, dispersant used in pharmaceutical prods.

Properties: Clear visc. oil; odorless; sol. in min. and castor oil, IPM, oleyl alcohol, anhyd. ethanol, and silicone fluid; sp.gr. 0.85-0.87; HLB 9; cloud pt. 0 C max.; acid no. 0.5 max.; sapon. no. 190-205; 100% conc.

Standamul® CTV. [Henkel/Cospha]

Chem. Descrip.: Decyl oleate

CAS 3687-46-5; EINECS 222-981-6

Uses: Emollient, spreading agent, carrier, base, dispersant used in pharmaceutical prods.

Properties: Clear visc. liq.; faint char. odor; sol. in min. and castor oil, IPM, oleyl alcohol and anhyd. ethanol; sp.gr. 0.86-0.87; HLB 9; cloud pt. 10 C max.; acid no. 0.5 max.; sapon. no. 130-150; 100% conc.

Standamul® G-32/36. [Henkel/Cospha]

Chem. Descrip.: Myristyl eicosanol

Uses: Emollient wax for topical pharmaceuticals; provides structure, stability, and lubricity; slip and nontackiness to antiperspirants sticks

Properties: Lt. soft wax; faint char. odor; sol. in min. and castor oil, IPM, oleyl alcohol; HLB 7; m.p. 33-40 C; acid no. 1.0 max.; sapon. no. 65-75.

Standamul® G-32/36 Stearate. [Henkel/Cospha]

Chem. Descrip.: Myristyl eicosyl stearate

Uses: Stabilizer, base, lubricant, opacifier, emollient used in pharmaceutical prods.

Properties: Lt. soft wax; faint char. odor; sol. in min. and castor oil, IPM, oleyl alcohol; m.p. 33-40 C; HLB 7; sapon. no. 65-75.

Standamul® HE. [Henkel/Cospha]

Chem. Descrip.: PEG-7 glyceryl cocoate

Uses: Emollient, refatting agent, solubilizer, coupler, emulsifier used in pharmaceutical prods.

Properties: Clear low visc. oil; faint char. odor; sol. in oleyl alcohol, castor oil, anhyd. ethanol, water; sp.gr. 1.050; visc. 200 cps; HLB 16; cloud pt. 0 C; acid no. 5.0 max.; sapon. no. 90-100; 100% conc.; nonionic.

Standard KCl. [Reheis]

Chem. Descrip.: Potassium chloride USP/FCC, BP, EP

CAS 7447-40-7; EINECS 231-211-8

Uses: Functional additive for tablet prod. and parenteral sol'ns.

Star. [Procter & Gamble]

Chem. Descrip.: Glycerin USP

CAS 56-81-5; EINECS 200-289-5

Uses: Humectant in pharmaceuticals

Properties: APHA 10 max. color; sp.gr. 1.2517.

Starch 1500®. [Colorcon]

Chem. Descrip.: Modified corn starch meeting NF specs. for pregelatinized starch
CAS 9005-25-8; EINECS 232-679-6
Uses: Excipient with good wet and dry binding, exc. flow props., self lubricating, good disintegration/dissolution; high performance capsule filler
Properties: Bulk dens. 0.619 g/cc.

Starch 1500® LM. [Colorcon]
Chem. Descrip.: Modified corn starch meeting NF specs. for pregelatinized starch
CAS 9005-25-8; EINECS 232-679-6
Uses: Low moisture excipient, mild desiccant with good wet and dry binding, exc. flow props., self lubricating, good disintegration/dissolution; high performance capsule filler; useful in moisture-sensitive formulations.

Sta-Rx®. [A.E. Staley Mfg.]
Chem. Descrip.: Corn starch NF meeting specs for food starch modified
CAS 9005-25-8; EINECS 232-679-6
Uses: Filler, absorbent, diluent, disintegration agent in pharmaceutical industry for tablets and powds.; wet binder in tablet granulations
Regulatory: FDA 21CFR §172.892
Properties: Wh. powd., free of objectionable odor, sl. char. taste; 0.5% max. on 80 mesh, 5% max. on 325 mesh; pH 64.5-7.0.0; 9.5-12.5% moisture.

Stearate 400 WL 817. [Gattefosse SA]
Chem. Descrip.: PEG-8 palmitostearate
Uses: Solv. and emulsifier for pharmaceutical emulsions
Properties: Drop pt. 29-34 C; HLB 11-12; acid no. < 6; iodine no. < 3; sapon. no. 70-95.

Stearate 1500. [Gattefosse SA]
Chem. Descrip.: PEG (1500) palmitostearate
Uses: Solv. and emulsifier for pharmaceutical emulsions
Properties: Drop pt. 46-50 C; HLB 16; acid no. < 6; iodine no. < 3; sapon. no. 30-45
Toxicology: Nonirritating to skin and eyes.

Stearate 6000 WL 1644. [Gattefosse SA]
Chem. Descrip.: PEG-150 palmitostearate
Uses: Solv. and emulsifier for pharmaceutical emulsions
Properties: Drop pt. 55-60 C; HLB 18; acid no. ≤ 2; iodine no. < 3; sapon. no. 15-25
Toxicology: Nonirritating to skin; sl. irritating to eyes.

Stepanol® AM. [Stepan; Stepan Canada]
Chem. Descrip.: Ammonium lauryl sulfate
CAS 2235-54-3; EINECS 218-793-9
Uses: Foamer, visc. booster used in pharmaceuticals
Properties: Pale yel. visc. liq.; water-sol.; pH 6-7 (10%); 28% act.; anionic.

Stepanol® AM-V. [Stepan; Stepan Canada]
Chem. Descrip.: Ammonium lauryl sulfate
CAS 2235-54-3; EINECS 218-793-9
Uses: Foamer, visc. booster used in pharmaceuticals
Properties: Visc. liq., lt. gel; water-sol.; pH 6-7 (10%); 27-29% act.; anionic.

Stepanol® DEA. [Stepan; Stepan Canada]
Chem. Descrip.: DEA-lauryl sulfate
CAS 143-00-0; EINECS 205-577-4
Uses: Foamer used in pharmaceuticals
Properties: Pale yel. clear liq.; water-sol.; pH 7.3-7.7 (10%); 34% act.; anionic.

Stepanol® ME Dry. [Stepan; Stepan Canada]
Chem. Descrip.: Sodium lauryl sulfate
CAS 151-21-3; EINECS 205-788-1
Uses: Foamer for dentifrices, tablets, pharmaceuticals
Properties: Wh. powd.; water-sol.; pH 7.5-1.0 (10%); 93% min. act.; anionic.

Stepanol® MG. [Stepan; Stepan Canada]
Chem. Descrip.: Magnesium lauryl sulfate
CAS 3097-08-3; EINECS 221-450-6
Uses: Foamer for pharmaceuticals
Properties: Water-sol.; pH 6.5-7.5 (10%); 28-30% act.; anionic.

Stepanol® WA-100. [Stepan; Stepan Canada; Stepan Europe]
Chem. Descrip.: Sodium lauryl sulfate USP/NF
CAS 151-21-3; EINECS 205-788-1
Uses: Foamer, wetting and suspending agent; dentrifice formulations where minimal taste contribution is important; pharmaceuticals
Properties: Wh. powd.; water-sol.; pH 7.5-10 (10%); 98.5% min. act.; anionic.

Stepanol® WAC. [Stepan; Stepan Canada; Stepan Europe]
Chem. Descrip.: Sodium lauryl sulfate
CAS 151-21-3; EINECS 205-788-1
Uses: Foamer, visc. booster for medicated ointments, pharmaceuticals
Properties: Pale yel. clear liq.; water-sol.; pH 7.5-8.5 (10%); 28-30% act.; anionic.

Stepanol® WA Extra. [Stepan; Stepan Canada]
Chem. Descrip.: Sodium lauryl sulfate
CAS 151-21-3; EINECS 205-788-1
Uses: Foamer, visc. booster for medicated ointments, pharmaceuticals
Properties: Clear liq.; water-sol.; pH 7.5-8.5 (10%); 29% act.; anionic.

Stepanol® WA Paste. [Stepan; Stepan Canada]
Chem. Descrip.: Sodium lauryl sulfate
CAS 151-21-3; EINECS 205-788-1
Uses: Foamer, visc. booster for medicated ointments, pharmaceuticals
Properties: Water-wh. clear paste; water-sol.; pH 7.5-8.5 (10%); 29% act.; anionic.

Stepanol® WAQ. [Stepan; Stepan Canada]
Chem. Descrip.: Sodium lauryl sulfate
CAS 151-21-3; EINECS 205-788-1
Uses: Foamer, visc. booster for medicated ointments, pharmaceuticals
Properties: Water-wh. clear visc. liq.; water-sol.; pH 7.5-8.5 (10%); 29% act.; anionic.

Stepanol® WA Special. [Stepan; Stepan Canada]
Chem. Descrip.: Sodium lauryl sulfate
CAS 151-21-3; EINECS 205-788-1
Uses: Foamer, visc. booster for medicated ointments, pharmaceuticals

Properties: Water-wh. clear liq.; water-sol.; pH 7.5-8.5 (10%); 29% act.; anionic.

Stepanol® WAT. [Stepan; Stepan Canada]
Chem. Descrip.: TEA-lauryl sulfate
CAS 139-96-8; EINECS 205-388-7
Uses: Foamer for pharmaceuticals
Properties: Water-wh. clear liq.; water-sol.; pH 7.0-8.5 (10%); 40% act.; anionic.

Stepan TAB®-2. [Stepan; Stepan Europe]
Chem. Descrip.: Dihydrogenated tallow phthalic acid amide
CAS 127733-92-0
Uses: Emulsifying, suspending agent for use in antidandruff shampoos
Properties: Off-wh. to sl. yel. solid, typ. mild fatty odor; sol. in min. and veg. oils, IPP, IPM; insol. in water; m.p. 45 C; flash pt. > 200 F; 99.7% solids
Toxicology: Nontoxic; nonirritating to skin; sl. conjunctival irritant; nonsensitizing.

Steraffine. [Laserson SA]
Chem. Descrip.: Stearyl alcohol
CAS 112-92-5; EINECS 204-017-6
Uses: Emollient, pharmaceutical raw material.

SteriLine 200. [Luzenac Am.]
Chem. Descrip.: Platy talc USP
CAS 14807-96-6; EINECS 238-877-9
Uses: General purpose, coarse talc for use in antiperspirant sticks.

Sterling® Purified USP Salt. [Akzo Salt]
Chem. Descrip.: Sodium chloride USP
CAS 7647-14-5; EINECS 231-598-3
Uses: High purity, food grade salt for use where highest quality is required, esp. in medical field as in the mfg. of saline sol'ns. for intravenous feeding, plasma separation, kidney dialysis, and other critical medical applics.
Regulatory: GRAS, FCC, kosher approvals
Properties: Cryst.; 16% retained 40 USS mesh, 51%-50 USS mesh, 25%-70 USS mesh; sol. 36 g/100 cc in water @ 20 C; sp.gr. 2.165; bulk dens. 1.15-1.28 g/cc; b.p. 1465 C (760 mm); flash pt. none
Toxicology: LD50 (oral, rat) 3.75 g/kg; MLD I.V. 2.5 g/kg
Storage: Store in dry, covered area at r.h. below 75% to retard caking.

Sterol TE 200. [Auschem SpA]
Chem. Descrip.: Blend of PEG esters
Uses: Self-emulsifying base for pharmaceutical o/w creams
Properties: Paste; 100% conc.; nonionic
Unverified

Sterotex®. [ABITEC]
Chem. Descrip.: Hydrog. cottonseed oil
CAS 68334-00-9; EINECS 269-804-9
Uses: Lubricant, emollient, moisturizer, visc. modifier for clinical nutriton, dermatologicals, encapsulation, suppositories, sustained release and tablet applics.
Properties: Lovibond 3R max. bead; m.p. 60-63 C; acid no. 0.4 max.; iodine no. 5 max.; sapon. no. 188-198.

Sterotex® C. [ABITEC]

Chem. Descrip.: Hydrog. soybean oil and carnauba wax
Uses: Tablet lubricant for pharmaceuticals, nutrition
Regulatory: Kosher
Properties: Wh. to lt. tan powd., odorless; insol. in water; sp.gr. 0.9 (100 F); m.p. 79-82 C; b.p. > 500 F; acid no. 2.5 max.; iodine no. 5 max.; sapon. no. 164-174; flash pt. (COC) > 500 F
Toxicology: Veg. oil mists classified as 'nuisance particles'
Precaution: Oil-soaked materials may spontaneously combust.

Sterotex® HM. [ABITEC]
Chem. Descrip.: Hydrog. soybean oils; conforms to hydrog. veg. oil NF
CAS 8016-70-4; EINECS 232-410-2
Uses: Lubricant in pharmaceutical tableting, nutrition, powd. compression applics., suppositories
Regulatory: Kosher
Properties: Wh. fine powd., yel. oil when melted; insol. in water; sp.gr. 0.9; m.p. 67-70 C; b.p. > 500 F; acid no. 0.4 max.; iodine no. 5 max.; sapon. no. 186-196; flash pt. (COC) > 550 F
Toxicology: Veg. oil mists classified as 'nuisance particles'
Precaution: Oil-soaked materials may spontaneously combust
Storage: Store in cool, dry place.

Sterotex® K. [ABITEC]
Chem. Descrip.: Hydrog. soybean oil, hydrog. castor oil
Uses: Tablet lubricant for pharmaceuticals; in clinical nutrition, dermatologicals, suppositories, sustained release
Regulatory: Kosher
Properties: Wh. to lt. tan powd., odorless; insol. in water; sp.gr. 0.9; bulk dens. 0.48; m.p. 81-84 C; b.p. > 500 f; acid no. 1 max.; iodine no. 5 max.; sapon. no. 185-195; flash pt. (COC) > 600 F
Toxicology: Nontoxic; veg. oil mists classified as 'nuisance particles'
Precaution: Oil-soaked materials may spontaneously combust.

Sterotex® NF. [ABITEC]
Chem. Descrip.: Hydrog. veg. oil
CAS 68334-00-9; EINECS 269-820-6
Uses: Lubricant for tableting and compaction in pharmaceuticals, nutritional supplements
Regulatory: Kosher
Properties: Wh. powd. @ R.T., lt. yel. oil when melted; insol. in water; sp.gr. 0.9; m.p. 140-145 F; b.p. > 500 F; acid no. 0.4 max.; iodine no. 5 max.; sapon. no. 188-198; flash pt. (COC) > 640 F
Toxicology: Veg. oil mists classified as 'nuisance particles'
Precaution: Oil-soaked materials may spontaneously combust.

Stripped Coconut Oil 6212, 6256. [Dial]
Chem. Descrip.: Coconut oil fatty acid
EINECS 262-978-7
Uses: Emulsifier used in pharmaceuticals, chem.

intermediates/derivs.
Properties: Acid no. 252-257; iodine no. 8-13; 0.1% max. moisture.

Sucro Ester 7. [Gattefosse SA]
Chem. Descrip.: Saccharose distearate
CAS 27195-16-0
Uses: Emulsifier; tableting agent and lipophilic matrix for pharmaceuticals
Properties: Fine powd., faint odor; sol. in water @ 75 C, in ethanol @ 60 C; insol. in veg. and min. oils; HLB 7.0; acid no. < 5; sapon. no. 115-135; 100% conc.; nonionic
Toxicology: LD0 (oral, rat) > 5 g/kg.

Sucro Ester 11. [Gattefosse SA]
Chem. Descrip.: Saccharose mono/distearate
Uses: Emulsifier; tableting agent and lipophilic matrix for pharmaceuticals
Properties: Fine powd., faint odor; sol. in water @ 75 C, in ethanol @ 60 C; insol. in min. and veg. oils; HLB 11.0; acid no. < 5; sapon. no. 110-130; 100% conc.; nonionic
Toxicology: LD0 (oral, rat) > 5 g/kg.

Sucro Ester 15. [Gattefosse SA]
Chem. Descrip.: Saccharose palmitate
CAS 26446-38-8; EINECS 247-706-7
Uses: Emulsifier; tableting agent and lipophilic matrix for pharmaceuticals
Properties: Fine powd., faint odor; sol. in water and ethanol @ 60 C; insol. in min. and veg. oils; HLB 15.0; acid no. < 5; sapon. no. 95-135; 100% conc.; nonionic
Toxicology: LD0 (oral, rat) > 8 g/kg.

Sugartab®. [Mendell]
Chem. Descrip.: Sucrose (90-93%), invert sugar (6-9%)
Uses: Inert base for directly compressible pharmaceutical tablets incl. chewables; flavor masking chars., noncloying sweetness, smooth disintegration, pleasant aftertaste, relatively low hygroscopicity
Properties: Wh. free-flowing powd.; avg. particle size 296 µ; 30% -80 mesh; very sol. in water; sl. sol. in alcohol; dens. (tapped) 0.6-0.9 g/ml.

Sunyl® 80. [SVO Enterprises]
Chem. Descrip.: High oleic sunflower oil
CAS 8001-21-6; EINECS 232-273-9
Uses: Pharmaceutical diluent, carrier, emulsifier, surfactant, emollient, nutrient, binder in tablets
Properties: Sp.gr. 0.915 (60 F); visc. 40 cSt (40 C); pour pt. -12 C; iodine no. 86; flash pt. 240 C.

Sunyl® 80 ES. [SVO Enterprises]
Chem. Descrip.: Low polyunsat. glyceryl trioleate with additional stabilizers
Uses: In pharmaceuticals as substitute for min. oils and high price esters
Properties: Sp.gr. 0.917 (60 F); visc. 45 cSt (40 C); iodine no. 75; sapon. no. 190; drop pt. 68 F; pour pt. 0 C; cloud pt. 80 F; flash pt. 240 C; ref. index 1.4584 (48 C).

Sunyl® 80 RBD. [SVO Enterprises]
Chem. Descrip.: High oleic sunflower oil, refined, bleached, deodorized

CAS 8001-21-6; EINECS 232-273-9
Uses: Food grade environmentally friendly veg. oil for use as feedstocks/raw materials in pharmaceuticals; oxidative and thermal stability; 77-82% oleic acid; readily biodeg.

Sunyl® 80 RBD ES. [SVO Enterprises]
Chem. Descrip.: High oleic sunflower oil, refined, bleached, deodorized
CAS 8001-21-6; EINECS 232-273-9
Uses: Extended stability, food grade, environmentally friendly veg. oil for use as feedstocks/raw materials in pharmaceuticals; oxidative and thermal stability; 77-82% oleic acid; readily biodeg.

Sunyl® 80 RBWD. [SVO Enterprises]
Chem. Descrip.: High oleic sunflower oil, refined, bleached, winterized, deodorized
CAS 8001-21-6; EINECS 232-273-9
Uses: Food grade, environmentally friendly veg. oil for use as feedstocks/raw materials in pharmaceuticals; oxidative and thermal stability; 77-82% oleic acid; readily biodeg.

Sunyl® 80 RBWD ES. [SVO Enterprises]
Chem. Descrip.: High oleic sunflower oil, refined, bleached, winterized, deodorized
CAS 8001-21-6; EINECS 232-273-9
Uses: Extended stability, food grade, environmentally friendly veg. oil for use as feedstocks/raw materials in pharmaceuticals; oxidative and thermal stability; 77-82% oleic acid; readily biodeg.

Sunyl® 90. [SVO Enterprises]
Chem. Descrip.: Very high oleic sunflower oil
CAS 8001-21-6; EINECS 232-273-9
Uses: Pharmaceutical diluent, carrier, emulsifier, surfactant, emollient, nutrient, binder in tablets; exc. high temp. oxidative stability
Properties: Sp.gr. 0.916 (60 F); visc. 40 cSt (40 C); pour pt. -18 C; iodine no. 82; flash pt. 240 C.

Sunyl® 90 RBD. [SVO Enterprises]
Chem. Descrip.: Very high oleic sunflower oil, refined, bleached, deodorized
CAS 8001-21-6; EINECS 232-273-9
Uses: Food grade, environmentally friendly veg. oil for use as feedstocks/raw materials in pharmaceuticals; oxidative and thermal stability; 85% min. oleic acid; readily biodeg.

Sunyl® 90 RBWD. [SVO Enterprises]
Chem. Descrip.: Very high oleic sunflower oil, refined, bleached, winterized, deodorized
CAS 8001-21-6; EINECS 232-273-9
Uses: Food grade, environmentally friendly veg. oil for use as feedstocks/raw materials in pharmaceuticals; oxidative and thermal stability; 85% min. oleic acid; readily biodeg.

Sunyl® 90E RBWD. [SVO Enterprises]
Chem. Descrip.: Very high oleic sunflower oil, refined, bleached, winterized, deodorized
CAS 8001-21-6; EINECS 232-273-9
Uses: Food grade, environmentally friendly veg. oil for use as feedstocks/raw materials in pharmaceuticals; oxidative and thermal stability; 85% min. oleic acid; readily biodeg.

Sunyl® 90E RBWD ES 1016. [SVO Enterprises]

Chem. Descrip.: Very high oleic sunflower oil, refined, bleached, winterized, deodorized
CAS 8001-21-6; EINECS 232-273-9
Uses: Extended stability, food grade, environmentally friendly veg. oil for use as feedstocks/raw materials in pharmaceuticals; oxidative and thermal stability; 87% min. oleic acid; readily biodeg.

Sunyl® HS 500. [SVO Enterprises]
Chem. Descrip.: High oleic sunflower oil, refined, bleached, deodorized, partially hydrog.
CAS 8001-21-6; EINECS 232-273-9
Uses: Extended stability, food grade, environmentally friendly veg. oil for use as feedstocks/raw materials in pharmaceuticals; very high oxidative and thermal stability; 77-82% oleic acid; readily biodeg.

Supercol® Guar Gum. [Hercules/Aqualon]
Chem. Descrip.: Guar gum
CAS 9000-30-0; EINECS 232-536-8
Uses: Thickener, protective colloid, stabilizer for pharmaceuticals; binding agent in tablets.

Super Corona Lanolin. [Croda Inc.]
Chem. Descrip.: Refined anhyd. lanolin USP
CAS 8006-54-0; EINECS 232-348-6
Uses: Superfatting emollient, moisturizer, emulsifier for topical pharmaceuticals; improves spreading, penetration, and aesthetic props.; for prods. for dry, itchy chapped skin, hemorrhoidal preps., suppositories, steroidal prods., acne prods., ophthalmics
Properties: Yel. soft solid, pract. odorless; partly sol. in min. oil; m.p. 38-44 C; acid no. 1.0 max; iodine no. 18-36
Toxicology: LD50 (oral, rat) > 20 g/kg; mild skin and eye irritant.

Superfine KCl. [Reheis]
Chem. Descrip.: Potassium chloride USP/FCC, BP, EP
CAS 7447-40-7; EINECS 231-211-8
Uses: Functional additive for use in microencapsulation in the pharmaceutical industry
Properties: Powd.; 100-200 mesh.

Superfine Lanolin. [Croda Inc.]
Chem. Descrip.: Lanolin USP
CAS 8006-54-0; EINECS 232-348-6
Uses: Superfatting emollient, emulsifier, moisturizer for topical pharmaceuticals, ointments, dressing creams, diaper rash and hemorrhoidal preps., acne formulations, ophthalmics
Properties: Yel./amber soft solid; low odor; partly sol. in min. oil; m.p. 38-44 C
Toxicology: LD50 (oral, rat) > 20 g/kg; mild skin and eye irritant.

Super Hartolan. [Croda Inc.; Croda Chem. Ltd.]
Chem. Descrip.: Lanolin alcohol NF
CAS 8027-33-6; EINECS 232-430-1
Uses: W/o emulsifier, thickener, stabilizer, and plasticizer in topical pharmaceutical emulsions; enhances stability of acid-contg. emulsions
Use level: 0.5-3%
Properties: Golden solid wax; sol. in IPA, partly sol. in min. oil, disp. in propylene glycol; m.p. 60-70 C

min.; HLB 1.0; acid no. 1.5 max.; sapon. no. 5 mg max.; 100% conc.; nonionic
Toxicology: LD50 (oral, rat) 20 g/kg; mild skin and eye irritant.

Superla® No. 5. [Amoco Petrol. Prods.]
Chem. Descrip.: Wh. min. oil USP
Uses: Lubricant for pharmaceuticals, medicinal prods.
Regulatory: FDA 21CFR §172.878, 178.3620, 5763.680, USDA approved; kosher
Properties: Colorless, odorless, tasteless; sp.gr. 0.844; visc. 8.4 cSt (40 C); pour pt. -12 C; flash pt. 150 C; ref. index 1.4660.

Superla® No. 6. [Amoco Petrol. Prods.]
Chem. Descrip.: Wh. min. oil USP
Uses: Lubricant for pharmaceuticals, medicinal prods.
Regulatory: FDA 21CFR §172.878, 178.3620, 5763.680, USDA approved; kosher
Properties: Colorless, odorless, tasteless; sp.gr. 0.847; visc. 10.9 cSt (40 C); pour pt. -12 C; flash pt. 169 C; ref. index 1.4664.

Superla® No. 7. [Amoco Petrol. Prods.]
Chem. Descrip.: Wh. min. oil USP
Uses: Lubricant for pharmaceuticals, medicinal prods.
Regulatory: FDA 21CFR §172.878, 178.3620, 5763.680, USDA approved; kosher
Properties: Colorless, odorless, tasteless; sp.gr. 0.845; visc. 12.1 cSt (40 C); pour pt. -12 C; flash pt. 173 C; ref. index 1.4666.

Superla® No. 9. [Amoco Petrol. Prods.]
Chem. Descrip.: Wh. min. oil USP
Uses: Lubricant for pharmaceuticals, medicinal prods.
Regulatory: FDA 21CFR §172.878, 178.3620, 5763.680, USDA approved; kosher
Properties: Colorless, odorless, tasteless; sp.gr. 0.850; visc. 16.0 cSt (40 C); pour pt. -12 C; flash pt. 194 C; ref. index 1.4715.

Superla® No. 10. [Amoco Petrol. Prods.]
Chem. Descrip.: Wh. min. oil USP
Uses: Lubricant for pharmaceuticals, medicinal prods.
Regulatory: FDA 21CFR §172.878, 178.3620, 5763.680, USDA approved; kosher
Properties: Colorless, odorless, tasteless; sp.gr. 0.848; visc. 19.3 cSt (40 C); pour pt. -12 C; flash pt. 199 C; ref. index 1.4728.

Superla® No. 13. [Amoco Petrol. Prods.]
Chem. Descrip.: Wh. min. oil USP
Uses: Lubricant for pharmaceuticals, medicinal prods.
Regulatory: FDA 21CFR §172.878, 178.3620, 5763.680, USDA approved; kosher
Properties: Colorless, odorless, tasteless; sp.gr. 0.854; visc. 26.2 cSt (40 C); pour pt. -12 C; flash pt. 206 C; ref. index 1.4728.

Superla® No. 18. [Amoco Petrol. Prods.]
Chem. Descrip.: Wh. min. oil USP
Uses: Lubricant for pharmaceuticals, medicinal prods.

Regulatory: FDA 21CFR §172.878, 178.3620, 5763.680, USDA approved; kosher
Properties: Colorless, odorless, tasteless; sp.gr. 0.857; visc. 36.3 cSt (40 C); pour pt. -12 C; flash pt. 216 C; ref. index 1.4738.

Superla® No. 21. [Amoco Petrol. Prods.]
Chem. Descrip.: Wh. min. oil USP
Uses: Lubricant for pharmaceuticals, medicinal prods.
Regulatory: FDA 21CFR §172.878, 178.3620, 5763.680, USDA approved; kosher
Properties: Colorless, odorless, tasteless; sp.gr. 0.859; visc. 40.2 cSt (40 C); pour pt. -12 C; flash pt. 220 C; ref. index 1.4744.

Superla® No. 31. [Amoco Petrol. Prods.]
Chem. Descrip.: Wh. min. oil USP
Uses: Lubricant for pharmaceuticals, medicinal prods.
Regulatory: FDA 21CFR §172.878, 178.3620, 5763.680, USDA approved; kosher
Properties: Colorless, odorless, tasteless; sp.gr. 0.865; visc. 60.5 cSt (40 C); pour pt. -12 C; flash pt. 230 C; ref. index 1.4763.

Superla® No. 35. [Amoco Petrol. Prods.]
Chem. Descrip.: Wh. min. oil USP
Uses: Lubricant for pharmaceuticals, medicinal prods.
Regulatory: FDA 21CFR §172.878, 178.3620, 5763.680, USDA approved; kosher
Properties: Colorless, odorless, tasteless; sp.gr. 0.865; visc. 69.3 cSt (40 C); pour pt. -12 C; flash pt. 236 C; ref. index 1.4772.

Superol. [Procter & Gamble]
Chem. Descrip.: Glycerin USP
CAS 56-81-5; EINECS 200-289-5
Uses: Humectant in pharmaceuticals
Properties: APHA 10 max. color; sp.gr. 1.2612.

Superpolystate. [Gattefosse SA]
Chem. Descrip.: PEG-6 stearate SE
CAS 9004-99-3
Uses: SE gelling base for pharmaceutical lotions
Properties: Gardner < 5 doughy solid; very sol. in chloroform, methylene chloride; disp. in water; insol. in ethanol, min. oils; drop pt. 33-37 C; HLB 9.0; acid no. < 6; iodine no. < 3; sapon. no. 90-110; hyd. no. 75-105; 100% conc.; nonionic
Toxicology: LD0 (oral, rat) > 2 g/kg; nonirritating to skin and eyes.

Super Refined® Almond Oil. [Croda Inc.; Croda Surf. Ltd.]
Chem. Descrip.: Almond oil NF
CAS 8007-69-0
Uses: Solv. and vehicle for pharmaceuticals (parenteral formulations for intramuscular administration, nutritional supplements, IV emulsions, liniments, ointments, orals, topicals); component of rose water ointment USP
Properties: APHA 40 oil, odorless, tasteless; sol. in min. oil, IPA
Toxicology: LD50 (oral, rat) > 5 g/kg; nonirritating to skin.

Super Refined® Corn Oil. [Croda Inc.]
Chem. Descrip.: Corn oil NF
CAS 8001-30-7; EINECS 232-281-2
Uses: Solv. and oleaginous vehicle for pharmaceuticals (parenteral formulations for intramuscular administration, nutritional supplements, IV emulsions, liniments, ointments, orals, topicals)
Properties: APHA 40 oil, odorless, tasteless; sol. in min. oil, IPA.

Super Refined® Cottonseed Oil. [Croda Inc.]
Chem. Descrip.: Cottonseed oil NF/USP
CAS 8001-29-4; EINECS 232-280-7
Uses: Emollient, solv., oleaginous vehicle for pharmaceuticals (orals, topicals, parenteral formulations for intramuscular administration, nutritional supplements, IV emulsions, liniments, ointments)
Properties: APHA 50 oil, odorless, tasteless; sol. in min. oil, IPA.

Super Refined® Menhaden Oil. [Croda Inc.]
Chem. Descrip.: Menhaden oil
CAS 8002-50-4; EINECS 232-311-4
Uses: Dietary supplement, therapeutic applics.; high in omega 3 fatty acids; for orals, topicals
Properties: APHA 100 oil, faint char. odor, tasteless; sol. in min. oil, IPA.

Super Refined® Olive Oil. [Croda Inc.; Croda Surf. Ltd.]
Chem. Descrip.: Olive oil
CAS 8001-25-0; EINECS 232-277-0
Uses: Emollient, lubricant, solv., oleaginous vehicle for pharmaceuticals (orals, topicals, parenteral formulations for intramuscular administration, nutritional supplements, IV emulsions, liniments, ointments)
Properties: APHA 30 oil, odorless, tasteless; sol. in min. oil, IPA.

Super Refined® Orange Roughy Oil. [Croda Inc.; Croda Surf. Ltd.]
Chem. Descrip.: Orange roughy oil
Uses: Wax ester as solubilizer for pharmaceuticals
Properties: APHA 30 liq., faint char. odor; sol. in min. oil, IPA
Toxicology: LD50 (oral, rat) > 5 g/kg; minimal skin irritant, nonirritating to eyes.

Super Refined® Peanut Oil. [Croda Inc.]
Chem. Descrip.: Peanut oil NF/USP
CAS 8002-03-7; EINECS 232-296-4
Uses: Solv. and oleaginous vehicle for pharmaceuticals (orals, topicals, parenteral formulations for intramuscular administration, nutritional supplements, IV emulsions, liniments, ointments)
Properties: APHA 30 oil, odorless, tasteless; sol. in min. oil, IPA.

Super Refined® Safflower Oil. [Croda Inc.; Croda Surf. Ltd.]
Chem. Descrip.: Safflower oil USP
CAS 8001-23-8; EINECS 232-276-5
Uses: Solv., oleaginous vehicle for pharmaceuticals (orals, topicals, parenteral formulations for intramuscular administration, nutritional supplements, IV emulsions, liniments, ointments)
Properties: APHA 30 mobile oil, odorless, tasteless; sol. in min. oil, IPA

Toxicology: LD50 (oral, rat) > 5 g/kg; minimal eye and skin irritant.

Super Refined® Sesame Oil. [Croda Inc.; Croda Surf. Ltd.]
Chem. Descrip.: Sesame oil NF/USP
CAS 8008-74-0; EINECS 232-370-6
Uses: Lubricant, emollient, solv., oleaginous vehicle for pharmaceuticals (orals, topicals, parenteral formulations for intramuscular administration, nutritional supplements, IV emulsions, liniments, ointments)
Regulatory: NF, BP compliance
Properties: APHA 30 clear oily liq., odorless, tasteless; sol. in min. oil, IPA; sp.gr. 0.916-0.921; iodine no. 103-116; sapon. no. 188-195; hyd. no. 5 max.; ref. index 1.472-1.476; 0.05% max. moisture
Toxicology: LD50 (oral, rat) > 5 g/kg; mild skin irritant, minimal eye irritant.

Super Refined® Shark Liver Oil. [Croda Inc.; Croda Surf. Ltd.]
Chem. Descrip.: Shark liver oil
CAS 68990-63-6; EINECS 273-616-2
Uses: Protectant that softens and smooths skin tissues; used for topical hemorrhoidal preps.
Regulatory: FDA recognized as skin protectant for OTC drugs @ 3% conc.
Properties: APHA 40 oil, faint char. odor, tasteless; sol. in min. oil, IPA
Toxicology: LD50 (oral, rat) > 5 g/kg; moderate skin irritant, minimal eye irritant.

Super Refined® Soybean Oil USP. [Croda Inc.; Croda Surf. Ltd.]
Chem. Descrip.: Soybean oil USP
CAS 8001-22-7; EINECS 232-274-4
Uses: Solv., oleaginous vehicle, nutritonal source, lubricant for pharmaceuticals (orals, topicals, parenteral formulations for intramuscular administration, nutritional supplements, IV emulsions, liniments, ointments)
Properties: APHA 60 max. clear oily liq., odorless, tasteless; sol. in min. oil, IPA; sp.gr. 0.916-0.922; iodine no. 120-141; sapon. no. 180-200; hyd. no. 5 max.; ref. index 1.465-1.475
Toxicology: LD50 (oral, rat) > 5 g/kg; mild skin irritant, minimal eye irritant.

Super Refined® Wheat Germ Oil. [Croda Inc.; Croda Surf. Ltd.]
Chem. Descrip.: Wheat germ oil
CAS 8006-95-9
Uses: Nutritional source, moisturizer for topical and oral pharmaceuticals
Properties: APHA 250 oil, odorless, tasteless.

Super-Sat. [R.I.T.A.]
Chem. Descrip.: Hydrog. lanolin
CAS 8031-44-5; EINECS 232-452-1
Uses: Plasticizer, emollient, spreading agent for pharmaceuticals; high water absorp.; vehicle for actives in skin prods.
Properties: Wh. to lt. yel. tacky solid; sol. in ethyl ether, chloroform; insol. in water; sp.gr. 0.855-0.865; m.p. 48-53 C; acid no. 2 max.; iodine no. 20

max.; sapon. no. 6 max.; hyd. no. 140-165; 100% act.; nonionic.

Super-Sat AWS-4. [R.I.T.A.]
Chem. Descrip.: PEG-20 hydrog. lanolin
CAS 68648-27-1
Uses: Emollient, emulsifier, visc. control agent, plasticizer, gellant, solubilizer for ointments, sun preps.
Properties: Amber solid, bland odor; slightly water-sol.; acid no. 1 mqx.; iodine no. 10 max.; sapon. no. 8 max.; hyd. no. 32-47; 100% conc.; nonionic.

Super-Sat AWS-24. [R.I.T.A.]
Chem. Descrip.: PEG-24 hydrog. lanolin
CAS 68648-27-1
Uses: Emollient, plasticizer, emulsifier, visc. control agent, gelling agent, solubilizer for ointments, sun preps.
Properties: Wh. flakes, bland odor; acid no. 1 max.; iodine no. 10 max.; sapon. no. 8 max.; hyd. no. 32-47; 100% conc.; nonionic.

Super Solan Flaked. [Croda Inc.]
Chem. Descrip.: PEG-75 lanolin
CAS 61790-81-6
Uses: Emollient, conditioner, superfatting agent, solubilizer, and plasticizer for topical pharmaceuticals; used in cleansing wipe formulations
Use level: 2-10%
Properties: Yel. flake; sol. in water, propylene glycol; sol. warm in IPA; m.p. 46-54 C
Toxicology: LD50 (oral, rat) > 5 g/kg; minimal skin irritant, nonirritating to eyes.

Super Sterol Ester. [Croda Inc.; Croda Chem. Ltd.]
Chem. Descrip.: C10-30 cholesterol/lanosterol esters
Uses: Emollient, lubricant, plasticizer, moisturizer for topical pharmaceuticals (ointments, dressing creams); softening agent in transdermal delivery systems due to its hypoallergenicity
Use level: 1-10%
Properties: Wh. soft solid, odorless; sol. in min. oil, IPA, esters; m.p. 30-38 C
Toxicology: LD50 (oral, rat) > 5 g/kg; mild skin irritant.

Super White Fonoline®. [Witco/Petroleum Spec.]
Chem. Descrip.: Wh. petrolatum USP
CAS 8027-32-5; EINECS 232-373-2
Uses: Low m.p. grade with superior snow white color, exhibiting elegant feel and texture; for premium pharmaceutical formulations, medicated ointments, petrol. jelly, suncare prods.
Regulatory: FDA §172.880
Properties: Lovibond 0.5Y color; visc. 9-14 cSt (100 C); m.p. 50-56 C.

Super White Protopet®. [Witco/Petroleum Spec.]
Chem. Descrip.: Wh. petrolatum USP
CAS 8027-32-5; EINECS 232-373-2
Uses: Lubricant; high purity, med. consistency, med. m.p. grade for premium pharmaceutical formulations where extra whiteness is preferred; for medicated ointments, dental adhesives, suncare prods.
Regulatory: FDA 21CFR §172.880

Properties: Lovibond 1.0Y max. color; visc. 10-16 cSt (100 C); m.p. 54-60 C.

Supoweiss A. [Unichema Int'l.; Unichema N. Am.]
Chem. Descrip.: Natural sat. fatty acid glycerides
Uses: Excipient, base for suppositories
Properties: Wh. to off-wh. flakes or pellets; m.p. 32-34 C; acid no. 0.5 max.; sapon. no. 225-245; hyd. no. 15-25
Storage: Store @ R.T. in a dry atmosphere.

Supoweiss B. [Unichema Int'l.; Unichema N. Am.]
Chem. Descrip.: Natural sat. fatty acid glycerides
Uses: Excipient, base for suppositories
Properties: Wh. to off-wh. flakes or pellets; m.p. 34-36 C; acid no. 0.2 max.; sapon. no. 235-245; hyd. no. 15-25
Storage: Store @ R.T. in a dry atmosphere.

Supoweiss B0. [Unichema Int'l.; Unichema N. Am.]
Chem. Descrip.: Natural sat. fatty acid glycerides
Uses: Excipient, base for suppositories
Properties: Wh. to off-wh. flakes or pellets; m.p. 34-36 C; acid no. 0.2 max.; sapon. no. 240-255; hyd. no. 1 max.
Storage: Store @ R.T. in a dry atmosphere.

Supoweiss B10. [Unichema Int'l.; Unichema N. Am.]
Chem. Descrip.: Natural sat. fatty acid glycerides
Uses: Excipient, base for suppositories
Properties: Wh. to off-wh. flakes or pellets; m.p. 33-35 C; acid no. 0.2 max.; sapon. no. 225-245; hyd. no. 8 max.
Storage: Store @ R.T. in a dry atmosphere.

Supoweiss B90. [Unichema Int'l.; Unichema N. Am.]
Chem. Descrip.: Natural sat. fatty acid glycerides
Uses: Excipient, base for suppositories
Properties: Wh. to off-wh. flakes or pellets; m.p. 34-36 C; acid no. 1.0 max.; sapon. no. 220-250; hyd. no. 80-100
Storage: Store @ R.T. in a dry atmosphere.

Supoweiss BV. [Unichema Int'l.; Unichema N. Am.]
Chem. Descrip.: Natural sat. fatty acid glycerides
Uses: Excipient, base for suppositories
Properties: Wh. to off-wh. flakes or pellets; m.p. 34-36 C; acid no. 0.3 max.; sapon. no. 225-245; hyd. no. 15 max.
Storage: Store @ R.T. in a dry atmosphere.

Supoweiss C. [Unichema Int'l.; Unichema N. Am.]
Chem. Descrip.: Natural sat. fatty acid glycerides
Uses: Excipient, base for suppositories
Properties: Wh. to off-wh. flakes or pellets; m.p. 36-38 C; acid no. 0.2 max.; sapon. no. 225-245; hyd. no. 15-25
Storage: Store @ R.T. in a dry atmosphere.

Supoweiss C2. [Unichema Int'l.; Unichema N. Am.]
Chem. Descrip.: Natural sat. fatty acid glycerides
Uses: Excipient, base for suppositories
Properties: Wh. to off-wh. flakes or pellets; m.p. 36-38 C; acid no. 0.2 max.; sapon. no. 240-255; hyd. no. 2 max.
Storage: Store @ R.T. in a dry atmosphere.

Supoweiss D. [Unichema Int'l.; Unichema N. Am.]
Chem. Descrip.: Natural sat. fatty acid glycerides
Uses: Excipient, base for suppositories
Properties: Wh. to off-wh. flakes or pellets; m.p. 40-

42 C; acid no. 0.2 max.; sapon. no. 225-245; hyd. no. 15-25
Storage: Store @ R.T. in a dry atmosphere.

Suppocire® A. [Gattefosse SA]
Chem. Descrip.: Hemisynthetic glycerides
Uses: Excipient for pharmaceutical suppositories
Properties: Very sol. in diethyl oxide, chloroform, CCl₄, toluene, petrol. ether (40-60 C); sl. sol. in ethanol; insol. in water; sp.gr. 0.955 (20 C); drop pt. 35-36.5 C; acid no. < 0.5; iodine no. < 2; sapon. no. 225-245; hyd. no. 20-30
Toxicology: LD50 (oral, rat) > 20 ml/kg, nonirritating rectally.

Suppocire® AI. [Gattefosse SA]
Chem. Descrip.: Hemisynthetic glycerides
Uses: Excipient for pharmaceutical suppositories
Properties: Very sol. in diethyl oxide, chloroform, CCl₄, toluene, petrol. ether (40-60 C); sl. sol. in ethanol; insol. in water; sp.gr. 0.955 (20 C); drop pt. 33-35 C; acid no. < 0.5; iodine no. < 2; sapon. no. 225-245; hyd. no. 20-30
Toxicology: LD0 (oral, rat) > 20 ml/kg; nonirritating rectally.

Suppocire® AIM. [Gattefosse SA]
Chem. Descrip.: Hemisynthetic glycerides
Uses: Excipient for pharmaceutical suppositories
Properties: Very sol. in diethyl oxide, chloroform, CCl₄, toluene, petrol. ether (40-60 C); sl. sol. in ethanol; insol. in water; sp.gr. 0.955 (20 C); drop pt. 33-35 C; acid no. < 0.2; iodine no. < 2; sapon. no. 225-245; hyd. no. < 6
Toxicology: LD50 (oral, rat) > 20 ml/kg, nonirritating rectally; sl. irritating to eyes.

Suppocire® AIML. [Gattefosse SA]
Chem. Descrip.: Hemisynthetic glycerides
Uses: Excipient for pharmaceutical suppositories
Properties: Very sol. in diethyl oxide, chloroform, CCl₄, toluene, petrol. ether (40-60 C); sl. sol. in ethanol; insol. in water; sp.gr. 0.955 (20 C); drop pt. 33-35 C; acid no. < 0.5; iodine no. < 3; sapon. no. 225-245; hyd. no. < 6
Toxicology: LD50 (oral, rat) > 20 ml/kg, nonirritating rectally.

Suppocire® AIP. [Gattefosse SA]
Chem. Descrip.: Saturated polyglycolized glycerides
Uses: Excipient for pharmaceutical suppositories; increased bioavailability; recommended where swift and massive release of active ingred. is required
Properties: Very sol. in diethyl oxide, chloroform, CCl₄, toluene, petrol. ether (40-60 C); sl. sol. in ethanol; insol. in water; sp.gr. 0.955 (20 C); drop pt. 30-33 C; acid no. < 1; iodine no. < 1; sapon. no. 205-225; hyd. no. < 1
Toxicology: LD0 > 20 ml/kg; nonirritating rectally.

Suppocire® AIX. [Gattefosse SA]
Chem. Descrip.: Hemisynthetic glycerides
Uses: Excipient for pharmaceutical suppositories
Properties: Very sol. in diethyl oxide, chloroform, CCl₄, toluene, petrol. ether (40-60 C); sl. sol. in ethanol; insol. in water; sp.gr. 0.955 (20 C); drop

pt. 33-35 C; acid no. < 0.5; iodine no. < 2; sapon. no. 220-240; hyd. no. 20-30
Toxicology: Nonirritating rectally.
Suppocire® AM. [Gattefosse SA]
Chem. Descrip.: Hemisynthetic glycerides
Uses: Excipient for pharmaceutical suppositories
Properties: Very sol. in diethyl oxide, chloroform, CCl_4, toluene, petrol. ether (40-60 C); sl. sol. in ethanol; insol. in water; sp.gr. 0.955 (20 C); drop pt. 33-36.5 C; acid no. < 0.2; iodine no. < 2; sapon. no. 225-245; hyd. no. < 6
Toxicology: LD50 (oral, rat) > 20 ml/kg, nonirritating rectally; sl. irritating to eyes.
Suppocire® AML. [Gattefosse SA]
Chem. Descrip.: Hemisynthetic glycerides
Uses: Excipient for pharmaceutical suppositories
Properties: Very sol. in diethyl oxide, chloroform, CCl_4, toluene, petrol. ether (40-60 C); sl. sol. in ethanol; insol. in water; sp.gr. 0.955 (20 C); drop pt. 35-36.5 C; acid no. < 0.5; iodine no. < 3; sapon. no. 225-245; hyd. no. < 6
Toxicology: LD50 (oral, rat) > 20 ml/kg, nonirritating rectally.
Suppocire® AP. [Gattefosse SA]
Chem. Descrip.: Saturated polyglycolized glycerides
Uses: Excipient for pharmaceutical suppositories; increased bioavailability; recommended where swift and massive release of active ingred. is required
Properties: Very sol. in diethyl oxide, chloroform, CCl_4, toluene, petrol. ether (40-60 C); sl. sol. in ethanol; insol. in water; sp.gr. 0.955 (20 C); drop pt. 30-39 C; acid no. < 1; iodine no. < 1; sapon. no. 200-220; hyd. no. < 1
Toxicology: LD0 > 20 ml/kg; nonirritating rectally.
Suppocire® AS2. [Gattefosse SA]
Chem. Descrip.: Hemisynthetic glycerides
Uses: Excipient for pharmaceutical suppositories
Properties: Very sol. in diethyl oxide, chloroform, CCl_4, toluene, petrol. ether (40-60 C); sl. sol. in ethanol; insol. in water; sp.gr. 0.955 (20 C); drop pt. 35-36.5 C; acid no. < 0.5; iodine no. < 2; sapon. no. 225-245; hyd. no. 15-25
Toxicology: LD50 (oral, rat) > 20 ml/kg.
Suppocire® AS2X. [Gattefosse SA]
Chem. Descrip.: Hemisynthetic glycerides
Uses: Excipient for pharmaceutical suppositories
Properties: Very sol. in diethyl oxide, chloroform, CCl_4, toluene, petrol. ether (40-60 C); sl. sol. in ethanol; insol. in water; sp.gr. 0.955 (20 C); drop pt. 35-36.5 C; acid no. < 0.5; iodine no. < 2; sapon. no. 225-245; hyd. no. 15-25
Toxicology: Nonirritating rectally.
Suppocire® B. [Gattefosse SA]
Chem. Descrip.: Hemisynthetic glycerides
Uses: Excipient for pharmaceutical suppositories
Properties: Very sol. in diethyl oxide, chloroform, CCl_4, toluene, petrol. ether (40-60 C); sl. sol. in ethanol; insol. in water; sp.gr. 0.955 (20 C); drop pt. 36-37.5 C; acid no. < 0.5; iodine no. < 2; sapon. no. 225-245; hyd. no. 20-30

Toxicology: LD50 (oral, rat) > 20 ml/kg, nonirritating rectally.
Suppocire® BM. [Gattefosse SA]
Chem. Descrip.: Hemisynthetic glycerides
Uses: Excipient for pharmaceutical suppositories
Properties: Very sol. in diethyl oxide, chloroform, CCl_4, toluene, petrol. ether (40-60 C); sl. sol. in ethanol; insol. in water; sp.gr. 0.955 (20 C); drop pt. 36-37.5 C; acid no. < 0.2; iodine no. < 2; sapon. no. 225-245; hyd. no. < 6
Toxicology: LD50 (oral, rat) > 20 ml/kg, nonirritating rectally; sl. irritating to eyes.
Suppocire® BML. [Gattefosse SA]
Chem. Descrip.: Hemisynthetic glycerides
Uses: Excipient for pharmaceutical suppositories
Properties: Very sol. in diethyl oxide, chloroform, CCl_4, toluene, petrol. ether (40-60 C); sl. sol. in ethanol; insol. in water; sp.gr. 0.955 (20 C); drop pt. 36-37.5 C; acid no. < 0.5; iodine no. < 3; sapon. no. 225-245; hyd. no. < 6
Toxicology: LD50 (oral, rat) > 20 ml/kg, nonirritating rectally.
Suppocire® BP. [Gattefosse SA]
Chem. Descrip.: Saturated polyglycolized glycerides
Uses: Excipient for pharmaceutical suppositories; increased bioavailability; recommended where swift and massive release of active ingred. is required
Properties: Very sol. in diethyl oxide, chloroform, CCl_4, toluene, petrol. ether (40-60 C); sl. sol. in ethanol; insol. in water; sp.gr. 0.955 (20 C); drop pt. 30-39 C; acid no. < 1; iodine no. < 1; sapon. no. 200-220; hyd. no. < 1
Toxicology: LD0 > 20 ml/kg; nonirritating rectally.
Suppocire® BS2. [Gattefosse SA]
Chem. Descrip.: Hemisynthetic glycerides
Uses: Excipient for pharmaceutical suppositories
Properties: Very sol. in diethyl oxide, chloroform, CCl_4, toluene, petrol. ether (40-60 C); sl. sol. in ethanol; insol. in water; sp.gr. 0.955 (20 C); drop pt. 36-37.5 C; acid no. < 0.5; iodine no. < 2; sapon. no. 225-245; hyd. no. 15-25
Toxicology: LD50 (oral, rat) > 20 ml/kg.
Suppocire® BS2X. [Gattefosse SA]
Chem. Descrip.: Hemisynthetic glycerides
Uses: Excipient for pharmaceutical suppositories
Properties: Very sol. in diethyl oxide, chloroform, CCl_4, toluene, petrol. ether (40-60 C); sl. sol. in ethanol; insol. in water; sp.gr. 0.955 (20 C); drop pt. 36-37.5 C; acid no. < 0.5; iodine no. < 2; sapon. no. 220-240; hyd. no. 15-25.
Suppocire® BT. [Gattefosse SA]
Chem. Descrip.: Hemisynthetic glycerides
Uses: Excipient for pharmaceutical suppositories
Properties: Very sol. in diethyl oxide, chloroform, CCl_4, toluene, petrol. ether (40-60 C); sl. sol. in ethanol; insol. in water; sp.gr. 0.955 (20 C); drop pt. 36-37.5 C; acid no. < 0.5; iodine no. < 2; sapon. no. 225-245; hyd. no. 25-35.
Suppocire® C. [Gattefosse SA]
Chem. Descrip.: Hemisynthetic glycerides

Uses: Excipient for pharmaceutical suppositories

Properties: Very sol. in diethyl oxide, chloroform, CCl_4, toluene, petrol. ether (40-60 C); sl. sol. in ethanol; insol. in water; sp.gr. 0.955 (20 C); drop pt. 38-40 C; acid no. < 0.5; iodine no. < 2; sapon. no. 220-240; hyd. no. 20-30

Toxicology: LD50 (oral, rat) > 20 ml/kg, nonirritating rectally.

Suppocire® CM. [Gattefosse]

Chem. Descrip.: Hydrog. palm glycerides, hydrog. palm kernel glycerides

Uses: Excipient for pharmaceutical suppositories

Properties: Very sol. in diethyl oxide, chloroform, CCl_4, toluene, petrol. ether (40-60 C); sl. sol. in ethanol; insol. in water; sp.gr. 0.955 (20 C); drop pt. 38-40 C; acid no. < 0.2; iodine no. < 2; sapon. no. 225-245; hyd. no. < 6

Toxicology: LD0 (oral, rat) > 20 ml/kg; sl. irritating to eyes, nonirritating to skin.

Suppocire® CP. [Gattefosse SA]

Chem. Descrip.: Saturated polyglycolized glycerides

Uses: Excipient for pharmaceutical suppositories; increased bioavailability; recommended where swift and massive release of active ingred. is required

Properties: Very sol. in diethyl oxide, chloroform, CCl_4, toluene, petrol. ether (40-60 C); sl. sol. in ethanol; insol. in water; sp.gr. 0.955 (20 C); drop pt. 30-39 C; acid no. < 1; iodine no. < 1; sapon. no. 195-215; hyd. no. < 1

Toxicology: LD0 > 20 ml/kg; nonirritating rectally.

Suppocire® CS2. [Gattefosse SA]

Chem. Descrip.: Hemisynthetic glycerides

Uses: Excipient for pharmaceutical suppositories

Properties: Very sol. in diethyl oxide, chloroform, CCl_4, toluene, petrol. ether (40-60 C); sl. sol. in ethanol; insol. in water; sp.gr. 0.955 (20 C); drop pt. 38-40 C; acid no. < 0.5; iodine no. < 2; sapon. no. 225-245; hyd. no. 15-25

Toxicology: LD50 (oral, rat) > 20 ml/kg.

Suppocire® CS2X. [Gattefosse SA]

Chem. Descrip.: Hemisynthetic glycerides

Uses: Excipient for pharmaceutical suppositories

Properties: Very sol. in diethyl oxide, chloroform, CCl_4, toluene, petrol. ether (40-60 C); sl. sol. in ethanol; insol. in water; sp.gr. 0.955 (20 C); drop pt. 38-40 C; acid no. < 0.5; iodine no. < 2; sapon. no. 220-240; hyd. no. 15-25.

Suppocire® CT. [Gattefosse SA]

Chem. Descrip.: Hemisynthetic glycerides

Uses: Excipient for pharmaceutical suppositories

Properties: Very sol. in diethyl oxide, chloroform, CCl_4, toluene, petrol. ether (40-60 C); sl. sol. in ethanol; insol. in water; sp.gr. 0.955 (20 C); drop pt. 38-40 C; acid no. < 0.5; iodine no. < 2; sapon. no. 220-240; hyd. no. 25-35.

Suppocire® D. [Gattefosse SA]

Chem. Descrip.: Hemisynthetic glycerides

Uses: Excipient for pharmaceutical suppositories

Properties: Very sol. in diethyl oxide, chloroform, CCl_4, toluene, petrol. ether (40-60 C); sl. sol. in ethanol; insol. in water; sp.gr. 0.955 (20 C); drop pt. 42-45 C; acid no. < 0.5; iodine no. < 2; sapon. no. 215-235; hyd. no. 20-30.

Suppocire® DM. [Gattefosse SA]

Chem. Descrip.: Hemisynthetic glycerides

Uses: Excipient for pharmaceutical suppositories

Properties: Very sol. in diethyl oxide, chloroform, CCl_4, toluene, petrol. ether (40-60 C); sl. sol. in ethanol; insol. in water; sp.gr. 0.955 (20 C); drop pt. 42-45 C; acid no. < 0.2; iodine no. < 2; sapon. no. 220-240; hyd. no. < 6.

Suppocire® NA. [Gattefosse SA]

Chem. Descrip.: Hemisynthetic glycerides

Uses: Excipient for pharmaceutical suppositories with exc. resist. to solvs., essential oils, or liposoluble active ingreds.

Properties: Very sol. in diethyl oxide, chloroform, CCl_4, toluene, petrol. ether (40-60 C); sl. sol. in ethanol; insol. in water; sp.gr. 0.955 (20 C); drop pt. 35.5-37.5 C; acid no. < 0.5; iodine no. < 2; sapon. no. 225-245; hyd. no. < 40.

Suppocire® NAI. [Gattefosse SA]

Chem. Descrip.: Hemisynthetic glycerides

Uses: Excipient for pharmaceutical suppositories with exc. resist. to solvs., essential oils, or liposoluble active ingreds.

Properties: Very sol. in diethyl oxide, chloroform, CCl_4, toluene, petrol. ether (40-60 C); sl. sol. in ethanol; insol. in water; sp.gr. 0.955 (20 C); drop pt. 33.5-40.5 C; acid no. < 0.5; iodine no. < 2; sapon. no. 225-245; hyd. no. < 40.

Suppocire® NAIL. [Gattefosse SA]

Chem. Descrip.: Hemisynthetic glycerides

Uses: Excipient for pharmaceutical suppositories with exc. resist. to solvs., essential oils, or liposoluble active ingreds.

Properties: Very sol. in diethyl oxide, chloroform, CCl_4, toluene, petrol. ether (40-60 C); sl. sol. in ethanol; insol. in water; sp.gr. 0.955 (20 C); drop pt. 33.5-35.5 C; acid no. < 1; iodine no. < 3; sapon. no. 225-245; hyd. no. < 40.

Suppocire® NAIX. [Gattefosse SA]

Chem. Descrip.: Hemisynthetic glycerides

Uses: Excipient for pharmaceutical suppositories with exc. resist. to solvs., essential oils, or liposoluble active ingreds.

Properties: Very sol. in diethyl oxide, chloroform, CCl_4, toluene, petrol. ether (40-60 C); sl. sol. in ethanol; insol. in water; sp.gr. 0.955 (20 C); drop pt. 33.5-35.5 C; acid no. < 0.5; iodine no. < 3; sapon. no. 225-245; hyd. no. < 40.

Suppocire® NAL. [Gattefosse SA]

Chem. Descrip.: Hemisynthetic glycerides

Uses: Excipient for pharmaceutical suppositories with exc. resist. to solvs., essential oils, or liposoluble active ingreds.

Properties: Very sol. in diethyl oxide, chloroform, CCl_4, toluene, petrol. ether (40-60 C); sl. sol. in ethanol; insol. in water; sp.gr. 0.955 (20 C); drop pt. 35.5-37.5 C; acid no. < 0.5; iodine no. < 2; sapon. no. 225-245; hyd. no. < 40.

Suppocire® NAX. [Gattefosse SA]

Chem. Descrip.: Hemisynthetic glycerides
Uses: Excipient for pharmaceutical suppositories with exc. resist. to solvs., essential oils, or liposoluble active ingreds.
Properties: Very sol. in diethyl oxide, chloroform, CCl_4, toluene, petrol. ether (40-60 C); sl. sol. in ethanol; insol. in water; sp.gr. 0.955 (20 C); drop pt. 35.5-37.5 C; acid no. < 0.5; iodine no. < 2; sapon. no. 220-240; hyd. no. < 40.

Suppocire® NB. [Gattefosse SA]
Chem. Descrip.: Hemisynthetic glycerides
Uses: Excipient for pharmaceutical suppositories with exc. resist. to solvs., essential oils, or liposoluble active ingreds.
Properties: Very sol. in diethyl oxide, chloroform, CCl_4, toluene, petrol. ether (40-60 C); sl. sol. in ethanol; insol. in water; sp.gr. 0.955 (20 C); drop pt. 36.5-38.5 C; acid no. < 0.5; iodine no. < 2; sapon. no. 225-245; hyd. no. < 40
Toxicology: LD50 (oral, rat) > 20 ml/kg, nonirritating rectally.

Suppocire® NBL. [Gattefosse SA]
Chem. Descrip.: Hemisynthetic glycerides
Uses: Excipient for pharmaceutical suppositories with exc. resist. to solvs., essential oils, or liposoluble active ingreds.
Properties: Very sol. in diethyl oxide, chloroform, CCl_4, toluene, petrol. ether (40-60 C); sl. sol. in ethanol; insol. in water; sp.gr. 0.955 (20 C); drop pt. 36.5-38.5 C; acid no. < 0.5; iodine no. < 3; sapon. no. 220-240; hyd. no. < 40.

Suppocire® NBX. [Gattefosse SA]
Chem. Descrip.: Hemisynthetic glycerides
Uses: Excipient for pharmaceutical suppositories with exc. resist. to solvs., essential oils, or liposoluble active ingreds.
Properties: Very sol. in diethyl oxide, chloroform, CCl_4, toluene, petrol. ether (40-60 C); sl. sol. in ethanol; insol. in water; sp.gr. 0.955 (20 C); drop pt. 36.5-38.5 C; acid no. < 0.5; iodine no. < 2; sapon. no. 215-235; hyd. no. < 40.

Suppocire® NC. [Gattefosse SA]
Chem. Descrip.: Hemisynthetic glycerides
Uses: Excipient for pharmaceutical suppositories with exc. resist. to solvs., essential oils, or liposoluble active ingreds.
Properties: Very sol. in diethyl oxide, chloroform, CCl_4, toluene, petrol. ether (40-60 C); sl. sol. in ethanol; insol. in water; sp.gr. 0.955 (20 C); drop pt. 38.5-40.5 C; acid no. < 0.5; iodine no. < 2; sapon. no. 220-240; hyd. no. < 40.

Suppocire® ND. [Gattefosse SA]
Chem. Descrip.: Hemisynthetic glycerides
Uses: Excipient for pharmaceutical suppositories with exc. resist. to solvs., essential oils, or liposoluble active ingreds.
Properties: Very sol. in diethyl oxide, chloroform, CCl_4, toluene, petrol. ether (40-60 C); sl. sol. in ethanol; insol. in water; sp.gr. 0.955 (20 C); drop pt. 42-45 C; acid no. < 0.5; iodine no. < 2; sapon. no. 210-230; hyd. no. < 40.

Supra A. [Luzenac Am.]

Chem. Descrip.: Platy talc USP
CAS 14807-96-6; EINECS 238-877-9
Uses: Extremely platy talc with high brightness, exc. slip; recommended for formulations with very sensitive fragrances and pigments; used in antiperspirants, creams, lotions
Properties: Powd.; 99% thru 200 mesh; median diam. 12 µ; tapped dens. 62 lb/ft^3; pH 9 (10% slurry).

Supra EF A. [Luzenac Am.]
Chem. Descrip.: Platy talc USP
CAS 14807-96-6; EINECS 238-877-9
Uses: Extrafine, extremely platy talc with exc. brightness, purity, surface passivity, and slip; used for antiperspirants, creams, lotions
Properties: Powd.; 99.6% thru 200 mesh; median diam. 8 µ; tapped dens. 59 lb/ft^3; pH 9 (10% slurry).

Supraene®. [Robeco]
Chem. Descrip.: Purified squalene
CAS 111-02-4; EINECS 203-826-1
Uses: Patented natural emollient, protective agent, vehicle for dermatological and medical use
Properties: Lt. straw-colored liq. oil, faint char. odor; misc. with veg. and min. oils, org. solvs., lipophilic substances, human sebum; insol. in water; m.w. 410.73; sp.gr. 0.855-0.865; visc. 15 cps; f.p. -75 C; b.p. 335 C; acid no. 1 max.; iodine no. 360-380; sapon. no. 2 max.; flash pt. 200 C; ref. index 1.4945-1.4960; 99% min. purity
Toxicology: Nontoxic
Precaution: Incompat. with oxidizing agents, oxygen; avoid elevated temps.

Suprafino A. [Luzenac Am.]
Chem. Descrip.: Talc USP
CAS 14807-96-6; EINECS 238-877-9
Uses: Extremely platy talc with high slip, brightness, and purity; for antiperspirants, creams and lotions
Properties: Powd.; 99.9% thru 325 mesh; median diam. 5 µ; tapped dens. 44 lb/ft^3; pH 9 (10% slurry).

Supralate® C. [Witco/H-I-P]
Chem. Descrip.: Sodium lauryl sulfate USP
CAS 151-21-3; EINECS 205-788-1
Uses: Emulsifier, dispersant, wetting agent for dental and medical preps.
Properties: Wh. spray-dried beads; mild fatty odor; water sol.; dens. 3.3 lb/gal; 90-96% conc.; anionic.

Supreme USP. [Luzenac Am.]
Chem. Descrip.: Talc
CAS 14807-96-6; EINECS 238-877-9
Uses: Glidant, anticaking agent, tablet lubricant, colorant.

Surelease®. [Colorcon]
Chem. Descrip.: Aq. fully plasticized liq. disp. of ethylcellulose
CAS 9004-57-3
Uses: Functional pharmceutical coating for controlled release, taste mask coatings, granulating applics., sealant/barrier coatings; provides pH-in-

dependent drug release.

Sureteric™. [Colorcon]
Chem. Descrip.: Aq. blend of polyvinyl acetate phthalate, plasticizers, and other ingreds.
Uses: Controlled release enteric coating for pharmaceuticals; provides optimum film-forming chars., resist. to gastric fluids, coated tablet stability.

Suspengel Elite. [Cimbar Perf. Minerals]
Chem. Descrip.: Purified dry colloidal hydrated aluminum silicate
CAS 1327-36-2; EINECS 215-475-1
Uses: Thixotropic thickener giving good sag control, leveling, and suspension props.; in pharmaceuticals
Regulatory: FDA GRAS §184.1155; kosher
Properties: Lt. cream-colored powd.; odorless, tasteless; avg. particle size 0.5 µ; surf. area 1.2 m²/cc; visc. 10,000 cps (6% solids); bulk dens. 38 lb/ft³ (loose); oil absorp. 47; pH 9.4; 8.7% moisture.

Suspengel Micro. [Cimbar Perf. Minerals]
Chem. Descrip.: Purified dry colloidal hydrated aluminum silicate
CAS 1327-36-2; EINECS 215-475-1
Uses: Thixotropic thickener giving good sag control, leveling, and suspension props.; in pharmaceuticals
Regulatory: FDA GRAS §184.1155; kosher
Properties: Lt. cream-colored powd.; odorless, tasteless; avg. particle size 1.0 µ; surf. area 0.9 m²/cc; visc. 10,000 cps (6% solids); bulk dens. 41 lb/ft³ (loose); oil absorp. 36; pH 9.4; 8.7% moisture.

Suspengel Ultra. [Cimbar Perf. Minerals]
Chem. Descrip.: Purified dry colloidal hydrated aluminum silicate
CAS 1327-36-2; EINECS 215-475-1
Uses: Thixotropic thickener giving good sag control, leveling, and suspension props.; in pharmaceuticals
Regulatory: FDA GRAS §184.1155; kosher
Properties: Lt. cream-colored powd.; odorless, tasteless; avg. particle size 0.18 µ; surf. area 1.8 m²/cc; visc. 15,000 cps (6% solids); bulk dens. 29 lb/ft³ (loose); oil absorp. 52; pH 9.4; 8.7% moisture.

Sweetrex®. [Mendell]
Chem. Descrip.: Dextrose, fructose, maltose, isomaltose, other polysaccharides
Uses: Directly compressible chewable tablet base with high sweetness, coolness and mouthfeel; binding capacity to 50% active ingreds.
Properties: Wh. gran. powd.; neutral odor; avg. particle size 210 µ; 25% -100 mesh; very sol. in water; dens. (tapped) 0.6-0.9 g/ml; pH 3.5-6.0 (10% aq.).

Syncal® CAS. [PMC Specialties]
Chem. Descrip.: Calcium saccharin USP/FCC/BP
CAS 6485-34-3; EINECS 229-349-9
Uses: Syn. sweetening agent for toothpastes, mouthwashes, pharmaceuticals

Regulatory: FDA 21CFR §180.37; BP compliance
Properties: Wh. fine free-flowing powd.; m.w. 404.45; 98% min. assay.

Syncal® GS. [PMC Specialties]
Chem. Descrip.: Sodium saccharin USP/FCC/BP
CAS 128-44-9; EINECS 204-886-1
Uses: Syn. sweetening agent for toothpastes, mouthwashes, pharmaceuticals
Regulatory: FDA 21CFR §180.37; BP compliance
Properties: Wh. nondusting, free-flowing gran., uniformly sized particles, odorless; sol. 46% in water; m.w. 241.20; sp.gr. > 1; 98-101% assay
Toxicology: LD50 (oral, rat) 14,200 mg/kg; nuisance dust ACGIH 10 mg/m³; potential for foreign body irritation to eyes, skin, respiratory tract; suspect carcinogen in rats on extreme exposure
Precaution: Incompat. with oxidizing agents; hazardous decomp. prods.: CO, NO_x, SO_2
Storage: Avoid excessive heat and humidity on storage to prevent caking.

Syncal® GSD. [PMC Specialties]
Chem. Descrip.: Sodium saccharin USP/FCC/BP
CAS 128-44-9; EINECS 204-886-1
Uses: Syn. sweetening agent for toothpastes, mouthwashes, pharmaceuticals
Regulatory: FDA 21CFR §180.37; BP compliance
Properties: Wh. nondusting gran., mixed sized particles, odorless; sol. 46% in water; m.w. 241.20; sp.gr. > 1; 98-101% assay
Toxicology: LD50 (oral, rat) 14,200 mg/kg; nuisance dust ACGIH 10 mg/m³; potential for foreign body irritation to eyes, skin, respiratory tract; suspect carcinogen in rats on extreme exposure
Precaution: Incompat. with oxidizing agents; hazardous decomp. prods.: CO, NO_x, SO_2
Storage: Avoid excessive heat and humidity on storage to prevent caking.

Syncal® S. [PMC Specialties]
Chem. Descrip.: Sodium saccharin USP/FCC/BP
CAS 128-44-9; EINECS 204-886-1
Uses: Syn. sweetening agent for toothpastes, mouthwashes, pharmaceuticals
Regulatory: FDA 21CFR §180.37; BP compliance
Properties: Wh. fine cryst. powd., odorless; m.w. 205.17; sp.gr. > 1; 98-101% assay
Toxicology: LD50 (oral, rat) 14,200 mg/kg; suspect carcinogen in rats on extreme exposure; nuisance dust
Storage: Avoid excessive heat and humidity to prevent caking.

Syncal® SDI. [PMC Specialties]
Chem. Descrip.: Saccharin insoluble USP/FCC/BP
CAS 81-07-2; EINECS 201-321-0
Uses: Syn. sweetening agent for toothpastes, mouthwashes, pharmaceuticals
Regulatory: FDA 21CFR §180.37; BP compliance
Properties: Wh. powd., odorless; sol. 0.03% in water; m.w. 183.18; sp.gr. > 1; m.p. 226-230 C; 98-101% assay
Toxicology: Nuisance dust ACGIH 10 mg/m³
Precaution: Incompat. with oxidizing agents
Storage: Avoid excessive heat and humidity on

storage to prevent caking.

Syncal® SDS. [PMC Specialties]
Chem. Descrip.: Sodium saccharin USP/FCC/BP
CAS 128-44-9; EINECS 204-886-1
Uses: Syn. sweetening agent for toothpastes, mouthwashes, pharmaceuticals; for applics. requiring free flow chars. and low degree of dust
Regulatory: FDA 21CFR §180.37; BP compliance
Properties: Wh. fine free-flowing spray-dried powd.; very fine particle size; sol. 46% in water; m.w. 205.17; sp.gr. > 1; 98-101% assay
Toxicology: Nuisance dust TLV 10 mg/m^3
Precaution: Incompat. with oxidizing agents
Storage: Avoid excessive heat on storage to prevent caking.

Syncal® US. [PMC Specialties]
Chem. Descrip.: Sodium saccharin USP/FCC/BP
CAS 128-44-9; EINECS 204-886-1
Uses: Syn. sweetening agent for toothpastes, mouthwashes, pharmaceuticals
Regulatory: FDA 21CFR §180.37; BP compliance
Properties: Wh. nondusting granules, unsized particles, odorless; sol. 46% in water; m.w. 241.20; sp.gr. > 1; 98-101% assay
Toxicology: LD50 (oral, rat) 14,200 mg/kg; nuisance dust ACGIH 10 mg/m^3; potential for foreign body irritation to eyes, skin, respiratory tract; suspect carcinogen in rats on extreme exposure
Precaution: Incompat. with oxidizing agents; hazardous decomp. prods.: CO, NO$_x$, SO$_2$
Storage: Avoid excessive heat and humidity on storage to prevent caking.

Syncrowax ERL-C. [Croda Inc.; Croda Surf. Ltd.]
Chem. Descrip.: C18-36 acid glycol ester
Uses: Emulsifier, emollient, opacifier, lubricant, stabilizer, suspending agent for topical pharmaceuticals; similar to candelilla
Use level: 1-4%
Properties: Lt. tan waxy flakes; mild waxy odor; m.p. 70-75 C; acid no. 10-15; iodine no. 3 max.; sapon. no. 155-160.

Syncrowax HGL-C. [Croda Inc.; Croda Surf. Ltd.]
Chem. Descrip.: C18-36 acid triglyceride
CAS 91052-08-3
Uses: Emulsifier, emollient, opacifier, lubricant, suspending agent, stabilizer, gloss improver for topical pharmaceuticals; props. like carnauba; rigidity for stick formulations
Use level: 4-12%
Properties: Lt. yel. waxy flakes; mild waxy odor; m.p. 70-75 C; acid no. 6-12; iodine no. 3 max.; sapon. no. 160-175.

Syncrowax HR-C. [Croda Inc.]
Chem. Descrip.: Glyceryl tribehenate
CAS 18641-57-1; EINECS 242-471-7
Uses: Emulsifier, emollient, opacifier, stiffening, suspending, and stabilizing agent for oral and topical pharmaceuticals; provides gloss; props. similar to beeswax
Use level: 4-12%
Regulatory: FDA 21CFR §184.1555
Properties: Off-wh. waxy flakes, mild waxy odor;

m.p. 60-65 C; acid no. 10 max.; iodine no. 3 max.; sapon. no. 170-175.

Synperonic NP1. [ICI Surf. Am.; ICI Surf. UK]
Chem. Descrip.: Nonoxynol-1
EINECS 248-762-5
Uses: Emulsifier for creams, lotions; solubilizer for topical pharmaceuticals
Properties: Pale yel. liq.; HLB 3.3.

Synperonic NP2. [ICI Surf. Am.; ICI Surf. UK]
Chem. Descrip.: Nonoxynol-2
EINECS 248-291-5
Uses: Emulsifier for creams, lotions; solubilizer for topical pharmaceuticals
Properties: Pale yel. liq.; HLB 5.7.

Synperonic NP4. [ICI Surf. Am.; ICI Surf. UK]
Chem. Descrip.: Nonoxynol-4
CAS 9016-45-9
Uses: Emulsifier for creams, lotions; solubilizer for topical pharmaceuticals
Properties: Pale yel. liq.; sol. in alcohol, glycol ethers, kerosene, and min. oil; dens. 1.022 g/ml; visc. 400 cps; HLB 8.9; pour pt. < 0 C; pH 6-8 (1% aq.); 99% min. act.; nonionic.

Synperonic NP5. [ICI Surf. Am.; ICI Surf. UK]
Chem. Descrip.: Nonoxynol-5
CAS 9016-45-9
Uses: Emulsifier for creams, lotions; solubilizer for topical pharmaceuticals
Properties: Pale yel. liq.; sol. in alcohol, glycol ethers, kerosene, min. oil; insol./disp. in water; dens. 1.035 g/ml; visc. 350 cps; HLB 10.5; pour pt. < 0 C; pH 6-8 (1% aq.); 99% min. act.; nonionic.

Synperonic NP5.5. [ICI Surf. Am.; ICI Surf. UK]
Chem. Descrip.: Nonoxynol-5.5
CAS 9016-45-9
Uses: Emulsifier for creams, lotions; solubilizer for topical pharmaceuticals
Properties: Pale yel. liq.; HLB 10.7.

Synperonic NP6. [ICI Surf. Am.; ICI Surf. UK]
Chem. Descrip.: Nonoxynol-6
CAS 9016-45-9
Uses: Emulsifier for creams, lotions; solubilizer for topical pharmaceuticals
Properties: Pale yel. liq.; sol. in alcohol, glycol ethers, min. oil; disp. in water; dens. 1.041 g/ml; visc. 355 cps; HLB 10.9; pour pt. < 0 C; pH 6-8 (1% aq.); 99% min. act.; nonionic.

Synperonic NP7. [ICI Surf. Am.; ICI Surf. UK]
Chem. Descrip.: Nonoxynol-7
CAS 9016-45-9; EINECS 248-292-0
Uses: Emulsifier for creams, lotions; solubilizer for topical pharmaceuticals
Properties: Pale yel. liq.; oil-sol.; HLB 11.7; 100% conc.; nonionic.

Synperonic NP8. [ICI Surf. Am.; ICI Surf. UK]
Chem. Descrip.: Nonoxynol-8
CAS 9016-45-9
Uses: Emulsifier for creams, lotions; solubilizer for topical pharmaceuticals
Properties: Pale yel. liq.; sol. in water, alcohol, glycol ethers; dens. 1.053 g/ml; visc. 355 cps; HLB 12.3; cloud pt. 30-34 C (1% aq.); pour pt. <

0 C; surf. tens. 29.4 dynes/cm (0.1%); pH 6-8 (1% aq.); 99% min. act.; nonionic.

Synperonic NP8.5. [ICI Surf. UK]
Chem. Descrip.: Nonoxynol-8.5
CAS 9016-45-9
Uses: Emulsifier for creams, lotions; solubilizer for topical pharmaceuticals
Properties: Pale yel. liq.; water-sol.; HLB 12.6; 100% conc.; nonionic.

Synperonic NP8.75. [ICI Surf. UK]
Chem. Descrip.: Nonoxynol-8.75
CAS 9016-45-9
Uses: Emulsifier for creams, lotions; solubilizer for topical pharmaceuticals
Properties: Pale yel. liq.; HLB 12.7.

Synperonic NP9. [ICI Surf. Am.; ICI Surf. UK]
Chem. Descrip.: Nonoxynol-9
CAS 9016-45-9
Uses: Emulsifier for creams, lotions; solubilizer for topical pharmaceuticals
Properties: Pale yel. liq.; sol. in water, alcohol, glycol ethers; dens. 1.058 g/ml; visc. 340 cps; HLB 12.8; cloud pt. 51-56 C (1% aq.); pour pt. 0 C; surf. tens. 30.6 dynes/cm; pH 6-8 (1% aq.); 99% min. act.; nonionic.

Synperonic NP9.5. [ICI Surf. UK]
Chem. Descrip.: Nonoxynol-9.5
CAS 9016-45-9
Uses: Emulsifier for creams, lotions; solubilizer for topical pharmaceuticals
Properties: Pale yel. liq.; HLB 13.0.

Synperonic NP9.75. [ICI Surf. UK]
Chem. Descrip.: Nonoxynol-9.75
CAS 9016-45-9; EINECS 248-294-1
Uses: Emulsifier for creams, lotions; solubilizer for topical pharmaceuticals
Properties: Pale yel. liq.; HLB 13.2.

Synperonic NP10. [ICI Surf. Am.; ICI Surf. UK]
Chem. Descrip.: Nonoxynol-10
CAS 9016-45-9; EINECS 248-294-1
Uses: Emulsifier for creams, lotions; solubilizer for topical pharmaceuticals
Properties: Pale yel. liq.; sol. in water, alcohol, glycol ethers; dens. 1.061 g/ml; visc. 360 cps; HLB 13.3; cloud pt. 62-67 C (1% aq.); pour pt. 5 C; surf. tens. 30.6 dynes/cm; pH 6-8 (1% aq.); 99% min. act.; nonionic.

Synperonic NP12. [ICI Surf. Am.; ICI Surf. UK]
Chem. Descrip.: Nonoxynol-12
CAS 9016-45-9
Uses: Emulsifier for creams, lotions; solubilizer for topical pharmaceuticals
Properties: Pale yel. liq.; sol. in water, alcohol, glycol ethers; dens. 1.062 g/ml; visc. 265 cps; HLB 13.9; cloud pt. 79-84 C (1% aq.); pour pt. 14 C; surf. tens. 35.2 dynes/cm; pH 6-8 (1% aq.); 99% min. act.; nonionic.

Synperonic NP13. [ICI Surf. Am.; ICI Surf. UK]
Chem. Descrip.: Nonoxynol-13
CAS 9016-45-9
Uses: Emulsifier for creams, lotions; solubilizer for topical pharmaceuticals

Properties: Pale yel. paste; sol. in water, alcohol, glycol ethers; dens. 1.068 g/ml; visc. 280 cps; HLB 14.4; cloud pt. 87-92 C (1% aq.); pour pt. 17 C; surf. tens. 34.8 dynes/cm; pH 6-8 (1% aq.); 99% min. act.; nonionic.

Synperonic NP15. [ICI Surf. Am.; ICI Surf. UK]
Chem. Descrip.: Nonoxynol-15
CAS 9016-45-9
Uses: Emulsifier for creams, lotions; solubilizer for topical pharmaceuticals
Properties: Pale yel. paste; sol. in water, alcohol, glycol ethers; dens. 1.058 g/ml (40 C); visc. 125 cps (40 C); HLB 15.0; cloud pt. 95-99 C (1% aq.); pour pt. 21 C; surf. tens. 33.4 dynes/cm; pH 6-8 (1% aq.); 99% min. act.; nonionic.

Synperonic NP17. [ICI Surf. Am.; ICI Surf. UK]
Chem. Descrip.: Nonoxynol-17
CAS 9016-45-9
Uses: Emulsifier for creams, lotions; solubilizer for topical pharmaceuticals
Properties: Pale yel. solid; HLB 15.4.

Synperonic NP20. [ICI Surf. Am.; ICI Surf. UK]
Chem. Descrip.: Nonoxynol-20
CAS 9016-45-9
Uses: Emulsifier for creams, lotions; solubilizer for topical pharmaceuticals
Properties: Pale yel. solid; sol. in water, alcohol, glycol ethers; dens. 1.073 g/ml (40 C); visc. 168 cps (40 C); HLB 16.0; cloud pt. > 100 C (1% aq.); pour pt. 30 C; surf. tens. 41.7 dynes/cm; pH 6-8 (1% aq.); 99% min. act.; nonionic.

Synperonic NP25. [ICI Surf. Am.; ICI Surf. UK]
Chem. Descrip.: Nonoxynol-25
CAS 9016-45-9
Uses: Emulsifier for creams, lotions; solubilizer for topical pharmaceuticals
Properties: Pale yel. solid; HLB 16.7.

Synperonic NP30. [ICI Surf. Am.; ICI Surf. UK]
Chem. Descrip.: Nonoxynol-30
CAS 9016-45-9
Uses: Emulsifier for creams, lotions; solubilizer for topical pharmaceuticals
Properties: Pale yel. solid; sol. in water, alcohol, glycol ethers; dens. 1.074 g/ml (50 C); visc. 150 cps (50 C); HLB 17.1; cloud pt. > 100 C (1% aq.); pour pt. 40 C; surf. tens. 42.8 dynes/cm; pH 6-8 (1% aq.); 99% min. act.; nonionic.

Synperonic NP30/70. [ICI Surf. Am.]
Chem. Descrip.: Nonoxynol-30
CAS 9016-45-9
Uses: Emulsifier for creams, lotions; solubilizer for topical pharmaceuticals; nonionic.

Synperonic NP35. [ICI Surf. Am.; ICI Surf. UK]
Chem. Descrip.: Nonoxynol-35
CAS 9016-45-9
Uses: Emulsifier for creams, lotions; solubilizer for topical pharmaceuticals
Properties: Pale yel. solid; HLB 17.5; 100% conc.; nonionic.

Synperonic NP40. [ICI Surf. Am.; ICI Surf. UK]
Chem. Descrip.: Nonoxynol-40
CAS 9016-45-9

Uses: Emulsifier for creams, lotions; solubilizer for topical pharmaceuticals
Properties: Pale yel. solid; HLB 17.8; 100% conc.; nonionic.

Synperonic NP50. [ICI Surf. Am.; ICI Surf. UK]
Chem. Descrip.: Nonoxynol-50
CAS 9016-45-9
Uses: Emulsifier for creams, lotions; solubilizer for topical pharmaceuticals
Properties: Pale yel. solid; HLB 18.2; 100% conc.; nonionic.

Synperonic OP3. [ICI Surf. Am.; ICI Surf. UK]
Chem. Descrip.: Octoxynol-3
CAS 9002-93-1
Uses: Emulsifier for creams, lotions; solubilizer for topical pharmaceuticals
Properties: Pale yel. liq.; oil-sol.; HLB 7.1; 100% conc.; nonionic.

Synperonic OP4.5. [ICI Surf. Am.; ICI Surf. UK]
Chem. Descrip.: Octoxynol-4.5
CAS 9002-93-1
Uses: Emulsifier for creams, lotions; solubilizer for topical pharmaceuticals
Properties: Pale yel. liq.; oil-sol.; HLB 9.4; 100% conc.; nonionic.

Synperonic OP6. [ICI Surf. Am.; ICI Surf. UK]
Chem. Descrip.: Octoxynol-6
CAS 9002-93-1
Uses: Emulsifier for creams, lotions; solubilizer for topical pharmaceuticals
Properties: Pale yel. liq.; HLB 10.5.

Synperonic OP7.5. [ICI Surf. Am.; ICI Surf. UK]
Chem. Descrip.: Octoxynol-7.5
CAS 9002-93-1
Uses: Emulsifier for creams, lotions; solubilizer for topical pharmaceuticals
Properties: Pale yel. liq.; HLB 11.7; 100% conc.; nonionic.

Synperonic OP8. [ICI Surf. Am.; ICI Surf. UK]
Chem. Descrip.: Octoxynol-8
CAS 9002-93-1
Uses: Emulsifier for creams, lotions; solubilizer for topical pharmaceuticals
Properties: Pale yel. liq.; HLB 12.6; 100% conc.; nonionic.

Synperonic OP10. [ICI Surf. Am.; ICI Surf. UK]
Chem. Descrip.: Octoxynol-10
CAS 9002-93-1
Uses: Emulsifier for creams, lotions; solubilizer for topical pharmaceuticals
Properties: Pale yel. liq.; sol. in water, alcohol, glycol ethers; dens. 1.062 g/ml; visc. 393 cps; HLB 13.3; cloud pt. 63-67 C (1% aq.); pour pt. 7 C; surf. tens. 31.8 dynes/cm; pH 6-8 (1% aq.); 99% min. act.; nonionic.

Synperonic OP10.5. [ICI Surf. Am.; ICI Surf. UK]
Chem. Descrip.: Octoxynol-10.5
CAS 9002-93-1
Uses: Emulsifier for creams, lotions; solubilizer for topical pharmaceuticals
Properties: Pale yel. liq.; HLB 13.5; 100% conc.; nonionic.

Synperonic OP11. [ICI Surf. Am.; ICI Surf. UK]
Chem. Descrip.: Octoxynol-11
CAS 9002-93-1
Uses: Emulsifier for creams, lotions; solubilizer for topical pharmaceuticals
Properties: Pale yel. liq.; sol. in water, alcohol, glycol ethers; dens. 1.067 g/ml; visc. 371 cps; HLB 13.6; cloud pt. 79-82 C (1% aq.); pour pt. 8 C; surf. tens. 31.0 dynes/cm; pH 6-8 (1% aq.); 99% min. act.; nonionic.

Synperonic OP12.5. [ICI Surf. Am.; ICI Surf. UK]
Chem. Descrip.: Octoxynol-12.5
CAS 9002-93-1
Uses: Emulsifier for creams, lotions; solubilizer for topical pharmaceuticals
Properties: Pale yel. liq.; water-sol.; HLB 14.3; 100% conc.; nonionic.

Synperonic OP16. [ICI Surf. Am.]
Chem. Descrip.: Octoxynol-16
CAS 9002-93-1
Uses: Emulsifier for creams, lotions; solubilizer for topical pharmaceuticals
Properties: Liq.; HLB 15.6; 70% conc.; nonionic
Unverified

Synperonic OP16.5. [ICI Surf. Am.; ICI Surf. UK]
Chem. Descrip.: Octoxynol-16.5
CAS 9002-93-1
Uses: Emulsifier for creams, lotions; solubilizer for topical pharmaceuticals
Properties: Pale yel. solid; HLB 15.3; 100% conc.; nonionic.

Synperonic OP20. [ICI Surf. Am.]
Chem. Descrip.: Octoxynol-20
CAS 9002-93-1
Uses: Emulsifier for creams, lotions; solubilizer for topical pharmaceuticals
Properties: Pale yel. solid; HLB 16.2; nonionic.

Synperonic OP25. [ICI Surf. Am.]
Chem. Descrip.: Octoxynol-25
CAS 9002-93-1
Uses: Emulsifier for creams, lotions; solubilizer for topical pharmaceuticals
Properties: Pale yel. solid; HLB 16.7; nonionic.

Synperonic OP30. [ICI Surf. Am.; ICI Surf. UK]
Chem. Descrip.: Octoxynol-30
CAS 9002-93-1
Uses: Emulsifier for creams, lotions; solubilizer for topical pharmaceuticals
Properties: Pale yel. solid; HLB 17.2; 100% conc.; nonionic.

Synperonic OP40. [ICI Surf. Am.; ICI Surf. UK]
Chem. Descrip.: Octoxynol-40
CAS 9002-93-1
Uses: Emulsifier for creams, lotions; solubilizer for topical pharmaceuticals
Properties: Pale yel. solid; HLB 17.4; 100% conc.; nonionic.

Synperonic OP40/70. [ICI Surf. UK]
Chem. Descrip.: Octoxynol-40
CAS 9002-93-1
Uses: Emulsifier for creams, lotions; solubilizer for topical pharmaceuticals

Properties: Liq.; HLB 17.4; 70% conc.; nonionic.

Synperonic PE/F127. [ICI Surf. Am.; ICI Surf. UK]
Chem. Descrip.: Poloxamer 407
CAS 9003-11-6
Uses: Emulsifier, dispersant for pharmaceutical preps. and mouthwashes
Properties: Wh. flake; cloud pt. > 100 C (10% aq.); 100% conc.; nonionic.

Synpro® Aluminum Monostearate NF. [Syn. Prods.]
Chem. Descrip.: Aluminum monostearate NF
CAS 7047-84-9; EINECS 230-325-5
Uses: Suspending agent, thickener used in ointments, tableting operations for pharmaceuticals
Regulatory: FDA 21CFR §181.29
Properties: Wh. fine free-flowing powd., mild fatty odor; negligible sol. in water; sp.gr. > 1.0; m.p. 220-250 C; flash pt. (PMCC) > 500 F
Toxicology: TLV 10 mg/m^3; dust can cause discomfort of nose, throat, upper respiratory tract, coughing; eye contact or prolonged skin contact may cause irritation; ingestion can cause gastrointestinal discomfort
Precaution: Incompat. with strong oxidizing agents; decomp. prods.: Al_2O_3, CO_2; dust explosions may occur in presence of igntion source
Storage: Store in cool, dry area away from heat, spark or flame.

Synpro® Aluminum Stearate USP. [Syn. Prods.]
Chem. Descrip.: Aluminum stearate
CAS 7047-84-9; EINECS 230-325-5
Uses: Suspending agent, thickener.

Synpro® Calcium Stearate NF. [Syn. Prods.]
Chem. Descrip.: Calcium stearate NF
CAS 1592-23-0; EINECS 216-472-8
Uses: Additive for pharmaceuticals, tableting operations, ointments
Regulatory: FDA 21CFR §177.2600, 178.2010
Properties: Wh. fine free-flowing powd., mild fatty odor; negligible sol. in water; 99% thru 325 mesh; sp.gr. > 1.0; apparent dens. 0.2 g/cc; m.p. 147-180 C; flash pt. (PMCC) > 500 F; 2.5% moisture
Toxicology: TLV 10 mg/m^3; inh. of dust can cause discomfort of nose, throat, upper respiratory tract, coughing, choking; eye contact and prolonged skin contact may cause irritation; ingestion may cause gastrointestinal discomfort
Precaution: Incompat. with strong oxidizing agents; decomp. prods.: CO_2, CaO; dust explosions can occur in presence of ignition source
Storage: Store in cool, dry area away from heat, spark, or flame.

Synpro® Magnesium Stearate NF. [Syn. Prods.]
Chem. Descrip.: Magnesium stearate NF
CAS 557-04-0; EINECS 209-150-3
Uses: Additive for pharmaceuticals, tableting operations, ointments
Regulatory: FDA 21CFR §181.29
Properties: Wh. fine free-flowing powd., mild fatty odor; 90% thru 200 mesh; negligible sol. in water; sp.gr. > 1.0; apparent dens. 0.3 g/cc; m.p. 155 C; flash pt. (PMCC) > 500 F
Toxicology: TLV 10 mg/m^3; inh. of dust can cause discomfort to nose, throat, upper respiratory tract, coughing, choking; eye contact or prolonged skin contact can cause discomfort; ingestion can cause gastrointestinal discomfort
Precaution: Incompat. with strong oxidizing agents; decomp. prods.: CO_2, MgO; dust explosions may occur in presence of ignition source
Storage: Store in cool, dry place away from heat, sparks, or flame.

Synpro® Zinc Stearate USP. [Syn. Prods.]
Chem. Descrip.: Zinc stearate
CAS 557-05-1; EINECS 209-151-9
Uses: Additive for pharmaceuticals
Regulatory: FDA 21CFR §177.2600, 178.2010
Properties: Wh. fine free-flowing powd., mild fatty odor; 99% thru 200 mesh; negligible sol. in water; sp.gr. > 1; apparent dens. 0.2 g/cc; m.p. 120-132 C; flash pt. (PMCC) > 500 F; 0.4% moisture
Toxicology: TLV/TWA 10mg/m^3 (ACGIH); inh. of dust can cause discomfort of nose, throat, upper respiratory tract, coughing, choking; ingestion can cause gastrointestinal discomfort; eye contact and prolonged skin contact can cause discomfort
Precaution: Incompat. with strong oxidizing agents; decomp. prods.: CO_2, ZnO; dust explosions can occur in presence of ignition source
Storage: Store in cool, dry area away from heat, sparks, or flame.

Syntase® 62. [Great Lakes]
Chem. Descrip.: Benzophenone-3
CAS 131-57-7; EINECS 205-031-5
Uses: Uv absorber for OTC sunscreen lotions
Regulatory: FDA 21CFR §177.1010
Properties: Pale cream powd.; sol. 75% in ethyl acetate, 68% in toluene, 65% in acetone, 60% in MEK; insol. in water; m.w. 228; sp.gr. 1.339; m.p. 62 C min.; pH 7.2 (10% aq. slurry); 99.5% min. purity.

T

Tagat® L2. [Goldschmidt; Goldschmidt AG]
Chem. Descrip.: PEG-20 glyceryl laurate
CAS 51248-32-9
Uses: Prep. of o/w emulsions for pharmaceuticals; solubilizer for flavors, vitamin oils; dispersant
Properties: Ivory liq.; sol. in water; insol. in veg. and min. oils; m.p. 60-80 C; HLB 15.7; acid no. 2 max.; iodine no. 4 max.; sapon. no. 50-70; hyd. no. 60-80; 100% conc.; nonionic.

Tagat® O2. [Goldschmidt; Goldschmidt AG]
Chem. Descrip.: PEG-20 glyceryl oleate
CAS 51192-09-7
Uses: Prep. of o/w emulsions for pharmaceuticals; solubilizer for flavors, vitamin oils; dispersant
Properties: Yel. liq.; sol. in water; insol. in veg. and min. oils; m.p. 70-85 C; HLB 15.0; acid no. 2 max.; iodine no. 21-27; sapon. no. 40-55; hyd. no. 70-85; 100% conc.; nonionic.

Tagat® R40. [Goldschmidt; Goldschmidt AG]
Chem. Descrip.: PEG-40 hydrog. castor oil
CAS 61788-85-0
Uses: Solubilizer for water-insol. substances, e.g., vitamins, pharmaceutical active ingreds.; coemulsifier for o/w emulsions
Properties: Ivory solid; sol. warm in water; sol. warm with sl. turbidity in veg. and min. oils; m.p. 55-75 C; HLB 13.0; acid no. 2 max.; iodine no. 2 max.; sapon. no. 45-65; hyd. no. 55-75; 100% conc.; nonionic.

Tagat® R60. [Goldschmidt; Goldschmidt AG]
Chem. Descrip.: PEG-60 hydrog. castor oil
CAS 61788-85-0
Uses: Solubilizer for water-insol. substances, e.g., vitamins, pharmaceutical active ingreds.; coemulsifier for o/w emulsions
Properties: Ivory solid; sol. warm in water; sol. warm with sl. turbidity in veg. and min. oils; HLB 15.0; acid no. 2 max.; iodine no. 2 max.; sapon. no. 35-52; hyd. no. 38-58; 100% conc.; nonionic.

Tagat® R63. [Goldschmidt; Goldschmidt AG]
Chem. Descrip.: PEG-60 hydrog. castor oil and propylene glycol
Uses: Solubilizer for water-insol. substances, e.g., vitamins, pharmaceutical active ingreds.; coemulsifier for o/w emulsions
Properties: Pale yel. liq.; sol. in water; insol. in veg. and min. oils; HLB 15.0; acid no. 2 max.; nonionic.

Tagat® S2. [Goldschmidt; Goldschmidt AG]

Chem. Descrip.: PEG-20 glyceryl stearate
CAS 51158-08-8
Uses: Prep. of o/w emulsions for pharmaceuticals; solubilizer for flavors, vitamin oils; dispersant
Properties: Ivory solid, partially liq.; sol. with sl. turbidity in water; insol. in veg. and min. oils; m.p. 65-85 C; HLB 15.0; acid no. 2 max.; iodine no. 2 max.; sapon. no. 40-60; hyd. no. 65-85; 100% conc.; nonionic.

Tauranol WS H.P. [Finetex]
Chem. Descrip.: Sodium methyl cocoyl taurate
Uses: Foamer for pharmaceuticals; tolerant to electrolytes, hard water
Properties: Powd.; 95% conc.; anionic.

TBC. [Morflex]
Chem. Descrip.: Tri-n-butyl citrate
CAS 77-94-1; EINECS 201-071-2
Uses: Plasticizer for aq. based pharmaceutical coatings; provides controlled sustained release of drugs; protects drugs from gastric juices but allows its release into the intestine
Regulatory: FDA 21CFR §175.105
Properties: Insol. in water; m.w. 360.4; sp.gr. 1.037-1.045; dens. 8.69 lb/gal; visc. 31.9 cps; b.p. 170 C (1 mm); pour pt. -80 F; flash pt. (COC) 185 C; ref. index 1.443-1.445; 99% min. assay.

TBP-HP. [Albright & Wilson Am.; Albright & Wilson UK]
Chem. Descrip.: Tributyl phosphite
CAS 102-85-2; EINECS 203-061-3
Uses: Intermediate in mfg. of phosphonate esters; reagent for dehalogenations, dehydrohalogenations and reductive cyclizations; scavenging agent for sulfur impurities
Properties: M.w. 250; dens. 0.93 g/cm^3; b.p. 120 C (7 mm); 94% min. assay.

Tebol™. [Arco]
Chem. Descrip.: Tert. butyl alcohol
CAS 75-65-0; EINECS 200-889-7
Uses: Solv., cosolvent, compatibilizer, coupling agent, processing aid for pharmaceuticals
Properties: Sol. 100% in water; m.w. 74.12; sp.gr. 0.80 (20/20 C); dens. 6.7 lb/gal (20 C); vapor pressure 30 mm Hg (20 C); b.p. 175 F; flash pt. 52 F.

Tebol™ 99. [Arco]
Chem. Descrip.: High purity tert. butyl alcohol
CAS 75-65-0; EINECS 200-889-7
Uses: Solv., cosolvent, compatibilizer, coupling

agent, processing aid for pharmaceuticals

Properties: Pt-Co ≤ 10 color; sol. in water; misc. with most org. solvs.; sp.gr. 0.78; dens. 6.5 lb/gal; visc. 3.3 cps (30 C); i.b.p. 81.5 C (760 mm Hg); f.p. 24.5 C; flash pt. (CC) 11 C; 99.3% act.

TEC. [Morflex]

Chem. Descrip.: Triethyl citrate NF/FCC

CAS 77-93-0; EINECS 201-070-7

Uses: Plasticizer for aq. based pharmaceutical coatings; provides controlled sustained release of drugs; protects drugs from gastric juices but allows its release into the intestine

Regulatory: FDA 21CFR §175.300, 175.320, 175.380, 175.390, 176.170, 177.1210, 181.27, 182.1911, 184.199, GRAS

Properties: Sol. 6.5 g/100 ml water; m.w. 276.3; sp.gr. 1.135-1.139; dens. 9.48 lb/gal; visc. 35.2 cps; b.p. 127 C (1 mm); pour pt. -50 F; flash pt. (COC) 155 C; ref. index 1.439-1.441; 99% min. assay.

Tecquinol® USP Grade. [Eastman]

Chem. Descrip.: Hydroquinone

CAS 123-31-9; EINECS 204-617-8

Uses: Antioxidant in suntan lotions.

Tefose® 63. [Gattefosse; Gattefosse SA]

Chem. Descrip.: PEG-6-32 stearate and glycol stearate

Uses: SE base for o/w pharmaceutical ointments, elegant cream formulations; exc. skin and mucosal tolerance; esp. for anti-mycotic preps.

Use level: 15-20%

Properties: Gardner < 5 pasty solid; weak odor; sol. in chloroform, methylene chloride; disp. in water; insol. in ethanol, min. oils; m.p. 40-45 C; drop pt. 46-53 C; HLB 10.0; acid no. < 6; iodine no. < 3; sapon. no. 110-120; 100% conc.; nonionic

Toxicology: Nonrritating to skin and eyes.

Tefose® 1500. [Gattefosse; Gattefosse SA]

Chem. Descrip.: PEG-6-32 stearate

CAS 9004-99-3

Uses: SE base for o/w pharmaceutical emulsions (thick lotions and creams)

Use level: 5-15%

Properties: Gardner < 5 pasty solid; weak odor; sol. in ethanol, chloroform, methylene chloride; insol. in water, min. oils; m.p. 39-45 C; drop pt. 42-46 C; HLB 11.0; acid no. < 6; iodine no. < 3; sapon. no. 75-95; 100% conc.; nonionic

Toxicology: Nonirritating to eyes; sl. irritating to skin.

Tefose® 2000. [Gattefosse; Gattefosse SA]

Chem. Descrip.: PEG-6 stearate, ceteth-20, steareth-20

Uses: SE base for o/w pharmaceutical emulsions (fluid, semifluid lotions, and creams)

Use level: 5-15%

Properties: Gardner < 5 pasty solid; weak odor; sol. in chloroform, methylene chloride; sparingly sol. in ethanol; disp. in water, n-hexane; insol. in min. oils; m.p. 32-37 C; HLB 11.0; acid no. < 6; iodine no. < 3; sapon. no. 65-85; 100% conc.; nonionic

Toxicology: Nonirritating to skin; sl. irritating to eyes.

Tefose® 2561. [Gattefosse; Gattefosse SA]

Chem. Descrip.: PEG-6 stearate, glyceryl stearate, and ceteth-20

Uses: Base for o/w pharmaceutical emulsions, creams, lotions, ointments

Use level: 5-15%

Properties: Gardner < 3 pasty solid; weak odor; HLB 10.0; m.p. 35-40 C; acid no. < 5; iodine no. < 3; sapon. no. 65-105; 100% conc.; nonionic

Toxicology: LD0 (oral, rat) > 2 g/kg; sl. irritating to skin and eyes.

Tegin®. [Goldschmidt]

Chem. Descrip.: Glyceryl stearate SE

Uses: SE emulsifier for pharmaceutical o/w emulsions

Properties: Powd.; HLB 5.5; 100% conc.; anionic.

Tegin® 90 NSE. [Goldschmidt; Goldschmidt AG]

Chem. Descrip.: Glyceryl stearate

Uses: Stabilizer for creamy and liq. o/w emulsions in pharmaceuticals

Properties: Wh.-ivory powd.; sol. warm in min. and veg. oils; insol. in water; m.p. 67-72 C; HLB 4.5; acid no. 3 max.; iodine no. 2 max.; sapon. no. 155-170; 100% conc.; nonionic.

Tegin® 4011. [Goldschmidt; Goldschmidt AG]

Chem. Descrip.: Glyceryl stearate

CAS 31566-31-1

Uses: Emulsifier for pharmaceuticals

Properties: Wh.-ivory powd.; sol. warm in veg. and min. oils; insol. in water; m.p. 54-60 C; HLB 3.8; acid no. 3 max.; iodine no. 3 max.; sapon. no. 162-173; 100% conc.; nonionic.

Tegin® 4100 NSE. [Goldschmidt; Goldschmidt AG]

Chem. Descrip.: Glyceryl stearate

CAS 31566-31-1

Uses: Stabilizer for pharmaceuticals

Properties: Wh.-ivory powd.; sol. warm in veg. and min. oils; insol. in water; m.p. 58-63 C; HLB 3.8; acid no. 2 max.; iodine no. 3 max.; sapon. no. 164-180; 100% conc.; nonionic.

Tegin® 4480. [Goldschmidt]

Chem. Descrip.: Glyceryl stearate

Uses: Emulsifier and stabilizer for pharmaceuticals

Properties: Semisolid; HLB 3.8; 100% conc.; nonionic.

Tegin® 4600 NSE. [Goldschmidt]

Chem. Descrip.: Glyceryl caprylate/caprate

Uses: Emulsifier for pharmaceutical prods.

Properties: Liq.; HLB 4.0; 100% conc.; nonionic.

Tegin® G. [Goldschmidt; Goldschmidt AG]

Chem. Descrip.: Glycol stearate SE

CAS 86418-55-5

Uses: SE sheen additive, opacifier for pharmaceuticals, o/w emulsions

Properties: Wh.-ivory waxy powd.; sol. warm in veg. and min. oils; disp. warm in water; m.p. 48-53 C; HLB 12.0; acid no. 36-38; iodine no. 3 max.; sapon. no. 150-165; 100% conc.; anionic.

Tegin® M. [Goldschmidt; Goldschmidt AG]

Chem. Descrip.: Glyceryl stearate

Uses: Emulsifier for o/w pharmaceutical systems

Properties: Wh.-ivory powd.; sol. warm in veg. and min. oils; insol. in water; m.p. 58-63 C; HLB 3.8; acid no. 2 max.; iodine no. 4 max.; sapon. no. 165-180; 100% conc.; anionic.

Tegin® O. [Goldschmidt; Goldschmidt AG]
Chem. Descrip.: Glyceryl mono/dioleate
CAS 25496-72-4
Uses: Emulsifier for w/o emulsions for pharmaceuticals
Properties: Pale yel. paste; sol. in veg. and min. oils; insol. in water; HLB 3.3; acid no. 2 max.; iodine no. 70-76; sapon. no. 158-175; 100% conc.; nonionic.

Tegin® P. [Goldschmidt; Goldschmidt AG]
Chem. Descrip.: Propylene glycol stearate SE
Uses: Emulsifier for o/w lotions and creams for pharmaceuticals
Properties: Wh.-ivory waxy solid; sol. warm in min. and veg. oils; disp. warm in water; m.p. 39-46 C; HLB 12.0; acid no. 16-18; iodine no. 3 max.; sapon. no. 150-170; 100% conc.; anionic.

Tegin® Spezial. [Goldschmidt; Goldschmidt AG]
Chem. Descrip.: Glyceryl stearate
Uses: Emulsifier for pharmaceutical o/w emulsions
Properties: Wh.-ivory powd.; sol. warm in veg. and min. oils; disp. warm in water; m.p. 54-60 C; HLB 12.0; acid no. 16-20; iodine no. 3 max.; sapon. no. 148-158; 100% conc.; anionic.

Tego®-Betaine L-7. [Goldschmidt; Goldschmidt AG]
Chem. Descrip.: Cocamidopropyl betaine
CAS 61789-40-0
Uses: Surfactant, emulsifier, foam stabilizer, visc. builder in low-irritation pharmaceuticals
Properties: Ivory powd. or yel. liq.; sp.gr. 1.040-1.050 (liq.); pH 5; 78-85% active. (powd.), 30% act. (liq.); amphoteric
Toxicology: LD50 (acute oral) 8.10 ml/kg; nonirritating to eyes.

Tego®-Betaine L-10 S. [Goldschmidt AG]
Chem. Descrip.: Lauramidopropyl betaine
EINECS 224-292-6
Uses: Surfactant for pharmaceutical prods.
Properties: Lt. clear liq.; pH 5.0; 30% act.; amphoteric.

Tego®-Betaine ZF. [Goldschmidt; Goldschmidt AG]
Chem. Descrip.: Cocamidopropyl betaine
CAS 61789-40-0
Uses: Mild surfactant, visc. and foam booster for use in dental prods.; amphoteric.

Tensopol USP 94. [Hickson Manro Ltd.]
Chem. Descrip.: Sodium fatty alcohol sulfate
CAS 73296-89-6
Uses: For pharmaceuticals, toothpaste
Properties: Powd.; 94% act.; anionic.

Tensopol USP 97. [Hickson Manro Ltd.]
Chem. Descrip.: Sodium fatty alcohol sulfate
CAS 73296-89-6
Uses: For pharmaceuticals, toothpaste
Properties: Powd.; 97% act.; anionic.

TEPA. [Albright & Wilson Am.; Albright & Wilson UK]
Chem. Descrip.: Triethyl phosphonoacetate
CAS 867-13-0

Uses: Intermediate in mfg. of substituted acrylic and acetic acids and their ethyl esters via the Horner-Emmons reaction
Properties: M.w. 224; dens. 1.12 g/cm^3; b.p. 140 C (8 mm); 97% min. assay.

Tepescohuite AMI Watersoluble. [Alban Muller]
Chem. Descrip.: Mimosa bark extract in water and propylene glycol
Uses: Natural ingred. with soothing props., regenerative agent for skin tissue; for pharmaceuticals, aftersun lotions, protection creams
Properties: Red brn.; sol. in water, alcohol; sp.gr. 1.035; b.p. 106 C; ref. index 1.3880-1.4090; pH 5.10-7.10.

Tepescohuite HG. [Alban Muller]
Chem. Descrip.: Mimosa bark extract in water and propylene glycol
Uses: Regenerative agent for skin tissue; for pharmaceuticals, aftersun lotions, protection creams
Properties: Dk. red; sol. in water, alcohol; sp.gr. 1.030; b.p. 100 C; ref. index 1.3880-1.4090; pH 5-7.

Tepescohuite HS. [Alban Muller]
Chem. Descrip.: Mimosa bark extract in propylene glycol (> 95%)
Uses: Regenerative agent for skin tissue; for pharmaceuticals, aftersun lotions, protection creams
Properties: Red brn.; sol. in water, alcohol; sp.gr. 1.045; b.p. 188.2 C; flash pt. (OC) 107 C; ref. index 1.4300-1.4360; pH 6-8.

Tepescohuite LS. [Alban Muller]
Chem. Descrip.: Mimosa bark extract in edible sunflower oil
Uses: Regenerative agent for skin tissue; for pharmaceuticals, aftersun lotions, protection creams
Properties: Yel.; sol. in org. solvs.; insol. in water; sp.gr. 0.915; acid no. < 3; iodine no. 105-135; sapon. no. 180-198; ref. index 1.4735-1.4785.

TEPF. [Albright & Wilson Am.; Albright & Wilson UK]
Chem. Descrip.: Triethyl phosphonoformate
Uses: Intermediate in mfg. of phosphonoformic acid and its esters and salts
Properties: M.w. 210; dens. 1.14 g/cm^3; b.p. 133 C (12.5 mm); 98% min. assay.

TEP-HP. [Albright & Wilson Am.; Albright & Wilson UK]
Chem. Descrip.: Triethyl phosphite
CAS 122-52-1; EINECS 204-552-5
Uses: Intermediate in mfg. of phosphonate esters; reagent for dehalogenations, dehydrohalogenations and reductive cyclizations
Properties: M.w. 166; dens. 0.97 g/cm^3; b.p. 65 C (24 mm); 98% min. assay.

Teric PEG 300. [ICI Australia]
Chem. Descrip.: PEG 300 USP
CAS 25322-68-3; EINECS 220-045-1
Uses: Binder for capsules/pills; also for liq. pharmaceutical preps., ointment bases
Properties: APHA 25 color; sol. in water and most polar org. solvs.; m.w. 285-315; sp.gr. 1.128; visc. 5.8 cst (99 C); pour pt. -12 C; flash pt. (OC) > 190 C; ref. index 1.463; pH 4.5-7.5; surf. tens. 44.6 dynes/cm; 99% act.; biodeg.

Teric PEG 400. [ICI Australia]
  Chem. Descrip.: PEG 400 USP
  CAS 25322-68-3; EINECS 225-856-4
  Uses: For pharmaceutical liq. preps., ointment bases, suppository bases; binder for capsules/pills; preservation of pathological specimens
  Properties: APHA 25 color; sol. in water and most polar org. solvs.; m.w. 380-420; sp.gr. 1.130; visc. 7.3 cst (99 C); pour pt. 6 C; flash pt. (OC) > 215 C; ref. index 1.465; pH 4.5-7.5; surf. tens. 44.6 dynes/cm; 99% act.; biodeg.

Teric PEG 600. [ICI Australia]
  Chem. Descrip.: PEG 600 USP
  CAS 25322-68-3; EINECS 229-859-1
  Uses: Used for pharmaceutical suppository bases; binder in capsules/pills
  Properties: APHA 10 color (25% aq.); sol. in water and most polar org. solvs.; m.w. 560-630; sp.gr. 1.127; visc. 10.4 cst (99 C); pour pt. 19 C; flash pt. (OC) > 230 C; ref. index 1.454; pH 4.5-7.5; surf. tens. 44.6 dynes/cm; 99% act.; biodeg.

Teric PEG 800. [ICI Australia]
  Chem. Descrip.: PEG 800
  CAS 25322-68-3
  Uses: Binder for pharmaceutical capsules/pills
  Properties: APHA 30 color (25% aq.); sol. in water and most polar org. solvs.; m.w. 760-840; sp.gr. 1.184; visc. 13.8 cst (99 C); pour pt. 28 C; flash pt. (OC) > 235 C; ref. index 1.455; pH 4.5-7.5; 99% act.; biodeg.

Teric PEG 1500. [ICI Australia]
  Chem. Descrip.: PEG 1500
  Uses: Used for ointment bases, suppository bases; preservation of pathological specimens
  Properties: APHA 30 color (25% aq.); sol. in water and most polar org. solvs.; m.w. 1430-1570; sp.gr. 1.208; visc. 28.4 cst (99 C); pour pt. 46 C; flash pt. (OC) > 260 C; ref. index 1.456; pH 4.5-7.5; surf. tens. 53.1 dynes/cm (50% aq.); 100% act.; biodeg.

Teric PEG 3350. [ICI Australia]
  Chem. Descrip.: PEG 3350 USP
  Uses: Used for suppository bases
  Properties: APHA 30 color (25% aq.); sol. in water and most polar org. solvs.; m.w. 3000-3700; sp.gr. 1.215; visc. 70-120 cst (99 C); pour pt. 53 C; flash pt. (OC) > 260 C; ref. index 1.456; pH 4.5-7.5; surf. tens. 54.0 dynes/cm (50% aq.); 100% act.; biodeg.

Teric PEG 4000. [ICI Australia]
  Chem. Descrip.: PEG 4000
  CAS 25322-68-3
  Uses: Used for pharmaceutical liq. preps., ointment and suppository bases; binder for capsules/pills; mounting of histological specimens
  Properties: APHA 50 color (25% aq.); sol. in water and most polar org. solvs.; m.w. 3300-4000; sp.gr. 1.217; visc. 130-180 cst (99 C); pour pt. 56 C; flash pt. (OC) > 260 C; ref. index 1.456; pH 4.5-7.5; surf. tens. 54.4 dynes/cm (50% aq.); 100% act.; biodeg.

Teric PEG 6000. [ICI Australia]

Chem. Descrip.: PEG 6000
  CAS 25322-68-3
  Uses: Used for pharmaceutical liq. preps., suppository bases; binder for capsules/pills; mounting of histological specimens
  Properties: APHA 50 color (25% aq.); sol. in water and most polar org. solvs.; m.w. 6000-7500; sp.gr. 1.217; visc. 330-500 cst (99 C); pour pt. 55-60 C; flash pt. (OC) > 260 C; ref. index 1.456; pH 4.5-7.5; surf. tens. 55.3 dynes/cm (50% aq.); 100% act.; biodeg.

Teric PEG 8000. [ICI Australia]
  Chem. Descrip.: PEG 8000 USP
  CAS 25322-68-3
  Uses: Suppository bases; binder for capsules/pills
  Properties: Sol. in water and most polar org. solvs.; m.w. 7000-9000; sp.gr. 1.2; visc. 700-900 cst (99 C); pour pt. 55-60 C; flash pt. (OC) > 260 C; ref. index 1.456; pH 4.5-7.5; 100% act.; biodeg.

Terra Alba 114836. [Allied Custom Gypsum]
  Chem. Descrip.: Calcium sulfate dihydrate
  CAS 7778-18-9; EINECS 231-900-3
  Uses: Pharmaceutical grade tablet diluent
  Regulatory: FDA 21CFR §184.1230, GRAS
  Properties: Wh. fine free-flowing powd., odorless, tasteless; 95% thru 325 sieve; m.w. 172.17; sp.gr. 2.32; bulk dens. 45 lb/ft^3 (loose); pH 7-7.5; 98% min. assay
  Toxicology: Nuisance particulate; high exposure to dust may cause eye and respiratory system irritation.

Terra-Dry™ FD Aloe Vera Powd. Decolorized FDD. [Terry Labs]
  Chem. Descrip.: Freeze-dried aloe vera gel powd., decolorized, deodorized
  Uses: Used in OTC pharmaceuticals (topical analgesics/anesthetics, hydrocortisone creams, first aid sprays, anti-acne preps., bedsore preps., as moisturizing base)
  Properties: Wh. to lt. beige fine cryst. powd.; After reconstitution 1:99: sp.gr. 0.997-1.004; pH 3.5-5.0; 8% max. moisture
  Storage: Preserve after reconstitution; may darken with age.

Terra-Dry™ FD Aloe Vera Powd. Reg. FDR. [Terry Labs]
  Chem. Descrip.: Freeze-dried aloe vera gel powd.
  Uses: Used in OTC pharmaceuticals (topical analgesics/anesthetics, hydrocortisone creams, first aid sprays, anti-acne preps., bedsore preps., as moisturizing base)
  Properties: Beige to lt. brn. fine cryst. powd.; After reconstitution 1:99: sp.gr. 0.997-1.004; pH 3.5-5.0; 8% max. moisture
  Storage: Preserve after reconstitution; may darken with age.

Terra-Pulp™ FD Whole Aloe Vera Gel Fillet. [Terry Labs]
  Chem. Descrip.: Freeze-dried whole aloe vera gel fillet
  Uses: Used in health care (after sun gel, natural first aid preps.)

Properties: Off-wh. to beige flakes, mod. veg. odor; After rehydration 1:99: visc. gel with pulp fiber; pH 3.5-5.0; < 10% moisture
Storage: Preserve after reconstitution; may darken with age.

Terra-Pure™ FD Non-Preserved Decolorized FDD. [Terry Labs]
Chem. Descrip.: Freeze-dried aloe vera gel powd. 200X, decolorized, deodorized
Uses: Used in OTC pharmaceuticals (topical analgesics/anesthetics, hydrocortisone creams, first aid sprays, anti-acne preps., medicated talcs, toothpaste)
Properties: Wh. to lt. beige fine cryst. powd.; After reconstitution 1:199: sp.gr. 0.997-1.004; pH 3.5-5.0; 8% max. moisture
Storage: Preserve after reconstitution; may darken with age.

Terra-Pure™ FD Non-Preserved Reg. FDR. [Terry Labs]
Chem. Descrip.: Freeze-dried aloe vera gel powd. 200X
Uses: Used in OTC pharmaceuticals (topical analgesics/anesthetics, hydrocortisone creams, first aid sprays, anti-acne preps., medicated talcs, toothpaste)
Properties: Lt. cream to beige fine cryst. powd.; After reconstitution 1:199: sp.gr. 0.997-1.004; pH 3.5-5.0; 8% max. moisture
Storage: Preserve after reconstitution; may darken with age.

Terra-Pure™ Non-Preserved Aloe Vera Powd. [Terry Labs]
Chem. Descrip.: Aloe vera gel spray-dried without preservatives
Uses: Additive in OTC pharmaceuticals
Properties: Lt. cream to beige fine powd., mod. veg. odor; disperses rapidly in most aq. sol'ns.; After reconsititing 1:199 with DI water: sp.gr. 0.997-1.004; pH 3.5-5.0; 12% max. moisture
Storage: Highly hygroscopic; store in cool, dry place with desiccant; add preservatives on reconstitution.

Terra-Spray™ Spray Dried Aloe Vera Powd. Decolorized SDD. [Terry Labs]
Chem. Descrip.: Aloe vera gel, decolorized, deodorized
Uses: Used in OTC pharmaceuticals (topical analgesics/anesthetics, hydrocortisone creams, first aid sprays, anti-acne preps., medicated talcs, as moisturizing agent)
Properties: Wh. to lt. beige fine powd.; After reconstitution 1:99: sp.gr. 0.997-1.004; pH 3.5-5.0; 8% max. moisture
Storage: Preserve after reconstitution; may darken with age.

Terra-Spray™ Spray Dried Aloe Vera Powd. Reg. SDR. [Terry Labs]
Chem. Descrip.: Aloe vera gel
Uses: Used in OTC pharmaceuticals (topical analgesics/anesthetics, hydrocortisone creams, first aid sprays, anti-acne preps., medicated talcs, as moisturizing agent)
Properties: Lt. cream to beige fine powd.; After reconstitution 1:99: sp.gr. 0.997-1.004; pH 3.5-5.0; 8% max. moisture
Storage: Preserve after reconstitution; may darken with age.

Tesal. [Gattefosse]
Chem. Descrip.: Propylene glycol stearate SE
Uses: SE base for pharmaceutical ointments, lotions, creams
Properties: Drop pt. 37-43 C; acid no. 90-110; iodine no. < 5; sapon. no. 160-180; anionic
Toxicology: Nonirritating to skin and eyes.

Tetraglyme. [Ferro/Grant]
Chem. Descrip.: Tetraethylene glycol dimethyl ether
Uses: Solv. for pharmaceuticals; drug carrier, stabilizer
Properties: Colorless clear; mild, nonresidual odor; water-sol.; misc. with ethanol, acetone, benzene, diethyl ether, octane; m.w. 222.28; sp.gr. 1.0132; dens. 8.45 lb/gal; visc. 4.1 cP; f.p. -29.7 C; b.p. 275 C; flash pt. (CC) 141 C; ref. index 1.4330 (20 C); pH neutral; surf. tens. 33.8 dynes/cm (20 C); 98.0% min. purity; slowly biodeg.
Toxicology: LD50 5100 mg/kg; low to mod. acute toxicity; chronic exposure may cause reproductive effects.

Tetronic® 304. [BASF]
Chem. Descrip.: Poloxamine 304
CAS 11111-34-5
Uses: Emulsifier, thickener, wetting agent, dispersant, solubilizer, stabilizer for pharmaceuticals
Properties: Colorless liq.; water-sol.; m.w. 1650; sp.gr. 1.06; visc. 450 cps; HLB 16; cloud pt. 94 C (1%); pour pt. -11 C; ref. index 1.4649; surf. tens. 53.0 dynes/cm (0.1%); Draves wetting > 360 s (0.1%); Ross-Miles foam 2 mm (0.1% aq., 50 C); 100% act.; nonionic
Toxicology: None to mild eye and minimal to moderate skin irritation.

Tewax TC 10. [Auschem SpA]
Chem. Descrip.: Ceteareth-9
CAS 68439-49-6
Uses: Emulsifier for pharmaceutical preps.
Properties: Flakes; HLB 12.0; 100% conc.; nonionic
Unverified

Tewax TC 65. [Auschem SpA]
Chem. Descrip.: Glyceryl stearate and PEG-100 stearate
Uses: Emulsifier for pharmaceutical preps.
Properties: Flakes; HLB 11.0; 100% conc.; nonionic.

Tewax TC 72. [Auschem SpA]
Chem. Descrip.: Steareth-8
CAS 9005-00-9
Uses: Emulsifier for pharmaceutical preps.
Properties: Solid; HLB 9.0; 100% conc.; nonionic
Unverified

Tewax TC 80. [Auschem SpA]
Chem. Descrip.: Glyceryl sorbitan oleo/stearate

Uses: W/o emulsifier for pharmaceutical preps.
Properties: Solid; HLB 4.6; 100% conc.; nonionic
Unverified

Tewax TC 81. [Auschem SpA]
Chem. Descrip.: Glyceryl sorbitan oleo/stearate,
beeswax
Uses: W/o emulsifier for pharmaceutical preps.
Properties: Solid; HLB 4.0; 100% conc.; nonionic
Unverified

Tewax TC 82. [Auschem SpA]
Chem. Descrip.: PEG-1 glyceryl sorbitan
isostearate
Uses: W/o emulsifier for pharmaceutical preps.
Properties: Solid; HLB 5.0; 100% conc.; nonionic
Unverified

Tewax TC 83. [Auschem SpA]
Chem. Descrip.: PEG-5 glyceryl stearate
CAS 51158-08-8
Uses: W/o emulsifier for pharmaceuticals
Properties: Solid; HLB 5.0; 100% conc.; nonionic
Unverified

Texapon® K-12 Needles. [Henkel/Cospha; Henkel
KGaA/Cospha]
Chem. Descrip.: Sodium lauryl sulfate
CAS 151-21-3; EINECS 205-788-1
Uses: Foamer for dentifrices, tablets
Properties: Wh. to lt. yel. needles, almost odorless;
dens. 400-500 g/l; pH 6.5-9.0 (1%); 88% act.;
anionic
Storage: 1 yr min. storage life in sealed orig.
containers in dry place at temps. below 40 C.

Texapon® K-12 Powd. [Henkel/Cospha; Henkel
KGaA/Cospha]
Chem. Descrip.: Sodium lauryl sulfate
CAS 151-21-3; EINECS 205-788-1
Uses: Wetting agent, dispersant, and foamer used
in toothpaste mfg.
Regulatory: NF, DAB, Ph.Eur., JP compliance
Properties: Wh. to sl. ylsh. fine powd., almost
odorless; dens. 200-300 g/l; pH 8.5-10.5 (1%);
90.5% min. act.; anionic
Storage: 1 yr min. storage stability in orig. un-
opened containers below 40 C, protected from
moisture.

Texapon® K-12 USP. [Henkel/Cospha]
Chem. Descrip.: Sodium lauryl sulfate
CAS 151-21-3; EINECS 205-788-1
Uses: Surfactant for dentifrices
Regulatory: USP compliance
Properties: Wh. powd.; 89% act.; anionic.

Texapon® K-1296 Needles. [Henkel KGaA/Cospha]
Chem. Descrip.: Sodium lauryl sulfate
CAS 151-21-3
Uses: Surfactant for toothpastes
Regulatory: DAB compliance
Properties: Wh. to sl. ylsh. needles, faint char. odor;
dens. 400-500 g/l; pH 8.5-10.5 (1%); 90% min.
act.; anionic
Storage: 1 yr min. storage life in orig. unopened
containers at temps. below 40 C, protected from
moisture.

Texapon® K-1296 Powd. [Henkel/Cospha; Henkel

Canada; Henkel KGaA/Cospha]
Chem. Descrip.: Sodium lauryl sulfate
CAS 151-21-3; EINECS 205-788-1
Uses: Dispersant, wetting agent, foamer for tooth-
pastes
Regulatory: NF, DAB, Ph.Eur., JP compliance
Properties: Wh. to sl. ylsh. powd., almost odorless;
dens. 2.08 lb/gal; pH 6-9 (1%); 96% act.; anionic
Storage: 1 yr min. storage stability in orig. un-
opened containers at temps. below 40 C, pro-
tected from moisture.

Texapon® K-1296 USP. [Henkel/Cospha]
Chem. Descrip.: Sodium lauryl sulfate
CAS 151-21-3; EINECS 205-788-1
Uses: Surfactant for dentifrices, tablets
Regulatory: USP compliance
Properties: Wh. powd.; 96% act.; anionic.

Texapon® SB-3. [Henkel Canada; Henkel KGaA/
Cospha]
Chem. Descrip.: Disodium laurethsulfosuccinate
EINECS 255-062-3
Uses: Base for pharmaceutical surfactant preps.
Properties: Pract. colorless clear liq., may become
cloudy on storage; acid no. 6 max.; cloud pt. < 0
C; pH 5.5-6.5; 40% conc.; anionic
Storage: Store at 20-25 C; may become cloudy on
storage-warm to 40 C to reverse.

Texapon® Z. [Henkel KGaA/Cospha]
Chem. Descrip.: Sodium lauryl sulfate C12-C14
CAS 151-21-3; EINECS 205-788-1
Uses: Wetting agent, foaming agent, dispersant for
pharmaceutical preps., toothpastes, mouth and
dental care prods.
Properties: Wh. to pale yel. powd.; sol. in cold
water; dens. 100 g/l; pH 6-9 (1%); 60% min. act.;
anionic.

Texapon® Z Highly Conc. Needles. [Henkel/
Cospha; Henkel KGaA/Cospha]
Chem. Descrip.: Sodium lauryl sulfate
CAS 68955-19-1
Uses: Foaming agent, dispersant, wetting agent for
toothpastes
Regulatory: NF, JP compliance
Properties: Wh. to sl. ylsh. needles; dens. 400-500
g/l; pH 6.5-9.0 (1%); 88% min. act.; anionic
Storage: 1 yr min. storage life in orig. unopened
containers at temps. below 40 C, protected from
moisture.

Texapon® Z Highly Conc. Powder. [Henkel/Cospha;
Henkel/Functional Prods.; Henkel KGaA/Cospha]
Chem. Descrip.: Sodium lauryl sulfate
CAS 68955-19-1
Uses: Foaming, dispersion, and wetting agent for
toothpastes
Regulatory: NF, JP compliance
Properties: Wh. to sl. ylsh. fine powd., faint odor;
dens. 200-300 g/l; pH 8.5-10.5 (1%); 90% min.
act.; anionic
Storage: 1 yr min. storage life in orig. unopened
containers at temps. below 40 C, protected from
moisture.

Thiamine Hydrochloride USP, FCC Regular Type

No. 601160. [Roche]
Chem. Descrip.: Vitamin B₁ hydrochloride USP FCC
CAS 67-03-8; EINECS 200-641-8
Uses: Nutrient, source of thiamine in pharmaceutical liqs. (polyvitamin drops), dry prods.; not recommended for dry prods. with high moisture content
Properties: Wh. fine cryst., char. sl. meat-like or yeast odor and taste; 90% thru 200 mesh; sol. 1 g/1 ml water, 1 g/100 ml alcohol; sol. in glycerin; insol. in ether, benzene; m.w. 337.27; pH 2.7-3.4 (1:100 aq.); 98-102% assay
Precaution: Avoid heat, alkalies, prolonged light exposure
Storage: Store in dry place in tightly closed container.

Thiamine Mononitrate USP, FCC Fine Powd. No. 601340. [Roche]
Chem. Descrip.: Vitamin B₁ mononitrate USP FCC
CAS 532-43-4; EINECS 208-537-4
Uses: Nutrient, thiamine source in dry mixts. that have appreciable moisture content, e.g., tablets; not recommended for sol'ns.
Regulatory: FDA GRAS
Properties: Wh. fine cryst. powd., char. sl. meat-like or yeasty odor and taste; 95% thru 200 mesh; sol. 1 g/35 ml water; sl. sol. in alcohol, chloroform; m.w. 327.36; pH 6.0-7.5 (2-100% aq.); 98-102% assay
Precaution: Avoid heat, alkalies, prolonged light exposure
Storage: Store in dry place in tight, light-resist. containers @ 72 F or below.

Thiovanol®. [Evans Chemetics]
Chem. Descrip.: Thioglycerin
CAS 96-27-5; EINECS 202-495-0
Uses: Pharmaceutical stabilizer
Properties: Practically clear and colorless sol'n.; mild char. odor; m.w. 108.2; b.p. 118 C (5 mm, anhyd.); misc. in all proportions with water and alcohol; insol. in ether; 90% aq. sol'n.

Thyroid 3X U.S.P. [Am. Labs]
Chem. Descrip.: Thyroid
Uses: Pharmaceutical additive, drug
Regulatory: USP compliance
Properties: Ylsh. to buff-colored amorphous powd., sl. char. meat-like odor, saline taste
Storage: Store in tight containers.

Thyroid U.S.P. [Am. Labs]
Chem. Descrip.: Thyroid
Uses: Pharmaceutical additive, drug
Regulatory: USP compliance
Properties: Ylsh. to buff-colored amorphous powd., sl. char. meat-like odor, saline taste
Storage: Store in tight containers.

Ticalose® 15. [TIC Gums]
Chem. Descrip.: Cellulose gum
CAS 9004-32-4
Uses: Low-visc. grade for pharmaceuticals where high solids levels, encapsulation, or film forming are desirable; thickener, moisture retention aid, binder, lubricant
Properties: Coarse (40 mesh), std. (80 mesh), or fine (120 mesh) particle size; visc. 10-15 cps (1%), 25-50 cps (2%); anionic.

Ticalose® 30. [TIC Gums]
Chem. Descrip.: Cellulose gum
CAS 9004-32-4
Uses: Low-visc. grade for pharmaceuticals where high solids levels, encapsulation, or film forming are desirable; thickener, moisture retention aid, binder, lubricant
Properties: Coarse (40 mesh), std. (80 mesh), or fine (120 mesh) particle size; visc. 20-30 cps (1%), 100-150 cps (2%); anionic.

Ticalose® 75. [TIC Gums]
Chem. Descrip.: Cellulose gum
CAS 9004-32-4
Uses: Med.-visc. grade for pharmaceuticals as viscosifier, texturizer, protein stabilizer
Properties: Coarse (40 mesh), std. (80 mesh), or fine (120 mesh) particle size; visc. 40-75 cps (1%), 400-600 cps (2%); anionic.

Ticalose® 100. [TIC Gums]
Chem. Descrip.: Cellulose gum
CAS 9004-32-4
Uses: Med.-visc. grade for pharmaceuticals as viscosifier, texturizer, protein stabilizer
Properties: Coarse (40 mesh), std. (80 mesh), or fine (120 mesh) particle size; visc. 70-110 cps (1%), 800-1200 cps (2%); anionic.

Ticalose® 150 R. [TIC Gums]
Chem. Descrip.: Cellulose gum, with high degree of substitution, providing better stability under high temp., low pH conditions, high salt concs., other high stress processes
CAS 9004-32-4
Uses: Thickener, binder, suspending aid, mouthfeel enhancer, moisture retention aid for pharmaceuticals
Properties: Coarse (40 mesh), std. (80 mesh), or fine (120 mesh) particle size; visc. 50-150 cps (1%), 600-1000 cps (2%); anionic.

Ticalose® 700 R. [TIC Gums]
Chem. Descrip.: Cellulose gum, with high degree of substitution, providing better stability under high temp., low pH conditions, high salt concs., other high stress processes
CAS 9004-32-4
Uses: Thickener, binder, suspending aid, mouthfeel enhancer, moisture retention aid for pharmaceuticals
Properties: Coarse (40 mesh), std. (80 mesh), or fine (120 mesh) particle size; visc. 200-400 cps (1%); anionic.

Ticalose® 750. [TIC Gums]
Chem. Descrip.: Cellulose gum
CAS 9004-32-4
Uses: High-visc. grade for pharmaceuticals as viscosifier
Properties: Coarse (40 mesh), std. (80 mesh), or fine (120 mesh) particle size; visc. 550-750 cps (1%); anionic.

Ticalose® 1200. [TIC Gums]
Chem. Descrip.: Cellulose gum
CAS 9004-32-4
Uses: High-visc. grade for pharmaceuticals as viscosifier, thickener, suspending agent, stabilizer
Properties: Coarse (40 mesh), std. (80 mesh), or fine (120 mesh) particle size; visc. 800-1200 cps (1%); anionic.

Ticalose® 2000 R. [TIC Gums]
Chem. Descrip.: Cellulose gum, with high degree of substitution, providing better stability under high temp., low pH conditions, high salt concs., other high stress processes
CAS 9004-32-4
Uses: Thickener, binder, suspending agent, mouthfeel enhancer, moisture retention aid for pharmaceuticals
Properties: Coarse (40 mesh), std. (80 mesh), or fine (120 mesh) particle size; visc. 1000-1500 cps (1%); anionic.

Ticalose® 2500. [TIC Gums]
Chem. Descrip.: Cellulose gum
CAS 9004-32-4
Uses: High-visc. grade for pharmaceuticals as viscosifier, thickener, suspending agent, stabilizer
Properties: Coarse (40 mesh), std. (80 mesh), or fine (120 mesh) particle size; visc. 1500-2500 cps (1%); anionic.

Ticalose® 4000. [TIC Gums]
Chem. Descrip.: Cellulose gum
CAS 9004-32-4
Uses: High-visc. grade for pharmaceuticals as viscosifier, thickener, suspending agent, stabilizer
Properties: Gran., 16 mesh particle size; visc. 2500-4000 cps (1%); anionic.

Ticalose® 4500. [TIC Gums]
Chem. Descrip.: Cellulose gum
CAS 9004-32-4
Uses: High-visc. grade for pharmaceuticals as viscosifier, thickener, suspending agent, stabilizer
Properties: Coarse (40 mesh), std. (80 mesh), or fine (120 mesh) particle size; visc. 3000-4500 cps (1%); anionic.

Ticalose® 5000 R. [TIC Gums]
Chem. Descrip.: Cellulose gum, with high degree of substitution, providing better stability under high temp., low pH conditions, high salt concs., other high stress processes
CAS 9004-32-4
Uses: Thickener, binder, suspending aid, mouthfeel enhancer, moisture retention aid for pharmaceuticals
Properties: Coarse (40 mesh), std. (80 mesh), or fine (120 mesh) particle size; visc. 2500-3500 cps (1%); anionic.

Ticaxan® Regular. [TIC Gums]
Chem. Descrip.: Xanthan gum
CAS 11138-66-2; EINECS 234-394-2
Uses: Stabilizer, thickener, emulsifier, suspending agent, binder, moisture control aid in pharmaceuticals (ointments, lotions, suspensions).

Ticolv. [TIC Gums]
Chem. Descrip.: Guar gum
CAS 9000-30-0; EINECS 232-536-8
Uses: Thickener, film-former, binder featuring high visc.; for pharmaceutical suspensions
Properties: Sol. in cold water.

TIC Pretested® Arabic FT-1 USP. [TIC Gums]
Chem. Descrip.: Gum arabic USP
CAS 9000-01-5; EINECS 232-519-5
Uses: Carrier for spray-dried flavors; retains flavors, protects them from oxidation, provides clean taste; may be labeled 'natural'
Regulatory: Kosher
Properties: Powd.; 85% min. dietary fiber, 15% max. moisture.

TIC Pretested® CMC 2500 S. [TIC Gums]
Chem. Descrip.: Sodium carboxymethylcellulose
CAS 9004-32-4
Uses: Thickener for pharmaceuticals
Regulatory: FDA GRAS, FCC
Properties: Off-wh. to tan free-flowing powd., odorless, bland flavor; 25% min. on 140 mesh, 65% max. thru 140 mesh; sol. in cold or hot water; visc. 1400-2400 cps; pH 6.0-8.5; 99.5% min. purity, 8% max. moisture.

TIC Pretested® CMC PH-2500. [TIC Gums]
Chem. Descrip.: Sodium carboxymethylcellulose USP/FCC
CAS 9004-32-4
Uses: Pre-hydrated thickener; protein stabilizer
Properties: Dust-free powd., odorless, tasteless; 60% min. on 100 mesh; sol. in hot or cold water; visc. 1000-2000 cps min.; pH 6.0-8.5; 99.5% min. purity.

TIC Pretested® Gum Agar Agar 100 FCC/NF Powd. [TIC Gums]
Chem. Descrip.: Agar agar gum
CAS 9002-18-0; EINECS 232-658-1
Uses: Rigid gel which must boil to hydrate; stable under low pH conditions; tolerates large percentages of salts without changes in gel structure; for dental impressions
Regulatory: Kosher approved
Properties: Med. mesh powd.; 90% thru 100 mesh; m.w. 5000-30,000; visc. forms gel on heating; gel pt. 88-103 F; pH 4-7; 20% max. moisture.

TIC Pretested® Tragacanth 440. [TIC Gums]
Chem. Descrip.: Gum tragacanth
CAS 9000-65-1; EINECS 232-552-5
Uses: Emulsifier providing med. visc., creamy texture to pharmaceutical suspensions; pH stable (3-9); slow to hydrate; exc. acid, heat, and salt tolerance
Properties: 95% min. thru 140 mesh; sol. in cold water; m.w. $\approx$ 850,000; visc. 300 cps min. (1%); pH 4-7; 15% max. moisture
Storage: Hygroscopic-store under cool, dry conditions.

Timica®. [Mearl]

Chem. Descrip.: Mica platelets coated with titanium dioxide or iron oxide
Uses: Luster pigment for analgesic body lotions, sunscreens
Properties: Wh. and colored powds.; sp.gr. ≈ 3.0.

TIPA 99. [Dow]
Chem. Descrip.: Triisopropanolamine
CAS 122-20-3; EINECS 204-528-4
Uses: Emulsifier for pharmaceuticals
Properties: Sp.gr. 0.988 (70/4 C); dens. 8.24 lb/gal (70 C); visc. 100 cps (60 C); f.p. 44 C; b.p. 306 C (760 mm Hg); flash pt. (COC) 320 F; ref. index 1.4595 (30 C).

TIPMDP. [Albright & Wilson Am.; Albright & Wilson UK]
Chem. Descrip.: Tetraisopropyl methylenediphosphonate
CAS 11660-95-3
Uses: Intermediate in mfg. of bisphosphonate esters, acids, and salts; reagent for phosphonate prep. via Horner-Emmons reaction
Properties: M.w. 344; dens. 1.08 g/cm^3; b.p. > 155 C (0.5 mm); 95% min. assay.

TIPP. [Albright & Wilson Am.; Albright & Wilson UK]
Chem. Descrip.: Triisopropyl phosphite
CAS 116-17-6
Uses: Intermediate in selective mfg. of phosphonate and bisphosphonate esters, acids, and salts
Properties: M.w. 419; dens. 0.89 g/cm^3; b.p. 162 C (0.3 mm); 96% min. assay.

Tixosil 311. [Rhone-Poulenc]
Chem. Descrip.: Hydrated silica, amorphous
CAS 7631-86-9; EINECS 215-683-2
Uses: Used in toothpaste, pharmaceuticals
Properties: Wh. powd.; 4 µ avg. particle size; < 0.1% retained 325 mesh; Hegman grind 6; sp.gr. 2.05; dens. 17.1 lb/gal; surf. area 250 m^2/g; oil absorp. 300%; ref. index 1.45; pH 7; 96% SiO_2.

Tixosil 321. [Rhone-Poulenc]
Chem. Descrip.: Precipitated silica, amorphous
EINECS 215-683-2
Uses: Used in toothpaste, pharmaceuticals
Properties: Wh. powd.; 3 µ avg. particle size; < 0.1% retained 325 mesh; Hegman grind > 6; dens. 17.1 lb/gal; surf. area 250 m^2/g; oil absorp. 300%; ref. index 1.45; pH 7; 96% SiO_2.

Tixosil 331. [Rhone-Poulenc]
Chem. Descrip.: Hydrated silica, amorphous
EINECS 215-683-2
Uses: Rheology control agent for solv. and water-based systems; used in toothpaste, pharmaceuticals
Properties: Wh. powd.; 3 µ avg. particle size; < 0.1% retained 325 mesh; Hegman grind 7; dens. 17.1 lb/gal; surf. area 310 m^2/g; oil absorp. 320%; ref. index 1.45; pH 7; 96% SiO_2.

Tixosil 333, 343. [Rhone-Poulenc]
Chem. Descrip.: Hydrated silica
EINECS 215-683-2
Uses: Rheology control agent for solv. and water-based systems; used in toothpaste, pharmaceuticals.

Tixosil 375. [Rhone-Poulenc]

Chem. Descrip.: Precipitated silica, amorphous
EINECS 215-683-2
Uses: Rheology control agent for solv. and water-based systems; used in toothpaste, pharmaceuticals
Properties: Wh. powd.; 2 µ avg. particle size; < 0.1% retained 325 mesh; Hegman grind 7; dens. 17.5 lb/gal; surf. area 180 m^2/g; oil absorp. 290%; ref. index 1.45; pH 6.6; 98% SiO_2.

T-Maz® 20. [PPG/Specialty Chem.]
Chem. Descrip.: Polysorbate 20
CAS 9005-64-5
Uses: Emulsifier, solubilizer, wetting agent, stabilizer, dispersant, visc. modifier, suspending agent for drug prods.
Regulatory: Kosher
Properties: Yel. liq.; sol. in water, ethanol, acetone, toluene, veg. oil, propylene glycol; sp.gr. 1.1; visc. 400 cps; HLB 16.7; acid no. 2 max.; sapon. no. 40-50; hyd. no. 96-108; flash pt. (PMCC) > 350 F; 97% act.; nonionic.

T-Maz® 28. [PPG/Specialty Chem.]
Chem. Descrip.: PEG-80 sorbitan laurate
CAS 9005-64-5
Uses: Emulsifier, solubilizer, wetting agent, stabilizer, dispersant, visc. modifier for drug prods.
Properties: Pale yel. liq.; sol. in water; sp.gr. 1.0; visc. 1100 cps; HLB 19.2; acid no. 2 max.; sapon. no. 5-15; hyd. no. 25-40; flash pt. (PMCC) > 350 F; 30% max. water.

T-Maz® 60K. [PPG/Specialty Chem.]
Chem. Descrip.: Polysorbate 60
CAS 9005-67-8
Uses: Emulsifier, solubilizer, wetting agent, stabilizer, dispersant, visc. modifier, suspending agent for drug prods.
Regulatory: FDA 21CFR §172.515, 172.836, 173.340, 573.840; kosher
Properties: Yel. to amber clear gel, bland odor; sol. in water, ethanol, min. spirits, toluene; disp. in propylene glycol; sp.gr. 1.08; m.p. 23-25 C; b.p. > 300 F; HLB 14.9; acid no. 2 max.; sapon. no. 45-55; hyd. no. 81-96; flash pt. (PMCC) > 350 F; 100% conc.; nonionic
Toxicology: LD50 (oral, rat) 64 g/kg; nonirritating
Storage: Store in well-ventilated area below 120 F.

T-Maz® 61. [PPG/Specialty Chem.]
Chem. Descrip.: Polysorbate 61
CAS 9005-67-8
Uses: Emulsifier, solubilizer, wetting agent, stabilizer, dispersant, visc. modifier, suspending agent for drug prods.
Properties: Gardner 5 paste; disp. @ 5% in water, min. oils, toluene, veg. oils; HLB 9.5; sapon. no. 98-113; hyd. no. 170-200; flash pt. (PMCC) > 350 F; 100% conc.; nonionic.

T-Maz® 65K. [PPG/Specialty Chem.]
Chem. Descrip.: Polysorbate 65
CAS 9005-71-4
Uses: Emulsifier, solubilizer, wetting agent, stabilizer, dispersant, visc. modifier, suspending agent for drug prods.

Regulatory: FDA 21CFR §172.838, 173.340; kosher

Properties: Tan waxy paste, char. ester odor; sol. @ 2% in ethanol, veg. oil, disp. in water, insol. in min. oil, propylene glycol; m.p. 30-32 C; b.p. > 300 F; HLB 10.5; acid no. 2 max.; sapon. no. 88-98; hyd. no. 44-60; flash pt. (PMCC) > 350 F; 100% conc.; nonionic

Toxicology: LD50 (oral, rat) > 39.8 g/kg; nonirritating, nonsensitizing

Storage: Store in well-ventilated area below 120 F.

T-Maz® 80. [PPG/Specialty Chem.]
Chem. Descrip.: Polysorbate 80
CAS 9005-65-6
Uses: Emulsifier, solubilizer, wetting agent, stabilizer, dispersant, visc. modifier, suspending agent for drug prods.
Properties: Yel. liq.; sol. in water, ethanol, veg. oil, toluol; sp.gr. 1.0; visc. 400 cps; HLB 15.0; sapon. no. 45-55; hyd. no. 65-80; flash pt. (PMCC) > 350 F; 97% min. act.; nonionic.

T-Maz® 80K. [PPG/Specialty Chem.]
Chem. Descrip.: Polysorbate 80
CAS 9005-65-6
Uses: Emulsifier, solubilizer, wetting agent, stabilizer, dispersant, visc. modifier for drug prods.
Regulatory: FDA 21CFR §172.840, 173.340, 573.860; kosher
Properties: Yel. clear liq., bland odor; sol. in water, ethanol, veg. oil; disp. in propylene glycol, toluene; sp.gr. 1.09; b.p. > 300 F; HLB 15.0; acid no. 2 max.; sapon. no. 45-55; hyd. no. 65-80; flash pt. (PMCC) > 350 F; 100% conc.; nonionic
Toxicology: LD50 (oral, rat) > 30 ml/kg (mild); nonirritating, noncomedogenic
Storage: Store in well-ventilated area below 120 F.

T-Maz® 80KLM. [PPG/Specialty Chem.]
Chem. Descrip.: Polysorbate 80, low melt pt.
CAS 9005-65-6
Uses: Emulsifier, solubilizer, wetting agent, stabilizer, dispersant, visc. modifier, suspending agent for drug prods.
Regulatory: Kosher
Properties: Gardner 5 liq.; sol. @ 5% in water, veg. oil, @ 2% in ethanol; disp. in toluene, propylene glycol; HLB 15.0; acid no. 2 max.; sapon. no. 45-55; hyd. no. 65-80; flash pt. (PMCC) > 350 F.

T-Maz® 81. [PPG/Specialty Chem.]
Chem. Descrip.: Polysorbate 81
CAS 9005-65-6
Uses: Emulsifier, solubilizer, wetting agent, stabilizer, dispersant, visc. modifier, suspending agent for drug prods.
Properties: Gardner 6 liq.; sol. in min. spirits; disp. in water, min. oils, toluene, veg. oils; HLB 10.0; sapon. no. 96-104; hyd. no. 134-150; flash pt. (PMCC) > 350 F; 100% conc.; nonionic.

T-Maz® 81K. [PPG/Specialty Chem.]
Chem. Descrip.: Polysorbate 81
CAS 9005-65-6
Uses: Emulsifier, solubilizer, wetting agent, stabilizer, dispersant, visc. modifier, suspending

agent for drug prods.
Regulatory: Kosher
Properties: Gardner 6 liq.; sol. in min. spirits; disp. in water, min. oils, toluene, veg. oils; HLB 10.0; sapon. no. 96-104; hyd. no. 134-150; flash pt. (PMCC) > 350 F; 100% conc.; nonionic.

T-Maz® 85. [PPG/Specialty Chem.]
Chem. Descrip.: Polysorbate 85
CAS 9005-70-3
Uses: Emulsifier, solubilizer, wetting agent, stabilizer, dispersant, visc. modifier, suspending agent for drug prods.
Properties: Lt. amber liq.; sol. in ethanol, min. spirits; disp. in water; sp.gr. 1.0; visc. 300 cps; HLB 11.1; sapon. no. 83-93; hyd. no. 39-52; flash pt. (PMCC) > 350 F; 95% min. act.; nonionic.

TMP-HP. [Albright & Wilson Am.; Albright & Wilson UK]
Chem. Descrip.: Trimethyl phosphite
CAS 121-45-9; EINECS 204-471-5
Uses: Intermediate in mfg. of phosphonate esters and vinyl phosphates; reagent for dehalogenations, dehydrohalogenations and reductive cyclizations
Properties: M.w. 124; dens. 1.05 g/cm³; b.p. 112 C; 98.5% min. assay.

T.P.L. Troches. [United-Guardian]
Chem. Descrip.: Contains Triamite
Uses: Anesthetic and antibacterial throat lozenges for medical and health-care use in clinics and hospitals.

Tragacanth Flake No. 27. [Meer]
Chem. Descrip.: Tragacanth gum
CAS 9000-65-1; EINECS 232-552-5
Uses: Thickener, water binder, suspending agent, emulsifier for toothpastes, medicinal emulsions, pharmaceutical jellies and creams
Properties: Water-sol.

Tragacanth Gum Ribbon No. 1. [Meer]
Chem. Descrip.: Tragacanth gum
CAS 9000-65-1; EINECS 232-552-5
Uses: Thickener, water binder, suspending agent, emulsifier for toothpastes, medicinal emulsions, pharmaceutical jellies and creams
Properties: Water-sol.

Transcutol. [Gattefosse SA]
Chem. Descrip.: Ethoxydiglycol USP
CAS 111-90-0; EINECS 203-919-7
Uses: Solv. for active ingreds. in pharmaceutical preps.; solubilizer for difficult-to-formulate compds. for oral, topical, sublingual, and transdermal applics., steroids, hormones; cosurfactant for microemulsions
Regulatory: Japanese compliance
Properties: Transparent limpid liq., faint odor; sol. in water, ethanol 96°; partly sol. in veg. oils; insol. in min. oil; sp.gr. 0.985-0.989 (20 C); f.p. -76 C; b.p. 195-202 C; acid no. < 0.10; flash pt. 96 C; ref. index 1.425-1.429 (20 C); 100% conc.
Toxicology: LD50 (oral, rat) 5.9 ml/kg; nontoxic; nonirritating to skin and eyes
Storage: Preserve in orig. hermetically closed container; stored under nitrogen; use rapidly after

opening.

Triamite. [United-Guardian]
Uses: Antibacterial, local anesthetic, and antioxidant for use in pharmaceuticals, mouthwashes, toothpastes, lozenges
Custom product

Triglyme. [Ferro/Grant]
Chem. Descrip.: Triethylene glycol dimethyl ether
CAS 112-49-2
Uses: Solv. for pharmaceuticals
Properties: Colorless clear; mild, nonresidual odor; water-sol.; misc. with ethanol, acetone, benzene, diethyl ether, octane; m.w. 178.22; sp.gr. 0.9862; dens. 8.23 lb/gal; visc. 3.8 cP; f.p. -45 C; b.p. 216 C; flash pt. (CC) 111 C; ref. index 1.4224; pH neutral; surf. tens. 29.4 dynes/cm (20 C); 98.0% min. purity; slowly biodeg.
Toxicology: LD50 5000 mg/kg; low to mod. acute toxicity; chronic exposure may cause reproductive effects.

Tri-K Vitamin E Acetate. [Tri-K Industries]
Chem. Descrip.: Dl-α-Tocopheryl acetate USP
CAS 7695-91-2; EINECS 231-710-0
Uses: Natural antioxidant for pharmaceuticals @ 0.1%; good stability
Properties: Colorless or yel. clear visc. liq., odorless; misc. with veg. and min. oils; insol. in water; sp.gr. 0.952-0.966; f.p. -27.5 C; b.p. 184 C (0.01 mm), 205 C (0.02 mm); Flash pt. (Cleveland) 266 C; 96-102% act.
Toxicology: Relatively nontoxic; LD50 (oral, rat) 20 g; possible allergic reaction or hypersensitivity
Precaution: Combustible; heated to decomp. or under fire conditions, emits toxic fumes; incompat. with oxidizing agents, alkalies
Storage: Preserve in tight containers, protected from light and heat; 2 yrs shelf life @ R.T.

Trilaxamin. [United-Guardian]
Uses: Rapid acting, mild laxative
Properties: Capsules or tablets
Custom product

Tris Amino® Conc. [ANGUS]
Chem. Descrip.: Tris (hydroxymethyl) aminomethane
CAS 77-86-1; EINECS 201-064-4
Uses: Pharmaceutical buffer and solubilizer
Properties: Misc. with water; 60% water.

Tris Amino® Crystals. [ANGUS]
Chem. Descrip.: Tris (hydroxymethyl) aminomethane
CAS 77-86-1; EINECS 201-064-4
Uses: Buffer in pharmaceutical, diagnostic, and biochemical applics.
Properties: Sol. 80 g/100 ml water (20 C); m.w. 121.14; m.p. 171-172 C; b.p. 219-220 C (10 mm); pH 10.4 (0.1M aq., 20 C); 60% water.

Tris Amino® Molecular Biology Grade. [ANGUS]
Chem. Descrip.: Tris (hydroxymethyl) aminomethane
CAS 77-86-1; EINECS 201-064-4
Uses: Pharmaceutical intermediate, buffer, solubilizer; pH buffer for analytical, reagent, diagnostic,

and biological applics., in prod. of enzymes; CO_2 scavenger and buffering agent for blood plasma; treatment or prevention for acidosis
Properties: Wh. cryst. solid; sol. 80 g/100 ml in water (20 C); sol. in alcohols, glycols; m.w. 121.14; m.p. 168-172 C; pH 10.4 (0.1M aq., 20 C); 0.5% max. water
Precaution: Mildly alkaline.

Tris Amino® Ultra Pure Standard. [ANGUS]
Chem. Descrip.: Tris (hydroxymethyl) aminomethane
CAS 77-86-1; EINECS 201-064-4
Uses: Intermediate, buffer, solubilizer, stabilizer; buffer for diagnostic/biological applics., contact lens cleaners, in prod. of enzymes; CO_2 scavenger/buffer for blood plasma; treats/prevents acidosis; for injectables, orals, topicals, ophthalmics
Regulatory: USP, German, Japananese pharmacopoeia compliance
Properties: Wh. cryst. solid; sol. 80 g/100 ml in water (20 C); sol. in alcohols, glycols; m.w. 121.14; m.p. 168-172 C; b.p. 219 C; pH 10.0-11.5 (5% aq.); 99.9-100.1% purity
Precaution: Mildly alkaline.

Trisynlane. [Tri-K Industries]
Chem. Descrip.: Hydrog. polyisobutene
Uses: Substitute for natural squalane for pharmaceuticals; provides exc. feel with good spreading and penetrating props. as base oil; good oxidation stability
Properties: Colorless liq., odorless, tasteless; misc. with veg. and min. oils.

Trypsin 1:75. [Am. Labs]
Chem. Descrip.: Trypsin
CAS 9002-07-7; EINECS 232-650-8
Uses: Proteolytic enzyme for pharmaceutical applics.; used for protein digestion, in tissue culture
Properties: Cream-colored amorphous powd., char. nonoffensive odor
Storage: Preserve in tight containers in cool, dry place.

Trypsin 1:80. [Am. Labs]
Chem. Descrip.: Trypsin
CAS 9002-07-7; EINECS 232-650-8
Uses: Proteolytic enzyme for pharmaceutical applics.; used for protein digestion, in tissue culture
Properties: Cream-colored amorphous powd., char. nonoffensive odor
Storage: Preserve in tight containers in cool, dry place.

Trypsin 1:150. [Am. Labs]
Chem. Descrip.: Trypsin
CAS 9002-07-7; EINECS 232-650-8
Uses: Proteolytic enzyme for pharmaceutical applics.; used for protein digestion, in tissue culture
Properties: Cream-colored amorphous powd., char. nonoffensive odor
Storage: Preserve in tight containers in cool, dry place.

Tullanox HM-100. [Tulco]
Chem. Descrip.: Precipitated silica
EINECS 215-683-2
Uses: Filler/additive, rheology control agent for pharmaceuticals.
Tullanox HM-150. [Tulco]
Chem. Descrip.: Precipitated silica
EINECS 215-683-2
Uses: Filler/additive, rheology control agent for pharmaceuticals.
Tullanox HM-250. [Tulco]
Chem. Descrip.: Hydrophobic precipitated silica, modified by org. silazane compd.
EINECS 215-683-2
Uses: Filler/additive, rheology control agent for pharmaceuticals
Properties: Wh. powd., extremely fine particle size; 0.3 μ particle diam.; sp.gr. 2.2; bulk dens. 5-6 lb/ft^3; surf. area 125 ± 20 m^2/g; ref. index 1.45-1.46; pH > 9 (4% in 50/50 IPA/water)
Toxicology: May cause eye irritation.
Turpinal® 4 NL. [Henkel/Cospha; Henkel KGaA/Cospha]
Chem. Descrip.: Tetrasodium etidronate
CAS 3794-83-0; EINECS 223-267-7
Uses: Chelating agent for heavy metal ions; stabilizer for pharmaceutical hair/skin preps.
Properties: Colorless to sl. ylsh. liq., neutral inherent odor; pH 10-12; 29-30% conc.
Turpinal® SL. [Henkel/Cospha; Henkel KGaA/Cospha]
Chem. Descrip.: Etidronic acid
CAS 2809-21-4; EINECS 220-552-8
Uses: Chelating agent for heavy metal ions; stabilizer, antioxidant for pharmaceutical hair/skin preps.
Properties: Colorless to sl. ylsh. liq., neutral inherent odor; sp.gr. 1.445-1.458; 58-61% conc.
Toxicology: Protect skin and eyes from contact
Precaution: Corrosive.
T-Wax. [Tri-K Industries]
Chem. Descrip.: Emulsifying wax NF
CAS 97069-99-0
Uses: Self-emulsifying wax, thickening agent, balanced emulsifying system for pharmaceuticals,

skin care prods.; stable at high and low pH
Properties: Wh. waxy flakes, mild char. odor; forms emulsion in water; sp.gr. 0.87; m.p. 48-52 C; b.p. > 400 F; iodine no. 3.5 max.; sapon. no. 14 max.; hyd. no. 178-192; flash pt. (PMCC) 300 F; pH 5-7 (3% aq. disp., 45 C); 100% act.; nonionic
Toxicology: LD50 (oral, rat) > 50 mg/kg; nonhazardous by skin and eye contact
Precaution: Hazardous decomp. prods.: CO, CO_2, hydrocarbons
Storage: Store in cool place; reseal containers tightly to avoid contamination; flakes may clump after storage under warm conditions.
28-1801. [Nat'l. Starch & Chem.]
Chem. Descrip.: Corn starch NF
CAS 9005-25-8; EINECS 232-679-6
Uses: Binder, filler, and disintegrant in pharmaceutical formulations
Properties: Wh. powd.; 12% volatiles.
Tylose® C, CB Series. [Hoechst Celanese/Colorants & Surf.]
Chem. Descrip.: Sodium CMC
CAS 9004-32-4
Uses: Thickener for pharmaceuticals
Properties: Gran., powd.; 100% act.; anionic.
Tylose® MH Grades. [Hoechst Celanese/Colorants & Surf.; Hoechst AG]
Chem. Descrip.: Methyl hydroxyethylcellulose
CAS 9032-42-2
Uses: Binder, thickener, pigment, foam, and filler stabilizer, dispersant, emulsifier, visc. control aid, protective colloid for pharmaceuticals
Properties: Gran.; water-sol.; 100% act.; nonionic.
Tylose® MHB. [Hoechst Celanese/Colorants & Surf.]
Chem. Descrip.: Methyl hydroxyethylcellulose
CAS 9032-42-2
Uses: Binder, thickener, pigment, foam, and filler stabilizer, dispersant, emulsifier, visc. control aid, protective colloid for pharmaceuticals; gran.; water-sol.; nonionic.
Type B Torula Dried Yeast. [Lake States]
Chem. Descrip.: Dried yeast USP
CAS 68876-77-7
Uses: Nutritional yeast; 45% min. protein
Storage: Store in cool, dry conditions.

U

Ultrafino. [Luzenac Am.]
Chem. Descrip.: Talc USP/FCC
CAS 14807-96-6; EINECS 238-877-9
Uses: Highly refined, extra-fine talc with exc. slip and lustrous, translucent appearance; recommended for formulations with sensitive fragrances and pigments, antiperspirants
Properties: Powd.; 99.96% thru 325 mesh; median diam. 4 μ; tapped dens. 35 lb/ft³; pH 9 (10% slurry).

Unamino GLUT. [Universal Preserv-A-Chem]
Chem. Descrip.: L-Glutamic acid
CAS 56-86-0; EINECS 200-293-7
Uses: Flavor enhancer, medicine/biochemical research.

Unibix AP (Acid Proof) [MLG Enterprises Ltd.]
Chem. Descrip.: Norbixin alkaline sol'n. (water, propylene glycol, polysorbate 80)
Uses: Natural colorant for pharmaceuticals
Regulatory: FDA 21CFR §73.30, 73.1030, 73.2030; EEC E160b; kosher incl. Passover use
Properties: Dk. red sol'n.; sol. in water; stable down to pH 1; 4% norbixin.
Storage: Store in cook, dark place; avoid exposure to air, heat, and light.

Unibix CUS. [MLG Enterprises Ltd.]
Chem. Descrip.: Encapsulated sodium norbixinate
Uses: Natural colorant providing yel. tint for pharmaceuticals
Regulatory: FDA 21CFR §73.30, 73.1030, 73.2030; EEC E160b; kosher incl. Passover use
Properties: Orange powd.; water-sol.; 1% norbixin.
Storage: Store in closed container @ 40 F; avoid exposure to air, heat, and light.

Unibix ENC (Acid Proof) [MLG Enterprises Ltd.]
Chem. Descrip.: Encapsulated sodium norbixinate
Uses: Natural colorant providing yel. tint for pharmaceuticals
Regulatory: FDA 21CFR §73.30, 73.1030, 73.2030; EEC E160b; kosher incl. Passover use
Properties: Orange powd.; water-sol.
Storage: Store in closed container @ 40 F; avoid exposure to air, heat, and light.

Unibix W. [MLG Enterprises Ltd.]
Chem. Descrip.: Annatto extract
CAS 8015-67-6
Uses: Natural colorant providing yel. to orange shades in pharmaceuticals

Regulatory: FDA 21CFR §73.30, 73.1030, 73.2030; EEC E160b; kosher incl. Passover use
Properties: Orange powd.; sol. in alkaline sol'n.s @ pH 10-11; 25-40% norbixin.
Storage: Store in closed container @ 40 F; avoid exposure to air, heat, and light.

Unicaine-B. [Universal Preserv-A-Chem]
Chem. Descrip.: Benzocaine
CAS 51-05-8
Uses: Local anesthetic in medicine and suntan preps..

Unichem ACETA. [Universal Preserv-A-Chem]
Chem. Descrip.: Acetic acid
CAS 64-19-7; EINECS 200-580-7
Uses: Intermediate, acidifying agent, vehicle for mfg. of pharmaceuticals.

Unichem BZBN. [Universal Preserv-A-Chem]
Chem. Descrip.: Benzyl benzoate
CAS 120-51-4; EINECS 204-402-9
Uses: External medicine.

Unichem Levula. [Universal Preserv-A-Chem]
Chem. Descrip.: Levulinic acid
CAS 123-76-2; EINECS 204-649-2
Uses: Pharmaceutical intermediate.

Unichem MC. [Universal Preserv-A-Chem]
Chem. Descrip.: Magnesium carbonate
CAS 546-93-0; EINECS 208-915-9
Uses: Used in pharmaceuticals, dentifrices.

Unichem MGC. [Universal Preserv-A-Chem]
Chem. Descrip.: Magnesium carbonate
CAS 546-93-0; EINECS 208-915-9
Uses: Used in pharmacueticals, dentifrices.

Unicide U-13. [Induchem AG; Lipo]
Chem. Descrip.: Imidazolidinyl urea
CAS 39236-46-9; EINECS 254-372-6
Uses: Preservative, biocide for pharmaceuticals, esp. for water phase; effective against Gram-negative bacteria; active over wide pH range
Use level: 0.2-0.6%
Regulatory: EEC, USA permitted
Properties: Wh. powd., odorless; sol. in water, aq. alcohol; sl. sol. in pure alcohol; insol. in lipoids; m.p. 150 C dec.; pH 7 ± 0.5 (2% aq.)
Toxicology: Nontoxic.

Unifilter U-41. [Induchem AG]
Chem. Descrip.: Butyl methoxydibenzoylmethane, octyl methoxycinnamate, 3-benzylidene camphor

Uses: Broad spectrum sunscreen and uv-absorbers for suntan prods., stabilization of light-sensitive prods.
Use level: 1-13%
Regulatory: EEC permitted
Properties: Ylsh. liq.; oil-sol.

Unifluorid D 401. [Induchem AG]
Chem. Descrip.: Stearyl trihydroxyethyl propylene diamine dihydrofluoride
CAS 6818-37-7
Uses: Pharmaceutical ingred. for caries prophylaxis; for toothpastes, gels, and mouthwashes
Use level: Up to 6%
Regulatory: EEC permitted
Properties: Yel. liq.; water-sol.

Unifluorid H 101. [Induchem AG]
Chem. Descrip.: Cetylamine hydrofluoride
CAS 3151-59-5; EINECS 221-588-7
Uses: Pharmaceutical ingred. for caries prophylaxis, toothpastes, gels, mouthwashes
Use level: Up to 2%
Regulatory: EEC permitted
Properties: Yel. liq.; water-sol.

Unihydag Wax 12. [Universal Preserv-A-Chem]
Chem. Descrip.: Lauryl alcohol
CAS 112-53-8; EINECS 203-982-0
Uses: Pharmaceutical raw material.

Unihydag Wax-14. [Universal Preserv-A-Chem]
Chem. Descrip.: Myristyl alcohol
CAS 112-72-1; EINECS 204-000-3
Uses: Pharmaceutical raw material.

Unihydag Wax-18. [Universal Preserv-A-Chem]
Chem. Descrip.: Stearyl alcohol
CAS 112-92-5; EINECS 204-017-6
Uses: Emollient, pharmaceutical raw material.

Unihydag Wax 22. [Universal Preserv-A-Chem]
Chem. Descrip.: Behenyl alcohol
CAS 661-19-8; EINECS 211-546-6
Uses: Pharmaceutical raw material.

Uninontan U 34. [Induchem AG]
Chem. Descrip.: Sodium citrate, lemon extract, and cucumber extract
Uses: Plant extract blend which inhibits tanning and lightens the skin; for suntan prods., sun protection prods.
Regulatory: USA, EEC, and Japan permitted
Properties: Ylsh. liq.; water-sol.

Unipabol U-17. [Induchem AG; Lipo]
Chem. Descrip.: PEG-25 PABA
CAS 113010-52-9
Uses: Uv-B sunscreen for pharmaceuticals, suntan prods., stabilization of light-sensitive prods.
Use level: 5-10%
Regulatory: EEC permitted
Properties: Ylsh. liq.; water-sol.

Unipertan P-24. [Induchem AG; Lipo]
Chem. Descrip.: Hydrolyzed collagen, acetyl tyrosine, riboflavin
Uses: Tanning accelerator complex for pharmaceuticals
Use level: 5%
Regulatory: EEC, USA permitted

Properties: Yel. liq.; water-sol.

Unipertan P-242. [Induchem AG; Lipo]
Chem. Descrip.: Hydrolyzed collagen, acetyl tyrosine, adenosine triphosphate
Uses: Tanning accelerator complex for pharmaceuticals
Use level: 5%
Regulatory: EEC, USA permitted
Properties: Brn. liq.; water-sol.

Unipertan P-2002. [Induchem AG]
Chem. Descrip.: Hydrolyzed collagen, acetyl tyrosine, adenosine triphosphate, and riboflavin
Uses: Tanning accelerator complex for suntan prods.
Use level: 5%
Regulatory: USA and EEC permitted
Properties: Yel. liq.

Unipertan VEG 24. [Induchem AG]
Chem. Descrip.: Butylene glycol, acetyl tyrosine, hydrolyzed vegetable protein, and riboflavin
Uses: Tanning accelerator complex
Use level: 5%
Regulatory: EEC and USA permitted
Properties: Yel. liq.; water-sol.

Unipertan VEG 242. [Induchem AG]
Chem. Descrip.: Butylene glycol, acetyl tyrosine, hydrolyzed vegetable protein, and adenosine triphosphate
Uses: Tanning accelerator complex
Use level: 5%
Regulatory: EEC and USA permitted
Properties: Brn. liq.; water-sol.

Uniphen P-23. [Induchem AG; Lipo]
Chem. Descrip.: Phenoxyethanol, methylparaben, ethylparaben, propylparaben, butylparaben
Uses: Preservative, bactericide, fungicide for pharmaceuticals, deodorants; esp. to preserve the oil phase of emulsions
Use level: 0.3-1.0%
Regulatory: USA, Japan, and Europe approvals
Properties: Colorless clear sl. visc. liq., faint aromatic odor; sol. in oil, ethanol, aq. ethanol, ethylene glycol, propylene glycol; misc. with acetone, chloroform; sl. sol. in water; sp.gr. 1.120-1.126; ref. index 1.540-1.543.

Uniquart CPC. [Universal Preserv-A-Chem]
Chem. Descrip.: Cetyl pyridinium chloride
CAS 123-03-5; EINECS 204-593-9
Uses: Emulsifier; antibacterial, preservative for pharmaceuticals.

Unisol S-22. [Induchem AG]
Chem. Descrip.: 3-Benzylidene camphor
CAS 15087-24-8; EINECS 239-139-9
Uses: Uv-B sunscreen for suntan prods., stabilization of light-sensitive prods.
Use level: 1-5%
Regulatory: EEC permitted
Properties: Colorless solid; oil-sol.

Unisweet 70. [Universal Preserv-A-Chem]
Chem. Descrip.: Sorbitol
CAS 50-70-4; EINECS 200-061-5
Uses: Humectant, nutritive sweetener, oleaginous

vehicle, tablet diluent.

Unisweet 70/CONC. [Universal Preserv-A-Chem]
Chem. Descrip.: Sorbitol
CAS 50-70-4; EINECS 200-061-5
Uses: Humectant, nutritive sweetener, oleaginous vehicle, tablet diluent.

Unisweet CALSAC. [Universal Preserv-A-Chem]
Chem. Descrip.: Calcium saccharin
CAS 6485-34-3; EINECS 229-349-9
Uses: Sweetener..

Unisweet Caramel. [Universal Preserv-A-Chem]
Chem. Descrip.: Caramel
CAS 8028-89-5; EINECS 232-435-9
Uses: Colorant.

Unisweet CONC. [Universal Preserv-A-Chem]
Chem. Descrip.: Sorbitol
CAS 50-70-4; EINECS 200-061-5
Uses: Humectant, nutritive sweetener, oleaginous vehicle, tablet diluent.

Unisweet EVAN. [Universal Preserv-A-Chem]
Chem. Descrip.: Ethyl vanillin
CAS 121-32-4; EINECS 204-464-7
Uses: Flavoring agent.

Unisweet L. [Universal Preserv-A-Chem]
Chem. Descrip.: Lactose
CAS 63-42-3; EINECS 200-559-2
Uses: Tablet/capsule diluent.

Unisweet Lactose. [Universal Preserv-A-Chem]
Chem. Descrip.: Lactose
CAS 63-42-3; EINECS 200-599-2
Uses: Tablet/capsule diluent.

Unisweet MAN. [Universal Preserv-A-Chem]
Chem. Descrip.: Mannitol
CAS 69-65-8; EINECS 200-711-8
Uses: Anticaking agent, humectant, sweetener, tonicity agent, bulking agent, tablet diluent.

Unisweet SAC. [Universal Preserv-A-Chem]
Chem. Descrip.: Saccharin
CAS 81-07-2; EINECS 201-321-0
Uses: Noncaloric sweetener, pharmaceutic aid.

Unisweet SOSAC. [Universal Preserv-A-Chem]
Chem. Descrip.: Sodium saccharin
CAS 128-44-9; EINECS 204-886-1
Uses: Artificial sweetener.

Unisweet VAN. [Universal Preserv-A-Chem]
Chem. Descrip.: Vanillin
CAS 121-33-5; EINECS 204-465-2
Uses: Flavoring agent.

Unitina HR. [Universal Preserv-A-Chem]
Chem. Descrip.: Hydrog. castor oil
CAS 8001-78-3; EINECS 232-292-2
Uses: Wax for pharmaceuticals.

Unitrienol T-27. [Induchem AG; Lipo]
Chem. Descrip.: Farnesyl acetate, farnesol, panthenyl triacetate
Uses: A bioactive complex with cell regenerating props. for pharmaceuticals
Use level: 2-8%
Regulatory: EEC and USA permitted
Properties: Ylsh. liq.; oil-sol.

USP-1. [Zinc Corp. of Am.]
Chem. Descrip.: French process zinc oxide USP
CAS 1314-13-2; EINECS 215-222-5
Uses: Protective astringent in dermatological ointments and lotions, e.g., calamine lotion, coal tar ointment, zinc gelation, zinc oxide ointment, zinc oxide paste; also in zinc-eugenol dental cement
Regulatory: FDA §73.1991
Properties: Powd.; 0.12 µ mean particle size; 99.99% thru 325 mesh; pkg. dens. 30 lb/ft^3; surf. area 9 m^2/g; oil absorp. 12 lb oil/100 lb ZnO; 99.6% zinc oxide.

USP-2. [Zinc Corp. of Am.]
Chem. Descrip.: Zinc oxide USP
CAS 1314-13-2; EINECS 215-222-5
Uses: Protective astringent in dermatological ointments and lotions, e.g., calamine lotion, coal tar ointment, zinc gelation, zinc oxide ointment, zinc oxide paste; also in zinc-eugenol dental cement
Properties: Powd.; 0.31 µ mean particle size; 99.99% thru 325 mesh; surf. area 3.2 m^2/g; sp.gr. 5.6; dens. 40 lb/ft^3; oil absorp. 12.

V

Vancide® 89 RE. [R.T. Vanderbilt]
Chem. Descrip.: Captan
CAS 133-06-2; EINECS 205-087-0
Uses: Antimicrobial and preservative for topical pharmaceuticals, veterinary prods.
Properties: Wh. to off-wh. fine powd.; sol. (g/100 g solv.): 7.5 g xylene, 5.8 g cyclohexanone, 5.3 g chloroform, 5.2 g tetrachloroethane, 5.0 g ethyl acetate, 4.2 g acetone; dens. 1.7 mg/m^3; m.p. 171-176 C; pH 5-6 (1% disp.); 97% assay.

Vaseline 335 G. [Ceca SA]
Chem. Descrip.: Vaseline meeting European and US pharmacopoeias
Uses: Excipient in pharmaceuticals, as ointments for skin where actives must remain on epidermis, base for laxatives, ophthalmologic ointments, creams, and salves, veterinary prods.
Properties: Mettler drop pt. 45-50 C.

Vaseline 7702. [Ceca SA]
Chem. Descrip.: Vaseline meeting European and US pharmacopoeias
Uses: Excipient in pharmaceuticals, as ointments for skin where actives must remain on epidermis, base for laxatives, ophthalmologic ointments, creams, and salves, veterinary prods.
Properties: Mettler drop pt. 46-52 C.

Vaseline 8332. [Ceca SA]
Chem. Descrip.: Vaseline meeting European and US pharmacopoeias
Uses: Excipient in pharmaceuticals, as ointments for skin where actives must remain on epidermis, base for laxatives, ophthalmologic ointments, creams, and salves, veterinary prods.
Properties: Mettler drop pt. 44-49 C.

Vaseline 10049 BL. [Ceca SA]
Chem. Descrip.: Vaseline BP/USP
Uses: Excipient in pharmaceuticals, as ointments for skin where actives must remain on epidermis, base for laxatives, ophthalmologic ointments, creams, and salves, veterinary prods.
Properties: Mettler drop pt. 55-60 C.

Vaseline A. [Ceca SA]
Chem. Descrip.: Vaseline meeting European and US pharmacopoeias
Uses: Excipient in pharmaceuticals, as ointments for skin where actives must remain on epidermis, base for laxatives, ophthalmologic ointments, creams, and salves, veterinary prods.
Properties: Mettler drop pt. 51-57 C.

Vee Gee Pharmaceutical Gelatins. [Vyse Gelatin]
Chem. Descrip.: Gelatin NF
CAS 9000-70-8; EINECS 232-554-6
Uses: Tablet binder for pharmaceutical and health food industries; gelling agent, protective colloid, film-former, stabilizer, binder, dispersant, softener, tenderizer, foaming/whipping agent, water imbiber, flocculator, clarifier, protein source
Regulatory: FDA GRAS
Properties: Lt. straw coarse gran. to fine powds., sl. typ. bouillon-like odor and flavor; insol. in cold water, but swells and softens on immersion; dissolves in hot water; insol. in alcohol; sp.gr. 1.2; b.p. dec. > 100 C; complete combustion > 500 C; nonflamm.
Toxicology: Nuisance dust limits apply, 15 mg/m^3, 10 mg/m^3 total dust
Precaution: Incompat. with strong oxidizing agents.

Veegum®. [R.T. Vanderbilt]
Chem. Descrip.: Complex colloidal magnesium aluminum silicate derived from natural smectite clays
CAS 12199-37-0; EINECS 235-374-6
Uses: Thickener, visc. modifier, emulsion stabilizer for pharmaceutical emulsions, suspensions, sol'ns., liqs., creams, and pastes, toothpaste; suspending agent, binder; disintegrating agent for tablets; improves spreadability of ointments, lotions, creams
Properties: Wh. to tan sm. flakes, odorless, tasteless; insol. in water or alcohol; swells to many times original vol. in water to form colloidal disp.; dens. 2.6 mg/m^3; visc. 250 cps ± 25% (5% aq. disp.); pH 9.5 (5% aq disp.); < 8% moisture.

Veegum® HV. [R.T. Vanderbilt]
Chem. Descrip.: Magnesium aluminum silicate
CAS 12199-37-0; EINECS 235-374-6
Uses: Thickener, visc. modifier, emulsion stabilizer for pharmaceutical emulsions, suspensions, sol'ns., liqs., creams, and pastes, toothpaste; suspending agent, binder; disintegrating agent for tablets; improves spreadability of ointments, lotions, creams
Properties: Wh. flakes, odorless, tasteless; insol. in water or alcohol; swells to many times original vol. in water to form colloidal disp.; visc. 187-312 cps

(4% aq. disp.); < 8% moisture.

Veegum® K. [R.T. Vanderbilt]
Chem. Descrip.: Magnesium aluminum silicate
CAS 12199-37-0; EINECS 235-374-6
Uses: Thickener, visc. modifier, emulsion stabilizer for pharmaceutical acid suspensions; has low acid demand and high acid compatibility
Properties: Wh. flakes, odorless, tasteless; insol. in water or alcohol; swells to many times original vol. in water to form colloidal disp.; visc. 165-275 cps (5.5% disp.); pH 9.5 (5% aq.); < 8% moisture.

Veegum® PRO. [R.T. Vanderbilt]
Chem. Descrip.: Tromethamine magnesium aluminum silicate
Uses: Emulsion stabilizer, suspending agent for pharmaceuticals, veterinary prods.; hydrates rapidly in cold or hot water to form high visc. disps.
Properties: Wh. flakes, odorless, tasteless; visc. 300-500 cps (1.5% aq. disp.).

Velsicure®. [Velsicol]
Chem. Descrip.: Benzophenone
CAS 119-61-9; EINECS 204-337-6
Uses: Intermediate for pharmaceuticals
Properties: Flake, powd.; 99.9% purity.

Veltol®. [Pfizer Food Science]
Chem. Descrip.: Maltol FCC
CAS 118-71-8; EINECS 204-271-8
Uses: Flavor/fragrance enhancer/modifier; provides creaminess and sweetness enhancement of aspartame, allowing reduced usage levels; antioxidant; masks bitterness in pharmaceuticals
Regulatory: FDA 21CFR §172.515, 27CFR §24.246; FCC compliance; FEMA GRAS
Properties: Wh. cryst. powd., sweet caramellic aroma with lesser warm, fruity notes; sol. in alcohol; sol. 1 g/82 ml water, 21 ml alcohol, 80 ml glycerin, 28 ml propylene glycol; m.w. 126.11; m.p. 160-164 C; ignition temp. (dust) 740 C; 99-100.5% assay
Toxicology: LD50 (oral, rat) 2330 mg/kg; may cause mild eye irritation on prolonged contact; avoid formation of dust.

Veltol®-Plus. [Pfizer Food Science]
Chem. Descrip.: Ethyl maltol FCC
CAS 4940-11-8
Uses: Flavor/fragrance enhancer/modifier; provides creaminess and sweetness enhancement of aspartame, allowing reduced usage levels; antioxidant; for pharmaceuticals
Regulatory: FDA 21CFR §172.515, 27CFR §24.246; FCC compliance; FEMA GRAS
Properties: Wh. cryst. powd., char. odor, faint fruit-like odor on dilution; sol. in alcohol; sol. 1/g in 55 ml water, 10 ml alcohol, 17 ml propylene glycol, 5 ml chloroform; m.w. 140.14; m.p. 90 C; ignition temp. (dust) 700 C; 99-100.5% assay
Toxicology: LD50 (oral, rat) 1150 mg/kg; may cause mild eye irritation on prolonged contact
Precaution: Avoid formation of heavy dust concs.-forms explosive mix
Storage: Store in tight containers.

Versene 100. [Dow]

Versene 100 EP. [Dow]
Chem. Descrip.: Tetrasodium EDTA
CAS 64-02-8; EINECS 200-573-9
Uses: Chelating agent controlling trace metal ions in pharmaceuticals; for heavy metal poisoning treatment and drug stabilization (deactivates metal ions that interfere with drug performance)
Properties: Lt. straw-colored liq.; m.w. 1.290-1.325; dens. 10.9 lb/gal; pH 11.0-11.8 (1% aq.); chel. value 102; 39% act.

Versene 100 EP. [Dow]
Chem. Descrip.: Tetrasodium EDTA
CAS 64-02-8; EINECS 200-573-9
Uses: Chelating agent controlling trace metal ions in pharmaceuticals; for heavy metal poisoning treatment and drug stabilization (deactivates metal ions that interfere with drug performance)
Properties: Liq.

Versene 100 LS. [Dow]
Chem. Descrip.: Tetrasodium EDTA
CAS 64-02-8; EINECS 200-573-9
Uses: Chelating agent controlling trace metal ions in pharmaceuticals; for heavy metal poisoning treatment and drug stabilization (deactivates metal ions that interfere with drug performance)
Properties: Liq.

Versene 100 SRG. [Dow]
Chem. Descrip.: Tetrasodium EDTA
CAS 64-02-8; EINECS 200-573-9
Uses: Chelating agent controlling trace metal ions in pharmaceuticals; for heavy metal poisoning treatment and drug stabilization (deactivates metal ions that interfere with drug performance)
Properties: Liq.

Versene 100 XL. [Dow]
Chem. Descrip.: Tetrasodium EDTA
CAS 64-02-8; EINECS 200-573-9
Uses: Chelating agent controlling trace metal ions in pharmaceuticals; for heavy metal poisoning treatment and drug stabilization (deactivates metal ions that interfere with drug performance)
Properties: Clear liq.; m.w. 380; sp.gr. 1.255-1.290; bulk dens. 10.5 lb/gal; pH 11.0-11.8 (1% aq.); chel. value 100; 38% min. act.

Versene 220. [Dow]
Chem. Descrip.: Tetrasodium EDTA tetrahydrate
CAS 64-02-8; EINECS 200-573-9
Uses: Chelating agent controlling trace metal ions in pharmaceuticals; for heavy metal poisoning treatment and drug stabilization (deactivates metal ions that interfere with drug performance)
Properties: Wh. cryst.; m.w. 452; dens. 45 lb/ft^3; pH 10.5-11.5 (1% aq.); chel. value 219; 99% act.

Versene Acid. [Dow]
Chem. Descrip.: EDTA
CAS 60-00-4; EINECS 200-449-4
Uses: Chelating agent controlling trace metal ions in pharmaceuticals; for heavy metal poisoning treatment and drug stabilization (deactivates metal ions that interfere with drug performance); intermediate for prep. of other salt forms of EDTA
Properties: Wh. powd.; m.w. 292; dens. 54 lb/ft^3; pH 2.5-3.0 (sat. aq. sol'n.); chel. value 339; 99% act.

Versene CA. [Dow]
Chem. Descrip.: Calcium-disodium EDTA
CAS 62-33-9; EINECS 200-529-9
Uses: Chelating agent controlling trace metal ions in pharmaceuticals and medical applics.; for heavy metal poisoning treatment and drug stabilization (deactivates metal ions that interfere with drug performance)
Regulatory: FCC, USP, and kosher compliance
Properties: Wh. powd.; m.w. 410; dens. 40 lb/ft³; pH 6.5-7.5 (1%); 97-102% act.

Versene Diammonium EDTA. [Dow]
Chem. Descrip.: Diammonium EDTA
CAS 20824-56-0; EINECS 244-063-4
Uses: Chelating agent controlling trace metal ions in pharmaceuticals; for heavy metal poisoning treatment and drug stabilization (deactivates metal ions that interfere with drug performance)
Properties: Lt. straw-colored liq.; m.w. 326; sp.gr. 1.19-1.22; dens. 10.0 lb/gal; pH 4.6-5.2; chel. value 137; 44.6% act.

Versene NA. [Dow]
Chem. Descrip.: Disodium EDTA dihydrate USP, FCC
CAS 139-33-3; EINECS 205-358-3
Uses: Chelating agent controlling trace metal ions in pharmaceuticals and medical applics.; for heavy metal poisoning treatment and drug stabilization (deactivates metal ions that interfere with drug performance)
Regulatory: FCC, USP, and Kosher compliance
Properties: Wh. cryst.; m.w. 372; dens. 67 lb/ft³; pH 4.3-4.7 (1%); chel. value 267; 99% act.

Versene Na₂. [Dow]
Chem. Descrip.: Disodium EDTA dihydrate USP, FCC
CAS 139-33-3; EINECS 205-358-3
Uses: Chelating agent
Properties: Wh. cryst.; m.w. 372; dens. 67 lb/ft³; pH 4.3-4.87 (1%); chel. value 267; 99% min. act.

Versene Tetraammonium EDTA. [Dow]
Chem. Descrip.: Tetraammonium EDTA
Uses: Chelating agent controlling trace metal ions in pharmaceuticals; for heavy metal poisoning treatment and drug stabilization (deactivates metal ions that interfere with drug performance)
Properties: Lt. straw-colored liq.; m.w. 360; sp.gr. 1.16-1.19; dens. 9.7 lb/gal; pH 9.0-9.5; chel. value 130; 46.8% act.

Versenex 80. [Dow]
Chem. Descrip.: Pentasodium DTPA
CAS 140-01-2; EINECS 205-391-3
Uses: Chelating agent controlling trace metal ions in pharmaceuticals; for heavy metal poisoning treatment and drug stabilization (deactivates metal ions that interfere with drug performance)
Properties: Lt. straw-colored liq.; m.w. 503; sp.gr. 1.28-1.32; dens. 10.8 lb/gal; pH 11.0-11.8 (1% aq.); chel. value 80; 40.2% act.

Versenol 120. [Dow]
Chem. Descrip.: Trisodium HEDTA
CAS 139-89-9; EINECS 205-381-9

Uses: Chelating agent controlling trace metal ions in pharmaceuticals; for heavy metal poisoning treatment and drug stabilization (deactivates metal ions that interfere with drug performance)
Properties: Lt. straw-colored liq.; m.w. 344; sp.gr. 1.26-1.31; dens. 10.7 lb/gal; pH 11.0-11.8 (1% aq.); chel. value 120; 41.3% act.

Vifcoll CCN-40, CCN-40 Powd. [Nikko Chem. Co. Ltd.]
Chem. Descrip.: N-Cocoyl collagen peptide, sodium salt
Uses: Emulsifier used in pharmaceuticals
Properties: Pale yel. liq. and wh. or pale yel. powd. resp.; m.w. 600; pH 5.5-7.5 (both, 3% aq. for powd.); 30% act. in water (CCN-40)
Unverified

Vigilan. [Fanning]
Chem. Descrip.: Lanolin oil
CAS 8038-43-5; EINECS 274-559-6
Uses: Emulsifier, emollient, conditioner, moisturizer for pharmaceuticals; coupling agent for castor and min. oils; spreads rapidly
Properties: Gardner 8 max. liq. (Regular), 6 max. (Superfine), pleasant mild odor; sol. in IPM, castor and min. oils, propylene glycol laurate, ethyl acetate, silicone fluids; insol. in water; acid no. 2.0 max.; iodine no. 36 max.; sapon. no. 95-110; cloud pt. 20 C; 100% conc.; nonionic.

Vigilan AWS. [Fanning]
Chem. Descrip.: PPG-12-PEG-65 lanolin oil
CAS 68458-58-8
Uses: O/w emulsifier; plasticizer, emollient, solubilizer, and wetting agent in pharmaceuticals
Properties: Gardner 9-11 color; sol. in water, ethanol, castor oil, propylene glycol laurate, acetone, ethyl acetate; HLB 13.5; acid no. 3.0 max.; iodine no. 15 max.; sapon. no. 10-25; pH 7 max. (10%); 100% conc.; nonionic.

Vitacote® B12 1%. [Particle Dynamics]
Chem. Descrip.: Microencapsuled cyanocobalamin
CAS 68-19-9; EINECS 200-680-0
Uses: Encapsulated vitamin for pharmaceutical tableting and nutritional supplements
Properties: Lt. pink to pink relatively free-flowing powd., typ. odor; 85% min. thru 60 mesh; dens. 0.5 g/cc; 0.9-1.1% assay.

Vitamin A Palmitate Type 250-CWS No. 65312. [Roche]
Chem. Descrip.: Vitamin A palmitate USP FCC compded. with acacia, sugar, modified food starch, and BHT, BHA, and dl-α-tocopherol (antioxidants)
Uses: For use in dry pharmaceutical prods. that are to be reconstituted with liqs.; not suitable where clarity of liqs. is essential or for tablet mfg.
Properties: Lt. yel. spherical dry free-flowing beadlets, nearly odorless; 90% min. thru 30 mesh, 25% max. thru 80 mesh; disp. in cold water, fruit juices, milk, infant formulas; 250,000 IU/g assay
Toxicology: Vitamin A: sustained daily intakes

exceeding 50,000 IU (adults), 20,000 IU (infants) may cause toxic effects (headache, vomiting, liver damage); US RDA 8000 IU (pregnant/lactating women)
Storage: Store in cool, dry place.

Vitamin A Palmitate Type PIMO/BH No. 638280100. [Roche]
Chem. Descrip.: Vitamin A palmitate, 1,000,000 IU/g, stabilized with BHA/BHT
CAS 79-81-2; EINECS 201-228-5
Uses: Antikeratinizing, moisturizing ingred. for skin care and after-sun tanning prods.; in aq. disps., oleaginous preps., capsulated prods. in pharmaceuticals field
Properties: Lt. yel. to amber clear liq., sl. char. odor, bland oily taste; misc. with edible oils and fats; sol. in ether, hydrocarbons, chlorinated hydrocarbons; sl. sol. in alcohol; insol. in water; m.w. 524.9; sp.gr. 0.90-0.95; 1,000,000 min. units vitamin A/g
Toxicology: Vitamin A: excessive daily intakes (> 50,000 IU in adults, 20,000 IU in infants) may cause toxic effects (headache, vomiting, liver damage); US RDA 8000 IU (pregnant/lactating women)
Storage: Store @ 70 F; refrigerate if stored for several mos, then hold @ R.T. for 24 h before use.

Vitamin A Palmitate USP, FCC Type P1.7/BHT No. 63693. [Roche]
Chem. Descrip.: Vitamin A palmitate USP FCC, stabilized with BHT
Uses: Used where max. vitamin A required for soft gelatin capsules, multivitamins; antikeratinizing, moisturizing ingred. for skin care and after-sun tanning prods.
Properties: Lt. yel. to amber clear liq., char. odor, bland oily taste; misc. with edible oils and fats; sol. in hydrocarbons, chlorinated hydrocarbons; sl. sol. in alcohol; insol. in water; m.w. 524.9; sp.gr. 0.90-0.95; 1,600,000 IU/g min. assay
Toxicology: Vitamin A: sustained daily intakes exceeding 50,000 IU (adults), 20,000 IU (infants) may cause toxic effects (headache, vomiting, liver damage); US RDA 8000 IU (pregnant/lactating women)
Storage: Sealed under inert gas; store in cool place under refrigeration; contents may cryst.; warm to 40 C before use.

Vitamin A Palmitate USP, FCC Type P1.7/E No. 63699. [Roche]
Chem. Descrip.: Vitamin A palmitate USP-FCC
CAS 79-81-2; EINECS 201-228-5
Uses: Used when max. vitamin A conc. required in soft gelatin capsules, multivitamins
Properties: Greenish-yel. to golden-yel. oily liq., char. odor; misc. with edible oils and fats; sol. in hydrocarbons, chlorinated hydrocarbons; sl. sol. in alcohol; insol. in water; m.w. 524.9; sp.gr. 0.90-0.95; 1,600,000 IU/g min.
Toxicology: Sustained daily intakes exceeding 50,000 IU (adults), 20,000 IU (infants) may cause toxic effects (headache, vomiting, liver damage);

US RDA 8000 IU (pregnant/lactating women)
Storage: Store in cool place under refrigeration; contents may crystallize; warm to 40 C to liquefy before use.

Vitamin A Palmitate USP, FCC Type P1.7 No. 262090000. [Roche]
Chem. Descrip.: Vitamin A palmitate
CAS 79-81-2; EINECS 201-228-5
Uses: Used when max. vitamin A conc. required in soft gelatin capsules, multivitamins; antikeratinizing, moisturizing ingred. for skin care and after-sun tanning prods.
Properties: Lt. yel. to amber clear liq., char. odor, bland oily taste; misc. with edible oils and fats; sol. in hydrocarbons and chlorinated hydrocarbons; sl. sol. in alcohol; insol. in water; sp.gr.0.90-0.95; m.w. 524.9; 1,600,000 IU/g assay
Toxicology: Vitamin A: sustained daily intakes exceeding 50,000 IU (adults), 20,000 IU (infants) may cause toxic effects (headache, vomiting, liver damage); US RDA 8000 IU (pregnant/lactating women)
Storage: Sealed under inert gas; store in cool place under refrigeration; contents may cryst.; warm to 40 C before use.

Vitamin B$_{12}$ 0.1% SD No. 65354. [Roche]
Chem. Descrip.: Cyanocobalamin stabilized in a matrix of modified food starch with sodium citrate, citric acid, preservatives (sodium benzoate, sorbic acid), silicon dioxide
Uses: Easy blending and distribution in pharmaceuticals, premixes, dry prods., liq. mixts. or suspensions
Properties: Pink fine powd.; sl. hygroscopic; 98% min. thru 40 mesh; disperses in cold or warm water; insol. in org. solvs.
Storage: Store in cool dry place in tightly closed container, optimally @ 46-59 C; avoid excessive heat.

Vitamin B$_{12}$ 1.0% SD No. 65305. [Roche]
Chem. Descrip.: Cyanocobalamin stabilized in a matrix of modified food starch with sodium citrate, citric acid, preservatives (sodium benzoate, sorbic acid), silicon dioxide
Uses: Easy blending and distribution in pharmaceuticals, premixes, dry prods., liq. mixts. or suspensions
Properties: Pink fine powd.; sl. hygroscopic; 98% min. thru 40 mesh; disperses in cold or warm water; insol. in org. solvs.
Storage: Store in cool dry place in tightly closed container, optimally @ 46-59 C; avoid excessive heat.

Vitamin B$_{12}$ 1% Trituration No. 69992. [Roche]
Chem. Descrip.: Cyanocobalamin USP with carrier (calcium phosphate dibasic)
Uses: Used in dry formulations, pharmaceutical tablets/capsules where water sol. is not critical and reducing agents or moisture are not present
Properties: Lt. pink fine powd.; 99% min. thru 100 mesh; insol. in water and org. solvs.; m.w. 1355.38

Storage: Store in cool dry place in tightly closed container, optimally @ 46-59 C.

Vitamin B₁₂ 1% Trituration No. 69993. [Roche]
Chem. Descrip.: Cyanocobalamin USP with mannitol carrier
Uses: Source of vitamin B₁₂ in liq. and solid pharmaceuticals
Properties: Lt. pink fine powd.; 99.5% min. thru 100 mesh; sol. 1 g/10 ml water (clear red sol'n.); m.w. 1355.38
Storage: Store in cool dry place in tightly closed container, optimally @ 46-59 C.

Vitamin E Acetate USP Oil. [BASF]
Chem. Descrip.: Vitamin E acetate USP
CAS 1406-70-8; EINECS 231-710-0
Uses: Antioxidant
Properties: Oil.

Vitamin E USP, FCC No. 60525. [Roche]
Chem. Descrip.: Dl-α-Tocopheryl acetate USP, FCC
CAS 1406-70-8; EINECS 231-710-0
Uses: Vitamin E source for pharmaceutical capsules and liqs., when precautions are taken to protect the formulation from oxygen; antioxidant in oil-based systems
Regulatory: FDA GRAS
Properties: Yel. to amber clear visc. liq., pract. odorless; freely sol. in alcohol; misc. with ether, chloroform, acetone, veg. oils; insol. in water; m.w. 430.72; 96-102% assay
Precaution: Unstable to air and light; degradation accelerated by ferric salts, cupric salts, silver salts, and rancid fats
Storage: Store @ 59-86 F in tight, light-resist. containers.

Vitamin E USP, FCC No. 60526. [Roche]
Chem. Descrip.: Dl-α-Tocopheryl acetate USP, FCC
CAS 1406-70-8; EINECS 231-710-0
Uses: Vitamin E source for pharmaceuticals, tablets, capsules, and liqs.
Regulatory: FDA GRAS
Properties: Yel. clear visc. oil, pract. odorless; may solidify at cold temps.; freely sol. in alcohol; misc. with ether, chloroform, acetone, veg. oils; insol. in water; m.w. 472.76; 96-102% assay
Storage: Store @ 59-86 F in tight, light-resist. containers.

Vitamin E USP Tocopherol. [BASF]
Chem. Descrip.: Vitamin E
Uses: Antioxidant, vitamin E source
Properties: Oil.

Vitinc® dl-alpha Tocopheryl Acetate USP XXII. [Vitamins, Inc.]
Chem. Descrip.: Dl-α-Tocopheryl acetate USP
CAS 1406-70-8; EINECS 231-710-0
Uses: Antioxidant, vitamin E source for pharmaceutical use.

Vivacel® 10. [J. Rettenmaier & Söhne]
Chem. Descrip.: Microcrystalline cellulose
CAS 9004-34-6
Uses: Tablet binder for pharmaceutical and health

food industries; carrier to soak up water and oil extracts
Properties: 35 μm avg. particle size; 6% max. moisture.

Vivacel® 12. [J. Rettenmaier & Söhne]
Chem. Descrip.: Microcrystalline cellulose
CAS 9004-34-6
Uses: Tablet binder for pharmaceutical and health food industries; very better flowability, suited for direct tableting
Properties: 150 μm avg. particle size; 6% max. moisture.

Vivacel® 20. [J. Rettenmaier & Söhne]
Chem. Descrip.: Microcrystalline cellulose
CAS 9004-34-6
Uses: Tablet binder for pharmaceutical and health food industries; recommended for spheronization
Properties: 25 μm avg. particle size; 6% max. moisture.

Vivacel® 101. [J. Rettenmaier & Söhne]
Chem. Descrip.: Microcrystalline cellulose NF, Ph.Eur., BP, DAB
CAS 9004-34-6
Uses: Tablet binder for pharmaceutical and health food industries, esp. for tableting and spheronization
Properties: 50 μm avg. particle size; bulk dens. 320 g/l, 2.2 ml/g (tapped); 6% max. moisture
Storage: Nearly unlimited shelf life when stored dry in orig. sealed bags; 36 mos guaranteed life.

Vivacel® 102. [J. Rettenmaier & Söhne]
Chem. Descrip.: Microcrystalline cellulose NF, Ph.Eur., BP, DAB
CAS 9004-34-6
Uses: Tablet binder for pharmaceutical and health food industries; better flowability than Vivacel 101, suited for direct tableting
Properties: 100 μm avg. particle size; bulk dens. 350 g/l, 1.9 ml/g (tapped); 6% max. moisture
Storage: Nearly unlimited shelf life when stored dry in orig. sealed bags; 36 mos guaranteed life.

Vivacel® 103. [J. Rettenmaier & Söhne]
Chem. Descrip.: Microcrystalline cellulose
CAS 9004-34-6
Uses: Tablet binder for pharmaceutical and health food industries, esp. for tableting of water-sensitive substances and spheronization
Properties: 50 μm avg. particle size; 3% max. moisture.

Vivacel® 105. [J. Rettenmaier & Söhne]
Chem. Descrip.: Microcrystalline cellulose
CAS 9004-34-6
Uses: Tablet binder for pharmaceutical and health food industries; antisedimentation agent in suspensions
Properties: 20 μm avg. particle size; 6% max. moisture.

Vivacel® 112. [J. Rettenmaier & Söhne]
Chem. Descrip.: Microcrystalline cellulose
CAS 9004-34-6
Uses: Tablet binder for pharmaceutical and health food industries; better flowability, suited for direct

tableting of water-sensitive substances
Properties: 100 μm avg. particle size; 3% max. moisture.

Vivacel® 200. [J. Rettenmaier & Söhne]
Chem. Descrip.: Microcrystalline cellulose
CAS 9004-34-6
Uses: Tablet binder for pharmaceutical and health food industries; best flowability, suited for direct tableting
Properties: 190 μm avg. particle size; 6% max. moisture.

Volclay® NF-BC. [Am. Colloid]
Chem. Descrip.: Sodium bentonite USP/NF
Uses: Suspending agent, gellant, binder for pharmaceuticals where color is not critical
Properties: Air-floated powd.; 99% thru 200 mesh; pH 9.5-10.5 (2% disp.); 63.02% SiO_2, 21.08% Al_2O_3; 5-8% moisture.

Volclay® NF-ID. [Am. Colloid]
Chem. Descrip.: Sterilized microfine sodium bentonite NF
Uses: Suspending agent, gellant, binder for use in pharmaceuticals where minimal microbial content is essential
Properties: Powd.; 99% min. thru 200 mesh; pH 9.5-10.5 (2% disp.); 5-8% moisture.

Volpo 3. [Croda Inc.]
Chem. Descrip.: Oleth-3
CAS 9004-98-2
Uses: W/o emulsifier, emollient, lubricant, solubilizer for topical pharmaceutical applics.; exc. petrolatum emulsifier in combination with Volpo S series
Use level: 0.5-5%
Properties: Off-wh. hazy liq.; sol. in alcohols, glycols, ketones, and chlorinated and aromatic solvs., min. oil, and nonpolar oils; insol. in water; HLB 6.6; acid no. 2.0 max.; iodine no. 57-62; hyd. no. 135-150; pH 5-7 (3% aq.); nonionic
Toxicology: LD50 (oral, rat) 12.2 g/kg; skin irritant; nonirritating to eyes.

Volpo 5. [Croda Inc.]
Chem. Descrip.: Oleth-5
CAS 9004-98-2
Uses: Emollient, lubricant, emulsifier, solubilizer for topical pharmaceutical applics.; exc. petrolatum emulsifier in combination with Volpo S series
Use level: 0.5-5%
Properties: Off-wh. hazy liq.; sol. in alcohols, glycols, ketones, and chlorinated and aromatic solvs., min. oil, and nonpolar oils; insol. in water; HLB 8.8; acid no. 2.0 max.; iodine no. 40-52; hyd. no. 120-135; pH 5-7 (3% aq.); 100% conc.; nonionic
Toxicology: LD50 (oral, rat) 5 g/kg; mild skin irritant, moderate eye irritant.

Volpo 10. [Croda Inc.]
Chem. Descrip.: Oleth-10 NF
CAS 9004-98-2
Uses: Emollient, lubricant, o/w emulsifier, solubilizer for topical pharmaceutical applics.
Use level: 0.5-5%

Properties: Off-wh. semisolid; sol. in alcohols, glycols, ketones, chlorinated and aromatic solvs., and water; HLB 12.4; acid no. 2.0 max.; iodine no. 31-37; hyd. no. 79-91; pH 5-7 (3% aq.); 100% conc.; nonionic
Toxicology: LD50 (oral, rat) 4.3 g/kg; skin irritant, nonirritating to eyes.

Volpo 20. [Croda Inc.]
Chem. Descrip.: Oleth-20
CAS 9004-98-2
Uses: Emollient, lubricant, o/w emulsifier, solubilizer for topical pharmaceutical applics.
Use level: 0.5-5%
Properties: Off-wh. soft solid; sol. in water, IPA, propylene glycol; HLB 15.4; cloud pt. 100 C (1% aq.); acid no. 2.0 max.; iodine no. 18-25; hyd. no. 50-58; pH 5-7 (3% aq.); 100% conc.; nonionic
Toxicology: LD50 (oral, rat) 15.1 g/kg; mild skin and eye irritant.

Volpo CS-20. [Croda Inc.; Croda Chem. Ltd.]
Chem. Descrip.: Ceteareth-20
CAS 68439-49-6
Uses: Emulsifier, dispersant, wetting agent, gellant for pharmaceutical applics.; solubilizer for perfumes and essential oils
Properties: Off-wh. hard waxy solid; sol. in water, ethanol, trichloroethylene, oleic acid; HLB 15.6; cloud pt. 78 C (1% aq.); surf. tens. 41.5 dynes/cm (0.1% aq.); pH 6.0-7.5 (3%); 97% conc.; nonionic
Toxicology: LD50 (oral, rat) 2.1 g/kg; mild skin irritant, moderate eye irritant.

Volpo L23. [Croda Chem. Ltd.]
Chem. Descrip.: C12-13 pareth-23
CAS 9002-92-0
Uses: O/w emulsifier and solubilizer for pharmaceuticals
Properties: Solid; 97% conc.; nonionic.

Volpo S-2. [Croda Inc.; Croda Chem. Ltd.]
Chem. Descrip.: Steareth-2
CAS 9005-00-9
Uses: Aux. emulsifier for o/w or w/o topical pharmaceutical emulsions; stable over wide pH range; synergistic with Volpo 3, 5 and Polychols
Use level: 0.5-5%
Properties: Wh. soft solid; sol. in alcohol, glycols, ketones, most chlorinated and aromatic solvs., keroesene, min. oil; cloud pt. < 55 C (1% aq.); HLB 4.9; acid no. 1.0 max.; hyd. no. 150-170; pH 6.0-7.0 (3%); 100% conc.; nonionic
Toxicology: LD50 (oral, rat) 21 g/kg; mild skin irritation, nonirritating to eyes.

Volpo S-10. [Croda Inc.; Croda Chem. Ltd.]
Chem. Descrip.: Steareth-10
CAS 9005-00-9
Uses: Primary emulsifier for o/w topical pharmaceutical emulsions; stable over wide pH range; synergistic with Polychol 15, Volpo 10 and 20; provides superior stability to systems contg. cetyl or stearyl alcohols
Use level: 0.5-5%
Properties: Wh. soft solid, low odor; sol. in alcohol, glycol, ketone, most chlorinated and aromatic

solvs.; insol. in oil; HLB 12.4; cloud pt. 65-75 C (1% aq.); acid no. 1.0 max.; hyd. no. 75-90; pH 6.0-7.0 (3%); 100% conc.; nonionic

Toxicology: LD50 (oral, rat) 2.1 g/kg; moderate skin irritant, severe eye irritant.

Volpo S-20. [Croda Inc.; Croda Chem. Ltd.]
Chem. Descrip.: Steareth-20
CAS 9005-00-9
Uses: Primary emulsifier for o/w topical pharma-

ceutical emulsions; stable over wide pH range
Use level: 0.5-5%
Properties: Wh. solid; sol. in water, alcohols, glycols, ketones, most chlorinated and aromatic solvs.; insol. in oil; cloud pt. > 100 C (1% aq.); HLB 15.3; acid no. 1.0 max.; hyd. no. 45-60; 100% conc.; nonionic
Toxicology: LD50 (oral, rat) 2.07 g/kg; nonirritating to skin; moderate eye irritant.

W

Wacker HDK® H20. [Wacker-Chemie GmbH; Wacker Silicones]
Chem. Descrip.: Fumed silica
EINECS 231-545-4
Uses: Hydrophobic thickener, thixotrope, excipient, free-flow aid for pharmaceuticals powds.
Properties: Wh. powd.; apparent dens. 40 g/l; surf. area 170 ± 30 m^2/g; ref. index 1.45; pH 3.8-4.5 (4% in 1:1 water/methanol disp.).

Wacker HDK® N20. [Wacker-Chemie GmbH; Wacker Silicones]
Chem. Descrip.: Fumed silica
EINECS 231-545-4
Uses: Hydrophilic thickener, thixotrope for pharmaceuticals (toothpaste, tablets, powds., aerosols, suspensions, ointments, creams)
Properties: Wh. powd.; apparent dens. 40 g/l; surf. area 200 ± 30 m^2/g; ref. index 1.45; pH 3.6-4.3 (4% aq.).

Wacker HDK® V15. [Wacker-Chemie GmbH; Wacker Silicones]
Chem. Descrip.: Fumed silica
EINECS 231-545-4
Uses: Hydrophilic thickener, thixotrope for pharmaceuticals (suspensions, ointments, creams)
Properties: Wh. powd.; apparent dens. 50 g/l; surf. area 150 ± 30 m^2/g; ref. index 1.45; pH 3.6-4.3 (4% aq.).

Wacker Silicone Antifoam Emulsion SE 9. [Wacker-Chemie GmbH]
Chem. Descrip.: Simethicone
CAS 8050-81-5
Uses: Antifoam, processing aid for pharmaceuticals
Regulatory: FDA §173.340, BGA II, VII
Properties: Milky wh. med. visc. o/w emulsion; sp.gr. 1.0; pH 6-8; 15-16% solids in water.

Wayhib® S. [Olin]
Chem. Descrip.: TEA phosphate ester, sodium salt
Uses: Emulsifier, sequestrant for pharmaceutical applics.
Properties: Gardner 1 liq.; misc. with water; sp.gr. 1.45; dens. 12.07 lb/gal; pH 4.6 (1% aq.); 70% act.; anionic
Toxicology: Irritating to skin and eyes.

Wecobee® FS. [Stepan Food Ingreds.]
Chem. Descrip.: Hydrog. veg. oil
CAS 68334-28-1; EINECS 269-820-6
Uses: Cocoa butter replacement, excipient, emollient for pharmaceuticals (suppositories, ointment bases)
Regulatory: FDA 21CFR §170.30, GRAS; avail. in kosher grade
Properties: Wh. to off-wh. soft solid, bland odor; m.p. 39 C; iodine no. 3; sapon. no. 240; 0-1% moisture
Toxicology: Nontoxic, nonirritating
Storage: Avoid prolonged storage above 90 F.

Wecobee® HTR. [Stepan Food Ingreds.]
Chem. Descrip.: Hydrog. veg. oil
CAS 68938-37-4; EINECS 269-820-6
Uses: Cocoa butter replacement, emollient for pharmaceuticals (suppositories, ointment and cream bases), antiperspirants; exc. mold release chars.
Properties: Wh. to off-wh. oil, bland odor; m.p. 36 C; iodine no. 1.2; 0.03% moisture
Storage: Avoid prolonged storage above 90 F.

Wecobee® M. [Stepan Food Ingreds.; Stepan Europe]
Chem. Descrip.: Hydrog. veg. oil
CAS 68938-37-4; EINECS 269-820-6
Uses: Cocoa butter replacement, excipient, emollient for pharmaceuticals (suppositories, ointment and cream bases)
Regulatory: FDA 21CFR §170.30, GRAS; avail. in kosher grade
Properties: Wh. to off-wh. soft solid, bland odor; visc. 13.5 cps (150 F); m.p. 35 C; acid no. 0.20 max.; iodine no. 3; sapon. value 242; 0.1% moisture
Storage: Avoid prolonged storage above 90 F.

Wecobee® R Mono. [Stepan Food Ingreds.]
Chem. Descrip.: Hydrog. veg. oil
CAS 68334-28-1; EINECS 269-820-6
Uses: Cocoa butter replacement, emollient for pharmaceuticals (suppositories, ointment and cream bases); exc. mold release chars.
Properties: Wh. to off-wh. oil, bland odor; m.p. 35 C; iodine no. 3; sapon. no. 189; 45% monoester
Storage: Avoid prolonged storage above 90 F.

Wecobee® S. [Stepan Food Ingreds.; Stepan Europe]
Chem. Descrip.: Hydrog. veg. oil
CAS 68334-28-1; EINECS 269-820-6
Uses: Cocoa butter replacement, emollient for pharmaceuticals (suppositories, ointment and cream bases)

Regulatory: FDA 21CFR §170.30, GRAS; avail. in kosher grade
Properties: Ivory or sl. yel. flakes, bland odor; visc. 14.0 cps (150 F); m.p. 46 C; acid no. 0.20 max.; iodine no. 3; sapon. value 238; 0.1% moisture
Storage: Avoid prolonged storage above 90 F.

Wecobee® SS. [Stepan Food Ingreds.]
Chem. Descrip.: Hydrog. veg. oil
CAS 68334-28-1; EINECS 269-820-6
Uses: Cocoa butter replacement, excipient, emollient for pharmaceuticals (suppositories, ointment bases)
Regulatory: FDA 21CFR §170.30, GRAS; avail. in kosher grade
Properties: Ivory to sl. yel. flakes, bland odor; m.p. 47 C; iodine no. 3; sapon. no. 237; 0.1% max. moisture
Storage: Avoid prolonged storage above 90 F.

Westchlor® 170. [Westwood]
Chem. Descrip.: Aluminum sesquichlorhydrate
CAS 11097-68-0
Uses: Antiperspirant active for aq. roll-ons or hydroalcoholic pump systems
Properties: Colorless clear liq., odorless; pH 3.9-4.3 (15% aq.); 45% aq., 11% Al, 8.25% Cl.

Westchlor® 170 Powd. [Westwood]
Chem. Descrip.: Aluminum sesquichloride
Uses: Antiperspirant active for hydroalcoholic and high basic sesquichlorhydrate systems
Properties: Off-wh., sl. yel. fine crystals, pract. odorless; sol. in 95% ethanol; pH 3.9-4.3 (15% aq.); 24.25% Al, 18.25% Cl.

Westchlor® 200. [Westwood]
Chem. Descrip.: Aluminum chlorhydrate
CAS 1327-41-9; EINECS 215-477-2
Uses: Antiperspirant active for aq. roll-on emulsions or creams
Properties: Colorless clear liq., odorless; sp.gr. 1.335-1.345; pH 4.0-4.4 (15% aq.); 50% aq., 12.2-12.7% Al, 7.9-8.4% Cl.

Westchlor® 200 Custom Powd. 10. [Westwood]
Chem. Descrip.: Basic aluminum chloride
CAS 1327-41-9
Uses: Antiperspirant active for anhyd. suspension systems and suspensoid sticks where low visc. are encountered
Properties: Wh. to off-wh. impalpable powd.; 85% min. < 10 μ; pH 4.0-4.4 (15% aq.); 46-48% Al_2O_3, 15.8-16.8% Cl.

Westchlor® 200 Impalpable. [Westwood]
Chem. Descrip.: Basic aluminum chloride
CAS 1327-41-9
Uses: Antiperspirant active for dry suspension formulas, aerosols, and creams
Properties: Wh. impalpable powd.; 97% min. thru 325 mesh; pH 4.0-4.4 (15% aq.); 46-48% Al_2O_3, 15.8-16.8% Cl.

Westchlor® A2Z 8106. [Westwood]
Chem. Descrip.: Aluminum zirconium pentachlorhydrex-gly, propylene glycol sol'n. with zinc glycinate as adjusting agent
Uses: Antiperspirant active for use in dibenzyl

sorbitol gellant formulations; features high pH, high efficacy, crystal clear solid formulas with no visible residue
Properties: Sl. yel. clear liq., faint glycolic odor; sp.gr. 1.230 ± 0.01; visc. 550 ± 150 cps; ref. index 1.460 ± 0.01; pH 4.75 ± 0.15 (10%); 30% act.; 5.50% Al, 2.40% Zr, 4.5% Cl.

Westchlor® DM 200 Impalpable. [Westwood]
Chem. Descrip.: Basic aluminum chloride
CAS 1327-41-9
Uses: Antiperspirant active for dry suspension formulas and aerosols; high efficacy
Properties: Off-wh. free-flowing powd., typ. odor; 60% min. < 10 μ; pH 4.0-4.5 (10% aq.); 25.5-26.4% Al, 16.3-17.9% Cl.

Westchlor® ZR 30B Custom Powd. 5. [Westwood]
Chem. Descrip.: Aluminum zirconium trichlorhydrex-gly
Uses: Antiperspirant active for anhyd. silicone suspensions and sticks; high efficacy; yields whiter formulations and lower degree of irritancy
Properties: Wh. to off-wh. free-flowing powd., pract. odorless; 100% thru 325 mesh, 90% < 10 μ; pH 3.8-4.4 (25% aq.); 14.0-15.2% Al, 13.6-16.3% Zr, 13.3-17.5% Cl, 13.5-16.5% glycine.

Westchlor® ZR 30B Custom Powd. 10. [Westwood]
Chem. Descrip.: Aluminum zirconium trichlorhydrex-gly
Uses: Antiperspirant active for anhyd. silicone suspensions and sticks; high efficacy; yields whiter formulations and lower degree of irritancy
Properties: Wh. to off-wh. free-flowing powd., pract. odorless; 100% thru 325 mesh, 80% < 10 μ; pH 3.8-4.4 (25% aq.); 14.0-15.2% Al, 13.6-16.3% Zr, 13.3-17.5% Cl, 13.5-16.5% glycine.

Westchlor® ZR 30B DM Custom Powd. 5. [Westwood]
Chem. Descrip.: Aluminum zirconium trichlorhydrex-gly
Uses: Patented enhanced efficacy antiperspirant active for anhyd. silicone suspensions and sticks
Properties: Wh. to off-wh. free-flowing powd., pract. odorless; 100% thru 325 mesh, 90% < 10 μ; pH 3.8-4.4 (25% aq.); 14.0-15.2% Al, 13.3-17.5% Cl, 13.5-16.5% glycine.

Westchlor® ZR 30B DM Custom Powd. 10. [Westwood]
Chem. Descrip.: Aluminum zirconium trichlorhydrex-gly
Uses: Patented enhanced efficacy antiperspirant active for anhyd. silicone suspensions and sticks
Properties: Wh. to off-wh. free-flowing powd., pract. odorless; 100% thru 325 mesh, 85% < 10 μ; pH 3.8-4.4 (25% aq.); 14.0-15.2% Al, 13.3-17.5% Cl, 13.5-16.5% glycine.

Westchlor® ZR 30B DM Powd. [Westwood]
Chem. Descrip.: Aluminum zirconium trichlorhydrex-gly
Uses: Antiperspirant active for anhyd. silicone suspensions and sticks; high efficacy
Properties: Wh. to off-wh. free-flowing powd., pract. odorless; 100% < 53 μ; pH 3.8-4.4 (25%

aq.); 14.0-15.2% Al, 13.3-17.5% Cl, 13.5-16.5% glycine.

Westchlor® ZR 30B Micro Powd. [Westwood]
Chem. Descrip.: Aluminum zirconium trichlorhydrex-gly
Uses: Antiperspirant active for anhyd. silicone suspensions and sticks; yields whiter formulations and lower irritancy levels
Properties: Wh. to off-wh. free-flowing powd., pract. odorless; 99.9% thru 200 mesh; pH 3.8-4.4 (25% aq.); 14.0-15.2% Al, 13.6-16.3% Zr, 13.3-17.5% Cl, 13.5-16.5% glycine.

Westchlor® ZR 35B [Westwood]
Chem. Descrip.: Aluminum zirconium tetrachlorhydrex-gly
Uses: Antiperspirant active for roll-on emulsion and creams; higher level of efficacy over basic aluminum chlorides
Properties: PH 3.7-4.1 (15% aq.); 35% aq., 5.0-5.7% Al, 4.7-5.4% Zr, 5.9-6.5% Cl.

Westchlor® ZR 35B Custom Powd. 5. [Westwood]
Chem. Descrip.: Aluminum zirconium tetrachlorhydrex-gly
Uses: Antiperspirant active for anhyd. silicone suspensions and sticks; good dispersion in anhyd. roll-ons; high aesthetic props.
Properties: Wh. to off-wh. impalpable powd., pract. odorless; 100% thru 325 mesh; 90% < 10 μ; pH 3.7-4.1 (15% aq.); 14.5-15.5% Al, 13.0-15.5% Zr, 17.0-18.5% Cl, 10.5-13.5% glycine.

Westchlor® ZR 35B Custom Powd. 10. [Westwood]
Chem. Descrip.: Aluminum zirconium tetrachlorhydrex-gly
Uses: Antiperspirant active for anhyd. silicone suspensions and sticks
Properties: Wh. to off-wh. impalpable powd., pract. odorless; 100% thru 325 mesh; 80% < 10 μ; pH 3.7-4.1 (15% aq.); 14.5-15.5% Al, 13.0-15.5% Zr, 17.0-18.5% Cl, 10.5-13.5% glycine.

Westchlor® ZR 35B DM Custom Powd. 5. [Westwood]
Chem. Descrip.: Aluminum zirconium tetrachlorhydrex-gly
Uses: Enhanced efficacy antiperspirant active with good suspension chars. in low-mod. visc. roll-on and suspensoid stick formulas, anhyd. silicone suspensions
Properties: Wh. to off-wh. impalpable powd., pract. odorless; 100% thru 325 mesh, 90% min. < 10 μ; pH 3.7-4.1 (15% aq.); 14.5-15.5% Al, 13.0-15.5% Zr, 17.0-18.5% Cl, 10.5-13.5% glycine.

Westchlor® ZR 35B DM Custom Powd. 10. [Westwood]
Chem. Descrip.: Aluminum zirconium tetrachlorhydrex-gly
Uses: Enhanced efficacy antiperspirant active with good suspension chars. in low-mod. visc. roll-on and suspensoid stick formulas, anhyd. silicone suspensions
Properties: Wh. to off-wh. impalpable powd., pract. odorless; 100% thru 325 mesh, 80% min. < 10 μ; pH 3.7-4.1 (15% aq.); 14.5-15.5% Al, 13.0-15.5%

Zr, 17.0-18.5% Cl, 10.5-13.5% glycine.

Westchlor® ZR 35B DM Powd. [Westwood]
Chem. Descrip.: Aluminum zirconium tetrachlorhydrex-gly
Uses: Antiperspirant active for anhyd. silicone suspensions and sticks; high efficacy
Properties: Off-wh. impalpable powd., pract. odorless; 98.5% min. thru 325 mesh; pH 3.6-4.0 (15% aq.); 14.5-15.5% Al, 13.0-15.5% Zr, 17-19% Cl, 10.5-13.5% glycine.

Westchlor® ZR 35B Micro Powd. [Westwood]
Chem. Descrip.: Aluminum zirconium tetrachlorhydrex-gly
Uses: Antiperspirant active for anhyd. silicone suspensions, sticks, and creams; offers higher efficacy than conventional aluminum chlorhydrate active suspension formulas
Properties: Wh. to off-wh. impalpable powd., pract. odorless; 98.5% min. < 325 mesh; pH 3.7-4.1 (15% aq.); 14.5-15.5% Al, 13.0-15.5% Zr, 17.0-18.5% Cl, 10.5-13.5% glycine.

Westchlor® ZR 41. [Westwood]
Chem. Descrip.: Aluminum zirconium tetrachlorhydrex-gly
Uses: Antiperspirant active allowing formulator greater flexibility in the use of nonaq. ingreds.
Properties: Pract. odorless; pH 3.70-4.00 (15% aq.); 45% aq., 6.5-7.2% Al, 5.85-6.40% Zr, 7.65-8.40% Cl.

Westchlor® ZR 58B DM Powd. [Westwood]
Chem. Descrip.: Aluminum zirconium trichlorhydrex-gly
Uses: Patented enhanced antiperspirant active for anhyd. silicone suspensions and sticks
Properties: Wh. to off-wh. free-flowing powd., pract. odorless; 100% thru 200 mesh, 98.5% thru 325 mesh; 17.5-18.5% Al, 10-11% Zr, 18.2-19.4% Cl, 10.5-13.5% glycine.

Westchlor® ZR 60B DM Powd. [Westwood]
Chem. Descrip.: Aluminum zirconium trichlorhydrex-gly
Uses: Patented enhanced antiperspirant active for anhyd. silicone suspensions and sticks
Properties: Wh. to off-wh. free-flowing powd., pract. odorless; 100% thru 200 mesh, 98.5% thru 325 mesh; 17.5-18.5% Al, 10-11% Zr, 15-17% Cl, 10.5-13.5% glycine.

Westchlor® ZR 80B DM Powd. [Westwood]
Chem. Descrip.: Aluminum zirconium pentachlorhydrex-gly
Uses: Antiperspirant active for anhyd. silicone suspensions and sticks
Properties: Wh. to off-wh. free-flowing powd., pract. odorless; 100% thru 200 mesh; 98.5% min. thru 325 mesh; 19-20% Al, 7.8-8.8% Zr, 15-17% Cl, 7-9% glycine.

Westchlor® ZR 82B DM Powd. [Westwood]
Chem. Descrip.: Aluminum zirconium octachlorhydrex-gly
Uses: Antiperspirant active for anhyd. silicone suspensions and sticks
Properties: Wh. to off-wh. free-flowing powd.,

pract. odorless; 98.5% min. thru 325 mesh; 18.4-19.4% Al, 7.6-8.6% Zr, 18.5-20.5% Cl, 7-9% glycine.

W.G.S. Cetyl Palmitate. [Werner G. Smith]
Chem. Descrip.: Cetyl palmitate
CAS 540-10-3; EINECS 208-736-6
Uses: Emollient, ointment base, consistency factor
Properties: Wh. flake, sl. fatty alcohol odor; negligible sol. in water; sp.gr. 0.82 (50 C); m.p. 45-55 C; acid no. 1 max.; iodine no. 5 max.; sapon. no. 110-130; flash pt. (COC) 450 F; 92% min. act.
Toxicology: Passes LD50 toxicity and rabbit skin and eye irritation tests; dust may cause eye irritation, tearing, redness; long term skin contact may cause dermatitis; inh. may cause respiratory irritation; ingestion may lead to gastrointestinal irritation
Precaution: Incompat. with strong oxidizing agents; hazardous decomp. prods.: oxides of carbon, smoke
Storage: Store in cool, dry place; keep in sealed container when not in use; keep away from heat and oxidizing agents.

W.G.S. Synaceti 116 NF/USP. [Werner G. Smith]
Chem. Descrip.: Cetyl esters (syn. spermaceti)
CAS 8002-23-1; EINECS 241-640-2
Uses: Emollient, bodying agent for pharmaceuticals
Regulatory: FDA 21CFR §175.105, 175.300
Properties: Wh. cryst. flakes, typ. waxy odor; negligible sol. in water; sp.gr. 0.82-0.84 (50 C); m.p. 43-47 C; acid no. 2 max.; iodine no. 1 max.; sapon. no. 109-120; flash pt. (COC) 450 F
Toxicology: Passes LD50 toxicity and rabbit eye and skin irritation tests; inh. may cause respiratory irritation; ingestion may cause gastrointestinal irritation
Precaution: Incompat. with oxidizing agents; hazardous decomp. prods.: oxides of carbon, smoke
Storage: Keep away from heat, sources of ignition; keep container closed when not in use.

White Swan. [Croda Chem. Ltd.]
Chem. Descrip.: Lanolin BP, anhyd.
CAS 8006-54-0; EINECS 232-348-6
Uses: Conditioner, moisturizer, w/o emulsifier, and emollient for pharmaceuticals; aids pigment dispersion
Properties: Yel. unctuous mass.

Wholecut KCl. [Reheis]
Chem. Descrip.: Potassium chloride USP/FCC, BP, EP
CAS 7447-40-7; EINECS 231-211-8
Uses: Functional additive for use in the pharmaceutical industry; designed to resemble the profile of evaporated sodium chloride for reduced separation in blends
Properties: Powd.; 100-200 mesh.

Wickenol® 142. [CasChem]
Chem. Descrip.: Octyldodecyl myristate
Uses: Emollient, plasticizer for pharmaceutical preps.
Properties: Gardner 2+ color; sol. in alcohol, animal, veg., and wh. oils; insol. in water; pour pt. 0 C; acid no. 0.1; ref. index 1.460.

Wickenol® 155. [CasChem]
Chem. Descrip.: Octyl palmitate
CAS 29806-73-3; EINECS 249-862-1
Uses: Emollient, moisturizer, pigment wetter/dispersant; increases water vapor porosity of fatty components used in topical pharmaceutical preparations
Properties: Gardner-1 color; sol. in alcohol, animal, veg., and min. oils; insol. in water; pour pt. -3 C; acid no. 0.10; ref. index 1.445.

Wickenol® 156. [CasChem]
Chem. Descrip.: Octyl stearate
Uses: Emollient, moisturizer, pigment wetter/dispersant; increases water vapor porosity of fatty components used in topical pharmaceutical preparations
Properties: Gardner-1 color; sol. in alcohol, animal, veg., and min. oils; pour pt. 5 C; acid no. 0.10; ref. index 1.4465.

Wickenol® 158. [CasChem]
Chem. Descrip.: Dioctyl adipate
CAS 103-23-1; EINECS 203-090-1
Uses: Emollient, moisturizer, pigment wetter/dispersant, cosolv.; increases water vapor porosity of fatty components used in topical pharmaceutical preparations
Properties: Gardner-1 color; sol. in alcohol, animal, veg., and min. oils; pour pt. -20 C; acid no. 0.10; ref. index 1.445.

Wickenol® 159. [CasChem]
Chem. Descrip.: Dioctyl succinate
CAS 2915-57-3; EINECS 220-836-1
Uses: Emollient, moisturizer, pigment wetter/dispersant; increases water vapor porosity of fatty components used in topical pharmaceutical preparations
Properties: Gardner-1 color; sol. in alcohol, animal, veg., and min. oils; pour pt. -18 C; acid no. 0.7; ref. index 1.443.

Wickenol® 160. [CasChem]
Chem. Descrip.: Octyl pelargonate
CAS 59587-44-9; EINECS 261-819-9
Uses: Emollient, moisturizer, pigment wetter/dispersant; increases water vapor porosity of fatty components used in topical pharmaceutical preparations; improves stick formulations
Properties: Gardner 2+ color; sol. in alcohol, animal, veg., and min. oils; pour pt. -18 C; acid no. 0.10; ref. index 1.437.

Wickenol® 161. [CasChem]
Chem. Descrip.: Dioctyl adipate, octyl stearate, octyl palmitate
Uses: Emollient, moisturizer, pigment wetter/dispersant; increases water vapor porosity of fatty components used in topical pharmaceutical preparations
Properties: Gardner-1 color; sol. in alcohol, animal, veg., and min. oils; pour pt. -12 C; acid no. 0.1; ref. index 1.446.

Wickenol® 171. [CasChem]

Chem. Descrip.: Octyl hydroxystearate
CAS 29383-26-4
Uses: Emollient, moisturizer, pigment wetter/dispersant; increases water vapor porosity of fatty components used in topical pharmaceutical preparations; refatting agent, counter-irritant, cosolv., solubilizer
Properties: Gardner 2+ color; sol. in acetone, castor, corn, and min. oil, chloroform, ethyl acetate, ethanol; pour pt. 5 C; acid no. 0.30; ref. index 1.456.

Witafrol® 7420. [Hüls Am.; Hüls AG]
Chem. Descrip.: Caprylic/capric glycerides
CAS 26402-26-6
Uses: Surfactant for pharmaceutical fields; emulsifier, solubilizer, dispersant, plasticizer, lubricant, consistency regulator, skin/mucous membrane protectant, refatting agent, penetrant, carrier, adsorp. promoter
Properties: Sl. ylsh. oil; sol. in water/ethanol (50/50), acetone; sol. cloudy in ether, heptane; dens. 1.02 kg/dm^3; visc. 190 mPa•s; acid no. 2 max.; iodine no. 1 max.; sapon. no. 230-260; flash pt. > 180 C; 40-42% monoglycerides.

Witch Hazel Lubrajel. [United-Guardian]
Chem. Descrip.: Lubrajel base contg. 35% pure extract of witch hazel
Uses: Astringent for the skin and for hemorrhoids, particularly since it stays in place when applied; for pharmaceutical, medical, health-care fields
Properties: Colorless glass-clear visc. gel, mild witch hazel odor
Custom product

Witconol™ MST. [Witco/H-I-P]
Chem. Descrip.: Glyceryl stearate
Uses: Emulsifier for pharmaceuticals, aerosol formulations
Properties: Flake; disp. in oil; sp.gr. 0.93; HLB 3.9; m.p. 58 C; 100% act.; nonionic.

Witco® Zinc Stearate U.S.P.-D. [Witco/H-I-P]
Chem. Descrip.: Zinc stearate
CAS 557-05-1; EINECS 209-151-9
Uses: Lubricant, w/o emulsifier for pharmaceuticals
Properties: Wh. powd.; 99.9% thru 325 mesh; sol. in hot turpentine, benzene, toluene, xylene, CCl$_4$, veg. and min. oils, waxes; sp.gr. 1.09; soften. pt. 120 C.

Witepsol® E75. [Hüls Am.; Hüls AG]
Chem. Descrip.: Hydrog. coco-glycerides
Uses: Suppository bases for pharmaceuticals
Properties: Pellets; m.p. 37-39 C; solid. pt. 32-36 C; acid no. 1.3 max.; iodine no. 3 max.; sapon. no. 220-230; hyd. no. 15 max.

Witepsol® E76. [Hüls Am.; Hüls AG]
Chem. Descrip.: Hydrog. coco-glycerides
Uses: Suppository bases for pharmaceuticals
Properties: Pellets; m.p. 37-39 C; solid. pt. 31-35 C; acid no. 0.3 max.; iodine no. 3 max.; sapon. no. 220-230; hyd. no. 30-40.

Witepsol® E85. [Hüls Am.; Hüls AG]
Chem. Descrip.: Hydrog. coco-glycerides

Uses: Suppository bases for hydrophilic and lipophilic drugs
Properties: Pellets; m.p. 42-44 C; solid. pt. 37-42 C; acid no. 0.3 max.; iodine no. 3 max.; sapon. no. 220-230; hyd. no. 15 max.

Witepsol® H5. [Hüls Am.; Hüls AG]
Chem. Descrip.: Hydrog. coco-glycerides
Uses: Suppository bases for pharmaceuticals
Properties: Pellets; m.p. 34-36 C; solid. pt. 33-35 C; acid no. 0.2 max.; iodine no. 2 max.; sapon. no. 235-245; hyd. no. 5 max.

Witepsol® H12. [Hüls Am.; Hüls AG]
Chem. Descrip.: Hydrog. coco-glycerides
Uses: Suppository bases for pharmaceuticals
Properties: Pellets; m.p. 32-33.5 C; solid. pt. 29-33 C; acid no. 0.2 max.; iodine no. 3 max.; sapon. no. 240-255; hyd. no. 15 max.

Witepsol® H15. [Hüls Am.; Hüls AG]
Chem. Descrip.: Hydrog. coco-glycerides
Uses: Suppository bases for pharmaceuticals
Properties: Pellets; m.p. 33.5-35.5 C; solid. pt. 32.5-34.5 C; acid no. 0.2 max.; iodine no. 3 max.; sapon. no. 230-245; hyd. no. 15 max.

Witepsol® H32. [Hüls Am.; Hüls AG]
Chem. Descrip.: Hydrog. coco-glycerides
Uses: Suppository bases for pharmaceuticals
Properties: Pellets; m.p. 31-33 C; solid. pt. 30-32.5 C; acid no. 0.2 max.; iodine no. 3 max.; sapon. no. 240-250; hyd. no. 3 max.

Witepsol® H35. [Hüls Am.; Hüls AG]
Chem. Descrip.: Hydrog. coco-glycerides
Uses: Suppository bases for pharmaceuticals
Properties: Pellets; m.p. 33.5-35.5 C; solid. pt. 32-35 C; acid no. 0.2 max.; iodine no. 3 max.; sapon. no. 240-250; hyd. no. 3 max.

Witepsol® H37. [Hüls Am.; Hüls AG]
Chem. Descrip.: Hydrog. coco-glycerides
Uses: Suppository bases for pharmaceuticals
Properties: Pellets; m.p. 36-38 C; solid. pt. 35-37 C; acid no. 0.2 max.; iodine no. 3 max.; sapon. no. 225-245; hyd. no. 3 max.

Witepsol® H175. [Hüls Am.; Hüls AG]
Chem. Descrip.: Hydrog. coco-glycerides
Uses: Suppository bases for pharmaceuticals
Properties: Pellets; m.p. 34.5-36.5 C; solid. pt. 32-34 C; acid no. 0.7 max.; iodine no. 3 max.; sapon. no. 225-245; hyd. no. 15 max.

Witepsol® H185. [Hüls Am.; Hüls AG]
Chem. Descrip.: Hydrog. coco-glycerides
Uses: Suppository bases for pharmaceuticals
Properties: Pellets; m.p. 38-39 C; solid. pt. 34-37 C; acid no. 0.2 max.; iodine no. 3 max.; sapon. no. 220-235; hyd. no. 15 max.

Witepsol® S51. [Hüls AG]
Chem. Descrip.: Hydrog. coco-glycerides
Uses: Suppository bases for pharmaceuticals
Properties: Pellets; m.p. 30-32 C; solid. pt. 25-27 C; acid no. 0.5 max.; iodine no. 8 max.; sapon. no. 215-230; hyd. no. 55-70.

Witepsol® S55. [Hüls AG]
Chem. Descrip.: Hydrog. coco-glycerides
Uses: Suppository bases for pharmaceuticals

Properties: Pellets; m.p. 33.5-35.5 C; solid. pt. 28-33 C; acid no. 1.0 max.; iodine no. 3 max.; sapon. no. 215-230; hyd. no. 50-65.

Witepsol® S58. [Hüls AG]
Chem. Descrip.: Hydrog. coco-glycerides
Uses: Suppository bases for pharmaceuticals
Properties: Pellets; m.p. 32-33.5 C; solid. pt. 27-29 C; acid no. 1.0 max.; iodine no. 7 max.; sapon. no. 215-225; hyd. no. 60-70.

Witepsol® W25. [Hüls Am.; Hüls AG]
Chem. Descrip.: Hydrog. coco-glycerides
Uses: Suppository bases for pharmaceuticals
Properties: Pellets; m.p. 33.5-35.5 C; solid. pt. 29-33 C; acid no. 0.3 max.; iodine no. 3 max.; sapon. no. 225-240; hyd. no. 20-30.

Witepsol® W31. [Hüls Am.; Hüls AG]
Chem. Descrip.: Hydrog. coco-glycerides
Uses: Suppository bases for pharmaceuticals
Properties: Pellets; m.p. 35-37 C; solid. pt. 30-33 C; acid no. 0.3 max.; iodine no. 3 max.; sapon. no. 225-240; hyd. no. 25-35.

Witepsol® W32. [Hüls Am.; Hüls AG]
Chem. Descrip.: Hydrog. coco-glycerides
Uses: Suppository bases for pharmaceuticals
Properties: Pellets; m.p. 32-33.5 C; solid. pt. 25-30 C; acid no. 0.5 max.; iodine no. 3 max.; sapon. no. 225-245; hyd. no. 40-50.

Witepsol® W35. [Hüls Am.; Hüls AG]
Chem. Descrip.: Hydrog. coco-glycerides
Uses: Suppository bases for pharmaceuticals
Properties: Pellets; m.p. 33.5-35.5 C; solid. pt. 27-32 C; acid no. 0.3 max.; iodine no. 3 max.; sapon. no. 225-235; hyd. no. 40-50.

Witepsol® W45. [Hüls Am.; Hüls AG]
Chem. Descrip.: Hydrog. coco-glycerides
Uses: Suppository bases for pharmaceuticals
Properties: Pellets; m.p. 33.5-35.5 C; solid. pt. 29-34C; acid no. 0.3 max.; iodine no. 3 max.; sapon. no. 225-235; hyd. no. 40-50.

XY

Xylitol C. [Xyrofin UK]
  Chem. Descrip.: Xylitol FCC, USP, NF
  CAS 87-99-0; EINECS 201-788-0
  Uses: Food grade sweetener for pharmaceutical
    applics.; stable to air and heat
  Properties: Wh. cryst. powd., pract. odorless, very
    sweet cool taste; very sol. in water; sparingly sol.
    in ethanol; m.w. 152.15; m.p. 92-96 C; pH 5-7
    (aq.); 98.5-101% assay
  Storage: 1 yr stability in original sealed pkg. stored
    below 25 C and < 65% r.h.; marginally hygro-
    scopic.

Yeast Lactase L-50,000. [Solvay Enzymes]
  Chem. Descrip.: Yeast lactase
  Uses: Enzyme for hydrolyzing lactose in pharma-
    ceuticals (digestive aids)
  Properties: Lt. amber liq., free from offensive odors
    and taste
  Storage: Store at refrigeration temp.

Yelkin F. [ADM Lecithin]
  Chem. Descrip.: Deoiled lecithin
  CAS 8030-76-0; EINECS 232-307-2
  Uses: Emulsifier, wetting agent, emollient, binder
    for pharmaceuticals
  Properties: Lt. gold fine gran.

Yelkin G. [ADM Lecithin]
  Chem. Descrip.: Deoiled lecithin
  CAS 8030-76-0; EINECS 232-307-2
  Uses: Emulsifier, wetting agent, emollient, binder
    for pharmaceuticals

  Properties: Lt. gold gran.
Yelkin P. [ADM Lecithin]
  Chem. Descrip.: Deoiled lecithin
  CAS 8030-76-0; EINECS 232-307-2
  Uses: Emulsifier, wetting agent, emollient, binder
    for pharmaceuticals
  Properties: Lt. gold powd.

Yeoman. [Croda Chem. Ltd.]
  Chem. Descrip.: Anhyd. lanolin BP
  CAS 8006-54-0; EINECS 232-348-6
  Uses: Emollient used in pharmaceuticals; aids
    dispersion of pigments into anhyd. systems
  Properties: Yel. unctuous mass; lipophilic.

York Krystal Kleer Castor Oil. [United Catalysts]
  Chem. Descrip.: Castor oil USP contg. an antioxi-
    dant
  CAS 8001-79-4; EINECS 232-293-8
  Uses: High quality oil imparting gloss and
    emollience; dye solv.; for pharmaceuticals
  Properties: Gardner 1 color; sp.gr. 0.959; dens.
    7.98 lb/gal; visc. 7.5 stokes; acid no. 1; iodine no.
    86; sapon. no. 180; hyd. no. 164.

York USP Castor Oil. [United Catalysts]
  Chem. Descrip.: Castor oil USP
  CAS 8001-79-4; EINECS 232-293-8
  Uses: High quality oil imparting gloss and
    emollience; dye solv.; for pharmaceuticals
  Properties: Gardner 1 color; sp.gr. 0.959; dens.
    7.98 lb/gal; visc. 7.5 stokes; acid no. 1; iodine no.
    86; sapon. no. 180; hyd. no. 164.

Z

Zea Red. [MLG Enterprises Ltd.]
  Chem. Descrip.: Extract of the antocyanins of purple corn, a variety of *Zea mays*, stabilized with phosphoric acid, spray-dried
  Uses: Natural colorant for pharmaceuticals
  Properties: Red powd.; sol. in water.

Zinc Oxide USP 66. [Whittaker, Clark & Daniels]
  Chem. Descrip.: Zinc oxide
  CAS 1314-13-2; EINECS 215-222-5
  Uses: Uv sunscreen.

Zinc Sulfate Monohydrate CP Grade. [United Min. & Chem.]
  Chem. Descrip.: Zinc sulfate monohydrate FCC/USP
  CAS 7446-19-7; EINECS 231-793-3

  Uses: Used in pharmaceuticals
  Properties: 99% min. assay.

Zoharpon LAS. [Zohar Detergent Factory]
  Chem. Descrip.: Sodium lauryl sulfate USP/BP
  CAS 151-21-3; EINECS 205-788-1
  Uses: Raw material for toothpaste, pharmaceutical preps.
  Properties: Liq. to paste; 30% conc.; anionic.

Zoharpon LAS Spray Dried. [Zohar Detergent Factory]
  Chem. Descrip.: Sodium lauryl sulfate USP/BP
  CAS 151-21-3; EINECS 205-788-1
  Uses: Raw material for mfg. of toothpaste, pharmaceutical preps.
  Properties: Powd.; 92% conc.; anionic.

Part II
Chemical Dictionary/
Cross-Reference

Chemical Dictionary/Cross-Reference

Absinthium oil. *See* Wormwood oil
Absolute alcohol. *See* Alcohol

Acacia
CAS 9000-01-5; EINECS 232-519-5
FEMA 2001
Synonyms: Acacia gum; Sudan gum; Gum hashab; Kordofan gum; Gum arabic; Acacia senegal; Arabic gum
Classification: Water-sol. gum
Definition: Dried gummy exudate from stems and branches of *Acacia farnesiana* or *A. senegal*
Properties: Ylsh.-wh. angular fragments, odorless; sol. in water; insol. in alcohol; m.w. 240,000
Precaution: Combustible
Toxicology: LD50 (oral, rat) 18 g/kg; inh. or ingestion may produce hives, eczema, angiodema, asthma; allergic responses; people prone to allergies should avoid acacia; heated to decomp., emits acrid smoke
Uses: Emulsifier, solubilizer, flavoring agent, tablet adhesive/binder/coating/excipient, suspending agent, stabilizer, visc.-increasing agent for orals; demulcent in cough drops and syrups; treatment of diarrhea, dysentery, catarrh; lubricant/emollient
Regulatory: FDA 21CFR §169.179, 169.182, 184.1330, GRAS; Japan approved; Europe listed; UK approved; ADI not specified (JECFA); USP/NF, Ph.Eur., BP compliance
Manuf./Distrib.: Ashland; Atomergic Chemetals; Chart; Commodity Services Int'l.; Frutarom Ltd; Gallard-Schlesinger Ind.; Gumix Int'l.; Dr. Madis Labs; Meer; Penta Mfg.; Robeco; Ruger; Spectrum Chem. Mfg.; TIC Gums; Universal Preserv-A-Chem
Manuf./Distrib. (pharm. & food): Aldrich; Ashland; Atomergic Chemetals; Bio-Botanica; Calaga Food Ingreds.; Chart; Commodity Services Int'l.; Cornelius; G Fiske; Florexco; Gumix Int'l.; Importers Service; Integra; Int'l. Ingreds.; Meer; Penta Mfg.; Quest; Rhone-Poulenc; Ruger; Spectrum Chem. Mfg.; Spice King; TIC Gums
Trade names: Granular Gum Arabic NF/FCC C-4010; Granular Gum Arabic Type A-1 NF Premium; Granular Gum Arabic Type A-2 NF Premium; Gum Arabic NF/FCC Clean Amber Sorts; Gum Arabic NF, Tech; Gum Arabic, Purified, Spray-Dried No. 1834; Natural Arabic Type Gum Purified, Spray-Dried; Powdered Gum Arabic NF/FCC G-150; Powdered Gum Arabic NF/FCC Superselect Type NB-4; Powdered Gum Arabic Type B-100 NF Premium; Powdered Gum Arabic Type B-200 NF Premium; Premium Spray Dried Gum Arabic; Spray Dried Gum Arabic NF/FCC CM; Spray Dried Gum Arabic NF/FCC CS (Low Bacteria); Spray Dried Gum Arabic NF/FCC CS-R; Spray Dried Gum Arabic NF Type CSP; Spray Dried Gum Arabic Type A-180 NF Premium; Spray Dried Gum Arabic Type A-230 NF Extra; Spray Dried Gum Talha (Acacia); Spray Dried Gum Talha (Acacia) Special; Spray Dried Kordofan Gum Arabic; TIC Pretested® Arabic FT-1 USP
Trade names containing: Cal-Tab®; Dry Phytonadione 1% SD No. 61748; Durkote Calcium Carbonate/Starch, Acacia Gum; Os-Tab™ 4455; Vitamin A Palmitate Type 250-CWS No. 65312

Acacia gum. *See* Acacia
Acacia senegal. *See* Acacia
Aceite de Algodon. *See* Cottonseed oil
Aceite de ricino. *See* Castor oil
Acesulfame K. *See* Acesulfame potassium

Acesulfame potassium
CAS 55589-62-3
Synonyms: Potassium 6-methyl-1,2,3-oxathiazine-4(3H)-1,2,2-dioxide; Potassium acesulfame; Acesulfame K; Sunnette
Definition: Potassium salt of 6-methyl-1,2,3-oxathiazine-4(3H)-one-2,2-dioxide
Empirical: $C_4H_4KNO_4S$
Properties: Wh. cryst. solid, odorless, sweet taste, very sl. bitter aftertaste; very sol. in water, DMF, DMSO;

Acetal

sol. in alcohol, glycerin-water; m.w. 201.24; about 200 times sweeter than sucrose; m.p. 250 C
Toxicology: Heated to decomp., emits toxic fumes of SO$_x$
Uses: Artficial sweetener
Regulatory: FDA 21CFR §172.800
Manuf./Distrib. (pharm. & food): Dietary Foods; Hoechst AG; Hoechst UK; Sunette; Vrymeer Commodities

Acetal
CAS 105-57-7; EINECS 203-310-6
FEMA 2002
Synonyms: Polyacetal; Acetaldehyde diethyl acetal; 1,1-Diethoxyethane; Diethyl acetal; Ethylidene diethyl ether
Empirical: C$_6$H$_{14}$O$_2$
Formula: CH$_3$CH(OC$_2$H$_5$)$_2$
Properties: Colorless volatile liq., fruity green flavor; sol. in heptane, ethyl acetate; misc. with alcohol, ether; m.w. 118.18; dens. 0.831; b.p. 103-104 C; flash pt. (CC) 36 C
Precaution: Highly flamm.; keep away from ignition sources; tends to polymerize on standing
Toxicology: LD50 (oral, rat) 4.57 g/kg; moderately toxic by ingestion, skin and eye irritant
Uses: Synthetic flavoring
Regulatory: FDA §172.515; FEMA GRAS
Manuf./Distrib.: Aldrich; Fluka
Manuf./Distrib. (pharm. & food): Aldrich

Acetaldehyde
CAS 75-07-0; EINECS 200-836-8
FEMA 2003
Synonyms: Acetic aldehyde; Ethyl aldehyde; Ethanal
Classification: Aldehyde
Empirical: C$_2$H$_4$O
Formula: CH$_3$CHO
Properties: Colorless fuming liq., pungent fruity odor; misc. in water, alcohol, ether; m.w. 44.06; dens. 0.788 (16/4 C); m.p. -123.5 C; b.p. 20.8 C; flash pt. (CC) -38 C; ref. index 1.3316 (20 C)
Precaution: Flamm. liq. (DOT); can react violently with acid anhydrides, alcohols, ketones, phenols, NH$_3$, halogens, etc.; reaction with oxygen may lead to detonation; keep cold
Toxicology: LD50 (oral, rat) 1930 mg/kg; poison by intratracheal/IV routes; human systemic irritant by inh.; narcotic; human mutagenic data; experimental tumorigen, teratogen; skin and severe eye irritant; heated to decomp., emits acrid smoke and fumes
Uses: Synthetic flavoring
Regulatory: FDA 21CFR §182.60, GRAS; FEMA GRAS
Manuf./Distrib.: Aldrich; J.T. Baker; BP Chem. Ltd.; Eastman; Hoechst-Celanese; Hüls UK; Mitsui Petrochem. Ind.; Wacker-Chemie GmbH
Manuf./Distrib. (pharm. & food): Aldrich; Eastman; Frutarom

Acetaldehyde benzyl β-methoxyethyl acetal. *See* Benzyl methoxyethyl acetal
Acetaldehyde diethyl acetal. *See* Acetal

Acetaldehyde phenethyl propyl acetal
CAS 7493-57-4
FEMA 2004
Synonyms: Acetal R; Pepital; Propyl phenethyl acetal
Definition: From acetaldehyde with a mixture of propyl and β-phenyl ethyl alcohols
Empirical: C$_{13}$H$_{20}$O$_2$
Properties: Colorless, stable liquid; strong odor of green leaves; m.w. 208.30; dens. 0.951; flash pt. 95 C
Uses: Syn. flavoring
Regulatory: FDA 21CFR §172.515; FEMA GRAS
Manuf./Distrib. (pharm. & food): Aldrich

Acetal R. *See* Acetaldehyde phenethyl propyl acetal

Acetanisole
CAS 100-06-1
FEMA 2005
Synonyms: p-Methoxyacetophenone; 4´-Methoxyacetophenone; p-Acetyl anisole; Novatone
Definition: From anisole and acetic acid in the presence of boron trifluoride
Empirical: C$_9$H$_{10}$O$_2$
Properties: Ylsh.-wh. cryst. @ R.T., floral, bitter; sl. sol. in water; sol. in most org. solvs.; bitter, unpleasant taste; m.w. 150.18; m.p. 38C; b.p. 152-154 C (26 mm)

Uses: Sweet buttery caramel, vanilla-like, fruity synthetic flavoring agent
Regulatory: FDA 21CFR §172.515; FEMA GRAS
Manuf./Distrib. (pharm. & food): Aldrich

Acetate C-8. *See* Octyl acetate
Acetate C-10. *See* Decyl acetate
Acetate C-12. *See* Lauryl acetate
Acetate PA. *See* Allyl phenoxyacetate
(Acetato)phenylmercury. *See* Phenylmercuric acetate

Acetic acid
CAS 64-19-7; EINECS 200-580-7
FEMA 2006; UN No. 2789, 2790
Synonyms: Ethanoic acid; Vinegar acid; Methanecarboxylic acid; Ethyllic acid; Pyroligneus acid
Classification: Aliphatic organic acid
Empirical: $C_2H_4O_2$
Formula: CH_3COOH
Properties: Clear colorless liq., pungent odor, sharply acid taste; misc. with water, alcohol, glycerol, ether;
   insol. in carbon disulfide; m.w. 60.03; dens. 1.0492 (20/4 C); m.p. 16.63 C; b.p. 118 C (765 mm); visc. 1.22
   cps (20 C); flash pt. (OC) 43 C; ref. index 1.3715 (20 C)
Precaution: Combustible; moderate fire risk; DOT: corrosive, flamm. liq.
Toxicology: Pure acetic acid: moderately toxic by ingestion, inhalation; dilute approved FDA for food use;
   strong irritant to skin and tissue; TLV 10 ppm in air; LD50 (oral, rat) 3310 mg/kg
Uses: Acidifying agent, buffering agent, solvent/vehicle, flavoring agent; used in ophthalmic pharmaceuticals,
   otics
Regulatory: FDA 21CFR §73.85, 133, 172.814, 178.1010, 184.1005, GRAS; USDA 9CFR §318.7; BP; Europe
   listed; UK approved; USP/NF, BP compliance
Manuf./Distrib.: Air Prods.; BASF; BP Chem.; General Chem.; Hoechst Celanese; Janssen Chimica; PMC;
   Quantum/USI; Ruger
Manuf./Distrib. (pharm. & food): Albright & Wilson; Aldrich; Daicel Chem. Ind.; Diamalt; Eastman; Ellis &
   Everard; Frutarom; Keith Harris; Hoechst AG; Integra; Integrated Ingreds.; Mallinckrodt; Penta; Pfaltz &
   Bauer; Ruger; Siber Hegner; Spectrum Chem. Mfg.; Tropic Agro; Van Waters & Rogers
Trade names: Unichem ACETA

Acetic acid ammonium salt. *See* Ammonium acetate
Acetic acid citronellyl ester. *See* Citronellyl acetate
Acetic acid cyclohexyl ester. *See* Cyclohexyl acetate
Acetic acid esters of mono- and diglycerides of fatty acids. *See* Acetylated mono- and diglycerides of fatty
acids
Acetic acid, ethenyl ester, homopolymer. *See* Polyvinyl acetate (homopolymer)
Acetic acid, ethenyl ester, polymer with ethene. *See* Ethylene/VA copolymer
Acetic acid, ethyl ester. *See* Ethyl acetate

Acetic acid, glacial
CAS 64-19-7; EINECS 200-580-7
FEMA 2006; UN No. 2789, 2790
Synonyms: Ethanoic acid; Ethanolic acid; Concentrated acetic acid; Vinegar acid; Glacial acetic acid
Classification: Aliphatic organic acid
Empirical: $C_2H_4O_2$
Formula: CH_3COOH
Properties: Clear colorless liq., pungent char. odor, acid taste when dil. with water; misc. with water, alcohol,
   acetone, glycerol, ether; insol. in chloroform; m.w. 60.05; dens. 1.049 (20/4 C); m.p. 16.2 C; b.p. 118 C;
   flash pt. 40 C; ref. index 1.3720
Precaution: DOT: Corrosive material
Toxicology: TLV:TWA 10 ppm; human poison by unspecified routes; mod. toxic by various routes; corrosive;
   severe eye and skin irritant; can produce lung obstruction
Uses: Acidifying agent, buffering agent, solvent; used in injectables, ophthalmic pharmaceuticals, orals, otics
Regulatory: USP/NF, BP, Ph.Eur. compliance
Manuf./Distrib.: Aldrich; Quantum/USI; Ruger
Manuf./Distrib. (pharm. & food): Aldrich; Ruger; Spectrum Chem. Mfg.

Acetic acid 1-methylethyl ester. *See* Isopropyl acetate
Acetic acid pentyl ester. *See* Amyl acetate
Acetic acid 2-phenylethyl ester. *See* 2-Phenylethyl acetate
Acetic acid potassium salt. *See* Potassium acetate

Acetic acid n-propyl ester. *See* Propyl acetate
Acetic acid sodium salt anhydrous. *See* Sodium acetate anhydrous
Acetic acid sodium salt trihydrate. *See* Sodium acetate trihydrate
Acetic acid, sulfo-, 1-dodecyl ester, sodium salt. *See* Sodium lauryl sulfoacetate
Acetic acid vinyl ester polymers. *See* Polyvinyl acetate (homopolymer)
Acetic aldehyde. *See* Acetaldehyde

Acetic anhydride
CAS 108-24-7; EINECS 203-564-8; UN No. 1715
Synonyms: Acetyl oxide; Acetic oxide
Empirical: $C_4H_6O_3$
Formula: $(CH_3CO)_2O$
Properties: Colorless liq., strong acetic odor; slowly sol. in water; sol. in chloroform, ether; m.w. 102.09; dens. 1.08 (15/4 C); m.p. -73 C; b.p. 138-140 C; flash pt. 49 C; ref. index 1.3904 (20 C)
Precaution: DOT: Corrosive material; readily combustible; fire hazard
Toxicology: LD50 (oral, rat) 1.78 g/kg; corrosive; produces irritation and necrosis of tissues in liq. or vapor state
Uses: Dehydrating and acetylating agent, acidifying agent for pharmaceuticals; used in orals, in the prod. of aspirin
Regulatory: FDA, esterifier for food starch, in combination with adipic anhydride (0.12% max. adipic anhydride, 5% max. acetic anhydride); BP compliance
Manuf./Distrib.: Ashland; BP Chem. Ltd.; Chisso; CPS; Eastman; Hoechst Celanese; Schweizerhall; Spectrum Chem. Mfg.; Union Carbide
Manuf./Distrib. (pharm. & food): Aldrich; Eastman

Acetic ether. *See* Ethyl acetate
Acetic oxide. *See* Acetic anhydride
Acetin. *See* Triacetin

Acetisoeugenol
CAS 93-29-8
FEMA 2470
Synonyms: 4-Acetoxy-3-methoxy-1-propenylbenzene; Acetyl isoeugenol; Isoeugenol acetate; 2-Methoxy-4-propenylphenyl acetate
Empirical: $C_{12}H_{14}O_3$
Properties: Wh. cryst., clove odor; sol. in alcohol, chloroform, ether; insol. in water; m.w. 206.26; flash pt. 153 F
Precaution: Combustible liq.
Toxicology: LD50 (oral, rat) 3450 mg/kg; mod. toxic by ingestion; heated to decomp., emits acrid smoke and irritating fumes
Uses: Synthetic flavoring agent
Regulatory: FDA 21CFR §172.515; FEMA GRAS

Acetoacetic acid ethyl ester. *See* Ethylacetoacetate
Acetoacetic ester. *See* Ethylacetoacetate
Acetoacetone. *See* Acetylacetone
Acetodiphosphonic acid. *See* Etidronic acid
Acetoin. *See* Acetyl methyl carbinol
β-Acetonaphthalene. *See* 2´-Acetonaphthone

2´-Acetonaphthone
CAS 93-08-3; EINECS 202-216-2
FEMA 2723
Synonyms: Orange crystals; Methyl 2-naphthyl ketone; Methyl β-naphthyl ketone; β-Acetonaphthalene; 2-Acetonaphthone; 2-Acetylnaphthalene
Empirical: $C_{12}H_{10}O$
Properties: Wh. or nearly wh. cryst. solid, orange blossom odor, strawberry-like flavor; sol. in most common org. solvs.; insol. in water; m.w. 170.21; m.p. 53 C; b.p. 301-303 C; flash pt. 168 C
Precaution: Combustible liq.
Toxicology: LD50 (oral, mouse) 599 mg/kg; mod. toxic by ingestion; skin irritant; heated to decomp., emits acrid smoke and fumes
Uses: Synthetic flavoring agent
Regulatory: FDA 21CFR §172.515; FEMA GRAS; Japan approved as flavoring
Manuf./Distrib. (pharm. & food): Aldrich

2-Acetonaphthone. *See* 2´-Acetonaphthone

Acetone
CAS 67-64-1; EINECS 200-662-2
FEMA 3326; UN No. 1090
Synonyms: Dimethylketone; 2-Propanone; β-Ketopropane; Pyroacetic ether
Classification: Aliphatic ketone
Empirical: C_3H_6O
Formula: CH_3COCH_3
Properties: Colorless volatile transparent liq., sweetish odor, pungent sweetish taste; misc. with water, alcohol, chloroform, ether, most volatile oils; m.w. 58.09; dens. 0.792 (20/20 C); m.p. -94.3 C; b.p. 56.2 C; flash pt. (OC) 15 F
Precaution: DOT: flamm. liq.; dangerous fire risk; explosive limit in air 2.6-12.8%
Toxicology: LD50 (oral, mouse) 3000 mg/kg; TLV 750 ppm in air; narcotic in high conc.; moderately toxic by ingestion and inhalation; lg. doses may cause narcosis; peeling and splitting of nails, skin rashes; inh. irritates lungs
Uses: Solvent for mfg. of pharmaceuticals; apple-, grape-, pear-, pineapaple-like flavoring agent
Regulatory: FDA 21CFR §73.1, 173.210, 30 ppm tolerance in spice oleoresins; FEMA GRAS; Japan approved with restrictions; USP/NF, BP compliance
Manuf./Distrib.: Allied-Signal; Ashland; BASF; BP Chem. Ltd; Dow; Eastman; Exxon; Mitsui Petrochem.; Montedipe SpA; Shell; Texaco; Union Carbide
Manuf./Distrib. (pharm. & food): Aldrich; Eastman; Ruger; Spectrum Chem. Mfg.

Acetone chloroform. *See* Chlorobutanol
'Acetone chloroforn'. *See* Chlorobutanol hemihydrate
Acetone dimethyl acetal. *See* Dimethoxypropane

Acetone sodium bisulfite
CAS 540-92-1
Synonyms: 2-Hydroxy-2-propane sulfonic acid sodium salt acetone sulfite; Sodium acetone bisulfite
Empirical: $C_3H_7NaO_4S$
Formula: $(CH_3)_2C(OH)SO_3Na$
Properties: Cryst., sl. SO_2 odor, fatty feel; sol. in water; sl. sol. in alcohol; m.w. 162.15
Precaution: Keep refrigerated
Uses: Used in injectables, inhalers
Regulatory: FDA approved
Manuf./Distrib.: Ruger
Manuf./Distrib. (pharm. & food): Ruger

Acetonic acid. *See* Lactic acid

Acetonitrile
CAS 75-05-8; EINECS 200-835-2; UN No. 1648
Synonyms: Methyl cyanide; Cyanomethane; Ethanenitrile
Empirical: C_2H_3N
Formula: CH_3CN
Properties: Colorless liq., ether-like odor; misc. with water, methanol, methyl acetate; m.w. 41.05; dens. 0.783; m.p. -45 C; b.p. 81.6 C; flash pt. 12.8 C; ref. index 1.3440
Precaution: DOT: Flamm. liq.; dangerous fire risk
Toxicology: LD50 (rat) 3800 mg/kg; poisonous; toxic by skin absorp. and inh.; skin irritant
Uses: Intermediate for mfg. of synthetic pharmaceuticals
Regulatory: BP compliance
Manuf./Distrib.: BP Chem. Ltd; DuPont; Enichem Am.; R.W. Greeff; ICC Ind.; Janssen Chimica; Mitsui Petrochem. Ind.; Mitsui Toatsu Chem.; Montedipe SpA; Penta Mfg.; Spectrum Chem. Mfg.
Manuf./Distrib. (pharm. & food): Aldrich; Mallinckrodt; Mitsui Toatsu Chem.; Penta Mfg.

Acetophenone
CAS 98-86-2; EINECS 202-708-7
FEMA 2009; UN No. 1993
Synonyms: Ketone methyl phenyl; Methyl phenyl ketone; Acetylbenzene; 1-Phenylethanone; Hypnone
Classification: Aromatic organic compd.
Empirical: C_8H_8O
Formula: $C_6H_5COCH_3$
Properties: Colorless liq., sweet pungent odor and taste; sol. in alcohol, chloroform, ether, fatty oils, glycerol; sl. sol. in water; m.w. 120.15; dens. 1.030 (20/20 C); m.p. 20.5 C; b.p. 201.7 C; flash pt. 82.2 C; ref. index 1.5339 (20 C)
Precaution: DOT: Combustible liq.

4-Acetoxy-3-methoxy-1-propenylbenzene

Toxicology: LD50 (oral, rat) 815 mg/kg; narcotic in high concs.; poison by intraperitoneal route; moderate toxicity by ingestion; skin and eye irritant; may cause allergic reaction
Uses: Intermediate for pharmaceuticals; sweet flavoring agent
Regulatory: FDA 21CFR §172.515; FEMA GRAS; Japan approved for flavoring
Manuf./Distrib.: ARCO; BP Chem. Ltd.; EniChem Am.; Janssen Chimica; Mitsui Petrochem. Ind.; Mitsui Toatsu Chem.; Montedipe SpA; Penta Mfg.
Manuf./Distrib. (pharm. & food): Aldrich; Mitsui Toatsu Chem.; Penta Mfg.

4-Acetoxy-3-methoxy-1-propenylbenzene. See Acetisoeugenol
Acetoxyphenylmercury. See Phenylmercuric acetate
α-Acetoxytoluene. See Benzyl acetate

Acetylacetone
CAS 123-54-6; EINECS 204-634-0; UN No. 1993
Synonyms: 2,4-Pentanedione; Diacetylmethane; Acetoacetone
Empirical: $C_5H_8O_2$
Formula: $CH_3COCH_2COCH_3$
Properties: Colorless to sl. yel. liq., pleasant odor; misc. with alcohol, benzene, ether, chloroform, acetone, glac. acetic acid, propylene glycol; insol. in water; m.w. 100.13; dens. 0.952-0.962; m.p. -23.2 C; b.p. 139 C (746 mm); flash pt. (OC) 105 F
Precaution: Flamm. liq. exposed to heat or flame; incompat. with oxidizing materials; light-sensitive; refrigerate
Toxicology: LD50 (oral, rat) 1000 mg/kg; mod. toxic by ingestion, IP, inh. routes; skin and severe eye irritant; narcotic in high doses
Uses: Pharmaceutical intermediate
Regulatory: FDA 21CFR §172.515; BP compliance
Manuf./Distrib.: Aceto; Aldrich; Penta Mfg.; Spectrum Chem. Mfg.; Union Carbide; Wacker Chem.
Manuf./Distrib. (pharm. & food): Aldrich; Mallinckrodt; Penta Mfg.

p-Acetyl anisole. See Acetanisole

Acetylated hydrogenated cottonseed glyceride
Synonyms: Glycerides, cottonseed-oil, mono-, hydrogenated, acetates
Definition: Acetyl ester of the monoglyceride derived from hydrogenated cottonseed oil
Uses: Plasticizer in film coatings; taste masking; sustained release solid dosage forms
Regulatory: FDA 21CFR §172.828, 175.230
Trade names: Myvacet® 5-07

Acetylated hydrogenated soybean oil glycerides
Uses: Plasticizer in film coatings
Trade names: Myvacet® 9-45

Acetylated hydrogenated vegetable oil glycerides
Uses: Plasticizer in film coatings; taste masking; sustained release solid dosage forms
Trade names: Myvacet® 7-07

Acetylated lanolin
CAS 61788-48-5; EINECS 262-979-2
Uses: Lubricant, emulsifier, and emollient for pharmaceutical prods.; repels water better than regular lanolin
Trade names: Acylan; Fancol Acel; Lanacet® 1705; Modulan®; Ritacetyl®

Acetylated lanolin alcohol
CAS 61788-49-6; EINECS 262-980-8
Synonyms: Lanolin, alcohols, acetates
Classification: Acetyl ester
Uses: Emollient for creams and lotions
Trade names containing: Crodalan AWS; Crodalan LA; Fancol ALA; Fancol ALA-10; Ritawax AEO; Ritawax ALA; Solulan® 97; Solulan® 98

Acetylated mono- and diglycerides of fatty acids
CAS 68990-55-6; 68990-58-9
Synonyms: Acetic acid esters of mono- and diglycerides of fatty acids
Definition: Partial or complete esters of glycerin with a mixture of acetic acid and edible fat-forming fatty acids
Properties: White to pale yel. liq., bland taste; sol. in alcohol, acetone; insol. in water; HLB 2-3
Toxicology: Heated to decomp., emits acrid smoke and fumes
Uses: Coating agent, emulsifier
Regulatory: FDA 21CFR §172.828; Europe listed; UK approved
Trade names: Lamegin® EE Range
Trade names containing: Chroma-Seal™ 859027; Chroma-Seal™ 889031

Acetylated POE (10) lanolin alcohol. *See* Laneth-10 acetate
Acetylbenzene. *See* Acetophenone

Acetyl butyryl
  CAS 3848-24-6; EINECS 223-350-8
  FEMA 2558
  Synonyms: 2,3-Hexanedione; Methyl propyl diketone; Acetyl-n-butyryl
  Empirical: $C_6H_{10}O_2$
  Formula: $CH_3CH_2CH_2COCOCH_3$
  Properties: Yel. oily liq., powerful creamy sweet buttery odor, butter cheese taste; sol. in alcohol, propylene glycol; sl. sol. in water; m.w. 114.15; dens. 0.934 (20/4 C); b.p. 128 C; flash pt. 83 F; ref. index 1.412 (20 C)
  Precaution: Flammable
  Toxicology: Irritant
  Uses: Sweet synthetic flavoring agent
  Regulatory: FDA 21CFR §172.515; FEMA GRAS
  Manuf./Distrib. (pharm. & food): Aldrich; BASF

Acetyl-n-butyryl. *See* Acetyl butyryl
Acetylcellulose. *See* Cellulose acetate

Acetyl chloride
  CAS 75-36-5; EINECS 200-865-6; UN No. 1717
  Synonyms: Ethanoyl chloride
  Empirical: C_2H_3ClO
  Formula: CH_3COCl
  Properties: Liq., pungent odor; misc. with benzene, chloroform, ether; m.w. 78.50; dens. 1.104; m.p. -112 C; b.p. 52 C; flash pt. 40 F; ref. index 1.398
  Precaution: DOT: Flamm. liq.; decomposed violently by water or alcohol
  Toxicology: Corrosive; irritant; extremely irritating to eyes; causes severe burns
  Uses: Pharmaceutical intermediate; acetylating agent for pharmaceuticals
  Manuf./Distrib.: Aceto; Elf Atochem SA; Hoechst Celanese; Penta Mfg.; Schweizerhall; Spectrum Chem. Mfg.

Acetylene trichloride. *See* Trichloroethylene
Acetyl formaldehyde. *See* Pyruvaldehyde
3-Acetyl-5-hydroxy-3-oxo-4-hexenoic acid Δ-lactone. *See* Dehydroacetic acid
Acetyl isoeugenol. *See* Acetisoeugenol

Acetyl methyl carbinol
  CAS 513-86-0; EINECS 208-174-1
  FEMA 2008; UN No. 2621
  Synonyms: Acetoin; 2,3-Butanolone; γ-Hydroxy-β-oxobutane; 3-Hydroxy-2-butanone; Dimethylketol
  Classification: Aliphatic organic compd.
  Empirical: $C_4H_8O_2$
  Formula: $CH_3COCH(OH)CH_3$
  Properties: Colorless to sl. yel. liq. or cryst. solid, buttery odor; sol. in ethanol; sl. sol. in ether; misc. with water, alcohol, propylene glycol; insol. in veg. oil; m.w. 88.12; dens. 1.016; b.p. 147-148 C; m.p. 15 C; flash pt. 106 F; ref. index 1.417
  Precaution: DOT: flamm. liq.
  Toxicology: Moderate skin irritant; heated to decomp., emits acrid smoke and fumes
  Uses: Flavoring agent, aroma carrier
  Regulatory: FDA §182.60, GRAS; FEMA GRAS
  Manuf./Distrib.: Aldrich; BASF; Penta Mfg.
  Manuf./Distrib. (pharm. & food): Aldrich; Ogawa & Co.; Penta Mfg.

3-Acetyl-6-methyl-1,2-pyran-2,4(3H)-dione. *See* Dehydroacetic acid
3-Acetyl-6-methyl-2,4-pyrandione. *See* Dehydroacetic acid
2-Acetylnaphthalene. *See* 2´-Acetonaphthone
Acetyl oxide. *See* Acetic anhydride
2-(Acetyloxy)-1,2,3-propanetricarboxylic acid, tributyl ester. *See* Acetyl tributyl citrate
2-(Acetyloxy)-1,2,3-propanetricarboxylic acid, triethyl ester. *See* Acetyl triethyl citrate
Acetylpropionic acid. *See* Levulinic acid
3-Acetylpropionic acid. *See* Levulinic acid
β-Acetylpropionic acid. *See* Levulinic acid

3-Acetylpyridine
CAS 350-03-8
FEMA 3424
Empirical: C₇H₇NO
Properties: Sweet, nutty, popcorn; m.w. 121.14; dens. 1.102; m.p. 13-14 C; b.p. 220 C; flash pt. 302 F
Uses: Sweet flavoring agent
Regulatory: FEMA GRAS
Manuf./Distrib.: Raschig
Manuf./Distrib. (pharm. & food): Aldrich

p-Acetyl toluene. *See* 4´-Methyl acetophenone

Acetyl tributyl citrate
CAS 77-90-7; EINECS 201-067-0
FEMA 3080
Synonyms: ATBC; 2-(Acetyloxy)-1,2,3-propanetricarboxylic acid, tributyl ester; Tributyl acetyl citrate
Classification: Aliphatic ester
Definition: Ester of citric acid
Empirical: C₂₀H₃₄O₈
Formula: CH₃COOC₃H₄(COOC₄H₉)₃
Properties: Colorless sl. visc. liq., sweet herbaceous odor; sol. in alcohol; insol. in water; m.w. 402.49; dens. 1.14; b.p. > 300 C; flash pt. 204 C; ref. index 1.4408
Toxicology: Heated to decomp., emits acrid smoke and irritating fumes
Uses: Sweet synthetic flavoring used in oral pharmaceuticals; plasticizer for aq. coatings; sustained-release drugs
Regulatory: FDA 21CFR §172.515, 175.105, 175.300, 175.320, 178.3910, 181.22, 181.27; FEMA GRAS
Manuf./Distrib.: Morflex; Pfizer Spec.; Unitex
Manuf./Distrib. (pharm. & food): Aldrich; Morflex; Pfizer Spec.
Trade names: ATBC

Acetyl triethyl citrate
CAS 77-89-4; EINECS 201-066-5
Synonyms: ATEC; 2-(Acetyloxy)-1,2,3-propanetricarboxylic acid, triethyl ester; Tricarballylic acid-β-acetoxytributyl ester; Triethyl acetylcitrate
Classification: Aliphatic ester
Empirical: C₁₄H₂₂O₈
Formula: CH₃COOC₃H₄(COOC₂H₅)₃
Properties: Colorless, odorless liq.; sl. sol. in water; m.w. 318.36; dens. 1.135 (25 C); flash pt. 187 C
Precaution: Combustible
Toxicology: Moderate toxicity by intraperitoneal route; mild toxicity by ingestion
Uses: Solvent; plasticizer for aq. coatings; sustained-release drugs
Regulatory: FDA 21CFR §175.105, 175.300, 175.320, 178.3910, 181.22, 181.27
Manuf./Distrib.: Morflex; Unitex
Manuf./Distrib. (pharm. & food): Morflex
Trade names: ATEC

Acetyltyrosine
CAS 537-55-3; EINECS 208-671-3
Synonyms: N-Acetyl-L-tyrosine
Uses: Ingred. in tanning accelerator complexes
Manuf./Distrib.: Degussa
Trade names containing: Unipertan P-24; Unipertan P-242; Unipertan P-2002; Unipertan VEG 24; Unipertan VEG 242

N-Acetyl-L-tyrosine. *See* Acetyltyrosine
Achilleic acid. *See* Aconitic acid
Achiote. *See* Annatto
Acid ammonium carbonate. *See* Ammonium bicarbonate
Acid blue 9. *See* CI 42090; FD&C Blue No. 1

Acid blue 9 aluminum lake. *See* FD&C Blue No. 1 aluminum lake
Acid blue 9 ammonium salt. *See* D&C Blue No. 4
Acid blue 74. *See* CI 73015
Acid calcium phosphate. *See* Calcium phosphate monobasic anhydrous
Acid fuchsine. *See* D&C Red No. 33
Acid green 25. *See* CI 61570; D&C Green No. 5
Acid orange 7. *See* CI 15510; D&C Orange No. 4
Acid orange 11. *See* D&C Orange No. 5
Acid potassium tartrate. *See* Potassium acid tartrate
Acid red 27. *See* Amarant
Acid red 33. *See* CI 17200; D&C Red No. 33
Acid red 51. *See* CI 45430; FD&C Red No. 3
Acid red 87. *See* CI 45380; D&C Red No. 22
Acid red 92. *See* CI 45410; D&C Red No. 28
Acid red 95. *See* CI 45425; D&C Orange No. 11
Acids, coconut. *See* Coconut acid
Acids, coconut, hydrogenated. *See* Hydrogenated coconut acid
Acids, lanolin. *See* Lanolin acid
Acids, menhaden, hydrogenated. *See* Hydrogenated menhaden acid
Acid sodium sulfite. *See* Sodium bisulfite
Acids, tallow. *See* Tallow acid
Acid yellow 1. *See* CI 10316; Ext. D&C Yellow No. 7
Acid yellow 3. *See* CI 47005; D&C Yellow No. 10
Acid yellow 23. *See* CI 19140; FD&C Yellow No. 5; Tartrazine
Acid yellow 73. *See* D&C Yellow No. 7
Acid yellow 73 sodium salt. *See* CI 45350; D&C Yellow No. 8
Acimetion. *See* DL-Methionine

Aconitic acid
　　CAS 499-12-7
　　FEMA 2010
　　Synonyms: 1,2,3-Propenetricarboxylic acid; Achilleic acid; Citridic acid; 1-Propene-1,2,3-tricarboxylic acid; Equisetic acid
　　Definition: Occurs in leaves and tubers of *Aconitum napellus* and other *Ranunculaceae*
　　Empirical: $C_6H_6O_6$
　　Formula: $C_3H_3(COOH)_3$
　　Properties: Wh. or ylsh. cryst. solid; sol. in water, alcohol; sl. sol. in ether; m.w. 174.11; m.p. > 195 C; dec. 198-199 C
　　Uses: Natural flavoring agent
　　Regulatory: FDA 21CFR §184.1007, GRAS; FEMA GRAS

Acrylamide/sodium acrylate copolymer
　　CAS 25085-02-3
　　Synonyms: 2-Propenamide, polymer with 2-propenoic acid, sodium salt; 2-Propenoic acid, sodium salt, polymer with 2-propenamide
　　Definition: Polymer of acrylamide and sodium acrylate monomers
　　Formula: $(C_3H_5NO \cdot C_3H_4O_2 \cdot Na)_x$
　　Uses: Thickener for pharmaceuticals
　　Regulatory: FDA 21CFR §173.310
　　Trade names: Pionier® NP 37

Acrylic acid/acrylonitrogens copolymer
　　CAS 61788-40-7; 136505-00-5; 136505-01-6
　　Definition: Polymer formed by the controlled hydrolysis of polyacrylonitrile
　　Uses: Emulsifier, thickener, gellant, film-former
　　Trade names: Hypan® SA100H; Hypan® SR150H

Acrylic acid methyl ester. *See* Methyl acrylate (monomer)
Acrylic acid polymers. *See* Polyacrylic acid
Activated alumina. *See* Alumina

Activated attapulgite. *See* Attapulgite
Activated charcoal. *See* Carbon, activated
Active carbon. *See* Carbon, activated
Adenosine, 5´-(tetrahydrogen triphosphate). *See* Adenosine triphosphate

Adenosine triphosphate
CAS 56-65-5; EINECS 200-283-2
Synonyms: ATP; Adenosine, 5´-(tetrahydrogen triphosphate)
Classification: Organic compd.
Empirical: $C_{10}H_{16}N_5O_{13}P_3$
Properties: M.w. 507.22; sol. in water
Toxicology: Poison by intraperitoneal route; toxic fumes when heated
Uses: Ingred. in tanning accelerator complexes
Manuf./Distrib.: Asahi Chem Industry Co Ltd; R.W. Greeff; Penta Mfg.
Trade names containing: Unipertan P-242; Unipertan P-2002; Unipertan VEG 242

Adeps lanae. *See* Lanolin
Adermine hydrochloride. *See* Pyridoxine HCl

Adipic acid
CAS 124-04-9; EINECS 204-673-3
FEMA 2011
Synonyms: Dicarboxylic acid C_6; Hexanedioic acid; 1,4-Butanedicarboxylic acid
Classification: Organic dicarboxylic acid
Empirical: $C_6H_{10}O_4$
Formula: $HOOC(CH_2)_4COOH$
Properties: Wh. monoclinic prisms, pract. odorless; very sol. in alcohol; sol. in acetone; sl. sol. in water; m.w. 146.16; dens. 1.360 (25/4 C); m.p. 152 C; b.p. 337.5 C; flash pt. (CC) 385 F
Precaution: Combustible
Toxicology: LD50 (oral, mouse) 1900 mg/kg; no known human toxicity; may cause occupational asthma
Uses: Buffer, neutralizer for pharmaceutical slow-release and microencapsulation prods.
Regulatory: FDA 21CFR §172.515, 184.1009, GRAS; FEMA GRAS; USDA 9CFR §318.7; Japan approved; Europe listed (ADI 0-5 mg/kg, free acid basis); UK approved
Manuf./Distrib.: AlliedSignal; Asahi Chem Industry Co Ltd; Ashland; DuPont; C.P. Hall; Monsanto; Penta Mfg.; Rhone-Poulenc; Samson; UCB SA; United Min. & Chem.; Van Waters & Rogers
Manuf./Distrib. (pharm. & food): Aldrich; Asahi Chem Industry Co Ltd; Mallinckrodt; Penta Mfg.; Spectrum Chem. Mfg.

AEP. *See* Aminoethylpiperazine
AEPD. *See* 2-Amino-2-ethyl-1,3-propanediol
Aesculus hippocastanum extract. *See* Horse chestnut extract
Agalmatolite. *See* Pyrophyllite

Agar
CAS 9002-18-0; EINECS 232-658-1
FEMA 2012
Synonyms: Agar-agar; Gelose; Bengal gelatin; Japan isinglass
Definition: A colloidal polygalactoside derived from *Gelidium* spp. or red algae; polysaccharide mixture of agarose and agaropectin
Properties: White to pale yel. flake, powd., or gran., either odorless or sl. char. odor; sol. in boiling water; insol. in cold water, org. solvs.
Toxicology: LD50 (oral, rat) 11 g/kg; mildly toxic by ingestion; occasional allergen; heated to decomp., emits acrid smoke and fumes
Uses: Protective colloid, stabilizer, carrier, emulsifier, emollient for orals, slow-release capsules, suppositories, surgical lubricants, emulsions; excipient, disintegrant in tablets; laxative, bulking agent; suspending agent for barium sulfate
Regulatory: FDA 21CFR §150.141, 150.161, 184.1115, GRAS; USDA 9CFR §318.7; FEMA GRAS; Europe listed; UK approved; USP/NF, BP, Ph.Eur. compliance
Manuf./Distrib.: Aldrich; Meer; Schweizerhall; Spice King; U.S. Biochemical
Manuf./Distrib. (pharm. & food): Aldrich; Am. Roland; Atomergic Chemetals; Browne & Dureau Int'l.; Calaga Food Ingreds.; Chart; Commodity Services; Diamalt; G Fiske; Gumix Int'l.; A C Hatrick; Hercules Ltd.; Honeywill & Stein; Meer; MLG Enterprises; Quest; Ruger; Spectrum Chem. Mfg.; Spice King; TIC Gums
Trade names: Agar-Agar; Agar Agar NF Flake #1; Powdered Agar Agar Bacteriological Grade; Powdered Agar Agar NF M-100 (Gracilaria); Powdered Agar Agar NF MK-60; Powdered Agar Agar NF MK-80-B; Powdered Agar Agar NF MK-80 (Bacteriological); Powdered Agar Agar NF S-100; Powdered Agar Agar NF S-100-

B; Powdered Agar Agar NF S-150; Powdered Agar Agar NF S-150-B; Powdered Agar Agar Type K-60; Powdered Agar Agar Type K-80; Powdered Agar Agar Type K-100; Powdered Agar Agar Type K-150; TIC Pretested® Gum Agar Agar 100 FCC/NF Powd.

Agar-agar. *See* Agar

Alabaster. *See* Calcium sulfate dihydrate

Albacol. *See* n-Propyl alcohol

Alba red. *See* D&C Red No. 39

Albumen

CAS 9006-50-2; EINECS 232-936-2

Synonyms: Dried egg white; Egg albumin; Albumin

Definition: Dried whites of chicken eggs

Properties: Yel. amorphous lumps, scales, or powd.; swells in water, then dissolves gradually; decomp. in moist air; dens. 1.035; m.p. -0.42 C; coagulating temp. 61 C; ref. index 1.356; pH 7.6

Toxicology: May cause allergic reactions in people allergic to milk or eggs

Uses: Emulsifier; binder, coagulant, film-former; in tablet film for erythromycin; antidote to mercury poisoning; in pharmaceutical compding. to make various albumates; microencapsulation

Regulatory: FDA 21CFR §160.145

Manuf./Distrib.: Fluka; Penta Mfg.; Schweizerhall; Spectrum Chem. Mfg.; Spice King; U.S. Biochemical

Manuf./Distrib. (pharm. & food): Am. Roland; Atomergic Chemetals; British Bakels; Farbest Brands; Food Additives & Ingreds.; Frigova Produce; R.W. Greeff; Igreca; Industrial Proteins; Mitsubishi; Moore Fine Foods; Penta Mfg.; Ruger; Spice King; Alfred L Wolff

Trade names: Sol-U-Tein EA

Albumin

Synonyms: Human albumin; Human serum albumin

Definition: Protein derived from human sources

Toxicology: May cause immune responses, anaphylactoid reactions

Uses: Buffering agent; used intravenously as plasma extenders; in microencapsulation, oral formulations; diluent for prep. of allergy extracts

Regulatory: BP compliance for albumin sol'n.

See also Albumen

Alcohol

CAS 64-17-5; EINECS 200-578-6

FEMA 2419; UN No. 1170, 1986

Synonyms: EtOH; Ethyl alcohol; Ethyl alcohol, undenatured; Ethanol; Ethanol, undenatured; Distilled spirits; Absolute alcohol

Definition: Undenatured ethyl alcohol

Empirical: C_2H_6O

Formula: CH_3CH_2OH

Properties: Colorless limpid, volatile liq., vinous odor, pungent taste; misc. with water, methanol, ether, chloroform, 95% acetone; m.w. 46.08; dens. 0.816 (15.5 C); b.p. 78.3 C; f.p. -117.3 C; flash pt. (CC) 12.7 C; ref. index 1.365 (15 C)

Precaution: DOT: Flamm. liq.; can react vigorously with oxidizers; reacts violently with many chemicals

Toxicology: Depressant drug; TLV 1000 ppm in air; moderately toxic by ingestion; experimental tumorigen, teratogen

Uses: Solvent, excipient used in oral pharmaceuticals; extraction medium; mfg. of tonics; component of flavored vehicles; active ingred. in OTC drug prods.; externally as an antiseptic; internally as a stimulant and hypnotic

Regulatory: FDA 21CFR §169.3, 169.175, 169.176, 169.177, 169.178, 169.180, 169.181, 172.340, 172.560, 175.105, 176.200, 176.210, 177.1440, 184.1293, GRAS; 27CFR §2.5, 2.12; FEMA GRAS; USP/NF, BP, Ph.Eur. compliance; Japan restricted

Manuf./Distrib.: BP Chem.; Coyne; Eastman; Georgia-Pacific Resins; Gist-brocades SpA; Grain Processing; Great Western; Quantum/USI; Union Carbide; Vista

Manuf./Distrib. (pharm. & food): ADM Ethanol Sales; Spectrum Chem. Mfg.

Trade names: Punctilious® SDA 1-1

Trade names containing: Filmex® A-2; Filmex® B; Filmex® C; Filmex® D-1; Filmex® D-2; Gantrez® ES-225; Gantrez® ES-425; Natipide® II; Phosal® 50 PG; Phosal® 53 MCT; Phosal® 75 SA; PVP/VA E-335; PVP/VA E-535; PVP/VA E-635; PVP/VA E-735

Alcohol C-3. *See* n-Propyl alcohol

Alcohol C-5. *See* n-Amyl alcohol

Alcohol C-6. *See* Hexyl alcohol

Alcohol C-7. *See* Heptyl alcohol
Alcohol C-8. *See* Caprylic alcohol
Alcohol C₈. *See* 2-Ethylhexanol
Alcohol C-9. *See* Nonyl alcohol
Alcohol C-10. *See* n-Decyl alcohol
Alcohol C-12. *See* Lauryl alcohol
Alcohol C16. *See* Cetyl alcohol
Alcohol C₂₂. *See* Behenyl alcohol
Alcohol C-11 undecylic. *See* Undecyl alcohol
Alcohols, lanolin. *See* Lanolin alcohol
Aldehyde C-1. *See* Formaldehyde
Aldehyde C-7. *See* Heptanal
Aldehyde C-8. *See* n-Octanal
Aldehyde C-9. *See* Nonanal
Aldehyde C-10. *See* Decanal
Aldehyde C-12. *See* Lauric aldehyde
Aldehyde C-14. *See* Myristaldehyde
Aldehyde C-18. *See* γ-Nonalactone
Aldehyde C-12 lauric. *See* Lauric aldehyde
Aldehyde C-14 pure. *See* γ-Undecalactone
Aldehyde C-16 pure. *See* Ethyl methylphenylglycidate
Aldehyde C-11 undecyclic. *See* Undecanal
Aldehyde C-11 Undecylenic. *See* 9-Undecenal
Aldehyde C-11 undecylenic. *See* 10-Undecenal

Alfalfa
  Synonyms: Lucerne
  Definition: Herb and seed from *Medicago sativa*
  Toxicology: No known toxicity
  Uses: Natural flavoring
  Regulatory: FDA 21CFR §182.10, GRAS
  Manuf./Distrib. (pharm. & food): Am. Roland; Chart; Dr. Madis

Alfalfa extract
  CAS 84082-36-0; EINECS 281-984-0
  FEMA 2013
  Synonyms: Medicago sativa extract; Lucerne extract; Purple medick extract
  Definition: Extract of alfalfa, *Medicago sativa*
  Uses: Natural flavoring agent
  Regulatory: FDA 21CFR §182.20, GRAS; FEMA GRAS
  Manuf./Distrib.: Bio-Botanica
  Manuf./Distrib. (pharm. & food): Chart

Algaroba. *See* Locust bean gum

Algin
  CAS 9005-38-3
  FEMA 2015
  Synonyms: Sodium alginate; Sodium polymannuronate; Alginic acid, sodium salt
  Classification: Hydrophilic polysaccharide
  Definition: Purified carbohydrate prod. extracted from brown seaweeds; sodium salt of alginic acid
  Empirical: $(C_6H_7O_6Na)_n$
  Properties: Cream-colored powd., pract. odorless and tasteless; sol. in water; insol. in alcohol, ether, chloroform; m.w. 198.11
  Toxicology: LD50 (IV, rat) 1000 mg/kg; poison by IV and intraperitoneal routes; heated to decomp., emits toxic fumes of Na_2O
  Uses: Suspending agent, gellant, thickening and emulsifying agent, excipient, tablet binder, stabilizer; used in orals; film-former for microencapsulation
  Regulatory: FDA 21CFR §133.133, 133.134, 133.162, 133.178. 133.179, 150.141, 150.161, 173.310, 184.1724, GRAS; FEMA GRAS; Japan approved; Europe listed; UK approved; FDA approved for orals; USP/NF, BP, Ph.Eur. compliance
  Manuf./Distrib.: Aldrich; Kelco
  Manuf./Distrib. (pharm. & food): Am. Roland; Multi-Kem; Spectrum Chem. Mfg.
  Trade names: Colloid 488T; KELCOSOL®; KELGIN® F; KELGIN® HV; KELGIN® LV; KELGIN® MV; KELGIN® XL; KELSET®; KELTONE®; KELTONE® HV; KELTONE® HVCR; KELTONE® LV;

KELTONE® LVCR; KELVIS®; Kimitsu Algin I-3; Kimitsu Algin I-7; Kimitsu Algin IS; MANUCOL DM; MANUCOL DMF; MANUCOL LB; MANUCOL LKX; Pronova™ LVG; Pronova™ LVM; Pronova™ MVG; Pronova™ MVM; Pronova™ P LVG; Pronova™ P MVG; Pronova™ UP MVG; Protanal LF 5/60; Protanal LF 10/40; Protanal LF 10/60; Protanal LF 20/200; Protanal LF 120 M; Protanal LF 200; Protanal LF 200 M; Protanal LF 200 RB; Protanal LF 200 S; Protanal LFR 5/60; Protanal SF; Protanal SF 120; Protanal SF 120 RB; Sobalg FD 100 Range

Alginic acid
CAS 9005-32-7; EINECS 232-680-1
Synonyms: Norgine; Polymannuronic acid
Definition: Hydrophilic colloidal carbohydrate derived from brown seaweeds, *Phaeophyceae*; polysaccharide composed of β-d-mannuronic acid residues
Formula: $(C_6H_8O_6)_n$
Properties: White to yel. powd., odorless, tasteless; sol. in alkaline sol'ns.; very sl. sol. in water; insol. in org. solvs.; capable of absorbing 200-300 times its wt. of water; m.w. ≈ 240,000; acid no. ≥ 230; pH 1.5-3.5 (3% disp.)
Toxicology: LD50 (IP, rat) 1600 mg/kg; ; moderately toxic by intraperitoneal route; heated to decomp., emits acrid smoke and irritating fumes
Uses: Emulsifier, tablet binder/disintegrant, suspending agent, visc.-increasing agent; used in ophthalmic pharmaceuticals, orals
Regulatory: FDA 21CFR §184.1011, GRAS; Japan approved; Europe listed; UK approved; USP/NF, BP, Ph.Eur. compliance
Manuf./Distrib.: Kelco; Mendell; Penta Mfg.; Protan Ltd.
Manuf./Distrib. (pharm. & food): Aceto; Aldrich; Kelco; Penta Mfg.; Protan Ltd.; Spectrum Chem. Mfg.
Trade names: Alginic Acid FCC; KELACID®; Kimitsu Acid; Protacid F 120; Satialgine™ H8; Sobalg FD 000 Range

Alginic acid, ammonium salt. *See* Ammonium alginate
Alginic acid, calcium salt. *See* Calcium alginate
Alginic acid, ester with 1,2-propanediol. *See* Propylene glycol alginate
Alginic acid, glyceryl ester. *See* Glyceryl alginate
Alginic acid, potassium salt. *See* Potassium alginate
Alginic acid, sodium salt. *See* Algin
Alizarine cyanine green F. *See* D&C Green No. 5
Alizurol purple SS. *See* D&C Violet No. 2
Alkane C-4. *See* Butane
Alkanes, C13-14-iso-. *See* C13-14 isoparaffin

Alkenyl succinic anhydride
Uses: Hardener for pharmaceuticals
Manuf./Distrib. (pharm. & food): Aceto

Acrylates/C10-30 alkyl acrylate crosspolymer
Definition: C10-30 alkyl acrylates and monomer(s) of acrylic or methacrylic acid or esters crosslinked with an allyl ether of sucrose or pentaerythritol
Uses: Emulsifier, rheology agent for pharmaceutical low-irritancy creams and lotions, topical gels
Trade names: Carbopol® 1342; Carbopol® 1382; Pemulen® TR-1; Pemulen® TR-2

Alkylbenzyldimethylammonium chloride. *See* Benzalkonium chloride
Alkyl dimethyl benzyl ammonium chloride. *See* Benzalkonium chloride

Allantoin
CAS 97-59-6; EINECS 202-592-8
Synonyms: (2,5-Dioxo-4-imidazolidinyl) urea; Urea-(2,5-dioxo-4-imidazolidine); Glyoxyldiureide; 5-Ureidohydrantoin
Definition: Heterocyclic organic compd.; prod. of animal metabolism, excreted in urine
Empirical: $C_4H_6N_4O_3$
Properties: White to colorless powd. or cryst., odorless, tasteless; sol. in hot water; sol. 1 g in 190 cc water or 500 cc alcohol; sol. alkaline media; almost insol. in ether; m.w. 158.08; m.p. 230 C (dec.); pH 5.5 (sat.)
Precaution: Conc. powd. may present an explosion hazard; hazardous decomp. prods.: above 230 C-CO_2, CO, NO_x, ammonia
Toxicology: Nontoxic by ingestion; nonirritating; nonallergenic
Uses: Biochemical research, medicine; soothing agent, active skin protectant; stimulates growth of healthy tissue
Regulatory: FDA approved as Category I (safe and effective) skin protectant
Manuf./Distrib.: 3-V; Atomergic Chemetals; EM Ind.; R.W. Greeff; ICI Am.; Penta Mfg.; Schweizerhall;

Alligator pear oil

Spectrum Chem. Mfg.; Sutton Labs; Tri-K Ind.
Manuf./Distrib. (pharm. & food): Aceto; Aldrich; Tri-K Ind.
Trade names: Allantoin

Alligator pear oil. *See* Avocado oil
Allomaleic acid. *See* Fumaric acid
all-rac-α-Tocopherol. *See* DL-α-Tocopherol
Allura™ Red. *See* FD&C Red No. 40
Allyl alcohol dibromide. *See* 2,3-Dibromo-1-propanol
Allyl 2-aminobenzoate. *See* Allyl anthranilate
Allyl o-aminobenzoate. *See* Allyl anthranilate
4-Allylanisole. *See* Estragole
p-Allylanisole. *See* Estragole

Allyl anthranilate
FEMA 2020
Synonyms: Allyl 2-aminobenzoate; Allyl o-aminobenzoate
Empirical: $C_{10}H_{11}NO_2$
Properties: M.w. 177.21
Uses: Synthetic flavoring agent
Regulatory: FDA 21CFR §172.515; FEMA GRAS

Allyl butyrate
CAS 2051-78-7
FEMA 2021
Empirical: $C_7H_{12}O_2$
Properties: M.w. 128.17; dens. 0.902; b.p. 44-45 C; flash pt. 107 F; ref. index 1.4158
Toxicology: Irritant
Uses: Apricot, peach-like synthetic flavoring agent
Regulatory: FDA 21CFR §172.515; FEMA GRAS
Manuf./Distrib. (pharm. & food): Aldrich

Allyl caproate
CAS 123-68-2; EINECS 204-642-4
FEMA 2032
Synonyms: 2-Propenyl hexanoate; Allyl capronate; Caproic acid allyl ester; Allyl hexanoate
Empirical: $C_9H_{16}O_2$
Properties: Colorless to lt. yel. liq., pineapple aroma; misc. with alcohol, ether; insol. in water; m.w. 156.23; dens. 0.887; b.p. 75-76 C; flash pt. 151 F; ref. index 1.4243
Toxicology: LD50 (oral, rat) 218 mg/kg; poison by ingestion and skin contact; skin irritant; heated to decomp., emits acrid smoke and irritating fumes
Uses: Pineapple-like flavoring agent
Regulatory: FDA 21CFR §172.515; FEMA GRAS; Japan approved
Manuf./Distrib.: Aldrich; BASF
Manuf./Distrib. (pharm. & food): Aldrich; Chr. Hansen's

Allyl capronate. *See* Allyl caproate
Allyl caprylate. *See* Allyl octanoate

Allyl cinnamate
CAS 1866-31-5
FEMA 2022
Synonyms: Allyl-3-phenylacrylate; Propenyl cinnamate; Vinyl carbinyl cinnamate
Empirical: $C_{12}H_{12}O_2$
Properties: Colorless to light yel. liq.; cherry odor; sol. in ether, alcohol; insol. in water; m.w. 188.24; dens. 1.052 (25/25 C); b.p. 150-152 C; flash pt. >230 F; ref. index 1.5661
Toxicology: LD50 (oral, rat) 1520 mg/kg; mod. toxic by ingestion; skin irritant; heated to decomp., emits acrid smoke and fumes
Uses: Peach-like synthetic flavoring agent
Regulatory: FDA 21CFR §172.515; FEMA GRAS
Manuf./Distrib. (pharm. & food): Aldrich

Allyl cyclohexaneacetate
FEMA 2023
Empirical: $C_{11}H_{18}O_2$
Properties: Liq., intense fruital aroma; m.w. 182.26; b.p. 66 C; ref. index 1.4574

Uses: Synthetic flavoring agent
Regulatory: FDA 21CFR §172.515; FEMA GRAS

Allyl cyclohexanebutyrate
FEMA 2024
Empirical: $C_{13}H_{22}O_2$
Properties: Liq., pineapple odor; m.w. 210.31; b.p. 104 C; ref. index 1.4608
Uses: Synthetic flavoring agent
Regulatory: FDA 21CFR §172.515; FEMA GRAS

Allyl cyclohexanehexanoate
FEMA 2025
Synonyms: Allyl cyclohexylcaproate; Allyl cyclohexylcapronate
Empirical: $C_{15}H_{26}O_2$
Properties: M.w. 238.37
Uses: Synthetic flavoring agent
Regulatory: FDA 21CFR §172.515; FEMA GRAS

Allyl cyclohexanepropionate
CAS 2705-87-5
FEMA 2026
Synonyms: Allyl-3-cyclohexanepropionate; 3-Allylcyclohexyl propionate; Allyl hexahydrophenylpropionate
Empirical: $C_{12}H_{20}O_2$
Properties: Colorless liq.; pineapple odor; misc. in alcohol, chloroform, ether; insol. in glycerin, water; m.w. 196.32; dens. 0.945-0.950; b.p. 91 C; flash pt. 212 F; ref. index 1.457-1.463
Precaution: Combustible liq.
Toxicology: LD50 (oral, rat) 585 mg/kg; LD50 (oral, guinea pig) 380 mg/kg; poison by ingestion; heated to decomp., emits acrid smoke and fumes
Uses: Sweet pineapple-like synthetic flavoring agent
Regulatory: FDA 21CFR §172.515; FEMA GRAS; Japan approved
Manuf./Distrib. (pharm. & food): Aldrich

Allyl-3-cyclohexanepropionate. *See* Allyl cyclohexanepropionate

Allyl cyclohexanevalerate
FEMA 2027
Synonyms: Allyl cyclohexylpentanoate
Empirical: $C_{14}H_{24}O_2$
Properties: Liq., char. fruital aroma; m.w. 224.34; b.p. 119 C; ref. index 1.4605
Uses: Synthetic flavoring agent
Regulatory: FDA 21CFR §172.515; FEMA GRAS

Allyl cyclohexylcaproate. *See* Allyl cyclohexanehexanoate
Allyl cyclohexylcapronate. *See* Allyl cyclohexanehexanoate
Allyl cyclohexylpentanoate. *See* Allyl cyclohexanevalerate
3-Allylcyclohexyl propionate. *See* Allyl cyclohexanepropionate
Allyl trans-2,3-dimethylacrylate. *See* Allyl tiglate
Allyl enanthate. *See* Allyl heptanoate
4-Allylguaiacol. *See* Eugenol
Allyl hendecenoate. *See* Allyl 10-undecenoate

Allyl heptanoate
CAS 142-19-8
FEMA 2031
Synonyms: Allyl heptoate; Allyl enanthate; Allyl heptylate; 2-Propenyl heptanoate
Empirical: $C_{10}H_{18}O_2$
Properties: Colorless to pale yel. liq., fruity sweet pineapple odor; m.w. 170.28; dens. 0.880; flash pt. 154 F; ref. index 1.426
Precaution: Combustible liq.
Toxicology: LD50 (oral, rat) 500 mg/kg; LD50 (oral, mouse) 630 mg/kg; mod. toxic by ingestion, skin contact; skin irritant; heated to decomp., emits acrid smoke and fume
Uses: Apricot, banana, berry, pineapple-like synthetic flavoring agent
Regulatory: FEMA GRAS
Manuf./Distrib. (pharm. & food): Aldrich

Allyl heptoate. *See* Allyl heptanoate
Allyl heptylate. *See* Allyl heptanoate

Allyl 2,4-hexadienoate. *See* Allyl sorbate
Allyl hexahydrophenylpropionate. *See* Allyl cyclohexanepropionate
Allyl hexanoate. *See* Allyl caproate
Allyl ionone. *See* Allyl α-ionone

Allyl α-ionone
CAS 79-78-7
FEMA 2033
Synonyms: 1-(2,6,6-Trimethyl-2-cyclohexene-1-yl)-1,6-heptadiene-3-one; Allyl ionone; Cetone V
Empirical: $C_{16}H_{24}O$
Properties: Colorless to yel. liq., fruity woody odor; sol. in alcohol; insol. in water; m.w. 232.40; dens. 0.928-0.935; b.p. 102-104 C; flash pt. 212 F; ref. index 1.503-1.507
Precaution: Combustible liq.
Toxicology: Skin irritant; heated to decomp., emits acrid smoke and fumes
Uses: Fruity synthetic flavoring agent
Regulatory: FDA 21CFR §172.515; FEMA GRAS
Manuf./Distrib. (pharm. & food): Aldrich

Allyl isosulfocyanate. *See* Allyl isothiocyanate

Allyl isothiocyanate
CAS 57-06-7; EINECS 200-309-2
FEMA 2034
Synonyms: Mustard oil; Isothiocyanic acid allyl ester; Allyl isosulfocyanate; 3-Isothiocyanato-1-propene
Definition: Obtained by the distillation of *Brassica* species
Empirical: C_4H_5NS
Formula: $CH_2=CHCH_2NCS$
Properties: Colorless to pale yel. liq., pungent irritable odor, sharp pungent mustard taste; misc. with alcohol, carbon disulfide, ether, most org. solvs.; sl. sol. in water; m.w. 99.16; dens. 1.013-1.016; m.p. -80 C; b.p. 150.7 C; flash pt. 115 F; ref. index 1.5
Precaution: Volatile; combustible liq.
Toxicology: LD50 (oral, rat) 339 mg/kg; poison by ingestion, skin contact; lachrymator; allergen; mutagenic; heated to decomp., emits highly toxic fumes
Uses: Synthetic flavoring agent; counter-irritant in external analgesic prods.
Regulatory: FDA 21CFR §172.515; FEMA GRAS; Japan approved as flavoring
Manuf./Distrib. (pharm. & food): Aldrich

Allyl isovalerate
CAS 2835-39-4
FEMA 2045
Synonyms: Isovaleric acid allyl ester; Allyl 3-methylbutyrate; 2-Propenyl isovalerate; 2-Propenyl 3-methylbutanoate
Empirical: $C_8H_{14}O_2$
Properties: Colorless to pale yel. liq., apple aroma; m.w. 142.20; b.p. 89-90 C; ref. index 1.4162
Toxicology: LD50 (oral, rat) 230 mg/kg; poison by ingestion; mod. toxic by skin contact; experimental carcinogen, tumorigen; skin irritant; heated to decomp, emits acrid smoke and fumes
Uses: Synthetic flavoring agent
Regulatory: FDA 21CFR §172.515; FEMA GRAS

4-Allyl-2-methoxyphenol. *See* Eugenol
Allyl trans-2-methyl-2-butenoate. *See* Allyl tiglate
Allyl 3-methylbutyrate. *See* Allyl isovalerate

Allyl nonanoate
CAS 7493-72-3
FEMA 2036
Synonyms: Allyl pelargonate
Empirical: $C_{12}H_{22}O_2$
Properties: Mobile liq., pineapple odor; m.w. 198.31; b.p. 151 C; ref. index 1.4302
Uses: Sweet, fruity synthetic flavoring agent
Regulatory: FDA 21CFR §172.515; FEMA GRAS
Manuf./Distrib. (pharm. & food): Aldrich

Allyl octanoate
CAS 4230-97-1
FEMA 2037

Synonyms: Allyl caprylate; Octanoic acid allyl ester; Allyl octylate
Empirical: $C_{11}H_{20}O_2$
Properties: Colorless liq., fruity odor; sol. in alcohol, fixed oils; sl. sol. in propylene glycol; insol. in glycerin, water; m.w. 184.31; dens. 0.8550; b.p. 87-88 C; flash pt. 151 F; ref. index 1.425
Toxicology: LD50 (oral, rat) 570 mg/kg; mod. toxic by ingestion; skin irritant; heated to decomp., emits acrid smoke and fumes
Uses: Banana, pineapple-like synthetic flavoring agent
Regulatory: FDA 21CFR §172.515; FEMA GRAS
Manuf./Distrib. (pharm. & food): Aldrich

Allyl octylate. *See* Allyl octanoate
Allyl pelargonate. *See* Allyl nonanoate

Allyl phenoxyacetate
CAS 7493-74-5
FEMA 2038
Synonyms: Acetate PA
Empirical: $C_{11}H_{12}O_3$
Properties: Liq., honey and pineapple-like aroma; m.w. 192.22; b.p. 100-102 C; ref. index 1.5131 (25.5 C)
Toxicology: LD50 (oral, rat) 475 mg/kg; mod. toxic by ingestion; heated to decomp., emits acrid smoke and fumes
Uses: Honey, pineapple-like synthetic flavoring agent
Regulatory: FDA 21CFR §172.515; FEMA GRAS
Manuf./Distrib. (pharm. & food): Aldrich

Allyl phenylacetate
CAS 1797-74-6
FEMA 2039
Synonyms: Allyl α-toluate; Benzeneacetic acid 2-propenyl ester
Empirical: $C_{11}H_{12}O_2$
Properties: Colorless to lt. yel. liq., fruit banana honey odor; m.w. 176.22; b.p. 89-93 C; ref. index 1.5122
Toxicology: LD50 (oral, rat) 650 mg/kg; mod. toxic by ingestion; human skin irritant; heated to decomp., emits acrid smoke and irritating fumes
Uses: Sweet, honey-like synthetic flavoring agent
Regulatory: FDA 21CFR §172.515; FEMA GRAS
Manuf./Distrib. (pharm. & food): Aldrich

Allyl-3-phenylacrylate. *See* Allyl cinnamate

Allyl propionate
FEMA 2040
Empirical: $C_6H_{10}O_2$
Properties: Liq., apple odor; m.w. 114.15; b.p. 122-123 C; ref. index 1.4105 (20 C), 1.4142 (14 C)
Uses: Synthetic flavoring agent in pharmaceuticals (imitation apricot aroma)
Regulatory: FDA 21CFR §172.515; FEMA GRAS

Allyl sorbate
FEMA 2041
Synonyms: Allyl 2,4-hexadienoate
Empirical: $C_9H_{12}O_2$
Properties: M.w. 152.19
Uses: Synthetic flavoring agent
Regulatory: FDA 21CFR §172.515; FEMA GRAS

Allyl tiglate
CAS 7493-71-2
FEMA 2043
Synonyms: Allyl trans-2,3-dimethylacrylate; Allyl trans-2-methyl-2-butenoate
Empirical: $C_8H_{12}O_2$
Properties: Fruity odor; m.w. 140.18; dens. 0.926; flash pt. 140 F
Uses: Berry, jam-like synthetic flavoring agent
Regulatory: FDA 21CFR §172.515; FEMA GRAS
Manuf./Distrib. (pharm. & food): Aldrich

Allyl α-toluate. *See* Allyl phenylacetate

Allyl 10-undecenoate
FEMA 2044

Allyl undecylenate

Synonyms: Allyl hendecenoate; Allyl undecylenate; Allyl undecylenoate
Empirical: $C_{14}H_{24}O_2$
Properties: Liq., pineapple odor; misc. with most org. solvs.; insol. in water; m.w. 224.34; b.p. 180 C; ref. index 1.4448
Uses: Synthetic flavoring agent
Regulatory: FDA 21CFR §172.515; FEMA GRAS

Allyl undecylenate. *See* Allyl 10-undecenoate
Allyl undecylenoate. *See* Allyl 10-undecenoate
Almond oil. *See* Sweet almond oil

Almond oil PEG-6 esters
Definition: Mixt. from the transesterification of almond oil and PEG-6
Uses: Amphiphilic agent improving drug delivery
Trade names: Labrafil® M 1966 CS

Almond oil, sweet. *See* Sweet almond oil
Aloe barbadensis extract. *See* Aloe extract

Aloe extract
CAS 85507-69-3; EINECS 305-181-2
FEMA 2047
Synonyms: Aloe barbadensis extract; Barbados aloe extract; Curacao aloe extract
Definition: Extract of leaves of one or more species of *Aloe*
Properties: Bitter char. flavor
Uses: Natural flavoring; thickener, stabilizer; used in health and pharmaceutical applics.
Regulatory: FDA 21CFR §172.510; FEMA GRAS; Japan approved
Manuf./Distrib. (pharm. & food): Chart
Trade names containing: Aloe Vera Lipo-Quinone Extract™ Cosmetic Grade; Aloe Vera Lipo-Quinone Extract™ Food Grade; Aloe Vera Lipo-Quinone Extract™ Low Odor (CG)

Aloe vera gel
Synonyms: First aid plant
Definition: Mucilage obtained from expression of juice from leaves of *Aloe barbadensis*
Toxicology: Cross-reacts with benzoin and balsam Peru in those who are allergic to these compds.
Uses: Moisturizer, soothing/healing aid for first aid preps., acne and facial preps., suncare prods.
Regulatory: FDA 21CFR §172.510
Manuf./Distrib. (pharm. & food): Bio-Botanica; R.W. Greeff
Trade names: Activera™ 1-1FA (Filtered); Activera™ 1-200 A; Activera™ 104; Aloe Con WG 40; Aloe Con WLG 200; Aloe Vera Gel 1X; Aloe Vera Gel 10X; Aloe Vera Gel 40X; Aloe Vera Gel Decolorized 1X; Aloe Vera Gel Decolorized 10X; Aloe Vera Gel Decolorized 40X; Aloe Vera Oil; Aloe Vera Powd. 200XXX Extract-Microfine; Cal-O-Vera 200XXX Powd.; Essential Aloe™ GII-1X; Essential Aloe™ GII-10X; Essential Aloe™ GII-100X; Essential Aloe™ GII-200X; Powdered Aloe Vera (1:200) Food Grade; Terra-Dry™ FD Aloe Vera Powd. Decolorized FDD; Terra-Dry™ FD Aloe Vera Powd. Reg. FDR; Terra-Pulp™ FD Whole Aloe Vera Gel Fillet; Terra-Pure™ FD Non-Preserved Decolorized FDD; Terra-Pure™ FD Non-Preserved Reg. FDR; Terra-Pure™ Non-Preserved Aloe Vera Powd.; Terra-Spray™ Spray Dried Aloe Vera Powd. Decolorized SDD; Terra-Spray™ Spray Dried Aloe Vera Powd. Reg. SDR
Trade names containing: Aloe-Moist™; Aloe-Moist™ A; Aloe Vera Gel Thickened FG; Cal-O-Vera 1:1; Cal-O-Vera 10:1; Cal-O-Vera 40:1

Alphazurine FG. *See* D&C Blue No. 4

Althea
Synonyms: Marshmallow; Hibiscus moscheutos
Definition: Dried root of *Althaea officinalis*
Toxicology: Nontoxic
Uses: Used in orals
Manuf./Distrib. (pharm. & food): Bio-Botanica

Althea extract
CAS 97676-24-9
FEMA 2048
Synonyms: Althea officinalis extract; Marshmallow root extract
Definition: Extract of the roots of the marshmallow, *Althea officinalis*
Uses: Natural flavoring
Regulatory: FDA 21CFR §172.510 (roots and flowers)

Manuf./Distrib.: Bio-Botanica
Manuf./Distrib. (pharm. & food): Chart

Althea officinalis extract. *See* Althea extract
Alum. *See* Aluminum sulfate
Alum. *See* Potassium alum dodecahydrate

Alumina
  CAS 1344-28-1; EINECS 215-691-6
  Synonyms: Aluminum oxide; Aluminum oxide (2:3); Tabular alumina; Alumina, tabular; Aluminium oxydes C; Aluminium oxide alumite; Calcined alumina; Alumina, calcined; Activated alumina; Alumina, activated; Alumite; Alundum
  Classification: Inorganic compd.
  Empirical: Al_2O_3
  Properties: Wh. powd., balls, or lumps, odorless, tasteless; insol. in water; very sl. sol. in min. acids; m.w. 101.96; dens. 3.5-4; m.p. 2050 C; b.p. 2977 C
  Precaution: Noncombustible; incompat. with hot chlorinated rubber; exothermic reaction above 200 C with halocarbon vapors produces toxic HCl and phosgene
  Toxicology: Toxic by inhalation of dust; TLV:TWA 10 mg/m^3 (dust); may be irritating to respiratory tract; eye irritant by mech. abrasion; skin drying, peeling; experimental tumorigen and neoplastigen by implant
  Uses: Colorant, dispersing agent; used in orals
  Regulatory: FDA 21CFR §73.1010, 177.1460; exempt from certification; BP compliance (anhyd., basic)
  Manuf./Distrib.: Air Prods.; Alcan; Alcoa; Aldrich; Atomergic Chemetals; BA Chem. Ltd.; Degussa; Ferro/Transelco; Hüls Am.; Lonza Sarl; Nissan Chem. Ind.; Norton Chem. Process Prods.; Rhone-Poulenc; San Yuan; Spectrum Chem. Mfg.; Sumitomo; Zircar
  Manuf./Distrib. (pharm. & food): Atomergic Chemetals
  Trade names containing: Aerosil® COK 84

Alumina, activated. *See* Alumina
Alumina, calcined. *See* Alumina
Alumina hydrate. *See* Alumina trihydrate
Alumina hydrate. *See* Aluminum hydroxide
Alumina hydrated. *See* Aluminum hydroxide
Alumina, tabular. *See* Alumina

Alumina trihydrate
  CAS 21645-51-2
  Synonyms: Alumina hydrate; Aluminum hydrate; Hydrated alumina; Aluminum hydroxide; Hydrated aluminum oxide; Aluminum trihydroxide
  Classification: Inorganic compd.
  Empirical: $Al_2O_3 \cdot 3H_2O$
  Properties: White powd., balls, or lumps; sol. in min. acids, caustic soda; insol. in water; m.w. 156.01; dens. 2.42; m.p. 2030 C; releases water on heating
  Toxicology: Irritant
  Uses: Stabilizer, filler, polishing agent, abrasive in dentifrices
  Regulatory: BP compliance
  Manuf./Distrib.: Alcan; Alcoa; Atomergic Chemetals; Climax Performance; Croxton & Garry Ltd; Franklin Ind. Min.; J.M. Huber; Nyco Minerals; Reheis
  Manuf./Distrib. (pharm. & food): Atomergic Chemetals; Croxton & Garry Ltd
  Trade names: Baco AF; Hydral® 710; SB-30
  See also Aluminum hydroxide

Aluminic acid. *See* Aluminum hydroxide
Aluminium oxide alumite. *See* Alumina
Aluminium oxydes C. *See* Alumina
Aluminophosphoric acid. *See* Aluminum orthophosphate
Aluminosilicic acid, magnesium salt. *See* Magnesium aluminum silicate

Aluminum
  CAS 7429-90-5; EINECS 231-072-3; UN No. 1396
  Synonyms: CI 77000; Aluminum powder; Aluminum bronze
  Classification: Metallic element
  Empirical: Al
  Properties: Silvery wh. cryst. solid; sol. in HCl, sulfuric acid; insol. in water, alcohol; m.w. 26.98; dens. 2.708; m.p. 660 C; b.p. 2450 C
  Precaution: Flamm. in air; explosive; no stable isotopes; moisture-sensitive; dangerous when wet

Aluminum acetate

Toxicology: TLV 10 mg/m^3 of air; (sol. salt) 2 mg/m^3 of air; (welding fumes) 5 mg/m^3 of air
Uses: Colorant for external pharmaceuticals
Regulatory: FDA 21CFR §73.1645, 73.2645, 175.105, 175.300, 177.1460; BP compliance; Japan approved
Manuf./Distrib.: Fluka
Manuf./Distrib. (pharm. & food): Aldrich; Integra

Aluminum acetate. *See* Aluminum diacetate
Aluminum bronze. *See* Aluminum
Aluminum chlorhydrate. *See* Aluminum chlorohydrate
Aluminum chlorhydrol. *See* Aluminum chlorohydrate
Aluminum chlorhydroxide. *See* Aluminum chlorohydrate

Aluminum chloride anhydrous
CAS 7446-70-0; EINECS 231-208-1; UN No. 2581
Classification: Inorganic compd.
Empirical: AlCl$_3$
Properties: Wh. or ylsh. cryst. powd, hydrochloric acid type odor, sweet very astringent taste; deliq.; very sol. in water; freely sol. in alcohol; sol. in glycerin; m.w. 133.34; dens. 2.44; m.p. 190 C
Precaution: Corrosive
Toxicology: Irritant; lethal to mammals when ingested in large doses; allergic reactions in susceptible persons
Uses: Mfg. of pharmaceuticals; antiseptic; the hexahydrate as a topical astringent
Regulatory: BP compliance
Manuf./Distrib.: Aldrich; Asada Chem Industry Co Ltd; Elf Atochem N. Am.; Fluka; Harcros Durham; Witco/ PAG
Manuf./Distrib. (pharm. & food): Mallinckrodt; Reheis; Witco

Aluminum chloride basic
CAS 1327-41-9
Synonyms: Polyaluminum chloride
Uses: Antiperspirant active
Trade names: Westchlor® 200 Custom Powd. 10; Westchlor® 200 Impalpable; Westchlor® DM 200 Impalpable

Aluminum chloride hydroxide. *See* Aluminum chlorohydrate

Aluminum chlorohydrate
CAS 1327-41-9; 12042-91-0 (dihydrate); EINECS 215-477-2
Synonyms: Aluminum chlorhydrate; Aluminum chloride hydroxide; Aluminum hydroxide chloride; Basic aluminum chlorate; Chlorhydrol; Aluminum chlorhydrol; Aluminum chlorohydrol; Aluminum hydroxychloride; Aluminum chlorohydroxide; Aluminum chlorhydroxide
Classification: Inorganic salt
Formula: [Al$_2$(OH)$_5$Cl]$_x$ or Al$_2$ClH$_5$O$_5$ • 2H$_2$O (dihydrate)
Properties: M.w. 174.46 (anhyd.), 210.48 (dihydrate); pH 4.0-4.4 (15%)
Toxicology: Mild skin irritant; TLV:TWA 2 mg(Al)/m^3; heated to decomp., emits toxic fumes of Cl⁻
Uses: Antiperspirant, deodorant
Manuf./Distrib.: Catomance Ltd; Reheis
Manuf./Distrib. (pharm. & food): Ruger; Spectrum Chem. Mfg.
Trade names: Chlorhydrol® 50% Sol'n.; Chlorhydrol® Granular; Chlorhydrol®, Impalpable; Chlorhydrol® Powd.; Macrospherical® 95; Micro-Dry®; Micro-Dry® Superultrafine; Micro-Dry® Ultrafine; Reach® 101; Reach® 103; Reach® 301; Reach® 301 Sol'n.; Reach® 501; Reach® 501 Sol'n.; Ritachlor 50%; Westchlor® 200

Aluminum chlorohydrex PG
Synonyms: Aluminum chlorohydrex propylene glycol complex
Definition: Coordination complex of aluminum chlorohydrate and propylene glycol in which some of the water molecules have been displaced by the propylene glycol
Properties: Sol. in alcohol
Uses: Antiperspirant, OTC active
Trade names: Rehydrol® II

Aluminum chlorohydrex propylene glycol complex. *See* Aluminum chlorohydrex PG
Aluminum chlorohydrol. *See* Aluminum chlorohydrate
Aluminum chlorohydroxide. *See* Aluminum chlorohydrate

Aluminum diacetate
CAS 142-03-0
Synonyms: Basic aluminum acetate; Aluminum acetate; Aluminum subacetate; Aluminum hydroxyacetate

Classification: Salt
Empirical: $C_4H_7AlO_5$
Formula: $Al(OH)(CH_3CO_2)_2$
Properties: Wh. amorphous powd.; m.w. 162.08
Toxicology: Skin irritant
Uses: Astringent in poison ivy/poison oak preps.; used in antiperspirants to combat body odor; used in rectals

Aluminum, dihydroxy (octadecanoato-o-). *See* Aluminum stearate

Aluminum distearate
CAS 300-92-5; EINECS 206-101-8
Definition: Aluminum salt of stearic acid
Empirical: $C_{36}H_{71}O_5Al$
Formula: $[CH_3(CH_2)_{16}COO]_2Al(OH)$
Properties: White powd.; insol. in water, alcohol, ether; forms gel w/ aliphatic and aromatic hydrocarbons; dens. 1.009; m.p. 145 C
Uses: Metal soap stabilizer
Regulatory: FDA 21CFR §172.863, 173.340, 175.105, 175.300, 175.320, 176.170, 176.200, 176.210, 177.1200, 177.1460, 177.2260, 178.3910, 179.45, 181.22, 181.29
Trade names: Haro® Chem ALMD-2

Aluminum hydrate. *See* Alumina trihydrate; Aluminum hydroxide

Aluminum hydroxide
CAS 21645-51-2; EINECS 244-492-7
Synonyms: Alumina hydrate; Alumina hydrated; Alumina trihydrate; Aluminic acid; Aluminum oxide hydrate; Aluminum hydrate ; Aluminum trihydroxide; Aluminum trihydrate; Hydrated alumina; Trihydrated alumina
Classification: Inorganic compd.
Empirical: AlH_3O_3
Formula: $Al(OH)_3$
Properties: White cryst. powd. or gran.; insol. in water; sol. in min. acids, caustic soda; m.w. 78.01; dens. 2.42; m.p. loses water @ 300 C
Precaution: Incompat. with chlorinated rubber
Toxicology: TLV:TWA 2 mg (Al)/m^3; poison by intraperitoneal route; human systemic effects by ing.; no known skin toxicity; mutagenic data
Uses: Filler, abrasive, mild astringent, adsorbent, protein binder; used in orals, antiperspirants, dentifrices, dusting powd., gastric antacid in medicine
Regulatory: FDA 21CFR §175.300, 177.1200, 177.2600, 182.90; BP compliance (dried, gel, mixt., oral susp.)
Manuf./Distrib.: Alcan; Alcoa; Atomergic Chemetals; BA Chem Ltd; J.M. Huber; Lohmann; Nyco Minerals; Reheis; Rhone-Poulenc; Seimi Chem.; Vista; Whittaker, Clark & Daniels
Manuf./Distrib. (pharm. & food): Integra; Ruger; Spectrum Chem. Mfg.
Trade names: F-500®; F-500® Low Sodium; F-1000®; F-1500™; F-1500™ Reductionized; F-2000®; F-2100®; F-2200®; F-2300™; F-4400™; Liquigel®; Liquigel® D4; Liquigel® HO; R-1000™; Rederm® Gel; Rederm® Powd.; Rehydragel® CG; Rehydragel® HPA; Rehydragel® LV; Rehydragel® T
Trade names containing: F-6000M™; F-MA 11®; F-MA 11® HD; F-MA 11® Reductionized; Liquigel® AM; Liquigel® AMS; R-MA 11®; R-MA 40®
See also Alumina trihydrate; CI 77002

Aluminum hydroxide. *See* Alumina trihydrate
Aluminum hydroxide. *See* CI 77002
Aluminum hydroxide chloride. *See* Aluminum chlorohydrate
Aluminum hydroxyacetate. *See* Aluminum diacetate
Aluminum hydroxychloride. *See* Aluminum chlorohydrate
Aluminum-L-2-hydroxypropionate. *See* Aluminum lactate

Aluminum lactate
CAS 18917-91-4
Synonyms: Aluminum-L-2-hydroxypropionate
Definition: Aluminum salt of L-lactic acid
Formula: $Al(CH_3CHOHCOO)_3$
Properties: Wh. powd.; m.w. 294
Uses: Pharmaceutical dietary supplement
Manuf./Distrib.: Lohmann
Trade names: Puramex® AL

Aluminum magnesium silicate. *See* Magnesium aluminum silicate

Aluminum monobasic stearate. *See* Aluminum stearate
Aluminum monostearate. *See* Aluminum stearate

Aluminum orthophosphate
CAS 7784-30-7
Synonyms: Aluminum phosphate; Aluminophosphoric acid; Phosphoric acid, aluminum salt (1:1)
Empirical: $AlPO_4$
Properties: Wh. cryst.; insol. in water and alcohol; sl. sol. in HCl, nitric acid; m.w. 121.95; dens. 2.566; m.p. 1500 C; isomorphous with quartz
Toxicology: Sol'ns. are corrosive to tissue
Uses: Lubricant; dental cements; antacid
Manuf./Distrib. (pharm. & food): Aldrich

Aluminum oxide. *See* Alumina
Aluminum oxide (2:3). *See* Alumina
Aluminum oxide hydrate. *See* Aluminum hydroxide
Aluminum phosphate. *See* Aluminum orthophosphate

Aluminum polyester
Uses: Used in injectables

Aluminum potassium sulfate. *See* Potassium alum dodecahydrate
Aluminum powder. *See* Aluminum; CI 77000

Aluminum sesquichloride
Uses: Antiperspirant active
Trade names: Westchlor® 170 Powd.

Aluminum sesquichlorohydrate
CAS 11097-68-0
Formula: $Al_2(OH)_{4.5}Cl_{1.5} \cdot nH_2O$
Uses: Active ingredient in antiperspirant formulations
Trade names: Westchlor® 170

Aluminum silicate
CAS 1327-36-2; 12141-46-7; 14504-95-1; EINECS 215-475-1; 235-253-8
Synonyms: Pyrophyllite; CI 77004
Definition: Complex inorganic salt with 1 mole alumina, 1-3 moles silica
Formula: Al_2O_5Si
Properties: Varying proportions of Al_2O_3 and SiO_2; wh. mass, crystals, or whiskers; high str.; m.w. 162.05; insol. in water
Toxicology: Essentially harmless when given orally or applied to skin
Uses: Thickener; mild abrasive for dentifrices; used in orals, dental cements; protective agent for stomach mucosa
Regulatory: FDA 21CFR §175.300, 177.1200, 177.1460, 177.2600, 184.1155
Manuf./Distrib.: R.E. Carroll; CE Minerals; Dry Branch Kaolin; ECC Int'l.; Kaopolite; Kyowa Chem. Ind.; Solvay; Takeda Chem. Ind.; Thiele Kaolin; Tomita Pharmaceutical; R.T. Vanderbilt
Manuf./Distrib. (pharm. & food): Tomita Pharmaceutical
Trade names: Kaopolite® 1147; Kaopolite® SF; Suspengel Elite; Suspengel Micro; Suspengel Ultra
See also Pyrophyllite

Aluminum sodium silicate. *See* Sodium silicoaluminate

Aluminum stearate
CAS 7047-84-9; EINECS 230-325-5
Synonyms: Aluminum, dihydroxy (octadecanoato-o-); Octadecanoic acid aluminum salt; Stearic acid aluminum dihydroxide salt; Aluminum monobasic stearate; Aluminum monostearate
Classification: Aliphatic organic compd.
Definition: Aluminum salt of stearic acid
Empirical: $C_{18}H_{37}AlO_4$
Formula: $CH_3(CH_2)_{16}COOAl(OH)_2$
Properties: Wh. to ylsh. fine powd., faint char. odor; insol. in water, alcohol, ether; sol. in alkali, petrol., turpentine oil; m.w. 344.48; dens. 1.070; m.p. 115 C
Toxicology: TLV:TWA 2 mg(Al)/m^3; no known toxicity; heated to decomp., emits acrid smoke and irritating fumes
Uses: Suspending agent, visc.-increasing agent for pharmaceuticals
Regulatory: FDA §121.1099, 172.863, 173.340, 181.29; USP/NF compliance
Manuf./Distrib.: Elf Atochem N. Am./Wire Mill; Ferro/Grant; Lohmann; Magnesia GmbH; Norac; Syn. Prods.;

Witco
Manuf./Distrib. (pharm. & food): Spectrum Chem. Mfg.
Trade names: Synpro® Aluminum Monostearate NF; Synpro® Aluminum Stearate USP
Trade names containing: Dehymuls® E; Dehymuls® F; Dehymuls® K

Aluminum subacetate. *See* Aluminum diacetate

Aluminum sulfate
CAS 10043-01-3 (anhyd.); 17927-65-0 (hydrate); EINECS 233-135-0; UN No. 1760 (sol'n.)
Synonyms: Alum; Pearl alum; Aluminum trisulfate; Cake alum
Classification: Inorganic salt
Empirical: $Al_2O_{12}S_3$
Formula: $Al_2(SO_4)_3 \cdot 14H_2O$
Properties: Wh. cryst. powd., odorless, sweet taste; hygroscopic; sol. in water; insol. in alcohol; m.w. 342.14
   (anhyd.); dens. 2.71; b.p. dec. @ 770 C; stable in air
Precaution: Forms sulfuric acid w/ water; decomposes to sulfur oxides at high temps.
Toxicology: Irritating to skin, eyes, respiratory tract; ingestion causes nausea, vomiting, abdominal pain; LD50
   (oral, mouse) 6207 mg/kg; TLV-TWA 2 mg/m^3(ACGIH)
Uses: Firming agent used in otics; antiseptic, astringent, and detergent in antiperspirants, skin treatments;
   20% sol'n. for treatment of insect or marine organism venom
Regulatory: FDA 21CFR §172.892, 173.3120, 182.1125, GRAS; USP/NF, BP, Ph.Eur. compliance
Manuf./Distrib.: Albemarle; Alcan; Aldrich; Am. Cyanamid; Asada Chem Industry Co Ltd; Ashland; BA Chem.
   Ltd.; General Chem.; Lohmann; Rasa Ind.; Rhone-Poulenc Basic
Manuf./Distrib. (pharm. & food): Integra; Mallinckrodt; Rhone-Poulenc; Spectrum Chem. Mfg.

Aluminum trihydrate. *See* Aluminum hydroxide
Aluminum trihydroxide. *See* Alumina trihydrate; Aluminum hydroxide
Aluminum trisulfate. *See* Aluminum sulfate

Aluminum zirconium octachlorohydrex GLY
Synonyms: Aluminum zirconium octachlorohydrex glycine complex
Definition: Coordination complex of aluminum zirconium octachlorohydrate and glycine
Uses: Active ingred. in OTC drug prods.; antiperspirant active
Trade names: Reach® AZO; Westchlor® ZR 82B DM Powd.

Aluminum zirconium octachlorohydrex glycine complex. *See* Aluminum zirconium octachlorohydrex GLY

Aluminum zirconium pentachlorohydrate
Classification: Complex basic aluminum zirconium chloride
Formula: $Al_8Zr(OH)_{23}Cl_5 \cdot nH_2O$
Uses: Antiperspirant active in OTC drug prods.
Trade names: Rezal® 67; Rezal® 67P

Aluminum zirconium pentachlorohydrex GLY
Synonyms: Aluminum zirconium pentachlorohydrex glycine complex
Definition: Coordination complex of aluminum zirconium pentachlorohydrate and glycine
Uses: Antiperspirant active in OTC drug prods.
Trade names: Westchlor® ZR 80B DM Powd.
Trade names containing: Westchlor® A2Z 8106

Aluminum zirconium pentachlorohydrex glycine complex. *See* Aluminum zirconium pentachlorohydrex
   GLY

Aluminum zirconium tetrachlorohydrex GLY
Synonyms: Aluminum zirconium tetrachlorohydrex glycine complex
Definition: Coordination complex of aluminum/zirconium tetrachlorohydrate and glycine where glycine
   replaces water molecule
Uses: Antiperspirant active in OTC drug prods.
Trade names: Reach® AZP-701; Reach® AZP-855; Reach® AZP-902; Reach® AZP-908; Rezal® 36; Rezal®
   36G; Rezal® 36G Conc.; Rezal® 36GP; Rezal® 36GP Superultrafine; Westchlor® ZR 35B; Westchlor®
   ZR 35B Custom Powd. 5; Westchlor® ZR 35B Custom Powd. 10; Westchlor® ZR 35B DM Custom Powd.
   5; Westchlor® ZR 35B DM Custom Powd. 10; Westchlor® ZR 35B DM Powd.; Westchlor® ZR 35B Micro
   Powd.; Westchlor® ZR 41
Trade names containing: Reach® AZP-908PG; Rezal® 36GPG

Aluminum zirconium tetrachlorohydrex glycine complex. *See* Aluminum zirconium tetrachlorohydrex
   GLY

329

Aluminum/zirconium trichlorohydrex GLY
> *Definition:* Coordination complex of aluminum zirconium trichlorohydrate and glycine where glycine replaces water molecule
> *Uses:* Antiperspirant active
> *Trade names:* Reach® AZZ-855; Reach® AZZ-902; Rezal® 33GP; Westchlor® ZR 30B Custom Powd. 5; Westchlor® ZR 30B Custom Powd. 10; Westchlor® ZR 30B DM Custom Powd. 5; Westchlor® ZR 30B DM Custom Powd. 10; Westchlor® ZR 30B DM Powd.; Westchlor® ZR 30B Micro Powd.; Westchlor® ZR 58B DM Powd.; Westchlor® ZR 60B DM Powd.
> *Trade names containing:* Reach® AZZ-908PG

Alumite. *See* Alumina
Alum lake of carminic acid. *See* Carmine
Alum, potassium. *See* Potassium alum dodecahydrate
Alundum. *See* Alumina

Amaranth
> CAS 915-67-3; EINECS 213-022-2
> *Synonyms:* FD&C Red No. 2; Acid red 27; Red dye No. 2; Naphthylamine red; Fast red; Naphthol red; Azorubin S; CI 16185
> *Classification:* Azo dye
> *Empirical:* $C_{20}H_{11}N_2Na_3O_{10}S_3$
> *Formula:* $NaSO_3C_{10}H_5N=NC_{10}H_4(SO_3Na)_2OH$
> *Properties:* Dk. red to purple powd.; sol. in water, glycerol, propylene glycol, citric acid, tartaric acid; very sl. sol. in alcohol; insol. in oil, fat, most org. solvs.; m.w. 604.48; dens. $\approx$ 1.50
> *Toxicology:* Possible carcinogen; may cause anaphylactic symptoms, urticaria
> *Uses:* Colorant, absorbent, diluent, disintegration agent, compression agent, nutrition, astringent
> *Regulatory:* Banned by FDA for use in foods, drugs, and cosmetics; UK approved; BP compliance
> *Manuf./Distrib.:* Spectrum Chem. Mfg.
> *Manuf./Distrib. (pharm. & food):* Aldrich
> *Trade names:* Amaranth Oil; Pre-Gel Amaranth Powd.

Amber. *See* Succinic acid
Amber acid. *See* Succinic acid
Ambrette seed liq. *See* Ambrette seed oil

Ambrette seed oil
> FEMA 2051
> *Synonyms:* Ambrette seed liq.
> *Definition:* Derived from *Hibiscus moschatus* or *H. abelmoschus*
> *Properties:* Oil; brandy-like odor; ref. index 1.4680 (20 C)
> *Toxicology:* Heated to decomp., emits acrid smoke and fumes
> *Uses:* Natural flavoring agent
> *Regulatory:* FDA 21CFR §182.10, 182.20, GRAS; FEMA GRAS; Japan approved
> *Manuf./Distrib. (pharm. & food):* Pierre Chauvet

American ash. *See* Potassium carbonate
American dill seed oil. *See* Dill seed oil
Ametriodinic acid. *See* Iodamide
Amine C$_4$. *See* n-Butylamine
Amine C$_5$. *See* Pentylamine
Aminoacetic acid. *See* Glycine
Amino acids, corn gluten. *See* Corn gluten amino acids
Aminoamylene glycol. *See* 2-Amino-2-ethyl-1,3-propanediol
2-Aminoanisole. *See* o-Anisidine
3-Aminoanisole. *See* m-Anisidine
4-Aminoanisole. *See* p-Anisidine
m-Aminobenzenesulfonic acid. *See* Metanilic acid
Aminobenzoic acid. *See* p-Aminobenzoic acid
4-Aminobenzoic acid. *See* p-Aminobenzoic acid

p-Aminobenzoic acid
> CAS 150-13-0; EINECS 205-753-0
> *Synonyms:* PABA; 4-Aminobenzoic acid; Aminobenzoic acid
> *Classification:* Aromatic organic compd.
> *Empirical:* $C_7H_7NO_2$
> *Formula:* $NH_2C_6H_4CO_2H$

Properties: Colorless to yel. monoclinic prisms; sol. in ethyl acetate, glac. acetic acid; sl. sol. in benzene; insol. in petrol. ether; m.w. 137.13; dens. 1.374; m.p. 187 C
Precaution: Light-sensitive
Toxicology: Irritant; can cause allergic eczema and lt. sensitivity in susceptible persons
Uses: Active ingred. in OTC drug prods.; UV absorber in pharmaceuticals; local anesthetic in sunburn prods.; pharmaceutical intermediate; to treath arthritis
Regulatory: BP compliance
Manuf./Distrib.: Am. Biorganics; R.W. Greeff; Nat'l. Starch & Chem.; Schweizerhall
Manuf./Distrib. (pharm. & food): Aldrich; R.W. Greeff; Koriyama Kasei; Spectrum Chem. Mfg.

2-Aminobenzoic acid methyl ester. *See* Methyl anthranilate
5-Amino-1,3-bis(2-ethylhexyl)-5-methyl-hexhydropyrimidine. *See* Hexetidine
1-Aminobutane. *See* n-Butylamine

2-Amino-1-butanol
CAS 96-20-8; 5856-63-3; EINECS 202-488-2
Synonyms: 2-Amino-n-butyl alcohol; 2-Aminobutan-1-ol
Classification: Amino alcohol
Empirical: $C_4H_{11}NO$
Formula: $CH_3CH_2CHNH_2CH_2OH$
Properties: Colorless liq.; misc. in water at 20 C, sol. in alcohols; m.w. 89.14; dens. 0.944 (20/20 C); m.p. -2 C; b.p. 178 C (760 mm); flash pt. 73.3 C; ref. index 1.453; corrosive to copper, brass, aluminum; moderate flamm.
Toxicology: Poison by intravenous, intraperitoneal routes, moderate toxicity by ingestion
Uses: Pharmaceutical intermediate for synthesis of ethambutol, an anti-tuberculosis drug; emulsifying agent
Regulatory: BP compliance
Manuf./Distrib. (pharm. & food): Aldrich
Trade names: AB®

2-Aminobutan-1-ol. *See* 2-Amino-1-butanol
2-Amino-n-butyl alcohol. *See* 2-Amino-1-butanol
Aminobutylene glycol. *See* 2-Amino-2-methyl-1,3-propanediol
3-Amino-N-(α-carboxyphenethyl) succinamic acid N-methyl ester. *See* Aspartame
m-Aminochlorobenzene. *See* m-Chloroaniline
o-Aminochlorobenzene. *See* o-Chloroaniline
p-Aminochlorobenzene. *See* p-Chloroaniline
2-Amino-1,7-dihydro-6H-purin-6-one. *See* CI 75170; Guanine
4-Aminodiphenylamine. *See* N-Phenyl-p-phenylenediamine
p-Aminodiphenylamine. *See* N-Phenyl-p-phenylenediamine
2-Aminoethanesulfonic acid. *See* Taurine
2-Aminoethanol. *See* Ethanolamine
2-Aminoethyl alcohol. *See* Ethanolamine

Aminoethylpiperazine
CAS 140-31-8; EINECS 205-411-0; UN No. 2815
Synonyms: AEP; 1-(2-Aminoethyl) piperazine; 2-Piperazinoethylamione
Classification: Amine
Empirical: $C_6H_{15}N_3$
Formula: $H_2NC_2H_4NCH_2CH_2NHCH_2CH_2$
Properties: Colorless or pale yel liq.; sol. in water; m.w. 129.24; dens. 0.9837; b.p. 222.0 C; f.p. 17.6 C; flash pt. 200 F; ref. index 1.499
Precaution: Combustible; corrosive
Toxicology: Strong irritant to tissue; poison by intraperitoneal route, toxic by ingestion and skin contact
Uses: Intermediate for pharmaceuticals, anthelmintics
Manuf./Distrib.: Akzo Nobel; Aldrich; Dow; Fabrichem; Texaco; Tosoh; Union Carbide
Manuf./Distrib. (pharm. & food): Aldrich; Tosoh

1-(2-Aminoethyl) piperazine. *See* Aminoethylpiperazine

2-Amino-2-ethyl-1,3-propanediol
CAS 115-70-8; EINECS 204-101-2
Synonyms: AEPD; Aminoamylene glycol
Classification: Aliphatic diol; amino glycol
Formula: $CH_2OHC(C_2H_5)NH_2CH_2OH$
Properties: Solid or viscous liq.; misc. in water; sol. in alcohols; m.w. 119.16; dens. 1.099 (20/20 C); m.p. 38 C
Uses: Pharmaceutical intermediate
Trade names: AEPD®

Aminoformamidine hydrochloride. *See* Guanidine hydrochloride
L-2-Aminoglutaric acid. *See* L-Glutamic acid
L-2-Aminoglutaric acid hydrochloride. *See* L-Glutamic acid hydrochloride
1-1-Amino-4-guanidovaleric acid. *See* L-Arginine
2-Amino-2-(hydroxymethyl)-1,3-propanediol. *See* Tris (hydroxymethyl) aminomethane
5-Amino-4-hydroxy-3-(phenylazo)-2,7-naphthalenedisulfonic acid disodium salt. *See* CI 17200; D&C Red
    No. 33
2-Amino-3-hydroxypropionic acid. *See* L-Serine
2-Amino-6-hydroxypurine. *See* CI 75170; Guanine
2-Aminohypoxanthine. *See* CI 75170; Guanine
α-Amino-β-imidazolepropionic acid. *See* L-Histidine
L-2-Amino-3-mercaptopropanoic acid. *See* L-Cysteine
L-2-Amino-3-mercaptopropanoic acid monohydrochloride. *See* Cysteine hydrochloride anhydrous
L-2-Amino-3-mercaptopropanoic acid monohydrochloride monohydrate. *See* Cysteine hydrochloride
    monohydrate
(+)-2-Amino-3-mercaptopropionic acid. *See* L-Cysteine
2-Amino-1-methyl-4-imidazolidinone. *See* Creatinine
(±)-2-Amino-4-(methylmercapto)butyric acid. *See* DL-Methionine
(S)-2-Amino-4-(methylmercapto)butyric acid. *See* L-Methionine

2-Amino-2-methyl-1,3-propanediol
    CAS 115-69-5; EINECS 204-100-7
    Synonyms: AMPD; Aminobutylene glycol; Butanediolamine
    Classification: Aliphatic diol; amino glycol
    Empirical: $C_4H_{11}NO_2$
    Formula: $CH_2OCH(CH_3)NH_2CH_2OH$
    Properties: Colorless crystals; sol. in water and alcohol; m.w. 105.14; m.p. 110 C; b.p. 151 C (10 mm); corrosive
        to copper, brass, aluminum
    Toxicology: Poison by ingestion; prolonged skin exposure may cause irritation
    Uses: Emulsifying agent in creams and lotions; used in medicines that reduce body water; pharmaceutical
        intermediate; alkaline buffer
    Manuf./Distrib.: Spectrum Chem. Mfg.
    Trade names: AMPD

Aminomethyl propanol. *See* 2-Amino-2-methyl-1-propanol

2-Amino-2-methyl-1-propanol
    CAS 124-68-5; EINECS 204-709-8
    Synonyms: AMP; Isobutanolamine; Aminomethyl propanol; Isobutanol-2 amine
    Classification: Substituted aliphatic alcohol
    Empirical: $C_4H_{11}NO$
    Formula: $CH_3(CH_3)(NH_2)CH_2OH$
    Properties: Solid or visc. liq.; misc. with water; sol. in alcohol; m.w. 89.1; dens. 0.93 (20/4 C); m.p. 30 C; b.p.
        165 C (760 mm); flash pt. (TOC) 153 F
    Precaution: Flamm. exposed to heat or flame
    Toxicology: Moderately toxic by ingestion
    Uses: Buffer in pharmaceutical, diagnostic, and biochem. applics.
    Regulatory: FDA 21CFR §175.105, 176.170
    Manuf./Distrib.: Allchem Ind.; ANGUS; Ashland; Janssen Chimica
    Trade names: AMP; AMP-95

3-[(4-Amino-2-methyl-5-pyrimidinyl)methyl]-4-(2-hydroxyethyl)-4-methylthiazolium nitrate (salt). *See*
    Thiamine nitrate
DL-2-Amino-4-methylthiobutanaoic acid. *See* DL-Methionine
2-Amino-4-(methylthio)butyric acid. *See* DL-Methionine; L-Methionine
2-Amino-6-oxypurine. *See* Guanine
1-Aminopentane. *See* Pentylamine
2-Aminopentanedioic acid. *See* L-Glutamic acid
2-Aminopentanedioic acid hydrochloride. *See* L-Glutamic acid hydrochloride
1-Amino-2-propanol. *See* Isopropanolamine

N-(3-Aminopropyl)diethanolamine
    UN No. 1760
    Synonyms: APDEA
    Properties: Clear liq.; sp.gr. 1.07; b.p. 167 C (760 mm); flash pt. (COC) 340 F; ref. index 1.4965

Uses: Mfg. of drugs
Manuf./Distrib.: Texaco

(+)-Aminosuccinic acid. *See* L-Aspartic acid
L-α-Aminosuccinic acid. *See* L-Aspartic acid
α-Amino-β-thiolpropionic acid. *See* L-Cysteine
Aminotrimethylolmethane. *See* Tris (hydroxymethyl) aminomethane

Ammonia
CAS 7664-41-7; EINECS 231-635-3
UN No. 1005 (anhyd.), 2672, 2073 (sol'ns.)
Classification: Inorganic compd.
Empirical: H₃N
Formula: NH₃
Properties: Colorless gas or liq., sharp, intensely irritating odor; easily liquefied by pressure; sol. in water, alcohol, ether; m.w. 17.03; f.p. -77 C; b.p. -33.5 C
Precaution: Moderate fire risk; caustic
Toxicology: Corrosive; inh. of conc. fumes may be fatal; irritating to eyes and mucous membranes; shown to produce cancer of the skin in human doses of 1000 mg/kg of body wt.
Uses: Alkalizing agent, buffer for pharmaceuticals; used in orals
Regulatory: FDA 27CFR §21.95; Japan approved; BP compliance
Manuf./Distrib.: Air Prods.; Allied-Signal; Am. Cyanamid; Asahi Chem Industry Co Ltd; Chevron; General Chem.; La Roche Ind.; Mitsui Toatsu Chem.; Molycorp; Monsanto; Nissan Chem. Ind.; Norsk Hydro A/S; Occidental; PPG Ind.
Manuf./Distrib. (pharm. & food): Aldrich

Ammonia solution, strong. *See* Ammonium hydroxide
Ammoniated glycyrrhizin. *See* Monoammonium glycyrrhizinate
Ammonia water. *See* Ammonium hydroxide

Ammonio methacrylate copolymer
Definition: Fully polymerized copolymer of acrylic and methacrylic acid esters with a low content of quat. ammonium groups
Properties: Colorless clear to wh.-opaque gran., faint amine odor; sol. in methanol, alcohol, IPA, acetone, ethyl acetate, methylene chloride; insol. in water, petrol. ether
Uses: Coating agent for sustained-release pharmaceuticals
Regulatory: USP/NF compliance
Trade names: Eudragit® RL 30 D; Eudragit® RS 30 D

Ammonium acetate
CAS 631-61-8; EINECS 211-162-9
Synonyms: Acetic acid ammonium salt
Classification: Aliphatic organic compd.
Empirical: C₂H₇NO₂
Formula: CH₃COONH₄
Properties: Colorless or wh.crystals, sl. acetous odor; hygroscopic, deliq.; sol. in alcohol; sl. sol. in acetone; m.w. 77.08; dens. 1.07; m.p. 114 C; pH 6.7-7.3 (5%)
Precaution: Combustible
Toxicology: Gastric irritant
Uses: Buffering agent; diuretic; used in injectables
Regulatory: BP compliance
Manuf./Distrib.: Aldrich; Allchem Ind.; Am. Biorganics; Daiwa Chem.; General Chem.; Great Western; Honig; Jarchem; Lohmann; Johnson Matthey; Magnablend; Schaefer Salt & Chem.; Spectrum Chem. Mfg.; Verdugt BV
Manuf./Distrib. (pharm. & food): Daiwa Chem.; Integra; Mallinckrodt

Ammonium alginate
CAS 9005-34-9
FEMA 2015
Synonyms: Ammonium polymannuronate; Alginic acid, ammonium salt
Definition: Ammonium salt of alginic acid
Formula: C₆H₇O₆ • NH₄
Properties: Filamentous, grainy, granular, or powd.; colorless or sl. yel.; sl. smell or taste; slowly sol. in water forming visc. sol'n.; insol. in alcohol; pH 5-6 (1%)
Toxicology: Heated to decomp., emits toxic fumes of NO_x
Uses: Thickening agent, gellant, stabilizer for pharmaceuticals

Ammonium, alkyldimethyl (phenylmethyl)-, chloride

> *Regulatory:* FDA 21CFR §173.310, 184.1133, GRAS; FEMA GRAS; USDA 9CFR 318.7; Europe listed; UK approved
> *Manuf./Distrib.:* Kelco Int'l.; Spectrum Chem. Mfg.
> *Manuf./Distrib. (pharm. & food):* Kelco Int'l.
> *Trade names:* Sobalg FD 300 Range
> *Trade names containing:* KELTOSE®

Ammonium, alkyldimethyl (phenylmethyl)-, chloride. *See* Benzalkonium chloride

Ammonium bicarbonate
CAS 1066-33-7; EINECS 213-911-5
Synonyms: Ammonium hydrogen carbonate; Acid ammonium carbonate; Carbonic acid, monoammonium salt
Classification: Inorganic salt
Empirical: $CH_2O_3 \cdot H_3N$
Formula: NH_4HCO_3
Properties: Colorless or wh. cryst., faint ammonia odor; sol. 17.4% in water (20 C); dec. by hot water; insol. in alcohol, acetone; m.w. 79.1; dens. 1.586; m.p. dec. 36-60 C; pH 7.0-7.8 (5%)
Precaution: Can cause skin rashes of scalp, forehead, or hands; evolves irritating fumes on heating to 35 C
Toxicology: Poison by intravenous route; LD50 (IV, mouse) 245 mg/kg; heated to decomp., emits toxic fumes of NO_x and NH_3
Uses: Prod. of pharmaceuticals; used medicinally as expectorant and to break up intestinal gas
Regulatory: FDA 21CFR §163.110, 182.1135, 184.1135, GRAS; Japan approved; Europe listed; UK approved; BP compliance
Manuf./Distrib.: BASF; General Chem.; Nissan Chem. Ind.; Norsk Hydro A/S; Rhone-Poulenc Basic; Spectrum Chem. Mfg.; Sumitomo; Ube
Manuf./Distrib. (pharm. & food): Aldrich; Browning; Integra; Mallinckrodt; Nissan Chem. Ind.; Spectrum Chem. Mfg.

Ammonium biphosphate. *See* Ammonium phosphate

Ammonium carbonate
CAS 506-87-6; 8000-73-5; 10361-29-2; EINECS 233-786-0
UN No. 9084
Synonyms: Carbonic acid, ammonium salt; Hartshorn
Definition: Mixt. of ammonium bicarbonate and ammonium carbamate
Empirical: $CH_2O_3 \cdot xH_3N$
Formula: $(NH_4)_2CO_3$
Properties: Wh. powd. or wh. or translucent hard mass, strong ammonia odor, sharp taste; slowly sol. in 4 parts water; dec. by hot water
Precaution: Light-sensistive; decomp. on exposure to air; volatilizes at 60 C; keep tightly closed in cool place; incompat. with acids, acid salts, salts of iron and zinc, alkaloids, alum, tartar emetic
Toxicology: LD50 (IV, mouse) 96 mg/kg; poison by subcutaneous and IV routes; heated to decomp., emits toxic fumes of NO_x and NH_3
Uses: Alkalizing agent, buffering agent for pharmaceuticals; source of ammonia
Regulatory: FDA 21CFR §184.1137, GRAS; BATF 27CFR 240.1051, limitation 0.2%; Japan approved; Europe listed; UK approved; USP/NF, BP compliance
Manuf./Distrib.: Spectrum Chem. Mfg.
Manuf./Distrib. (pharm. & food): Aldrich; Integra; Mallinckrodt; Ruger; Spectrum Chem. Mfg.

Ammonium dihydrogen orthophosphate. *See* Ammonium phosphate
Ammonium dihydrogen phosphate. *See* Ammonium phosphate
Ammonium ferric citrate. *See* Iron ammonium citrate
Ammonium glycyrrhizinate. *See* Monoammonium glycyrrhizinate
Ammonium glycyrrhizinate, pentahydrate. *See* Monoammonium glycyrrhizinate
Ammonium hydrogen carbonate. *See* Ammonium bicarbonate

Ammonium hydroxide
CAS 1336-21-6; EINECS 215-647-6
UN No. 2672
Synonyms: Ammonia solution, strong; Strong ammonia solution; Ammonia water; Aqueous ammonia; Aqua ammonium; Spirit of Hartshorn
Classification: Inorganic base
Empirical: H_5NO
Formula: NH_4OH
Properties: Clear colorless liq., very pungent odor; sol. in water; m.w. 35.06; dens. 0.90; m.p. -77 C; flash pt. none

Precaution: DOT: Corrosive material
Toxicology: LD50 (oral, rat) 350 mg/kg; poison by ingestion; inhalation irritant; severe eye irritant; liq. can inflict burns; heated to decomp., emits NH_3 and NO_x
Uses: Alkalizing agent; used in orals
Regulatory: FDA 21CFR §163.110, 182.90, 184.1139, GRAS; Europe listed; UK approved; USP/NF compliance
Manuf./Distrib.: Spectrum Chem. Mfg.
Manuf./Distrib. (pharm. & food): Aldrich; Integra; Mallinckrodt; Ruger; Spectrum Chem. Mfg.

Ammonium-L-2-hydroxy propionate. *See* Ammonium lactate

Ammonium lactate
CAS 515-98-0
Synonyms: Lactic acid, ammonium salt; Ammonium-L-2-hydroxy propionate
Empirical: $C_3H_9NO_3$
Formula: $CH_3CHOHCOONH_4$
Properties: Colorless to yel. syrupy liq.; sol. in water, alcohol; m.w. 107.08; dens. 1.19-1.21 (15 C)
Uses: Pharmaceutical intermediate
Manuf./Distrib.: AMRESCO; Kraft; Lohmann; Magnablend; Penta Mfg.; Purac Am.; Spectrum Chem. Mfg.; Universal Preserv-A-Chem
Manuf./Distrib. (pharm. & food): Aldrich
Trade names: Purasal® NH 70

Ammonium laureth sulfate
CAS 32612-48-9 (generic); 67762-19-0
Synonyms: Ammonium lauryl ether sulfate
Definition: Ammonium salt of ethoxylated lauryl sulfate
Formula: $(C_2H_4O)_n \cdot C_{12}H_{26}O_4S \cdot H_3N$, n = 1-4
Toxicology: Moderate toxicity by ingestion; skin and eye irritant
Uses: Surfactant in pharmaceutical creams and lotions
Regulatory: FDA 21CFR §175.105
Manuf./Distrib.: Aquatec Quimica SA; Ashland; Great Western; Lonza; Pilot; Rhone-Poulenc Spec.; Sandoz; Sea-Land; Witco/Oleo-Surf.

Ammonium lauryl ether sulfate. *See* Ammonium laureth sulfate

Ammonium lauryl sulfate
CAS 2235-54-3; 68081-96-9; EINECS 218-793-9
Synonyms: Sulfuric acid, monododecyl ester, ammonium salt
Definition: Ammonium salt of lauryl sulfate
Formula: $C_{12}H_{26}O_4S \cdot H_3N$
Properties: M.w. 283.48
Toxicology: Skin and eye irritant
Uses: Foamer, visc. booster
Regulatory: FDA 21CFR §175.105, 175.210, 176.170, 177.1200
Manuf./Distrib.: Aquatec Quimica SA; Ashland; Lonza; Pilot; Rhone-Poulenc Spec.; Sandoz; Sea-Land; Stepan; Witco/Oleo-Surf.
Trade names: Stepanol® AM; Stepanol® AM-V

Ammonium phosphate
CAS 7722-76-1; EINECS 231-764-5
Synonyms: MAP; Monoammonium phosphate; Primary ammonium phosphate; Ammonium dihydrogen orthophosphate; Ammonium phosphate monobasic; Ammonium biphosphate; Ammonium dihydrogen phosphate
Empirical: H_6NO_4P
Formula: $NH_4H_2PO_4$
Properties: Brilliant wh. cryst. or powd., odorless; mildly acidic in reaction; moderately sol. in water; sl. sol. in alcohol; pract. insol. in acetone; m.w. 115.04; dens. 1.803; m.p. 190 C
Uses: Mold culture nutrient in mfg. of pharmaceuticals
Regulatory: FDA 21CFR §184.1141a, GRAS; Japan approved
Manuf./Distrib.: Albright & Wilson; Aldrich; Chisso; EniChem SpA; Fluka; Heico; IMC Fertilizer; Monsanto; Occidental; Rhone-Poulenc Food Ingreds.; Showa Denko
Manuf./Distrib. (pharm. & food): Albright & Wilson Am.; Rhone-Poulenc Food Ingreds.
Trade names: Albrite® Monoammonium Phosphate Food Grade

Ammonium phosphate, dibasic
CAS 7783-28-0; EINECS 231-987-8
Synonyms: DAP; Diammonium phosphate; Phosphoric acid diammonium salt; Diammonium hydrogen phosphate; Diammonium hydrogen orthophosphate; Secondary ammonium phosphate
Classification: Inorganic salt
Empirical: $H_9N_2O_4P$
Formula: $(NH_4)_2HPO_4$
Properties: Wh. cryst. or powd., odorless, cooling salty taste; mildly alkaline in reaction; sol. 1 g/1.7 ml in water; pract. insol. in alcohol, acetone; m.w. 132.07; dens. 1.619; m.p. 155 C (dec.); pH ≈ 8 (1%)
Precaution: Noncombustible; keep well closed
Toxicology: Low to moderate toxicity; heated to decomp., emits very toxic fumes of PO_x, NO_x, and NH_3
Uses: Buffering agent, processing aid for pharmaceuticals
Regulatory: FDA 21CFR §573.320, 184.1141b, GRAS; BATF 27CFR 240.1051, limitation 0.17% as yeast nutrient in wine prod., 0.8% in sparkling wines; Japan approved; USP/NF compliance
Manuf./Distrib.: Albright & Wilson; Aldrich; Chisso; Heico; IMC Fertilizer; La Roche Ind.; Monsanto; Occidental; Rhone-Poulenc Food Ingreds.
Manuf./Distrib. (pharm. & food): Albright & Wilson Am.; Rhone-Poulenc Food Ingreds.; Spectrum Chem. Mfg.
Trade names: Albrite® Diammonium Phosphate Food Grade

Ammonium phosphate monobasic. *See* Ammonium phosphate
Ammonium polymannuronate. *See* Ammonium alginate

Ammonium xylenesulfonate
CAS 26447-10-9; EINECS 247-710-9
Synonyms: Benzenesulfonic acid, dimethyl-, ammonium salt
Definition: Ammonium salt of ring sulfonated mixed xylene isomers
Formula: $C_8H_{10}O_3S \cdot H_3N$
Properties: Sol. in water
Precaution: Flamm.
Toxicology: Chronic toxicity or skin effects are not known; narcotic in high doses

Amorphous sodium polyphosphate. *See* Sodium hexametaphosphate
AMP. *See* 2-Amino-2-methyl-1-propanol
AMPD. *See* 2-Amino-2-methyl-1,3-propanediol

Amyl acetate
CAS 628-63-7; EINECS 211-047-3
Synonyms: Amylacetic ester; Banana oil; Pear oil; Acetic acid pentyl ester; Pentyl acetate
Definition: Ester of amyl alcohol and acetic acid
Empirical: $C_7H_{12}O_2$
Formula: $CH_3COOC_5H_{11}$
Properties: Liq.; m.w. 130.19; dens. 0.876; m.p. -100; f.p. 75 F; b.p. 142 C; flash pt. 75 F
Precaution: Flamm.
Toxicology: Irritant
Uses: Banana-like flavoring agent
Regulatory: FDA 21CFR §175.105; FEMA GRAS; BP compliance
Manuf./Distrib.: Aldrich; Ashland; BP Chem. Ltd; Chemcentral; Penta Mfg; Union Carbide; Van Waters & Rogers
Manuf./Distrib. (pharm. & food): Aldrich; Penta Mfg.

Amylacetic ester. *See* Amyl acetate

n-Amyl alcohol
CAS 71-41-0; EINECS 200-752-1
FEMA 2056; UN No. 1105
Synonyms: 1-Pentanol; Pentan-1-ol; Alcohol C-5; Pentyl alcohol
Empirical: $C_5H_{12}O$
Formula: $CH_3(CH_2)_4OH$
Properties: Clear liq., somewhat sweet balsamic odor; sol. in water; misc. with alcohol, ether; m.w. 88.15; dens. 0.812 (20/4 C); m.p. -79 C; b.p. 137-139 C; flash pt. (CC) 38 C; ref. index 1.409
Precaution: DOT: Flamm. liq.
Toxicology: LD50 (oral, rat) 3030 mg/kg; highly toxic and narcotic; ingestion of 30 mg can cause death in humans; irritating to eyes, respiratory tract
Uses: Raw material for pharmaceutical preps.; sweet syn. flavoring agent
Regulatory: FDA 21CFR §172.515; FEMA GRAS; BP compliance

Manuf./Distrib.: Ashland; Hoechst Celanese; MTM Spec. Ltd.; Union Carbide; Vista
Manuf./Distrib. (pharm. & food): Aceto; Aldrich; Ashland

sec-n-Amyl alcohol. *See* 3-Pentanol

t-Amyl alcohol
CAS 75-85-4; EINECS 200-908-9; UN No. 1105
Synonyms: 2-Methyl-2-butanol; t-Pentyl alcohol; t-Pentanol; Dimethyl ethyl carbinol; Amylene hydrate
Empirical: $C_5H_{12}O$
Formula: $CH_3CH_2C(CH_3)_2OH$
Properties: Colorless clear volatile liq., char. camphoraceous odor, burning taste; sol. in 8 parts water; misc. with alcohol, ether, benzene, chloroform, glycerin, oils; m.w. 88.15; dens. 0.808 (20/4 C); m.p. -9 C; b.p. 100-103 C; ref. index 1.405
Precaution: DOT: Flamm. liq.; keep tightly closed; protect from light
Toxicology: LD50 (oral, rat) 1 g/kg; mod. irritating to human mucous membranes; narcotic in high concs.
Uses: Solvent for pharmaceuticals; hypnotic
Regulatory: USP/NF compliance
Manuf./Distrib.: Allchem Ind.; BASF
Manuf./Distrib. (pharm. & food): Aceto; Aldrich; Mallinckrodt

n-Amylamine. *See* Pentylamine

Amylase
CAS 9000-92-4; EINECS 232-567-7
Synonyms: Mylase 100; 1,4-D-Glucan glucanohydrolase
Classification: Enzyme
Definition: Starch-degrading enzyme
Properties: Off-white powd. or suspension
Toxicology: May produce hypersensitivity reactions
Uses: Ingred. in digestive enzyme preps.; reduces respiratory tract inflammation and local swelling
Trade names: Biodiastase 1000; Biodiastase Conc.; Diastase JP
Trade names containing: Pancreatin 3X USP Powd.; Pancreatin 4X USP Powd.; Pancreatin 5X USP Powd.; Pancreatin 6X USP Powd.; Pancreatin 8X USP Powd.; Pancreatin USP Powd.; Pancrelipase USP; SPL High Lipase Pancreatic Enzyme Conc. (PEC); SPL Pancreatin 3X USP; SPL Pancreatin 4X USP; SPL Pancreatin 5X USP; SPL Pancreatin 6X USP; SPL Pancreatin 7X USP; SPL Pancreatin 8X USP; SPL Pancreatin USP; SPL Pancrelipase USP; SPL Undiluted Pancreatic Enzyme Conc. (PEC)

Amyl butyrate
CAS 540-18-1; EINECS 208-739-2
FEMA 2059; UN No. 2620
Synonyms: Pentyl butyrate; n-Amyl butyrate; Butanoic acid pentyl ester
Empirical: $C_9H_{18}O_2$
Formula: $CH_3CH_2CH_2COOCH_2(CH_2)_3CH_3$
Properties: Colorless liq.; strong, penetrating apricot-like odor, sweet taste; very sol. in alcohol, ether; sol. 0.54 g/l in water (50 C); m.w. 158.24; dens. 0.8713 (15/4 C); m.p. -73.2 C; b.p.185-186 C; ref. index 1.4110 (20 C)
Toxicology: LD50 (oral, rat) 12,210 mg/kg; no known toxicity
Uses: Synthetic flavoring agent for pharmaceuticals; imitation banana flavor; also used in apricot, cherry, pear, plum, and pineapple flavors
Regulatory: FDA 21CFR §172.515
Manuf./Distrib. (pharm. & food): Aldrich
See also Isoamyl butyrate

n-Amyl butyrate. *See* Amyl butyrate
γ-N-Amylbutyrolactone. *See* γ-Nonalactone
Amylcarbinol. *See* Hexyl alcohol

α-Amylcinnamaldehyde
CAS 122-40-7
FEMA 2061
Synonyms: Amylcinnamaldeyhde; α-Pentylcinnamaldehyde; α-Amyl β-phenylacrolein; Jasminaldehyde; Amyl cinnamic aldehyde
Empirical: $C_{14}H_{18}O$
Properties: Yellow liq.; floral odor; sol. in most fixed oils; m.w. 202.30; dens. 0.970; b.p. 153-154 C (10 mm); flash pt. > 230 F; ref. index 1.5552 (20 C)
Toxicology: LD50 (oral, rat) 3730 mg/kg: mod. toxic by ingestion; mild skin irritant; heated to decomp., emits acrid smoke and fumes

α-Amylcinnamaldehyde dimethyl acetal

Uses: Synthetic flavoring agent, fragrance for pharmaceuticals
Regulatory: FDA 21CFR §172.515; FEMA GRAS; Japan approved as flavoring
Manuf./Distrib. (pharm. & food): Aldrich

α-Amylcinnamaldehyde dimethyl acetal
CAS 91-87-2
FEMA 2062
Synonyms: 1,1-Dimethoxy-2-amyl-3-phenyl-2-propene
Empirical: $C_{16}H_{24}O_2$
Properties: M.w. 248.37
Uses: Lemon-like synthetic flavoring agent
Regulatory: FDA 21CFR §172.515; FEMA GRAS
Manuf./Distrib. (pharm. & food): Aldrich

Amylcinnamaldeyhde. *See* α-Amylcinnamaldehyde
n-Amyl cinnamic alcohol. *See* α-Amylcinnamyl alcohol
Amyl cinnamic aldehyde. *See* α-Amylcinnamaldehyde

α-Amylcinnamyl alcohol
FEMA 2065
Synonyms: n-Amyl cinnamic alcohol; α-Pentylcinnamyl alcohol; 2-Amyl-3-phenyl-2-propen-1-ol; 2-Benzylidene-heptanol
Empirical: $C_{14}H_{20}O$
Properties: Ylsh. liq.; m.w. 204.31; flash pt. > 100 C; ref. index 1.5330-1.5400 (20 C)
Uses: Synthetic flavoring agent for pharmaceuticals
Regulatory: FDA 21CFR §172.515; FEMA GRAS

Amylene hydrate. *See* t-Amyl alcohol

Amyl formate
CAS 638-49-3
FEMA 2068
Empirical: $C_6H_{12}O_2$
Properties: M.w. 116.16
Uses: Fruity flavoring agent
Regulatory: FEMA GRAS
Manuf./Distrib. (pharm. & food): Aldrich
See also Isoamyl formate

Amyl hexanoate. *See* Isoamyl hexanoate
Amyl isovalerate. *See* Isoamyl isovalerate
n-Amyl methyl ketone. *See* Methyl n-amyl ketone

Amyl octanoate
FEMA 2079
Synonyms: Isoamyl octanoate; Isoamyl caprylate; Pentyl octanoate
Empirical: $C_{13}H_{26}O_2$
Properties: Liq., orris odor; m.w. 214.35; sp.gr. 0.8562; m.p. -34 C; b.p. 260 C; ref. index 1.4262 (25 C)
Uses: Sweet synthetic flavoring agent
Regulatory: FDA 21CFR §172.515; FEMA GRAS
Manuf./Distrib. (pharm. & food): Aldrich

α-Amyl β-phenylacrolein. *See* α-Amylcinnamaldehyde
2-Amyl-3-phenyl-2-propen-1-ol. *See* α-Amylcinnamyl alcohol

Amyl salicylate
CAS 87-20-7; EINECS 218-080-2
FEMA 2084
Synonyms: 2-Hydroxybenzoic acid, pentyl ester; Isoamyl salicylate; Isopentyl salicylate; Isoamyl 2-hydroxybenzoate; Isoamyl o-hydroxybenzoate
Definition: Ester of amyl alcohol and salicylic acid
Empirical: $C_{12}H_{16}O_3$
Properties: Wh. liq., orchid-like odor; sol. in alcohol, ether; insol. in water, glycerol; m.w. 208.26; dens. 1.053; b.p. 277-278 C; flash pt. > 230 F
Precaution: Combustible
Uses: Synthetic flavoring agent, fragrance for pharmaceuticals
Regulatory: FDA 21CFR §172.515; FEMA GRAS
Manuf./Distrib. (pharm. & food): Aldrich

Amyl valerate. *See* Isoamyl isovalerate
Amyl-Δ-valerolactone. *See* Δ-Decalactone
Analgesine. *See* Antipyrine
Anesthesol. *See* Benzocaine
Anethol. *See* Anethole

Anethole
CAS 104-46-1; 4180-23-8 (E isomer); EINECS 203-205-5
FEMA 2086
Synonyms: Anethol; Anetol; 1-Methoxy-4-propenylbenzene; p-Methoxypropenylbenzene; p-Propenylanisole; Anise camphor; p-Methoxy-β-methylstyrene
Classification: Substituted aromatic ether
Definition: Obtained from anise oil and other sources or prepared synthetically
Empirical: $C_{10}H_{12}O$
Properties: Leaves or lt. yel. liq. above 23 C, anise odor, sweet taste; very sl. sol. in water; misc. with abs. alcohol, ether, chloroform; m.w. 148.22; dens. 0.991 (20/20 C); m.p. 22.5 C; b.p. 235.3 C; flash pt. 90 C; ref. index 1.557-1.561
Precaution: Combustible; light-sensitive
Toxicology: LD50 (oral, rat) 2090 mg/kg; poison by ingestion; skin contact may cause hives, scaling, blisters; experimental tumorigen; may cause human intolerance reaction; heated to decomp., emits acrid smoke and irritating fumes
Uses: Flavoring agent, perfume for orals, mouthwashes, toothpastes, denture creams
Regulatory: FDA 21CFR §182.60, GRAS; FEMA GRAS; USP/NF, BP compliance
Manuf./Distrib. (pharm. & food): Acme-Hardesty; Koyo Chem.; Mallinckrodt; Spectrum Chem. Mfg.

Anethum graveolens oil. *See* Dillweed oil
Anetol. *See* Anethole
Aneurine hydrochloride. *See* Thiamine HCl
Aneurine mononitrate. *See* Thiamine nitrate
Angelica archangelica extract. *See* Angelica extract

Angelica extract
CAS 84775-41-7; EINECS 283-871-1
FEMA 2087
Synonyms: Angelica root extract; Angelica archangelica extract; Archangelica officinalis; European angelica extract
Definition: Extract of roots of *Angelica archangelica*
Properties: Pale yel. to amber liq., pungent odor, bitter-sweet taste; sol. in fixed oils; sl. sol. in min. oil
Toxicology: May cause skin rash or swelling when exposed to lt.; heated to decomp., emits acrid smoke and irritating fumes
Uses: Natural flavoring agent for toothpastes, mouthwashes; used medicinally for gas, to increase sweating, and reduce body water; aromatic, stimulant, carminative, diuretic, diaphoretic
Regulatory: FDA 21CFR §182.10, 182.20, GRAS; FEMA GRAS
Manuf./Distrib. (pharm. & food): Bio-Botanica; Chart; Dr. Madis

Angelica lactone. *See* Pentadecalactone
Angelica root extract. *See* Angelica extract
Anhydrite (natural form). *See* Calcium sulfate
1,4-Anhydro-D-glucitol, 6-hexadecanoate. *See* Sorbitan palmitate
1,4-Anhydro-D-glucitol, 6-isooctadecanoate. *See* Sorbitan isostearate
Anhydrohexitol sesquioleate. *See* Sorbitan sesquioleate
Anhydrosorbitol monoisostearate. *See* Sorbitan isostearate
Anhydrosorbitol monolaurate. *See* Sorbitan laurate
Anhydrosorbitol monooleate. *See* Sorbitan oleate
Anhydrosorbitol monostearate. *See* Sorbitan stearate
Anhydrosorbitol sesquioleate. *See* Sorbitan sesquioleate
Anhydrosorbitol trioleate. *See* Sorbitan trioleate
Anhydrosorbitol tristearate. *See* Sorbitan tristearate
Anhydrous gypsum. *See* Calcium sulfate
Anhydrous lanolin. *See* Lanolin
Aniline-3-sulfonic acid. *See* Metanilic acid
Anisaldehyde. *See* p-Anisaldehyde
o-Anisaldehyde. *See* o-Methoxybenzaldehyde

p-Anisaldehyde

CAS 123-11-5; EINECS 204-602-6
FEMA 2670
Synonyms: 4-Methoxybenzaldehyde; Anisic aldehyde; Anisaldehyde; Aubépine; p-Methoxybenzaldehyde
Empirical: $C_8H_8O_2$
Properties: Colorless oil, hawthorn odor; sol. in propylene glycol; misc. in alcohol, ether, fixed oils; insol. in glycerin, water; m.w. 136.15; dens. 1.123 (20/4 C); m.p. 2.5 C; b.p. 247-248 C; flash pt. 121 C; ref. index 1.571-1.574
Precaution: Combustible; volatile in steam
Toxicology: LD50 (oral, rat) 1510 mg/kg; mod. toxic by ingestion; skin irritant; mutagenic data; heated to decomp., emits acrid smoke and irritating fumes
Uses: Sweetly floral, hawthorn-like fragrance and flavoring
Regulatory: FDA 21CFR §172.515; FEMA GRAS; Japan approved for flavoring; BP compliance
Manuf./Distrib.: Allied-Signal; BASF
Manuf./Distrib. (pharm. & food): Aldrich

Anise

FEMA 2093
Synonyms: Anise seed; Aniseed; Anise fruit
Definition: Pimpinella anisum
Properties: Sweet, soft, mild flavor
Precaution: Protect from light
Toxicology: Can cause contact dermatitis
Uses: Natural flavoring agent; carminative, mildly expectorant; used to break up intestinal gas
Regulatory: FEMA GRAS; Japan approved; BP, Ph.Eur. compliance
Manuf./Distrib. (pharm. & food): Bio-Botanica; Chart

Anise alcohol. *See* Anisyl alcohol
Anise camphor. *See* Anethole
Aniseed. *See* Anise
Aniseed oil. *See* Anise oil
Anise fruit. *See* Anise

Anise oil

CAS 8007-70-3
FEMA 2094
Synonyms: Aniseed oil; Pimpinella anisum oil; Star anise oil
Definition: Volatile oil derived from the dried ripe fruit and seeds of *Pimpinella anisum* or *Illicium verum*, contg. 80-90% anethole, methylchavicol, anisaldehyde
Properties: Colorless or pale yel. liq.; char. odor, sweet aromatic taste; sol. in 3 vols. alcohol; freely sol. in chloroform, ether; sl. sol. in water; dens. 0.978-0.988 (25/25 C); solid. pt. 15 C min.; ref. index 1.553-1.560
Precaution: Keep cool in well-closed containers; protect from light; do not store in PVC bottles
Toxicology: May cause contact dermatitis due to anethole content; anethole is quite toxic in animals, but considered safe in humans @ 2.5 mg/kg dose
Uses: Natural flavoring; carminative, mildly expectorant; used in buccal, orals; common ingred. in cough preps.
Regulatory: FDA 21CFR §182.10, 182.20, GRAS; 27CFR §21.65, 21.151; BP compliance
Manuf./Distrib. (pharm. & food): Chart; Florida Treatt; Ruger; Spectrum Chem. Mfg.

Anise seed. *See* Anise

p-Anisic acid

CAS 100-09-4
Empirical: $C_8H_8O_3$
Properties: M.w. 152.15; m.p. 183-186 C
Uses: Sweet flavoring agent
Manuf./Distrib. (pharm. & food): Aldrich

p-Anisic acid ethyl ester. *See* Ethyl-p-anisate
Anisic alcohol. *See* Anisyl alcohol
Anisic aldehyde. *See* p-Anisaldehyde
Anisic ketone. *See* 1-(p-Methoxyphenyl)-2-propanone

m-Anisidine

CAS 536-90-3; EINECS 208-651-4
UN No. 2431
Synonyms: 3-Aminoanisole; 3-Methoxyaniline; m-Methoxyaniline

Classification: Aromatic organic compd.
Empirical: C_7H_9NO
Properties: M.w. 123.16; dens. 1.102 (20/4 C); b.p. 251 C; flash pt. 126 C; ref. index 1.581 (20 C)
Precaution: Photosensitive
Toxicology: Anisidine and its hydrochloride may reasonably be expected to be carcinogens
Uses: Pharmaceutical intermediate
Manuf./Distrib.: Fluka
Manuf./Distrib. (pharm. & food): Aceto; Aldrich

o-Anisidine
CAS 90-04-0; EINECS 201-963-1
UN No. 2431
Synonyms: o-Methoxyaniline; 2-Aminoanisole; 2-Methoxyaniline
Classification: Aromatic organic compd.
Empirical: C_7H_9NO
Properties: Lt. yel. liq.; sol. in water, dil. acid, org. solvs.; insol. in water; m.w. 123.16; sp.gr. 1.098 (15/15 C); m.p. 5 C; b.p. 225 C; flash pt. 100 C; ref. index 1.575 (20 C)
Precaution: Photosensitive
Toxicology: Anisidine and its hydrochloride may reasonably be expected to be carcinogens
Uses: Pharmaceutical intermediate
Manuf./Distrib.: Fluka
Manuf./Distrib. (pharm. & food): Aceto; Aldrich; Daiwa Chem.

p-Anisidine
CAS 104-94-9; EINECS 203-254-2
UN No. 3143
Synonyms: 4-Aminoanisole; 4-Methoxyaniline; p-Methoxyaniline
Classification: Aromatic organic compd.
Empirical: C_7H_9NO
Properties: Sol. in water, org. solvs.; m.w. 123.16; m.p. 56-59 C; flash pt. 122 C
Precaution: Photosensitive
Uses: Pharmaceutical intermediate
Manuf./Distrib. (pharm. & food): Aceto; Aldrich; Daiwa Chem.

Anisyl acetate
CAS 104-21-2
FEMA 2098
Synonyms: p-Methoxybenzyl acetate
Empirical: $C_{10}H_{12}O_3$
Properties: Colorless to sl. yellow liq.; floral, fruit-like odor; sweet taste; sol. in alcohol; insol. in water; m.w. 180.21; b.p. 270 C; ref. index 1.511-1.516 (20 C)
Precaution: Combustible liq.
Toxicology: Heated to decomp., emits acrid smoke and fumes
Uses: Vanilla, plum-like synthetic flavoring agent
Regulatory: FDA 21CFR §172.515; FEMA GRAS
Manuf./Distrib. (pharm. & food): Aldrich

Anisyl acetone. See 4-p-Methoxyphenyl-2-butanone

Anisyl alcohol
CAS 105-13-5; EINECS 203-273-6
FEMA 2099
Synonyms: Anise alcohol; Anisic alcohol; 4-Methoxybenzenemethanol; p-Methoxybenzyl alcohol; 4-Methoxybenzyl alcohol
Empirical: $C_8H_{10}O_2$
Properties: Need. or colorless to sl. yellow liq.; floral odor; fruity (peach) taste; sol. in most fixed oils, alcohol, ether; pract. insol. in water; m.w. 138.17; dens. 1.113 (15/15 C); m.p. 25 C; b.p. 259 C; flash pt. 112 C; ref. index 1.543-1.545
Precaution: Combustible liq.
Toxicology: LD50 (oral, rat) 1200 mg/kg; moderately toxic by ingestion; skin irritant; allergen; heated to decomp., emits acrid smoke and irritating fumes
Uses: Caramel, chocolate, vanilla-like, fruity fragrance and flavoring for pharmaceuticals
Regulatory: FDA 21CFR §172.515; FEMA GRAS
Manuf./Distrib.: Aldrich; BASF
Manuf./Distrib. (pharm. & food): Aldrich; Allied-Signal

Anisyl formate
Anisyl formate
CAS 122-91-8
FEMA 2101
Synonyms: p-Methoxybenzyl formate
Empirical: $C_9H_{10}O_3$
Properties: Colorless liq.; sweet, floral odor; strawberry taste; sol. in most organic solvents; insol. in water; m.w. 166.18; dens. 1.035; b.p. 220 C; flash pt. 100 C ref. index 1.5220-1.5240 (20 C)
Precaution: Combustible
Uses: Sweet synthetic flavoring agent
Regulatory: FDA 21CFR §172.515; FEMA GRAS
Manuf./Distrib. (pharm. & food): Aldrich

Anisylmethyl ketone. *See* 1-(p-Methoxyphenyl)-2-propanone

Anisyl phenylacetate
FEMA 3740
Synonyms: Anisyl α-toluate
Empirical: $C_{16}H_{16}O_3$
Properties: Colorless, oily liq.; honey-like odor; sol. in alcohol; m.w. 256.30; b.p. 370 C
Uses: Synthetic flavoring agent
Regulatory: FDA 21CFR §172.515; FEMA GRAS

Anisyl propionate
CAS 7549-33-9
FEMA 2102
Synonyms: p-Methoxybenzyl propionate
Empirical: $C_{11}H_{14}O_3$
Properties: Herbaceous odor; fruity taste; m.w.194.23; dens. 1.070; b.p. 277 C; flash pt. >230 F; ref. index 1.5490 (20 C)
Uses: Fruity vanilla-like synthetic flavoring agent
Regulatory: FDA 21CFR §172.515; FEMA GRAS
Manuf./Distrib. (pharm. & food): Aldrich

Anisyl α-toluate. *See* Anisyl phenylacetate

Annatto
CAS 1393-63-1; EINECS 215-735-4
FEMA 2104
Synonyms: CI 75120 (EEC); Achiote; Arnatta; Annotta; Arnotta; Annatto seed; Arnotta seed; Annotta seed; Natural orange 4
Definition: Vegetable dye from seeds of *Bixa orellana* containing ethyl bixin
Formula: $C_{27}H_{34}O_4$
Properties: Sol. in alcohol, ether, oils
Toxicology: LD50 (intraperitoneal, mouse) 700 mg/kg; moderately toxic by intraperitoneal route; human systemic effect by skin contact; heated to decomp., emits acrid smoke and irritating fumes
Uses: Colorant for pharmaceuticals
Regulatory: FDA 21CFR §73.30, 73.1030, 73.2030; USDA 9CFR §318.7, 381.147; FEMA GRAS; Japan approved (water-sol.); Europe listed; UK approved; approved for use in ingested drugs in 1963 and for external drugs in 1977
Manuf./Distrib.: Crompton & Knowles; Haarmann & Reimer/Food Ingred.; Meer; Penta Mfg.; Pfizer; Warner-Jenkinson
Manuf./Distrib. (pharm. & food): Am. Roland; Chart; Consolidated Flavor; Crompton & Knowles; Haarmann & Reimer/Food Ingred.; MLG Enterprises; Quest Int'l.
Trade names: Annatto Powd. WS
See also CI 75120

Annatto extract
CAS 8015-67-6; EINECS 289-561-2 (annatto tree extract)
FEMA 2103
Synonyms: Natural orange 4; Arnotta extract; Annotta extract; CI 75120 (EEC); Bixin
Definition: Carotenoid color contg. bixin (oil/fat extract) or norbixin (alkaline aq. extract), derived from *Bixa orellana*
Empirical: $C_{25}H_{30}O_4$ (bixin); $C_{24}H_{28}O_4$ (norbixin)
Properties: Bixin: brownish-red cryst.; m.w. 394.51; m.p. 198 C; Norbixin: m.w. 380.48
Toxicology: May cause asthma, rashes
Uses: Colorant for pharmaceuticals

Regulatory: FEMA GRAS; Japan restricted use; permanently listed as a color in 1977
Manuf./Distrib.: Bio-Botanica
Manuf./Distrib. (pharm. & food): Chr. Hansen's
Trade names: Bixin Crystal 95; Natural Yellow Colour Q-500, Q-1000, Q-2000; Norbixin 40; Unibix W
Trade names containing: Annatto OS #2894; Annatto OS #2922; Annatto OS #2923; Annatto Liq. #3968, Acid Proof
See also Annatto; CI 75120

Annotta. *See* Annatto
Annotta extract. *See* Annatto extract
Anodynine. *See* Antipyrine
9,10-Anthracenedione, 1,4-bis[(4-methylphenyl)amino]-. *See* CI 61565; D&C Green No. 6

Anthranilic acid
CAS 118-92-3; EINECS 204-287-5
Synonyms: o- or 2-Aminobenzoic acid; o- or 2-Carboxyaniline; Vitamin L
Classification: Aromatic organic compd.
Formula: $C_6H_4(NH_2)(CO_2H)$
Properties: Yellowish crystals, sweetish taste; sol. in hot water, alcohol, ether; m.w. 137.14; m.p. 144-146 C, sublimes
Precaution: Combustible
Toxicology: Experimental tumorigen and reproductive effects; moderate toxicity by intraperitoneal route; irritant
Uses: In drugs, pharmaceuticals
Regulatory: BP compliance
Manuf./Distrib.: Aldrich; PMC Spec.; Spectrum Chem. Mfg.
Manuf./Distrib. (pharm. & food): Aldrich; Mallinckrodt; Yamamoto Chem.

Anthranilic acid methyl ester. *See* Methyl anthranilate
Antimony (III) chloride. *See* Antimony trichloride

Antimony trichloride
CAS 10025-91-9; EINECS 233-047-2; UN No. 1733
Synonyms: Trichlorostibine; Butter of antimony; Antimony (III) chloride; Caustic antimony
Empirical: Cl_3Sb
Formula: $SbCl_3$
Properties: Faintly yel. orthorhombic cryst.; hygroscopic; sol. in alcohol, benzene, ether, acetone; insol. in pyridine, quinoline; m.w. 228.13; dens. 3.14; m.p. 73 C; b.p. 223.5 C
Precaution: DOT: Corrosive material; moisture-sensitive
Toxicology: Irritant; corrosive
Uses: Chlorinating agent in pharmaceuticals
Regulatory: BP compliance
Manuf./Distrib.: Akzo; Aldrich; Hoechst Celanese; Nihon Kagaku Sangyo; Spectrum Chem. Mfg.
Manuf./Distrib. (pharm. & food): Mallinckrodt

Antipyrine
CAS 60-80-0; EINECS 200-486-6
Synonyms: Analgesine; Anodynine; Dimethyloxychinizin; Phenazone; 2,3-Dimethyl-1-phenyl-3-pyrazolin-5-one
Empirical: $C_{11}H_{12}N_2O$
Properties: Wh. powd., odorless, sl. bitter taste; sol. in water, chloroform, alcohol; sl. sol. in ether; m.w. 188.22; dens. 1.19; m.p. 111 C; b.p. 319 C
Toxicology: LD50 (rat) 1.8 g/kg; irritant
Uses: Used in ophthalmic pharmacy
Manuf./Distrib.: Spectrum Chem. Mfg.
Manuf./Distrib. (pharm. & food): Aldrich; Ruger

APDEA. *See* N-(3-Aminopropyl)diethanolamine
APM. *See* Aspartame
Apple acid. *See* N-Hydroxysuccinic acid

Apricot kernel oil
CAS 72869-69-3
FEMA 2105
Synonyms: Persic oil; Prunus armeniaca
Definition: Oil expressed from kernels of *Prunus armeniaca*

Apricot kernel oil PEG-6 esters

Properties: Colorless or pale straw clear oily liq., nearly odorless, bland taste; sl. sol. in alcohol; misc. with chloroform, ether, petrol. spirit; sp.gr. 0.910-0.923; acid no. 1 max.; iodine no. 90-115; sapon. no. 185-195; ref. index 1.4635-1.4655 (40 C)
Toxicology: No known toxicity
Uses: Oily vehicle, emollient, lubricant for pharmaceuticals
Regulatory: FDA 21CFR §182.40, GRAS; FEMA GRAS; USP/NF compliance
Trade names: Lipovol P

Apricot kernel oil PEG-6 esters
CAS 97488-91-0
Definition: Complex mixture formed from the transesterification of apricot kernel oil and PEG-6
Uses: Hydrophilic oil, solv., emulsifier for pharmaceuticals
Trade names: Labrafil® M 1944 CS

Aqua ammonium. *See* Ammonium hydroxide
Aqua fortis. *See* Nitric acid
Aqueous ammonia. *See* Ammonium hydroxide
Arabic gum. *See* Acacia

L-Arabinose
FEMA 3255
Synonyms: Pectin sugar
Uses: Natural sweetener
Regulatory: FEMA GRAS; BP compliance; Japan approved
Manuf./Distrib.: Lonza; U.S. Biochemical

d-Araboascorbic acid. *See* Erythorbic acid

Arachidyl alcohol
CAS 629-96-9; EINECS 211-119-4
Synonyms: 1-Eicosanol
Formula: $CH_3(CH_2)_{18}CH_2OH$
Properties: White wax-like solid; insol. in water; sol. in alcohol, hot benzene; m.w. 298.56; m.p. 66.5 C; b.p. 369 C
Precaution: Combustible
Uses: Raw material; emollient; lubricant, consistency factor for creams, ointments, liniments, lotions, sticks
Manuf./Distrib. (pharm. & food): Aldrich
Trade names: Nacol® 20-95

Arachidyl propionate
CAS 65591-14-2; EINECS 265-839-9
Synonyms: Eicosanyl propanoate
Definition: Ester of arachidyl alcohol and behenic acid
Properties: Sol. in min. oil, IPM, chloroform; insol. in water, propylene glycol, glycerin, 95% ethanol
Uses: Wax and emollient used to soothe the skin

Arachis oil. *See* Peanut oil
Archangelica officinalis. *See* Angelica extract

L-Arginine
CAS 74-79-3; EINECS 200-811-1
Synonyms: 1-1-Amino-4-guanidovaleric acid
Classification: Amino acid
Empirical: $C_6H_{14}N_4O_2$
Formula: $H_2NCNHNHCH_2CH_2CH_2CHNH_2COOH$
Properties: Wh. cryst. powd.; sol. in water; sl. sol. in alcohol; insol. in ether; m.w. 174.20; m.p. 235 C (dec.); strongly alkaline
Toxicology: Heated to decomp., emits toxic fumes of NO_x
Uses: Used in injectables; in treatment of liver disease; ammonia detoxicant (hepatic failure); diagnostic aid (pituitary function)
Regulatory: FDA 21CFR §172.320, limitation 6.6%; Japan approved; BP, Ph.Eur. compliance
Manuf./Distrib.: Degussa; Penta; U.S. Biochemical
Manuf./Distrib. (pharm. & food): Ajinomoto; Aldrich; Am. Roland; R.W. Greeff; Ruger; Spectrum Chem. Mfg.

Arheol. *See* Sandalwood oil
Aritolochia extract. *See* Serpentaria extract
Arnatta. *See* Annatto
Arnotta extract. *See* Annatto extract

Aromatic elixir USP/NF
UN No. 1170
Precaution: DOT: Flamm. liq.
Uses: Vehicle for pharmaceuticals
Regulatory: USP/NF compliance
Manuf./Distrib. (pharm. & food): Spectrum Chem. Mfg.

Arsenic chloride. *See* Arsenic trichloride

Arsenic trichloride
CAS 7784-34-1; EINECS 232-059-5
UN No. 1560
Synonyms: Arsenic chloride; Butter of arsenic; Arsenious chloride; Arsenous chloride; Fuming liquid arsenic
Classification: Inorg. compd.
Empirical: $AsCl_3$
Properties: Colorless oily liq.; misc. with chloroform; m.w. 181.28; dens. 2.1497; m.p. -16 C; b.p. 130 C; ref. index 1.6006
Precaution: Decomp. by UV rays
Toxicology: DOT: Poisonous material; strong irritant to eyes and skin
Uses: Intermediate for pharmaceuticals
Manuf./Distrib.: Atomergic Chemetals; Nippon Sanso; Noah Chem.
Manuf./Distrib. (pharm. & food): Nippon Sanso

Arsenious chloride. *See* Arsenic trichloride
Arsenous chloride. *See* Arsenic trichloride
Artemisia absinthium oil. *See* Wormwood oil
Artificial almond oil. *See* Benzaldehyde
Artificial oil of ants. *See* Furfural
1-Ascorbic acid. *See* L-Ascorbic acid

L-Ascorbic acid
CAS 50-81-7; EINECS 200-066-2
FEMA 2109
Synonyms: 1-Ascorbic acid; Vitamin C; Cevitamic acid
Empirical: $C_6H_8O_6$
Properties: Wh. or sl. yel. cryst. or powd.; sol. in water; sl. sol. in alcohol; insol. in ether, chloroform, benzene, petrol. ether, oils, fats; m.w. 176.14; m.p. 192 C; flash pt. 99 C
Precaution: Combustible liq.; light-sensitive, oxygen-sensitive
Toxicology: LD50 (IV, mouse) 518 mg/kg; moderately toxic; human blood systemic effects by IV route; extremely high repeated doses may cause nausea, diarrhea, GI disturbances, flatus; emits acrid smoke and irritating fumes when heated
Uses: Antioxidant; used in injectables, inhalers, orals, ophthalmics
Regulatory: FDA 21CFR §137.105, 137.155, 137.160, 137.165, 137.170, 137.175, 137.180, 137.185, 137.200, 137.205, 145.110, 145.115, 145.116, 145.135, 145.136, 145.170, 145.171, 146.113, 146.187, 150.141, 150.161, 155.200, 156.145, 161.175,; 182.3013, 182.3041, 182.5013, 182.8013, 240.1044, GRAS; BATF 27CFR §240.1051; USDA 9CFR §318.7; FEMA GRAS; Japan approved; Europe listed; UK approved; USP/NF, BP, Ph.Eur. compliance
Manuf./Distrib. (pharm. & food): ADM; Aldrich; Am. Roland; Browning; Gist-brocades Food Ingreds.; Int'l. Sourcing; Jungbunzlauer; Mallinckrodt; Ruger; Spectrum Chem. Mfg.
Trade names: Ascorbic Acid USP/FCC, 100 Mesh; Ascorbic Acid USP, FCC Fine Gran. No. 6045655; Ascorbic Acid USP, FCC Fine Powd. No. 6045652; Ascorbic Acid USP, FCC Gran. No. 6045654; Ascorbic Acid USP, FCC Type S No. 6045660; Ascorbic Acid USP, FCC Ultra-Fine Powd No. 6045653; Descote® Ascorbic Acid 60%
Trade names containing: Coated Ascorbic Acid 97.5% No. 60482; Durkote Vitamin C/Hydrog. Veg. Oil; Oxynex® K; Palma-Sperse® Type 250-S No. 65322; Palma-Sperse® Type 250A/50 D-S No. 65221

Ascorbic acid calcium salt. *See* Calcium ascorbate
L-Ascorbic acid, 6-hexadecanoate. *See* Ascorbyl palmitate
L-Ascorbic acid monosodium salt. *See* Sodium ascorbate
Ascorbic acid palmitate. *See* Ascorbyl palmitate
L-Ascorbic acid palmitate. *See* Ascorbyl palmitate
L-Ascorbic acid 6-palmitate. *See* Ascorbyl palmitate
L(+)-Ascorbic acid sodium salt. *See* Sodium ascorbate

Ascorbyl palmitate
CAS 137-66-6; EINECS 205-305-4
Synonyms: L-Ascorbic acid, 6-hexadecanoate; L-Ascorbic acid 6-palmitate; L-Ascorbic acid palmitate; Palmitoyl L-ascorbic acid; Ascorbic acid palmitate
Definition: Ester of ascorbic acid and palmitic acid
Empirical: $C_{22}H_{38}O_7$
Properties: White or yel.-wh. powd., citrus odor; sol. in alcohol, animal and veg. oils; sl. sol. in water; m.w. 414.54; m.p. 107-117 C
Toxicology: Heated to decomp., emits acrid smoke and irritating fumes
Uses: Antioxidant preservative in pharmaceutical creams and lotions to prevent rancidity
Regulatory: FDA 21CFR §166.110, 182.3149, GRAS; USDA 9CFR §318.7 (0.02% max. in margarine); Japan approved; Europe listed; UK approved; USP/NF, BP, Ph.Eur. compliance
Manuf./Distrib. (pharm. & food): Spectrum Chem. Mfg.
Trade names: Ascorbyl Palmitate NF, FCC No. 60412
Trade names containing: 24% Beta Carotene HS-E in Veg. Oil No. 65671; Canthaxanthin Beadlets 10%; Dry Beta Carotene Beadlets 10% CWS No. 65633; Dry Beta Carotene Beadlets 10% No. 65661; Oxynex® 2004; Oxynex® K; Oxynex® LM

Asparagic acid. *See* L-Aspartic acid

Aspartame
CAS 22839-47-0; EINECS 245-261-3
Synonyms: APM; 3-Amino-N-(α-carboxyphenethyl) succinamic acid N-methyl ester; Aspartylphenylalanine methyl ester; 1-Methyl N-L-α-aspartyl-L-phenylalanine
Classification: Dipeptide
Definition: Consists of L-aspartic acid and the methyl ester of L-phenylalanine; artificial sweetener
Empirical: $C_{14}H_{18}N_2O_5$
Formula: $HOOCCH_2CH(NH_2)CONHCH(CH_2C_6H_5)COOCH_3$
Properties: Wh. cryst. powd. or colorless need., odorless, sweet taste, prolonged sweet aftertaste; sl. sol. in water, alcohol; m.w. 294.34; m.p. 246-248 C; 160 times sweeter than sucrose
Toxicology: Human systemic effects by ingestion (allergic dermatitis); possible link to neural problems; headaches; experimental reproductive effects; should not be used by individuals with PKU; heated to decomp., emits toxic fumes of NO_x
Uses: Sweetening agent; used in OTC pharmaceuticals and in some prescription drugs, esp. chewable tablets and sugar-free prods.
Regulatory: FDA 21CFR §172.804; Japan, Canada approved; USP/NF compliance
Manuf./Distrib.: Ajinomoto; Browne & Dureau Int'l.; Calaga Food Ingreds.; Quimdis; Sanofi; Sweeteners Plus; Tosoh; EH Worlee GmbH
Manuf./Distrib. (pharm. & food): Ajinomoto; Aldrich; Browne & Dureau Int'l.; Calaga Food Ingreds.; Holland Sweetener; NutraSweet AG; Quimdis; Sanofi; Scanchem; Spectrum Chem. Mfg.; Sweeteners Plus; Tosoh; EH Worlee GmbH
Trade names: HSC Aspartame

L-Aspartic acid
CAS 56-84-8; EINECS 200-291-6
FEMA 3656
Synonyms: (+)-Aminosuccinic acid; L-α-Aminosuccinic acid; Asparagic acid
Classification: Amino acid
Empirical: $C_4H_7NO_4$
Properties: Colorless to wh. cryst., acid taste; sol. in acids, alkalies; sl. sol. in water; insol. in alcohol, ether; m.w. 133.11; dens. 1.661 (12.5 C); m.p. 270 C
Toxicology: Possible brain damage; heated to decomp., emits toxic fumes of NO_x
Uses: Used in injectables
Regulatory: FDA 21CFR §172.320, 7% max. by wt.; FEMA GRAS; Japan approved; BP, Ph.Eur. compliance
Manuf./Distrib.: Ajinomoto; Dainippon Pharmaceutical; Degussa; Mitsubishi

Aspartylphenylalanine methyl ester. *See* Aspartame
ATBC. *See* Acetyl tributyl citrate
ATEC. *See* Acetyl triethyl citrate
ATP. *See* Adenosine triphosphate

Attapulgite
CAS 1337-76-4
Synonyms: Fuller's earth; Activated attapulgite; Colloidal activated attapulgite; Palygorskite; Dioctrahedral smectite

Definition: A hydrated aluminum-magnesium silicate, chief ingredient in Fuller's earth
Toxicology: Nuisance dust when < 1% cryst. silica is present (PEL 5.00 mg/m^3, TLV/TWA 10 mg/m^3 total dust, 5 mg/m^3 respirable)
Uses: Suspending agent, visc.-increasing agent, adsorbent; used in orals, antidiarrheal prods.
Regulatory: FDA GRAS; USP/NF, BP compliance
Trade names: Pharmasorb Colloidal Pharmaceutical Grade

Attar of rose. *See* Rose oil
Aubépine. *See* p-Anisaldehyde
Avobenzone. *See* Butyl methoxy dibenzoyl methane

Avocado oil
CAS 8024-32-6; EINECS 232-428-0
Synonyms: Alligator pear oil
Definition: Oil obtained by pressing dehydrated avocado pear Persea americana; consists principally of glycerides of fatty acids
Properties: Yellowish-green to brownish-green oil, faint char. odor; sol. in min. oil, isopropyl esters, ethanol; insol. in water; dens. 0.908-0.925; iodine no. 84-95; sapon. no. 177-198; ref. index 1.460-1.470
Uses: Emollient used in topicals
Manuf./Distrib.: Arista Industries; Tri-K
Manuf./Distrib. (pharm. & food): Am. Roland; Arista Industries

Azacycloheptane. *See* Hexamethyleneimine
Azacyclotridecane-2-one, homopolymer. *See* Nylon-12
Azacyclotridecane-2-one polyamide. *See* Nylon-12
Azeite. *See* Olive oil
1H-Azepine, hexahydro. *See* Hexamethyleneimine
Azorubin S. *See* Amaranth
Azotic acid. *See* Nitric acid

Baking soda. *See* Sodium bicarbonate
Balm. *See* Balm mint

Balm mint
FEMA 2111
Synonyms: Lemon balm; Balm; Melissa
Definition: Leaves of balm mint, *Melissa officinalis* contg. chiefly citral
Properties: Citral odor, tonic-like flavor
Toxicology: May cause hypersensitivity reactions
Uses: Natural flavoring agent, carminative; in herbal remedies
Regulatory: FDA 21CFR §182.10, GRAS; FEMA GRAS

Balsam Oregon
Synonyms: Douglas fir oil
Definition: Resin from *Pseudotsuga menziesi*
Uses: Used in topicals
Regulatory: Approved for use in topicals

Balsam Peru
CAS 8007-00-9; 8016-42-0; EINECS 232-352-8
FEMA 2116
Synonyms: Myroxylon pereirae oleoresin; China oil; Peruvian balsam; Black balsam; Indian balsam
Definition: Oleoresin extracted from *Myroxylon pereirae*; mixt. of resins and chemicals incl. benzyl benzoate, benzyl cinnamate, cinnamic acid, benzoic acid, and vanillin
Properties: Dk. brn. visc. liq., pleasant vanilla odor; sol. in fixed oils; sl. sol. in propylene glycol; insol. in glycerin; dens. 1.150-1.170
Precaution: Combustible when heated
Toxicology: Mild allergen; can cause contact dermatitis and stuffy nose; common sensitizer; may crossreact with benzoin, rosin, benzoic acid, benzyl alcohol, cinnamic acid, essential oils, storax, etc.; heated to decomp., emits acrid smoke and irritating fumes
Uses: Flavor ingred.; mildly antiseptic; scabicide; skin ulcer therapy
Regulatory: FDA 21CFR §182.20, GRAS; FEMA GRAS; Japan approved; BP, Ph.Eur. compliance
Manuf./Distrib.: Bio-Botanica
Manuf./Distrib. (pharm. & food): Bio-Botanica; Florida Treatt; Ruger

Balsam tolu
CAS 8011-89-0; 9000-64-0; EINECS 232-550-4
FEMA 3070
Synonyms: Resin tolu; Thomas balsam; Opobalsam; Toluifera balsamam resin; Tolu resin; Tolu balsam
Definition: Resin derived from *Toluifera balsamam*
Properties: Ylsh.-brn. solid, pleasant aromatic odor and taste; sol. in alcohol, benzene, chloroform, ether; pract. insol. in water, hexane; acid no. 112-168; sapon. no. 154-220
Uses: Natural flavoring agent for pharmaceuticals; vehicle for expectorants
Regulatory: FDA 21CFR §172.510; FEMA GRAS; Japan approved
Manuf./Distrib.: Spectrum Chem. Mfg.
Manuf./Distrib. (pharm. & food): Chart (extract); Ruger; Spectrum Chem. Mfg.

Banana oil. *See* Amyl acetate
BAPP. *See* Bis(aminopropyl)piperazine
Barbados aloe extract. *See* Aloe extract

Barium hydroxide lime
CAS 17194-00-2 (anhyd.); 12230-71-6 (octahydrate)
Definition: Mixt. of barium hydroxide octahydrate and calcium hydroxide
Properties: Wh. or grayish wh. gran.
Toxicology: Toxic if ingested
Uses: Sorbent for carbon dioxide for pharmaceuticals, aesthetic apparatus
Regulatory: USP compliance

Barium sulfate
CAS 7727-43-7; EINECS 231-784-4; UN No. 1564
Synonyms: Barytes (natural); Sulfuric acid barium salt (1:1); Barium sulfate (1:1); Blanc fixe (artificial, precipitated); Precipitated barium sulfate; Basofor
Classification: Inorganic salt
Empirical: BaO_4S
Formula: $BaSO_4$
Properties: White or yellowish fine powd. free from grittiness, odorless, tasteless; sol. in conc. sulfuric acid; pract. insol. in water, dilute acids, alcohol; m.w. 233.40; dens. 4.25-4.5; m.p. 1580 C
Toxicology: TLV:TWA 10/mg^3 (total dust); poisonous when ingested; frequently causes skin reactions when applied
Uses: X-ray contrast media; used in intrauterine pharmaceuticals
Regulatory: FDA approved for use in intrauterine prods.; BP compliance
Manuf./Distrib.: Am. Biorganics; Barium & Chems.; Barker Ind.; R.E. Carroll; Cyprus Ind. Min.; EM Ind.; J.M. Huber; Mallinckrodt; Mitsubishi; Ore & Chem.; Sachtleben Chemie GmbH; San Yuan; Spectrum Chem. Mfg.
Manuf./Distrib. (pharm. & food): Aldrich; Fushimi Pharmaceutical; Mallinckrodt; Sakai Chem. Industry; Spectrum Chem. Mfg.

Barium sulfate (1:1). *See* Barium sulfate

Barley extract
CAS 94349-67-4; EINECS 286-476-2
Synonyms: Extract of barley
Definition: Extract of the cereal grass *Hordeum distichum* or *H. sativum*
Uses: Flavor, colorant, and humectant in pharmaceuticals
Trade names containing: Extramalt Light

Barm. *See* Yeast
Barytes (natural). *See* Barium sulfate
Basic aluminum acetate. *See* Aluminum diacetate
Basic aluminum chlorate. *See* Aluminum chlorohydrate
Basic bismuth chloride. *See* Bismuth oxychloride
Basic bismuth gallate. *See* Bismuth subgallate
Basic violet 10. *See* D&C Red No. 19
Basofor. *See* Barium sulfate
Battery acid. *See* Sulfuric acid

Batyl alcohol
CAS 544-62-7; EINECS 208-874-7
Synonyms: Stearyl glyceryl ether; 3-(Octadecyloxy)-1,2-propanediol; Monooctadecyl ether of glycerol
Definition: Monooctadecyl ether of glycerin

Empirical: $C_{21}H_{44}O_3$
Properties: Sol. in common fat solvs.; m.w. 344.58; m.p. 71-73 C
Toxicology: No known toxicity; irritant
Uses: Emulsifier, emollient, hydrotrope, thickener for pharmaceutical preps.
Manuf./Distrib.: Aldrich
Manuf./Distrib. (pharm. & food): Aldrich
Trade names: Nikkol Batyl Alcohol 100, EX

Bay leaf oil. *See* Bay oil

Bay oil
CAS 8006-78-8
FEMA 2122
Synonyms: Bay leaf oil; Myrcia oil; West Indian bay leaf oil
Definition: Volatile oil distilled from leaves of *Pimenta acris*, contg. 40-55% eugenol, myrcene, chavicol, etc.
Properties: Yel. to brnsh.-yel. liq., pleasant odor, sharp spicy taste; very sol. in alcohol, CS_2, glac. acetic acid; insol. in water; dens. 0.962-0.990 (25/25 C); ref. index 1.500-1.520
Precaution: Light-sensitive
Toxicology: LD50 (oral, rat) 1800 mg/kg; moderately toxic by ingestion; may cause human skin irritation and intolerance reaction; heated to decomp., emits acrid smoke
Uses: Astringent and antiseptic oil; natural flavoring
Regulatory: FDA 21CFR §182.10, 182.20, GRAS; 27CFR §21.75, 21.151; FEMA GRAS
Manuf./Distrib. (pharm. & food): Chart; Florida Treatt; Spectrum Chem. Mfg.

Beeswax
CAS 8006-40-4 (white); 8012-89-3 (yellow); EINECS 232-383-7
FEMA 2126 (wh.)
Synonyms: Cera alba; White wax; White beeswax; Beeswax, white; Yellow wax; Yellow beeswax; Beeswax, yellow
Definition: Purified wax from the honeycomb of the bee, *Apis mellifera*; commonly called white wax when bleached, yellow wax when not bleached
Properties: Brown or white (bleached) solid with faint odor; insol. in water; sl. sol. in alcohol; sol. in chloroform, ether, and oils; dens. 0.95; m.p. 62-65 C; acid no. 17-24; sapon. no. 84
Precaution: Combustible when heated
Toxicology: Essentially nontoxic; mild allergen; may cause contact dermatitis, human intolerance reaction
Uses: Stiffening agent, emulsifier, tablet coating agent; pharmaceutic aid, filler; used in orals, topicals, ointments, suppositories, vaginals, adhesive plasters, mouth and throat preps. (troches, lozenges)
Regulatory: FDA 21CFR §184.1973, GRAS; FEMA GRAS (white); Japan approved; Europe listed; UK approved; FDA approved for orals, topicals; USP/NF, BP, Ph.Eur. compliance
Manuf./Distrib.: British Wax Refining; Fluka; ICI Spec.; Koster Keunen; Maruzen Fine Chem.; Strahl & Pitsch
Manuf./Distrib. (pharm. & food): Aldrich; C.A.L.-Pfizer; Pierre Chauvet; Integra; Ruger; Spectrum Chem. Mfg.
Trade names: Koster Keunen Beeswax; Ross Beeswax
Trade names containing: Alcolan® 40; Dehymuls® E; Dehymuls® K; Montane® 481; Tewax TC 81
See also Beeswax, white; Beeswax, yellow

Beeswax, synthetic. *See* Synthetic beeswax

Beeswax, white
CAS 8006-40-4
Synonyms: Bleached beeswax; Bleached wax; White beeswax; White wax
Definition: Bleached and purified yellow wax obtained from the honeycomb of the bee, *Apis mellifera*
Properties: Ylsh.-wh. solid, char. odor, tasteless; sol. in chloroform, ether, fixed oils; insol. in water; dens. 0.95; m.p. 62-65 C
Uses: Stiffening agent; used in orals, topicals, vaginals
Regulatory: FDA approved for orals, topicals, vaginals; BP, Ph.Eur. compliance
Manuf./Distrib. (pharm. & food): Aldrich; Ruger

Beeswax, yellow
CAS 8012-89-3
Synonyms: Beeswax; Yellow beeswax; Yellow wax
Definition: Purified wax from the honeycomb of the bee *Apis mellifera*
Properties: Ylsh. to grayish brn. solid, honeylike odor, faint char. taste; sol. in chloforom, ether, fixed oils; sl. sol. in alcohol; insol. in water; dens. 0.95; m.p. 62-65 C
Uses: Stiffening agent; used in orals, topicals
Regulatory: FDA approved for orals, topicals; BP, Ph.Eur. compliance
Manuf./Distrib. (pharm. & food): Aldrich; Ruger

Beet powder
CAS 89957-89-1; EINECS 289-610-8
Synonyms: Beetroot red; Dehydrated beets; Beets, dehydrated
Definition: Color additive from edible beets, contg. red pigments, betacyanins (principally betanine, CAS 7659-95-2) and yel. pigments, betaxanthins, collectively known as betalains
Properties: Dk. red powd.; readily dissolves in water
Precaution: Degrades readily at temps. as low as 50 C, esp. on air/light exposure
Uses: Colorant for pharmaceuticals
Regulatory: FDA 21CFR §73.40; Europe listed; UK approved; Japan restricted
Manuf./Distrib.: Crompton & Knowles
Manuf./Distrib. (pharm. & food): Am. Roland; Cham Foods (Israel); Chart; Crompton & Knowles; Quest Int'l.
Trade names containing: Natural Red Beet Powd. 654200

Beetroot red. *See* Beet powder
Beets, dehydrated. *See* Beet powder
Beet sugar. *See* Sucrose

Behenalkonium chloride
CAS 16841-14-8; EINECS 240-865-3
Synonyms: Behenyl dimethyl benzyl ammonium chloride; Benzyldocosyldimethylammonium chloride
Classification: Quaternary ammonium salt
Empirical: $C_{31}H_{58}N \cdot Cl$
Uses: Mild emulsifier for topical pharmaceutical creams and emulsions
Trade names containing: Incroquat B65C

Behenic acid
CAS 112-85-6; EINECS 204-010-8
Synonyms: Docosanoic acid
Classification: Fatty acid
Empirical: $C_{22}H_{44}O_2$
Formula: $CH_3(CH_2)_{20}COOH$
Properties: Colorless waxy solid; water-sol.; m.w. 340.57; dens. 0.8221 (100/4 C); m.p. 80 C; b.p. 306 C (60 mm), 265 C (15 mm); ref. index 1.4270 (100 C)
Toxicology: No known toxicity
Uses: Opacifier, lubricant, emulsifier
Manuf./Distrib. (pharm. & food): Aldrich
Trade names: Hystrene® 7022; Hystrene® 9022

Behenic acid, dihydroabietyl ester. *See* Dihydroabietyl behenate
Behenic acid, isocetyl ester. *See* Isocetyl behenate
Behenic acid, isohexadecyl ester. *See* Isocetyl behenate

Behentrimonium methosulfate
CAS 81646-13-1
Synonyms: Behenyl trimethyl ammonium methyl sulfate; 1-Docosanaminium, N,N,N-trimethyl-, chloride
Classification: Quaternary ammonium salt
Empirical: $C_{26}H_{57}NO_4S$
Uses: Used in topical pharmaceutical creams and emulsions
Trade names containing: Incroquat Behenyl TMS

Behenyl alcohol
CAS 661-19-8; EINECS 211-546-6
Synonyms: 1-Docosanol; Alcohol C_{22}
Definition: Mixture of fatty alcohols chiefly of n-docosanol
Empirical: $C_{22}H_{46}O$
Formula: $CH_3(CH_2)_{20}CH_2OH$
Properties: Colorless waxy solid; insol. in water, sol. in ethanol, chloroform; m.w. 326.61; m.p. 71 C; b.p. 180 C (0.22 mm)
Toxicology: Low toxicity
Uses: Pharmaceutical raw material, consistency factor, emollient; as an antihistamine
Regulatory: FDA 21CFR §178.3910
Manuf./Distrib.: Brown; Fluka; M. Michel; Schweizerhall; Vista
Manuf./Distrib. (pharm. & food): Aldrich
Trade names: Cachalot® Behenyl Alcohol BE-22; Dehydag® Wax 22 (Lanette); Lanette® 22 Flakes; Nacol® 22-97; Nikkol Behenyl Alcohol 65, 80; Unihydag Wax 22

Behenyl behenate
CAS 17671-27-1; EINECS 241-646-5
Synonyms: Docosanoic acid, docosyl ester
Definition: Ester of behenic acid and behenyl alcohol
Empirical: $C_{44}H_{48}O_2$
Formula: $CH_3(CH_2)_{20}COOCH_2(CH_2)_{20}CH_3$
Uses: Emollient, visc. builder for topical pharmaceuticals
Trade names: Pelemol® BB

Behenyl dimethyl benzyl ammonium chloride. *See* Behenalkonium chloride
Behenyl trimethyl ammonium methyl sulfate. *See* Behentrimonium methosulfate
Bengal gelatin. *See* Agar
Benne oil. *See* Sesame oil
Bentanol. *See* Benzyl alcohol

Bentonite
CAS 1302-78-9; EINECS 215-108-5
Synonyms: Soap clay; Mineral soap; Wilkinite; CI 77004
Definition: Native hydrated colloidal aluminum silicate clay
Formula: $Al_2O_3 \cdot 4SiO_2 \cdot nH_2O$
Properties: Light to cream-colored impalpable powd., odorless, sl. earthy taste; hygroscopic; forms colloidal suspension in water, thixotropic properties; insol. in water and org. solvs.; pH 9.5-10.5
Toxicology: LD50 (IV, rat) 35 mg/kg; poison by intravenous route causing blood clotting; inert and generally nontoxic
Uses: Protective colloid, emulsifier, suspending agent, visc. increasing agent in orals, topicals, medicated jellies and ointments, calamine lotion, o/w emulsions, suspending powds.
Regulatory: FDA 21CFR §175.105, 175.300, 177.1460, 184.1155, GRAS; Japan restricted (0.5% max. residual); Europe listed; UK approved; USP/NF, BP, Ph.Eur. compliance; FDA approved for orals, topicals; USP/NF compliance
Manuf./Distrib.: Am. Colloid; Dry Branch Kaolin; Fluka; Norsk Hydro AS; L. A. Salomon; Southern Clay; R.T. Vanderbilt
Manuf./Distrib. (pharm. & food): Aldrich; Integra; Spectrum Chem. Mfg.
Trade names: Albagel Premium USP 4444; Bentonite USP BC 670; Korthix H-NF; Polargel® HV; Polargel® NF; Polargel® T

Bentonite magma
Definition: A prep. of bentonite with purified water
Uses: Suspending agent, visc.-increasing agent used in topicals
Regulatory: FDA approved for topicals; USP/NF compliance
Manuf./Distrib. (pharm. & food): Spectrum Chem. Mfg.

Benylate. *See* Benzyl benzoate
Benyl phenylformate. *See* Benzyl benzoate
Benzalacetone. *See* Benzylidene acetone

Benzaldehyde
CAS 100-52-7; EINECS 202-860-4
FEMA 2127; UN No. 1989, 1990
Synonyms: Benzoic aldehyde; Benzic aldehyde; Benzene methylal; Benzene carbonal; Artificial almond oil; Benzenecarbaldehyde
Classification: Aromatic org. compd.
Empirical: C_7H_6O
Formula: C_6H_5CHO
Properties: Colorless liq., bitter almond odor, burning taste; sl. sol. in water; misc. in alcohol, ether, oils; m.w. 106.13; sp.gr. 1.041; m.p. -26 C; b.p 179 C; flash pt. 148 F; ref. index 1.544
Precaution: DOT: Combustible liq.; light-sensitive; strong reducing agent; acts violently with oxidizers
Toxicology: LD50 (oral, rat) 1300 mg/kg; highly toxic; poison by ingestion and intraperitoneal routes; allergen; feeble local anesthethic; skin irritant; CNS depressant; 1 g/kg may be fatal in humans
Uses: Synthetic flavoring agent, perfume for mfg. of pharmaceuticals; elixir as vehicle
Regulatory: FDA 21CFR §182.60, GRAS; FEMA GRAS; Japan approved as flavoring; USP/NF, BP compliance
Manuf./Distrib.: Aceto; Aldrich; DSM; Elf Atochem SA; Fluka; R.W. Greeff; Haarmann & Reimer; Janssen Chimica; Mitsubishi Chem.; Penta Mfg.; Snia (UK); Spectrum Chem. Mfg.
Manuf./Distrib. (pharm. & food): Aldrich; Berje; Britannia Natural Prods.; H E Daniel; Dragoco Australia; Foote & Jenkins; R.W. Greeff; Mitsubishi Chem.; Naturex; O'Laughlin Industries; Penta Mfg.; Quimdis; Ruger; Spectrum Chem. Mfg.

Benzalkonium chloride

Benzalkonium chloride
CAS 8001-54-5; 61789-71-7; 68391-01-5; 68424-85-1; 68989-00-4; 85409-22-9; EINECS 204-479-9; 263-080-8; 269-919-4; 270-325-2; 273-544-1; 287-089-1
UN No. 1760
Synonyms: Alkyl dimethyl benzyl ammonium chloride; Alkylbenzyldimethylammonium chloride; Ammonium, alkyldimethyl (phenylmethyl)-, chloride
Classification: Quaternary ammonium salt
Definition: Mixt. of alkylbenzyldimethylammonium chlorides
Formula: $C_6H_5CH_2N(CH_3)_2RCl$, R = C_8H_{17} to $C_{18}H_{37}$
Properties: White or yellowish-white, amorphous powd., aromatic odor, bitter; sol. in water, alcohol, acetone; insol. in ether; m.p. 34-37 C
Precaution: DOT: Corrosive material
Toxicology: LD50 (rats, oral) 400 mg/kg; highly toxic; poison by parenteral, ingestion, intraperitoneal, intravenous routes; large systemic doses can cause nausea, vomiting, muscle paralysis, CNS depression, local tissue damage; eye irritant
Uses: Cationic antimicrobial preservative, disinfectant, wetting agent, solubilizer; used in ophthalmic prods., injectables, otics, topicals; enhances antiseptic effects; preservative in contact lens soaking sol'ns., nebulizer sol'ns.
Usage level: 0.1-0.3%
Regulatory: USA not restricted; FDA 21CFR §175.105, 178.1010; FDA approved for ophthalmics, injectables, otics, topicals; Japan, Europe listed; USP/NF, BP, Ph.Eur. compliance
Manuf./Distrib.: Akzo; Chemron; EM Industries; Lonza AG; Rhone-Poulenc France; Stepan; Witco/H-I-P
Manuf./Distrib. (pharm. & food): Aldrich; Ruger; Spectrum Chem. Mfg.
Trade names: Empigen® BAC50; Empigen® BAC50/BP; Empigen® BAC90; Gardiquat 1450; Gardiquat 1480; Hyamine® 3500 50%; Pentonium 24 BP; Querton 246; RSP 50-5 BZK; RSP 451-5 BZK; Sanisol C; Sanisol CPR, CR, CR-80%; Sanisol HTPR; Sanisol OPR, TPR
Trade names containing: Arquad® B-100

2-Benzazine. *See* Isoquinoline
Benzeneacetaldehyde. *See* Phenylacetaldehyde
Benzeneacetic acid. *See* Phenylacetic acid
Benzeneacetic acid 2-propenyl ester. *See* Allyl phenylacetate
Benzenecarbaldehyde. *See* Benzaldehyde
Benzene carbonal. *See* Benzaldehyde
Benzenecarboxylic acid. *See* Benzoic acid
1,2-Benzenedicarboxylic acid, dibutyl ester. *See* Dibutyl phthalate
1,2-Benzenedicarboxylic acid diethyl ester. *See* Diethyl phthalate
1,2-Benzenedicarboxylic acid dioctyl ester. *See* Dioctyl phthalate
1,2-Benzenediol. *See* Pyrocatechol
1,3-Benzenediol. *See* Resorcinol
1,4-Benzenediol. *See* Hydroquinone
Benzeneethanol. *See* Phenethyl alcohol
Benzene, ethenyl-, homopolymer. *See* Polystyrene
Benzene formic acid. *See* Benzoic acid
Benzenemethanol. *See* Benzyl alcohol
Benzene methylal. *See* Benzaldehyde
Benzenepropanal. *See* Hydrocinnamaldehyde
Benzenepropanoic acid. *See* Hydrocinnamic acid
Benzenesulfonic acid butyl amide. *See* N,N-Butyl benzene sulfonamide
Benzenesulfonic acid, dimethyl-, ammonium salt. *See* Ammonium xylenesulfonate
Benzenethiol. *See* Thiophenol
1,2,3-Benzenetriol. *See* Pyrogallol

Benzethonium chloride
CAS 121-54-0; EINECS 204-479-9
Synonyms: N,N-Dimethyl-N-[2-[2-[4-(1,1,3,3-tetramethylbutyl) phenoxy] ethoxy] ethyl] benzenemethan-aminium chloride; Diisobutylphenoxyethoxyethyl dimethyl benzyl ammonium chloride; Phemerol chloride
Classification: Quaternary ammonium salt
Empirical: $C_{27}H_{42}ClNO_2$
Properties: Colorless, odorless plates, bitter; sol. in water, alcohol, acetone, chloroform; m.w. 448.15; m.p. 164-166 C
Precaution: Light-sensitive
Toxicology: Poison by oral, subcutaneous, intraperitoneal, intravenous routes; severe eye irritant; LD50 (rats) 420 mg/kg

Uses: Antimicrobial preservative, germicide, wetting agent, solubilizer, topical anti-infective and antiseptic; used in injectables, ophthalmics, otics, topical sol'ns., tinctures
Usage level: 1000 ppm
Regulatory: FDA 21CFR §175.105, EPA registered, Japan approved, Europe listed; approved for use in injectables, ophthalmics, otics; USP/NF compliance
Manuf./Distrib.: Lonza
Manuf./Distrib. (pharm. & food): Aldrich; Lonza; Ruger; Spectrum Chem. Mfg.
Trade names: Hyamine® 1622 50%; Hyamine® 1622 Crystals

Benzic aldehyde. *See* Benzaldehyde
Benzilidene acetone. *See* Benzylidene acetone
1,2-Benzisothiazolin-3-one 1,1-dioxide. *See* Saccharin
1,2-Benzisothiazol-3(2H)-one, 1,1-dioxide, calcium salt. *See* Calcium saccharin
1,2-Benzisothiazol-3(2H)-one, 1,1-dioxide, calcium salt hydrate. *See* Calcium saccharin
Benzoate of soda. *See* Sodium benzoate
Benzoate sodium. *See* Sodium benzoate

Benzocaine
CAS 51-05-8
Synonyms: Ethyl-p-aminobenzoate hydrochloride; Procaine hydrochloride; Anesthesol
Properties: Wh. cryst. powd., odorless, tasteless; sol. in dil. acids; less sol. in chloroform, ether, alcohol; very sl. sol. in water; m.p. 88-92 C
Toxicology: Toxic by ingestion; systemic CNS excitation reported in adults
Uses: Local anesthetic in medicine, suntan prep; used in rectals, intramuscular injectables
Regulatory: FDA approved for use in rectals, intramuscular injectables; BP, Ph.Eur. compliance
Manuf./Distrib.: R.W. Greeff; Nat'l. Starch & Chem.; Nipa Labs; Roussel Labs Ltd; Schweizerhall
Manuf./Distrib. (pharm. & food): Avrachem; R.W. Greeff; Integra; Ruger
Trade names: Unicaine-B

1,2-Benzodihydropyrone. *See* Dihydrocoumarin
1,3-Benzodioxole. *See* 1,2-Methylenedioxybenzene
1,3-Benzodioxole-5-carboxaldehyde. *See* Heliotropine
3,4-Benzodioxole-5-carboxaldehyde. *See* Heliotropine

Benzoic acid
CAS 65-85-0; EINECS 200-618-2
FEMA 2131
Synonyms: Benzenecarboxylic acid; Benzene formic acid; Carboxybenzene; Phenylformic acid; Phenylcarboxylic acid; Dracylic acid
Classification: Aromatic acid
Empirical: $C_7H_6O_2$
Properties: White scales, needles, crystals, benzoin odor; sol. in alcohol, ether, chloroform, benzene, carbon disulfide; sl. sol. in water; m.w. 122.13; dens. 1.2659; m.p. 121.25 C; b.p. 249.2 C; subl. at 100 C; flash pt. 121.1 C
Precaution: Combustible when exposed to heat or flame; reactive with oxidizing materials
Toxicology: LD50 (oral, rat) 2530 mg/kg; mod. toxic by ingestion, IP routes; poison by subcut. route; severe eye/skin irritant; may cause human intolerance reaction, asthma, hyperactivity in children; heated to decomp., emits acrid smoke and irritating fumes
Uses: Antimicrobial preservative for oral liq. and parenteral prods. at 0.1% conc.; antiseptic; antifungal agent; also for rectals, topicals
Regulatory: FDA 21CFR §150.141, 150.161, 166.40, 166.110, 175.300, 184.1021, GRAS 0.1% max. in foods; USA EPA registered; Japan 0.2% max.; Europe listed 0.5% max.; FEMA GRAS; cleared by MID to retard flavor reversion in oleomargarine at 0.1%; Japan approved with limitations; Europe listed; UK approved; approved for orals, rectals, topicals; USP/NF, BP, Ph.Eur. compliance
Manuf./Distrib.: Aldrich; Ashland; Jan Dekker; Elf Atochem SA; Fluka; R.W. Greeff; Int'l. Sourcing; Mallinckrodt; E. Merck; Mitsubishi Chem.; Napp; Penta Mfg.; Schaefer Salt; Velsicol
Manuf./Distrib. (pharm. & food): Aldrich; Ashland; Avrachem; R.W. Greeff; Integra; Int'l. Sourcing; E. Merck; Mitsubishi Chem.; Nipa Hardwicke; Penta Mfg.; Ruger; Spectrum Chem. Mfg.
Trade names: Benzoic Acid U.S.P./F.C.C.
Trade names containing: Dow Corning® Q7-2587

Benzoic acid, benzyl ester. *See* Benzyl benzoate
Benzoic acid ethyl ester. *See* Ethyl benzoate
Benzoic acid, 4-hydroxy-, phenylmethyl ester. *See* Benzylparaben
Benzoic acid methyl ester. *See* Methyl benzoate

Benzoic acid phenylmethyl ester

Benzoic acid phenylmethyl ester. *See* Benzyl benzoate
Benzoic acid potassium salt. *See* Potassium benzoate
Benzoic acid sodium salt. *See* Sodium benzoate
o-Benzoic acid sulfimide. *See* Saccharin
Benzoic aldehyde. *See* Benzaldehyde

Benzoin
   CAS 119-53-9; EINECS 204-331-3
   FEMA 2132
   Synonyms: α-Hydroxybenzyl phenyl ketone; 2-Hydroxy-2-phenylacetophenone; α-Hydroxy-α-phenylacetophenone; Bitter almond oil camphor
   Classification: Aromatic org. compd.
   Empirical: $C_{14}H_{12}O_2$
   Formula: $C_6H_5CH(OH)COC_6H_5$
   Properties: Wh. or ylsh. cryst., sl. camphor odor; sol. in acetone, pyridine, hot water; sl. sol. in water, ether; m.w. 212.22; m.p. 137 C; b.p. 344 C (163 mm)
   Precaution: Combustible
   Toxicology: No known toxicity; mutagenic data; heated to decomp., emits acrid smoke and irritating fumes
   Uses: Pharmaceutical intermediate; preservative in creams and ointments; medicinal, vanilla-like flavoring agent; used in orals; stimulant, expectorant; externally applied to wounds
   Regulatory: FDA 21CFR §73.1, no residue, 172.515; FEMA GRAS; Japan approved; FDA approved for orals; BP compliance
   Manuf./Distrib.: Aceto; Aldrich; Janssen Chimica; Dr. Madis Labs; Snia (UK); Spectrum Chem. Mfg.; Wako Pure Chem. Ind.
   Manuf./Distrib. (pharm. & food): Aldrich; Bio-Botanica; C.A.L.-Pfizer; Dr. Madis; Ruger; Wako Pure Chem. Ind.

Benzoin gum. *See* Gum benzoin
Benzoin resin. *See* Gum benzoin
Benzoperoxide. *See* Benzoyl peroxide

Benzophenone
   CAS 119-61-9; EINECS 204-337-6
   FEMA 2134
   Synonyms: Benzoylbenzene; Diphenyl ketone; Diphenylmethanone
   Classification: Organic compd.
   Empirical: $C_{13}H_{10}O$
   Properties: Wh. rhombic cryst., persistent rose-like odor; sol. in fixed oils; sl. sol. in propylene glycol; m.w. 182.23; sp.gr. 1.0976 (α, 50/50 C), 1.108 (β, 23/40 C); m.p. 49 C (α), 26 C (β), 47 C (γ); b.p. 305 C
   Precaution: Combustible when heated; incompat. with oxidizers
   Toxicology: LD50 (oral, mouse) 2895 mg/kg; moderately toxic by ingestion and intraperitoneal routes; heated to decomp., emits acrid and irritating fumes
   Uses: Apricot, peach-like synthetic flavoring agent, fragrance for pharmaceuticals
   Regulatory: FDA 21CFR §172.515; FEMA GRAS; BP compliance
   Manuf./Distrib.: Aldrich; Allchem Ind.; Berje; Elf Atochem N. Am.; Fluka; R.W. Greeff; Penta Mfg.; Plastics & Chems.; Reedy Int'l.; Schweizerhall; Spectrum Chem. Mfg.; 3V; Velsicol
   Manuf./Distrib. (pharm. & food): Aldrich
   Trade names: Velsicure®

Benzophenone-3
   CAS 131-57-7; EINECS 205-031-5
   Synonyms: 2-Hydroxy-4-methoxybenzophenone; (2-Hydroxy-4-methoxyphenyl) phenylmethanone; Oxybenzone
   Classification: Organic benzophenone deriv.
   Empirical: $C_{14}H_{12}O_3$
   Properties: Yellowish cryst., rose-like odor; sol. in min. oil, peanut oil, ethanol, PEG-8, oleyl alcohol, castor oil; insol. in water; m.w. 228.26; m.p. 62-63.5 C
   Toxicology: Poison by intraperitoneal route; mild toxicity by ingestion; LD50 (rat, oral) > 10 g/kg; LD50 (rabbit, dermal) > 16 g/kg
   Uses: UV stabilizer, sunscreen agent used in mfg. of sunscreens; prevents deterioration of ingreds. that could be affected by UV light
   Regulatory: FDA 21CFR §177.1010
   Manuf./Distrib.: Aceto; EM Industries; Ferro/Bedford; R.W. Greeff; Haarmann & Reimer; Hoechst Celanese; Quest Int'l.; Sartomer; Spectrum Chem. Mfg.
   Manuf./Distrib. (pharm. & food): Aldrich
   Trade names: Escalol® 567; Spectra-Sorb® UV 9; Syntase® 62

Benzophenone-4
CAS 4065-45-6; EINECS 223-772-2
Synonyms: 2-Hydroxy-4-methoxybenzophenone-5-sulfonic acid; Sulisobenzone; 2-Hydroxy-4-methoxy-5-sulfo benzophenone
Classification: Organic benzophenone deriv.
Empirical: $C_{14}H_{12}O_6S$
Properties: Wh. flakey solid, rose-like odor; sol. in most fixed oils and min. oil; acid no. 190 max.; pH 1-2 (1%)
Toxicology: Toxic when injected; may induce hives and contact sensitivity, photoallergic reaction
Uses: UV absorber in sunscreen prods.; prevents deterioration of ingreds. that might be affected by uv rays
Manuf./Distrib.: Aceto; EM Industries; Ferro/Bedford; R.W. Greeff; Haarmann & Reimer; Hoechst Celanese; Quest Int'l.; Sartomer; Spectrum Chem. Mfg.
Manuf./Distrib. (pharm. & food): Aldrich

1-Benzoxy-1-(2-methoxyethoxy)-ethane. *See* Benzyl methoxyethyl acetal
Benzoylbenzene. *See* Benzophenone

Benzoyl peroxide
CAS 94-36-0; EINECS 202-327-6; UN No. 3102, 3104, 3106, 3108
Synonyms: Dibenzoyl peroxide; Benzoperoxide; Benzoyl superoxide
Classification: Aromatic organic peroxide
Empirical: $C_{14}H_{10}O_4$
Formula: $[C_6H_5C(O)]_2O_2$
Properties: Colorless to wh. gran., solid, faint odor of benzaldehyde, tasteless; sl. sol. in alcohols, veg. oils, water; sol. in benzene, chloroform, ether; m.w. 242.23; dens. 1.3340 (25 C); m.p. 103-105 C
Precaution: Flamm. oxidizing liq.; explosion hazard
Toxicology: LD50 (oral, rat) 7710 mg/kg; highly toxic; TLV 5 mg/m³; poison by ingestion, intraperitoneal routes; allergen; eye irritant
Uses: Used in ophthalmics
Regulatory: FDA 21CFR §184.1157, GRAS; Japan approved with limitations; FDA approved for ophthalmics; BP, Ph.Eur. compliance
Manuf./Distrib.: Abco Ind. Ltd; Akzo; Aztec Peroxides; Elf Atochem N. Am.; Fluka; Great Western; Norac
Manuf./Distrib. (pharm. & food): Aldrich; Kawaguchi Chem.; Mallinckrodt; Ruger; Sanken Chem.; Spectrum Chem. Mfg.

Benzoyl superoxide. *See* Benzoyl peroxide
Benzylacetaldehyde. *See* Hydrocinnamaldehyde

Benzyl acetate
CAS 140-11-4; EINECS 205-399-7
FEMA 2135
Synonyms: Phenylmethyl acetate; α-Acetoxytoluene; Benzyl ethanoate
Classification: Aromatic org. compd.
Definition: Ester of benzyl alcohol and acetic acid
Empirical: $C_9H_{10}O_2$
Formula: $CH_3COOCH_2C_6H_5$
Properties: Colorless liq., sweet floral fruity odor; sol. in alcohol, most fixed oils, propylene glycol; insol. in water, glycerin; m.w. 150.19; sp.gr. 1.06; m.p. -51.5 C; b.p. 213.5 C; flash pt. (CC) 216 F; ref. index 1.501
Precaution: Combustible liq.
Toxicology: LD50 (oral, rat) 2490 mg/kg; moderately toxic by ingestion and subcutaneous routes; poison by inhalation; antipsychotic; heated to decomp., emits irritating fumes
Uses: Apple, apricot, cherry, plum-like synthetic flavoring agent
Regulatory: FDA 21CFR §172.515; FEMA GRAS; Japan approved as flavoring
Manuf./Distrib.: Aldrich; Fluka; Haarmann & Reimer; Janssen Chimica; Koyo Chem.; MTM Spec. Ltd; Penta Mfg.; Quest Int'l.
Manuf./Distrib. (pharm. & food): Aceto; Aldrich; Haarmann & Reimer; Chr. Hansen's; Koyo Chem.; Penta Mfg.; Quest Int'l.

Benzylacetic acid. *See* Hydrocinnamic acid

Benzyl acetoacetate
CAS 5396-89-4; EINECS 226-416-4
FEMA 2136
Synonyms: Benzyl acetyl acetate; Benzyl β-ketobutyrate; Benzyl 3-oxobutanoate
Empirical: $C_{11}H_{12}O_3$
Formula: $CH_3COCH_2COOCH_2C_6H_5$
Properties: Oily liq.; sol. in alkali solutions at room temp.; m.w. 192.22; dens. 1.112; b.p. 156-159 C (10 mm);

Benzylacetone

flash pt. >230 F
Toxicology: Irritating to skin, eyes
Uses: Fruity synthetic flavoring agent
Regulatory: FDA 21CFR §172.515; FEMA GRAS
Manuf./Distrib. (pharm. & food): Aldrich

Benzylacetone. *See* Benzylidene acetone
Benzyl acetyl acetate. *See* Benzyl acetoacetate

Benzyl alcohol
CAS 100-51-6; EINECS 202-859-9
FEMA 2137
Synonyms: Bentanol; α-Hydroxytoluene; Phenylmethanol; Phenylcarbinol; Benzenemethanol
Classification: Aromatic alcohol
Empirical: $C_6H_5CH_2OH$
Formula: C_7H_8O
Properties: Water-wh. liq., faint aromatic odor, sharp burning taste; misc. with alcohol, chloroform, ether, water
@ 206 C (dec.); m.w. 108.15; sp.gr. 1.042; m.p. -15.3 C; b.p. 205.7 C; flash pt. (CC) 213 F; ref. index 1.540
Precaution: Combustible liq.; light-sensitive; dec. explosively at 180 C with sulfuric acid
Toxicology: LD50 (oral, rat) 1230 mg/kg; poison by ingestion, intraperitoneal, IV routes; mod. toxic by inh., skin
contact; mod. skin and severe eye irritant; may crossreact with balsam Peru in sensitive persons; heated
to decomp., emits acrid smoke and fumes
Uses: Antimicrobial preservative, solubilizer (@ 5% or more); citrus berry cherry-like flavoring; disinfectant,
local anesthetic; used in multiple-use parenterals; orals, topical antiseptics, vaginals; mouth/throat preps;
astringent in poison ivy preps.
Usage level: 10% (disinfectant, local anesthetic), 1% (additive to injectables)
Regulatory: FDA 21CFR §172.515; FEMA GRAS; USA EPA registered; Japan approved as flavoring; Europe
listed; FDA approved for use in injectables, parenterals, orals, topicals; USP/NF, BP, Ph.Eur. compliance
Manuf./Distrib.: Aldrich; Ashland; Elf Atochem SA; Fluka; Givaudan Iberica SA; R.W. Greeff; Haarmann &
Reimer; Janssen Chimica; E. Merck; Osaka Org. Chem. Ind.; Penta Mfg.; Quest Int'l.; Takasago; Tosoh
Manuf./Distrib. (pharm. & food): Aldrich; Ashland; Haarmann & Reimer; Mallinckrodt; E. Merck; Osaka Org.
Chem. Ind.; Penta Mfg.; Quest Int'l.; Ruger; Spectrum Chem. Mfg.; Tosoh

Benzyl benzene carboxylate. *See* Benzyl benzoate

Benzyl benzoate
CAS 120-51-4; EINECS 204-402-9
FEMA 2138; UN No. 2810
Synonyms: Benylate; Benzyl benzene carboxylate; Benyl phenylformate; Phenylmethyl benzoate; Benzoic
acid phenylmethyl ester; Benzoic acid, benzyl ester
Definition: Ester of benzyl alcohol and benzoic acid
Empirical: $C_{14}H_{12}O_2$
Formula: $C_6H_5COOCH_2C_6H_5$
Properties: Colorless oily liq., sl. aromatic odor; misc. with alcohol, chloroform, ether; insol. in water, glycerin;
m.w. 212.26; sp.gr. 1.116-1.120; m.p. 21 C; b.p. 324 C; flash pt. (CC) 298 F; ref. index 1.568
Precaution: Combustible liq.; light-sensitive; reactive with oxidizing materials
Toxicology: LD50 (oral, rat) 500 mg/kg; mod. toxic by ingestion, skin contact; heated to decomp., emits acrid
and irritating fumes and smoke
Uses: Solvent, preservative; sweet, cherry, pineapple, strawberry-like flavoring agent; used in injectables,
orals, topicals, external medicine; scabicide; pediculicide
Regulatory: FDA 21CFR §172.515, 175.105; FEMA GRAS; FDA approved for injectables, orals; USP/NF, BP,
Ph.Eur. compliance
Manuf./Distrib.: Aldrich; Berje; Fluka; Haarmann & Reimer; Janssen Chimica; Kalama; Morflex; Penta Mfg.;
Pentagon Chems. Ltd; Schweizerhall
Manuf./Distrib. (pharm. & food): Aldrich; Haarmann & Reimer; Mallinckrodt; Ogawa & Co.; Pentagon Chems.
Ltd.; Penta Mfg.; Ruger; Spectrum Chem. Mfg.
Trade names: Unichem BZBN

Benzyl butanoate. *See* Benzyl butyrate
Benzylbutyl alcohol. *See* α-Propylphenethyl alcohol

Benzyl butyrate
CAS 103-37-7
FEMA 2140
Synonyms: Benzyl butanoate
Empirical: $C_{11}H_{14}O_2$

Properties: M.w. 178.23; dens. 1.009; b.p. 240 C; flash pt. 225 F
Uses: Apricot, berry, peach, pear, plum-like flavoring agent
Regulatory: FEMA GRAS
Manuf./Distrib. (pharm. & food): Aldrich

Benzyl carbinol. *See* Phenethyl alcohol
Benzylcarbinyl acetate. *See* 2-Phenylethyl acetate
Benzyl carbinyl anthranilate. *See* Phenethyl anthranilate

Benzyl cinnamate
CAS 103-41-3; EINECS 203-109-3
FEMA 2142
Synonyms: Cinnamein; Benzyl β-phenylacrylate; Phenylmethyl 3-phenyl-2-propenoate; Benzyl 3-phenylpropenoate
Definition: Ester of benzyl alcohol and cinnamic acid
Empirical: $C_{16}H_{14}O_2$
Properties: Wh. cryst., aromatic odor; sol. in fixed oils; insol. in glycerin, propylene glycol; m.w. 238.30; m.p. 39 C; b.p. 350 C; flash pt. 100 C
Precaution: Combustible liq.
Toxicology: Mod. toxic by ingestion; mild allergen and skin irritant; heated to decomp., emits acrid smoke and irritating fumes
Uses: Chocolate, apricot, cherry, peach, pineapple-like synthetic flavoring agent
Regulatory: FDA 21CFR §172.515; FEMA GRAS; BP compliance
Manuf./Distrib.: Aldrich; BASF; Fluka
Manuf./Distrib. (pharm. & food): Aldrich

Benzyldiethyl [(2,6-xylylcarbomoyl)methyl]ammonium benzoate. *See* Denatonium benzoate
Benzyl dimethylcarbinyl butyrate. *See* α,α-Dimethylphenethyl butyrate
Benzyldimethyldodecylammonium chloride. *See* Lauralkonium chloride
Benzyldocosyldimethylammonium chloride. *See* Behenalkonium chloride
Benzyl ethanoate. *See* Benzyl acetate

Benzyl ether
CAS 103-50-4; EINECS 203-118-2
FEMA 2371
Synonyms: Dibenzyl ether; 1,1´-[Oxybis(methylene)]bis[benzene]
Empirical: $C_{14}H_{14}O$
Formula: $(C_6H_5CH_2)_2O$
Properties: Colorless to pale yel. unstable liq.; misc. with ethanol, ether, chloroform, acetone; pract. insol. in water; m.w. 198.28; dens. 1.043 (20/4 C); m.p. 5 C; b.p. 298 C (dec.); flash pt. (CC) 275 F; ref. index 1.557
Precaution: Combustible exposed to heat or flame; reactive with oxidizing materials; mod. explosion hazard by spontaneous chemical reaction
Toxicology: LD50 (oral, rat) 2500 mg/kg; mod. toxic by ingestion; vapors may be narcotic in high conc.; skin and eye irritant
Uses: Sweet chocolate-like, fruity synthetic flavoring agent
Regulatory: FDA 21CFR §172.515; FEMA GRAS
Manuf./Distrib. (pharm. & food): Aldrich

Benzylhexadecyldimethylammonium chloride. *See* Cetalkonium chloride
Benzyl o-hydroxybenzoate. *See* Benzylsalicylate
Benzyl p-hydroxybenzoate. *See* Benzylparaben

Benzylidene acetone
CAS 122-57-6; EINECS 204-555-1
FEMA 2881
Synonyms: Benzalacetone; Benzylacetone; Benzilidene acetone; Cinnamyl methyl ketone; Methyl styryl ketone; trans-4-Phenyl-3-buten-2-one; 4-Phenyl-3-buten-2-one
Classification: Aromatic compd.
Empirical: $C_{10}H_{10}O$
Formula: $C_6H_5CH{:}CHCOCH_3$
Properties: Colorless cryst., odor of coumarin, sweet pungent floral flavor; sol. in alcohol, ether, benzene, chloroform; insol. in water; m.w. 146.19; dens. 1.0097; m.p. 39-42 C; b.p. 260-262 C; flash pt. 150 F
Precaution: Combustible
Toxicology: Irritant
Uses: Sweet synthetic flavoring agent
Regulatory: FDA 21CFR §172.515; FEMA GRAS

Manuf./Distrib.: Aldrich; Fluka; Penta Mfg.; Raschig; Schweizerhall
Manuf./Distrib. (pharm. & food): Aldrich; Penta Mfg.

3-Benzylidene camphor
CAS 15087-24-8; EINECS 239-139-9
Synonyms: 1,7,7-Trimethyl-3-(phenylmethylene)bicyclo[2.2.1]heptan-2-one
Classification: Polycyclic org. compd.
Empirical: $C_{17}H_{20}O$
Uses: UV-B sunscreen for suntan prods., stabilization of light-sensitive prods.
Trade names: Unisol S-22
Trade names containing: Unifilter U-41

2-Benzylidene-heptanol. *See* α-Amylcinnamyl alcohol
Benzyl isoamyl alcohol. *See* α-Isobutylphenethyl alcohol
Benzyl isobutyl carbinol. *See* α-Isobutylphenethyl alcohol
Benzyl isobutyl ketone. *See* 4-Methyl-1-phenyl-2-pentanone

Benzyl isobutyrate
CAS 103-28-6
FEMA 2141
Synonyms: Isobutyric acid benzyl ester; Benzyl-2-methylpropionate; Benzyl 2-methyl propanoate
Empirical: $C_{11}H_{14}O_2$
Properties: Colorless liq., fruity floral jasmine odor; sol. in alcohol, fixed oils; sl. sol. in propylene glycol; insol.
in glycerin; m.w. 178.25; dens. 1.001-1.005; b.p. 105-108 C (4 mm); flash pt. 100 C; ref. index 1.489-1.4920
(20 C)
Precaution: Combustible liq.
Toxicology: LD50 (oral, rat) 2850 mg/kg; mod. toxic by ingestion; heated to decomp, emits acrid smoke and
fumes
Uses: Fruity synthetic flavoring agent
Regulatory: FDA 21CFR §172.515; FEMA GRAS
Manuf./Distrib.: Hüls
Manuf./Distrib. (pharm. & food): Aldrich; Hüls

Benzyl isoeugenol. *See* Isoeugenyl benzyl ether

Benzyl isovalerate
CAS 103-38-8
FEMA 2152
Synonyms: Benzyl 3-methyl butyrate
Empirical: $C_{12}H_{16}O_2$
Properties: Colorless liq.; apple, pineapple odor; sol. in alcohol, most fixed oils; insol. in water; m.w. 192.26;
dens. 0.988; b.p. 245 C; flash pt. >230 F; ref. index 1.486-1.490
Uses: Apple, pineapple-like synthetic flavoring agent
Regulatory: FDA 21CFR §172.515; FEMA GRAS
Manuf./Distrib. (pharm. & food): Aldrich

Benzyl β-ketobutyrate. *See* Benzyl acetoacetate

Benzyl methoxyethyl acetal
FEMA 2148
Synonyms: Acetaldehyde benzyl β-methoxyethyl acetal; 1-Benzoxy-1-(2-methoxyethoxy)-ethane; 1-
Benzyloxy-1-(β-methoxy)ethoxy ethane
Empirical: $C_{12}H_{18}O_3$
Properties: Colorless liq.; fruital odor; m.w.210.27
Uses: Synthetic flavoring agent
Regulatory: FDA 21CFR §172.515; FEMA GRAS

Benzyl 3-methyl butyrate. *See* Benzyl isovalerate
Benzyl 2-methyl propanoate. *See* Benzyl isobutyrate
Benzyl-2-methylpropionate. *See* Benzyl isobutyrate
Benzyl 3-oxobutanoate. *See* Benzyl acetoacetate
1-Benzyloxy-1-(β-methoxy)ethoxy ethane. *See* Benzyl methoxyethyl acetal

Benzylparaben
CAS 94-18-8; EINECS 202-311-9
Synonyms: Benzoic acid, 4-hydroxy-, phenylmethyl ester; Benzyl p-hydroxybenzoate; Phenylmethyl 4-
hydroxybenzoate
Definition: Ester of benzyl alcohol and p-hydroxybenzoic acid

Empirical: C$_{14}$H$_{12}$O$_3$
Uses: Preservative, bactericide, fungicide
Regulatory: BP compliance
Trade names: Nipabenzyl

Benzyl phenylacetate
FEMA 2149
Synonyms: Benzyl α-toluate
Empirical: C$_{15}$H$_{14}$O$_2$
Properties: Colorless liq.; floral odor; honey-like taste; misc. with alcohol, chloroform, ether; m.w. 226.28; dens. 1.097-1.099; b.p. 320 C; flash pt. >100 C; ref. index 1.553-1.558
Precaution: Combustible liq.
Toxicology: Heated to decomp., emits acrid smoke and fumes
Uses: Synthetic flavoring agent
Regulatory: FDA 21CFR §172.515; FEMA GRAS
Manuf./Distrib. (pharm. & food): Chr. Hansen's

Benzyl β-phenylacrylate. *See* Benzyl cinnamate
Benzyl 3-phenylpropenoate. *See* Benzyl cinnamate
Benzyl propanoate. *See* Benzyl propionate

Benzyl propionate
CAS 122-63-4
FEMA 2150
Synonyms: Benzyl propanoate
Empirical: C$_{10}$H$_{12}$O$_2$
Properties: Colorless liq.; floral-fruity odor; sol. in alcohol, most fixed oils; insol. in water; m.w. 164.20; dens. 1.036; b.p. 219-220 C; flash pt. 100 C; ref. index 1.496-1.500
Precaution: Combustible
Toxicology: Heated to decomp., emits acrid smoke and fumes
Uses: Sweet, berry-like synthetic flavoring agent
Regulatory: FDA 21CFR §172.515; FEMA GRAS; Japan approved as flavoring
Manuf./Distrib. (pharm. & food): Aldrich

Benzylpropyl carbinol. *See* α-Propylphenethyl alcohol
Benzyl-n-propyl carbinol. *See* α-Propylphenethyl alcohol

Benzylsalicylate
CAS 118-58-1; EINECS 204-262-9
FEMA 2151
Synonyms: Phenylmethyl 2-hydroxybenzoate; Benzyl o-hydroxybenzoate
Definition: Ester of benzyl alcohol and salicylic acid
Empirical: C$_{14}$H$_{12}$O$_3$
Properties: Colorless visc. liq., pleasant odor; sol. in fixed oils; insol. in glycerin, propylene glycol; m.w. 228.26; sp.gr. 1.175 (20 C); b.p. 208 C (26 mm); ref. index 1.579
Precaution: Combustible when heated or exposed to flame; incompat. with oxidizing materials
Toxicology: LD50 (oral, rat) 2227 mg/kg; mod. toxic by ingestion; heated to decomp., emits acrid smoke and irritating fumes
Uses: Synthetic flavoring agent for pharmaceuticals
Regulatory: FDA 21CFR §172.515; FEMA GRAS

Benzyl α-toluate. *See* Benzyl phenylacetate
Benzytol. *See* Chloroxylenol
Bergamiol. *See* Linalyl acetate
Bergamol. *See* Linalyl acetate
Betanin. *See* Betanine

Betanine
CAS 7659-95-2
Synonyms: Betanin
Definition: Coloring principal in beets
Properties: M.w. 568.5
Uses: Colorant; limited stability to heat, light, oxygen, and SO$_2$
Trade names: Natural Red Beet Liq. 275280
See also Beet powd.

BHA

CAS 25013-16-5; EINECS 204-442-7; 246-563-8
FEMA 2183
Synonyms: Butylated hydroxyanisole; t-Butyl-4-methoxyphenol; (1,1-Dimethylethyl)-4-methoxyphenol; 3-t-Butyl-4-hydroxyanisole
Definition: Mixture of isomers of tertiary butyl-substituted 4-methoxyphenols
Empirical: $C_{11}H_{16}O_2$
Properties: Wh. or sl. yel. waxy solid, faint char. odor; insol. in water; sol. in petrol. ether, 50% or higher alcohol, propylene glycol, chloroform, fats, oils; m.w. 180.27; m.p. 48-55 C; b.p. 264-270 C (733 mm)
Precaution: Combustible
Toxicology: LD50 (oral, mouse) 2000 mg/kg; suspected carcinogen; moderate toxicity by ingestion, intraperitoneal routes; may cause rashes, hyperactivity; heated to decomp., emits acrid and irritating fumes
Uses: Antioxidant, preservative for orals, rectals, topicals
Usage level: 0.02% max. (preservation of fixed oils, fats, vitamin oil concs.)
Regulatory: FDA 21CFR §166.110, 172.110, 172.515, 172.615, 173.340, 175.105, 175.125, 175.300, 175.380, 175.390, 176.170, 176.210, 177.1010, 177.1210, 177.1350, 178.3120, 178.3570, 179.45,; 181.22, 181.24 (0.005% migrating from food pkg.), 182.3169 (0.02% max. of fat or oil), GRAS; FEMA GRAS; USDA 9CFR 318.7, 381.147; Japan approved 0.2-1 g/kg; Europe approved; UK approved; approved for orals, rectals, topicals; USP/NF, BP compliance
Manuf./Distrib.: Aceto; Allchem Ind.; Eastman; Fluka; Penta Mfg.; Spectrum Chem. Mfg.; UOP
Manuf./Distrib. (pharm. & food): Ruger; Spectrum Chem. Mfg.
Trade names containing: Arlacel® 186; Cetiol®; Dry Vitamin D₃ Beadlets Type 850 No. 652550401, 652550601; Durkex 25BHA; Palmabeads® Type 500 No. 65332; Palma-Sperse® Type 250-S No. 65322; Palma-Sperse® Type 250A/50 D-S No. 65221; Vitamin A Palmitate Type 250-CWS No. 65312

BHT

CAS 128-37-0; EINECS 204-881-4
FEMA 2184
Synonyms: DBPC; Butylated hydroxytoluene; 2,6-Di-t-butyl-4-methylphenol; 2,6-Di-t-butyl-p-cresol; 2,6-Bis (1,1-dimethylethyl)-4-methylphenol
Classification: Substituted toluene
Empirical: $C_{15}H_{24}O$
Formula: $[C(CH_3)_3]_2CH_3C_6H_2OH$
Properties: White cryst. solid, faint char. odor; insol. in water, propylene glycol; sol. in toluene, alcohols, MEK, acetone, Cellosolve, petrol. ether, chloroform, benzene, most HC solvs.; m.w. 220.39; sp.gr. 1.048 (20/4 C); m.p. 68 C; b.p. 265 C; flash pt. (TOC) 260 F
Precaution: Combustible exposed to heat or flame; reactive with oxidizing materials
Toxicology: TLV: 10 mg/m³; LD50 (oral, rat) 890 mg/kg; moderately toxic by ingestion; poison by IP, IV routes; suspected carcinogen; human skin irritant; eye irritant; may cause rashes, hyperactivity; heated to decomp., emits acrid smoke and fumes
Uses: Antioxidant, preservative for orals, injectables, rectals, topicals
Usage level: 0.02% max. (preservation of fixed oils, fats, vitamin oil concs.)
Regulatory: FDA 21CFR §137.350, 166.110, 172.115, 172.615 (0.1% max.), 173.340 (0.1% of defoamer), 175.105, 175.125, 175.300, 175.380, 175.390, 176.170, 176.210, 177.1010, 177.1210, 177.1350, 177.2260, 177.2600, 178.3120, 178.3570, 179.45, 181.22; 181.24 (0.005% migrating from food pkg.), 182.3173 (0.02% max. of fat/oil), GRAS; USDA 9CFR §318.7, 381.147; Japan 0.2-1 g/kg; Europe, UK; USP/NF, BP, Ph.Eur. compliance
Manuf./Distrib.: Aceto; Aldrich; Ashland; Fluka; Great Lakes; Penta Mfg.; PMC Specialties; Raschig; Uniroyal
Manuf./Distrib. (pharm. & food): Aldrich; Am. Roland; Ruger; Spectrum Chem. Mfg.; Wako Pure Chem. Ind.
Trade names: CAO®-3
Trade names containing: CAO®-3/Blend 29; Dry Vitamin A Palmitate Type 250-SD No. 65378; Dry Vitamin D₃ Beadlets Type 850 No. 652550401, 652550601; Hydagen® DEO; Oxynex® 2004; Palmabeads® Type 500 No. 65332; Palma-Sperse® Type 250-S No. 65322; Palma-Sperse® Type 250A/50 D-S No. 65221; Vitamin A Palmitate Type 250-CWS No. 65312; Vitamin A Palmitate USP, FCC Type P1.7/BHT No. 63693

Bicarbonate of soda. *See* Sodium bicarbonate

d-Biotin

CAS 58-85-5; EINECS 200-399-3
Synonyms: [3aS-(3a-α,4b,6aα)]-Hexahydro-2-oxo-1H-thieno]3,4-d]imidazole-4-pentanoic acid; Vitamin H; cis-Hexahydro-2-oxo-1H-thieno (3,4)-imidazole-4-valeric acid; Coenzyme R
Classification: Organic compd.
Empirical: $C_{10}H_{16}N_2O_3S$
Properties: Wh. cryst. powd.; sl. sol. in water, alcohol; insol. in common org. solvs.; m.w. 244.31; m.p. 231-

233 C
Toxicology: No human toxic symptoms reported on heavy dosage; heated to decomp., emits toxic fumes of NO$_x$, SO$_x$
Uses: Nutrient; in enzyme systems
Regulatory: FDA 21CFR §182.5159, 182.8159, GRAS
Manuf./Distrib.: Fluka; Sumitomo Pharmaceuticals
Manuf./Distrib. (pharm. & food): Am. Roland
Trade names: d-Biotin USP, FCC No. 63345
Trade names containing: Bitrit-1™ (1% Biotin Trituration No. 65324)

Birthwort extract. *See* Serpentaria extract

Bisabolol
CAS 515-69-5; EINECS 208-205-9
Synonyms: α,4-Dimethyl-α-(4-methyl-3-pentenyl)-3-cyclohexene-1-methanol
Classification: Terpene
Empirical: C$_{15}$H$_{26}$O
Uses: Antiphlogistic active
Trade names: Hydagen® B

(-)-α-Bisabolol. *See* Levomenol
N,N´-Bis(2-aminoethyl)-1,2-ethanediamine. *See* Triethylenetetramine

Bis(aminopropyl)piperazine
Synonyms: BAPP
Classification: Heterocyclic organic compd.
Properties: Clear liq.; sp.gr. 0.97; b.p. 295 C; flash pt. (COC) 325 F; ref. index 1.5001
Uses: Pharmaceutical intermediate; dietary supplement
Manuf./Distrib.: Texaco
Manuf./Distrib. (pharm. & food): Aldrich

Bis-[3,3-bis-(4´-hydroxy-3´-t-butylphenyl butanoic acid]-glycol ester. *See* Hydrocinnamic acid
N-[2-[Bis(carboxymethyl)amino]ethyl]-N-(2-hydroxyethyl)glycine, trisodium salt. *See* Trisodium HEDTA
1,6-Bis (5-(p-chlorophenyl) bi-guanidino) hexane diacetate. *See* Chlorhexidine diacetate
N,N´-Bis (4-chlorophenyl)-3,12-diimino-2,4,11,13-tetraazatetradecane-diimidamide compd. with D-gluconic acid. *See* Chlorhexidine digluconate

Bis-diglyceryl caprylate/caprate/isostearate/stearate/hydroxystearate adipate
Definition: Adipic acid diester of a mixed diglyceryl ester of caprylic, capric, stearic, isostearic and hydroxystearic acids
Uses: Emollient, ointment base, stabilizer
Trade names: Softisan® 649

1,4-Bis(3,4-dihydroxyphenyl)-2,3-dimethylbutane. *See* Nordihydroguaiaretic acid
2,6-Bis (1,1-dimethylethyl)-4-methylphenol. *See* BHT
Bis(dimethylthiocarbamyl) disulfide. *See* Tetramethylthiuram disulfide
Bis(dodecyloxycarbonylethyl) sulfide. *See* Dilauryl thiodipropionate
Bis (2-ethylhexyl) butanedioate. *See* Dioctyl succinate
1,3-Bis(2-ethylhexyl)hexahydro-5-methyl-5-pyrimidiamine. *See* Hexetidine
Bis(2-ethylhexyl) hexanedioate. *See* Dioctyl adipate
Bis (2-ethylhexyl) phthalate. *See* Dioctyl phthalate
Bis(D-gluconato) copper. *See* Copper gluconate
Bis(2-hydroxyethyl)amine. *See* Diethanolamine
Bis(2-hydroxyethyl)-ammonium hexadecylphosphate. *See* DEA-cetyl phosphate
N,N-Bis (2-hydroxyethyl) coco amides. *See* Cocamide DEA
N,N-Bis(2-hydroxyethyl)dodecanamide. *See* Lauramide DEA
N,N-Bis(2-hydroxyethyl)myristamide. *See* Myristamide DEA
N,N-Bis(2-hydroxyethyl) octadecanamide. *See* Stearamide DEA
N,N-Bis(2-hydroxyethyl)palm kernel oil acid amide. *See* Palm kernelamide DEA
N,N-Bis(2-hydroxyethyl) stearamide. *See* Stearamide DEA
N,N-Bis(2-hydroxyethyl)tetradecanamide. *See* Myristamide DEA
N-[1,3-Bis(hydroxymethyl)-2,5-dioxo-4-imidazolidinyl]-. *See* Diazolidinyl urea
2,2-Bis(hydroxymethyl)propionic acid. *See* Dimethylolpropionic acid
1,3-Bis(hydroxymethyl) urea. *See* Diazolidinyl urea
Bis[1-hydroxy-2(1H)-pyridinethinato-O,S]-(T-4) zinc. *See* Zinc pyrithione
Bis (2-methoxyethyl) ether. *See* Diethylene glycol dimethyl ether

Bis(1-methylethyl) decanedioate

Bis(1-methylethyl) decanedioate. *See* Diisopropyl sebacate
Bis(1-methylethyl)hexanedioate. *See* Diisopropyl adipate
1,4-Bis[(4-methylphenyl)-amino-9,10-anthracenedione. *See* CI 61565; D&C Green No. 6

Bismuth
CAS 7440-69-9; EINECS 231-177-4
Classification: Metallic element
Formula: Bi
Properties: Brittle metal, reddish; sol. in nitric and HCl; at. wt. 208.9804; dens. 9.8 (20 C); m.p. 271 C; b.p. 1560 C; flamm. in powd. form
Precaution: Flamm. solid
Uses: Pharmaceuticals and medicinals
Manuf./Distrib.: Aldrich; Asarco; Atomergic Chemetals; Dowa Mining; Fry's Metals Ltd; Mitsubishi Materials; Noah Chem.; Spectrum Chem. Mfg.; Toho Zinc
Manuf./Distrib. (pharm. & food): Aldrich

Bismuth carbonate basic. *See* Bismuth subcarbonate
Bismuth chloride oxide. *See* Bismuth oxychloride
Bismuth nitrate, basic. *See* Bismuth subnitrate
Bismuth oxycarbonate. *See* Bismuth subcarbonate

Bismuth oxychloride
CAS 7787-59-9; EINECS 232-122-7
Synonyms: Basic bismuth chloride; Bismuth chloride oxide; Bismuth subchloride; CI 77163; Chlorooxobismuthine; Synthetic pearl; Pearl white; Pigment white 14
Classification: Inorganic pigment
Empirical: BiClO
Formula: BiOCl
Properties: White crystalline powd.; sol. in acids; insol. in water; m.w. 260.48; dens. 7.717
Uses: Color additive for external pharmaceuticals; skin protectant
Regulatory: FDA 21CFR §73.1162, 73.2162; permanently listed
Manuf./Distrib.: Atomergic Chemetals; Great Western; ISP Van Dyk; Mallinckrodt; Mearl; Spectrum Chem. Mfg.
Manuf./Distrib. (pharm. & food): Aldrich; Ruger
See also CI 77163

Bismuth oxynitrate. *See* Bismuth subnitrate
Bismuth salicylate basic. *See* Bismuth subsalicylate

Bismuth subcarbonate
CAS 5892-10-4
Synonyms: Bismuth oxycarbonate; Bismuth carbonate basic
Empirical: CBi_2O_5
Formula: $(BiO)_2CO_3$
Properties: Wh. powd., odorless; sol. in nitric acid; insol. in water, alcohol; m.w. 510.01; dens. 6.860
Precaution: Light-sensitive
Uses: Adsorbent in antidiarrheal prods.; used in orals
Regulatory: FDA approved for orals; BP, Ph.Eur. compliance
Manuf./Distrib.: Atomergic Chemetals; Mallinckrodt; Spectrum Chem. Mfg.
Manuf./Distrib. (pharm. & food): Aldrich; Integra; Ruger

Bismuth subchloride. *See* Bismuth oxychloride

Bismuth subgallate
CAS 99-26-3; 12263-40-0
Synonyms: Basic bismuth gallate; Gallic acid, bismuth basic salt
Empirical: $C_7H_5BiO_6$
Properties: Hydrate, bright yel. powd., odorless, tasteless; dissolves readily with decomp. in warm, mod. dil. hydrochloric, nitric, or sulfuric acids; pract. insol. in water, alcohol, chloroform, ether; insol. in very dil. min. acids; m.w. 394.09; stable in air
Precaution: Light-sensitive
Uses: Protective, antiseptic, astringent, antacid; used in rectals and dusting powds.
Regulatory: FDA approved for rectals
Manuf./Distrib. (pharm. & food): Integra; Ruger; Spectrum Chem. Mfg.

Bismuth subnitrate
CAS 1304-85-4; EINECS 215-136-8

Synonyms: Bismuth nitrate, basic; Bismuth oxynitrate
Classification: Inorganic salt
Empirical: $Bi_5H_9N_4O_{22}$
Formula: $Bi_5(OH)_9(NO_3)_4O$
Uses: Antidarrheal adsorbent; protectant for diaper rash and prickly heat
Manuf./Distrib.: Atomergic Chemetals; Celtic Chem. Ltd; R.W. Greeff; Mallinckrodt

Bismuth subsalicylate
CAS 14882-18-9
Synonyms: Bismuth salicylate basic
Formula: $Bi(C_7H_5O_3)_3Bi_2O_3$
Uses: Antidiarrheal adsorbent
Manuf./Distrib.: Atomergic Chemetals; R.W. Greeff; Mallinckrodt; Spectrum Chem. Mfg.

Bisodium tartrate. *See* Sodium tartrate
1,4-Bis(phenylamino)benzene. *See* N,N´-Diphenyl-p-phenylenediamine
4-Bis(polyethoxy)-p-aminobenzoic acid polyethoxyethyl ester. *See* PEG-25 PABA
Bis (trimethylsilyl) amine. *See* Hexamethyldisilazane
Bitter almond oil camphor. *See* Benzoin
Bitter ash. *See* Quassia
Bitter fennel oil. *See* Fennel oil
Bitter root. *See* Gentian
Bitter wood. *See* Quassia
Bixin. *See* Annatto extract
Black balsam. *See* Balsam Peru
Blanc fixe (artificial, precipitated). *See* Barium sulfate
Bleached beeswax. *See* Beeswax, white
Bleached shellac. *See* Shellac
Bleached wax. *See* Beeswax, white
Bleaching sol'n. *See* Sodium hypochlorite
BLO. *See* Butyrolactone
Blood sugar. *See* D-Glucose anhyd.
Blue copperas. *See* Cupric sulfate pentahydrate
Blue No. 3. *See* FD&C Blue No. 1 aluminum lake
Blue No. 1 (Japan). *See* FD&C Blue No. 1 aluminum lake
Blue stone. *See* Cupric sulfate pentahydrate
Blue vitriol. *See* Cupric sulfate pentahydrate
Blue X. *See* FD&C Blue No. 2
BNPD. *See* 2-Bromo-2-nitropropane-1,3-diol
Boletic acid. *See* Fumaric acid
Bolus alba. *See* Kaolin
Boracic acid. *See* Boric acid
Borax. *See* Sodium borate decahydrate
Borax, fused. *See* Sodium borate

Boric acid
CAS 10043-35-3; EINECS 233-139-2
Synonyms: Boracic acid; Orthoboric acid
Classification: Inorganic acid
Empirical: BH_3O_3
Formula: H_3BO_3
Properties: Wh. or colorless cryst. powd., gran., odorless, almost tasteless or sl. acidic taste; sol. in water, alcohol, glycerol; insol. in ether, benzene; m.w. 61.83; dens. 1.435; m.p. 171 C
Precaution: Hygroscopic
Toxicology: Acute poisoning causes digestive upsets in man, CNS stimulation, depression, renal damage, circulatory collapse; irritant; contraindicated with perforated eardrum or broken skin
Uses: Antimicrobial preservative, buffering agent in eye drops; weak bacteriostat and fungistat; antiseptic; used for temp. relief of burns, abrasions, insect bites; to treat external ear canal infections; used in ophthalmics, otics, topicals
Usage level: 0.01-1.0%
Regulatory: FDA 21CFR §175.105, 176.180, 181.22, 181.30; USA not restricted; Europe listed; permitted in Switzerland and Sweden as preservative in some processed seafoods; FDA approved for ophthalmics, otics, topicals; USP/NF, BP, Ph.Eur. compliance
Manuf./Distrib.: Dragoco; Janssen Chimica; Nippon Denko; Occidental; U.S. Borax

Boric acid disodium salt

Manuf./Distrib. (pharm. & food): Aldrich; Dragoco; Integra; Mallinckrodt; Nippon Denko; Ruger; Spectrum Chem. Mfg.

Boric acid disodium salt. See Sodium borate decahydrate
2-Bornanone. See Camphor
Bornan-2-one. See Camphor
Borneol acetate. See Bornyl acetate

Bornyl acetate
CAS 76-49-3
FEMA 2159
Synonyms: levo-Bornyl acetate; Borneol acetate; 1,7,7-Trimethylbicyclo[2.2.1]heptan-2-ol acetate; Bornyl acetic ether; Bornyl ethanoate
Empirical: $C_{12}H_{20}O_2$
Properties: Colorless liq., white crystalline solid; piney odor; fresh, burning taste; sol. in alcohol, most fixed oils; sl. sol. in water; insol. in propyl glycol; m.w. 196.29; m.p. 27.5 C; b.p. 225-226 C; flash pt. 89 C; ref. index 1.462-1.466
Precaution: Combustible liq.
Toxicology: Heated to decomp., emits acrid smoke and fumes
Uses: Synthetic flavoring agent, solv.; used in aromatic preps. for treatment of coughs, other respiratory-tract disorders, musculoskeletal and joint disorders
Regulatory: FDA 21CFR §172.515; FEMA GRAS
Manuf./Distrib. (pharm. & food): Aldrich; Chr. Hansen's

levo-Bornyl acetate. See Bornyl acetate
Bornyl acetic ether. See Bornyl acetate
Bornyl ethanoate. See Bornyl acetate
Bourbonal. See Ethyl vanillin
Brassica campestris oil. See Rapeseed oil
Brazil wax. See Carnauba
Bread sugar. See D-Glucose monohydrate
Brilliant Blue FCF. See FD&C Blue No. 1
Brilliant lake red R. See D&C Red No. 31
Brilliant red. See D&C Red No. 9
Brimstone. See Sulfur
British gum. See Dextrin
Bromoethylene. See Vinyl bromide
Bromofluoroesceic acid. See D&C Red No. 22

2-Bromo-2-nitropropane-1,3-diol
CAS 52-51-7; EINECS 200-143-0; UN No. 3241
Synonyms: BNPD; 1,3-Propanediol, 2-bromo-2-nitro; Bronopol; 2-Bromo-2-nitro-1,3-propanediol
Classification: Substituted aliphatic diol
Empirical: $C_3H_6BrNO_4$
Properties: Cryst., odorless; sol. in water, alcohol; sl. sol. in chloroform, acetone, ether; m.w. 200.01; m.p. 130-133 C
Toxicology: Poison by ingestion, subcutaneous, intravenous, intraperitoneal routes; moderately toxic by skin contact; eye and skin irritant
Uses: Antimicrobial preservative for topical preps. and suppositories, esp. water-sol. creams and lotions; generates its antimicrobial effect by release of formaldehyde
Usage level: 0.01-0.1%
Regulatory: USA CIR approved to 0.1%, EPA registered; Europe listed; BP compliance
Manuf./Distrib.: Aldrich
Manuf./Distrib. (pharm. & food): Aldrich
Trade names: Bronopol; Bronopol-Boots® BP
Trade names containing: Nipaguard® BPX

2-Bromo-2-nitro-1,3-propanediol. See 2-Bromo-2-nitropropane-1,3-diol
Bronopol. See 2-Bromo-2-nitropropane-1,3-diol

Bronze powder
CAS 7440-50-8; EINECS 231-159-6
Synonyms: CI 77400 (EEC)
Definition: Inorganic metal consisting of powdered bronze
Uses: Color additive for external pharmaceuticals
Regulatory: FDA 21CFR §73.1646, 73.2646

Manuf./Distrib.: Atomergic Chemetals; Canbro; Crescent Bronze Powd.; Lenape Ind.; Obron Atlantic; Punda
   Mercantile; Reade Advanced Materials; SCM Metal Prods.; Sheffield Bronze Paint; U.S. Bronze Powds.;
   Whittaker, Clark & Daniels
See also CI 77400; Copper

Bucrilate. *See* Bucrylate

Bucrylate
   CAS 1069-55-2
   Synonyms: Isobutyl 2-cyanoacrylate; Bucrilate
   Empirical: $C_8H_{11}NO_2$
   Properties: M.w. 153.18
   Uses: Tissue adhesive; surgical aid

Bulgarian rose oil. *See* Rose oil
Burnt lime. *See* Calcium oxide
Burnt sugar. *See* Caramel
Burnt sugar coloring. *See* Caramel
n-Butanal. *See* n-Butyraldehyde
1-Butanamine. *See* n-Butylamine

Butane
   CAS 106-97-8; EINECS 203-448-7; UN No. 1011
   Synonyms: n-Butane; Alkane C-4
   Classification: Hydrocarbon
   Empirical: C_4H_{10}
   Formula: $CH_3CH_2CH_2CH_3$
   Properties: Colorless gas, faint disagreeable odor; easily liquefied under pressure @ R.T.; one vol. water
      dissolves 0.15 vol.; 1 vol. alcohol dissolves 18 vol.s (17 C, 770 mm); m.w. 58.12; dens. 0.599; vapor
      pressure 1620 mm Hg (17 psig, 21 C); f.p. -138 C; b.p. -0.5 C; flash pt. (CC) -76 F
   Precaution: Flamm. gas; very dangerous fire hazard exposed to heat, flame, oxidizers; highly explosive;
      explosive limits 1.9-8.5%
   Toxicology: TLV:TWA 800 ppm; mildly toxic by inh.; causes drowsiness; asphyxiant; narcotic in high concs.;
      heated to decomp., emits acrid smoke and fumes
   Uses: Aerosol propellant used in topicals
   Regulatory: FDA 21CFR §173.350, 184.1165, GRAS; approved for topicals; USP/NF compliance
   Manuf./Distrib.: Air Prods.; Electrochem Ltd; Phillips 66; Stanchem
   Manuf./Distrib. (pharm. & food): Aldrich

n-Butane. *See* Butane
1,4-Butanedicarboxylic acid. *See* Adipic acid
1,4-Butanedioic acid. *See* Succinic acid
Butanedioic acid, bis(2-ethylhexyl) ester. *See* Dioctyl succinate
Butanedioic acid, hydroxy-, bis(2-ethylhexyl) ester. *See* Dioctyl malate
Butanedioic anhydride. *See* Succinic anhydride
1,3-Butanediol. *See* Butylene glycol
Butanediolamine. *See* 2-Amino-2-methyl-1,3-propanediol
Butanenitrile. *See* Butyronitrile
Butanoic acid pentyl ester. *See* Amyl butyrate
Butanoic acid 1,2,3-propanetriyl ester. *See* Tributyrin
1-Butanol. *See* Butyl alcohol
Butan-1-ol. *See* Butyl alcohol
4-Butanolide. *See* Butyrolactone
2,3-Butanolone. *See* Acetyl methyl carbinol

Butan-3-one-2-yl butyrate
   FEMA 3332
   Empirical: $C_8H_{14}O_3$
   Properties: Wh. to sl. yel. liq., red berry odor; sol. in alcohol, propylene glycol, most oils; insol. in water; m.w.
      158.19; dens. 0.972-0.992; flash pt. 179 F; ref. index 1.408-1.429
   Toxicology: Heated to decomp., emits acrid smoke and irritating fumes
   Uses: Berry-like flavoring agent
   Regulatory: FDA GRAS; FEMA GRAS
   Manuf./Distrib.: Aldrich
   Manuf./Distrib. (pharm. & food): Aldrich

Butcherbroom extract
CAS 84012-38-4
Synonyms: Rusco extract; Ruscus aculeatus extract
Definition: Extract of the rhizome of *Ruscus aculeatus*
Uses: Used in anti-inflammatory sun care and eye care prods.
Trade names containing: Biophytex®

2-Butenedioic acid. *See* Fumaric acid; Maleic acid
cis-Butenedioic acid. *See* Maleic acid
trans-Butenedioic acid. *See* Fumaric acid
2-Butenedioic acid ferrous salt. *See* Ferrous fumarate
2-Butenedioic acid, polymer with methoxyethene, butyl ester. *See* PVM/MA copolymer, butyl ester
2-Butenedioic acid (Z)-, polymer with methoxyethene, calcium, sodium salt. *See* Calcium/sodium PVM/MA copolymer
2-Butenedioic acid, polymer with methoxyethene, 1-methylethyl ester. *See* PVM/MA copolymer, isopropyl ester
cis-Butenedioic anhydride. *See* Maleic anhydride
1-Butene, homopolymer. *See* Polybutene
2-Butenoic acid. *See* Crotonic acid
(2-Butenylidene) acetic acid. *See* Sorbic acid
Butter of antimony. *See* Antimony trichloride
Butter of arsenic. *See* Arsenic trichloride
Butter of zinc. *See* Zinc chloride
Button lac. *See* Shellac
Butylacetic acid. *See* Caproic acid

Butyl alcohol
CAS 71-36-3; EINECS 200-751-6
FEMA 2178; UN No. 1120
Synonyms: n-Butyl alcohol; 1-Butanol; Butan-1-ol; Propyl carbinol
Classification: Aliphatic alcohol
Empirical: $C_4H_{10}O$
Formula: $CH_3(CH_2)_2CH_2OH$
Properties: Colorless clear mobile liq., char. penetrating vinous odor; sol. in water; misc. with alcohol, ether, many org. solvs.; m.w. 74.14; dens. 0.8109 (20/20 C); m.p. -90 C; f.p. -89.0 C; b.p. 117.7 C; flash pt. 35 C; ref. index 1.3993 (20 C)
Precaution: DOT: Flamm. liq.; mod. explosive exposed to flame; incompat. with Al, oxidizing materials
Toxicology: TLV:CL 50 ppm in air; LD50 (oral, rat) 790 mg/kg; poison by IV route; mod. toxic by skin contact, ingestion, subcutaneous, IP routes; skin and severe eye irritant; may be narcotic in high doses; heated to decomp., emits acrid smoke and fumes
Uses: Solv. used in orals; medicinal flavoring agent
Regulatory: FDA 21CFR §73.1, 172.515, 172.560, 175.105, 175.320, 176.200, 177.1200, 177.1440, 177.1650; 27CFR §21.99; FEMA GRAS; FDA approved for orals; USP/NF, BP compliance
Manuf./Distrib.: Ashland; BASF; BP Chem Ltd; Eastman; Fluka; Hoechst Celanese; Shell; Union Carbide; Vista
Manuf./Distrib. (pharm. & food): Aldrich; Eastman
Trade names: Nacol® 4-99

n-Butyl alcohol. *See* Butyl alcohol

t-Butyl alcohol
CAS 75-65-0; EINECS 200-889-7; UN No. 1120
Synonyms: TBA; 2-Methyl-2-propanol; Trimethyl carbinol; 2-Propanol, 2-methyl-
Empirical: $C_4H_{10}O$
Formula: $(CH_3)_3COH$
Properties: Colorless liq., unpleasant odor; m.w. 74.12; dens. 0.775; m.p. 25-26 C; b.p. 83 C; flash pt. 11 C; ref. index 1.3870 (20 C)
Precaution: DOT: Flamm. liq.
Toxicology: Irritant to mucous membranes; inh. of 25 ppm causes pulmonary problems in man; ingestion can cause headache, dizziness, drowsiness; skin contact can cause contact dermatitis
Uses: Processing aid for pharmaceuticals; denaturant and solv.
Regulatory: FDA 21CFR §176.200, 178.3910, 27CFR §21.100
Manuf./Distrib.: AC Ind.; Aldrich; Allchem Ind.; Arco; Ashland; Fluka; Hüls Am.; Spectrum Chem. Mfg.
Trade names: Tebol™; Tebol™ 99

n-Butylaldehyde. *See* n-Butyraldehyde
Butylamine. *See* n-Butylamine

n-Butylamine
CAS 109-73-9; EINECS 203-699-2
FEMA 3130; UN No. 1125
Synonyms: Amine C_4; 1-Aminobutane; 1-Butanamine; Butylamine
Classification: Aliphatic organic compd.
Empirical: $C_4H_{11}N$
Formula: $CH_3(CH_2)_3NH_2$
Properties: Colorless liq., amine odor; misc. with water, alcohol, ether; m.w. 73.14; dens. 0.7327; m.p. -50 C; b.p. 78 C; flash pt. 30 F; ref. index 1.4010
Precaution: DOT: Flamm. liq.; refrigerate
Toxicology: LD50 (rat) 500 mg/kg; potent irritant to eyes, mucous membranes; direct skin contact causes severe primary irritation and blistering
Uses: Intermediate for pharmaceuticals; flavoring agent
Regulatory: FEMA GRAS; BP compliance
Manuf./Distrib.: Air Prods.; Aldrich; Ashland; BASF; Elf Atochem N. Am.; Spectrum Chem. Mfg.
Manuf./Distrib. (pharm. & food): Aldrich; Daicel Chem. Co.; Mallinckrodt

Butyl-2-aminobenzoate. *See* Butyl anthranilate
Butyl-o-aminobenzoate. *See* Butyl anthranilate

Butyl anthranilate
CAS 7756-96-9
FEMA 2181
Synonyms: Butyl-2-aminobenzoate; Butyl-o-aminobenzoate
Empirical: $C_{11}H_{15}NO_2$
Properties: Liq. @ R.T.; m.w. 193.25; sp.gr. 1.060 (15.5 C); m.p. $\approx$0 C; b.p. 303 C; ref. index 1.5420 (20 C)
Uses: Sweet plum-like synthetic flavoring agent
Regulatory: FDA 21CFR §172.515; FEMA GRAS
Manuf./Distrib. (pharm. & food): Aldrich

Butylated hydroxyanisole. *See* BHA
Butylated hydroxytoluene. *See* BHT

N,N-Butyl benzene sulfonamide
CAS 3622-84-2; EINECS 222-823-6
Synonyms: Benzenesulfonic acid butyl amide
Empirical: $C_{20}H_{19}NO_2S$
Formula: $C_6H_5SO_2NHC_3H_9$
Properties: Amber to straw liq., pleasant odor; m.w. 337.46; dens. 1.148; b.p. 189-190 C (4.5 mm); ref. index 1.5235
Toxicology: Toxic by ingestion
Uses: Synthesis of pharmaceuticals
Manuf./Distrib.: Advance Coatings; Allchem Ind.; Hardwicke; Unitex

n-Butyl n-butanoate. *See* Butyl butyrate

Butyl butyrate
CAS 109-21-7; EINECS 203-656-8
FEMA 2186
Synonyms: n-Butyl n-butanoate; n-Butyl butyrate; n-Butyl n-butyrate
Empirical: $C_8H_{16}O_2$
Formula: $CH_3CH_2CH_2COO(CH_2)_3CH_3$
Properties: Colorless liq., pineapple odor; misc. with alcohol, ether, veg. oils; sl. sol. in propylene glycol, water; m.w. 144.24; dens. 0.67-0.871; b.p. 166 C; flash pt. (OC) 128 F; ref. index 1.405
Precaution: Combustible liq.; incompat. with oxidizers
Toxicology: LD50 (oral, rabbit) 9520 mg/kg, (IP, rat) 2300 mg/kg; mod. toxic by IP; mildly toxic by ingestion; mod. irritating to eyes, skin, mucous membranes; narcotic in high concs.; heated to decomp., emits acrid smoke and irritating fumes
Uses: Apple, banana, berry, peach, pear-like synthetic flavoring agent
Regulatory: FDA 21CFR §172.515; FEMA GRAS; Japan approved as flavoring
Manuf./Distrib.: Aldrich
Manuf./Distrib. (pharm. & food): Aldrich

n-Butyl butyrate. *See* Butyl butyrate

n-Butyl n-butyrate. *See* Butyl butyrate
Butyl γ-butyrolactone. *See* Butyl levulinate
Butyl caproate. *See* Butyl hexanoate
Butyl capronate. *See* Butyl hexanoate
Butyl citrate. *See* Tributyl citrate

Butyl 2-decenoate
FEMA 2194
Synonyms: n-Butyl decylenate
Empirical: $C_{14}H_{26}O_2$
Properties: Colorless liq., peach/apricot odor, fruity green taste; sol. in alcohol; insol. in water; m.w. 226.36
Uses: Synthetic flavoring agent
Regulatory: FDA 21CFR §172.515; FEMA GRAS

n-Butyl decylenate. *See* Butyl 2-decenoate

Butylene glycol
CAS 107-88-0; EINECS 203-529-7
Synonyms: 1,3-Butanediol; 1,3-Butylene glycol
Classification: Aliphatic diol
Empirical: $C_4H_{10}O_2$
Formula: $HOCH_2CH_2CHOHCH_3$
Properties: Visc. liq., sweet flavor with bitter aftertaste; m.w. 90.12; dens. 1.004-1.006 (20/20 C); b.p. 207.5 C; f.p. < -50 C; flash pt. 250 F
Precaution: Combustible when exposed to heat or flame; incompat. with oxidizing materials
Toxicology: LD50 (oral, rat) 23 g/kg; mildly toxic by ingestion and subcutaneous routes; eye irritant; heated to decomp., emits acrid smoke and irritating fumes
Uses: Active ingred. in topical ointments, creams, lotions; carrier, vehicle, and solv. for injectable prods.
Regulatory: FDA 21CFR §173.220, 184.1278 GRAS
Manuf./Distrib.: Fluka; Hüls AG
Trade names containing: Unipertan VEG 24; Unipertan VEG 242

1,3-Butylene glycol. *See* Butylene glycol

Butylene glycol dicaprylate/caprate
Uses: Emollient, dispersant, lubricant, suspending agent, solubilizer, carrier/vehicle, penetrant, spreading agent
Trade names: Miglyol® 8810

Butyl ester of PVM/MA copolymer. *See* PVM/MA copolymer, butyl ester
Butyl ethyl ketone. *See* 3-Heptanone

Butyl formate
CAS 592-84-7; EINECS 209-772-5
FEMA 2196
Synonyms: Formic acid butyl ester
Empirical: $C_5H_{10}O_2$
Formula: $HCOO(CH_2)_3CH_3$
Properties: Colorless liq., plum-like odor; sl. sol. in water; misc. with alcohol, ether; m.w. 102.14; m.p. -90 C; b.p. 106.8 C; flash pt. 64 C; ref. index 1.3890-1.3891
Precaution: Flamm. liq.
Toxicology: Irritant
Uses: Plum-like synthetic flavoring agent
Regulatory: FDA 21CFR §172.515; FEMA GRAS
Manuf./Distrib. (pharm. & food): Aldrich

Butyl heptanoate
CAS 5454-28-4
FEMA 2199
Synonyms: Butyl heptoate; Butyl heptylate
Empirical: $C_{11}H_{22}O_2$
Properties: Colorless liq., sl. fruity odor; sol. in most org. solvs.; m.w. 186.30; sp.gr. 0.85553; m.p. -68.4 C; b.p. 226.2 C; ref. index 1.42280 (20 C)
Uses: Apple-like synthetic flavoring agent
Regulatory: FDA 21CFR §172.515; FEMA GRAS
Manuf./Distrib. (pharm. & food): Aldrich

Butyl heptoate. *See* Butyl heptanoate

Butyl heptylate. *See* Butyl heptanoate

Butyl hexanoate
 CAS 626-82-4
 FEMA 2201
 Synonyms: Butyl caproate; Butyl caproanate; Butyl hexylate
 Empirical: $C_{10}H_{20}O_2$
 Properties: Liq., pineapple-like odor; m.w. 172.27; sp.gr. 0.8623; m.p. -63 to -64 C; b.p. 208 C; ref. index 1.4153
 Uses: Fruity synthetic flavoring agent
 Regulatory: FDA 21CFR §172.515; FEMA GRAS
 Manuf./Distrib. (pharm. & food): Aldrich

Butyl hexylate. *See* Butyl hexanoate

t-Butyl hydroquinone
 CAS 1948-33-0; EINECS 217-752-2
 Synonyms: TBHQ; Mono-t-butyl hydroquinone; 2-(1,1-Dimethylethyl)-1,4-benzenediol
 Classification: Aromatic organic compd.
 Empirical: $C_{10}H_{14}O_2$
 Properties: Wh. to lt. tan cryst. solid; sol. in ethyl alcohol, ethyl acetate, acetone, ether; sl. sol. in water; m.w. 166.24; m.p. 126.5-128.5 C; flash pt. (COC) 171 C
 Toxicology: LD50 (oral, rat) 700 mg/kg; poison by intraperitoneal route; moderately toxic by ingestion; irritant; heated to decomp., emits acrid smoke and irritating fumes
 Uses: Antioxidant
 Regulatory: FDA 21CFR 172.185 (limitation 0.02% of oil), 177.2420; USDA 9CFR §318.7 (limitation 0.003% in dry sausage, 0.006% with BHA/BHT, 0.01% in rendered animal fat, 0.02% with BHA and/or BHT, 0.02% in margarine), 381.147 (limitation 0.01% on fat in poultry)
 Manuf./Distrib.: AC Ind.; Aceto; Allchem Ind.; Charkit; Eastman; Penta Mfg.; Schweizerhall; Showa Denko; UOP
 Manuf./Distrib. (pharm. & food): Aceto; Aldrich; Eastman; Penta Mfg.; UOP

3-t-Butyl-4-hydroxyanisole. *See* BHA
n-Butyl p-hydroxybenzoate. *See* Butylparaben
Butyl p-hydroxybenzoate. *See* Butylparaben
n-Butyl-4-hydroxybenzoate potassium salt. *See* Potassium butyl paraben
4-Butyl-4-hydroxyoctanoic acid, γ-lactone. *See* 4,4-Dibutyl-γ-butyrolactone
Butyl 2-hydroxypropanoate. *See* Butyl lactate
Butyl α-hydroxypropionate. *See* Butyl lactate
n-Butyl-S(-)-2-hydroxypropionate. *See* Butyl lactate

Butyl isobutyrate
 CAS 97-87-0
 FEMA 2188
 Synonyms: n-Butyl 2-methyl propanoate
 Empirical: $C_8H_{16}O_2$
 Properties: Colorless liq., fruity odor, pineapple taste; insol. in water; m.w. 144.21; dens. 0.862; b.p. 155-156 C; flash pt. 110 F; ref. index 1.4025
 Precaution: Combustible liq.
 Toxicology: Heated to decomp., emits acrid smoke and fumes
 Uses: Apple, banana-like synthetic flavoring agent
 Regulatory: FDA 21CFR §172.515; FEMA GRAS
 Manuf./Distrib. (pharm. & food): Aldrich

n-Butyl isopentanoate. *See* n-Butyl isovalerate

n-Butyl isovalerate
 CAS 109-19-3
 FEMA 2218
 Synonyms: Isovaleric acid butyl ester; n-Butyl isopentanoate; Butyl 3-methylbutyrate
 Empirical: $C_9H_{18}O_2$
 Properties: Colorless to pale yel. liq., fruity odor; misc. with alcohol, fixed oils; sl. sol. in propylene glycol; insol. in water; m.w. 158.27; dens. 0.851-0.857; b.p. 150 C; ref. index 1.407
 Precaution: Flamm. when exposed to heat, flames, sparks, oxidizers
 Toxicology: LD50 (oral, rat) 8200 mg/kg; mildly toxic by ingestion; skin irritant; heated to decomp, emits acrid smoke and fumes
 Uses: Apple, peach-like synthetic flavoring agent

Butyl lactate

Regulatory: FDA 21CFR §172.515; FEMA GRAS
Manuf./Distrib. (pharm. & food): Aldrich

Butyl lactate

CAS 138-22-7
FEMA 2205
Synonyms: n-Butyl lactate; n-Butyl-S(-)-2-hydroxypropionate; Butyl 2-hydroxypropanoate; Butyl α-hydroxypropionate
Classification: Ester
Empirical: $C_7H_{14}O_3$
Formula: $CH_3CHOHCOOC_4H_9$
Properties: Water-wh. liq., mild odor; misc. with many lacquer solvs., diluents, oils; sl. sol. in water; hydrolyzed in acids and alkalies; m.w. 146.19; dens. 0.974-0.984 (20/20 C); m.p. -43 C; flash pt. (TOC) 75.5 C
Precaution: Combustible
Toxicology: TLV 5 ppm in air
Uses: Sweet synthetic flavoring agent; pharmaceutical intermediate
Regulatory: FDA 21CFR §172.515; FEMA GRAS
Manuf./Distrib.: CPS; Penta Mfg.; Purac Biochem BV; Van Waters & Rogers
Manuf./Distrib. (pharm. & food): Aldrich; Penta Mfg.; Purac Biochem BV
Trade names: Purasolv® BL

n-Butyl lactate. *See* Butyl lactate

Butyl levulinate

CAS 2052-15-5
FEMA 2207
Synonyms: Butyl γ-butyrolactone; Butyl 4-oxopentanoate
Empirical: $C_9H_{16}O_3$
Properties: Liq., bitter taste; sol. in ether, alcohol, chloroform; sl. sol. in water; m.w. 172.23; dens. 0.974; b.p. 238 C; flash pt. 197 F; ref. index 1.4283 (20 C)
Uses: Fruity synthetic flavoring agent
Regulatory: FDA 21CFR §172.515; FEMA GRAS
Manuf./Distrib. (pharm. & food): Aldrich

Butyl methoxy dibenzoyl methane

CAS 70356-09-1; EINECS 274-581-6
Synonyms: 1-[4-(1,1-Dimethylethyl)phenyl]-3-(4-methoxyphenyl)-1,3-propanedione; Avobenzone
Classification: Substituted aromatic compd.
Empirical: $C_{20}H_{22}O_3$
Trade names containing: Unifilter U-41

t-Butyl-4-methoxyphenol. *See* BHA
Butyl 3-methylbutyrate. *See* n-Butyl isovalerate
t-Butyl methyl ether. *See* Methyl t-butyl ether
n-Butyl 2-methyl propanoate. *See* Butyl isobutyrate
Butyl octadecanoate. *See* Butyl stearate
n-Butyl octadecanoate. *See* Butyl stearate

2-Butyl-1-octanol

CAS 3913-02-8; EINECS 223-470-0
Synonyms: Isododecanol; Isolauryl alcohol
Classification: Branch chain alcohol
Empirical: $C_{12}H_{26}O$
Formula: $CH_3(CH_2)_5CHCH_2OHCH_2(CH_2)_2CH_3$
Properties: M.w. 186; flash pt. (COC) 120 C
Uses: Solubilizer
Trade names: Isofol® 12

Butyl 4-oxopentanoate. *See* Butyl levulinate

Butylparaben

CAS 94-26-8; EINECS 202-318-7
FEMA 2203
Synonyms: Butyl p-hydroxybenzoate; Butyl parasept; 4-Hydroxybenzoic acid butyl ester; n-Butyl p-hydroxybenzoate
Definition: Ester of butyl alcohol and p-hydroxybenzoic acid
Empirical: $C_{11}H_{14}O_3$

Properties: Colorless or wh. cryst. powd.; very sl. sol. in water, glycerin; freely sol. in acetone, alcohols, ether, chloroform, propylene glcyol; m.w. 194.22; m.p. 68-72 C
Precaution: Preserve in well-closed containers
Toxicology: Poison by intraperitoneal route; skin irritant
Uses: Antimicrobial preservative, antifungal, flavoring; used in injectables, orals, rectals, topicals
Regulatory: FDA 21CFR §172.515; FEMA GRAS; EPA registered; Japan approved (0.012-1 g/kg as p-hydroxybenzoic acid); Europe listed; approved for injectables, orals, rectals, topicals; USP/NF, BP compliance
Manuf./Distrib.: Aldrich; Ashland; Inolex; Int'l. Sourcing; E. Merck; Napp; Nipa Labs; Penta Mfg.; Tri-K Ind.
Manuf./Distrib. (pharm. & food): Aldrich; Ashland; Int'l. Sourcing; E. Merck; Penta Mfg.; Spectrum Chem. Mfg.; Tri-K Ind.
Trade names: Butyl Parasept® NF; Lexgard® B; Nipabutyl
Trade names containing: LiquaPar® Oil; Nipastat; Phenonip; Uniphen P-23

Butylparaben, potassium salt. *See* Potassium butyl paraben
Butylparaben, sodium salt. *See* Sodium butylparaben
Butyl parasept. *See* Butylparaben
n-Butyl pentanoate. *See* Butyl valerate

Butyl phenylacetate
CAS 122-43-0
FEMA 2209
Synonyms: Butyl α-toluate
Empirical: $C_{12}H_{16}O_2$
Properties: Colorless liq., honey-like odor; m.w. 192.26; dens. 0.991-0.994 (25/25 C); b.p. 260 C; flash pt. 74 C; ref. index 1.488-1.490 (20 C)
Precaution: Combustible
Uses: Honey-like synthetic flavoring agent
Regulatory: FDA 21CFR §172.515; FEMA GRAS
Manuf./Distrib. (pharm. & food): Aldrich; Chr. Hansen's

Butyl phthalate. *See* Dibutyl phthalate
Butyl propionate. *See* n-Butyl propionate

n-Butyl propionate
CAS 590-01-2
FEMA 2211
Synonyms: Propanoic acid butyl ester; Butyl propionate
Empirical: $C_7H_{14}O_2$
Formula: $CH_3CH_2COOC_4H_9$
Properties: Colorless liq., earthy faintly sweet odor, apricot-like taste; very sol. in alcohol, ether; very sl. sol. in water; m.w. 130.19; dens. 0.8754 (20/4 C); m.p. -89 C; f.p. 32 C; b.p. 145-146 C; ref. index 1.401 (20 C)
Precaution: Flamm.
Toxicology: Skin and eye irritant
Uses: Banana-like synthetic flavoring agent
Regulatory: FDA 21CFR §172.515; FEMA GRAS
Manuf./Distrib.: Aldrich; Penta Mfg.; Union Carbide
Manuf./Distrib. (pharm. & food): Aldrich; Penta Mfg.

Butyl rubber. *See* Isobutylene/isoprene copolymer

Butyl stearate
CAS 123-95-5; EINECS 204-666-5
FEMA 2214
Synonyms: Butyl octadecanoate; n-Butyl octadecanoate; Octadecanoic acid butyl ester
Definition: Ester of butyl alcohol and stearic acid
Empirical: $C_{22}H_{44}O_2$
Formula: $CH_3(CH_2)_{16}COO(CH_2)_3CH_3$
Properties: Crystals; sl. sol. in water; sol. in alcohol, ether; m.w. 340.60; dens. 0.86 (20/4 C); m.p. 17-22 C; b.p. 343 C; flash pt. (CC) 160 C; ref. index 1.4430 (20 C)
Toxicology: No known toxicity; heated to decomp., emits acrid smoke and irritating fumes
Uses: Synthetic flavoring agent; used in topicals
Regulatory: FDA 21CFR §172.515, 173.340, 175.105, 175.300, 175.320, 176.200, 176.210, 177.2600, 177.2800, 178.3910, 181.22, 181.27; FDA approved for topicals; FEMA GRAS
Manuf./Distrib.: Amerchol; Aquatec Quimica SA; Ashland; C.P. Hall; Henkel/Organic Prods.; Inolex; Kenrich

Butyl α-toluate

Petrochem.; Mosselman NV; Penta Mfg.; Sea-Land; Spectrum Chem. Mfg.; Stepan; Union Camp; Unitex; Witco/Oleo-Surf.
Manuf./Distrib. (pharm. & food): Aldrich

Butyl α-toluate. *See* Butyl phenylacetate

Butyl valerate
CAS 591-68-4
FEMA 2217
Synonyms: n-Butyl valerate; n-Butyl pentanoate; n-Butyl-n-valerianate
Empirical: $C_9H_{18}O_2$
Formula: Liq., fruity odor; sol. in propylene glycol; sl. sol. in water; m.w. 158.24; sp.gr. 0.8680 (20 C); b.p. 186.5 C; ref. index 1
Properties: M.w. 158.24; dens. 0.868; b.p. 186-187 C; flash pt. 152 F
Uses: Apple, raspberry-like synthetic flavoring agent
Regulatory: FDA 21CFR §172.515; FEMA GRAS
Manuf./Distrib. (pharm. & food): Aldrich

n-Butyl valerate. *See* Butyl valerate
n-Butyl-n-valerianate. *See* Butyl valerate
1,4-Butynediol. *See* But-2-yne-1,4-diol

But-2-yne-1,4-diol
CAS 110-65-6; EINECS 203-788-6; UN No. 2716
Synonyms: 1,4-Butynediol
Empirical: $C_4H_6O_2$
Formula: $HOCH_2=CCH_2OH$
Properties: Straw to amber crystals; m.w. 86.10; m.p. 57.5 C; b.p. 194 (100 mm); flash pt. 152 C
Toxicology: Poison by ingestion; skin sensitizer
Uses: Pharmaceutical intermediate; synthesis of histamine and pyridoxine; alternative route for vitamin B6
Manuf./Distrib.: BASF; ISP
Manuf./Distrib. (pharm. & food): ISP

n-Butyraldehyde
CAS 123-72-8; EINECS 204-646-6
FEMA 2219
Synonyms: n-Butylaldehyde; Butyric aldehyde; n-Butanal
Classification: Aldehyde
Empirical: C_4H_8O
Formula: $CH_3CH_2CH_2CHO$
Properties: Colorless liq.; sol. in water; misc. with ether @ 75 C; m.w. 72.10; sp.gr. 0.800; m.p. -99 C; f.p. 12 F; b.p. 75-76 C; ref. index 1.3843
Precaution: Flamm. liq. (DOT); incompat. with oxidizng materials; reacts vigorously with chlorosulfonic acid
Toxicology: LD50 (oral, rat) 2490mg/kg; mod. toxic by ingestion, inh., skin contact, intraperitoneal, and subcutaneous routes; severe skin and eye irritant; heated to decomp., emits acrid smoke and fumes
Uses: Fruity synthetic flavoring agent
Regulatory: FDA 21CFR §172.515; FEMA GRAS
Manuf./Distrib.: Aldrich; Eastman; Fluka; Hoechst Celanese; Neste UK; Penta Mfg.; Union Carbide
Manuf./Distrib. (pharm. & food): Aldrich; Penta Mfg.

Butyric acid, 3,3-bis(3-t-butyl-4-hydroxyphenyl) ethylene ester. *See* Hydrocinnamic acid
Butyric acid isoamyl ester. *See* Isoamyl butyrate
Butyric acid nitrile. *See* Butyronitrile
Butyric aldehyde. *See* n-Butyraldehyde
Butyric ether. *See* Ethyl butyrate
Butyrin. *See* Tributyrin
Butyrolactam. *See* 2-Pyrrolidone

Butyrolactone
CAS 96-48-0; EINECS 202-509-5
FEMA 3291
Synonyms: BLO; Dihydro-2(3H)-furanone; 4-Hydroxybutanoic acid lactone; γ-Butyrolactone; 4-Butanolide
Classification: Lactone
Empirical: $C_4H_6O_2$
Properties: Colorless oily liq., mild caramel odor; misc. with water; sol. in methanol, ethanol, acetone, ether, benzene; m.w. 86.09; dens. 1.120; m.p. -45 C; b.p. 204-205 C; flash pt. 98 C; ref. index 1.4348

Precaution: Combustible when exposed to heat or flame; reactive with oxidizing materials
Toxicology: LD50 (oral, rat) 1800 mg/kg; mod. toxic by ingestion, IV, intraperitoneal routes; suspected tumorigen; heated to decomp., emits acrid and irritating fumes
Uses: Solvent, stabilizer; pharmaceutical intermediate
Regulatory: FEMA GRAS
Manuf./Distrib.: Aldrich; Allchem Ind.; BASF; Gelest; Great Western; ISP; Janssen Chimica; Schweizerhall; Spectrum Chem. Mfg.; UCB SA
Manuf./Distrib. (pharm. & food): Aldrich; Spectrum Chem. Mfg.
Trade names: BLO®

γ-Butyrolactone. *See* Butyrolactone
Butyrone. *See* 4-Heptanone

Butyronitrile
CAS 109-74-0; EINECS 203-700-6; UN No. 2411
Synonyms: Propyl cyanide; Butyric acid nitrile; Nitrile C₄; Butanenitrile
Empirical: C_4H_7N
Formula: $CH_3CH_2CH_2CN$
Properties: Colorless liq.; misc. with alcohol, ether; m.w. 69.11; dens. 0.794; m.p. -112 C; b.p. 115-117 C; flash pt. 16 C; ref. index 1.3840
Precaution: Flamm.
Toxicology: LD50 (oral, rat) 0.14 g/kg; highly toxic
Uses: Basic material in pharmaceutical intermediates and prods.
Manuf./Distrib.: Air Prods.; Aldrich; Eastman; Janssen Chimica; Lonza
Manuf./Distrib. (pharm. & food): Aldrich

Butyrophenone
CAS 495-40-9
Empirical: $C_{10}H_{12}O$
Properties: M.w. 148.21; dens. 1.021; b.p. 220-222 C; flash pt. 192 F
Uses: Cherry-like flavoring agent
Manuf./Distrib. (pharm. & food): Aldrich

CA. *See* Cellulose acetate
CAB. *See* Cellulose acetate butyrate
Cacao butter. *See* Cocoa butter
C-8 acid. *See* Caprylic acid

C18-36 acid glycol ester
Definition: Ester of ethylene glycol and C18-36 acid
Formula: $CH_3(CH_2)_xCOOCH_2CH_2OH$, avg. x = 16-34
Uses: Emollient, conditioner, emulsifier, lubricant, stabilizer, suspending agent
Trade names: Syncrowax ERL-C

C18-36 acid triglyceride
CAS 91052-08-3
Definition: Triester of glycerin and C18-36 acid
Formula: $(CH_2OCO(CH_2)_xCH_3)_2HCOCO(CH_2)_xCH_3$, x=16-34
Uses: Emollient, conditioner, thickener
Trade names: Syncrowax HGL-C

CADG. *See* Cocamidopropyl betaine

Caffeine
CAS 58-08-2; EINECS 200-362-1
FEMA 2224
Synonyms: Theine; Coffeine; Guaramine; Methyltheobromine; 1,3,7-Trimethyl-2,6-dioxopurine; 1,3,7-Trimethylxanthine
Classification: Heterocyclic organic compd.
Empirical: $C_8H_{10}N_4O_2$
Properties: Wh. fleecy mass, powd. or need., odorless, bitter taste; sparingly sol. in water, alcoholl freely sol. in chloroform; sl. sol. in ether; m.w. 194.22; dens. 1.23; m.p. 238 C; pH neutral; hydrate is efflorescent in air
Toxicology: Possible teratogen; diuretic effect; can cause heartburn, upset stomach, diarrhea; 200-500 mg

can cause headache, tremors, nervousness, and irritability

Uses: Flavoring agent, synergist for pharmaceuticals; CNS stimulant (medicine)

Regulatory: FDA 21CFR §165.175, 182.1180 (limitation 0.02%), GRAS; FEMA GRAS; BP, Ph.Eur. compliance

Manuf./Distrib.: Am. Bio-Synthetics; Bell Flavors & Fragrances; R.W. Greeff; Janssen Chimica; Knoll AG; Penta Mfg.; Pfizer Food Science

Manuf./Distrib. (pharm. & food): Aldrich; Alfa; Am. Roland; Ashland; Bell Flavors & Fragrances; Berk; Ellis & Everard; Food Ingred. Tech.; R.W. Greeff; Jungbunzlauer; Mallinckrodt; MLG Enterprises; Penta Mfg.; Pfizer; Quimdis; Robt. Bryce; Ruger; Scanchem; Spectrum Chem. Mfg.; Tesco; Van Waters & Rogers

Cajeputene. *See* d-Limonene; dl-Limonene

Cajeputi oil. *See* Cajeput oil

Cajeput oil

FEMA 2225; UN No. 1993

Synonyms: Cajeputi oil; White tea tree; Tea tree

Definition: Volatile oil from fresh leaves and twigs of *Melaleuca leucadendron*, contg. 50-60% eucalyptol and l-pinene, terpineol, and aldehydes

Properties: Colorless of ylsh. liq., agreeable camphor odor, bitter aromatic taste; misc. with alcohol, chloroform, ether, CS_2; very sl. sol. in water; sol. in 1 vol. 80% alcohol; dens. 0.912-0.925; ref. index 1.4660-1.4710 (20 C)

Precaution: DOT: Flamm. liq.; keep well closed, cool, protected from light

Toxicology: LD50 (oral, rat) 3870 mg/kg

Uses: Natural flavoring; expectorant, counterirritant, scabicide, rubefacient, topical antimycotic; used to treat fungus infections such as athlete's foot; liniment; antiseptic for cuts; stimulant; antispasmodic, diaphoretic

Regulatory: FDA 21CFR §172.510; FEMA GRAS; Japan approved

Manuf./Distrib.: Spectrum Chem. Mfg.

Manuf./Distrib. (pharm. & food): Ruger

Cajeputol. *See* Eucalyptol

Cake alum. *See* Aluminum sulfate

Calcaria absorbens. *See* Soda lime

Calcined alumina. *See* Alumina

Calcined magnesia. *See* Magnesium oxide

Calciofon. *See* Calcium gluconate

Calciol. *See* Cholecalciferol

Calcium acetate

CAS 62-54-4 (anhyd.); 5743-26-0 (monohydrate); EINECS 200-540-9

FEMA 2228

Synonyms: Vinegar salts; Gray acetate; Lime acetate

Definition: Calcium salt of acetic acid

Empirical: $C_4H_6CaO_4$ (anhyd.) or $C_4H_6CaO_4 \cdot H_2O$ (monohydrate)

Formula: $(CH_3COO)_2Ca$ (anhyd.) or $(CH_3COO)_2Ca \cdot H_2O$ (monohydrate)

Properties: Wh. powd., odorless or almost odorless, sl. bitter taste; hygroscopic; sol. in water; sl. sol. in alcohol; pract. insol. in acetone, dehydrated alc., benzene; m.w. 158.18 (anhyd.), 176.17 (monohydrate); dens. 1.50; heated above 160 C, dec. to $CaCO_3$ and acetone

Precaution: Combustible

Toxicology: LD50 (IV, mouse) 52 mg/kg; poison by IV route; heated to decomp., emits acrid smoke and fumes

Uses: Preservative; used in orals, topicals

Regulatory: FDA 21CFR §175.300, 181.22, 181.29, 182.6197, 184.1185, GRAS; FEMA GRAS; Europe listed; UK approved; approved for orals, topicals; BP compliance

Manuf./Distrib.: General Chem.; Lohmann; Mallinckrodt; Niacet; Schaefer Salt; Spectrum Chem. Mfg; Verdugt BV

Manuf./Distrib. (pharm. & food): Aldrich; Integra; Lohmann; Mallinckrodt; Niacet; Ruger; Spectrum Chem. Mfg.

Calcium alginate

CAS 9005-35-0

FEMA 2015

Synonyms: Alginic acid, calcium salt

Classification: Aliphatic organic compd.

Definition: Calcium salt of alginic acid

Empirical: $[(C_6H_7O_6)_2Ca]_n$

Properties: White or cream-colored powd. or filaments, sl. odor and taste; insol. in water, acid; sol. in alkaline sol'n.; m.w. 195.16

Precaution: Flamm.
Toxicology: Heated to decomp., emits acrid smoke and irritating fumes
Uses: Emulsifier, stabilizer, thickener for pharmaceutical prods.; film-former for microencapsulation
Regulatory: FDA 21CFR §184.1187, GRAS; FEMA GRAS; Europe listed (ADI 0-25 mg/kg, as alginic acid); UK approved
Manuf./Distrib.: Fluka
Manuf./Distrib. (pharm. & food): Pronova; Tomiyama Pure Chem. Ind.
Trade names: Protanal TFX 200; Sobalg FD 460
Trade names containing: KELTOSE®

Calcium ascorbate
CAS 5743-27-1; 5743-28-2 (dihydrate)
Synonyms: Ascorbic acid calcium salt
Empirical: $C_{12}H_{14}CaO_{12}$ • $2H_2O$ (dihydrate)
Properties: Wh. to sl. yel. cryst. powd., pract. odorless; freely sol. in water; sl. sol. in alcohol; insol. in ether, methanol, ethanol; m.w. 426.35
Toxicology: Heated to decomp., emits acrid smoke and irritating fumes
Uses: Antioxidant, preservative in orals; vitamin C source; antiscorbutic vitamin
Regulatory: FDA 21CFR §182.3189, GRAS; Europe listed; UK approved; approved for orals
Manuf./Distrib. (pharm. & food): Spectrum Chem. Mfg
Trade names: Calcium Ascorbate FCC No. 60475

Calcium benzoate
CAS 2090-05-3; EINECS 218-235-4
Definition: Calcium salt of benzoic acid
Empirical: $C_{14}H_{10}O_4$ • $3H_2O$
Properties: Orthorhombic cryst. or powd.; sol. in water; m.w. 374.26; dens. 1.44
Precaution: Combustible exposed to heat or flame
Toxicology: May cause an intolerance reaction in some people; heated to decomp., emits acrid smoke and irritating fumes
Uses: Preservative
Regulatory: FDA 21CFR §166.110, 178.2010; USDA 9CFR §318.7; Europe listed

Calcium o-benzosulfimide. *See* Calcium saccharin
Calcium biphosphate. *See* Calcium phosphate monobasic anhydrous

Calcium borogluconate
CAS 5743-34-0
Synonyms: D-Gluconic acid cyclic 4,5-ester with boric acid calcium salt; Calcium diborogluconate
Empirical: $C_{12}H_{20}B_2C_9O_{16}$
Properties: Cryst.; freely sol. in water; m.w. 482.01
Uses: Mineral source for pharmaceutical prods.
Trade names: Gluconal® CA M B

Calcium carbonate
CAS 471-34-1; 1317-65-3; EINECS 207-439-9
Synonyms: Carbonic acid calcium salt (1:1); Calcium carbonate (1:1); CI 77220; Precipitated calcium carbonate; Precipitated chalk
Classification: Inorganic salt
Empirical: $CaCO_3$
Properties: White powd. or colorless crystals, odorless, tasteless; hygroscopic; very sl. sol. in water; sol. in acids with CO_2; insol. in alcohol; m.w. 100.09; dens. 2.7-2.95; m.p. 825 C (dec.); stable in air
Precaution: Ignites on contact with F_2; incompat. with acids, alum, ammonium salts
Toxicology: TLV 5 mg/m³ of air; LD50 (oral, rat) 6450 mg/kg; no known toxicity; severe eye and moderate skin irritant
Uses: Alkali, neutralizing agent, colorant, opacifying agent used in implants, orals, otics; tablet/capsule diluent; tooth polish in dentifrices; filler in deodorants; gastric antacid; antidiarrheal medicine
Regulatory: FDA 21CFR §73.1070, 137.105, 137.155, 137.160, 137.165, 137.170, 137.175, 137.180, 137.185, 137.350, 169.115, 175.300, 177.1460, 181.22, 181.29, 182.5191, 184.1191, 184.1409, GRAS; BATF 27CFR §240.1051, limitation 30 lb/1000 gal of wine; Japan approved (1-2%); Europe listed; UK approved; FDA approved for implants, orals, otics; USP/NF, BP, Ph.Eur. compliance
Manuf./Distrib.: AluChem; Am. Ingreds.; BASF; R.E. Carroll; Cerac; ECC Int'l.; EM Industries; Genstar Stone Prods.; Georgia Marble; J.M. Huber; Lohmann; Mallinckrodt; Nichia Kagaku Kogyo; Pfizer; Whittaker, Clark & Daniels
Manuf./Distrib. (pharm. & food): Aldrich; Am. Roland; Integra; Int'l. Sourcing; Mallinckrodt; Ruger; Spectrum Chem. Mfg.

Calcium carbonate (1:1)

Trade names: Micro-White® 10 Codex; Micro-White® 25 Codex; Micro-White® 50 Codex; Micro-White® 100 Codex; Pharma-Carb®
Trade names containing: Cal-Carb® 4450; Cal-Carb® 4450 PG; Cal-Carb® 4457; Cal-Carb® 4462; Destab™ Calcium Carbonate 90; Destab™ Calcium Carbonate 95
See also CI 77220

Calcium carbonate (1:1). See Calcium carbonate

Calcium carboxymethyl cellulose
CAS 9050-04-8
Synonyms: Calcium cellulose glycolate; Cellulose carboxymethyl ether calcium salt; Carmellose calcium; Carboxymethylcellulose calcium
Definition: Calcium salt of a polycarboxymethyl ether of cellulose
Properties: Wh. to lt. yel. powd., odorless
Uses: Thickener, suspending agent, stabilizer, gellant; tablet disintegrant; used in orals
Regulatory: Japan approved; restricted; FDA approved for orals; USP/NF, BP, Ph.Eur. compliance
Manuf./Distrib.: Daicel Chem. Ind.; Nichirin Chem. Ind.
Trade names: Nymcel® ZSC

Calcium carrageenan
CAS 9049-05-2
Definition: Calcium salt of carrageenan
Uses: Emulsifier, stabilizer, thickener used in orals
Regulatory: FDA 21CFR §136.110, 136.115, 136.130, 136.160, 136.180, 139.121, 139.122, 150.141, 150.161, 172.626, 176.170; approved for orals

Calcium cellulose glycolate. See Calcium carboxymethyl cellulose

Calcium chloride
CAS 10043-52-4 (anhyd.); 10035-04-8 (dihydrate); EINECS 233-140-8
Classification: Inorganic salt
Empirical: $CaCl_2 \cdot 2H_2O$ (dihydrate)
Properties: Wh. deliq. cryst., granules, lumps, or flakes; deliq.; freely sol. in water and alcohol; m.w. 110.99 (anhyd.), 147.01 (dihydrate); dens. 2.150; b.p. > 1600 C; m.p. 782 C; pH 4.5-9.2 (5%)
Precaution: Hygroscopic; keep well closed
Toxicology: LD50 (oral rat) 1000 mg/kg, (intraperitoneal, rat) 264 mg/kg; poison by intravenous, intramuscular, intraperitoneal, subcutaneous routes; moderately toxic by ingestion causing stomach and heart disturbances
Uses: Firming agent, antimicrobial, desiccant; used in injectables, ophthalmics, orals; antiseptic in eye lotions; diuretic; urinary acidifier
Regulatory: FDA 21CFR §184.1193, GRAS; USDA 9CFR §318.7, 381.147, 3% max.; Japan approved (1% max.); Europe listed (ADI not specified); UK approved; WHO limitation: 350-800 mg/kg (canned fruits/veg.), 200 mg/kg (preserves, processed cheese); approved for injectables, ophthalmics, orals; USP/NF, BP, Ph.Eur. compliance
Manuf./Distrib.: Akzo Salt; Allied-Signal; EM Industries; Fluka; Gist-brocades Food Ingreds.; Kemira Kemi UK; Lohmann; Mallinckrodt; Nichia Kagaku Kogyo; Occidental; Schaefer Salt
Manuf./Distrib. (pharm. & food): Aldrich; Browning; Gist-brocades Food Ingreds.; Integra; Int'l. Sourcing; Lohmann; Mallinckrodt; Ruger; Spectrum Chem. Mfg.

Calcium citrate
CAS 813-94-5 (anhyd.); 5785-44-4 (tetrahydrate); EINECS 212-391-7
Synonyms: Lime citrate; Tricalcium citrate; Calcium citrate tertiary; Dicalcium citrate
Empirical: $C_{12}H_{10}Ca_3O_{14} \cdot 4H_2O$ (tetrahydrate)
Formula: $Ca_3(C_6H_5O_7)_2 \cdot 4H_2O$ (tetrahydrate)
Properties: Wh. fine powd., odorless; sl. sol. in water; insol. in alcohol; sol. in dil. HCl and nitric acid; m.w. 570.50 (tetrahdyrate)
Toxicology: Heated to decomp., emits acrid smoke and irritating fumes
Uses: Dietary supplement, nutrient, sequestrant, buffer; used in orals
Regulatory: FDA 21CFR §182.1195, 182.5195, 182.6195, 182.8195, GRAS; Japan approved (1% max. as calcium); Europe listed; UK approved; approved for orals
Manuf./Distrib.: EM Industries; Lohmann; Rit-Chem; Rottapharm SpA
Manuf./Distrib. (pharm. & food): Clofine; CRS; Integra; Int'l. Sourcing; Jungbunzlauer; Lohmann; Penta Mfg.; Ruger; Qualcepts Nutrients; Quimdis; Spectrum Chem. Mfg.

Calcium citrate tertiary. See Calcium citrate
Calcium diborogluconate. See Calcium borogluconate

Calcium N-(2,4-dihydroxy-3,3-dimethyl-1-oxobutyl-β-alanine. *See* Calcium D-pantothenate
Calcium dioctyl sulfosuccinate. *See* Dioctyl calcium sulfosuccinate
Calcium diphosphate. *See* Calcium pyrophosphate
Calcium disodium edetate. *See* Calcium disodium EDTA

Calcium disodium EDTA
CAS 62-33-9 (anhyd.); 23411-34-9; EINECS 200-529-9
Synonyms: Calcium disodium ethylenediamine tetraacetic acid; Disodium[(ethylenedinitrilo)tetraacetate], calciate (2-) hydrate; Edetate calcium disodium; Calcium disodium edetate
Classification: Substituted diamine
Definition: Mixt. of calcium disodium ethylenediaminetetraacetate dihydrate (predominantly) and trihydrate
Empirical: $C_{10}H_{12}CaN_2Na_2O_8 \cdot 2H_2O$
Formula: $CaNa_2C_{10}H_{12}N_2O_8 \cdot xHOH$
Properties: White cryst. powd. or gran., odorless, faint salt taste; sl. hygroscopic; sol. in water; insol. in org. solvs.; m.w. 374.27 (anhyd.), 410.30; pH 6.5-8.0; stable in air
Toxicology: Nontoxic; possible link to liver damage in test animals
Uses: Sequestrant, chelating agent for control of trace metal contamination in pharmaceutical prods.; preservative; used in injectables (IM, IV), intravenous, orals
Regulatory: FDA 21CFR §172.120; USDA 9CFR §318.7; Japan approved (0.035 g/kg max.); Europe listed; permitted in UK only in canned fish, shellfish; FDA approved for injectables (IM, IV), intravenous, orals
Manuf./Distrib.: Akzo Nobel; Am. Biorganics; Hampshire; Hickson Danchem
Manuf./Distrib. (pharm. & food): R.W. Greeff; Int'l. Sourcing
Trade names: Versene CA

Calcium disodium ethylenediamine tetraacetic acid. *See* Calcium disodium EDTA
Calcium D-glucarate (1:1) tetrahydrate. *See* Calcium saccharate

Calcium gluceptate
CAS 17140-60-2; 29039-00-7 (dihydrate)
Synonyms: Glucoheptonic acid, calcium salt (2:1); Calcium glucoheptonate (1:2)
Definition: Calcium salt of the alpha epimer of glucoheptonic acid
Empirical: $C_{14}H_{26}CaO_{16}$ (anhyd.), $C_{14}H_{26}CaO_{16} \cdot 2H_2O$ (dihydrate)
Properties: Wh. to very lt. yel. amorphous powd.; sol. in water; insol. in alcohol, many org. solvs.; m.w. 490.43 (anhyd.), 526.46 (dihydrate); pH 6-8 (10%)
Precaution: Stable in air, but hydrous forms may lose part of their water of hydration on standing
Uses: Replenisher (calcium); used in injectables
Regulatory: Approved for injectables
Manuf./Distrib. (pharm. & food): Spectrum Chem. Mfg.

Calcium glucoheptonate (1:2). *See* Calcium gluceptate

Calcium gluconate
CAS 299-28-5 (anhyd.); 18016-24-5 (monohydrate); EINECS 206-075-8
Synonyms: Gluconic acid calcium salt; D-Gluconic acid calcium salt; Calciofon; Glucal
Definition: Calcium salt of gluconic acid
Empirical: $C_{12}H_{22}O_{14} \cdot Ca$
Formula: $Ca[HOCH_2(CHOH)_4COO]_2$
Properties: Wh. fluffy powd. or gran., odorless, pract. tasteless; sol. in hot water; insol. in alcohol, acetic acid, other org. solvs.; sparingly and slowly sol. in water; stable in air; m.w. 430.4 (anhyd.), 448.39 (monohydrate); m.p. loses water @ 120 C; pH neutral
Toxicology: LD50 (IV, rat) 950 mg/kg; moderately toxic by subcutaneous, intraperitoneal, intravenous routes; may cause gastrointestinal and cardiac disturbances; heated to decomp., emits acrid smoke and fumes
Uses: Mineral source for pharmaceutical prods.; buffer, firming agent, sequestrant
Regulatory: FDA 21CFR §184.1199, GRAS; Japan restricted (1% max. as calcium); Europe listed; UK approved; WHO limitation 350 ppm max. (fruits, veg.), 200 ppm (jams, jellies); BP, Ph.Eur. compliance
Manuf./Distrib.: Akzo; EM Industries; Lipo; Lohmann; Mallinckrodt; Pfizer
Manuf./Distrib. (pharm. & food): Aldrich; Am. Roland; Integra; Int'l. Sourcing; Ruger; Spectrum Chem. Mfg.
Trade names: Gluconal® CA A; Gluconal® CA M

Calcium hydrate. *See* Calcium hydroxide
Calcium hydrogen orthophosphate. *See* Calcium phosphate dibasic
Calcium hydrogen phosphate. *See* Calcium phosphate dibasic
Calcium hydrogen phosphate anhydrous. *See* Calcium phosphate dibasic
Calcium hydrogen phosphate dihydrate. *See* Calcium phosphate dibasic dihydrate

Calcium hydroxide
CAS 1305-62-0; EINECS 215-137-3
Synonyms: Calcium hydrate; Hydrated lime; Slaked lime; Lime water
Classification: Inorganic base
Empirical: CaH_2O_2
Formula: $Ca(OH)_2$
Properties: Soft, white cryst. powd., alkaline sl. bitter taste; sl. sol. in water; sol. in glycerol, syrup, acid; insol. in alcohol; m.w. 74.10; dens. 2.34; m.p. loses water at 580 C
Precaution: Violent reaction with maleic anhydride, nitroethane, nitromethane, nitroparaffins, etc.
Toxicology: TLV 5 mg/m^3 in air; LD50 (oral, rat) 7.34 g/kg; mildly toxic by ingestion; severe eye irritant; skin, mucous membrane irritant; dust is industrial hazard
Uses: Used in injectables, orals, topicals
Regulatory: FDA 21CFR §135.110, 184.1205, GRAS; USDA 9CFR §318.7; Japan restricted (1% max. as calcium); Europe listed; UK approved; FDA approved for injectables, orals, topicals; BP compliance
Manuf./Distrib.: Am. Biorganics; EM Industries; Janssen Chimica; Lohmann; Mallinckrodt; Pfizer; Smith Lime Flour; Spec. Mins.; U.S. Gypsum
Manuf./Distrib. (pharm. & food): Aldrich; Integra; Pfizer; Ruger; Spectrum Chem. Mfg.
Trade names: Calcium Hydroxide USP 802

Calcium hydroxide phosphate. *See* Calcium phosphate tribasic
Calcium-L-2-hydroxypropionate. *See* Calcium lactate

Calcium lactate
CAS 814-80-2 (anhyd.); 41372-22-9 (monohydrate, trihydrate); 63690-56-2 (pentahydrate); EINECS 212-406-7
Synonyms: 2-Hydroxypropanoic acid, calcium salt; Calcium-L-2-hydroxypropionate
Empirical: $C_6H_{10}CaO_6$ • xH_2O, x < 5
Formula: $[CH_3CH(OH)COO]_2Ca$ • xH_2O
Properties: Wh. to cream-colored cryst. powd. or granules containing up to 5 moles of water of crystallization, almost odorless; pentahydrate is somethwat efflorescent, is sol. in water, pract. insol. in alcohol; becomes anhyd. at 120 C; m.w. 218.22 (anhyd.), 236.24 (monohydrate), 272.27 (trihydrate), 308.30 (pentahydrate)
Toxicology: May cause gastrointestinal and cardiac disturbances; heated to decomp., emits acrid smoke and irritating fumes
Uses: Nutrient supplement; used in dentifrices, calcium deficiency
Regulatory: FDA 21CFR §184.1207, GRAS except for infant foods/formulas; USDA 9CFR §318.7 (0.6% max.); Japan approved (1% max. as calcium); Europe listed; UK approved; BP, Ph.Eur. compliance
Manuf./Distrib.: Am. Biorganics; Am. Ingreds.; Atomergic Chemetals; EM Ind.; Lohmann; Spectrum Chem. Mfg.; Wilke Int'l.
Manuf./Distrib. (pharm. & food): Am. Roland; Integra; Int'l. Sourcing; Jungbunzlauer; Lohmann; Qualcepts Nutrients; Ruger; Spectrum Chem. Mfg.
Trade names: Puracal® PG; Puracal® PP; Puracal® TG

Calcium monohydrogen phosphate. *See* Calcium phosphate dibasic
Calcium monohydrogen phosphate dihydrate. *See* Calcium phosphate dibasic dihydrate
Calcium octadecanoate. *See* Calcium stearate
Calcium orthophosphate. *See* Calcium phosphate tribasic

Calcium oxide
CAS 1305-78-8; EINECS 215-138-9
Synonyms: Lime; Quicklime; Calx; Burnt lime
Classification: Inorganic oxide
Empirical: CaO
Properties: White or gray cryst. or powd., odorless; sol. in acids, glycerol, sugar sol'n.; sol. in water forming $Ca(OH)_2$ and generating heat; pract. insol. in alcohol; m.w. 56.08; dens. 3.40; m.p. 2570 C; b.p. 2850 C
Precaution: Noncombustible; powd. may react explosively with water; mixts. with ethanol may ignite if heated
Toxicology: TLV 2 mg/m^3; strong caustic; may cause severe irritation to skin, mucous membranes, eyes
Uses: Used in dermatological preps.; in sulfurated lime
Regulatory: FDA 21CFR §182.1210, 182.5210, 184.1210, GRAS; USDA 9CFR §318.7, 381.147; Europe listed; UK approved
Manuf./Distrib.: AluChem; Ash Grove Cement; Cerac; GE; Hüls Am.; Mallinckrodt; Pfizer; Spec. Mins.; Smith Lime Flour; U.S. Gypsum
Manuf./Distrib. (pharm. & food): Pfizer

Calcium D-pantothenate
CAS 137-08-6; EINECS 205-278-9

Synonyms: Calcium N-(2,4-dihydroxy-3,3-dimethyl-1-oxobutyl-β-alanine; Vitamin B_5, calcium salt; d-Calcium pantothenate; Calcium d-pantothenate
Definition: Calcium salt of pantothenic acid
Empirical: $C_9H_{16}NO_5 \cdot {}^1/_2Ca$
Properties: Wh. powd., sl. hygroscopic, odorless, sweetish taste with sl. bitter aftertaste; stable in air; sol. in water, glycerol; insol. in alcohol, chloroform, ether; m.w. 490.63; m.p. 170-172 C; dec. 195-196 C
Toxicology: LD50 (oral, mouse) 10 g/kg; (IV, rat) 830 mg/kg; moderately toxic by intraperitoneal, subcutaneous, and intravenous routes; mildly toxic by ingestion; heated to decomp., emits toxic fumes of NO_x
Uses: Source of pantothenic acid for solid dosage forms, multivitamin prods.
Regulatory: FDA 21CFR §182.5212, 184.1212, GRAS; Japan approved (1% max. as calcium); BP, Ph.Eur. compliance
Manuf./Distrib.: BASF; Hoffmann-La Roche; Schweizerhall; Takeda USA; Tanabe USA
Manuf./Distrib. (pharm. & food): Am. Roland; Daiichi Pharmaceutical; Unipex
Trade names: Calcium Pantothenate USP, FCC Type SD No. 63924

d-Calcium pantothenate. *See* Calcium D-pantothenate
Calcium d-pantothenate. *See* Calcium D-pantothenate

Calcium phosphate dibasic
CAS 7757-93-9; EINECS 231-826-1
Synonyms: DCP-0; Dicalcium phosphate; Dicalcium orthophosphate anhyd. (E341); Calcium monohydrogen phosphate; Calcium hydrogen phosphate; Calcium hydrogen phosphate anhydrous; Calcium hydrogen orthophosphate; Phosphoric acid calcium salt (1:1)
Classification: Inorganic salt
Empirical: $CaHPO_4$
Properties: Wh. cryst. powd., odorless, tasteless; deliq.; sol. in dilute HCl, nitric, and acetic acids; insol. in alcohol; sl. sol. in water; m.w. 136.07; dens. 2.306; loses water at 109 C; stable in air
Toxicology: No known toxicity; skin and eye irritant; nuisance dust
Uses: Tablet and/or capsule diluent, dispersant; nutrient source in multivitamin prods.; abrasive in dentifrices; used in dentals, orals
Regulatory: FDA 21CFR §181.29, 182.1217, 182.5217, 182.8217, GRAS; Japan approved (1% max. as calcium); Europe listed; UK approved; FDA approved for dentals, orals; USP/NF, BP, Ph.Eur. compliance
Manuf./Distrib.: Albright & Wilson; EM Industries; FMC; GE; Janssen Chimica; Lohmann; Mallinckrodt; Occidental; Rhone-Poulenc Basic
Manuf./Distrib. (pharm. & food): Albright & Wilson Am.; Browning; FMC; Mallinckrodt; Rhone-Poulenc Food Ingreds.; Ruger
Trade names: Albrite® Dicalcium Phosphate Anhyd; Anhydrous Emcompress®
Trade names containing: Bitrit-1™ (1% Biotin Trituration No. 65324); Folic Acid 10% Trituration No. 69997; Vitamin B_{12} 1% Trituration No. 69992

Calcium phosphate dibasic dihydrate
CAS 7789-77-7; EINECS 231-826-1
Synonyms: DCP-2; Dicalcium phosphate dihydrate; Calcium monohydrogen phosphate dihydrate; Calcium hydrogen phosphate dihydrate; Dicalcium phosphate
Empirical: $CaHPO_4 \cdot 2H_2O$
Properties: Monoclinic cryst.; deliq.; loses water of cryst. slowly below 100 C; sol. in dil. HCl or HNO_3; sl. sol. in dil. acetic acid; pract. insol. in water, alcohol; m.w. 172.09; dens. 2.31
Toxicology: Irritant; heated to decomp., emits acrid smoke and irritating fumes
Uses: Tablet/capsule diluent, excipient, filler; abrasive in dentifrices; phosphorus source in multivitamin prods.; used in orals
Regulatory: FDA 21CFR §181.29; FDA approved for orals; USP/NF compliance
Manuf./Distrib.: Albright & Wilson; Aldrich
Manuf./Distrib. (pharm. & food): Albright & Wilson Am.; Lohmann; Rhone-Poulenc Food Ingreds.; Ruger; Spectrum Chem. Mfg.
Trade names: Emcompress®

Calcium phosphate monobasic. *See* Calcium phosphate monobasic anhydrous

Calcium phosphate monobasic anhydrous
CAS 7758-23-8
Synonyms: MCP/A; Monocalcium phosphate anhydrous; Calcium tetrahydrogen diorthophosphate; Phosphoric acid calcium salt (2:1); Calcium phosphate monobasic; Acid calcium phosphate; Calcium biphosphate
Formula: $Ca(H_2PO_4)_2$
Properties: Wh. powd.; m.w. 234.05
Uses: Used in pharmaceutical preps.

Calcium phosphate tertiary

Regulatory: Europe listed
Manuf./Distrib. (pharm. & food): Albright & Wilson Am.; Browning; Rhone-Poulenc Food Ingreds.

Calcium phosphate tertiary. *See* Calcium phosphate tribasic

Calcium phosphate tribasic
CAS 7758-87-4; 12167-74-7; EINECS 231-840-8
FEMA 3081
Synonyms: TCP; Tricalcium phosphate; Tribasic calcium phosphate; Calcium hydroxide phosphate; Tricalcium orthophosphate; Calcium orthophosphate; Calcium phosphate tertiary; Precipitated calcium phosphate
Empirical: $Ca_3(PO_4)_2$
Formula: $3Ca_3(PO_4)_2 \cdot Ca(OH)_2$
Properties: Wh. cryst. powd., odorless, tasteless; sol. in acid; insol. in water, alcohol, acetic acid; m.w. 1004.64; dens. 3.18; m.p. 1670 C; ref. index 1.63; stable in air
Toxicology: Skin and eye irritant; nuisance dust
Uses: Tablet and/or capsule diluent; nutrient source; abrasive ingred. in dentifrices; used in orals
Regulatory: FDA 21CFR §137.105, 137.155, 137.160, 137.165, 137.170, 137.175, 137.180, 137.185, 169.179, 169.182, 175.300, 181.29, 182.1217, 182.5217, 182.8217, GRAS; USDA 9CFR §318.7; FEMA GRAS; Japan approved (1% max. as calcium), restricted; Europe listed; UK approved; FDA approved for orals; USP/NF compliance
Manuf./Distrib.: Albright & Wilson; FMC; Mallinckrodt; Monsanto; Rhone-Poulenc Basic
Manuf./Distrib. (pharm. & food): Albright & Wilson Am.; Aldrich; Browning; FMC; Integra; Lohmann; Rhone-Poulenc Food Ingreds.; Ruger; Spectrum Chem. Mfg.
Trade names: Calfos
Trade names containing: Lecigran™ C; Lecigran™ T; Palmabeads® Type 500 No. 65332

Calcium polycarbophil
CAS 9003-97-8
Definition: Calcium salt of polyacrylic acid crosslinked with divinyl glycol
Properties: Wh. to creamy wh. powd.; insol. in water, dil. acids, dil. alkalies, common org. solvs.
Uses: Bulking agent for laxative prods.
Manuf./Distrib. (pharm. & food): BFGoodrich; R.W. Greeff
Trade names: Noveon® CA-1; Noveon® CA-2

Calcium propionate
CAS 4075-81-4 (anhyd.); EINECS 223-795-8
Synonyms: Propionic acid, calcium salt; Propanoic acid, calcium salt
Definition: Calcium salt of propionic acid
Empirical: $C_6H_{10}CaO_4$
Formula: $Ca(OOCCH_2CH_3)_2$
Properties: White cryst. or cryst. powd., faint odor of propionic acid; sol. in water; sl. sol. in alcohol; m.w. 186.23; m.p. > 300 C
Precaution: Hygroscopic
Toxicology: Irritant; heated to decomp., emits acrid smoke and irritating fumes
Uses: Antimicrobial preservative in antifungal medication for the skin
Regulatory: FDA 21CFR §133.123, 133.124, 133.173, 133.179, 136.110, 136.115, 136.130, 136.160, 136.180, 150.141, 150.161, 179.45, 181.22, 181.23, 184.1221, GRAS;; USDA 9CFR §318.7, 0.32% max. on wt. of flour, 381.147, 0.3% max. on wt. of flour in fresh pie dough; Japan approved with limitations; Europe listed
Manuf./Distrib.: Gist-brocades Food Ingreds.; Lohmann; Niacet; Verdugt BV
Manuf./Distrib. (pharm. & food): Aldrich; Browning; Gist-brocades Food Ingreds.; Integra; Lohmann; Ruger; Spectrum Chem. Mfg.

Calcium pyrophosphate
CAS 7790-76-3; EINECS 232-221-5
Synonyms: Calcium diphosphate; Diphosphoric acid, calcium salt (1:2)
Classification: Inorganic salt
Properties: Wh. fine powd., tasteless; sol. in dilute HCl, insol. in water; dens. 3.09; m.p. 1230 C
Toxicology: No known toxity; nuisance dust
Uses: Buffer, neutralizing agent, nutrient, abrasive; used in dentals, orals
Regulatory: FDA 21CFR §182.5223, 182.8223, GRAS; approved for dentals, orals
Manuf./Distrib. (pharm. & food): Aldrich

Calcium saccharate
CAS 5793-88-4 (anhyd.); 5793-89-5 (tetrahydrate)

Synonyms: D-Glucaric acid, calcium salt (1:1) tetrahydrate; Calcium D-glucarate (1:1) tetrahydrate; Calcium D-saccharate
Definition: Calcium salt of D-saccharic acid
Empirical: $C_6H_8CaO_8 \cdot 4H_2O$
Properties: Wh. cryst. powd., odorless; very sl. sol. alcohol, cold water; pract. insol. in chloroform and ether; sol. in dil. min. acids, calcium gluconate sol'ns.; m.w. 320.27
Uses: Stabilizing agent in sol'ns. of calcium gluconate for injection
Regulatory: USP/NF compliance (tetrahydrate)
Manuf./Distrib.: Lohmann

Calcium D-saccharate. *See* Calcium saccharate

Calcium saccharin
CAS 6485-34-3 (anhyd.); 6381-91-5 (hydrate); EINECS 229-349-9
Synonyms: 1,2-Benzisothiazol-3(2H)-one, 1,1-dioxide, calcium salt; 1,2-Benzisothiazol-3(2H)-one, 1,1-dioxide, calcium salt hydrate; Calcium o-benzosulfimide; Saccharin calcium
Classification: Organic compd.
Empirical: $C_{14}H_8CaN_2O_6S_2 \cdot 3\frac{1}{2}H_2O$
Properties: Wh. cryst. powd., faint aromatic odor, intensely sweet taste; sol. in water; sl. sol. in alcohol; m.w. 404.44 (anhyd.), 467.48 (hydrate)
Toxicology: Heated to decomp., emits toxic fumes of NO_x
Uses: Nonnutritive sweetener; used in orals
Regulatory: FDA 21CFR §180.37; USDA 9CFR §318.7 (limitation 0.01% in bacon); FDA approved for orals; USP/NF compliance
Manuf./Distrib. (pharm. & food): Boots; Integra; Int'l. Sourcing; Ruger; Spectrum Chem. Mfg.
Trade names: Syncal® CAS; Unisweet CALSAC

Calcium salicylate
CAS 824-35-1
Uses: Used in orals
Regulatory: Approved for orals

Calcium silicate
CAS 1344-95-2; 10101-39-0; EINECS 215-710-8
Synonyms: Silicic acid, calcium salt; Okenite
Definition: Hydrous or anhydrous silicate with varying proportions of calcium oxide and silica
Empirical: Common forms: $CaSiO_3$, Ca_2SiO_4, Ca_3SiO_5
Properties: White or cream-colored powd.; pract. insol. in water; forms a gel with min. acids; dens. 2.10; bulk dens. 15-16 lb/ft^3; absorp. power 600% (water); surf. area 95-175 m^2/g; pH 8.4-10.2 (5% aq. susp.)
Toxicology: Pract. nontoxic orally, but inh. may cause respiratory tract irritation; nuisance dust
Uses: Filler, glidant and/or anticaking agent used in orals; antacid (pharmacology)
Regulatory: FDA 21CFR §172.410, 175.300, 177.1460, 182.2227, GRAS (limitation 2% in table salt, 5% in baking powd.); Europe listed; UK approved; approved for orals; USP/NF compliance
Manuf./Distrib.: Celite; Crosfield; Degussa; Great Western; J.M. Huber; Kraft; R.T. Vanderbilt
Manuf./Distrib. (pharm. & food): Aldrich; Crosfield; Degussa
Trade names: Micro-Cel® C
Trade names containing: Lecigran™ Super A

Calcium/sodium PVM/MA copolymer
CAS 62386-95-2
Synonyms: 2-Butenedioic acid (Z)-, polymer with methoxyethene, calcium, sodium salt
Definition: Mixed calcium and sodium salt of PVM/MA copolymer
Formula: $(C_4H_4O_4 \cdot C_3H_6O)_n \cdot Ca_xNa_y$
Uses: Film-former in spray bandages; visc. modifier/stabilizer; enteric sustained-release tablet coating
Trade names: Gantrez® MS-955D

Calcium stearate
CAS 1592-23-0; EINECS 216-472-8
Synonyms: Calcium octadecanoate; Stearic acid calcium salt; Octadecanoic acid calcium salt
Classification: Aliphatic organic compd.
Definition: Calcium salt of stearic acid
Empirical: $C_{18}H_{35}O_2 \cdot \frac{1}{2}Ca$
Formula: $Ca(C_{18}H_{35}O_2)_2$
Properties: White impalpable powd., sl. char. odor; insol. in water, alcohol, ether; sl. sol. in hot alcohol, hot veg. and min. oils; m.w. 707.00; bulk dens. 20 lb/ft^3; m.p. 149 C
Toxicology: Nontoxic; heated to decomp., emits acrid smoke and irritating fumes

Calcium stearoyl lactylate

Uses: Conditioning agent, tablet/capsule lubricant for implants, orals, rectals, topicals
Regulatory: FDA 21CFR §169.179, 169.182, 172.863, 173.340; must conform to FDA specs for fats or fatty acids derived from edible oils, 175.105, 175.300, 175.320, 176.170, 176.200, 176.210, 177.1200, 177.2260, 177.2410, 177.2600, 178.2010, 179.45; 181.22, 181.29, 184.1229, GRAS; FDA approved for implants, orals, rectals, topicals; USP/NF, BP, Ph.Eur. compliance
Manuf./Distrib.: Adeka Fine Chem.; Cometals; Eka Nobel Ltd; Elf Atochem N. Am./Wire Mill; Ferro/Grant; Henkel/Organic Prods.; Lohmann; Mallinckrodt; Miljac; PPG Industries; R.T. Vanderbilt; Witco
Manuf./Distrib. (pharm. & food): Lohmann; PPG Industries; Ruger; Sankyo Org. Chems.; Spectrum Chem. Mfg.
Trade names: Haro® Chem CPR-2; Synpro® Calcium Stearate NF

Calcium stearoyl lactylate
CAS 5793-94-2; EINECS 227-335-7
Synonyms: Calcium stearoyl-2-lactylate; Calcium stearyl-2-lactylate; Calcium stelate
Definition: Calcium salt of stearic acid ester of lactyl lactate
Empirical: $C_{24}H_{44}O_6 \cdot {}^1/_2Ca$
Properties: Cream-colored nonhygroscopic powd., caramel odor; sparingly sol. in water; m.w. 895.30; HLB 5-6; acid no. 50-86
Toxicology: No known toxicity; when heated to decomp., emits acrid smoke and irritating fumes
Uses: Emulsifier for pharmaceuticals
Regulatory: FDA 21CFR §172.844; must conform to FDA specs for fats or fatty acids derived from edible oils; Japan approved with restrictions; Europe listed; UK approved

Calcium stearoyl-2-lactylate. *See* Calcium stearoyl lactylate
Calcium stearyl-2-lactylate. *See* Calcium stearoyl lactylate
Calcium stelate. *See* Calcium stearoyl lactylate

Calcium sulfate
CAS 7778-18-9 (anhyd.); EINECS 231-900-3
Synonyms: Anhydrite (natural form); Calcium sulfate (1:1); Calcium sulfonate; Gypsum; Anhydrous gypsum; Plaster of Paris
Classification: Inorganic salt
Empirical: CaO_4S
Formula: $Ca \cdot H_2O_4S$
Properties: Wh. to sl. yel.-wh. powd. or crystals, odorless, tasteless; sl. sol. in water; sol. in 3 N HCl; m.w. 136.14; dens. 2.964; m.p. 1450 C
Precaution: Reacts violently with aluminum when heated; mixts. with phosphorus ignite at high temps.
Toxicology: Ingestion may result in intestinal obstruction because it absorbs water and hardens; no known toxicity on the skin; irritant; heated to decomp., emits toxic fumes of SO_x
Uses: Excipient, tablet/capsule diluent, dessicant; used in tablets prepared by direct compression, orals; abrasive and firming agent in tooth powds.
Regulatory: FDA 21CFR §133, 133.102, 133.106, 133.111, 133.141, 133.165, 133.181, 133.195, 137.105, 137.155, 137.160, 137.165, 137.170, 137.175, 137.180, 137.185, 150.141, 150.161, 155.200, 175.300, 177.1460, 184.1230, GRAS;; BATF 27CFR §240.1051, limitation 16.69 lb/1000 gal; Japan approved with restrictions (1% max.); Europe listed; UK approved; FDA approved for orals; USP/NF compliance
Manuf./Distrib.: Am. Ingreds.; EM Ind.; Fluka; Kemira Kemi AB; Lohmann; U.S. Gypsum
Manuf./Distrib. (pharm. & food): Aldrich; Am. Roland; Integra; Mallinckrodt
Trade names: Terra Alba 114836

Calcium sulfate (1:1). *See* Calcium sulfate

Calcium sulfate dihydrate
CAS 10101-41-4; EINECS 231-900-3
Synonyms: Native calcium sulfate; Precipitated calcium sulfate; Gypsum; Alabaster
Empirical: $CaO_4S \cdot 2H_2O$
Formula: $CaSO_4 \cdot 2H_2O$
Properties: Lumps or powd.; hygroscopic; sol. in water; very slowly sol. in glycerol; pract. insol. in most org. solvs.; m.w. 172.10; dens. 2.32
Toxicology: Irritant
Uses: Excipient, filler, desiccant, tablet/capsule diluent; used in orals
Regulatory: FDA approved for orals; USP/NF, BP, JP compliance
Manuf./Distrib.: Aldrich; R.E. Carroll; EM Ind.; Fluka; Franklin Ind. Mins.
Manuf./Distrib. (pharm. & food): Aldrich; Ruger; Spectrum Chem. Mfg.
Trade names: Compactrol®
Trade names containing: Cal-Tab®

Calcium sulfate hemihydrate
CAS 10034-76-1; EINECS 231-900-3
Synonyms: Dried calcium sulfate; Dried gypsum; Plaster of Paris
Formula: CaO$_4$S • $^1/_2$H$_2$O
Properties: Wh. or almost wh. fine powd., odorless, tasteless; hygroscopic; sl. sol. in water; more sol. in dil.
  min. acids; pract. insol. in alcohol; m.w. 145.15
Toxicology: Irritant
Uses: Used for prep. of plaster of Paris bandage for immobilization of limbs and fractures; for dental casts;
  in orals
Regulatory: FDA approved for orals; BP, JP compliance
Manuf./Distrib.: Aldrich
Manuf./Distrib. (pharm. & food): Aldrich

Calcium sulfonate. *See* Calcium sulfate
Calcium tetrahydrogen diorthophosphate. *See* Calcium phosphate monobasic anhydrous
Calcium trisodium pentetate. *See* Pentetate calcium trisodium
Calcium 10-undecenoate. *See* Calcium undecylenate

Calcium undecylenate
Synonyms: Calcium 10-undecenoate; 10-Undecenoic acid, calcium (2+) salt
Empirical: C$_{22}$H$_{38}$O$_4$Ca
Properties: M.w. 406.62
Uses: Antimicrobial in diaper rash and prickly heat prods.
Manuf./Distrib.: Elf Atochem

C-8 alcohols. *See* Caprylic alcohol
C16-18 alcohols. *See* Cetearyl alcohol
C12-15 alcohols lactate. *See* C12-15 alkyl lactate

Calendula extract
CAS 84776-23-8; EINECS 283-949-5
Synonyms: Calendula officinalis extract; Marigold extract; Extract of calendula
Definition: Extract of flowers of *Calendula officinalis*
Uses: Anti-inflammatory and colorant in sun care and eye care prods.
Regulatory: FDA GRAS; not listed as approved colorant for cosmetics under FDA 21CFR §73 and 74
Manuf./Distrib. (pharm. & food): Chart
Trade names containing: Biophytex®

Calendula officinalis extract. *See* Calendula extract

C12-15 alkyl lactate
Synonyms: C12-15 alcohols lactate
Definition: Ester of lactic acid and C12-15 alcohols
Formula: H$_3$CCHOCOOR, R = C12-15 mixed linear alcohols
Properties: Liq.; sol. in oil, ethanol, propylene glycol, IPM, oleyl alcohol; partly sol. in water, glycerin; sp.gr.
  0.900-0.920; ref. index 1.4430-1.4450
Toxicology: LD50 (rat, oral) 21 ± 9.2 ml/kg; moderately irritating to eyes and skin
Uses: Emollient for topical pharmaceuticals; antitack in antiperspirants
Trade names: Ceraphyl® 41

Cal sodada. *See* Soda lime
Calx. *See* Calcium oxide
Calx sodica. *See* Soda lime
2-Camphanone. *See* Camphor

Camphor
CAS 76-22-2 (DL); 464-49-3 (D-+); EINECS 207-355-2
FEMA 2230 (D-); UN No. 1325, 2717
Synonyms: 1,7,7-Trimethylbicyclo[2.2.1] heptan-2-one; Gum camphor; Camphora; 2-Camphanone; 2-
  Bornanone; Bornan-2-one
Classification: Aliphatic cyclohexyl compd.
Definition: Ketone derived from wood of the camphor tree, *Cinnamomum camphora* or prepared synthetically
Empirical: C$_{10}$H$_{16}$O
Properties: Colorless or wh. translucent cryst. mass, char. fragrant penetrating odor, sl. bitter cooling taste;
  sol. in alc., chloroform, ether, fixed/volatile oils; sl. sol. in water; m.w. 152.24; dens. 0.992 (25/4 C); m.p.
  179.7 C; b.p. 204 C; subl. @ ambient temp./pressure; flash pt. 150 F
Precaution: Combustible; keep tightly closed away from heat; incompat. with potassium permanganate

Toxicology: LD50 (IP, mouse) 3000 mg/kg; ingestion by humans may cause nausea, vomiting, vertigo, mental confusion, delirium, coma, respiratory failure, death; may cause transient hepatic and renal damage

Uses: Medicinal-type flavoring; active OTC drug prod. ingred.; topical preps. to create cooling sensation in liniments and for inhalation; sedative, anodyne, antispasmodic, diaphoretic, anthelmintic; anesthetic, analgesic in cold sore prods.

Regulatory: FDA 21CFR §172.510, 172.515, 175.105, 27CFR §21.65, 21.151; FEMA GRAS; Japan approved; banned in U.S. for internal use

Manuf./Distrib.: Buckton Scott Ltd; R.W. Greeff; Lonza; Penta Mfg.; Quest Int'l.; Schweizerhall

Manuf./Distrib. (pharm. & food): Aldrich; Bio-Botanica; Chart; R.W. Greeff; Robeco; Spectrum Chem. Mfg.

Camphora. *See* Camphor
Cananga. *See* Cananga oil

Cananga oil
FEMA 2232
Synonyms: Cananga
Definition: Oil derived from *Cananga odorata*
Properties: Sl. woody floral odor, burning taste; sp.gr. 0.906-0.923 (20/20 C); ref. index 1.495-1.503 (20 C)
Toxicology: Sensitizer; heated to decomp., emits acrid smoke and fumes
Uses: Natural flavoring agent in pharmaceuticals
Regulatory: FDA 21CFR §182.20, GRAS; FEMA GRAS
Manuf./Distrib. (pharm. & food): Florida Treatt

Candelilla wax
CAS 8006-44-8; EINECS 232-347-0
FEMA 3479
Definition: Wax from various *Euphorbiaceae* species
Properties: Yel.-brown to translucent solid; pract. insol. in water; sparingly sol. in alcohol; sol. in acetone, benzene, carbon disulfide, hot petrol. ether, gasoline, oils, turpentine, CCl_4; dens. 0.983; m.p. 67-68 C; acid no. 10-20; sapon. no. 50-65; ref. index 1.4555
Precaution: Combustible
Toxicology: No known toxicity; heated to decomp., emits acrid smoke and irritating fumes
Uses: Protects skin from moisture loss; used in orals, topicals
Regulatory: FDA 21CFR §175.105, 175.320, 176.180, 184.1976, GRAS; FEMA GRAS; Japan approved; approved for orals, topicals
Manuf./Distrib.: Koster Keunen; Penta Mfg.; Frank B. Ross; Spectrum Chem. Mfg.; Stevenson Cooper; Strahl & Pitsch
Manuf./Distrib. (pharm. & food): Ruger; Penta Mfg.
Trade names containing: Ross Beeswax Substitute 628/5

Cane sugar. *See* Sucrose

Canola oil
CAS 8002-13-9; 120962-03-0
Synonyms: Rapeseed; Rapeseed oil
Definition: Low-erucic rapeseed oil
Properties: Oil, odorless, bland flavor; iodine no. 110-120; sapon. no. 180-193
Toxicology: Can cause acne-like skin eruptions
Uses: Lubricant
Manuf./Distrib.: ABITEC; Arista Industries; Tri-K
Manuf./Distrib. (pharm. & food): ABITEC; Arista Industries; C&T Refinery; Calgene; CanAmera Foods; Cargill; Colombus Foods; De Choix Specialty; Penta Mfg.; Spectrum Naturals; Tri-K Industries; Wensleydale Foods
Trade names: Lipex 201
See also Rapeseed oil

Canola oil (low erucic acid rapeseed oil). *See* Rapeseed oil
Cantha. *See* Canthaxanthine
Canthaxanthin. *See* Canthaxanthine; CI 40850

Canthaxanthine
CAS 514-78-3; EINECS 208-187-2
Synonyms: Cantha; Canthaxanthin; 4,4´-Diketo-β-carotene; β-Carotene-4,4´-dione; Food Orange 8; CI 40850
Definition: Synthetic non-provitamin A carotenoid
Empirical: $C_{40}H_{52}O_2$

Properties: Violet cryst. solid; sol. in chloroform and various oils; very sl. sol. in acetone; insol. in water; easily absorbed by fat; m.w. 564.86; m.p. 211-213 C (dec.)
Precaution: Sensitive to light and oxygen; store under inert gas at low temps.
Toxicology: Oral intake may cause loss of night vision; patients at risk for retinopathy should avoid excessive use; heated to decomp., emits acrid smoke and irritating fumes
Uses: Noncertifiable color additive for ingested drugs; used in sugar-coated tablets to impart a peach to red color; also in oil, aq. sol'ns., gelatin capsules
Regulatory: FDA 21CFR §73.75, 73.1075; Europe listed; UK approved
Manuf./Distrib.: Fluka
Manuf./Distrib. (pharm. & food): Am. Roland
Trade names containing: Canthaxanthin Beadlets 10%
See also CI 40850

CAP. *See* Cellulose acetate phthalate; Cellulose acetate propionate
Capraldehyde. *See* Decanal

Capric acid
CAS 334-48-5; EINECS 206-376-4
FEMA 2364
Synonyms: Decanoic acid; n-Decanoic acid; Decoic acid; Decylic acid; n-Capric acid; Carboxylic acid C_{10}
Classification: Fatty acid
Empirical: $C_{10}H_{20}O_2$
Formula: $CH_3(CH_2)_8COOH$
Properties: White crystals, unpleasant odor; sol. in org. solvs.; insol. in water; m.w. 172.27; dens. 0.8858 (40 C); m.p. 31.5 C; b.p. 270 C; ref. index 1.4288 (40 C)
Precaution: Combustible
Toxicology: LD50 (IV, mouse) 129 mg/kg; poison by IV route; mutagenic data; skin irritant; heated to decomp., emits acrid smoke and irritating fumes
Uses: Citrus-like flavoring agent
Regulatory: FDA 21CFR §172.860; FEMA GRAS
Manuf./Distrib.: Akzo; Aldrich; Henkel/Emery; Mirachem Srl; Procter & Gamble; Witco
Manuf./Distrib. (pharm. & food): Acme-Hardesty; Aldrich

n-Capric acid. *See* Capric acid
Capric aldehyde. *See* Decanal
Caprinaldehyde. *See* Decanal

Caproic acid
CAS 142-62-1; EINECS 205-550-7
FEMA 2559; UN No. 1760
Synonyms: Carboxylic acid C-6; Hexanoic acid; Hexoic acid; Butylacetic acid; Pentylformic acid
Empirical: $C_6H_{12}O_2$
Formula: $CH_3(CH_2)_4COOH$
Properties: Colorless oily liq., odor of Limburger cheese; very sol. in ether, fixed oils; sl. sol. in water; m.w. 116.18; dens. 0.9295 (20/20 C); f.p. -3.4 C; b.p. 205 C; flash pt. (COC) 215 F; ref. index 1.415-1.418
Precaution: DOT: Corrosive material; combustible
Toxicology: No known toxicity
Uses: Mfg. of pharmaceuticals; synthetic flavoring agent
Regulatory: FDA 21CFR §172.515; FEMA GRAS; Japan approved as flavoring
Manuf./Distrib.: Aldrich; Chisso Am.; Janssen Chimica; Penta Mfg.; Schweizerhall; Spectrum Chem. Mfg.
Manuf./Distrib. (pharm. & food): Acme-Hardesty; Aldrich

Caproic acid allyl ester. *See* Allyl caproate
γ-Caprolactone. *See* γ-Hexalactone
Capryl alcohol. *See* Caprylic alcohol
Caprylaldehyde. *See* n-Octanal

Caprylic acid
CAS 124-07-2; EINECS 204-677-5
FEMA 2799
Synonyms: n-Octanoic acid; Octanoic acid; Octoic acid; n-Octylic acid; C-8 acid
Classification: Fatty acid
Empirical: $C_8H_{16}O_2$
Formula: $CH_3(CH_2)_6COOH$
Properties: Colorless leaf or oily liq.; unpleasant odor; sl. sol. in water; sol. in alcohol, chloroform, ether, carbon disulfide, petrol. ether, glacial acetic acid; m.w. 144.21; dens. 0.91 (20/4 C); m.p. 16 C; b.p. 237.5 C; ref.

Caprylic acid, 1,2,3-propanetriyl ester

index 1.4280

Toxicology: LD50 (oral, rat) 10,080 mg/kg; moderately toxic by intravenous route; mildly toxic by ingestion; skin irritant; yields irritating vapors which can cause coughing; heated to decomp., emits acrid smoke and irritating fumes

Uses: Mfg. of drugs; flavoring agent

Regulatory: FDA 21CFR §172.210, 172.860, 173.340, 175.105, 175.320, 176.170, 176.200, 176.210, 177.1010, 177.1200, 177.2260, 177.2600, 177.2800, 178.3570, 178.3910, 184.1025, 186.1025,GRAS; GRAS as indirect additive; FEMA GRAS; BP compliance

Manuf./Distrib.: Akzo; Aldrich; Henkel/Emery; Procter & Gamble; Spectrum Chem. Mfg.; Unichema

Manuf./Distrib. (pharm. & food): Acme-Hardesty; Aldrich

Caprylic acid, 1,2,3-propanetriyl ester. *See* Tricaprylin
Caprylic acid sodium salt. *See* Sodium caprylate

Caprylic alcohol

CAS 111-87-5; EINECS 203-917-6

FEMA 2800

Synonyms: n-Octyl alcohol; pri-Octyl alcohhol; Heptyl carbinol; 1-Octanol; n-Octanol; C-8 alcohols; Alcohol C-8; Capryl alcohol

Classification: Fatty alcohol

Empirical: $C_8H_{18}O$

Formula: $CH_3(CH_2)_6CH_2OH$

Properties: Colorless liq., fresh orange-rose odor, sl. herbaceous taste; sol. in water; misc. in alcohol, ether, and chloroform; m.w. 130.26; dens. 0.827; m.p. -16.7 C; b.p. 194.5 C; flash pt. 178 F; ref. index 1.429 (20 C)

Precaution: Combustible liq. when exposed to heat or flame; can react with oxidizers

Toxicology: LD50 (oral, mouse) 1790 mg/kg; poison by intravenous route; moderately toxic by ingestion; skin irritant

Uses: Citrus synthetic flavoring agent

Regulatory: FDA 21CFR §172.230, 172.515 (only for encapsulating lemon, dist. lime, orange, peppermint, and spearmint oils), 172.864, 173.280, 175.105, 175.300, 176.210, 177.1010, 177.1200, 177.2800, 178.3480; FEMA GRAS

Manuf./Distrib.: Albemarle; Aldrich; M. Michel; Penta Mfg.; Schweizerhall; Spectrum Chem. Mfg.; Union Camp; Van Waters & Rogers; Vista

Manuf./Distrib. (pharm. & food): Aldrich; Penta Mfg.

Trade names: Nacol® 8-97; Nacol® 8-99

Caprylic aldehyde. *See* n-Octanal

Caprylic/capric diglyceryl succinate

Classification: Mixed ester

Definition: Mixed ester of diglycerin with caprylic, capric, and succinic acids

Uses: Emollient, suspending agent for pharmaceutical topicals

Caprylic/capric/disuccinic triglyceride

Uses: Emollient, suspending agent for pharmaceutical topicals, cream and liq. emulsions, oral suspensions, and capsules

Trade names: Miglyol® 829

Caprylic/capric glycerides

CAS 26402-26-6

Definition: Mixture of mono-, di-, and triglycerides of caprylic and capric acids

Uses: Solv. for lipophilic ingreds.; solubilizer, carrier for lipophilic drugs

Trade names: Imwitor® 742; Witafrol® 7420

Caprylic/capric/lauric triglyceride

CAS 68991-68-4

Definition: Mixed triester of glycerin with caprylic, capric and lauric acids

Uses: Emollient, solv., carrier, fixative, and extender for pharmaceutical and nutritional applics.

Trade names: Captex® 350

Caprylic/capric/linoleic triglyceride

CAS 67701-28-4

Definition: Mixed triester of glycerin with caprylic, capric, and linoleic acids

Uses: Emollient, solv., carrier, fixative, and extender for pharmaceutical and nutritional applics.

Trade names: Captex® 810A; Captex® 810D; Miglyol® 818

Caprylic/capric/oleic triglyceride

CAS 67701-28-4

Caprylic/capric/stearic triglyceride
Definition: Mixed triester of glycerin with caprylic, capric and stearic acids
Uses: Ointment base, emollient, moisturizer, stabilizer; filler/carrier for gelatin capsules
Trade names: Softisan® 378

Caprylic/capric triglyceride
CAS 65381-09-1; 85409-09-2; 73398-61-5; EINECS 265-724-3
Synonyms: Octanoic/decanoic acid triglyceride
Definition: Mixed triester of glycerin and caprylic and capric acids
Uses: Emollient, solubilizer, suspending agent in pharmaceutical topicals; carrier/vehicle
Regulatory: Approved for topicals
Trade names: Aldo® MCT KFG; Aldo® TC; Calgene CC-33; Calgene CC-33-F; Calgene CC-33-L; Calgene
   CC-33-S; Captex® 300; Captex® 355; Crodamol GTCC; Estasan GT 8-40 3578; Estasan GT 8-60 3575;
   Estasan GT 8-60 3580; Estasan GT 8-65 3577; Estasan GT 8-65 3581; Estasan GT 8-70 3579; Labrafac®
   LIPO; Labrafac® Lipophile WL 1349; Lexol® GT-855; Lexol® GT-865; Miglyol® 810; Miglyol® 812;
   Myritol® 312; Myritol® 318; Neobee® 1053; Neobee® M-5; Neobee® O; Pelemol® CCT; Standamul® 318;
   Standamul® 7105
Trade names containing: Miglyol® Gel B; Miglyol® Gel T; Palma-Sperse® Type 250-S No. 65322; Palma-
   Sperse® Type 250A/50 D-S No. 65221; Phosal® 53 MCT

Caprylic/capric triglyceride PEG-4 esters
Definition: Complex mixture formed from transesterification of caprylic/capric triglyceride and PEG-4
Uses: Hydrophilic oil for pharmaceutical creams, lotions, ointments
Trade names: Labrafac® Hydro; Labrafac® Hydro WL 1219

Capryloyl animal collagen amino acids. *See* Capryloyl collagen amino acids

Capryloyl collagen amino acids
CAS 68989-52-6
Synonyms: Capryloyl animal collagen amino acids
Definition: Condensation prod. of caprylic acid chloride and collagen amino acids
Uses: Antimicrobial, antiseborrheic, antiacneic, antiseptic for dermal preps.
Trade names: Lipacide C8CO

Caprylyl/capryl glucoside
CAS 68515-73-1
Classification: Alkyl glucoside
Formula: $[CH_2(OH)_4O]_xOR$, R = blend of caprylyl and capryl radicals
Uses: Foaming surfactant, solubilizer for dermopharmaceutical prods.
Trade names: Oramix® CG 110-60

Capsicin. *See* Capsicum oleoresin

Capsicum; EINECS 297-599-6 (*C. annuum* extract)
FEMA 2266
Synonyms: Cayenne; Cayenne pepper; Red pepper
Definition: Plant material derived from dried ripe fruit of *Capsicum frutescens* or *C. annuum*
Toxicology: In large doses, can cause diarrhea and weight loss
Uses: Natural flavoring agent; OTC drug active ingred.
Regulatory: FDA 21CFR §182.10, GRAS; FEMA GRAS; Japan approved
Manuf./Distrib. (pharm. & food): Bio-Botanica; Dr. Madis; Ruger

Capsicum extract
CAS 84625-29-6; EINECS 288-920-0
FEMA 2233
Synonyms: Capsicum frutescens extract
Definition: Extract from *Capsicum frutescens*
Uses: Natural flavoring agent
Regulatory: FDA §182.20, GRAS; FEMA GRAS

Capsicum frutescens extract. *See* Capsicum extract

Capsicum oleoresin
CAS 8023-77-6
Synonyms: Capsicin; Oleoresin capsicum Africanus
Definition: Resinous extract of *Capsicum frutescens*
Uses: Natural flavoring for OTC drugs, orals; counter-irritant in external analgesic prods.
Regulatory: FDA 21CFR §182.20; approved for orals

Captan

CAS 133-06-2; EINECS 205-087-0

Synonyms: cis-N-[(Trichloromethyl) thio]-4-cyclohexene-1,2-dicarboximide; N-Trichloromethylthio-4-cyclohexene-1,2-dicarboximide; N-Trichloromethylthiotetrahydrophthalimide

Classification: Organic compd.

Empirical: $C_9H_8Cl_3NO_2S$

Properties: Crystal, odorless; pract. insol. in water; partly sol. in benzene, chloroform, tetrachloroethane; m.w. 300.59; dens. 1.74; m.p. 178 C

Toxicology: Moderately toxic by inhalation; irritant; TLV 5 mg/m³ of air; LD50 (rat, oral) 9000 mg/kg

Uses: Antimicrobial preservative for topical pharmaceuticals

Regulatory: FDA 21CFR §176.170

Manuf./Distrib.: Industrias Quimicas del Valles SA; R.T. Vanderbilt

Trade names: Vancide® 89 RE

Caramel

CAS 8028-89-5; EINECS 232-435-9

FEMA 2235

Synonyms: Burnt sugar coloring; Burnt sugar; Caramel color; Natural Brown 10

Definition: Conc. sol'n. obtained from heating sucrose or glucose sol'ns.

Properties: Dk. brn. to black liq. or solid, char. burnt sugar odor, pleasant bitter taste; sol. in water (colloidal); sol. in dil. alc. up to 55% (v/v); insol. in most org. solvs.; sp.gr. 1.25-1.38

Toxicology: Mutagenic data; may reduce wh. blood cells and destroy vitamin B_6; heated to decomp., emits acrid smoke and irritating fumes

Uses: Colorant, sweetener, synthetic flavoring for pharmaceuticals; used in orals, rectals, topicals, cough syrups, placebo sol'ns.; soothing agent in skin lotions

Regulatory: FDA 21CFR §73.85, 73.1085, 73.2085, 182.1235, GRAS; FEMA GRAS; Japan restricted; Europe listed; UK approved; approved for orals, rectals, topicals; permanently listed by FDA; USP/NF compliance

Manuf./Distrib. (pharm. & food): Booths; Bradleys; Cairn Foods; Cerestar Int'l.; Crompton & Knowles; Dena AG; Ellis & Everard; Flavors of N. Am.; Foote & Jenkins; Frutarom; Hershey Import; Kraft; Moore Fine Foods; Pacific Foods; Penta Mfg.; Ruger; Spectrum Chem. Mfg.; Universal Flavors

Trade names: Acid Proof Caramel Powd.; B&C Caramel Powd.; Caramel Color Double Strength; Caramel Color Single Strength; Double Strength Acid Proof Caramel Colour; Powdered Caramel Color 986010; Powdered Caramel Color, Acid Proof; Powdered Caramel Colour Non-Ammoniated-All Natural T-717; Single Strength Acid Proof Caramel Colour; Unisweet Caramel

Caramel color. *See* Caramel

Caraway oil

CAS 8000-42-8; EINECS 288-921-6 (extract)

FEMA 2238

Synonyms: Carum carvi oil

Definition: Volatile oil distilled from the dried ripe fruit of *Carum carvi*, contg. carvone, d-limonene

Properties: Colorless to pale yel. clear oily liq., caraway odor and taste; darkens and thickens with age; sol. in 8 vols. 80% alcohol; pract. insol. in water; dens. 0.900-0.910 (25/25 C); ref. index 1.485-1.497 (20 C)

Precaution: Keep cool, well closed; protect from light

Toxicology: LD50 (oral, rat) 3500 mg/kg; mod. toxic by ingestion, skin contact; skin irritant; mutagenic data; heated to decomp., emits acrid smoke and irritating fumes

Uses: Natural flavoring agent; carminative expelling gas from alimentary canal; relieves colic, flatulence; stimulant

Regulatory: FDA 21CFR §182.10, 182.20, GRAS; FEMA GRAS; Japan approved; BP compliance

Manuf./Distrib.: Spectrum Chem. Mfg.

Manuf./Distrib. (pharm. & food): Chart; Florida Treatt; Spectrum Chem. Mfg.

Carbamide. *See* Urea
Carbamide peroxide. *See* Urea peroxide
Carbamidic acid. *See* Urea
Carbanthrene blue. *See* D&C Blue No. 9
Carbinol. *See* Methyl alcohol
'Carbitol'. *See* Ethoxydiglycol

Carbomer

CAS 9007-16-3; 9003-01-4; 9007-17-4; 9007-20-9; 76050-42-5

Synonyms: Carboxypolymethylene

Definition: Homopolymer of acrylic acid crosslinked with an allyl ether of pentaerythritol or an allyl ether of sucrose

Properties: Wh. fluffy powd., odorless; hygroscopic; dens. 1.41
Toxicology: Essentially nontoxic
Uses: Emulsifier, thickener, suspending agent, dispersant for pharmaceuticals; enteric film-former; forms gels or aq. ointments at higher concs.; used in orals, rectals, topicals, prolonged action preps.; as bulk laxative
Usage level: 0.4% (suspending agent), 0.5-5% (aq. ointment base)
Regulatory: FDA approved for orals, rectals, topicals; BP compliance
Trade names: Acritamer® 934; Acritamer® 934P; Acritamer® 940; Acritamer® 941; Carbopol® 910; Carbopol® 934; Carbopol® 934P; Carbopol® 940; Carbopol® 941; Carbopol® 971P; Carbopol® 974P; Carbopol® 980; Carbopol® 981; Carbopol® 2984; Carbopol® 5984

Carbomer 910
CAS 9003-01-4
Definition: Polymer of acrylic acid crosslinked with allyl ether of pentaerythritol
Properties: Wh. fluffy powd., sl. char. odor; hygroscopic; when neutralized with alkali hydroxides or with amines, dissolves in water, alcohol, and glycerin; m.w. nominally 750,000; visc. 3000-7000 cps (1% aq. disp.); pH 3 (1% disp.)
Uses: Suspending agent and/or visc.-increasing agent for pharmaceuticals
Regulatory: USP/NF compliance
Manuf./Distrib.: Spectrum Chem. Mfg.

Carbomer 934
CAS 9003-01-4; 9007-16-3
Definition: Polymer of acrylic acid crosslinked with allyl ether of sucrose
Properties: Wh. fluffy powd., sl. char. odor; hygroscopic; when neutralized with alkali hydroxides or with amines, dissolves in water, alcohol, and glycerin; m.w. nominally 3,000,000; visc. 30,500-39,400 cps (0.5% aq. disp.); pH 3 (1% disp.)
Toxicology: No known toxicity
Uses: Thickener, suspending agent, visc.-increasing agent, dispersant, emulsifier; used in orals, rectals, topicals; reacts with fat particles to form thick stable emulsions of oils in water
Regulatory: FDA approved for orals, rectals, topicals; USP/NF compliance
Manuf./Distrib. (pharm. & food): Spectrum Chem. Mfg.

Carbomer 934P
CAS 9003-01-4
Synonyms: Carpolene
Definition: Polymer of acrylic acid crosslinked with allyl ether of sucrose
Properties: Wh. fluffy powd., sl. char. odor; hygroscopic; when neutralized with alkali hydroxides or with amines, dissolves in water, alcohol, and glycerin; m.w. nominally 3,000,000; visc. 29,400-39,400 cps (0.5% aq. disp.); pH 3 (1% disp.)
Uses: Emulsifying agent, suspending and/or visc. agent, thickening agent for pharmaceuticals
Regulatory: USP/NF compliance
Manuf./Distrib.: BFGoodrich; Spectrum Chem. Mfg.

Carbomer 940
CAS 9003-01-4; 9007-17-4
Definition: Polymer of acrylic acid crosslinked with allyl ether of pentaerythritol
Properties: Wh. fluffy powd., sl. char. odor; hygroscopic; when neutralized with alkali hydroxides or with amines, dissolves in water, alcohol, and glycerin; m.w. nominally 4,000,000; visc. 40,000-60,000 cps (0.5% aq. disp.); pH 3 (1% disp.)
Toxicology: No known toxicity
Uses: Thickener, suspending agent, dispersant, emulsifier; used in ophthalmics, topicals; reacts with fat particles to form thick stable emulsions of oils in water
Regulatory: FDA approved for ophthalmics, topicals; USP/NF compliance
Manuf./Distrib.: Spectrum Chem. Mfg.

Carbomer 941
CAS 9003-01-4
Definition: Polymer of acrylic acid crosslinked with allyl ether of pentaerythritol
Properties: Wh. fluffy powd., sl. char. odor; hygroscopic; when neutralized with alkali hydroxides or with amines, dissolves in water, alcohol, and glycerin; m.w. nominally 1,250,000; visc. 4000-11,000 cps (0.5% aq. disp.); pH 3 (1% disp.)
Toxicology: No known toxicity
Uses: Thickener, suspending agent, dispersant, emulsifier; used in topicals; reacts with fat particles to form thick stable emulsions of oils in water
Regulatory: FDA approved for topicals; USP/NF compliance
Manuf./Distrib.: Spectrum Chem. Mfg.

Carbomer 1342
  Definition: Polymer of acrylic acid crosslinked with allyl ether of pentaerythritol
  Properties: Wh. fluffy powd., sl. char. odor; hygroscopic; when neutralized with alkali hydroxides or with amines, dissolves in water, alcohol, and glycerin; visc. 9500-26,500 cps (1% aq.disp.); pH 3 (1% disp.)
  Uses: Suspending agent and/or visc.-increasing agent for pharmaceuticals
  Regulatory: USP/NF compliance
  Manuf./Distrib.: Spectrum Chem. Mfg.

Carbon, activated
  CAS 7440-44-0; 64365-11-3; EINECS 231-153-3
  Synonyms: Active carbon; Activated charcoal; Decolorizing carbon
  Empirical: C
  Properties: Black porous solid, coarse gran., or powd.; insol. in water, org. solvs.; m.w. 12.01; dens. 0.08-0.5
  Precaution: Flamm. solid; combustible exposed to heat; dust is flamm. and explosive when exposed to heat, flame, or oxides
  Toxicology: Dust irritant, esp. to eyes and mucous membranes
  Uses: Activated charcoal in medicine as antidote, adsorptive, for odor control; refining of pharmaceutical chemicals
  Regulatory: FDA 21CFR §240.361, 240.365, 240.401, 240.405, 240.527, 240.527a, GRAS; BATF 27CFR §240.1051; USDA 9CFR §318.7
  Manuf./Distrib.: Allied-Signal; Calgon Carbon; Ceca SA; Elf Atochem N. Am.; Norit Am.; United Catalysts; Westvaco
  Manuf./Distrib. (pharm. & food): Aldrich; Calgon Carbon
  Trade names: Calgon® Type 114A AWD; Calgon® Type ADP; Calgon® Type APA; Calgon® Type BL®; Calgon® Type CAL®; Calgon® Type CPG®; Calgon® Type CPG® LF; Calgon® Type OL®; Calgon® Type PWA®; Calgon® Type RB®; Calgon® Type RC®; Calgon® Type SGL®

Carbonate magnesium. *See* Magnesium carbonate

Carbon dioxide
  CAS 124-38-9; EINECS 204-696-9
  UN No. 1013, 2187, 1845
  Synonyms: Carbonic acid gas; Carbonic anhydride
  Classification: Gas
  Empirical: CO_2
  Properties: Colorless gas, odorless; sol. 1 vol. dissolves in about 1 vol. of water; m.w. 44.01; m.p. subl. @ -78.5 C
  Precaution: Noncombustible; various dusts explode in CO_2 atmospheres
  Toxicology: TLV 5000 ppm; asphyxiant at > 10%; experimental teratogen; skin contact can cause burns
  Uses: Provides air displacement in inhalants
  Regulatory: FDA 21CFR §169.115, 169.140, 169.150, 184.120, GRAS, 193.45 (modified atm. for pest control); USDA 9CFR §318.7, 381.147; BATF 27CFR 240.1051; Japan approved; Europe listed; UK approved; FDA approved for inhalants; USP/NF, BP, Ph.Eur. compliance
  Manuf./Distrib.: Air Prods.; BOC Gases; Carbonic Ind.; Coastal; Great Western; Nissan Chem. Ind.; Norsk Hydro AS; Scott Spec. Gases; Showa Denko
  Manuf./Distrib. (pharm. & food): ADM Ethanol Sales; Aldrich

Carbonic acid, ammonium salt. *See* Ammonium carbonate
Carbonic acid calcium salt (1:1). *See* Calcium carbonate; CI 77220
Carbonic acid dipotassium salt. *See* Potassium carbonate
Carbonic acid disodium salt. *See* Sodium carbonate
Carbonic acid gas. *See* Carbon dioxide
Carbonic acid magnesium salt. *See* Magnesium carbonate
Carbonic acid, monoammonium salt. *See* Ammonium bicarbonate
Carbonic acid monopotassium salt. *See* Potassium bicarbonate
Carbonic acid monosodium salt. *See* Sodium bicarbonate
Carbonic acid, 1,2-propylene glycol ester. *See* Propylene carbonate
Carbonic anhydride. *See* Carbon dioxide
Carbonyldiamide. *See* Urea
Carboxybenzene. *See* Benzoic acid
Carboxylic acid C$_5$. *See* 2-Methylbutyric acid
Carboxylic acid C-6. *See* Caproic acid; Diethylacetic acid
Carboxylic acid C$_{10}$. *See* Capric acid
Carboxylic acid C$_{18}$. *See* Stearic acid

Carboxymethylcellulose
CAS 9000-11-7
FEMA 2239
Synonyms: Cellulose carboxymethyl ether
Classification: Synthetic gum
Toxicology: Shown to cause cancer in animals when ingested; toxicity on skin not known; may cause immune responses
Uses: Flavoring agent; used in orals, dentifrices; medicinally as laxative and antacid
Regulatory: FDA approved for orals; FEMA GRAS; BP compliance
Manuf./Distrib.: Aqualon; Chemcentral; Hercules; Hoechst Celanese; Punda Mercantile; Van Waters & Rogers
Manuf./Distrib. (pharm. & food): Aldrich; Integra; Ruger

Carboxymethylcellulose calcium. *See* Calcium carboxymethyl cellulose

Carboxymethylcellulose sodium
CAS 9004-32-4; EINECS 265-995-8; 215-185-5; 201-178-4
Synonyms: CMC; Cellulose gum; Cellulose carboxymethyl ether sodium salt; Carmellose sodium; Sodium carboxymethylcellulose; Sodium CMC
Definition: Sodium salt of the carboxylic acid R-O-CH$_2$COONa
Formula: $[(C_6H_7O_2(OH)_2OCH_2COOH]_n$
Properties: Colorless or wh. powd. or gran., odorless; hygroscopic; water sol. depends on degree of substitution; insol. in org. liqs.; m.w. 21,000-500,000; visc. various; m.p. > 300 C; pH 6.5-8.5 (1%)
Toxicology: Nontoxic; LD50 (oral, rat) 27,000 mg/kg
Uses: Suspending agent, tablet binder/excipient, visc.-increasing agent, coating agent; used in dentals, injectables, orals, topicals, vaginals, mouth and throat preps. such as troches, saliva substitutes, lozenges
Regulatory: FDA 21CFR §133.134, 133.178, 133.179, 150.141, 150.161, 173.310, 175.105, 175.300, 182.70, 182.1745, GRAS; USDA 9CFR 318.7, limitation 1.5%, must be added dry; 9CFR 381.147; Japan restricted (2% max.); Europe listed; UK approved; approved for dentals, injectables, orals, topicals; USP/NF, BP, Ph.Eur. compliance
Manuf./Distrib.: Aldrich; Aqualon; Courtaulds Water Soluble Polymers; J.W.S. Delavau; FMC; Hercules
Manuf./Distrib. (pharm. & food): Am. Roland; Multi-Kem; Robeco; Spectrum Chem. Mfg.
Trade names: Aqualon® Cellulose Gum; Cekol® 30; Cekol® 150; Cekol® 300; Cekol® 700; Cekol® 2000; Cekol® 4000; Cekol® 10000; Cekol® 30000; Cekol® 50000; Cellogen HP; CMC Daicel 1150; CMC Daicel 1160; CMC Daicel 1220; CMC Daicel 1260; Nymcel® ZSB-10; Nymcel® ZSB-16; Nymcel® ZSD-16; Ticalose® 15; Ticalose® 30; Ticalose® 75; Ticalose® 100; Ticalose® 150 R; Ticalose® 700 R; Ticalose® 750; Ticalose® 1200; Ticalose® 2000 R; Ticalose® 2500; Ticalose® 4000; Ticalose® 4500; Ticalose® 5000 R; TIC Pretested® CMC 2500 S; TIC Pretested® CMC PH-2500; Tylose® C, CB Series

N-(Carboxymethyl)N,N-dimethyl-3-[(1-oxododecyl)amino]-1-propanaminium hydroxide, inner salt. *See* Lauramidopropyl betaine

Carboxymethylmethylcellulose
Uses: Thickener, stabilizer, rheology control agent, film-former, suspending agent, water-retention aid, binder

Carboxymethyl starch sodium salt. *See* Sodium starch glycolate
Carboxyphenol. *See* Ethylparaben
Carboxypolymethylene. *See* Carbomer
Cardam fruit. *See* Cardamom

Cardamom
FEMA 2240
Synonyms: Grains of paradise; Cardamom fruit; Cardam fruit; Cardamom seed
Definition: Dried ripe seeds of *Elettaria cardamomum*
Toxicology: No known toxicity
Uses: Aromatic and flavoring agent used in orals; carminative; breaks up intestinal gas; stomachic
Regulatory: FDA approved for orals; FEMA GRAS; BP, JP compliance
Manuf./Distrib. (pharm. & food): Bio-Botanica

Cardamom fruit. *See* Cardamom

Cardamom oil
CAS 8000-66-6; EINECS 288-922-1 (extract)
FEMA 2241
Synonyms: Elettaria cardamomum oil; Cardamon oil; Cardamom seed oil
Definition: Volatile oil obtained from the dried ripe seeds of *Elettaria cardamomum*, contg. eucalyptol, sabinene, etc.

Cardamom seed

Properties: Colorless to pale yel. oily liq., aromatic penetrating odor of cardamom, pungent taste; sol. in ether; misc. with alcohol; insol. in water; dens. 0.917-0.947 (25/4 C); ref. index 1.4630-1.4660 (20 C)
Toxicology: Mutagenic data; heated to decomp., emits acrid smoke and fumes
Uses: Natural flavoring agent; carminative
Regulatory: FDA 21CFR §182.10, 182.20, GRAS; FEMA GRAS; Japan approved; BP compliance
Manuf./Distrib. (pharm. & food): Chart; Pierre Chauvet; Florida Treatt

Cardamom seed. *See* Cardamom
Cardamom seed oil. *See* Cardamom oil
Cardamon oil. *See* Cardamom oil
Carmellose calcium. *See* Calcium carboxymethyl cellulose
Carmellose sodium. *See* Carboxymethylcellulose sodium

Carmine
CAS 1390-65-4; 8022-93-3; EINECS 215-724-4
FEMA 2242
Synonyms: CI 75470; Alum lake of carminic acid; Carminic acid; Cochineal extract; Natural Red 4
Definition: Aluminum lake of the coloring agent, cochineal; cochineal is a natural pigment derived from the dried female insect *Coccus cacti*
Empirical: $C_{22}H_{20}O_{13}$
Properties: Bright red cryst., easily powdered; sol. in alkali, borax; insol. in dilute acids; sl. sol. in hot water; m.w. 492.39; decomp. @ 250 C
Toxicology: Suspected of causing food intolerance; may cause allergic cheilitis, occupational asthma in sensitive patients; heated to decomp., emits acrid smoke and irritating fumes
Uses: Colorant used in oral pharmaceuticals, medicine (pill coatings); as marker to measure gastrointestinal transit time (up to 500 mg dose)
Regulatory: FDA 21CFR §73.100, must be pasteurized to destroy *Salmonella*, 73.1100, 73.2087; FEMA GRAS; Europe listed; UK approved; FDA approved for orals
Manuf./Distrib.: Aceto; R.W. Greeff; Hilton Davis; Penta Mfg.; Spectrum Chem. Mfg.; Warner-Jenkinson
Manuf./Distrib. (pharm. & food): Aldrich; Allchem Int'l.; Am. Fruit Processors; Am. Roland; Burlington Bio-Medical; Crompton & Knowles; Ellis & Everard; Food Additives & Ingreds.; Hilton Davis; Mallinckrodt; MLG Enterprises; Penta Mfg.; Quest Int'l.; Ruger; Spectrum Chem. Mfg.; Universal Flavors; Warner-Jenkinson
Trade names: Carmacid Y; Carmine FG; Carmine PG; Carmine Powd. 272010, 272015, 272020; Carmine Powd. WS; Carmine XY/UF; Carminic Acid 90; Carmisol A; Carmisol NA; Natural Liquid AP Carmine Colorant; Natural Liquid Carmine Colorant (Type 100, 50, and Simple); Natural Soluble Carmine Powd.; Natural Soluble Powder AP Carmine Colorant
Trade names containing: Carmine AS; Red Soluble Powd. Natural Colorant
See also CI 75470

Carmine solution
CAS 8001-80-7
Uses: Used in orals
Regulatory: FDA approved for orals

Carminic acid. *See* Carmine; CI 75470

Carnauba
CAS 8015-86-9; EINECS 232-399-4
Synonyms: Brazil wax; Carnauba wax; Cera carnauba
Definition: Exudate from leaves of Brazilian wax palm tree *Copernicia prunifera*
Properties: Yel. greenish brown lumps, solid, char. odor; sol. in ether, alkalis, warm benzene, warm chloroform, toluene; sl. sol. in boiling alcohol; insol. in water; dens. 0.995 (15/15 C); m.p. 82-85.5 C; acid no. 2-7; sapon. no. 78-89; ref. index 1.4500
Precaution: Protect from light
Toxicology: Essentially nontoxic; heated to decomp., emits acrid smoke and irritating fumes
Uses: Coating agent for use in orals, topicals; plasticizer for dental compds.
Regulatory: FDA 21CFR §175.320, 184.1978, GRAS; Japan approved; Europe listed (permitted only in chocolate prods.); UK approved; approved for orals, topicals; USP/NF, BP, Ph.Eur., JP compliance
Manuf./Distrib.: Penta Mfg.; Spectrum Chem. Mfg.; Stevenson Cooper; Strahl & Pitsch
Manuf./Distrib. (pharm. & food): Aldrich; Penta Mfg.; C.E. Roeper GmbH; Ruger
Trade names: Koster Keunen Carnauba; Koster Keunen Carnauba, Powd.; Ross Carnauba Wax
Trade names containing: Sterotex® C

Carnauba wax. *See* Carnauba
Carob bean gum. *See* Locust bean gum
Carob flour. *See* Locust bean gum

Carotene
CAS 7235-40-7; EINECS 230-636-6
Synonyms: β-Carotene; Provitamin A; Food Orange 5; Natural Yellow 26; CI 40800; CI 75130
Empirical: $C_{40}H_{56}$
Properties: Purple hexagonal prisms, red leaflets; sol. in carbon disulfide, benzene, chloroform; moderately sol. in ether, petrol. ether, oils; pract. insol. in water; m.w. 536.89; m.p. 178-179 C
Precaution: Sensitive to alkali, air, and light; refrigerate
Toxicology: Nontoxic on skin; massive doses may cause yellowing of the skin; heated to decomp., emits acrid smoke and irritating fumes
Uses: Colorant for pharmaceuticals
Regulatory: FDA 21CFR §73.95, 73.1095, 73.2095, 166.110, 182.5245, 184.1245, GRAS; Japan restricted; Europe listed; UK approved
Manuf./Distrib.: BASF; Hoffmann-La Roche; Penta Mfg.; Schweizerhall; Spectrum Chem. Mfg.; Warner-Jenkinson
Manuf./Distrib. (pharm. & food): Aldrich; Allchem Int'l.; Am. Roland; Atomergic Chemetals; Bronson & Jacobs; Cornelius; Ellis & Everard; Henkel; Hilton Davis; Hoffmann-La Roche; Penta Mfg.; Phytone Ltd.; Produits Roche; Quest Int'l.; Quimdis; Spice King; Universal Flavors
Trade names containing: Aloe-Moist™ A; 24% Beta Carotene HS-E in Veg. Oil No. 65671; 24% Beta Carotene Semi-Solid Suspension No. 65642; 30% Beta Carotene in Veg. Oil No. 65646; Dry Beta Carotene Beadlets 10% CWS No. 65633; Dry Beta Carotene Beadlets 10% No. 65661

β-Carotene. *See* Carotene; CI 40800; CI 75130
β-Carotene-4,4'-dione. *See* Canthaxanthine
β,β-Carotene-4,4'-dione. *See* CI 40850
Carpolene. *See* Carbomer 934P
Carrageen. *See* Carrageenan

Carrageenan
CAS 9000-07-1; EINECS 232-524-2
Synonyms: Chondrus; Carrageen; Irish moss
Classification: Sulfated polysaccharide
Definition: Hydrocolloid obtained from various members of the *Gigartinaceae* or *Solieriaceae* familes of the red seaweed, *Rhodophyceae*; consists of sulfite esters of galactose and 3,6-anhydrogalactose copolymers
Properties: Yel. white powd., odorless, tasteless; sol. in hot water, hot conc. NaCl sol'n.; insol. in oils and org. solvs.
Toxicology: Poison by intravenous route; experimental tumorigen; suspected carcinogen; linked to ulcers in colon, fetal damage in test animals; heated to decomp., emits acrid smoke and fumes
Uses: Emulsifier, binder, extender, stabilizer, thickener, gelling agent, suspending agent; bulk laxative; used in orals, topicals; soothes the skin
Usage level: 1-5%
Regulatory: FDA 21CFR §172.620, 172.623, 172.626, limitation 5% polysorbate 80 in carrageenan and 500 ppm in final prod., 182.7255, GRAS; USDA 9CFR §318.7, 1.5% max. in restructured meat food prods., 381.147; ; Japan approved; JSCI, European listed; UK approved; FDA approved for orals, topicals; USP/NF compliance
Manuf./Distrib.: G Fiske & Co Ltd; FMC; Hercules
Manuf./Distrib. (pharm. & food): Browne & Dureau Int'l.; Browning; Calaga Food; Carrageenan Co.; Chart; Diamalt; G Fiske; FMC; Grindsted UK; A C Hatrick; Hercules; Honeywill & Stein; Hormel Foods; Marine Colloids; Meer; Mitsubishi; Quest Int'l.; Spectrum Chem. Mfg.; Spice King; TIC Gums
Trade names: Aquagel SP 399; CI-100; CM-80; Cracked Bleached Irish Moss; Genu® Carrageenan; Genugel® Series; Genuvisco; Soageena®; Soageena® LX7; Soageena® LX26; Soageena® WX87; Stamere® CK-S; Stamere® N-325; Stamere® N-350; Stamere® N-350 S; Stamere® NI
Trade names containing: Aloe Vera Gel Thickened FG; CI-90

Carrageenan extract
CAS 8015-95-0
FEMA 2596
Synonyms: Chondrus crispus extract; Irish moss extract; Chondrus extract
Definition: Extract of *Chondrus crispus*
Properties: Ylsh. or tan to wh. powd., odorless, mucilaginous taste; sol. in water
Toxicology: Possible carcinogen
Uses: Emulsifier used in nasals, topicals
Regulatory: FDA 21CFR §182.7255, GRAS; FEMA GRAS; FDA approved for nasals, topicals
Manuf./Distrib.: Bio-Botanica
Manuf./Distrib. (pharm. & food): Carrageenan Co.; Cheil Foods (UK); Croda Colloids; Penta Mfg.; Siber Hegner

Carthanus tinctorious oil. *See* Safflower oil
Carum carvi oil. *See* Caraway oil
(+)-Carvene. *See* d-Limonene

Carveol
CAS 99-48-9
FEMA 2247
Synonyms: p-Mentha-6,8-dien-2-ol; 1-Methyl-4-isopropenyl-6-cyclohexen-2-ol; l-Carveol
Empirical: $C_{10}H_{16}O$
Properties: M.w. 152.24; dens. 1.496; b.p. 226-227 C (15 mm); flash pt. 209 F
Toxicology: Irritant
Uses: Minty synthetic flavoring agent
Regulatory: FDA 21CFR §172.515; FEMA GRAS
Manuf./Distrib. (pharm. & food): Aldrich

l-Carveol. *See* Carveol
Carvol. *See* l-Carvone
(-)-Carvone. *See* l-Carvone

l-Carvone
CAS 6485-40-1; EINECS 229-352-5
FEMA 2249
Synonyms: 1-1-Methyl-4-isopropenyl-6-cyclohexen-2-one; 1-6,8(9)-p-Menthadien-2-one; (-)-Carvone; Carvol
Empirical: $C_{10}H_{14}O$
Properties: Colorless to pale yel. liq., spearmint odor; sol. in propylene glycol, fixed oils; misc. in alcohol; insol. in glycerin; m.w. 150.22; dens. 0.956-0.960; b.p. 227-230 C; flash pt. 192 F; ref. index 1.495-1.499
Toxicology: LD50 (oral, rat) 1640 mg/kg; mod. toxic by ingestion; heated to decomp., emits acrid smoke and irritating fumes
Uses: Minty synthetic flavoring agent
Regulatory: FDA 21CFR §172.515, 182.60, GRAS; FEMA GRAS
Manuf./Distrib.: Fluka
Manuf./Distrib. (pharm. & food): Acme-Hardesty; Aldrich; Commodity Services Int'l.; Frutarom

Carvyl acetate
CAS 97-42-7
FEMA 2250
Empirical: $C_{12}H_{18}O_2$
Properties: Colorless liq., spearmint-like odor; m.w. 194.27; dens. 0.976; b.p. 115-116 C; flash pt. 208 F
Toxicology: Irritant
Uses: Minty synthetic flavoring agent
Regulatory: FDA 21CFR §172.515; FEMA GRAS
Manuf./Distrib. (pharm. & food): Aldrich

Carvyl propionate
CAS 97-45-0
FEMA 2251
Synonyms: l-Carvyl propionate; l-p-Mentha-6,8-dien-2-yl propionate
Empirical: $C_{13}H_{20}O_2$
Properties: Colorless liq., minty/fruity odor, sweet fruity minty taste; sol. in alcohol; insol. in water; m.w. 208.30; dens. 0.952; b.p. 239 C; flash pt. 226 F
Uses: Sweet, minty synthetic flavoring agent
Regulatory: FDA 21CFR §172.515; FEMA GRAS
Manuf./Distrib. (pharm. & food): Aldrich

l-Carvyl propionate. *See* Carvyl propionate
Caryophyllic acid. *See* Eugenol

Casanthranol
CAS 8024-48-4
Uses: Stimulant in laxative prods.
Manuf./Distrib.: Bio-Botanica

Cascara extract
CAS 84650-55-5; EINECS 232-400-8
FEMA 2253
Synonyms: Rhamnus purshiana extract

Definition: Extract of dried bark of *Rhamnus purshiana*
Uses: Natural flavoring; stimulant in laxative prods.
Regulatory: FDA 21CFR §172.510; FEMA GRAS; Japan approved
Manuf./Distrib.: Bio-Botanica

Casein
CAS 9000-71-9; EINECS 232-555-1
Synonyms: Milk protein, casein
Definition: Mixt. of phosphoproteins obtained from cow's milk
Toxicology: Mild sensitive reactions in persons allergic to cow's milk
Uses: Used in slow-release and microencapsulation prods.
Regulatory: FDA 21CFR §166.110, 182.90, GRAS; Japan restricted; BP compliance
Manuf./Distrib.: Am. Casein; Browning; Ultra Additives
Manuf./Distrib. (pharm. & food): Am. Roland; Blossom Farm Prods.
See also Milk protein

Cassava starch. *See* Tapioca starch

Cassia gum
Uses: Tonic, stomachic, carminative; used in buccals
Regulatory: Japan approved; FDA approved for buccals

Cassia oil. *See* Cinnamon oil

Castor oil
CAS 1323-38-2; 8001-79-4; EINECS 232-293-8
FEMA 2263
Synonyms: Ricinus oil; Aceite de ricino; Huile de ricini; Oleum ricini; Ricini oleum; Oil of Palma Christi; Tangantangan oil
Definition: Fixed oil obtained from seeds of *Ricinus communis*
Properties: Colorless to pale yel. viscous liq., characteristic odor; sol. in alcohol; misc. with glac. acetic acid, chloroform, ether; dens. 0.961; m.p. -12 C; b.p. 313 C; flash pt. (CC) 445 F; iodine no. 83-88; sapon. no. 176-187; hyd. no. 160-168; ref. index 1.478
Precaution: Combustible when exposed to heat; spontaneous heating may occur
Toxicology: Moderately toxic by ingestion; allergen; eye irritant; purgative, laxative in large doses
Uses: Oleaginous vehicle, emollient, lubricant, plasticizer, laxative; solv. in intramuscular injectables, solid oral dosage forms, topical pharmaceuticals, capsules, emulsions; soothing to eyes; cathartic, purgative
Usage level: 0.08-23 mg (solid oral dosage forms); 5-12.5% (topicals)
Regulatory: FDA 21CFR §73.1, 172.510, 172.876, 175.300, 176.210, 177.2600, 177.2800, 178.3120, 178.3570, 178.3910, 181.22, 181.26, 181.28; FEMA GRAS; FDA approved for injectables, orals, topicals; USP/NF, BP, Ph.Eur., JP compliance
Manuf./Distrib.: Air Prods.; Amber Syn.; Arista Industries; Ashland; CasChem; Climax Performance; Degen; Fanning; Harcros; Lipo; Norman, Fox; Süd-Chemie; Van Waters & Rogers; Zeochem
Manuf./Distrib. (pharm. & food): Aldrich; Arista Industries; Ashland; CasChem; R.W. Greeff; Ruger; Spectrum Chem. Mfg.
Trade names: AA USP; Castor Oil USP; Cosmetol® X; Crystal® O; Crystal® Crown; Crystal® Crown LP; Diamond Quality®; EmCon CO; Lanaetex CO; York Krystal Kleer Castor Oil; York USP Castor Oil

Castor oil, hydrogenated. *See* Hydrogenated castor oil
Castor oil sulfated. *See* Sulfated castor oil
Castorwax. *See* Hydrogenated castor oil

Catalase
CAS 9001-05-2; EINECS 232-577-1
Classification: Oxidizing enzyme
Definition: Derived from bovine liver
Properties: M.w. $\approx$ 240,000
Toxicology: Heated to decomp., emits acrid smoke and irritating fumes
Uses: Used in treatment of wounds, skin ulcers, eczema
Regulatory: FDA 21CFR §173.135; Canada, UK, Japan approved

Catechol. *See* Pyrocatechol
Caustic antimony. *See* Antimony trichloride
Caustic potash. *See* Potassium hydroxide
Caustic soda. *See* Sodium hydroxide
Cayenne. *See* Capsicum
Cayenne pepper. *See* Capsicum

CCC. *See* Chlorophyllin-copper complex

C10-30 cholesterol/lanosterol esters
Definition: Mixture of esters derived from reaction of C10-30 acids with a blend of cholesterol and lanosterol
Uses: Emollient, lubricant for pharmaceuticals
Trade names: Super Sterol Ester

Cedro oil. *See* Lemon oil
Cellacephate. *See* Cellulose acetate phthalate

Cellulase
CAS 9012-54-8; EINECS 232-734-4
Classification: Enzyme complex
Definition: Derived from *Aspergillus niger*
Properties: Off-white powd.; m.w. ≈ 31,000
Precaution: Refrigerate
Uses: Enzyme; digestive aid in medicine; aids bacteria in the hydrolysis of cellulose
Regulatory: FDA 21C FR §173.120, GRAS; UK, Japan approved
Manuf./Distrib.: Schweizerhall; Spectrum Chem. Mfg.
Trade names: Cellulase 4000; Cellulase AP 3; Cellulase T-AP6; Cellulase Tr Conc.; Cellulase TRL

Celluloid. *See* Nitrocellulose

Cellulose
CAS 9004-34-6; 65996-61-4; EINECS 232-674-9
Synonyms: Wood pulp, bleached; Crystalline cellulose; α-Cellulose; Cotton fiber; Cellulose powder; Powdered cellulose; Cellulose gel
Definition: Natural polysaccharide derived from plant fibers
Properties: Colorless to wh. solid, odorless; sl. sol. in sodium hdyroxide sol'n.; insol. in water, dil. acids, and org. solvs.; m.w. 160,000-560,000; dens. ≈ 1.5
Toxicology: No known toxicity; cannot be digested by humans; nuisance dust; heated to decomp., emits acrid smoke and irritating fumes
Uses: Tablet and capsule diluent; tablet disintegrant; suspending and/or visc.-increasing agent; filtering aid, sorbent (powd.); used in buccals, dentals, orals; bulk laxative effect
Usage level: 5-20% (tablet binders, disintegrants), 30% (capsule diluent)
Regulatory: FDA 21CFR §177.2260; GRAS; Europe listed; use in baby foods not permitted in UK; FDA approved for buccals, dentals, orals; powdered USP/NF, BP, Ph.Eur., JP compliance
Manuf./Distrib.: Degussa; Eastman; FMC Int'l.; Hercules Ltd; Edw. Mendell; Spectrum Chem. Mfg.
Manuf./Distrib. (pharm. & food): Aldrich; Allchem Int'l.; Am. Roland; Bioengineering AG; Courtaulds; Croxton & Garry; Dow Europe; FMC; A C Hatrick; Hercules BV; Honeywill & Stein; Mid-Am. Food Sales; Multi-Kem; Quimdis; Siber Hegner; Welding
Trade names: Elcema® F150; Elcema® G250; Elcema® P100; Justfiber® CL-40-H; Justfiber® CL-60-H; Justfiber® CL-80-H; Keycel®; Solka-Floc®; Solka-Floc® BW-40; Solka-Floc® BW-100; Solka-Floc® BW-200; Solka-Floc® BW-2030; Solka-Floc® Fine Granular
See also Microcrystalline cellulose

α-Cellulose. *See* Cellulose

Cellulose acetate
CAS 9004-35-7
Synonyms: CA; Cellulose acetate ester; Acetylcellulose
Classification: Cellulosics
Properties: Triacetate insol. in water, alcohol, ether, sol. in glacial acetic acid; tetraacetate insol. in water, alcohol, ether, glacial acetic acid, methanol; pentaacetate insol. in water, sol. in alcohol; m.w. ≈ 37,000; dens. 1.300
Uses: Polymer membrane, coating agent for pharmaceuticals
Regulatory: FDA 21CFR §182.90, GRAS; USP/NF, BP, Ph.Eur. compliance
Manuf./Distrib.: Aldrich; Courtaulds Acetate; Eastman; FMC; Rotuba Extruders; Scientific Adsorbents
Trade names: Eastman® CA

Cellulose, acetate, 1,2-benzenedicarboxylate. *See* Cellulose acetate phthalate
Cellulose, acetate butanoate. *See* Cellulose acetate butyrate

Cellulose acetate butyrate
CAS 9004-36-8
Synonyms: CAB; Cellulose acetobutyrate; Cellulose, acetate butanoate
Definition: Butyric acid ester of a partially acetylated cellulose
Properties: Dens. 1.250

Uses: Excipient for formulation of drug-loaded microparticles
Regulatory: FDA 21CFR §175.105, 175.230, 175.300, 177.1200
Manuf./Distrib.: Allchem Ind.; Eastman; FMC; Van Waters & Rogers; Whitfield Chem. Ltd
Trade names: Eastman® CAB

Cellulose acetate ester. *See* Cellulose acetate

Cellulose acetate phthalate
CAS 9004-38-0
Synonyms: CAP; Cellulose, acetate, 1,2-benzenedicarboxylate; Cellacephate
Definition: Reaction prod. of phthalic anhydride and a partial acetate ester of cellulose
Properties: Wh. free-flowing powd., sl. odor of acetic acid; sol. in acetone, dioxane; insol. in water, alcohol
Uses: Enteric film former; coating agent, excipient for coating of tablets and capsules; used in orals
Regulatory: FDA approved for orals; USP/NF, BP, Ph.Eur., JP compliance
Manuf./Distrib.: Eastman; FMC
Trade names: C-A-P Enteric Coating Material

Cellulose, acetate propanoate. *See* Cellulose acetate propionate

Cellulose acetate propionate
CAS 9004-39-1
Synonyms: CAP; Cellulose propionate; Cellulose acetate propionate ester; Cellulose, acetate propanoate
Definition: Propionic acid ester of a partially acetylated cellulose
Uses: Excipient
Regulatory: FDA 21CFR §175.105, 175.230, 175.300, 177.1200
Manuf./Distrib.: Aldrich; Eastman; SAF Bulk Chems.
Trade names: Eastman® CAPr

Cellulose acetate propionate ester. *See* Cellulose acetate propionate

Cellulose acetate trimellitate
Uses: Excipient; enteric film-coatings; matrix binder
Manuf./Distrib.: Eastman
Trade names: C-A-T Enteric Coating Polymer

Cellulose acetobutyrate. *See* Cellulose acetate butyrate
Cellulose carboxymethyl ether. *See* Carboxymethylcellulose
Cellulose carboxymethyl ether calcium salt. *See* Calcium carboxymethyl cellulose
Cellulose carboxymethyl ether sodium salt. *See* Carboxymethylcellulose sodium
Cellulose ethyl ether. *See* Ethylcellulose
Cellulose gel. *See* Cellulose; Microcrystalline cellulose
Cellulose gum. *See* Carboxymethylcellulose sodium
Cellulose, 2-hydroxyethyl ether. *See* Hydroxyethylcellulose
Cellulose, 2-hydroxypropyl ether. *See* Hydroxypropylcellulose
Cellulose hydroxypropyl methyl ether. *See* Hydroxypropyl methylcellulose
Cellulose 2-hydroxypropyl methyl ether. *See* Hydroxypropyl methylcellulose
Cellulose methyl ether. *See* Methylcellulose
Cellulose, nitrate. *See* Nitrocellulose
Cellulose, oxidized. *See* Oxidized cellulose
Cellulose powder. *See* Cellulose
Cellulose propionate. *See* Cellulose acetate propionate
Cellulose tetranitrate. *See* Nitrocellulose
Centella asiatica extract. *See* Hydrocotyl extract
Cera alba. *See* Beeswax
Cera carnauba. *See* Carnauba

Ceresin
CAS 8001-75-0; EINECS 232-290-1
Synonyms: White ozokerite wax; Cerin; Ceresin wax; Earth wax; Mineral wax
Definition: Waxy mixture of hydrocarbons obtained by purification of ozokerite
Properties: White or yel. waxy cake; sol. in alcohol, benzene, chloroform, naphtha, hot oils; insol. in water; dens. 0.92-0.94; m.p. 68-72 C
Precaution: Combustible
Toxicology: May cause allergic reactions
Uses: Thickener used in protective creams; in dentistry for making wax impressions
Regulatory: FDA 21CFR §175.105
Manuf./Distrib.: M. Argueso & Co.; Astor Wax; Jonk BV; Koster Keunen; Frank B. Ross; Scheel; Spectrum

Ceresin wax

Chem. Mfg.; Stevenson Cooper; Strahl & Pitsch
Trade names: Koster Keunen Ceresine; Ross Ceresine Wax
Trade names containing: Dehymuls® K
See also Ozokerite

Ceresin wax. *See* Ceresin
Cerin. *See* Ceresin
Ceruleinum. *See* FD&C Blue No. 2

Cetalkonium chloride
CAS 122-18-9; EINECS 204-526-3
Synonyms: Cetyl dimethyl benzyl ammonium chloride; Benzylhexadecyldimethylammonium chloride; N-Hexadecyl-N,N-dimethylbenzenemethanaminium chloride
Classification: Quaternary ammonium salt
Empirical: $C_{25}H_{46}N•Cl$
Formula: $C_6H_5CH_2N(CH_3)_2(C_{16}H_{33})Cl$
Properties: Colorless crystalline powd., odorless; sol. in water, alcohol, acetone, esters, propylene glycol, glycerol, CCl_4; m.w. 396.12; m.p. 58-60 C
Uses: Cationic antimicrobial, antiseptic, surfactant for pharmaceutical preps. and medical devices
Regulatory: FDA 21CFR §173.320, 175.105, 178.1010

Ceteareth-7
CAS 68439-49-6 (generic)
Synonyms: PEG-7 cetyl/stearyl ether
Uses: Ingred. in pharmaceutical creams and lotions
Trade names containing: Cromul EM 0685

Ceteareth-9
CAS 68439-49-6 (generic)
Synonyms: PEG-9 cetyl/stearyl ether; POE (9) cetyl/stearyl ether
Definition: PEG ether of cetearyl alcohol
Formula: $R(OCH_2CH_2)_nOH$, R = blend of cetyl and stearyl radicals, avg. n = 9
Uses: Emulsifier
Trade names: Tewax TC 10

Ceteareth-10
CAS 68439-49-6 (generic)
Synonyms: PEG-10 cetyl/stearyl ether; POE (10) cetyl/stearyl ether
Definition: PEG ether of cetearyl alcohol
Formula: $R(OCH_2CH_2)_nOH$, R = blend of cetyl and stearyl radicals, avg. n = 10
Uses: Conditioner and emollient for pharmaceuticals
Regulatory: FDA 21CFR §177.2800

Ceteareth-11
CAS 68439-49-6 (generic)
Synonyms: PEG-11 cetyl/stearyl ether; POE (11) cetyl/stearyl ether
Definition: PEG ether of cetearyl alcohol
Formula: $R(OCH_2CH_2)_nOH$, R = blend of cetyl and stearyl radicals, avg. n = 11
Uses: Solubilizer, emulsifier for pharmaceutical preps.
Regulatory: FDA 21CFR §177.2800
Trade names: Britex CS 110; Cremophor® A 11; Rewopal® CSF 11

Ceteareth-12
CAS 68439-49-6 (generic)
Synonyms: PEG-12 cetyl/stearyl ether; POE (12) cetyl/stearyl ether
Definition: PEG ether of cetearyl alcohol
Formula: $R(OCH_2CH_2)_nOH$, R = blend of cetyl and stearyl radicals, avg. n = 12
Uses: Emulsifier, emollient, bodying agent
Regulatory: FDA 21CFR §177.2800
Trade names: Eumulgin® B1
Trade names containing: Emulgade® SE

Ceteareth-14
CAS 68439-49-6 (generic)
Synonyms: PEG-14 cetyl/stearyl ether; POE (14) cetyl/stearyl ether
Definition: PEG ether of cetearyl alcohol

Formula: $R(OCH_2CH_2)_nOH$, R = blend of cetyl and stearyl radicals, avg. n = 14
Uses: Conditioner and emollient for pharmaceuticals

Ceteareth-15
CAS 68439-49-6 (generic)
Synonyms: PEG-15 cetyl/stearyl ether; POE (15) cetyl/stearyl ether
Definition: PEG ether of cetearyl alcohol
Formula: $R(OCH_2CH_2)_nOH$, R = blend of cetyl and stearyl radicals, avg. n = 15
Uses: Emollient used in topicals
Regulatory: FDA 21CFR §177.2800; approved for topicals

Ceteareth-16
CAS 68439-49-6 (generic)
Synonyms: PEG-16 cetyl/stearyl ether; POE (16) cetyl/stearyl ether
Definition: PEG ether of cetearyl alcohol
Formula: $R(OCH_2CH_2)_nOH$, R = blend of cetyl and stearyl radicals, avg. n = 16
Uses: Emulsifier and solubilizer for pharmaceuticals
Trade names containing: Simulsol® 5719

Ceteareth-20
CAS 9005-00-9; 68439-49-6 (generic)
Synonyms: PEG-20 cetyl/stearyl ether; POE (20) cetyl/stearyl ether; Polyoxyl 20 cetostearyl ether
Definition: PEG ether of cetearyl alcohol
Formula: $R(OCH_2CH_2)_nOH$, R = blend of cetyl and stearyl radicals, avg. n = 20
Properties: Cream-colored waxy unctuous mass, melting to brnsh. yel. clear liq.; sol. in water, alcohol, acetone; insol. in hexane; acid no. 0.5 max.; sapon. no. 2 max.; hyd. no. 42-60; pH 4.5-7.5 (10%)
Uses: Emollient, nonionic emulsifier, solubilizer, wetting agent used in topicals
Regulatory: FDA 21CFR §177.2800; FDA approved for topicals; USP/NF compliance
Manuf./Distrib. (pharm. & food): Spectrum Chem. Mfg.
Trade names: Acconon W230; Britex CS 200 B; Eumulgin® B2; Incropol CS-20; Volpo CS-20
Trade names containing: Brookswax™ G; Cosmowax J; Cosmowax K; Emerwax® 1266; Emulgade® 1000 NI; Emulgade® SE; Galenol® 1618 AE; Lexemul® CS-20; Macol® 124; Macol® 125; Promulgen® D; Promulgen® G

Ceteareth-25
CAS 68439-49-6 (generic)
Synonyms: PEG-25 cetyl/stearyl ether; POE (25) cetyl/stearyl ether
Definition: PEG ether of cetearyl alcohol
Formula: $R(OCH_2CH_2)_nOH$, R = blend of cetyl and stearyl radicals, avg. n = 25
Uses: Emulsifier for pharmaceutical preps.
Regulatory: FDA 21CFR §177.2800
Trade names: Britex CS 250; Cremophor® A 25; Emulgator E 2568
Trade names containing: Softisan® 601

Ceteareth-30
CAS 68439-49-6 (generic)
Synonyms: PEG-30 cetyl/stearyl ether; POE (30) cetyl/stearyl ether
Definition: PEG ether of cetearyl alcohol
Formula: $R(OCH_2CH_2)_nOH$, R = blend of cetyl and stearyl radicals, avg. n = 30
Uses: Emulsifier and emollient used in topicals
Regulatory: FDA 21CFR §177.2800; approved for topicals
Trade names: Eumulgin® B3; Rhodasurf® E-15

Ceteareth-33
CAS 68439-49-6 (generic)
Synonyms: PEG-33 cetyl/stearyl ether; PEG (33) cetyl/stearyl ether; POE (33) cetyl/stearyl ether
Definition: PEG ether of cetearyl alcohol
Formula: $R(OCH_2CH_2)_nOH$, R = blend of cetyl/stearyl alcohol, avg. n = 33
Uses: Emulsifier, gellant, stabilizer, solubilizer
Regulatory: FDA 21CFR §177.2800
Trade names: Simulsol® CS
Trade names containing: Cire Lanol® CTO

Cetearyl alcohol
CAS 8005-44-5; 67762-27-0; EINECS 267-008-6
Synonyms: Cetostearyl alcohol; Cetyl/stearyl alcohol; C16-18 alcohols

Cetearyl glucoside

Definition: Mixture of fatty alcohols, predominantly cetyl and stearyl alcohols
Properties: Wh. unctuous flakes or gran., faint char. odor, bland mild taste; sol. in alcohol, ether; insol. in water; m.p. 48-55 C; acid no. ≤ 2; iodine no. ≤ 4; hyd. no. 208-228
Uses: Emulsifying wax, emollient, stiffening agent, consistency factor for pharmaceutical creams; antiseptic in topical anti-infective prods.; used in orals, otics, topicals
Regulatory: FDA 21CFR §175.105; FDA approved for orals, otics, topicals; USP/NF, BP, Ph.Eur. compliance
Manuf./Distrib. (pharm. & food): Spectrum Chem. Mfg.
Trade names: Cetostearyl Alcohol BP; Cetostearyl Alcohol NF; Dehydag® Wax O; Lanette® O; Laurex® CS; Laurex® CS/D; Nafol® 1618 H
Trade names containing: Argobase EUC 2; Cire Lanol® CTO; Cosmowax J; Crodex A; Crodex C; Crodex N; Emerwax® 1266; Empiwax SK; Empiwax SK/BP; Emulgade® 1000 NI; Emulgade® F; Emulgade® SE; Galenol® 1618 AE; Galenol® 1618 CS; Galenol® 1618 DSN; Galenol® 1618 KS; Incroquat Behenyl TMS; Lanbritol Wax N21; Lanette® N; Lanette® W; Lanette® Wax SX, SXBP; Lexemul® CS-20; Macol® 124; Macol® CPS; Mazawax® 163R; Mazawax® 163SS; Pionier® MAA; Promulgen® D; Ritachol® 1000; Ritachol® 2000; Ritachol® 3000; Sebase

Cetearyl glucoside
Uses: Emulsifier for dermopharmaceutical prods.
Trade names: Montanol® 68

Cetearyl isononanoate
Synonyms: Isononanoic acid, cetyl/stearyl ether
Definition: Ester of cetearyl alcohol and a branched chain of nanoic acid
Uses: Emollient, oily component for pharmaceutical skin care and sun protection prods.
Trade names: Cetiol® SN

Cetearyl octanoate
CAS 59130-70-7; EINECS 261-619-1
Synonyms: Cetyl/stearyl 2-ethyl hexanoate; 2-Ethylhexanoic acid, cetyl/stearyl ester
Definition: Ester of cetearyl alcohol and octanoic acid
Uses: Emollient, waterproofing agent in pharmaceuticals, skin care preps.
Trade names: Luvitol® EHO
Trade names containing: Crodamol CAP

Cetearyl palmitate
CAS 85341-79-3
Synonyms: Hexadecanoic acid, cetyl/stearyl ether
Definition: Ester of cetearyl alcohol and palmitic acid
Uses: Emollient, plasticizer for topical pharmaceuticals
Trade names: Crodamol CSP

Ceteth-2
CAS 9004-95-9 (generic); 5274-61-3
Synonyms: PEG-2 cetyl ether; POE (2) cetyl ether; PEG 100 cetyl ether
Definition: Polyethylene glycol ether of cetyl alcohol
Formula: $CH_3(CH_2)_{14}CH_2(OCH_2CH_2)_nOH$, avg. n = 2
Uses: Emulsifier used in topicals
Regulatory: Approved for topicals
Trade names: Britex C

Ceteth-5
CAS 9004-95-9 (generic), 4478-97-1
Synonyms: PEG-5 cetyl ether; POE (5) cetyl ether; 3,6,9,12,15-Pentaoxahentriacontan-1-ol
Definition: PEG ether of cetyl alcohol
Formula: $CH_3(CH_2)_{14}CH_2(OCH_2CH_2)_nOH$, avg. n = 5
Uses: Emulsifier for pharmaceutical creams and lotions
Trade names containing: Cromul EM 0685

Ceteth-6
CAS 9004-95-9 (generic); 5168-91-2
Synonyms: PEG-6 cetyl ether; POE (6) cetyl ether; 3,6,9,12,15,18-Hexaoxatetratricontan-1-ol
Definition: PEG ether of cetyl alcohol
Formula: $CH_3(CH_2)_{14}CH_2(OCH_2CH_2)_nOH$, avg. n = 6
Uses: Emulsifier for pharmaceuticals
Regulatory: FDA 21CFR §176.200
Trade names: Nikkol BC-5.5

Ceteth-7
CAS 9004-95-9 (generic)
Synonyms: PEG-7 cetyl ether; POE (7) cetyl ether
Definition: PEG ether of cetyl alcohol
Formula: $CH_3(CH_2)_{14}CH_2(OCH_2CH_2)_nOH$, avg. n = 7
Uses: Emulsifier for pharmaceuticals
Trade names: Nikkol BC-7

Ceteth-10
CAS 9004-95-9 (generic); 14529-40-9
Synonyms: PEG-10 cetyl ether; PEG 500 cetyl ether; POE (10) cetyl ether; 3,6,9,12,15,18,21,24,27,30-Dexaoxahexatetracontan-1-ol
Definition: PEG ether of cetyl alcohol
Formula: $CH_3(CH_2)_{14}CH_2(OCH_2CH_2)_nOH$, avg. n = 10
Uses: Emulsifier for lotions and creams
Regulatory: FDA 21CFR §176.200
Trade names: Britex C 100; Nikkol BC-10TX

Ceteth-12
CAS 9004-95-9 (generic); 13149-83-2
Synonyms: PEG-12 cetyl ether; POE (12) cetyl ether; PEG 600 cetyl ether
Definition: PEG ether of cetyl alcohol
Formula: $CH_3(CH_2)_{14}CH_2(OCH_2CH_2)_nOH$, avg. n = 12
Uses: Emulsifier for pharmaceuticals
Regulatory: FDA 21CFR §177.2800
Trade names containing: Lanbritol Wax N21

Ceteth-15
CAS 9004-95-9 (generic)
Synonyms: PEG-15 cetyl ether; POE (15) cetyl ether
Definition: PEG ether of cetyl alcohol
Formula: $CH_3(CH_2)_{14}CH_2(OCH_2CH_2)_nOH$, avg. n = 15
Uses: Emulsifier
Regulatory: FDA 21CFR §177.2800
Trade names: Nikkol BC-15TX

Ceteth-16
CAS 9004-95-9 (generic)
Synonyms: PEG-16 cetyl ether; POE (16) cetyl ether
Definition: PEG ether of cetyl alcohol
Formula: $CH_3(CH_2)_{14}CH_2(OCH_2CH_2)_nOH$, avg. n = 16
Uses: Emulsifier for pharmaceuticals
Regulatory: FDA 21CFR §176.200

Ceteth-20
CAS 9004-95-9 (generic)
Synonyms: PEG-20 cetyl ether; POE (20) cetyl ether; Cetomacrogol 1000
Definition: PEG ether of cetyl alcohol
Formula: $CH_3(CH_2)_{14}CH_2(OCH_2CH_2)_nOH$, avg. n = 20
Uses: Emulsifier, emulsion stabilizer for pharmaceuticals; used in topicals
Regulatory: FDA approved for topicals; BP compliance
Trade names: Britex C 200; Cetomacrogol 1000 BP; Nikkol BC-20TX; Simulsol® 58
Trade names containing: Crodex N; Tefose® 2000; Tefose® 2561

Ceteth-23
CAS 9004-95-9 (generic)
Synonyms: PEG-23 cetyl ether; POE (23) cetyl ether
Definition: PEG ether of cetyl alcohol
Formula: $CH_3(CH_2)_{14}CH_2(OCH_2CH_2)_nOH$, avg. n = 23
Uses: Emulsifier for pharmaceuticals
Trade names: Nikkol BC-23

Ceteth-24
CAS 9004-95-9 (generic)
Synonyms: PEG-24 cetyl ether; POE (24) cetyl ether
Definition: PEG ether of cetyl alcohol

Ceteth-25

    Formula: $CH_3(CH_2)_{14}CH_2(OCH_2CH_2)_nOH$, avg. n = 24
    Uses: Emulsifier for pharmaceuticals
    Regulatory: FDA 21CFR §177.2800
    Trade names containing: Forlan C-24

Ceteth-25

    CAS 9004-95-9 (generic)
    Synonyms: PEG-25 cetyl ether; POE (25) cetyl ether
    Definition: PEG ether of cetyl alcohol
    Formula: $CH_3(CH_2)_{14}CH_2(OCH_2CH_2)_nOH$, avg. n = 25
    Uses: Emulsifier for pharmaceuticals
    Regulatory: FDA 21CFR §176.200, 177.2800
    Trade names: Nikkol BC-25TX
    Trade names containing: Hydrolactol 70; Solulan® 25

Ceteth-30

    CAS 9004-95-9 (generic)
    Synonyms: PEG-30 cetyl ether; POE (30) cetyl ether
    Definition: PEG ether of cetyl alcohol
    Formula: $CH_3(CH_2)_{14}CH_2(OCH_2CH_2)_nOH$, avg. n = 30
    Uses: Emulsifier for pharmaceuticals
    Regulatory: FDA 21CFR §176.200, 177.2800
    Trade names: Nikkol BC-30TX

Ceteth-40

    CAS 9004-95-9 (generic)
    Synonyms: PEG-40 cetyl ether; POE (40) cetyl ether
    Definition: PEG ether of cetyl alcohol
    Formula: $CH_3(CH_2)_{14}CH_2(OCH_2CH_2)_nOH$, avg. n = 40
    Uses: Emulsifier for pharmaceuticals
    Trade names: Nikkol BC-40TX

Cetin. *See* Cetyl palmitate

Cetoleth-22

    CAS 68920-66-1
    Uses: Emulsifier
    Trade names: Britex CO 220

Cetomacrogol 1000. *See* Ceteth-20
Cetone V. *See* Allyl α-ionone
Cetostearyl alcohol. *See* Cetearyl alcohol
Cetrimide. *See* Cetrimonium bromide

Cetrimonium bromide

    CAS 57-09-0; EINECS 200-311-3
    Synonyms: Cetyltrimethylammonium bromide; Cetrimide; Hexadecyltrimethylammonium bromide; N,N,N-Trimethyl-1-hexadecanaminium bromide
    Classification: Quaternary ammonium salt
    Formula: $CH_3(CH_2)_{15}N(CH_3)_3Br$
    Properties: White powd.; sol. in water, alcohol, chloroform; m.w. 364.46; m.p. > 230 C (dec.)
    Toxicology: LD50 (mice, iv) 32.0 mg/kg; large systemic doses may cause nausea, vomiting, muscle paralysis, CNS depression, hypotension, local tissue damage
    Uses: Cationic surfactant; topical antiseptic in higher concs., preservative in lower concs.
    Regulatory: USA EPA registered, Japan approved, Europe listed; BP, Ph.Eur. compliance
    Manuf./Distrib.: Aceto; Aldrich; Chemron; E. Merck; Witco; Zeeland
    Trade names containing: Crodex C

Cetrimonium chloride

    CAS 112-02-7; EINECS 203-928-6
    Synonyms: Cetyl trimethyl ammonium chloride; Palmityl trimethyl ammonium chloride;; Hexadecyl trimethyl ammonium chloride
    Classification: Quaternary ammonium salt
    Formula: $C_{16}H_{33}(CH_3)_3NCl$
    Uses: Emulsifier, emollient, bactericide; used in topicals; coagulating agent in mfg. of antibiotics
    Regulatory: FDA approved for topicals

Manuf./Distrib.: Witco/Oleo-Surf.
Trade names: Barquat® CT-29; Carsoquat® CT-429

Cetyl acetate
CAS 629-70-9; EINECS 211-103-7
Synonyms: Hexadecyl acetate; 1-Hexadecanol, acetate
Definition: Ester of cetyl alcohol and acetic acid
Empirical: $C_{18}H_{36}O_2$
Formula: $CH_3COOCH_2(CH_2)_{14}CH_3$
Uses: Used in pharmaceutical topicals
Trade names: Pelemol® CA
Trade names containing: Crodalan AWS; Crodalan LA; Fancol ALA; Fancol ALA-10; Ritawax AEO; Ritawax ALA; Solulan® 97; Solulan® 98

Cetyl alcohol
CAS 124-29-8; 36653-82-4; EINECS 253-149-0
FEMA 2554
Synonyms: Palmityl alcohol; C16 linear primary alcohol; Alcohol C16; 1-Hexadecanol; Hexadecyl alcohol
Classification: Fatty alcohol
Empirical: $C_{16}H_{34}O$
Formula: $CH_3(CH_2)_{14}CH_2OH$
Properties: Wh. waxy solid; partially sol. in alcohol and ether; insol. in water; m.w. 242.27; dens. 0.8176 (49.5 C); m.p. 49.3 C; b.p. 344 C; acid no. ≤ 2; iodine no. ≤ 5; hyd. no. 218-238; flash pt. > 110 C; ref. index 1.4283
Precaution: Flamm. when exposed to heat or flame; can react with oxidizing materials
Toxicology: LD50 (oral, rat) 6400 mg/kg; mod. toxic by ingestion, intraperitoneal routes; eye and human skin irritant; can cause hives; heated to decomp., emits acrid smoke and fumes
Uses: Emulsifier, opacifier, emollient, visc.-increasing agent, stiffening agent, foam booster, filler; used in ophthalmics, orals, otics, rectals, topicals; sometimes used as a laxative
Regulatory: FDA 21CFR §73.1, 73.1001, 172.515, 172.864, 175.105, 175.300, 176.200, 177.1010, 177.1200, 177.2800, 178.3480, 178.3910; FEMA GRAS; FDA approved for ophthalmics, orals, otics, rectals, topicals; USP/NF, BP, Ph.Eur. compliance
Manuf./Distrib.: Aarhus Oliefabrik A/S; Albemarle; Aldrich; Amerchol; Chemron; Croda; Lipo; Lonza; M. Michel; Norman, Fox; Procter & Gamble; Stepan; Vista
Manuf./Distrib. (pharm. & food): Aarhus Oliefabrik A/S; Aldrich; Lipo; Lonza; Procter & Gamble; Ruger; Spectrum Chem. Mfg.
Trade names: Crodacol C-95NF; Dehydag® Wax 16; Epal® 16NF; Hyfatol 16-98; Lanette® 16; Nacol® 16-95; Nacol® 16-98
Trade names containing: Amerchol® 400; Incroquat B65C; Ritachol® 3000; Ritachol® 4000; Ross Beeswax Substitute 628/5

Cetylamine hydrofluoride
CAS 3151-59-5; EINECS 221-588-7
Synonyms: Hexadecylamine hydrofluoride; Hexadecylammonium fluoride
Empirical: $C_{16}H_{36}NF$
Formula: $CH_3(CH_2)_{15}NH_2$ • HF
Uses: Caries prophylaxis; toothpastes, mouthwashes
Trade names: Unifluorid H 101

Cetyl DEA phosphate. *See* DEA-cetyl phosphate

Cetyl dimethicone
Classification: Dimethyl siloxane polymer
Formula: $(CH_3)_3SiO-[CH_3SiO(CH_2)_{15}CH_3]_x[CH_3SiOCH_3]_y-Si(CH_3)_3$
Uses: Emollient, spreading agent, pigment solubilizer
Trade names: Abil®-Wax 9801; Abil®-Wax 9814

Cetyl dimethicone copolyol
Definition: Copolymer of cetyl dimethicone and dimethicone copolyol
Uses: Surfactant, emollient, emulsifier
Trade names: Abil® EM-90
Trade names containing: Abil® WE 09

Cetyl dimethyl benzyl ammonium chloride. *See* Cetalkonium chloride

Cetyl esters
CAS 8002-23-1; 17661-50-6; 136097-97-7; EINECS 241-640-2
Synonyms: Synthetic spermaceti; Synthetic spermaceti wax; Cetyl esters wax

Cetyl esters wax

Classification: Synthetic wax
Definition: A mixt. of sat. fatty alcohols (C14 to C18) and sat. fatty acids (C14 to C18)
Properties: Wh. to off. wh. translucent flakes, faint odor, bland mild taste; sol. in boiling alcohol, ether, chloroform; insol. in water; dens. 0.820; m.p. 43-47 C; acid no. 5 max.; iodine no. 1 max.; sapon. no. 109-120
Uses: Emollient, stiffening agent, and visc. builder for pharmaceutical preps.; used in orals, topicals
Regulatory: FDA approved for orals, topicals; USP/NF compliance
Manuf./Distrib.: Koster Keunen; Robeco; Werner G. Smith; Spectrum Chem. Mfg.; Witco/Oleo-Surf.
Manuf./Distrib. (pharm. & food): Spectrum Chem. Mfg.
Trade names: Crodamol SS; Koster Keunen Synthetic Spermaceti; Ritaceti; Ross Spermaceti Wax Substitute 573; Spermwax®; W.G.S. Synaceti 116 NF/USP
Trade names containing: Cetina

Cetyl esters wax. *See* Cetyl esters

Cetyl glyceryl ether
Uses: Emulsifier, hydrotrope, emollient, thickener
Trade names: Nikkol Chimyl Alcohol 100

Cetyl hydroxyethyl cellulose
Definition: Ether of cetyl alcohol and hydroxyethylcellulose
Uses: Thickener, stabilizer, film-former, suspending agent
Trade names: Natrosol® Plus CS, Grade 330

Cetylic acid. *See* Palmitic acid

Cetyl lactate
CAS 35274-05-6; EINECS 252-478-7
Synonyms: n-Hexadecyl lactate; 2-Hydroxypropanoic acid hexadecyl ester; 1-Hexadecanol lactate
Definition: Ester of cetyl alcohol and lactic acid
Empirical: $C_{19}H_{38}O_3$
Formula: $CH_3CHOHCOO(CH_2)_{15}CH_3$
Properties: Waxy solid; sol. in oil, ethanol, IPM, oleyl alcohol; partly sol. in water, propylene glycol; m.w. 314.49; m.p. 41 C; b.p. 132 C (0.1 mm), 170 C (1 mm); ref. index 1.4410
Toxicology: LD50 (rat, oral) > 20 ml/kg; no known toxicity; nonirritating to eyes and skin
Uses: Emollient, lubricant for pharmaceutical topicals
Manuf./Distrib.: Am. Biorganics
Trade names: Ceraphyl® 28; Pelemol® CL

Cetyl palmitate
CAS 540-10-3; EINECS 208-736-6
Synonyms: Hexadecanoic acid, hexadecyl ester; Palmitic acid, hexadecyl ester; Cetin
Definition: Ester of cetyl alcohol and palmitic acid
Formula: $C_{15}H_{31}COOC_{16}H_{33}$
Properties: White crystalline wax-like substance; sol. in abs. alcohol, ether; insol. in water; m.w. 480.50; dens. 0.832; m.p. 50 C; b.p. 360 C; acid no. max.; iodine no. 5 max.; sapon. no. 110-130; ref. index 1.4398
Precaution: Combustible
Toxicology: Nontoxic
Uses: Emollient, consistency factor, base for ointments; used in topicals
Regulatory: FDA approved for topicals
Manuf./Distrib.: Croda; Werner G. Smith; Spectrum Chem. Mfg.; Stepan; Witco
Manuf./Distrib. (pharm. & food): Ruger
Trade names: Crodamol CP; Cutina® CP; Kessco® 653; Kessco CP; Pelemol® CP; Precifac ATO; Standamul® 1616; W.G.S. Cetyl Palmitate
Trade names containing: Emulgade® SE

Cetylpyridinium chloride
CAS 123-03-5 (anhyd.); 6004-24-6 (monohydrate); EINECS 204-593-9
Synonyms: 1-Hexadecylpyridinium chloride
Classification: Quaternary ammonium salt
Empirical: $C_{21}H_{38}ClN$ (anhyd.), $C_{21}H_{38}ClN \cdot H_2O$ (monohydrate)
Properties: White powd.; sol. in water, alcohol, chloroform; m.w. 339.99 (anhyd.), 358.01 (monohydrate); m.p. 77-83 C
Toxicology: LD50 (rat, oral) 200 mg/kg
Uses: Antimicrobial preservative in cough syrups and lozenges; topical anti-infective; wetting agent, solubilizer; antiseptic in oral rinse and hemorrhoidal prods.; used in inhalants, orals

Usage level: 0.1%
Regulatory: U.S. not restricted; Japan not approved, Europe listed; FDA approved for inhalants, orals; USP/NF, BP, Ph.Eur. compliance
Manuf./Distrib.: E. Merck; Schweizerhall; Spectrum Chem. Mfg.; Weiders Farmasoytiske A/S; Zeeland
Manuf./Distrib. (pharm. & food): Ruger; Spectrum Chem. Mfg.; Zeeland
Trade names: CPC; CPC Sumquat 6060; Uniquart CPC

Cetyl ricinoleate
CAS 10401-55-5; EINECS 233-864-4
Synonyms: Hexadecyl 12-hydroxy-9-octadecenoate; 12-Hydroxy-9-octadecenoic acid ester
Definition: Ester of cetyl alcohol and ricinoleic acid
Empirical: $C_{34}H_{66}O_3$
Uses: Emollient for pharmaceutical topicals, tanning preps.
Trade names: Pelemol® CR

Cetyl/stearyl alcohol. *See* Cetearyl alcohol
Cetyl/stearyl 2-ethyl hexanoate. *See* Cetearyl octanoate
Cetyltrimethylammonium bromide. *See* Cetrimonium bromide
Cetyl trimethyl ammonium chloride. *See* Cetrimonium chloride
Cevitamic acid. *See* L-Ascorbic acid
CFC 12. *See* Dichlorodifluoromethane
CFC 114. *See* Dichlorotetrafluoromethane

Charcoal, activated
CAS 16291-96-6
UN No. 1362
Definition: The residue from the destructive distillation of various org. materials, treated to increase its adsorptive power
Empirical: C
Properties: Blk. fine powd. free from gritty matter, odorless, tasteless; a.w. 12.01
Precaution: DOT: Spontaneously combustible material
Uses: Adsorbent for pharmaceuticals, antidiarrheal prods.
Regulatory: USP/NF, BP, Ph.Eur. compliance
Manuf./Distrib. (pharm. & food): Aldrich; Ruger; Spectrum Chem. Mfg.

Chavicol methyl ether. *See* Estragole
Chavicyl methyl ether. *See* Estragole

Cherry juice
CAS 8012-99-5
Uses: Used in orals
Regulatory: FDA approved for orals

Chile saltpeter. *See* Sodium nitrate
China clay. *See* Kaolin
Chinaldine. *See* Quinaldine
China oil. *See* Balsam Peru
Chinese bean oil. *See* Soybean oil
Chinese cinnamon oil. *See* Cinnamon oil
Chinese white. *See* Zinc oxide
Chinosol. *See* 8-Hydroxyquinoline sulfate
Chloracetamide. *See* Chloroacetamide
Chlorallyl methenamine chloride. *See* Quaternium-15
Chlorate of soda. *See* Sodium chlorate
Chlorbutol. *See* Chlorobutanol
Chloretone. *See* Chlorobutanol
Chlorhexidine acetate. *See* Chlorhexidine diacetate

Chlorhexidine diacetate
CAS 56-95-1; EINECS 200-302-4
Synonyms: Chlorhexidine acetate; 1,1´-Hexamethylene bis [5-(4-chlorophenyl) biguanide] diacetate; 1,6-Bis (5-(p-chlorophenyl) bi-guanidino) hexane diacetate; 1,6-Di (4´-chlorophenyldiguanidino) hexane diacetate
Definition: Salt of chlorhexidine and acetic acid
Formula: $C_{22}H_{30}Cl_2N_{10} \cdot 2C_2H_4O_2$
Properties: Crystals; sol. 1.5 g in 100 ml water; sol. in alcohols, glycerol, propylene glycol, polyethylene glycols; m.w. 643.56; m.p. 154-156 C (dec.)

Chlorhexidine digluconate

 Toxicology: LD50 (mice, oral) 2 g/kg; poison by subcutaneous, intravenous, intraperitoneal routes; moderately toxic by ingestion, skin irritant
 Uses: Antimicrobial for pharmaceuticals, hospital disinfectants, veterinary prods., anti-plaque dental prods.
 Regulatory: BP, Ph.Eur. compliance
 Manuf./Distrib.: Lonza
 Manuf./Distrib. (pharm. & food): Lonza

Chlorhexidine digluconate

 CAS 18472-51-0; 14007-07-9; EINECS 242-354-0
 Synonyms: N,N´-Bis (4-chlorophenyl)-3,12-diimino-2,4,11,13-tetraazatetradecane-diimidamide compd. with D-gluconic acid; Chlorhexidine gluconate
 Definition: Salt of chlorhexidine and gluconic acid
 Empirical: $C_{22}H_{30}Cl_2N_{10} \cdot 2C_6H_{12}O_7$
 Properties: Sol. > 50% in water; m.w. 897.76
 Precaution: Light-sensitive
 Toxicology: LD50 (oral, mice), 1800 mg/kg; (IV, mice) 22 mg/kg; poison by intravenous route; moderately toxic by ingestion; may cause contact dermatitis; heated to dec., emits very toxic fumes of NO_x and Cl^-
 Uses: Topical antiseptic, antimicrobial, skin sterilizing agent, mouthwashes, European feminine hygiene sprays; anti-plaque dental prods.
 Usage level: 0.01-0.1%
 Regulatory: Japan approved; Europe listed; BP, Ph.Eur. compliance
 Manuf./Distrib.: Degussa; Int'l. Sourcing; Lonza AG; Rhone-Poulenc France; Spectrum Chem. Mfg.
 Trade names: Spectradyne® G

Chlorhexidine gluconate. *See* Chlorhexidine digluconate
Chlorhydric acid. *See* Hydrochloric acid
Chlorhydrol. *See* Aluminum chlorohydrate

Chloroacetamide

 CAS 79-07-2; EINECS 201-174-2
 Synonyms: Chloracetamide; 2-Chloroacetamide
 Classification: Chlorinated compd.
 Empirical: C_2ClH_4NO
 Formula: $ClCH_2CONH_2$
 Properties: M.w. 93.51; m.p. 116-118 C
 Toxicology: May cause dermatitis; irritant; potent sensitizer in extremely low concs. (0.015-0.1%)
 Uses: Antimicrobial preservative; used in topical pharmaceuticals in Europe
 Regulatory: U.S. EPA registered; Europe listed; not registered or approved for use in the U.S. (pharm.)
 Manuf./Distrib.: Aldrich
 Manuf./Distrib. (pharm. & food): Aldrich

2-Chloroacetamide. *See* Chloroacetamide

Chloroacetophenone

 CAS 532-27-4
 UN No. 1697
 Synonyms: α-Chloroacetophenone; 2-Chloroacetophenone; Phenacyl chloride
 Formula: $C_6H_5COCH_2Cl$
 Properties: Wh. cryst., floral odor; sol. in acetone, benzene; insol. in water; m.w. 154.60; dens. 1.324; m.p. 54-56 C; b.p. 244-245 C
 Toxicology: Strong eye and tissue irritant
 Uses: Pharmaceutical intermediate
 Manuf./Distrib.: Janssen Chimica; Penta Mfg.; Schweizerhall

2-Chloroacetophenone. *See* Chloroacetophenone
α-Chloroacetophenone. *See* Chloroacetophenone
N-(3-Chloroallyl)hexaminium chloride. *See* Quaternium-15
1-(3-Chloroallyl)-3,5,7-triaza-1-azoniaadamantane chloride. *See* Quaternium-15
3-Chloroaniline. *See* m-Chloroaniline
4-Chloroaniline. *See* p-Chloroaniline

m-Chloroaniline

 CAS 108-42-9; EINECS 203-581-0
 UN No. 2018, 2019
 Synonyms: m-Aminochlorobenzene; 3-Chloroaniline
 Formula: $ClC_6H_4NH_2$

Properties: Colorless to lt. amber liq.; sol. in org. solvs.; insol. in water; m.w. 127.57; dens. 1.206; m.p. -11 to -9 C; b.p. 95-96 C (11 mm); flash pt. 123 C; ref. index 1.5940
Toxicology: Irritant
Uses: Pharmaceutical intermediate
Manuf./Distrib.: Aceto; Aldrich; DuPont; Janssen Chimica; Schweizerhall
Manuf./Distrib. (pharm. & food): Aldrich

o-Chloroaniline

CAS 95-51-2
UN No. 2018, 2019
Synonyms: o-Aminochlorobenzene
Formula: $ClC_6H_4NH_2$
Uses: Pharmaceutical intermediate
Manuf./Distrib.: Aceto; DuPont

p-Chloroaniline

CAS 106-47-8; EINECS 203-401-0
UN No. 2018, 2019
Synonyms: p-Aminochlorobenzene; 4-Chloroaniline
Formula: $ClC_6H_4NH_2$
Properties: Wh. or pale yel. solid; sol. in hot water, org. solvs.; m.w. 127.57; m.p. 68-71 C; b.p. 232 C
Toxicology: Irritant
Uses: Pharmaceutical intermediate
Regulatory: BP compliance
Manuf./Distrib.: Aceto; Aldrich; DuPont; Janssen Chimica; Mitsui Toatsu
Manuf./Distrib. (pharm. & food): Aldrich

Chlorobutanol

CAS 57-15-8 (anhyd.); 6001-64-5 (hemihydrate); EINECS 200-317-6
Synonyms: Trichloro-t-butyl alcohol; Chlorbutol; Chloretone; 1,1,1-Trichloro-2-methyl-2-propanol; Acetone chloroform
Empirical: $C_4Cl_3H_7O$
Formula: $Cl_3CC(CH_3)_2OH$
Properties: Colorless to wh. cryst., camphoraceous odor; sol. in chloroform, ether, volatile oils; sl. sol. in water; m.w. 177.46 (anhyd.), 186.46 (hemihydrate); m.p. 76 C
Precaution: Unstable in alkali
Toxicology: Hypersensitivity and toxic reactions have occurred; no known skin toxicity; eye irritant; CNS depressant
Uses: Antimicrobial preservative, anesthetic, antiseptic; mild sedative; topical analgesic; used in parenterals, ophthalmic prods., topicals, otics, inhalants
Usage level: 0.0001-0.5% (parenterals); 0.2-0.65% (ophthalmics)
Regulatory: USA EPA registered; Europe listed; FDA approved for injectables, inhalants, nasals, ophthalmics, otics, topicals; USP/NF, BP, Ph.Eur. compliance
Manuf./Distrib.: Aldrich; EM Industries; R.W. Greeff; Penta Mfg.; Spectrum Chem. Mfg.
Manuf./Distrib. (pharm. & food): Integra; Ruger; Spectrum Chem. Mfg.

Chlorobutanol hemihydrate

CAS 6001-64-5; EINECS 200-317-6
Synonyms: 1,1,1-Trichloro-2-methyl-2-propanol hemihydrate; β,β,β-Trichloro-t-butyl alcohol; 'Acetone chloroforn'
Empirical: $C_4H_7Cl_3O \cdot {}^1/_2H_2O$
Formula: $Cl_3CC(CH_3)_2OH \cdot {}^1/_2H_2O$
Properties: M.w. 186.46
Uses: Antimicrobial preservative; used in intramuscular injectables
Regulatory: FDA approved for injectables; USP/NF, BP, Ph.Eur. compliance
Manuf./Distrib.: Fluka
Manuf./Distrib. (pharm. & food): Spectrum Chem. Mfg.

6-Chloro-2-(6-chloro-4-methyl-3-oxobenzo[b]thien-2(3H)-ylidene)-4-methylbenzo[b]thiophen-3(2H)-one.
See CI 73360; D&C Red No. 30
Chlorocresol. *See* p-Chloro-m-cresol
4-Chloro-m-cresol. *See* p-Chloro-m-cresol

p-Chloro-m-cresol
   CAS 59-50-7; EINECS 200-431-6
   UN No. 2669
   Synonyms: PCMC; 4-Chloro-3-methyl phenol; 4-Chloro-m-cresol; Parachlorometacresol; Chlorocresol; 2-
      Chloro-5-hydroxytoluene
   Empirical: C_7CIH_7O
   Properties: Colorless dimorphous cryst., phenolic odor; very sol. in alcohol; sol. in ether, fixed oils, hot water;
      m.w. 142.59; m.p. 65-68 C; b.p. 235 C
   Toxicology: Weak irritant; may produce digestive disturbances, nervous disorders, fainting, dizziness, mental
      changes, skin eruptions; eye irritant
   Uses: Antimicrobial preservative for injectable prods. (intravenous heparin prods.), topical creams and lotions,
      eye lotions, dentifrices, mouthwashes
   Usage level: 0.1-0.15% (injectables), 0.075-0.12% (topicals)
   Regulatory: FDA approved for topicals; USP/NF, BP compliance
   Trade names containing: Sebase

1-Chloro-2,2-dichloroethylene. *See* Trichloroethylene
5-Chloro-2(2,4-dichlorophenoxy)phenol. *See* Triclosan
6-Chloro-3,4-dihydro-2H-1,2,4-benzothiadiazine-7-sulfonamide-1,1-dioxide. *See* Hydrochlorothiazide
1-Chloro-2-dimethylaminoethane hydrochloride. *See* Dimethylaminoethyl chloride hydrochloride
2-Chloro-N,N-dimethylethylamine hydrochloride. *See* Dimethylaminoethyl chloride hydrochloride
4-Chloro-3,5-dimethylphenol. *See* Chloroxylenol
Chloroethene. *See* Vinyl chloride
Chloroethene homopolymer. *See* Polyvinyl chloride
N-(2-Chloroethyl)dimethylamine hydrochloride. *See* Dimethylaminoethyl chloride hydrochloride
Chloroethylene. *See* Vinyl chloride
Chloroethylene polymer. *See* Polyvinyl chloride

Chloroform
   CAS 67-66-3; EINECS 200-663-8
   UN No. 1888
   Synonyms: Trichloromethane; Methane, trichloro-
   Empirical: $CHCl_3$
   Properties: Colorless clear mobile liq., ethereal odor, sweet burning taste; misc. with alcohol, benzene,
      hexane, acetone; m.w. 119.38; dens. 1.474-1.478; m.p. -63 C; b.p. 61 C; flash pt. none; ref. index 1.4460
   Precaution: DOT: Poisonous material; light-sensitive
   Toxicology: Respiratory and skin allergies; poisonous in large doses; suspected carcinogen
   Uses: Preservative; solvent; sweet pleasant flavor in aq. ('chloroform water'), alcoholic ('spirits'), and emulsion
      formulations; potent systemic anesthetic
   Regulatory: BP compliance
   Manuf./Distrib.: Elf Atochem N. Am.; Hüls AG; Mallinckrodt; Mitsui Toatsu Chem.; Occidental; Spectrum
      Chem. Mfg.
   Manuf./Distrib. (pharm. & food): Aldrich; Mallinckrodt; Ruger; Tokuyama

2-Chloro-5-hydroxytoluene. *See* p-Chloro-m-cresol
Chloromethylisothiazolinone. *See* Methylchloroisothiazolinone
5-Chloro-2-methyl-4-isothiazolin-3-one. *See* Methylchloroisothiazolinone
4-Chloro-3-methyl phenol. *See* p-Chloro-m-cresol
1-[(2-Chloro-4-nitrophenyl)azo]-2-naphthalenol. *See* CI 12085; D&C Red No. 36
Chlorooxobismuthine. *See* Bismuth oxychloride; CI 77163
Chlorophyll. *See* CI 75810

Chlorophyllin-copper complex
   CAS 11006-34-1; EINECS 234-242-5
   Synonyms: CCC; Potassium sodium copper chlorophyllin; Chlorophyllin, copper sodium complex; Copper
      sodium chlorophyllin; CI 75810
   Definition: Obtained from chlorophyll from dehydrated alfalfa by replacing the methyl and phytyl ester groups
      with alkali and replacing the magnesium with copper
   Properties: Grn.-blk. powd.
   Uses: Colorant for dentifrices; deodorant drug for internal use; wound healing remedy
   Usage level: 0.1% max. (dentifrices)
   Regulatory: FDA 21CFR §73.1125, 73.2125; banned by FDA as a colorant
   Trade names: Potassium Sodium Copper Chlorophyllin 033280
   See also CI 75810

Chlorophyllin, copper sodium complex. *See* Chlorophyllin-copper complex

2-Chloropyridine
CAS 109-09-1; EINECS 203-646-3
UN No. 2822
Empirical: C_5H_4ClN
Properties: M.w. 113.55; sol. 2.5 g/100 g water; b.p. 168-170 C; ref. index 1.532
Uses: Pharmaceutical intermediate; prod. of antihistamines
Manuf./Distrib.: Aceto; Expansia SA; Olin; Penta Mfg.; Reilly Ind.; Schweizerhall
Manuf./Distrib. (pharm. & food): Aldrich

1-(4-Chloro-o-sulfo-5-tolylazo)-2-nahthol monosodium salt. *See* D&C Red No. 8
1-(4-Chloro-o-sulfo-5-tolylazo)-2-naphthol monobarium salt. *See* D&C Red No. 9
Chlorosulthiadil. *See* Hydrochlorothiazide

Chlorothen
CAS 148-65-2
Synonyms: Chlorothenylpyramine
Empirical: $C_{14}H_{18}ClN_3S$
Properties: Sol. in water; insol. in ether, chloroform, benzene; m.w. 295.85; b.p. 155-156 C
Toxicology: LD50 (IP, mus) 105 mg/kg
Uses: Used in orals
Regulatory: Approved for orals

Chlorothenylpyramine. *See* Chlorothen

Chlorotrifluoromethane
CAS 75-72-9; EINECS 200-894-4
UN No. 1022
Empirical: $CClF_3$
Properties: Colorless gas, ethereal odor; m.w. 104.5; b.p. -81.4 C; f.p. -181 C
Precaution: Nonflamm.
Toxicology: Toxic by inhalation, sl. irritant
Uses: Pharmaceutical processing
Manuf./Distrib.: Elf Atochem N. Am.; PCR
Manuf./Distrib. (pharm. & food): Aldrich

Chloroxylenol
CAS 88-04-0; EINECS 201-793-8
Synonyms: PCMX; p-Chloro-m-xylenol; Benzytol; 4-Chloro-3,5-xylenol; 4-Chloro-3,5-dimethylphenol; Parachlorometaxylenol
Classification: Organic compd.
Empirical: C_8H_9OCl
Formula: $C_6H_2(CH_3)_2OHCl$
Properties: Wh. cryst. or cryst. powd., char. phenolic odor; sol. in 1 part of 95% alcohol, ether, benzene, terpenes, fixed oils; very sl. sol. in water; m.w. 156.61; m.p. 114-116 C; b.p. 246 C
Toxicology: Toxic by ingestion; strong irritant absorbed by skin
Uses: Antimicrobial preservative for otics and topicals; antiseptic base
Usage level: 0.2-0.8%; 0.1-0.15% (otics, topicals)
Regulatory: USA EPA registered; Japan approved; Europe listed; FDA approved for otics, topicals; BP compliance
Manuf./Distrib. (pharm. & food): Aldrich; Spectrum Chem. Mfg.
Trade names: Nipacide® PX-R; Ottasept®; Ottasept® Extra
Trade names containing: Phenosept

4-Chloro-3,5-xylenol. *See* Chloroxylenol
p-Chloro-m-xylenol. *See* Chloroxylenol
Chlorzide. *See* Hydrochlorothiazide

Cholecalciferol
CAS 67-97-0; EINECS 200-673-2
Synonyms: 5,7-Cholestadien-3-β-ol; 9,10-seco(5Z,7E)-5,7,10(19)-Cholestatrien-3-ol; 7-Dehydrocholesterol; Calciol; Vitamin D_3
Classification: Sterol; vitamin
Empirical: $C_{27}H_{44}O$
Properties: Colorless to wh. cryst., odorless; unstable in light and air; sol. in acetone, alcohol, chloroform, fatty oils; insol. in water; m.w. 384.71; m.p. 84-88 C

Precaution: Affected by air and light
Toxicology: LD50 (oral, rat) 42 mg/kg; poison by ingestion; experimental teratogen; heated to decomp., emits acrid smoke and irritating fumes
Uses: Medicine (antirachitic vitamin); nutrient
Regulatory: FDA 21CFR §166.110, 182.5953, 184.1950, GRAS; Japan approved; BP, Ph.Eur. compliance
Manuf./Distrib. (pharm. & food): Am. Roland; Spectrum Chem. Mfg.
Trade names containing: Dry Vitamin D_3 Beadlets Type 850 No. 652550401, 652550601; Dry Vitamin D_3 Type 100 CWS No. 65242; Liquid Vitamin D_3 No. 63643

5,7-Cholestadien-3-β-ol. *See* Cholecalciferol
Cholest-5-en-3β-ol. *See* Cholesterol
Cholesteric esters. *See* Cholesterol
Cholesterin. *See* Cholesterol

Cholesterol
CAS 57-88-5; EINECS 200-353-2
Synonyms: Cholesterin; Cholest-5-en-3β-ol; Cholesteric esters
Classification: Steroid alcohol
Definition: Mono-unsaturated sec. alcohol of the cyclopentenophenanthrene system
Empirical: $C_{27}H_{46}O$
Properties: White or faintly yellow pearly granules or crystals, almost odorless; yel. to tan color on prolonged exposure to light; sol. in acetone, chloroform, dioxane, ethyl acetate, hexane, benzene, petrol. ether, oils, fats; sl. sol. in water, alcohol; m.w. 386.67; dens. 1.067; m.p. 148.5 C; b.p. 360 C (dec.)
Precaution: Light-sensitive; refrigerate
Toxicology: Nontoxic to skin
Uses: Emulsifier/solubilizer used in ophthalmics, topicals
Regulatory: Japan approved; approved for ophthalmics, topicals; USP/NF, BP compliance
Manuf./Distrib.: Croda; EM Industries; Fluka; Schweizerhall; Solvay Duphar BV; U.S. Biochemical
Manuf./Distrib. (pharm. & food): Robeco; Ruger; Spectrum Chem. Mfg.
Trade names: Cholesterol NF; Cholesterol NF; Fancol CH; Loralan-CH

Choleth-24
CAS 27321-96-6 (generic)
Synonyms: PEG-24 cholesteryl ether
Definition: Polyethylene glycol ether of cholesterol
Uses: Emulsifier, solubilizer, thickener for topicals
Regulatory: Approved for topicals
Trade names containing: Forlan C-24

Cholinphosphoric acid diglyceride ester. *See* Hydrogenated lecithin

Chondroitin sulfate
CAS 9007-28-7
Synonyms: Chondroitinsulfuric acid
Classification: Mucopolysaccharide
Definition: Major constituent of the cartilagenous tissue in the body
Properties: M.w. ≈ 50,000
Uses: Nutritive additive; antihyperlipoproteinemic
Manuf./Distrib.: Croda; Kraeber GmbH
Trade names containing: Soluble Trachea CS 16 Substance

Chondroitinsulfuric acid. *See* Chondroitin sulfate
Chondrus. *See* Carrageenan
Chondrus crispus extract. *See* Carrageenan extract
Chondrus extract. *See* Carrageenan extract
Chromic oxide. *See* Chromium oxide greens; CI 77288
Chromic oxide hydrated. *See* Chromium hydroxide green; CI 77289
Chromic sesquioxide. *See* Chromium oxide greens

Chromium-cobalt-aluminum oxide
Definition: Obtained by calcining a mixt. of chromium oxide, cobalt carbonate, and aluminum oxide
Properties: Blue-green pigment
Toxicology: Inh. of chromium dust can cause irritation and ulceration; ingestion results in violent gastrointestinal irritation; applic.to skin may result in allergic reaction
Uses: Color additive for polyethylene sutures
Usage level: 2% max. (sutures)

Chromium hydroxide green
CAS 12001-99-9; 12182-82-0
Synonyms: Chromic oxide hydrated; Hydrated chromic sesquioxide; Hydrated chromium sesquioxide; Veridian; Guignet's green; CI 77289 (EEC); Pigment green 18
Classification: Inorganic pigment
Empirical: $Cr_2O_3 \cdot xH_2O$
Properties: Bluish/brilliant green transparent
Toxicology: Applic. to skin may cause allergic reaction; ingestion results in violent gastrointestinal irritation
Uses: Color additive for external pharmaceuticals
Regulatory: FDA 21CFR §73.1326, 173.2326; permanently listed
Manuf./Distrib. (pharm. & food): Hilton Davis
See also CI 77289

Chromium oxide greens
CAS 1308-38-9; EINECS 215-160-9
Synonyms: Chromic oxide; Chromic sesquioxide; Chromium sesquioxide; Dichromium trioxide; Pigment green 17; CI 77288
Classification: Inorganic pigment
Empirical: Cr_2O_3
Properties: Ylsh. (sage) green; hygroscopic; m.w. 151.99
Uses: Color additive for external pharmaceuticals
Regulatory: FDA 21CFR §72.2327, 173.1327
Manuf./Distrib.: Spectrum Chem. Mfg.
Manuf./Distrib. (pharm. & food): Aldrich; Hilton Davis
See also CI 77288

Chromium sesquioxide. *See* Chromium oxide greens

CI 10316
CAS 846-70-8; EINECS 212-690-2
Synonyms: 2,4-Dinitro-1-naphthol-7-sulfonic acid disodium salt; 8-Hydroxy-5,7-dinitro-2-naphthalenesulfonic acid disodium salt; Acid yellow 1
Classification: Nitro color
Formula: $C_{10}H_6N_2O_8S \cdot 2Na$
Uses: Color additive for external pharmaceuticals
Manuf./Distrib. (pharm. & food): Aldrich
See also Ext. D&C Yellow No. 7

CI 12075. *See* D&C Orange No. 17

CI 12085
CAS 2814-77-9; EINECS 220-562-2
Synonyms: 1-[(2-Chloro-4-nitrophenyl)azo]-2-naphthalenol; Pigment red 4
Classification: Monoazo color
Formula: $C_{16}H_{10}ClN_3O_3$
Properties: M.w. 327.73
Uses: Color additive for pharmaceuticals
See also D&C Red No. 36

CI 13058. *See* D&C Red No. 39

CI 14700
CAS 4548-53-2; EINECS 224-909-9
Synonyms: 3-[(2,4-Dimethyl-5-sulfophenyl)azo]-4-hydroxy-1-naphthalenesulfonic acid disodium salt; Ponceau SX; Food red 1
Classification: Monoazo color
Formula: $C_{18}H_{16}N_2O_7S_2 \cdot 2Na$
Properties: M.w. 480.14
Uses: Colorant for external pharmaceuticals
See also FD&C Red No. 4

CI 15510
CAS 633-96-5; EINECS 211-199-0
Synonyms: 4-[(2-Hydroxy-1-naphthalenyl)azo]benzenesulfonic acid monosodium salt; Orange II; Acid orange 7
Classification: Monoazo color
Formula: $C_{16}H_{12}N_2O_4S \cdot Na$
Properties: M.w. 350.32

CI 15585

Uses: Color additive for external pharmaceuticals
Manuf./Distrib. (pharm. & food): Aldrich
See also D&C Orange No. 4

CI 15585. See D&C Red No. 8
CI 15585:1. See D&C Red No. 9
CI 15800:1. See D&C Red No. 31

CI 15850
CAS 5858-81-1; EINECS 227-497-9
Synonyms: 3-Hydroxy-4-[(4-methyl-2-sulfophenyl)azo]-2-naphthalenecarboxylic acid disodium salt; Pigment red 57
Classification: Monoazo color
Formula: $C_{18}H_{14}N_2O_6S \cdot 2Na$
Uses: Color additive for pharmaceuticals
See also D&C Red No. 6

CI 15850:1. See D&C Red No. 7
CI 15880:1. See D&C Red No. 34

CI 15985
CAS 2783-94-0; EINECS 220-491-7
Synonyms: 6-Hydroxy-5-[(4-sulfophenyl)azo]-2-naphthalenesulfonic acid disodium salt; Sunset yellow; Food yellow 3
Classification: Monoazo color
Definition: Disodium salt of 1-p-sulfophenylazo-2-naphthol-6-sulfonic acid
Empirical: $C_{16}H_{10}N_2O_7S_2Na_2$
Formula: $C_{16}H_{10}N_2O_7S_2 \cdot 2Na$
Properties: Reddish-yel. powd., gran.; sol. (oz/gal): 23 oz dist. water, 14 oz glycerin, 2 oz propylene glycol; sol. in conc. sulfuric acid; sl. sol. in abs. alcohol; m.w 452.36
Toxicology: LD50 (IP, rat) 4600 mg/kg; mod. toxic by IP route; may cause allergies, kidney tumors, chromosomal damage; heated to decomp., emits very toxic fumes of NO_x and SO_x
Uses: Colorant for pharmaceuticals
See also FD&C Yellow No. 6

CI 16035
CAS 25956-17-6
Synonyms: 6-Hydroxy-5-[(2-methoxy-5-methyl-4-sulfophenyl)azo]-2-naphthalenesulfonic acid disodium salt; Food red 17; Curry red
Classification: Monoazo color
Empirical: $C_{18}H_{16}N_2O_8S_2Na_2$
Formula: $C_{18}H_{16}N_2O_8S_2 \cdot 2Na$
Properties: Ylsh.-red powd., gran.; sol. (oz/gal): 26 oz dist. water, 4 oz glycerin, 2 oz propylene glycol; m.w. 498.46
Toxicology: Experimental reproductive effects; may cause lymph tumors; heated to decomp., emits very toxic fumes of NO_x and SO_x
Uses: Colorant for oral drug prods., topicals; exhibits orange-red hue in sol'n.
See also FD&C Red No. 40

CI 16185. See Amaranth

CI 17200
CAS 3567-66-6; EINECS 222-656-9
Synonyms: 5-Amino-4-hydroxy-3-(phenylazo)-2,7-naphthalenedisulfonic acid disodium salt; Acid red 33
Classification: Monoazo color
Formula: $C_{16}H_{13}N_3O_7S_2 \cdot 2Na$
Uses: Color additive for pharmaceuticals
See also D&C Red No. 33

CI 19140
CAS 1934-21-0; EINECS 217-699-5
Synonyms: 4,5-Dihydro-5-oxo-1-(4-sulfophenyl)-4-[(4-sulfophenyl)azo]-1H-pyrazole-3-carboxylic acid trisodium salt; Tartrazine; Acid yellow 23
Classification: Pyrazole color
Empirical: $C_{16}H_9N_4O_9S_2Na_3$
Formula: $C_{16}H_9N_4O_9S_2 \cdot 3Na$
Properties: Lemon yel. powd., gran.; greenish-yel. in sol'n.; sol. (oz/gal): 28 oz glycerin, 17 oz dist. water, 12

oz propylene glycol; m.w. 534.36

Precaution: Heated to dec., emits very toxic fumes of NO_x, SO_x, and Na_2O

Toxicology: LD50 (oral, mouse) 12,750 mg/kg; mildly toxic by ingestion; experimental teratogen, reproductive effects; human mutagenic data; may cause allergies, asthma, rashes, hyperactivity, thyroid tumors, lyphocytic lymphomas

Uses: Colorant for oral and topical pharmaceuticals

Manuf./Distrib. (pharm. & food): Aldrich

See also FD&C Yellow No. 5; Tartrazine

CI 26100

CAS 85-86-9

Synonyms: 1-[[4-(Phenylazo)phenyl]azo]-2-naphthalenol; Sudan III; Solvent red 23

Classification: Diazo color

Empirical: $C_{22}H_{16}N_4O$

Properties: M.w. 352.40

Uses: Color additive for external pharmaceuticals

Manuf./Distrib. (pharm. & food): Aldrich

See also D&C Red No. 17

CI 40800

CAS 7235-40-7; EINECS 230-636-6

Synonyms: β-Carotene; Synthetic carotene; Food orange 5

Classification: Carotenoid color

Empirical: $C_{40}H_{56}$

Uses: Color additive for pharmaceuticals

See also Carotene, CI 75130

CI 40850

CAS 514-78-3; EINECS 208-187-2

Synonyms: Canthaxanthin; Canthaxanthine; β,β-Carotene-4,4´-dione; Food orange 8

Classification: Carotenoid color

Empirical: $C_{40}H_{52}O_2$

Uses: Colorant for ingested pharmaceuticals

See also Canthaxanthine

CI 42053

CAS 2353-45-9; EINECS 219-091-5

Synonyms: Fast green FCF; Food green 3

Classification: Triphenylmethane color

Empirical: $C_{37}H_{36}O_{10}N_2S_3Na_2$

Properties: Red to brn.-violet powd.; sol. in water, conc. sulfuric acid, ethanol; m.w. 810.91

Toxicology: LD50 (oral, rat) > 2 g/kg; experimental neoplastigen; may cause bladder tumors; mutagenic data; heated to decomp., emits very toxic fumes of NO_x and SO_x

Uses: Colorant for pharmaceuticals

Manuf./Distrib. (pharm. & food): Aldrich

See also FD&C Green No. 3

CI 42090

CAS 3844-45-9

Synonyms: Acid blue 9

Classification: Triphenylmethane color

Empirical: $C_{37}H_{36}N_2O_9S_3 \cdot 2H_3N$

Properties: M.w. 783.01

Uses: Color additive for pharmaceuticals

Manuf./Distrib. (pharm. & food): Aldrich

See also FD&C Blue No. 1; D&C Blue No. 4

CI 42090:2. *See* FD&C Blue No. 1 aluminum lake

CI 45170. *See* D&C Red No. 19

CI 45170:1. *See* D&C Red No. 37

CI 45350

CAS 518-47-8; EINECS 208-253-0

Synonyms: 3´,6´-Dihydroxyspiro[isobenzofuran-1(3H),9´-[9H]xanthen]-3-one disodium salt; Sodium fluorescein; Acid yellow 73 sodium salt

Classification: Xanthene color

CI 45350:1

Formula: $C_{20}H_{12}O_5 \cdot 2Na$
Properties: M.w. 376.28
Uses: Color additive for external pharmaceuticals
Manuf./Distrib. (pharm. & food): Aldrich
See also D&C Yellow No. 8

CI 45350:1. See D&C Yellow No. 7
CI 45370:1. See D&C Orange No. 5

CI 45380

CAS 548-26-5; 17372-87-1; EINECS 241-409-6
Synonyms: 2',4',5',7'-Tetrabromo-3',6'-dihydroxyspiro[isobenzofuran-1(3H),9'-[9H]xanthen]-3-one disodium salt; Acid red 87
Classification: Xanthene color
Formula: $C_{20}H_8O_5Br_4Na_2$
Uses: Color additive for pharmaceuticals
Manuf./Distrib. (pharm. & food): Aldrich
See also D&C Red No. 22

CI 45380:2. See D&C Red No. 21

CI 45410

CAS 18472-87-2; EINECS 242-355-6
Synonyms: 2',4',5',7'-Tetrabromo-4,5,6,7-tetrachloro-3',6'-dihydroxyspiro[isobenzofuran-1(3H),9'-[9H]xanthen]-3-one disodium salt; Acid red 92
Classification: Xanthene color
Formula: $C_{20}H_4Br_4Cl_4O_5 \cdot 2Na$
Uses: Color additive for pharmaceuticals
Manuf./Distrib. (pharm. & food): Aldrich
See also D&C Red No. 28

CI 45410:1. See D&C Red No. 27

CI 45425

CAS 68424-94-2
Synonyms: 3',6'-Dihydroxy-4',5'-diiodospiro[isobenzofuran-1(3H),9'-[9H]xanthen]-3-one disodium salt; Acid red 95
Classification: Xanthene color
Empirical: $C_{20}H_{10}I_2O_5 \cdot 2Na$
Uses: Color additive for external pharmaceuticals

CI 45425:1. See D&C Orange No. 10

CI 45430

CAS 16423-68-0; EINECS 240-474-8
Synonyms: 3',6'-Dihydroxy-2',4',5',7'-tetraiodospiro[isobenzofuran-1(3H),9'-(9H)xanthen]-3-one disodium salt; Erythrosine; Acid red 51
Classification: Xanthene color
Definition: Disodium salt of 2',4',5',7'-tetraiodofluorescein
Formula: $C_{20}H_6I_4O_5 \cdot 2Na$
Properties: Bluish pink to brn. powd., gran.; sol. (oz/gal): 30 oz glycerin, 28 oz propylene glycol, 12 oz dist. water, 2 oz 95% ethanol; m.w. 879.84
Precaution: Photosensitizer
Toxicology: LD50 (oral, rat) 1840 mg/kg; poison by IV route; mod. toxic by ingestion; human mutagenic data; may cause thyroid tumors, chromosomal damage, asthma, rashes, hyperactivity; heated to decomp., emits very toxic fumes of Na_2O and I.
Uses: Colorant for ingested drugs and other uses
Manuf./Distrib. (pharm. & food): Aldrich
See also FD&C Red No. 3

CI 47000

CAS 8003-22-3; EINECS 232-318-2
Synonyms: 2-(2-Quinolyl)-1,3-indandione; Solvent yellow 33
Classification: Quinoline color
Empirical: $C_{18}H_{11}NO_2$
Properties: M.w. 273.29

Uses: Color additive for external pharmaceuticals
Manuf./Distrib. (pharm. & food): Aldrich
See also D&C Yellow No. 11

CI 47005
CAS 8004-92-0
Synonyms: Quinoline Yellow; Acid yellow 3
Classification: Quinoline color
Definition: Mixt. of the disodium salt of the mono- and disulfonic acids of 2-(2-quinolyl)-1H-indene-1,3(2H)-dione
Empirical: $C_{18}H_9NO_8S_2Na_2$
Properties: M.w. 477.37
Uses: Color additive for pharmaceuticals
Manuf./Distrib. (pharm. & food): Aldrich
See also D&C Yellow No. 10

CI 59040
CAS 6358-69-6; EINECS 228-783-6
Synonyms: 8-Hydroxy-1,3,6-pyrenetrisulfonic acid trisodium salt; Solvent green 7
Classification: Pyrene color
Formula: $C_{16}H_7O_{10}S_3$ • 3Na
Properties: M.w. 524.37
Uses: Color additive for external pharmaeuticals
See also D&C Green No. 8

CI 60725
CAS 81-48-1; EINECS 201-353-5
Synonyms: 1-Hydroxy-4-[(4-methylphenyl)amino]-9,10-anthracenedione; Solvent violet 13
Classification: Anthraquinone color
Empirical: $C_{21}H_{15}NO_3$
Properties: M.w. 329.35
Uses: Color additive for external pharmaceuticals
See also D&C Violet No. 2

CI 61565
CAS 128-80-3; EINECS 204-909-5
Synonyms: 9,10-Anthracenedione, 1,4-bis[(4-methylphenyl)amino]-; 1,4-Bis[(4-methylphenyl)-amino-9,10-anthracenedione; Solvent green 3
Classification: Anthraquinone color
Empirical: $C_{28}H_{22}N_2O_2$
Properties: M.w. 418.50
Uses: Color additive for PET and polyglycolic acid sutures for ophthalmic and general surgical use, external pharmaceuticals
Manuf./Distrib. (pharm. & food): Aldrich
See also D&C Green No. 6

CI 61570
CAS 4403-90-1; EINECS 224-546-6
Synonyms: 2,2′-[(9,10-Dihydro-9,10-dioxo-1,4-anthracenediyl)diimino]bis(5-methyl)benzenesulfonic acid disodium salt; Acid green 25
Classification: Anthraquinone color
Empirical: $C_{28}H_{20}N_2Na_2O_8S_2$
Formula: $C_{28}H_{20}N_2O_8S_2$ • 2Na
Properties: M.w. 622.57
Uses: Color additive for nylon 6 and 6/6 nonabsorbable surgical sutures and other uses
Manuf./Distrib. (pharm. & food): Aldrich
See also D&C Green No. 5

CI 69825
CAS 130-20-1; EINECS 240-980-2
Synonyms: 7,16-Dichloro-6.15-dihydro-5,9,14,18-anthrazinetetrone; Vat blue 6
Classification: Anthraquinone color
Empirical: $C_{28}H_{12}Cl_2N_2O_4$
Formula: $C_{28}H_{12}N_2O_4Cl_2$
Properties: M.w. 511.32

CI 73000

Uses: Color additive for sutures, incl. ophthalmic use
See also D&C Blue No. 9

CI 73000

CAS 482-89-3; EINECS 207-586-9
Synonyms: 2-(1,3-Dihydro-3-oxo-2H-indol-2-ylidene)-1,2-dihydro-3H-indol-3-one; Indigo; Vat blue 1
Classification: Indigoid color
Empirical: $C_{16}H_{10}N_2O$
Properties: M.w. 246.28
Uses: Color additive; used in sutures incl. ophthalmic surgical use
Manuf./Distrib. (pharm. & food): Aldrich
See also D&C Blue No. 6

CI 73015

CAS 860-22-0; EINECS 212-728-8
Synonyms: 2-(1,3-Dihydro-3-oxo-5-sulfo-2H-indol-2-ylidene)-2,3-dihydro-3-oxo-1H-indole-5-sulfonic acid
disodium salt; Indigotine; Indigo carmine; Acid blue 74
Classification: Indigoid color
Formula: $C_{16}H_8N_2O_8S_2$ • 2Na
Toxicology: Intravenous use may produce severe headache, acute pulmonary edema with cardiac arrest,
hypertension
Uses: Color additive for ingested drugs and nylon sutures; diagnostic marker in urology
Manuf./Distrib. (pharm. & food): Aldrich
See also FD&C Blue No. 2

CI 73360

CAS 2379-74-0; EINECS 219-163-6
Synonyms: 6-Chloro-2-(6-chloro-4-methyl-3-oxobenzo[b]thien-2(3H)-ylidene)-4-methylbenzo[b]thiophen-
3(2H)-one; Vat red 1
Classification: Thioindigoid color
Empirical: $C_{18}H_{10}O_2S_2Cl_2$
Properties: M.w. 393.30
Uses: Color additive for pharmaceuticals
See also D&C Red No. 30

CI 74160. See Copper phthalocyanine blue

CI 75120

CAS 1393-63-1; EINECS 215-735-4
Synonyms: Annatto; Natural orange 4
Definition: Coloring matter from Bixa orellana
Uses: Colorant for pharmaceuticals
See also Annatto; Annatto extract

CI 75130

CAS 7235-40-7; EINECS 230-636-6
Synonyms: β-Carotene; Natural carotene; Natural brown 5; Natural yellow 26
Classification: Carotenoid color
Empirical: $C_{40}H_{56}$
Uses: Colorant for pharmaceuticals
See also Carotene, CI 40800

CI 75170

CAS 73-40-5; EINECS 200-799-8
Synonyms: 2-Amino-1,7-dihydro-6H-purin-6-one; 2-Aminohypoxanthine; 2-Amino-6-hydroxypurine; Gua-
nine; Natural pearl essence; Natural white 1; Pearl essence
Classification: Natural purine
Empirical: $C_5H_5N_5O$
Properties: Colorless rhombic crystals; insol. in water; sparingly sol. in alcohol, ether; freely sol. in ammonium
hydroxide, dilute acids; m.w. 151.15; dec. > 360 C
Toxicology: Suspected tumorigen; human mutagenic data
Uses: Color additive for external pharmaceuticals
See also Guanine

CI 75290. See Logwood extract

CI 75470

CAS 1260-17-9; EINECS 215-724-4

Synonyms: Carminic acid; Carmine; Natural red 4
Classification: Naturally derived color
Empirical: $C_{22}H_{20}O_{13}$
Properties: M.w. 492.39
Uses: Color additive for pharmaceuticals
Manuf./Distrib. (pharm. & food): Aldrich
See also Carmine

CI 75810

CAS 11006-34-1; EINECS 234-242-5
Synonyms: Potassium sodium copper chlorophyllin; Chlorophyll; Chlorophyllin-copper complex; Natural green 3
Definition: Botanically derived color obtained from green plants
Uses: Colorant for dentifrices
Usage level: 0.1% max. (dentifrices)
See also Chlorophyllin-copper complex

CI 76515. *See* Pyrogallol

CI 77000

CAS 7429-90-5; EINECS 231-072-3
Synonyms: Aluminum powder; Pigment metal 1
Classification: Inorganic color
Definition: Consists of finely powdered aluminum
Empirical: Al
Uses: Color additive for external pharmaceuticals
See also Aluminum

CI 77002

CAS 1332-73-6; EINECS 215-573-4
Synonyms: Aluminum hydroxide; Pigment white 24
Classification: Inorganic color
Definition: Consists predominantly of aluminum hydroxide
Empirical: AlH_3O_3
Uses: Colorant for pharmaceuticals

CI 77004. *See* Aluminum silicate; Bentonite
CI 77019. *See* Mica; Talc

CI 77163

CAS 7787-59-9; EINECS 232-122-7
Synonyms: Bismuth oxychloride; Chlorooxobismuthine; Pigment white 14
Classification: Inorganic color
Empirical: BiClO
Formula: BiOCl
Uses: Color additive for external pharmaceuticals
See also Bismuth oxychloride

CI 77220

CAS 471-34-1; EINECS 207-439-9
Synonyms: Calcium carbonate; Carbonic acid calcium salt (1:1); Pigment white 18
Classification: Inorganic color
Empirical: $CaCO_3$
Uses: Color additive for pharmaceuticals
See also Calcium carbonate

CI 77288

CAS 1308-38-9; EINECS 215-160-9
Synonyms: Chromic oxide; Chromium oxide greens; Dichromium trioxide; Pigment green 17
Classification: Inorganic color
Empirical: Cr_2O_3
Uses: Color additive for external pharmaceuticals
See also Chromium oxide greens

CI 77289

CAS 12001-99-9
Synonyms: Chromic oxide hydrated; Chromium hydroxide green; Hydrated chromium sesquioxide; Pigment green 18

CI 77400

Classification: Inorganic color
Formula: $Cr_2O(OH)_4$
Uses: Color additive for external pharmaceuticals
See also Chromium hydroxide green

CI 77400

CAS 7440-50-8; EINECS 231-159-6
Synonyms: Bronze powder; Copper powder; Pigment metal 2
Classification: Inorganic color
Definition: Finely powdered metal consisting chiefly of copper or copper-zinc alloys with small amts. of aluminum or tin
Uses: Colorant for external pharmaceuticals
See also Bronze powder; Copper powder

CI 77489

CAS 1345-25-1; EINECS 215-721-8
Synonyms: Ferrous oxide; Iron oxides
Classification: Inorganic color
Definition: Consists chiefly of ferrous oxide
Empirical: FeO
Uses: Color additive for ingested drugs (5 mg/day as Fe)
See also Iron oxides

CI 77491

CAS 1309-37-1; EINECS 215-168-2
Synonyms: Ferric oxide; Iron oxides; Pigment brown 6; Pigment brown 7; Pigment red 101; Pigment red 102
Classification: Inorganic color
Definition: Consists chiefly of ferric oxide
Empirical: Fe_2O_3
Properties: Dense dk. red powd. or lumps; sol. in acids; insol. in water; dens. 5.12-5.24; m.p.1565 C
Uses: Color additive for ingested drugs (5 mg/day as Fe)
See also Iron oxides; Ferric oxide

CI 77492

CAS 20344-49-4
Synonyms: Hydrated ferric oxide; Iron hydroxide oxide; Iron oxides; Pigment brown 6; Pigment brown 7; Pigment yellow 42; Pigment yellow 43
Classification: Inorganic color
Definition: Consists chiefly of hydrated ferrous oxide
Empirical: $FeO(OH) \cdot nH_2O$
Uses: Color additive for ingested drugs (5 mg/day as Fe)
See also Iron oxides; Iron (III) oxide hydrated

CI 77499

CAS 1309-37-1; 1317-61-9; 1345-25-1
Synonyms: Ferrous-ferric oxide; Iron oxides; Pigment black 11; Pigment brown 6; Pigment brown 7
Classification: Inorganic color
Definition: Consists chiefly of ferrous-ferric oxide
Uses: Color additive for ingested drugs (5 mg/day as Fe)
See also Iron oxides

CI 77510

CAS 14038-43-8; EINECS 237-875-5
Synonyms: Ferric ferrocyanide; Pigment blue 27; Prussian blue
Classification: Inorganic color
Empirical: $C_6FeN_6 \cdot {}_{4/3}Fe$
Properties: M.w. 286.38
Uses: Color additive for external pharmaceuticals
See also Ferric ferrocyanide

CI 77713. See Magnesium carbonate
CI 77820. See Silver

CI 77891

CAS 13463-67-7; EINECS 236-675-5
Synonyms: Titanium dioxide; Pigment white 6
Classification: Inorganic color

Empirical: O_2Ti
Formula: TiO_2
Properties: Wh. amorphous powd.; insol. in water, HCl, HNO_3, dil. H_2SO_4; sol. in HF, hot conc. H_2SO_4; m.w. 79.90; Anatase: dens. 3.90; Rutile: dens. 4.23
Precaution: Violent or incandescent reaction with metals (e.g., aluminum, calcium, magnesium, potassium, sodium, zinc, lithium)
Toxicology: TLV:TWA 10 mg/m^3 of total dust; experimental carcinogen, neoplastigen, tumorigen; human skin irritant; nuisance dust
Uses: Opacifying agent, color additive; used in ophthalmics, orals, topicals, tableted drugs
See also Titanium dioxide

CI 77947
CAS 1314-13-2; EINECS 215-222-5
Synonyms: Zinc oxide; Pigment white 4
Classification: Inorganic color
Empirical: OZn
Formula: ZnO
Properties: White to gray powd. or crystals, odorless, bitter taste; sol. in dilute acetic or min. acids, alkalies; insol. in water, alcohol; m.w. 81.38; dens. 5.67; m.p. 1975 C; ref. index 2.0041-2.0203; pH 6.95 (Amer. process), 7.37 (French process)
Precaution: Heated to decomp., emits toxic fumes of ZnO
Toxicology: TLV/TWA 5 mg/m^3; LD50 (IP, rat) 240 mg/kg; poison by IP route; fumes may cause metal fume fever with chills, fever, tightness in chest, cough, leukocytes; experimental teratogen; mutagenic data; skin/eye irritant
Uses: Color addtive for external pharmaceuticals
See also Zinc oxide

CI 42090 (ammonium salt). *See* D&C Blue No. 4
CI 75120. *See* Annatto; Annatto extract
CI 77289. *See* Chromium hydroxide green
CI 77400. *See* Bronze powder
Cinene. *See* d-Limonene; dl-Limonene
Cineol. *See* Eucalyptol

Cinnamal
CAS 104-55-2; 14371-10-9; EINECS 203-213-9
FEMA 2286
Synonyms: Cinnamaldehyde; Phenylacrolein; Cinnamic aldehyde; 3-Phenylpropenal; 3-Phenyl-2-propenal
Classification: Aromatic aldehyde
Definition: A syn. liq. with strong cinnamon odor isolated from a wood-rotting fungus
Empirical: C_9H_8O
Formula: $C_6H_5CH:CHCHO$
Properties: Ylsh. oily liq., strong cinnamon odor, burning aromatic taste; very sl. sol. in water; misc. with alcohol, ether, chloroform, fixed oils; m.w. 132.16; dens. 1.048-1.052; m.p. -7.5 C; b.p. 246 C (760 mm); flash pt. 248 F; ref. index 1.619-1.623 (20 C)
Precaution: Combustible liq.; may ignite after delay in contact with NaOH; volatile with steam
Toxicology: LD50 (oral, rat) 2220 mg/kg; poison by IV route; mod. toxic by ingestion and intraperitoneal routes; severe human skin irritant; one of the most common allergens; heated to decomp., emits acrid smoke and fumes
Uses: Cinnamon-, vanilla-like synthetic flavoring agent used in orals, mouthwashes, and toothpaste; topical sunscreens, ointments
Regulatory: FDA 21CFR §182.60, GRAS; 27CFR §21.65, 21.151; FEMA GRAS; Japan approved as flavoring; FDA approved for orals; BP compliance
Manuf./Distrib.: Aldrich; Nipa Labs; Penta Mfg.; Quest Int'l.
Manuf./Distrib. (pharm. & food): Aldrich; Florida Treatt

Cinnamaldehyde. *See* Cinnamal

Cinnamaldehyde ethylene glycol acetal
FEMA 2287
Synonyms: Cinnamic aldehyde ethylene glycol acetal; Cinncloval; 2-Styryl-1,3-dioxolane; 2-Styryl-m-dioxolane
Definition: From cinnamic aldehyde and ethylene glycol
Empirical: $C_{11}H_{12}O_2$

Cinnamein

Properties: Colorless oily liq., cinnamon-like odor and flavor; sol. in alcohol; insol. in water; m.w. 176.22; b.p. 265 C
Uses: Synthetic flavoring agent
Regulatory: FDA 21CFR §172.515; FEMA GRAS

Cinnamein. See Benzyl cinnamate
Cinnamene. See Styrene

Cinnamic acid
CAS 140-10-3, 621-82-9; EINECS 205-398-1
FEMA 2288
Synonyms: β-Phenylacrylic acid; trans-3-Phenylacrylic acid; 3-Phenylpropenoic acid; Cinnamylic acid
Empirical: $C_9H_8O_2$
Formula: $C_6H_5CH:CHCOOH$
Properties: Wh. monoclinic cryst., honey floral odor; sol. in benzene, ether, acetone, glac. acetic acid, carbon disulfide, fixed oils; m.w. 148.17; dens. 1.2475 (4/4 C); m.p. 133 C; b.p. 300 C; flash pt. > 212 F
Precaution: Combustible liq.
Toxicology: LD50 (oral, rat) 2500 mg/kg; poison by IV and intraperitoneal routes; mod. toxic by ingestion; skin irritant; heated to decomp., emits acrid smoke and fumes
Uses: Sweet, cinnamon-like synthetic flavoring agent
Regulatory: FDA 21CFR §172.515; FEMA GRAS; Japan approved as flavoring; BP compliance
Manuf./Distrib.: Aceto; Aldrich; Hüls Am.; Penta Mfg.; Raschig
Manuf./Distrib. (pharm. & food): Aceto; Aldrich; Penta Mfg.

Cinnamic alcohol. See Cinnamyl alcohol
Cinnamic aldehyde. See Cinnamal
Cinnamic aldehyde ethylene glycol acetal. See Cinnamaldehyde ethylene glycol acetal
Cinnamol. See Styrene
Cinnamomum cassia oil. See Cinnamon oil

Cinnamon oil
CAS 8007-80-5; EINECS 284-635-0 (extract)
FEMA 2256
Synonyms: Cassia oil; Cinnamomum cassia oil; Chinese cinnamon oil; Saigon cinnamon
Definition: Volatile oil distilled from the leaves and twigs of Cinnamomum cassia, contg. 80-90% cinnamaldehyde, plus cinnamyl acetate, eugenol
Properties: Ylsh. to brnsh. liq., cinnamon odor, spicy burning taste; darkens and thickens on exposure to air; sol. in fixed oils, propylene glycol; sl. sol. in water; insol. in glycerin, min. oil; dens. 1.045-1.063 (25/25 C); ref. index 1.6020-1.6060 (20 C)
Precaution: Keep cool, well closed; protect from light
Toxicology: LD50 (oral, rat) 2800 mg/kg; poison by skin contact; mod. toxic by ingestion, IP routes; human skin irritant; suspected weak carcinogen; mutagenic data; heated to decomp., emits acrid smoke and irritating fumes
Uses: Natural flavoring agent used in orals, dentifrices, mouthwashes; mild anesthetic in dentistry; carminative; aromatic, astringent, stimulant
Regulatory: FDA 21CFR §145.135, 145.140, 145.145, 145.180, 145.181, 182.10, 182.20, GRAS, 27CFR §21.151; FDA approved for orals; BP compliance
Manuf./Distrib. (pharm. & food): Berje; Formula One; Integra; Kato Worldwide; Meer; Penta Mfg.; Ruger; SKW Chems.; Spectrum Chem. Mfg.

Cinnamyl alcohol
CAS 104-54-1; EINECS 203-212-3
FEMA 2294
Synonyms: 3-Phenyl-2-propen-1-ol; Cinnamic alcohol; γ-Phenylallyl alcohol; Styroen; Styryl carbinol
Classification: Organic compd.
Empirical: $C_9H_{10}O$
Formula: $C_6H_5CH:CHCH_2OH$
Properties: Needles or cryst. mass, hyacinth odor; sol. in water, glycerol, propylene glycol, alcohol, ether, other common org. solvs.; m.w. 134.19; dens. 1.0397 (35/35 C); m.p. 33 C; b.p. 250 C; flash pt. > 230 F; ref. index 1.58190
Toxicology: LD50 (oral, rat) 2000 mg/kg; mod. toxic by ingestion; skin irritant; can cause allergic reaction; heated to decomp., emits acrid smoke and fumes
Uses: Balsamic, sweetly floral fragrance and flavoring; used in deodorants
Regulatory: FDA 21CFR §172.515; FEMA GRAS; Japan approved as flavoring

Manuf./Distrib.: Aldrich; BASF
Manuf./Distrib. (pharm. & food): Aldrich

Cinnamyl butyrate
CAS 103-61-7
FEMA 2296
Synonyms: Phenyl propenyl-n-butyrate
Empirical: $C_{13}H_{16}O_2$
Properties: Colorless to ylsh. liq., fruity sl. floral odor, honey-like taste; insol. in water; m.w. 204.27; dens. 1.010-1.015 (25/25 C); b.p. 300 C; flash pt. > 100 C
Uses: Fruity synthetic flavoring agent
Regulatory: FDA 21CFR §172.515; FEMA GRAS
Manuf./Distrib. (pharm. & food): Aldrich

Cinnamylic acid. *See* Cinnamic acid

Cinnamyl isobutyrate
CAS 103-59-3
FEMA 2297
Empirical: $C_{13}H_{16}O_2$
Properties: Colorless to ylsh. liq., sweet balsamic fruital odor; insol. in water; m.w. 204.27; dens. 1.01; b.p. 254 C; flash pt. > 230 F; ref. index 1.5230-1.5280 (20 C)
Uses: Sweet, fruity synthetic flavoring agent
Regulatory: FDA 21CFR §172.515; FEMA GRAS
Manuf./Distrib. (pharm. & food): Aldrich

Cinnamyl methyl ketone. *See* Benzylidene acetone

Cinnamyl phenylacetate
FEMA 2300
Synonyms: Cinnamyl α-toluate
Empirical: $C_{17}H_{16}O_2$
Properties: Colorless liq., honey-like flavor; sol. in alcohol; insol. in water; m.w. 252.32; dens. 1.09; b.p. 333-335 C
Uses: Synthetic flavoring agent
Regulatory: FDA 21CFR §172.515; FEMA GRAS

Cinnamyl propionate
CAS 103-56-0
FEMA 2301
Synonyms: γ-Phenylallyl propionate; 3-Phenyl-2-propenyl propanoate
Definition: Obtained by esterification of cinnamic alcohol with propionic acid
Empirical: $C_{12}H_{14}O_2$
Properties: Colorless to ylsh. liq., spicy fruital odor; insol. in water; m.w. 190.24; dens. 1.0370-1.0410 (15 C); b.p. 289 C; flash pt. > 100 C; ref. index 1.5180-1.5240 (20 C)
Precaution: Combustible liq.
Toxicology: Heated to decomp., emits acrid smoke and fumes
Uses: Fruity synthetic flavoring agent
Regulatory: FDA 21CFR §172.515; FEMA GRAS
Manuf./Distrib. (pharm. & food): Aldrich

Cinnamyl α-toluate. *See* Cinnamyl phenylacetate
Cinncloval. *See* Cinnamaldehyde ethylene glycol acetal
CI 45425 (sodium salt). *See* D&C Orange No. 11

C13-14 isoparaffin
CAS 64742-48-9
Synonyms: Alkanes, C13-14-iso-
Definition: Mixture of branched chain aliphatic hydrocarbons with 13 or 14 carbons in the alkyl chain
Uses: Used in antibiotic gels
Trade names containing: Sepigel 305

Citral
CAS 5392-40-5; EINECS 226-394-6
FEMA 2303
Synonyms: 3,7-Dimethyl-2,6-octadienal; 2,6-Dimethyloctadien-2,6-al-8; Geranial; Neral
Classification: Aldehyde
Empirical: $C_{10}H_{16}O$

Citral diethyl acetal

Formula: $(CH_3)_2C:CHCH_2CHC(CH_3)CHCHO$
Properties: Pale yel. mobile liq., strong lemon odor; sol. in glycerin, propylene glycol, min. oil, fixed oils, 95% alcohol; insol. in water; m.w. 152.24; dens. 0.891-0.987 (15 C); b.p. 220-225 C; flash pt. 198 F; ref. index 1.486-1.490
Precaution: Combustible liq.
Toxicology: LD50 (oral, rat) 4960 mg/kg; mod. toxic by intraperitoneal route; mildly toxic by ingestion; experimental reproductive effects; human skin irritant; heated to decomp., emits acrid smoke and irritating fumes
Uses: Fragrance and flavoring for medicinal preps.
Regulatory: FDA 21CFR §172.515, 182.60, GRAS; FEMA GRAS; Japan approved as flavoring; BP compliance
Manuf./Distrib.: BASF; Lucta SA; Penta Mfg.; Schweizerhall; SCM Glidco Organics
Manuf./Distrib. (pharm. & food): Florida Treatt

Citral diethyl acetal

CAS 7492-66-2
FEMA 2304
Synonyms: 3,7-Dimethyl-2,6-octadienal diethyl acetal; Citral diethyl acetate
Empirical: $C_{14}H_{26}O_2$
Properties: Colorless liq., mild green citrus odor; sol. in propylene glycol; insol. in water; m.w. 226.36; dens. 0.8745-0.8790 (15 C); b.p. 230 C; flash pt. 79 C; ref. index 1.4520-1.4545
Uses: Citrus synthetic flavoring agent
Regulatory: FDA 21CFR §172.515; FEMA GRAS
Manuf./Distrib. (pharm. & food): Aldrich

Citral diethyl acetate. *See* Citral diethyl acetal

Citral dimethyl acetal

CAS 7549-37-3
FEMA 2305
Synonyms: 3,7-Dimethyl-2,6-octadienal dimethyl acetal
Empirical: $C_{12}H_{22}O_2$
Properties: Colorless to ylsh. liq., fresh lemon-like odor; m.w. 198.31; dens. 0.885; b.p. 198 C; flash pt. 180 F; ref. index 1.4560-1.4630 (20 C)
Uses: Lemon-like synthetic flavoring agent
Regulatory: FDA 21CFR §172.515; FEMA GRAS
Manuf./Distrib. (pharm. & food): Aldrich

Citric acid

CAS 77-92-9 (anhyd.); EINECS 201-069-1
FEMA 2306
Synonyms: 2-Hydroxy-1,2,3-propanetricarboxylic acid; β-Hydroxytricarballylic acid
Classification: Organic acid
Empirical: $C_6H_8O_7$
Formula: $HOC(COOH)(CH_2COOH)_2$
Properties: Colorless translucent crystals or powd., odorless, strongly acidic tart taste; very sol. in water and alcohol; very sl. sol. in ether; m.w. 192.43; dens. 1.542; m.p. 153 C
Precaution: Combustible; potentially explosive reaction with metal nitrates
Toxicology: LD50 (oral, rat) 6730 mg/kg; poison by IV; mod. toxic by subcutaneous and intraperitoneal routes; mildly toxic by ingestion; severe eye, mod. skin irritant; some allergenic props.; erodes tooth enamel; heated to decomp., emits acrid smoke, fumes
Uses: Prep. of citrates; acidifier, buffering agent, pH adjuster, flavoring extracts; used in injectables, buccals, inhalants, nasals, ophthalmics, orals, otics, topicals; effervescent tablets; citrate sol'n. as blood anticoagulant; keratin softener
Regulatory: FDA 21CFR §131.111, 131.112, 131.136, 131.138, 131.144, 131.146, 133, 145.131, 145.145, 146.187, 150.141, 150.161, 155.130, 161.190, 166.40, 166.110, 169.115, 169.140, 169.150, 172.755, 173.160, 173.165, 173.280, 182.1033, 182.6033, GRAS; USDA 9CFR §318.7, 381.147; BATF 27CFR §240.1051, limitation 5.8 lb/1000 gal; FEMA GRAS; Japan approved; Europe listed; UK approved; FDA approved for injectables, buccals, inhalants, nasals, ophthalmics, topicals, orals, otics; USP/NF, BP, Ph.Eur.
Manuf./Distrib.: Cargill; R.W. Greeff; Haarmann & Reimer; Hoffmann-La Roche; Lohmann; Penta Mfg.; PMC; Schweizerhall; U.S. Petrochem. Ind.
Manuf./Distrib. (pharm. & food): ADM; Albright & Wilson; Aldrich; Am. Roland; Ashland; Browning; Consolidated Flavor; Ellis & Everard; Frutarom; R.W. Greeff; Haarmann & Reimer; Hoffmann-La Roche; Integra; Jungbunzlauer; Lohmann; Norman Fox; Penta Mfg.; Pfizer Food Science; Ruger; Spectrum Chem. Mfg.;

Spice King
Trade names: Citric Acid Anhyd. USP/FCC; Citric Acid USP FCC Anhyd. Fine Gran. No. 69941; Citric Acid
USP FCC Anhyd. Gran. No. 69942; Descote® Citric Acid 50%
Trade names containing: Arlacel® 186; 24% Beta Carotene HS-E in Veg. Oil No. 65671; Cal-O-Vera 1:1; Cal-
O-Vera 10:1; Cal-O-Vera 40:1; Dur-Em® 117; Dur-Em® 207-E; Oxynex® 2004; Oxynex® K; Oxynex® LM;
Vitamin B_{12} 0.1% SD No. 65354; Vitamin B_{12} 1.0% SD No. 65305

Citric acid monohydrate
CAS 5949-29-1
FEMA 2306
Synonyms: Hydrous citric acid; 2-Hydroxy-1,2,3-propanetricarboxylic acid monohydrate
Empirical: $C_6H_8O_7 \cdot H_2O$
Properties: Wh. or colorless cryst. or powd., odorless; sol. in water, alcohol (1:1.5); sl. sol. in ether; m.w. 210.14;
efflorescent in dry air
Precaution: Airtight storage
Toxicology: May cause dental erosion or local irritation if ingested frequently or in large amts.
Uses: Acidifier, buffering agent, effervescent; synergist for antioxidants; used in preps. to dissolve renal calculi,
alkalize the urine; in anticoagulant sol'ns.; treatment of GI disturbances; used in ophthalmics, orals, topicals
Regulatory: FDA approved for ophthalmics, orals, topicals; USP, BP, Ph.Eur., German Pharmacopoeia, JP
compliance
Manuf./Distrib. (pharm. & food): Aldrich; Mallinckrodt; Spectrum Chem. Mfg.

Citric acid monosodium salt. *See* Sodium citrate
Citric acid, octadecyl ester. *See* Stearyl citrate
Citric acid tripotassium salt. *See* Potassium citrate
Citric acid trisodium salt. *See* Trisodium citrate
Citridic acid. *See* Aconitic acid

Citronellal
CAS 106-23-0; EINECS 203-376-6
FEMA 2307
Synonyms: 3,7-Dimethyl-6-octenal; Rhodinal
Empirical: $C_{10}H_{18}O$
Properties: Colorless to sl. yel. liq., strong lemon-citronnella-rose odor; sol. in alcohol, most oils; sl. sol. in
propylene glycol; insol. in glycerin, water; m.w. 154.25; dens. 0.850-0.860; b.p. 83-85 C (11 mm); flash pt.
170 F; ref. index 1.446-1.456
Precaution: Combustible liq.
Toxicology: Heated to decomp., emits acrid smoke and irritating fumes
Uses: Synthetic flavoring agent
Regulatory: FDA 21CFR §172.515; FEMA GRAS; Japan approved as flavoring
Manuf./Distrib.: BASF; Penta Mfg.; PMC Specialties; Schweizerhall
Manuf./Distrib. (pharm. & food): Florida Treatt

Citronellal hydrate. *See* Hydroxycitronellal

β-Citronellol
CAS 106-22-9; EINECS 203-375-0
FEMA 2309
Synonyms: 3,7-Dimethyl-6-octen-1-ol; (±)-β-Citronellol; d-Citronellol
Empirical: $C_{10}H_{20}O$
Formula: $(CH_3)_2C{:}CHCH_2CH_2CH(CH_3)CH_2CH_2OH$
Properties: Colorless oily liq., rose odor; sol. in fixed oils, propylene glycol; sl. sol. in water; insol. in glycerin
@ 225 C; m.w. 156.30; dens. 0.850-0.860; b.p. 99 C (10 mm); flash pt. 215 F; ref. index 1.454-1.462
Precaution: Combustible liq.
Toxicology: LD50 (oral, rat) 3450 mg/kg; poison by IV route; mod. toxic by ingestion, skin contact; heated to
decomp., emits acrid smoke and irritating fumes
Uses: Fresh floral, rose-like fragrance and flavoring for pharmaceuticals
Regulatory: FDA 21CFR §172.515
Manuf./Distrib.: BASF; Int'l. Flavors & Fragrances; Penta Mfg.; SCM Glidco Organics
Manuf./Distrib. (pharm. & food): Int'l. Flavors & Fragrances; Penta Mfg.

(±)-β-Citronellol. *See* β-Citronellol
d-Citronellol. *See* β-Citronellol

Citronellyl acetate
CAS 150-84-5; EINECS 205-775-0

Citronellyl butyrate

FEMA 2311
Synonyms: Acetic acid citronellyl ester; 3,7-Dimethyl-6-octen-1-ol acetate; 3,7-Dimethyl-6-octen-1-yl acetate
Definition: Ester of citronellol and acetic acid
Empirical: $C_{12}H_{22}O_2$
Properties: Colorless liq., fruity odor; sol. in alcohol, fixed oils; insol. in glycerin, propylene glycol, water @ 229 C; m.w. 198.34; dens. 0.883-0.893; b.p. 240 C; flash pt. > 212 F; ref. index 1.440-1.450
Precaution: Combustible liq.
Toxicology: LD50 (oral, rat) 6800 mg/kg; mildly toxic by ingestion; human skin irritant; heated to decomp., emits acrid smoke and irritating fumes
Uses: Synthetic flavoring agent
Regulatory: FDA 21CFR §172.515, 182.60, GRAS; FEMA GRAS; Japan approved as flavoring
Manuf./Distrib. (pharm. & food): Chr. Hansen's

Citronellyl butyrate

CAS 141-16-2
FEMA 2312
Synonyms: 3,7-Dimethyl-6-octen-1-yl butyrate
Empirical: $C_{14}H_{26}O_2$
Properties: Colorless liq., rose-like odor, sweet plum-like taste; m.w. 226.36; dens. 0.880-0.886; b.p. 134-135 C (12 mm); flash pt. > 230 F; ref. index 1.444-1.448
Precaution: Combustible liq.
Toxicology: Heated to decomp., emits acrid smoke and fumes
Uses: Sweet, fruity synthetic flavoring agent
Regulatory: FDA 21CFR §172.515; FEMA GRAS
Manuf./Distrib. (pharm. & food): Aldrich
See also Rhodinyl butyrate

Citronellyl formate

CAS 105-85-1
FEMA 2314
Synonyms: 3,7-Dimethyl-6-octen-1-yl formate
Empirical: $C_{11}H_{20}O_2$
Properties: Colorless oily liq., fruity rose-like odor, sweet fruity taste; insol. in water; m.w. 184.28; dens. 0.897; b.p. 235 C; flash pt. 198 F; ref. index 1.4430-1.4490
Precaution: Combustible liq.
Toxicology: LD50 (oral, rat) 8400 mg/kg; mildly toxic by ingestion; human skin irritant; heated to decomp., emits acrid smoke and fumes
Uses: Synthetic flavoring agent
Regulatory: FDA 21CFR §172.515; FEMA GRAS; Japan approved as flavoring
Manuf./Distrib. (pharm. & food): Aldrich

Citronellyl phenylacetate

FEMA 2315
Synonyms: Citronellyl α-toluate; 3,7-Dimethyl-6-octen-1-yl phenylacetate
Empirical: $C_{18}H_{26}O_2$
Properties: Honey rose-like odor; m.w. 274.41; dens. 0.992 (15.5 C); b.p. 342 C; ref. index 1.5100
Uses: Synthetic flavoring agent
Regulatory: FDA 21CFR §172.515; FEMA GRAS

Citronellyl propionate

FEMA 2316
Synonyms: 3,7-Dimethyl-6-octen-1-yl propionate
Definition: Obtained by direct esterification of citronellol with propionic acid under azeotropic conditions or using propionic anhydride
Empirical: $C_{13}H_{24}O_2$
Properties: Colorless liq., rose-like odor, bittersweet plum-like taste; m.w. 212.33; dens. 0.8810-0.8840; b.p. 242 C; flash pt. > 100 C; ref. index 1.4430-1.4490
Precaution: Combustible liq.
Toxicology: Heated to decomp., emits acrid smoke and fumes
Uses: Synthetic flavoring agent
Regulatory: FDA 21CFR §172.515; FEMA GRAS
Manuf./Distrib. (pharm. & food): Chr. Hansen's
See also Rhodinyl propionate

Citronellyl α-toluate. *See* Citronellyl phenylacetate

Citronellyl valerate
CAS 7540-53-6
FEMA 2317
Synonyms: 3,7-Dimethyl-6-octen-1-yl valerate
Empirical: $C_{15}H_{28}O_2$
Properties: Liq., rose herb honey-like odor; m.w. 240.39; dens. 0.890; b.p. 237 C; flash pt. > 230 F; ref. index 1.4435
Uses: Honey-like synthetic flavoring agent
Regulatory: FDA 21CFR §172.515; FEMA GRAS
Manuf./Distrib. (pharm. & food): Aldrich

Citrucel. *See* Methylcellulose
Citrus limon extract. *See* Lemon extract
Citrus limon oil. *See* Lemon oil
Citrus pectin. *See* Pectin
Citrus sinensis extract. *See* Orange extract
Citrus sinensis oil. *See* Orange oil
Clarified honey. *See* Honey
C18 linear alcohol. *See* Stearyl alcohol
C-12 linear primary alcohol. *See* Lauryl alcohol
C16 linear primary alcohol. *See* Cetyl alcohol
Clove bud oil. *See* Clove oil
Clove leaf oil. *See* Clove oil

Clove oil
CAS 8000-34-8
FEMA 2323 (bud), 2325 (leaf), 2328 (stem)
Synonyms: Eugenia caryophyllus oil; Clove bud oil; Clove leaf oil; Clove stem oil
Definition: Volatile oil distilled from the dried flower buds of *Eugenia caryophyllus*, contg. 82-87% eugenol, 10% acetyleugenol, etc.
Properties: Colorless to pale yel. volatile liq.; char. odor and taste of clove; becomes darker and thicker with age; very sol. in strong alcohol, ether, glac. acetic acid; insol. in water; dens. 1.036-1.060; b.p. 250 C; ref. index 1.527-1.538 (20 C)
Precaution: Keep cool, well closed; protect from light
Toxicology: LD50 (oral, rodents) 2-3 g/kg; strongly irritating to skin; causes allergic skin rashes; may cause hypersensitivity
Uses: Natural flavoring agent and adjuvant; used in buccals, orals; carminative that is sometimes used in treatment of flatulence; local anesthetic (toothache); counterirritant
Regulatory: FDA 21CFR §184.1257, GRAS; 27CFR §21.65, 21.151; FEMA GRAS; Council of Europe listed; FDA approved for buccals, orals; BP compliance
Manuf./Distrib. (pharm. & food): Chart; Pierre Chauvet; Florida Treatt; Ruger; Spectrum Chem. Mfg.

Clove stem oil. *See* Clove oil
CMC. *See* Carboxymethylcellulose sodium

Cobalt gluconate
CAS 71957-08-9
Empirical: $C_{12}H_{22}O_{14}Co$
Properties: M.w. 449.3
Uses: Mineral source for pharmaceuticals
Manuf./Distrib.: Spectrum Chem. Mfg.
Manuf./Distrib. (pharm. & food): Am. Roland
Trade names: Gluconal® CO

Cocamide DEA
CAS 8051-30-7; 61791-31-9; 68603-42-9; EINECS 263-163-9
Synonyms: Coconut diethanolamide; Cocoyl diethanolamide; N,N-Bis (2-hydroxyethyl) coco amides
Definition: Ethanolamides of coconut acid
Formula: $RCO-N(CH_2CH_2OH)_2$, RCO represents the coconut acid radical
Toxicology: May produce contact sensitivity
Uses: Mild surfactant, thickener, emulsifier, solubilizer; used in topical dermatological prods.
Regulatory: FDA 21CFR §172.710, 173.322 (0.2% max.), 175.105, 176.210, 177.1200, 177.2260, 177.2800; FDA approved for topicals
Manuf./Distrib.: Aquatec Quimica SA
Trade names: Comperlan® COD

Cocamide MEA

CAS 68140-00-1; EINECS 268-770-2

Synonyms: Coconut monoethanolamide; N-(2-hydroxyethyl) coco fatty acid amide; Coconut fatty acid monoethanolamide

Definition: Mixture of ethanolamides of coconut acid

Formula: $RCO-NHCH_2CH_2OH$, RCO represents the coconut acid radical

Properties: Cream flakes; sol. in ethanol, propylene glycol, oleyl alcohol; disp. in min. oil, IPM; insol. in water; m.p. 70-74 C

Uses: Foam booster/stabilizer, thickener, emulsifier

Trade names: Mazamide® CMEA

Cocamide mercaptoethyl amine

Uses: Used in topicals

Regulatory: Approved for topicals

N-Cocamidoethyl-N-2-hydroxyethyl-N-carboxyethylglycine, sodium salt. *See* Disodium cocamphodiacetate

Cocamidopropylamine oxide

CAS 68155-09-9; EINECS 268-938-5

Synonyms: Cocamidopropyl dimethylamine oxide; Coco amides, N-[3-(dimethylamino)propyl], N-oxide; N-[3-(Dimethylamino)propyl]coco amides-N-oxide

Classification: Tertiary amine oxide

Formula: $RCO-NH(CH_2)_3N(CH_3)_3O$, RCO- represents the coconut fatty acids

Uses: Surfactant, emulsifier

Trade names: Aminoxid WS 35

Cocamidopropyl betaine

CAS 61789-40-0; 70851-07-9; 83138-08-3; 86438-79-1; EINECS 263-058-8; 274-923-4

Synonyms: CADG; Cocamidopropyl dimethyl glycine

Classification: Zwitterion (inner salt)

Formula: $RCO-NH(CH_2)_3N^+(CH_3)_2CH_2COO^-$, RCO represents the coconut acid radical

Properties: Stable when exposed to air

Toxicology: May cause allergic skin rashes

Uses: Ointment base; surfactant, emulsifier, foam booster/stabilizer

Manuf./Distrib.: Chemron; Goldschmidt; Henkel/Emery; Huntington Labs; Inolex; McIntyre; Mona; Scher; Witco

Trade names: Amonyl® 380 BA; Amonyl® 440 NI; Dehyton® K; Tego®-Betaine L-7; Tego®-Betaine ZF

Cocamidopropyl dimethylamine oxide. *See* Cocamidopropylamine oxide
Cocamidopropyl dimethyl glycine. *See* Cocamidopropyl betaine
Cochin. *See* Lemongrass oil East Indian
Cochineal extract. *See* Carmine

Cocoa butter

CAS 8002-31-1

Synonyms: Theobroma oil; Cacao butter

Definition: Ylsh. wh. solid obtained from roasted seeds of *Theobroma cacao*

Properties: Ylsh.-wh. solid, chocolate-like odor and taste; sol. in ether, chloroform; sl. sol. in alcohol; insol. in water; dens. 0.858-0.864 (100/25 C); m.p. 30-35 C; iodine no. 33-42; sapon. no. 188-198; ref. index 1.4537-1.4585 (40 C)

Precaution: Combustible

Toxicology: May cause allergic skin reactions

Uses: Emollient, carrier, filler, suppository base; used in orals, rectals, topicals; used in massage oils and suppositories because it melts at body temp.; suntan lotions; protectant in hemorrhoidal prods.

Regulatory: FDA 21CFR §182.20, GRAS; FDA approved for orals, rectals, topicals; USP/NF, BP compliance

Manuf./Distrib.: ABITEC; Vrymeer Commodities

Manuf./Distrib. (pharm. & food): ABITEC; Ruger; Spectrum Chem. Mfg.

Trade names: Fancol CB; Fancol CB Extra

Coco amides, N-[3-(dimethylamino)propyl], N-oxide. *See* Cocamidopropylamine oxide
Cocoamphocarboxyglycinate. *See* Disodium cocamphodiacetate
Cocoamphocarboxypropionate. *See* Disodium cocamphodipropionate
Cocoamphodiacetate. *See* Disodium cocamphodiacetate
Cocoamphodipropionate. *See* Disodium cocamphodipropionate

Coco-betaine
CAS 68424-94-2; 85409-25-2; EINECS 270-329-4
Synonyms: Quat. ammonium compds., carboxymethyl (coco alkyl) dimethyl hydroxides, inner salts; Coconut betaine; Coco dimethyl betaine; Coco dimethyl glycine
Classification: Zwitterion (inner salt)
Uses: Amphoteric surfactant, detergent, foamer, visc. modifier, emulsifier; used in therapeutic shampoos
Manuf./Distrib.: Aquatec Quimica SA
Trade names: Amonyl® 265 BA; Dehyton® AB-30

Coco caprylate/caprate
Definition: Mixture of esters of coconut alcohol with caprylic acid and capric acid
Uses: Emollient, carrier, superfatting agent
Trade names: Cetiol® LC
Trade names containing: Copherol® 950LC

Coco dimethyl betaine. *See* Coco-betaine
Coco dimethyl glycine. *See* Coco-betaine
Coco fatty acid. *See* Coconut acid

Cocoglycerides
CAS 67701-26-2
Synonyms: Glycerides, coconut, mono-, di-, and tri-
Definition: Mixture of mono-, di-, and triglycerides derived from coconut oil
Uses: Suppository bases
Trade names: Novata® 299; Novata® A; Novata® AB; Novata® B; Novata® BBC; Novata® BC; Novata® BCF; Novata® BD; Novata® C; Novata® D
Trade names containing: Novata® E

Cocohydroxyethyl PEG-imidazolinium chloride phosphate
Uses: Cationic emulsifier, solubilizer, dispersant, thickener, wetting agent, bactericide for pharmaceuticals
Trade names: Phospholipid PTZ

Cocomonoethanolamide
Uses: Used in topicals
Regulatory: FDA approved for topicals

Coconut acid
CAS 61788-47-4; 8037-14-7; 67701-05-7; 68937-85-9; EINECS 262-978-7
Synonyms: Coco fatty acid; Coconut oil acids; Coconut fatty acids; Acids, coconut
Definition: Mixtures of fatty acids
Uses: Emulsifier used in topicals
Regulatory: FDA 21CFR §175.105, 175.320, 176.200, 176.210, 177.1010, 177.2260, 177.2600, 177.2800, 178.3570, 178.3910; approved for topicals
Manuf./Distrib.: ABITEC; Akzo Nobel; Norman, Fox; Procter & Gamble; Witco/Oleo-Surf.
Trade names: Distilled Whole Coconut Oil 6226 6222; Low I.V. Coconut Oil 6227, 6228; Split Coconut Oil 6254, 6255; Stripped Coconut Oil 6212, 6256
Trade names containing: Hystrene® 1835

Coconut acid, hydrogenated. *See* Hydrogenated coconut acid
Coconut acid, potassium salt. *See* Potassium cocoate
Coconut aldehyde. *See* γ-Nonalactone
Coconut betaine. *See* Coco-betaine
Coconut butter. *See* Coconut oil
Coconut diethanolamide. *See* Cocamide DEA
Coconut fatty acid monoethanolamide. *See* Cocamide MEA
Coconut fatty acids. *See* Coconut acid
Coconut monoethanolamide. *See* Cocamide MEA

Coconut oil
CAS 8001-31-8; EINECS 232-282-8
Synonyms: Copra oil; Coconut butter; Coconut palm oil
Classification: Saturated fat
Definition: Fixed oil obtained from kernels of seeds of *Cocos nucifera*
Properties: Wh. fatty solid or liq., sweet nutty taste; very sol. in chloroform, ether, CS_2; pract. insol. in water; dens. 0.903 (0/4 C); m.p. 21-27 C; acid no. < 6; iodine no. 8-9.5; sapon. no. 255-258; ref. index 1.4485-1.4495; surf. tens. 33.4 dynes/cm

Coconut oil acids

Precaution: Flamm. solid when exposed to heat or flame; may spontaneously heat and ignite if stored wet and hot

Toxicology: May cause allergic skin reaction

Uses: Emollient, emulsifier, excipient, ointment base for pharmaceuticals; coating agent; used in orals, topicals, massage creams

Regulatory: FDA 21CFR §175.105, 175.300, 176.200, 176.210, 177.2800, 182.70; GRAS; FDA approved for orals, topicals; BP compliance

Manuf./Distrib.: ABITEC; Akzo; Amber Syn.; Arista Industries; Spectrum Chem. Mfg.; Tri-K

Manuf./Distrib. (pharm. & food): Aarhus; ABITEC; Arista Industries; British Arkady; Calgene; Croda Singapore; Edw. Gittens; Integra; Penta Mfg.; Ruger; Spectrum Naturals

Trade names: Cobee 76; Coconut Oil® 76; Coconut Oil® 92; Pureco® 76

Trade names containing: Aloe Vera Lipo-Quinone Extract™ Cosmetic Grade; Aloe Vera Lipo-Quinone Extract™ Low Odor (CG); Dry Vitamin A Palmitate Type 250-SD No. 65378

Coconut oil acids. *See* Coconut acid
Coconut oil fatty acid, sodium salt. *See* Sodium cocoate
Coconut oil, hydrogenated. *See* Hydrogenated coconut oil
Coconut palm oil. *See* Coconut oil
Cocoyl diethanolamide. *See* Cocamide DEA
N-Cocoyl-N-methyl glycine. *See* Cocoyl sarcosine

Cocoyl sarcosine

CAS 68411-97-2; EINECS 270-156-4

Synonyms: N-Cocoyl-N-methyl glycine; N-Methyl-N-(1-coconut alkyl) glycine

Definition: N-cocoyl deriv. of sarcosine

Properties: Yel. liq.; dens. 0.970; m.p. 22-28 C

Toxicology: No known toxicity

Uses: Foam booster/stabilizer, emulsifier, lubricant; used to make antienzyme agents for toothpaste to prevent decay

Regulatory: FDA 21CFR §178.3130

Manuf./Distrib.: Chemplex; Hampshire; R.T. Vanderbilt

Trade names: Sarkosyl® LC

Cocoyl sodium isethionate. *See* Sodium cocoyl isethionate

Cod liver oil

CAS 8001-69-2; EINECS 232-289-6

Synonyms: Morrhua oil

Definition: Fixed oil expressed from fresh livers of *Gadus morrhua* and other species of codfish, contg. vitamins A and D, omega 3 fatty acid

Properties: Amber thin oily liq., sl. fishy odor and taste; sol. in ether, chloroform, ethyl acetate, carbon disulfide, petroleum ether; sl. sol. in alcohol; dens. 0.918-0.927; iodine no. 145-180; sapon. no. 180-192; ref. index 1.4705-1.4745

Precaution: Combustible

Toxicology: No known toxicity

Uses: Medicine (vitamin A and D content); dietary supplement; used in skin ointments and special skin creams to promote healing; protectant in diaper rash ointment

Regulatory: FDA 21CFR §175.105, 176.200, 176.210, 177.2800; GRAS for use in dietary supplements; BP compliance

Manuf./Distrib.: Arista Industries; R.W. Greeff; Penta Mfg.

Manuf./Distrib. (pharm. & food): Am. Roland; Arista Industries; R.W. Greeff; Integra; Ruger; Spectrum Chem. Mfg.

Coenzyme R. *See* d-Biotin
Coffeine. *See* Caffeine
Cognac oil, synthetic. *See* Ethyl heptanoate

Collagen

CAS 9007-34-5; EINECS 232-697-4

Synonyms: Collagen fiber; Ossein

Definition: Fibrous protein derived from connective tissues in animals

Formula: Clear to hazy, colorless; m.w. $\approx$ 100,000

Toxicology: May cause urticaria

Uses: Forms tissue-compat. sheets and fibers for medical and health-care prods., e.g., implants, skin substitutes

Regulatory: BP compliance (collagen suture, sterile reconstituted)

Manuf./Distrib.: Croda; Hormel; Inolex; Maybrook; RITA; U.S. Biochemical
Trade names: Collagenite

Collagen fiber. See Collagen
Collagen hydrolysates. See Hydrolyzed collagen

Collodion
CAS 9004-70-0
UN No. 2059
Synonyms: Nitrocellulose; Cellulose nitrate; Collodion wool
Definition: A solution of pyroxylin (nitrocellulose) in ether and alcohol
Properties: Colorless or pale yel. syrupy liq., ether odor; immiscible with water; sp.gr. 0.765-0.775; flash pt.
   0 F
Precaution: DOT: Flamm. liq.
Toxicology: May cause allergic skin reactions
Uses: Solvent for drugs, corn removers; coating wounds and abrasions
Regulatory: BP compliance (collodion, flexible)
Manuf./Distrib.: Spectrum Chem. Mfg.
Manuf./Distrib. (pharm. & food): Mallinckrodt; Ruger; Spectrum Chem. Mfg.
See also Nitrocellulose

Collodion cotton. See Nitrocellulose
Colloidal activated attapulgite. See Attapulgite
Colloidal silicon dioxide. See Silica
Cologel. See Methylcellulose
Colophane. See Rosin
Colophonium. See Rosin
Colophony. See Rosin
Columbian spirits. See Methyl alcohol
Colza oil. See Rapeseed oil
Common salt. See Sodium chloride
Common thyme. See Thyme
Concentrated acetic acid. See Acetic acid, glacial
Confectioner's sugar. See Sucrose

Copper
CAS 7440-50-8; EINECS 231-159-6
Synonyms: Bronze powder; Copper bronze; Gold bronze
Formula: Cu
Properties: Reddish metal; at.wt. 63.54; dens. 8.96; m.p. 1083 C; b.p. 2595 C
Toxicology: TLV 0.2 mg/m^3 (fume), 1 mg/m^3 (dusts and mists); poison to humans by ingestion
Uses: Ingred. in dental amalagam
Regulatory: FDA 21CFR §193.90, herbicides residue tolerance 1 ppm in potable water; GRAS for use in dietary
   supplements; Japan restricted; BP compliance
Manuf./Distrib.: Aldrich; Asarco; Noah Chem.

Copperas. See Ferrous sulfate
Copper bronze. See Copper

Copper gluconate
CAS 527-09-3; EINECS 208-408-2
Synonyms: Bis(D-gluconato) copper; Cupric gluconate
Definition: Copper salt of gluconic acid
Empirical: $C_{12}H_{22}O_{14}Cu$
Formula: $[HOCOO\,CHOHCHCHOHCHOHCH_2OH]_2Cu^{++}$
Properties: Lt. blue powd., odorless; sol. in water; sl. sol. in alcohol; insol. in acetone, ether; m.w. 453.8
Toxicology: Heated to decomp., emits acrid smoke and irritating fumes
Uses: Mineral source for pharmaceuticals; nutrient, dietary supplement, synergist
Regulatory: FDA 21CFR §182.5260, 184.1260, GRAS; Japan approved (0.6 mg/L as copper in milk)
Manuf./Distrib.: Akzo; Glucona; Lohmann; Spectrum Chem. Mfg.
Manuf./Distrib. (pharm. & food): Aldrich; Am. Roland; Ruger; Spectrum Chem. Mfg.
Trade names: Descote® Copper Gluconate 20%; Gluconal® CU

Copper (III) nitrate. See Copper nitrate (ic)
Copper metallic powder. See Copper powder

Copper nitrate (ic)

Copper nitrate (ic)
CAS 10031-43-3; EINECS 221-838-5
UN No. 1479
Synonyms: Cupric nitrate trihydrate; Cupric nitrate hexahydrate; Cupric nitrate; Copper (III) nitrate
Empirical: $CuN_2O_6 \cdot 3H_2O$ or $CuN_2O_6 \cdot 6H_2O$
Formula: $Cu(NO_3)_2 \cdot 3H_2O$ or $Cu(NO_3)_2 \cdot 6H_2O$
Properties: Trihydrate: Dk. blue cryst., deliq.; sol. in water and ethanol; m.w. 241.60; Hexahydrate: Blue cryst. flakes, deliq.; sol. in water, ethanol; m.w. 295.66; sp.gr. 2.0
Uses: In pharmaceuticals
Manuf./Distrib.: Blythe, William Ltd; Mallinckrodt
Manuf./Distrib. (pharm. & food): Aldrich

Copper phthalocyanine. *See* Copper phthalocyanine blue

Copper phthalocyanine blue
CAS 147-14-8; EINECS 205-685-1
Synonyms: Copper phthalocyanine; Phthalocyanine blue; Pigment blue 15; CI 74160
Definition: Bright blue copper phthalocyanine pigment
Empirical: $C_{32}H_{16}N_8Cu$
Formula: $(C_6H_4C_2N)_4N_4Cu$
Properties: Bright blue microcryst. with purple luster; insol. in water, alcohol; m.w. 576.08
Uses: Used in topicals
Regulatory: FDA approved for topicals
Manuf./Distrib.: Aldrich; Spectrum Chem. Mfg.
Manuf./Distrib. (pharm. & food): Aldrich

Copper powder
CAS 7440-50-8; EINECS 231-159-6
UN No. 3089
Synonyms: CI 77400; Copper metallic powder
Definition: Color additive consisting of powdered metallic copper
Empirical: Cu
Properties: Powd.; a.w. 63.54
Precaution: DOT: Flamm. solid
Toxicology: TLV 0.2 mg/m^3 (fume), 1 mg/m^3 (dusts and mists); poison to humans by ingestion
Uses: Color additive for external pharmaceuticals
Regulatory: FDA 21CFR §73.1647, 73.2647
Manuf./Distrib.: Aarbor Int'l.; Am. Chemet; Atomergic Chemetals; BASF; Canbro; Crescent Bronze Powd.; Lenape Ind.; Obron Atlantic; Punda Mercantile; Reade Advanced Materials; SCM Metal Prods.; Sheffield Bronze Paint; Spectrum Chem. Mfg.; U.S. Bronze Powds.
See also CI 77400

Copper sodium chlorophyllin. *See* Chlorophyllin-copper complex
Copper sulfate. *See* Cupric sulfate anhyd.
Copper sulfate (ic). *See* Cupric sulfate pentahydrate
Copper sulfate pentahydrate. *See* Cupric sulfate pentahydrate
Copra oil. *See* Coconut oil
Cordycepic acid. *See* D-Mannitol

Coriander oil
CAS 8008-52-4
FEMA 2334
Definition: Volatile oil from steam distillation of ripe fruit of *Coriandrum sativum*, contg. d-linalool and its acetate
Properties: Colorless to pale yel. liq., char. odor and taste; very sol. in chloroform, ether, glac. acetic acid; sol. in stronger alcohol; pract. insol. in water; dens. 0.863-0.875 (25/25 C); ref. index 1.4620-1.4720 (20 C)
Precaution: Keep cool, well closed; protect from light
Toxicology: LD50 (oral, rat) 4130 mg/kg; mod. toxic by ingestion; skin irritant; can cause allergic reaction, esp. of the skin; mutagenic data; heated to decomp., emits acrid smoke and fumes
Uses: Natural flavoring agent; aromatic; stimulant; carminative; used in orals
Regulatory: FDA 21CFR §182.10, 182.20, GRAS; FEMA GRAS; Japan approved; Council of Europe listed; FDA approved for orals; BP compliance
Manuf./Distrib. (pharm. & food): Chart; Pierre Chauvet; Commodity Services; Florida Treatt; Ruger; Spectrum Chem. Mfg.

Corn bran
  Uses: Natural fiber for high-fiber formulations, pharmaceuticals
  Trade names: Stabilized Micro-Lite Corn Bran

Corn gluten amino acids
  CAS 65072-01-7
  Synonyms: Maize gluten amino acids; Amino acids, corn gluten
  Definition: Mixt. of amino acids resulting from the complete hydrolysis of corn gluten protein
  Uses: Ingred. in pharmaceuticals
  Trade names containing: Amino Gluten MG

Corn oil
  CAS 8001-30-7; EINECS 232-281-2
  Synonyms: Maize oil; Zea mays oil
  Definition: Refined fixed oil obtained from wet milling of corn, *Zea mays*
  Properties: Pale yel. oily liq., faint char. odor and taste; insol. in water; sol. in ether, chloroform, amyl acetate, benzene, CS_2; sl. sol. in alcohol; dens. 0.914-0.921; m.p. -10 C; acid no. 2-6; iodine no. 109-133; sapon. no. 187-193; flash pt. 321 C; ref. index 1.470-1.474
  Precaution: Combustible liq. when exposed to heat or flame; dangerous spontaneous heating may occur; light-sensitive
  Toxicology: Nontoxic; human skin irritant; experimental teratogen; may be an allergen
  Uses: Solvent, oleaginous vehicle for injections; used in injectables, orals, topicals
  Regulatory: FDA 21CFR §175.105, 175.300, 176.200, 176.210, GRAS; FDA approved for injectables, orals, topicals; USP/NF, BP, JP compliance
  Manuf./Distrib.: ABITEC; Arista Industries; Grain Processing; Penta Mfg.; A.E. Staley Mfg.; Tri-K
  Manuf./Distrib. (pharm. & food): ADM; Arista Industries; British Arkady; Calgene; Cargill; Cerestar Int'l.; Colombus Foods; Ruger; Spectrum Chem. Mfg.; Spectrum Naturals; A E Staley Mfg.; Vandemoortele Professional; Wensleydale Foods
  Trade names: Lipex 104; Super Refined® Corn Oil
  Trade names containing: Docusate Calcium USP in Corn Oil NF Sol'n.; Liquid Vitamin D_3 No. 63643

Corn oil PEG-6 complex. *See* Corn oil PEG-6 esters

Corn oil PEG-6 esters
  CAS 85536-08-9
  Synonyms: Corn oil PEG-6 complex
  Definition: Complex mixture formed from the transesterification of corn oil and PEG-6
  Uses: Hydrophilic oil; amphilic agent improving drug delivery; solubilizer, cosurfactant
  Trade names: Labrafil® M 2125 CS

Corn oil PEG-8 esters
  Definition: Complex mixture formed from transesterification of corn oil and PEG-8
  Uses: Bioavailability enhancer, solubilizer, excipient, emulsifier
  Trade names: Labrafil® WL 2609 BS

Corn starch
  CAS 9005-25-8; EINECS 232-679-6
  Synonyms: Starch, corn; Maize starch
  Definition: Granules obtained from mature grains of corn, *Zea mays*; carbohydrate polymer consisting primarily of amylose and amylopectin
  Properties: White powd. or spheroidal gran.
  Toxicology: No ill effects unless massive doses are given; use of powd. in rubber gloves may cause contact urticaria
  Uses: Excipient; filler; tablet-disintegrant; source of glucose; thickener; for solid oral medicinals; powd. in rubber gloves
  Regulatory: FDA 21CFR §175.105, 178.3520, 182.70, 182.90; GRAS for use in dietary supplements; BP, Ph.Eur. compliance
  Manuf./Distrib.: Am. Maize Prods.; Cerestar UK; Grain Processing; Nat'l. Starch & Chem.; A.E. Staley Mfg.
  Manuf./Distrib. (pharm. & food): ADM; Am. Maize Prods.; Cerestar UK; Grain Processing; Nat'l. Starch & Chem.; Ruger; Spectrum Chem. Mfg.; A.E. Staley Mfg.
  Trade names: Pharma-Gel™; Pure-Dent® B700; Pure-Dent® B810; Pure-Dent® B812; Pure-Dent® B815; Pure-Dent® B816; Pure-Dent® B852; Pure-Dent® B880; Pure Food Starch Bleached 142-A; Purity® 21; Starch 1500®; Starch 1500® LM; Sta-Rx®; 28-1801
  Trade names containing: Pure-Dent® B851; Rocoat® Riboflavin $33^1/_3$ No. 60288

Corn starch, pregelatinized
Synonyms: Maize starch, pregelatinized
Uses: Tablet binder, tablet disintegrant, and table and/or capsule diluent
Usage level: 3-15% (tablet disintegrant)
Regulatory: BP compliance

Corn sugar. *See* D-Glucose anhyd.
Corn sugar gum. *See* Xanthan gum
Corn sugar syrup. *See* Corn syrup

Corn syrup
CAS 8029-43-4; EINECS 232-436-4
Synonyms: Glucose syrup; Corn sugar syrup
Definition: Mixture of D-glucose, maltose, and maltodextrins; obtained by partial hydrolysis of corn starch
Properties: Aq. syrup
Toxicology: May cause allergic reaction
Uses: Sweetener used in orals; texturizer and carrying agent; used in aspirin
Regulatory: FDA 21CFR §182.1866, 184.1865, GRAS; cleared by MID to flavor sausage, hamburger, meat loaf, luncheon meat, chopped or pressed ham; for use alone at 2% or in combination with corn syrup solids or glucose syrup, with combination totaling 2% on dry basis; approved for orals
Manuf./Distrib.: Am. Maize Prods.; Gist-brocades Food Ingreds.; A.E. Staley Mfg.
Manuf./Distrib. (pharm. & food): ADM; Am. Maize Prods.; Gist-brocades Food Ingreds.; Jungbunzlauer; A.E. Staley Mfg.
Trade names: 42/43 Corn Syrup; Jungbunzlauer GS 7097
See also Glucose, liquid

Corn syrup, high fructose
Synonyms: HFCS; High fructose corn syrup
Uses: Used in orals
Regulatory: FDA approved for orals

Corn syrup, hydrogenated. *See* Hydrogenated starch hydrolysate

Corn syrup solids
CAS 68131-37-3
Synonyms: Glucose syrup solids
Properties: Clear visc. syrup
Uses: Coating and binding agent, flavoring agent for pharmaceuticals
Trade names: Maltrin® M200; Maltrin® M250; Maltrin® QD M600
Trade names containing: Extramalt 10; Extramalt 35; Natural Octacosanol GF; Octacosanol GF

Cosbiol. *See* Squalane
Cosmetic talc. *See* Talc
Cotton fiber. *See* Cellulose
Cotton oil. *See* Cottonseed oil

Cottonseed oil
CAS 8001-29-4; EINECS 232-280-7
Synonyms: Deodorized winterized cottonseed oil; Cotton oil; Oleum Gossypii seminis; Aceite de Algodon
Definition: Refined fixed oil from seeds of *Gossypium hirsutum*
Properties: Pale yel. oily liq., nearly odorless; sol. in ether, benzene, chloroform; sl. sol. in alcohol; dens. 0.915-0.921; f.p. 0-5 C; solid. pt. 31-33 C; iodine no. 109-120; sapon. no. 190-198; flash pt. (CC) 486 F
Precaution: Combustible liq. when exposed to heat of flame; may be dangerous hazard due to spontaneous heating; light-sensitive
Toxicology: Experimental tumorigen and teratogen; allergen
Uses: Oleaginous vehicle, solvent for intramuscular preps. and solid oral dosage forms, topical formulations, intravenous nutrition
Usage level: 56-92% (intramuscular preps.), 0.002-402 mg (solid oral dosage forms)
Regulatory: FDA 21CFR §175.105, 175.300, 176.200, 176.210, 177.2800, GRAS; FDA approved for intramuscular injectables, orals; USP/NF compliance
Manuf./Distrib.: ABITEC; Amber Syn.; Arista Industries; Tri-K
Manuf./Distrib. (pharm. & food): ABITEC; Aldrich; Arista Industries; British Arkady; Calgene; Cargill; Colombus Foods; Good Food; Nat'l. Cottonseed; Penta Mfg.; Ruger; Spectrum Chem. Mfg.
Trade names: Super Refined® Cottonseed Oil

C12-13 pareth-23
CAS 9002-92-0

Uses: O/w emulsifier, solubilizer
Trade names: Volpo L23

C12-15 pareth-12

CAS 68131-39-5 (generic)
Synonyms: Pareth 25-12
Definition: PEG ether of a mixture of syn. C12-15 fatty alcohols with avg. 12 moles of ethylene oxide
Uses: Emollient
Trade names: Rhodasurf® LA-12

C12-15 pareth-2 phosphate

Synonyms: Pareth-25-2 phosphate; PEG-2-C12-15 alcohols phosphate
Definition: Complex mixture of esters of phosphoric acid and C12-15 pareth-2
Uses: Emulsifier, solubilizer for drugs
Trade names: Nikkol TDP-2

C-11 primary alcohol. See Undecyl alcohol
Cream of tartar. See Potassium acid tartrate

Creatinine

CAS 60-27-5; EINECS 200-466-7
Synonyms: 2-Amino-1-methyl-4-imidazolidinone
Definition: Anhydride of creatine
Empirical: $C_4H_7N_3O_2$
Properties: Colorless to yel. liq., odorless; sl. sol. in water, alcohol, benzene, chloroform, ether; m.w. 113.12; dens. 1.092; m.p. 255 C (dec.); flash pt. 290 C
Uses: Bulking agent for freeze-drying; used in injectables, ophthalmics, otics, topicals
Regulatory: FDA approved for injectables, ophthalmics, otics, topicals; USP/NF compliance
Manuf./Distrib.: Aldrich; Spectrum Chem. Mfg.
Manuf./Distrib. (pharm. & food): Aldrich

Creosol. See 2-Methoxy-4-methylphenol
4-Cresol. See p-Cresol

m-Cresol

CAS 108-39-4; EINECS 203-577-9
FEMA 3530; UN No. 2076
Synonyms: 3-Methylphenol; m-Cresylic acid
Classification: Phenol
Empirical: C_7H_8O
Formula: $CH_3C_6H_4OH$
Properties: Colorless to yel. liq., phenolic odor; hygroscopic; sol. in water; misc. with alcohol, chloroform, ether, glycerin; m.w. 108.14; dens. 1.034 (20/4 C); m.p. 12 C; b.p. 203 C; flash pt. (CC) 187 F; ref. index 1.5400
Precaution: Corrosive
Toxicology: LD50 (rat, oral) 2.02 g/kg; chronic poisoning may occur from oral ingestion or absorption through the skin; can produce digestive disturbances, skin eruptions, jaundice, uremia
Uses: Antimicrobial preservative; medicinal flavoring agent; used in injectables, eye lotions, antiseptic, insulin prods.
Regulatory: FDA 21CFR §177.2410; FEMA GRAS; FDA approved for injectables; USP/NF, BP compliance
Manuf./Distrib.: Allchem Industries; Mitsui Petrochem. Ind.; Penta Mfg.; Schweizerhall; Spectrum Chem. Mfg.
Manuf./Distrib. (pharm. & food): Aldrich

o-Cresol

CAS 95-48-7; EINECS 202-423-8
FEMA 3480
Synonyms: 2-Methylphenol
Empirical: C_7H_8O
Properties: M.w. 108.14; m.p. 30-34 C; b.p. 191 C; flash pt. 178 F
Uses: Medicinal flavoring agent
Regulatory: FEMA GRAS; BP compliance
Manuf./Distrib.: Allchem Industries; Crowley Tar Prods.; Penta Mfg.; PMC Specialties
Manuf./Distrib. (pharm. & food): Aldrich

p-Cresol

CAS 106-44-5; EINECS 203-398-6
FEMA 2337
Synonyms: 4-Methylphenol; p-Cresylic acid; 4-Cresol

m-Cresylic acid

Empirical: C_7H_8O
Formula: $CH_3C_6H_4OH$
Properties: Crystalline mass, phenolic odor; sol. in alcohol, ether, chloroform, hot water; m.w. 108.14; dens. 1.0341 (20/4 C); m.p. 32-35 C; b.p. 202 C; flash pt. (CC) 86 C; ref. index 1.5395
Toxicology: LD50 (oral, rat) 1.8 g/kg
Uses: Medicinal synthetic flavoring agent
Regulatory: FDA 21CFR §172.515; FEMA GRAS
Manuf./Distrib.: Allchem Industries; Am. Biorganics; Penta Mfg.; PMC Specialties; Spectrum Chem. Mfg.
Manuf./Distrib. (pharm. & food): Aldrich; Allchem Industries; Penta Mfg.; PMC Specialties; Spectrum Chem. Mfg.

m-Cresylic acid. *See* m-Cresol
p-Cresylic acid. *See* p-Cresol
Crispmint oil. *See* Spearmint oil

Croscarmellose sodium
CAS 74811-65-7
Synonyms: Crosslinked NaCMC
Definition: A crosslinked polymer of carboxymethylcellulose sodium
Properties: Wh. free-flowing powd.; partly sol. in water; insol. in ether, alcohol, org. solvs.; pH 5-7 (1% disp.)
Uses: Tablet disintegrant; used in intramuscular injectables, orals
Regulatory: FDA approved for intramuscular injectables, orals; USP/NF compliance
Manuf./Distrib. (pharm. & food): Spectrum Chem. Mfg.
Trade names: Nymcel® ZSX

Crospovidone
CAS 9003-39-8
Synonyms: 1-Ethenyl-2-pyrrolidinone homopolymer; 2-Pyrrolidinone, 1-ethenyl-, homopolymer; Crosslinked PVP; 1-Vinyl-2-pyrrolidinone homopolymer; Poly(vinylpolypyrrolidone); Polyvidonum insoluble, crosslinked
Definition: Water-insol. synthetic crosslinked homopolymer of N-vinyl-2-pyrrolidinone
Empirical: $(C_6H_9NO)_n$
Properties: Wh. powd., faint odor; hygroscopic; insol. in water and most org. solvs.
Uses: Tablet disintegrating agent, suspension stabilizer; used in implants, ophthalmics, orals, injectables (percutaneous), topicals
Regulatory: FDA approved for implants, ophthalmics, orals, injectables, topicals; USP/NF, BP, Ph.Eur. compliance
Manuf./Distrib.: ISP
Trade names: Kollidon® CL; Polyplasdone® INF-10; Polyplasdone® XL; Polyplasdone® XL-10

Crosslinked NaCMC. *See* Croscarmellose sodium
Crosslinked PVP. *See* Crospovidone

Crotonic acid
CAS 3724-65-0
UN No. 2823
Synonyms: β-Methacrylic acid; 2-Butenoic acid
Classification: Aliphatic organic compd.
Empirical: $C_4H_6O_2$
Formula: $CH_3CH:CHCOOH$
Properties: M.w. 86.09; sp.gr. 1.018
Precaution: DOT: Corrosive material
Uses: Synthesis of drugs
Manuf./Distrib.: Aldrich; Allchem Industries; Atomergic Chemetals; Chisso Am.; Eastman; Hoechst Celanese; Spectrum Chem. Mfg.

Cryflourane. *See* Dichlorotetrafluoromethane

Cryofluorane
CAS 76-14-2
Properties: Colorless gas, odorless or ether-like odor; m.w. 170.93; dens. 1.5312; m.p. -94 C; b.p. 4.1 C; ref. index 1.3092
Uses: Aerosol propellant; used in inhalants, nasals, rectals, topicals
Regulatory: FDA approved for inhalants, nasals, rectals, topicals

Crystalline cellulose. *See* Cellulose
CSP. *See* Cupric sulfate pentahydrate

Cubeb oil
FEMA 2339
Synonyms: Tailed pepper; Java pepper; Cubebs oil
Definition: Volatile oil from unripe fruit of *Piper cubeba*, contg. dipentene, cadinene, cubeb camphor
Properties: Colorless, pale grn. or ylsh. liq.; sol. in 10 vols alcohol; misc. with abs. alcohol, chloroform; insol. in water; dens. 0.905-0.925 (25/25 C); ref. index 1.4800-1.5020 (20 C)
Precaution: Keep cool, well closed; protect from light
Toxicology: Heated to decomp., emits acrid smoke and fumes
Uses: Natural flavoring agent; stimulant and diuretic used for chronic bladder troubles; reputed to increase flow of urine; aromatic; expectorant; stimulating effect on mucous membrane
Regulatory: FDA 21CFR §172.510; FEMA GRAS

Cubebs oil. *See* Cubeb oil
Cubic niter. *See* Sodium nitrate

Cucumber extract
CAS 89998-01-6
Synonyms: Cucumis sativus extract
Trade names containing: Uninontan U 34

Cucumis sativus extract. *See* Cucumber extract
Cumaldehyde. *See* Cuminaldehyde
o-Cumaric aldehyde methyl ether. *See* o-Methoxycinnamaldehyde
Cuminal. *See* Cuminaldehyde

Cuminaldehyde
CAS 122-03-2; EINECS 204-516-9
FEMA 2341
Synonyms: Cuminal; Cumaldehyde; p-Cuminic aldehyde; p-Isopropylbenzaldehyde; 4-Isopropylbenzaldehyde; 4-(1-Methylethyl)benzaldehyde
Definition: Constituent of eucalyptus, myrrh, cassia, cumin, and other essential oils or prepared synthetically
Empirical: $C_{10}H_{12}O$
Formula: $(CH_3)_2CHC_6H_4CHO$
Properties: Colorless to ylsh. oily liq., strong persistent aromatic odor, acrid burning taste; sol. in alcohol, ether, toluene; pract. insol. in water; m.w. 148.21; dens. 0.978 (20 C); b.p. 235-236 C (760 mm); flash pt. (COC) 104 C; ref. index 1.5301 (20 C)
Toxicology: LD50 (oral, rat) 1390 mg/kg; skin and eye irritant
Uses: Synthetic flavoring agent; pharmaceutical intermediate
Regulatory: FDA 21CFR §172.515; FEMA GRAS
Manuf./Distrib. (pharm. & food): Aldrich

Cuminic acetaldehyde. *See* p-Isopropylphenylacetaldehyde
p-Cuminic aldehyde. *See* Cuminaldehyde
Cupric gluconate. *See* Copper gluconate
Cupric nitrate. *See* Copper nitrate (ic)
Cupric nitrate hexahydrate. *See* Copper nitrate (ic)
Cupric nitrate trihydrate. *See* Copper nitrate (ic)
Cupric sulfate. *See* Cupric sulfate pentahydrate

Cupric sulfate anhyd.
CAS 7758-98-7; EINECS 231-847-6
Synonyms: Copper sulfate
Empirical: CuO_4S
Formula: $CuSO_4$
Properties: Blue cryst. or cryst. gran. or powd., nauseous metallic taste; sol. in water; insol. in alcohol; m.w. 159.60; dens. 3.6
Precaution: Reacts violently with hydroxylamine, magnesium
Toxicology: LD50 (oral, rat) 300 mg/kg; strong irritant; experimental tumorigen; human poison, systemic effects by ingestion: gastritis, diarrhea, nausea, vomiting, hemolysis; no known skin toxicity; mutagenic data; heated, emits toxic fumes of SO_x
Uses: Fungicide used in orals; antidote to phosphorus
Regulatory: Japan approved (0.6 mg/L as copper in milk); FDA approved for orals
Manuf./Distrib.: Allchem Industries; Farleyway Chem. Ltd; Spectrum Chem. Mfg.

Cupric sulfate pentahydrate
CAS 7758-99-8; EINECS 231-847-6

Curacao aloe extract

Synonyms: CSP; Copper sulfate pentahydrate; Copper sulfate (ic); Cupric sulfate; Blue vitriol; Blue stone; Blue copperas
Classification: Inorganic salt
Empirical: $CuO_4S \cdot 5H_2O$
Formula: $CuSO_4 \cdot 5H_2O$
Properties: Blue cryst. or cryst. gran. or powd., nauseous metallic taste; very sol. in water; sol. in methanol, glycerin; sl. sol. in ethanol; m.w. 249.70; dens. 2.286 (15.6/4 C)
Toxicology: TLV:TWA 1 mg (Cu)/m^3; LD50 (oral, rat) 960 mg/kg; human poison by unspecified routes; moderately toxic by ingestion; heated to dec., emits toxic fumes of SO_x
Uses: In pharmaceuticals
Regulatory: FDA 21CFR §184.1261, GRAS
Manuf./Distrib.: Allchem Industries; Farleyway Chem. Ltd; Spectrum Chem. Mfg.
Manuf./Distrib. (pharm. & food): Allchem Industries; Spectrum Chem. Mfg.; Wako Pure Chem. Ind.

Curacao aloe extract. *See* Aloe extract
Curled mint oil. *See* Spearmint oil
Curry red. *See* CI 16035
Curry red. *See* FD&C Red No. 40
Cyamopsis gum. *See* Guar gum

Cyanocobalamin
CAS 68-19-9; EINECS 200-680-0
Synonyms: Vitamin B_{12}; Cyanocon(III)alamin; α-(5,6-Dimethylbenzimidazolyl)cyanocobamide
Classification: Organic compd.
Definition: Produced commercially from cultures of *Streptomyces griseus*
Empirical: $C_{63}H_{88}CoN_{14}O_{14}P$
Properties: Dark red cryst. or powd., odorless and tasteless; very hygroscopic; sl. sol. in water; sol. in alcohol; insol. in acetone, ether; m.w. 1355.55
Precaution: Light-sensitive
Toxicology: No hazard to humans from excessive ingestion in foods; poison by subcutaneous route; moderately toxic by intraperitoneal route; experimental teratogen, reproductive effects; heated to decomp., emits very toxic fumes of PO_x, NO_x
Uses: Vitamin B_{12} source; hematopoietic vitamin
Regulatory: FDA 21CFR §182.5945, 184.1945, GRAS; Japan approved; BP, Ph.Eur. compliance
Manuf./Distrib.: EM Industries; Hoffmann-La Roche; Roussel Uclaf; Schweizerhall
Manuf./Distrib. (pharm. & food): Am. Roland; R.W. Greeff; Spectrum Chem. Mfg.
Trade names: Cyanocobalamin USP Cryst. No. 69932; Vitacote® B12 1%
Trade names containing: Vitamin B_{12} 0.1% SD No. 65354; Vitamin B_{12} 1.0% SD No. 65305; Vitamin B_{12} 1% Trituration No. 69992; Vitamin B_{12} 1% Trituration No. 69993

Cyanocon(III)alamin. *See* Cyanocobalamin
Cyanoguanidine. *See* Dicyandiamide
Cyanomethane. *See* Acetonitrile
Cyclic dimethyl polysiloxane with n= 3-6. *See* Cyclomethicone
Cyclic dimethylsiloxane. *See* Cyclomethicone
Cyclic ethylene carbonate. *See* Ethylene carbonate

β-Cyclocitral
CAS 432-25-7
FEMA 3639
Synonyms: 2,6,6-Trimethyl-1 and 2-cyclohexen-1-carboxyaldehyde
Empirical: $C_{10}H_{16}O$
Properties: M.w. 152.24; dens. 0.943; b.p. 62—63 C (3 mm); flash pt. > 230 F
Uses: Medicinal flavoring agent
Regulatory: FEMA GRAS
Manuf./Distrib. (pharm. & food): Aldrich

α-Cyclocitrylideneacetone. *See* α-Ionone

Cyclodextrin
CAS 7585-39-9 (β); 10016-20-3 (α); 17465-86-0 (γ); EINECS 231-493-2 (β); 233-007-4 (α); 241-482-4 (γ)
Synonyms: α: α-Cyclodextrin; Cyclomaltohexaose; Schardinger α-dextrin; β: β-Cyclodextrin; Cyclomaltoheptaose; γ: γ-Cyclodextrin; Cyclomaltooctaose
Definition: Cyclic polysaccharide comprised of six to eight glucopyranose units
Properties: M.w. 972.86; m.p. 278 (dec.)
Uses: Bioavailability enhancer; taste/odor masking; stabilizer

Regulatory: Japan approved; not permitted in certain foods
Manuf./Distrib.: Am. Maize Prods.; Janssen Chimica; Pfanstiehl Labs; U.S. Biochemical; Wacker
Trade names: Alpha W6 Pharma Grade; Beta W7; Beta W7 P; Cavitron Cyclo-dextrin™; Gamma W8

α-**Cyclodextrin.** *See* Cyclodextrin

β-**Cyclodextrin**
CAS 7585-39-9; EINECS 231-493-2
Synonyms: Cyclomaltoheptaose; Schardinger β-dextrin
Definition: Cyclic polysaccharide comprised of 7 glucopyranosyl units
Empirical: $C_{42}H_{70}O_{35}$
Formula: $(C_6H_{10}O_5)_7$
Properties: Wh. fine cryst. powd., pract. odorless, sl. sweet taste; sparingly sol. in water; m.p. 290-300 C (dec.)
Uses: Sequestering agent; complex hosting guest molecules; increases the sol. and bioavailability of other
    substances; masks flavor, odor, or coloration; stabilizes against light, oxidation, heat, and hydrolysis; turns
    liqs. or volatiles into stable solids
Regulatory: USP/NF compliance
Manuf./Distrib.: Am. Maize Prods.
Manuf./Distrib. (pharm. & food): Aldrich
See also Cyclodextrin

γ-**Cyclodextrin.** *See* Cyclodextrin
Cyclo-1,13-ethylenedioxytridecane-1,13-dione. *See* Ethylene brassylate
Cyclohexamethyleneimine. *See* Hexamethyleneimine

Cyclohexane
CAS 110-82-7; EINECS 203-806-2
UN No. 1145
Synonyms: Hexahydrobenzene; Hexamethylene; Hexanaphthene
Classification: Aliphatic organic compd.
Formula: C_6H_{12}
Properties: Colorless mobile liq., pungent odor; insol. in water; sol. in alcohol, acetone, benzene; m.w. 84.16;
    dens. 0.779 (20/4 C); m.p. 6.5 C; b.p. 80.7 C; f.p. 6.3 C; flash pt. (CC) -18.3 C; ref. index 1.4264; flamm.
Precaution: DOT: Flamm. liq.; dangerous fire hazard exposed to heat or flame; reactive with oxidizers; mod.
    explosion hazard as vapor exposed to flame; explosive mixed hot with liq. dinitrogen tetraoxide
Toxicology: TLV 300 ppm in air; LD50 (oral, rat) 29,820 mg/kg; poison by IV; mod. toxic by ingestion, inhalation,
    skin contact; systemic and skin irritant; high concs. may act as narcotic; mutagenic data; heated to
    decomp., emits acrid smoke, irritating fumes
Uses: Used in orals
Regulatory: FDA approved for orals; BP compliance
Manuf./Distrib.: Exxon Europe; Phillips 66; Spectrum Chem. Mfg.; Texaco
Manuf./Distrib. (pharm. & food): Aldrich

Cyclohexane, 1,3-bis(2-ethylhexyl)-. *See* Dioctyl cyclohexane
Cyclohexane, diisooctyl-. *See* Dioctyl cyclohexane
Cyclohexaneethyl acetate. *See* Cyclohexylethyl acetate
Cyclohexane ethyl propionate. *See* Ethyl cyclohexanepropionate

Cyclohexyl acetate
CAS 622-45-7; EINECS 210-736-6
FEMA 2349
Synonyms: Acetic acid cyclohexyl ester
Empirical: $C_8H_{14}O_2$
Properties: Oily liq.; misc. with alcohol, ether; insol. in water; m.w. 142.20; dens. 0.966; b.p. 172-173 C; flash
    pt. 136 F; ref. index 1.4400-1.4410
Precaution: Flammable when exposed to heat or flame
Toxicology: LD50 (oral, rat) 6730 mg/kg; mod. toxic by subcutaneous route; mildly toxic by ingestion, skin
    contact; human systemic effects by inhalation: conjunctiva irritation and unspecified respiratory changes;
    systemic irritant to humans
Uses: Fruity synthetic flavoring agent
Regulatory: FDA 21CFR §172.515; FEMA GRAS; Japan approved as flavoring
Manuf./Distrib. (pharm. & food): Aldrich

Cyclohexyl 2-aminobenzoate. *See* Cyclohexyl anthranilate
Cyclohexyl o-aminobenzoate. *See* Cyclohexyl anthranilate

Cyclohexyl anthranilate

Cyclohexyl anthranilate
FEMA 2350
Synonyms: Cyclohexyl 2-aminobenzoate; Cyclohexyl o-aminobenzoate
Definition: Obtained from isatoic anhydride and cyclohexanol
Empirical: $C_{13}H_{17}NO_2$
Properties: Pale yel. liq., orange blossom odor, grape-like taste; sol. in alcohol; insol. in water; m.w. 219.28; dens. 1.01; b.p. 318 C
Uses: Synthetic flavoring agent
Regulatory: FDA 21CFR §172.515; FEMA GRAS

Cyclohexyl butyrate
CAS 1551-44-6
FEMA 2351
Definition: Obtained from esterification of cyclohexanol with isobutyric acid
Empirical: $C_{10}H_{18}O_2$
Properties: Colorless liq., fresh floral odor, intense sweet taste; sol. in alcohol; almost insol. in water; m.w. 170.25; dens. 0.957; b.p. 212 C; flash pt. 173 F; ref. index 1.4490
Uses: Apple-, pineapple-like synthetic flavoring agent
Regulatory: FDA 21CFR §172.515; FEMA GRAS; Japan approved as flavoring
Manuf./Distrib. (pharm. & food): Aldrich

Cyclohexylethyl acetate
CAS 21722-83-8
FEMA 2348
Synonyms: 2-Cyclohexylethyl acetate; Cyclohexaneethyl acetate; Hexahydrophenethyl acetate
Definition: Obtained from the corresponding alcohol by acetylation with sodium acetate in acetic acid sol'n.
Empirical: $C_{10}H_{18}O_2$
Properties: Liq., sweet fruity odor; m.w. 170.25; dens. 0.950; b.p. 104 C (15 mm); flash pt. 178 F
Uses: Sweet synthetic flavoring agent
Regulatory: FDA 21CFR §172.515; FEMA GRAS
Manuf./Distrib.: Aldrich; BASF
Manuf./Distrib. (pharm. & food): Aldrich; BASF

2-Cyclohexylethyl acetate. *See* Cyclohexylethyl acetate

Cyclohexyl formate
FEMA 2353
Empirical: $C_7H_{12}O_2$
Properties: Lt. colorless liq., cherry-like odor; sol. in alcohol; insol. in water; m.w. 128.17; b.p. 162-163 C; ref. index 1.4417 (24 C)
Uses: Synthetic flavoring agent
Regulatory: FDA 21CFR §172.515; FEMA GRAS

Cyclohexyl isovalerate
CAS 7774-44-9
FEMA 2355
Definition: Synthesized from cyclohexane and isovaleric acid in the presence of perchloric acid
Empirical: $C_{11}H_{20}O_2$
Properties: Liq., apple-banana odor; m.w. 184.28; dens. 0.925; b.p. 223 C; flash pt. 192 F; ref. index 1.4410
Uses: Fruity synthetic flavoring agent
Regulatory: FDA 21CFR §172.515; FEMA GRAS
Manuf./Distrib. (pharm. & food): Aldrich

Cyclohexyl propionate
CAS 6222-35-1
FEMA 2354
Empirical: $C_9H_{16}O_2$
Formula: Liq., apple-banana odor; m.w. 156.22; dens. 0.954; b.p. 72-73 C (10 mm); flash pt. 154 F; ref. index 1.4430
Properties: M.w. 156.22; dens. 0.954; b.p. 72-73 C (10 mm); flash pt. 154 F
Uses: Sweet banana, pineapple-like synthetic flavoring agent
Regulatory: FDA 21CFR §172.515; FEMA GRAS
Manuf./Distrib. (pharm. & food): Aldrich

Cyclomaltoheptaose. *See* Cyclodextrin; β-Cyclodextrin
Cyclomaltohexaose. *See* Cyclodextrin

Cyclomaltooctaose. *See* Cyclodextrin

Cyclomethicone
CAS 69430-24-6
Synonyms: Cyclic dimethylsiloxane; Cyclic dimethyl polysiloxane with n= 3-6; Cyclopolydimethylsiloxane
Definition: Fully methylated cyclic silioxane
Empirical: $(C_2H_6OSi)_n$
Formula: $[-(CH_3)_2SiO-]_n$, avg. n = 3-6
Uses: Water repelling agent; used in orals, injectables (percutaneous), topicals
Regulatory: FDA approved for orals, injectables, topicals; USP/NF compliance
Trade names containing: Fancorsil A; Fancorsil P

Cyclopentadecanolide. *See* Pentadecalactone
Cyclopolydimethylsiloxane. *See* Cyclomethicone
Cydonia oblonga seed. *See* Quince seed
p-Cymen-7-carboxaldehyde. *See* p-Isopropylphenylacetaldehyde

p-Cymene
CAS 99-87-6; EINECS 202-796-7
FEMA 2356
Synonyms: Cymol; 4-Isopropyl-1-methylbenzene; 1-Isopropyl-4-methylbenzene; p-Isopropyltoluene; 4-Isopropyltoluene
Definition: Obtained chiefly from the wash water of sulfite paper
Empirical: $C_{10}H_{14}$
Formula: $(CH_3)_2CHC_6H_4CH_3$
Properties: Colorless to pale yel. liq., odorless; sol. in alcohol, ether, acetone, benzene; m.w. 134.24; dens. 0.853; m.p. -68 C; b.p. 176 C; flash pt. (CC) 117 F; ref. index 1.489
Precaution: Flamm. or combustible liq.; sl. explosion hazard in vapor form
Toxicology: LD50 (oral, rat) 4750 mg/kg; mildly toxic by ingestion; human CNS effects at low doses; mutagenic data; skin irritant; heated to decomp., emits acrid smoke and fumes
Uses: Citrus synthetic flavoring agent
Regulatory: FDA 21CFR §172.515; FEMA GRAS
Manuf./Distrib.: Aldrich
Manuf./Distrib. (pharm. & food): Aldrich

3-p-Cymenol. *See* Thymol
p-Cymen-3-ol. *See* Thymol
Cymol. *See* p-Cymene

L-Cysteine
CAS 52-90-4; EINECS 200-158-2
FEMA 3263
Synonyms: (+)-2-Amino-3-mercaptopropionic acid; L-2-Amino-3-mercaptopropanoic acid; α-Amino-β-thiolpropionic acid; l-Cysteine; 3,3´-Dithiobis(2-aminopropanoic acid)
Classification: A nonessential amino acid
Empirical: $C_3H_7NO_2S$
Formula: $HSCH_2CH(NH_2)COOH$
Properties: M.w. 121.16; m.p. 220 C (dec.)
Toxicology: Irritant
Uses: Used in injectables
Regulatory: FDA 21CFR §172.320 (2.3% max. by wt.), 184.1271, GRAS; FEMA GRAS; FDA approved for injectables; BP compliance
Manuf./Distrib.: Aldrich; Diamalt GmbH; Nippon Rikagakuyakuhin; Showa Denko
Manuf./Distrib. (pharm. & food): Aldrich; Am. Roland; Int'l. Sourcing

l-Cysteine. *See* L-Cysteine
Cysteine chlorhydrate. *See* Cysteine hydrochloride anhydrous
Cysteine chlorhydrate monohydrate. *See* Cysteine hydrochloride monohydrate
Cysteine HCl. *See* Cysteine hydrochloride anhydrous
Cysteine HCl monohydrate. *See* Cysteine hydrochloride monohydrate
L-Cysteine hydrochloride. *See* Cysteine hydrochloride anhydrous

Cysteine hydrochloride anhydrous
CAS 52-89-1; EINECS 200-157-7
Synonyms: L-Cysteine hydrochloride; L-2-Amino-3-mercaptopropanoic acid monohydrochloride; Cysteine chlorhydrate; Cysteine HCl; L-Cysteine monohydrochloride

Cysteine hydrochloride monohydrate

Empirical: $C_3H_7NO_2S$ • HCl
Formula: $HSCH_2CH(NH_2)COOH$ • HCl
Properties: Wh. cryst. powd., char. acetic taste; sol. in water, alcohol; m.w. 157.62; m.p. 175 C (dec.)
Toxicology: LD50 (IP, mouse) 1250 mg/kg; mod. toxic by intraperitoneal, IV routes; mutagenic data; heated to decomp., emits very toxic fumes of NO_x, SO_x, and Cl⁻
Uses: Used in orals
Regulatory: FDA 21CFR §172.320, limitation 2.3%, 184.1272, GRAS; Japan approved; Europe listed; UK approved; FDA approved for orals; BP, Ph.Eur. compliance
Manuf./Distrib.: Bretagne Chimie Fine SA; Degussa; EM Industries; Fluka; R.W. Greeff; Nippon Rikagakuyakuhin; Penta Mfg.; Tanabe USA; U.S. Biochemical
Manuf./Distrib. (pharm. & food): Am. Roland

Cysteine hydrochloride monohydrate

CAS 7048-04-6; EINECS 200-157-7
Synonyms: L-Cysteine hydrochloride monohydrate; L-2-Amino-3-mercaptopropanoic acid monohydrochloride monohydrate; Cysteine chlorhydrate monohydrate; Cysteine HCl monohydrate; L-Cysteine monohydrochloride monohydrate
Empirical: $C_3H_7NO_2S$ • HCl • H_2O
Formula: $HSCH_2CH(NH_2)COOH$ • HCl • H_2O
Properties: Colorless to wh. powd.; sol. in water, alcohol, acetone; insol. in ether; m.w. 175.64
Uses: Used in injectables
Regulatory: Approved for injectables
Manuf./Distrib.: Ajinomoto; Fluka; Tanabe Seiyaku
Manuf./Distrib. (pharm. & food): Aldrich; Spectrum Chem. Mfg.

L-Cysteine hydrochloride monohydrate. *See* Cysteine hydrochloride monohydrate
L-Cysteine monohydrochloride. *See* Cysteine hydrochloride anhydrous
L-Cysteine monohydrochloride monohydrate. *See* Cysteine hydrochloride monohydrate

Dakins sol'n. *See* Sodium hypochlorite
DAP. *See* Ammonium phosphate, dibasic
DBP. *See* Dibutyl phthalate
DBPC. *See* BHT
DBS. *See* Dibutyl sebacate

D&C Blue No. 4

CAS 2650-18-2; 37307-56-5; 6371-85-3
Synonyms: CI 42090 (ammonium salt); Acid blue 9 ammonium salt (noncertified); Alphazurine FG; Erioglaucine
Classification: Triphenylmethane color
Definition: Ammonium salt of FD&C Blue No. 1
Empirical: $C_{37}H_{42}N_4O_9S_3$
Formula: $C_{37}H_{36}N_2O_9S_3$ • $2H_3N$
Properties: M.w. 783.01
Uses: Colorant for external pharmaceuticals
Regulatory: FDA 21CFR §74.1104, 74.2104, 82.1104
See also CI 42090

D&C Blue No. 6

CAS 482-89-3
Synonyms: CI 73000; Indigo; Vat blue 1
Classification: Indigoid color
Empirical: $C_{16}H_{10}N_2O$
Properties: M.w. 246.28
Uses: Color additive; used in sutures incl. ophthalmic surgical use, implants, orals
Regulatory: FDA approved for implants, orals
Manuf./Distrib. (pharm. & food): Ruger
See also CI 73000

D&C Blue No. 9

CAS 130-20-1; EINECS 240-980-2
Synonyms: 7,16-dichloro-6,15-dihydro-5,9,14,18-anthrazinetetrone; CI 69825; Indanthrene blue; Carbanthrene blue; Vat blue 6

Classification: Anthraquinone color
Empirical: $C_{28}H_{12}N_2O_4Cl_2$
Properties: M.w. 511.32
Uses: Color additive for sutures, incl. ophthalmic use
Usage level: 2.5% max. (sutures)
Manuf./Distrib. (pharm. & food): Ruger
See also CI 69825

DCDMH. *See* 1,3-Dichloro-5,5-dimethyl hydantoin

D&C Green No. 5
CAS 4403-90-1; EINECS 224-546-6
Synonyms: 2,2´-[(9,10-Dihydro-9,10-dioxo-1,4-anthracenediyl)diimino]bis(5-methyl)benzenesulfonic acid disodium salt; Acid green 25 (noncertified); Alizarine cyanine green F; CI 61570
Classification: Anthraquinone color
Empirical: $C_{28}H_{20}N_2Na_2O_8S_2$
Formula: $C_{28}H_{20}N_2O_8S_2$ • 2Na
Properties: Dullish blue-grn.; m.w. 622.57
Toxicology: Low skin toxicity; may cause skin irritation and sensitivity
Uses: Color additive for nylon 6 and 6/6 nonabsorbable surgical sutures and other uses
Usage level: 0.6% max. (sutures)
Regulatory: FDA 21CFR §74.1205, 74.2205, 82.1205; permanently listed
Manuf./Distrib. (pharm. & food): Crompton & Knowles; Hilton Davis; Ruger
See also CI 61570

D&C Green No. 6
CAS 128-80-3; EINECS 204-909-5
Synonyms: 9,10-Anthracenedione, 1,4-bis[(4-methylphenyl)amino]-; 1,4-Bis[(4-methylphenyl)-amino-9,10-anthracenedione; CI 61565; Quinizarin green SS; Solvent green 3 (noncertified
Classification: Anthraquinone color
Empirical: $C_{28}H_{22}N_2O_2$
Properties: Dull blue-grn.; m.w. 418.50
Uses: Color additive for PET and polyglycolic acid sutures for ophthalmic and general surgical use, external pharmaceuticals; used in implants, topicals
Regulatory: FDA 21CFR §74.1206, 74.2206, 74.3206, 82.1206; FDA approved for implants, topicals; permanently listed
Manuf./Distrib. (pharm. & food): Hilton Davis; Ruger
See also CI 61565

D&C Green No. 8
CAS 6358-69-6; EINECS 228-783-6
Synonyms: 8-Hydroxy-1,3,6-pyrenetrisulfonic acid trisodium salt; CI 59040; Pyranine conc.; Solvent green 7 (noncertified)
Classification: Pyrene color
Empirical: $C_{16}H_7Na_3O_{10}S_3$
Formula: $C_{16}H_{10}O_{10}S_3$ • 3Na
Properties: Ylsh. grn.; m.w. 524.37
Uses: Color additive for external pharmaceuticals
Usage level: 0.01% max. (external pharmaceuticals)
Regulatory: FDA 21CFR §74.1208, 74.2208; permanently listed
Manuf./Distrib. (pharm. & food): Hilton Davis; Ruger
See also CI 59040

DCM. *See* Methylene chloride

D&C Orange No. 4
CAS 633-96-5; EINECS 211-199-0
Synonyms: 4-[(2-Hydroxy-1-naphthalenyl)azo]benzenesulfonic acid monosodium salt; CI 15510; Orange II; Acid orange 7 (noncertified)
Classification: Monoazo color
Formula: $C_{16}H_{12}N_2O_4S$ • Na
Properties: M.w. 350.32
Uses: Color additive for external pharmaceuticals
Regulatory: FDA 21CFR §74.1254, 74.2254, 82.1254; permanently listed
Manuf./Distrib. (pharm. & food): Crompton & Knowles; Hilton Davis; Ruger
See also CI 15510

D&C Orange No. 5
CAS 596-03-2; EINECS 209-876-0
Synonyms: 4′,5′-Dibromo-3′,6′-dihydroxyspiro[isobenzofuran-1(3H),9′-[9H]xanthen]-3-one; Dibromo-fluorescein; CI 45370:1; Acid orange 11; Solvent red 72 (noncertified)
Classification: Fluoran color
Empirical: $C_{20}H_{10}Br_2O_5$
Properties: Reddish-orange; m.w. 490.10
Uses: Color additive for ingested mouthwashes and dentifrices and externally applied drugs
Regulatory: FDA 21CFR §74.1255, 74.2255, 81.25, 82.1255; permanently listed

D&C Orange No. 10
CAS 518-40-1; 38577-97-8
Synonyms: 3′,6′-Dihydroxy-4′,5′-diiodospiro[isobenzofuran-1(3H),9′-[9H]xanthen]-3-one; CI 45425:1; Diiodofluorescein; Solvent red 73 (noncertified)
Classification: Fluoran color
Empirical: $C_{20}H_{10}I_2O_5$
Properties: Orange-red powd.; m.w. 584.10
Uses: Color additive for external pharmaceuticals
Regulatory: FDA 21CFR §74.1260, 74.2260, 82.1260

D&C Orange No. 11
CAS 33239-19-9; EINECS 251-419-2
Synonyms: 3′,6′-Dihydroxy-4′,5′-diiodospiro[isobenzofuran-1(3H),9′-[9H]xanthen]-3-one disodium salt; Erythrosine yellowish NA; CI 45425 (sodium salt); Acid red 95 (noncertified)
Classification: Xanthene color
Definition: Sodium salt of D&C Orange No. 10
Empirical: $C_{20}H_{10}N_2O_5I_2$
Formula: $C_{20}H_{10}I_2O_5$ • 2Na
Properties: Clear red; m.w. 628.07
Uses: Color additive for external pharmaceuticals
Regulatory: FDA 21CFR §74.1261, 74.2261, 82.1261
See also CI 45425

D&C Orange No. 17
CAS 3468-63-1
Synonyms: 1-(2,4-Dinitrophenylazo)-2-naphthol; Permatone orange; Permanent orange; Pigment orange 5; CI 12075
Classification: Monoazo color
Empirical: $C_{16}H_{10}N_4O_5$
Properties: Bright orange; m.w. 338.28
Uses: Color additive for external pharmaceuticals
Regulatory: Color no longer authorized for use in U.S.
See also CI 12075

DCP-0. *See* Calcium phosphate dibasic
DCP-2. *See* Calcium phosphate dibasic dihydrate
DCPC. *See* 1,2-Dicaproyl-sn-glycero(3) phosphatidylcholine

D&C Red No. 6
CAS 5858-81-1; EINECS 227-497-9
Synonyms: 3-Hydroxy-4-[(4-methyl-2-sulfophenyl)azo]-2-naphthalenecarboxylic acid disodium salt; Lithol rubin B; Pigment red 57 (noncertified); CI 15850
Classification: Monoazo color
Empirical: $C_{18}H_{14}N_2O_6SNa_2$
Formula: $C_{18}H_{14}N_2O_6S$ • 2Na
Properties: Med. red; m.w. 432.38
Uses: Color additive for pharmaceuticals; topical antiseptic
Regulatory: FDA 21CFR §74.1306, 74.2306, 82.1306
Manuf./Distrib. (pharm. & food): Hilton Davis; Ruger
See also CI 15850

D&C Red No. 7
CAS 5281-04-9; EINECS 226-109-5
Synonyms: 3-Hydroxy-4-[(4-methyl-2-sulfophenyl)azo]-2-naphthalenecarboxylic acid calcium salt; Lithol rubin B Ca; Pigment red 57:1 (noncertified); CI 15850:1
Classification: Monoazo color

Definition: Calcium salt of D&C Red No. 6
Empirical: $C_{18}H_{14}N_2O_6SCa$
Formula: $C_{18}H_{14}N_2O_6S \cdot Ca$
Properties: Bluish red; m.w. 426.45
Uses: Color additive for pharmaceuticals; topical antiseptic
Usage level: Not to exceed 5 mg per daily dose of drug
Regulatory: FDA 21CFR §74.1307, 74.2307, 82.1307; permanently listed

D&C Red No. 8
CAS 2092-56-0
Synonyms: 1-(4-Chloro-o-sulfo-5-tolylazo)-2-nahthol monosodium salt; Lake red C; Pigment red 53; CI 15585
Classification: Monoazo color
Empirical: $C_{17}H_{12}N_2O_4SNaCl$
Properties: M.w. 398.80
Toxicology: Carcinogenic in animals
Uses: Color additive for pharmaceuticals
Regulatory: No longer authorized for use in U.S.

D&C Red No. 9
CAS 5160-02-1
Synonyms: 1-(4-Chloro-o-sulfo-5-tolylazo)-2-naphthol monobarium salt; Lake red C Ba; Brilliant red; Pigment red 53:1; CI 15585:1
Classification: Monoazo color
Definition: Barium salt of D&C Red No. 8
Empirical: $C_{17}H_{12}N_2O_4SBa_{1/2}Cl$
Properties: M.w. 444.46
Toxicology: Carcinogenic in animals
Uses: Color additive for pharmaceuticals
Regulatory: No longer authorized for use in U.S.

D&C Red No. 17
CAS 85-86-9
Synonyms: 1-[[4-(Phenylazo)phenyl]azo]-2-naphthalenol; Sudan III; Toney red; Solvent red 23; CI 26100
Classification: Diazo color
Empirical: $C_{22}H_{16}N_4O$
Properties: M.w. 352.40
Toxicology: Carcinogenic in animals
Uses: Color additive for external pharmaceuticals
Manuf./Distrib. (pharm. & food): Hilton Davis
See also CI 26100

D&C Red No. 19
CAS 81-88-9
Synonyms: 3-Ethochloride of 9-o-carboxyphenyl-6-diethylamino-3-ethylimino-3-isoxanthene; Rhodamine B; Food red 15; Basic violet 10; CI 45170
Classification: Xanthene color
Empirical: $C_{28}H_{31}N_2O_3Cl$
Properties: Greenish cryst. or yel. powd.; turns violet in sol'n.; m.w. 479.02
Toxicology: Carcinogenic
Uses: Color additive for external pharmaceuticals
Regulatory: Permanently listed in 1988; ruling reversed, no longer authorized for use in U.S.

D&C Red No. 21
CAS 15086-94-9; EINECS 239-138-3
Synonyms: 2´,4´,5´,7´-Tetrabromo-3´,6´-dihydroxyspiro[isobenzofuran-1(3H),9´-[9H]xanthen]-3-one; Tetrabromofluorescein; Solvent red 43 (noncertified); CI 45380:2
Classification: Fluoran color
Empirical: $C_{20}H_8Br_4O_5$
Properties: Bluish-pink stain; insol. in water; m.w. 647.90
Uses: Color additive for pharmaceuticals
Regulatory: FDA 21CFR §74.1321, 74.2321, 82.1321; permanently listed
Manuf./Distrib. (pharm. & food): Hilton Davis

D&C Red No. 22
CAS 548-26-5; 17372-87-1; EINECS 208-953-6
Synonyms: 2´,4´,5´,7´-Tetrabromo-3´,6´-dihydroxyspiro[isobenzofuran-1(3H),9´-[9H]xanthen]-3-one diso-

D&C Red No. 27

dium salt; Eosine G; Eosin YS; Eosin disodium; Acid red 87 (noncertified); Tetrabromofluorescein; CI 45380; Bromofluoroesceic acid
Classification: Indelible xanthene color
Definition: Disodium salt of eosin
Empirical: $C_{20}H_8O_5Na_2Br_4$
Properties: Red cryst. with bluish tinge or brnsh. red powd.; freely sol. in water; m.w. 693.90
Uses: Color additive for pharmaceuticals; used in oral capsules and tablets
Regulatory: FDA 21CFR §74.1322, 74.2122, 82.1322; FDA approved for orals; permanently listed
Manuf./Distrib. (pharm. & food): Hilton Davis; Ruger
See also CI 45380

D&C Red No. 27
CAS 13473-26-2; EINECS 236-747-6
Synonyms: 2´,4´,5´,7´-Tetrabromo-4,5,6,7-tetrachloro-3´,6´-dihydroxyspiro[isobenzofuran-1(3H),9´-[9H]xanthen]-3-one; Tetrachlorotetrabromofluorescein; Tetrabromotetrachlorofluorescein; Solvent red 48; CI 45410:1
Classification: Fluoran color
Empirical: $C_{20}H_4Br_4Cl_4O_5$
Properties: Deep bluish red stain; m.w. 785.68
Uses: Color additive for pharmaceuticals
Regulatory: FDA 21CFR §74.1327, 74.2327, 82.1327; permanently listed
Manuf./Distrib. (pharm. & food): Hilton Davis

D&C Red No. 28
CAS 18472-87-2; EINECS 242-355-6
Synonyms: 2´,4´,5´,7´-Tetrabromo-4,5,6,7-tetrachloro-3´,6´-dihydroxyspiro[isobenzofuran-1(3H),9´-[9H]xanthen]-3-one disodium salt; Phloxine B; Acid red 92 (noncertified); CI 45410
Classification: Xanthene color
Definition: Sodium salt of D&C Red No. 27
Empirical: $C_{20}H_4O_5Na_2Cl_4B4_4$
Formula: $C_{20}H_4Br_4Cl_4O_5 \cdot 2Na$
Properties: M.w. 829.64
Uses: Color additive for pharmaceuticals
Regulatory: FDA 21CFR §74.1328, 74.2328, 82.1328; permanently listed
Manuf./Distrib. (pharm. & food): Hilton Davis; Ruger
See also CI 45410

D&C Red No. 30
CAS 2379-74-0; EINECS 219-163-6
Synonyms: 6-Chloro-2-(6-chloro-4-methyl-3-oxobenzo[b]thien-2(3H)-ylidene)-4-methylbenzo[b]thiophen-3(2H)-one; Helindone pink CN; Vat red 1 (noncertified); CI 73360
Classification: Indigoid color
Empirical: $C_{18}H_{10}O_2S_2Cl_2$
Properties: Bluish pink; m.w. 393.30
Uses: Colorant used in orals
Regulatory: FDA 21CFR §74.1330, 74.2330, 82.1330; FDA approved for orals
Manuf./Distrib. (pharm. & food): Hilton Davis; Ruger
See also CI 73360

D&C Red No. 31
CAS 6371-76-2; EINECS 228-899-7
Synonyms: 3-Hydroxy-4-(phenylazo)-2-naphthalenecarboxylic acid calcium salt; Brilliant lake red R; Pigment red 64:1 (noncertified); CI 15800:1
Classification: Monoazo color
Empirical: $C_{17}H_{11}N_2O_3Ca_{1/2}$
Formula: $C_{17}H_{12}N_2O_3 \cdot {}^1/_2Ca$
Properties: M.w. 311.33
Uses: Colorant used in external pharmaceuticals
Regulatory: FDA 21CFR §74.1331, 74.2331, 82.1331

D&C Red No. 33
CAS 3567-66-6; EINECS 222-656-9
Synonyms: 5-Amino-4-hydroxy-3-(phenylazo)-2,7-naphthalenedisulfonic acid disodium salt; Acid fuchsine; Acid red 33 (noncertified); CI 17200
Classification: Monoazo color

Empirical: $C_{16}H_{13}N_3O_7S_2Na_2$
Formula: $C_{16}H_{13}N_3O_7S_2$ • 2Na
Properties: Dull bluish red; m.w. 469.42
Uses: Color additive for pharmaceuticals
Regulatory: FDA 21CFR §82.1333
Manuf./Distrib.: Spectrum Chem. Mfg.
Manuf./Distrib. (pharm. & food): Crompton & Knowles; Hilton Davis; Ruger
See also CI 17200

D&C Red No. 34
CAS 6417-83-0; EINECS 229-142-3
Synonyms: 3-Hydroxy-4-[(1-sulfo-2-naphthalenyl)azo]-2-naphthalenecarboxylic acid calcium salt (1:1); Deep marron; Fanchon marron; Lake bordeaux B; Pigment red 63:1 (noncertified); CI 15880:1
Classification: Monoazo color
Empirical: $C_{21}H_{14}N_2O_6SCa$
Properties: M.w. 462.48
Uses: Color additive for external pharmaceuticals
Regulatory: FDA 21CFR §74.1334, 74.2334, 82.1334
Manuf./Distrib. (pharm. & food): Ruger

D&C Red No. 36
CAS 2814-77-9; EINECS 220-562-2
Synonyms: 1-[(2-Chloro-4-nitrophenyl)azo]-2-naphthalenol; Flaming red; Pigment red 4 (noncertified); Tiger orange; Vulcan red R; CI 12085
Classification: Monoazo color
Formula: $C_{16}H_{10}ClN_3O_3$
Properties: M.w. 327.73
Uses: Colorant used in orals, topicals
Regulatory: FDA 21CFR §74.1333, 74.1336, 74.2333, 74.2336, 82.1336; FDA approved for orals, topicals
Manuf./Distrib. (pharm. & food): Ruger
See also CI 12085

D&C Red No. 37
CAS 6363-07-5
Synonyms: 3-Ethostearate of 9-o-carboxyphenyl-6-diethylamino-3-ethylimino-3-isoxanthene; Rhodamine B stearate; CI 45170:1
Classification: Xanthene color
Empirical: $C_{46}H_{66}N_2O_5$
Properties: M.w. 727.04
Uses: Color additive for external pharmaceuticals
Regulatory: Banned in 1988 in U.S.

D&C Red No. 39
CAS 6371-55-7
Synonyms: o[p-(β,β´-Dihydroxydiethylamino)phenylazo] benzoic acid; Alba red; Pigment red 100; CI 13058
Classification: Monoazo color
Empirical: $C_{17}H_{19}N_3O_4$
Properties: M.w. 329.36
Uses: Color additive for externally applied quat. ammonium germicides
Usage level: 0.1% max. (quat. germicides)

D&C Red No. 30 aluminum lake
Synonyms: Thioindigoid pink R
Classification: Thioindigoid color
Uses: Colorant used in orals
Regulatory: FDA approved for orals

D&C Violet No. 2
CAS 81-48-1; EINECS 201-353-5
Synonyms: 1-Hydroxy-4-[(4-methylphenyl)amino]-9,10-anthracenedione; Alizurol purple SS; Solvent violet 13 (noncertified); CI 60725
Classification: Anthraquinone color
Empirical: $C_{21}H_{15}NO_3$
Properties: Dull bluish violet; m.w. 329.35
Uses: Color additive for external pharmaceuticals, sun tan oils
Regulatory: FDA 21CFR §74.1602, 74.2602, 74.3602, 82.1602

D&C Yellow No. 7

Manuf./Distrib. (pharm. & food): Hilton Davis; Ruger
See also CI 60725

D&C Yellow No. 7
CAS 2321-07-5; EINECS 219-031-8
Synonyms: 3′,6′-Dihydroxyspiro[isobenzofuran-1(3H),9′-[9H]xanthen]-3-one; Fluorescein; Solvent yellow 94; Acid yellow 73 (noncertified); CI 45350:1
Classification: Fluoran color
Empirical: $C_{20}H_{12}O_5$
Properties: Ylsh.-red powd.; freely sol. in water; water-absorbing; fluorescence disappears when sol'n. is made acid and reappears when made neutral; m.w. 332.31
Toxicology: Believed to be nontoxic to humans
Uses: Color additive for external pharmaceuticals
Regulatory: FDA 21CFR §74.1707, 74.2707, 82.1707
Manuf./Distrib. (pharm. & food): Ruger

D&C Yellow No. 8
CAS 518-47-8; EINECS 208-253-0
Synonyms: 3′,6′-Dihydroxyspiro[isobenzofuran-1(3H),9′-[9H]xanthen]-3-one disodium salt; Naphthol yellow S; Sodium fluorescein; Uranine; Acid yellow 73 sodium salt (noncertified); CI 45350
Classification: Xanthene color
Empirical: $C_{20}H_{10}O_5Na_2$
Properties: Lt. yel. or orange yel. powd.; sol. in water; m.w. 376.27
Uses: Color additive for external pharmaceuticals
Regulatory: FDA 21CFR §74.1708, 74.2708, 82.1708
Manuf./Distrib. (pharm. & food): Hilton Davis; Ruger
See also CI 45350

D&C Yellow No. 10
CAS 8004-92-0
Synonyms: Quinoline Yellow; Quinoline Yellow WS; Acid yellow 3 (noncertified); CI 47005
Classification: Quinoline color
Definition: Mixt. of the disodium salt of the mono- and disulfonic acids of 2-(2-quinolyl)-1H-indene-1,3(2H)-dione
Empirical: $C_{18}H_9NO_8S_2Na_2$
Properties: Brn. greenish yel.; m.w. 454.21
Toxicology: Potential allergen
Uses: Color additive; used in dentals, implants, orals, rectals, sublinguals, topicals
Regulatory: FDA 21CFR §74.2710, 74.3710, 82.1710; FDA approved for dentals, implants, orals, rectals, sublinguals, topicals
Manuf./Distrib.: Spectrum Chem. Mfg.
Manuf./Distrib. (pharm. & food): Crompton & Knowles; Hilton Davis; Ruger
See also CI 47005

D&C Yellow No. 11
CAS 8003-22-3; EINECS 232-318-2
Synonyms: 2-(2-Quinolyl)-1,3-indandione; Quinoline yellow SS; Quinoline yellow spirit soluble; Solvent yellow 33 (noncertified); CI 47000
Classification: Quinoline color
Empirical: $C_{18}H_{11}NO_2$
Properties: Bright greenish yel.; m.w. 273.29
Uses: Color additive for external pharmaceuticals, suntan oils
Regulatory: FDA 21CFR §74.1711, 74.2711
Manuf./Distrib. (pharm. & food): Hilton Davis; Ruger
See also CI 47000

DDH. *See* 1,3-Dichloro-5,5-dimethyl hydantoin
DEA. *See* Diethanolamine

DEA-cetyl phosphate
CAS 61693-41-2
Synonyms: Cetyl DEA phosphate; Bis(2-hydroxyethyl)-ammonium hexadecylphosphate
Definition: Diethanolamine salt of cetyl phosphate
Formula: $CH_3(CH_2)_{14}CH_2OPO_3H_2 \cdot HN(CH_2CH_2OH)_2$
Uses: Emulsifier, emulsion stabilizer
Trade names: Amphisol®

Deadburned magnesite. *See* Magnesium oxide
DEAE. *See* Diethylaminoethanol

DEA-lauryl sulfate
CAS 143-00-0; 68585-44-4; EINECS 205-577-4
Synonyms: Sulfuric acid, monododecyl ester, compd. with 2,2′-iminodiethanol (1:1); Diethanolamine lauryl sulfate
Formula: $C_{12}H_{26}O_4S•C_4H_{11}NO_2$
Uses: Foaming agent
Trade names: Stepanol® DEA

Deanol. *See* Dimethylethanolamine

DEA-oleth-3 phosphate
CAS 58855-63-3
Synonyms: Diethanolamine oleth-3 phosphate; Diethanolammonium POE (3) oleyl ether phosphate
Definition: Diethanolamine salt of a complex mixture of esters of phosphoric acid and oleth-3
Uses: Surfactant, conditioner, emulsifier, gellant for pharmaceuticals; corrosion inhibitor and antigelling agent in aerosol antiperspirant systems

DEA-oleth-10 phosphate
CAS 58855-63-3
Synonyms: Diethanolamine oleth-10 phosphate; Diethanolammonium POE (10) oletyl ether phosphate
Definition: Diethanolamine salt of a complex mixture of esters of phosphoric acid and oleth-10
Uses: Surfactant, conditioner, antistat, emulsifier, gelling agent for cosmetics, pharmaceuticals, and toiletries; corrosion inhibitor and antigelling agent in aerosol antiperspirant systems

2-trans,4-trans-Decadienal. *See* trans-trans-2,4-Decadienal

trans-trans-2,4-Decadienal
CAS 25152-84-5; EINECS 246-668-9
FEMA 3135
Synonyms: 2-trans,4-trans-Decadienal
Empirical: $C_{10}H_{16}O$
Properties: Powerful fatty citrus odor; m.w. 152.24; dens. 0.871; b.p. 114-116 C (10 mm); flash pt. 214 F
Precaution: Combustible liq.
Toxicology: Heated to decomp., emits acrid smoke and fumes
Uses: Citrus synthetic flavoring agent
Regulatory: FEMA GRAS
Manuf./Distrib. (pharm. & food): Aldrich

Decaglycerin dioleate. *See* Polyglyceryl-10 dioleate
Decaglycerin distearate. *See* Polyglyceryl-10 distearate
Decaglycerin monoisostearate. *See* Polyglyceryl-10 isostearate
Decaglycerin monolaurate. *See* Polyglyceryl-10 laurate
Decaglycerin monolinoleate. *See* Polyglyceryl-10 linoleate
Decaglycerin monomyristate. *See* Polyglyceryl-10 myristate
Decaglycerin monooleate. *See* Polyglyceryl-10 oleate
Decaglycerin monostearate. *See* Polyglyceryl-10 stearate
Decaglycerol decaoleate. *See* Polyglyceryl-10 decaoleate
Decaglycerol decastearate. *See* Polyglyceryl-10 decastearate
Decaglycerol dioleate. *See* Polyglyceryl-10 dioleate
Decaglycerol octaoleate. *See* Polyglyceryl-10 octaoleate
Decaglycerol tetralinoleate. *See* Polyglyceryl-10 tetralinoleate
Decaglycerol tetraoleate. *See* Polyglyceryl-10 tetraoleate
Decaglyceryl decaoleate. *See* Polyglyceryl-10 decaoleate
Decaglyceryl decastearate. *See* Polyglyceryl-10 decastearate
Decaglyceryl dioleate. *See* Polyglyceryl-10 dioleate
Decaglyceryl distearate. *See* Polyglyceryl-10 distearate
Decaglyceryl hexaoleate. *See* Polyglyceryl-10 hexaoleate
Decaglyceryl monoisostearate. *See* Polyglyceryl-10 isostearate
Decaglyceryl monolaurate. *See* Polyglyceryl-10 laurate
Decaglyceryl monooleate. *See* Polyglyceryl-10 oleate
Decaglyceryl monostearate. *See* Polyglyceryl-10 stearate
Decaglyceryl octaoleate. *See* Polyglyceryl-10 octaoleate
Decaglyceryl tetraoleate. *See* Polyglyceryl-10 tetraoleate

Δ-Decalactone
CAS 705-86-2; EINECS 211-889-1
FEMA 2361
Synonyms: Amyl-Δ-valerolactone; Decanolide-1,5
Classification: Heterocyclic compd.
Empirical: $C_{10}H_{18}O_2$
Properties: Colorless liq., coconut fruity odor, butterlike on dilution; very sol. in alcohol, propylene glycol; insol. in water; m.w. 170.28; m.p. -27 C; b.p. 117-120 C (0.02 mm); flash pt. > 230 F; ref. index 1.456-1.459
Toxicology: Skin and eye irritant; heated to decomp., emits acrid smoke and irritating fumes
Uses: Coconut, peach-like synthetic flavoring agent
Regulatory: FDA 21CFR §172.515; FEMA GRAS
Manuf./Distrib. (pharm. & food): Aldrich

γ-Decalactone
CAS 706-14-9
FEMA 2360
Synonyms: 4-Hydroxydecanoic acid, γ-lactone
Empirical: $C_{10}H_{18}O_2$
Properties: Colorless liq., fruity peach odor; sl. sol. in water; m.w. 170.25 dens. 0.952; b.p. 281 C; flash pt. > 230 F
Uses: Peach-like synthetic flavoring agent
Regulatory: FDA 21CFR §172.515; FEMA GRAS
Manuf./Distrib. (pharm. & food): Acme-Hardesty; Aldrich

Decanal
CAS 112-31-2; EINECS 203-957-4
FEMA 2362
Synonyms: Aldehyde C-10; Capraldehyde; Capric aldehyde; Caprinaldehyde; 1-Decyl aldehyde; n-Decyl aldehyde; Decylic aldehyde
Empirical: $C_{10}H_{20}O$
Formula: $CH_3(CH_2)_8CH_3$
Properties: Colorless to lt. yel. liq., floral fatty odor; sol. in 80% alcohol, fixed oils, volatile oils, min. oils; insol. in water, glycerin; m.w. 156.30; dens. 0.830 (15/4 C); m.p. 17-18 c; b.p. 208 C; flash pt. 185 F; ref. index 1.4260-1.4300
Precaution: Combustible liq.
Toxicology: LD50 (oral, rat) 3730 mg/kg; mod. toxic by ingestion; mildly toxic by skin contact; severe skin irritant; heated to decomp., emits acrid smoke and irritating fumes
Uses: Citrus flavoring agent
Regulatory: FDA 21CFR §182.60, GRAS; FEMA GRAS; Japan approved as flavoring
Manuf./Distrib.: BASF
Manuf./Distrib. (pharm. & food): Aldrich; BASF; Florida Treatt

Decanedioic acid, bis(1-methylethyl) ester. *See* Diisopropyl sebacate
Decanedioic acid, dibutyl ester. *See* Dibutyl sebacate
Decanoic acid. *See* Capric acid
n-Decanoic acid. *See* Capric acid
Decanoic acid ethyl ester. *See* Ethyl decanoate
Decanoic acid, 1-methyl-1,2-ethanediyl ester mixed with 1-methyl-1,2-ethanediyl dioctanoate. *See* Propylene glycol dicaprylate/dicaprate
Decanoic acid, mixed esters with neopentyl glycol and octanoic acid. *See* Neopentyl glycol dicaprylate/dicaprate
1-Decanol. *See* n-Decyl alcohol
Decanolide-1,5. *See* Δ-Decalactone

3-Decanone
CAS 928-80-3
Empirical: $C_{10}H_{20}O$
Properties: M.w. 156.27; dens. 0.825; m.p. -4 to -3 C; b.p. 204-205 C; flash pt. 80 F
Uses: Citrus, orange flavoring agent
Manuf./Distrib. (pharm. & food): Aldrich

Decanyl acetate. *See* Decyl acetate
2-Decenal. *See* trans-2-Decenal
4-Decenal. *See* cis-4-Decen-1-al

cis-4-Decen-1-al
  CAS 21662-09-9
  FEMA 3264
  Synonyms: 4-Decenal
  Empirical: C$_{10}$H$_{18}$O
  Properties: Colorless to sl. yel. liq., orange-like fatty odor; sol. in alcohol; insol. in water; m.w. 154.28; dens. 0.847-0.848; ref. index 1.442-1.444
  Toxicology: Heated to decomp., emits acrid smoke and irritating fumes
  Uses: Orange-like synthetic flavoring agent
  Regulatory: FEMA GRAS
  Manuf./Distrib. (pharm. & food): Aldrich

trans-2-Decenal
  CAS 3913-71-1; EINECS 223-472-1
  FEMA 2366
  Synonyms: 2-Decenal; Decenaldehyde
  Empirical: C$_{10}$H$_{18}$O
  Properties: M.w. 154.25; dens. 0.841; b.p. 78-80 C (3 mm); flash pt. 205 F
  Toxicology: LD50 (oral, rat) 5000 mg/kg; mod. toxic by skin contact; mildly toxic by ingestion; severe skin irritant; heated to decomp., emits acrid smoke and fumes
  Uses: Citrus synthetic flavoring agent
  Regulatory: FDA 21CFR §172.515; FEMA GRAS
  Manuf./Distrib. (pharm. & food): Aldrich

Decenaldehyde. *See* trans-2-Decenal

Decene-1
  CAS 872-05-9; EINECS 212-819-2
  Synonyms: Linear C10 alpha olefin; Decylene; 1-Decene
  Empirical: C$_{10}$H$_{20}$
  Formula: H$_2$C:CH(CH$_2$)$_7$CH$_3$
  Properties: Colorless liq., mild hydrocarbon odor; sol. in alcohol; sl. sol. in water; m.w. 140.27; dens. 0.741 (20/4 C); f.p. -66.3 C; b.p. 166-171 C; flash pt. (Seta) 114 F; ref. index 1.421 (20 C)
  Precaution: Combustible
  Toxicology: Irritating to skin and eyes; low acute inhalation toxicity; sl. toxic by ingestion
  Uses: Intermediate for surfactants and specialty chemicals for the pharmaceutical industry
  Manuf./Distrib.: Albemarle; Aldrich; Chevron; Monomer-Polymer & Dajac; Shell
  Manuf./Distrib. (pharm. & food): Aldrich

1-Decene. *See* Decene-1

3-Decen-2-one
  CAS 10519-33-2; EINECS 234-059-0
  FEMA 3532
  Synonyms: Heptylidene acetone; Oenanthylidene acetone
  Empirical: C$_{10}$H$_{18}$O
  Properties: Needles, fruital-floral jasmine-like odor; sol. in alcohol, perfume oils; insol. in water; m.w. 154.25; m.p. 16-17 C; b.p. 125-126 C (12 mm)
  Uses: Fruity synthetic flavoring agent
  Regulatory: FDA 21CFR §172.515; FEMA GRAS
  Manuf./Distrib. (pharm. & food): Aldrich

Decoic acid. *See* Capric acid
Decolorizing carbon. *See* Carbon, activated

Decyl acetate
  CAS 112-17-4; EINECS 203-942-2
  FEMA 2367
  Synonyms: Acetate C-10; Decanyl acetate
  Definition: Synthesized by direct acetylation of n-decanol with acetic acid
  Empirical: C$_{12}$H$_{24}$O$_2$
  Formula: CH$_3$(CH$_2$)$_9$OOCCH$_3$
  Properties: Liq., floral orange-rose odor; sol. in 80% alcohol, ether, benzene; insol. in water; m.w. 200.32; dens. 0.862-0.866; b.p. 187-190 C; ref. index 1.4250-1.4300
  Precaution: Combustible
  Uses: Orange-, pineapple-like synthetic flavoring agent

3-Decylacrolein

Regulatory: FDA 21CFR §172.515; FEMA GRAS
Manuf./Distrib. (pharm. & food): Aldrich

3-Decylacrolein. *See* 2-Tridecenal

n-Decyl alcohol
CAS 112-30-1; 68526-85-2; EINECS 203-956-9
FEMA 2365
Synonyms: Alcohol C-10; Noncarbinol; Nonylcarbinol; 1-Decanol; Decylic alcohol
Classification: Fatty alcohol
Empirical: $C_{10}H_{22}O$
Formula: $CH_3(CH_2)_8CH_2OH$
Properties: Mod. visc. liq., sweet odor; sol. in alcohol, ether; insol. in water; m.w. 158.32; dens. 0.8297 (20/ 4 C); m.p. 7 C; b.p. 232.9 C; flash pt. (OC) 180 F; ref. index 1.43587
Precaution: Flamm. when exposed to heat or flame
Toxicology: LD50 (oral, rat) 4720 mg/kg; moderately toxic by skin contact; irritating to eyes, skin, respiratory system; heated to decomp., emits acrid smoke and irritating fumes
Uses: Pharmaceutical raw material; fruity synthetic flavoring agent
Regulatory: FDA 21CFR §172.515, 172.864, 175.300, 176.170, 178.3480, 178.3910; FEMA GRAS; Japan approved as flavoring
Manuf./Distrib.: Albemarle; Aldrich; Brown; M. Michel; Penta Mfg.; Schweizerhall; Vista
Manuf./Distrib. (pharm. & food): Aldrich; Penta Mfg.
Trade names: Cachalot® DE-10; Nacol® 10-97; Nacol® 10-99

1-Decyl aldehyde. *See* Decanal
n-Decyl aldehyde. *See* Decanal

Decyl butyrate
CAS 5454-09-1
FEMA 2368
Empirical: $C_{14}H_{28}O_2$
Properties: Oily liq., apricot-like odor; m.w. 228.37; dens. 0.862; b.p. 134-135 C (8 mm); flash pt. > 230 F
Uses: Citrus synthetic flavoring agent
Regulatory: FDA 21CFR §172.515; FEMA GRAS
Manuf./Distrib. (pharm. & food): Aldrich

Decyl dodecanol
Uses: Solubilizer for lipid-sol. actives in creams, ointments, emulsions, sticks
Trade names: Isofol® 24

Decylene. *See* Decene-1

Decyl glucoside
CAS 54549-25-6; EINECS 259-218-1
Definition: Decyl ether of glucose
Uses: Foaming cosurfactant for dermopharmaceutical prods.
Trade names: Oramix® NS 10

Decylic acid. *See* Capric acid
Decylic alcohol. *See* n-Decyl alcohol
Decylic aldehyde. *See* Decanal
Decyl 9-octadecenoate. *See* Decyl oleate
Decyl octyl alcohol. *See* Stearyl alcohol

Decyl oleate
CAS 3687-46-5; 59231-34-4; EINECS 222-981-6
Synonyms: Decyl 9-octadecenoate
Definition: Ester of decyl alcohol and oleic acid
Empirical: $C_{28}H_{54}O_2$
Formula: $CH_3(CH_2)_7CH=CH(CH_2)_7COOCH_2(CH_2)_8CH_3$
Properties: Wh. to straw liq.; sol. in min. oil, 95% ethanol, IPM, oleyl alcohol; insol. in water; sp.gr. 0.855-0.865; ref. index 1.4530-1.4555
Uses: Emollient, lubricant
Trade names: Ceraphyl® 140; Cetiol® V; Pelemol® DO; Standamul® CTV
Trade names containing: Dehymuls® K

Decyl propionate
CAS 5454-19-3

FEMA 2369
Empirical: $C_{13}H_{26}O_2$
Properties: Liq., ethereal rum fruity odor; m.w. 214.35; dens. 0.864; b.p. 123-134 C (8 mm); flash pt. 225 F; ref. index 1.4291
Uses: Fruity synthetic flavoring agent
Regulatory: FDA 21CFR §172.515; FEMA GRAS
Manuf./Distrib. (pharm. & food): Aldrich

Deep marron. *See* D&C Red No. 34
DEHP. *See* Dioctyl phthalate
Dehydrated beets. *See* Beet powder

Dehydroacetic acid
CAS 520-45-6; 771-03-9; EINECS 208-293-9, 212-227-4
Synonyms: DHA; DHS; 3-Acetyl-5-hydroxy-3-oxo-4-hexenoic acid Δ-lactone; Methylacetopyronone; 3-Acetyl-6-methyl-1,2-pyran-2,4(3H)-dione; 3-Acetyl-6-methyl-2,4-pyrandione
Classification: Cyclic ketone
Empirical: $C_8H_8O_4$
Properties: Wh. cryst. or cryst. powd.; mod. sol. in water and org. solvs.; m.w. 168.16; m.p. 109-111 C; b.p. 269 C
Precaution: Combustible when exposed to heat or flame
Toxicology: LD50 (oral, rat) 500 mg/kg; poison by ingestion and IV routes; mod. toxic by intraperitoneal route; experimental tumorigen; heated to decomp., emits acrid smoke and irritating fumes
Uses: Antimicrobial preservative for pharmaceuticals
Regulatory: FDA 21CFR §172.130, 65 ppm max. residue in or on prepared squash, GRAS; 175.105; USP/NF compliance
Manuf./Distrib. (pharm. & food): Aldrich

7-Dehydrocholesterol. *See* Cholecalciferol
Dehydroxymenthofurolactone. *See* Menthalactone

Denatonium benzoate
CAS 3734-33-6 (anhyd.); 86398-53-0 (monohydrate); EINECS 223-095-2
Synonyms: N-[2-[(2,6-Dimethylphenyl)amino]-2-oxoethyl]-N,N-diethylbenzenemathanaminium benzoate; Benzyldiethyl [(2,6-xylylcarbomoyl)methyl]ammonium benzoate; Lignocaine benzyl benzoate
Classification: Organic compd.
Empirical: $C_{28}H_{34}N_2O_3$ or $C_{28}H_{34}N_2O_3 \cdot H_2O$
Formula: $C_{21}H_{29}N_2O \cdot C_7H_5O_2$
Properties: Wh. cryst. powd., odorless, extremely bitter; very sol. in chloroform, methanol; sol. in water, alcohol; sparingly sol. in acetone; pract. insol. in ether; m.w. 446.59 (anhyd.); m.p. 174-176 C; pH 6.5-7.5 (3%)
Uses: Pharmaceutical aid, alcohol denaturant, flavor; added to toxic substances as a deterrent to ingestion
Regulatory: FDA 27CFR §21.151; USP/NF compliance
Manuf./Distrib.: Atomergic Chemetals; EM Industries; Macfarlan Smith Ltd
Manuf./Distrib. (pharm. & food): Aldrich; Atomergic Chemetals; Robeco; Spectrum Chem. Mfg.

Deodorized winterized cottonseed oil. *See* Cottonseed oil
Deoiled lanolin. *See* Lanolin wax
7-Deoxycholic acid sodium salt. *See* Sodium desoxycholate
6-Deoxy-L-mannose. *See* Rhamnose
1-Deoxy-1-(methylamino)-D-glucitol. *See* Meglumine
DEP. *See* Diethyl phthalate
DETDA. *See* Diethyl toluene diamine
Devitalized wheat gluten. *See* Wheat gluten
Dewaxed lanolin. *See* Lanolin oil
3,6,9,12,15,18,21,24,27,30-Dexaoxadotetracontan-1-ol. *See* Laureth-10
3,6,9,12,15,18,21,24,27,30-Dexaoxahexatetracontan-1-ol. *See* Ceteth-10
Dexpanthenol. *See* D-Panthenol; DL-Panthenol

Dextran
CAS 9004-54-0; EINECS 232-677-5
Synonyms: Macrose
Definition: Polymers of glucose with chain-like structures and m.w. to 200,000
Formula: $(C_6H_{10}O_5)_n$
Precaution: Combustible
Toxicology: Histamine-releasing props.; may cause anaphylactoid reactions
Uses: Visc. agent in artificial tear prods., topical ophthalmic preps.; plasma substitute

Dextrates

Regulatory: FDA 21CFR §186.1275, GRAS as indirect additive; Japan approved
Manuf./Distrib.: Accurate Chem. & Scientific; Am. Biorganics; Pharmacia AB; Schweizerhall; Spectrum Chem. Mfg.; U.S. Biochemical
Manuf./Distrib. (pharm. & food): Spectrum Chem. Mfg.

Dextrates

Definition: Purified mixt. of saccharides resulting from controlled enzymatic hydrolysis of starch; either anhyd. or hydrated
Properties: Wh. free-flowing porous spherical gran., odorless, sweet taste producing cooling sensation in mouth; freely sol. in water; sol. in dil. acids and alkalies, basic org. solvs.; insol. in common org. solvs.; pH 3.8-5.8 (20%); DE 93-99%
Toxicology: Essentially nontoxic
Uses: Sweetening agent; tablet and capsule diluent, excipient; may be compressed directly into self-binding tablets
Regulatory: USP/NF compliance

Dextrin

CAS 9004-53-9; EINECS 232-675-4
Synonyms: Dextrine; British gum; Starch gum; Tapioca; Vegetable gum
Definition: Gum produced by incomplete hydrolysis of starch
Empirical: $(C_6H_{10}O_5)_n \cdot xH_2O$
Properties: Yel. or wh. powd. or gran.; hygroscopic; sol. in water; insol. in alcohol, ether; colloidal in props.
Toxicology: Mildly toxic by IV route; heated to decomp., emits acrid smoke and irritating fumes
Uses: Emulsifier, suspending or visc.-increasing agent; tablet binder/diluent; used in orals (infant formulas), topicals; as adhesive and stiffener in surgical dressings
Regulatory: FDA 21CFR §184.1277, 186.1275, GRAS; USDA 9CFR §318.7, 381.147; FDA approved for orals, topicals; USP/NF compliance
Manuf./Distrib.: Am. Maize Prods.; Avebe BV; Grain Processing; Nat'l. Starch & Chem.; Spectrum Chem. Mfg.; A.E. Staley Mfg.
Manuf./Distrib. (pharm. & food): Aldrich; Am. Maize Prods.; Avebe; Cerestar Int'l.; Grain Processing; Integra; Mallinckrodt; Nat'l. Starch & Chem.; Roquette UK

Dextrine. *See* Dextrin
Dextronic acid. *See* D-Gluconic acid
Dextrose. *See* D-Glucose anhyd.
Dextrose monohydrate. *See* D-Glucose monohydrate
DHA. *See* Dehydroacetic acid; Dihydroxyacetone
DHS. *See* Dehydroacetic acid
1,2-Diacetoxypropane. *See* Propylene glycol diacetate

Diacetylated monoglycerides

CAS 8029-92-3
Definition: Glycerin esterified with edible fatty acids and acetic acid
Properties: Clear liq.; sol. in 80% aq. alcohol, veg. and min. oils; acid no. 3 max.; sapon. no. 365-395; hyd. no. 15 max.
Uses: Excipient, solv., plasticizer; used in orals, parenterals
Regulatory: FDA approved for orals; USP/NF compliance

Diacetylmethane. *See* Acetylacetone
1,2-Diacyl-sn-glycero-3-phosphocholine. *See* Hydrogenated lecithin

Diallyl maleate

CAS 999-21-3; EINECS 213-658-0
Empirical: $C_{10}H_{12}O_4$
Formula: $CH_2{:}CHCH_2OCOCH{:}CHCOOCH_2CH{:}CH_2$
Uses: Pharmaceutical intermediate
Manuf./Distrib.: Aceto; Ashland
Manuf./Distrib. (pharm. & food): Aldrich

α, ϵ-**Diaminocaproic acid.** *See* L-Lysine
1,2-Diaminoethane. *See* Ethylenediamine
2,6-Diaminohexanoic acid. *See* L-Lysine
Diammonium edetate. *See* Diammonium EDTA

Diammonium EDTA

CAS 20824-56-0; EINECS 244-063-4
Synonyms: Diammonium edetate; Diammonium N,N´-1,2-ethanediylbis[N-(carboxymethyl)glycine];

Diammonium ethylene diamine tetraacetate; Edetate diammonium
Classification: Substituted diamine
Empirical: $C_{10}H_{16}N_2O_8 \cdot 2H_3N$
Formula: $NCH_2CH_2N(CH_2COOH)_2(CH_2COONH_4)_2$
Uses: Chelating agent; drug stabilizing agent
Trade names: Versene Diammonium EDTA

Diammonium N,N´-1,2-ethanediylbis[N-(carboxymethyl)glycine]. *See* Diammonium EDTA
Diammonium ethylene diamine tetraacetate. *See* Diammonium EDTA
Diammonium hydrogen orthophosphate. *See* Ammonium phosphate, dibasic
Diammonium hydrogen phosphate. *See* Ammonium phosphate, dibasic
Diammonium phosphate. *See* Ammonium phosphate, dibasic
1,4-Dianilinobenzene. *See* N,N´-Diphenyl-p-phenylenediamine

Diatomaceous earth
CAS 6067-86-0; 7631-86-9; 68855-54-9; EINECS 231-545-4
Synonyms: Kieselguhr; Diatomite; Diatomaceous silica; Infusorial earth; Siliceous earth
Definition: Mineral material consisting chiefly of the siliceous frustules and fragments of various species of diatoms
Properties: Wh. to pale buff soft bulky solid; insol. in acids except HF; sol. in strong alkalies; dens. 1.9-2.35; bulk dens. 8-15 lb/ft³; oil absorp. 135-185%; 88% silica
Precaution: Noncombustible
Toxicology: TLV:TWA 10 mg/m³ (dust); poison by inhalation and ingestion; dust may cause fibrosis of the lungs
Uses: Filtering aid, sorbent; used in dentifrices; absorbent for liq.
Regulatory: FDA 21CFR §73.1, 133.146, 160.105, 160.185, 172.230, 172.480, 173.340, 175.300, 177.1460, 177.2410, 182.90, 193.135, 561.145, 573.940; USDA 9CFR §318.7; Japan restricted (0.5% max. residual); USP/NF, BP compliance
Manuf./Distrib.: Ashland; Celite; Coyne; CR Mins.; Great Western; Grefco; L.A. Salomon; Seefast (Europe) Ltd; Spectrum Chem. Mfg.
Manuf./Distrib. (pharm. & food): Aldrich
Trade names: Hyflo Super-Cel

Diatomaceous silica. *See* Diatomaceous earth
Diatomite. *See* Diatomaceous earth

Diatrizoic acid
CAS 117-96-4
Uses: Used in injectables
Regulatory: FDA approved for injectables; BP, Ph.Eur. compliance (dihydrate)

Diazolidinyl urea
CAS 78491-02-8; EINECS 278-928-2
Synonyms: N-[1,3-Bis(hydroxymethyl)-2,5-dioxo-4-imidazolidinyl]-; 1,3-Bis(hydroxymethyl) urea; Oxymethurea
Classification: Heterocyclic substituted urea
Empirical: $C_8H_{14}N_4O_7$
Precaution: May release formaldehyde
Uses: Antimicrobial preservative; antiseptic; keratin softener in dry skin prods.; used in topical pharmaceutical prods.
Regulatory: USA CIR approved; Europe listed; Japan not approved
Trade names: Germall® II
Trade names containing: Germaben® II

Dibasic potassium phosphate. *See* Potassium phosphate dibasic
Dibasic sodium phosphate. *See* Sodium phosphate dibasic anhydrous
Dibasic sodium phosphate heptahydrate. *See* Sodium phosphate dibasic heptahydrate
Dibenzoyl peroxide. *See* Benzoyl peroxide
Dibenzyl ether. *See* Benzyl ether
DIBK. *See* Diisobutyl ketone
4´,5´-Dibromo-3´,6´-dihydroxyspiro[isobenzofuran-1(3H),9´-[9H]xanthen]-3-one. *See* D&C Orange No. 5
Dibromofluorescein. *See* D&C Orange No. 5
β-Dibromo hydrin. *See* 2,3-Dibromo-1-propanol

2,3-Dibromo-1-propanol
CAS 96-13-9; EINECS 202-480-9
Synonyms: Allyl alcohol dibromide; β-Dibromo hydrin

2,2´-Dibutoxyethyl ether

Classification: Aliphatic organic compd.
Empirical: $C_3H_6Br_2O$
Formula: $CH_2BrCHBrCH_2OH$
Properties: Colorless liq.; sol. in acetone, alcohol, ether, benzene; m.w. 217.90; dens. 2.120 (20/4 C); b.p. 219 C; flash pt. > 110 C; ref. index 1.5590
Toxicology: Carcinogenic
Uses: Intermediate for pharmaceuticals
Manuf./Distrib.: Aldrich; ICI Am.; Schweizerhall
Manuf./Distrib. (pharm. & food): Honjo; MANAC; Tosoh

2,2´-Dibutoxyethyl ether. *See* Diethylene glycol dibutyl ether

Dibutyl adipate

CAS 105-99-7; EINECS 203-350-4
Synonyms: Hexanedioic acid, dibutyl ester
Definition: Diester of butyl alcohol and adipic acid
Empirical: $C_{14}H_{26}O_4$
Formula: $[-CH_2CH_2CO_2(CH_2)_3CH_3]_2$
Properties: M.w. 258.36; dens. 0.962; b.p. 305 C; flash pt. > 110 C
Uses: Emolllient, oily component in sun and skin protective oils
Manuf./Distrib.: Aquatec Quimica SA
Trade names: Cetiol® B

Dibutyl-1,2-benzene dicarboxylate. *See* Dibutyl phthalate
Dibutyl butyrolactone. *See* 4,4-Dibutyl-γ-butyrolactone

4,4-Dibutyl-γ-butyrolactone

FEMA 2372
Synonyms: Dibutyl butyrolactone; 4-Butyl-4-hydroxyoctanoic acid, γ-lactone; 4,4-Dibutyl-4-hydroxybutyric acid, γ-lactone
Definition: Synthesized from butyl pentanol and methyl acrylate using a catalyst
Empirical: $C_{12}H_{22}O_2$
Properties: Colorless oily liq., oily coconut-butter odor, coconut-like flavor; sol. in alcohol; insol. in water; m.w. 198.31
Uses: Synthetic flavoring agent
Regulatory: FDA 21CFR §172.515; FEMA GRAS

Dibutyl 'Carbitol'. *See* Diethylene glycol dibutyl ether
2,6-Di-t-butyl-p-cresol. *See* BHT
Dibutyl decanedioate. *See* Dibutyl sebacate
4,4-Dibutyl-4-hydroxybutyric acid, γ-lactone. *See* 4,4-Dibutyl-γ-butyrolactone
2,6-Di-t-butyl-4-methylphenol. *See* BHT

Dibutyl phthalate

CAS 84-74-2; EINECS 201-557-4
Synonyms: DBP; 1,2-Benzenedicarboxylic acid, dibutyl ester; Dibutyl-1,2-benzene dicarboxylate; Butyl phthalate
Definition: Aromatic diester of butyl alcohol and phthalic acid
Empirical: $C_{16}H_{22}O_4$
Formula: $C_6H_4(COOC_4H_9)_2$
Properties: Colorless stable oily liq., odorless; misc. with common org. solvs.; insol. in water; m.w. 278.17; dens. 1.0484 (20/20 C); b.p. 340 C; f.p. -35 C; flash pt. (COC) 340 F; ref. index 1.4920
Toxicology: Toxic; TLV 5 mg/m³ of air; irritant; if ingested can cause gastrointestinal upset; vapor irritating to eyes and mucous membranes
Uses: Used in orals
Regulatory: FDA 21CFR §175.105, 175.300, 176.170, 176.300, 177.1200, 177-2420, 177.2600; FDA approved for orals; BP, Ph.Eur. compliance
Manuf./Distrib.: Aldrich; Allchem Ind.; Aristech; Ashland; BP Chem. Ltd; Chisso Am.; Coyne; Daihachi Chem. Ind.; Eastman; Great Western; C.P. Hall; Mitsubishi Gas; Spectrum Chem. Mfg.; Unitex
Manuf./Distrib. (pharm. & food): Ruger

Dibutyl sebacate

CAS 109-43-3; EINECS 203-672-5
FEMA 2373
Synonyms: DBS; Dibutyl decanedioate; Di-n-butyl sebacate; Decanedioic acid, dibutyl ester
Definition: Diester of butyl alcohol and sebacic acid

Empirical: $C_{18}H_{34}O_4$
Formula: $C_4H_9OCO(CH_2)_8OCOC_4H_9$
Properties: Colorless clear liq., odorless; sol. in alcohol, IPA, min. oil; sl. sol. in propylene glycol; insol. in water; m.w. 314.47; dens. 0.936 (20/20 C); b.p. 349 C (760 mm); f.p. -11 C; acid no. 0.1 max.; sapon. no. 352-357; flash pt. 350 F; ref. index 1.429-1.441
Precaution: Combustible when exposed to heat or flame; can react with oxidizing materials
Toxicology: LD50 (oral, rat) 16 g/kg; mildly toxic by ingestion; experimental reproductive effects; heated to decomp., emits acrid smoke and fumes
Uses: Plasticizer; used in orals
Regulatory: FDA 21CFR §172.515, 175.105, 175.300, 175.320, 176.170, 177.2600, 178.3910, 181.22, 181.27; FEMA GRAS; FDA approved for orals; USP/NF compliance
Manuf./Distrib.: C.P. Hall; Harwick; Richman; Union Camp; Unitex; Velsicol

Di-n-butyl sebacate. *See* Dibutyl sebacate
Dicalcium citrate. *See* Calcium citrate
Dicalcium orthophosphate anhyd. *See* Calcium phosphate dibasic
Dicalcium phosphate. *See* Calcium phosphate dibasic; Calcium phosphate dibasic dihydrate
Dicalcium phosphate dihydrate. *See* Calcium phosphate dibasic dihydrate

1,2-Dicaproyl-sn-glycero(3) phosphatidylcholine
CAS 3436-44-0
Synonyms: DCPC
Uses: Emulsifier, solubilizer
Trade names: Phospholipon® CC

Dicapryl ether. *See* Dioctyl ether
Dicarboxylic acid C_3. *See* Malonic acid
Dicarboxylic acid C_6. *See* Adipic acid
Dicarboxylic acid C_8. *See* Suberic acid
Dichlorantin. *See* 1,3-Dichloro-5,5-dimethyl hydantoin
1,4-Dichlorobenzene. *See* p-Dichlorobenzene

p-Dichlorobenzene
CAS 106-46-7; EINECS 203-400-5
UN No. 1592
Synonyms: 1,4-Dichlorobenzene
Empirical: $C_6H_4Cl_2$
Properties: Wh. cryst., penetrating odor; sol. in alcohol, benzene, ether; insol. in water; m.w. 147.00; dens. 1.241; m.p. 54-56 C; b.p. 173 C; flash pt. 65 C
Precaution: Combustible
Toxicology: DOT: Poisonous material; eye irritant; suspected carcinogen
Uses: Mfg. of intermediates, pharmaceuticals
Manuf./Distrib.: Aldrich; Ashland; Mitsubishi Gas; Monsanto; PPG Industries; Spectrum Chem. Mfg.
Manuf./Distrib. (pharm. & food): Aldrich; Ruger

2,4-Dichlorobenzenemethanol. *See* Dichlorobenzyl alcohol

Dichlorobenzyl alcohol
CAS 1777-82-8; EINECS 217-210-5
Synonyms: 2,4-Dichlorobenzenemethanol
Classification: Substituted aromatic compd.
Empirical: $C_7H_6Cl_2O$
Properties: Crystals; sol. clear 1 g/10 ml methanol; m.w. 177.03; m.p. 57-59 C
Uses: Topical antiseptic; antifungal, preservative
Usage level: 0.05-0.5%
Regulatory: USA CIR approved; Europe listed 0.15% max.; Japan not approved
Manuf./Distrib. (pharm. & food): Aldrich
Trade names: Myacide® SP

1,1-Dichloro-2-chloroethylene. *See* Trichloroethylene

Dichlorodifluoromethane
CAS 75-71-8; EINECS 200-893-9
UN No. 1028
Synonyms: Difluorodichloromethane; CFC 12; Fluorocarbon-12; Food Freezant 12
Empirical: CCl_2F_2
Formula: $ClCF_2Cl$

7,16-Dichloro-6,15-dihydro-5,9,14,18-anthrazinetetrone

> *Properties:* Colorless gas, odorless; noncorrosive; insol. in water; sol. in most org. solvs.; m.w. 120.9; b.p. -29.8 C; f.p. -158 C
> *Precaution:* Nonflamm. gas; can react violently with Al
> *Toxicology:* TLV 1000 ppm in air; human systemic effects; narcotic in high concs.; heated to decomp., emits highly toxic fumes of phosgene, Cl⁻, and F⁻
> *Uses:* Aerosol propellant; used in implants, inhalers, rectals, topicals
> *Regulatory:* FDA 21CFR §173.355; FDA approved for implants, inhalers, rectals, topicals; USP/NF, BP compliance
> *Manuf./Distrib.:* Air Prods.; Elf Atochem N. Am.; ICI Spec.; PCR

7,16-Dichloro-6,15-dihydro-5,9,14,18-anthrazinetetrone. *See* CI 69825; D&C Blue No. 9

1,3-Dichloro-5,5-dimethyl hydantoin

> CAS 118-52-5
> *Synonyms:* DDH; Dichlorantin; DCDMH
> *Formula:* CINCONCIOC(CH₃)₂
> *Properties:* White powd., mild chlorine odor; sl. sol. in water; sol. in benzene, chloroform, ethylene dichloride, alcohol; m.w. 197.02; m.p. 132-134 C
> *Precaution:* Combustion with evolution of chlorine
> *Toxicology:* Toxic by inhalation; skin irritant; TLV 0.2 mg/m³ of air; causes cancer when injected into rats
> *Uses:* Pharmaceutical intermediate

Dichlorofluoromethane

> CAS 75-43-4
> UN No. 1029
> *Empirical:* FCHCl₂
> *Properties:* M.w. 102.92; m.p. -135 C; b.p. 8.9 C
> *Uses:* Used in orals
> *Regulatory:* FDA approved for orals
> *Manuf./Distrib. (pharm. & food):* Aldrich

Dichloromethane. *See* Methylene chloride

1,6-Di (4´-chlorophenyldiguanidino) hexane diacetate. *See* Chlorhexidine diacetate

Dichlorotetrafluoroethane

> CAS 76-14-2
> UN No. 1958
> *Synonyms:* sym-Dichlorotetrafluoroethane; 1,2-Dichlorotetrafluoroethane; Fluorocarbon-114; Tetrafluorodichloroethane
> *Empirical:* C₂Cl₂F₄
> *Formula:* CClF₂CClF₂
> *Properties:* Colorless clear gas, nearly odorless to faint ethereal odor; insol. in water; m.w. 170.9; vapor pressure 1620 mm Hg; b.p. 3.55 C; f.p. -94 C
> *Precaution:* Nonflamm.
> *Toxicology:* Toxic by inhalation; TLV 1000 ppm in air
> *Uses:* Aerosol propellant for pharmaceuticals
> *Regulatory:* USP/NF, BP compliance

1,2-Dichlorotetrafluoroethane. *See* Dichlorotetrafluoroethane

Dichlorotetrafluoromethane

> *Synonyms:* CFC 114; Cryflourane; Tetrafluorodichloromethane
> *Empirical:* C₂Cl₂F₄
> *Formula:* ClCF₂CF₂Cl
> *Uses:* Aerosol propellant

Dichromium trioxide. *See* Chromium oxide greens; CI 77288

Dicocoyl pentaerythrityl distearyl citrate

> *Classification:* Organic compd.
> *Uses:* Emulsifier
> *Trade names:* Dehymuls® FCE
> *Trade names containing:* Dehymuls® F; Dehymuls® K

Dicyandiamide

> CAS 461-58-5; EINECS 207-312-8
> *Synonyms:* Cyanoguanidine
> *Classification:* Aliphatic organic compd.

Empirical: C$_2$H$_4$N$_4$
Formula: NH$_2$C(NH)(NHCN)
Properties: Pure white crystals; sol. in liq. ammonia; partly sol. in hot water; m.w. 84.08; dens. 1.4 (25 C); m.p. 207-209 C; stable when dry
Precaution: Nonflamm.
Uses: Pharmaceuticals
Regulatory: BP compliance
Manuf./Distrib.: Allchem Ind.; Andrulex Trading Ltd; CVC Spec.; San Yuan; SKW
Manuf./Distrib. (pharm. & food): Aldrich; Nippon Carbide Ind.

Dicyclohexyl disulfide
CAS 2550-40-5
FEMA 3448
Empirical: C$_{12}$H$_{22}$S$_2$
Properties: M.w. 230.44; dens. 1.046; b.p. 162-163 C (6 mm); flash pt. > 230 F
Uses: Berry-like flavoring agent
Regulatory: FEMA GRAS
Manuf./Distrib. (pharm. & food): Aldrich

Didodecyl 3,3´-thiodipropionate. *See* Dilauryl thiodipropionate

Diethanolamine
CAS 111-42-2; EINECS 203-868-0
UN No. 1760
Synonyms: DEA; 2,2´-Iminobisethanol; Bis(2-hydroxyethyl)amine; Di(2-hydroxyethyl) amine; 2,2´-Iminodiethanol
Classification: Aliphatic amine
Empirical: C$_4$H$_{11}$NO$_2$
Formula: (HOCH$_2$CH$_2$)$_2$NH
Properties: Colorless cryst. or liq., mild ammoniacal odor; very sol. in water and alcohol; misc. with acetone, chloroform, glycerin; insol. in ether, benzene; m.w. 105.09; dens. 1.0881 (30/4 C); m.p. 28 C; b.p. 268 C; flash pt. 300 F; ref. index 1.4770
Precaution: Combustible; DOT: corrosive material; light-sensitive
Toxicology: LD50 (rat, oral) 12.76 g/kg; TLV 3 ppm in air; may be irritating to skin and mucous membranes
Uses: Alkalizing agent, emulsifier, solubilizer, and dispersant in pharmaceuticals; used in injectables (IV), ophthalmics
Regulatory: FDA 21CFR §175.105, 176.170, 176.180, 176.210, 177.2600; FDA approved for injectables (IV), ophthalmics; USP/NF, BP compliance
Manuf./Distrib.: Akzo Nobel; Allchem Ind.; Ashland; Coyne; Great Western; Hüls AG; Oxiteno; Union Carbide
Manuf./Distrib. (pharm. & food): Aldrich; Ruger; Spectrum Chem. Mfg.

Diethanolamine lauric acid amide. *See* Lauramide DEA
Diethanolamine lauryl sulfate. *See* DEA-lauryl sulfate
Diethanolamine oleth-3 phosphate. *See* DEA-oleth-3 phosphate
Diethanolamine oleth-10 phosphate. *See* DEA-oleth-10 phosphate
Diethanolamine palm kernel oil acid amide. *See* Palm kernelamide DEA
Diethanolamine stearic acid amide. *See* Stearamide DEA
Diethanolammonium POE (10) oletyl ether phosphate. *See* DEA-oleth-10 phosphate
Diethanolammonium POE (3) oleyl ether phosphate. *See* DEA-oleth-3 phosphate
1,1-Diethoxyethane. *See* Acetal
Diethyl acetal. *See* Acetal

Diethylacetic acid
CAS 88-09-5; EINECS 201-796-4
FEMA 2429
Synonyms: 2-Ethyl butanoic acid; Carboxylic acid C-6; α-Ethylbutyric acid; 3-Pentanecarboxylic acid; 2-Ethylbutyric acid
Empirical: C$_6$H$_{12}$O$_2$
Formula: (C$_2$H$_5$)$_2$CHCOOH
Properties: Colorless volatile liq., rancid odor; sol. in alcohol, ether; sl. sol. in water; m.w. 116.18; dens. 0.917; m.p. -15 C; b.p. 194-195 C; flash pt. (CC) 78 F
Precaution: Flamm. liq.
Toxicology: LD50 (oral, rat) 2200 mg/kg; mod. toxic by ingestion, skin contact; irritant to skin, mucous membranes; severe eye irritant; narcotic in high concs.; heated to decomp., emits acrid smoke and irritating fumes

Diethylamine

Uses: Caramel or berry-like synthetic flavoring agent
Regulatory: FDA 21CFR §172.515; FEMA GRAS
Manuf./Distrib. (pharm. & food): Aldrich

Diethylamine
CAS 109-89-7; EINECS 203-716-3
UN No. 1154
Synonyms: N-Ethylethanamine
Classification: Aliphatic organic compd.
Empirical: $C_4H_{11}N$
Formula: $(C_2H_5)_2NH$
Properties: Liq.; misc. with water, alcohol; m.w. 73.14; dens. 0.707; m.p. -50 C; b.p. 55 C; flash pt. -28 C; ref. index 1.3850 (20 C)
Precaution: DOT: Flamm. liq.
Toxicology: Corrosive
Uses: Used in injectables (IM, IV)
Regulatory: FDA approved for injectables (IM, IV); BP compliance
Manuf./Distrib.: AC Ind.; Air Prods.; Aldrich; Allchem Ind.; Ashland; BASF; Coyne; Elf Atochem N. Am.; Spectrum Chem. Mfg.; Union Carbide
Manuf./Distrib. (pharm. & food): Daicel Chem. Ind.; Mallinckrodt; Mitsubishi Gas

α-Diethylaminoaceto-2,6-xylidide. See Lidocaine

Diethylaminoethanol
CAS 100-37-8; EINECS 202-845-2
UN No. 2686
Synonyms: DEAE; 2-Diethylaminoethanol; Diethylethanolamine; N,N-Diethyl-2-aminoethanol; 2-Hydroxytriethylamine; β-Diethylaminoethyl alcohol
Empirical: $C_6H_{15}NO$
Formula: $(C_2H_5)_2NCH_2CH_2OH$
Properties: Colorless hygroscopic liq. base having props. of amines and alcohols; sol. in water, alcohol, ether, benzene; m.w. 117.19; dens. 0.88-0.89 (20/20 C); b.p. 161 C; flash pt. (OC) 140 F; f.p. -70 C; ref. index 1.4389
Precaution: DOT: Flamm. liq.; moderate fire risk; reactive with oxidizing materials
Toxicology: TLV 10 ppm in air; LD50 (oral, rat) 1300 mg/kg; poison by IP, IV routes; mod. toxic by ingestion, skin contact, subcut. routes; human systemic effects; skin, severe eye irritant; corrosive; heated to decomp., emits toxic fumes of NO_x
Uses: Pharmaceuticals
Regulatory: FDA 21CFR §173.310 (15 ppm max. in steam)
Manuf./Distrib.: Ashland; BASF; Elf Atochem N. Am.; Union Carbide
Manuf./Distrib. (pharm. & food): Aldrich

2-Diethylaminoethanol. See Diethylaminoethanol
N,N-Diethyl-2-aminoethanol. See Diethylaminoethanol
β-Diethylaminoethyl alcohol. See Diethylaminoethanol
N-[2-Diethylamino)ethyl]octadecanamide. See Stearamidoethyl diethylamine
2-(Diethylamino) ethyl octadecanoate. See Diethylaminoethyl stearate
Diethylaminoethyl stearamide. See Stearamidoethyl diethylamine

Diethylaminoethyl stearamide phosphate
CAS 7490-88-2
Uses: Miscellaneous pharmaceutical applics.

Diethylaminoethyl stearate
CAS 3179-81-5; EINECS 221-662-9
Synonyms: 2-(Diethylamino) ethyl octadecanoate; Octadecanoic acid, 2-(diethylamino) ethyl ester
Classification: Aliphatic ester
Empirical: $C_{24}H_{50}NO_2$
Properties: Straw to amber liq. to semisolid, amine odor; sol. in ethanol, IPM, oleyl alcohol; partly sol. in min. oil; disp. in water; sp.gr. 0.860-0.880; pH 9.5-10.5 (3%); sapon. no. 150-160
Uses: Emulsifier, dispersant for topical pharmaceuticals
Trade names: Cerasynt® 303

Diethyl 1,2-benzenedicarboxylate. See Diethyl phthalate
Diethyl carbinol. See 3-Pentanol

Diethyl cyanomethylphosphonate
CAS 2537-48-6
Uses: Intermediate
Manuf./Distrib.: Albright & Wilson
Manuf./Distrib. (pharm. & food): Aldrich
Trade names: DECMP

Diethyl decanedioate. *See* Diethyl sebacate
Diethyl 2,3-dihydroxybutanedioate. *See* Diethyl tartrate
Diethyl 2,3-dihydroxysuccinate. *See* Diethyl tartrate
Diethylene diamine. *See* Piperazine
Diethylene dioxide. *See* 1,4-Dioxane
1,4-Diethylene dioxide. *See* 1,4-Dioxane
Diethylene ether. *See* 1,4-Dioxane

Diethylene glycol dibutyl ether
CAS 112-73-2; EINECS 204-001-9
Synonyms: 2,2′-Dibutoxyethyl ether; Dibutyl 'Carbitol'
Empirical: $C_{12}H_{26}O_3$
Formula: $C_4H_9O(C_2H_4O)_2C_4H_9$
Properties: Almost colorless liq.; sl. sol. in water; m.w. 218.38; dens. 0.8853 (20/20 C); f.p. -60.2 C; b.p. 256 C; flash pt. 118 C
Precaution: Combustible
Toxicology: Moderately toxic by ingestion; mildly toxic by skin contact; skin and eye irritant; heated to dec., emits acrid smoke and irritating fumes
Uses: Solv., drug carrier, stabilizer
Manuf./Distrib.: Brand-Nu Labs; Ferro/Grant; Fluka; Great Western; Hoechst AG
Trade names: Butyl Diglyme; Ethyl Diglyme

Diethylene glycol dimethyl ether
CAS 111-96-6; EINECS 203-924-4
Synonyms: Diglycol methyl ether; Dimethyldiglycol; Diglyme; Dimethoxydiglycol; 2-Methoxyethyl ether; Bis (2-methoxyethyl) ether
Empirical: $C_6H_{14}O_3$
Formula: $CH_3(OCH_2CH_2)_2OCH_3$
Properties: Colorless liq., mild odor; misc. with water and hydrocarbons; m.w. 134.18; dens. 0.9451 (20/20 C); b.p. 162 C; f.p. -68 C; visc. 1.089 cP (20 C)
Precaution: Combustible
Uses: Solvent
Manuf./Distrib.: Brand-Nu Labs; Ferro/Grant; Great Western; Hoechst AG
Trade names: Diglyme

Diethylene glycol dodecyl ether. *See* Laureth-2
Diethylene glycol ethyl ether. *See* Ethoxydiglycol
Diethylene glycol monoethyl ether. *See* Ethoxydiglycol
Diethylene glycol stearate. *See* PEG-2 stearate
Diethyleneimide oxide. *See* Morpholine
Diethylene oxide. *See* 1,4-Dioxane
Diethylene oximide. *See* Morpholine
Diethylethanolamine. *See* Diethylaminoethanol
Diethyl ether. *See* Ethyl ether
Di(2-ethylhexyl) adipate. *See* Dioctyl adipate
Di(2-ethylhexyl) phthalate. *See* Dioctyl phthalate
Di(2-ethylhexyl) succinate. *See* Dioctyl succinate
Diethylhydroxysuccinate. *See* Diethyl malate

Diethyl malate
CAS 626-11-9
FEMA 2374
Synonyms: Diethylhydroxysuccinate; Ethyl malate
Empirical: $C_8H_{14}O_5$
Properties: Liq., fruital odor; m.w. 190.20; dens. 1.128; b.p. 122-124 C (12 mm); flash pt. 185 F
Uses: Fruity synthetic flavoring agent
Regulatory: FDA 21CFR §172.515; FEMA GRAS
Manuf./Distrib. (pharm. & food): Aldrich

Diethyl maleate
CAS 141-05-9
Empirical: $C_8H_{12}O_4$
Properties: M.w. 172.18; dens. 1.064; m.p. -10 C; b.p. 225 C; flash pt. 200 F
Uses: Fruity, mild citrus banana-like flavoring agent
Manuf./Distrib. (pharm. & food): Aldrich

Diethyl malonate
CAS 105-53-3; EINECS 203-305-9
FEMA 2375
Synonyms: Ethyl malonate; Malonic ester; Propanedioic acid diethyl ester
Classification: Aliphatic organic compd.
Empirical: $C_7H_{12}O_4$
Formula: $CH_2(COOC_2H_5)_2$
Properties: Liq., sl. aromatic pleasant odor; misc. with alcohol, ether; sol. 1 g/50 ml in water; m.w. 160.17; dens.
    1.055 (20/4 C); m.p. -50 C; b.p. 94-95 C (11 mm); flash pt. 80 C; ref. index 1.413 (20 C)
Precaution: Combustible
Uses: Fruity synthetic flavoring agent
Regulatory: FDA 21CFR §172.515; FEMA GRAS
Manuf./Distrib.: Aldrich; Spectrum Chem. Mfg.
Manuf./Distrib. (pharm. & food): Aldrich; Juzen; Lonza Ltd; Mitsubishi Chem.; Tateyama Kasei

Diethyl 1,8-octanedicarboxylate. *See* Diethyl sebacate

Diethyl phthalate
CAS 84-66-2; EINECS 201-550-6
Synonyms: DEP; Ethyl phthalate; 1,2-Benzenedicarboxylic acid diethyl ester; Phthalic acid, diethyl ester;
    Diethyl 1,2-benzenedicarboxylate
Definition: Aromatic diester of ethyl alcohol and phthalic acid
Empirical: $C_{12}H_{14}O_4$
Formula: $C_6H_4(CO_2C_2H_5)_2$
Properties: Water-wh. oily liq., odorless, bitter taste; misc. with alcohol, ketones, esters, aromatic HC; insol.
    in water; m.w. 222.24; dens. 1.120 (25/25 C); f.p. -40.5 C; b.p. 298 C; flash pt. (OC) 325 F; visc. 31.3 cs
    (0 C); ref. index 1.500-1.505; stable
Precaution: Combustible when exposed to heat or flame; heated to decomp., emits acrid smoke and irritating
    fumes
Toxicology: TLV 5 mg/m^3 of air; LD50 (oral, rat) 8600 mg/kg; poison by IV route; mod. toxic by ingestion,
    subcut., IP routes; human systemic effects; strong irritant to eyes and mucous membranes; narcotic in high
    concs.; experimental reproductive effects
Uses: Plasticizer, fragrance; used in orals
Regulatory: FDA 21CFR §175.105, 175.300, 175.320, 178.3910, 181.22, 181.27, 212.177; 27CFR §21.105;
    FDA approved for orals; USP/NF, BP compliance
Manuf./Distrib.: Allan; Allchem Ind.; Berje; BP Chem. Ltd; Daihachi Chem. Ind.; Eastman; Hüls Am.; Morflex;
    Penta Mfg.; Spectrum Chem. Mfg.; Unitex
Manuf./Distrib. (pharm. & food): Eastman; Morflex; Penta Mfg.; Aldrich; Spectrum Chem. Mfg.

3,3-Diethyl-2,4(1H,3H)-pyridinedione. *See* Pyrithyldione

Diethyl sebacate
CAS 110-40-7; EINECS 203-764-5
FEMA 2376
Synonyms: Diethyl decanedioate; Ethyl sebacate; Diethyl 1,8-octanedicarboxylate
Empirical: $C_{14}H_{26}O_4$
Properties: Colorless to sl. yel. liq., faint fruity odor; misc. with alcohol, ether, other org. solvs., fixed oils; insol.
    in water; m.w. 258.40; dens. 0.960-0.965; m.p. 1-3 C; b.p. 312 C; flash pt. > 230 F; ref. index 1.435
Toxicology: LD50 (oral, rat) 14,470 mg/kg; mildly toxic by ingestion; skin irritant; heated to decomp., emits acrid
    smoke and irritating fumes
Uses: Quince-like synthetic flavoring agent; used in topicals
Regulatory: FDA 21CFR §172.515; FEMA GRAS; FDA approved for topicals
Manuf./Distrib. (pharm. & food): Aldrich

Diethyl tartrate
CAS 87-91-2; EINECS 201-783-3
FEMA 2378
Synonyms: Diethyl 2,3-dihydroxybutanedioate; (R)-2,3-Dihydroxybutanedioic acid diethyl ester; Ethyl tar-
    trate; (+)-Diethyl L-tartrate; Diethyl 2,3-dihydroxysuccinate

Empirical: $C_8H_{14}O_6$
Formula: $C_2H_5OOCCH(OH)CH(OH)COOC_2H_5$
Properties: Colorless thick oily liq.; sl. sol. in water; misc. with alcohol, ether; m.w. 206.19; dens. 1.204 (20/4 C); m.p. 17 C; b.p. 280 C; flash pt. 93 C; ref. index 1.4476 (20 C)
Uses: Fruity synthetic flavoring agent
Regulatory: FDA 21CFR §172.515; FEMA GRAS
Manuf./Distrib. (pharm. & food): Aldrich

(+)-Diethyl L-tartrate. *See* Diethyl tartrate

2,5-Diethyltetrahydrofuran
FEMA 3743
Empirical: $C_8H_{16}O$
Properties: Colorless liq., sweet herbaceous caramellic odor; sol. in alcohol, propylene glycol; sl. sol. in water; m.w. 128.21; b.p. 116 C
Uses: Synthetic flavoring agent
Regulatory: FDA 21CFR §172.515; FEMA GRAS

Diethyl toluene diamine
CAS 68479-98-1
Synonyms: DETDA
Classification: Orthoalkylated aromatic
Uses: Intermediate for pharmaceuticals

Difluorodichloromethane. *See* Dichlorodifluoromethane
Diglyceryl dioleate. *See* Polyglyceryl-2 dioleate
Diglyceryl monooleate. *See* Polyglyceryl-2 oleate
Diglyceryl monostearate. *See* Polyglyceryl-2 stearate
Diglyceryl PEG-4 stearate. *See* Polyglyceryl-2-PEG-4 stearate
Diglyceryl sesquiisostearate. *See* Polyglyceryl-2 sesquiisostearate
Diglyceryl sesquioleate. *See* Polyglyceryl-2 sesquioleate

Diglycol cyclohexane dimethanol isophthalate sulfoisophthalates copolymer
Uses: Raw material for pharmaceuticals

Diglycol methyl ether. *See* Diethylene glycol dimethyl ether
Diglycol stearate. *See* PEG-2 stearate
Diglyme. *See* Diethylene glycol dimethyl ether
Diheptadecyl ketone. *See* Stearone
Dihydroabietyl alcohol. *See* Hydroabietyl alcohol

Dihydroabietyl behenate
CAS 127036-29-7
Synonyms: Behenic acid, dihydroabietyl ester
Definition: Ester of dihydroabietyl alcohol and behenic acid
Properties: Sol. in oil, insol. in water
Uses: Emollient for pharmaceutical topicals
Trade names: Pelemol® HAB

Dihydrocarveol
CAS 17699-09-1
FEMA 2379
Synonyms: 8-p-Menthen-2-ol; 6-Methyl-3-isopropenylcyclohexanol; Tuberyl alcohol
Definition: Synthesized by reducing carvone and separating the resulting isomers
Empirical: $C_{10}H_{18}O$
Properties: Almost colorless straw-colored liq., floral woody odor, sweet somewhat spicy flavor; sol. in alcohol; m.w. 154.24; dens. 0.924; b.p. 224-225 C; flash pt. 197 F
Precaution: Combustible liq.
Toxicology: Moderate skin and eye irritant; heated to decomp., emits acrid smoke and fumes
Uses: Minty synthetic flavoring agent
Regulatory: FDA 21CFR §172.515; FEMA GRAS
Manuf./Distrib. (pharm. & food): Aldrich

d-Dihydrocarvone
CAS 7764-50-3
FEMA 3565
Synonyms: d-2-Methyl-5-(1-methylethenyl)-cyclohexanone; p-Menth-8-en-2-one
Empirical: $C_{10}H_{16}O$

Dihydrocarvyl acetate

Properties: Herbaceous spearmint odor; m.w. 152.24; dens. 0.926; b.p. 87-88 C (6 mm); flash pt. 178 F
Toxicology: Mod. toxic by subcutaneous route; heated to decomp., emits acrid smoke and fumes
Uses: Minty flavoring agent
Regulatory: FDA 21CFR §172.515; FEMA GRAS
Manuf./Distrib. (pharm. & food): Aldrich

Dihydrocarvyl acetate
CAS 20777-49-5; EINECS 244-029-9
FEMA 2380
Synonyms: 8-p-Menthen-2-yl acetate; l-Dihydrocarvyl acetate; 6-Methyl-3-isopropenyl cyclohexyl acetate; p-Menth-8-(9)-en-2-yl acetate
Definition: Acetylation of dihydrocarveol
Empirical: $C_{12}H_{20}O_2$
Properties: Colorless liq., sweet floral rose-like odor, sl. minty flavor; sol. in aclohol; sl. sol. in water; m.w. 196.29; dens. 0.96; b.p. 232-234 C; flash pt. 194 F
Uses: Medicinal, minty synthetic flavoring agent
Regulatory: FDA 21CFR §172.515; FEMA GRAS
Manuf./Distrib. (pharm. & food): Aldrich

l-Dihydrocarvyl acetate. *See* Dihydrocarvyl acetate
Dihydrochlorothiazide. *See* Hydrochlorothiazide
Dihydrocinnamaldehyde. *See* Hydrocinnamaldehyde
Dihydrocitronellol. *See* 3,7-Dimethyl-1-octanol

Dihydrocoumarin
CAS 119-84-6; EINECS 204-354-9
FEMA 2381
Synonyms: Hydrocoumarin; 3,4-Dihydrocoumarin; 1,2-Benzodihydropyrone; Melilotin
Classification: Heterocyclic compd.
Empirical: $C_9H_8O_2$
Properties: Colorless to pale yel. liq., coconut odor; m.w. 148.17; dens. 1.186; m.p. 24-25 C; b.p. 272 C; flash pt. 266 F; ref. index 1.555
Precaution: Combustible liq.
Toxicology: LD50 (oral, rat) 1460 mg/kg; poison by intraperitoneal route; mod. toxic by ingestion; skin irritant; heated to decomp., emits acrid smoke and fumes
Uses: Synthetic flavoring agent
Regulatory: FEMA GRAS
Manuf./Distrib.: Aldrich
Manuf./Distrib. (pharm. & food): Aldrich

3,4-Dihydrocoumarin. *See* Dihydrocoumarin
2,2´-[(9,10-Dihydro-9,10-dioxo-1,4-anthracenediyl)diimino]bis(5-methyl)benzenesulfonic acid disodium salt. *See* CI 61570; D&C Green No. 5
Dihydro-2,5-furandione. *See* Succinic anhydride
Dihydro-2(3H)-furanone. *See* Butyrolactone

Dihydrogenated tallow phthalic acid amide
CAS 127733-92-0
Classification: Organic compd.
Uses: Emulsifier, suspending agent for antidandruff shampoos
Trade names: Stepan TAB®-2

2-(1,3-Dihydro-3-oxo-2H-indol-2-ylidene)-1,2-dihydro-3H-indol-3-one. *See* CI 73000
2-(1,3-Dihydro-3-oxo-5-sulfo-2H-indol-2-ylidene)-2,3-dihydro-3-oxo-1H-indole-5-sulfonic acid disodium salt. *See* CI 73015; FD&C Blue No. 2
4,5-Dihydro-5-oxo-1-(4-sulfophenyl)-4-[(4-sulfophenyl)azo]-1H-pyrazole-3-carboxylic acid trisodium salt. *See* CI 19140

Dihydroxyacetone
CAS 96-26-4; EINECS 202-494-5
Synonyms: DHA; 1,3-Dihydroxydimethyl ketone; 1,3-Dihydroxy-2-propanone; Oxatone chromelin
Classification: Aliphatic ketone
Empirical: $C_3H_6O_3$
Formula: $HOCH_2COCH_2OH$
Properties: Almost wh. crystals, char. odor, sweet taste; sol. in water, ethanol; m.w. 90.09; pH 4-6 (5% aq.)
Toxicology: LD50 (oral, rat) 16 g/kg; no known skin toxicity; can cause allergic contact dermatitis

Uses: Color additive for external pharmaceuticals imparting color to the human body; stain for suntan lotion
Regulatory: FDA 21CFR §73.1150, 73.2150
Manuf./Distrib.: EM Industries; Gist-brocades Food Ingreds.; Janssen Chimica; Penta Mfg.; Spectrum Chem. Mfg.
Manuf./Distrib. (pharm. & food): R.W. Greeff

3,4-Dihydroxybenzaldehyde
CAS 139-85-5
Empirical: $C_7H_6O_3$
Properties: M.w. 138.12
Uses: Medicinal flavoring agent
Manuf./Distrib. (pharm. & food): Aldrich

1,2-Dihydroxybenzene. *See* Pyrocatechol
m-Dihydroxybenzene. *See* Resorcinol
o-Dihydroxybenzene. *See* Pyrocatechol
p-Dihydroxybenzene. *See* Hydroquinone
2,5-Dihydroxybenzoic acid. *See* Gentisic acid
2,5-Dihydroxybenzoic acid ethanolamide. *See* Gentisic acid ethanolamide
2 3-Dihydroxy-1,2-benzothiazolin-3-one-1,1-dioxide. *See* Saccharin
2,3-Dihydroxybutanedioic acid. *See* Tartaric acid
2,3-Dihydroxybutanedioic acid, monopotassium monosodium salt. *See* Potassium sodium tartrate anhyd.
o[p-(β,β′-Dihydroxydiethylamino)phenylazo] benzoic acid. *See* D&C Red No. 39
3′,6′-Dihydroxy-4′,5′-diiodospiro[isobenzofuran-1(3H),9′-[9H]xanthen]-3-one. *See* D&C Orange No. 10
3′,6′-Dihydroxy-4′,5′-diiodospiro[isobenzofuran-1(3H),9′-[9H]xanthen]-3-one disodium salt. *See* CI 45425; D&C Orange No. 11
1,3-Dihydroxydimethyl ketone. *See* Dihydroxyacetone
Di(2-hydroxyethyl) amine. *See* Diethanolamine
2,4-Dihydroxy-N-(3-hydroxypropyl)-3,3-dimethylbutanamide. *See* D-Panthenol; DL-Panthenol
1,2-Dihydroxypropane. *See* Propylene glycol
1,3-Dihydroxy-2-propanone. *See* Dihydroxyacetone
2,3-Dihydroxypropyl docosanoate. *See* Glyceryl behenate
2,3-Dihydroxypropyl octadecanoate. *See* Glyceryl stearate
3′,6′-Dihydroxyspiro[isobenzofuran-1(3H),9′-[9H]xanthen]-3-one. *See* D&C Yellow No. 7
3′,6′-Dihydroxyspiro[isobenzofuran-1(3H),9′-[9H]xanthen]-3-one disodium salt. *See* CI 45350; D&C Yellow No. 8
Dihydroxysuccinic acid. *See* Tartaric acid
α,β-Dihydroxysuccinic acid. *See* Tartaric acid
3′,6′-Dihydroxy-2′,4′,5′,7′-tetraiodospiro[isobenzofuran-1(3H),9′-(9H)xanthen]-3-one disodium salt. *See* CI 45430; FD&C Red No. 3
Diiodofluorescein. *See* D&C Orange No. 10
Diisobutyl cresoxy ethoxy ethyl dimethyl benzyl ammonium chloride. *See* Methylbenzethonium chloride

Diisobutyl ketone
CAS 108-83-8; EINECS 203-620-1
FEMA 3537
Synonyms: DIBK; 2,6-Dimethyl-4-heptanone; Isovalerone
Empirical: $C_9H_{18}O$
Formula: $(CH_3)_2CHCH_2COCH_2CH(CH_3)_2$
Properties: M.w. 142.24; sp.gr. 0.8076; b.p. 325 F; flash pt. (TCC) 120 F; ref. index 1.4130 (20 C)
Precaution: Flamm.
Toxicology: LD50 (oral, rat) 4300 mg/kg; ACGIH TLV 100 ppm, STEL 150 ppm; OSHA PEL 100 ppm; irritant to respiratory system
Uses: Fruity flavoring agent
Regulatory: FEMA GRAS
Manuf./Distrib.: Aldrich; Allchem Ind.; Ashland; Coyne; Eastman; Fluka; Great Western; Hüls AG; Union Carbide
Manuf./Distrib. (pharm. & food): Aldrich

Diisobutylphenoxyethoxyethyl dimethyl benzyl ammonium chloride. *See* Benzethonium chloride

Diisopropanolamine
CAS 110-97-4; EINECS 203-820-9
Synonyms: DIPA; 1,1′-Iminobis-2-propenol; 1,1′-Iminobis(propan-2-ol)
Classification: Aliphatic amine

Diisopropyl adipate

Empirical: $C_6H_{15}NO_2$
Formula: $HN(CH_2CHOHCH_3)_2$
Properties: Wh. cryst. solid; misc. with water; m.w. 133.19; dens. 1.004; m.p. 44.5-45.5 C; b.p. 249-250 C (745 mm); flash pt. 126 C
Precaution: Combustible; protect from light
Uses: Emulsifier for topicals
Regulatory: FDA 21CFR § 175.105, 176.210; FDA approved for topicals; USP/NF
Manuf./Distrib.: Aldrich; Ashland; BASF; Coyne; Ruger; Van Waters & Rogers
Manuf./Distrib. (pharm. & food): Aldrich
Trade names: DIPA Commercial Grade; DIPA Low Freeze Grade 85; DIPA Low Freeze Grade 90; DIPA NF Grade

Diisopropyl adipate

CAS 6938-94-9; EINECS 230-072-0
Synonyms: Bis(1-methylethyl)hexanedioate; Hexanedioic acid, bis (1-methylethyl) ester
Definition: Diester of isopropyl alcohol and adipic acid
Empirical: $C_{12}H_{22}O_4$
Formula: $(CH_3)_2CHOCO(CH_2)_4COOCH(CH_3)_2$
Properties: Clear liq.; sol. in min. oil, ethanol, propylene glycol, IPM, oleyl alcohol; insol. in water, glycerin; sp.gr. 0.950-0.962; ref. index 1.4216-1.4245
Toxicology: LD50 (rat, oral) > 20 ± 3 ml/kg; nonirritating to eyes and skin
Uses: Emollient used in topicals
Regulatory: FDA approved for topicals
Manuf./Distrib.: Inolex; ISP Van Dyk; Union Camp
Trade names: Ceraphyl® 230

Diisopropyl sebacate

CAS 7491-02-3; EINECS 231-306-4
Synonyms: Bis(1-methylethyl) decanedioate; Decanedioic acid, bis(1-methylethyl) ester
Definition: Diester of isopropyl alcohol and sebacic acid
Empirical: $C_{16}H_{30}O_4$
Formula: $(CH_3)_2CHOCO(CH_2)_8COOCH(CH_3)_2$
Properties: Sp.gr. 0.936; flash pt. (COC) 190 C; ref. index 1.4310
Uses: Emollient, solubilizer, coupling agent in creams, lotions
Manuf./Distrib.: Union Camp
Trade names: Pelemol® DIPS

4,4′-Diketo-β-carotene. See Canthaxanthine
2,5-Diketotetrahydrofuran. See Succinic anhydride
Dilaurin. See Glyceryl dilaurate

1,2-Dilauroyl-sn-glycero(3) phosphocholine

CAS 18285-71-7
Uses: For mfg. of liposomes and mixed micelles
Trade names: Phospholipon® LC

Dilauryl thiodipropionate

CAS 123-28-4; EINECS 204-614-1
Synonyms: Didodecyl 3,3′-thiodipropionate; Thiobis(dodecyl propionate); Thiodipropionic acid dilauryl ester; Bis(dodecyloxycarbonylethyl) sulfide
Classification: Diester
Definition: Diester of lauryl alcohol and 3,3′-thiodipropionic acid
Empirical: $C_{30}H_{58}O_4S$
Formula: $(C_{12}H_{25}OOCCH_2CH_2)_2S$
Properties: White flakes, sweetish odor; insol. in water; sol. in benzene, toluene, acetone, ether, chloroform; sl. sol. in alcohols, ethyl acetate; m.w. 514.94; dens. 0.975; m.p. 40 C; b.p. 240 C (1 mm); acid no. < 1
Toxicology: LD50 (oral, rat) > 10.3 g/kg; no known toxicity; eye irritant; heated to decomp., emits toxic fumes
Uses: Antioxidant, preservative for pharmaceuticals
Regulatory: FDA 21CFR §175.300, 181.22, 181.24 (0.005% migrating from food pkg.), 182.3280 (0.02% max. fat/oil)
Manuf./Distrib.: Cytec; Evans Chemetics; Morton Int'l.; Witco/PAG
Manuf./Distrib. (pharm. & food): Witco; Yoshitomi Pharmaceutical
Trade names: PAG DLTDP

Dill oil. See Dillweed oil

Dill seed oil
 CAS 8016-06-6
 FEMA 2383
 Synonyms: American dill seed oil; European dill seed oil
 Definition: Volatile oil from dried ripe fruit of *Anethum graveolens*, contg. 50% carvone, d-limonene, phellandrene, other terpenes
 Properties: Colorless or pale yel. liq., char. odor; sol. in 1 vol. 90% alcohol; insol. in water; dens. 0.900-0.915 (15/15 C); ref. index 1.481-1.492 (20 C)
 Precaution: Keep cool, well closed; protect from light
 Uses: Flavoring agent in pharmaceuticals; aromatic carminative
 Regulatory: FDA 21CFR §184.1282, GRAS; FEMA GRAS; BP compliance

Dillweed oil
 CAS 8006-75-5
 Synonyms: Dill oil; Anethum graveolens oil
 Toxicology: LD50 (oral, rat) 4040 mg/kg; mildly toxic by ingestion; skin irritant; mutagenic data; heated to decomp., emits acrid smoke and fumes
 Uses: Flavoring agent in pharmaceuticals
 Regulatory: FDA 21CFR §184.1282, GRAS; FEMA GRAS; Europe listed, no restrictions
 Manuf./Distrib. (pharm. & food): Florida Treatt

Dimagnesium trisilicate. *See* Magnesium trisilicate

Dimethicone
 CAS 9006-65-9; 9016-00-6; 63148-62-9; 68037-74-1 (branched)
 Synonyms: PDMS; Dimethylpolysiloxane; Dimethyl silicone; Polydimethylsiloxane
 Definition: Silicone oil consisting of dimethylsiloxane polymers
 Empirical: $(C_2H_6OSi)_xC_4H_{12}Si$
 Formula: $(CH_3)_3SiO[Si(CH_3)_2O]_nSi(CH_3)_3$
 Properties: Colorless clear visc. oily liq., odorless; sol. in hydrocarbon solvs., benzene, toluene, xylene, hexane, petrol. spirits, amyl acetate; misc. in chloroform, ether; insol. in water, methanol, acetone, alcohol; m.w. 340-250,000; dens. 0.96-0.97; visc. 20-12,500 cst; ref. index 1.400-1.404
 Toxicology: Very low toxicity; suspected neoplastigen; heated to dec., emits acrid smoke and irritating fumes
 Uses: Ointment and topical drug ingred., skin protectant, antifoaming agent, water repelling agent; for topicals as barrier former; lubricant and coating for syringes, vials, etc.
 Regulatory: FDA 21CFR §145.180, 145.181, 146.185, 173.340, 175.105, 175.300, 176.170, 176.200, 176.210, 177.2260, 177.2600, 177.2800, 178.3570, 178.3910, 181.22, 181.28; USDA 9CFR §318.7, 381.147; Europe listed; UK approved; FDA approved for topicals; USP/NF, BP, Ph.Eur. compliance
 Manuf./Distrib.: Dow Corning
 Trade names: Dimethicone L-45 Series; Dow Corning® 360 Medical Fluid (20 cs); Dow Corning® 360 Medical Fluid (100 cs); Dow Corning® 360 Medical Fluid (350 cs); Dow Corning® 360 Medical Fluid (1000 cs); Dow Corning® 360 Medical Fluid (12,500 cs); Dow Corning® 365; Foamkill® 810F; Foamkill® 830F
 Trade names containing: Fancorsil A; Fancorsil P

Dimethicone copolyol
 CAS 63148-55-0; 64365-23-7; 67762-96-3
 Synonyms: Dimethylsiloxane-glycol copolymer
 Classification: Polymer
 Toxicology: Very low toxicity
 Uses: Surfactant, antifoam, dispersant, emulsifier; leveling and flow control agent used in injectables (percutaneous)
 Regulatory: FDA approved for injectables (percutaneous)
 Trade names: Silwet® L-720; Silwet® L-7500; Silwet® L-7602

Dimethicone copolyol eicosanate
 CAS 157479-50-0; 157479-51-1
 Uses: Emollient, conditioner for topical pharmaceuticals
 Trade names: Fancorsil LIM 1; Fancorsil LIM 2; Fancorsil LIM 3

Dimethicone copolyol phosphate
 CAS 132207-31-9
 Definition: Partial ester of dimethicone copolyol and phosphoric acid
 Uses: Emulsifier, pigment wetting and dispersing agent for topical pharmaceuticals
 Trade names: Pecosil® PS-100; Pecosil® WDS-100

Dimethicone copolyol undecylenate
CAS 159100-33-1
Synonyms: Dimethicone copolyol undecylinate
Uses: Emollient, coupling agent, cosolvent used in pharmaceuticals
Trade names: Pecosil® DCU

Dimethicone copolyol undecylinate. *See* Dimethicone copolyol undecylenate

Dimethicone propylethylenediamine behenate
CAS 132207-30-8; 133448-12-1
Synonyms: Siloxanes and silicones, 3-[(2-aminoethyl amino]propyl, methyl, dimethyl, docosanoates
Uses: Film-former, humectant, protective barrier for pharmaceutical topicals
Trade names: Pecosil® OS-100B

1,1-Dimethoxy-2-amyl-3-phenyl-2-propene. *See* α-Amylcinnamaldehyde dimethyl acetal
3,4-Dimethoxybenzaldehyde. *See* Veratraldehyde
1,3-Dimethoxybenzene. *See* m-Dimethoxybenzene

m-Dimethoxybenzene
CAS 151-10-0; EINECS 205-783-4
FEMA 2385
Synonyms: 1,3-Dimethoxybenzene; Dimethylresorcinol; Resorcinol dimethyl ether
Definition: Synthesized from resorcinol by methylation using dimethyl sulfate and alkali
Empirical: $C_8H_{10}O_2$
Properties: Liq., acrid fruity odor reminiscent of nerolin; sol. in alcohol, ether, benzene; sl. sol. in water; m.w. 138.17; dens. 1.067 (20/4 C); b.p. 85-87 C (10 mm); flash pt. 190 F; ref. index 1.525 (20 C)
Toxicology: Skin irritant
Uses: Coconut-like synthetic flavoring agent
Regulatory: FDA 21CFR §172.515; FEMA GRAS
Manuf./Distrib. (pharm. & food): Aldrich

3,4-Dimethoxybenzenecarbonal. *See* Veratraldehyde
Dimethoxydiglycol. *See* Diethylene glycol dimethyl ether
1,2-Dimethoxyethane. *See* Ethylene glycol dimethyl ether

Dimethoxypropane
CAS 77-76-9; EINECS 201-056-0
UN No. 1993
Synonyms: Acetone dimethyl acetal; 2,2-Dimethoxypropane
Classification: Aliphatic organic compd.
Definition: Protein precipitant
Empirical: $C_5H_{12}O_2$
Formula: $(CH_3)_2C(OCH_3)_2$
Properties: Colorless liq.; sol. in water; misc. with alcohol, ether; m.w. 104.15; dens. 0.849 (20/4 C); m.p. -47 C; b.p. 81-83 C; flash pt. (CC) -6.7 C; ref. index 1.3780
Precaution: Very dangerous fire hazard when exposed to heat, flame or oxidizers
Toxicology: Irritant; heated to dec., emits acrid smoke and fumes
Uses: Chemical intermediate for pharmaceuticals (dehydrator)
Manuf./Distrib.: Aldrich; Janssen Chimica; Penta Mfg.; Ube Ind.
Manuf./Distrib. (pharm. & food): Ube Ind.
Trade names: DMP

2,2-Dimethoxypropane. *See* Dimethoxypropane

2,4-Dimethylacetophenone
CAS 89-74-7; EINECS 201-935-9
FEMA 2387
Synonyms: Methyl 2,4-dimethylphenyl ketone
Definition: Obtained by condensation of acetyl chloride and m-xylene in presence of aluminum or ferric chloride
Empirical: $C_{10}H_{12}O$
Properties: Colorless to ylsh. oil liq., floral sweet odor; m.w. 148.21; dens. 0.998 (20/4 C); b.p. 120 C (10 mm); flash pt. > 100 C; ref. index 1.543 (20 C)
Precaution: Combustible
Uses: Sweet synthetic flavoring agent
Regulatory: FDA 21CFR §172.515; FEMA GRAS
Manuf./Distrib. (pharm. & food): Aldrich

3,3-Dimethylallyl alcohol. *See* 3-Methyl-2-buten-1-ol

2-Dimethylaminoethanol. *See* Dimethylethanolamine
N,N-Dimethylaminoethanol. *See* Dimethylethanolamine

Dimethylaminoethyl chloride hydrochloride
CAS 4584-46-7; EINECS 224-970-1
Synonyms: DMC; 1-Chloro-2-dimethylaminoethane hydrochloride; 2-Chloro-N,N-dimethylethylamine hydro-
chloride; N-(2-Chloroethyl)dimethylamine hydrochloride
Empirical: $C_4H_{10}ClN \cdot HCl$
Formula: $(CH_3)_2NCH_2CH_2Cl \cdot HCl$
Properties: M.w. 144.05; m.p. 205-208 C
Toxicology: Irritant
Uses: Mfg. of antihistamines and other pharmaceuticals
Manuf./Distrib.: Aldrich; ICI Spec.; Janssen Chimica; Lonza; Schweizerhall
Manuf./Distrib. (pharm. & food): Aldrich; R.W. Greeff

N-[3-(Dimethylamino)propyl]coco amides-N-oxide. *See* Cocamidopropylamine oxide
N-[3-(Dimethylamino)propyl]octadecanamide. *See* Stearamidopropyl dimethylamine
Dimethylaminopropyl stearamide. *See* Stearamidopropyl dimethylamine

Dimethyl anthranilate
CAS 85-91-6; EINECS 201-642-6
FEMA 2718
Synonyms: MMA; Methyl methylaminobenzoate; N-Methyl methyl anthranilate; 2-Methylamino methyl
benzoate
Empirical: $C_9H_{11}NO_2$
Properties: Pale yel. liq., grape-like odor; sol. in fixed oils; sl. sol. in propylene glycol; insol. in water, glycerin;
m.w. 165.21; dens. 1.126-1.132; flash pt. 196 F; ref. index 1.578-1.581
Precaution: Combustible
Toxicology: Poison by IV route; mod. toxic by ingestion; heated to decomp., emits toxic fumes of NO_x
Uses: Orange, grape-like synthetic flavoring
Regulatory: FDA 21CFR §172.515; FEMA GRAS; Japan approved as flavoring
Manuf./Distrib.: Am. Bio-Synthetics; Bell Flavors & Fragrances; Penta Mfg.
Manuf./Distrib. (pharm. & food): Aldrich; Florida Treatt

2,4-Dimethylbenzaldehyde
CAS 15764-16-6
FEMA 3427
Empirical: $C_9H_{10}O$
Properties: M.w. 134.18; dens. 0.962; m.p. -9 C; b.p. 102-103 C (14 mm); flash pt. 192 F
Uses: Sweet, cherry-like flavoring agent
Regulatory: FEMA GRAS
Manuf./Distrib. (pharm. & food): Aldrich

Dimethylbenzene sulfonic acid, sodium salt. *See* Sodium xylenesulfonate
α-(5,6-Dimethylbenzimidazolyl)cyanocobamide. *See* Cyanocobalamin
Dimethylbenzylcarbinyl butyrate. *See* α,α-Dimethylphenethyl butyrate
4,5-Dimethyl-2-benzyl-1,3-dioxolan. *See* Phenylacetaldehyde 2,3-butylene glycol acetal

α,α-Dimethylbenzyl isobutyrate
FEMA 2388
Synonyms: Phenyldimethyl carbinyl isobutyrate; 2-Phenylpropan-2-yl isobutyrate
Definition: Obtained by esterification of dimethylphenyl carbinol with isobutyric acid
Empirical: $C_{13}H_{18}O_2$
Properties: Colorless liq., sweet fruity apricot/peach/plum odor, plum-like flavor; sol. in alcohol; insol. in water;
m.w. 206.28
Uses: Synthetic flavoring agent
Regulatory: FDA 21CFR §172.515; FEMA GRAS

Dimethyl benzyl tallow ammonium chloride. *See* Tallowalkonium chloride
Dimethyl butanedioate. *See* Dimethyl succinate
4,4´-(2,3-Dimethyl-1,4-butanediyl)bis[1,2-benzenediol]. *See* Nordihydroguairetic acid
Dimethyl carbinol. *See* Isopropyl alcohol
2,5-Di-o-methyl-1,4:3,6-dianhydro-D-glucitol. *See* Dimethyl isosorbide
2,3-Dimethyl-1,4-diazine. *See* 2,3-Dimethylpyrazine
Dimethyldiglycol. *See* Diethylene glycol dimethyl ether

Dimethyl dioctadecylammonium bentonite

Dimethyl dioctadecylammonium bentonite
  Uses: Used in rectals
  Regulatory: FDA approved for rectals

N,N-Dimethyl-1-dodecanamine-N-oxide. *See* Lauramine oxide
N,N-Dimethyl-N-dodecylbenzenemethanaminium chloride. *See* Lauralkonium chloride
Dimethylenediamine. *See* Ethylenediamine
Dimethylene oxide. *See* Ethylene oxide

Dimethylethanolamine
  CAS 108-01-0; EINECS 203-542-8
  UN No. 2051
  Synonyms: DMAE; 2-Dimethylaminoethanol; N,N-Dimethylaminoethanol; Deanol; N,N-Dimethyl ethanolamine
  Empirical: $C_4H_{11}NO$
  Formula: $(CH_3)_2NCH_2CH_2OH$
  Properties: Colorless liq., amine odor; sol. in water, alcohol, ether; m.w. 89.14; dens. 0.8866 (20/4 C); visc. 3.8 cps (20 C); f.p. -64 C; b.p. 133 C; flash pt. (OC) 105 F; ref. index 1.430
  Precaution: Flamm.
  Toxicology: Moderately toxic by ingestion, inhalation, skin contact, intraperitoneal, subcutaneous routes; skin and eye irritant; central nervous system stimulant
  Uses: Synthesis of pharmaceuticals
  Manuf./Distrib.: Air Prods.; Aldrich; Allchem Ind.; Ashland; BASF; Elf Atochem N. Am.; Great Western; Nippon Nyukazai; Pelron; Texaco; Union Carbide
  Manuf./Distrib. (pharm. & food): Aldrich

N,N-Dimethyl ethanolamine. *See* Dimethylethanolamine
Dimethyl ether protocatechualdehyde. *See* Veratraldehyde
2-(1,1-Dimethylethyl)-1,4-benzenediol. *See* t-Butyl hydroquinone
Dimethyl ethyl carbinol. *See* t-Amyl alcohol
(1,1-Dimethylethyl)-4-methoxyphenol. *See* BHA
1-[4-(1,1-Dimethylethyl)phenyl]-3-(4-methoxyphenyl)-1,3-propanedione. *See* Butyl methoxy dibenzoyl methane
Dimethyl ethynyl carbinol. *See* Methyl butynol
2,6-Dimethyl-4-heptanone. *See* Diisobutyl ketone

2,6-Dimethyl-5-heptenal
  CAS 106-72-9
  FEMA 2389
  Empirical: $C_9H_{16}O$
  Properties: Pale yel. liq., melon odor; m.w. 140.23; dens. 0.852-0.858; b.p. 80 C (19 mm); flash pt. 144 F; ref. index 1.443-1.448
  Toxicology: Skin and eye irritant; heated to decomp., emits acrid smoke and irritating fumes
  Uses: Melon-like synthetic flavoring agent
  Regulatory: FDA 21CFR §172.515; FEMA GRAS
  Manuf./Distrib. (pharm. & food): Aldrich

Dimethylhydroxybenzene. *See* Xylenol
3,7-Dimethyl-7-hydroxy-octane-1-al. *See* Hydroxycitronellal

Dimethyl isosorbide
  CAS 5306-85-4; EINECS 226-159-8
  Synonyms: DMI; 2,5-Di-o-methyl-1,4:3,6-dianhydro-D-glucitol; D-Glucitol, 1,4:3,6-dianhydro-2,5-di-o-methyl; Isosorbide dimethyl ether
  Definition: Dimethyl ether of an anhydride of an isomer of sorbitol
  Empirical: $C_8H_{14}O_4$
  Properties: Wh. to ylsh. visc. liq.; m.w. 174.20; dens. 1.150; b.p. 93-95 C (0.1 mm); flash pt. 108 C; ref. index 1.4610
  Uses: Carrier, solvent for pharmaceutical
  Manuf./Distrib.: Aldrich
  Manuf./Distrib. (pharm. & food): Aldrich; EMS-Dottikon AG

Dimethylketol. *See* Acetyl methyl carbinol
Dimethylketone. *See* Acetone

Dimethyl lauramine
  CAS 112-18-5; 67700-98-5; EINECS 203-943-8; 266-922-2

Synonyms: Lauryl dimethylamine; Dodecyldimethylamine
Classification: Tertiary aliphatic amine
Empirical: $C_{14}H_{31}N$
Formula: $CH_3(CH_2)_{10}CH_2N(CH_3)_2$
Properties: M.w. 213.46
Toxicology: Moderately toxic by ingestion; severe skin and eye irritant; heated to dec., emits toxic NO_x
Uses: Bactericide precursor
Regulatory: FDA 21CFR §177.1680
Manuf./Distrib.: Albemarle; Lonza; Mason
Trade names: Empigen® 5073

Dimethylmethane. *See* Propane
6,6-Dimethyl-2-methylenebicyclo[3.1.1]heptane. *See* β-Pinene
α,4-Dimethyl-α-(4-methyl-3-pentenyl)-3-cyclohexene-1-methanol. *See* Bisabolol
N,N-Dimethyl-N-octadecylbenzenemethanaminium chloride. *See* Stearalkonium chloride
Dimethyloctadecylbenzyl ammonium chloride. *See* Stearalkonium chloride
2,6-Dimethyloctadien-2,6-al-8. *See* Citral
3,7-Dimethyl-2,6-octadienal. *See* Citral
3,7-Dimethyl-2,6-octadienal diethyl acetal. *See* Citral diethyl acetal
3,7-Dimethyl-2,6-octadienal dimethyl acetal. *See* Citral dimethyl acetal
2,6-Dimethyl-2,7-octadien-6-ol. *See* Linalool
3,7-Dimethyl-1,6-octadien-3-ol. *See* Linalool
trans-3,7-Dimethyl-2,6-octadien-1-ol. *See* Geraniol
3,7-Dimethyl-1,6-octadien-3-ol acetate. *See* Linalyl acetate
trans-3,7-Dimethyl-2,6-octadien-1-ol acetate. *See* Geranyl acetate
3,7-Dimethyl-1,6-octadien-3-yl acetate. *See* Linalyl acetate
cis-3,7-Dimethyl-2,6-octadien-1-yl-acetate. *See* Neryl acetate
3,7-Dimethyl-1,6-octadien-3-yl anthranilate. *See* Linalyl anthranilate
3,7-Dimethyl-1,6-octadien-3-yl formate. *See* Linalyl formate
3,7-Dimethyl-2,6-octadien-3-yl propionate. *See* Linalyl propionate
3,7-Dimethyloctane-1,7-diol. *See* Hydroxycitronellol
3,7-Dimethyl-1,7-octanedol. *See* Hydroxycitronellol
Dimethyl octanol. *See* 3,7-Dimethyl-1-octanol

3,7-Dimethyl-1-octanol
   CAS 106-21-8; EINECS 203-374-5
   FEMA 2391
   Synonyms: Dimethyl octanol; Tetrahydrogeraniol; Dihydrocitronellol
   Definition: Usually prepared by hydrogenation of geraniol, citronellol, or citronellal
   Empirical: $C_{10}H_{22}O$
   Formula: $(CH_3)_2CH(CH_2)_3CH(CH_3)CH_2CH_2OH$
   Properties: Colorless liq., sweet rosy odor, bitter taste; sol. in min. oil; insol. in glycerol; m.w. 158.29; dens.
      0.828 (20/4 C); b.p. 98-99 C (9 mm); flash pt. 97 C; ref. index 1.435 (20 C)
   Precaution: Combustible
   Toxicology: LD50 (skin, rabbit) 2400 mg/kg; mod. toxic by skin contact; skin irritant; heated to decomp., emits
      acrid smoke and fumes
   Uses: Sweet synthetic flavoring agent
   Regulatory: FDA 21CFR §172.515; FEMA GRAS
   Manuf./Distrib. (pharm. & food): Aldrich

3,7-Dimethyl-6-octenal. *See* Citronellal
3,7-Dimethyl-6-octen-1-ol. *See* β-Citronellol
3,7-Dimethyl-6-octen-1-ol acetate. *See* Citronellyl acetate
3,7-Dimethyl-6-octen-1-yl acetate. *See* Citronellyl acetate
3,7-Dimethyl-6-octen-1-yl butyrate. *See* Citronellyl butyrate
3,7-Dimethyl-6-octen-1-yl formate. *See* Citronellyl formate
3,7-Dimethyl-6-octen-1-yl phenylacetate. *See* Citronellyl phenylacetate
3,7-Dimethyl-6-octen-1-yl propionate. *See* Citronellyl propionate
3,7-Dimethyl-6-octen-1-yl valerate. *See* Citronellyl valerate
Dimethylol dimethyl hydantoin. *See* DMDM hydantoin
1,3-Dimethylol-5,5-dimethyl hydantoin. *See* DMDM hydantoin

Dimethylolpropionic acid
   CAS 4767-03-7
   Synonyms: DMPA; 2,2-Bis(hydroxymethyl)propionic acid

Dimethyl oxazolidine

Empirical: $C_5H_{10}O_4$
Properties: Off-wh. cryst. solid; sol. in water and methanol; sl. sol. in acetone; insol. in benzene; m.w. 134; m.p. 192-194 C
Toxicology: Essentially nontoxic; LD50 (mouse, oral) > 5000 mg/kg; sl. irritating to abraded skin; moderately irritating to eyes
Uses: Pharmaceutical intermediate
Manuf./Distrib.: Allchem Ind.; Fabrichem; Hoechst AG
Trade names: DMPA®

Dimethyl oxazolidine
CAS 51200-87-4; EINECS 257-048-2
Synonyms: 4,4-Dimethyloxazolidine; Oxazolidine A
Classification: Heterocyclic compd.
Empirical: $C_5H_{11}NO$
Properties: M.w. 101.17; sol. in water and oil
Toxicology: Moderately toxic by ingestion and skin contact; mildly toxic by inhalation
Uses: Antimicrobial, antibacterial for topical aq. pharmaceuticals
Regulatory: USA not restricted; Euorpe listed
Trade names: Oxaban®-A

4,4-Dimethyloxazolidine. *See* Dimethyl oxazolidine
Dimethyloxychinizin. *See* Antipyrine

α,α-Dimethylphenethyl butyrate
FEMA 2394
Synonyms: Benzyl dimethylcarbinyl butyrate; Dimethylbenzylcarbinyl butyrate; DMBC butyrate
Definition: Obtained by esterification of dimethyl benzyl carbinol with n-butyric acid
Empirical: $C_{14}H_{20}O_2$
Properties: Colorless liq., plum-prune odor, apricot/peach/plum-like taste; sol. in alcohol; insol. in water; m.w. 220.31
Precaution: Combustible liq.
Toxicology: Heated to decomp., emits acrid smoke and fumes
Uses: Synthetic flavoring agent
Regulatory: FDA 21CFR §172.515; FEMA GRAS

Dimethylphenol. *See* Xylenol
2,6-Dimethylphenol. *See* 2,6-Xylenol
N,N-Dimethyl-N-(2-phenoxyethyl)-1-dodecanaminium bromide. *See* Domiphen bromide
N-[2-[(2,6-Dimethylphenyl)amino]-2-oxoethyl]-N,N-diethylbenzenemathanaminium benzoate. *See* Denatonium benzoate
2,3-Dimethyl-1-phenyl-3-pyrazolin-5-one. *See* Antipyrine
Dimethylpolysiloxane. *See* Dimethicone
2,2-Dimethylpropanoic acid, isooctadecyl ester. *See* Isostearyl neopentanoate

2,3-Dimethylpyrazine
CAS 5910-89-4
FEMA 3271
Synonyms: 2,3-Dimethyl-1,4-diazine
Empirical: $C_6H_8N_2$
Properties: Colorless liq., nutty cocoa odor; misc. with water, org. solvs.; m.w. 108.16; dens. 1.000-1.022 (20 C); b.p. 182 C; flash pt. (OC) 147 F; ref. index 1.506-1.509
Precaution: Combustible liq.
Toxicology: LD50 (oral, rat) 613 mg/kg; mod. toxic by ingestion and intraperitoneal routes; heated to decomp., emits toxic fumes of NO_x
Uses: Synthetic flavoring agent
Regulatory: FEMA GRAS
Manuf./Distrib.: Aldrich
Manuf./Distrib. (pharm. & food): Aldrich

2,5-Dimethylpyrazine
CAS 123-32-0; EINECS 204-618-3
FEMA 3272
Empirical: $C_6H_8N_2$
Properties: M.w. 108.14; dens. 0.990; b.p. 155 C; flash pt. 147 F
Precaution: Combustible liq.
Toxicology: LD50 (oral, rat) 1020 mg/kg; irritant; mod. toxic by ingestion and IP routes; mutagenic data; heated

to decomp., emits toxic fumes of NO_x
Uses: Medicinal synthetic flavoring agent
Regulatory: FEMA GRAS
Manuf./Distrib. (pharm. & food): Aldrich

2,6-Dimethylpyridine. *See* 2,6-Lutidine
Dimethylresorcinol. *See* m-Dimethoxybenzene
6,7-Dimethyl-9-d-ribitylisoalloxazine. *See* Riboflavin
7,8-Dimethyl-10-(d-ribityl) isoalloxazine. *See* Riboflavin
Dimethyl silicone. *See* Dimethicone
Dimethylsiloxane-glycol copolymer. *See* Dimethicone copolyol
Dimethyl siloxy stearoxy siloxane polymer. *See* Stearoxy dimethicone

Dimethyl succinate
CAS 106-65-0; EINECS 203-419-9
FEMA 2396
Synonyms: Dimethyl butanedioate; Methyl succinate
Empirical: $C_6H_{10}O_4$
Formula: $CH_3OCOCH_2CH_2COOCH_3$
Properties: Colorless liq., ethereal winey odor; m.w. 146.14; dens. 1.119 (20/4 C); m.p. 16-19 C; b.p. 190-193 C; flash pt. 90 C; ref. index 1.419
Uses: Fruity synthetic flavoring agent
Regulatory: FDA 21CFR §172.515; FEMA GRAS
Manuf./Distrib.: Ashland; Chemie Linz N. Am.; DuPont; Penta Mfg.; Schweizerhall
Manuf./Distrib. (pharm. & food): Aldrich

3-[(2,4-Dimethyl-5-sulfophenyl)azo]-4-hydroxy-1-naphthalenesulfonic acid disodium salt. *See* CI 14700; FD&C Red No. 4

Dimethyl sulfoxide
CAS 67-68-5; EINECS 200-664-3
Synonyms: DMSO; Methyl sulfoxide; Sulfinylbis (methane)
Classification: Aliphatic organic compd.
Empirical: C_2H_6OS
Formula: $(CH_3)_2SO$
Properties: Colorless liq., strong char. odor; hygroscopic; sol. in water; pract. insol. in alcohol, benzene, acetone, chloroform, ether; m.w. 78.13; dens. 1.101; m.p. 18.4 C; b.p. 189 C; flash pt. 95 C; ref. index 1.4790 (20 C)
Precaution: Combustible
Toxicology: Little systemic toxicity, but a primary irritant when used topically (may cause contact urticaria, shortness of breath, facial swelling, GI disturbances, headache, nausea, diarrhea, photophobia)
Uses: Carrier, solubilizer, solv. for pharmaceuticals; helps anti-inflammatory medicine penetrate the skin; dissolves highly lipophilic materials; used in treatment of scleroderma, systemically for rheumatoid arthritis
Regulatory: BP, Ph.Eur. compliance
Manuf./Distrib.: Aldrich; Allchem Ind.; Elf Atochem N. Am.; Gaylord; Itochu Spec.; Monomer-Polymer & Dajac; Spectrum Chem. Mfg.; Toray Fine Chems.
Manuf./Distrib. (pharm. & food): R.W. Greeff; Mallinckrodt; Toray Fine Chems.
Trade names: DMSO

N,N-Dimethyl-N-tetradecylbenzenemethanaminium chloride. *See* Myristalkonium chloride
N,N-Dimethyl-N-[2-[2-[4-(1,1,3,3-tetramethylbutyl) phenoxy] ethoxy] ethyl] benzenemethanaminium chloride. *See* Benzethonium chloride
4,4´-(2,3-Dimethyltetramethylene)dipyrocatechol. *See* Nordihydroguairetic acid
7,8-Dimethyltocol. *See* (+)-γ-Tocopherol
1,2-Dimyristoyl phosphatidylcholine. *See* 1,2-Dimyristoyl-sn-glycero(3) phosphatidylcholine

1,2-Dimyristoyl-sn-glycero(3) phosphatidylcholine
CAS 18194-24-6; 13699-48-4
Synonyms: DMPC; 1,2-Dimyristoyl phosphatidylcholine
Uses: Emulsifier, solubilizer
Trade names: Phospholipon® MC

1,2-Dimyristoyl-sn-glycero(3)phosphoglycerol sodium salt. *See* Sodium 1,2-dimyristoyl-sn-glycero(3) phosphatidylcholine

Dimyristyl thiodipropionate
CAS 16545-54-3; EINECS 240-613-2

Dinitrogen monoxide

Synonyms: Ditetradecyl 3,3′-thiobispropanoate; Propanoic acid, 3,3′-thiobis-, ditetradecyl ester
Classification: Diester
Definition: Diester of myristyl alcohol and thiodipropionic acid
Empirical: $C_{34}H_{66}O_4S$
Formula: $S(CH_2CH_2COOC_{14}H_{29})_2$
Properties: M.w. 570; m.p. 48-50 C; acid no. 1.0 max.
Uses: Antioxidant for pharmaceuticals
Regulatory: FDA 21CFR §178.2010
Manuf./Distrib.: Evans Chemetics; Witco/PAG
Manuf./Distrib. (pharm. & food): Witco

Dinitrogen monoxide. *See* Nitrous oxide
2,4-Dinitro-1-naphthol-7-sulfonic acid disodium salt. *See* CI 10316; Ext. D&C Yellow No. 7
1-(2,4-Dinitrophenylazo)-2-naphthol. *See* D&C Orange No. 17
Dinkum oil. *See* Eucalyptus oil
Dioctadecyl dimethyl ammonium chloride. *See* Distearyldimonium chloride
3,3′-Dioctadecyl thiodipropionate. *See* Distearyl thiodipropionate
Dioctrahedral smectite. *See* Attapulgite

Dioctyl adipate
CAS 103-23-1; EINECS 203-090-1
Synonyms: DOA; Bis(2-ethylhexyl) hexanedioate; Di(2-ethylhexyl) adipate; Hexanedioic acid, bis (2-ethylhexyl) ester
Classification: Aliphatic organic compd.
Definition: Diester of 2-ethylhexyl alcohol and adipic acid
Empirical: $C_{22}H_{42}O_4$
Formula: $[CH_2CH_2COOCH_2CH(C_2H_5)C_4H_9]_2$
Properties: Lt.-colored oily liq.; insol. in water; m.w. 370.64; dens. 0.9268 (20/20 C); b.p. 417 C; flash pt. 196 C; ref. index 1.4472
Toxicology: Suspected carcinogen and tetratogen; moderately toxic by IV route; mildly toxic by ingestion and skin contact; mutagenic data; eye and skin irritant
Uses: Emollient, moisturizer, pigment dispersant, cosolv. used in injectables
Regulatory: FDA 21CFR §175.105, 175.300, 177.1200, 177.1210, 177.1400, 177.2600, 178.3740; FDA approved for injectables
Manuf./Distrib.: Allchem Ind.; Ashland; BASF; Chisso Am.; Coyne; Eastman; Esprit; Hüls AG; Inolex; Monsanto
Trade names: Wickenol® 158
Trade names containing: Wickenol® 161

Dioctyl calcium sulfosuccinate
Synonyms: Docusate calcium; Calcium dioctyl sulfosuccinate
Uses: Pharmaceutical surfactant used in stool softeners, vitamin formulations, ear wax removal compds.; lubricant/emollient in laxative prods.
Trade names containing: Docusate Calcium USP in Corn Oil NF Sol'n.

Dioctyl cyclohexane
CAS 84753-08-2; 100182-46-5; EINECS 283-854-9
Synonyms: Cyclohexane, 1,3-bis(2-ethylhexyl)-; 1,3 Dioctyl cyclohexane; Cyclohexane, diisooctyl-
Classification: Organic compd.
Empirical: $C_{22}H_{44}$
Uses: Emollient, superfatting agent for pharmaceutical creams and emulsions
Trade names: Cetiol® S

1,3 Dioctyl cyclohexane. *See* Dioctyl cyclohexane

Dioctyl ether
CAS 629-82-3
Synonyms: Dicapryl ether
Uses: Emollient, spreading agent
Trade names: Cetiol® OE

Dioctyl malate
CAS 15763-02-7; 56235-92-8; EINECS 260-070-5
Synonyms: Butanedioic acid, hydroxy-, bis(2-ethylhexyl) ester
Uses: Emollient; fragrance coupler; solubilizer; antitack in antiperspirants, carbomer formulations
Trade names: Ceraphyl® 45

Dioctyl phthalate
CAS 117-81-7; 117-84-0; EINECS 204-211-0
Synonyms: DOP; DEHP; Di(2-ethylhexyl) phthalate; Bis (2-ethylhexyl) phthalate; Di-s-octyl phthalate; 1,2-Benzenedicarboxylic acid dioctyl ester
Definition: Diester of 2-ethylhexyl alcohol and phthalic acid
Empirical: $C_{24}H_{38}O_4$
Formula: $C_6H_4[COOCH_2CH(C_2H_5)C_4H_9]_2$
Properties: Lt.-colored liq., odorless, bitter taste; insol. in water; misc. with min. oil; m.w. 390.62; dens. 0.9861 (20/20 C); b.p. 231 C (5 mm); flash pt. 218 C; ref. index 1.4836
Precaution: Combustible
Toxicology: TLV 5 mg/m^3; STEL 10 mg/m^3; LD50 (oral, rat) 30,600 mg/kg; poison by IV; mildly toxic by ingestion; skin and severe eye irritant; suspected human carcinogen; experimental teratogen; affects human GI tract; heated to decomp., emits acrid smoke
Uses: Solvent, fixative; used in ophthalmics, injectables
Regulatory: FDA 21CFR §175.105, 175.300, 175.310, 715.380, 175.390, 176.170, 176.210, 176.1210, 177.1010, 177.1200, 177.1210, 177.1400, 177.2600, 178.3120, 178.3910, 181.22, 181.27; FDA approved for ophthalmics, injectables; BP compliance
Manuf./Distrib.: Allchem Ind.; Aristech; BASF; Chemisphere Ltd; Chisso Am.; Coyne; Daihachi Chem. Ind.; Eastman; Great Western; C.P. Hall; Hoechst AG; Hüls AG; Mitsubishi Gas; Spectrum Chem. Mfg.; UCB SA
Manuf./Distrib. (pharm. & food): Aldrich; Eastman; Integra

Di-s-octyl phthalate. *See* Dioctyl phthalate

Dioctyl sodium sulfosuccinate
CAS 577-11-7; 1369-66-3; EINECS 209-406-4
Synonyms: DSS; Sodium dioctyl sulfosuccinate; Sodium 1,4-bis(2-ethylhexyl) sulfosuccinate; Sodium di(2-ethylhexyl) sulfosuccinate; Docusate sodium
Definition: Sodium salt of the diester of 2-ethylhexyl alcohol and sulfosuccinic acid
Empirical: $C_{20}H_{38}O_7S \cdot Na$
Formula: $C_8H_{17}OOCCH_2CH(SO_3Na)COOC_8H_{17}$
Properties: Wh. wax-like solid, char. octyl alcohol odor; slowly sol. in water; freely sol. in alcohol, glycerol, CCl$_4$, acetone, xylene, hexane; m.w. 445.63; m.p. 173-179 C
Precaution: Hygroscopic
Toxicology: LD50 (oral, rat) 1900 mg/kg; moderately toxic by ingestion, intraperitoneal routes; poison by intravenous route; skin, severe eye irritant; heated to decomp., emits toxic fumes of SO$_x$ and Na$_2$O
Uses: Emulsifier, wetting agent, solubilizer in pharmaceuticals; adjuvant in tablet formation; stool softener; lubricant/emollient in laxative prods.; used in injectables (IM), orals, topicals, vaginals
Regulatory: FDA 21CFR §73.1, with cocoa, 131.130, 131.132, 133.124, 133.133, 133.134, 133.162, 133.178, 133.179, 163.114, 163.117, 169.115, 169.150, 172.520, 172.808, 172.810, 175.105, 175.300, 175.320, 176.170, 176.210, 177.1200, 177.2800, 178.1010, 178.3400; USDA 9 CFR §318.7, 381.147; FDA approved for injectables (IM), orals, topicals; USP/NF, BP compliance
Manuf./Distrib.: Alco; Aquatec Quimica SA; Brotherton Ltd; Calgene; Cytec; Eastern Color & Chem.; EM Industries; Finetex; Hart Prod.; Henkel/Organic Prods.; McIntyre; Mona; Witco/Oleo-Surf.
Manuf./Distrib. (pharm. & food): Aldrich; Am. Cyaamid; R.W. Greeff; Ruger; Spectrum Chem. Mfg.
Trade names: Docusate Sodium USP; Nikkol OTP-100S
Trade names containing: Docusate Sodium USP in Polyethylene Glycol 400 NF; DSS Granular; DSS Tablet Grade; Monawet MO-70R

Dioctyl succinate
CAS 2915-57-3; EINECS 220-836-1
Synonyms: Bis (2-ethylhexyl) butanedioate; Butanedioic acid, bis(2-ethylhexyl) ester; Di(2-ethylhexyl) succinate
Definition: Diester of 2-ethylhexyl alcohol and succinic acid
Empirical: $C_{20}H_{38}O_4$
Formula: $C_8H_{17}OCOCH_2CH_2COOC_8H_{17}$
Properties: Liq.; sol. < 0.01% in water @ 20 C; dens. 0.9346 (20/20 C); b.p. 257 C (50 mm); f.p. set to glass < -60 C; flash pt. (OC) 157 C
Toxicology: No known skin toxicity
Uses: Wetting agent used in compounding calamine lotion; emollient, moisturizer, pigment dispersant/wetter
Trade names: Wickenol® 159

1,4-Dioxacycloheptadecane-5,17-dione. *See* Ethylene brassylate
1,3-Dioxaindane. *See* 1,2-Methylenedioxybenzene
1,4-Dioxan. *See* 1,4-Dioxane

1,4-Dioxane
  CAS 123-91-1; EINECS 204-661-8
  UN No. 1165
  Synonyms: Diethylene ether; p-Dioxane; 1,4-Dioxan; 1,4-Diethylene dioxide; Diethylene dioxide; Diethylene oxide
  Classification: Aliphatic organic compd.; ether
  Empirical: $C_4H_8O_2$
  Formula: $OCH_2CH_2OCH_2CH_2$
  Properties: Colorless liq., ethereal odor; stable; misc. with water, most org. solvs.; m.w. 88.11; dens. 1.0356 (20/20 C); b.p. 101.3 C; f.p. 10-12 C; flash pt. 18.3 C; ref. index 1.4220
  Precaution: DOT: Flamm. liq.
  Toxicology: Carcinogen; toxic by inhalation, absorbed by skin; TLV 25 ppm in air; OSHA 100 ppm min. air
  Uses: Solv. for prod. of pharmaceuticals
  Regulatory: BP compliance
  Manuf./Distrib.: AC Ind.; Alemark; Allchem Ind.; Amber Syn.; Ashland; J.T. Baker; BASF; CPS; Ferro/Grant; Fluka; Mallinckrodt; Osaka Org. Chem. Ind.; Spectrum Chem. Mfg.; Toho; Union Carbide; Van Waters & Rogers
  Manuf./Distrib. (pharm. & food): Aldrich; Ferro/Grant; Mercian; Nisso Petrochem. Ind.

p-Dioxane. *See* 1,4-Dioxane
1,1-Dioxide-1,2-benzisothiazol-3(2H)-one sodium salt. *See* Saccharin sodium
(2,5-Dioxo-4-imidazolidinyl) urea. *See* Allantoin
1,3-Dioxolan-2-one. *See* Ethylene carbonate
1,3-Dioxolan-2-one, 4-methyl. *See* Propylene carbonate
Dioxolone-2. *See* Ethylene carbonate
Dioxymethyleneprotocatechuic aldehyde. *See* Heliotropine
DIPA. *See* Diisopropanolamine
L-α-1,2-Dipalmitoyl phosphatidylcholine. *See* 1,2-Dipalmitoyl-sn-glycero(3) phosphatidylcholine

1,2-Dipalmitoyl-sn-glycero(3) phosphatidylcholine
  CAS 2644-64-6
  Synonyms: DPPC; L-α-1,2-Dipalmitoyl phosphatidylcholine
  Uses: For mfg. of liposomes and mixed micelles
  Trade names: Phospholipon® PC

L-α-1,2-Dipalmitoyl-sn-phosphatidylglycerol sodium salt. *See* Sodium 1,2-dipalmitoyl-sn-glycero(3) phosphatidylcholine
Dipentene. *See* d-Limonene, dl-Limonene
N,N-Diphenyl-1,4-benzenediamine. *See* N,N´-Diphenyl-p-phenylenediamine

Diphenyl chlorophosphate
  CAS 2524-64-3
  Uses: Intermediate
  Manuf./Distrib.: Albright & Wilson
  Manuf./Distrib. (pharm. & food): Aldrich
  Trade names: DPCP

Diphenyl ketone. *See* Benzophenone
Diphenylmethanone. *See* Benzophenone

N,N´-Diphenyl-p-phenylenediamine
  CAS 74-31-7; EINECS 200-806-4
  Synonyms: DPPD; 1,4-Bis(phenylamino)benzene; N,N-Diphenyl-1,4-benzenediamine; 1,4-Dianilinobenzene
  Classification: Aromatic organic compd.
  Empirical: $C_{18}H_{16}N_2$
  Formula: $(C_6H_5NH)_2C_6H_4$
  Properties: Gray powd.; insol. in water; sol. in acetone, benzene, monochlorobenzene, isopropyl acetate, DMF, ether, chloroform, ethyl acetate, glacial acetic acid; m.w. 260.36; dens. 1.28; m.p. 145-152 C
  Precaution: Combustible; emits toxic fumes of NO_x
  Toxicology: Poison by intravenous, intraperitoneal routes; moderately toxic by ingestion; eye irritant
  Uses: Intermediate for drugs
  Manuf./Distrib.: Kawaguchi Chem. Ind.; Sumitomo
  Manuf./Distrib. (pharm. & food): Seiko Chem.

N,N´-Diphenylthiocarbamide. *See* N,N´-Diphenylthiourea

1,2-Diphenyl-2-thiourea. *See* N,N´-Diphenylthiourea

N,N´-Diphenylthiourea
CAS 102-08-9; EINECS 203-004-2
Synonyms: sym-Diphenylthiourea; 1,2-Diphenyl-2-thiourea; Thiocarbanilide; N,N´-Diphenylthiocarbamide
Classification: Aromatic organic compd.
Empirical: $C_{13}H_{12}N_2S$
Formula: $CS(NHC_6H_5)_2$
Properties: White to faint gray powd., bitter taste; pract. insol. in water; sol. in acetone, alcohol, ether, chloroform; m.w. 228.33; dens. 1.32 (25 C); m.p. 153-154 C; b.p. dec.
Precaution: Combustible
Toxicology: Moderately toxic by ingestion and intraperitoneal routes; MLD (rabbit, oral) 1.5 g/kg; heated to dec., emits highly toxic fumes of SO_x and NO_x
Uses: Synthetic organic pharmaceuticals
Manuf./Distrib.: Aldrich; Charkit; Fluka; Ouchi Shinko Chem.
Manuf./Distrib. (pharm. & food): Aldrich; Ouchi Shinko Chem.

Diphosphoric acid, calcium salt (1:2). *See* Calcium pyrophosphate
Diphosphoric acid tetrasodium salt. *See* Tetrasodium pyrophosphate
Diphosphoric acid tin (2+) salt. *See* Stannous pyrophosphate
Dipotassium carbonate. *See* Potassium carbonate
Dipotassium dichloride. *See* Potassium chloride
Dipotassium disulfite. *See* Potassium metabisulfite

Dipotassium glycyrrhizate
CAS 68797-35-3; EINECS 272-296-1
Synonyms: Dipotassium glycyrrhizinate
Properties: Pale yel. cryst. powd.; water-sol.
Uses: Flavoring and colorant; anti-inflammatory, anti-allergenic surfactant; soothes skin
Manuf./Distrib.: Nikko Chem. Co. Ltd.
Trade names: Nikkol Dipotassium Glycyrrhizinate

Dipotassium glycyrrhizinate. *See* Dipotassium glycyrrhizate
Dipotassium hydrogen orthophosphate. *See* Potassium phosphate dibasic
Dipotassium hydrogen phosphate. *See* Potassium phosphate dibasic
Dipotassium orthophosphate. *See* Potassium phosphate dibasic
Dipotassium persulfate. *See* Potassium persulfate
Dipotassium phosphate. *See* Potassium phosphate dibasic
Dipotassium pyrosulfite. *See* Potassium metabisulfite
Dipotassium L-(+)-tartrate. *See* Potassium acid tartrate

Dipropylene glycol salicylate
CAS 7491-14-7
Synonyms: POP (2) monosalicylate; PPG-2 salicylate; PPG (2) monosalicylate
Definition: Ester of dipropylene glycol and salicylci acid
Empirical: $C_7H_6O_3 \cdot xC_6H_{14}O_3$
Properties: Insol. in water
Uses: Plasticizer, emollient, UV absorber in pharmaceutical specialties, sunscreen lotions
Trade names: Dipsal

Dipropyl ketone. *See* 4-Heptanone
Diresorcinolphthalein. *See* Fluorescein
Disodium carbonate. *See* Sodium carbonate

Disodium cocoamphodiacetate
CAS 61791-32-0; 68650-39-5; EINECS 272-043-5
Synonyms: N-Cocamidoethyl-N-2-hydroxyethyl-N-carboxyethylglycine, sodium salt; Cocoamphodiacetate; Cocoamphocarboxyglycinate
Classification: Amphoteric organic compd.
Formula: $RCO-NH(CH_2)_5ON(COO)_2Na_2$, RCO- represents the coconut acid radical
Uses: Emulsifier, solubilizer, stabilizer
Trade names: Miranol® C2M Conc. NP

Disodium cocoamphodipropionate
CAS 86438-35-9; 83138-08-3; 86438-79-1; 68411-57-4; 68604-71-7; 68910-41-5; 68919-40-4; EINECS 270-131-8; 272-897-9
Synonyms: Cocoamphocarboxypropionate; Cocoamphodipropionate

Disodium disulfite

Classification: Amphoteric organic compd.
Formula: RCO-NH(CH$_2$)$_8$ON(COO)$_2$Na$_2$, RCO- represents the coconut acid radical

Disodium disulfite. *See* Sodium metabisulfite
Disodium edetate. *See* Disodium EDTA

Disodium EDTA
CAS 139-33-3 (anhyd.); 6381-92-6 (dihydrate); EINECS 205-358-3
Synonyms: Disodium edetate; Disodium ethyenediamine tetraacetate; Glycine, N,N´-1,2-ethanediylbis[N-(carboxymethyl)-, disodium salt dihydrate; Ethylenediaminetetraacetic acid, disodium salt; Edetate disodium
Classification: Substituted diamine
Empirical: C$_{10}$H$_{14}$N$_2$Na$_2$O$_8$ • 2H$_2$O
Properties: Wh. cryst. powd.; freely sol. in water; m.w. 336.24 (anhyd.), 372.24 (dihydrate); m.p. 252 (dec.); pH 4-6
Toxicology: LD50 (oral, rat) 2 g/kg; poison by intravenous route; moderately toxic by ingestion; experimental teratogen, reproductive effects; mutagenic data; heated to decomp., emits toxic fumes of NO$_x$ and Na$_2$O
Uses: Pharmaceutical aid; chelating agent, complexing agent; preservative in nasal drops, decongestant prods.; used in injectables, inhalants, intravenous, ophthalmics, orals, otics, rectals, topicals
Regulatory: FDA 21CFR §155.200, 169.115, 169.140, 169.150, 172.135, 175.105, 176.150, 176.170, 177.1200, 177.2800, 178.3570, 178.3910, 573.360; USDA 9CFR §318.7; Japan approved (0.25 g/kg max. as calcium disodium EDTA); FDA approved for injectables, inhalants, IV, ophthalmics, orals, otics, rectals, topicals; USP/NF, BP, Ph.Eur. compliance
Manuf./Distrib.: Aldrich; R.W. Greeff; Hampshire; Int'l. Sourcing
Manuf./Distrib. (pharm. & food): Int'l. Sourcing; Spectrum Chem. Mfg.
Trade names: Sequestrene® NA2; Versene NA; Versene Na$_2$

Disodium ethyenediamine tetraacetate. *See* Disodium EDTA
Disodium[(ethylenedinitrilo)tetraacetate], calciate (2-) hydrate. *See* Calcium disodium EDTA

Disodium guanylate
CAS 5550-12-9 (anhyd.)
FEMA 3668
Synonyms: GMP; Sodium guanylate; Guanosine 5´-disodium phosphate; Disodium 5´-guanylate; Guanylic acid sodium salt; Sodium guanosine-5´-monophosphate
Empirical: C$_{10}$H$_{14}$N$_5$O$_8$P•2Na
Formula: Na$_2$C$_{10}$H$_{12}$N$_5$O$_8$P•2HOH
Properties: Colorless to wh. cryst., char. taste; sol. in cold water, very sol. in hot water; sl. sol. in alcohol; insol. in ether; m.w. 409.24
Toxicology: LD50 (oral, mouse) 15 g/kg; moderately toxic by ingestion, intraperitoneal, subcutaneous, intravenous routes; mildly toxic by ingestion; heated to decomp., emits toxic fumes of PO$_x$, NO$_x$, Na$_2$O
Uses: Flavoring agent; in eye drops for treatment of corneal damage
Regulatory: FDA 21CFR §172.530; USDA 9CFR §318.7, 381.147; FEMA GRAS; Japan approved; Europe listed; UK approved

Disodium 5´-guanylate. *See* Disodium guanylate
Disodium hydrogen phosphate. *See* Sodium phosphate dibasic anhydrous
Disodium hydrogen phosphate heptahydrate. *See* Sodium phosphate dibasic heptahydrate
Disodium IMP. *See* Disodium inosinate
Disodium indigo-5,5-disulfonate. *See* FD&C Blue No. 2

Disodium inosinate
CAS 4691-65-0 (anhyd.)
FEMA 3669
Synonyms: IMP; Disodium IMP; Disodium inosine 5´-monophosphate; Sodium inosinate; Sodium 5´-inosinate; Disodium 5´-inosinate; Inosine 5´-disodium phosphate
Definition: A 5´-nucleotide derived from seaweed or dried fish
Empirical: C$_{10}$H$_{13}$N$_4$O$_8$P • 2Na
Properties: Colorless to wh. cryst., char. taste; sol. in water; sl. sol. in alcohol; insol. in ether; m.w. 394.22
Toxicology: LD50 (oral, rat) 15,900 mg/kg; moderately toxic by several routes; experimental teratogen; mutagenic data; heated to decomp., emits toxic fumes of PO$_x$, NO$_x$, Na$_2$O
Uses: Flavoring agent; treatment of visual disturbances; in orals, topicals
Regulatory: FDA 21CFR §172.535, must contain ≤ 150 ppm sol. barium; USDA 9CFR §318.7, 381.147; FEMA GRAS; UK, Japan approved
Manuf./Distrib.: Penta Mfg.; Schweizerhall

Disodium 5´-inosinate. *See* Disodium inosinate
Disodium inosine 5´-monophosphate. *See* Disodium inosinate

Disodium laureth sulfosuccinate
CAS 39354-45-5 (generic); 40754-59-4; 42016-08-0; 58450-52-5; EINECS 255-062-3
Synonyms: Sulfobutanedioic acid, 4-[2-[2-[2-(dodecyloxy)ethoxy]ethoxy]ethyl]ester, disodium salt; Disodium lauryl ether sulfosuccinate
Definition: Disodium salt of an ethoxylated lauryl alcohol half ester of sulfosuccinic acid
Formula: $(C_2H_4O)_xC_{16}H_{30}O_7S \cdot 2Na$
Uses: Surfactant base for pharmaceuticals
Trade names: Texapon® SB-3

Disodium lauryl ether sulfosuccinate. *See* Disodium laureth sulfosuccinate

Disodium lauryl sulfosuccinate
CAS 13192-12-6; 19040-44-9; 26838-05-1; 36409-57-1; EINECS 248-030-5; 236-149-5
Synonyms: Sulfobutanedioic acid, 1-dodecyl ester, disodium salt
Definition: Disodium salt of a lauryl alcohol half ester of sulfosuccinic acid
Empirical: $C_{16}H_{30}O_7S \cdot 2Na$
Uses: Surfactant

Disodium monohydrogen orthophosphate. *See* Sodium phosphate dibasic anhydrous
Disodium orthophosphate. *See* Sodium phosphate dibasic anhydrous
Disodium orthophosphate heptahydrate. *See* Sodium phosphate dibasic heptahydrate

Disodium pamoate
Empirical: $C_{23}H_{14}O_6Na_2$
Properties: Yel. to tan powd.; m.w. 432.33
Uses: Used to produce pamoate salts of drug prods.; masks bitter taste in pharmaceutical prods.; permits slow release of active drugs
Trade names: Disodium Pamoate

Disodium PEG-8 ricinosuccinate
Classification: Dicarboxylic acid
Formula: $CH_3(CH_2)_5CHOHCH_2CH:CHCH(CH_2)_6COONaCHCOONaCH_2CO(OCH_2CH_2)_nOH$, avg. n = 8
Uses: Ingred. in antiperspirants
Trade names containing: Grillocin® AT Basis

Disodium phosphate. *See* Sodium phosphate dibasic anhydrous
Disodium phosphate heptahydrate. *See* Sodium phosphate dibasic heptahydrate
Disodium pyrosulfite. *See* Sodium metabisulfite
Disodium succinate. *See* Sodium succinate
Disodium sulfate. *See* Sodium sulfate
Disodium tartrate. *See* Sodium tartrate
Disodium L-(+)-tartrate. *See* Sodium tartrate
Disodium thiosulfate. *See* Sodium thiosulfate anhydrous

Disofenin
CAS 65717-97-7
Uses: Used in injectables (IV, infusion)
Regulatory: FDA approved for injectables (IV, infusion)

Distarch phosphate
CAS 55963-33-2
Synonyms: Phosphate cross-linked starch
Definition: Prod. from crosslinking of starch with sodium metaphosphate
Toxicology: No known toxicity
Uses: Absorbable dusting powd. for surgical gloves; production aid, filler, carrier; water softener, sequestering agent, and texturizer in dandruff shampoos
Trade names: Corn Po 4
Trade names containing: Corn Po 4 Ster

L-α-1,2-Distearoylphosphatidylcholine. *See* 1,2-Distearoyl-sn-glycero(3) phosphatidylcholine

1,2-Distearoyl-sn-glycero(3) phosphatidylcholine
CAS 816-94-4
Synonyms: DSPC; L-α-1,2-Distearoylphosphatidylcholine
Uses: For mfg. of liposomes and mixed micelles
Trade names: Phospholipon® SC

1,2-Distearoyl-sn-glycero(3)phosphoglycerol sodium salt. *See* Sodium 1,2-distearoyl-sn-glycero(3) phosphatidylcholine

Distearyl dimethyl ammonium chloride. *See* Distearyldimonium chloride

Distearyldimonium chloride
CAS 107-64-2; EINECS 203-508-2
Synonyms: Distearyl dimethyl ammonium chloride; Quaternium-5; Dioctadecyl dimethyl ammonium chloride
Classification: Quaternary ammonium salt
Empirical: $C_{38}H_{80}N \cdot Cl$
Uses: Visc. builder in pharmaceutical prods.
Regulatory: FDA 21CFR §172.712, 177.1200

Distearyl thiodipropionate
CAS 693-36-7; EINECS 211-750-5
Synonyms: DSTDP; 3,3′-Thiobispropanoic acid, dioctadecyl ester; 3,3′-Dioctadecyl thiodipropionate; Thiodipropionic acid, distearyl ester
Classification: Aliphatic organic compd.
Definition: Diester of stearyl alcohol and 3,3′-thiodipropionic acid
Empirical: $C_{42}H_{82}O_4S$
Formula: $(C_{18}H_{37}OOCCH_2CH_2)_2S$
Properties: White flakes; insol. in water; sol. in benzene, toluene, chloroform, and olefin polymers; m.w. 683; m.p. 58-62 C; b.p. 360 C (dec.)
Toxicology: Nonhazardous; heated to decomp., emits toxic fumes of SO_x
Uses: Antioxidant for pharmaceuticals
Regulatory: FDA 21CFR §175.105, 175.300, 181.22, 181.24 (0.005% migrating from food pkg.)
Manuf./Distrib.: Cytec; Evans Chemetics; Hampshire; Morton Int'l.; Witco/PAG
Manuf./Distrib. (pharm. & food): Sumitomo; Witco; Yoshitomi Pharmaceuticals
Trade names: PAG DSTDP

Distilled spirits. *See* Alcohol
Disulfurous acid dipotassium salt. *See* Potassium metabisulfite
Disulfurous acid disodium salt. *See* Sodium metabisulfite
Ditetradecyl 3,3′-thiobispropanoate. *See* Dimyristyl thiodipropionate
3,3′-Dithiobis(2-aminopropanoic acid). *See* L-Cysteine
Ditin diphosphate. *See* Stannous pyrophosphate

Ditridecyl thiodipropionate
CAS 10595-72-9; EINECS 234-206-9
Synonyms: 3,3′-Thiobispropanoic acid, ditridecyl ester; Di(tridecyl) thiodipropionate
Definition: Diester of tridecyl alcohol and 3,3′-thiodipropionic acid
Empirical: $C_{32}H_{62}O_4S$
Formula: $S(CH_2CH_2COOC_{13}H_{27})_2$
Properties: Colorless liq.; sol. in most org. solvs.; sl. sol. in methanol; insol. in water; m.w. 542.91; b.p. 265 C (0.25 mm)
Precaution: Combustible
Toxicology: LD50 (rat, oral) > 10 ml/kg, (rabbit, dermal) > 5 ml/kg
Uses: Sec. antioxidant for pharmaceuticals
Manuf./Distrib.: Cytec; Hampshire; Witco/PAG
Manuf./Distrib. (pharm. & food): Aldrich; Witco

Di(tridecyl) thiodipropionate. *See* Ditridecyl thiodipropionate
DKP. *See* Potassium phosphate dibasic
DMAE. *See* Dimethylethanolamine
DMBC butyrate. *See* α,α-Dimethylphenethyl butyrate
DMC. *See* Dimethylaminoethyl chloride hydrochloride

DMDM hydantoin
CAS 6440-58-0; EINECS 229-222-8
Synonyms: 1,3-Dimethylol-5,5-dimethyl hydantoin; 2,4-Imidazolidinedione, 1,3-bis(hydroxymethyl)-5,5-dimethyl-; Dimethylol dimethyl hydantoin
Classification: Organic compd.
Empirical: $C_7H_{12}N_2O_4$
Precaution: May release formaldehyde
Uses: Preservative used in topicals
Regulatory: USA CIR approved, EPA registered; Europe listed 0.6% max.; FDA approved for topicals

DME. *See* Ethylene glycol dimethyl ether
DMI. *See* Dimethyl isosorbide
DMPA. *See* Dimethylolpropionic acid
DMPC. *See* 1,2-Dimyristoyl-sn-glycero(3) phosphatidylcholine
DMSO. *See* Dimethyl sulfoxide
DOA. *See* Dioctyl adipate
1-Docosanaminium, N,N,N-trimethyl-, chloride. *See* Behentrimonium methosulfate
Docosanoic acid. *See* Behenic acid
Docosanoic acid, docosyl ester. *See* Behenyl behenate
Docosanoic acid dodecyl ester. *See* Lauryl behenate
Docosanoic acid, isocetyl ester. *See* Isocetyl behenate
Docosanoic acid, isooctadecyl ester. *See* Isostearyl behenate
Docosanoic acid, 1,2,3-propanetriyl ester. *See* Tribehenin
1-Docosanol. *See* Behenyl alcohol
13-Docosenoic acid, 9-octadecenyl ester. *See* Oleyl erucate
Docusate calcium. *See* Dioctyl calcium sulfosuccinate
Docusate sodium. *See* Dioctyl sodium sulfosuccinate
Dodecahydro-1,4a-dimethyl-7-(1-methylethyl)-1-phenanthrenemethanol. *See* Hydroabietyl alcohol
Dodecahydrosqualene. *See* Squalane

δ-Dodecalactone
  CAS 713-95-1
  FEMA 2401
  Synonyms: 5-Hydroxydodecanoic acid, δ-lactone
  Definition: Obtained by lactonization of 5-hydroxydodecanoic acid
  Empirical: $C_{12}H_{22}O_2$
  Properties: Colorless to very pale straw-yel. visc. liq., fresh-fruit oily odor; sol. in alcohol; insol. in water; m.w. 198.31; dens. 0.942; m.p. -12 C; b.p. 140-141 C (1 mm); flash pt. > 230 F
  Uses: Coconut, peach-like synthetic flavoring agent
  Regulatory: FDA 21CFR §172.515; FEMA GRAS
  Manuf./Distrib. (pharm. & food): Aldrich

γ-Dodecalactone
  CAS 2305-05-7
  FEMA 2400
  Synonyms: 4-Hydroxydodecanoic acid γ-lactone; Dodecanolide-1,4; γ-Octyl-γ-butyrolactone
  Empirical: $C_{12}H_{22}O_2$
  Properties: Colorless oily liq., fatty peachy odor, butter peach-like flavor; sol. in alcohol; insol. in water; m.w. 198.31; dens. 0.936; m.p. 17-18 C; b.p. 258 C
  Uses: Fruity synthetic flavoring agent
  Regulatory: FDA 21CFR §172.515; FEMA GRAS
  Manuf./Distrib. (pharm. & food): Acme-Hardesty; Aldrich

Dodecanal. *See* Lauric aldehyde
1-Dodecanaminium, N,N-dimethyl-N-(2-phenoxyethyl)-, bromide. *See* Domiphen bromide
Dodecanoic acid. *See* Lauric acid
n-Dodecanoic acid. *See* Lauric acid
Dodecanoic acid, 2,2-bis[[(1-oxododecyl)oxy]methyl-1,3-propanediyl ester. *See* Pentaerythrityl tetralaurate
Dodecanoic acid, diester with 1,2,3-propanetriol. *See* Glyceryl dilaurate
Dodecanoic acid, diester with 1,23,-propanetriol. *See* Glyceryl dilaurate SE
Dodecanoic acid, 2,3-dihydroxypropyl ester. *See* Glyceryl laurate
Dodecanoic acid 1,2-ethanediyl ester. *See* Glycol dilaurate
Dodecanoic acid ethyl ester. *See* Ethyl laurate
Dodecanoic acid, hexyl ester. *See* Hexyl laurate
Dodecanoic acid, 2-hydroxypropyl ester. *See* Propylene glycol laurate
Dodecanoic acid methyl ester. *See* Methyl laurate
Dodecanoic acid, 1-methylethyl ester. *See* Isopropyl laurate
Dodecanoic acid, monoester with 1,2-propanediol. *See* Propylene glycol laurate
Dodecanoic acid, monoester with 1,2,3-propanetriol. *See* Glyceryl laurate
Dodecanoic acid, 1,2,3-propanetriyl ester. *See* Trilaurin
1-Dodecanol. *See* Lauryl alcohol
Dodecan-1-ol. *See* Lauryl alcohol
Dodecanolide-1,4. *See* γ-Dodecalactone
1-Dodecanol, 2-octyl-. *See* Octyldodecanol

Dodecanyl acetate

Dodecanyl acetate. *See* Lauryl acetate
2,6,10-Dodecatrien-1-ol, 3,7,11-trimethyl-, acetate. *See* Farnesyl acetate
2-Dodecenal
  EINECS 225-402-5
  FEMA 2402
  Synonyms: n-Dodecen-2-ol; 3-Nonyl acrolein; trans-2-Dodecen-1-al
  Empirical: $C_{12}H_{22}O$
  Properties: Colorless oily liq., orange-like odor, mandarin taste; sol. in alcohol; insol. in water; m.w. 182.31;
    b.p. 272 C
  Toxicology: Heated to decomp., emits acrid smoke and fumes
  Uses: Synthetic flavoring agent
  Regulatory: FDA 21CFR §172.515; FEMA GRAS

trans-2-Dodecen-1-al. *See* 2-Dodecenal
n-Dodecen-2-ol. *See* 2-Dodecenal
Dodecoic acid. *See* Lauric acid
Dodecyl acetate. *See* Lauryl acetate
Dodecyl alcohol. *See* Lauryl alcohol
n-Dodecyl aldehyde. *See* Lauric aldehyde
N-Dodecyl-*ar*-ethyl-N,N-dimethylbenzenemethanaminium chloride. *See* Quaternium-14
Dodecylbenzene sodium sulfonate. *See* Sodium dodecylbenzenesulfonate
Dodecylbenzenesulfonic acid sodium salt. *See* Sodium dodecylbenzenesulfonate
Dodecyldimethylamine. *See* Dimethyl lauramine
Dodecyl dimethyl benzyl ammonium chloride. *See* Lauralkonium chloride
Dodecyl dimethyl ethylbenzyl ammonium chloride. *See* Quaternium-14
Dodecyldimethyl (2-phenoxyethyl) ammonium bromide. *See* Domiphen bromide
Dodecyl docosanoate. *See* Lauryl behenate

Dodecyl gallate
  CAS 1166-52-5; EINECS 214-620-6
  Synonyms: 3,4,5-Trihydroxybenzoic acid, dodecyl ester; Dodecyl-3,4,5-trihydroxybenzoate; Lauryl gallate
  Definition: Ester of gallic acid
  Empirical: $C_{19}H_{30}O_5$
  Properties: M.w. 338.49; m.p. 96-97 C
  Toxicology: LD50 (oral, mouse) 1600 mg/kg; mod. toxic by ingestion; may cause intolerance and liver damage;
    can irritate intestines; heated to decomp., emits acrid smoke and irritating fumes
  Uses: Antioxidant for pharmaceuticals
  Regulatory: FDA 21CFR §166.110; USDA 9CFR §318.7; Europe listed; UK approved; BP compliance
  Manuf./Distrib.: Aldrich

Dodecyl 2-hydroxypropanoate. *See* Lauryl lactate
2-[2-(Dodecyloxy)ethoxy]ethanol. *See* Laureth-2
2-[2-[2-(Dodecyloxy)ethoxy]ethoxy]ethanol. *See* Laureth-3
Dodecyl sodium sulfate. *See* Sodium lauryl sulfate
Dodecylsulfate sodium salt. *See* Sodium lauryl sulfate
Dodecyl-3,4,5-trihydroxybenzoate. *See* Dodecyl gallate
Dodecyl trimethyl ammonium chloride. *See* Laurtrimonium chloride

Domiphen bromide
  CAS 538-71-6; EINECS 208-702-0
  Synonyms: PDDB; Dodecyldimethyl (2-phenoxyethyl) ammonium bromide; Phenododecinium bromide; 1-
    Dodecanaminium, N,N-dimethyl-N-(2-phenoxyethyl)-, bromide; N,N-Dimethyl-N-(2-phenoxyethyl)-1-
    dodecanaminium bromide
  Classification: Quaternary ammonium salt
  Formula: $(C_6H_5OC_2H_4N(C_{12}H_{25})(CH_3)_2Br$
  Properties: Crystals, mild char. odor, bitter taste; sol. in water, ethanol, acetone, ethyl acetate, chloroform; very
    sl. sol. in benzene; m.w. 414.54; m.p. 112 C
  Toxicology: Poison by intraperitoneal and intravenous routes
  Uses: Antimicrobial, fungicide for use in mouthwashes, cold sterilization; antiseptic in oral rinse prods.; anti-
    infective
  Regulatory: BP compliance

DOP. *See* Dioctyl phthalate
Douglas fir oil. *See* Balsam Oregon
DPPC. *See* 1,2-Dipalmitoyl-sn-glycero(3) phosphatidylcholine

DPPD. *See* N,N´-Diphenyl-p-phenylenediamine
Dracylic acid. *See* Benzoic acid
Dried calcium sulfate. *See* Calcium sulfate hemihydrate
Dried egg white. *See* Albumen
Dried gypsum. *See* Calcium sulfate hemihydrate
DSP-0. *See* Sodium phosphate dibasic anhydrous
DSP-7. *See* Sodium phosphate dibasic heptahydrate
DSPC. *See* 1,2-Distearoyl-sn-glycero(3) phosphatidylcholine
DSS. *See* Dioctyl sodium sulfosuccinate
DSTDP. *See* Distearyl thiodipropionate
DTPANa$_5$. *See* Pentasodium pentetate

Earthnut oil. *See* Peanut oil
Earth wax. *See* Ceresin
East Indian lemongrass oil. *See* Lemongrass oil East Indian
East Indian nutmeg oil. *See* Nutmeg oil
East Indian sandalwood oil. *See* Sandalwood oil
EC. *See* Ethylcellulose

Echinacin
 Definition: Polysaccharide fraction derived from the dried rhizomes and roots of *Echinacea pallida*
 Uses: Used in raw materials for pharmaceuticals
 Trade names containing: Lipocare HA/EC

EDA. *See* Ethylenediamine
Edathamil. *See* Edetic acid
Edetate. *See* Edetic acid
Edetate calcium disodium. *See* Calcium disodium EDTA
Edetate diammonium. *See* Diammonium EDTA
Edetate disodium. *See* Disodium EDTA
Edetate sodium. *See* Tetrasodium EDTA
Edetate trisodium. *See* Trisodium EDTA

Edetic acid
 CAS 60-00-4; EINECS 200-449-4
 Synonyms: EDTA; N,N´-1,2-Ethanediylbis[N-(carboxymethyl) glycine]; (Ethylenedinitrilo) tetraacetic acid; Ethylene diamine tetraacetic acid; Edathamil; Edetate
 Classification: Substituted diamine
 Empirical: $C_{10}H_{16}N_2O_8$
 Formula: $(HOOCCH_2)_2NCH_2CH_2N(CH_2COOH)_2$
 Properties: Colorless or wh. cryst. powd.; sol. in alkali hydroxide sol'ns.; very sl. sol. in water; insol. in common org. solvs.; m.w. 292.28; dec. 240 C
 Toxicology: Irritant; poison by intraperitoneal route; mutagenic data
 Uses: Chelating agent, metal complexing agent, excipient, preservative; used in otics, rectals, topicals, ophthalmics, ear/eye/nose drops, local anesthetics, antibiotics, antihistamines; diagnosis/treatment of heavy metal poisoning and iron overload
 Regulatory: FDA 21CFR §175.105, 176.170; FDA approved for otics, rectals, topicals; USP/NF compliance
 Manuf./Distrib.: Akzo Nobel; Aldrich; Allchem Ind.; Allied Colloids; Chemplex; Hampshire; Protex SA; Showa Denko
 Manuf./Distrib. (pharm. & food): Spectrum Chem. Mfg.
 Trade names: Versene Acid

EDTA. *See* Edetic acid
EDTA Na$_4$. *See* Tetrasodium EDTA
EEA. *See* Ethylacetoacetate
EGDS. *See* Glycol distearate
Egg albumin. *See* Albumen
EGMS. *See* Glycol stearate
2-EH. *See* 2-Ethylhexanol
1-Eicosanol. *See* Arachidyl alcohol
Eicosanyl propanoate. *See* Arachidyl propionate
Eicosyl erucate. *See* 2-Octyldodecyl erucate

Elainic acid. *See* Oleic acid

Elastin
Definition: Fibrous protein found in animal connective tissue
Uses: Natural ingred. for pharmaceuticals, medicinal soaps
Trade names: Kelisema Bovine Natural Insoluble Elastin

Electrolyte acid. *See* Sulfuric acid
Elettaria cardamomum oil. *See* Cardamom oil

Elm bark extract
Synonyms: Ulmus campestris extract
Definition: Extract of *Ulmus campestris*
Uses: Used in orals, herbal medicine to soothe the skin
Regulatory: FDA approved for orals
Manuf./Distrib.: Bio-Botanica

Emulsifying wax NF
CAS 97069-99-0
Definition: A waxy solid derived from cetostearyl alcohol contg. a polyoxyethylene deriv. of a fatty acid ester of sorbitan
Properties: Creamy wh. waxy solid, mild char. odor; sol. in alcohol, ether, chloroform, hydrocarbon solvs., aerosol propellants; insol. in water; m.p. 50-54 C; iodine no. 3.5 max.; sapon. no. 14 max.; hyd. no. 178-192; pH 5.5-7.0 (3% disp.)
Uses: Emulsifier, solubilizer, suspending agent, stiffening agent for pharmaceuticals
Regulatory: USP/NF compliance
Trade names: Emerwax® 1257; Koster Keunen Emulsifying Wax; Polawax®; Polawax® A31; T-Wax

Enanthal. *See* Heptanal
Enanthaldehyde. *See* Heptanal
Enanthic alcohol. *See* Heptyl alcohol
Enanthyl alcohol. *See* Heptyl alcohol
Engraver's acid. *See* Nitric acid
Enocianina. *See* Grape skin extract
Enocyanin. *See* Grape skin extract
Entsufon. *See* Sodium octoxynol-2 ethane sulfonate
Entsufon sodium. *See* Sodium octoxynol-2 ethane sulfonate
Enzactin. *See* Triacetin
EO. *See* Ethylene oxide

EO/PO block polymer or copolymer
CAS 106392-12-5
Uses: Wetting agent, dispersant, defoamer, gellant, solubilizer, lubricant base for medical and pharmaceutical applics.
See also Poloxamer Series

Eosin disodium. *See* D&C Red No. 22
Eosine G. *See* D&C Red No. 22
Eosin YS. *See* D&C Red No. 22
Epoxyethane. *See* Ethylene oxide
1,2-Epoxyethane. *See* Ethylene oxide
1,8-Epoxy-p-menthane. *See* Eucalyptol
1,2-Epoxy-3-phenoxypropane. *See* Phenyl glycidyl ether

Epoxy resin
CAS 25928-94-3
Definition: Derived from epichlorohydrin and diethylene glycol
Formula: $-OCH_2CHOCH_2$
Toxicology: Strong skin irritant in uncured state; poison by inhalation; moderately toxic by ingestion
Uses: Biomaterial for topicals, slow-release and microencapsulation prods.
Manuf./Distrib.: Asahi Chem Industry Co Ltd; Ciba-Geigy; Conap; Ferro/Bedford; Hardman; Henkel; Key Polymer; Morton Int'l.; Reichhold; Rhone-Poulenc/Perf. Resins; Sartomer; Shell; Union Carbide; Witco/ PAG

Epsom salts. *See* Magnesium sulfate anhyd.
Equisetic acid. *See* Aconitic acid
Erioglaucine. *See* D&C Blue No. 4
Erucic acid, 2-octyldodecyl ester. *See* 2-Octyldodecyl erucate

Erucic acid, oleyl ester. *See* Oleyl erucate

Erythorbic acid
  CAS 89-65-6; EINECS 201-928-0
  FEMA 2410
  Synonyms: D-Erythro-hex-2-enonic acid, γ-lactone; Isoascorbic acid; D-Isoascorbic acid; d-Araboascorbic acid
  Definition: Isomer of ascorbic acid
  Empirical: $C_6H_8O_6$
  Properties: Wh. or sl. yel. cryst. or powd.; darkens on exposure to light; sol. in water, alcohol; sl. sol. in glycerin; m.p. 164-171 C (dec.)
  Toxicology: Nontoxic; heated to decomp., emits acrid smoke and irritating fumes
  Uses: Antioxidant, preservative
  Regulatory: FDA 21CFR §101.33, 145.110, 175.105, 182.3041, GRAS; FEMA GRAS; USDA 9CFR §318.7, 381.147; Japan restricted for purpose of antioxidation
  Manuf./Distrib.: Ashland; Pfizer Food Science; Spice King
  Manuf./Distrib. (pharm. & food): Aldrich; Pfizer Food Science; Spectrum Chem. Mfg.

D-Erythro-hex-2-enonic acid, γ-lactone. *See* Erythorbic acid
Erythrosine. *See* CI 45430; FD&C Red No. 3
Erythrosine bluish. *See* FD&C Red No. 3
Erythrosine yellowish NA. *See* D&C Orange No. 11
Esdragol. *See* Estragole
Essence of rose. *See* Rose oil

Estragole
  CAS 140-67-0
  FEMA 2411
  Synonyms: p-Allylanisole; 4-Allylanisole; Esdragol; p-Methoxyallylbenzene; 1-Methoxy-4-(2-propenyl) benzene; Chavicyl methyl ether; Chavicol methyl ether; Methyl chavicol
  Definition: Main constituent of tarragon oil derived from *Artemisia dracunculus*
  Empirical: $C_{10}H_{12}O$
  Properties: Liq.; sol. in alcohol, chloroform; forms azeotropic mixts. with water; m.w. 148.20; dens. 0.9645 (21/4 C); b.p. 216 C (764 mm); flash pt. 178 F; ref. index 1.5230 (17.5 C)
  Toxicology: LD50 (oral, rat) 1820 mg/kg
  Uses: Sweet, minty synthetic flavoring agent
  Regulatory: FDA 21CFR §172.515; FEMA GRAS
  Manuf./Distrib. (pharm. & food): Aldrich

Ethanal. *See* Acetaldehyde
1,2-Ethanediamine. *See* Ethylenediamine
1,2-Ethanedicarboxylic acid. *See* Succinic acid
1,2-Ethanediol. *See* Glycol
Ethane-1,2-diol. *See* Glycol
N,N′-1,2-Ethanediylbis[N-(carboxymethyl) glycine]. *See* Edetic acid
Ethanenitrile. *See* Acetonitrile
Ethanoic acid. *See* Acetic acid; Acetic acid, glacial
Ethanol. *See* Alcohol

Ethanolamine
  CAS 141-43-5; EINECS 205-483-3
  UN No. 2491
  Synonyms: MEA; 2-Aminoethanol; 2-Aminoethyl alcohol; Monoethanolamine; Glycinol; 2-Hydroxyethylamine
  Classification: Monoamine
  Empirical: C_2H_7NO
  Formula: $NH_2CH_2CH_2OH$
  Properties: Colorless clear mod. visc. liq., ammoniacal odor; hygroscopic; misc. with water, alcohol, acetone, glycerin; sol. in chloroform; sl. sol. in benzene; m.w. 61.10; dens. 1.012; m.p. 10.5 C; b.p. 170 C; flash pt. 93 C; ref. index 1.4540
  Precaution: DOT: Corrosive material; flamm. exposed to heat or flame; powerful reactive base
  Toxicology: TLV:TWA 3 ppm; LD50 (oral, rat) 214 mg/kg, (skin, rat) 1500 mg/kg; poison by IP route; mod. toxic by ingestion, skin contact, subcut., IV routes; corrosive irritant to eyes, skin, mucous membranes; heated to decomp., emits toxic fumes of NO_x
  Uses: Emulsifier for pharmaceuticals
  Regulatory: FDA 21CFR §173.315, 175.105, 176.210, 176.300, 178.3120; not permitted for use in foods

Ethanolic acid

intended for babies and young infants in UK; USP/NF, BP compliance
Manuf./Distrib.: BP Chem. Ltd; Occidental; Spectrum Chem. Mfg.; Texaco; Union Carbide
Manuf./Distrib. (pharm. & food): Aldrich; Spectrum Chem. Mfg.
Trade names: MEA Commercial Grade; MEA Low Freeze Grade; MEA Low Iron Grade; MEA Low Iron-Low Freeze Grade; MEA NF Grade

Ethanolic acid. *See* Acetic acid, glacial
Ethanol, undenatured. *See* Alcohol
Ethanoyl chloride. *See* Acetyl chloride
Ethene, homopolymer. *See* Polyethylene
Ethene oxide. *See* Ethylene oxide
Ethene polymer. *See* Polyethylene
Ethenol homopolymer. *See* Polyvinyl alcohol
Ethenyl acetate, homopolymer. *See* Polyvinyl acetate (homopolymer)
Ethenylbenzene. *See* Styrene
Ethenylbenzene, homopolymer. *See* Polystyrene
1-Ethenyl-2-pyrrolidinone homopolymer. *See* Crospovidone; PVP
1-Ethenyl-2-pyrrolidinone, polymer with acetic acid ethenyl ester. *See* PVP/VA copolymer
Ether. *See* Ethyl ether
Ethinyl trichloride. *See* Trichloroethylene
Ethocel. *See* Ethylcellulose
3-Ethochloride of 9-o-carboxyphenyl-6-diethylamino-3-ethylimino-3-isoxanthene. *See* D&C Red No. 19
3-Ethostearate of 9-o-carboxyphenyl-6-diethylamino-3-ethylimino-3-isoxanthene. *See* D&C Red No. 37
Ethovan. *See* Ethyl vanillin
6-Ethoxy-m-anol. *See* Propenylguaethol
4-Ethoxybenzaldehyde. *See* p-Ethoxybenzaldehyde

p-Ethoxybenzaldehyde
CAS 10031-82-0; EINECS 233-093-3
FEMA 2413
Synonyms: 4-Ethoxybenzaldehyde
Definition: Obtained by ethylation of p-hydroxybenzaldehyde using aluminum chloride catalyst
Empirical: $C_9H_{10}O_2$
Properties: Red-brn., sweet floral odor and taste; sol. in alcohol; pract. insol. in water; m.w. 150.18; dens. 1.081 (20/4 C); m.p. 13-16 C; b.p. 255 C; flash pt. 75 C; ref. index 1.559 (20 C)
Toxicology: Skin irritant
Uses: Sweet synthetic flavoring agent
Regulatory: FDA 21CFR §172.515; FEMA GRAS
Manuf./Distrib. (pharm. & food): Aldrich

Ethoxycarbonylethylene. *See* Ethyl acrylate

Ethoxydiglycol
CAS 111-90-0; EINECS 203-919-7
Synonyms: Diethylene glycol monoethyl ether; Diethylene glycol ethyl ether; 'Carbitol'; 2-(2-Ethoxyethoxy) ethanol
Classification: Ether alcohol
Formula: $CH_2OHCH_2OCH_2CH_2OC_2H_5$
Properties: Colorless liq., mild pleasant odor; hygroscopic; misc. with water, common org. solvs.; m.w. 134.20; dens. 1.0272 (20/20 C); b.p. 195-202 C; flash pt. 96.1 C; ref. index 1.425 (25 C)
Precaution: Combustible
Toxicology: Nonirritating and nonpenetrating when applied to human skin
Uses: Solvent, solubilizer, cosurfactant
Regulatory: FDA 21CFR §175.105, 176.180
Manuf./Distrib.: Allchem Ind.; Ashland; Eastman; Great Western; Oxiteno; Spectrum Chem. Mfg.; Union Carbide
Trade names: Transcutol
Trade names containing: Simulsol® 5719

2-(2-Ethoxyethoxy) ethanol. *See* Ethoxydiglycol
3-Ethoxy-4-hydroxybenzaldehyde. *See* Ethyl vanillin
1-Ethoxy-2-hydroxy-4-propenylbenzene. *See* Propenylguaethol

Ethyl acetate
CAS 141-78-6; EINECS 205-500-4
FEMA 2414; UN No. 1173

Synonyms: Acetic ether; Acetic acid, ethyl ester; Vinegar naphtha
Classification: Aliphatic organic compd.
Definition: Ester of ethyl alcohol and acetic acid
Empirical: $C_4H_8O_2$
Formula: $CH_3COOC_2H_5$
Properties: Colorless liq., fragrant fruity odor, acetous burning taste; sol. in chloroform, alcohol, ether; sl. sol. in water; m.w. 88.12; dens. 0.902 (20/4 C); bulk dens. 0.8945 g/ml (25 C); b.p. 77 C; f.p. -83.6 C; flash pt. -4.4 C; ref. index 1.3723
Precaution: DOT: Flamm. liq.; very dangerous fire hazard exposed to heat or flame; can react vigorously with oxidizers
Toxicology: TLV 400 ppm in air; LD50 (oral, rat) 5620 mg/kg; poison by inhalation; mildly toxic by ingestion; irritant to eyes, skin, mucous membranes; mutagenic data; mildly narcotic; CNS depressant; heated to decomp., emits acrid smoke and irritating fumes
Uses: Solvent, pineapple-like flavoring agent; used in ophthalmics, orals, topicals
Regulatory: FDA 21CFR § 73.1, 172.560, 173.228, 175.320, 177.1200, 182.60, GRAS; 27CFR §21.106; FEMA GRAS; Japan approved with restrictions; FDA approved for ophthalmics, orals, topicals; USP/NF, BP, Ph.Eur. compliance
Manuf./Distrib.: Allchem Industries; Berje; BP Chem. Ltd; Brown; Chisso Am.; Eastman; Hoechst Celanese; Hüls AG; Lonza AG; Mallinckrodt; Monsanto; Penta Mfg.; Union Carbide
Manuf./Distrib. (pharm. & food): Aldrich; Chisso Petrochem.; Daicel Chem. Ind.; Mallinckrodt; Spectrum Chem. Mfg.; Tokuyama Petrochem.
Trade names containing: Filmex® C

Ethylacetoacetate
CAS 141-97-9; EINECS 205-516-1
FEMA 2415; UN No. 1993
Synonyms: EEA; 3-Oxobutanoic acid ethyl ester; Acetoacetic acid ethyl ester; Acetoacetic ester; Ethyl 3-oxobutanoate
Classification: Aliphatic organic compd.
Empirical: $C_6H_{10}O_3$
Formula: $CH_3COCH_2COOC_2H_5$
Properties: Colorless liq., fruity odor; sol. in ≈ 35 parts water; misc. with common org. solvs.; m.w. 130.14; dens. 1.0213 (25/4 C); m.p. -45 C; b.p. 180.8 C (760 mm); flash pt. (CC) 184 F; ref. index 1.4180-1.4195
Precaution: DOT: Flamm. liq.; combustible liq. when exposed to heat or flame; can react with oxidizing materials
Toxicology: LD50 (oral, rat) 3.98 g/kg; mod. toxic by ingestion; mod. irritating to skin, mucous membranes, eyes; heated to decomp., emits acrid smoke and irritating fumes
Uses: Pharmaceutical intermediate, sweet syn. flavoring agent
Regulatory: FDA 21CFR §172.515; FEMA GRAS; Japan approved as flavoring
Manuf./Distrib.: Aceto; Aldrich; Berje; Eastman; Lonza; Penta Mfg.; Spectrum Chem. Mfg.
Manuf./Distrib. (pharm. & food): Aldrich; Daicel Chem. Ind.; Mallinckrodt; Nippon Syn. Chem. Ind.

Ethyl acetone. *See* Methyl propyl ketone
Ethyl α-acetylhydrocinnamate. *See* Ethyl 2-acetyl-3-phenylpropionate

Ethyl 2-acetyl-3-phenylpropionate
CAS 620-79-1
FEMA 2416
Synonyms: Ethylbenzyl acetoacetate; Ethyl α-acetylhydrocinnamate
Empirical: $C_{13}H_{16}O_3$
Properties: M.w. 220.27; dens. 1.036; b.p. 276 C; flash pt. > 230 F
Uses: Fruity synthetic flavoring agent
Regulatory: FDA 21CFR §172.515; FEMA GRAS
Manuf./Distrib. (pharm. & food): Aldrich

Ethyl acrylate
CAS 140-88-5; EINECS 205-438-8
FEMA 2418
Synonyms: Ethyl propenoate; Ethoxycarbonylethylene
Definition: Esterification of acrylic acid
Empirical: $C_5H_8O_2$
Properties: Liq., penetrating and persistent odor; sl. sol. in water; m.w. 100.12; sp.gr. 0.918; m.p. -71 to -75 C; f.p. 60 F; b.p. 99-100 C; ref. index 1.4068
Precaution: Flamm. liq.; very dangerous fire hazard exposed to heat/flame; can react vigorously with oxidizers
Toxicology: LD50 (oral, rat) 800 mg/kg; poison by ingestion and inh.; mod. toxic by skin contact and

Ethyl acrylate/methyl methacrylate copolymer

    intraperitoneal routes; suspected human carcinogen; skin and eye irritant; heated to decomp., emits acrid smoke and irritating fumes
    Uses: Fruity synthetic flavoring agent
    Regulatory: FDA 21CFR §172.515; FEMA GRAS; BP compliance
    Manuf./Distrib.: Aldrich
    Manuf./Distrib. (pharm. & food): Aldrich

Ethyl acrylate/methyl methacrylate copolymer
    Uses: For controlled-release permeable film coatings
    Trade names: Eudragit® NE 30 D

Ethyl alcohol. *See* Alcohol
Ethyl alcohol, undenatured. *See* Alcohol
Ethyl aldehyde. *See* Acetaldehyde
Ethyl 2-aminobenzoate. *See* Ethyl anthranilate
Ethyl o-aminobenzoate. *See* Ethyl anthranilate
Ethyl-p-aminobenzoate hydrochloride. *See* Benzocaine

Ethyl-p-anisate
    CAS 94-30-4
    FEMA 2420
    Synonyms: p-Anisic acid ethyl ester; Ethyl-4-methoxybenzoate; Ethyl-p-methoxybenzoate
    Definition: Obtained by esterification of anisic acid with ethanol in presence of an acid catalyst
    Empirical: $C_{10}H_{12}O_3$
    Properties: Colorless liq., fruity anise odor; sol. in alcohol, ether; sl. sol. in water; m.w. 180.21; dens. 1.103; m.p. 7-8 C; b.p. 269-270 C; flash pt. > 100 C; ref. index 1.522-1.526
    Precaution: Combustible liq.
    Toxicology: LD50 (oral, rat) 2040 mg/kg; mod. toxic by ingestion; heated to decomp., emits acrid smoke and irritating fumes
    Uses: Fruity synthetic flavoring agent
    Regulatory: FDA 21CFR §172.515; FEMA GRAS
    Manuf./Distrib. (pharm. & food): Aldrich

Ethyl anthranilate
    CAS 87-25-2; EINECS 201-735-1
    FEMA 2421
    Synonyms: Ethyl o-aminobenzoate; Ethyl 2-aminobenzoate
    Definition: Obtained by esterification of anthranilic acid with ethanol in presence of acid catalysts
    Empirical: $C_9H_{11}NO_2$
    Formula: $NH_2C_6H_4COOC_2H_5$
    Properties: M.w. 165.19; dens. 1.118 (20/4 C); m.p. 13-15 C; b.p. 264-268 C; ref. index 1.564 (20 C)
    Precaution: Combustible liq.
    Toxicology: LD50 (oral, rat) 3750 mg/kg; mod. toxic by ingestion; skin irritant; heated to decomp., emits toxic fumes of NO_x
    Uses: Sweet grape-like synthetic flavoring agent
    Regulatory: FDA 21CFR §172.515; FEMA GRAS
    Manuf./Distrib. (pharm. & food): Aldrich

4-Ethylbenzaldehyde. *See* p-Ethylbenzaldehyde

p-Ethylbenzaldehyde
    CAS 4748-78-1; EINECS 225-268-8
    FEMA 3756
    Synonyms: 4-Ethylbenzaldehyde
    Empirical: $C_9H_{10}O$
    Formula: $C_2H_5C_6H_4CHO$
    Properties: Liq., aromatic odor; sol. in ethanol, ether, toluene; insol. in water; m.w. 134.2; dens. 0.979; b.p. 221 C; flash pt. 92 C; ref. index 1.5390 (20 C)
    Toxicology: LD50 (oral, rat) 1700 mg/kg; eye and skin irritant
    Uses: Pharmaceutical intermediate; sweet flavoring agent
    Regulatory: FEMA GRAS
    Manuf./Distrib.: Aldrich; Esprit; Jonas; Penta Mfg.
    Manuf./Distrib. (pharm. & food): Aldrich
    Trade names: Ebal

Ethyl benzeneacetate. *See* Ethyl phenylacetate

Ethyl benzenecarboxylate. *See* Ethyl benzoate

Ethyl benzoate
  CAS 93-89-0; EINECS 202-284-3
  FEMA 2422
  Synonyms: Benzoic acid ethyl ester; Ethyl benzenecarboxylate
  Empirical: $C_9H_{10}O_2$
  Formula: $C_6H_5COOC_2H_5$
  Properties: Colorless liq., aromatic odor; misc. with alcohol, chloroform, ether, petroleum ether; pract. insol.
    in water; m.w. 150.18; dens. 1.046 (20/4 C); m.p. -34 C; b.p. 211-214 C; flash pt. 184 F; ref. index 1.505
    (20 C)
  Precaution: Combustible liq.
  Toxicology: LD50 (oral, rat) 2100 mg/kg; mod. toxic by ingestion; mildly toxic by skin contact; skin and eye
    irritant; vapors cause cough; heated to decomp., emits acrid smoke and fumes
  Uses: Banana-, cherry-, plum-like synthetic flavoring agent
  Regulatory: FDA 21CFR §172.515; FEMA GRAS; BP compliance
  Manuf./Distrib. (pharm. & food): Aldrich

Ethylbenzyl acetoacetate. *See* Ethyl 2-acetyl-3-phenylpropionate

α-Ethylbenzyl butyrate
  FEMA 2424
  Synonyms: Ethyl phenyl carbinyl butyrate; α-Phenylpropyl butyrate
  Empirical: $C_{13}H_{18}O_2$
  Properties: Liq., floral fruity odor, sweet plum-like taste; m.w. 206.28; dens. 0.9875-0.9905 (15 C); b.p. 282
    C; flash pt. 118 C; ref. index 1.4875-1.4895
  Uses: Synthetic flavoring agent
  Regulatory: FDA 21CFR §172.515; FEMA GRAS

7-Ethyl bicyclooxazolidine
  CAS 7747-35-5; EINECS 231-810-4
  Uses: Antibacterial for topical pharmaceuticals
  Regulatory: USA not restricted; Europe provisional list 3000 ppm max.
  Trade names: Oxaban®-E

Ethyl brassylate. *See* Ethylene brassylate
Ethyl butanoate. *See* Ethyl butyrate
2-Ethyl butanoic acid. *See* Diethylacetic acid
Ethyl butylacetate. *See* Ethyl caproate

2-Ethylbutyl acetate
  CAS 10031-87-5
  FEMA 2425
  Definition: Obtained by reacting 2-ethylbutanol with acetic anhydride in the presence of sulfuric acid
  Empirical: $C_8H_{16}O_2$
  Properties: Liq.; m.w. 144.21; dens. 0.876; b.p. 160-163 C; flash pt. 52 C; ref. index 1.4109
  Precaution: Moderate fire risk
  Uses: Fruity synthetic flavoring agent
  Regulatory: FDA 21CFR §172.515; FEMA GRAS
  Manuf./Distrib. (pharm. & food): Aldrich

Ethyl butyl ketone. *See* 3-Heptanone
Ethyl-n-butyl ketone. *See* 3-Heptanone

Ethyl butyrate
  CAS 105-54-4; EINECS 203-306-4
  FEMA 2427
  Synonyms: Ethyl butanoate; Ethyl n-butyrate; Butyric ether
  Definition: Obtained by esterification of n-butyric acid with ethyl alcohol in presence of Twitchell's reagent or
    $MgCl_2$
  Empirical: $C_6H_{12}O_2$
  Formula: $CH_3CH_2CH_2COOC_2H_5$
  Properties: Colorless liq., banana-pineapple odor; sol. in water, fixed oils, propylene glycol; misc. with alcohol,
    ether; insol. in glycerin @ 121 C; m.w. 116.18; dens. 0.874; m.p. -100.8 C; b.p. 121.6 C; flash pt. (CC) 78
    F; ref. index 1.391
  Precaution: Flamm. liq.; can react vigorously with oxidizing materials
  Toxicology: LD50 (oral, rat) 13 g/kg; mildly toxic by ingestion; skin irritant; heated to decomp., emits acrid

Ethyl n-butyrate

    smoke and irritating fumes
    Uses: Banana-, pineapple-like synthetic flavoring agent
    Regulatory: FDA 21CFR §182.60, GRAS; FEMA GRAS; Japan approved as flavoring
    Manuf./Distrib.: BASF
    Manuf./Distrib. (pharm. & food): Aldrich; BASF

Ethyl n-butyrate. *See* Ethyl butyrate
2-Ethylbutyric acid. *See* Diethylacetic acid
α-**Ethylbutyric acid.** *See* Diethylacetic acid
Ethyl butyrolactone. *See* γ-Hexalactone
Ethyl caprate. *See* Ethyl decanoate

Ethyl caproate
    CAS 123-66-0; EINECS 204-640-3
    FEMA 2439
    Synonyms: Ethyl hexanoate; Ethyl capronate; Ethyl hexylate; Ethyl butylacetate; Hexanoic acid ethyl ester
    Definition: Obtained by esterification of caproic acid with ethyl alcohol in presence of conc. H_2SO_4 or HCl
    Empirical: $C_8H_{16}O_2$
    Formula: $CH_3(CH_2)_4COOC_2H_5$
    Properties: Colorless to ylsh. liq., mild wine odor; sol. in fixed oils; sl. sol. in propylene glycol; misc. with alcohol, ether; insol. in water, glycerin; m.w. 144.24; dens. 0.867-0.871; b.p. 163 C; flash pt. (OC) 130 F; ref. index 1.406-1.409
    Precaution: Flamm. or combustible liq.; can react with oxidizing materials
    Toxicology: Skin irritant; heated to decomp., emits acrid smoke and irritating fumes
    Uses: Apple-, banana-, pineapple-like synthetic flavoring agent
    Regulatory: FDA 21CFR §172.515; FEMA GRAS; Japan approved as flavoring
    Manuf./Distrib.: BASF
    Manuf./Distrib. (pharm. & food): Aldrich; BASF

Ethyl capronate. *See* Ethyl caproate
Ethyl caprylate. *See* Ethyl octanoate
Ethyl carbinol. *See* n-Propyl alcohol

Ethylcellulose
    CAS 9004-57-3
    Synonyms: EC; Cellulose ethyl ether; Ethocel
    Definition: Ethyl ether of cellulose
    Properties: Wh. to lt. tan powd.; sol. in most org. liqs.; insol. in water, glycerol, propylene glycol; dens. 1.07-1.18; ref. index 1.47
    Toxicology: No known toxicity; irritant; heated to decomp., emits acrid smoke and irritating fumes
    Uses: Protective coating agent and tablet binder in pharmaceutical vitamin/mineral preps.; used in orals, topicals
    Regulatory: FDA 21CFR §73.1, 172.868, 175.300, 182.90, 573.420, GRAS; FDA approved for orals, topicals; USP/NF, BP, Ph.Eur. compliance
    Manuf./Distrib.: Aqualon; Ashland; Chemcentral; Colorcon; FMC; Hercules; Hoechst Celanese; Punda Mercantile; Van Waters & Rogers
    Manuf./Distrib. (pharm. & food): FMC; Ruger; Spectrum Chem. Mfg.
    Trade names: Ethocel Medium Premium; Ethocel Standard Premium; Surelease®
    Trade names containing: Chroma-Seal™ 859027; Chroma-Seal™ 889031; Coated Ascorbic Acid 97.5% No. 60482

Ethyl cinnamate
    CAS 103-36-6; EINECS 203-104-6
    FEMA 2430
    Synonyms: Ethyl-trans-cinnamate; Ethyl phenylacrylate; Ethyl-β-phenylacrylate; Ethyl-3-phenylpropenoate; Ethyl (E)-3-phenylprop-2-enoate
    Definition: Obtained by heating cinnamic acid, alcohol, and sulfuric acid to 100 C in presence of aluminum sulfate
    Empirical: $C_{11}H_{12}O_2$
    Properties: Nearly colorless oily liq., faint cinnamon odor; misc. with alcohol, ether, fixed oils; insol. in glycerin, water; m.w. 176.23; dens. 1.049 (20/4 C); m.p. 9 C; b.p. 271 C; flash pt. > 212 F; ref. index 1.558-1.561
    Precaution: Combustible liq.
    Toxicology: LD50 (oral, rat) 4000 mg/kg; mod. toxic by ingestion; heated to decomp., emits acrid smoke and irritating fumes
    Uses: Sweet cinnamon, plum-like synthetic flavoring agent

Regulatory: FDA 21CFR §172.515; FEMA GRAS; Japan approved as flavoring; BP compliance
Manuf./Distrib.: Aldrich
Manuf./Distrib. (pharm. & food): Aldrich

Ethyl-trans-cinnamate. *See* Ethyl cinnamate
Ethyl citrate. *See* Triethyl citrate

Ethyl cyclohexanepropionate
　　CAS 10094-36-7
　　FEMA 2431
　　Synonyms: Cyclohexane ethyl propionate; Ethyl cyclohexylpropionate; Ethyl 3-cyclohexylpropanoate; Hexahydro phenylethyl propionate
　　Definition: Obtained by esterification of ethyl cyclohexanol with propionic acid or anhydride
　　Empirical: $C_{11}H_{20}O_2$
　　Properties: Colorless oily liq., fruity sweet pineapple-like odor; sol. in alcohol; insol. in water; m.w. 184.28; dens. 0.940; b.p. 91-94 C (8 mm); flash pt. 122 F; ref. index 1.4480
　　Uses: Sweet peach, pear-like synthetic flavoring agent
　　Regulatory: FDA 21CFR §172.515; FEMA GRAS
　　Manuf./Distrib. (pharm. & food): Aldrich

Ethyl 3-cyclohexylpropanoate. *See* Ethyl cyclohexanepropionate
Ethyl cyclohexylpropionate. *See* Ethyl cyclohexanepropionate

Ethyl decanoate
　　CAS 110-38-3; EINECS 203-761-9
　　FEMA 2432
　　Synonyms: Ethyl caprate; Decanoic acid ethyl ester; Ethyl decylate
　　Definition: Obtained by esterification of decanoic acid and ethyl alcohol in presence of HCl or H_2SO_4
　　Empirical: $C_{12}H_{24}O_2$
　　Formula: $CH_3(CH_2)_8COOC_2H_5$
　　Properties: Colorless liq.; misc. with alcohol, chloroform, ether; insol. in water; m.w. 200.32; dens. 0.862 (20 C); m.p. -20 C; b.p. 243-245 C; flash pt. 216 F; ref. index 1.425 (20 C)
　　Precaution: Combustible liq.
　　Toxicology: Skin irritant; reacts with oxidizing materials; heated to decomp., emits acrid smoke and fumes
　　Uses: Grape, pear-like synthetic flavoring agent
　　Regulatory: FDA 21CFR §172.515; FEMA GRAS; Japan approved as flavoring
　　Manuf./Distrib. (pharm. & food): Aldrich

Ethyl decylate. *See* Ethyl decanoate
Ethyl trans-2,3-dimethyl acrylate. *See* Ethyl tiglate

2-Ethyl-3,5(6)-dimethylpyrazine
　　CAS 55031-15-7
　　FEMA 3149
　　Empirical: $C_8H_{12}N_2$
　　Properties: M.w. 136.20; dens. 0.965; b.p. 180-181 C; flash pt. 157 F
　　Precaution: Combustible liq.
　　Toxicology: Heated to decomp., emits toxic fumes of NO_x
　　Uses: Chocolate synthetic flavoring agent
　　Regulatory: FEMA GRAS
　　Manuf./Distrib. (pharm. & food): Aldrich

Ethyl dodecanoate. *See* Ethyl laurate
Ethyl dodecylate. *See* Ethyl laurate
Ethyl enanthate. *See* Ethyl heptanoate
Ethylene alcohol. *See* Glycol

Ethylene brassylate
　　CAS 105-95-3; EINECS 203-347-8
　　FEMA 3543
　　Synonyms: 1,4-Dioxacycloheptadecane-5,17-dione; Cyclo-1,13-ethylenedioxytridecane-1,13-dione; Ethylene undecane dicarboxylate; Ethylene glycol brassylate cyclic diester; Ethyl brassylate
　　Classification: Cyclic ester
　　Definition: Obtained by esterification of brassylic acid
　　Empirical: $C_{15}H_{26}O_4$
　　Properties: Wh. to lt. yel. liq., sweet odor; sol. in alcohol, most org. solvs.; insol. in water; m.w. 270.37; dens. 1.05; b.p. 332 C; ref. index 1.4690-1.4730

Ethylene carbonate

Uses: Synthetic flavoring agent
Regulatory: FDA 21CFR §172.515; FEMA GRAS

Ethylene carbonate
CAS 96-49-1; EINECS 202-510-0
Synonyms: Glycol carbonate; Dioxolone-2; 1,3-Dioxolan-2-one; Cyclic ethylene carbonate
Empirical: $C_3H_4O_3$
Formula: $(-CH_2O)_2CO$
Properties: Colorless solid or liq., odorless; misc. (40%) in water, alcohol, ethyl acetate, benzene, chloroform; sol. in ether, n-butanol, CCl_4; m.w. 88.07; dens. 1.3218 (39/4 C); m.p. 36.4 C; b.p. 248 C; flash pt. 143 C; ref. index 1.4158 (50 C)
Precaution: Combustible
Toxicology: Moderately toxic by intraperitoneal route; mildly toxic by ingestion; skin and eye irritant
Uses: Intermediate for pharmaceuticals
Manuf./Distrib.: Aldrich; Fluka; Hüls AG; Monomer-Polymer & Dajac
Manuf./Distrib. (pharm. & food): Aldrich

Ethylenediamine
CAS 107-15-3 (anhyd.); 6780-13-8 (monohydrate); EINECS 203-468-6
UN No. 1604
Synonyms: EDA; 1,2-Diaminoethane; 1,2-Ethanediamine; Dimethylenediamine
Classification: Aliphatic organic compd.; alkaline compd.
Empirical: $C_2H_8N_2$
Formula: $NH_2CH_2CH_2NH_2$
Properties: Colorless to sl. yel. clear volatile liq., ammonia-like odor; hygroscopic; misc. with water, alcohol; m.w. 60.12; dens. 0.8994 (20/4 C); m.p. 8.5 C; b.p. 117.2 C; flash pt. (CC) 110 F; ref. index 1.4565
Precaution: DOT: Corrosive material; flamm. exposed to heat, flame, oxidizers; can react violently with acetic acid, acetic anhydride, acrylic acid, epichlorohydrin, many others
Toxicology: TLV:TWA 10 ppm; LD50 (oral, rat) 500 mg/kg; human irritant poison by inh.; mod. toxic by ingestion, skin contact; corrosive; severe skin and eye irritant; allergen, sensitizer; mutagenic data; heated to decomp., emits toxic fumes of NO_x and NH_3
Uses: Stabilizer, buffer; used in intravenous drugs, injectables, orals, rectals, topicals; aminophylline formulations, antihistamines, topical steroids, topical creams incl. Mycolog cream
Regulatory: FDA 21CFR §173.315, 173.320 (1 ppm max.), 178.3120, 556.270, 181.30; FDA approved for IV, injectables, orals, rectals, topicals; USP, BP, Ph.Eur., JP compliance
Manuf./Distrib.: Aldrich; Allchem Industries; BASF; Spectrum Chem. Mfg.; Texaco; Tosoh; Union Carbide
Manuf./Distrib. (pharm. & food): Kanto Denka Kogyo; Spectrum Chem. Mfg.; Sumitomo Seika Chems.; Tosoh

Ethylenediamine dihydrochloride
CAS 333-18-6; EINECS 206-369-6
Empirical: $C_2H_8N_2 \cdot 2HCl$
Formula: $H_2NCH_2CH_2NH_2 \cdot 2HCl$
Properties: Hygroscopic; m.w. 133.02; m.p. > 300 C
Toxicology: Irritant
Uses: Used in topicals
Regulatory: FDA approved for topicals
Manuf./Distrib.: Aldrich; Spectrum Chem. Mfg.
Manuf./Distrib. (pharm. & food): Aldrich

Ethylene diamine tetraacetic acid. *See* Edetic acid
Ethylenediaminetetraacetic acid, disodium salt. *See* Disodium EDTA
Ethylene diamine tetraacetic acid, sodium salt. *See* Tetrasodium EDTA
trans-1,2-Ethylenedicarboxylic acid. *See* Fumaric acid
(Ethylenedinitrilo) tetraacetic acid. *See* Edetic acid
Ethylenedinitrilotetra-2-propanol. *See* Tetrahydroxypropyl ethylenediamine
Ethylene glycol. *See* Glycol
Ethylene glycol brassylate cyclic diester. *See* Ethylene brassylate
Ethylene glycol dilaurate. *See* Glycol dilaurate

Ethylene glycol dimethyl ether
CAS 110-71-4
UN No. 2252
Synonyms: DME; 1,2-Dimethoxyethane; Monoglyme; Glycol dimethyl ether
Formula: $CH_3OCH_2CH_2OCH_3$
Properties: Water-white liq., sharp ethereal odor; misc. with water, alcohol; sol. in hydrocarbons; m.w. 90.12;

dens. 0.86285 (20/4 C); m.p. -58 C; b.p. 82-83 (760 mm); flash pt. 4.5 C; ref. index 1.3813 (20 C)
Precaution: DOT: Flamm. liq.; fire hazard
Toxicology: Experimental reproductive effects
Uses: Solvent, vehicle
Regulatory: BP compliance
Manuf./Distrib.: Ferro/Grant; Spectrum Chem. Mfg.
Manuf./Distrib. (pharm. & food): Aldrich
Trade names: Monoglyme

Ethylene glycol distearate. *See* Glycol distearate
Ethylene glycol monohydroxystearate. *See* Glycol hydroxystearate
Ethylene glycol monophenyl ether. *See* Phenoxyethanol
Ethylene glycol monostearate. *See* Glycol stearate
Ethylene glycol monostearate SE. *See* Glycol stearate SE
Ethylene glycol nonyl phenyl ether. *See* Nonoxynol-1
Ethylene glycol octyl phenyl ether. *See* Octoxynol-1
Ethylene glycol phenyl ether. *See* Phenoxyethanol
Ethylene glycol stearate. *See* Glycol stearate
Ethylene homopolymer. *See* Polyethylene

Ethylene oxide
CAS 75-21-8; EINECS 200-849-9
FEMA 2433; UN No. 1040
Synonyms: EO; ETO; Oxacyclopropane; Oxane; Oxidoethane; Oxirane; Ethene oxide; Epoxyethane; 1,2-Epoxyethane; Dimethylene oxide
Empirical: C_2H_4O
Properties: Colorless gas; sol. in org. solvs.; misc. with water, alcohol; very sol. in ether; m.w. 44.06; dens. 0.8711 (20/20 C); m.p. -111.3 C; b.p. 10.73 C; flash pt. 0 F
Precaution: Flamm.; severe explosion hazard exposed to flame; violent polymerization on contact with ammonia, alkali hydroxides, amines, acids, etc.; heated to decomp., emits acrid smoke and irritating fumes
Toxicology: LD50 (oral, rat) 72 mg/kg; OSHA PEL: TWA 1 ppm; poison by ingestion, IP, subcutaneous, IV routes; mod. toxic by inh.; skin and eye irritant; suspected human carcinogen; human systemic effects by inh. (convulsions, nausea, vomiting); mutagenic data
Uses: Sterilant; used in ophthalmics, topicals
Regulatory: FEMA GRAS; FDA approved for ophthalmics, topicals; BP compliance
Manuf./Distrib.: BASF; Hoechst Celanese; Hüls AG; Mitsubishi Petrochem.; Mitsui Petrochem. Ind.; Mitsui Toatsu Chem.; Occidental; Shell; Union Carbide
Manuf./Distrib. (pharm. & food): Aldrich

Ethylene polymers. *See* Polyethylene
Ethylenesuccinic acid. *See* Succinic acid
Ethylene undecane dicarboxylate. *See* Ethylene brassylate

Ethylene/VA copolymer
CAS 24937-78-8
Synonyms: EVA; EVA copolymer; Ethylene vinyl acetate; Ethylene/vinyl acetate copolymer; Acetic acid, ethenyl ester, polymer with ethene
Definition: Polymer of ethylene and vinyl acetate monomers
Formula: $(C_4H_6O_2 \cdot C_2H_4)_x$
Properties: Dens. 0.930
Uses: Used in ophthalmics, otics, topicals, slow-release and microencapsulation prods.
Regulatory: FDA 21CFR §175.300, 177.1200, 177.1210, 177.1350, 178.1005; FDA approved for ophthalmics, otics
Manuf./Distrib.: AlliedSignal; Bayer; Chemcentral; Focus; Tamms Ind.

Ethylene vinyl acetate. *See* Ethylene/VA copolymer
Ethylene/vinyl acetate copolymer. *See* Ethylene/VA copolymer
Ethyl ester of PVM/MA copolymer. *See* PVM/MA copolymer, ethyl ester
N-Ethylethanamine. *See* Diethylamine

Ethyl ether
CAS 60-29-7; EINECS 200-467-2
UN No. 1155
Synonyms: Diethyl ether; Ether
Empirical: $C_4H_{10}O$
Formula: $CH_3CH_2OCH_2CH_3$

Ethyl formate

Properties: Clear volatile liq., sweet pungent odor; hygroscopic; sol. in water, chloroform; misc. with alcohol, ether; m.w. 74.12; dens. 0.7135 (20/4 C); m.p. -116.2 C; b.p. 34.6 C; flash pt. -49 F
Precaution: DOT: Flamm. liq.
Toxicology: TLV:TWA 400 ppm (air); moderately toxic by ingestion, intraperitoneal, intravenous routes; poison by subcutaneous route; mildly toxic by inhalation
Uses: Antiseptic, analgesic, expectorant; used in transmucosal pharmaceuticals
Regulatory: FDA approved for transmucosal pharmaceuticals
Manuf./Distrib.: Aldrich; J.T. Baker; Exxon; Hüls AG; Mallinckrodt; Quantum/USI; Spectrum Chem. Mfg.; Van Waters & Rogers
Trade names: Ethyl Ether USP/ACS

Ethyl formate

CAS 109-94-4; EINECS 203-721-0
FEMA 2434; UN No. 1190
Synonyms: Ethyl formic ester; Formic acid ethyl ester; Ethyl methanoate; Formic ether
Classification: Aliphatic organic compd.
Definition: Ester of ethyl alcohol and formic acid
Empirical: $C_3H_6O_2$
Formula: $HCOOC_2H_5$
Properties: Colorless liq., sharp rum-like odor; sol. in fixed oils, propylene glycol, water (dec.); sl. sol. in min. oil; m.w. 74.09; dens. 0.9236 (20/20 C); m.p. -79 C; b.p. 54 C; flash pt. (CC) -4 F; ref. index 1.359
Precaution: DOT: Flamm. liq.; dangerous fire and explosion hazard exposed to heat, flame, oxidizers
Toxicology: LD50 (oral, rat) 1850 mg/kg; mod. toxic by ingestion, subcutaneous routes; mildly toxic by skin contact and inh.; experimental tumorigen; skin and eye irritant; heated to decomp., emits acrid smoke and irritating fumes
Uses: Intermediate for prod. of pharmaceuticals; fruity synthetic flavoring agent and adjuvant
Regulatory: FDA 21CFR §172.515, 184.1295, GRAS; 193.210, insecticide residue tolerance of 250 ppm in raisins and currants; FEMA GRAS
Manuf./Distrib.: BASF
Manuf./Distrib. (pharm. & food): Aldrich; Hasegawa; Ogawa & Co.; San-Ei Gen F.F.I.

Ethylformic acid. See Propionic acid
Ethyl formic ester. See Ethyl formate

2-Ethylfuran

CAS 3208-16-0
FEMA 3673
Definition: Obtained by dehydration of furyl methyl carbinol followed by reduction
Empirical: C_6H_8O
Properties: Colorless liq., powerful sweet burnt odor, coffee-like flavor; sol. in alcohol; almost insol. in water; m.w. 96.13; dens. 0.912; b.p. 92-93 C; flash pt. 28 F; ref. index 1.4390
Precaution: Flamm. liq.
Uses: Sweet synthetic flavoring agent
Regulatory: FDA 21CFR §172.515; FEMA GRAS
Manuf./Distrib. (pharm. & food): Aldrich

Ethyl hendecanoate. See Ethyl undecanoate
Ethyl 10-hendecenoate. See Ethyl 10-undecenoate

Ethyl heptanoate

CAS 106-30-9; EINECS 203-382-9
FEMA 2437
Synonyms: Ethyl heptoate; Ethyl n-heptoate; Heptanoic acid ethyl ester; Ethyl enanthate; Cognac oil, synthetic; Oil of grapes; Ethyl oenanthate
Definition: Ester of heptoic acid
Empirical: $C_9H_{18}O_2$
Formula: $CH_3(CH_2)_5COOC_2H_5$
Properties: Liq., fruity wine-like odor and taste with burning aftertaste; misc. with alcohol, ether, chloroform; insol. in water; m.w. 158.24; dens. 0.868 (20/4 C); m.p. -66.3 C; b.p. 186-188 C; flash pt. 74 C; ref. index 1.413 (20 C)
Precaution: Combustible liq.
Toxicology: LD50 (oral, rat) > 34,640 mg/kg; no known toxicity; heated to decomp., emits acrid smoke and fumes
Uses: Berry, melon, peach, pineapple, plum-like synthetic flavoring agent

Regulatory: FDA 21CFR §172.515; FEMA GRAS; Japan approved as flavoring
Manuf./Distrib. (pharm. & food): Aldrich

Ethyl heptotate. *See* Ethyl heptanoate
Ethyl n-heptoate. *See* Ethyl heptanoate
Ethyl-2,4-hexadienoate. *See* Ethyl sorbate
Ethyl hexanoate. *See* Ethyl caproate
2-Ethylhexanoic acid, cetyl/stearyl ester. *See* Cetearyl octanoate
2-Ethylhexanoic acid, 1-methyl-1,2-ethanediyl ester. *See* Propylene glycol dioctanoate

2-Ethylhexanol
CAS 104-76-7; EINECS 203-234-3
FEMA 3151
Synonyms: 2-EH; 2-Ethylhexyl alcohol; 2-Ethyl-1-hexanol; Octyl alcohol; Alcohol C_8
Empirical: $C_8H_{18}O$
Formula: $CH_3(CH_2)_3CHC_2H_5CH_2OH$
Properties: Colorless liq., mild oily sweet sl. rose fragrance; misc. with most org. solvs.; sl. sol. in water; m.w. 130.26; dens. 0.83 (20 C); b.p. 183.5 C; f.p. -76 C; flash pt. 81.1 C; ref. index 1.4300 (20 C)
Toxicology: Moderately toxic by ingestion, skin contact, IP, SQ, parenteral routes; severe eye irritant; moderate skin irritant; LD50 (rat, oral) 12.46 ml/kg
Uses: Sweet synthetic flavoring agent
Regulatory: FEMA GRAS
Manuf./Distrib.: Aristech; Ashland; BASF; BP Chem. Ltd; Coyne; Eastman; Hoechst AG; Penta Mfg.; Shell
Manuf./Distrib. (pharm. & food): Aldrich

2-Ethyl-1-hexanol. *See* 2-Ethylhexanol
2-Ethylhexyl aceetate. *See* Octyl acetate
2-Ethylhexyl alcohol. *See* 2-Ethylhexanol
Ethyl hexylate. *See* Ethyl caproate
2-Ethylhexyl 2-cyano-3,3-diphenylacrylate. *See* Octocrylene
2-Ethylhexyl 2-cyano-3,3-diphenyl-2-propenoate. *See* Octocrylene
2-Ethylhexyl-4(dimethylamino) benzoate. *See* Octyl dimethyl PABA
2-Ethylhexyl p-dimethylaminobenzoate. *See* Octyl dimethyl PABA
2-Ethylhexyl hexadecanoate. *See* Octyl palmitate
2-Ethylhexyl 2-hydroxybenzoate. *See* Octyl salicylate
2-Ethylhexylhydroxystearate. *See* Octyl hydroxystearate
2-Ethylhexyl isononanoate. *See* Octyl isononanoate
2-Ethylhexyl methoxycinnamate. *See* Octyl methoxycinnamate
Ethylhexyl p-methoxycinnamate. *See* Octyl methoxycinnamate
2-Ethylhexyl 3-(4-methoxyphenyl)-2-propenoate. *See* Octyl methoxycinnamate
2-Ethylhexyl octadecanoate. *See* Octyl stearate
2-Ethylhexyl oxystearate. *See* Octyl hydroxystearate
2-Ethylhexyl palmitate. *See* Octyl palmitate
2-Ethylhexyl pelargonate. *See* Octyl pelargonate
2-Ethylhexyl salicylate. *See* Octyl salicylate
2-Ethylhexyl stearate. *See* Octyl stearate
Ethyl hydrocinnamate. *See* Ethyl-3-phenylpropionate
Ethyl 4-hydroxybenzoate. *See* Ethylparaben
Ethyl-o-hydroxybenzoate. *See* Ethyl salicylate
Ethyl p-hydroxybenzoate. *See* Ethylparaben
Ethyl-4-hydroxybenzoate potassium salt. *See* Potassium ethylparaben
Ethyl α-hydroxypropionate. *See* Ethyl lactate
Ethyl-S(-)-2-hydroxypropionate. *See* Ethyl lactate
2-Ethyl-3-hydroxy-4H-pyran-4-one. *See* Ethyl maltol
Ethylidene diethyl ether. *See* Acetal
Ethylidenelactic acid. *See* Lactic acid

Ethyl isobutyrate
CAS 97-62-1; EINECS 202-595-4
FEMA 2428
Synonyms: 2-Methylpropanoic acid ethyl ester
Empirical: $C_6H_{12}O_2$
Formula: $(CH_3)_2CHCOOC_2H_5$
Properties: Liq., aromatic fruity odor; misc. with alcohol, ether; sl. sol. in water; m.w. 116.16; dens. 0.867 (20/4 C); m.p. -88 C; b.p. 107-110 C; flash pt. 20 C; ref. index 1.388

Ethyl isovalerate

Precaution: Flammable liq.
Toxicology: LD50 (IP, mouse) 800 mg/kg; mod. toxic by IP route; skin irritant; reacts with oxidizing materials; heated to decomp., emits acrid smoke and fumes
Uses: Strawberry-like synthetic flavoring agent
Regulatory: FDA 21CFR §172.515; FEMA GRAS
Manuf./Distrib. (pharm. & food): Aldrich

Ethyl isovalerate
CAS 108-64-5; EINECS 203-602-3
FEMA 2463
Synonyms: Isovaleric acid ethyl ester; 3-Methylbutanoic acid ethyl ester; Ethyl 3-methylbutyrate; Ethyl β-methylbutyrate
Definition: Obtained by esterification of isovaleric acid with ethyl alcohol in presence of conc. H_2SO_4
Empirical: $C_7H_{14}O_2$
Formula: $(CH_3)_2CHCH_2COOC_2H_5$
Properties: Colorless oily liq., apple odor; sol. in propylene glycol; sl. sol. in water @ 135 C; misc. with alcohol, fixed oils, benzene, ether; m.w. 130.21; dens. 0.868 (20/20 C); b.p. 135 C; m.p. -99 C; flash pt. 77 F; ref. index 1.395-1.399
Precaution: Flamm. liq. when exposed to heat, flame, or sparks
Toxicology: LD50 (oral, rabbit) 7031 mg/kg; mod. toxic by intraperitoneal route; mildly toxic by ingestion; skin irritant; heated to decomp., emits acrid smoke and fumes
Uses: Apple-like synthetic flavoring agent
Regulatory: FDA 21CFR §172.515; FEMA GRAS; Japan approved as flavoring
Manuf./Distrib.: BASF
Manuf./Distrib. (pharm. & food): Aldrich; BASF

Ethyl α-ketopropionate. *See* Ethyl pyruvate
Ethyl γ-ketovalerate. *See* Ethyl levulinate

Ethyl lactate
CAS 97-64-3
FEMA 2440; UN No. 1192
Synonyms: Lactic acid ethyl ester; Ethyl α-hydroxypropionate; Ethyl-S(-)-2-hydroxypropionate
Definition: Ethyl ester of lactic acid
Empirical: $C_5H_{10}O_3$
Formula: $CH_3CHOHCOOC_2H_5$
Properties: Colorless liq., mild odor; misc. with water, alcohol, ketones, esters, hydrocarbons, oil; m.w. 118.13; dens. 1.020-1.036 (20/20 C); m.p. -26 C; b.p. 154 C; flash pt. 46.1 C; ref. index 1.410-1.420
Precaution: Flamm. or combustible; can react with oxidizers; sl. explosion hazard in vapor form exposed to flame
Toxicology: LD50 (oral, mouse) 2500 mg/kg; moderately toxic by ingestion, intraperitoneal, subcutaneous, intravenous routes; heated to decomp., emits acrid smoke and irritating fumes
Uses: Fruity synthetic flavoring agent
Regulatory: FDA 21CFR §172.515; FEMA GRAS
Manuf./Distrib.: Aldrich; CPS; Farleyway Chem. Ltd; Penta Mfg.
Manuf./Distrib. (pharm. & food): Aldrich; Jungbunzlauer

Ethyl laurate
CAS 106-33-2; EINECS 203-386-0
FEMA 2441
Synonyms: Dodecanoic acid ethyl ester; Ethyl dodecanoate; Ethyl dodecylate
Definition: Synthesized from lauroyl chloride and ethyl alcohol in presence of Mg in ether sol'n.
Empirical: $C_{14}H_{28}O_2$
Properties: Colorless oily liq., fruity-floral odor; misc. with alcohol, chloroform, ether; insol. in water; m.w. 228.37; dens. 0.858; b.p. 272-273 C; flash pt. > 212 F; ref. index 1.430
Precaution: Combustible liq.
Toxicology: Heated to decomp., emits acrid smoke and irritating fumes
Uses: Fruity synthetic flavoring agent
Regulatory: FDA 21CFR §172.515; FEMA GRAS
Manuf./Distrib.: Aldrich
Manuf./Distrib. (pharm. & food): Aldrich

Ethyl levulinate
CAS 539-88-8; EINECS 208-728-2
FEMA 2442

Synonyms: Ethyl γ-ketovalerate; Ethyl-4-oxopentanoate; 4-Oxopentanoic acid ethyl ester
Definition: Ester of levulinic acid and ethyl alcohol
Empirical: $C_7H_{12}O_3$
Formula: $CH_3COCH_2CH_2COOC_2H_5$
Properties: Liq.; freely sol. in water; misc. with alcohol; m.w. 144.17; dens. 1.012 (20/4 C); b.p. 203-205 C; flash pt. 94 C; ref. index 1.423 (20 C)
Precaution: Combustible
Uses: Apple, pineapple-like synthetic flavoring agent
Regulatory: FDA 21CFR §172.515; FEMA GRAS
Manuf./Distrib. (pharm. & food): Aldrich

Ethyllic acid. *See* Acetic acid

Ethyl linoleate
CAS 544-35-4; EINECS 208-868-4
Synonyms: Linoleic acid ethyl ester; Vitamin F; 9,12-Octadecadienoic acid ethyl ester
Definition: Ester of ethyl alcohol and linoleic acid
Empirical: $C_{20}H_{36}O_2$
Toxicology: Large doses can cause nausea and vomiting; no known skin toxicity
Uses: Vitamin deriv.; used in emulsifiers and vitamins
Manuf./Distrib. (pharm. & food): Aldrich; Avrachem
Trade names: Safester A-75
Trade names containing: Safester A 75 WS

Ethyl malate. *See* Diethyl malate
Ethyl malonate. *See* Diethyl malonate

Ethyl maltol
CAS 4940-11-8
FEMA 3487
Synonyms: 3-Hydroxy-2-ethyl-4-pyrone; 2-Ethyl-3-hydroxy-4H-pyran-4-one
Empirical: $C_7H_8O_3$
Properties: Caramel sweet odor; m.w. 140.14; m.p. 88-92 C
Toxicology: Mod. toxic by ingestion, subcutaneous routes; mutagenic data; heated to decomp., emits acrid smoke and fumes
Uses: Synthetic flavoring agent imparting sweet taste; flavor enhancer; processing aid; used for orals
Regulatory: FDA 21CFR §172.515; FEMA GRAS; Europe listed; UK approved; FDA approved for orals
Manuf./Distrib.: Spectrum Chem. Mfg.
Manuf./Distrib. (pharm. & food): Aldrich; Spectrum Chem. Mfg.
Trade names: Veltol®-Plus

2-(Ethylmercuriomercapto)benzoic acid sodium salt. *See* Thimerosal
Ethyl methanoate. *See* Ethyl formate
Ethyl-4-methoxybenzoate. *See* Ethyl-p-anisate
Ethyl-p-methoxybenzoate. *See* Ethyl-p-anisate
Ethyl trans-2-methyl-2-butenoate. *See* Ethyl tiglate

Ethyl 2-methylbutyrate
CAS 7452-79-1; EINECS 231-225-4
FEMA 2443
Empirical: $C_7H_{14}O_2$
Formula: $CH_3CH_2CH(CH_3)COOC_2H_5$
Properties: Powerful green fruity pungent odor; m.w. 130.19; dens. 0.868 (20/4 C); b.p. 130-133 C; flash pt. 26 C; ref. index 1.397 (20 C)
Precaution: Combustible liq.
Toxicology: Heated to decomp., emits acrid smoke and fumes
Uses: Apple, plum-like synthetic flavoring agent
Regulatory: FDA 21CFR §172.515; FEMA GRAS
Manuf./Distrib. (pharm. & food): Aldrich

Ethyl 3-methylbutyrate. *See* Ethyl isovalerate
Ethyl β-methylbutyrate. *See* Ethyl isovalerate

Ethyl methylphenylglycidate
CAS 77-83-8
FEMA 2444
Synonyms: Aldehyde C-16 pure; Ethyl 3-methyl-3-phenylglycidate; Strawberry aldehyde; 3-Methyl-3-phenyl

Ethyl 3-methyl-3-phenylglycidate

glycidic acid ethyl ester
Empirical: $C_{12}H_{14}O_3$
Properties: Colorless to pale yel. liq., fruity strawberry-like odor; sol. in most fixed oils; m.w. 206.24; dens. 1.104-1.123; ref. index 1.509-1.511
Precaution: Combustible liq.
Toxicology: Mildly toxic by ingestion; heated to decomp., emits acrid smoke and fumes
Uses: Sweet strawberry-like synthetic flavoring agent
Regulatory: FDA 21CFR §182.60, GRAS; FEMA GRAS
Manuf./Distrib. (pharm. & food): Aldrich

Ethyl 3-methyl-3-phenylglycidate. *See* Ethyl methylphenylglycidate

Ethyl 3-(methylthio)propionate
CAS 13327-56-5
FEMA 3343
Empirical: C_6H_9NS
Properties: M.w. 148.23
Uses: Citrus, pineapple flavoring agent
Regulatory: FEMA GRAS
Manuf./Distrib. (pharm. & food): Aldrich

Ethyl nonanoate. *See* Ethyl pelargonate
Ethyl 9-octadecenoate. *See* Ethyl oleate

Ethyl octanoate
CAS 106-32-1; EINECS 203-385-5
FEMA 2449
Synonyms: Ethyl caprylate; Ethyl octoate; Ethyl octylate; Octanoic acid ethyl ester
Definition: Ester of caprylic acid and ethyl alcohol
Empirical: $C_{10}H_{20}O_2$
Formula: $CH_3(CH_2)_6COOC_2H_5$
Properties: Colorless very mobile liq., pleasant pineapple odor; misc. with alcohol, ether; insol. in water; m.w. 172.27; dens. 0.867 (20/4 C); m.p. -47 C; b.p. 207-209; flash pt. 167 F; ref. index 1.418 (20 C)
Precaution: Combustible liq.
Toxicology: LD50 (oral, rat) 25,960 mg/kg; mildly toxic by ingestion; skin irritant; heated to decomp., emits acrid smoke and fumes
Uses: Apricot, pineapple-like synthetic flavoring agent
Regulatory: FDA 21CFR §172.515; FEMA GRAS; Japan approved as flavoring
Manuf./Distrib. (pharm. & food): Aldrich

Ethyl octoate. *See* Ethyl octanoate
Ethyl octylate. *See* Ethyl octanoate
Ethyl oenanthate. *See* Ethyl heptanoate

Ethyl oleate
CAS 111-62-6; 85049-36-1; EINECS 203-889-5; 285-206-0
FEMA 2450
Synonyms: 9-Octadecenoic acid ethyl ester; Ethyl 9-octadecenoate
Definition: Ester of ethyl alcohol and oleic acid
Empirical: $C_{20}H_{38}O_2$
Formula: $CH_3(CH_2)_7CH:CH(CH_2)_7COOC2H_5$
Properties: Ylsh. oily liq.; misc. with alcohol, ether, veg. oils; insol. in water; m.w. 310.52; dens. 0.870 (20/4 C); visc. 75.15 cp; m.p. -32 C; b.p. 216-218 (15 mm); acid no. 0.5 max.; iodine no. 75-85; sapon. no. 177-188; flash pt. 175 C; ref. index 1.451
Precaution: Combustible
Toxicology: No known toxicity
Uses: Oleaginous vehicle, solv.; used in intramuscular injectables, parenterals, topicals
Regulatory: FDA 21CFR §172.515; FEMA GRAS; USP/NF, BP compliance
Manuf./Distrib. (pharm. & food): Aldrich
Trade names: Crodamol EO

Ethyl 3-oxobutanoate. *See* Ethylacetoacetate
Ethyl-4-oxopentanoate. *See* Ethyl levulinate
Ethyl 2-oxopropanoate. *See* Ethyl pyruvate

Ethylparaben
CAS 120-47-8; EINECS 204-399-4

Synonyms: Ethyl 4-hydroxybenzoate; 4-Hydroxybenzoic acid ethyl ester; Ethyl p-hydroxybenzoate; Carboxyphenol; Ethyl parahydroxybenzoate
Definition: Ester of ethyl alcohol and p-hydroxybenzoic acid
Empirical: $C_9H_{10}O_3$
Formula: $HOC_6H_4CO_2C_2H_5$
Properties: Colorless to wh. cryst. or powd.; sol. in alcohol, ether, acetone, propylene glycol; almost insol. in water; m.w. 166.19; m.p. 115-118 C; b.p. 297 C (dec.)
Toxicology: Moderately toxic by ingestion, intraperitoneal route; irritant; local anesthetic effect; mutagenic data; may cause asthma, rashes, hyperactivity
Uses: Antimicrobial preservative; used in orals, topicals, parenterals; dental anesthetics
Usage level: 0.08-1.0%; 0.1% in mixts.
Regulatory: USA CIR approved, EPA registered; Japan approved; Europe listed; UK permitted; FDA approved for orals, topicals; USP/NF, BP compliance
Manuf./Distrib.: Ashland; Inolex; Int'l. Sourcing; E. Merck; Napp; Nipa Labs; Penta Mfg.
Manuf./Distrib. (pharm. & food): Int'l. Sourcing; Spectrum Chem. Mfg.; Tri-K Ind.
Trade names: Ethyl Parasept® NF; Nipagin A
Trade names containing: Nipastat; Phenonip; Uniphen P-23

Ethylparaben, potassium salt. *See* Potassium ethylparaben
Ethylparaben, sodium salt. *See* Sodium ethylparaben
Ethyl parahydroxybenzoate. *See* Ethylparaben

Ethyl pelargonate
CAS 123-29-5; EINECS 204-615-7
FEMA 2447
Synonyms: Ethyl nonanoate; Nonanoic acid ethyl ester; Wine ether
Definition: Ester of ethyl alcohol and pelargonic acid
Empirical: $C_{11}H_{22}O_2$
Formula: $CH_3(CH_2)_7COOCH_2CH_3$
Properties: Colorless liq., fruity odor; insol. in water; sol. in alcohol, ether; m.w. 186.33; dens. 0.866 (18/4 C); b.p. ≈ 220 C; f.p. -44 C; flash pt. 185 F; ref. index 1.4220 (20 C)
Precaution: Combustible liq.
Toxicology: LD50 (oral, rat) > 43,000 mg/kg; mildly toxic by ingestion; skin irritant; heated to decomp., emits acrid smoke and irritating fumes
Uses: Fruity synthetic flavoring agent
Regulatory: FDA 21C FR §172.515; FEMA GRAS
Manuf./Distrib.: Aldrich
Manuf./Distrib. (pharm. & food): Aldrich

Ethyl phenacetate. *See* Ethyl phenylacetate

p-Ethylphenol
Uses: Medicinal flavoring agent
Manuf./Distrib. (pharm. & food): Aldrich

Ethyl phenylacetate
CAS 101-97-3; EINECS 202-993-8
FEMA 2452
Synonyms: Ethyl benzeneacetate; α-Toluic acid ethyl ester; Ethyl phenacetate; Ethyl-2-phenylethanoate; Ethyl-α-toluate
Definition: Ester of ethyl alcohol and phenylacetic acid
Empirical: $C_{10}H_{12}O_2$
Properties: Colorless liq., sweet honey-like odor; sol. in fixed oils; insol. in glycerin, propylene glycol, water; m.w. 164.22; dens. 1.033 (20 C); b.p. 227 C; flash pt. > 100 C; ref. index 1.496-1.500
Precaution: Combustible liq.
Toxicology: LD50 (oral, rat) 3300 mg/kg; mod. toxic by ingestion; heated to decomp., emits acrid smoke and irritating fumes
Uses: Sweet apricot, cherry-like synthetic flavoring agent
Regulatory: FDA 21CFR §172.515; FEMA GRAS; Japan approved as flavoring
Manuf./Distrib.: Aldrich
Manuf./Distrib. (pharm. & food): Aldrich

Ethyl phenylacrylate. *See* Ethyl cinnamate
Ethyl-β-phenylacrylate. *See* Ethyl cinnamate
Ethyl phenylbutyrate. *See* Ethyl-4-phenylbutyrate

Ethyl-4-phenylbutyrate
FEMA 2453
Synonyms: Ethyl phenylbutyrate; Ethyl-γ-phenylbutyrate
Definition: Ester of ethanol and γ-phenylbutyric acid
Empirical: $C_{12}H_{16}O_2$
Properties: Colorless somewhat oily liq., plum-like odor, plum-prune taste; sol. in alcohol; insol. in water; m.w. 192.26
Uses: Synthetic flavoring agent
Regulatory: FDA 21CFR §172.515; FEMA GRAS

Ethyl-γ-phenylbutyrate. *See* Ethyl-4-phenylbutyrate
Ethyl phenyl carbinyl butyrate. *See* α-Ethylbenzyl butyrate
Ethyl 3-phenyl-2,3-epoxypropionate. *See* Ethyl phenylglycidate
Ethyl-2-phenylethanoate. *See* Ethyl phenylacetate

Ethyl phenylglycidate
CAS 121-39-1
FEMA 2454
Synonyms: Ethyl 3-phenylglycidate; Ethyl 3-phenyl-2,3-epoxypropionate
Empirical: $C_{11}H_{12}O_3$
Properties: Colorless to pale yel. liq., fruity odor; m.w. 192.22; flash pt. > 100 C; ref. index 1.5190-1.5230
Toxicology: Irritant; mutagenic data; mod. toxic by ingestion; heated to decomp., emits acrid smoke and fumes
Uses: Caramel, strawberry-like synthetic flavoring agent
Regulatory: FDA 21CFR §172.515; FEMA GRAS
Manuf./Distrib. (pharm. & food): Aldrich

Ethyl 3-phenylglycidate. *See* Ethyl phenylglycidate
Ethyl-3-phenylpropenoate. *See* Ethyl cinnamate
Ethyl (E)-3-phenylprop-2-enoate. *See* Ethyl cinnamate

Ethyl-3-phenylpropionate
CAS 2021-28-5; EINECS 217-966-6
FEMA 2455
Synonyms: Ethyl hydrocinnamate
Empirical: $C_{11}H_{14}O_2$
Formula: $C_6H_5CH_2CH_2COOC_2H_5$
Properties: Colorless liq., floral odor; sol. in most org. solvs.; insol. in water; m.w. 178.23; dens. 1.013 (20/4 C); b.p. 247-249 C; flash pt. > 98 C; ref. index 1.494 (20 C)
Uses: Fruity synthetic flavoring agent
Regulatory: FDA 21CFR §172.515; FEMA GRAS
Manuf./Distrib. (pharm. & food): Aldrich

Ethyl phthalate. *See* Diethyl phthalate
Ethyl propenoate. *See* Ethyl acrylate

Ethyl propionate
CAS 105-37-3; EINECS 203-291-4
FEMA 2456; UN No. 1195
Synonyms: Propanoic acid ethyl ester
Definition: Ester of propionic acid and ethyl alcohol
Empirical: $C_5H_{10}O_2$
Formula: $CH_3CH_2COOC_2H_5$
Properties: Colorless liq., fruity odor; sol. in ≈ 60 parts water; misc. with alcohol, ether; m.w. 102.14; dens. 0.890 (20/4 C); m.p. -73 C; b.p. 96-99 C; flash pt. (CC) 12 C; ref. index 1.384 (20 C)
Precaution: Highly flamm. liq.
Toxicology: LD50 (oral, rabbit) 3500 mg/kg; mod. toxic by ingestion and IP routes; skin irritant; reacts with oxidizing materials; heated to decomp., emits acrid smoke and fumes
Uses: Pineapple-like synthetic flavoring agent
Regulatory: FDA 21CFR §172.515; FEMA GRAS; Japan approved as flavoring
Manuf./Distrib.: Union Carbide
Manuf./Distrib. (pharm. & food): Aldrich

Ethyl pyruvate
CAS 617-35-6; EINECS 210-511-2
FEMA 2457
Synonyms: Ethyl α-ketopropionate; Ethyl 2-oxopropanoate

Definition: Ester of pyruvic acid and absolute ethyl alcohol
Empirical: $C_5H_8O_3$
Formula: $CH_3COCOOC_2H_5$
Properties: Liq., vegetable caramel odor; sl. sol. in water; misc. with alcohol, ether; m.w. 116.12; dens. 1.047 (20/4 C); m.p. -50 c; b.p. 148-150 C; flash pt. 114 F; ref. index 1.405
Uses: Synthetic flavoring agent
Regulatory: FDA 21CFR §172.515; FEMA GRAS
Manuf./Distrib.: Aldrich
Manuf./Distrib. (pharm. & food): Aldrich

Ethyl salicylate
CAS 118-61-6; EINECS 204-265-5
FEMA 2458
Synonyms: Ethyl-o-hydroxybenzoate; Salicylic ethyl ester; Sal ethyl; Salicylic ether
Definition: Ester of salicylic acid and ethyl alcohol
Empirical: $C_9H_{10}O_3$
Formula: $HO \cdot C_6H_4 \cdot CO_2 \cdot C_2H_5$
Properties: Colorless liq., wintergreen odor; sol. in alcohol, ether, acetic acid, fixed oils; sl. sol. in water, glycerin; m.w. 166.18; dens. 1.127; m.p. 1.3 C; b.p. 233-234 C; flash pt. 225 F; ref. index 1.520
Precaution: Combustible
Toxicology: LD50 (oral, rat) 1320 mg/kg; mod. toxic by ingestion, subcutaneous routes; skin irritant; heated to decomp., emits acrid smoke and irritating fumes
Uses: Sweet, fruity, minty synthetic flavoring agent
Regulatory: FDA 21CFR §172.515; FEMA GRAS
Manuf./Distrib.: Aldrich
Manuf./Distrib. (pharm. & food): Aldrich

Ethyl sebacate. *See* Diethyl sebacate
Ethyl (sodium o-mercaptobenzoato) mercury. *See* Thimerosal

Ethyl sorbate
CAS 2396-84-1
FEMA 2459
Synonyms: Ethyl-2,4-hexadienoate; Sorbic acid ethyl ester
Definition: Ester of sorbyl chloride and ethyl alcohol
Empirical: $C_8H_{12}O_2$
Properties: Warm fruity ethereal odor; m.w. 140.18; dens. 0.956; b.p. 81 C (15 mm); flash pt. 157 F; ref. index 1.502
Uses: Fruity synthetic flavoring agent
Regulatory: FDA 21CFR §172.515; FEMA GRAS
Manuf./Distrib.: Penta Mfg.
Manuf./Distrib. (pharm. & food): Aldrich

Ethyl tartrate. *See* Diethyl tartrate

Ethyl tiglate
CAS 5837-78-5
FEMA 2460
Synonyms: Ethyl trans-2,3-dimethyl acrylate; Ethyl trans-2-methyl-2-butenoate
Definition: Ester of tiglic acid and ethyl alcohol
Empirical: $C_7H_{12}O_2$
Properties: Liq., fruity caramel odor; sol. in most org. solvs.; m.w. 128.17; dens. 0.923; b.p. 154-156 C; flash pt. 112 F; ref. index 1.4347 (16.8 C)
Uses: Raspberry-like synthetic flavoring agent
Regulatory: FDA 21CFR §172.515; FEMA GRAS
Manuf./Distrib. (pharm. & food): Aldrich

Ethyl-α-toluate. *See* Ethyl phenylacetate

Ethyl undecanoate
CAS 627-90-7
FEMA 3492
Synonyms: Ethyl hendecanoate; Ethyl undecylate
Empirical: $C_{13}H_{26}O_2$
Properties: Liq., cognac coconut odor; insol. in water; m.w. 214.35; dens. 0.859; b.p. 255 C; flash pt. > 230 F; ref. index 1.9325

Ethyl 10-undecenoate

    Uses: Coconut-like synthetic flavoring agent
    Regulatory: FDA 21CFR §172.515; FEMA GRAS
    Manuf./Distrib. (pharm. & food): Aldrich

Ethyl 10-undecenoate
    CAS 692-86-4
    FEMA 2461
    Synonyms: Ethyl 10-hendecenoate; Ethyl undecylenoate
    Empirical: $C_{13}H_{24}O_2$
    Properties: Colorless to pale yel. liq., wine-like odor; m.w. 212.34; dens. 0.879; b.p. 258-259 C; flash pt. > 230
      F; ref. index 1.4382
    Uses: Fruity synthetic flavoring agent
    Regulatory: FDA 21CFR §172.515; FEMA GRAS
    Manuf./Distrib. (pharm. & food): Aldrich

Ethyl undecylate. *See* Ethyl undecanoate
Ethyl undecylenoate. *See* Ethyl 10-undecenoate

Ethyl valerate
    CAS 539-82-2; EINECS 208-726-1
    FEMA 2462
    Synonyms: Ethyl n-valerate
    Empirical: $C_7H_{14}O_2$
    Formula: $CH_3(CH_2)_3COOC_2H_5$
    Properties: Liq.; misc. with alcohol; insol. in water; m.w. 130.19; dens. 0.877 (20/4 C); b.p. 142-146 C; flash
      pt. 34 C; ref. index 1.372-1.400 (20 C)
    Precaution: Flamm.
    Toxicology: Irritant
    Uses: Apple-like synthetic flavoring agent
    Regulatory: FDA 21CFR §172.515; FEMA GRAS
    Manuf./Distrib. (pharm. & food): Aldrich

Ethyl n-valerate. *See* Ethyl valerate

Ethyl vanillin
    CAS 121-32-4; EINECS 204-464-7
    FEMA 2464
    Synonyms: 3-Ethoxy-4-hydroxybenzaldehyde; Bourbonal; Ethovan; Vanillal
    Classification: Substituted phenolic; aromatic organic compd.
    Empirical: $C_9H_{10}O_3$
    Properties: Fine, wh. cryst., vanilla odor; sol in alc., chloroform, and ether; sl. sol. in water; m.w. 166.19; m.p.
      76.5 C; b.p. 285 C; flash pt. > 212 F
    Precaution: Flamm. liq.; light-sensitive
    Toxicology: Mod. toxic by ingestion, intraperitoneal, subcutaneous, and IV routes; human skin irritant; heated
      to decomp., emits acrid smoke and irritating fumes
    Uses: Sweet, vanilla-like synthetic flavoring agent, perfume; used in orals
    Regulatory: FDA 21CFR §163.111, 163.112, 163.113, 163.114, 163.117, 163.123, 163.130, 163.135,
      163.140, 163.145, 163.150, 163.153, 163.155, 182.60, 182.90, GRAS; FEMA GRAS; Japan approved as
      flavoring; FDA approved for orals; USP/NF compliance
    Manuf./Distrib.: Aldrich; Boehringer Mannheim GmbH; Penta Mfg.; Schweizerhall
    Manuf./Distrib. (pharm. & food): Aldrich; Am. Fruit Processors; Avrachem; Berje; Calaga Food Ingreds.; Chart;
      H E Daniel; Dragoco Australia; Flavors of N. Am.; Foote & Jenkins; Ikeda; Penta Mfg.; Quimdis; Rhone-
      Poulenc Food Ingreds.; Soda Aromatic USA; Spectrum Chem. Mfg.; R C Treatt; Van Waters & Rogers
    Trade names: Unisweet EVAN

Etidronic acid
    CAS 2809-21-4; EINECS 220-552-8
    Synonyms: HEDPA; (1-Hydroxyethylidene) bisphosphonic acid; (1-Hydroxyethylidene) diphosphonic acid;
      Acetodiphosphonic acid
    Classification: Organic diphosphonic acid
    Empirical: $C_2H_8O_7P_2$
    Formula: $CH_3C(OH)(PO_3H_2)_2$
    Properties: M.w. 206.03; heated above 200 C, dec. violently emitting toxic fumes
    Uses: Antioxidant for pharmaceutical skin/hair preps.; chelating agent, sequestrant for radioactive pharma-
      ceuticals

Regulatory: FDA 21CFR §173.310
Trade names: Turpinal® SL

ETO. *See* Ethylene oxide
EtOH. *See* Alcohol

Eucalyptol
CAS 470-82-6; EINECS 207-431-5
FEMA 2465
Synonyms: Cineol; Cajeputol; 1,8-Epoxy-p-menthane; 1,3,3-Trimethyl-2-oxabicyclo[2.2.2]octane
Definition: Constituent of oil of eucalyptus
Empirical: $C_{10}H_{18}O$
Properties: Colorless liq., camphor-like odor, spicy cooling taste; misc. with alcohol, chloroform, ether, glac. acetic acid, oils; pract. insol. in water; m.w. 154.25; dens. 0.924 (20/4 C); m.p. > 1.5 C; b.p. 175-179 C; flash pt. 49 C; ref. index 1.458 (20 C)
Precaution: Combustible liq.
Toxicology: LD50 (oral, rat) 2480 mg/kg; poison by subcutaneous and intramuscular routes; mod. toxic by ingestion; experimental reproductive effects; heated to decomp., emits acrid smoke and fumes
Uses: Synthetic flavoring; antiseptic in oral rinse prods.; used in dentals
Regulatory: FDA 21CFR §172.515; 27CFR §21.65, 21.151; FEMA GRAS; Japan approved as flavoring; FDA approved for dentals
Manuf./Distrib.: Aldrich; Penta Mfg.; Quest Int'l.; Ungerer
Manuf./Distrib. (pharm. & food): Aldrich; Florida Treatt; Ruger

Eucalyptus oil
CAS 8000-48-4
FEMA 2466
Synonyms: Dinkum oil
Definition: Volatile oil obtained from leaves of *Eucalyptus globulus* or other species, contg. 70-80% eucalyptol
Properties: Colorless to pale yel. liq., char. camphoraceous odor, pungent spicy cooling taste; sol. in 5 vols 70% alcohol; misc. with abs. alcohol, oils, fats; pract. insol. in water; dens. 0.905-0.925; m.p. -15.4 C; ref. index 1.458-1.470 (20 C)
Precaution: Keep cool, well closed; protect from light
Toxicology: LD50 (oral, rat) 2480 mg/kg; human poison and human systemic effects by ingestion; skin and eye irritant; can cause allergic reaction; heated to decomp., emits acrid smoke and irritating fumes
Uses: Natural flavoring agent used in orals; used as local antiseptic; antispasmodic, stimulant
Regulatory: FDA 21CFR §172.510, 27CFR §21.65, 21.151; FEMA GRAS; Japan approved; Europe listed, no restrictions; FDA approved for orals; BP, Ph.Eur. compliance
Manuf./Distrib. (pharm. & food): Chart; Florida Treatt; Ruger; Spectrum Chem. Mfg.

Eugenia caryophyllus oil. *See* Clove oil
Eugenic acid. *See* Eugenol

Eugenol
CAS 97-53-0; EINECS 202-589-1
FEMA 2467
Synonyms: 4-Allyl-2-methoxyphenol; 2-Methoxy-4-(2-propenyl) phenol; Caryophyllic acid; Eugenic acid; 4-Allylguaiacol
Classification: Substituted phenol
Empirical: $C_{10}H_{14}O_2$
Properties: Colorless or ylsh. liq., pungent clove odor; sol. in alcohol, chloroform, ether, volatile oils; very sl. sol. in water; m.w. 164.22; dens. 1.064-1.070; m.p. 10.3 C; b.p. 253.5 C; flash pt. 219 F; ref. index 1.540
Precaution: Combustible liq.; light-sensitive
Toxicology: LD50 (oral, rat) 1930 mg/kg; mod. toxic by ingestion, intraperitoneal, and subcutaneous routes; human skin irritant; potential allergen; experimental carcinogen, tumorigen; human mutagenic data; heated to decomp., emits acrid smoke, irritating fumes
Uses: Synthetic flavoring agent and adjuvant; used in orals, periodontal dressings, zinc oxide cement, impression pastes; also as a local antiseptic; anesthetic/analgesic for mouth pain and cold sore prods.
Regulatory: FDA 21CFR §177.2800, 184.1257, GRAS; 27CFR §21.65, 21.151; FEMA GRAS; Japan approved as flavoring; FDA approved for orals; BP compliance
Manuf./Distrib.: Aldrich; Firmenich; Lucta SA; Penta Mfg.; Schweizerhall; Spectrum Chem. Mfg.; Ungerer
Manuf./Distrib. (pharm. & food): Aldrich; Florida Treatt; Spectrum Chem. Mfg.

European angelica extract. *See* Angelica extract
European dill seed oil. *See* Dill seed oil
EVA. *See* Ethylene/VA copolymer

EVA copolymer. *See* Ethylene/VA copolymer

Ext. D&C Yellow No. 7
CAS 846-70-8; EINECS 212-690-2
Synonyms: 2,4-Dinitro-1-naphthol-7-sulfonic acid disodium salt; 8-Hydroxy-5,7-dinitro-2-naphthalenesulfonic acid disodium salt; Naphthol yellow S; Acid yellow 1 (noncertified); CI 10316
Classification: Nitro color
Formula: $C_{10}H_6N_2O_8S \cdot 2Na$
Properties: M.w. 358.19
Uses: Color additive for external pharmaceuticals
Regulatory: FDA 21CFR §74.1707a, 74.2707a, 82.2707a
See also CI 10316

Extract of barley. *See* Barley extract
Extract of calendula. *See* Calendula extract
Extract of logwood. *See* Logwood extract

FAC. *See* Iron ammonium citrate
Fanchon marron. *See* D&C Red No. 34

Farnesol
CAS 4602-84-0; EINECS 225-004-1
FEMA 2478
Synonyms: 3,7,11-Trimethyl-2,6,10-dodecatrien-1-ol; Farnesyl alcohol
Classification: Organic compd.
Empirical: $C_{15}H_{26}O$
Properties: Lt. yel. liq., mild oily odor; insol. in water; dens. 0.8871 (20/4 C); b.p. 111 C; ref. index 1.487-1.492
Precaution: Combustible
Toxicology: LD50 (oral, rat) 6000 mg/kg; mod. toxic by intraperitoneal route; mildly toxic by ingestion; mutagenic data; heated to decomp., emits acrid smoke and irritating fumes
Uses: Synthetic flavoring agent; used in topicals
Regulatory: FDA 21CFR §172.515; FEMA GRAS
Manuf./Distrib.: Aldrich
Manuf./Distrib. (pharm. & food): Aldrich
Trade names containing: Unitrienol T-27

Farnesyl acetate
CAS 29548-30-9; EINECS 249-689-1
Synonyms: 2,6,10-Dodecatrien-1-ol, 3,7,11-trimethyl-, acetate; 3,7,11-Trimethyl-2,6,10-dodecatrien-1-ol, acetate
Definition: Ester of farnesol and acetic acid
Empirical: $C_{17}H_{28}O_2$
Trade names containing: Unitrienol T-27

Farnesyl alcohol. *See* Farnesol
Fast green FCF. *See* CI 42053
Fast green FCF. *See* FD&C Green No. 3
Fast red. *See* Amaranth
Fatty acids, coco, hydrogenated. *See* Hydrogenated coconut acid
Fatty acids, coconut oil, potassium salts. *See* Potassium cocoate
Fatty acids, coconut oil, sodium salts. *See* Sodium cocoate
Fatty acids, coconut oil, sulfoethyl esters, sodium salts. *See* Sodium cocoyl isethionate
Fatty acids, montan wax. *See* Montan acid wax
Fatty acids, tallow. *See* Tallow acid

FD&C Blue No. 1
CAS 2650-18-2; 3844-45-9; EINECS 223-339-8
Synonyms: Acid Blue 9 (noncertified); Patent Blue AC; Brilliant Blue FCF; CI 42090; Food blue 2
Classification: Triphenylmethane color
Empirical: $C_{37}H_{36}N_2O_9S_3 \cdot 2H_3N$
Properties: Greenish-blue powd., gran.; sol. (oz/gal): 52 oz propylene glycol, 36 oz glycerin, 25 oz dist. water, 2 oz 95% ethanol; sol. in ether, conc. sulfuric acid; m.w. 783.01
Toxicology: May cause allergic reactions; produces malignant tumors at site of injection and by injgestion in

rats; experimental neoplastigen; mutagenic data; heated to decomp., emits very toxic fumes of NO_x, Na_2O, and SO_x

Uses: Color additive; used in oral and topical drugs, buccals

Regulatory: FDA 21CFR §74.101, 74.1101, 74.2101, 82.101; banned in France, Finland; FDA approved for buccals, orals, topicals; permanently listed

Manuf./Distrib.: Crompton & Knowles; Hilton Davis; Tricon Colors

Manuf./Distrib. (pharm. & food): Crompton & Knowles; Hilton Davis; Spectrum Chem. Mfg.; Tricon Colors

See also CI 42090

FD&C Blue No. 2

CAS 860-22-0; EINECS 212-728-8

Synonyms: 2-(1,3-Dihydro-3-oxo-5-sulfo-2H-indol-2-ylidene)-2,3-dihydro-3-oxo-1H-indole-5-sulfonic acid disodium salt; Indigotine; Indigo carmine; Disodium indigo-5,5-disulfonate; Ceruleinum; Food Blue 1; CI 73015; Blue X

Classification: Indigoid color

Definition: Disodium salt of 5,5´-indigotin disulfonic acid

Empirical: $C_{16}H_8N_2O_8S_2$ • 2Na

Properties: Blue-brn. to red-brn. powd.; sol. in water, conc. sulfuric acid; sl. sol. in alcohol; m.w. 466.36

Precaution: Sensitive to light, oxidizing agents

Toxicology: LD50 (oral, rat) 2 g/kg; poison by IV route mod. toxic by ingestion, subcut. routes; experimental neoplastigen; mutagenic data; may cause brain tumors, asthma, rashes, hyperactivity; heated to decomp., emits very toxic fumes of SO_x, NO_x, Na_2O

Uses: Color additive; used in oral tablets and capsules, nylon surgical sutures, buccals

Regulatory: FDA 21CFR §74.102, 74.1102, 81.1; Europe listed; banned in Norway; FDA approved for orals, buccals

Manuf./Distrib.: Crompton & Knowles; Hilton Davis; Tricon Colors

Manuf./Distrib. (pharm. & food): Crompton & Knowles; Hilton Davis; Ruger; Spectrum Chem. Mfg.; Tricon Colors

See also CI 73015

FD&C Blue No. 1 aluminum lake

CAS 15792-67-3; 53026-57-6; 68921-42-6

Synonyms: Acid blue 9 aluminum lake (noncertified); Blue No. 3 (EEC); Blue No. 1 (Japan); CI 42090:2

Definition: Aluminum salt of FD&C Blue No. 1 extended on an alumina substrate

Formula: $C_{37}H_{36}N_2O_9S_3$ • xAl

Properties: Water-insol.

Uses: Pigment exhibiting bright blue hue in dispersion; used in orals, topicals

Regulatory: FDA 21CFR §81.1, 82.50, 82.51, 82.101, 176.180

Manuf./Distrib.: Crompton & Knowles

Manuf./Distrib. (pharm. & food): Hilton Davis; Ruger

FD&C Green No. 3

CAS 2353-45-9; EINECS 219-091-5

Synonyms: Fast Green FCF (noncertified); Food Green 3; CI 42053

Classification: Triphenylmethane color

Empirical: $C_{37}H_{36}O_{10}N_2S_3Na_2$

Properties: Red to brn.-violet powd.; sol. in water, conc. sulfuric acid, ethanol; m.w. 810.91

Toxicology: LD50 (oral, rat) > 2 g/kg; experimental neoplastigen; may cause bladder tumors; mutagenic data; heated to decomp., emits very toxic fumes of NO_x and SO_x

Uses: Colorant for orals, topicals; exhibits blueish-grn. hue in sol'n.

Regulatory: FDA 21CFR §74.203, 74.1203, 74.2203, 82.203; banned in EEC; FDA approved for orals, topicals

Manuf./Distrib.: Crompton & Knowles

Manuf./Distrib. (pharm. & food): Crompton & Knowles; Ruger; Spectrum Chem. Mfg.; Tricon Colors

See also CI 42053

FD&C Red No. 2. *See* Amaranth

FD&C Red No. 3

CAS 16423-68-0; EINECS 240-474-8

Synonyms: 3´,6´-Dihydroxy-2´,4´,5´,7´-tetraiodospiro[isobenzofuran-1(3H),9´-(9H)xanthen]-3-one disodium salt; Erythrosine; Erythrosine bluish; Acid red 51; Tetraiodofluorescein sodium salt; CI 45430; Food red 14

Classification: Xanthene color

Definition: Disodium salt of 2´,4´,5´,7´-tetraiodofluorescein

Empirical: $C_{20}H_6O_5I_4Na_2$

Properties: Bluish pink to brn. powd., gran.; sol. (oz/gal): 30 oz glycerin, 28 oz propylene glycol, 12 oz dist.

FD&C Red No. 4

water, 2 oz 95% ethanol; m.w. 879.84

Precaution: Suspected phototoxicity

Toxicology: LD50 (oral, rat) 1840 mg/kg; poison by IV route; mod. toxic by ingestion; human mutagenic data; may cause thyroid tumors, chromosomal damage, asthma, rashes, hyperactivity; heated to decomp., emits very toxic fumes of Na_2O and I^-

Uses: Colorant for tablets, capsules, and liq. oral formulations

Regulatory: FDA 21CFR §74.303, 74.1303, 81.1; Europe listed; FDA approved for orals

Manuf./Distrib.: Crompton & Knowles; Hilton Davis

Manuf./Distrib. (pharm. & food): Crompton & Knowles; Hilton Davis; Spectrum Chem. Mfg.; Tricon Colors

See also CI 45430

FD&C Red No. 4

CAS 4548-53-2; EINECS 224-909-9

Synonyms: 3-[(2,4-Dimethyl-5-sulfophenyl)azo]-4-hydroxy-1-naphthalenesulfonic acid disodium salt; Ponceau SX (noncertified); Food red 1; CI 14700

Classification: Monoazo color and coal tar dye

Empirical: $C_{18}H_{14}N_2O_7S_2Na_2$

Properties: M.w. 480.42

Toxicology: Shown to cause urinary bladder polyps and atrophy of adrenal gland in animals

Uses: Colorant for external pharmaceuticals

Regulatory: FDA 21CFR §74.1304, 174.2304, 82.304

Manuf./Distrib.: Crompton & Knowles

Manuf./Distrib. (pharm. & food): Crompton & Knowles; Hilton Davis

See also CI 14700

FD&C Red No. 40

CAS 25956-17-6

Synonyms: 6-Hydroxy-5-[(2-methoxy-5-methyl-4-sulfophenyl)azo]-2-naphthalenesulfonic acid disodium salt; Food red 17; NT red; Allura™ Red; Curry red (noncertified); CI 16035

Classification: Monoazo color

Empirical: $C_{18}H_{16}N_2O_8S_2Na_2$

Properties: Ylsh.-red powd., gran.; sol. (oz/gal): 26 oz dist. water, 4 oz glycerin, 2 oz propylene glycol; m.w. 498.46

Toxicology: Experimental reproductive effects; may cause lymph tumors; heated to decomp., emits very toxic fumes of NO_x and SO_x

Uses: Colorant for oral drug prods., topicals; exhibits orange-red hue in sol'n.

Regulatory: FDA 21CFR §74.340, 74.1340, 74.2340; banned in EEC, Japan, Norway, Sweden, Finland, Austria; FDA approved for orals, topicals

Manuf./Distrib.: Crompton & Knowles; Hilton Davis

Manuf./Distrib. (pharm. & food): Crompton & Knowles; Hilton Davis; Ruger; Spectrum Chem. Mfg.; Tricon Colors

See also CI 16035

FD&C Yellow No. 5

CAS 1934-21-0; EINECS 217-699-5

Synonyms: Trisodium-3-carboxy-5-hydroxy-1-p-sulfophenyl-4-p-sulfophenylazopyrazole; Tartrazine; Acid yellow 23 (noncertified); Food yellow 4; CI 19140

Classification: Pyrazole color

Empirical: $C_{16}H_9N_4O_9S_2Na_3$

Properties: Lemon yel. powd., gran.; greenish-yel. in sol'n.; sol. (oz/gal): 28 oz glycerin, 17 oz dist. water, 12 oz propylene glycol; m.w. 534.36

Precaution: Heated to dec., emits very toxic fumes of NO_x, SO_x, and Na_2O

Toxicology: LD50 (oral, mouse) 12,750 mg/kg; mildly toxic by ing.; experimental teratogen, reproductive effects; human mutagenic data; may cause allergies, asthma, rashes, hyperactivity, thyroid tumors, lyphocytic lymphomas; avoid for aspirin-sensitive persons

Uses: Colorant for OTC and prescription oral and topical pharmaceuticals

Regulatory: FDA 21CFR §74.705, 74.1705, 74.2705, 82.705; Europe listed; banned in Norway, Austria; FDA approved for orals

Manuf./Distrib.: Crompton & Knowles; Hilton Davis

Manuf./Distrib. (pharm. & food): Crompton & Knowles; Hilton Davis; Ruger; Spectrum Chem. Mfg.; Tricon Colors

See also CI 19140; Tartrazine

FD&C Yellow No. 6

CAS 2783-94-0; EINECS 220-491-7

Synonyms: 6-Hydroxy-5-[(4-sulfophenyl)azo]-2-naphthalenesulfonic acid disodium salt; Sunset yellow (noncertified); Food yellow 3; Orange yellow S; CI 15985
Classification: Coal tar monoazo color
Definition: Disodium salt of 1-p-sulfophenylazo-2-naphthol-6-sulfonic acid
Empirical: $C_{16}H_{10}N_2O_7S_2Na_2$
Properties: Reddish-yel. powd., gran.; sol. (oz/gal): 23 oz dist. water, 14 oz glycerin, 2 oz propylene glycol; sol. in conc. sulfuric acid; sl. sol. in abs. alcohol; m.w. 452.36
Toxicology: LD50 (IP, rat) 4600 mg/kg; mod. toxic by IP route; may cause allergies, kidney tumors, chromosomal damage; heated to decomp., emits very toxic fumes of NO_x and SO_x
Uses: Colorant for inhalants, orals, topicals
Regulatory: FDA 21CFR §74.706, 74.1706, 74.2706, 81.1, 82.706, 201.20; banned in Norway, Sweden; FDA approved for inhalants, orals, topicals; pernanently listed
Manuf./Distrib.: Crompton & Knowles; Hilton Davis
Manuf./Distrib. (pharm. & food): Crompton & Knowles; Hilton Davis; Ruger; Spectrum Chem. Mfg.; Tricon Colors
See also CI 15985

Feculose
Uses: Used in orals
Regulatory: FDA approved for orals

2-Fenchanol. *See* Fenchyl alcohol
Fenchol. *See* Fenchyl alcohol
(+)-Fenchol. *See* Fenchyl alcohol

l-Fenchone
CAS 7787-20-4
Empirical: $C_{10}H_{16}O$
Properties: M.w. 152.24; dens. 0.948; m.p. 5-6 C; b.p. 192-194 C; flash pt. 127 F
Uses: Sweet flavoring agent
Manuf./Distrib. (pharm. & food): Aldrich

Fenchyl alcohol
CAS 1632-73-1; EINECS 216-639-5
FEMA 2480
Synonyms: (1S)-1,3,3-Trimethylbicyclo[2.2.1]heptan-2-ol; Fenchol; (+)-Fenchol; 2-Fenchanol; 1,3,3-Trimethyl-2-norbornanol
Empirical: $C_{10}H_{18}O$
Properties: Camphor-like odor; sol. in alcohol; sl. sol. in water; m.w. 154.25; m.p. 40-43 C; b.p. 201-202 C; flash pt. 165 F; ref. index 1.473
Uses: Lemon-like synthetic flavoring agent
Regulatory: FDA 21CFR §172.515; FEMA GRAS
Manuf./Distrib. (pharm. & food): Aldrich; Chr. Hansen's

Fennel
FEMA 2481, 2482 (sweet)
Synonyms: Foeniculum; Foeniculum vulgare; Fennel fruit; Fennel seed; Sweet fennel
Definition: Dried ripe fruit of cultivated varieties of *Foeniculum vulgare*
Precaution: Protect from light
Uses: Natural flavoring agent, carminative; in herbal remedies for respiratory tract disorders
Regulatory: FEMA GRAS; JP compliance; Japan approved
Manuf./Distrib. (pharm. & food): Chart

Fennel fruit. *See* Fennel

Fennel oil
CAS 8006-84-6
FEMA 2483
Synonyms: Bitter fennel oil; Sweet fennel oil
Definition: Volatile oil from steam distillation of *Foeniculum vulgare*, contg. 50-60% anethole, 20% fenchone, pinene, limonene, dipentene, phellandrene
Properties: Colorless to pale yel. liq., fennel odor and taste; sol. in 1 vol 90% alcohol; very sol. in chloroform, ether; sl. sol. in water; dens. 0.953-0.973 (25/25 C); ref. index 1.5280-1.5380 (20 C)
Precaution: Keep cool, well closed; protect from light
Toxicology: LD50 (oral, rat) 3120 mg/kg; mod. toxic by ingestion; mutagenic data; severe skin irritant; heated to decomp., emits acrid smoke and irritating fumes

Fennel seed

Uses: Natural flavoring agent; aromatic carminative; in herbal remedies for respiratory tract disorders
Regulatory: FDA 21CFR §182.10, 182.20, GRAS; FEMA GRAS; JP compliance
Manuf./Distrib. (pharm. & food): Chart

Fennel seed. *See* Fennel
Ferrate(4-), hexakis(cyano-C)-, iron(3+) 3:4). *See* Ferric ferrocyanide
Ferric ammonium citrate. *See* Iron ammonium citrate
Ferric ammonium citrate, green. *See* Iron ammonium citrate

Ferric ammonium ferrocyanide
CAS 25869-00-5; 12240-15-2
Synonyms: Iron blue
Classification: Inorganic salt
Uses: Color additive for external pharmaceuticals
Regulatory: FDA 21CFR §73.1298, 73.2298

Ferric ferrocyanide
CAS 14038-43-8; EINECS 237-875-5
Synonyms: Ferrate(4-), hexakis(cyano-C)-, iron(3+) 3:4); CI 77510; CI 77520; Pigment blue 27; Prussian blue
Classification: Inorganic salt
Formula: $C_6FeN_6 \cdot {}^4/_3Fe$
Properties: M.w. 286.38
Uses: Color additive for external pharmaceuticals
Regulatory: FDA 21CFR §73.1299, 73.2299; permanently listed
Manuf./Distrib. (pharm. & food): Hilton Davis
See also CI 77510

Ferric oxide
CAS 1309-37-1 (anhyd.); EINECS 215-168-2
Synonyms: Ferric oxide red; Iron (III) oxide; Red iron trioxide; Red iron oxide; Ferrosoferric oxide
Empirical: Fe_2O_3
Properties: Red-brn. to blk. cryst.; sol. in acids; insol. in water, alcohol, ether; m.w. 159.69; dens. 5.240; m.p. 1538 C (dec.)
Precaution: Catalyzes the potentially explosive polymerization of ethylene oxide
Toxicology: TLV:TWA 5 mg (Fe)/m^3 (vapor, dust); LD50 (IP, rat) 5500 mg/kg; irritant; poison by subcutaneous route; suspected human carcinogen; experimental tumorigen
Uses: Colorant for oral pharmaceuticals
Regulatory: FDA 21CFR §73.200 (limitation 0.25%), 186.1300, 186.1374, GRAS as indirect food additive; FDA approved for orals; USP/NF compliance
Manuf./Distrib.: Aldrich; BASF; Bayer Inc.; Crompton & Knowles; Kerr-McGee; Spectrum Chem. Mfg.
Manuf./Distrib. (pharm. & food): Aldrich
See also CI 77491

Ferric oxide red. *See* Ferric oxide

Ferric pyrophosphate
CAS 10058-44-3 (anhyd.); EINECS 233-190-0
Synonyms: Iron (III) pyrophosphate
Empirical: $Fe_4(P_{207})_3 \cdot xH_2O$
Properties: Tan or ylsh. wh. powd.; sol. in min. acids; pract. insol. in water, acetic acid; m.w. 745.25 (anhyd.)
Toxicology: Heated to decomp., emits toxic fumes of PO$_x$
Uses: Source of nutritional iron in iron supplement preps.
Regulatory: FDA 21CFR §182.5304, 184.1304, GRAS; Japan approved
Manuf./Distrib.: Lohmann
Manuf./Distrib. (pharm. & food): Lohmann

Ferrosoferric oxide. *See* Ferric oxide

Ferrous citrate
CAS 23383-11-1 (anhyd.); 22242-53-1; EINECS 245-625-1
Synonyms: Iron (II) citrate
Empirical: $C_6H_6FeO_7$
Properties: Sl. colored powd. or wh. cryst.; sol. in water; insol. in alcohol; m.w. 245.96
Toxicology: Heated to decomp., emits acrid smoke and irritating fumes
Uses: Used in intravenous pharmaceuticals
Regulatory: FDA 21CFR §184.1307c, GRAS; FDA approved for intravenous
Manuf./Distrib.: Lohmann

Ferrous-ferric oxide. *See* CI 77499

Ferrous fumarate
CAS 141-01-5; EINECS 205-447-7
Synonyms: Iron (II) fumarate; 2-Butenedioic acid ferrous salt
Definition: A salt of ferrous iron combined with fumaric acid, contg. 31.3% min. total iron, $\leq$ 2% ferric iron
Empirical: $C_4H_2O_4$ • Fe
Formula: $FeC_4H_2O_4$
Properties: Reddish-orange to reddish-brn. gran. powd., odorless, almost tasteless; sol. 0.14 g/100 ml water, < 0.01 g/100 ml alcohol; m.w. 169.91; dens. 2.435
Toxicology: LD50 (oral, rat) 3850 mg/kg; poison by intraperitoneal route; mod. toxic by ingestion and subcutaneous routes; heated to decomp., emits acrid smoke and irritating fumes; ACGIH TLV: TWA 1 mg/(Fe)/m^3
Uses: Dietary supplement; source of iron in iron supplement preps.
Regulatory: FDA 21CFR §172.350, 184.1307d, GRAS; BP compliance
Manuf./Distrib.: Chemie Linz UK; Hüls AG; Lohmann; Nichia Kagaku Kogyo; Schweizerhall
Manuf./Distrib. (pharm. & food): Am. Roland; Int'l. Sourcing; Lohmann; Ruger; Spectrum Chem. Mfg.
Trade names: Descote® Ferrous Fumarate 60%
Trade names containing: Cap-Shure® FF-165-60; Durkote Ferrous Fumarate/Hydrog. Veg. Oil

Ferrous gluconate
CAS 299-29-6 (anhyd.); 6047-12-7; 12389-15-0; EINECS 206-076-3
Synonyms: Iron (II) gluconate; Niconate
Empirical: $C_{12}H_{22}O_{14}Fe$ • $2H_2O$
Formula: $Fe(C_6H_{11}O_7)_2$•$2H_2O$
Properties: Yellowish-gray or pale greenish-yel. fine powd. or gran., sl. odor of caramel; sol. in water, glycerol; insol. in alcohol; m.w. 446.1 (anhyd.), 482.18 (dihydrate)
Precaution: Combustible
Toxicology: LD50 (oral, rat) 2237 mg/kg; poison by intraperitoneal and intravenous routes; moderately toxic by ingestion; experimental tumorigen and teratogen; heated to decomp., emits acrid smoke and irritating fumes; ACGIH TLV:TWA 1 mg(Fe)/m^3
Uses: Mineral source for pharmaceuticals; source of iron in iron supplement preps.
Regulatory: FDA 21CFR §73.160, 182.5308, 182.8308, 184.1308, GRAS; Japan approved (0.15 g/kg max. as iron); BP, Ph.Eur. compliance
Manuf./Distrib.: Lohmann
Manuf./Distrib. (pharm. & food): Am. Roland; Int'l. Sourcing; Lohmann; Ruger; Spectrum Chem. Mfg.
Trade names: Gluconal® FE

Ferrous lactate
CAS 5905-52-2; EINECS 227-608-0
Synonyms: Iron (II) lactate; Lactic acid iron (2+) salt (2:1)
Empirical: $C_6H_{10}O_6$ • Fe (anhyd.); $C_6H_{10}FeO_6$ • $3H_2O$ (trihydrate)
Formula: $Fe(CH_3CHOHCOO)_2$ • xH_2O
Properties: Anhyd.: m.w. 233.99; Trihydrate: Greenish-wh. powd., sl. char. odor, mild sweet ferruginous taste; deliq.; sol. in water, alkali citrates; almost insol. in alcohol; m.w. 287.97
Precaution: Combustible; keep well closed and protected from light
Toxicology: TLV:TWA 1 mg(Fe)/m^3; LD50 (oral, mouse) 147 mg/kg, (IV, rabbits) 287 mg/kg; poison by ingestion; experimental tumorigen; heated to decomp, emits acrid smoke and irritating fumes
Uses: Nutrient supplement
Regulatory: FDA 21CFR §182.5311, 182.8311, 184.1311, GRAS; Japan approved
Manuf./Distrib.: Lohmann; Spectrum Chem. Mfg.
Manuf./Distrib. (pharm. & food): Am. Roland
Trade names: Puramex® FE

Ferrous oxide. *See* CI 77489

Ferrous sulfate
CAS 7720-78-7 (anhyd.); 7782-63-0 (heptahydrate)
Synonyms: Iron sulfate (ous); Iron (II) sulfate (1:1); Iron vitriol; Copperas; Green vitriol; Sal chalybis
Empirical: O_4S • Fe (anhyd.), FeO_4S • $7H_2O$ (heptahydrate)
Properties: Grayish wh. to buff powd., odorless; hygroscopic; efflorescent in dry air; slowly sol. in water; insol. in alcohol; m.w. 151.91 (anhyd.), 278.01 (heptahydrate); dens. 1.89; m.p. 64 C
Toxicology: TLV:TWA 1 mg(Fe)/m^3; LD50 (oral, rat) 319 mg/kg; human poison by ingestion; human systemic effects; experimental tumorigen, reproductive effects; mutagenic data; heated to decomp., emits toxic fumes of SO_x

First aid plant

Uses: Astringent and deodorant; used medicinally as a source of iron in iron supplement preps.
Regulatory: FDA 21CFR §182.5315, 182.8315, GRAS; Japan approved; BP, Ph.Eur. compliance
Manuf./Distrib.: EM Industries; J.M. Huber; Lohmann; Mallinckrodt; Spectrum Chem. Mfg.
Manuf./Distrib. (pharm. & food): Int'l. Sourcing; Mallinckrodt; Ruger; Spectrum Chem. Mfg.
Trade names: Descote® Ferrous Sulfate 60%
Trade names containing: Durkote Ferrous Sulfate/Hydrog. Veg. Oil

First aid plant. *See* Aloe vera gel

Fish glycerides
CAS 100085-40-3
Definition: Mixture of mono, di and triglycerides expressed or extracted from menhaden, hake or similar oil-bearing fish
Uses: Ingred. in pharmaceutical waxes
Trade names containing: Ross Japan Wax Substitute 525

Flaming red. *See* D&C Red No. 36
Flavaxin. *See* Riboflavin
Flaxseed oil. *See* Linseed oil
Flour, soy. *See* Soy flour
Flowers of zinc. *See* Zinc oxide

Fluorescein
CAS 2321-07-5; EINECS 219-031-8
Synonyms: Resorcinolphthalein; Diresorcinolphthalein
Empirical: $C_{20}H_{12}O_5$
Uses: Diagnostic marker for viable tissue; topical agent to detect corneal lacerations
Usage level: 15-30 mg/kg (IV dose)
Regulatory: BP compliance
Manuf./Distrib.: EM Industries; R.W. Greeff; Hilton Davis; Kraeber GmbH; U.S. Biochemical

Fluorescein. *See* D&C Yellow No. 7
Fluorocarbon-11. *See* Trichlorofluoromethane
Fluorocarbon-12. *See* Dichlorodifluoromethane
Fluorocarbon-114. *See* Dichlorotetrafluoroethane
4-Fluorophenol. *See* p-Fluorophenol

p-Fluorophenol
CAS 371-41-5; EINECS 206-736-0
Synonyms: 4-Fluorophenol
Empirical: C_6H_5FO
Formula: FC_6H_4OH
Properties: Wh. cryst. solid; sol. in water; m.w. 112.10; dens. 1.1889; m.p. 46-48 C; b.p. 185 C; flash pt. 68 C
Toxicology: Irritant
Uses: Intermediate for pharmaceuticals
Manuf./Distrib.: Aldrich; ICI Am.; PCR; Schweizerhall
Manuf./Distrib. (pharm. & food): Aldrich

Fluorotrichloromethane. *See* Trichlorofluoromethane
Foeniculum. *See* Fennel
Foeniculum vulgare. *See* Fennel
Folacin. *See* Folic acid
Folate. *See* Folic acid

Folic acid
CAS 59-30-3; EINECS 200-419-0
Synonyms: Folacin; Folate; Pteroylglutamic acid; Vitamin Bc; Vitamin M
Empirical: $C_{19}H_{19}N_7O_6$
Properties: Orange-yel. need. or platelets, odorless; sol. in dil. alkali hydroxide, carbonate sol'ns.; sl. sol. in water; insol. in lipid solvs., acetone, alcohol, ether; m.w. 441.45
Toxicology: LD50 (IV, rat) 500 mg/kg; poison by intraperitoneal and IV routes; experimental teratogen, reproductive effects; mutagenic data; heated to decomp., emits toxic fumes of NO_x
Uses: Vitamin
Regulatory: FDA 21CFR §172.345; Japan approved; BP, Ph.Eur. compliance
Manuf./Distrib. (pharm. & food): Am. Roland; Unipex

Trade names: Folic Acid USP, FCC No. 20383
Trade names containing: Folic Acid 10% Trituration No. 69997

Food blue 1. *See* FD&C Blue No. 2
Food blue 2. *See* FD&C Blue No. 1
Food freezant 12. *See* Dichlorodifluoromethane
Food green 3. *See* CI 42053; FD&C Green No. 3
Food orange 5. *See* Carotene; CI 40800
Food orange 8. *See* Canthaxanthine; CI 40850
Food red 1. *See* CI 14700; FD&C Red No. 4
Food red 14. *See* FD&C Red No. 3
Food red 15. *See* D&C Red No. 19
Food red 17. *See* CI 16035; FD&C Red No. 40

Food starch modified
CAS 53124-00-8; 65996-62-5; 65996-63-6
Synonyms: Modified food starch
Properties: Wh. powd., odorless, tasteless; insol. in water, alcohol, ether, chloroform
Toxicology: Heated to decomp., emits acrid smoke and irritating fumes
Uses: Binder, diluent, absorbent, and disintegrant in tablets
Regulatory: FDA 21CFR §172.892, 178.3520
Manuf./Distrib. (pharm. & food): ADM; Avebe BV; Cargill; Cerestar Int'l.; Grain Processing; Humphrey; Nat'l. Starch & Chem.; Norba; Penwest Foods; J L Priestley; Roquette UK; Sandoz Nutrition; A E Staley Mfg.; Zumbro
Trade names: Pure-Dent® B890
Trade names containing: Canthaxanthin Beadlets 10%; Dry Beta Carotene Beadlets 10% CWS No. 65633; Dry Beta Carotene Beadlets 10% No. 65661; Dry Vitamin A Palmitate Type 250-SD No. 65378; Dry Vitamin D_3 Beadlets Type 850 No. 652550401, 652550601; Palma-Sperse® Type 250-S No. 65322; Palma-Sperse® Type 250A/50 D-S No. 65221; Vitamin A Palmitate Type 250-CWS No. 65312; Vitamin B_{12} 0.1% SD No. 65354; Vitamin B_{12} 1.0% SD No. 65305

Food yellow 3. *See* CI 15985; FD&C Yellow No. 6
Food yellow 4. *See* FD&C Yellow No. 5

Formaldehyde
CAS 50-00-0; EINECS 200-001-8
UN No. 1198, 2209
Synonyms: Oxymethylene; Formalin; Formic aldehyde; Aldehyde C-1; Methanal
Empirical: CH_2O
Formula: HCHO
Properties: Colorless gas, strong pungent odor; avail. commercially as aq. sol'ns. (37-50% in methanol); sol. in water, alcohol; m.w. 30.03; dens. 1.083; b.p. -19 C; f.p. -118 C; flash pt. 56 C; ref. index 1.3765
Precaution: Combustible when exposed to heat, or flame; mod. fire risk; explosive limits 7-73%; can react vigorously with oxidizers
Toxicology: TLV 1 ppm in air; LD50 (oral, rat) 800 mg/kg; human poison by ing., systemic effects, skin/eye irritant, mutagenic data; toxic by inh.; vapor intensely irritating to mucous membranes; suspected human carcinogen; heated to decomp., emits acrid smoke
Uses: Antimicrobial preservative used in biologics, topicals, hepatitis B vaccine; sterilizer for kidney dialyzer membranes
Regulatory: FDA 21CFR §173.340 (1% of dimethicone content), 175.105, 175.210, 176.170, 1876.180, 176.200, 176.210, 177.2410, 177.2800, 178.3120, 573.460; FDA approved for topicals; BP compliance (sol'n.)
Manuf./Distrib.: Aqualon; DuPont; Farleyway Chem. Ltd; Georgia-Pacific Resins; Hoechst Celanese; Mallinckrodt; Mitsubishi Gas; Monsanto; Spectrum Chem. Mfg.
Manuf./Distrib. (pharm. & food): Hoechst Celanese; Monsanto; Aldrich; Ruger; Spectrum Chem. Mfg.

p-Formaldehyde. *See* Paraformaldehyde
Formalin. *See* Formaldehyde
Formic acid butyl ester. *See* Butyl formate
Formic acid ethyl ester. *See* Ethyl formate
Formic acid propyl ester. *See* Propyl formate
Formic aldehyde. *See* Formaldehyde
Formic ether. *See* Ethyl formate
4-Formyl phenol. *See* p-Hydroxybenzaldehyde
p-Formyl phenol. *See* p-Hydroxybenzaldehyde

Fossil wax. *See* Ozokerite
Fo-ti-tieng extract. *See* Hydrocotyl extract
Frambinone. *See* 4-(p-Hydroxyphenyl)-2-butanone
French chalk. *See* Talc
β-D-Fructofuranosyl-α-D-glucopyranoside. *See* Sucrose

Fructose
CAS 57-48-7 (D-); 7660-25-5; EINECS 200-333-3 (D-)
Synonyms: Levulose; Laevulose; D-Fructose; Fruit sugar; Laevosan
Definition: Sugar occurring in fruit and honey
Empirical: $C_6H_{12}O_6$
Properties: Colorless cryst. or wh. cryst. powd., odorless, sweet taste; hygroscopic; sol. in methanol, ethanol, water, pyridine; m.w. 180.18; dens. 1.6; m.p. 103-105 C
Toxicology: Experimental tumorigen; heated to decomp., emits acrid smoke and fumes
Uses: Nutritive sweetener, tablet/capsule diluent; used in orals
Regulatory: GRAS; FDA approved for orals; USP/NF, BP, Ph.Eur. compliance
Manuf./Distrib.: Am. Maize Prods.; Corn Prods.; Laevosan GmbH; Pfanstiehl Labs; A.E. Staley Mfg.
Manuf./Distrib. (pharm. & food): Advanced Sweeteners; Aldrich; Am. Roland; British Arkady; Cargill; Cerestar Int'l.; Corn Prods.; Farbest Brands; Maruzen Fine Chems.; MLG Enterprises; Penta Mfg.; Ruger; Siber Hegner; Spectrum Chem. Mfg.; A.E. Staley Mfg.; Xyrofin UK
Trade names: CornSweet® Crystalline Fructose; Fructofin® C
Trade names containing: Sweetrex®

D-Fructose. *See* Fructose
Fruit sugar. *See* Fructose
Fuller's earth. *See* Attapulgite

Fumaric acid
CAS 110-17-8; EINECS 203-743-0
FEMA 2488
Synonyms: Allomaleic acid; Boletic acid; trans-1,2-Ethylenedicarboxylic acid; 2-Butenedioic acid; trans-Butenedioic acid; Lichenic acid
Classification: Dicarboxylic acid
Empirical: $C_4H_4O_4$
Formula: HOOCCH:CHCOOH
Properties: Wh. cryst., odorless, acidic taste; sol. in alcohol; sl. sol. in water, ether; very sl. sol. in chloroform; m.w. 116.08; dens. 1.635 (20/4 C); m.p. 287 C; b.p. 290 C; flash pt. (COC) 282 C
Precaution: Combustible when exposed to heat or flame; can react vigorously with oxidizers
Toxicology: LD50 (oral, rat) 10,700 mg/kg, (dermal, rabbit) 20,000 mg/kg; poison by intraperitoneal route; mildly toxic by ingestion and skin contact; skin and eye irritant; heated to decomp., emits acrid smoke and irritating fumes
Uses: Acidifying agent; antidandruff ingred.; cleaning agent for dentures; used in orals
Regulatory: FDA 21CFR §172.350; USDA 9CFR §318.7, 381.147; BATF 27CFR §240.1051, limitation 25 lb/ 1000 gal wine; FEMA GRAS; Japan approved; Europe listed; UK approved; FDA approved for orals; USP/ NF, BP compliance
Manuf./Distrib.: Aceto; Ashland; Browning; The Chemical Co.; Chemie Linz UK; Haarmann & Reimer; Hüls Am.; Lonza; Mitsubishi Gas; Monsanto; Schaefer Salt; Schweizerhall; United Min. & Chem.; Van Waters & Rogers
Manuf./Distrib. (pharm. & food): AB Tech.; Aldrich; Am. Roland; Ashland; Bartek; Browne & Dureau Int'l.; Browning; Cheil Foods UK; Cornelius; Forum Chems.; Haarmann & Reimer; Int'l. Sourcing; Jungbunzlauer; W Kündig; Penta Mfg.; Pfizer; Ruger; Spectrum Chem. Mfg.; Tesco; Thymly Prods.; Unipex

Fumed silica. *See* Silica
Fuming liquid arsenic. *See* Arsenic trichloride
2-Furaldehyde. *See* Furfural
2-Furancarbinol. *See* Furfuryl alcohol
2-Furancarboxaldehyde. *See* Furfural
Furan-2-carboxylic acid. *See* 2-Furoic acid
2,5-Furandione. *See* Maleic anhydride
2,5-Furandione, polymer with methoxyethylene. *See* PVM/MA copolymer
2-Furanmethanol. *See* Furfuryl alcohol

Furan polymer
CAS 110-00-9
UN No. 2389

Synonyms: Furan resin; Divniylene oxide; Furfuran
Uses: Pharmaceutical intermediate
Manuf./Distrib.: QO; Spectrum Chem. Mfg.
Manuf./Distrib. (pharm. & food): Aldrich
Trade names: QO® Furan

Furan resin. *See* Furan polymer

Furfural
CAS 98-01-1; EINECS 202-627-7
FEMA 2489
Synonyms: 2-Furaldehyde; 2-Furancarboxaldehyde; Artificial oil of ants
Classification: Cyclic aldehyde
Empirical: $C_5H_4O_2$
Formula: C_4H_3OCHO
Properties: Colorless liq. (pure); reddish-brown (on exposure to air and light); almond-like odor; sol. in alcohol, ether, benzene, 8.3% in water; m.w. 96.08; dens. 1.1598 (20/4 C); f.p. -36.5 C; b.p. 161.7 C; ref. index 1.5260 (20 C); flash pt. 60 C
Precaution: Flamm. or combustible
Toxicology: LD50 (oral, rat) 65 mg/kg; poison by ingestion, intraperitoneal, subcutaneous routes; moderately toxic by inhalation; TLV 2 ppm in air; irritates mucous membranes, acts on CNS
Uses: Sweet synthetic flavoring agent
Regulatory: FDA 21CFR §175.105; FEMA GRAS; Japan approved as flavoring
Manuf./Distrib.: Aldrich; Allchem Ind.; Penta Mfg.; QO; Spectrum Chem. Mfg.
Manuf./Distrib. (pharm. & food): Aldrich

Furfuralcohol. *See* Furfuryl alcohol

Furfuryl acetate
CAS 623-17-6
FEMA 2490
Empirical: $C_7H_8O_3$
Properties: M.w. 140.14; dens. 1.118; b.p. 175-177 C; flash pt. 150 F
Uses: Fruity banana-like flavoring agent
Regulatory: FEMA GRAS
Manuf./Distrib. (pharm. & food): Aldrich

Furfuryl alcohol
CAS 98-00-0; EINECS 202-626-1
FEMA 2491
Synonyms: 2-Furancarbinol; 2-Furanmethanol; 2-Hydroxymethylfuran; α-Furylcarbinol; 2-Furylcarbinol; Furfuralcohol
Empirical: $C_5H_6O_2$
Formula: $C_4H_3OCH_2OH$
Properties: Colorless mobile liq., brn.-dk. red (air/lt. exposed), low odor, cooked sugar taste; sol. in alc., chloroform, benzene; misc. with water but unstable; m.w. 98.10; dens. 1.1285 (20/4 C); m.p. -29 C; b.p. 170 C; flash pt. (OC) 75 C; ref. index 1.485
Toxicology: TLV 10 ppm in air; TLV:TWA 2 ppm (skin); LD50 (rat, oral) 275 mg/kg; poisonous
Uses: Synthetic flavoring agent
Regulatory: FEMA GRAS
Manuf./Distrib.: AC Ind.; Aldrich; Allchem Ind.; Ashland; Browning; Great Lakes; Penta Mfg.; QO; Schweizerhall; Spectrum Chem. Mfg.; Van Waters & Rogers
Manuf./Distrib. (pharm. & food): Aldrich

Furfuryl butyrate
CAS 623-21-2
Empirical: $C_9H_{12}O_3$
Properties: M.w. 168.19; dens. 1.053; b.p. 129-130 C (52 mm); flash pt. 195 F
Uses: Fruity grape-like flavoring agent
Manuf./Distrib. (pharm. & food): Aldrich

2-Furoic acid
CAS 88-14-2; EINECS 201-803-0
Synonyms: Furan-2-carboxylic acid; Pyromucic acid
Empirical: $C_5H_4O_3$
Properties: Monoclinic prisms; sol. 1 g/26 ml water (15 C); sol. in alcohol, ether; m.w. 112.09; m.p. 128-130

2-Furylcarbinol

C; b.p. 230-232 C (760 mm)
Toxicology: Irritant
Manuf./Distrib.: R.W. Greeff; Penta Mfg.; QO
Manuf./Distrib. (pharm. & food): Aldrich

2-Furylcarbinol. *See* Furfuryl alcohol
α-Furylcarbinol. *See* Furfuryl alcohol

4-O-β-D-Galactopyranosyl-D-glucitol. *See* Lactitol monohydrate
4-O-β-Galactopyranosyl D-glucose. *See* Lactose

D-Galactose
CAS 59-23-4; EINECS 200-416-4
Classification: Monosaccharide
Empirical: $C_6H_{12}O_6$
Properties: Wh. cryst.; hygroscopic; sol. in hot water; sl. sol. in glycerol; m.w. 180.16; m.p. 168-170 C (dec.)
Uses: Sweetener; used in orals, as a diagnostic aid
Regulatory: FDA approved for orals; BP compliance
Manuf./Distrib.: Fluka; Spectrum Chem. Mfg.
Manuf./Distrib. (pharm. & food): Aldrich; Fluka; Ruger

Gallic acid
CAS 149-91-7; 5995-86-8 (monohydrate); EINECS 205-749-9
Synonyms: 3,4,5-Trihydroxybenzoic acid
Empirical: $C_7H_6O_5$ (anhyd.) or $C_7H_6O_5 \cdot H_2O$ (monohydrate)
Formula: $C_6H_2(OH)_3CO_2H$ (anhyd.) or $C_6H_2(OH)_3CO_2H \cdot H_2O$ (monohydrate)
Properties: Need.; hygroscopic; sol. (1 g/ml): 87 ml water, 6 ml alcohol, 100 ml ether, 10 ml glycerin, 5 ml acetone; pract. insol. in benzene, chloroforom, petroleum ether; m.w. 170.12 (anhyd.), 188.14 (monohydrate); dens. 1.694; m.p. 258-265 C (dec.)
Precaution: Protect from light
Toxicology: LD50 (oral, rabbit) 5 g/kg; irritant
Uses: Astringent and antioxidant in pharmaceuticals
Regulatory: Japan approved; BP compliance
Manuf./Distrib.: Aceto; Fuji Chem. Ind.; Mallinckrodt; Penta Mfg.; Spectrum Chem. Mfg.; U.S. Biochemical
Manuf./Distrib. (pharm. & food): Aldrich; Integra; Mallinckrodt; Penta Mfg.; Ruger

Gallic acid, bismuth basic salt. *See* Bismuth subgallate
Gallic acid propyl ester. *See* Propyl gallate
Gallotannic acid. *See* Tannic acid
Gallotannin. *See* Tannic acid
Gardenol. *See* α-Methylbenzyl acetate
Garden sage. *See* Sage
Garden thyme. *See* Thyme
GDL. *See* Gluconolactone

Gelatin
CAS 9000-70-8; EINECS 232-554-6
Synonyms: Gelatine; White gelatin
Definition: Obtained from partial hydrolysis of collagen derived from animal skin, connective tissues, and bones; Type A is derived from acid-treated precursor, Type B from alkali-treated precursor
Properties: Faint yel. or amber flake or powd., sl.char. bouillon-like odor in sol'n., tasteless; sol. in warm water, glycerol, acetic acid; insol. in org. solvs., alcohol, chloroform, ether, fixed and volatile oils; amphoteric
Precaution: Stable in air when dry, but subject to microbic decomp. when moist or in sol'n.
Toxicology: LD50 (rat, oral) 5 g/kg; may cause anaphylactoid reactions
Uses: Emulsifier, vehicle, binder, suspending agent, tablet binder/coating (hard/soft capsules, microencapsulation), wound/burn healing, surgical sponges, ointments, suppositories, dentals, inhalants, IM injectables, intravenous, orals, topicals, vaginals
Regulatory: FDA 21CFR §133.133, 133.134, 133.162, 133.178.133.179, 182.70; GRAS; Japan approved; FDA approved for dentals, inhalants, intramuscular injectables, intravenous, IV (infusion), orals, topicals; USP/NF, BP, Ph.Eur. compliance
Manuf./Distrib.: Ashland; Croda; DynaGel; G Fiske & Co Ltd; Hormel; Nitta Gelatin
Manuf./Distrib. (pharm. & food): Aldrich; Alfa; Browning; Cheil Foods UK; Chemcolloids Ltd.; Croda Food;

Dena AG; DynaGel; Ellis & Everard; Foodtech; Gelatine Prods.; Hormel Foods; N I Ibrahim; Integra; Mallinckrodt; Lucas Meyer; Penta Mfg.; Ruger; Sanofi; Siber Hegner; Spectrum Chem. Mfg.; Spice King; Vyse Gelatine; World Trade Service

Trade names: Bone Gelatin Type B 200 Bloom; Croda 50 Bloom Gelatin; Croda 60 Bloom Alkaline Processed Gelatin; Croda 160 Bloom Limed Gelatin; Croda 190 Bloom Acid Ossein Gelatin; Croda 250 Bloom Acid Ossein Gelatin; Crodyne BY-19; Edible Beef Gelatin; Gelatin USP/NF, Type A; Gelatin XF; Liquid Fish Gelatin Conc.; P-4 Pharmaceutical Gelatin; P-5 Pharmaceutical Gelatin; P-6 Pharmaceutical Gelatin; P-7 Pharmaceutical Gelatin; P-8 Pharmaceutical Gelatin; P-9 Pharmaceutical Gelatin; P-10 Pharmaceutical Gelatin; Spray Dried Fish Gelatin; Spray Dried Hydrolysed Fish Gelatin; Vee Gee Pharmaceutical Gelatins

Trade names containing: Canthaxanthin Beadlets 10%; Dry Beta Carotene Beadlets 10% CWS No. 65633; Dry Beta Carotene Beadlets 10% No. 65661; Dry Vitamin D_3 Beadlets Type 850 No. 652550401, 652550601; Dry Vitamin D_3 Type 100 CWS No. 65242; Dry Vitamin E Acetate 50% Type CWS/F No. 652530001; Palma-Sperse® Type 250-S No. 65322; Palma-Sperse® Type 250A/50 D-S No. 65221; Spray Dried Fish Gelatin/Maltodextrin

Gelatine. *See* Gelatin

Gellan gum
CAS 71010-52-1; EINECS 275-117-5
Synonyms: Gum gellan
Definition: High m.w. heteropolysaccharide gum produced by pure-culture fermentation of a carbohydrate with *Pseudomonas elodea*
Uses: Gellant
Regulatory: FDA 21CFR §172.665; Japan, JECFA, Canada approvals
Manuf./Distrib. (pharm. & food): Kelco Int'l.; Spectrum Chem. Mfg.
Trade names: GELRITE®

Gelose. *See* Agar

Gentian
Synonyms: Bitter root; Gentiana; Gentiana lutea; Gentian root
Definition: Dried rhizome and roots of *Gentiana lutea*
Precaution: Protect from light
Uses: Bitter in alcoholic infusions, bitter mixts., homeopathic medicine
Regulatory: FDA 21CFR §172.510; BP, Ph.Eur., JP compliance
Manuf./Distrib. (pharm. & food): Chart

Gentiana. *See* Gentian
Gentiana lutea. *See* Gentian
Gentian root. *See* Gentian

Gentisic acid
CAS 490-79-9; EINECS 207-718-5
Synonyms: 2,5-Dihydroxybenzoic acid
Empirical: $C_7H_6O_4$
Formula: $(HO)_2C_6H_3CO_2H$
Properties: Cryst.; sol. in water, alcohol, ether; insol. in chloroform, benzene; m.w. 154.12; m.p. 205 C (dec.)
Toxicology: Irritant
Uses: Used in intravenous
Regulatory: FDA approved for intravenous
Manuf./Distrib.: Aldrich
Manuf./Distrib. (pharm. & food): Aldrich

Gentisic acid ethanolamide
Synonyms: 2,5-Dihydroxybenzoic acid ethanolamide
Empirical: $C_9H_{11}NO_4$
Properties: Wh. to tan powd.; sol. in acetone, methanol, alcohol; sl. sol. in ether, water; pract. insol. in chloroform; m.w. 197.2; m.p. 149 C
Uses: Complexing agent; used in parenterals
Regulatory: FDA approved for parenterals; USP/NF compliance

Gentisic acid ethanolamine
CAS 7491-35-2
Uses: Used in intravenous, IV (infusion)
Regulatory: FDA approved for intravenous, IV (infusion)

Geranial. *See* Citral

Geraniol

Geraniol
CAS 106-24-1; EINECS 203-377-1
FEMA 2507
Synonyms: trans-3,7-Dimethyl-2,6-octadien-1-ol; Geranyl alcohol; Guaniol
Classification: Aliphatic organic compd.; a terpene alcohol
Empirical: $C_{10}H_{18}O$
Properties: Colorless to pale yel. oily liq., pleasant geranium odor; sol. in fixed oils, propylene glycol; sl. sol. in water; insol. in glycerin; m.w. 154.28; dens. 0.870-0.890 (15 C); m.p. 15 C; b.p. 230 C; flash pt. 214 F; ref. index 1.469-1.478
Precaution: Combustible
Toxicology: LD50 (oral, rat) 3600 mg/kg; poison by IV route; mod. toxic by ingestion and intramuscular routes; can cause allergic reaction; heated to decomp., emits acrid smoke and irritating fumes
Uses: Sweet apple, apricot, berry-like synthetic flavoring agent; fragrance
Regulatory: FDA 21CFR §182.60, GRAS; FEMA GRAS; Japan approved as flavoring; BP compliance
Manuf./Distrib.: Aldrich; Penta Mfg.; Schweizerhall; SCM Glidco Organics
Manuf./Distrib. (pharm. & food): Aldrich; Florida Treatt

Geraniol acetate. *See* Geranyl acetate

Geranium oil
CAS 8000-46-2
FEMA 2508
Synonyms: Pelargonium oil; Rose geranium oil Algerian
Definition: Volatile oil from steam distillation of leaves from *Pelargonium graveolens* or *Geranium maculatum*
Properties: Yel. liq., rose and geraniol odor; sol. in fixed oils, min. oil; insol. in glycerin; dens. 0.886-0.898; ref. index 1.454-1.472 (20 C)
Precaution: Keep cool, well closed; protect from light
Toxicology: Skin irritant; sensitizer; heated to decomp., emits acrid smoke and irritating fumes
Uses: Natural flavoring agent for pharmaceuticals
Regulatory: FDA 21CFR §182.10, 182.20, GRAS
Manuf./Distrib. (pharm. & food): Pierre Chauvet; Commodity Services; Florida Treatt

Geranyl acetate
CAS 105-87-3; 16409-44-2; EINECS 203-341-5, 240-458-0
FEMA 2509
Synonyms: Geraniol acetate; trans-3,7-Dimethyl-2,6-octadien-1-ol acetate
Empirical: $C_{12}H_{20}O_2$
Formula: $(CH_3)_2C{:}CHCH_2CH_2C(CH_3){:}CHCH_2OCOCH_3$
Properties: Colorless clear liq., lavender oil, sweet taste; sol. in alcohol, fixed oils, ether; sl. sol. in propylene glycol; insol. in water, glycerin; m.w. 196.32; dens. 0.907-0.918 (15 C); b.p. 128-129 C; flash pt. 219 F; ref. index 1.458-1.464
Precaution: Combustible
Toxicology: LD50 (oral, rat) 6330 mg/kg; mildly toxic by ingestion; heated to decomp., emits acrid smoke and irritating fumes
Uses: Sweet synthetic flavoring agent
Regulatory: FDA 21CFR §182.60, GRAS; FEMA GRAS; Japan approved as flavoring
Manuf./Distrib.: Aldrich; Firmenich; Int'l. Flavors & Fragrances; Penta Mfg.; SCM Glidco Organics
Manuf./Distrib. (pharm. & food): Aldrich; Firmenich; Int'l. Flavors & Fragrances; Penta Mfg.

Geranyl alcohol. *See* Geraniol

Geranyl isobutyrate
FEMA 2513
Empirical: $C_{14}H_{24}O_2$
Properties: Liq., lt. rose odor, sweet apricot-like taste; sol. in most org. solvs.; insol. in water; m.w. 224.34; dens. 0.8997 (15 C); ref. index 1.4576
Uses: Synthetic flavoring agent
Regulatory: FDA 21CFR §172.515; FEMA GRAS
Manuf./Distrib. (pharm. & food): Chr. Hansen's

Ghatti gum. *See* Gum ghatti
Gingelly oil. *See* Sesame oil
Gingilli oil. *See* Sesame oil
Glacial acetic acid. *See* Acetic acid, glacial
Glauber's salt. *See* Sodium sulfate
Glaze, pharmaceutical. *See* Pharmaceutical glaze

Glicerol. *See* Glycerin
Glucal. *See* Calcium gluconate
1,4-D-Glucan glucanohydrolase. *See* Amylase
D-Glucaric acid, calcium salt (1:1) tetrahydrate. *See* Calcium saccharate

Gluceptate sodium
　　CAS 13007-85-7
　　Uses: Used in intravenous
　　Regulatory: FDA approved for intravenous

D-Glucitol. *See* Sorbitol
D-Glucitol, 1-deoxy-1-(methylamino)-,. *See* Meglumine
D-Glucitol, 1,4:3,6-dianhydro-2,5-di-o-methyl. *See* Dimethyl isosorbide
Glucoheptonic acid, calcium salt (2:1). *See* Calcium gluceptate
γ-Gluconamidopropyl dimethyl 2-hydroxyethyl ammonium chloride. *See* Quaternium-22

D-Gluconic acid
　　CAS 526-95-4; EINECS 208-401-4
　　Synonyms: Glyconic acid; Glycogenic acid; Pentahydroxycaproic acid; Dextronic acid; Maltonic acid
　　Empirical: $C_6H_{12}O_7$
　　Formula: $CH_2OH(CHOH)_4COOH$
　　Properties: Pure: crystals, mild acid taste; sol. in water; sl. sol. in alcohol; insol. in most org. solvs.; m.w. 196.16;
　　　　m.p. 131 C; Commercial 50% aq. sol'n.: lt. amber, faint odor of vinegar; dens. 1.24 (25/4 C); flash pt. none;
　　　　ref. index 1.4161
　　Toxicology: No known toxicity; irritant
　　Uses: Chelating agent, sequestrant, dietary supplement; used in orals
　　Regulatory: FDA GRAS; Japan approved; FDA approved for orals
　　Manuf./Distrib.: Akzo; Am. Biorganics; Faesy & Besthoff; Glucona; Lohmann; PMP Fermentation Prods.;
　　　　Spectrum Chem. Mfg.
　　Manuf./Distrib. (pharm. & food): Aldrich; Jungbunzlauer; PMP Fermentation Prods.

Gluconic acid calcium salt. *See* Calcium gluconate
D-Gluconic acid calcium salt. *See* Calcium gluconate
D-Gluconic acid cyclic 4,5-ester with boric acid calcium salt. *See* Calcium borogluconate
D-Gluconic acid δ-lactone. *See* Gluconolactone
D-Gluconic acid magnesium salt. *See* Magnesium gluconate
D-Gluconic acid monopotassium salt. *See* Potassium D-gluconate
D-Gluconic acid monosodium salt. *See* Sodium gluconate
D-Gluconic acid potassium salt. *See* Potassium D-gluconate
Gluconic acid sodium salt. *See* Sodium gluconate

Gluconolactone
　　CAS 90-80-2; EINECS 202-016-5
　　Synonyms: GDL; D-Gluconic acid δ-lactone; Glucono Δ-lactone; D-Glucono-1,5-lactone
　　Empirical: $C_6H_{10}O_6$
　　Properties: Wh. cryst. powd., pract. odorless; sol. in water; sl. sol. in alcohol; insol. in ether, chloroform; m.w.
　　　　178.14; m.p. 153 C (dec.)
　　Precaution: Moisture-sensitive; avoid dust formation
　　Toxicology: May cause eye irritation; heated to decomp., emits acrid smoke and irritating fumes
　　Uses: Digestible carbohydrate, natural flavor, mild acidulant; used in orals, topicals
　　Regulatory: FDA 21CFR §131.144, 133.129, 184.1318, GRAS; USDA 9CFR §318.7 (limitation 8 oz/100 lb
　　　　meat, 6 oz/100 lb genoa salami); Japan approved; Europe listed; UK approved; FDA approved for orals,
　　　　topicals
　　Manuf./Distrib. (pharm. & food): ADM; Aldrich; Am. Roland; Int'l. Sourcing; Jungbunzlauer; PMP Fermentation
　　　　Prods.; Spectrum Chem. Mfg.

Glucono Δ-lactone. *See* Gluconolactone
D-Glucono-1,5-lactone. *See* Gluconolactone
α-D-Glucopyranose. *See* D-Glucose anhyd.
α-D-Glucopyranoside, β-D-fructofuranosyl, dioctadecanoate. *See* Sucrose distearate
α-D-Glucopyranoside, β-D-fructofuranosyl, monododecanoate. *See* Sucrose laurate
α-D-Glucopyranoside, β-D-fructofuranosyl, monooctadecanoate. *See* Sucrose stearate
α-D-Glucopyranoside, 1,3,4,6-tetra-O-acetyl-β-D-fructofuranosyl, tetraacetate. *See* Sucrose octaacetate
4-O-β-D-Glucopyranosyl-D-glucitol. *See* Maltitol
r-O-α-D-Glucopyranosyl-D-glucose. *See* Maltose
4-O-α-Glucopyranosyl-D-sorbitol. *See* Maltitol

D-Glucose anhyd.

CAS 50-99-7 (anhyd.); 492-62-6; EINECS 200-075-1; 207-757-8

Synonyms: Dextrose; Grape sugar; Blood sugar; Corn sugar; α-D-Glucopyranose

Definition: Sugar obtained from the hydrolysis of starch

Empirical: $C_6H_{12}O_6$

Properties: Colorless cryst. or wh. gran. powd., odorless, sweet taste; sol. in water; sl. sol. in alcohol; m.w. 180.18 (anhyd.); dens. 1.544; m.p.146 C

Precaution: Potentially explosive reaction with potassium nitrate + sodium peroxide on heating

Toxicology: LD50 (oral, rat) 25,800 mg/kg; mildly toxic by ingestion; experimental reproductive effects; mutagenic data; large doses can cause diabetes; heated to decomp., emits acrid smoke and irritating fumes; mixts. with alkali release CO on heating

Uses: Excipient, sweetening agent, coloring agent, tonicity agent for pharmaceuticals; tablet diluent, filler esp. for chewable tablets; used in injectables

Regulatory: FDA 21CFR §133.124, 133.178. 133.179, 145, 145.134, 145.180, 145.181, 146, 155.170, 155.194, 155.200, 163.123, 163.150, 163.153, 168.110, 168.111, 169.175, 169.176, 169.177, 169.178, 169.179, 169.180, 169.181,169.182, 184.1857, GRAS; USDA 9CFR §318.7, 381.147; FDA approved for injectables; USP/NF, BP compliance

Manuf./Distrib.: Am. Biorganics; Amerchol Europe; Avebe BV; Corn Prods.; Mallinckrodt; Mendell; Spectrum Chem. Mfg.; U.S. Biochemical

Manuf./Distrib. (pharm. & food): ADM; Aldrich; Am. Roland; Avebe; Bestoval; Browning; Cargill; Cerestar Int'l.; Corn Prods.; Farbest Brands; Penta Mfg.; Penwest Foods; Ragus Sugars; Roquette UK; Sefcol; Siber Hegner; Spectrum Chem. Mfg.; A.E. Staley; Sweeteners Plus; Van Waters & Rogers

Trade names: Candex®; Clintose® A; Clintose® L

Trade names containing: Candex® Plus; CI-90; Dry Phytonadione 1% SD No. 61748; Emdex®; Emdex® Plus; Sweetrex®

Glucose, liquid

CAS 8027-56-3

Synonyms: Corn syrup; Starch syrup

Definition: Obtained by the incomplete hydrolysis of starch, contg. principally dextrose, dextrins, maltose, and water

Properties: Colorless or ylsh. thick syrupy liq., odorless, sweet taste; misc. with water; sparingly sol. in alcohol

Uses: Tablet binder, coating agent, diluent; used in orals

Regulatory: FDA approved for orals; USP/NF compliance

Manuf./Distrib. (pharm. & food): Ruger

D-Glucose monohydrate

CAS 5996-10-1; EINECS 200-075-1

Synonyms: Dextrose monohydrate; Bread sugar

Empirical: $C_6H_{12}O_6 \cdot H_2O$

Properties: Cryst.; m.w. 198.17; m.p. 83 C

Toxicology: LD50 (IV, rabbit) 35 g/kg

Uses: Sweetening agent, tonicity agent; used in injectables (IM, IV), inhalers, orals

Regulatory: FDA 21CFR §184.1857, GRAS; FDA approved for injectables (IM, IV), inhalers, orals; USP/NF, BP, Ph.Eur. compliance

Manuf./Distrib.: Spectrum Chem. Mfg.

Manuf./Distrib. (pharm. & food): Fluka; Spectrum Chem. Mfg.

Glucose oxidase

CAS 9001-37-0; EINECS 232-601-0

Synonyms: Oxidase, glucose

Definition: Enzyme which catalyzes the oxidation of glucose to gluconic acid; derived from *Aspergillus niger*

Properties: Amorphous powd. or crystal; sol. in water; m.w. ≈ 186,000

Toxicology: Poison by subcutaneous, intravenous, intraperitoneal routes

Uses: Enzyme, preservative; mfg. of fertility and diabetic tests; ingred. in toothpastes for dental caries prophylaxis

Regulatory: FDA GRAS; Canada, UK, Japan approved

Glucose syrup. *See* Corn syrup

Glucose syrup solids. *See* Corn syrup solids

α-Glutamic acid. *See* L-Glutamic acid

L-Glutamic acid

CAS 56-86-0; EINECS 200-293-7

FEMA 3285

Synonyms: α-Glutamic acid; L-2-Aminoglutaric acid; 2-Aminopentanedioic acid
Classification: Amino acid
Empirical: $C_5H_9NO_4$
Properties: Wh. free-flowing cryst. or cryst. powd., odorless; sl. sol. in water; m.w. 147.15; dens. 1.538 (20/4 C); m.p. 224-225 C
Toxicology: Human systemic effects by ingestion and IV route (headache, vomiting); heated to decomp., emits toxic fumes of NO_x
Uses: Flavor enhancer; biochemical research; used in medicine
Regulatory: FDA 21CFR §172.320 (12.4% max.), 182.1045, GRAS; FEMA GRAS; Japan approved; Europe listed; UK approved; BP compliance
Manuf./Distrib.: Aldrich; Am. Biorganics; Degussa; R.W. Greeff; Penta Mfg.; Spectrum Chem. Mfg.; U.S. Biochemical
Manuf./Distrib. (pharm. & food): Aldrich; R.W. Greeff; Penta Mfg.; Ruger; Spectrum Chem. Mfg.
Trade names: Unamino GLUT

L-Glutamic acid hydrochloride
CAS 138-15-8; EINECS 205-315-9
Synonyms: L-2-Aminoglutaric acid hydrochloride; 2-Aminopentanedioic acid hydrochloride
Empirical: $C_5H_9NO_4$ • HCl
Formula: $HOOCCH_2CH_2CH(NH_2)COOH$ • HCl
Properties: Orthorombic bisphenoidal plates; m.w. 183.60; dec. 214 C
Precaution: Light-sensitive
Uses: Used in injectables (IM, IV), orals
Regulatory: FDA 21CFR §182.1047, GRAS; FDA approved for injectables (IM, IV), orals
Manuf./Distrib.: Degussa
Manuf./Distrib. (pharm. & food): Aldrich; Ruger; Spectrum Chem. Mfg.

Glutamic acid monosodium salt. *See* MSG
γ-Glutamylcysteinyglycine. *See* Glutathione

Glutaral
CAS 111-30-8; EINECS 203-856-5
Synonyms: Glutaraldehyde; Glutaric dialdehyde; Pentanedial
Classification: Dialdehyde
Formula: $OHC(CH_2)_3CHO$
Properties: Liq.; sol. in water, alcohol; m.w. 100.12; dens. 0.72; b.p. 188 C (dec.); f.p. -14 C; flash pt. none
Precaution: Corrosive
Toxicology: Irritant; TLV (ceiling) 0.1 ppm in air; may cause upper or lower respiratory symptoms, contact dermatitis
Uses: Sterilizing agent for medical and dental equip., fiberoptic endoscopes; bactericidal, fungicidal, sproicidal,and viricidal activity
Regulatory: FDA 21CFR §173.320 (250 ppm max.), 173.357, 175.105, 176.170, 176.180; EPA reg. 10352-39; Japan MITI; Europe provisional list 0.1% max.; BP compliance (sol'n.)
Manuf./Distrib.: Aldrich; Allchem Industries; BASF; Transol Chem. UK Ltd; Union Carbide
Manuf./Distrib. (pharm. & food): Allchem Industries

Glutaraldehyde. *See* Glutaral
Glutaric dialdehyde. *See* Glutaral

Glutathione
CAS 70-18-8; EINECS 200-725-4
Synonyms: γ-Glutamylcysteinyglycine
Empirical: $C_{10}H_{17}O_6N_3S$
Properties: Wh. cryst. powd., odorless, sour taste; sol. in water, dilute alcohol; m.w. 307.33; m.p. 192-195 C (dec.)
Precaution: Refrigerate
Uses: Used in intramuscular injectables
Regulatory: FDA approved for intramuscular injectables
Manuf./Distrib.: Aldrich; Spectrum Chem. Mfg.
Manuf./Distrib. (pharm. & food): Aldrich

Gluten. *See* Wheat gluten
Glyccyrrhiza. *See* Licorice

Glycereth-26
CAS 31694-55-0 (generic)

Glycereth-7 benzoate

Synonyms: PEG-26 glyceryl ether; POE (26) glyceryl ether
Definition: PEG ether of glycerin with avg. ethoxylation value of 26
Uses: Emulsifier, humectant, lubricant for pharmaceutical uses
Regulatory: FDA 21CFR §175.105
Trade names: Ethosperse® G-26

Glycereth-7 benzoate
CAS 12804-12-8
Synonyms: PEG-7 glyceryl ether benzoate; POE (7) glyceryl ether benzoate
Definition: Ester of benzoic acid with a PEG ether of glycerin containing an avg. 7 moles of ethylene oxide
Properties: Clear water-white to pale yel. liq., mild odor; disp. in water; sp.gr. 1.17; b.p. 210 C; flash pt. (COC) 210 C
Precaution: Store away from strong oxidizing agents; avoid excessive heat
Toxicology: Nonhazardous
Uses: Emollient, lubricant
Trade names: Pelemol® G7B

Glycereth-5 lactate
CAS 125804-13-9; 125804-28-6
Synonyms: PEG-5 glyceryl ether lactate; POE (5) glyceryl ether lactate
Definition: Ester of lactic acid with PEG ether of glycerin containing avg. 5 moles EO
Formula: $C_3H_7O_3(CH_2CH_2O)_4.5C_3H_5O_2$
Properties: Pale yel. visc. liq., carmel odor; sol. in water; sp.gr. 1.155; b.p. dec. > 210 C; flash pt. (COC) 210 C
Precaution: Store away from strong oxidizing agents; avoid excessive heat
Toxicology: May cause mild skin and eye irritation on prolonged contact
Uses: Emollient, humectant for pharmaceutical topicals
Trade names: Pelemol® G45L

Glycereth polyacrylate copolyol
Uses: Used in topical ointments, emulsions
Trade names: Fancorsil HA Super

Glycereth-7 triacetate
CAS 57569-76-3
Synonyms: PEG-7 glyceryl ether triacetate; POE (7) glyceryl ether triacetate
Definition: Triester of acetic acid with a PEG ether of glycerin containing an avg. 7 moles ethylene oxide
Empirical: $C_{23}H_{42}O_{13}$
Properties: Clear pale yel. liq., mild typ. odor; sol. in water; m.w. 526; sp.gr. 1.15; b.p. > 200 C
Precaution: Store away from strong oxidizing agents; avoid excessive heat
Toxicology: May cause mild skin and eye irritation on prolonged contact
Uses: Humectant, emollient, solubilizer; solv. for sunscreen ingreds.
Trade names: Pelemol® G7A

Glycerides, coconut, mono-, di-, and tri-. See Cocoglycerides
Glycerides, coconut oil mono-. See Glyceryl cocoate
Glycerides, cottonseed-oil, mono-, hydrogenated, acetates. See Acetylated hydrogenated cottonseed glyceride
Glycerides, hydrogenated lard mono-. See Hydrogenated lard glyceride
Glycerides, hydrogenated tallow mono-. See Hydrogenated tallow glyceride
Glycerides, lard mono-. See Lard glyceride
Glycerides, lard mono-, di- and tri-, hydrogenated. See Hydrogenated lard glycerides
Glycerides, palm oil mono-, di- and tri-. See Palm glycerides
Glycerides, palm oil mono-, di- and tri, hydrogenated. See Hydrogenated palm glycerides
Glycerides, palm oil mono-, hydrogenated. See Hydrogenated palm glyceride
Glycerides, soybean oil, hydrogenated, mono. See Hydrogenated soy glyceride
Glycerides, sunflower seed mono-. See Sunflower seed oil glyceride
Glycerides, sunflower seed mono-, di- and tri-. See Sunflower seed oil glycerides
Glycerides, tallow mono-. See Tallow glyceride
Glycerides, tallow mono-, di- and tri-. See Tallow glycerides
Glycerides, tallow mono-, di- and tri-, hydrogenated. See Hydrogenated tallow glycerides
Glycerides, tallow mono-, hydrogenated, lactates. See Hydrogenated tallow glyceride lactate

Glycerin
CAS 56-81-5; EINECS 200-289-5
FEMA 2525

Synonyms: Glicerol; Glycerol; Glycyl alcohol; 1,2,3-Propanetriol; Propane-1,2,3-triol; Glycerine; Trihydroxypropane glycerol
Classification: Polyhydric alcohol
Empirical: $C_3H_8O_3$
Formula: $HOCH_2COHHCH_2OH$
Properties: Clear colorless syrupy liq., odorless, sweet taste; hygroscopic; sol. in water, alcohol; insol. in ether, benzene, chloroform; m.w. 92.09; dens. 1.26201 (25/25 C); m.p. 17.8 C; b.p. 290 C (dec.); flash pt. (OC) 176 C; ref. index 1.4730 (25 C)
Precaution: Combustible liq. exposed to heat, flame, strong oxidizers; highly explosive with hydrogen peroxide
Toxicology: LD50 (oral, ratl) > 20 ml/kg, (IV, rat) 4.4 ml/kg; poison by subcutaneous route; mildly toxic by ingestion; human systemic and GI effects by ingestion; human mutagenic data; skin and eye irritant; nuisance dust; heated to dec., emits acrid smoke
Uses: Plasticizer, solv., solubilizer; emollient, humectant in topicals; tonicity agent; in orals, parenterals, ophthalmics, IM injectables, rectals, dentifrices; ear wax softener; vehicle solv. for antimicrobials; sweetener; preservative @ > 20% conc.
Usage level: 0.2-65.7% (topicals), 1-50% (liq. orals), 50% (parenterals), 7-10% (dentifrices), 0.5-3.0% (ophthalmics)
Regulatory: FDA 21CFR §169.175, 169.176, 169.177, 169.178, 169.180, 169.181, 172.866, 175.300, 178.3500, 182.90, 182.1320, GRAS; FEMA GRAS; FDA approved for orals, parenterals, ophthalmics, dentifrices, intramuscular injectables, rectals; USP/NF compliance; Japan approved; Europe listed; UK approved; BP compliance
Manuf./Distrib.: Alba Int'l.; Asahi Denka Kogyo; Dial; Farleyway Chem. Ltd; Fina; Henkel/Emery; Lonza; Procter & Gamble; Unichema; Witco
Manuf./Distrib. (pharm. & food): Acme-Hardesty; Asahi Denka Kogyo; Ashland; Avrachem; Browne & Dureau Int'l.; Croda; Crompton & Knowles; Ellis & Everard; Fina; Grünau; K&K Greeff; Henkel; Integra; Int'l. Sourcing; Norman Fox; Penta Mfg.; Procter & Gamble; Ruger; Spectrum Chem. Mfg.; Thew Arnott; Van Waters & Rogers
Trade names: Croderol GA7000; Emery® 912; Emery® 916; Emery® 917; Emery® 918; Glycerine (Pharmaceutical); Glycon® G 100; Glycon® G-300; Kemstrene® 96.0% USP; Kemstrene® 99.0%; Kemstrene® 99.7% USP; Natural Glycerine USP 96%; Natural Glycerine USP 99%; Natural Glycerine USP 99.5%; Pricerine 9088; Star; Superol
Trade names containing: Grillocin® AT Basis; Lipo PE Base G-55; Lipo PE Base GP-55

Glycerine. *See* Glycerin
Glycerite. *See* Tannic acid
Glycerol. *See* Glycerin
Glycerol formal. *See* Glyceryl formal
Glycerol mono coconut oil. *See* Glyceryl cocoate
Glycerol monoricinoleate. *See* Glyceryl ricinoleate
Glycerol ricinoleate. *See* Glyceryl ricinoleate
Glycerol shortening. *See* Glyceryl mono shortening
Glycerol trilaurate. *See* Trilaurin

Glycerophosphocholine
CAS 28319-77-9
Uses: Natural raw material for pharmaceuticals
Trade names: GPC

Glyceryl alginate
Synonyms: Alginic acid, glyceryl ester
Definition: Ester of glycerin and alginic acid
Uses: Moisturizer, carrier
Trade names: Karajel

Glyceryl behenate
CAS 6916-74-1; 30233-64-8; EINECS 250-097-0
Synonyms: 2,3-Dihydroxypropyl docosanoate; Glyceryl monobehenate
Definition: Monoester of glycerin and behenic acid
Properties: Fine powd., faitn odor; sol. in chloroform; pract. insol. in water and alcohol; m.p. 70 C; acid no. 4 max.; iodine no. 3 max.; sapon. no. 145-165
Toxicology: Heated to decomp., emits acrid smoke and irritating fumes
Uses: Excipient, lubricant, binding agent for tablets/capsules
Regulatory: FDA 21CFR §184.1328, GRAS; USP/NF compliance

Glyceryl caprylate

CAS 26402-26-6; EINECS 247-668-1
Synonyms: Glyceryl monocaprylate; Octanoic acid, monoester with 1,2,3-propanetriol; Monooctanoin
Definition: Monoester of glycerin and caprylic acid
Empirical: $C_{11}H_{22}O_4$
Formula: $CH_3(CH_2)_6COOCH_2COHHCH_2OH$
Properties: Crystals; m.p. 39.5-40.5 C
Uses: Solubilizer, emulsifier for pharmaceutical drugs
Regulatory: FDA 21CFR §176.210, 177.2800
Trade names: Capmul® MCMC8; Imwitor® 308; Imwitor® 988

Glyceryl caprylate/caprate

Definition: Mixture of monoglycerides of caprylic and capric acids
Uses: Solv., dispersant, emulsifier, solubilizer, vehicle/carrier, penetrant
Regulatory: FDA 21CFR §176.210, 177.2800
Trade names: Capmul® MCM; Capmul® MCM-90; Tegin® 4600 NSE

Glyceryl citrate/lactate/linoleate/oleate

CAS 9174-23-9
Definition: Ester of glycerin and a blend of citric, lactic, linoleic and oleic acids
Uses: Emulsifier
Trade names: Imwitor® 375

Glyceryl cocoate

CAS 61789-05-7; EINECS 263-027-9
Synonyms: Glycerides, coconut oil mono-; Glycerol mono coconut oil; Glyceryl coconate
Definition: Monoester of glycerin and coconut fatty acids
Formula: $RCO-OCH_2COHHCH_2OH$, RCO- represents the fatty acids derived from coconut oil
Uses: Surfactant, emulsifier, solubilizer, dispersant, plasticizer, lubricant, cosistency regulator, skin protectant, penetrant, carrier
Regulatory: FDA 21CFR §175.105, 176.210, 177.2800
Trade names: Imwitor® 928
Trade names containing: Softisan® 601

Glyceryl coconate. *See* Glyceryl cocoate

Glyceryl dilaurate

CAS 27638-00-2; EINECS 248-586-9
Synonyms: Dilaurin; Dodecanoic acid, diester with 1,2,3-propanetriol
Definition: Diester of glycerin and lauric acid
Empirical: $C_{27}H_{52}O_5$
Formula: $C_{11}H_{23}COOCH_2CHCH_2OHOCOC_{11}H_{23}$
Properties: Wh. to off-wh. solid; sol. in min. oil, 95% ethanol, IPM, oleyl alcohol, castor oil; insol. in water, glycerin, propylene glycol; sapon. no. 219-229; ref. index 1.4520-1.4560 (35 C)
Toxicology: LD50 (rat, oral) > 5 g/kg; nonirritating to eyes and skin
Uses: Emulsifier, emollient, solubilizer, dispersant
Regulatory: FDA 21CFR §175.105, 1876.210
Manuf./Distrib. (pharm. & food): Ruger
Trade names: Capmul® GDL; Kemester® GDL

Glyceryl dilaurate SE; EINECS 248-586-9

Synonyms: Dodecanoic acid, diester with 1,23,-propanetriol
Uses: Emulsifier, dispersant

Glyceryl dioleate

CAS 25637-84-7; EINECS 247-144-2
Synonyms: 9-Octadecenoic acid, diester with 1,2,3-propanetriol
Definition: Diester of glycerin and oleic acid
Empirical: $C_{39}H_{72}O_5$
Uses: Surfactant, emulsifier, stabilizer, lubricant for pharmaceuticals
Regulatory: FDA 21CFR §175.105, 176.210, 177.2800
Manuf./Distrib. (pharm. & food): Ruger

Glyceryl dioleate SE

Uses: Emulsifier, coemulsifier, stabilizer, wetting agent, lubricant used in pharmaceutical applics.

Glyceryl distearate

CAS 1323-83-7; EINECS 215-359-0

Synonyms: Octadecanoic acid, diester with 1,2,3-propanetriol
Definition: Diester of glycerin and stearic acid
Empirical: $C_{39}H_{76}O_5$
Uses: Emulsifier, coemulsifier, stabilizer, wetting agent, lubricant used in pharmaceuticals, orals
Regulatory: FDA 21CFR §175.105, 176.210, 177.2800; Europe listed; FDA approved for orals
Trade names: Kessco® Glycerol Distearate 386F

Glyceryl distearate SE
Uses: Emulsifier, coemulsifier, stabilizer, wetting agent, lubricant for pharmaceuticals

Glyceryl di/tripalmitostearate
CAS 8067-32-1
Uses: Additive for tablets, binder, lubricant

Glyceryl di/tristearate
CAS 8067-32-1
Uses: Additive for tablets mfg.
Trade names: Precirol WL 2155 ATO

Glyceryl formal
CAS 4740-78-7; EINECS 225-248-9
Synonyms: Glycerol formal
Empirical: $C_4H_8O_3$
Properties: Colorless liq., low odor; hygroscopic; m.w. 104.11; dens. 1.218 (20/4 C); b.p. 95-97 C (20 mm); ref. index 1.451 (20 C)
Toxicology: Low toxicity
Uses: Solvent for pharmaceutical compds.; vehicle for veterinary injectables (sulphadiazine and trimethoprin)
Manuf./Distrib.: Pentagon Chems. Ltd
Manuf./Distrib. (pharm. & food): Pentagon Chems. Ltd

Glyceryl isostearate
CAS 32057-14-0; 66085-00-5; 61332-02-3; EINECS 262-710-9; 266-124-4
Synonyms: Glyceryl monoisostearate; Isooctadecanoic acid, monoester with 1,2,3-propanetriol
Definition: Monoester of glycerin and isostearic acid
Empirical: $C_{21}H_{42}O_4$
Properties: Pale yel. paste
Toxicology: Lethal when injected in large doses in mice
Uses: Surfactant, emulsifier, dispersant for pharmaceutical applics.
Trade names: Emalex GWIS-100
Trade names containing: Hydrolactol 70; Protegin® W; Protegin® WX

Glyceryl laurate
CAS 142-18-7; EINECS 205-526-6
Synonyms: Glyceryl monolaurate; Dodecanoic acid, monoester with 1,2,3-propanetriol; Dodecanoic acid, 2,3-dihydroxypropyl ester
Definition: Monoester of glycerin and lauric acid
Empirical: $C_{15}H_{30}O_4$
Formula: $CH_3(CH_2)_{10}COOCH_2COHHCH_2OH$
Properties: Cream-colored paste, faint odor; disp. in water; sol. in methanol, ethanol, toluene, naphtha, min. oil; dens. 0.98; m.p. 23-27 C; pH 8-8.6
Precaution: Combustible
Uses: Emulsifier, stabilizer, solubilizer, carrier
Regulatory: FDA 21CFR §175.105, 176.210, 177.2800, GRAS; Japan approved; Europe listed
Manuf./Distrib.: Grindsted; Henkel/Emery; Inolex; Lonza; Protameen; Velsicol
Manuf./Distrib. (pharm. & food): Grindsted; Lonza
Trade names: Cithrol GML N/E; Hodag GML; Imwitor® 312
Trade names containing: Acconon CON

Glyceryl laurate SE
CAS 27215-38-9
Definition: Self-emulsifying grade of glyceryl laurate containing some sodium and/or potassium laurate
Uses: Emulsifier, coemulsifier, stabilizer, wetting agent, lubricant for pharmaceutical applics.
Trade names: Aldo® MLD

Glyceryl linoleate
CAS 2277-28-3; EINECS 218-901-4
Synonyms: Monolinolein; 9,12-Octadecadienoic acid, 2,3-dihydroxypropyl ester; 9,12-Octadecadienoic acid,

Glyceryl monobehenate

monoester with 1,2,3-propanetriol
Definition: Monoester of glycerin and linoleic acid
Empirical: $C_{21}H_{38}O_4$
Uses: Matrix material for sustained-release formulations, gelatin capsules
Trade names: Myverol® 18-92

Glyceryl monobehenate. *See* Glyceryl behenate
Glyceryl monocaprylate. *See* Glyceryl caprylate

Glyceryl mono/dioleate
CAS 25496-72-4
Properties: Yel. oil or soft solid; dens. 0.95; m.p. 14-19 C
Precaution: Combustible
Uses: Emulsifier, solubilizer for pharmaceuticals

Glyceryl monoisostearate. *See* Glyceryl isostearate
Glyceryl monolaurate. *See* Glyceryl laurate
Glyceryl monomyristate. *See* Glyceryl myristate
Glyceryl monooleate. *See* Glyceryl oleate
Glyceryl monoricinoleate. *See* Glyceryl ricinoleate

Glyceryl mono shortening
Synonyms: Glyceryl shortening; Glycerol shortening
Uses: Emulsifier, dispersant, stabilizer
Trade names: Drewmulse® 10K

Glyceryl monostearate. *See* Glyceryl stearate
Glyceryl monostearate SE. *See* Glyceryl stearate SE
Glyceryl monotristearate. *See* Tristearin

Glyceryl myristate
CAS 589-68-4; 67701-33-1
Synonyms: Glyceryl monomyristate; Monomyristin; Tetradecanoic acid, monoester with 1,2,3-propanetriol
Definition: Monoester of glycerin and myristic acid
Empirical: $C_{17}H_{34}O_4$
Formula: $CH_3(CH_2)_{12}COOCH_2COHHCH_2OH$
Uses: Coemulsifier, solubilizer, carrier for lipophilic drugs
Regulatory: FDA 21CFR §175.105, 176.210, 177.2800

Glyceryl oleate
CAS 111-03-5; 25496-72-4; 37220-82-9; EINECS 203-827-7; 253-407-2
FEMA 2526
Synonyms: Glyceryl monooleate; Monoolein; 9-Octadecenoic acid, monoester with 1,2,3-propanetriol
Definition: Monoester of glycerin and oleic acid
Empirical: $C_{21}H_{40}O_4$
Formula: $CH_3(CH_2)_7CH=CH(CH_2)_7COOCH_2CCH_2OHHOH$
Properties: Sp.gr. 0.940-0.960; acid no. 3 max.; sapon. no. 166-174
Toxicology: Heated to decomp., emits acrid smoke and irritating fumes
Uses: Emulsifier, coemulsifier, stabilizer, wetting agent, lubricant for pharmaceuticals; used in orals
Regulatory: FDA 21CFR §175.105, 175.300, 176.210, 177.2800, 181.22, 181.27, 182.4505, 184.1323,
    GRAS; FEMA GRAS; FDA approved for orals
Manuf./Distrib.: ABITEC; Am. Ingreds.; Aquatec Quimica SA; Calgene; Croda Surf.; Ferro/Keil; Grindsted;
    Henkel/Emery; ICI Surf. Am.; Inolex; Lonza; Mona; Spectrum Chem. Mfg.; Stepan; Unichema N. Am.;
    Witco/Oleo-Surf.
Manuf./Distrib. (pharm. & food): ABITEC; Am. Ingreds.; Calgene; Grindsted
Trade names: Aldo® MO FG; Capmul® GMO; Cithrol GMO N/E; Drewmulse® 85K; Drewmulse® GMOK;
    Hodag GMO; Hodag GMO-D; Monomuls® 90-O18; Myverol® 18-99; Rheodol MO-60; Tegin® O
Trade names containing: Arlacel® 186; Dehymuls® F; Oxynex® LM; Protegin®; Protegin® X

Glyceryl oleate SE
CAS 111-03-5; 25496-72-4
Definition: Self-emulsifying grade of glyceryl oleate that contains some sodium and/or potassium oleate
Uses: Emulsifier, coemulsifier, stabilizer, wetting agent, lubricant used for pharmaceuticals
Trade names: Cithrol GMO S/E

Glyceryl palmitate
CAS 26657-96-5; EINECS 247-887-2
Uses: Surfactant used in rectals, topicals

Regulatory: FDA approved for rectals, topicals
Trade names: Emalex GMS-P

Glyceryl polymethacrylate
CAS 37310-95-5
Definition: Ester of glycerin and polymethacrylic acid
Uses: Autoclavable lubricant, moisturizer for medical/surgical use, for pre-lubricating catheters, thermometers, enema tips; additive to body lotions
Trade names: Lubrajel® Oil; Lubrajel® WA
Trade names containing: Aloe-Moist™; Aloe-Moist™ A; Lubrajel® CG; Lubrajel® DV; Lubrajel® MS; Lubrajel® TW

Glyceryl ricinoleate
CAS 141-08-2; EINECS 205-455-0
Synonyms: 12-Hydroxy-9-octadecenoic acid, monoester with 1,2,3-propanetriol; Monoricinolein; Glycerol ricinoleate; Glycerol monoricinoleate; Glyceryl monoricinoleate
Definition: Monoester of glycerin and ricinoleic acid
Formula: $C_3H_5(OOCC_{16}H_{32}OH)_3$
Properties: Sp.gr. 0.981; m.p. < -50 C; flash pt. (COC) 265 C; ref. index 1.4770
Uses: Emulsifier, stabilizer, solubilizer; used in orals, topicals
Regulatory: FDA 21CFR §175.105, 176.170, 176.210, 178.3130; FDA approved for orals, topicals
Manuf./Distrib.: CasChem; Lonza
Trade names: Aldo® MR; Cithrol GMR N/E; Hodag GMR; Hodag GMR-D; Rilanit GMRO; Softigen® 701

Glyceryl ricinoleate SE
Synonyms: Glyceryl triricinoleate SE
Uses: Emulsifier, coemulsifier, stabilizer, wetting agent, lubricant used in pharmaceuticals
Trade names: Cithrol GMR S/E

Glyceryl shortening. *See* Glyceryl mono shortening

Glyceryl sorbitan oleo/stearate
Uses: Emulsifier
Trade names: Tewax TC 80
Trade names containing: Tewax TC 81

Glyceryl stearate
CAS 123-94-4; 11099-07-3; 31566-31-1; 85666-92-8; 85251-77-0; EINECS 250-705-4; 234-325-6; 204-664-4; 286-490-9
FEMA 2527
Synonyms: Monostearin; 1,2,3-Propanetriol octadecanoate; Octadecanoic acid, monoester with 1,2,3,-propanetriol; Glyceryl monostearate; 2,3-Dihydroxypropyl octadecanoate
Definition: Monoester of glycerin and stearic acid
Empirical: $C_{21}H_{42}O_4$
Formula: $CH_3(CH_2)_{16}COOCH_2COHHCH_2OH$
Properties: Wh. to cream wax-like flakes, sl. fatty odor and taste; sol. in hot org. solvs.; insol. in water, ethanol, glycerin, propylene glycol; disp. in min. oil; m.p. 56-59 C; acid no. 6 max.; iodine no. 3 max.; sapon. no. 162-175; hyd. no. 300-330
Precaution: Combustible; affected by light
Toxicology: LD50 (IP, mouse) 200 mg/kg; poison by IP route; heated to decomp., emits acrid smoke and irritating fumes
Uses: Emulsifier, solubilizer used in ophthalmics, orals, otics, rectals, topicals
Regulatory: FDA 21CFR §139.110, 139.115, 139.117, 139.120, 139.121, 139.122, 139.125, 139.135, 139.138, 139.140, 139.150, 139.155, 139.160, 139.165, 139.180, 175.105, 175.210, 175.300, 176.200, 176.210, 177.2800, 184.1324, GRAS; FEMA GRAS; Europe listed; FDA approved for orals, ophthalmics, otics, rectals, topicals; USP/NF, BP, Ph.Eur. compliance
Manuf./Distrib.: ABITEC; Am. Ingreds.; Aquatec Quimica SA; Croda Surf.; Eastman; Goldschmidt; Grindsted; Hart Prod.; Henkel/Emery; ICI Surf.; Inolex; ISP Van Dyk; Lanaetex; Lipo; Lonza; Protameen; Spectrum Chem. Mfg.; Stepan; Witco/Oleo-Surf.
Manuf./Distrib. (pharm. & food): AB Tech.; Alfa; Calgene; Croda; Eastman; Fina; Grindsted; Grünau; A C Hatrick; Henkel; Honeywill & Stein; Hüls; Nordmann Rassmann; Norman Fox; Penta Mfg.; PPG; Quest; Riken Vitamin; Spectrum Chem. Mfg.; Stepan; Unipex; Van Den Bergh; Peter Whiting
Trade names: Aldo® MS; Aldo® MSA; Aldo® MSC; Capmul® GMS; Cerasynt® GMS; Cerasynt® SD; Cithrol GMS N/E; Cutina® GMS; Cutina® MD; Drewmulse® 200K; Drewmulse® 900K; Drewmulse® TP; Drewmulse® V; Emalex GMS-A; Emalex GMS-B; Geleol; Hodag GMS; Imwitor® 191; Imwitor® 900; Kessco® Glyceryl Monostearate Pure; Lexemul® 55G; Lexemul® 503; Lexemul® 515; Mazol® GMS-90;

Glyceryl stearate citrate

Mazol® GMS-K; Myvaplex® 600; Myvaplex® 600P NF; Nissan Monogly M; Rheodol MS-50, MS-60, SEM; Tegin® 90 NSE; Tegin® 4011; Tegin® 4100 NSE; Tegin® 4480; Tegin® M; Tegin® Spezial; Witconol™ MST

Trade names containing: Aldosperse® O-20 KFG; 24% Beta Carotene Semi-Solid Suspension No. 65642; Cerasynt® 945; Cerasynt® WM; Ches® 500; Drewmulse® 700K; Drewmulse® 1128; Drewmulse® HM-100; Emulgade® SE; Gelot 64®; Hodag GMS-A; Hydrolactol 70; Lexemul® AR; Lexemul® AS; Mazol® 165C; Myvatex® TL; Oxynex® 2004; Oxynex® LM; Pionier® OEWA-II; Simulsol® 165; Tefose® 2561; Tewax TC 65

Glyceryl stearate citrate
CAS 39175-72-9; 91744-38-6
Synonyms: 2-Hydroxy-1,2,3-propanetricarboxylic acid, monoester with 1,2,3-propanetriol monoocta-decanoate
Definition: Citric acid ester of glyceryl stearate
Empirical: $C_{27}H_{48}O_{10}$
Uses: Emulsifier, consistency regulator, solubilizer
Trade names: Imwitor® 370

Glyceryl stearate SE
CAS 31566-31-1; 11099-07-3; 85666-92-8
Synonyms: GMS-SE; Glyceryl monostearate SE
Definition: Self-emulsifying grade of glyceryl stearate containg some sodium and/or potassium stearate
Properties: Wh. to cream flakes; sol. in oleyl alcohol; partly sol. in water, veg. oil, ethanol, propylene glycol; m.p. 57-59 C; sapon. no. 150-160
Uses: Aux. emulsifier, solubilizer; used in topicals
Regulatory: FDA approved for topicals
Trade names: Aldo® MSD; Cerasynt® Q; Cithrol GMS Acid Stable; Cithrol GMS S/E; Drewmulse® V-SE; Emalex GMS-10SE; Emalex GMS-15SE; Emalex GMS-20SE; Emalex GMS-25SE; Emalex GMS-45RT; Emalex GMS-50; Emalex GMS-55FD; Emalex GMS-195; Emalex GMS-ASE; Imwitor® 960 Flakes; Mazol® GMS-D; Tegin®
Trade names containing: Cutina® KD16

Glyceryl triacetate. *See* Triacetin
Glyceryl tribehenate. *See* Tribehenin
Glyceryl tributyrate. *See* Tributyrin

Glyceryl tricaprate/caprylate
Uses: Emollient, plasticizer, solubilizer for pharmaceuticals

Glyceryl tricaprylate. *See* Tricaprylin

Glyceryl tricocoate
Uses: Suppository base
Trade names: Novata® PK

Glyceryl tridodecanoate. *See* Trilaurin
Glyceryl tri(2-ethylhexanoate). *See* Trioctanoin

Glyceryl triheptanoate
Uses: Emollient, plasticizer, solubilizer for pharmaceuticals

Glyceryl tri(12-hydroxystearate). *See* Trihydroxystearin

Glyceryl trilactate
Uses: Used in pharmaceutical topicals
Trade names: Pelemol® GTL

Glyceryl trilaurate. *See* Trilaurin
Glyceryl trimyristate. *See* Trimyristin
Glyceryl trioctanoate. *See* Trioctanoin
Glyceryl trioleate. *See* Triolein
Glyceryl tripalmitate. *See* Tripalmitin
Glyceryl triricinoleate SE. *See* Glyceryl ricinoleate SE
Glyceryl tristearate. *See* Tristearin

Glycine
CAS 56-40-6; EINECS 200-272-2
FEMA 3287
Synonyms: Aminoacetic acid; Glycocoll

Classification: Aliphatic organic compd.; amino acid
Empirical: $C_2H_5NO_2$
Formula: H_2NCH_2COOH
Properties: Wh. cryst. powd., odorless, sweet taste; sol. in water; very sl. sol. in alcohol, ether; m.w. 75.08; dens. 1.1607; m.p. 232-236 C (dec.)
Toxicology: LD50 (oral, rat) 7930 mg/kg; moderately toxic by IV route; mildly toxic by ingestion; heated to decomp., emits toxic fumes of NO_x
Uses: Dietary supplement, bufffering agent; gastric antacid; used in injectables (IM, IV, SC), orals, rectals; in irrigant solutions
Regulatory: FDA 21CFR §170.50, GRAS for animal feed (582.5049), 172.320, limitation 3.5%, 172.812, 0.2% in finished beverage; USDA 9CFR §318.7, 0.01% in rendered animal fat; Japan approved; FEMA GRAS; FDA approved for injectables (IM, IV, SC), orals, rectals; BP, Ph.Eur. compliance
Manuf./Distrib.: Aldrich; Allchem Industries; Degussa; Hampshire; Spectrum Chem. Mfg.; U.S. Biochemical
Manuf./Distrib. (pharm. & food): Aldrich; Allchem Industries; Degussa; R.W. Greeff; Hamari Chems.; Mallinckrodt; Robeco; Spectrum Chem. Mfg.

Glycine, N,N'-1,2-ethanediylbis[N-(carboxymethyl)-, disodium salt dihydrate. *See* Disodium EDTA
Glycinol. *See* Ethanolamine
Glycocoll. *See* Glycine
Glycogenic acid. *See* D-Gluconic acid

Glycol
CAS 107-21-1; EINECS 203-473-3
Synonyms: Ethylene glycol; 1,2-Ethanediol; Ethane-1,2-diol; Ethylene alcohol
Classification: Aliphatic diol
Empirical: $C_2H_6O_2$
Formula: $HOCH_2CH_2OH$
Properties: Clear liq., sweet taste (poisonous); very hygroscopic; misc. with water, lower aliphatic alcohols, glycerol; m.w. 62.07; dens. 1.1135 (20/4 C); visc. 17.3 cps (25 C); m.p. -13 C; b.p. 197.6 C (760 mm); flash pt. (OC) 115 C; ref. index 1.43063
Toxicology: Irritant; toxic by ingestion; lethal human dose 1.4 ml/kg; TLV 50 ppm (vapor ceiling)
Uses: Solvent; used in topicals, ear drops
Regulatory: FDA 21CFR §175.105, 176.300; FDA approved for topicals; BP compliance
Manuf./Distrib.: Aldrich; Ashland; BASF; Eastman; Hoechst Celanese; Mitsui Petrochem. Ind.; Mitsui Toatsu; Mobil; Occidental; Olin; Shell; Spectrum Chem. Mfg.; Texaco; Union Carbide
Manuf./Distrib. (pharm. & food): Aldrich

Glycol carbonate. *See* Ethylene carbonate

Glycol dilaurate
CAS 624-04-4; EINECS 210-827-0
Synonyms: Ethylene glycol dilaurate; Lauric acid, 1,2-ethanediyl ester; Dodecanoic acid 1,2-ethanediyl ester
Definition: Diester of ethylene glycol and lauric acid
Empirical: $C_{26}H_{50}O_4$
Formula: $CH_3(CH_2)_{10}COOCH_2CH_2OCO(CH_2)_{10}CH_3$
Properties: Colorless amorphous mass; insol. in alcohol, ether; m.w. 426.66; m.p. 50-52 C; b.p. 188 C (20 mm)
Uses: Emollient
Trade names: Kemester® EGDL

Glycol dimethyl ether. *See* Ethylene glycol dimethyl ether

Glycol distearate
CAS 627-83-8; EINECS 211-014-3
Synonyms: EGDS; Ethylene glycol distearate; Octadecanoic acid, 1,2-ethanediyl ester
Definition: Diester of ethylene glycol and stearic acid
Formula: $CH_3(CH_2)_{16}COOCH_2CH_2OCO(CH_2)_{16}CH_3$
Properties: Sp.gr. 0.97; m.p. 60 C; flash pt. (COC) 171 C
Uses: Surfactant, thickener, pearlescent, and opacifier
Regulatory: FDA 21CFR §73.1, 176.210
Manuf./Distrib.: Inolex
Trade names: Kemester® EGDS; Mapeg® EGDS; Pegosperse® 50 DS

Glycol hydroxystearate
CAS 33907-46-9; EINECS 251-732-4
Synonyms: Ethylene glycol monohydroxystearate; Glycol monohydroxystearate; Hydroxyoctadecanoic acid, 2-hydroxyethyl ester

Glycolic acid phenyl ether

    Definition: Ester of ethylene glycol and hydroxystearic acid
    Empirical: $C_{20}H_{40}O_4$
    Formula: $CH_3(CH_2)_5COHH(CH_2)_{10}COOCH_2CH_2OH$
    Uses: Wax modifier, firming agent in pharmaceuticals

Glycolic acid phenyl ether. *See* Phenoxyacetic acid
Glycol monohydroxystearate. *See* Glycol hydroxystearate
Glycol monostearate. *See* Glycol stearate

Glycol stearate

    CAS 111-60-4; 97281-23-7; EINECS 203-886-9; 306-522-8
    Synonyms: EGMS; Ethylene glycol monostearate; Ethylene glycol stearate; Glycol monostearate; 2-Hydroxyethyl octadecanoate
    Definition: Ester of ethylene glycol and stearic acid
    Formula: $CH_3(CH_2)_{16}COOCH_2CH_2OH$
    Properties: Yel. waxy solid; sol. in alcohol, hot ether, acetone; insol. in water; m.w. 328.60; dens. 0.96 (25 C); m.p. 57-60 C
    Precaution: Combustible
    Toxicology: Poison by intraperitoneal route; skin irritant
    Uses: Emulsifier, solubilizer, base used in topicals
    Regulatory: FDA 21CFR §176.210; FDA approved for topicals
    Manuf./Distrib.: Ashland; C.P. Hall; Inolex; ISP Van Dyk; Witco/Oleo-Surf.
    Trade names: Cerasynt® M; Kemester® EGMS; Lexemul® EGMS; Mapeg® EGMS; Monthyle; Nikkol MYS-1EX
    Trade names containing: Cerasynt® IP; Sedefos 75®; Tefose® 63

Glycol stearate SE

    CAS 86418-55-5
    Synonyms: Ethylene glycol monostearate SE
    Definition: Self-emulsifying grade of glycol stearate containg. some sodium and/or potassium stearate
    Properties: Wh. to cream flakes; disp. in water, peanut oil, oleyl alcohol; insol. in min. oil, ethanol, glycerin, propylene glycol, IPM; m.p. 57-60 C; sapon. no. 181-191
    Uses: Emulsifier, visc. builder, base used in topical pharmaceuticals
    Trade names: Cerasynt® MN; Tegin® G

Glyconic acid. *See* D-Gluconic acid
Glycyl alcohol. *See* Glycerin

Glycyrrhetinic acid

    CAS 471-53-4; EINECS 207-444-6
    Properties: Wh. cryst. powd.
    Uses: Anti-inflammatory, anti-allergenic for pharmaceuticals
    Regulatory: BP compliance
    Manuf./Distrib.: Nikko Chem. Co. Ltd.
    Trade names: Nikkol Glycyrrhetinic Acid

Glycyrrhiza extract. *See* Licorice extract
Glycyrrhiza glabra extract. *See* Licorice extract

Glycyrrhizic acid

    CAS 1405-86-3; EINECS 215-785-7
    Synonyms: Glycyrrhizin; Glycyrrhizinic acid
    Definition: Natural material extracted from *Glycyrrhiza glabra*
    Empirical: $C_{41}H_{62}O_{16}$
    Properties: White powd.; water-sol.
    Uses: Anti-inflammatory, anti-allergenic surfactant for pharmaceuticals
    Manuf./Distrib.: Nikko Chem. Co. Ltd.
    Trade names: Nikkol Glycyrrhizic Acid

Glycyrrhizin. *See* Glycyrrhizic acid
Glycyrrhizinic acid. *See* Glycyrrhizic acid
Glyoxaline-5-alanine. *See* L-Histidine
Glyoxyldiureide. *See* Allantoin
GMP. *See* Disodium guanylate
GMS-SE. *See* Glyceryl stearate SE

Gold
CAS 7440-57-5; EINECS 231-165-9
Classification: Metallic element
Empirical: Au
Properties: Yel. soft metal; at.wt. 196.9665
Toxicology: Metallic gold may cause hypersensitivity reactions
Uses: Used in dental alloys; compds. for treatment of rheumatoid arthritis; radiopharmacy
Regulatory: UK approved; BP approved (colloidal gold injection)
Manuf./Distrib.: Cerac; Degussa; Koch Chem. Ltd; Noah Chem.

Gold bronze. *See* Copper
Gomenoleo oil. *See* Olive oil
Gotu kola extract. *See* Hydrocotyl extract
Graham's salt. *See* Sodium hexametaphosphate
Grains of paradise. *See* Cardamom
Granulated sugar. *See* Sucrose

Grape juice conc.
Uses: Ingred. in pharmaceutical tableting
Trade names containing: FruitSource® Granular; FruitSource® Liquid Sweetener; FruitSource® Liquid Sweetener Plus

Grape skin extract
Synonyms: Enocianina; Enocyanin
Definition: From aq. extraction of fresh deseeded marc remaining after grapes are pressed to produce wine or juice; contains anthocyanins, tartaric acid, tannins, sugars, minerals
Properties: Deep purple; sol. in water
Uses: Colorant
Regulatory: FDA 21CFR §73.170; Japan restricted
Manuf./Distrib. (pharm. & food): Am. Roland
Trade names: Grape Skin Extract, 2X #3850; Grape Skin Extract, Double Strength; Grape Skin Extract, Powd. 282730; Grape Skin Extract, Single Strength

Grape sugar. *See* D-Glucose anhyd.
Gray acetate. *See* Calcium acetate
Green vitriol. *See* Ferrous sulfate
Groundnut oil. *See* Peanut oil
Guadidium chloride. *See* Guanidine hydrochloride

Guaiacol
CAS 90-05-1; EINECS 201-964-7
FEMA 2532
Synonyms: Methylcatechol; Pyrocatechol methyl ether; o-Methoxyphenol; 2-Methoxyphenol; o-Hydroxyanisole
Classification: Aromatic organic compd.
Definition: Obtained from hardwood tar
Empirical: $C_7H_8O_2$
Formula: $OHC_6H_4OCH_3$
Properties: Wh. to sl. yel. cryst. or colorless to ylsh. liq., char. odor; sol. (1 g/ml): 60-70 ml water, 1 ml glycerin; misc. with alcohol, chloroform, ether, oils, glac. acetic acid; m.w. 124.14; dens. 1.129 (cryst.), 1.112 (liq.); m.p. 26-29 C; b.p. 204-206 C
Precaution: Combustible; light-sensitive
Toxicology: LD50 (oral, rat) 725 mg/kg; irritant; ingestion causes irritation of intestinal tract and heart failure; penetrates the skin; when applied to mucous membranes, produces pain, burning, and then loss of sensitivity
Uses: Medicinal synthetic flavor; expectorant; counter-irritant in external analgesic prods.
Regulatory: FDA 21CFR §172.515; FEMA GRAS; BP compliance
Manuf./Distrib.: Aldrich; Penta Mfg.; Schweizerhall; Société Chimique Roche; Spectrum Chem. Mfg.
Manuf./Distrib. (pharm. & food): Aldrich; Penta Mfg.; Ruger; Ube Ind.

Guanidine hydrochloride
CAS 50-01-1; EINECS 200-002-3
Synonyms: Aminoformamidine hydrochloride; Guanidinium chloride; Guadidium chloride
Classification: Aliphatic organic compd.
Empirical: $CH_5N_3 \cdot HCl$
Formula: $NH_2C(:NH)NH_2 \cdot HCl$

Guanidinium chloride

Properties: Hygroscopic; m.w. 95.53; m.p. 181-183 C
Toxicology: Irritant
Uses: Used in intravenous
Regulatory: FDA approved for intravenous
Manuf./Distrib.: Aldrich; Am. Biorganics; Fluka; Heico; Monomer-Polymer & Dajac; Spectrum Chem. Mfg.; U.S. Biochemical
Manuf./Distrib. (pharm. & food): Aldrich; R.W. Greeff; Sanwa Chem.

Guanidinium chloride. *See* Guanidine hydrochloride

Guanine
CAS 73-40-5; EINECS 200-799-8
Synonyms: 2-Amino-1,7-dihydro-6H-purin-6-one; 2-Aminohypoxanthine; 2-Amino-6-hydroxypurine; 2-Amino-6-oxypurine; CI 75170; Natural pearl essence; Natural white 1; Pearl essence
Classification: Natural purine
Definition: Crystalline material obtained from fish sacles, consisting of 75-97% guanine and 3-25% hypoxanthine (CAS 68-94-0)
Empirical: $C_5H_5N_5O$
Properties: Colorless rhombic crystals; insol. in water; sparingly sol. in alcohol, ether; freely sol. in ammonium hydroxide, dilute acids; m.w. 151.15; m.p. 300 C min.; dec. > 360 C
Toxicology: Suspected tumorigen; human mutagenic data
Uses: Color additive for external pharmaceuticals
Regulatory: FDA 21CFR §73.1329, 73.2329; BP compliance
Manuf./Distrib.: R.W. Greeff; Henley; Janssen Chimica; Mearl; Penta Mfg.; Spectrum Chem. Mfg.
Manuf./Distrib. (pharm. & food): R.W. Greeff
Trade names containing: Mearlmaid® AA; Mearlmaid® TR
See also CI 75170

Guaniol. *See* Geraniol
Guanosine 5´-disodium phosphate. *See* Disodium guanylate
Guanylic acid sodium salt. *See* Disodium guanylate
Guaramine. *See* Caffeine
Guar flour. *See* Guar gum

Guar gum
CAS 9000-30-0; EINECS 232-536-8
FEMA 2537
Synonyms: Guar flour; Jaguar gum; Gum cyamopsis; Cyamopsis gum
Definition: Natural material derived from the ground endosperms of *Cyamopsis tetragonolobus*; consists of high m.w. hydrocolloidal polysaccharide composed of galactomannan units
Properties: Yellowish-white free-flowing powd.; aq. sol'ns. tasteless, odorless; sol. in hot or cold water; insol. in oil, greases, hydrocarbons, ketones, esters; m.w. ≈ 220,000
Toxicology: Mildly toxic by ingestion; may cause contact dermatitis; heated to decomp., emits acrid smoke and irritating fumes
Uses: Binding agent in tablets; protective colloid, stabilizer, thickener, emulsifier, suspending or visc.-increasing agent; as bulk laxative, appetite suppressant; treatment of peptic ulcers; used in buccals, orals, lotions, creams, toothpastes
Regulatory: FDA 21CFR §133.124, 133.133, 133.134, 133.162, 133.178, 133.179, 150.141, 150.161, 184.1339, GRAS; FEMA GRAS; FDA approved for buccals, orals; USP/NF compliance; Japan approved; Europe listed; UK approved; ADI not specified (WHO)
Manuf./Distrib.: Aqualon; Hercules; Multi-Kem; Nat'l. Starch & Chem.; Rhone-Poulenc; Stan Chem Int'l. Ltd
Manuf./Distrib. (pharm. & food): Aldrich; Ashland; Atomergic Chemetals; Bio-Botanica; Chart; Commodity Services Int'l.; Cornelius; Courtaulds; Diamalt; Ellis & Everard; Goorden; Grindsted; Gumix Int'l.; A C Hatrick; Hercules; Lucas Meyer; Meer; Multi-Kem; Quest; Rhone-Poulenc; Ruger; Sanofi; Seah Int'l.; Spectrum Chem. Mfg.; Spice King; TIC Gums
Trade names: Edicol®; Edicol® P; Edicol® ULV Series; Powdered Guar Gum Type A; Powdered Guar Gum Type AA; Powdered Guar Gum Type B; Powdered Guar Gum Type BB; Powdered Gum Guar NF Type 80 Mesh B/T; Powdered Gum Guar Type 140 Mesh B/T; Powdered Gum Guar Type ECM; Powdered Gum Guar Type M; Powdered Gum Guar Type MM FCC; Powdered Gum Guar Type MM (HV); Powdered Gum Guar Type MMM $^1/_2$; Powdered Gum Guar Type MMW; Supercol® Guar Gum; Ticolv

Guatemala lemongrass oil. *See* Lemongrass oil West Indian
Guignet's green. *See* Chromium hydroxide green
Gum arabic. *See* Acacia
Gum Benjamin. *See* Gum benzoin

Gum benzoin
 CAS 9000-05-9; EINECS 232-523-7
 FEMA 2133
 Synonyms: Benzoin gum; Benzoin resin; Gum sumatra; Gum Benjamin; Siam benzoin; Sumatra benzoin
 Definition: Balsamic resin obtained from various *Styrax* species
 Toxicology: No known toxicity
 Uses: Natural flavoring agent; preservative, skin protectant, antiseptic in topicals, creams and ointments; ingred. in inhalants for treatment of catarrh of the upper respiratory tract
 Regulatory: FDA 21CFR §73.1, 172.510; FEMA GRAS; Japan approved; BP compliance

Gum camphor. *See* Camphor
Gum cyamopsis. *See* Guar gum
Gum dragon. *See* Tragacanth gum
Gum gellan. *See* Gellan gum

Gum ghatti
 CAS 900-28-6
 FEMA 2519
 Synonyms: Indian gum; Ghatti gum
 Definition: Exudate from wounds in the bark of *Anogeissus latifolia*
 Toxicology: Can cause allergy
 Uses: Emulsifier, suspending agent, stabilizer, binder; pharmaceutical tablets and coatings; imparts consistency to troches and emulsions
 Regulatory: FDA 21CFR §184.1333, GRAS; FEMA GRAS; Japan approved
 Manuf./Distrib. (pharm. & food): Importers Service
 Trade names: Granular Gum Ghatti #1; Powdered Gum Ghatti #1; Powdered Gum Ghatti #2; Premium Powdered Gum Ghatti G-1; Staform P

Gum hashab. *See* Acacia
Gum rosin. *See* Rosin
Gum sumatra. *See* Gum benzoin
Gum tragacanth. *See* Tragacanth gum
Guncotton. *See* Nitrocellulose

Gutta percha
 Synonyms: trans-Polyisoprene
 Definition: Geometric isomer of natural rubber
 Properties: Brn. to gray lumps or blocks, sl. char. odor; insol. in water; partly sol. in CS_2, turpentine oil; 90% sol. in chloroform; m.p.100 C
 Precaution: Protect from light
 Uses: Used in dressings, as filling for dental impression compds.
 Regulatory: USP compliance; Japan approved

Gypsum. *See* Calcium sulfate
Gypsum. *See* Calcium sulfate dihydrate

Haematoxylon capechianum extract. *See* Logwood extract
Hamamelis extract. *See* Witch hazel extract
Hard paraffin. *See* Paraffin
Hartshorn. *See* Ammonium carbonate
H.E. cellulose. *See* Hydroxyethylcellulose
Heavy mineral oil. *See* Mineral oil
HEC. *See* Hydroxyethylcellulose
Hector clay. *See* Hectorite

Hectorite
 CAS 12173-47-6; EINECS 235-340-0
 Synonyms: Hector clay
 Definition: One of the montmorillonite minerals that are the principal constituent of bentonite clay
 Formula: $\approx Na_{0.67}(Mg,Li)_6Si_8O_{20}(OH,F)_4$
 Toxicology: No known toxicity to skin; dust can be irritating to respiratory tract
 Uses: Emulsifier, extender, stabilizer, suspension agent, thickener
 Trade names: Hectabrite® AW; Hectabrite® DP

HEDPA. *See* Etidronic acid
HEDTANa₃. *See* Trisodium HEDTA
Helindone pink CN. *See* D&C Red No. 30
Helioptropyl isobutyrate. *See* Piperonyl isobutyrate
Heliotropin. *See* Heliotropine

Heliotropine
CAS 120-57-0; EINECS 204-409-7
FEMA 2911
Synonyms: Heliotropin; Piperonal; Piperonyl aldehyde; Dioxymethyleneprotocatechuic aldehyde; 3,4-
Methylenedioxybenzaldehyde; 3,4-Benzodioxole-5-carboxaldehyde; 1,3-Benzodioxole-5-carboxalde-
hyde; 3,4-Methylene dihydroxybenzaldehyde
Classification: Diazo dye
Empirical: $C_8H_6O_3$
Properties: Colorless lustrous cryst., floral heliotrope odor; very sol. in alcohol, ether; sol. in propylene glycol,
fixed oils; insol. in water, glycerin; m.w. 150.14; m.p. 37 C; b.p. 263 C; flash pt. > 230 F
Precaution: Combustible when exposed to heat, flame; reactive with oxidizers; keep in cool place;
photosensitive-protect from light
Toxicology: LD50 (oral, rat) 2700 mg/kg; mod. toxic by ingestion and intraperitoneal routes; can cause CNS
depression; skin irritant; may cause allergic skin reactions
Uses: Synthetic flavoring agent (cherry and vanilla flavors); used in orals
Regulatory: FDA 21CFR §182.60, GRAS; FEMA GRAS; FDA approved for orals
Manuf./Distrib.: Aldrich; Spectrum Chem. Mfg.
Manuf./Distrib. (pharm. & food): Aldrich; Chr. Hansen's

Heliotropyl acetate. *See* Piperonyl acetate

Hemicellulase
CAS 9025-56-3
Uses: Enzyme
Trade names: Hemi-Cellulase Amano 90

Hendecanal. *See* Undecanal
Hendecanoic alcohol. *See* Undecyl alcohol
1-Hendecanol. *See* Undecyl alcohol
Hendecenal. *See* 10-Undecenal
Hendecen-9-al. *See* 9-Undecenal
Hendecyl alcohol. *See* Undecyl alcohol

Heparin ammonium
CAS 60800-63-7; EINECS 232-681-7
Synonyms: Heparin ammonium salt
Uses: Anticoagulant; laboratory reagent
Manuf./Distrib.: Fluka
Trade names: SPL Heparin Ammonium

Heparin ammonium salt. *See* Heparin ammonium

Heparin lithium
CAS 9045-22-1; EINECS 232-681-7
Definition: Lithium salt of heparinic acid
Properties: Wh. powd.; sol. in water
Uses: Anticoagulant; in medical devices, laboratory reagent
Manuf./Distrib.: Fluka
Trade names: SPL Heparin Lithium

Heparin sodium
CAS 9041-08-1; EINECS 232-681-7
Synonyms: Heparin sodium salt
Definition: Sodium salt of a sulfated glycosaminoglycan of mixed mucopolysaccharides
Properties: Wh. powd.; hygroscopic; sol. in water; pH 5.0-7.5 (1%)
Toxicology: Possible hemorrhage, irritation, mild pain; hypersensitive reactions incl. chills, fever, itching, runny
nose, burning of feet, red eyes, tearing, joint pain, and hives
Uses: Anticoagulant, pharmaceutical agent; prevents and treats deep vein blood clots; used to flush and
maintain catheters
Regulatory: USP/NF, BP, Ph.Eur. compliance
Manuf./Distrib.: Fluka

Manuf./Distrib. (pharm. & food): Spectrum Chem. Mfg.
Trade names: SPL Heparin Sodium USP

Heparin sodium salt. *See* Heparin sodium

γ-Heptalactone
CAS 105-21-5
FEMA 2539
Synonyms: 4-Hydroxyheptanoic acid, γ-lactone
Empirical: $C_7H_{12}O_2$
Properties: Colorless sl. oily liq., sweet nut-like caramel odor; sol. in alcohol; insol. in water; m.w. 128.17
Uses: Sweet caramel, coconut-like synthetic flavoring agent
Regulatory: FDA 21CFR §172.515; FEMA GRAS
Manuf./Distrib. (pharm. & food): Aldrich

Heptaldehyde. *See* Heptanal
1-Heptaldehyde. *See* Heptanal

Heptanal
CAS 111-71-7; EINECS 203-898-4
FEMA 2540
Synonyms: Aldehyde C-7; 1-Heptanal; Enanthal; Oenanthol; Heptaldehyde; 1-Heptaldehyde; Heptylaldehyde; Enanthaldehyde; Oenanthaldehyde
Empirical: $C_7H_{14}O$
Formula: $CH_3(CH_2)_5CHO$
Properties: Liq., penetrating fruity odor; misc. with alcohol, ether; sl. sol. in water; m.w. 114.19; dens. 0.80902 (30/4 C); visc. 0.977 cp (15 C); m.p. -43.3 C; b.p. 152.8 C (760 mm); flash pt. 95 F; ref. index 1.42571 (20 C)
Precaution: Flamm.
Uses: Synthetic flavoring agent
Regulatory: FDA 21CFR §172.515; FEMA GRAS
Manuf./Distrib. (pharm. & food): Aldrich

1-Heptanal. *See* Heptanal
Heptanoic acid ethyl ester. *See* Ethyl heptanoate
Heptanoic acid methyl ester. *See* Methyl heptanoate
Heptanoic acid, octadecyl ester. *See* Stearyl heptanoate
1-Heptanol. *See* Heptyl alcohol
2-Heptanone. *See* Methyl n-amyl ketone

3-Heptanone
CAS 106-35-4; EINECS 203-388-1
FEMA 2545
Synonyms: Ethyl butyl ketone; Butyl ethyl ketone; Ethyl-n-butyl ketone
Empirical: $C_7H_{14}O$
Formula: $CH_3(CH_2)_3COC_2H_5$
Properties: Colorless liq., powerful green fatty fruity odor, melon banana flavor; insol. in water; m.w. 114.19; dens. 0.818 (20/4 C); m.p. -39 C; b.p. 145-148 C; flash pt. 38 C; ref. index 1.409 (20 C)
Precaution: Flamm.
Toxicology: Eye irritant
Uses: Sweet, fruity synthetic flavoring agent
Regulatory: FDA 21CFR §172.515; FEMA GRAS
Manuf./Distrib. (pharm. & food): Aldrich; Hüls

4-Heptanone
CAS 123-19-3; EINECS 204-608-9
FEMA 2546
Synonyms: Dipropyl ketone; Butyrone
Empirical: $C_7H_{14}O$
Formula: $(CH_3CH_2CH_2)_2CO$
Properties: Colorless liq., penetrating odor, burning taste; misc. with alcohol, ether; insol. in water; m.w. 114.19; dens. 0.814 (20/4 C); m.p. -32.6 C; b.p. 142-144 C; flash pt. 49 C; ref. index 1.4073 (22 C)
Precaution: Flamm.
Uses: Pineapple-like synthetic flavoring agent
Regulatory: FDA 21CFR §172.515; FEMA GRAS
Manuf./Distrib. (pharm. & food): Aldrich; Hüls

3,6,9,12,15,18,21-Heptaoxanonatriacontan-1-ol

3,6,9,12,15,18,21-Heptaoxanonatriacontan-1-ol. *See* Steareth-7
3,6,9,12,15,18,21-Heptaoxatricosane-1,2,3-diol. *See* PEG-8
3,6,9,12,15,18,21-Heptaoxatritriacontan-1-ol. *See* Laureth-7

Heptyl acetate
CAS 112-06-1
FEMA 2547
Empirical: $C_9H_{18}O_2$
Properties: Colorless liq., pear-like odor, apricot-like taste; sol. in alcohol, ether; insol. in water; m.w. 150.18; dens. 0.87505 (15 C); m.p. -50 C; b.p. 192-193 C; flash pt. 154 F; ref. index 1.4150
Uses: Citrus, apricot, pear-like synthetic flavoring agent
Regulatory: FDA 21CFR §172.515; FEMA GRAS
Manuf./Distrib. (pharm. & food): Aldrich

Heptyl alcohol
CAS 111-70-6; EINECS 203-897-9
FEMA 2548
Synonyms: 1-Heptanol; Hydroxy heptane; pri-Heptyl alcohol; Alcohol C-7; Enanthyl alcohol; Enanthic alcohol
Empirical: $C_7H_{16}O$
Formula: $CH_3(CH_2)_6OH$
Properties: Colorless liq., citrus odor; sl. sol. in water @ 175 C; misc. with alcohol, fixed oils, ether; m.w. 116.23; dens. 0.824 (20/4 C); m.p. -34.6 C; b.p. 175.8 C; flash pt. 70 C; ref. index 1.423-.1427
Precaution: Combustible liq.; reactive with oxidizing materials
Toxicology: LD50 (oral, rat) 500 mg/kg; mod. toxic by ingestion, skin contact; mildly toxic by inh.; heated to decomp., emits acrid smoke and fumes
Uses: Citrus synthetic flavoring agent
Regulatory: FDA 21CFR §172.515; FEMA GRAS
Manuf./Distrib.: Aldrich; Elf Atochem N. Am.; Penta Mfg.; Suchema AG
Manuf./Distrib. (pharm. & food): Aldrich

Heptylaldehyde. *See* Heptanal
n-Heptyl-n-butanoate. *See* Heptyl butyrate

Heptyl butyrate
CAS 5870-93-9
FEMA 2549
Synonyms: n-Heptyl-n-butanoate; n-Heptyl-n-butyrate
Empirical: $C_{11}H_{22}O_2$
Properties: Colorless liq., fruity camomile-like odor, sweet green tea-like taste; sol. in alcohol; almost insol. in water; m.w. 186.30; m.p. -58 C; b.p. 225-226 C; flash pt. 195 F; ref. index 1.4231
Uses: Sweet synthetic flavoring agent
Regulatory: FDA 21CFR §172.515; FEMA GRAS
Manuf./Distrib. (pharm. & food): Aldrich

n-Heptyl-n-butyrate. *See* Heptyl butyrate
γ-Heptyl butyrolactone. *See* γ-Undecalactone
Heptyl carbinol. *See* Caprylic alcohol

Heptyl formate
CAS 112-23-2
FEMA 2552
Empirical: $C_8H_{16}O_2$
Properties: Colorless liq., fruity floral odor, plum-like taste; sol. in ether; insol. in water
Uses: Apple, plum-like synthetic flavoring agent
Regulatory: FDA 21CFR §172.515; FEMA GRAS
Manuf./Distrib. (pharm. & food): Aldrich

Heptylidene acetone. *See* 3-Decen-2-one
Heptyl methyl ketone. *See* 2-Nonanone

Herbacol
CAS 6365-83-9
Uses: Used in topicals
Regulatory: FDA approved for topicals

Hexachlorophene
CAS 70-30-4
UN No. 2875

Synonyms: 2,2´-Methylenebis (3,4,6-trichlorophenol)
Empirical: $C_{13}H_6Cl_6O_2$
Formula: $CH_2[C_6H(Cl)_3OH]_2$
Properties: Wh. free-flowing powd., odorless or sl. phenolic odor; sol. in acetone, alcohol, ether; insol. in water; m.w. 406.91; m.p. 163-165 C
Precaution: DOT: Poisonous material
Toxicology: Irritant
Uses: Antibacterial used in topicals
Usage level: Up to 0.75%
Regulatory: FDA approved for topicals; USP/NF, BP compliance
Manuf./Distrib. (pharm. & food): Aldrich; Spectrum Chem. Mfg.

Hexadecanoic acid. *See* Palmitic acid
Hexadecanoic acid, cetyl/stearyl ether. *See* Cetearyl palmitate
Hexadecanoic acid, hexadecyl ester. *See* Cetyl palmitate
Hexadecanoic acid, 1-methylethyl ester. *See* Isopropyl palmitate
Hexadecanoic acid, 1,2,3-propanetriyl ester. *See* Tripalmitin
1-Hexadecanol. *See* Cetyl alcohol
1-Hexadecanol, acetate. *See* Cetyl acetate
1-Hexadecanol lactate. *See* Cetyl lactate
Hexadecyl acetate. *See* Cetyl acetate
Hexadecyl alcohol. *See* Cetyl alcohol
Hexadecylamine hydrofluoride. *See* Cetylamine hydrofluoride
Hexadecylammonium fluoride. *See* Cetylamine hydrofluoride
N-Hexadecyl-N,N-dimethylbenzenemethanaminium chloride. *See* Cetalkonium chloride
Hexadecyl 12-hydroxy-9-octadecenoate. *See* Cetyl ricinoleate
Hexadecylic acid. *See* Palmitic acid
n-Hexadecyl lactate. *See* Cetyl lactate
1-Hexadecylpyridinium chloride. *See* Cetylpyridinium chloride
Hexadecyltrimethylammonium bromide. *See* Cetrimonium bromide
Hexadecyl trimethyl ammonium chloride. *See* Cetrimonium chloride
Hexadienic acid. *See* Sorbic acid
2,4-Hexadienoic acid. *See* Sorbic acid
2,4-Hexadienoic acid potassium salt. *See* Potassium sorbate
Hexaethylene glycol. *See* PEG-6
Hexaglycerin monooleate. *See* Polyglyceryl-6 oleate
Hexaglycerol dioleate. *See* Polyglyceryl-6 dioleate
Hexaglycerol distearate. *See* Polyglyceryl-6 distearate
Hexaglyceryl dioleate. *See* Polyglyceryl-6 dioleate
Hexaglyceryl distearate. *See* Polyglyceryl-6 distearate
Hexaglyceryl oleate. *See* Polyglyceryl-6 oleate
Hexahydro azepine. *See* Hexamethyleneimine
Hexahydrobenzene. *See* Cyclohexane
[3aS-(3a-α,4b,6aα)]-Hexahydro-2-oxo-1H-thieno]3,4-d]imidazole-4-pentanoic acid. *See* d-Biotin
cis-Hexahydro-2-oxo-1H-thieno (3,4)-imidazole-4-valeric acid. *See* d-Biotin
Hexahydrophenethyl acetate. *See* Cyclohexylethyl acetate
Hexahydro phenylethyl propionate. *See* Ethyl cyclohexanepropionate
Hexahydropyridine. *See* Piperidine
Hexahydrothymol. *See* Menthol

γ-Hexalactone
  CAS 695-06-7
  FEMA 2556
  Synonyms: 4-Hydroxyhexanoic acid γ-lactone; Ethyl butyrolactone; Tonkalide; γ-Caprolactone
  Empirical: $C_6H_{10}O_2$
  Properties: Colorless liq., herbaceous sweet odor, sweet coumarin-caramel taste; sol. in alcohol, propylene glycol; sl. sol. in water; m.w. 114.15; dens. 1.023; m.p. -18 C; b.p. 220 C; flash pt. 209 F
  Uses: Sweet synthetic flavoring agent
  Regulatory: FDA 21CFR §172.515; FEMA GRAS
  Manuf./Distrib. (pharm. & food): Aldrich

Hexamethyldisilazane
  CAS 999-97-3; EINECS 213-668-5
  Synonyms: HMDS; Bis (trimethylsilyl) amine

Hexamethylene

Empirical: $C_6H_{19}NSi_2$
Formula: $(CH_3)_3SiNHSi(CH_3)_3$
Properties: Liq.; sol. in acetone, benzene, ethyl ether, heptane, perchloroethylene; m.w. 161.44; dens. 0.77; b.p. 125 C; flash pt. 25 C; ref. index 1.4057
Precaution: Fire hazard
Toxicology: Moderately toxic by intraperitoneal route; experimental tumorigen; PEL 6 mg/m^3
Uses: Used in pharmaceutical mfg. processes
Regulatory: BP compliance
Manuf./Distrib.: Aldrich; Austin; Dow Corning; FAR Research; Gelest; Great Western; Hüls Am.; Janssen Chimica; PCR; Schweizerhall; Wacker Chemie GmbH
Trade names containing: Cab-O-Sil® TS-530

Hexamethylene. *See* Cyclohexane
1,1´-Hexamethylene bis [5-(4-chlorophenyl) biguanide] diacetate. *See* Chlorhexidine diacetate

Hexamethyleneimine

CAS 111-49-9; EINECS 203-875-9
UN No. 2493
Synonyms: HMI; 1H-Azepine, hexahydro; Hexahydro azepine; Hexamethylenimine; Cyclohexamethylene-imine; Homopiperidine; Azacycloheptane
Empirical: $C_6H_{13}N$
Properties: Colorless clear liq., ammonia-like odor; m.w. 99.2; sp.gr. 0.88; vapor pressure 9 mm Hg; m.p. -37 C; b.p. 138 C (760 mm); flash pt. (CC) 22 C; ref. index 1.463 (20 C)
Precaution: Flamm., corrosive
Toxicology: Corrosive to skin and eyes; tissue irritant; avoid inh. of vapor
Uses: Intermediate for pharmaceuticals
Manuf./Distrib.: BASF; DuPont; Fluka; Monomer-Polymer & Dajac
Manuf./Distrib. (pharm. & food): Aldrich

Hexamethylenimine. *See* Hexamethyleneimine
2,6,10,15,19,23-Hexamethyl-2,6,10,14,18,22-tetracosahexaene. *See* Squalene
2,6,10,15,19,23-Hexamethyltetracosane. *See* Squalane

Hexamidine diisethionate

CAS 659-40-5; EINECS 211-533-5
Classification: Organic salt
Properties: Wh. powd.
Uses: Antimicrobial preservative; cutaneous asepticizer; topical antiseptic
Usage level: 0.1%
Regulatory: USA not restricted; Europe listed
Trade names: Elestab® HP 100

Hexanaphthene. *See* Cyclohexane
Hexanedioic acid. *See* Adipic acid
Hexanedioic acid, bis (2-ethylhexyl) ester. *See* Dioctyl adipate
Hexanedioic acid, bis (1-methylethyl) ester. *See* Diisopropyl adipate
Hexanedioic acid, dibutyl ester. *See* Dibutyl adipate
2,3-Hexanedione. *See* Acetyl butyryl
1,2,3,4,5,6-Hexanehexol. *See* D-Mannitol; Sorbitol
Hexanoic acid. *See* Caproic acid
Hexanoic acid ethyl ester. *See* Ethyl caproate
1-Hexanol. *See* Hexyl alcohol

3-Hexanol

CAS 623-37-0
FEMA 3351
Empirical: $C_6H_{14}O$
Properties: M.w. 102.18; dens. 0.819; b.p. 134-135 C; flash pt. 107 F
Uses: Medicinal flavoring agent
Regulatory: FEMA GRAS
Manuf./Distrib. (pharm. & food): Aldrich

n-Hexanol. *See* Hexyl alcohol

3-Hexanone

CAS 589-38-8
FEMA 3290

Empirical: $C_6H_{12}O$
Properties: M.w. 100.16; dens. 0.815; b.p. 123 C; flash pt. 95 F
Uses: Grape-like flavoring agent
Regulatory: FEMA GRAS
Manuf./Distrib. (pharm. & food): Aldrich

3,6,9,12,15,18-Hexaoxatetratricontan-1-ol. *See* Ceteth-6
3,6,9,12,15,18-Hexaoxatriacontan-1-ol. *See* Laureth-6
Hexazane. *See* Piperidine

2-Hexenal
CAS 6728-26-3; EINECS 229-778-1
FEMA 2560
Synonyms: α-β-Hexylenaldehyde; trans-2-Hexenal; β-Propyl acrolein
Empirical: $C_6H_{10}O$
Properties: Oily liq., char. green leafy odor; sol. in most org. solvs.; m.w. 98.15; dens. 0.844; b.p.47-48 C (17 mm); flash pt. 101 F; ref. index 1.446 (20 C)
Precaution: Flamm.
Toxicology: Skin irritant
Uses: Sweet apple, plum-like synthetic flavoring agent
Regulatory: FDA 21CFR §172.515; FEMA GRAS
Manuf./Distrib. (pharm. & food): Aldrich

trans-2-Hexenal. *See* 2-Hexenal
2-Hexene-1-yl acetate. *See* trans-2-Hexenyl acetate

2-Hexenol
CAS 928-95-0; EINECS 213-191-2
FEMA 2562
Synonyms: 2-Hexen-1-ol; α,β-Hexenol; trans-2-Hexen-1-ol; γ-Propylallyl alcohol
Empirical: $C_6H_{12}O$
Properties: Colorless liq., powerful fruity green wine-like odor, sweet fruity flavor; sol. in alcohol, propylene glycol; sl. sol. in water; m.w. 100.16; dens. 0.843 (20/4 C); b.p. 158-160 C; flash pt. 64 C; ref. index 1.438 (20 C)
Toxicology: Irritant
Uses: Fruity synthetic flavoring agent
Regulatory: FDA 21CFR §172.515; FEMA GRAS
Manuf./Distrib. (pharm. & food): Aldrich

2-Hexen-1-ol. *See* 2-Hexenol
α,β-Hexenol. *See* 2-Hexenol
trans-2-Hexen-1-ol. *See* 2-Hexenol
2-Hexen-1-yl acetate. *See* trans-2-Hexenyl acetate

trans-2-Hexenyl acetate
CAS 2497-18-9
FEMA 2564
Synonyms: 2-Hexen-1-yl acetate; 2-Hexene-1-yl acetate
Empirical: $C_8H_{14}O_2$
Properties: Liq., pleasant fruity odor and taste; m.w. 142.19; dens. 0.898; b.p. 165-166 C; flash pt. 58 C; ref. index 1.4270
Toxicology: Irritant
Uses: Synthetic flavoring agent
Regulatory: FDA 21CFR §172.515; FEMA GRAS
Manuf./Distrib. (pharm. & food): Aldrich

3-Hexenyl 2-methylbutanoate. *See* cis-3-Hexenyl 2-methylbutyrate
3-Hexenyl-2-methylbutyrate. *See* cis-3-Hexenyl 2-methylbutyrate

cis-3-Hexenyl 2-methylbutyrate
CAS 10094-41-4
FEMA 3497
Synonyms: 3-Hexenyl-2-methylbutyrate; cis-3-Hexenyl-α-methylbutyrate; 3-Hexenyl 2-methylbutanoate
Empirical: $C_{11}H_{20}O_2$
Properties: Colorless liq., warm fruity apple-like odor, sweet apple-like taste; sol. in alcohol; insol. in water; m.w. 184.28; dens. 0.878; flash pt. 182 F
Uses: Apple-like flavoring agent

cis-3-Hexenyl-α-methylbutyrate

Regulatory: FDA 21CFR §172.515; FEMA GRAS
Manuf./Distrib. (pharm. & food): Aldrich

cis-3-Hexenyl-α-methylbutyrate. See cis-3-Hexenyl 2-methylbutyrate

Hexetidine
CAS 141-94-6; EINECS 205-513-5
Synonyms: 5-Amino-1,3-bis(2-ethylhexyl)-5-methyl-hexhydropyrimidine; 1,3-Bis(2-ethylhexyl)hexahydro-5-methyl-5-pyrimidiamine; Substituted hexa hydropyrimidine
Classification: Heterocyclic organic compd.
Empirical: $C_{21}H_{45}N_3$
Uses: Antimicrobial, antifungal agent for topical antifungal and feminine hygiene prods.
Usage level: 100-1000 ppm
Regulatory: USA EPA registered; Europe listed 0.1% max.
Manuf./Distrib.: ANGUS
Manuf./Distrib. (pharm. & food): Aldrich
Trade names: Hexetidine 90; Hexetidine 99

Hexoic acid. See Caproic acid
Hexone. See Methyl isobutyl ketone

Hexyl acetate
CAS 142-92-7; EINECS 205-572-7
FEMA 2565
Empirical: $C_8H_{16}O_2$
Formula: $CH_3COO(CH_2)_5CH_3$
Properties: Colorless oily liq., pleasant fruity odor, bittersweet taste; sol. in alcohol, ether; insol. in water; m.w. 144.22; dens. 0.873 (20/4 C); m.p. -81 C; b.p. 167-169 C; flash pt. 41 C; ref. index 1.409 (20 C)
Precaution: Flamm.
Uses: Sweet apple, cherry, pear-like synthetic flavoring agent
Regulatory: FDA 21CFR §172.515; FEMA GRAS
Manuf./Distrib. (pharm. & food): Aldrich

2-Hexyl-4-acetoxytetrahydrofuran
FEMA 2566
Synonyms: 2-Hexyl-tetrahydrofuran-4-yl acetate
Empirical: $C_{12}H_{22}O_3$
Properties: Colorless liq., sweet floral-fruity odor, peach-apricot taste; sol. in alcohol; sl. sol. in water; m.w. 214.31
Uses: Synthetic flavoring agent
Regulatory: FDA 21CFR §172.515; FEMA delisted

Hexyl alcohol
CAS 111-27-3; 68526-79-4; EINECS 203-852-3
FEMA 2567
Synonyms: 1-Hexanol; n-Hexanol; Alcohol C-6; Pentylcarbinol; Amylcarbinol
Classification: Aliphatic alcohol
Empirical: $C_6H_{14}O$
Formula: $CH_3(CH_2)_4CH_2OH$
Properties: Colorless liq., fruity odor, aromatic flavor; sol. in alcohol and ether; sl. sol. in water; m.w. 102.20; dens. 0.8186; f.p. -51.6 C; b.p. 157.2 C; flash pt. (TOC) 65 C; ref. index 1.1469 (25 C)
Precaution: Flamm. or combustible liq.; reactive with oxidizing materials
Toxicology: LD50 (rat, oral) 4.59 g/kg; poison by intravenous route; moderately toxic by ingestion, skin contact; skin and severe eye irritant
Uses: Synthetic flavoring agent; pharmaceuticals (antiseptics, perfume esters)
Regulatory: FDA 21CFR §172.515, 172.864, 178.3480; FEMA GRAS
Manuf./Distrib.: Albemarle; Aldrich; Ashland; Penta Mfg.; Vista
Manuf./Distrib. (pharm. & food): Aldrich
Trade names: Nacol® 6-98

Hexyl-2-butenoate
CAS 19089-92-0
FEMA 3354
Synonyms: Hexyl trans-2-butenoate; N-Hexyl 2-butenoate
Empirical: $C_{10}H_{18}O_2$
Properties: Fruity pineapple odor; m.w. 170.25; dens. 0.885; flash pt. 193 F

Uses: Pineapple-like flavoring agent
Regulatory: FEMA GRAS
Manuf./Distrib. (pharm. & food): Aldrich

N-Hexyl 2-butenoate. *See* Hexyl-2-butenoate
Hexyl trans-2-butenoate. *See* Hexyl-2-butenoate

Hexyl butyrate
CAS 2639-63-6
FEMA 2568
Empirical: $C_{10}H_{20}O_2$
Properties: Liq., apricot-like odor, pineapple-like taste; m.w. 172.27; dens. 0.851; m.p. -78 C; b.p. 205 C
Uses: Sweet apricot, pineapple-like synthetic flavoring agent
Regulatory: FDA 21CFR §172.515; FEMA GRAS
Manuf./Distrib. (pharm. & food): Aldrich

Hexyl caprylate. *See* Hexyl octanoate

2-Hexyl-1-decanol
CAS 2425-77-6; EINECS 219-370-1
Classification: Aliphatic alcohol
Empirical: $C_{16}H_{34}O$
Uses: Solubilizer for lipid-sol. actives for pharmaceutical creams, ointments, emulsions, sticks
Trade names: Isofol® 16

α-β-Hexylenaldehyde. *See* 2-Hexenal

Hexylene glycol
CAS 107-41-5; EINECS 203-489-0
Synonyms: 2-Methyl-2,4-pentanediol; 4-Methyl-2,4-pentanediol; α,α,α´-Trimethyltrimethyleneglycol
Classification: Aliphatic alcohol
Empirical: $C_6H_{14}O_2$
Formula: $(CH_3)_2COHCH_2CHOHCH_3$
Properties: Colorless liq., nearly odorless; hygroscopic; misc. with water, hydrocarbons, fatty acids; m.w. 118.18; dens. 0.9216 (20/4 C); b.p. 198.3 C; flash pt. (OC) 93 C; ref. index 1.4276 (20 C)
Toxicology: TLV:Cl 25 ppm in air; LD50 (rat, oral) 4.70 g/kg
Uses: Pharmaceutic aid, humectant, solvent; used in topicals
Regulatory: FDA 21CFR §175.105, 176.180, 176.200, 176.210, 177.1210, 177.2800; FDA approved for topicals; USP/NF compliance
Manuf./Distrib.: Allchem Ind.; Ashland; BP Chem. Ltd; Coyne; Elf Atochem SA; Great Western; Mitsui Petrochem. Ind.; Penta Mfg.; Shell; Union Carbide
Manuf./Distrib. (pharm. & food): Aldrich; Ruger; Spectrum Chem. Mfg.

Hexyl formate
CAS 629-33-4
FEMA 2570
Empirical: $C_7H_{14}O_2$
Properties: Colorless liq., green fruity odor, sweet taste; sl. sol. in water; misc. with alcohol, ether; m.w. 130.19; dens. 0.879; m.p. -63 C; b.p. 155-156 C; flash pt. 118 F; ref. index 1.4071
Uses: Synthetic flavoring agent
Regulatory: FDA 21CFR §172.515; FEMA GRAS
Manuf./Distrib. (pharm. & food): Aldrich

Hexyl isobutyrate
CAS 2349-07-7
FEMA 3172
Empirical: $C_{10}H_{20}O_2$
Properties: M.w. 172.27; dens. 0.860; flash pt. 164 F
Uses: Grape-like flavoring agent
Regulatory: FEMA GRAS
Manuf./Distrib. (pharm. & food): Aldrich

n-Hexyl isopentanoate. *See* Hexyl isovalerate

Hexyl isovalerate
CAS 10032-13-0
FEMA 3500
Synonyms: n-Hexyl isopentanoate; Hexyl 3-methylbutanoate

Hexyl laurate

Definition: Ester of n-hexanol and isovaleric acid
Empirical: $C_{11}H_{22}O_2$
Properties: Colorless liq., pungent fruity odor; sol. in alcohol, fixed oils; insol. in water; m.w. 186.30; dens. 0.853; flash pt. 215 C; ref. index 1.417
Toxicology: Heated to decomp, emits acrid smoke and irritating fumes
Uses: Synthetic flavoring agent
Regulatory: FDA 21CFR §172.515; FEMA GRAS
Manuf./Distrib. (pharm. & food): Aldrich

Hexyl laurate

CAS 34316-64-8; EINECS 251-932-1
Synonyms: Dodecanoic acid, hexyl ester
Definition: Ester of hexyl alcohol and lauric acid
Formula: $CH_3(CH_2)_{10}COO(CH_2)_5CH_3$
Uses: Emulsifier, emollient, spreading agent, carrier, base, dispersant used in pharmaceuticals
Trade names: Cetiol® A; Standamul® CTA
Trade names containing: Abil® WE 09

Hexyl 2-methylbutanoate. *See* Hexyl 2-methylbutyrate
Hexyl 3-methylbutanoate. *See* Hexyl isovalerate

Hexyl 2-methylbutyrate

CAS 10032-15-2
FEMA 3499
Synonyms: 2-Methylbutanoic acid n-hexyl ester; Hexyl 2-methylbutanoate
Definition: Ester of n-hexanol and 2-methylbutanoic acid
Empirical: $C_{11}H_{22}O_2$
Properties: Colorless liq., strong green fruity odor, unripe strawberry taste; sol. in alcohol; insol. in water; m.w. 186.30; dens. 0.858; flash pt. 183 F
Uses: Apple, strawberry-like, fruity flavoring agent
Regulatory: FDA 21CFR §172.515; FEMA GRAS
Manuf./Distrib. (pharm. & food): Aldrich

Hexyl methyl ketone. *See* Methyl hexyl ketone

Hexyl octanoate

CAS 1117-55-1
FEMA 2575
Synonyms: Hexyl caprylate; n-Hexyl-n-octanoate; n-Hexyl octylate
Definition: Ester of n-hexanol and caproic acid
Empirical: $C_{14}H_{28}O_2$
Properties: Liq., sl. fruity odor, sweet green fruity taste; sol. in alcohol; insol. in water; m.w. 228.37; dens. 0.87; m.p. -31 C; b.p. 277 C
Uses: Synthetic flavoring agent
Regulatory: FDA 21CFR §172.515; FEMA GRAS
Manuf./Distrib. (pharm. & food): Aldrich

n-Hexyl-n-octanoate. *See* Hexyl octanoate
n-Hexyl octylate. *See* Hexyl octanoate
n-Hexyl propanoate. *See* Hexyl propionate

Hexyl propionate

CAS 2445-76-3
FEMA 2576
Synonyms: n-Hexyl propanoate
Definition: Ester of n-hexanol and propionic acid
Empirical: $C_9H_{18}O_2$
Properties: Liq., earthy acrid odor, sweet metallic-fruity taste; sol. in alcohol, propylene glycol; insol. in water; m.w. 158.24; dens. 0.871; b.p. 180 C; flash pt. 149 F; ref. index 1.4105
Uses: Pear-like synthetic flavoring agent
Regulatory: FEMA GRAS
Manuf./Distrib. (pharm. & food): Aldrich

2-Hexyl-tetrahydrofuran-4-yl acetate. *See* 2-Hexyl-4-acetoxytetrahydrofuran
HFCS. *See* Corn syrup, high fructose
Hibiscus moscheutos. *See* Althea
High fructose corn syrup. *See* Corn syrup, high fructose

Histidine. *See* L-Histidine

L-Histidine
CAS 71-00-1; EINECS 200-745-3
FEMA 3694
Synonyms: Histidine; L-α-4(or 5)-Imidazolepropionic acid; α-Amino-β-imidazolepropionic acid; Glyoxaline-5-alanine
Classification: Essential amino acid
Empirical: $C_6H_9N_3O_2$
Formula: $HOOCCH(NH_2)CH_2C_3H_3N_2$
Properties: Wh. need., plates, or cryst. powd., odorless, sl. bitter taste; sol. in water; very sl. sol. in alcohol; insol. in ether; m.w. 155.16; m.p. 285-287 C (dec.); pH 7.0-8.5 (2%)
Toxicology: Experimental reproductive effects; human mutagenic data; heated to decomp., emits toxic fumes of NO_x
Uses: Nutrient used in orals and creams
Regulatory: FDA 21CFR §172.310, limitation 2.4%, 172.320; FEMA GRAS; Japan approved; FDA approved for orals; BP, Ph.Eur. compliance
Manuf./Distrib.: Degussa; R.W. Greeff; Janssen Chimica; Penta Mfg.; Spectrum Chem. Mfg.; Tanabe USA
Manuf./Distrib. (pharm. & food): Aldrich; Degussa; Penta Mfg.; Ruger; Spectrum Chem. Mfg.

HMDS. *See* Hexamethyldisilazane
HMI. *See* Hexamethyleneimine
Homoanisic acid. *See* p-Methoxyphenylacetic acid
Homo-cuminic aldehyde. *See* p-Isopropylphenylacetaldehyde
Homopiperidine. *See* Hexamethyleneimine

Honey
CAS 8028-66-8
Synonyms: Mel; Clarified honey; Strained honey
Definition: Saccharic secretion gathered by honey bees, *Apis mellifera*
Properties: Lt. ylsh. to reddish brn. thick syrupy liq., char. odor, sweet faintly acrid taste
Uses: Sweetener
Regulatory: BP complliance (purified)
Trade names containing: Hony-Tab®

Horse chestnut extract
CAS 90045-79-7
Synonyms: Aesculus hippocastanum extract
Definition: Extract derived from *Aesculus hippocastanum*
Uses: Ingred. in sun care and eye care prods.
Manuf./Distrib.: Bio-Botanica
Trade names containing: Biophytex®

HPC. *See* Hydroxypropylcellulose
HPMCAS. *See* Hydroxypropyl methylcellulose acetate succinate
HPMCP. *See* Hydroxypropyl methylcellulose phthalate
Huile de ricini. *See* Castor oil
Human albumin. *See* Albumin
Human serum albumin. *See* Albumin
Hyacinthin. *See* Phenylacetaldehyde

Hyaluronic acid
CAS 9004-61-9; EINECS 232-678-0
Definition: Natural mucopolysaccharide formed by bonding N-acetyl-D-glucosamine with glucuronic acid
Empirical: $(C_{14}H_{21}NO_{11})_N$
Uses: Used in raw materials for pharmaceuticals
Manuf./Distrib.: Am. Biorganics; Croda; Solabia; Worthington Biochemical
Trade names containing: Lipocare HA/EC

Hybrid safflower oil
Synonyms: Safflower oil, hybrid
Definition: Oil derived from safflower seeds; contains predominantly oleic acid triglyceride
Properties: Bland liq.; insol. in water; sol. in oil
Uses: Solubilizer, emollient, solvent for pharmaceuticals

2-Hydoxyethyl octadecanoate. *See* Glycol stearate
Hydrargyrum. *See* Mercury

Hydrated alumina. *See* Alumina trihydrate; Aluminum hydroxide
Hydrated aluminum oxide. *See* Alumina trihydrate
Hydrated aluminum silicate. *See* Kaolin; Pyrophyllite
Hydrated chromic sesquioxide. *See* Chromium hydroxide green
Hydrated chromium sesquioxide. *See* Chromium hydroxide green; CI 77289
Hydrated ferric oxide. *See* CI 77492
Hydrated lime. *See* Calcium hydroxide
Hydratropyl butyrate. *See* 2-Phenylpropyl butyrate
Hydratropyl isobutyrate. *See* 2-Phenylpropyl isobutyrate

Hydriodic acid
CAS 10034-85-2; EINECS 233-109-9
UN No. 1787
Synonyms: Hydroiodic acid
Classification: Acid
Empirical: HI
Properties: Colorless to pale yel. liq., odorless; misc. with water, alcohol; m.w. 127.91; dens. 1.7; b.p. 127 C; flash pt. none
Precaution: Light-sensitive
Toxicology: Eye and skin irritant
Uses: Prep. of iodine salts, org. preps., analytical reagent; expectorant
Regulatory: BP compliance
Manuf./Distrib.: Janssen Chimica; Spectrum Chem. Mfg.
Manuf./Distrib. (pharm. & food): Aldrich

Hydroabietyl alcohol
CAS 1333-89-7; 26266-77-3; EINECS 247-574-0
Synonyms: Dihydroabietyl alcohol; Dodecahydro-1,4a-dimethyl-7-(1-methylethyl)-1-phenanthrenemethanol
Definition: Organic alcohol derived from wood rosin
Empirical: $C_{20}H_{34}O$
Formula: $C_{19}H_{31}CH_2OH$
Properties: Solid; insol. in water; dens. 1.007-1.008; m.p. 32-33 C; flash pt. (COC) 185 C; ref. index 1.526 (20 C)
Precaution: Combustible
Uses: Pharmaceutical excipient
Regulatory: FDA 21CFR §175.105, 176.180
Manuf./Distrib.: Hercules

Hydrocarbon 40
CAS 8041-63-2
Uses: Used in topicals for its water repellency
Regulatory: FDA approved for topicals

Hydrochloric acid
CAS 7647-01-0; EINECS 231-595-7
UN No. 1789
Synonyms: Muriatic acid; Chlorhydric acid; Spirit of salt
Classification: Inorganic acid
Empirical: CIH
Formula: HCl
Properties: Colorless fuming gas or liq., pungent odor; misc. with water, alcohol; m.w. 36.46; dens. 1.639 g/L (gas, 0 C), 1.194 (liq., -26 C); m.p. -114.3 C; b.p. -84.8 C
Precaution: Nonflamm. gas; explosive reaction with many chems.; potentially dangerous reaction with sulfuric acid releases HCl gas; strongly corrosive
Toxicology: TLV: CL 5 ppm; human poison; mildly toxic to humans by inh.; corrosive irritant to skin, eyes, mucous membranes; mutagenic data; experimental teratogen; 35 ppm causes throat irritation on short exposure; heated to decomp., emits toxic fumes of Cl⁻
Uses: Acidifying agent, buffer and neutralizing agent; preservative in soft lens prods.; used in injectables, parenterals, inhalants, intravenous, ophthalmics, orals, otics, topicals
Regulatory: FDA 21CFR §131.144, 131.129, 160.105, 160.185, 172, 172.560, 182.1057, GRAS; Japan restricted; Europe listed; UK approved; FDA approved for injectables, parenterals, inhalants, intravenous, ophthalmics, orals, otics, topicals; USP/NF, BP, Ph.Eur., JP compliance
Manuf./Distrib.: Allied-Signal; Asahi Chem Industry Co Ltd; Asahi Denka Kogyo; Bayer; Dover; DuPont; Elf Atochem; Hüls AG; ICI; Nissan Chem. Ind.; Occidental; PPG Industries; Rasa Ind.; Showa Denko; Vista; Witco/PAG

Manuf./Distrib. (pharm. & food): Aldrich; Asahi Chem Industry Co Ltd; Avrachem; Hüls AG; Integra; PPG Industries; Spectrum Chem. Mfg.

Hydrochlorothiazide
CAS 58-93-5
Synonyms: 6-Chloro-3,4-dihydro-2H-1,2,4-benzothiadiazine-7-sulfonamide-1,1-dioxide; Chlorosulthiadil; Chlorzide; Dihydrochlorothiazide
Empirical: $C_7H_8ClN_3O_4S_2$
Properties: Wh. or pract. wh. cryst. powd., odorless; sol. in sodium hydroxide sol'n., dimethylformamide, dil. ammonia, NaOH; insol. in water, chloroform, ether, dil. min. acids; m.w. 297.75; m.p. 273-275 C
Toxicology: LD50 (oral, mouse) 2830 mg/kg; poison by IP and IV routes; mod. toxic by ing. and subcutaneous routes; mutagenic data; diuretic; heated to decomp., emits very toxic fumes of SO_x, Cl^-, and NO_x
Uses: Used in orals
Regulatory: FDA approved for orals; BP, Ph.Eur. compliance
Manuf./Distrib. (pharm. & food): Avrachem; Spectrum Chem. Mfg.

Hydrocinnamaldehyde
CAS 104-53-0; EINECS 203-211-8
FEMA 2887
Synonyms: Benzenepropanal; Benzylacetaldehyde; Dihydrocinnamaldehyde; Hydrocinnamic aldehyde; 3-Phenylpropanal; 3-Phenylpropionaldehyde
Empirical: $C_9H_{10}O$
Formula: $C_6H_5CH_2CH_2CHO$
Properties: Colorless to sl. yel. liq., strong floral hyacinth odor; misc. with alcohol, ether; insol. in water; m.w. 134.19; dens. 1.010-1.020; b.p. 221-224 C; flash pt. 203 F; ref. index 1.520-1.532
Precaution: Combustible liq.
Toxicology: LD50 (IV, mouse) 56 mg/kg; poison by IV route; human skin irritant; eye irritant; heated to decomp, emits acrid smoke and irritating fumes
Uses: Cinnamon, cherry, plum-like synthetic flavoring agent
Regulatory: FDA 21CFR §172.515; FEMA GRAS
Manuf./Distrib. (pharm. & food): Aldrich; Hüls AG

Hydrocinnamic acid
CAS 501-52-0; EINECS 207-924-5
FEMA 2889
Synonyms: Bis-[3,3-bis-(4´-hydroxy-3´-t-butylphenyl butanoic acid]-glycol ester; 3-Phenylpropionic acid; Butyric acid, 3,3-bis(3-t-butyl-4-hydroxyphenyl) ethylene ester; Benzylacetic acid; Benzenepropanoic acid
Empirical: $C_9H_{10}O_2$
Formula: $C_6H_5CH_2CH_2COOH$
Properties: Wh. cryst. powd., sweet rosy odor; sol. in 170 parts cold water; sol. in alcohol, benzene, chloroform, ether, glac. acetic acid, petroleum ether, CS_2; m.w. 150.18; m.p. 45-48 C; b.p. 280 C; flash pt. > 230 F
Uses: Sweet synthetic flavoring agent
Regulatory: FDA 21CFR §172.515; FEMA GRAS
Manuf./Distrib.: Aldrich; R.W. Greeff; Janssen Chimica; Penta Mfg.
Manuf./Distrib. (pharm. & food): Aldrich

Hydrocinnamic aldehyde. *See* Hydrocinnamaldehyde
Hydrocinnamic isobutyrate. *See* 3-Phenylpropyl isobutyrate
Hydrocinnamyl isobutyrate. *See* 3-Phenylpropyl isobutyrate
Hydrocinnamyl isovalerate. *See* 3-Phenylpropyl isovalerate

Hydrocotyl extract
CAS 84776-24-9; 84696-21-9
Synonyms: Centella asiatica extract; Fo-ti-tieng extract; Gotu kola extract
Definition: Extract of the leaves or roots of *Hydrocotyl asiatica*
Uses: Provides local anti-inflammatory and anti-irritant action in sun care and eye care prods.
Trade names containing: Biophytex®

Hydrocoumarin. *See* Dihydrocoumarin
Hydrogeanted palm/palm kernel oil PEG-6 complex. *See* Hydrogenated palm/palm kernel oil PEG-6 esters

Hydrogenated castor oil
CAS 8001-78-3; EINECS 232-292-2
Synonyms: Opalwax; Castorwax; Castor oil, hydrogenated
Definition: End prod. of controlled hydrogenation of castor oil, consisting mainly of the triglyceride of hydroxystearic acid

Hydrogenated coco-glycerides

Properties: Hard white wax; very insol. in water and in the more common org. solvs.; m.w. ≈ 932; m.p. 86-88 C; iodine no. 5 max.; sapon. no. 176-182; hyd. no. 154-162
Toxicology: Ingestion of large amts. may cause pelvic congestion
Uses: Stiffening agent, wax for ointments; lubricant, tableting aid; tablet coatings; solv. for intramuscular injectables; laxative effect; for orals, topicals
Regulatory: FDA 21CFR §175.105, 175.300, 176.170, 176.210, 177.1200, 177.1210, 177.2420, 177.2800, 178.3280; USP/NF compliance
Manuf./Distrib.: Akzo Nobel; Amber Syn.; Arista Ind.; Hoechst AG; Southern Clay Prods.
Trade names: Castorwax® MP-70; Castorwax® NF; Cutina® HR Powd.; Ross Castor Wax; Unitina HR
Trade names containing: Protegin® W; Protegin® WX; Sterotex® K

Hydrogenated coco-glycerides

Definition: Mixture of mono, di, and triglycerides of hydrogenated coconut oil
Uses: Emollient, ointment base, consistency regulator for pharmaceuticals; suppository bases
Trade names: Softisan® 100; Softisan® 133; Softisan® 134; Softisan® 138; Softisan® 142; Witepsol® E75; Witepsol® E76; Witepsol® E85; Witepsol® H5; Witepsol® H12; Witepsol® H15; Witepsol® H32; Witepsol® H35; Witepsol® H37; Witepsol® H175; Witepsol® H185; Witepsol® S51; Witepsol® S55; Witepsol® S58; Witepsol® W25; Witepsol® W31; Witepsol® W32; Witepsol® W35; Witepsol® W45

Hydrogenated coconut acid

CAS 68938-15-8
Synonyms: Acids, coconut, hydrogenated; Coconut acid, hydrogenated; Fatty acids, coco, hydrogenated
Definition: End prod. of controlled hydrogenation of coconut acid
Uses: Emulsifier; chemical intermediate for pharmaceuticals
Regulatory: FDA 21CFR §175.105, 176.210, 177.2600, 177.2800, 178.3570
Trade names: Hystrene® 5012; Industrene® 223

Hydrogenated coconut oil

CAS 68334-28-1; EINECS 284-283-8
Synonyms: Coconut oil, hydrogenated
Definition: End prod. of controlled hydrogenation of coconut oil
Uses: Lubricant, moisturizer, coatings, gelatin capsules, suppositories, base
Regulatory: FDA 21CFR §175.105, 176.210, 177.2800
Trade names: Lipex 401; Pureco® 100; Special Fat 42/44
Trade names containing: 24% Beta Carotene Semi-Solid Suspension No. 65642; Softisan® 601

Hydrogenated corn syrup. *See* Hydrogenated starch hydrolysate

Hydrogenated cottonseed oil

CAS 68334-00-9; EINECS 269-804-9
Definition: End prod. of controlled hydrogenation of cottonseed oil
Properties: Pale yel.; dens. 0.915-0.921; flash pt. 486 F
Precaution: Combustible
Toxicology: May cause allergic reaction
Uses: Crystallization promoter, m.p. modifier, bodying agent, binder, vehicle, lubricant, moisturizer
Regulatory: FDA 21CFR §175.105, 176.210, 177.2800
Trade names: Akolizer C; C-Flakes; Duratex; Emvelop®; Lipex 109; Lubritab®; Sterotex®
Trade names containing: Akopol R; Akorex B; 24% Beta Carotene HS-E in Veg. Oil No. 65671; 30% Beta Carotene in Veg. Oil No. 65646; Cap-Shure® KCL-140-50

Hydrogenated isomaltulose. *See* Isomalt

Hydrogenated lanolin

CAS 8031-44-5; EINECS 232-452-1
Synonyms: Lanolin, hydrogenated
Definition: End prod. of controlled hydrogenation of lanolin
Properties: Lt. yel. to wh. tacky solid; sol. in ethyl ether; insol. in water
Uses: Emollient, moisturizer, lubricant, plasticizer, chemical intermediate, humectant, mold release agent for pharmaceuticals
Trade names: Distilled Lipolan; Fancol HL; Lipolan S; Lipolan Distilled; Super-Sat

Hydrogenated lard glyceride

CAS 8040-05-9
Synonyms: Glycerides, hydrogenated lard mono-
Definition: End prod. of controlled hydrogenation of lard glyceride
Uses: Emulsifier, stabilizer, dispersant for drugs

Regulatory: FDA 21CFR §175.105, 176.210
Trade names: Monomuls® 90-15

Hydrogenated lard glycerides
Synonyms: Hydrogenated lard mono-, di- and tri- glycerides; Glycerides, lard mono-, di- and tri-, hydrogenated
Definition: End prod. of controlled hydrogenation of lard glycerides
Uses: Emulsifier, stabilizer, dispersant for drugs
Regulatory: FDA 21CFR §175.105, 176.210
Trade names: Monomuls® 60-15

Hydrogenated lard mono-, di- and tri- glycerides. *See* Hydrogenated lard glycerides

Hydrogenated lecithin
CAS 92128-87-5; 97281-48-6; EINECS 295-786-7; 306-549-5
Synonyms: Lecithin, hydrogenated; Cholinphosphoric acid diglyceride ester; Hydrogenated soya phosphatidylcholine; (3-sn-Phosphatidyl)choline, soya, hydrogenated; 1,2-Diacyl-sn-glycero-3-phosphocholine
Definition: End prod. of controlled hydrogenation of lecithin
Empirical: $C_{44}H_{82}O_8PN$
Properties: M.w. 783
Uses: Prep. of liposomes for pharmaceuticals; increases skin humidity
Trade names: Phospholipon® 80 H; Phospholipon® 90 H; Phospholipon® 100 H

Hydrogenated menhaden acid
Synonyms: Acids, menhaden, hydrogenated; Menhaden acid, hydrogenated
Definition: End prod. of controlled hydrogenation of fatty acids obtained from menhaden oil
Uses: Chemical intermediate; emulsifier, lubricant, mold release agent; used in pharmaceuticals
Regulatory: FDA 21CFR §175.105, 176.210, 177.2800, 178.3570
Trade names: Hystrene® 3022

Hydrogenated menhaden oil
CAS 93572-53-3; 68002-72-2
Synonyms: Menhaden oil, hydrogenated
Definition: End prod. of controlled hydrogenation of menhaden oil
Properties: Wh. opaque solid, odorless; iodine no. 10 max.; sapon. no. 180-200
Uses: Pharmaceutical intermediate
Regulatory: FDA 21CFR §175.105, 176.170, 176.210, 177.2800, 184.1472, 186.1551

Hydrogenated palatinose. *See* Isomalt

Hydrogenated palm glyceride
CAS 67784-87-6; 97593-29-8
Synonyms: Palm oil glyceride, hydrogenated; Glycerides, palm oil mono-, hydrogenated
Definition: End prod. of controlled hydrogenation of palm glyceride
Uses: Emulsifier, stabilizer, dispersant
Regulatory: FDA 21CFR §176.210, 177.2800
Trade names: Monomuls® 90-35

Hydrogenated palm glycerides
Synonyms: Hydrogenated palm mono-, di- and tri-glycerides; Glycerides, palm oil mono-, di- and tri, hydrogenated
Definition: End prod. of controlled hydrogenation of palm oil glycerides
Uses: Emulsifier, stabilizer, dispersant
Trade names: Monomuls® 60-35
Trade names containing: Suppocire® CM

Hydrogenated palm kernel glycerides
Definition: End prod. of controlled hydrogenation of palm kernel glycerides
Uses: For pharmaceutical applics.
Trade names containing: Suppocire® CM

Hydrogenated palm kernel oil
CAS 68990-82-9
Synonyms: Oils, palm kernel, hydrogenated; Palm kernel oil, hydrogenated
Definition: End prod. of controlled hydrogenation of palm kernel oil
Uses: Used in ointments
Trade names: Paramount B
Trade names containing: Paramount C

Hydrogenated palm mono-, di- and tri-glycerides. *See* Hydrogenated palm glycerides

Hydrogenated palm oil

Hydrogenated palm oil
CAS 8033-29-2; 68514-74-9
Synonyms: Oils, palm, hydrogenated; Palm oil, hydrogenated
Definition: End prod. of controlled hydrogenation of palm oil
Uses: Hard wax for pharmaceutical preps.; emollient; consistency regulator, lubricant, m.p. modifier
Regulatory: FDA 21CFR §175.105, 176.210, 177.2800
Trade names: Akolizer P; Softisan® 154
Trade names containing: BBS

Hydrogenated palm/palm kernel oil PEG-6 esters
Synonyms: Hydrogeanted palm/palm kernel oil PEG-6 complex
Definition: Complex mixture formed from transesterification of hydrog. palm kernel oil, hydrog. palm oil, and PEG-6
Uses: Hydrophilic wax; amphphilic agent for improving drug delivery
Trade names: Labrafil® M 2130 BS
Trade names containing: Labrafil® M 2130 CS

Hydrogenated polyisobutene
CAS 61693-08-1; 68937-10-0
Synonyms: Polyisobutane
Classification: Branched chain aliphatic hydrocarbon
Formula: $[CH_2C(CH_3)_2]_n$, avg. n = 6-8
Toxicology: Nonirritating to eyes and skin, noncomedogenic, nontoxic when ingested
Uses: Emollient oil component for pharmaceuticals
Regulatory: FDA 21CFR §176.105, 175.300, 178.3740
Trade names: Trisynlane

Hydrogenated soya phosphatidylcholine. *See* Hydrogenated lecithin
Hydrogenated soybean glyceride. *See* Hydrogenated soy glyceride

Hydrogenated soybean glycerides
CAS 68201-48-9
Synonyms: Hydrogenated soybean oil mono-, di- and tri- glycerides; Hydrogenated soybean oil glycerides
Definition: End prod. of controlled hydrogenation of a mixture of mono, di and triglycerides derived from soybean oil
Uses: Emulsifier, stabilizer, dispersant
Regulatory: FDA 21CFR §176.210, 177.2800
Trade names: Monomuls® 60-45

Hydrogenated soybean oil
CAS 8016-70-4; 68002-71-1; EINECS 232-410-2
Synonyms: Soybean oil hydrogenated
Definition: End prod. of controlled hydrogenation of soybean oil
Uses: Pharmaceutical intermediate; crystallization promoter, m.p. modifier, bodying agent, lubricant, moisturizer, diluent
Regulatory: FDA 21CFR §175.105, 176.210, 177.2800, 182.70, 182.170
Manuf./Distrib. (pharm. & food): Ruger
Trade names: Akolizer S; Clarity; Neustrene® 064; Sterotex® HM
Trade names containing: Akopol R; Akorex B; BBS; 24% Beta Carotene HS-E in Veg. Oil No. 65671; 30% Beta Carotene in Veg. Oil No. 65646; Cap-Shure® FF-165-60; Cap-Shure® KCL-165-70; Durkex 25BHA; Ross Japan Wax Substitute 966; Sterotex® C; Sterotex® K

Hydrogenated soybean oil glycerides. *See* Hydrogenated soybean glycerides
Hydrogenated soybean oil mono-, di- and tri- glycerides. *See* Hydrogenated soybean glycerides
Hydrogenated soybean oil monoglyceride. *See* Hydrogenated soy glyceride

Hydrogenated soy glyceride
CAS 61789-08-0; 68002-71-1
Synonyms: Hydrogenated soybean oil monoglyceride; Glycerides, soybean oil, hydrogenated, mono; Hydrogenated soybean glyceride
Definition: End prod. of controlled hydrogenation of soybean monoglycerides
Uses: Emulsifier, stabilizer, dispersant for drugs
Regulatory: FDA 21CFR §176.210, 177.2800
Trade names: Dimodan PV; Monomuls® 90-45

Hydrogenated starch hydrolysate
CAS 68425-17-2

Synonyms: Hydrogenated corn syrup; Corn syrup, hydrogenated
Definition: End prod. of controlled hydrogenation of corn syrup
Uses: Lubricant, humectant for dentifrices
Trade names: Hystar® 3375; Hystar® 4075; Hystar® 5875; Hystar® 6075; Hystar® CG; Hystar® HM-75; Hystar® TPF

Hydrogenated tallow
CAS 8030-12-4; EINECS 232-442-7
Synonyms: Tallow, hydrogenated
Definition: End prod. of controlled hydrogenation of tallow
Uses: Raw material for pharmaceuticals; hydrophobing agent
Regulatory: FDA 21CFR §173.340, 175.105, 176.170, 176.210, 177.2800, 182.70
Trade names: Special Fat 168T

Hydrogenated tallow glyceride
CAS 61789-09-1; EINECS 263-031-0
Synonyms: Hydrogenated tallow monoglyceride; Glycerides, hydrogenated tallow mono-
Definition: Monoglyceride of hydrogenated tallow
Uses: Emulsifier, stabilizer, dispersant
Regulatory: FDA 21CFR §176.210, 177.2800
Trade names: Monomuls® 90-25
Trade names containing: Monomuls® 90-25/2; Monomuls® 90-25/5

Hydrogenated tallow glyceride lactate
CAS 68990-06-7; EINECS 273-576-6
Synonyms: Glycerides, tallow mono-, hydrogenated, lactates
Definition: Lactic acid ester of hydrogenated tallow glyceride
Uses: Emulsifier, emollient, plasticizer for pharmaceuticals
Trade names: Lamegin® GLP 10, 20

Hydrogenated tallow glycerides
CAS 68308-54-3; 67701-27-3; EINECS 269-658-6
Synonyms: Hydrogenated tallow mono-, di- and tri- glycerides; Glycerides, tallow mono-, di- and tri-, hydrogenated
Definition: Mixture of mono, di and triglycerides of hydrogenated tallow acid
Uses: Emulsifier, stabilizer, dispersant, opacifier for drugs
Regulatory: FDA 21CFR §176.210, 177.2800
Trade names: Monomuls® 60-25; Neustrene® 060
Trade names containing: Monomuls® 60-25/2; Ross Beeswax Substitute 628/5

Hydrogenated tallow mono-, di- and tri- glycerides. *See* Hydrogenated tallow glycerides
Hydrogenated tallow monoglyceride. *See* Hydrogenated tallow glyceride
Hydrogenated tallow trimethyl ammonium chloride. *See* Hydrogenated tallowtrimonium chloride

Hydrogenated tallowtrimonium chloride
CAS 61788-78-1; EINECS 263-005-9
Synonyms: Hydrogenated tallow trimethyl ammonium chloride
Classification: Quaternary ammonium salt
Formula: $RN(CH_3)_2CH_3Cl$, R represents the alkyl groups derived from hydrog. tallow
Uses: Additive for antibiotics mfg.
Trade names: Noramium MSH 50

Hydrogenated vegetable oil
CAS 67701-26-2; 67784-82-1; 68334-00-9; 68334-28-1; 68938-37-4; EINECS 269-820-6
Synonyms: Vegetable oil, hydrogenated
Definition: End prod. of controlled hydrogenation of vegetable oil; mixt. of triglycerides of fatty acids
Properties: Wh. fine powd., pale yel. oily liq. above its m.p.; insol. in water; sol. in hot IPA, hexane, chloroform; Type I: m.p. 57-70 C; acid no. 4 max.; iodine no. 0-5; sapon. no. 175-205; Type II: m.p. 20-50 C; acid no. 4 max.; iodine no. 55-80; sapon. no.185-200
Toxicology: May cause skin reactions
Uses: Lubricant in pharmaceutical tableting (type I), suppositories; cocoa butter replacement; emollient wax; ointment base (type II)
Regulatory: FDA 21CFR §175.105, 176.210; USP/NF and JP compliance
Manuf./Distrib.: ABITEC; Arista Industries; Int'l. Flora Tech.; Lipo; A.E. Staley Mfg.
Manuf./Distrib. (pharm. & food): ABITEC; Arista Industries; Lipo; Ruger; A.E. Staley Mfg.
Trade names: Caprol® ET; Hydrokote® 95; Hydrokote® 97; Hydrokote® 102; Hydrokote® 108; Hydrokote®

Hydrogen dioxide

112; Hydrokote® 118; Hydrokote® 175; Hydrokote® M; Paramount H; Paramount X; Paramount XX; Sterotex® NF; Wecobee® FS; Wecobee® HTR; Wecobee® M; Wecobee® R Mono; Wecobee® S; Wecobee® SS

Trade names containing: Durkote Ferrous Fumarate/Hydrog. Veg. Oil; Durkote Ferrous Sulfate/Hydrog. Veg. Oil; Durkote Potassium Chloride/Hydrog. Veg. Oil; Durkote Vitamin B-1/Hydrog. Veg. Oil; Durkote Vitamin C/Hydrog. Veg. Oil

Hydrogen dioxide. *See* Hydrogen peroxide

Hydrogen peroxide
CAS 7722-84-1; EINECS 231-765-0
UN No. 2014
Synonyms: Hydrogen dioxide
Classification: Inorganic oxide
Empirical: H_2O_2
Formula: HOOH
Properties: Colorless visc. liq., cryst. solid at low temp., bitter taste; sol. in ether, alcohol; misc. with water; dec. by many org. solvs.; m.w. 34.02; dens. (liq.) 1.450 g/cc (20 C); f.p. -0.41 C; b.p. 150.2 C
Precaution: Dangerous fire hazard by chem. reaction with flamm. materials; explosion hazard; strong oxidizer
Toxicology: LD50 (oral, mouse) 2 g/kg; mod. toxic by inh., ingestion, skin contact; corrosive irritant to skin, eyes, mucous membranes; tumorigenic; human mutagenic data; TLV: 1 ppm in air
Uses: Antiseptic to cleanse wounds, skin ulcers, local infections, in oral rinse prods.; in treatment of inflammatory conditions of the external ear canal; foaming agent in dentifrices; used in topicals, mouthwash gargles
Regulatory: FDA 21CFR §133.133, 160.105, 160.145, 160.185, 172.814, 172.892, 175.105, 178.1005, 178.1005 (35% sol'n. max.), 178.1010, 184.1366, GRAS; BATF 27CFR §240.1051 (3 ppm max. in wine), 240.1051a (200 ppm max. in distilling materials); Japan restricted; FDA approved for topicals; BP compliance (sol'n.)
Manuf./Distrib.: AlliedSignal; Ashland; J.T. Baker; Browning; Degussa; DuPont; Elf Atochem N. Am.; Farleyway Chem. Ltd; FMC; C.P. Hall; Harcros; Mallinckrodt; Mitsubishi Gas; Spectrum Chem. Mfg.; Stanchem; Van Waters & Rogers
Manuf./Distrib. (pharm. & food): Aldrich; Browning; Integra; Spectrum Chem. Mfg.
Trade names: Albone® 35 CG; Albone® 50 CG; Albone® 70CG
Trade names containing: Ringwell

Hydrogen peroxide carbamide. *See* Urea peroxide
Hydrogen sulfate. *See* Sulfuric acid
Hydroiodic acid. *See* Hydriodic acid
Hydrolysed gelatin. *See* Hydrolyzed gelatin
Hydrolyzed animal protein. *See* Hydrolyzed collagen
Hydrolyzed casein. *See* Hydrolyzed milk protein

Hydrolyzed collagen
CAS 9015-54-7; EINECS 295-635-5
Synonyms: Collagen hydrolysates; Hydrolyzed animal protein; Protein hydrolysate; Proteins, collagen, hydrolysate
Definition: Hydrolysate of animal collagen derived by acid, enzyme or other method of hydrolysis
Uses: Conditioner and emollient for pharmaceutical creams and lotions; used in orals, topicals
Regulatory: FDA 21CFR §161.190, 573.200; FDA approved for orals, topicals
Trade names containing: Lanotein AWS 30; Unipertan P-24; Unipertan P-242; Unipertan P-2002

Hydrolyzed gelatin
CAS 68410-45-7; EINECS 270-082-2
Synonyms: Hydrolysed gelatin
Uses: Tablet binder, excipient, film-former, coating agent, emulsion stabilizer; adjuvant protein
Regulatory: BP compliance
Trade names: Byco A; Byco C; Byco E; Byco O; Polypro 5000® Pharmaceutical Grade; Polypro 15000® Pharmaceutical Grade

Hydrolyzed milk protein
CAS 65072-00-6; 92797-39-2; EINECS 265-363-1
Synonyms: Proteins, milk, hydrolysate; Hydrolyzed casein
Definition: Hydrolysate of milk protein derived by acid, enzyme or other method of hydrolysis
Properties: Sol. in water
Toxicology: Heated to decomp., emits acrid smoke and irritating fumes
Uses: Ingred. in sun care and eye care prods.

Regulatory: USDA 9CFR §318.7
Trade names containing: Biophytex®

Hydrolyzed protein
CAS 73049-73-7
Uses: Used in pharmaceutical supplements
Trade names containing: Dry Vitamin E Acetate 50% SD No. 65356

Hydrolyzed vegetable protein
CAS 100209-45-8
Synonyms: Vegetable protein hydrolysate; Proteins, vegetable, hydrolysate
Definition: Hydrolysate of vegetable protein derived by acid, enzyme or other method of hydrolysis
Properties: Sol. in water
Toxicology: Heated to decomp., emits acrid smoke and irritating fumes
Uses: Flavoring, flavor enhancer; skin protectant
Regulatory: USDA 9CFR §318.7
Manuf./Distrib.: Tri-K Ind.
Manuf./Distrib. (pharm. & food): Am. Roland
Trade names containing: Unipertan VEG 24; Unipertan VEG 242

Hydrolyzed wheat protein/dimethicone copolyol phosphate copolymer
Classification: Vegetable protein/silicone compd.
Definition: Polymer of hydrolyzed wheat protein and dimethicone copolyol phosphate monomers
Properties: Amber liq.
Uses: Used in pharmaceutical topicals
Trade names: Pecosil® SWP-83

Hydrolyzed yeast protein
CAS 100684-36-4
Synonyms: Yeast protein hydrolysate
Definition: Hydrolysate of yeast protein, derived by acid, enzyme or other method of hydrolysis
Uses: Ingred. in sun care and eye care prods.
Trade names containing: Biophytex®

Hydroquinol. *See* Hydroquinone

Hydroquinone
CAS 123-31-9; EINECS 204-617-8
UN No. 2662
Synonyms: 1,4-Benzenediol; p-Dihydroxybenzene; Hydroquinol
Classification: Aromatic organic compd.
Empirical: $C_6H_6O_2$
Formula: $C_6H_4(OH)_2$
Properties: White crystals; sol. in water, alcohol, ether; m.w. 110.11; dens. 1.330; m.p.170 C; b.p. 285 C
Precaution: Combustible; light-sensitive
Toxicology: LD50 (rat, oral) 320 mg/kg; TLV 2 mg/m³ of air; toxic by ingestion and inhalation; irritant; ingestion of large amts. has caused nausea, vomiting, ringing in ears, delirium, sense of suffocation, and collapse
Uses: Antioxidant used in suntan lotions
Regulatory: FDA 21CFR §175.105, 176.170, 177.2420; BP compliance
Manuf./Distrib.: Aldrich; Alfa; Allchem Ind.; Charkit; Eastman; Goodyear Tire & Rubber; Kraeber GmbH; Penta Mfg.; San Yuan; Spectrum Chem. Mfg.
Manuf./Distrib. (pharm. & food): Ruger; Spectrum Chem. Mfg.
Trade names: Tecquinol® USP Grade

Hydroquinone methyl ether. *See* Hydroquinone monomethyl ether

Hydroquinone monomethyl ether
CAS 150-76-5; EINECS 205-769-8
Synonyms: MEHQ; Hydroquinone methyl ether; 4-Methoxyphenol; p-Hydroxyanisole
Classification: Substituted phenolic compd.
Definition: Monomethyl ether of hydroquinone
Empirical: $C_7H_8O_2$
Formula: $CH_3OC_6H_4OH$
Properties: White waxy solid; hygroscopic; sl. sol. in water; sol. in benzene, acetone, ethyl acetate, alcohol; m.w. 124.14; dens. 1.55 (20/20 C); m.p. 52.5 C; b.p. 243 C
Precaution: Combustible
Uses: Mfg. of antioxidants, pharmaceuticals

Hydrotalcite

Regulatory: FDA 21CFR §177.1010
Manuf./Distrib.: Alemark; Alfa; Arenol; ChemDesign; Eastman; Fluka; Kincaid Enterprises; Penta Mfg.; Specialty Chem. Prods.; Spectrum Chem. Mfg.

Hydrotalcite

Definition: A hydrated form of aluminum magnesium basic carbonate
Formula: $Al_2Mg_6(OH_{16}CO_3 \cdot 4H_2O$
Uses: Antacid active, compressible powd. for direct compression tablets and caplets; stabilizes intragastric pH @ 3-5
Regulatory: BP compliance
Trade names: Hydrotalcite Powd. BP

Hydrous citric acid. *See* Citric acid monohydrate
Hydrous magnesium calcium silicate. *See* Talc
Hydrous magnesium silicate. *See* Talc
4-Hydroxy-m-anisaldehyde. *See* Vanillin
o-Hydroxyanisole. *See* Guaiacol
p-Hydroxyanisole. *See* Hydroquinone monomethyl ether
4-Hydroxybenzaldehyde. *See* p-Hydroxybenzaldehyde

p-Hydroxybenzaldehyde

CAS 123-08-0; EINECS 204-599-1
Synonyms: 4-Hydroxybenzaldehyde; 4-Formyl phenol; p-Formyl phenol
Empirical: $C_7H_6O_2$
Formula: HOC_6H_4CHO
Properties: Colorless need., sl. agreeable aromatic odor; sol. in alcohol, ether, acetone, MIBK, hot water; m.w. 122.12; dens. 1.129; m.p. 114-117 C
Toxicology: Irritant
Uses: Sweet flavoring agent
Regulatory: BP compliance
Manuf./Distrib.: Hoechst Celanese; Mitsubishi; Nippon Fine Chem.; Penta Mfg.; Schweizerhall; Spectrum Chem. Mfg.
Manuf./Distrib. (pharm. & food): Aldrich

4-Hydroxybenzenesulfonic acid. *See* Phenol sulfonic acid
2-Hydroxybenzoic acid. *See* Salicylic acid
o-Hydroxybenzoic acid. *See* Salicylic acid
4-Hydroxybenzoic acid butyl ester. *See* Butylparaben
4-Hydroxybenzoic acid ethyl ester. *See* Ethylparaben
4-Hydroxybenzoic acid, ethyl ester, sodium salt. *See* Sodium ethylparaben
2-Hydroxybenzoic acid, 2-ethylhexyl ester. *See* Octyl salicylate
4-Hydroxybenzoic acid, methyl ester. *See* Methylparaben
4-Hydroxybenzoic acid, methyl ester, potassium salt. *See* Potassium methylparaben
4-Hydroxybenzoic acid, methyl ester, sodium salt. *See* Sodium methylparaben
4-Hydroxybenzoic acid, 1-methylethyl ester. *See* Isopropylparaben
4-Hydroxybenzoic acid, 2-methylpropyl ester. *See* Isobutylparaben
2-Hydroxybenzoic acid, pentyl ester. *See* Amyl salicylate
4-Hydroxybenzoic acid, propyl ester. *See* Propylparaben
4-Hydroxybenzoic acid, propyl ester, sodium salt. *See* Sodium propylparaben
p-Hydroxybenzyl acetone. *See* 4-(p-Hydroxyphenyl)-2-butanone
α-Hydroxybenzyl phenyl ketone. *See* Benzoin
Hydroxybutanedioic acid. *See* N-Hydroxysuccinic acid
4-Hydroxybutanoic acid lactone. *See* Butyrolactone
3-Hydroxy-2-butanone. *See* Acetyl methyl carbinol

Hydroxycetyl phosphate

Synonyms: Phosphoric acid, hydroxycetyl ester
Definition: Complex mixts. of esters of phosphoric acid and hydroxycetyl alcohol
Uses: O/w emulsifier for pharmaceutical emulsions
Trade names: Forlanit® E

Hydroxycitronellal

CAS 107-75-5; EINECS 203-518-7
FEMA 2583
Synonyms: 3,7-Dimethyl-7-hydroxy-octane-1-al; Citronellal hydrate; 7-Hydroxy-3,7-dimethyloctanol; Lilyl aldehyde

548

Empirical: C$_{10}$H$_{20}$O$_2$
Formula: CH$_3$CH$_3$OHCCH$_2$CH$_2$CH$_2$CH$_3$CHCH$_2$CHO
Properties: Colorless liq., sweet floral, lily odor; sol. in fixed oils, propylene glycol; insol. in glycerin; m.w. 172.30; dens. 0.918-0.923; b.p. 94-96 C (1 mm); flash pt. > 212 F; ref. index 1.447-1.450
Precaution: Combustible liq.
Toxicology: Skin irritant; allergen; heated to decomp., emits acrid smoke and irritating fumes
Uses: Synthetic flavoring agent for pharmaceuticals
Regulatory: FDA 21CFR §172.515; FEMA GRAS; Japan approved as flavoring
Manuf./Distrib.: BASF
Manuf./Distrib. (pharm. & food): BASF

Hydroxycitronellol
CAS 107-74-4
FEMA 2586
Synonyms: 3,7-Dimethyloctane-1,7-diol; 3,7-Dimethyl-1,7-octanedol
Empirical: C$_{10}$H$_{22}$O$_2$
Properties: Colorless visc. liq., rosy grape odor; sl. sol. in toluene, benzene; m.w. 174.29; dens. 0.935; b.p. 156 C (15 mm); flash pt. > 100 C; ref. index 1.4550-1.4600
Uses: Synthetic flavoring agent
Regulatory: FEMA GRAS
Manuf./Distrib.: BASF
Manuf./Distrib. (pharm. & food): BASF

3-Hydroxy-p-cymene. *See* Thymol
4-Hydroxydecanoic acid, γ-lactone. *See* γ-Decalactone
3-Hydroxy-4,5-dihydroxymethyl-2-methylpyridine HCl. *See* Pyridoxine HCl
Hydroxydimethylbenzene. *See* Xylenol

4-Hydroxy-2,5-dimethyl-3(2H)furanone
CAS 3658-77-3
FEMA 3174
Empirical: C$_6$H$_8$O$_3$
Properties: M.w. 128.13; m.p. 78-80 C
Uses: Strawberry-like flavoring agent
Regulatory: FEMA GRAS
Manuf./Distrib. (pharm. & food): Aldrich

7-Hydroxy-3,7-dimethyloctanol. *See* Hydroxycitronellal
8-Hydroxy-5,7-dinitro-2-naphthalenesulfonic acid disodium salt. *See* CI 10316; Ext. D&C Yellow No. 7
4-Hydroxydodecanoic acid γ-lactone. *See* γ-Dodecalactone
5-Hydroxydodecanoic acid, δ-lactone. *See* δ-Dodecalactone
1-Hydroxyethane 1-carboxylic acid. *See* Lactic acid
1-Hydroxy-1,2-ethanedicarboxylic acid. *See* N-Hydroxysuccinic acid
2-Hydroxyethylamine. *See* Ethanolamine

Hydroxyethylcellulose
CAS 9004-62-0
Synonyms: HEC; Cellulose, 2-hydroxyethyl ether; H.E. cellulose
Definition: Partially substituted poly(hydroxyethyl) ether of cellulose
Formula: C$_6$H$_7$O$_2$(OH)$_2$OCH$_2$CH$_2$OH
Properties: White free-flowing powd., odorless, tasteless; nonionic; hygroscopic; insol. in org. solvs.; sol. in hot or cold water; grease and oil resistant; m.p. 288-290 C (dec.); ref. index 1.336; pH 6.0-8.5 (1%)
Precaution: Combustible
Uses: Thickener, suspending agent, protective colloid, binder, stabilizer; used in ophthalmics, orals, otics, topicals; visc. agent in eye lens prods.
Regulatory: FDA 21CFR §175.105, 175.300; FDA approved for ophthalmics, orals, otics, topicals; USP/NF, BP, Ph.Eur. compliance
Manuf./Distrib.: Allchem Ind.; Amerchol Europe; Aqualon; Spectrum Chem. Mfg.; Sumisho Plaschem; Union Carbide
Manuf./Distrib. (pharm. & food): Spectrum Chem. Mfg.
Trade names: Natrosol® 250; Natrosol® Hydroxyethylcellulose

N-(2-hydroxyethyl) coco fatty acid amide. *See* Cocamide MEA
(1-Hydroxyethylidene) bisphosphonic acid. *See* Etidronic acid
(1-Hydroxyethylidene)bisphosphonic acid, tetrasodium salt. *See* Tetrasodium etidronate
(1-Hydroxyethylidene) diphosphonic acid. *See* Etidronic acid

3-(1-Hydroxyethylidene)-6-methyl-2H-pyran-2,4(3H)-dione sodium salt

3-(1-Hydroxyethylidene)-6-methyl-2H-pyran-2,4(3H)-dione sodium salt. *See* Sodium dehydroacetate
Hydroxyethylmethylcellulose. *See* Methyl hydroxyethylcellulose
3-Hydroxy-2-ethyl-4-pyrone. *See* Ethyl maltol
N-(2-Hydroxyethyl)tetradecanamide. *See* Myristamide MEA
Hydroxy heptane. *See* Heptyl alcohol
4-Hydroxyheptanoic acid, γ-lactone. *See* γ-Heptalactone
4-Hydroxyhexanoic acid γ-lactone. *See* γ-Hexalactone

Hydroxylated lanolin
    CAS 68424-66-8; EINECS 270-315-8
    Synonyms: Lanolin, hydroxylated
    Definition: Prod. obtained by the controlled hydroxylation of lanolin
    Uses: Emulsifier, stabilizer, emollient for pharmaceutical topical preps.
    Trade names: Hydroxylan; OHlan®; Ritahydrox

Hydroxylated lecithin
    CAS 8029-76-3; EINECS 232-440-6
    Synonyms: Lecithin, hydroxylated
    Definition: Prod. obtained by the controlled hydroxylation of lecithin
    Properties: Lt. yel. liq. to paste, char. odor; mod. sol. in water
    Toxicology: Nontoxic; heated to decomp., emits acrid smoke and irritating fumes
    Uses: Emulsifier, suspending agent for topicals
    Regulatory: FDA 21CFR §136.110, 136.115, 136.130, 136.160, 136.165, 136.180, 172.814, 173.340, 176.170, 176.200
    Trade names: Alcolec® Z-3

4-Hydroxy-3-methoxybenzaldehyde. *See* Vanillin
2-Hydroxy-4-methoxybenzophenone. *See* Benzophenone-3
2-Hydroxy-4-methoxybenzophenone-5-sulfonic acid. *See* Benzophenone-4
6-Hydroxy-5-[(2-methoxy-5-methyl-4-sulfophenyl)azo]-2-naphthalenesulfonic acid disodium salt. *See* CI 16035
6-Hydroxy-5-[(2-methoxy-5-methyl-4-sulfophenyl)azo]-2-naphthalenesulfonic acid disodium salt. *See* FD&C Red No. 40
4-(4-Hydroxy-3-methoxyphenyl)-2-butanone. *See* Zingerone
(4-Hydroxy-3-methoxyphenyl)ethyl methyl ketone. *See* Zingerone
(2-Hydroxy-4-methoxyphenyl) phenylmethanone. *See* Benzophenone-3
1-Hydroxy-2-methoxy-4-propenylbenzene. *See* Isoeugenol
4-Hydroxy-3-methoxystyrene. *See* 2-Methoxy-4-vinylphenol
2-Hydroxy-4-methoxy-5-sulfo benzophenone. *See* Benzophenone-4
Hydroxymethyl anethole. *See* Propenylguaethol
2-Hydroxy-5-methylanisole. *See* 2-Methoxy-4-methylphenol
2-Hydroxymethylfuran. *See* Furfuryl alcohol
4-Hydroxy-3-methyl-1-methylbenzene. *See* 2-Methoxy-4-methylphenol
1-Hydroxy-4-[(4-methylphenyl)amino]-9,10-anthracenedione. *See* CI 60725; D&C Violet No. 2
3-Hydroxy-2-methyl-4H-pyran-4-one. *See* Maltol
5-Hydroxy-6-methyl-3,4-pyridinedimethanol hydrochloride. *See* Pyridoxine HCl
3-Hydroxy-2-methyl-4-pyrone. *See* Maltol
3-Hydroxy-2-methyl-γ-pyrone. *See* Maltol
3-Hydroxy-4-[(4-methyl-2-sulfophenyl)azo]-2-naphthalenecarboxylic acid calcium salt. *See* D&C Red No. 7
3-Hydroxy-4-[(4-methyl-2-sulfophenyl)azo]-2-naphthalenecarboxylic acid disodium salt. *See* CI 15850; D&C Red No. 6
4-[(2-Hydroxy-1-naphthalenyl)azo]benzenesulfonic acid monosodium salt. *See* CI 15510; D&C Orange No. 4
4-Hydroxynonanoic acid, γ-lactone. *See* γ-Nonalactone
12-Hydroxyoctadecanoic acid, 2-ethylhexyl ester. *See* Octyl hydroxystearate
Hydroxyoctadecanoic acid, 2-hydroxyethyl ester. *See* Glycol hydroxystearate
12-Hydroxyoctadecanoic acid, 1,2,3-propanetriyl ester. *See* Trihydroxystearin
12-Hydroxy-9-octadecenoic acid. *See* Ricinoleic acid
12-Hydroxy-9-octadecenoic acid ester. *See* Cetyl ricinoleate
12-Hydroxy-9-octadecenoic acid, monoester with 1,2-propanediol. *See* Propylene glycol ricinoleate
12-Hydroxy-9-octadecenoic acid, monoester with 1,2,3-propanetriol. *See* Glyceryl ricinoleate
12-Hydroxy-9-octadecenoic acid, zinc salt. *See* Zinc ricinoleate
4-Hydroxyoctanoic acid, γ-lactone. *See* γ-Octalactone

d-12-Hydroxyoleic acid. *See* Ricinoleic acid
γ-Hydroxy-β-oxobutane. *See* Acetyl methyl carbinol
15-Hydroxypentadecanoic acid, ω-lactone. *See* Pentadecalactone
2-Hydroxy-2-phenylacetophenone. *See* Benzoin
α-Hydroxy-α-phenylacetophenone. *See* Benzoin
3-Hydroxy-4-(phenylazo)-2-naphthalenecarboxylic acid calcium salt. *See* D&C Red No. 31

4-(p-Hydroxyphenyl)-2-butanone
    CAS 5471-51-2
    FEMA 2588
    Synonyms: p-Hydroxybenzyl acetone; Frambinone; Raspberry ketone; Oxyphenalon
    Empirical: $C_{10}H_{12}O_2$
    Properties: Wh. cryst. solid, raspberry odor; sol. in alcohol, ether; m.w. 164.22; m.p. 81-86 C; flash pt. > 212 F
    Precaution: Combustible liq.
    Toxicology: LD50 (oral, rat) 1320 mg/kg; poison by IP route; mod. toxic by ingestion; heated to decomp., emits
        acrid smoke and irritating fumes
    Uses: Sweet raspberry-like synthetic flavoring agent
    Regulatory: FDA 21CFR §172.515; FEMA GRAS
    Manuf./Distrib. (pharm. & food): Aldrich; Chr. Hansen's

2-Hydroxy-2-propane sulfonic acid sodium salt acetone sulfite. *See* Acetone sodium bisulfite
2-Hydroxy-1,2,3-propanetricarboxylic acid. *See* Citric acid
2-Hydroxy-1,2,3-propanetricarboxylic acid, monoester with 1,2,3-propanetriol monooctadecanoate. *See*
    Glyceryl stearate citrate
2-Hydroxy-1,2,3-propanetricarboxylic acid monohydrate. *See* Citric acid monohydrate
2-Hydroxy-1,2,3-propanetricarboxylic acid, monooctadecyl ester. *See* Stearyl citrate
2-Hydroxy-1,2,3-propanetricarboxylic acid, tributyl ester. *See* Tributyl citrate
2-Hydroxy-1,2,3-propanetricarboxylic acid, triethyl ester. *See* Triethyl citrate
2-Hydroxy-1,2,3-propanetricarboxylic acid, tris(2-octyldodecyl) ester. *See* Trioctyldodecyl citrate
2-Hydroxypropanoic acid. *See* Lactic acid
2-Hydroxypropanoic acid, calcium salt. *See* Calcium lactate
2-Hydroxypropanoic acid, dodecyl ester. *See* Lauryl lactate
2-Hydroxypropanoic acid hexadecyl ester. *See* Cetyl lactate
2-Hydroxypropanoic acid, isostearyl ester. *See* Isostearyl lactate
2-Hydroxypropanoic acid, 5-methyl-2-(1-methylethyl)cyclohexyl ester. *See* Menthyl lactate
2-Hydroxypropanoic acid monosodium salt. *See* Sodium lactate
2-Hydroxypropanoic acid, tetradecyl ester. *See* Myristyl lactate
2-Hydroxypropionic acid. *See* Lactic acid
α-Hydroxypropionic acid. *See* Lactic acid
(S)-2-Hydroxypropionic acid sodium salt. *See* Sodium L-lactate
Hydroxypropyl alginate. *See* Propylene glycol alginate
2-Hydroxypropylamine. *See* Isopropanolamine

Hydroxypropylcellulose
    CAS 9004-64-2
    Synonyms: HPC; Cellulose, 2-hydroxypropyl ether; Oxypropylated cellulose; Hyprolose
    Definition: Partially substituted poly(hydroxypropyl) ether of cellulose
    Properties: Wh. powd., odorless, tasteless; sol. in water, methanol, ethanol, other org. solvs.; insol. in water
        > 37.7 C; thermoplastic; can be extruded and molded; softens at 130 C; visc.various; ref. index 1.337; pH
        5-8.5 (1%)
    Precaution: Combustible
    Toxicology: LD50 (oral, rat) 10,200 mg/kg; sl. toxic by ingestion; heated to decomp., emits acrid smoke and
        fumes
    Uses: Binder, thickener, granulation agent, stabilizer, suspending agent; tablet film coating aid; protectant in
        topicals; also in orals
    Regulatory: FDA 21CFR §172.870, 177.1200; Europe listed; UK approved; FDA approved for orals, topicals;
        USP/NF, BP, Ph.Eur. compliance
    Manuf./Distrib.: Nippon Soda; Shin-Etsu Chem.
    Manuf./Distrib. (pharm. & food): Aldrich; Spectrum Chem. Mfg.
    Trade names: Klucel® 'F' Grades

Hydroxypropyl-α-cyclodextrin
    CAS 99241-24-4
    Properties: M.p. 245 C

Hydroxypropyl-β-cyclodextrin

 Uses: Bioavailability enhancer; odor/taste masking; stabilizer
 Trade names: Alpha W6 HP 0.6

Hydroxypropyl-β-cyclodextrin
CAS 94035-02-6
Properties: M.w. 1500 (avg.)
Uses: Complex hosting guest molecules; increases the sol. and bioavailability of other substances; masks flavor, odor, or coloration; stabilizes against light, oxidation, heat, and hydrolysis; turns liqs. or volatiles into stable solid powds.
Manuf./Distrib. (pharm. & food): Aldrich
Trade names: Beta W7 HP 0.9; Encapsin HPB

Hydroxypropyl-γ-cyclodextrin
CAS 99241-25-5
Properties: M.p. 250 C
Uses: Drug delivery system; bioavailability enhancer; odor/taste masking; stabilizer
Manuf./Distrib. (pharm. & food): Aldrich
Trade names: Encapsin HPG; Gamma W8 HP0.6

Hydroxypropyl methylcellulose
CAS 9004-65-3
Synonyms: MHPC; Methyl hydroxypropyl cellulose; Cellulose hydroxypropyl methyl ether; Cellulose 2-hydroxypropyl methyl ether; Hypromellose
Definition: Propylene glycol ether of methyl cellulose
Properties: White powd.; swells in water to produce a clear to opalescent visc. colloidal sol'n.; nonionic; insol. in anhyd. alcohol, ether, chloroform; sol. in most polar solvs.
Precaution: Combustible
Toxicology: LD50 (intraperitoneal, rat) 5200 mg/kg; mildly toxic by intraperitoneal route; heated to decomp., emits acrid smoke and fumes
Uses: Thickener, dispersing agent, tablet binder, coating aid, suspending and/or visc.-increasing agent; used in ophthalmics, orals, topicals
Regulatory: FDA 21CFR §172.874, 175.105, 175.300; Europe listed; FDA approved for ophthalmics, orals, topicals; USP/NF compliance
Manuf./Distrib.: Aceto; Ashland
Manuf./Distrib. (pharm. & food): Aldrich; Aqualon; S Black; Cornelius; Courtaulds; Croxton & Garry; Hercules; Nordmann Rassmann; Penta; SPCI; Spectrum Chem. Mfg.
Trade names: Benecel® Hydroxypropyl Methylcellulose; Methocel® E3 Premium; Methocel® E4M Premium; Methocel® E5P; Methocel® E6 Premium; Methocel® E10MP CR; Methocel® E15LV Premium; Methocel® E50LV Premium; Methocel® E50P; Methocel® E Premium; Methocel® F4M Premium; Methocel® F Premium; Methocel® J Premium; Methocel® K3 Premium; Methocel® K4M Premium; Methocel® K15M Premium; Methocel® K100LV Premium; Methocel® K100M Premium; Methocel® K Premium

Hydroxypropyl methylcellulose acetate succinate
Synonyms: HPMCAS
Uses: Used in enteric polymer matrix for controlled-release tablets of amoxicillin trihydrate

Hydroxypropyl methylcellulose phthalate
Synonyms: HPMCP
Definition: A monophthalic acid ester of hydroxypropyl methylcellulose
Properties: Wh. powd., odorless, tasteless; pract. insol. in water
Uses: Enteric film-former; coating agent, excipient, matrix binder for solid dosage forms; used in orals
Regulatory: FDA approved for orals; USP/NF, Ph.Eur., JP compliance
Trade names: HPMCP 50; HPMCP 55; HPMCP 55S

8-Hydroxy-1,3,6-pyrenetrisulfonic acid trisodium salt. *See* CI 59040; D&C Green No. 8

8-Hydroxyquinoline
CAS 148-24-3; EINECS 205-711-1
Synonyms: 8-Quinolinol; Oxine; Oxyquinoline
Empirical: C_9H_7NO
Formula: C_9H_6NOH
Properties: Wh. cryst. or powd.; sol. in alcohol, acetone, chloroform, benzene; insol. in water; m.w. 145.16; m.p. 73-75 C; b.p. 267 C
Precaution: Light-sensitive
Toxicology: Toxic by ingestion
Uses: Antifungal agent in topical anti-infective prods.; used in intravenous

Regulatory: FDA approved for intravenous; BP compliance
Manuf./Distrib.: Penta Mfg.; Spectrum Chem. Mfg.; Tanabe USA
Manuf./Distrib. (pharm. & food): R.W. Greeff; Ruger

8-Hydroxyquinoline sulfate

CAS 134-31-6
Synonyms: 8-Quinolinol sulfate (2:1) (salt); 8-Quinolinol hydrogen sulfate (2:1); Chinosol; 8-Quinolinol sulfate; Oxyquinoline sulfate; Oxine sulfate
Formula: $(C_9H_7NO)_2 \cdot H_2SO_4$
Properties: Yel. powd.; very sol. in water; freely sol. in methanol; sl. sol. in alcohol; pract. insol. in acetone, ether; m.w. 388.40; m.p. ≈ 185 C
Toxicology: LD50 (oral, rat) 2038 mg/kg; poison by ingestion; human mutagenic data; heated to decomp., emits very toxic fumes of SO_x and NO_x
Uses: Complexing agent; antimicrobial in wet dressings
Regulatory: USP/NF compliance

N-Hydroxysuccinic acid

CAS 6915-15-7 (±); 97-67-6 (L); 617-48-1 (DL); 636-61-3 (+); EINECS 202-601-5
FEMA 2655
Synonyms: Malic acid; Apple acid; 1-Hydroxy-1,2-ethanedicarboxylic acid; Hydroxybutanedioic acid
Empirical: $C_4H_6O_5$
Formula: $COOHCH_2CH(OH)COOH$
Properties: Wh. or colorless cryst. powd. or gran., strongly acid taste; dl, l, and d isomeric forms; very sol. in water, alcohol; sl. sol. in ether; m.w. 134.09; dens. 1.595 (20/40 C, d or l), 1.601 (dl); m.p. 100 C (d or l), 128 C (dl); b.p. 140 C (dec.)
Toxicology: Mod. toxic by ingestion; skin and severe eye irritant; dust and aq. sol'ns. may irritate skin, eyes, mucous membranes; heated to decomp., emits acrid smoke and irritating fumes
Uses: Acidifier; enhances flavors, masks undesirable tastes/odors of medicines (throat lozenges, cough syrups, effervescent powds.); in toothpastes, mouthwashes, germicidal prods.; pH control in nutritional supplements; rejuvenates skin in facial prods.
Regulatory: FDA 21CFR §146.113, 150, 150.161, 169.115, 169.140, 169.150, 184.1069, GRAS; USDA 9CFR §318.7, 0.01% max.; BATF 27CFR §240.1051, GRAS; not for use in baby foods; FEMA GRAS; Japan approved; Europe listed; UK approved; FDA approved for orals; USP/NF, BP compliance
Manuf./Distrib.: Aldrich; Allchem Industries; Croda Colloids Ltd; Haarmann & Reimer; Janssen Chimica; Schweizerhall; Spectrum Chem. Mfg.
Manuf./Distrib. (pharm. & food): AB Tech.; Ashland; Bartek; Browning; Cornelius; Croda Colloids; Ellis & Everard; Haarmann & Reimer; Honeywill & Stein; Int'l. Sourcing; Jungbunzlauer; Penta Mfg.; Quimdis; Spectrum Chem. Mfg.; Van Waters & Rogers
Trade names containing: Durkote Malic Acid/Maltodextrin

2-Hydroxy-5-sulfobenzoic acid. *See* 5-Sulfosalicylic acid

3-Hydroxy-4-[(1-sulfo-2-naphthalenyl)azo]-2-naphthalenecarboxylic acid calcium salt (1:1). *See* D&C Red No. 34

6-Hydroxy-5-[(4-sulfophenyl)azo]-2-naphthalenesulfonic acid disodium salt. *See* CI 15985; FD&C Yellow No. 6

14-Hydroxytetradecanoic acid. *See* Pentadecalactone
α-Hydroxytoluene. *See* Benzyl alcohol
β-Hydroxytricarballylic acid. *See* Citric acid
2-Hydroxytriethylamine. *See* Diethylaminoethanol
5-Hydroxyundecanoic acid lactone. *See* δ-Undecalactone
5-Hydroxyundecanoic acid γ-lactone. *See* γ-Undecalactone
α-Hydroxy-ω-hydroxy poly(oxy-1,2-ethanediyl). *See* Polyethylene glycol
Hydroxyxylene. *See* Xylenol
Hypnone. *See* Acetophenone
Hypo. *See* Sodium thiosulfate anhydrous

Hypophosphorous acid

CAS 6303-21-5; 14332-09-3; EINECS 228-601-5
UN No. 1760
Synonyms: Phosphinic acid
Classification: Acid
Definition: Phosphorus treated with a resin
Empirical: H_3PO_2
Formula: HPH_2O_2
Properties: Colorless oily liq. or deliquescent cryst., sour odor; sol. in water, ethanol; m.w. 66; dens. 1.439;

Hyprolose

m.p. 26.5 C; dec. above 100 C; flash pt. none
Precaution: DOT: Corrosive material; fire and explosion risk in contact with oxidizing agents
Uses: Antioxidant for pharmaceuticals
Regulatory: USP/NF compliance; BP compliance (dilute)
Manuf./Distrib.: Albright & Wilson; Aldrich; Nippon Chem. Industrial
Manuf./Distrib. (pharm. & food): Aldrich; Mallinckrodt; Ruger; Spectrum Chem. Mfg.

Hyprolose. *See* Hydroxypropylcellulose
Hypromellose. *See* Hydroxypropyl methylcellulose

Hyssop extract
FEMA 2590
Definition: Extract from *Hyssopus officinalis*
Properties: Warm aromatic camphor-like odor, warm sweet sl. burning flavor
Toxicology: No known toxicity
Uses: Natural flavoring agent; stimulant, carminative, pectoral
Regulatory: FDA 21CFR §182.10, 182.20, GRAS; FEMA GRAS; Japan approved
Manuf./Distrib. (pharm. & food): Chart; Pierre Chauvet (oil)

IIR. *See* Isobutylene/isoprene copolymer
2,4-Imidazolidinedione, 1,3-bis(hydroxymethyl)-5,5-dimethyl-. *See* DMDM hydantoin

Imidazolidinyl urea
CAS 39236-46-9; EINECS 254-372-6
Synonyms: N,N´´-Methylenebis[N´-[1-(hydroxymethyl)-2,5-dioxo-4-imidazolindinyl]urea]; Imidurea
Classification: Heterocyclic substituted urea
Empirical: $C_9H_{16}O_8N_8$
Properties: Wh. powd., odorless, tasteless; very water-sol.; sol. in glycerin; sl. sol. in propylene glycol; insol.
in most org. solvs.; m.w. 388.30 pH 6.0-7.5 (1%)
Toxicology: Low systemic toxicity by ingestion or on applic. to abraded skin; may cause contact dermatitis
Uses: Formaldehyde-releasing antimicrobial preservative for topical pharmaceuticals, esp. water-sol. creams
and lotions; keratin softener for dry skin prods.
Usage level: 0.2-0.6%
Regulatory: USA CIR approved; Europe listed 0.6% max.; FDA approved for topicals
Manuf./Distrib.: Ashland; Int'l. Sourcing; Nipa Labs; Tri-K
Manuf./Distrib. (pharm. & food): Spectrum Chem. Mfg.; Tri-K
Trade names: Biopure® 100; Germall® 115; Unicide U-13

Imidurea. *See* Imidazolidinyl urea
2,2´-Iminobisethanol. *See* Diethanolamine
1,1´-Iminobis(propan-2-ol). *See* Diisopropanolamine
1,1´-Iminobis-2-propenol. *See* Diisopropanolamine
2,2´-Iminodiethanol. *See* Diethanolamine
IMP. *See* Disodium inosinate
Inactive limonene. *See* dl-Limonene
Indanthrene blue. *See* D&C Blue No. 9
Indian balsam. *See* Balsam Peru
Indian gum. *See* Gum ghatti
Indian tragacanth. *See* Karaya gum
India tragacanth. *See* Karaya gum
Indigo. *See* CI 73000; D&C Blue No. 6
Indigo carmine. *See* CI 73015; FD&C Blue No. 2
Indigotine. *See* CI 73015; FD&C Blue No. 2
Industrial talc. *See* Talc
Infusorial earth. *See* Diatomaceous earth
Inosine 5´-disodium phosphate. *See* Disodium inosinate

Invert sugar
CAS 8013-17-0
Synonyms: Invert sugar syrup; Invert syrup
Definition: Aq. sol'n. of inverted/partly inverted refined/partly refined sucrose; mixt. of approx. 50% dextrose
and 50% fructose

Properties: Colorless sol'n., odorless, sweet flavor
Uses: Sweetening agent; used in orals
Regulatory: FDA 21CFR §184.1859, GRAS; FDA approved for orals; BP compliance
Manuf./Distrib. (pharm. & food): MLG Enterprises
Trade names containing: Nu-Tab®; Sugartab®

Invert sugar syrup. *See* Invert sugar
Invert syrup. *See* Invert sugar

Iodamide
CAS 440-58-4
Synonyms: Ametriodinic acid
Definition: Crystals from acetic acid
Properties: Sol. in water; m.p. 255-257 C
Uses: Used in parenterals, intravenous, IV (infusion)
Regulatory: FDA approved for intravenous, IV (infusion)

Iodine
CAS 7553-56-2; EINECS 231-442-4
UN No. 1759
Classification: Nonmetallic halogen element
Empirical: I_2
Properties: Bluish-black scales or plates, metallic luster, char. odor, sharp acrid taste; sol. (g/100 g): 14.09 benzene, 16.47 CS_2, 21.43 ethanol; sol. in chloroform, CCl_4, glac. acetic acid; very sl. sol. in water; m.w. 253.81; dens. 4.98; m.p. 113.6 C; b.p. 185.24 C
Precaution: DOT: Corrosive material; incompat. with alkaloids, starch, tannins
Toxicology: Human ingestion of large quantities causes abdominal pain, nausea, vomiting, diarrhea, asthma, anaphylactic shock; 2-4 g have been fatal; intensely irritating to eyes, skin, mucous membranes
Uses: Medicinal soaps, x-ray contrast media; artifically synthesized I_{131} in diagnostic and medical treatment, radiation treatment; used in expectorants and thinners, treatment of asthma in cough medicines; topical antiseptic and anesthetics
Regulatory: BP, Ph.Eur. compliance
Manuf./Distrib.: Aldrich; Andeno BV; Atomergic Chemetals; Cerac; Mallinckrodt; Mitsui Toatsu; Nippoh Chems.; Yanagishima Pharmaceutical
Manuf./Distrib. (pharm. & food): Atomergic Chemetals; Avrachem; Integra; Ruger; Spectrum Chem. Mfg.; Yanagishima Pharmaceutical

Iodipamide
CAS 606-17-7
Empirical: $C_{20}H_{14}I_6N_2O_6$
Properties: Wh. cryst. solid, nearly odorless; sl. sol. in alcohol, chloroform, ether; insol. in water; m.w. 1139.81
Toxicology: Toxic by ingestion
Uses: Used in parenterals
Regulatory: FDA approved for parenterals; BP compliance

Iodohippurate sodium
CAS 133-17-5
Empirical: $C_9H_7INN_2O_3$
Properties: Cryst.; sol. in water, alcohol; m.w. 327.05
Uses: Used in intravenous
Regulatory: FDA approved for intravenous

Iofetamine hydrochloride
Uses: Used in intravenous
Regulatory: FDA approved for intravenous

α-Ionone
CAS 127-41-3; EINECS 204-841-6
FEMA 2594
Synonyms: 4-(2,6,6-Trimethyl-2-cyclohexene-1-yl)-3-butene-2-one; α-Cyclocitrylideneacetone
Empirical: $C_{13}H_{20}O$
Properties: Colorless oil, woody violet odor; sol. in alcohol, fixed oils, propylene glycol; sl. sol. in water; misc. with ether; insol. in glycerin; m.w. 192.33; dens. 0.930; b.p. 136 C; flash pt. 118 C; ref. index 1.497-1.502
Toxicology: LD50 (oral, rat) 4590 mg/kg; mildly toxic by ingestion; heated to decomp., emits acrid smoke and fumes
Uses: Cherry, raspberry-like synthetic flavoring agent

Ioxaglic acid

Regulatory: FDA 21CFR §172.515; FEMA GRAS
Manuf./Distrib.: BASF
Manuf./Distrib. (pharm. & food): Aldrich; BASF

Ioxaglic acid
CAS 59017-64-0
Empirical: $C_{24}H_{21}I_6N_5O_8$
Properties: M.w. 1268.90
Uses: Used in intravenous
Regulatory: FDA approved for intravenous

IPA. *See* Isopropyl alcohol
IPG. *See* Isopentyldiol
IPM. *See* Isopropyl myristate
IPP. *See* Isopropyl palmitate
Irish moss. *See* Carrageenan
Irish moss extract. *See* Carrageenan extract

Iron ammonium citrate
CAS 1185-57-5 (green); 1185-57-6 (brown); 1333-00-2; 1332-98-5; EINECS 214-686-6
Synonyms: FAC; Ferric ammonium citrate; Ammonium ferric citrate; Iron (III) ammonium citrate; Ferric ammonium citrate, green
Classification: A complex salt
Empirical: $C_6H_8O_7 \cdot xFe \cdot H_4N$
Properties: Transparent grn. scales, gran., powd., or cryst., ammoniacal odor, mild iron-metallic taste; deliq.; sol. in water; insol. in alcohol; deliq.; m.w. 709.44
Precaution: Light-sensitive
Toxicology: Heated to decomp., emits acrid smoke and irritating fumes
Uses: Color additive with pyrogallol in sutures for use in general and ophthalmic surgery
Usage level: 3% max. total citrate-pyrogallol complex (sutures)
Regulatory: FDA 21CFR §172.430, 25 ppm max. in finished salt, 184.1296, GRAS; Japan approved; Europe listed; UK approved
Manuf./Distrib.: Lohmann
Manuf./Distrib. (pharm. & food): Lohmann; Spectrum Chem. Mfg.

Iron blue. *See* Ferric ammonium ferrocyanide
Iron hydroxide oxide. *See* CI 77492
Iron (II) citrate. *See* Ferrous citrate
Iron (II) fumarate. *See* Ferrous fumarate
Iron (II) gluconate. *See* Ferrous gluconate
Iron (III) ammonium citrate. *See* Iron ammonium citrate
Iron (III) oxide. *See* Ferric oxide

Iron (III) oxide hydrated
CAS 20344-49-4
Synonyms: CI 77492
Formula: FeO(OH)
Properties: Sol. in min. acids; pract. insol. in w ater, alcohol; m.w. 88.85
Uses: Color additive
Manuf./Distrib.: Aldrich
See also CI 77492

Iron (III) pyrophosphate. *See* Ferric pyrophosphate
Iron (II) lactate. *See* Ferrous lactate
Iron (II) sulfate (1:1). *See* Ferrous sulfate

Iron oxides
CAS 1309-37-1 (Fe_2O_3); 1345-25-1 (FeO); 1317-61-9 (Fe_3O_4); EINECS 215-168-2 (Fe_2O_3), 215-721-8 (FeO), 215-277-5
Synonyms: CI 77489; CI 77491; CI 77492; CI 77499
Definition: Inorganic compd. consisting of any one or combinations of synthetically prepared iron oxides incl. the hydrated forms
Uses: Color additive for ingested drugs (5 mg/day as Fe)
Regulatory: FDA 21CFR §73.200, 73.1200, 73.2250, 175.300, 177.1460, 177.2600, 182.90, 186.1300, 186.1374, 522.940

Manuf./Distrib.: R.E. Carroll; Spectrum Chem. Mfg.
See also Ferric oxide; CI 77489; CI 77491; CI 77492; CI 77499

Iron sulfate (ous). *See* Ferrous sulfate
Iron vitriol. *See* Ferrous sulfate

Isoamyl acetate
CAS 123-92-2; EINECS 204-662-3
FEMA 2055
Synonyms: 3-Methyl-1-butanol acetate; β-Methylbutyl acetate; Isopentyl alcohol acetate; Isopentyl acetate
Definition: Ester of isoamyl alcohol and acetic acid
Empirical: $C_7H_{14}O_2$
Formula: $CH_3COOCH_2CH_2CH(CH_3)_2$
Properties: Colorless liq., banana-like odor; sl. sol. in water; misc. with alcohol, ether, ethyl acetate, fixed oils; insol. in glycerin, propylene glycol; m.w. 130.21; dens. 0.876; b.p. 142 C; flash pt. 77 F; ref. index 1.400
Precaution: Highly flamm.; exposed to het or flame, can react vigorously with reducing materials
Toxicology: TLV 100 ppm; LD50 (oral, rat) 16,600 mg/kg; mildly toxic by ingestion, inh., subcutaneous routes; heated to decomp., emits acrid smoke and fumes
Uses: Banana, pear-like synthetic flavoring agent
Regulatory: FDA 21CFR §172.515; FEMA GRAS; Japan approved as flavoring
Manuf./Distrib.: Aldrich; Penta Mfg.; Spectrum Chem. Mfg.
Manuf./Distrib. (pharm. & food): Aldrich; Chr. Hansen's; Penta Mfg.

Isoamyl acetoacetate
FEMA 3551
Synonyms: Isoamyl β-ketobutyrate; Isoamyl 3-oxobutanoate
Empirical: $C_9H_{16}O_3$
Properties: Colorless liq., sweet winey odor, green-apple flavor; sol. in alcohol; insol. in water; m.w. 172.23; dens. 0.954 (10 C); b.p. 222-224 C
Uses: Synthetic flavoring agent
Regulatory: FDA 21CFR §172.515; FEMA GRAS

Isoamyl alcohol
CAS 123-51-3; EINECS 204-633-5
FEMA 2057; UN No. 1105
Synonyms: 3-Methylbutanol; 3-Methyl-1-butanol; Isopentyl alcohol; Isobutyl carbinol
Classification: Aliphatic organic compd.
Empirical: $C_5H_{12}O$
Formula: $(CH_3)_2CHCH_2CH_2OH$
Properties: Colorless liq., pungent taste, disagreeable odor; sl. sol. in water; misc. with alcohol, ether; m.w. 88.15; dens. 0.813 (15/4 C); b.p. 132 C; f.p. -117.2 C; flash pt. (CC) 42.7 C; ref. index 1.407 (20 C)
Precaution: DOT: Flamm. liq.; explosive limits in air 1.2-9%; vapor is toxic and irritant
Toxicology: TLV 100 ppm in air; highly toxic; ing. has caused human deaths from respiratory failure; may cause heart, lung, kidney damage; CNS depressant; vapor exposure has caused marked irritation of eyes, nose, throat, and headache
Uses: Synthetic flavoring agent
Regulatory: FDA 21CFR §172.515; FEMA GRAS
Manuf./Distrib.: Aldrich; CPS; Spectrum Chem. Mfg.
Manuf./Distrib. (pharm. & food): Aldrich; Chr. Hansen's; Kuraray; Osaka Org. Chem. Ind.
Trade names: Isoamyl Alcohol 95%; Isoamyl Alcohol 99%

Isoamyl aldehyde. *See* Isovaleraldehyde

Isoamyl butyrate
CAS 106-27-4
FEMA 2060
Synonyms: Butyric acid isoamyl ester; Amyl butyrate; Isopentyl butyrate
Definition: Ester of isoamyl alcohol and butyric acid
Empirical: $C_9H_{18}O_2$
Properties: Colorless liq., fruity odor; sol. in alcohol, fixed oils; insol. in glycerin, propylene glycol, water; m.w. 158.24; dens. 0.860; flash pt. 149 F; ref. index 1.409-1.414
Precaution: Combustible liq.
Toxicology: Heated to decomp., emits acrid smoke and irritating fumes
Uses: Apricot, banana, pineapple-like synthetic flavoring agent
Regulatory: FDA 21CFR §172.515; FEMA GRAS; Japan approved as flavoring

Isoamyl caproate

    Manuf./Distrib.: BASF
    Manuf./Distrib. (pharm. & food): Aldrich; BASF

Isoamyl caproate. *See* Isoamyl hexanoate
Isoamyl caprylate. *See* Amyl octanoate

Isoamyl formate
    CAS 110-45-2
    FEMA 2069
    Synonyms: Amyl formate; Isopentyl formate
    Empirical: $C_6H_{12}O_2$
    Properties: Colorless liq., plum-like odor; sol. in alcohol; sl. sol. in water; misc. with ether; m.w. 116.16; dens. 0.859; b.p. 123-124 C; flash pt. 86 F; ref. index 1.3960-1.40
    Precaution: Combustible
    Toxicology: Strong irritant
    Uses: Plum-like synthetic flavoring agent
    Regulatory: FDA 21CFR §172.515; FEMA GRAS; Japan approved as flavoring
    Manuf./Distrib. (pharm. & food): Aldrich

Isoamyl hexanoate
    CAS 2198-61-0
    FEMA 2075
    Synonyms: Amyl hexanoate; Isoamyl caproate; Isopentyl hexanoate
    Definition: Ester of caproic acid and isomeric amyl alcohols
    Empirical: $C_{11}H_{22}O_2$
    Properties: Colorless liq., fruity odor; insol. in water; m.w. 186.30; dens. 0.860; b.p. 94-96 C (10 mm); flash pt. 88 C
    Uses: Sweet apple, pineapple-like synthetic flavoring agent
    Regulatory: FDA 21CFR §172.515; FEMA GRAS
    Manuf./Distrib. (pharm. & food): Aldrich

Isoamyl 2-hydroxybenzoate. *See* Amyl salicylate
Isoamyl o-hydroxybenzoate. *See* Amyl salicylate

Isoamyl isobutyrate
    CAS 2050-01-3
    FEMA 3507
    Synonyms: Isopentyl isobutyrate; 3-Methylbutyl 2-methylpropanoate; Isoamyl 2-methylpropanoate
    Empirical: $C_9H_{18}O_2$
    Properties: Liq.; m.w. 158.24; dens. 0.8627; b.p. 170 C
    Uses: Apricot, grape, pineapple, honey-like synthetic flavoring agent
    Regulatory: FDA 21CFR §172.515; FEMA GRAS
    Manuf./Distrib. (pharm. & food): Aldrich

Isoamyl isovalerate
    CAS 659-70-1
    FEMA 2085
    Synonyms: Amyl valerate; Amyl isovalerate; Isopentyl isovalerate
    Empirical: $C_{10}H_{20}O_2$
    Properties: Liq., fruity odor, apple-like flavor; sol. in most org. solvs.; insol. in water; m.w. 172.27; dens. 0.8583; b.p. 193 C; flash pt. 72 C; ref. index 1.4125-1.4135
    Uses: Apple-like synthetic flavoring agent
    Regulatory: FDA 21CFR §172.515; FEMA GRAS; Japan approved as flavoring
    Manuf./Distrib. (pharm. & food): Aldrich

Isoamyl β-ketobutyrate. *See* Isoamyl acetoacetate
Isoamyl 2-methylpropanoate. *See* Isoamyl isobutyrate

Isoamyl nonanoate
    CAS 7779-70-6
    FEMA 2078
    Synonyms: Isoamyl nonylate; Isoamyl pelargonate; Isopentyl nonanoate; Nonate
    Empirical: $C_{14}H_{28}O_2$
    Properties: Colorless oily liq., nutty oily apricot-like odor, fruity winey cognac-rum flavor; sol. in alcohol; insol. in water; m.w. 228.37; dens. 0.86; b.p. 260-265 C
    Uses: Apricot-like synthetic flavoring agent

Regulatory: FDA 21CFR §172.515; FEMA GRAS
Manuf./Distrib. (pharm. & food): Aldrich

Isoamyl nonylate. *See* Isoamyl nonanoate
Isoamyl octanoate. *See* Amyl octanoate
Isoamyl 3-oxobutanoate. *See* Isoamyl acetoacetate
Isoamyl pelargonate. *See* Isoamyl nonanoate

Isoamyl propionate
CAS 105-68-0
FEMA 2082
Synonyms: Isopentyl propionate
Empirical: $C_8H_{16}O_2$
Properties: M.w. 144.21; dens. 0.871; b.p. 156 C; flash pt. 118 F
Uses: Apricot, pineapple-like flavoring agent
Regulatory: FEMA GRAS
Manuf./Distrib. (pharm. & food): Aldrich

Isoamyl salicylate. *See* Amyl salicylate
Isoascorbic acid. *See* Erythorbic acid
D-Isoascorbic acid. *See* Erythorbic acid
Isobutanal. *See* 2-Methylpropanal

Isobutane
CAS 75-28-5; EINECS 200-857-2
UN No. 1969
Synonyms: 2-Methylpropane
Classification: Hydrocarbon gas
Definition: A constituent of natural gas and illuminating gas
Empirical: C_4H_{10}
Formula: $CH(CH_3)_3$
Properties: Colorless gas, odorless; easily liquefied under pressure at R.T.; insol. in water; m.w. 58.12; dens.
   0.5572; vapor pressure 2950 mm Hg (31 psig, 21 C); f.p. -159 C; b.p. -11.73 C
Precaution: Highly flamm. gas; explosive
Toxicology: Asphyxiant; narcotic at high concs.
Uses: Aerosol propellant used in topicals
Regulatory: FDA 21CFR §184.1165; FDA approved for topicals; USP/NF compliance
Manuf./Distrib.: Air Prods.; Hüls Am.; Phillips 66
Manuf./Distrib. (pharm. & food): Aldrich

Isobutanol. *See* Isobutyl alcohol
Isobutanolamine. *See* 2-Amino-2-methyl-1-propanol
Isobutanol-2 amine. *See* 2-Amino-2-methyl-1-propanol

Isobutyl acetate
CAS 110-19-0; EINECS 203-745-1
FEMA 2175
Synonyms: 2-Methylpropyl acetate; β-Methylpropyl ethanoate
Definition: Ester of isobutyl alcohol and acetic acid
Empirical: $C_6H_{12}O_2$
Formula: $CH_3COOCH_2CH(CH_3)_2$
Properties: Colorless liq., fruit-like odor; very sol. in alcohol, fixed oils, propylene glycol; sl. sol. in water; m.w.
   116.18; dens. 0.8685 (15 C); m.p. -98.9 C; b.p. 118 C; flash pt. (CC) 18 C; ref. index 1.389
Precaution: Highly flamm.; very dangerous fire and mod. explosion hazard on exposure to heat, flame,
   oxidizers
Toxicology: TLV 150 ppm; LD50 (oral, rat) 13,400 mg/kg; mildly toxic by ingestion and inh.; skin and eye irritant;
   heated to decomp., emits acrid smoke and fumes
Uses: Sweet apple, banana-like synthetic flavoring agent
Regulatory: FDA 21CFR §172.515; FEMA GRAS; BP compliance
Manuf./Distrib.: Aldrich; BASF; Eastman; Hoechst Celanese; Janssen Chimica; Union Carbide
Manuf./Distrib. (pharm. & food): Aldrich; Eastman

Isobutyl acetoacetate
CAS 7779-75-1
FEMA 2177
Synonyms: Isobutyl β-ketobutyrate; Isobutyl-3-oxobutanoate

Isobutyl alcohol

Empirical: $C_8H_{14}O_3$
Properties: Colorless liq., brandy-like odor, sweet sl. fruity flavor; sol. in alcohol; insol. in water; m.w. 158.20; dens. 0.9697; b.p. 84.5 C (11 mm); flash pt. 173 F; ref. index 1.4219
Uses: Fruity synthetic flavoring agent
Regulatory: FDA 21CFR §172.515; FEMA GRAS
Manuf./Distrib. (pharm. & food): Aldrich

Isobutyl alcohol
CAS 78-83-1; EINECS 201-148-0
FEMA 2179; UN No. 1212
Synonyms: Isobutanol; Isopropylcarbinol; 2-Methyl-1-propanol; 2-Methylpropanol
Classification: Alcohol
Empirical: $C_4H_{10}O$
Formula: $(CH_3)_2CHCH_2OH$
Properties: Colorless liq., sweet odor; partly sol. in water; sol. in alcohol, ether; m.w. 74.12; dens. 0.806 (15 C); m.p. -108 C; b.p. 106-109 C; f.p. -108 C; flash pt. (TCC) 29 C; ref. index 1.396
Precaution: Flamm.; dangerous fire hazard with heat, flame; mod. explosive as vapor with heat, flame, oxidizers
Toxicology: TLV 50 ppm in air; LD50 (oral, rat) 2460 mg/kg; poison by IV, intraperitoneal route; mod. toxic by ingestion, skin contact; experimental carcinogen, tumorigen; severe skin/eye irritant; mutagenic data; heated to decomp., emits acrid smoke and fumes
Uses: Fruity synthetic flavoring agent; used in pharmaceutical processing
Regulatory: FDA 21CFR §172.515; FEMA GRAS
Manuf./Distrib.: Aldrich; BASF; CPS; Eastman; Hoechst Celanese; Neste UK; Penta Mfg.; Shell; Union Carbide
Manuf./Distrib. (pharm. & food): Aldrich; Eastman
Trade names containing: Filmex® B

Isobutyl aldehyde. *See* 2-Methylpropanal

p-Isobutylbenzaldehyde
Empirical: $C_{11}H_{14}O$
Properties: Liq.; sol. in ethanol, ether, toluene; insol. in water; m.w. 162.2; sp.gr. 0.960 (20 C); b.p. 240 C; flash pt. (COC) 122 C
Toxicology: LD50 (oral, rat) 1000-5000 mg/kg; eye and skin irritant
Uses: Intermediate for pharmaceuticals
Trade names: Ibbal

Isobutyl benzyl carbinol. *See* α-Isobutylphenethyl alcohol

Isobutyl-2-butenoate
CAS 589-66-2
FEMA 3432
Synonyms: Isobutyl trans-2-butenoate
Empirical: $C_8H_{14}O_2$
Properties: Fruity odor; m.w. 142.19; dens. 0.890; b.p. 171 C; flash pt. 131 F
Uses: Fruity flavoring agent
Regulatory: FEMA GRAS
Manuf./Distrib. (pharm. & food): Aldrich

Isobutyl trans-2-butenoate. *See* Isobutyl-2-butenoate

Isobutyl butyrate
CAS 539-90-2
FEMA 2187
Synonyms: Isobutyl n-butyrate; 2-Methyl propanyl butyrate
Definition: Ester of butyric acid and isobutyl alcohol
Empirical: $C_8H_{16}O_2$
Formula: $CH_3CH_2CH_2COOCH_2CH(CH_3)_2$
Properties: Liq., fruity odor, sweet rum-like flavor; sl. sol. in water; misc. with alcohol, ether; m.w. 144.21; dens. 0.866; b.p. 157 C; flash pt. 114 F; ref. index 1.4035 (20 C)
Uses: Fruity synthetic flavoring agent
Regulatory: FDA 21CFR §172.515; FEMA GRAS
Manuf./Distrib. (pharm. & food): Aldrich

Isobutyl n-butyrate. *See* Isobutyl butyrate
Isobutyl caproate. *See* Isobutyl hexanoate

Isobutyl capronate. *See* Isobutyl hexanoate
Isobutyl carbinol. *See* Isoamyl alcohol

Isobutyl cinnamate
CAS 122-67-8
FEMA 2193
Synonyms: Isobutyl-3-phenylpropenoate; Isobutyl-β-phenylacrylate
Empirical: $C_{13}H_{16}O_2$
Properties: Colorless liq., sweet fruity balsamic odor, sweet taste; m.w. 204.27; dens. 1.003; b.p. 287 C; flash pt. > 230 F; ref. index 1.541
Precaution: Combustible
Uses: Sweet, fruity synthetic flavoring agent
Regulatory: FDA 21CFR §172.515; FEMA GRAS
Manuf./Distrib. (pharm. & food): Aldrich

Isobutyl 2-cyanoacrylate. *See* Bucrylate

Isobutylene/isoprene copolymer
CAS 9010-85-9
Synonyms: IIR; Butyl rubber; 3-Methyl-1,3-butadiene polymer with 2-methyl-1-propene
Definition: Copolymer of isobutylene and isoprene monomers
Formula: $(C_5H_8 • C_4H_8)_x$
Toxicology: Heated to decomp., emits acrid smoke and irritating fumes
Uses: Pharmaceuticals
Regulatory: FDA 21CFR §172.615, 175.105, 177.1210, 177.2600
Manuf./Distrib.: Nat'l. Chem. Co.
Manuf./Distrib. (pharm. & food): Aldrich

Isobutyl formate
CAS 542-55-2
FEMA 2197
Synonyms: Tetryl formate
Empirical: $C_5H_{10}O_2$
Formula: $HCOOCH_2CH(CH_3)_2$
Properties: Liq., fruity ether-like odor, rum-like taste; sol. in 100 parts water; misc. with alcohol, ether; m.w. 102.13; dens. 0.885 (20/4 C); m.p. -95 C; b.p. 98-99 C; flash pt. 50 F; ref. index 1.3858 (20 C)
Precaution: Flamm. liq.
Uses: Sweet, fruity synthetic flavoring agent
Regulatory: FDA 21CFR §172.515; FEMA GRAS
Manuf./Distrib. (pharm. & food): Aldrich

Isobutyl hexanoate
CAS 105-79-3
FEMA 2202
Synonyms: Isobutyl caproate; Isobutyl capronate; Isobutyl hexylate
Empirical: $C_{10}H_{20}O_2$
Properties: Colorless liq., fruity apple-like odor; m.w. 172.27; dens. 0.856; flash pt. 169 F; ref. index 1.412-1.416
Uses: Chocolate, apple-like synthetic flavoring agent
Regulatory: FDA 21CFR §172.515; FEMA GRAS
Manuf./Distrib. (pharm. & food): Aldrich

Isobutyl hexylate. *See* Isobutyl hexanoate
Isobutyl p-hydroxybenzoate. *See* Isobutylparaben

Isobutyl isobutyrate
CAS 97-85-8; EINECS 202-612-5
FEMA 2189
Synonyms: 2-Methylpropanoic acid 2-methylpropyl ester
Empirical: $C_8H_{16}O_2$
Formula: $(CH_3)_2CHCOOCH_2CH(CH_3)_2$
Properties: Liq., fruity odor; misc. with alcohol; insol. in water; m.w. 144.22; dens. 0.854 (20/4 C); m.p. -81 C; b.p. 149-151 C; flash pt. 40 C; ref. index 1.399 (20 C)
Precaution: Flamm.
Toxicology: Irritant
Uses: Grape-like synthetic flavoring agent

Isobutyl β-ketobutyrate

Regulatory: FDA 21CFR §172.515; FEMA GRAS
Manuf./Distrib.: Eastman
Manuf./Distrib. (pharm. & food): Aldrich

Isobutyl β-ketobutyrate. See Isobutyl acetoacetate
2-Isobutyl-5-methylcyclohexanol. See d-Neomenthol
Isobutyl methyl ketone. See Methyl isobutyl ketone
Isobutyl-3-oxobutanoate. See Isobutyl acetoacetate

Isobutylparaben
CAS 4247-02-3; EINECS 224-208-8
Synonyms: Isobutyl p-hydroxybenzoate; 4-Hydroxybenzoic acid, 2-methylpropyl ester; Isobutyl parahydroxybenzoate
Definition: Ester of isobutyl alcohol and p-hydroxybenzoic acid
Uses: Broad-spectrum preservative for topical pharmaceuticals
Regulatory: FDA 21CFR §176.200
Trade names containing: LiquaPar® Oil

Isobutyl parahydroxybenzoate. See Isobutylparaben

α-Isobutylphenethyl alcohol
FEMA 2208
Synonyms: Isobutyl benzyl carbinol; Benzyl isobutyl carbinol; 4-Methyl-1-phenyl-2-pentanol; Benzyl isoamyl alcohol
Empirical: $C_{12}H_{18}O$
Properties: Colorless oily liq., green floral herbaceous odor, buttery oily caramellic flavor; sol. in alcohol; insol. in water; m.w. 178.27; dens. 0.96; b.p. 250 C
Uses: Synthetic flavoring agent
Regulatory: FDA 21CFR §172.515; FEMA GRAS

Isobutyl phenylacetate
FEMA 2210
Synonyms: Isobutyl α-toluate
Definition: Ester of phenylacetic acid and isobutyl alcohol
Empirical: $C_{12}H_{16}O_2$
Properties: Colorless liq., sweet musk-like fragrance, sweet honey-like flavor; sol. in most fixed oils; insol. in glycerol; m.w. 192.26; dens. 0.984-0.988; b.p. 253 C; flash pt. 116 C; ref. index 1.4860-1.4880
Uses: Synthetic flavoring agent
Regulatory: FDA 21CFR §172.515; FEMA GRAS; Japan approved as flavoring
Manuf./Distrib. (pharm. & food): Chr. Hansen's

Isobutyl-β-phenylacrylate. See Isobutyl cinnamate
Isobutyl-3-phenylpropenoate. See Isobutyl cinnamate

Isobutyl stearate
CAS 646-13-9; 85865-69-6; EINECS 211-466-1; 288-668-1
Synonyms: 2-Methylpropyl octadecanoate; Stearic acid, 2-methylpropyl ester
Definition: Ester of isobutyl alcohol and stearic acid
Empirical: $C_{22}H_{44}O_2$
Formula: $CH_3(CH_2)_{16}COOCH_2CH(CH_3)_2$
Properties: Waxy crystalline solid; m.w. 340.57; m.p. 20 C
Toxicology: No known toxicity
Uses: Emollient for topical pharmaceuticals, ointments
Regulatory: FDA 21CFR §176.210, 177.2260, 177.2800, 178.3910
Trade names: Pelemol® IBS

Isobutyl α-toluate. See Isobutyl phenylacetate
Isobutyraldehyde. See 2-Methylpropanal
Isobutyric acid benzyl ester. See Benzyl isobutyrate
Isobutyric aldehyde. See 2-Methylpropanal

Isoceteth-20
Synonyms: PEG-20 isocetyl ether; POE (20) isohexadecyl ether; PEG 1000 isocetyl ether
Definition: PEG ether of isocetyl alcohol
Formula: $C_{16}H_{33}(OCH_2CH_2)_nOH$, avg. n = 20
Uses: Surfactant, emulsifier, solubilizer

Isoceteth-30

Synonyms: PEG-30 isocetyl ether; POE (30) isocetyl ether
Definition: PEG ether of isocetyl alcohol
Formula: $C_{16}H_{33}(OCH_2CH_2)_nOH$, avg. n = 30
Uses: Emulsifier, solubilizer used in pharmaceuticals
Trade names: Nikkol BEG-1630

Isocetyl alcohol

CAS 36311-34-9; EINECS 252-964-9
Synonyms: Isohexadecanol; Isohexadecyl alcohol; Isopalmityl alcohol
Definition: Mixture of branched chain C16 aliphatic alcohols
Empirical: $C_{16}H_{34}O$
Formula: $C_8H_{17}CHC_6H_{13}CH_2OH$
Properties: Liq.; sol. in min. oil, 95% ethanol, IPM, oleyl alcohol, castor oil, cyclomethicone; insol. in water, glycerin, propylene glycol; m.w. 242; sp.gr. 0.830-0.840; flash pt. (COC) 156 C
Toxicology: LD50 (rat, oral) > 50 g/kg; mildly irritating to skin and eyes
Uses: Emollient, carrier, extender, pigment dispersant, spreading agent
Trade names: Ceraphyl® ICA; Eutanol® G16

Isocetyl behenate

CAS 94247-28-6; EINECS 304-205-9
Synonyms: Behenic acid, isocetyl ester; Behenic acid, isohexadecyl ester; Docosanoic acid, isocetyl ester
Definition: Ester of isocetyl alcohol and behenic acid
Empirical: $C_{38}H_{76}O_2$
Formula: $CH_3(CH_2)_{20}COOC_{16}H_{33}$
Properties: Sol. in oil; insol. in water, alcohol
Uses: Emollient for pharmaceutical topicals
Trade names: Pelemol® ICB

Isocetyl isostearate

Definition: Ester of isocetyl alcohol and isostearic acid
Uses: Emollient for pharmaceutical topicals
Trade names: Pelemol® ICIS

Isocetyl laurate

CAS 20834-06-4
Uses: Used in pharmaceutical topicals
Trade names: Pelemol® ICLA

Isocetyl octanoate

CAS 125804-19-5
Synonyms: Isohexadecyl octanoate
Uses: Used in pharmaceutical topicals
Trade names: Pelemol® ICO

Isocetyl stearate

CAS 25339-09-7; EINECS 246-868-6
Definition: Ester of isocetyl alcohol and stearic acid
Empirical: $C_{34}H_{68}O_2$
Formula: $CH_3(CH_2)_{16}COOC_{16}H_{33}$
Properties: Oily liq., pract. odorless; insol. in water; sol. in most org. solvs.; dens. 0.862; f.p. 57 C; visc. 29 cp (25 C); ref. index 1.446-1.456
Precaution: Combustible
Toxicology: LD50 (rabbit, oral) > 5 g/kg; minimal eye irritation, nonirritating to skin
Uses: Emollient, lubricant for pharmaceutical topicals
Trade names: Ceraphyl® 494; Pelemol® ICS; Standamul® 7061

Isocetyl stearoyl stearate

CAS 97338-28-8
Classification: Ester
Properties: Lt. to straw liq., char. mild odor; sol. in min. oil, IPP, IPM, oleyl alcohol; insol. in propylene glycol, glycerin; sp.gr. 0.865-0.885; ref. index 1.4560-1.4590
Toxicology: Nonirritating, nonsensitizing
Uses: Pigment dispersant, emollient, lubricant, spreading agent for topical pharmaceuticals
Trade names: Ceraphyl® 791

Isocholesterol. *See* Lanosterol

Isodecyl oleate
  CAS 59231-34-4; EINECS 261-673-6
  Synonyms: 9-Octadecenoic acid, isodecyl ester
  Definition: Ester of branched chain decyl alcohols and oleic acid
  Empirical: $C_{28}H_{54}O_2$
  Formula: $CH_3(CH_2)_7CH=CH(CH_2)_7COOC_{10}H_{21}$
  Properties: Wh. to straw liq., char. mild odor; sol. in peanut oil, 95% ethanol, IPM, oleyl alcohol; insol. in water, glycerin, propylene glycol; sp.gr. 0.858-0.864; ref. index 1.4540-1.4560
  Toxicology: LD50 (rat, oral) > 40 ml/kg; nonirritating to eyes; mildly irritating to skin
  Uses: Emollient, cosolv., solubilizer for pharmaceutical topicals
  Trade names: Ceraphyl® 140-A; Pelemol® IDO

Isododecanol. *See* 2-Butyl-1-octanol
Isodulcit. *See* Rhamnose
Isoeicosyl alcohol. *See* Octyldodecanol

Isoeugenol
  CAS 97-54-1; EINECS 202-589-1
  FEMA 2468
  Synonyms: 1-Hydroxy-2-methoxy-4-propenylbenzene; 2-Methoxy-4-propenylphenol; 4-Propenylguaiacol
  Empirical: $C_{10}H_{12}O_2$
  Properties: Pale yel. oil, carnation odor; sol. in fixed oils, propylene glycol; very sl. sol. in water; misc. with alcohol, ether; insol. in glycerin; m.w. 164.22; dens. 1.079-1.085; m.p. -10 C; b.p. 266 C; flash pt. > 230 F; ref. index 1.572-1.577
  Precaution: Combustible
  Toxicology: LD50 (oral, rat) 1560 mg/kg; mod. toxic by ingestion; allergen; sensitizer; human mutagenic data; heated to decomp., emits acrid smoke and fumes
  Uses: Sweet synthetic flavoring agent
  Regulatory: FDA 21CFR §172.515; FEMA GRAS; Japan approved as flavoring
  Manuf./Distrib.: Aldrich
  Manuf./Distrib. (pharm. & food): Aldrich

Isoeugenol acetate. *See* Acetisoeugenol
trans-Isoeugenol benzyl ether. *See* Isoeugenyl benzyl ether

Isoeugenyl benzyl ether
  CAS 92666-21-2
  FEMA 3698
  Synonyms: Benzyl isoeugenol; trans-Isoeugenol benzyl ether
  Empirical: $C_{17}H_{18}O_2$
  Properties: Wh. to ivory-colored cryst. powd., rose-carnation odor; m.w. 254.33; b.p. 282 C; m.p. 59-63 C
  Uses: Sweet synthetic flavoring agent
  Regulatory: FDA 21CFR §172.515; FEMA GRAS
  Manuf./Distrib. (pharm. & food): Aldrich

Isoeugenyl phenylacetate
  CAS 120-24-1
  FEMA 2477
  Synonyms: 2-Methoxy-4-propenylphenyl phenylacetate
  Empirical: $C_{18}H_{18}O_3$
  Properties: Ylsh. visc. liq.; insol. in water; m.w 282.34; dens. 1.119; flash pt. > 230 F; ref. index 1.575-1.577
  Uses: Sweet cinnamon, apple, honey-like synthetic flavoring agent
  Regulatory: FDA 21CFR §172.515; FEMA GRAS
  Manuf./Distrib. (pharm. & food): Aldrich

Isohexadecanol. *See* Isocetyl alcohol
Isohexadecyl alcohol. *See* Isocetyl alcohol
Isohexadecyl octanoate. *See* Isocetyl octanoate
Isolauryl alcohol. *See* 2-Butyl-1-octanol

Isomalt
  Synonyms: Hydrogenated isomaltulose; Hydrogenated palatinose
  Toxicology: 50% metabolized in humans; breaks down to form sorbitol, mannitol, and glucose; short-term animal studies show increase in bilirubin levels
  Uses: Nutritive sweetener, sugar substitute

Isomaltose
  CAS 499-40-1
  Empirical: $C_{12}H_{22}O_{11}$
  Properties: M.w. 342.30
  Uses: Vehicle for direct compression of pharmaceutical tablets
  Trade names containing: Sweetrex®

Isononanoic acid, cetyl/stearyl ether. *See* Cetearyl isononanoate
Isononanoic acid, 2-ethylhexyl ester. *See* Octyl isononanoate

Isononyl isononanoate
  CAS 42131-25-9
  Synonyms: 3,5,5-Trimethylhexanoic acid, 3,5,5-trimethylhexyl ester
  Definition: Ester of a branched chain nonyl alcohol with a branched chain nonanoic acid
  Empirical: $C_{18}H_{36}O_2$
  Properties: Sol. in alcohol, animal and vegetable oils, min. oil; insol. in water, glycerin, propylene glycol
  Toxicology: No known toxicity
  Uses: Emollient for pharmaceutical topicals, mouthwashes
  Trade names: Pelemol® IN-2

Isooctadecanoic acid, diester with triglycerol. *See* Polyglyceryl-3 diisostearate
Isooctadecanoic acid, isooctadecyl ester. *See* Isostearyl isostearate
Isooctadecanoic acid, monoester with 1,2-propanediol. *See* Propylene glycol isostearate
Isooctadecanoic acid, monoester with 1,2,3-propanetriol. *See* Glyceryl isostearate
Isooctanoic acid, monoester with tetraglycerol. *See* Polyglyceryl-4 isostearate

Isooctyl acrylate
  CAS 29590-42-9
  Classification: Monomer
  Properties: M.w. 184.0
  Uses: Used in topicals
  Regulatory: FDA approved for topicals

Isopalmityl alcohol. *See* Isocetyl alcohol
Isopentaldehyde. *See* Isovaleraldehyde
Isopentyl acetate. *See* Isoamyl acetate
Isopentyl alcohol. *See* Isoamyl alcohol
Isopentyl alcohol acetate. *See* Isoamyl acetate
Isopentyl butyrate. *See* Isoamyl butyrate

Isopentyldiol
  CAS 2568-33-4
  Synonyms: IPG; 3-Methyl-1,3-butanediol; Isoprene glycol
  Classification: Diol
  Empirical: $C_5H_{12}O_2$
  Uses: Humectant, moisturizer for skin prods.
  Manuf./Distrib.: Kuraray Co. Ltd.; Robeco
  Manuf./Distrib. (pharm. & food): Kuraray Co. Ltd.; Robeco

Isopentyl formate. *See* Isoamyl formate
Isopentyl hexanoate. *See* Isoamyl hexanoate
Isopentyl isobutyrate. *See* Isoamyl isobutyrate
Isopentyl isovalerate. *See* Isoamyl isovalerate
Isopentyl nonanoate. *See* Isoamyl nonanoate
Isopentyl propionate. *See* Isoamyl propionate
Isopentyl salicylate. *See* Amyl salicylate

Isophorone
  CAS 78-59-1; EINECS 201-126-0
  FEMA 3553
  Synonyms: 3,3,5-Trimethyl-2-cyclohexen-1-one
  Empirical: $C_9H_{14}O$
  Properties: Sp.gr. 0.923
  Uses: Sweet flavoring agent
  Regulatory: FEMA GRAS
  Manuf./Distrib.: Aceto; Allchem Ind.; Ashland; BP Chem.; Chemcentral; Coyne; Elf Atochem N. Am.; Exxon;

Isoprene glycol

Fabrichem; Great Western; Hüls AG; Stanchem; Sunnyside; Union Carbide; Van Waters & Rogers
Manuf./Distrib. (pharm. & food): Aldrich

Isoprene glycol. *See* Isopentyldiol
Isopropanol. *See* Isopropyl alcohol

Isopropanolamine
CAS 78-96-6; EINECS 201-162-7
Synonyms: MIPA; 1-Amino-2-propanol; Monoisopropanolamine; 2-Hydroxypropylamine
Classification: Aliphatic amine
Empirical: C_3H_9ON
Formula: $H_2NCH_2CHOHCH_3$
Properties: Liq., sl. ammonia odor; sol. in water; m.w. 75.13; dens. 0.969; m.p. 1.4 C; flash pt. 171 F
Precaution: Combustible
Toxicology: Poison by intraperitoneal route; moderately toxic by ingestion and skin contact; skin and severe eye irritant
Uses: Emulsifier used in orals
Regulatory: FDA 21CFR §175.105, 176.210; FDA approved for orals
Manuf./Distrib.: Ashland; BASF; Mitsui Toatsu Chem.
Manuf./Distrib. (pharm. & food): Aldrich

Isopropenyl carbinyl-n-butyrate. *See* 2-Methylallyl butyrate
4-Isopropenyl-1-cyclohexene-1-carboxaldehyde. *See* Perillaldehyde

Isopropyl acetate
CAS 108-21-4; EINECS 203-561-1
FEMA 2926
Synonyms: Acetic acid 1-methylethyl ester; 2-Propyl acetate; 1-Methylethyl acetate
Empirical: $C_5H_{10}O_2$
Formula: $CH_3COOCH(CH_3)2$
Properties: Colorless aromatic liq., fruity odor; sl. sol. in water; misc. with alcohol, ether, fixed oils; m.w. 102.15; dens. 0.874 (20/20 C); m.p. 073 C; f.p. -69.3 C; b.p. 88.4 C; flash pt. 40 F; ref. index 1.377
Precaution: Highly flamm.; dangerous fire hazard with heat, flame, oxidizers; mod. explosive with heat or flame
Toxicology: TLV 250 ppm; LD50 (oral, rat) 3000 mg/kg; mod. toxic by ingestion; mildly toxic by inh.; human systemic effects on inh.; narcotic in high conc.; chronic exposure can cause liver damage
Uses: Sweet banana-like synthetic flavoring agent
Regulatory: FDA 21CFR §172.515, 175.105, 177.1200; FEMA GRAS
Manuf./Distrib.: Aldrich; Ashland; J.T. Baker; Chemcentral; Eastman; Harcros; Samson; Stanchem; Sunnyside; Union Carbide; Van Waters & Rogers
Manuf./Distrib. (pharm. & food): Aldrich

Isopropylacetone. *See* Methyl isobutyl ketone

Isopropyl alcohol
CAS 67-63-0; EINECS 200-661-7
FEMA 2929; UN No. 1219
Synonyms: IPA; Isopropanol; Petrohol; 2-Propanol; Dimethyl carbinol
Classification: Aliphatic alcohol
Empirical: C_3H_8O
Formula: $(CH_3)_2CHOH$
Properties: Colorless volatile liq., pleasant odor, sl. bitter taste; sol. in water, alcohol, ether, chloroform; m.w. 60.11; dens. 0.7863 (20/20 C); f.p. -86 C; b.p. 82.4 C (760 mm); flash pt. (TOC) 11.7 C; ref. index 1.3756 (20 C)
Precaution: DOT: Flamm. liq.; very dangerous fire hazard with heat, flame, oxidizers; reacts with air to form dangerous peroxides; heated to decomp., emits acrid smoke and fumes
Toxicology: TLV:TWA 400 ppm; STEL 500 ppm; LD50 (oral, rat) 5045 mg/kg; poison by ingestion, subcutaneous routes; human systemic effects by ingestion/inhalation (headache, nausea, vomiting, narcosis); 100 ml can be fatal; experimental reproductive effects
Uses: Synthetic flavoring, solv., color diluent; antiseptic in topical anti-infective prods.; externally as 'rubbing alcohol' for topical sterilization, cooling and soothing props.; used in orals, topicals
Regulatory: FDA 21CFR §73.1 (no residue), 73.1001, 172.515, 172.560, 172.712, 173.240 (limitation 50 ppm in spice oleoresins, 6 ppm in lemon oil, 2% in hops extract), 173.340; 175.105, 176.200, 176.210, 177.1200, 177.2800, 178.1010, 178.3910; 27CFR §21.112; use in bread is permitted in Ireland and Japan; FEMA GRAS; FDA approved for orals, topicals; USP/NF, BP compliance
Manuf./Distrib.: Aldrich; Arco; Eastman; Exxon; Hüls AG; Mallinckrodt; Mitsui Toatsu; Shell; Union Carbide
Manuf./Distrib. (pharm. & food): Aldrich; Eastman; Mallinckrodt; Mitsui Toatsu; Nippon Petrochems.; Ruger;

Spectrum Chem. Mfg.; Tokuyama
Trade names containing: Arquad® B-100; Chroma-Seal™ 859027; Chroma-Seal™ 889031; Filmex® D-1; Gantrez® ES-335; Gantrez® ES-435; Mearlmaid® AA; Mearlmaid® TR; PVP/VA I-235; PVP/VA I-335; PVP/VA I-535; PVP/VA I-735

4-Isopropylbenzaldehyde. *See* Cuminaldehyde
p-Isopropylbenzaldehyde. *See* Cuminaldehyde

Isopropyl butyrate
CAS 638-11-9
FEMA 2935
Empirical: $C_7H_{14}O_2$
Properties: Colorless liq., fruity odor; m.w. 130.19; dens. 0.859; b.p. 130-131 C; flash pt. 86 F; ref. index 1.3936
Uses: Fruity synthetic flavoring agent
Regulatory: FDA 21CFR §172.515; FEMA GRAS
Manuf./Distrib. (pharm. & food): Aldrich

Isopropyl caproate. *See* Isopropyl hexanoate
Isopropyl capronate. *See* Isopropyl hexanoate
Isopropylcarbinol. *See* Isobutyl alcohol

Isopropyl cinnamate
FEMA 2939
Synonyms: Isopropyl β-phenylacrylate; Isopropyl 3-phenylpropenoate
Definition: Ester of isopropanol and cinnamic acid
Empirical: $C_{12}H_{14}O_2$
Properties: Colorless visc. liq., balsamic sweet dry amber-like odor, fresh fruity flavor; sol. in alcohol; insol. in water; m.w. 190.24; dens. 1.03; b.p. 268-270 C
Uses: Synthetic flavoring agent
Regulatory: FDA 21CFR §172.515; FEMA GRAS

6-Isopropyl-m-cresol. *See* Thymol
Isopropyl ester of PVM/MA copolymer. *See* PVM/MA copolymer, isopropyl ester

Isopropyl formate
FEMA 2944
Empirical: $C_4H_8O_2$
Properties: Colorless liq., fruity ether-like odor, plum-like taste; sl. sol. in water; misc. with alcohol, ether; m.w. 88.10; dens. 0.8774; b.p. 67-68 C; ref. index 1.3678
Uses: Synthetic flavoring agent
Regulatory: FDA 21CFR §172.515; FEMA GRAS

Isopropyl hex. *See* Isopropyl hexanoate
Isopropyl n-hexadecanoate. *See* Isopropyl palmitate

Isopropyl hexanoate
FEMA 2950
Synonyms: Isopropyl capronate; Isopropyl caproate; Isopropyl hex
Definition: Ester of hexanoic acid and isopropyl alcohol
Empirical: $C_9H_{18}O_2$
Properties: Colorless liq., pineapple-like odor, fresh sweet berry-like taste; sol. in alcohol; insol. in water; m.w. 158.24; dens. 0.8570; b.p. 176 C
Uses: Synthetic flavoring agent
Regulatory: FDA 21CFR §172.515; FEMA GRAS

Isopropyl p-hydroxybenzoate. *See* Isopropylparaben

Isopropyl isobutyrate
FEMA 2937
Empirical: $C_7H_{14}O_2$
Properties: Liq., intense fruity ether-like odor; sol. in most org. solvs.; insol. in water; m.w. 130.18; dens. 0.8687 (0 C); b.p. 121 C
Uses: Pear, pineapple-like synthetic flavoring agent
Regulatory: FDA 21CFR §172.515; FEMA GRAS
Manuf./Distrib. (pharm. & food): Aldrich

Isopropyl isovalerate
FEMA 2961
Empirical: $C_8H_{16}O_2$

Isopropyl lanolate

Properties: Liq., ether-like odor, sweet apple-like taste; sol. in most org. solvs.; insol. in water; m.w. 144.21; b.p. 68-70 C (55 mm); ref. index 1.3960
Uses: Synthetic flavoring agent
Regulatory: FDA 21CFR §172.515; FEMA GRAS

Isopropyl lanolate

CAS 63393-93-1; EINECS 264-119-1
Synonyms: Lanolin fatty acids, isopropyl esters
Definition: Ester of isopropyl alcohol and lanolin acid
Toxicology: Eye and skin irritant; may cause skin sensitization
Uses: Lubricant, emollient, emulsifier, stabilizer for pharmaceuticals
Trade names: Amerlate® P; Amerlate® W; Fancor IPL; Lanesta SA-30; Ritasol

Isopropyl laurate

CAS 10233-13-3; EINECS 233-560-1
Synonyms: Dodecanoic acid, 1-methylethyl ester; 1-Methylethyl dodecanoate
Definition: Ester of isopropyl alcohol and lauric acid
Formula: $CH_3(CH_2)_{10}COOCH(CH_3)_2$
Uses: Emollient and lubricant for pharmaceuticals
Regulatory: FDA 21CFR §176.210, 177.2800

Isopropyl metacresol. See Thymol
1-Isopropyl-4-methylbenzene. See p-Cymene
4-Isopropyl-1-methylbenzene. See p-Cymene
Isopropyl α-methyl crotonic acid. See Isopropyl tiglate
1-Isopropyl-4-methyl-1,4-cyclohexadiene. See γ-Terpinene
5-Isopropyl-2-methyl-1,3-cyclohexadiene. See α-Phellandrene
2-Isopropyl-5-methylcyclohexanol. See Menthol
2-Isopropyl-5-methylphenol. See Thymol

Isopropyl myristate

CAS 110-27-0; EINECS 203-751-4
FEMA 3556
Synonyms: IPM; 1-Methylethyl tetradecanoate; Tetradecanoic acid, 1-methylethyl ester; Myristic acid isopropyl ester
Classification: Synthetic fatty alcohol
Definition: Ester of isopropyl alcohol and myristic acid
Empirical: $C_{17}H_{34}O_2$
Formula: $CH_3(CH_2)_{12}COOCH(CH_3)_2$
Properties: Colorless oily liq., odorless; sol. in most org. solvs., veg. oil, alcohol; dissolves waxes; insol. in water; m.w. 270.44; dens. 0.850-0.860; f.p. 3 C; b.p. 192.6 C (20 mm); dec. 208 C; acid no. 1 max.; iodine no. 1 max.; sapon.no. 202-212; ref. index 1.432-1.436 (20 C)
Precaution: Light-sensitive
Toxicology: Suspected tumorigen; human skin irritant; causes blackheads
Uses: Oleaginous vehicle; emollient, lubricant, spreading agent; used as solvent for topical medicinals
Regulatory: FDA 21CFR §176.210, 177.2800; FEMA GRAS; FDA approved for topicals; USP/NF, BP, Ph.Eur. compliance
Manuf./Distrib.: Amerchol; Aquatec Quimica SA; Goldschmidt; Henkel/Emery; Inolex; Lanaetex; Penta Mfg.; Pentagon Chems. Ltd; Stepan; Unichema
Manuf./Distrib. (pharm. & food): Aldrich; Pentagon Chems. Ltd; Ruger; Spectrum Chem. Mfg.
Trade names: Isopropylmyristat; RITA IPM
Trade names containing: Crodamol CAP; Lexol® 60; Lexol® 3975

Isopropyl palmitate

CAS 142-91-6; EINECS 205-571-1
Synonyms: IPP; Isopropyl n-hexadecanoate; Hexadecanoic acid, 1-methylethyl ester; 1-Methylethyl hexandecanoate
Definition: Ester of isopropyl alcohol and palmitic acid
Empirical: $C_{19}H_{38}O_2$
Formula: $CH_3(CH_2)_{14}COOCH(CH_3)_2$
Properties: Colorless mobile liq., very sl. odor; sol. in 4 parts 90% alcohol, min. oil, fixed oils, acetone, castor oil, chloroform, cottonseed oil, ethyl acetate; insol. in water, glycerin, propylene glycol; m.w. 298.57; dens. 0.850-0.855; m.p. 14 C; acid no. 1 max.; iodine no. 1 max.; sapon. no. 183-193; flash pt. > 230 F; ref. index 1.4350-1.4390 (20 C)
Precaution: Combustible; Light-sensitive

Toxicology: Poison by intraperitoneal route; human skin irritant
Uses: Emollient, emulsifier, oleaginous vehicle; used in topicals
Regulatory: FDA 21CFR §176.210, 177.2800; FDA approved for topicals; USP/NF, BP, Ph.Eur. compliance
Manuf./Distrib.: Amerchol; Aquatec Quimica SA; Goldschmidt; Henkel/Emery; Inolex; Lanaetex; Penta Mfg.; Stepan; Unichema
Manuf./Distrib. (pharm. & food): Aldrich; Ruger; Spectrum Chem. Mfg.
Trade names: Isopropylpalmitat; Lexol® IPP; Lexol® IPP-A; Lexol® IPP-NF; RITA IPP
Trade names containing: Lexol® 60; Lexol® 3975; Pionier® OEWA-II

Isopropylparaben
CAS 4191-73-5; EINECS 224-069-3
Synonyms: Isopropyl p-hydroxybenzoate; 1-Methylethyl-4-hydroxybenzoate; 4-Hydroxybenzoic acid, 1-methylethyl ester
Definition: Ester of isopropyl alcohol and p-hdyroxybenzoic acid
Uses: Preservative for topical pharmaceuticals
Trade names containing: LiquaPar® Oil

2-Isopropylphenol. *See* o-Isopropylphenol
4-Isopropylphenol. *See* p-Isopropylphenol

o-Isopropylphenol
CAS 88-69-7; EINECS 201-852-8
FEMA 3461
Synonyms: OIPP; 2-Isopropylphenol
Empirical: $C_9H_{12}O$
Formula: $(CH_3)_2CHC_6H_4OH$
Properties: Medicinal, creosote odor; m.w. 136.19; dens. 1.012; m.p. 15-16 C; b.p. 212-213 C; flash pt. 88 C; ref. index 1.5620 (20 C)
Precaution: Corrosive
Toxicology: Toxic
Uses: Medicinal flavoring agent
Regulatory: FEMA GRAS
Manuf./Distrib.: Albemarle; Aldrich; Fluka
Manuf./Distrib. (pharm. & food): Aldrich

p-Isopropylphenol
CAS 99-89-8
Synonyms: PIPP; 4-Isopropylphenol
Empirical: $C_9H_{12}O$
Properties: M.w. 136.19; m.p. 60-64 C; b.p. 212-213 C
Uses: Medicinal flavoring agent
Manuf./Distrib.: AC Ind.; Alemark; Amber Syn.
Manuf./Distrib. (pharm. & food): Aldrich

p-Isopropylphenylacetaldehyde
FEMA 2954
Synonyms: p-Cymen-7-carboxaldehyde; Cuminic acetaldehyde; Homo-cuminic aldehyde
Empirical: $C_{11}H_{14}O$
Properties: Colorless liq., char. bark odor, citrus bittersweet fruity flavor; m.w. 162.23; dens. 0.0955; b.p. 230 C; ref. index 1.5200
Uses: Synthetic flavoring agent
Regulatory: FDA 21CFR §172.515; FEMA GRAS

Isopropyl phenylacetate
CAS 4861-85-2
FEMA 2956
Synonyms: Isopropyl α-toluate
Empirical: $C_{11}H_{14}O_2$
Properties: Liq., fragrant rose-like scent, honey-like flavor; m.w. 178.23; dens. 1.0096; b.p. 253 C
Uses: Honey-like synthetic flavoring agent
Regulatory: FDA 21CFR §172.515; FEMA GRAS
Manuf./Distrib. (pharm. & food): Aldrich

Isopropyl β-phenylacrylate. *See* Isopropyl cinnamate
Isopropyl 3-phenylpropenoate. *See* Isopropyl cinnamate

Isopropyl propionate
FEMA 2959
Empirical: $C_6H_{12}O_2$
Properties: Liq., plum-like taste; misc. with alcohol; m.w. 116.16; dens. 0.8660; b.p. 108-110 C; ref. index 1.3872
Uses: Synthetic flavoring agent
Regulatory: FDA 21CFR §172.515; FEMA GRAS

Isopropyl stearate
CAS 112-10-7; EINECS 203-934-9
Synonyms: 1-Methylethyl octadecanoate; Octadecanoic acid, 1-methylethyl ester
Definition: Ester of isopropyl alcohol and stearic acid
Empirical: $C_{21}H_{42}O_2$
Formula: $CH_3(CH_2)_{16}COOCH(CH_3)_2$
Uses: Emollient, lubricant used in topicals
Regulatory: FDA 21CFR §176.210, 177.2800; FDA approved for topicals
Trade names containing: Lexol® 60; Lexol® 3975

Isopropyl tiglate
CAS 1733-25-1
FEMA 3229
Synonyms: Isopropyl α-methyl crotonic acid
Empirical: $C_8H_{14}O_2$
Properties: M.w. 142.20; dens. 0.896; flash pt. 123 F
Uses: Sweet, minty, medicinal flavoring agent
Regulatory: FEMA GRAS
Manuf./Distrib. (pharm. & food): Aldrich

Isopropyl α-toluate. *See* Isopropyl phenylacetate
4-Isopropyltoluene. *See* p-Cymene
p-Isopropyltoluene. *See* p-Cymene

Isopulegol
CAS 7786-67-6
FEMA 2962
Synonyms: p-Menth-4-en-3-ol; p-Menth-8-en-3-ol; 1-Methyl-4-isopropenyl cyclohexan-3-ol
Classification: Terpene deriv.
Empirical: $C_{10}H_{18}O$
Properties: Colorless liq., mint-like odor; m.w. 154.24; dens. 0.904-0.911; ref. index 1.471-1.474
Precaution: Combustible
Uses: Minty synthetic flavoring agent
Regulatory: FDA 21CFR §172.515; FEMA GRAS
Manuf./Distrib. (pharm. & food): Aldrich

Isopulegyl acetate
CAS 89-49-6; 57576-09-7
FEMA 2965
Empirical: $C_{12}H_{20}O_2$
Properties: Colorless liq., sweet mint-like odor; m.w. 196.29; dens. 0.932-0.936; b.p. 104-105 C (10 mm); flash pt. 87 C; ref. index 1.4572
Uses: Minty synthetic flavoring agent
Regulatory: FDA 21CFR §172.515; FEMA GRAS
Manuf./Distrib. (pharm. & food): Aldrich

Isoquinoline
CAS 119-65-3; EINECS 204-341-8
FEMA 2978
Synonyms: 2-Benzazine
Empirical: C_9H_7N
Properties: Colorless plates or liq.; sol. in most org. solvs.; sl. sol. in water; m.w. 129.16; dens. 1.09 (20/4 C); m.p. 23-25 C; b.p. 243 C; flash pt. 102 C; ref. index 1.615
Precaution: Combustible
Toxicology: Skin and eye irritant
Uses: Sweet synthetic flavoring agent
Regulatory: FDA 21CFR §172.515; FEMA GRAS
Manuf./Distrib. (pharm. & food): Aldrich

Isosafroeugenol. *See* Propenylguaethol
Isosorbide dimethyl ether. *See* Dimethyl isosorbide

Isosorbide dinitrate
CAS 87-33-2
UN No. 2907
Synonyms: 1,4:3,6-Dianhydrosorbitol 2,5-dinitrate; Isotrate; Nitrosorbide
Empirical: $C_6H_8N_2O_8$
Properties: M.w. 236.16
Uses: Preservative for pharmaceuticals
Regulatory: BP compliance
Trade names: Nipa ISDN

Isostearyl behenate
CAS 125804-16-2
Synonyms: Docosanoic acid, isooctadecyl ester
Definition: Ester of isostearyl alcohol and behenic acid
Empirical: $C_{40}H_{80}O_2$
Formula: $CH_3(CH_2)_{20}COOC_{18}H_{37}$
Properties: Off-wh. paste; sol. in oil, insol. in water
Uses: Emollient, moisture barrier in pharmaceutical topicals
Trade names: Pelemol® ISB

Isostearyl diglyceryl succinate
CAS 66085-00-5
Definition: Mixed ester of succincic acid with isostearyl alcohol and a glycerin polymer containg. an avg. of 2 units
Uses: W/o emulsifier for pharmaceutical preps.
Trade names: Imwitor® 780 K

Isostearyl isostearate
CAS 41669-30-1; EINECS 255-485-3
Synonyms: Isooctadecanoic acid, isooctadecyl ester
Definition: Ester of isostearyl alcohol and isostearic acid
Empirical: $C_{36}H_{62}O_2$
Properties: Liq.; insol. in water, sol. in hydrocarbons
Toxicology: No known toxicity
Uses: Emollient, lubricant for pharmaceuticals
Manuf./Distrib.: Gattefosse
Trade names: Iso Isotearyle WL 3196

Isostearyl lactate
CAS 42131-28-2; EINECS 255-674-0
Synonyms: 2-Hydroxypropanoic acid, isostearyl ester
Definition: Ester of isostearyl alcohol and lactic acid
Empirical: $C_{21}H_{42}O_3$
Uses: Emollient, substantivity agent, softener, slip agent, lubricant, cosolvent, solubilizer for pharmaceutical preps.
Trade names: Pelemol® ISL

Isostearyl neopentanoate
CAS 58958-60-4; EINECS 261-521-9
Synonyms: 2,2-Dimethylpropanoic acid, isooctadecyl ester
Classification: Ester
Definition: Ester of isostearyl alcohol and neopentanoic acid
Empirical: $C_{23}H_{46}O_2$
Properties: Pale yel. liq.; sol. in IPM, oleyl alcohol, 95% ethanol, min. oil; insol. in water, glycerin, propylene glycol; sp.gr. 0.850-0.870; ref. index 1.4450-1.4497
Toxicology: LD50 (rat, oral) > 40 ml/kg; nonirritating to skin and eyes
Uses: Emollient, spreading agent for topical pharmaceuticals; antitack for antiperspirants
Trade names: Ceraphyl® 375

4-Isothiazolin-3-one, 5-chloro-2-methyl-. *See* Methylchloroisothiazolinone
3(2H)-Isothiazolone, 2-methyl-. *See* Methylisothiazolinone
3-Isothiocyanato-1-propene. *See* Allyl isothiocyanate
Isothiocyanic acid allyl ester. *See* Allyl isothiocyanate

Isotonic sodium chloride sol'n.

Isotonic sodium chloride sol'n.
  CAS 8028-77-1
  Uses: Used in injectables, parenterals, ophthalmics, orals
  Regulatory: FDA approved for injectables, parenterals, ophthalmics, orals

Isourea. *See* Urea
Isovaleral. *See* Isovaleraldehyde

Isovaleraldehyde
  CAS 590-86-3; EINECS 209-691-5
  FEMA 2692
  Synonyms: 3-Methylbutyraldehyde; 3-Methylbutanal; Isopentaldehyde; Isovaleral; Isoamyl aldehyde; Isovaleric aldehyde
  Empirical: $C_5H_{10}O$
  Formula: $(CH_3)_2CHCH_2CHO$
  Properties: Colorless liq., pungent apple-like odor; sparingly sol. in water; misc. with alcohol, ether; m.w. 86.14; dens. 0.797 (20/4 C); m.p. -51 C; b.p. 91-93 C; flash pt. -5 C; ref. index 1.388 (20 C)
  Precaution: Highly flamm.
  Toxicology: Irritating to eyes, respiratory tract
  Uses: Peach-like synthetic flavoring agent
  Regulatory: FEMA GRAS
  Manuf./Distrib.: Aldrich; Hercules; Hoechst Celanese; Pfaltz & Bauer
  Manuf./Distrib. (pharm. & food): Aldrich

Isovaleric acid allyl ester. *See* Allyl isovalerate
Isovaleric acid butyl ester. *See* n-Butyl isovalerate
Isovaleric acid ethyl ester. *See* Ethyl isovalerate
Isovaleric aldehyde. *See* Isovaleraldehyde
Isovalerone. *See* Diisobutyl ketone

Jaguar gum. *See* Guar gum
Japan isinglass. *See* Agar
Japan tallow. *See* Japan wax

Japan wax
  CAS 8001-39-6; 67701-27-3
  Synonyms: Rhus succedanea wax; Japan tallow; Sumac wax
  Definition: Fat expressed from the mesocarp of the fruit of *Rhus succedanea*, contg. 10-15% palmitin, stearin, olein, 1% japanic acid
  Properties: Pale yel. solid, greasy feel, rancid odor and taste; sol. in benzene, CS_2, ether, hot alcohol, alkalies; insol. in water; dens. 0.97-0.98; m.p. 53.5-55 C; acid no. 22-23; iodine no. 10-15; sapon. no. 217-237
  Precaution: Combustible
  Uses: Wax used for pharmaceuticals
  Regulatory: FDA 21CFR §73.1, 175.105, 175.350, 176.170, 182.70
  Trade names: Koster Keunen Synthetic Japan Wax; Ross Japan Wax

Jasminaldehyde. *See* α-Amylcinnamaldehyde

cis-Jasmone
  CAS 488-10-8
  FEMA 3196
  Synonyms: 3-Methyl-2-(2-pentenyl)-2-cyclopenten-1-one
  Classification: Ketone
  Empirical: $C_{11}H_{16}O$
  Properties: Odor of jasmine; m.w. 164.25; dens. 0.940; b.p. 134-135 C (12 mm); flash pt. 225 F
  Uses: Fruity flavoring agent
  Regulatory: FDA 21CFR §172.515; FEMA GRAS
  Manuf./Distrib. (pharm. & food): Aldrich

Java pepper. *See* Cubeb oil

Jelene
  CAS 8049-66-9
  Uses: Used in ophthalmics, topicals
  Regulatory: FDA approved for ophthalmics, topicals

Jerusalem artichoke flour
Uses: Bulking agent, nutraceutical ingred. for health food tablets/capsules, gastric upset prods.
Trade names: Jerusalem Arthichoke Flour (JAF)

Jojoba oil
CAS 61789-91-1
Synonyms: Oils, jojoba
Definition: Oil from the seeds of the Jojoba desert shrub (*Simmondsia chinensis*)
Properties: Colorless waxy liq., odorless; m.p. 6.8-7 C
Toxicology: May cause allergic reaction
Uses: Lubricant used in sunscreens; skin protectant; antifoam in antibiotic fermentation; coating material, carrier
Manuf./Distrib.: Arista Industries; R.W. Greeff; Int'l. Flora Tech.; Lipo; Tri-K
Manuf./Distrib. (pharm. & food): Am. Roland; Arista Industries
Trade names: Simchin® Natural; Simchin® Refined

Juglans nigra extract. *See* Walnut extract
Juglans regia extract. *See* Walnut extract
Juniper berry oil. *See* Juniper oil

Juniper oil
CAS 8012-91-7, 73049-62-4
FEMA 2604
Synonyms: Juniper berry oil
Definition: Volatile oil obtained from the berries of *Juniperus communis*, contg. pinene, cadinene, camphene, terpineol, juniper camphor
Properties: Colorless to pale grnsh.-yel. liq., aromatic bitter taste; sol. in fixed oils, min. oil; pract. insol. in water; insol. in glycerin, propylene glycol; dens. 0.854-0.879 (25/25 C); ref. index 1.4780-1.4840 (20 C)
Precaution: Keep cool, well closed; protect from light
Toxicology: LD50 (oral, rat) 6280 mg/kg; mildly toxic by ingestion; human skin and systemic irritant; allergen; taken internally may cause severe kidney irritation; heated to decomp., emits acrid smoke and fumes
Uses: Natural flavoring agent; carminative; in herbal remedies for urinary tract disorders, muscle and joint pain
Regulatory: FDA 21CFR §182.20, GRAS; FEMA GRAS; Japan approved
Manuf./Distrib. (pharm. & food): Acme-Hardesty; Chart; Pierre Chauvet; Florida Treatt

Kadaya gum. *See* Karaya gum
Kalinite. *See* Potassium alum dodecahydrate

Kaolin
CAS 1332-58-7; EINECS 296-473-8
Synonyms: Bolus alba; China clay; Hydrated aluminum silicate
Definition: Native hydrated aluminum silicate
Formula: $\approx Al_2O_3 \cdot 2SiO_2 \cdot 2H_2O$
Properties: White to yel. or grayish fine powd., clay-like odor when moist, earthy taste; insol. in water, dilute acids, alkali hydroxides; dens. 1.8-2.6
Toxicology: Nuisance dust; large doses may cause obstructions, perforations, or granuloma (tumor formation)
Uses: Tablet and/or capsule diluent; adsorbent in antidiarrheal prods.; used medicinally to treat intestinal disorders; used in orals
Regulatory: FDA 21CFR §178.3550, 182.2727, 182.2729, 186.1256, GRAS as indirect additive; BATF 27CFR §240.1051; Japan restricted (0.5% max. residual); Europe listed; UK approved; FDA approved for orals; USP/NF, BP compliance
Manuf./Distrib.: Burgess Pigment; Dry Branch Kaolin; ECC Int'l.; Feldspar; J.M. Huber; Kaopolite; San Yuan; Thiele Kaolin; R.T. Vanderbilt; Whittaker, Clark & Daniels
Manuf./Distrib. (pharm. & food): Aldrich; ECC Int'l.; Ruger; Spectrum Chem. Mfg.
Trade names: Peerless® No. 1; Peerless® No. 2; Peerless® No. 3; Peerless® No. 4

Karaya gum
CAS 9000-36-6; EINECS 232-539-4
FEMA 2605
Synonyms: Sterculia gum; Sterculia urens gum; India tragacanth; Indian tragacanth; Kadaya gum
Definition: A hydrophilic polysaccharide from trunks of the genus *Sterculia*
Properties: Wh. fine powd., sl. acetic acid odor; insol. in alcohol; swells in water to a gel; produces highly stable emulsions, resist. to acids

Toxicology: Very mildly toxic by ingestion; mild allergen causing hay fever, dermatitis, gastrointestinal diseases, and asthma; may cause intolerance; laxative effect, may reduce nutrient intake

Uses: Protective colloid, stabilizer, thickener, emulsifier, suspending agent for pharmaceuticals; tablet excipient; bulk laxative; denture adhesive powds.; imparts consistency to troches and in prep. of emulsions

Regulatory: FDA 21CFR §133.133, 133.134, 133.162, 133.178, 133.179, 150.141, 150.161, 184.1349, GRAS; FEMA GRAS; Japan approved; Europe listed; UK approved; BP compliance

Manuf./Distrib.: Meer; Penta Mfg.; Rhone-Poulenc Perf. Resins; TIC Gums

Manuf./Distrib. (pharm. & food): Aarhus Olie; Agrisales; Ashland; Bio-Botanica; Arthur Branwell; Bronson & Jacobs; Browne & Dureau Int'l.; Colloides Naturels; Florexco; Gum Tech.; Importers Service; Mar-Gel; Meer; Penta Mfg.; Red Carnation; Ruger; Spectrum Chem. Mfg.; Thew Arnott; TIC Gums

Trade names: Karaya Gum #1 FCC; Powdered Gum Karaya Superfine #1 FCC; Powdered Gum Karaya Superfine XXXX FCC; Premium Powdered Gum Karaya No. 1; Premium Powdered Gum Karaya No. 1 Special

Katchung oil. *See* Peanut oil
Kautschin. *See* d-Limonene

Kelp
FEMA 2606
Definition: Dehydrated seaweed from *Macrocystis pyriferae, Laminaria digitata, L. saccharina, L. cloustoni*
Properties: Dk. grn. to olive-brn. color, salty char. taste
Toxicology: Heated to decomp., emits acrid smoke and irritating fumes
Uses: Natural flavoring agent; in dietary supplements, herbal preps.; source of iodine
Regulatory: FDA 21CFR §172.365, 184.1120, 184.1121; FEMA GRAS
Manuf./Distrib. (pharm. & food): Am. Roland; Chart

Keratinase
CAS 9025-41-6
Definition: Proteolytic enzyme obtained from cultures of *Streptomyces fradiae*, which can digest keratin
Uses: Enzyme; ingred. in topical antibiotic ointments, presumably to aid penetration of active substances

Ketone C-7. *See* Methyl n-amyl ketone
Ketone methyl phenyl. *See* Acetophenone
β-Ketopropane. *See* Acetone
2-Ketopropopnaldehyde. *See* Pyruvaldehyde
γ-Ketovaleric acid. *See* Levulinic acid
Kieselguhr. *See* Diatomaceous earth
Kordofan gum. *See* Acacia

Labarrque's sol'n. *See* Sodium hypochlorite
Lacca. *See* Shellac
Lacolin. *See* Sodium lactate

Lactic acid
CAS 50-21-5; 598-82-3 (DL); 79-33-4 (L); 10326-41-7 (D); EINECS 200-018-0; 209-954-4 (DL); 201-296-2 (L); 233-713-2 (D)
FEMA 2611; UN No. 1760
Synonyms: 2-Hydroxypropanoic acid; 1-Hydroxyethane 1-carboxylic acid; 2-Hydroxypropionic acid; α-Hydroxypropionic acid; Milk acid; Acetonic acid; Ethylidenelactic acid
Classification: Organic acid
Definition: Prod. of the metabolism of glucose and glycogen
Empirical: $C_3H_6O_3$
Formula: $CH_3CHOHCOOH$
Properties: Colorless to yellowish cryst. or syrupy liq., nearly odorless; hygroscopic; misc. with water, alcohol, glycerol, furfural; insol. in chloroform; m.w. 90.09; dens. 1.249; m.p. 18 C; b.p. 122 C (15 mm); flash pt. > 230 F; ref. index 1.4251
Precaution: DOT: Corrosive material; mixts. with nitric acid + hydrofluoric acid may react vigorously
Toxicology: LD50 (oral, rat) 3730 mg/kg; mod. toxic by ingestion, rectal routes; mutagenic data; severe skin and eye irritant; heated to decomp., emits acrid smoke and irritating fumes
Uses: Acidulant, buffering agent, antimicrobial; used in injectables, parenterals, orals, topicals, vaginals, digestive aid prods.; treatment of infective skin and vaginal disorders; keratin softener for dry skin prods.
Usage level: Up to 10%
Regulatory: FDA 21CFR §131.144, 133, 150.141, 150.161, 172.814, 184.1061, GRAS; USDA 9CFR §318.7,

381.147; BATF 27CFR §240.1051, GRAS; not for use in infant foods; FEMA GRAS; Japan approved; Europe listed; UK approved; FDA approved for injectables, parenterals, orals, topicals, vaginals; USP/NF, BP, Ph.Eur., JP compliance

Manuf./Distrib.: Lohmann; Penta Mfg.; Pfanstiehl Labs; Purac Biochem BV

Manuf./Distrib. (pharm. & food): AB Tech.; ADM; Aldrich; Ashland; Ellis & Everard; Chr Hansen's Lab; Honeywill & Stein; Integra; Int'l. Sourcing; Jungbunzlauer; Lohmann; Malalinckrodt; Mitsubishi; Penta Mfg.; Pointing; Purac Am.; Ruger; Siber Hegner; Spectrum Chem. Mfg.; Tesco; Todd's; Van Waters & Rogers

Trade names: Lactic Acid 88% USP/FCC; Patlac® LA USP; Purac® PH 88; Purac® USP 88

Lactic acid, ammonium salt. *See* Ammonium lactate
Lactic acid ethyl ester. *See* Ethyl lactate
Lactic acid iron (2+) salt (2:1). *See* Ferrous lactate
Lactic acid menthyl ester. *See* Menthyl lactate
L-Lactic acid sodium salt. *See* Sodium L-lactate

Lactitol monohydrate
CAS 81025-04-9
Synonyms: 4-O-β-D-Galactopyranosyl-D-glucitol
Classification: Disaccharide sugar alcohol
Empirical: $C_{12}H_{24}O_{11} \cdot H_2O$
Properties: M.w. 362.37; m.p. 95-98 C
Toxicology: Large doses may cause diarrhea
Uses: Sweetener
Manuf./Distrib. (pharm. & food): Am. Xyrofin
Trade names: Lactitol MC

Lactoflavin. *See* Riboflavin

Lactose
CAS 63-42-3; EINECS 200-559-2
Synonyms: 4-O-β-Galactopyranosyl D-glucose; Lactosum; Milk sugar; Saccharum lactis
Classification: Disaccharide
Empirical: $C_{12}H_{22}O_{11}$
Formula: $C_6H_7O(OH)_4OC_6H_7O(OH)_4$
Properties: Wh. hard cryst. mass or white powd., odorless to sl. char. odor but readily absorbs odors, mildly sweet taste, odorless; sol. in water, alcohol, ether; sl. sol. in alcohol; m.w. 342.34; dens. 1.525 (20 C); m.p. dec. 203.5 C; b.p. dec.; stable in air
Toxicology: Moderately toxic by intravenous route; found to cause tumors when injected under skin of mice; derivs. can be irritating to the colon
Uses: Tablet/capsule diluent, filler; sweetener; in solid oral dosage forms; injectables; inhalation capsules; rectal syrups and tablets; topical creams, ointments, powds.; vaginal creams, suppositories; transdermal ointments and patches; eye lotion base
Regulatory: FDA 21CFR §133.124, 133.178, 133.179, 168.122, 169.179, 169.182, GRAS; FDA approved for orals, buccals, inhalants, rectals, topicals, vagnials, transdermals; USP/NF, BP, Ph.Eur., JP compliance
Manuf./Distrib.: Monomer-Polymer & Dajac; Penta Mfg.; Schweizerhall; Simonis BV
Manuf./Distrib. (pharm. & food): Aldrich; Allchem Int'l.; Am. Dairy Prods.; Arla; Calaga Food Ingreds.; DMV Int'l.; G Fiske; K&K Greeff; Integra; Land O'Lakes; New Zealand Milk Prods.; Penta Mfg.; Ruger; Quest USA; Spectrum Chem. Mfg.; Tesco; Unilait France; Van Waters & Rogers; Westin
Trade names: Unisweet L; Unisweet Lactose
Trade names containing: Dry Phytonadione 1% SD No. 61748; Dry Vitamin A Palmitate Type 250-SD No. 65378

Lactose monohydrate
CAS 10039-26-6; 64044-51-5; EINECS 200-559-2
Definition: A natural disaccharide consisting of one glucose and one galactose moiety (obtained from milk)
Empirical: $C_{12}H_{22}O_{11} \cdot H_2O$
Properties: Wh. fine cryst. powd.; sol. in water; insol. in alcohol; m.w. 360.31
Uses: Tablet/capsule diluent; used in parenterals, orals
Regulatory: FDA approved for parenterals, orals; USP, Ph.Eur., JP
Manuf./Distrib. (pharm. & food): Aldrich; Spectrum Chem. Mfg.

Lactosum. *See* Lactose
Laevosan. *See* Fructose
Laevulose. *See* Fructose
Lake bordeaux B. *See* D&C Red No. 34
Lake red C. *See* D&C Red No. 8

Lake red C Ba. *See* D&C Red No. 9

Landalgene
Uses: Used in orals
Regulatory: FDA approved for orals

Laneth-5
CAS 61791-20-6 (generic)
Synonyms: PEG-5 lanolin ether; POE (5) lanolin ether; PEG-5 lanolin alcohol
Definition: PEG ether of lanolin alcohol with avg. ethoxylation value of 5
Uses: Nonionic emulsifier, emollient, stabilizer, solubilizer, wetting agent, dispersant, conditioner for pharmaceuticals
Trade names: Polychol 5

Laneth-10
CAS 61791-20-6 (generic)
Synonyms: PEG-10 lanolin ether; POE (10) lanolin ether; PEG 500 lanolin ether
Definition: PEG ether of lanolin alcohol with avg. ethoxylation value of 10
Uses: Emulsifier, thickener
Trade names: Polychol 10

Laneth-15
CAS 61791-20-6 (generic); 84650-19-1
Synonyms: PEG-15 lanolin ether; POE (15) lanolin ether
Definition: PEG ether of lanolin alcohol with avg. ethoxylation value of 15
Uses: Nonionic emulsifier, emollient, stabilizer, solubilizer, wetting agent, dispersant, conditioner for topical pharmaceuticals
Trade names: Fancol LA-15; Polychol 15

Laneth-16
CAS 61791-20-6 (generic)
Synonyms: PEG-16 lanolin ether; POE (16) lanolin ether
Definition: PEG ether of lanolin alcohol with avg. ethoxylation value of 16
Uses: Emulsifier
Trade names containing: Ritachol® 3000

Laneth-20
CAS 61791-20-6 (generic)
Synonyms: PEG-20 lanolin ether; POE (20) lanolin ether; PEG 1000 lanolin ether
Definition: PEG ether of lanolin alcohol with avg. ethoxylation value of 20
Uses: Emulsifier, thickener
Trade names: Polychol 20

Laneth-25
CAS 61791-20-6 (generic)
Synonyms: PEG-25 lanolin ether; POE (25) lanolin ether
Definition: PEG ether of lanolin alcohol with avg. ethoxylation value of 25
Uses: Used in pharmaceuticals
Trade names containing: Solulan® 25

Laneth-40
CAS 61791-20-6 (generic)
Synonyms: PEG-40 lanolin ether; POE (40) lanolin ether; PEG 2000 lanolin ether
Definition: PEG ether of lanolin alcohol with avg. ethoxylation value of 40
Uses: Emulsifier, thickener
Trade names: Polychol 40

Laneth-10 acetate
CAS 65071-98-9 (generic)
Synonyms: Acetylated POE (10) lanolin alcohol; PEG-10 lanolin ether, acetylated; PEG 500 lanolin ether acetate
Definition: Acetylated ester of an ethoxylated ether of lanolin alcohol with avg. ethoxylation value of 10
Toxicology: May cause allergic contact skin rashes
Uses: Emulsifier used in topicals

Lanolic acids. *See* Lanolin acid

Lanolin
CAS 8006-54-0 (anhyd.); 8020-84-6 (hyd.); EINECS 232-348-6

Synonyms: Anhydrous lanolin; Adeps lanae; Wool wax; Wool fat
Definition: Deriv. of unctuous fatty sebaceous secretion of sheep, *Ovis aries*, consistg. of complex mixt. of esters of high m.w. aliphatic, steroid, or triterpenoid alcohol and fatty acids
Properties: Yel.-wh. semisolid; sol. in chloroform, ether; insol. in water; m.p. 38-42 C; iodine no. 18-36; flash pt. > 230 F
Precaution: Heated to decomp., emits acrid smoke and irritating fumes
Toxicology: Can cause allergic reactions, contact dermatitis
Uses: Emollient, ointment base, filler, emulsifier, vehicle; used in ophthalmics, topicals, suppositories; protectant in diaper rash, hemorrhoidal, and antibiotic ointments
Regulatory: FDA 21CFR §172.615, 175.300, 176.170, 176.210, 177.1200, 177.2600, 178.3910; Japan approved; FDA approved for ophthalmics, topicals; USP/NF, BP, Ph.Eur. compliance
Manuf./Distrib.: Amerchol; Croda; Henkel/Emery; RITA; Stevenson Cooper; Westbrook Lanolin
Manuf./Distrib. (pharm. & food): Aldrich; Croda; Integra; Ruger; Spectrum Chem. Mfg.
Trade names: Anhydrous Lanolin Grade 1; Anhydrous Lanolin Grade 2; Anhydrous Lanolin P.80; Anhydrous Lanolin P.95; Anhydrous Lanolin Superfine; Anhydrous Lanolin USP; Anhydrous Lanolin USP Cosmetic; Anhydrous Lanolin USP Cosmetic AA; Anhydrous Lanolin USP Cosmetic Grade; Anhydrous Lanolin USP Deodorized AAA; Anhydrous Lanolin USP Pharmaceutical; Anhydrous Lanolin USP Pharmaceutical; Anhydrous Lanolin USP Pharmaceutical Grade; Anhydrous Lanolin USP Pharmaceutical Light Grade; Anhydrous Lanolin USP Superfine; Anhydrous Lanolin USP Ultrafine; Anhydrous Lanolin USP X-tra Deodorized; Clearlan® 1650; Corona PNL; Corona Lanolin; Coronet Lanolin; Cosmetic Lanolin; Cosmetic Lanolin Anhydrous USP; Emery® 1650; Emery® 1656; Emery® 1660; Emery® HP-2050; Emery® HP-2060; Ivarlan™ Light; Lanolin Anhydrous USP; Lanolin Anhydrous USP; Lanolin Pharmaceutical; Lanolin U.S.P.; Lanolin USP; Medilan™; Pharmaceutical Lanolin; RITA Lanolin; Sorba; Super Corona Lanolin; Superfine Lanolin; White Swan; Yeoman
Trade names containing: Alcolan® 36W; Alcolan® 40; Amerchol® 400; Amerchol® BL; Amerchol® C; Amerchol® H-9; Cremba; Emery® 1740; Emery® 1747; Fancol CAB

Lanolin acid
CAS 68424-43-1; EINECS 270-302-7
Synonyms: Lanolic acids; Lanolin fatty acids; Acids, lanolin
Definition: Mixture of organic acids obtained from hydrolysis of lanolin
Uses: Emollient, stabilizer, emulsifier
Trade names: Fancor LFA

Lanolin alcohol
CAS 8027-33-6; EINECS 232-430-1
Synonyms: Alcohols, lanolin; Wool wax alcohol
Definition: Mixture of organic alcohols obtained from hydrolysis of lanolin
Properties: Amber waxy solid, char. odor; sol. in ether, chloroform; sl. sol. in alcohol; insol. in water; m.p. 56 C; acid no. 2 max.; sapon. no. 12 max.
Toxicology: Less likely to cause allergic reaction than lanolin
Uses: Emulsifier, solubilizer; used in ophthalmics, topicals
Regulatory: FDA approved for ophthalmics, topicals; USP/NF compliance
Manuf./Distrib.: ChemMark; Croda; Henkel/Emery; Heterene
Trade names: Fancol LA; Hartolan; Ritawax; Ritawax Super; Super Hartolan
Trade names containing: Alcolan®; Amerchol® 400; Amerchol® BL; Amerchol® C; Amerchol® CAB; Amerchol® H-9; Amerchol L-101®; Amerchol® L-500; Argobase 125T; Argobase EU; Argobase EUC 2; Cremba; Emery® 1732; Emery® 1747; Fancol CAB; Fancol LAO; Lexate® PX; Liquid Absorption Base Type A; Liquid Absorption Base Type T; Pionier® MAA; Protegin®; Protegin® X; Ritachol®

Lanolin, alcohols, acetates. *See* Acetylated lanolin alcohol
Lanolin fatty acids. *See* Lanolin acid
Lanolin fatty acids, isopropyl esters. *See* Isopropyl lanolate
Lanolin, hydrogenated. *See* Hydrogenated lanolin
Lanolin, hydroxylated. *See* Hydroxylated lanolin

Lanolin oil
CAS 8038-43-5; 70321-63-0; 8006-54-0; EINECS 274-559-6
Synonyms: Dewaxed lanolin; Oils, lanolin
Definition: Liq. fraction of lanolin obtained by physical means from whole lanolin
Toxicology: LD50 (rat, oral) > 20 g/kg; may cause allergic reactions, contact skin rashes
Uses: Ointment base, emollient, penetrant, superfatting agent for topical pharmaceuticals, ointments, creams, lotions
Manuf./Distrib.: ChemMark
Trade names: Fluilan; Lantrol® 1673; Lantrol® 1674; Lantrol® HP-2073; Lantrol® HP-2074; Ritalan®; Vigilan
Trade names containing: Emery® 1740

Lanolin wax

Lanolin wax
CAS 68201-49-0; EINECS 269-220-4
Synonyms: Deoiled lanolin
Definition: Semisolid fraction of lanolin obtained by physical means from whole lanolin
Uses: Emollient, lubricant, emulsifier, humectant, film-former for pharmaceuticals
Trade names: Fancor Lanwax; Lanfrax® 1776; Lanfrax® 1779

Lanosta-8,24-dien-3-ol, (3beta)-. *See* Lanosterol

Lanosterol
CAS 79-63-0; EINECS 201-214-9
Synonyms: Isocholesterol; Lanosta-8,24-dien-3-ol, (3beta)-
Classification: Sterol
Definition: Unsaturated sterol obtained from lanolin
Empirical: $C_{30}H_{50}O$
Properties: Cryst.; m.w. 426.70; m.p. 139-140 C
Uses: Used in topicals
Regulatory: FDA approved for topicals

Lard glyceride
CAS 61789-10-4; 97593-29-8; EINECS 263-032-6
Synonyms: Lard monoglyceride; Glycerides, lard mono-
Definition: Monoglyceride derived from lard
Uses: Emulsifier, stabilizer, dispersant
Trade names: Monomuls® 90-10

Lard glycerides
Synonyms: Lard mono-, di- and tri-glycerides
Definition: Mixture of mono-, di-, and triglycerides derived from lard
Properties: Wh. soft unctuous mass; insol. in water
Uses: Emulsifier, stabilizer, dispersant, opacifier for drug industry
Trade names: Monomuls® 60-10

Lard mono-, di- and tri-glycerides. *See* Lard glycerides
Lard monoglyceride. *See* Lard glyceride
Larixinic acid. *See* Maltol
Laughing gas. *See* Nitrous oxide
Lauraldehyde. *See* Lauric aldehyde

Lauralkonium chloride
CAS 139-07-1; EINECS 205-351-5
Synonyms: Lauryl dimethyl benzyl ammonium chloride; Benzyldimethyldodecylammonium chloride; N,N-Dimethyl-N-dodecylbenzenemethanaminium chloride; Dodecyl dimethyl benzyl ammonium chloride
Classification: Quaternary ammonium salt
Empirical: $C_{21}H_{38}N \cdot Cl$
Properties: M.w. 340.05
Toxicology: Skin and eye irritant; heated to decomp., emits very toxic fumes of NO_x, NH_3, and Cl^-
Uses: Germicide, disinfectant for medical/pharmaceutical applics.
Regulatory: FDA 21CFR §172.165 (limitation 0.25-1.0 ppm), 173.320 (0.05 ± 0.005 ppm), 175.105
Trade names: Catinal MB-50A

Lauramide DEA
CAS 120-40-1; 52725-64-1; EINECS 204-393-1
Synonyms: Lauric diethanolamide; N,N-Bis(2-hydroxyethyl)dodecanamide; Diethanolamine lauric acid amide
Definition: Mixture of ethanolamides of lauric acid
Empirical: $C_{16}H_{33}NO_3$
Formula: $CH_3(CH_2)_{10}CON(CH_2CH_2OH)_2$
Properties: M.w. 287.50
Toxicology: Moderately toxic by ingestion; may produce contact sensitivity
Uses: Emulsifier used in topical dermatological prods.
Regulatory: FDA 21CFR §172.710, 173.315, 175.105, 176.180, 176.210, 177.2260, 177.2800, 178.3130; FDA approved for topicals
Manuf./Distrib.: ABITEC; Chemron; Mona; Norman, Fox; Pilot; Protameen; Sandoz; Scher; Stepan; Witco/Oleo-Surf.

Lauramide/myristamide DEA
Synonyms: Lauric/myristic DEA; Lauric/myristic diethanolamide
Definition: Mixture of ethanolamides of a blend of lauric and myristic acids
Formula: RCO-N(CH_2CH_2OH)2, RCO- represents the lauric/myristic acid radical
Uses: Used in topicals
Regulatory: FDA approved for topicals

Lauramide/myristamide MEA
Synonyms: Lauric/myristic MEA; Lauric/myristic monoethanolamide
Definition: Mixture of ethanolamides of a blend of lauric and myrstic acids
Uses: Used in topicals
Regulatory: FDA approved for topicals

Lauramidopropyl betaine
CAS 4292-10-8; 86438-78-0; EINECS 224-292-6
Synonyms: N-(Carboxymethyl)N,N-dimethyl-3-[(1-oxododecyl)amino]-1-propanaminium hydroxide, inner salt
Classification: Zwitterion (inner salt)
Empirical: $C_{19}H_{38}N_2O_3$
Formula: $CH_3(CH_2)_{10}CONH(CH_2)_3N^+(CH_3)_2CH_2COO^-$
Uses: Surfactant
Trade names: Tego®-Betaine L-10 S

Lauramidopropyl PEG-dimonium chloride phosphate
CAS 83682-78-4
Uses: Bactericide, emulsifier, solubilizer, dispersant, thickener, wetting agent
Trade names: Phospholipid PTD

Lauramine oxide
CAS 1643-20-5; 70592-80-2; EINECS 216-700-6
Synonyms: Lauryl dimethylamine oxide; N,N-Dimethyl-1-dodecanamine-N-oxide
Classification: Tertiary amine oxide
Empirical: $C_{14}H_{31}NO$
Uses: Thickener, emollient used in topicals; foaming agent for surgical scrubs
Regulatory: FDA approved for topicals
Trade names: Empigen® OB

Laurdimonium hydroxypropyl hydrolyzed collagen

Laureth-2
CAS 3055-93-4 (generic); 9002-92-0; 68002-97-1; 68439-50-9; EINECS 221-279-7
Synonyms: Diethylene glycol dodecyl ether; PEG-2 lauryl ether; 2-[2-(Dodecyloxy)ethoxy]ethanol
Definition: PEG ether of lauryl alcohol
Empirical: $C_{16}H_{34}O_3$
Formula: $CH_3(CH_2)_{10}CH_2(OCH_2CH_2)_nOH$, avg. n = 2
Uses: Thickener, emulsifier, solubilizer
Trade names: Arlypon® F; Britex L 20; Dehydol® LS 2 DEO

Laureth-3
CAS 3055-94-5; 9002-92-0 (generic); 68002-97-1; 68439-50-9; EINECS 221-280-2
Synonyms: Triethylene glycol dodecyl ether; 2-[2-[2-(Dodecyloxy)ethoxy]ethoxy]ethanol; PEG-3 lauryl ether
Definition: PEG ether of lauryl alcohol
Empirical: $C_{18}H_{38}O_4$
Formula: $CH_3(CH_2)_{10}CH_2(OCH_2CH_2)_nOH$, avg. n = 3
Uses: Emulsifier, solubilizer
Trade names: Dehydol® LS 3 DEO

Laureth-4
CAS 5274-68-0; 68002-97-1; 68439-50-9; EINECS 226-097-1
Synonyms: PEG-4 lauryl ether; PEG 200 lauryl ether; 3,6,9,12-Tetraoxatetracosan-1-ol
Definition: PEG ether of lauryl alcohol
Empirical: $C_{20}H_{42}O_5$
Formula: $CH_3(CH_2)_{10}CH_2(OCH_2CH_2)_nOH$, avg. n = 4
Uses: Lubricant, emollient, emulsifier, solubilizer used in topicals
Regulatory: FDA 21CFR §178.3520; FDA approved for topicals
Trade names: Britex L 40; Dehydol® LS 4 DEO; Ethosperse® LA-4; Rhodasurf® L-4; Simulsol® P4

Laureth-6
CAS 3055-96-7; EINECS 221-282-3
Synonyms: PEG-6 lauryl ether; POE (6) lauryl ether; 3,6,9,12,15,18-Hexaoxatriacontan-1-ol
Definition: PEG ether of lauryl alcohol
Empirical: $C_{24}H_{50}O_7$
Formula: $CH_3(CH_2)_{10}CH_2(OCH_2CH_2)_nOH$, avg. n = 6
Uses: Emulsifier, wetting agent
Trade names: Dehydol® PID 6

Laureth-7
CAS 3055-97-8; 9002-92-0 (generic); EINECS 221-283-9
Synonyms: PEG-7 lauryl ether; POE (6) lauryl ether; 3,6,9,12,15,18,21-Heptaoxatritriacontan-1-ol
Definition: PEG ether of lauryl alcohol
Empirical: $C_{26}H_{54}O_8$
Formula: $CH_3(CH_2)_{10}CH_2(OCH_2CH_2)_nOH$, avg. n = 7
Uses: Emulsifier for antibiotic gels
Trade names containing: Sepigel 305

Laureth-10
CAS 6540-99-4; 9002-92-0 (generic);; EINECS FDA 21CFR §177.2800
Synonyms: PEG-10 lauryl ether; POE (10) lauryl ether; 3,6,9,12,15,18,21,24,27,30-Dexaoxadotetracontan-1-ol
Definition: PEG ether of lauryl alcohol
Empirical: $C_{32}H_{66}O_{11}$
Formula: $CH_3(CH_2)_{10}CH_2(OCH_2CH_2)_nOH$, avg. n = 10
Uses: Emulsifier
Trade names: Britex L 100

Laureth-12
CAS 3056-00-6; 9002-92-0 (generic); EINECS 221-286-5
Synonyms: PEG-12 lauryl ether; POE (12) lauryl ether; PEG 600 lauryl ether
Definition: PEG ether of lauryl alcohol
Empirical: $C_{36}H_{64}O_{13}$
Formula: $CH_3(CH_2)_{10}CH_2(OCH_2CH_2)_nOH$, avg. n = 12
Properties: M.w. 1199.57; m.p. 41-45 C; b.p. 100 C; flash pt. > 110 C
Uses: Emulsifier for pharmaceutical uses; anti-irritant in deodorants and antiperspirants
Regulatory: FDA 21CFR §177.2800
Trade names: Ethosperse® LA-12

Laureth-23
CAS 9002-92-0 (generic)
Synonyms: PEG-23 lauryl ether; POE (23) lauryl ether
Definition: PEG ether of lauryl alcohol
Formula: $CH_3(CH_2)_{10}CH_2(OCH_2CH_2)_nOH$, avg. n = 23
Uses: Emollient, emulsifier, thickener, stabilizer; used in topicals; anti-irritant in deodorants and antiperspirants
Regulatory: FDA 21CFR §177.2800; FDA approved for topicals
Trade names: Britex L 230; Ethosperse® LA-23; Rhodasurf® L-25; Simulsol® P23
Trade names containing: Cerasynt® 945

Laureth-2 acetate
CAS 32289-26-2
Synonyms: PEG-2 lauryl ether acetate; PEG 100 lauryl ether acetate; POE (2) lauryl ether acetate
Definition: Ester of laureth-2 and acetic acid
Formula: $CH_3(CH_2)_{10}CH_2(OCH_2CH_2)_nOCOCH_3$, avg. n = 2
Properties: Liq.; sol. in ethanol; disp. in water
Uses: Emollient, coupling agent for pharmaceutical topicals
Trade names: Pelemol® L2A

Laureth-5 carboxylic acid, sodium salt. *See* Sodium laureth-5 carboxylate

Lauric acid
CAS 143-07-7; EINECS 205-582-1
FEMA 2614
Synonyms: n-Dodecanoic acid; Dodecanoic acid; Dodecoic acid
Classification: Fatty acid

Empirical: $C_{12}H_{24}O_2$
Formula: $CH_3(CH_2)_{10}COOH$
Properties: Colorless needles; insol. in water; sol. in benzene and ether; m.w. 200.36; dens. 0.833; m.p. 44 C; b.p. 225 (100 mm); ref. index 1.4323 (45 C)
Precaution: Combustible when exposed to het or flame; reactive with oxidizing materials
Toxicology: LD50 (oral, rat) 12 g/kg; poison by intravenous route; mildly toxic by ingestion; mutagenic data; heated to decomp., emits acrid smoke and irritating fumes
Uses: Lubricant, emulsifier; pharmaceutical intermediate
Regulatory: FDA 21CFR §172.210, 172.860, 173.340, 175.105, 175.320, 176.170, 176.200, 176.210, 177.1010, 177.1200, 177.2260, 177.2600, 177.2800, 178.3570, 178.3910; FEMA GRAS
Manuf./Distrib.: Akzo Nobel; Aldrich; Brown; Condor; Henkel/Emery; Mirachem Srl; Penta Mfg.; Spectrum Chem. Mfg.; Unichema; Welch, Holme & Clark; Witco/Oleo-Surf.
Manuf./Distrib. (pharm. & food): Acme-Hardesty; Aldrich
Trade names: Hystrene® 9512; Philacid 1200

Lauric acid, 1,2-ethanediyl ester. *See* Glycol dilaurate
Lauric acid triglyceride. *See* Trilaurin

Lauric aldehyde
CAS 112-54-9; EINECS 203-983-6
FEMA 2615
Synonyms: Aldehyde C-12; Aldehyde C-12 lauric; Dodecanal; n-Dodecyl aldehyde; Lauryl aldehyde; Laurinaldehyde; Lauraldehyde
Empirical: $C_{12}H_{24}O$
Formula: $CH_3(CH_2)_{10}CHO$
Properties: Colorless to yel. liq., char. fatty odor; m.w. 184.32; dens. 0.830 (20/4 C); b.p. 237 C; flash pt. 101 C; ref. index 1.435 (20 C)
Toxicology: Skin irritant
Uses: Sweet synthetic flavoring agent
Regulatory: FDA 21CFR §172.515; FEMA GRAS
Manuf./Distrib. (pharm. & food): Aldrich

Lauric diethanolamide. *See* Lauramide DEA
Lauric/myristic DEA. *See* Lauramide/myristamide DEA
Lauric/myristic diethanolamide. *See* Lauramide/myristamide DEA
Lauric/myristic MEA. *See* Lauramide/myristamide MEA
Lauric/myristic monoethanolamide. *See* Lauramide/myristamide MEA
Laurinaldehyde. *See* Lauric aldehyde

Lauroyl sarcosine
CAS 97-78-9; EINECS 202-608-3
Synonyms: N-Methyl-N-(1-oxododecyl) glycine
Definition: N-lauryl deriv. of N-methylglycine
Empirical: $C_{15}H_{29}NO_3$
Formula: $CH_3(CH_2)_{10}CONCH_3CH_2COOH$
Toxicology: No known toxicity
Uses: Emulsifier used in dentifrices, pharmaceuticals
Regulatory: FDA 21CFR §177.1200, 178.3130
Manuf./Distrib.: Chemplex; Hampshire; R.T. Vanderbilt
Trade names: Sarkosyl® L

N-Lauroylsarcosine sodium salt. *See* Sodium lauroyl sarcosinate

Laurtrimonium chloride
CAS 112-00-5; EINECS 203-927-0
Synonyms: Lauryl trimethyl ammonium chloride; Dodecyl trimethyl ammonium chloride; N,N,N-Trimethyl-1-dodecanaminium chloride
Classification: Quaternary ammonium salt
Empirical: $C_{15}H_{34}N \cdot Cl$
Precaution: Nonflammable
Uses: Bactericide for antiseptics
Regulatory: USA permitted; JSCI, Europe listed
Trade names: Empigen® 5089

Lauryl acetate
CAS 112-66-3
FEMA 2616

Lauryl alcohol

Synonyms: Acetate C-12; Dodecanyl acetate; Dodecyl acetate
Empirical: $C_{14}H_{28}O_2$
Properties: Colorless liq., citrus-rose odor; sol. in most org. solvs.; m.w. 228.38; dens. 0.865; b.p. 150 C 915 mm); flash pt. > 230 F
Uses: Citrus synthetic flavoring agent
Regulatory: FDA 21CFR §172.515; FEMA GRAS
Manuf./Distrib. (pharm. & food): Aldrich

Lauryl alcohol

CAS 112-53-8; 68526-86-3; EINECS 203-982-0
FEMA 2617
Synonyms: 1-Dodecanol; Dodecan-1-ol; C-12 linear primary alcohol; Alcohol C-12; Dodecyl alcohol
Classification: Fatty alcohol
Empirical: $C_{12}H_{26}O$
Formula: $CH_3(CH_2)_{10}CH_2OH$
Properties: Colorless leaflets, liq. above 21 C, floral odor; insol. in water; sol. in alcohol, ether; m.w. 186.33; dens. 0.8309 (24/4 C); m.p. 24 C; b.p. 259 C (760 mm); flash pt. (CC) > 212 F; ref. index 1.440-1.444
Precaution: Combustible; reactive with oxidizing materials
Toxicology: LD50 (oral, rat) 12,800 mg/kg; moderately toxic by intraperitoneal route; mildly toxic by ingestion; severe human skin irritant; heated to decomp., emits acrid smoke and irritating fumes
Uses: Honey, coconut-like synthetic flavoring agent; mfg. of sulfuric acid esters, pharmaceuticals
Regulatory: FDA 21CFR §172.515, 172.864, 175.105, 175.300, 177.1010, 177.1200, 177.2800, 178.3480, 178.3910; FEMA GRAS; BP compliance
Manuf./Distrib.: Albemarle; Aldrich; M. Michel; Penta Mfg.; Procter & Gamble; Schweizerhall; Spectrum Chem. Mfg.; Vista
Manuf./Distrib. (pharm. & food): Aldrich
Trade names: Cachalot® L-90; Nacol® 12-96; Nacol® 12-99; Unihydag Wax 12

Lauryl aldehyde. *See* Lauric aldehyde

Lauryl behenate

CAS 42233-07-8
Synonyms: Dodecyl docosanoate; Docosanoic acid dodecyl ester
Definition: Ester of lauryl alcohol and behenic acid
Empirical: $C_{34}H_{68}O_2$
Uses: Pharmaceutical topicals
Trade names: Pelemol® LB

Lauryl dimethylamine. *See* Dimethyl lauramine
Lauryl dimethylamine oxide. *See* Lauramine oxide
Lauryl dimethyl benzyl ammonium chloride. *See* Lauralkonium chloride
Lauryl gallate. *See* Dodecyl gallate

Lauryl lactate

CAS 6283-92-7; EINECS 228-504-8
Synonyms: Dodecyl 2-hydroxypropanoate; 2-Hydroxypropanoic acid, dodecyl ester
Definition: Ester of lauryl alcohol and lactic acid
Empirical: $C_{15}H_{30}O_3$
Formula: $CH_3COHHCOOCH_2(CH_2)_{10}CH_3$
Properties: Lt. yel. liq., faint char. odor; sol. in oil, ethanol, propylene glycol, IPM, oleyl alcohol; insol. in water; sp.gr. 0.910-0.922; ref. index 1.4417-1.4456
Toxicology: LD50 (rat, oral) > 20 ml/kg; nonirritating to eyes, mildly irritating to skin
Uses: Emollient, lubricant for topical pharmaceuticals; antitack agent in antiperspirants
Trade names: Ceraphyl® 31

Lauryl/stearyl thiodipropionate

Uses: Antioxidant
Trade names: Mark® 5095

Lauryl sulfate

CAS 151-41-7
Uses: Used in orals
Regulatory: FDA approved for orals

Lauryl trimethyl ammonium chloride. *See* Laurtrimonium chloride
Lavender flowers oil. *See* Lavender oil

Lavender oil
CAS 8000-28-0
FEMA 2622
Synonyms: Lavendula officinalis oil; Lavender flowers oil
Definition: Volatile oil obtained from flowers of *Lavendula officinalis*, contg. linalyl acetate, linalool, pinene, limonene, geraniol, etc.
Properties: Colorless to yel. liq., camphor-lavender odor; sol. in 4 vols 70% alcohol; misc. with abs. alcohol, CS_2; sl. sol. in water; dens. 0.875-0.888; ref. index 1.459-1.470 (20 C)
Precaution: Keep cool, well closed; protect from light
Toxicology: LD50 (oral, rat) 9040 mg/kg; mildly toxic by ingestion; skin irritant; may cause adverse skin reactions when the skin is exposed to sunlight; can cause allergic reaction; heated to decomp., emits acrid smoke and irritating fumes
Uses: Colorant, flavoring agent; odor masking for unpleasant odors in ointments; carminative; perfumes; used in topicals, mouthwashes, dentifrices; externally as insect repellent
Usage level: 0.5 mg/kg considered safe oral dose
Regulatory: FDA 21CFR §182.10, 182.20, GRAS; 27CFR §21.65, 21.151; FEMA GRAS; Japan approved; FDA approved for topicals
Manuf./Distrib.: Spectrum Chem. Mfg.
Manuf./Distrib. (pharm. & food): C.A.L.-Pfizer; Chart; Pierre Chauvet; Florida Treatt; Ruger

Lavendula officinalis oil. *See* Lavender oil

Lecithin
CAS 8002-43-5; 8029-76-3; 8030-76-0; 97281-47-5; EINECS 232-307-2
Synonyms: Soya lecithin
Definition: Mixture of the diglycerides of stearic, palmitic and oleic acids linked to the choline ester of phosphoric acid; found in plants and animals
Formula: $C_8H_{17}O_5NRR'$, R and R' are fatty acid groups
Properties: Nearly wh. to yel. or brn. waxy mass or thick fluid, nutlike odor, bland taste; insol. but swells in water and salt sol'ns.; sol. in chloroform, ether, petrol. ether, min. oils, fatty acids; dens. 1.0305 (24/4 C); sapon. no. 196
Toxicology: May cause bronchoconstriction in people with asthma; heated to decomp., emits acrid smoke and irritating fumes
Uses: Edible surfactant, emulsifier, stabilizer, solubilizer, wetting agent, emollient for pharmaceuticals; used in liposome technology, orals, topicals; nutritional in gel capsules and tablet form; binding agent in tableting; choline source in dementia
Regulatory: FDA 21CFR §133.169, 133.173, 133.179, 136.110, 136.115, 136.130, 137.160, 136.165, 136.180, 163.123, 163.130, 163.135, 163.140, 163.145, 163.150, 163.155, 166.40, 166.110, 169.115, 169.140, 169.150, 175.300, 184.1400, GRAS;; USDA 9CFR §318.7, 0.5% max. in oleomargarine, 381.147; Japan approved; Europe listed; UK approved; FDA approved for orals, topicals; USP/NF compliance
Manuf./Distrib.: ADM Lecithin; Am. Lecithin; Central Soya; W.A. Cleary; Great Western; Landers-Segal Color; Lucas Meyer GmbH; Penta Mfg.; Reichhold; Solvay Duphar BV; Spice King; U.S. Biochemical
Manuf./Distrib. (pharm. & food): ADM Lecithin; Am. Lecithin; Am. Roland; D F Anstead; CanAmera Foods; Central Soya; W A Cleary; K&K Greeff; Grünau; A C Hatrick; Lucas Meyer GmbH; Penta Mfg.; Quest UK; Rhone-Poulenc; Riken Vitamin; Ruger; Siber Hegner; Spectrum Chem. Mfg.; Stern-France; Vamo Mills; Westin
Trade names: Alcolec® Granules; Asol; Capcithin™; Capsulec 51-SB; Capsulec 51-UB; Capsulec 56-SB; Capsulec 56-UB; Capsulec 62-SB; Capsulec 62-UB; Centrolex® F; Centrolex® P; Dulectin; Emulmetik™ 970; Lecigran™ 5750; Lecigran™ 6750; Lecigran™ A; Lecigran™ F; Lecigran™ M; PhosPho F-97; PhosPho LCN-TS; Phospholipon® 80; Phospholipon® 90; Phospholipon® 90 G; Phospholipon® 100, 100G; Yelkin F; Yelkin G; Yelkin P
Trade names containing: Annatto OS #2894; Lecigran™ C; Lecigran™ Super A; Lecigran™ T; Natipide® II; Natipide® II PG; Oxynex® LM; Paramount C; Phosal® 50 SA; Phosal® 53 MCT; Phosal® 60 PG; Phosal® 75 SA; Phosal® NAT-50-PG

Lecithin, hydrogenated. *See* Hydrogenated lecithin
Lecithin, hydroxylated. *See* Hydroxylated lecithin
Lemon balm. *See* Balm mint

Lemon extract
CAS 8008-56-8; 84929-31-7
FEMA 2623
Synonyms: Citrus limon extract
Definition: Extract of the lemon, *Citrus limon*

583

Lemongrass oil East Indian

Properties: Char. lemon-leaf odor, sour bitter taste
Uses: Natural flavoring agent; ingred. in sun protection prods.
Regulatory: FDA 21CFR §182.20, GRAS; FEMA GRAS; Japan approved (lemon)
Trade names containing: Uninontan U 34

Lemongrass oil East Indian
FEMA 2624
Synonyms: Cochin; East Indian lemongrass oil
Definition: Oil from steam distillation of grasses of *Cymbopogon flexosus* and *Andropogon nardus*, contg. citral
Properties: Dk. yel. to brn.-red liq., heavy lemon odor; sol. in min. oil, propylene glycol, alcohol; insol. in water, glycerin; dens. 0.894-0.902; ref. index 1.483
Precaution: Protect from light
Toxicology: LD50 (oral, rat) 5600 mg/kg; mildly toxic by ingestion; skin irritant; heated to decomp, emits acrid smoke and irritating fumes
Uses: Natural flavoring agent, carminative
Regulatory: FDA 21CFR §182.20, GRAS; FEMA GRAS; Europe listed, no restrictions
Manuf./Distrib. (pharm. & food): Chart; Florida Treatt

Lemongrass oil West Indian
CAS 8007-02-1; EINECS 289-752-0 (extract)
FEMA 2624
Synonyms: West Indian lemongrass oil; Guatemala lemongrass oil; Madagascar lemongrass oil
Definition: Volatile oil from steam distillation of fresh *Cymbopogon citratus* grasses
Properties: Lt. yel. to brn. liq., lt. lemon odor; sol. in min. oil, propylene glycol; insol. in water; dens. 0.869-0.894; ref. index 1.483
Precaution: Keep cool, well closed; protect from light
Toxicology: Skin irritant; heated to decomp., emits acrid smoke and irritating fumes
Uses: Natural flavoring agent, carminative
Regulatory: FDA 21CFR §182.20, GRAS; FEMA GRAS; Europe listed, no restrictions
Manuf./Distrib. (pharm. & food): Florida Treatt

Lemon juice
CAS 68916-88-1
Definition: Liq. expressed from the fresh pulp of *Citrus limon*
Toxicology: Can cause allergic reactions
Uses: Natural flavoring agent used in orals; tonic, refrigerant, antisorbutic
Regulatory: FDA 21CFR §182.20, GRAS; FDA approved for orals
Manuf./Distrib. (pharm. & food): Vicente Trapani SA

Lemon oil
CAS 8008-56-8; 84929-31-7
FEMA 2625
Synonyms: Citrus limon oil; Cedro oil
Definition: Volatile oil expressed from the fresh peel of fruit of *Citrus limon*, contg. limonene, terpinene, phellandrene, pinene
Properties: Pale yel. to greenish-yel. liq., lemon peel odor and taste; misc. with dehydrated alcohol, CS_2, glac. acetic acid; sl. sol. in water; dens. 0.849-0.855 (25/25 C); ref. index 1.4742-1.4755 (20 C)
Precaution: Keep cool, well closed; protect from light; do not use if terebinthine odor can be detected
Toxicology: LD50 (oral, rat) 2840 mg/kg; mod. toxic by ingestion; experimental tumorigen; skin irritant; heated to decomp., emits acrid smoke and irritating fumes
Uses: Natural flavoring agent; used in orals, topicals; mfg. of terpeneless lemon oil
Usage level: ADI 500 µg/kg (WHO)
Regulatory: FDA 21CFR §146.114, 146.120, 146.121, 146.126, 161.190, 182.20, GRAS; FEMA GRAS; Europe listed, no restrictions; FDA approved for orals, topicals; BP, Ph.Eur. compliance
Manuf./Distrib. (pharm. & food): Commodity Services; Florida Treatt; Ruger; Spectrum Chem. Mfg.

Levomenol
CAS 23089-26-1
Synonyms: (-)-α-Bisabolol; (-)-6-Methyl-2-(4-methyl-3-cyclohexen-1-yl)-5-hepten-2-ol
Empirical: $C_{15}H_{26}O$
Properties: M.w. 222.4
Uses: Transepidermal penetration enhancer for topicals

Levulic acid. *See* Levulinic acid

Levulinic acid
CAS 123-76-2; EINECS 204-649-2

FEMA 2627; UN No. 1759
Synonyms: γ-Ketovaleric acid; 4-Oxo-n-valeric acid; Acetylpropionic acid; β-Acetylpropionic acid; 3-Acetylpropionic acid; 4-Oxopentanoic acid; Levulic acid
Empirical: $C_5H_8O_3$
Formula: $CH_3COCH_2CH_2COOH$
Properties: Yel. plates or leaflets; freely sol. in water, alcohol, ether; insol. in aliphatic hydrocarbons; m.w. 116.12; dens. 1.1447; m.p. 33-35 C; b.p. 245-246 C; flash pt. ≈ 98 C; ref. index 1.442 (16 C)
Precaution: Light-sensitive
Uses: Synthetic flavoring agent; intermediate for pharmaceuticals
Regulatory: FDA 21CFR §172.515; FEMA GRAS
Manuf./Distrib.: Aldrich; Chemie Linz UK Ltd; Otsuka Chem.; Penta Mfg.; QO; Schweizerhall; Spectrum Chem. Mfg.
Manuf./Distrib. (pharm. & food): Aldrich; Otsuka Chem.; Penta Mfg.
Trade names: Unichem Levula

Levulose. *See* Fructose
Licareol. *See* Linalool
Lichenic acid. *See* Fumaric acid

Licorice
CAS 68916-91-6
Synonyms: Glyccyrrhiza; Licorice root; Liquorice
Definition: Dried rhizome and roots of *Glycyrrhiza glabra*
Uses: Natural flavoring agent, flavor enhancer; strong lingering sweet taste; counteracts excessive saltiness
Regulatory: FDA 21CFR §184.1408, GRAS; not permitted as nonnutritive sweetener in sugar substitutes; Japan approved; BP, Ph.Eur. compliance
Manuf./Distrib. (pharm. & food): Biddle Sawyer; Bio-Botanica; Arthur Branwell; Chart; Cornelius; Dr Madis Labs; Mafco Worldwide; Maruzen Fine Chems.; Meer; MLG Enterprises; Penta Mfg.; Rhone-Poulenc; Roeper; W Ruitenberg; E H Worlee GmbH

Licorice extract
CAS 97676-23-8; 84775-66-6
FEMA 2628
Synonyms: Glycyrrhiza glabra extract; Glycyrrhiza extract
Definition: Extract of *Glycyrrhiza glabra* and other species
Uses: Natural flavoring agent, flavor enhancer; expectorant in cough preps.; sun care and eye care prods.
Regulatory: FDA 21CFR §184.1408; FEMA GRAS; Japan approved
Manuf./Distrib.: Bio-Botanica
Manuf./Distrib. (pharm. & food): Chart
Trade names containing: Biophytex®

Licorice root. *See* Licorice

Lidocaine
CAS 137-58-6
Synonyms: α-Diethylaminoaceto-2,6-xylidide
Formula: $C_6H_3(CH_3)_2NHCOCH_2N(C_2H_5)_2$
Uses: Anesthetic/analgesic in mouth pain and cold sore prods.
Manuf./Distrib.: Atomergic Chemetals; R.W. Greeff; Wyckoff

Lidofenin
CAS 59160-29-1
Uses: Used in injectables
Regulatory: FDA approved for injectables

Light magnesium carbonate. *See* Magnesium carbonate
Light mineral oil. *See* Mineral oil
Lignocaine benzyl benzoate. *See* Denatonium benzoate
Lilyl aldehyde. *See* Hydroxycitronellal
Lime. *See* Calcium oxide
Lime acetate. *See* Calcium acetate
Lime citrate. *See* Calcium citrate

Lime oil
CAS 8008-26-2
FEMA 2631
Synonyms: Lime oil, distilled

Lime oil, distilled

Definition: Oil from *Citrus aurantifolia*
Properties: Intensely fresh citrus aroma, astringent sweet-sour flavor
Uses: Natural flavoring agent; used in orals
Regulatory: FDA 21CFR §182.20, GRAS; FEMA GRAS; Japan approved (lime); Europe listed, no restrictions; FDA approved for orals
Manuf./Distrib. (pharm. & food): Chart; Pierre Chauvet; Commodity Services; Florida Treatt

Lime oil, distilled. *See* Lime oil
Lime-tree extract. *See* Linden extract
Lime water. *See* Calcium hydroxide
(±)-Limonene. *See* dl-Limonene

d-Limonene
CAS 5989-27-5; EINECS 227-813-5
FEMA 2633
Synonyms: d-p-Mentha-1,8-diene; Cinene; Dipentene; Cajeputene; Kautschin; R(+)-Limonene; (+)-Carvene; (R)-4-Isopropenyl-1-methyl-1-cyclohexene
Classification: Terpene
Empirical: $C_{10}H_{16}$
Properties: Colorless liq., citrus odor; insol. in water; misc. with alcohol and ether; m.w. 136.26; dens. 0.8411 (20 C); b.p. 176-176.4 C; ref. index 1.471
Toxicology: LD50 (oral, rat) 4400 mg/kg; poison by IV route; mod. toxic by intraperitoneal route; mildly toxic by ingestion; skin irritant; experimental tumorigen, reproductive effects; heated to decomp., emits acrid smoke and irritating fumes
Uses: Citrus synthetic flavoring agent
Regulatory: FDA 21CFR §182.60, GRAS; FEMA GRAS
Manuf./Distrib.: Aldrich; Allchem Industries; Int'l. Flavors & Fragrances; Langley Smith Ltd; Penta Mfg.; SCM Glidco Organics
Manuf./Distrib. (pharm. & food): Aldrich; Allchem Industries; Int'l. Flavors & Fragrances; Penta Mfg.

dl-Limonene
CAS 138-86-3; EINECS 205-341-0
UN No. 2052
Synonyms: Dipentene; Cinene; Cajeputene; Inactive limonene; (±)-Limonene
Empirical: $C_{10}H_{16}$
Properties: Colorless liq., pleasant lemon-like odor; misc. with alcohol; pract. insol. in water; m.w. 136.23; dens. 0.847 (15.5/15.5 C); m.p. -96.9 C; b.p. 175-176 C (763 mm); ref. index 1.4744
Precaution: DOT: Flamm. liq.
Toxicology: LD50 (oral, rat) 5000 mg/kg; skin irritant and sensitizer
Uses: Used in topicals
Regulatory: FDA 21CFR §175.105, 177.2600, 182.60, GRAS; FDA approved for topicals
Manuf./Distrib.: Aldrich; Arizona; Hercules; Penta Mfg.; SCM Glidco Organics; Spectrum Chem. Mfg.; Veitsiluoto Oy
Manuf./Distrib. (pharm. & food): Penta Mfg.

Linalol. *See* Linalool

Linalool
CAS 78-70-6; EINECS 201-134-4
FEMA 2635
Synonyms: 2,6-Dimethyl-2,7-octadien-6-ol; 3,7-Dimethyl-1,6-octadien-3-ol; Licareol; Linalyl alcohol; Linalol
Classification: Terpene
Empirical: $C_{10}H_{18}O$
Properties: Colorless liq., odor similar to Bergamot oil, French lavender; sol. in alcohol, ether, fixed oils, propylene glycol; insol. in glycerin; m.w. 154.28; dens. 0.858-0.868; b.p. 195-199 C; flash pt. 172 F; ref. index 1.461
Toxicology: LD50 (oral, rat) 2790 mg/kg; mod. toxic by ingestion, mildly toxic by skin contact; skin irritant; heated to decomp., emits acrid smoke and irritating fumes
Uses: Citrus synthetic flavoring agent; raw material in synthesis of isophytol and vitamin E
Regulatory: FDA 21CFR §182.60, GRAS; FEMA GRAS; Japan approved as flavoring; BP compliance
Manuf./Distrib.: Aldrich; BASF
Manuf./Distrib. (pharm. & food): Aldrich; BASF; Florida Treatt
Trade names: Linalool 95

Linalyl acetate
CAS 115-95-7; EINECS 204-116-4

FEMA 2636
Synonyms: 3,7-Dimethyl-1,6-octadien-3-ol acetate; 3,7-Dimethyl-1,6-octadien-3-yl acetate; Bergamiol; Bergamol
Definition: Ester of linalool and acetic acid
Empirical: $C_{12}H_{20}O_2$
Formula: $CH_3COOC_{10}H_{17}$
Properties: Colorless clear oily liq., bergamot odor; sol. in alcohol, ether, diethyl phthalate, benzyl benzoate, min. oil, fixed oils; sl. sol. in propylene glycol; insol. water; m.w. 196.32; dens. 0.898-0.914; b.p. 108-110 C; flash pt. 185 F; ref. index 1.4500
Precaution: Combustible
Toxicology: LD50 (oral, rat) 14,550 mg/kg; mildly toxic by ingestion; heated to decomp., emits acrid smoke and irritating fumes
Uses: Pear-like synthetic flavoring agent
Regulatory: FDA 21CFR §182.60, GRAS; FEMA GRAS; Japan approved as flavoring
Manuf./Distrib.: Aldrich; BASF
Manuf./Distrib. (pharm. & food): Aldrich; BASF; Florida Treatt

Linalyl alcohol. *See* Linalool
Linalyl 2-aminobenzoate. *See* Linalyl anthranilate

Linalyl anthranilate
FEMA 2637
Synonyms: 3,7-Dimethyl-1,6-octadien-3-yl anthranilate; Linalyl 2-aminobenzoate
Empirical: $C_{17}H_{23}NO_2$
Properties: Liq., sweet orange-like flavor; sol. in alcohol; insol. in water; m.w. 273.38; b.p. 350 C; ref. index 1.4970
Uses: Synthetic flavoring agent
Regulatory: FDA 21CFR §172.515; FEMA GRAS

Linalyl butyrate
CAS 78-36-4
FEMA 2639
Synonyms: Linalyl-n-butyrate
Empirical: $C_{14}H_{24}O2$
Properties: Colorless or ylsh. liq., fruity banana odor; m.w. 224.34; dens. 0.8890-0.8903; b.p. 232 C; flash pt. > 100 C; ref. index 1.4510-1.4560 (20 C)
Uses: Synthetic flavoring agent
Regulatory: FDA 21CFR §172.515; FEMA GRAS
Manuf./Distrib. (pharm. & food): Aldrich

Linalyl-n-butyrate. *See* Linalyl butyrate

Linalyl cinnamate
FEMA 2641
Synonyms: Linalyl 3-phenylpropenoate
Empirical: $C_{19}H_{24}O_2$
Properties: Colorless liq., soft floral odor, fruity flavor; sol. in alcohol; insol. in water; m.w. 284.40
Uses: Synthetic flavoring agent
Regulatory: FDA 21CFR §172.515; FEMA GRAS

Linalyl formate
CAS 115-99-1
FEMA 2642
Synonyms: 3,7-Dimethyl-1,6-octadien-3-yl formate
Empirical: $C_{11}H_{18}O_2$
Properties: M.w. 182.27; dens. 0.914; b.p. 100-103 C (10 mm); flash pt. 186 F
Uses: Citrus synthetic flavoring agent
Regulatory: FDA 21CFR §172.515; FEMA GRAS
Manuf./Distrib. (pharm. & food): Aldrich

Linalyl isovalerate
CAS 1118-27-0
FEMA 2646
Empirical: $C_{15}H_{26}O_2$
Properties: M.w. 238.37
Uses: Apple-like synthetic flavoring agent

Linalyl 3-phenylpropenoate

Regulatory: FDA 21CFR §172.515; FEMA GRAS
Manuf./Distrib. (pharm. & food): Aldrich

Linalyl 3-phenylpropenoate. See Linalyl cinnamate

Linalyl propionate
CAS 144-39-8
FEMA 2645
Synonyms: 3,7-Dimethyl-2,6-octadien-3-yl propionate
Empirical: $C_{13}H_{22}O_2$
Properties: M.w. 210.32
Uses: Pear-like synthetic flavoring agent
Regulatory: FDA 21CFR §172.515; FEMA GRAS
Manuf./Distrib. (pharm. & food): Aldrich

Linden extract
CAS 84929-52-2
Synonyms: Lime-tree extract; Tilia cordata extract
Definition: Extract of the flowers of the linden tree, Tilia cordata or T. europa
Toxicology: No known toxicity
Uses: Natural flavoring
Regulatory: FDA 21CFR §172.510; Japan approved
Manuf./Distrib.: Bio-Botanica

Linear C10 alpha olefin. See Decene-1

Linoleic acid
CAS 60-33-3; EINECS 200-470-9
Synonyms: 9,12-Octadecadienoic acid; (Z,Z)-9,12-Octadecadienoic acid; Linolic acid
Classification: Unsaturated essential fatty acid
Empirical: $C_{18}H_{32}O_2$
Formula: $CH_3(CH_2)_4=CHCH_2CH=CH(CH_2)_7COOH$
Properties: Colorless to pale yel. oil; freely sol. in ether; sol. in chloroform, abs. alcohol; misc. with dimethylformamide, fat solvs., oils; insol. in water; m.w. 280.44; dens. 0.9007 (22/4 C); m.p. -12 C; b.p. 230 C (16 mm); ref. index 1.4699 (20 C)
Precaution: Combustible; easily oxidized by air; refrigerate
Toxicology: Human skin irritant; ingestion can cause nausea and vomiting; heated to decomp., emits acrid smoke and irritating fumes
Uses: Used in emulsifiers and vitamins, drug delivery for orals and topicals
Regulatory: FDA 21CFR §175.105, 182.5065, 184.1065, GRAS
Manuf./Distrib.: Arizona; CasChem; Henkel/Emery; Hercules; Langley Smith Ltd; Spectrum Chem. Mfg.
Manuf./Distrib. (pharm. & food): Aldrich; CasChem; Hercules
Trade names: Crossential LS

Linoleic acid ethyl ester. See Ethyl linoleate

Linolenic acid
CAS 463-40-1; EINECS 207-334-8
Synonyms: 9,12,15-Octadecatrienoic acid; α-Linolenic acid
Classification: Unsaturated fatty acid
Empirical: $C_{18}H_{30}O_2$
Formula: $CH_3CH_2CHCHCH_2CHCHCH_2CHCH(CH_2)_7COOH$
Properties: Colorless liq.; sol. in most org. solvs.; insol. in water; m.w. 278.44; dens. 0.916 (20/4 C); f.p. -11 C; b.p. 230 C (17 mm); ref. index 1.480
Precaution: Combustible; photosensitive; refrigerate
Toxicology: Sl. irritating to mucous membranes
Uses: Nutrient; drug delivery
Manuf./Distrib.: Spectrum Chem. Mfg.
Manuf./Distrib. (pharm. & food): Aldrich
Trade names: Crossential ALA

α-Linolenic acid. See Linolenic acid

γ-Linolenic acid
CAS 506-26-3
Synonyms: 6,9,12-Octadecatrienoic acid
Classification: Unsaturated fatty acid
Empirical: $C_{18}H_{30}O_2$

Properties: Flash pt. > 110 C; ref. index 1.471 (20 C)
Precaution: Photosensitive
Uses: Drug delivery
Manuf./Distrib. (pharm. & food): Aldrich
Trade names: Crossential GLA

Linolic acid. *See* Linoleic acid

Linseed oil
CAS 8001-26-1; EINECS 232-278-6
Synonyms: Oils, linseed; Flaxseed oil; Linseed oil, raw; Raw linseed oil
Definition: Expressed oil from the dried ripe seed of *Linum usitatissimum*
Properties: Golden-yel., amber, or brown drying oil, peculiar odor, bland taste; sol. in ether, chloroform, carbon disulfide, turpentine; sl. sol. in alcohol; dens. 0.921-0.936; m.p. -19 C; b.p. 343 C; flash pt. 222 C
Precaution: Combustible liq. exposed to heat or flame; can react with oxidizers; subject to spontaneous heating; violent reaction with Cl_2
Toxicology: Allergen and skin irritant to humans
Uses: Demulcent, emollient; used in medicinal soaps; soothing to skin; pectoral; used in cough medicines; purgative in veterinary medicine
Regulatory: FDA 21CFR §175.105, 175.300, 176.200, 176.210, 181.22, 181.26; BP compliance
Manuf./Distrib.: Arista Industries; Ferro/Bedford; Penta Mfg.; John L Seaton Ltd; Spectrum Chem. Mfg.
Manuf./Distrib. (pharm. & food): Penta Mfg.; Ruger

Linseed oil, raw. *See* Linseed oil

Lipase
CAS 9001-62-1; EINECS 232-619-9
Classification: Esterase
Definition: Digestive enzyme
Uses: Fat-splitting enzyme; ingred. for vitamin-mineral mixes
Regulatory: FDA GRAS; Canada approved; BP compliance (solv.)
Manuf./Distrib.: Atomergic Chemetals; Gist-brocades Food Ingreds.; U.S. Biochemical
Trade names: Lipase 8 Powd.; Lipase 16 Powd.; Lipase 24 Powd.; Lipase 30 Powd.; Pancreatic Lipase 250
Trade names containing: Pancreatin 3X USP Powd.; Pancreatin 4X USP Powd.; Pancreatin 5X USP Powd.; Pancreatin 6X USP Powd.; Pancreatin 8X USP Powd.; Pancreatin USP Powd.; Pancrelipase USP; SPL High Lipase Pancreatic Enzyme Conc. (PEC); SPL Pancreatin 3X USP; SPL Pancreatin 4X USP; SPL Pancreatin 5X USP; SPL Pancreatin 6X USP; SPL Pancreatin 7X USP; SPL Pancreatin 8X USP; SPL Pancreatin USP; SPL Pancrelipase USP; SPL Undiluted Pancreatic Enzyme Conc. (PEC)

Liquid paraffin. *See* Mineral oil
Liquid petrolatum. *See* Mineral oil
Liquid rosin. *See* Tall oil
Liquid silver. *See* Mercury
Liquid storax. *See* Storax
Liquorice. *See* Licorice

Lithium
CAS 7439-93-2; EINECS 231-102-5
UN No. 1415, 1760
Definition: Metallic element; at. no. 3
Empirical: Li
Properties: Very soft silvery light metal; sol. in liq. ammonia; at. wt. 6.941; dens. 0.534 (20 C); m.p. 179 C; b.p. 1317 C; Mohs hardness 0.6
Precaution: Ignites in air near its m.p.; dangerous fire/explosive risk exposed to water, acids
Toxicology: Toxic to CNS
Uses: Pharmaceuticals
Regulatory: BP compliance
Manuf./Distrib.: Atomergic Chemetals; Cerac; Eagle-Picher; FMC; Leverton-Clarke Ltd; Noah
Manuf./Distrib. (pharm. & food): Aldrich

Lithol rubin B. *See* D&C Red No. 6
Lithol rubin B Ca. *See* D&C Red No. 7
Liver of sulfur. *See* Sulfurated potash
Lysine, compd. with 5-oxo-L-proline (1:1). *See* Lysine PCA

Locust bean gum
CAS 9000-40-2; EINECS 232-541-5

Locust gum

FEMA 2648
Synonyms: Carob flour; Carob bean gum; Locust gum; St. John's bread; Algaroba
Classification: Polysaccharide plant mucilage
Definition: Ground seed of the ripe fruit of St. John's Bread (*Ceratonia siliqua*)
Properties: Wh. powd., odorless, tasteless; swells in cold water; insol. in org. solvs.; visc. increases when heated; m.w. ≈ 310,000
Precaution: Combustible
Toxicology: LD50 (oral, rat) 13 g/kg; mildly toxic by ingestion; heated to decomp., emits acrid smoke and irritating fumes
Uses: Stabilizer, thickener, emulsifier, suspending agent for pharmaceuticals (lotions, creams, toothpaste); excipient for tablets
Regulatory: FDA 21CFR §133.133, 133.134, 133.162, 133.178. 133.179, 150.141, 150.161, 182.20, 184.1343, 240.1051, GRAS; FEMA GRAS; Japan approved; Europe listed; UK approved; ADI not specified (JECFA)
Manuf./Distrib.: Grindsted; Hercules; Rhone-Poulenc Food Ingreds.
Manuf./Distrib. (pharm. & food): Agrisales; Ashland; Bio-Botanica; Calaga Food Ingreds.; Chart; Diamalt; Grindsted; Gumix Int'l.; Hercules Ltd.; Lucas Meyer; Meer; Multi-Kem; Quest UK; Rhone-Poulenc Food Ingreds.; Sanofi; Seah Int'l.; Spectrum Chem. Mfg.; Thew Arnott; TIC Gums; Valmar; E H Worlee GmbH
Trade names: Locust Bean Gum Pharmaceutical Grade; Locust Bean Gum Speckless Type D-200; Locust Bean Gum Type A-100; Locust Bean Gum Type A-250; Locust Bean Gum Type A-270; Powdered Locust Bean Gum Type D-200; Powdered Locust Bean Gum Type D-300; Powdered Locust Bean Gum Type P-100; Powdered Locust Bean Gum Type PP-100; Seagel L

Locust gum. *See* Locust bean gum

Logwood extract
Synonyms: Extract of logwood; Haematoxylon capechianum extract; CI 75290
Definition: Extract of the heartwood of *Haematoxylon capechianum* contg. active colorant substance hematein
Properties: Reddish brn. to blk. liq. or solid extract
Toxicology: May cause allergic reaction in hypersensitive persons
Uses: Color additive for nylon 6 and 6/6 and silk nonabsorbable sutures for general and ophthalmic surgery; mild astringent
Usage level: 1.0% max. (sutures)
Regulatory: Not listed as an approved colorant for cosmetics under FDA 21CFR §73 and 74

Lucerne. *See* Alfalfa
Lucerne extract. *See* Alfalfa extract

2,6-Lutidine
CAS 108-48-5; EINECS 203-587-3
FEMA 3540; UN No. 1993
Synonyms: 2,6-Dimethylpyridine
Empirical: C_7H_9N
Properties: Colorless liq., peppermint odor; hygroscopic; sol. in water, alcohol, ether; m.w. 107.16; dens. 0.920; f.p. -6 C; b.p. 143-145 C; flash pt. 33 C; ref. index 1.4970
Precaution: DOT: Flamm. liq.
Uses: Flavoring agent
Regulatory: FEMA GRAS
Manuf./Distrib.: Aldrich; Janssen Chimica; Koei Chem.; Raschig; Reilly Industries; Spectrum Chem. Mfg.
Manuf./Distrib. (pharm. & food): Aldrich

Lye. *See* Potassium hydroxide; Sodium hydroxide

L-Lysine
CAS 56-87-1; EINECS 200-294-2
Synonyms: α, ε-Diaminocaproic acid; 2,6-Diaminohexanoic acid
Classification: Amino acid
Definition: Essential amino acid isolated from casein, fibrin, or blood
Empirical: $C_6H_{14}N_2O_2$
Properties: Need. or hexagonal plates; very sol. in water; very sl. sol. in alcohol; pract. insol. in ether; m.w. 146.19; m.p. 215 C (dec.)
Toxicology: No known toxicity
Uses: Used in parenterals; biochemical and nutritional research; culture media
Regulatory: FDA 21CFR §172.320; Japan approved; FDA approved for parenterals; BP compliance
Manuf./Distrib.: Degussa; R.W. Greeff; U.S. Biochemical; Walton Pharmaceuticals Ltd
Manuf./Distrib. (pharm. & food): Alrich; Degussa

Lysine aspartate
Synonyms: L-Lysine L-aspartate
Definition: Lysine salt of aspartic acid
Manuf./Distrib.: Degussa

L-Lysine L-aspartate. *See* Lysine aspartate
Lysine 5-oxo-prolinate. *See* Lysine PCA

Lysine PCA
CAS 30657-38-6; EINECS 250-275-8
Synonyms: Lysine pyroglutamate; Lysine 5-oxo-prolinate; Lysine, compd. with 5-oxo-L-proline (1:1)
Definition: Lysine salt of 2-pyrrolidone-5-carboxylic acid
Empirical: $C_{11}H_{21}N_3O_5$
Formula: $C_6H_{14}N_2O_2 \cdot C_3H_7NO_3$
Uses: Moisturizer, cellular regenerative agent, antioxidant, free radical scavenger
Trade names: Lysidone®

Lysine pyroglutamate. *See* Lysine PCA

MAA. *See* Methyl acetoacetate

Mace oil
FEMA 2653
Definition: Volatile oil derived from the arillus of the seed of *Myristica fragrans* by distillation
Precaution: Protect from light
Toxicology: Large doses may cause epileptiform convulsions and hallucinations
Uses: Natural flavoring agent, carminative; in herbal preps. for treatment of respiratory tract disorders
Regulatory: FDA 21CFR §182.10, 182.20, GRAS; FEMA GRAS; Europe listed (< 1 to 15 ppm safrole levels)
Manuf./Distrib. (pharm. & food): Chart; Pierre Chauvet

Macrogol 300. *See* PEG-6
Macrogol 400. *See* PEG-8
Macrogol 600. *See* PEG-12
Macrogol 1000. *See* PEG-20
Macrogol 1540. *See* PEG-32
Macrogol 4000. *See* PEG-4M
Macrogol 6000. *See* PEG-150
Macrogol 120 methyl glucose dioleate. *See* PEG-120 methyl glucose dioleate
Macrose. *See* Dextran
Madagascar lemongrass oil. *See* Lemongrass oil West Indian
MAG. *See* Monoammonium glycyrrhizinate

Magaldrate
Definition: Basic magnesium-aluminum complex
Formula: $Al_5Mg_{10}(OH)_{31}(SO)_4 \cdot xH_2O$
Uses: Antacid active
Regulatory: BP compliance
Manuf./Distrib.: Lohmann
Manuf./Distrib. (pharm. & food): Reheis
Trade names: Magaldrate Fluid Gel; Magaldrate Powd. USP

Magnesia. *See* Magnesium oxide
Magnesia alba. *See* Magnesium carbonate
Magnesia clinker. *See* Magnesium oxide
Magnesia magma. *See* Magnesium hydroxide
Magnesia usta. *See* Magnesium oxide
Magnesite. *See* Magnesium carbonate

Magnesium alginate
Uses: Useful in pharmaceuticals for treatment of esophageal reflux
Trade names: Protanal LFMg 5/60

Magnesium aluminum silicate
CAS 1327-43-1; 12199-37-0; EINECS 235-374-6
Synonyms: Aluminum magnesium silicate; Aluminosilicic acid, magnesium salt

Magnesium carbonate

Definition: Complex silicate refined from naturally occurring minerals; blend of colloidal montmorillonite and saponite

Empirical: $Al_2MgO_8Si_2$

Properties: Fine powd. or sm. flakes, odorless, tasteless; swells in water or glycerin; insol. in water or alcohol; m.w. 262.45; visc. 100-2200 cps; pH 9-10 (5% susp.)

Toxicology: Not harmful at presently used levels; WHO recommends further studies because of kidney damage in dogs that ingested it

Uses: Stabilizer, suspending agent, thickener, tablet disintegrant/binder; antacid; used in dentals, orals, rectals, topicals, vaginals, medicated jellies and ointments

Regulatory: FDA approved for dentals, orals, rectals, topicals, vaginals; USP/NF, BP compliance

Manuf./Distrib.: Am. Colloid; Dry Branch Kaolin; ECC Int'l.; Kaopolite; R.T. Vanderbilt; Volclay Ltd

Manuf./Distrib. (pharm. & food): Ruger; Spectrum Chem. Mfg.

Trade names: Magnabrite® F; Magnabrite® FS; Magnabrite® HS; Magnabrite® HV; Magnabrite® K; Magnabrite® S; Veegum®; Veegum® HV; Veegum® K

Magnesium carbonate

CAS 546-93-0 (anhyd.); 23389-33-5 (hydrate); 39409-82-0 (basic); EINECS 208-915-9; 235-192-7 (basic)

Synonyms: Magnesium (II) carbonate (1:1); Magnesite; Light magnesium carbonate; Magnesia alba; CI 77713; Magnesium carbonate precipitated; Magnesium carbonate basic; Carbonate magnesium; Carbonic acid magnesium salt

Classification: Crystalline salt

Definition: Basic dehydrated magnesium carbonate or normal hydrated magnesium carbonate

Empirical: $CO_3 \cdot Mg$

Properties: Light bulky wh. powd., odorless; sol. in acids; insol. in alcohol, water; m.w. 84.32 (anhyd.); dens. 3.04; dec. 350 C; ref. index 1.52

Precaution: Noncombustible; incompat. with formaldehyde

Toxicology: TLV:TWA 10 mg/m^3; heated to decomp., emits acrid smoke and irritating fumes

Uses: Anticaking agent, coloring agent; buffering agent; abrasive ingred. in dentifrice prods.; antacid in medicine; retarding and spraying; used in orals

Regulatory: FDA 21CFR §133.102, 133.106, 133.111, 133.141, 133.165, 133.181, 133.183, 133.195, 137.105, 137.155 137.160, 137.165, 137.170, 137.175, 137.180, 137.185, 163.110, 177.2600, 184.1425, GRAS; Japan approved (0.5% max.); Europe listed; UK approved; FDA approved for orals; BP, Ph.Eur. compliance

Manuf./Distrib.: Giulini; Lohmann; Lonza; Magnesia GmbH; Mallinckrodt; Marine Magnesium; Martin Marietta; Morton Int'l.; Tomita Pharmaceutical; Whittaker, Clark & Daniels

Manuf./Distrib. (pharm. & food): Integra; Mallinckrodt; Ruger; Spectrum Chem. Mfg.; Tomita Pharmaceutical

Trade names: Basic Magnesium Carbonate USP Heavy; Basic Magnesium Carbonate USP Heavy Low Moisture; Basic Magnesium Carbonate USP Light; Basic Magnesium Carbonate USP Pregranular Heavy; Basic Magnesium Carbonate USP Pregranular Light; Marinco® CH; Marinco® CH-Granular; Marinco® CL; Unichem MC; Unichem MGC

Trade names containing: F-MA 11®; F-MA 11® HD; F-MA 11® Reductionized; R-MA 11®; R-MA 40®

Magnesium (II) carbonate (1:1). *See* Magnesium carbonate
Magnesium carbonate basic. *See* Magnesium carbonate
Magnesium carbonate precipitated. *See* Magnesium carbonate

Magnesium chloride

CAS 7786-30-3; EINECS 232-094-6

Synonyms: Magnesium chloride anhydrous

Classification: Inorganic salt

Empirical: Cl_2Mg

Formula: $MgCl_2$

Properties: Wh. to opaque gray gran. or flakes, odorless; deliq.; sol. in water evolving heat, alcohol; m.w. 95.21; dens. 2.325; m.p. 708 C; b.p. 1412 C

Precaution: Causes steel to rust very rapidly in humid environments

Toxicology: LD50 (oral, rat) 2800 mg/kg; poison by intraperitoneal and IV routes; mod. toxic by ingestion, subcutaneous routes; human mutagenic data; heated to decomp., emits toxic fumes of Cl$^-$

Uses: Electrolyte replenisher; used in intramuscular injectables, intraocular injectables, ophthalmics

Regulatory: FDA 21CFR §172.560, 177.1650, 182.5446, 184.1426, GRAS; USDA 9CFR §318.7, 381.147, limitation ≤3% of 0.8 molar sol'n.; Japan approved; FDA approved for intramuscular injectables, intraocular injectables, ophthalmics; BP, Ph.Eur. compliance

Manuf./Distrib.: Aldrich; Lohmann; Magnesia GmbH; Mallinckrodt; Schaefer Salt & Chem.; Tomita Pharmaceutical

Manuf./Distrib. (pharm. & food): Integra; Mallinckrodt; Ruger; Spectrum Chem. Mfg.; Tomita Pharmaceutical

Magnesium chloride anhydrous. *See* Magnesium chloride

Magnesium gluconate
CAS 3632-91-5 (anhyd.); EINECS 222-848-2
Synonyms: Magnesium D-gluconate; D-Gluconic acid magnesium salt
Definition: Inorg. salt of gluconic acid
Empirical: $C_{12}H_{22}MgO_{14}$
Formula: $(C_6H_{11}O_7)_2Mg$
Properties: Wh. powd. or fine need., odorless; sol. in water; sl. sol. in alcohol; insol. in ether; m.w. 414.6; flash pt. > 100 C
Precaution: Combustible
Uses: Mineral source for pharmaceutical prods.
Manuf./Distrib.: Akzo; Atomergic Chemetals; Lohmann; Rhone-Poulenc; Spectrum Chem. Mfg.
Manuf./Distrib. (pharm. & food): Aldrich; Am. Roland; Integra; Ruger; Spectrum Chem. Mfg.
Trade names: Gluconal® MG

Magnesium D-gluconate. *See* Magnesium gluconate
Magnesium hydrate. *See* Magnesium hydroxide
Magnesium hydrogen metasilicate. *See* Talc

Magnesium hydroxide
CAS 1309-42-8 (anhyd.); EINECS 215-170-3
Synonyms: Magnesium hydrate; Milk of magnesia; Magnesia magma
Classification: Inorganic base
Empirical: H_2MgO_2
Formula: $Mg(OH)_2$
Properties: White amorphous powd., odorless; sol. in sol'n. of ammonium salts and dilute acids; almost insol. in water and alcohol; m.w. 58.33; dens. 2.36; m.p. 350 C (dec.)
Precaution: Noncombustible; incompat. with maleic anhdyride
Toxicology: Variable toxicity; toxic when ihaled; harmless to skin
Uses: Alkali in dentifrices; soothes skin in skin creams; used in orals; medicine (antacid, laxative); milk of magnesia
Regulatory: FDA 21CFR §184.1428, GRAS; Europe listed; UK approved; FDA approved for orals; BP, Ph.Eur. compliance
Manuf./Distrib.: Aldrich; Climax Performance; Croxton & Garry Ltd; J.W.S. Delavau; J.M. Huber; Lohmann; Mallinckrodt; Morton Int'l.; Reheis; Tomita Pharmaceutical
Manuf./Distrib. (pharm. & food): Croxton & Garry Ltd; Integra; Lohmann; Mallinckrodt; Ruger; Spectrum Chem. Mfg.; Tomita Pharmaceutical
Trade names: Hydro-Magma; Magnesium Hydroxide Fluid 25; Magnesium Hydroxide HD; Magnesium Hydroxide Paste; Magnesium Hydroxide Powd.; Magnesium Hydroxide USP; Magnesium Hydroxide USP DC; Marinco H-USP
Trade names containing: F-6000M™; Liquigel® AM; Liquigel® AMS

Magnesium-L-2-hydroxy propionate. *See* Magnesium lactate

Magnesium lactate
CAS 18917-93-6
Synonyms: Magnesium-L-2-hydroxy propionate
Formula: $Mg(CH_3CHOHCOO)_2 \cdot 2H_2O$
Properties: Wh. powd.; sol. 5.2 g/100 ml water; m.w. 202 (anhyd.)
Uses: Nutrient supplement
Manuf./Distrib.: Lohmann
Trade names: Puramex® MG

Magnesium lauryl sulfate
CAS 3097-08-3; 68081-97-0; EINECS 221-450-6
Synonyms: Magnesium monododecyl sulfate; Sulfuri acid, monododecyl ester, magnesium salt
Definition: Magnesium salt of lauryl sulfate
Empirical: $C_{12}H_{26}O_4S \cdot {}^1/_2Mg$
Formula: $[CH_3(CH_2)_{10}CH_2OSO_3]_2^-Mg^{++}$
Properties: Pale yel. liq., mild odor; sol. in methanol, acetone, water; insol. in kerosene
Precaution: Combustible
Uses: Foaming agent
Regulatory: FDA 21CFR §1175.105, 176.170, 177.1200
Trade names: Stepanol® MG

Magnesium monododecyl sulfate

Magnesium monododecyl sulfate. *See* Magnesium lauryl sulfate
Magnesium octadecanoate. *See* Magnesium stearate

Magnesium oxide
CAS 1309-48-4; EINECS 215-171-9
Synonyms: Magnesia; Periclase; Magnesia clinker; Deadburned magnesite; Calcined magnesia; White charcoal; Magnesia usta
Classification: Inorganic oxide
Definition: Inorganic salt of magnesium
Empirical: MgO
Properties: White powd., odorless; sol. in acids, ammonium salt sol'ns.; sl. sol. in water; insol. in alcohol; m.w. 40.31; dens. 0.36; m.p. 2800 C; b.p. 3600 C
Precaution: Noncombustible; violent reaction or ignition with interhalogens; incandescent reaction with phopshorus pentachloride; moisture-sensitive
Toxicology: Toxic by inhalation of fume; experimental tumorigen; TLV (as magnesium) 10 mg/m^3 (fume)
Uses: Antacid, mild laxative; alkaline buffer; mineral supplement; used in orals
Regulatory: FDA 21CFR §163.110, 175.300, 177.1460, 177.2400, 177.2600, 182.5431, 184.1431, GRAS; Japan restricted; Europe listed; FDA approved for orals; BP, Ph.Eur. compliance
Manuf./Distrib.: Cerac; EM Industries; Harwick; Hüls Am.; Lohmann; Magnesia GmbH; Mallinckrodt; Marine Magnesium; Morton Int'l.; Premier Services; Tomita Pharmaceutical
Manuf./Distrib. (pharm. & food): Aldrich; Integra; Lohmann; Mallinckrodt; Morton Int'l.; Ruger; Spectrum Chem. Mfg.; Tomita Pharmaceutical
Trade names: Magnesium Oxide USP 30 Light; Magnesium Oxide USP 60 Light; Magnesium Oxide USP 90 Light; Magnesium Oxide USP Heavy; Marinco OH; Marinco OL
Trade names containing: Corn Po 4 Ster; Pure-Dent® B851

Magnesium silicate
CAS 1343-88-0; EINECS 215-681-1
Synonyms: Silicic acid, magnesium salt (1:1)
Classification: Inorganic salt of variable composition
Definition: Compd. of magnesium oxide and silicon dioxide
Empirical: MgO • SiO$_2$ • xH$_2$O
Properties: Wh. fine effervescent powd., odorless, tasteless; insol. in water, alcohol; decomp. by acids; pH 7-10.8 (10% aq. susp.)
Precaution: Noncombustible
Toxicology: Toxic by inhalation; use in foods restricted to 2%
Uses: Glidant, anticaking agent; used in orals; used medicinally to reduce stomach acidity with slow neutralizing action
Regulatory: FDA 21CFR §169.179, 169.182, 182.2437 (2% max.), GRAS; Europe listed; UK approved; FDA approved for orals; USP/NF compliance
Manuf./Distrib.: Cyprus Industrial Min.; Lohmann; PQ Corp.; R.T. Vanderbilt
Manuf./Distrib. (pharm. & food): Aldrich; Spectrum Chem. Mfg.

Magnesium stearate
CAS 557-04-0; EINECS 209-150-3
Synonyms: Magnesium octadecanoate; Octadecanoic acid, magnesium salt
Definition: Magnesium salt of stearic acid
Empirical: C$_{36}$H$_{70}$MgO$_4$
Formula: [CH$_3$(CH$_2$)$_{16}$COO]$_2$Mg
Properties: Wh. soft oily powd., tasteless, odorless; insol. in water, alcohol, ether; dec. by dilute acids; m.w. 591.27; dens. 1.028; m.p. 88.5 C (pure)
Precaution: Nonflamm.
Toxicology: No known toxicity; heated to decomp., emits acrid smoke and toxic fumes
Uses: Coloring agent, tablet/capsule lubricant used in buccals, parenterals, orals, vaginals; anticaking agent, stabilizer
Regulatory: FDA 21CFR §172.863, 173.340; 175.105, 175.300, 175.320, 176.170, 176.200, 176.210, 177.1200, 177.2260, 178.3910, 179.45, 181.22, 181.29, 184.1440, GRAS; must conform to FDA specs for salts of fats or fatty acids derived from edible oils; Europe listed; UK approved; FDA approved for buccals, parenterals, orals, vaginals; USP/NF, BP, Ph.Eur., JP compliance
Manuf./Distrib.: Cometals; Cookson Specialty; EM Industries; Ferro/Grant; Lohmann; Magnesia GmbH; Mallinckrodt; Miljac; Norac; San Yuan; Syn. Prods.; Witco/PAG
Manuf./Distrib. (pharm. & food): Avrachem; Ruger; Spectrum Chem. Mfg.
Trade names: Cecavon MG 51; Haro® Chem MF-2; Petrac® Magnesium Stearate MG-20 NF; Synpro® Magnesium Stearate NF

Trade names containing: Candex® Plus; Chroma-Seal™ 859027; Chroma-Seal™ 889031; DSS Tablet Grade; Emdex® Plus; Nu-Tab®

Magnesium sulfate anhyd.
CAS 7487-88-9; EINECS 231-298-2
Synonyms: Sulfuric acid magnesium salt (1:1); Epsom salts
Classification: Inorganic salt
Empirical: $O_4S \cdot Mg$
Formula: $MgSO_4$
Properties: Colorless crystals, odorless, saline bitter taste; sol. in water; slowly sol. in glycerin; sl. sol. in alcohol; m.w. 120.37; dens. 2.65; dec. at 1124 C
Precaution: Noncombustible; potentially explosive when heated with ethoxyethynyl alcohols
Toxicology: Mod. toxic by ingestion, intraperitoneal, subcutaneous routes; potential adverse reactions incl. drowsiness, depressed reflexes, paralysis, low blood pressure, circulatory collapse; experimental teratogen; heated to decomp., emits toxic fumes of SO_x
Uses: Used in orals; medicine (laxative, local painkiller, antidote)
Regulatory: FDA 21CFR §182.5443, 184.1443, GRAS; Japan approved; Europe listed; UK approved; FDA approved for orals; BP, Ph.Eur. compliance
Manuf./Distrib.: Blythe, William Ltd; Heico; Lohmann; Mallinckrodt; PQ Corp.; Spectrum Chem. Mfg.; Tomita Pharmaceutical
Manuf./Distrib. (pharm. & food): Aldrich; Heico; Ruger; Tomita Pharmaceutical

Magnesium trisilicate
CAS 14987-04-3 (anhyd.); EINECS 239-076-7
Synonyms: Silicic acid, magnesium salt (1:2); Dimagnesium trisilicate
Classification: Inorg. compd.
Empirical: $H_4O_8Si_3 \cdot 2Mg$
Formula: $2MgO \cdot 3SiO_2 \cdot xH_2O$
Properties: Wh. powd., odorless, tasteless; hygroscopic; insol. in water, alcohol; m.w. 260.86 (anhyd.)
Uses: Colorant used in orals
Regulatory: FDA approved for orals; BP, Ph.Eur. compliance
Manuf./Distrib.: Lohmann
Manuf./Distrib. (pharm. & food): Ruger; Spectrum Chem. Mfg.

Maize gluten amino acids. *See* Corn gluten amino acids
Maize oil. *See* Corn oil
Maize starch. *See* Corn starch
Maize starch, pregelatinized. *See* Corn starch, pregelatinized
MAK. *See* Methyl n-amyl ketone

Maleated soybean oil
CAS 68648-66-8
Synonyms: Soybean oil, maleated; Oils, soybean, maleated
Definition: Modified soybean oil where some of the unsaturation is converted to a cyclic dicarboxylic acid
Properties: Amber-yel. visc. oily liq., mild char. odor; sol. in castor oil, IPM, dioctyl maleate, lauramide DEA (1:1), cocamide DEA (2:1); insol. in water, glycerin, propylene glycol, 90% ethanol; sapon. no. 230-250; ref. index 1.4750-1.4850
Toxicology: LD50 (rat, oral) > 5 g/kg; nonirritating to eyes; mildly irritating to skin
Uses: Moisturizer, skin softener for topical pharmaceuticals, water-resist. sunscreens, creams, lotions
Trade names: Ceraphyl® GA-D

Maleic acid
CAS 110-16-7; EINECS 203-742-5
UN No. 2215
Synonyms: Maleinic acid; cis-Butenedioic acid; 2-Butenedioic acid; Toxilic acid
Classification: Cis unsaturated organic acid
Empirical: $C_4H_4O_4$
Formula: HOOCCH:CHCOOH
Properties: Wh. cryst. powd., odorless; sol. in water, alcohol, acetone; m.w. 116.07; dens. 1.590; m.p. 132-140 C; flash pt. 100 C
Precaution: DOT: Corrosive material
Toxicology: Toxic by ingestion; irritant
Uses: Rancidity retardant; pharmaceutical intermediate; used in intramuscular injectables, orals
Regulatory: FDA 21CFR §175.105, 177.1200; FDA approved for intramuscular injectables, orals; BP, Ph.Eur. compliance

Maleic anhydride

    Manuf./Distrib.: Croda Colloids Ltd; Gen'l. Chem.; Penta Mfg.; Spectrum Chem. Mfg.; Thor
    Manuf./Distrib. (pharm. & food): Aldrich; Croda Colloids Ltd; Mallinckrodt

Maleic anhydride
    CAS 108-31-6; EINECS 203-571-6
    UN No. 2215
    Synonyms: 2,5-Furandione; Toxilic anhydride; cis-Butenedioic anhydride
    Empirical: $C_4H_2O_3$
    Properties: Colorless needles; sol. in water, acetone, alcohol, dioxane; partly sol. in chloroform, benzene; m.w.
        98.06; dens. 0.934 (20/4 C); m.p. 53 C; b.p. 200 C; flash pt. 218 F
    Precaution: DOT: Corrosive material
    Toxicology: Irritant to tissues; TLV 0.25 ppm in air
    Uses: Preservative for pharmaceuticals
    Regulatory: BP compliance
    Manuf./Distrib.: Allchem Ind.; Amoco; Aristech; Ashland; BP Chem.; Brown; Elf Atochem SA; Hüls AG; Mitsui
        Toatsu; Monsanto; NOF; Occidental; Primachem; Spectrum Chem. Mfg.
    Manuf./Distrib. (pharm. & food): Aldrich; Mallinckrodt

Maleinic acid. *See* Maleic acid
Malic acid. *See* N-Hydroxysuccinic acid

Malonic acid
    CAS 141-82-2; EINECS 205-503-0
    Synonyms: Dicarboxylic acid C_3; Methanedicarbonic acid; Propanedioic acid
    Empirical: $C_3H_4O_4$
    Formula: $CH_2(COOH)_2$
    Properties: Wh. cryst.; sol. in water, alcohol, ether; m.w. 104.06; dens. 1.63; m.p. 135-137 C
    Toxicology: Strong irritant; large doses injected into mice are lethal
    Uses: Intermediate for pharmaceuticals
    Manuf./Distrib.: Aldrich; R.W. Greeff; Lonza; Penta Mfg.; Spectrum Chem. Mfg.
    Manuf./Distrib. (pharm. & food): R.W. Greeff; Lonza Ltd

Malonic ester. *See* Diethyl malonate
Malonic methyl ester nitrile. *See* Methyl cyanoacetate

Malt extract
    CAS 8002-48-0; EINECS 232-310-9
    Synonyms: Maltine; Malt syrup
    Definition: Dark syrup obtained by evaporating an aq. extract of partially germinated and dried barley seeds;
        derived from *Hordeum vulgare*; contains dextrin, maltose, a little glucose, and an amylolytic enzyme
    Properties: Lt. brown, visc. liq., sweet; sol. in cold water; dens. 1.35-1.43
    Toxicology: Heated to decomp., emits acrid smoke and irritating fumes
    Uses: Emulsifying agent; humectant, nutritive sweetener, colorant; used in orals
    Regulatory: FDA 21CFR §133.178, 184.1445, GRAS; USDA 9CFR §318.7, limitation 2.5% in cured meats,
        381.147; FDA approved for orals
    Manuf./Distrib. (pharm. & food): Beck Flavors; Calgene; Chart; Diamalt; Enco Prods.; Folexco; Grünau;
        Goorden; Henkel; Malt Prods.; Mid-Am. Food Sales; MLG Enterprises; J W Pike; Pure Malt Prods.;
        Regency Mowbray; Sandoz Nutrition; Wander
    Trade names: Extramalt Dark; Non-Diastatic Malt Syrup #40600; Pure Malt Colorant A6000; Pure Malt
        Colorant A6001
    Trade names containing: Extramalt 10; Extramalt 35; Extramalt Light

Maltine. *See* Malt extract

Maltitol
    CAS 585-88-6; EINECS 209-567-0
    Synonyms: 4-O-α-Glucopyranosyl-D-sorbitol; 4-O-β-D-Glucopyranosyl-D-glucitol
    Empirical: $C_{12}H_{24}O_{11}$
    Properties: Liq., cryst.; easily sol. in water; m.w. 344.32; m.p. 149-152 C; very stable at different pH conditions
        and temps.
    Toxicology: LD50 (oral) > 24 g/kg; low acute toxicity; nonmutagenic; nonteratogenic
    Uses: Nutritive sweetener
    Manuf./Distrib. (pharm. & food): Aldrich
    Trade names: Amalty®; Finmalt L

Maltobiose. *See* Maltose

Maltodextrin

CAS 9050-36-6; EINECS 232-940-4

Classification: Saccharide

Definition: Saccharide material obtained by hydrolysis of starch; consists of D-glucose units with a DE < 20

Empirical: $(C_6H_{10}O_5)_n$

Properties: Wh. powd. or sol'n.; hygroscopic; sol. in water; pract. insol. in anhyd. alcohol; pH 4-7 (20%)

Toxicology: Heated to decomp., emits acrid smoke and irritating fumes

Uses: Nonsweet nutritive polymer, carrier, bulking agent, absorbent for pharmaceuticals; tablet/capsule diluent, coating agent, tablet binder, visc.-increasing agent; functions in spray drying

Regulatory: FDA 21CFR §184.144, GRAS

Manuf./Distrib. (pharm. & food): Aldrich; Avebe UK; Cerestar Int'l.; Clofine; Grain Processing; Kingfood Australia; Nat'l. Starch & Chem. UK; Roquette UK; Spectrum Chem. Mfg.; Sweeteners Plus; Westin; Zumbro

Trade names: Maltrin® M040; Maltrin® M050; Maltrin® M100; Maltrin® M150; Maltrin® M180; Maltrin® M510; Maltrin® M700; Maltrin® QD M440; Maltrin® QD M500; Maltrin® QD M550; Maltrin® QD M580

Trade names containing: Cal-Carb® 4450; Cal-Carb® 4450 PG; Dry Vitamin E Acetate 50% Type CWS/F No. 652530001; Durkote Malic Acid/Maltodextrin; Natural Red Beet Powd. 654200; Os-Tab™ 4455; Spray Dried Fish Gelatin/Maltodextrin

Maltol

CAS 118-71-8; EINECS 204-271-8

FEMA 2656

Synonyms: 3-Hydroxy-2-methyl-4-pyrone; 3-Hydroxy-2-methyl-γ-pyrone; 2-Methyl pyromeconic acid; 3-Hydroxy-2-methyl-4H-pyran-4-one; Larixinic acid

Empirical: $C_6H_6O_3$

Properties: Wh. cryst. powd., fragrant caramel-like odor; sol. 1 g/85 ml water; freely sol. in hot water, chloroform; sol. in alcohol; sparingly sol. in benzene, ether, petroleum ether; m.w. 126.11; m.p. 160-162 C; begins to sublime @ 93 C; pH 5.3 (0.5% aq.)

Precaution: Volatile with steam

Toxicology: No known toxicity; skin irritant

Uses: Chocolate synthetic flavoring agent and enhancer; antioxidant; used in orals

Regulatory: FDA 21CFR §172.515; FEMA GRAS; Japan approved as flavoring; Europe listed; UK approved; FDA approved for orals

Manuf./Distrib. (pharm. & food): Aldrich

Trade names: Veltol®

Maltonic acid. *See* D-Gluconic acid

Maltose

CAS 69-79-4; 6363-53-7 (monohydrate); EINECS 200-716-5

Synonyms: Malt sugar; Maltobiose; r-O-α-D-Glucopyranosyl-D-glucose

Classification: Malt sugar, an isomer of cellobiose

Empirical: $C_{12}H_{22}O_{11} \cdot H_2O$

Properties: Anhyd.: m.w. 342.31; Monohydrate: Colorless cryst.; hygroscopic; sol. in water, sl. sol. in alcohol; pract. insol. in ether; m.w. 360.32; m.p. 102-103 C; about one-third as sweet as sucrose

Precaution: Combustible

Toxicology: No known toxicity

Uses: Nutrient, sweetener, culture media, stabilizer

Manuf./Distrib.: Am. Biorganics; Avebe BV; Penta Mfg.; Pfanstiehl Labs; Spectrum Chem. Mfg.

Manuf./Distrib. (pharm. & food): Alfa; Cargill; Cerestar Int'l.; K&K Greeff; Integra; Mallinckrodt; Mid-Am. Food Sales; Mitsubishi; North Western; Penta Mfg.; Ragus Sugars; Ruger

Trade names containing: Sweetrex®

Malt sugar. *See* Maltose
Malt syrup. *See* Malt extract

Maltyl isobutyrate

CAS 65416-14-0

FEMA 3462

Empirical: $C_{10}H_{12}O_4$

Properties: M.w. 196.20; dens. 1.149; flash pt. > 230 F

Uses: Sweet, strawberry-like flavoring agent

Regulatory: FEMA GRAS

Manuf./Distrib. (pharm. & food): Aldrich

Mandarin oil. *See* Mandarin orange oil

Mandarin oil, coldpressed. *See* Mandarin orange oil
Mandarin oil, expressed. *See* Mandarin orange oil

Mandarin orange oil
CAS 8008-31-9; 84696-35-5
FEMA 2657
Synonyms: Mandarin oil; Mandarin oil, expressed; Mandarin oil, coldpressed
Definition: Oil expressed from the peel of *Citrus reticulata*
Properties: Clear orange to brn.-orange liq., orange odor; sol. in fixed oils, min. oil; sl. sol. in propylene glycol; insol. in glycerin; dens. 0.846; ref. index 1.473-1.477
Precaution: Light-sensitive
Toxicology: Heated to decomp., emits acrid smoke and irritating fumes
Uses: Natural flavoring agent used in orals
Regulatory: FDA 21CFR §182.20, GRAS; FEMA GRAS; Europe listed, no restrictions; FDA approved for orals
Manuf./Distrib. (pharm. & food): Commodity Services; Florida Treatt; Spectrum Chem. Mfg.

Manganese gluconate
CAS 6485-39-8; EINECS 229-350-4
Synonyms: Manganese (II) gluconate
Empirical: $C_{12}H_{22}O_{14}Mn \cdot 2H_2O$
Formula: $Mn(C_6H_{11}O_7)_2 \cdot 2H_2O$
Properties: Lt. pinkish powd. or gran.; sol. in water; insol. in alc. and benzene; m.w. 481.27 (dihydrate)
Precaution: Combustible
Toxicology: Heated to decomp., emits toxic fumes of manganese
Uses: Mineral source for pharmaceutical prods.
Regulatory: FDA 21CFR §182.5452, 184.1452, GRAS
Manuf./Distrib.: Akzo; Lohmann; Spectrum Chem. Mfg.
Manuf./Distrib. (pharm. & food): Lohmann; Spectrum Chem. Mfg.
Trade names: Gluconal® MN

Manganese (II) gluconate. *See* Manganese gluconate
Manganese-L-2-hydroxy propionate. *See* Manganese lactate

Manganese lactate
CAS 16039-56-8
Synonyms: Manganese-L-2-hydroxy propionate
Formula: $Mn(CH_3CHOHCOO)_2 \cdot 2H_2O$
Properties: pink powd.; sol. 10 g/100 ml water; m.w. 233 (anhyd.)
Uses: Nutrient supplement
Manuf./Distrib.: Lohmann
Trade names: Puramex® MN

Mango seed oil
Definition: Oil expressed from the kernels of *Magnifera indica*
Uses: Natural oil for pharmaceutical formulations
Trade names: Lipex 203

Manna sugar. *See* D-Mannitol
Mannite. *See* D-Mannitol
Mannitol. *See* D-Mannitol

D-Mannitol
CAS 69-65-8; EINECS 200-711-8
Synonyms: 1,2,3,4,5,6-Hexanehexol; Mannitol; Mannite; Cordycepic acid; Manna sugar; Mannose sugar
Classification: Hexahydric alcohol
Empirical: $C_6H_{14}O_6$
Properties: Orthorhombic need., odorless, sweetish taste; hygroscopic; sol. 1 g/5.5 ml water, 1 g/18 ml glycerol; 1 g/83 ml alcohol; sol. in pyridine, aniline, aq. sol'ns. of alkalies; m.w. 182.18; dens. 1.52 (20 C); m.p. 165-167 C; b.p. 290-295 C (3.5 mm)
Toxicology: Excess consumption may have a laxative effect; may cause diarrhea and flatulence
Uses: Anticaking agent, humectant, sweetener, tonicity agent; bulking agent for freeze-drying; stabilizer, thickener, processing aid; tablet inert base/diluent; used in parenterals, injectables (IM, IP, intrapleural), intravenous, ophthalmics, orals
Regulatory: FDA 21CFR §180.25; GRAS; Japan approved; Europe listed; UK approved; FDA approved for parenterals, intramuscular injectables, interaperitoneal injectables, intrapleural injectables, intravenous, ophthalmics, orals; USP/NF, BP, Ph.Eur. compliance

Manuf./Distrib. (pharm. & food): Aldrich; Allchem Int'l.; Am. Roland; Atomergic Chemetals; Cerestar Int'l.; Food
  Additives & Ingreds.; R.W. Greeff; ICI Atkemix; Int'l. Sourcing; E Merck; Penta Mfg.; Roquette UK; Ruger;
  Spectrum Chem. Mfg.; Van Waters & Rogers; Peter Whiting
Trade names: Unisweet MAN
Trade names containing: Vitamin B$_{12}$ 1% Trituration No. 69993

L-Mannomethylose. *See* Rhamnose

D-Mannose
  CAS 530-26-7; 3458-28-4
  Empirical: C$_6$H$_{12}$O$_6$
  Properties: M.w. 180.16
  Uses: Used in orals
  Regulatory: FDA approved for orals; BP compliance
  Manuf./Distrib.: Spectrum Chem. Mfg.
  Manuf./Distrib. (pharm. & food): Aldrich; Mallinckrodt

Mannose sugar. *See* D-Mannitol
MAP. *See* Ammonium phosphate
Marigold extract. *See* Calendula extract
Marshmallow. *See* Althea
Marshmallow root extract. *See* Althea extract
Maw oil. *See* Poppyseed oil
MC. *See* Methylcellulose
MCC. *See* Microcrystalline cellulose
MCP/A. *See* Calcium phosphate monobasic anhydrous
MDB. *See* 1,2-Methylenedioxybenzene
MEA. *See* Ethanolamine

Meadowfoam seed oil
  Definition: Oil extracted from the seeds of the meadowfoam plant, *Limnanthes alba*
  Uses: Color enhancer, conditioner in pharmaceuticals
  Trade names: EmCon Limnanthes Alba
  Trade names containing: Fancol VB

Medicago sativa extract. *See* Alfalfa extract

Medronate disodium
  CAS 25681-89-4
  Uses: Used in intravenous
  Regulatory: FDA approved for intravenous

Medronic acid
  CAS 1984-15-2
  Uses: Used in intravenous
  Regulatory: FDA approved for intravenous

Meglumine
  CAS 6284-40-8
  Synonyms: D-Glucitol, 1-deoxy-1-(methylamino)-,; 1-Deoxy-1-(methylamino)-D-glucitol; N-Methylglucamine;
    1-Methylamino-1-deoxy-D-glucitol
  Empirical: C$_7$H$_{17}$NO$_5$
  Properties: Wh. to faintly ylsh. cryst. or powd., odorless; sol. in water; sl. sol. in alcohol; pract. insol. in
    chloroform, ether; m.w. 195.21; m.p. 128-132 C
  Uses: Pharmaceutic aid; organic base used for preps. of salts of org. acids incl. many used as contrast media;
    used in injectables, intravenous
  Regulatory: FDA approved for injectables, intravenous; USP, BP, JP compliance
  Manuf./Distrib. (pharm. & food): Spectrum Chem. Mfg.

MEHQ. *See* Hydroquinone monomethyl ether
Mel. *See* Honey

Melanin
  CAS 8049-97-6; 77465-45-3
  Definition: Pigment responsible for color of animal skin, hair, feathers, and fur; not approved for cosmetics
    under FDA
  Uses: Pharmaceutical raw material
  Regulatory: Use prohibited in U.S.
  Trade names: Lipo Melanin

Melilotin. *See* Dihydrocoumarin
Melissa. *See* Balm mint
Menhaden acid, hydrogenated. *See* Hydrogenated menhaden acid

Menhaden oil
  CAS 8002-50-4; EINECS 232-311-4
  Synonyms: Oils, menhaden; Pogy oil; Mossbunker oil
  Definition: Oil obtained from the small North Atlantic fish, *Brevoortia tyrannus*
  Properties: Yellowish-brown or reddish-brown oil, characteristic fishy odor and taste; sol. in ether, benzene, petrol. ether, naphtha, kerosene, CS_2; dens. 0.925-0.933; m.p. 38.5-47.2 C; iodine no. 115-160; sapon. no. 191-200; ref. index 1.480 (20 C)
  Precaution: Combustible
  Toxicology: No known toxicity
  Uses: Nutritonal supplements, therapeutic uses; in soaps and creams
  Regulatory: FDA 21CFR §175.300, 176.200, 176.210, 177.2800
  Manuf./Distrib.: ABITEC; Arista Industries
  Trade names: Super Refined® Menhaden Oil
  Trade names containing: Neobee® SL-120; Neobee® SL-140

Menhaden oil, hydrogenated. *See* Hydrogenated menhaden oil
p-Mentha-1,8-dien-7-al. *See* Perillaldehyde
d-p-Mentha-1,8-diene. *See* d-Limonene
p-Mentha-1,3-diene. *See* α-Terpinene
p-Mentha-1,4-diene. *See* γ-Terpinene
p-Mentha-1,5-diene. *See* α-Phellandrene
p-Mentha-6,8-dien-2-ol. *See* Carveol
1-6,8(9)-p-Menthadien-2-one. *See* l-Carvone
l-p-Mentha-6,8-dien-2-yl propionate. *See* Carvyl propionate

Menthalactone
  CAS 13341-72-5
  FEMA 3764
  Synonyms: Mintlactone; 3,6-Dimethyl5,6,7,7a-tetrahydro-2(4H)-benzofuranone; Dehydroxymenthofuro-lactone
  Empirical: $C_{10}H_{14}O_2$
  Properties: M.w. 166.22; dens. 1.058; b.p. 87-89 C (25 mm); flash pt. 176 F
  Uses: Medicinal flavoring agent
  Regulatory: FEMA GRAS
  Manuf./Distrib. (pharm. & food): Aldrich

3-p-Menthanol. *See* Menthol
p-Menthan-3-ol. *See* Menthol
l-p-Menthan-3-one. *See* l-Menthone
dl-p-Menthan-3-yl acetate. *See* dl-Menthyl acetate
Mentha piperita leaves. *See* Peppermint leaves
Mentha piperita oil. *See* Peppermint oil
Mentha spicata oil. *See* Spearmint oil

p-Mentha-8-thiol-3-one
  CAS 38462-22-5
  FEMA 3177
  Synonyms: 8-Mercapto-p-menthane-3-one
  Empirical: $C_{10}H_{18}OS$
  Properties: M.w. 186.32; dens. 1.00; b.p. 56 C (0.1 mm); flash pt. 227 F
  Uses: Berry-like flavoring agent
  Regulatory: FEMA GRAS
  Manuf./Distrib. (pharm. & food): Aldrich

Mentha viridis. *See* Spearmint
p-Menthen-1-en-8-ol. *See* α-Terpineol
8-p-Menthen-2-ol. *See* Dihydrocarveol
p-Menth-1-en-8-ol. *See* α-Terpineol
p-Menth-4-en-3-ol. *See* Isopulegol
p-Menth-8-en-3-ol. *See* Isopulegol
p-Menth-1-en-3-one. *See* d-Piperitone
p-Menth-4(8)-en-3-one. *See* Pulegone

p-Menth-8-en-2-one. *See* d-Dihydrocarvone
8-p-Menthen-2-yl acetate. *See* Dihydrocarvyl acetate
p-Menth-8-(9)-en-2-yl acetate. *See* Dihydrocarvyl acetate
p-Menth-1-en-8-yl formate. *See* Terpinyl formate
Menthofuran. *See* 4,5,6,7-Tetrahydro-3,6-dimethylbenzofuran

Menthol
CAS 89-78-1; 1490-04-6; 15356-60-2 (+); 2216-51-5 (-); 15356-70-4 (±); EINECS 201-939-0
FEMA 2665
Synonyms: Hexahydrothymol; 2-Isopropyl-5-methylcyclohexanol; 3-p-Menthanol; p-Menthan-3-ol; 5-Methyl-
2-isopropyl hexahydrophenol; 5-Methyl-2-(1-methylethyl) cyclohexanol; 5-Methyl-2-isopropylcyclo-
hexanol; Racemic menthol; Peppermint camphor
Classification: Diterpene alcohol
Definition: Alcohol obtained from diverse mint oils or prepared synthetically; may be levorotatory (l-), from
natural or syn. sources, or racemic (dl-)
Empirical: $C_{10}H_{20}O$
Formula: $CH_3C_6H_9(C_3H_7)OH$
Properties: Wh. cryst., cooling peppermint-like odor and taste; very sol. in alcohol, light petrol. solv., glacial
acetic acid, min. oil, fixed/volatile oils; sl. sol. in water; m.w. 156.26; dens. 0.89; m.p. 42.5 C; b.p. 215 C;
flash pt. 200 F; ref. index 1.461
Precaution: Combustible; incompat. with phenol, β-naphthol, others
Toxicology: LD50 (oral, rat) 3180 mg/kg; poison by IV route; mod. toxic by ingestion, IP routes; severe eye
irritant; irritant to mucous membranes on inh.; may cause human intolerance reaction; heated to decomp.,
emits acrid smoke and irritating fumes
Uses: Minty synthetic flavoring agent, perfume used in buccals, dentals, inhalants, orals, topicals; in
formulations for bronchitis and sinusitis, topically for its cooling effect, esp. for localized pain; antiseptic in
oral rinse prods.
Usage level: < 3%
Regulatory: FDA 21CFR §172.515, 182.20, GRAS; 27CFR §21.65, 21.151; FEMA GRAS; Japan approved
as flavoring; FDA approved for buccals, dentals, inhalants, orals, topicals; USP/NF, BP compliance
Manuf./Distrib.: Aldrich; Haarmann & Reimer; Janssen Chimica; Penta Mfg.; Quest Int'l.; Robeco
Manuf./Distrib. (pharm. & food): Acme-Hardesty; Aldrich; Am. Fruit Processors; Berje; Berk; Biddle Sawyer;
Charabot; Chart; Commodity Services Int'l.; Diamalt; Forrester Wood; Frutarom UK; R.W. Greeff;
Haarmann & Reimer; Ikeda; Penta Mfg.; Polarome; Quimdis; Robeco; Robt. Bryce; Ruger; Spectrum
Chem. Mfg.; R C Treatt

l-Menthone
CAS 14073-97-3
FEMA 2667
Synonyms: l-p-Menthan-3-one
Empirical: $C_{10}H_{18}O$
Properties: M.w. 154.25; dens. 0.893; b.p. 207-210 C; flash pt. 163 F
Uses: Minty synthetic flavoring agent
Regulatory: FDA 21CFR §172.515; FEMA GRAS
Manuf./Distrib. (pharm. & food): Aldrich

dl-Menthyl acetate
CAS 16409-45-3
FEMA 2668
Synonyms: dl-p-Menthan-3-yl acetate
Empirical: $C_{12}H_{22}O_2$
Properties: Fruity, berry, minty, woody; m.w. 198.31; dens. 0.922; b.p. 228-229 C; flash pt. 198 F
Uses: Berry-like, minty flavoring agent
Regulatory: FEMA GRAS; BP compliance
Manuf./Distrib. (pharm. & food): Aldrich

Menthyl o-aminobenzoate. *See* Menthyl anthranilate

Menthyl anthranilate
CAS 134-09-8; EINECS 205-129-8
Synonyms: Menthyl o-aminobenzoate; 5-Methyl-2(1-methylethyl)cyclohexanol-2-aminobenzoate
Definition: Ester of menthol and o-anthranilic acid
Empirical: $C_{17}H_{25}NO_2$
Properties: M.w. 275.38
Precaution: Store away from strong oxidizing agents

Menthyl lactate

    Toxicology: Mildly irritating to skin and eyes on prolonged contact
    Uses: UV-A absorber for sunscreens; active ingred. in OTC drug prods.

Menthyl lactate

    CAS 59259-38-0; EINECS 261-678-3
    Synonyms: Lactic acid menthyl ester; 2-Hydroxypropanoic acid, 5-methyl-2-(1-methylethyl)cyclohexyl ester
    Definition: Ester of menthol and lactic acid
    Empirical: $C_{13}H_{24}O_3$
    Uses: Minty flavoring agent
    Manuf./Distrib. (pharm. & food): Aldrich

l-Menthyl lactate

    CAS 61597-98-6
    FEMA 3748
    Empirical: $C_{13}H_{24}O_3$
    Properties: Mild cooling odor, sweet menthol taste; m.w. 228.33; m.p. 42-47 C; b.p. 142 C (5 mm); flash pt.
      > 230 F
    Uses: Mild cooling flavoring
    Regulatory: FEMA GRAS
    Manuf./Distrib. (pharm. & food): Aldrich

Menthyl salicylate. *See* Wintergreen oil
Meparfynol. *See* Methyl pentynol
Mercaptoacetic acid sodium salt. *See* Sodium thioglycolate

2-Mercaptoethanol

    CAS 60-24-2; EINECS 200-464-6
    UN No. 2966
    Synonyms: Thioethylene glycol; Thioglycol
    Classification: Aliphatic organic compd.
    Empirical: C_2H_6OS
    Formula: $HSCH_2CH_2OH$
    Properties: Water-wh. mobile liq., disagreeable odor; misc. with water; m.w. 78.13; dens. 1.114; b.p. 157 C;
      flash pt. 165 F; ref. index 1.5006
    Precaution: Combustible
    Toxicology: DOT: Poisonous material
    Uses: Intermediate for pharmaceuticals
    Manuf./Distrib.: Aldrich; BASF; Morton Int'l.; Spectrum Chem. Mfg.; Toray Thiokol
    Manuf./Distrib. (pharm. & food): Aldrich

8-Mercapto-p-menthane-3-one. *See* p-Mentha-8-thiol-3-one
3-Mercapto-1,2-propanediol. *See* Thioglycerin
Mercuric acetate. *See* Mercury acetate (ic)
Mercuric oxide. *See* Mercury oxide (ic), red and yellow

Mercury

    CAS 7439-97-6; EINECS 231-106-7
    Synonyms: Quicksilver; Hydrargyrum; Liquid silver
    Classification: Metallic element
    Empirical: Hg
    Properties: Metallic element, silvery heavy liq.; insol. in water, alcohol, ether, HCl; sol. in sulfuric acid, lipids;
      readily sol. in nitric acid; at.wt. 200.59; extremely high surf. tension
    Toxicology: Highly toxic by skin absorption and inhalation of fume or vapor, absorbed by respiratory and
      intestinal tract; TLV (as Hg) 0.05 mg/m^3 of air; low allergic potential
    Uses: Main ingred. in amalgam dental fillings
    Regulatory: BP compliance
    Manuf./Distrib.: Aldrich; Atomergic Chemetals; Cerac; Cox Chem. Ltd; Spectrum Chem. Mfg.

Mercury acetate (ic)

    CAS 1600-27-7; EINECS 216-491-1
    UN No. 1629
    Synonyms: Mercuric acetate; Mercury (II) acetate
    Empirical: $C_4H_6HgO_4$
    Formula: $(CH_3COO)_2Hg$
    Properties: Wh. cryst. powd.; sol. in alcohol, water; m.w. 318.68; dens. 3.2544; m.p. 178-180 C
    Precaution: Light-sensitive

Toxicology: DOT: Poisonous material; toxic by ingestion, inhalation; irritant
Uses: Catalyst for pharmaceuticals
Regulatory: BP compliance
Manuf./Distrib.: Atomergic Chemetals; Cerac; Noah Chem.; Thor
Manuf./Distrib. (pharm. & food): Aldrich

Mercury, ethyl(2-mercaptobenzoato-S)-, sodium salt. *See* Thimerosal
Mercury (II) acetate. *See* Mercury acetate (ic)
Mercury (II) oxide. *See* Mercury oxide (ic), red and yellow

Mercury oxide (ic), red and yellow
CAS 21908-53-2; EINECS 244-654-7
UN No. 1641
Synonyms: Mercuric oxide; Yellow oxide of mercury; Red precipitate; Yellow precipitate; Mercury (II) oxide
Empirical: HgO
Properties: M.w. 216.59; m.p. 500 C (dec.)
Precaution: Light-sensitive
Toxicology: DOT: Poisonous material
Uses: Red: Pharmaceuticals, antiseptic; Yellow: Antiseptic
Regulatory: BP compliance
Manuf./Distrib.: BASF; Cerac; Noah Chem.; Spectrum Chem. Mfg.; Thor UK
Manuf./Distrib. (pharm. & food): Aldrich

Meroxapol 105
CAS 9003-11-6 (generic)
Classification: Polyoxypropylene, polyoxyethylene block polymer
Formula: $HO(CHCH_3CH_2O)_x(CH_2CH_2O)_y(CH_2CHCH_3O)_z)H$, avg. x=7, y=22, z=7
Properties: Nonionic liq.
Uses: Surfactant used in creams
Regulatory: FDA 21CFR §172.808, 173.340

Meroxapol 172
CAS 9003-11-6 (generic)
Classification: Polyoxypropylene, polyoxyethylene block polymer
Formula: $HO(CHCH_3CH_2O)_x(CH_2CH_2O)_y(CH_2CHCH_3O)_z)H$, avg. x=12, y=9, z=12
Uses: Emulsifier, wetting agent

Meroxapol 174
CAS 9003-11-6 (generic)
Classification: Polyoxypropylene, polyoxyethylene block polymer
Formula: $HO(CHCH_3CH_2O)_x(CH_2CH_2O)_y(CH_2CHCH_3O)_z)H$, avg. x=12, y=23, z=12
Uses: Emulsifier, wetting agent

Meroxapol 251
CAS 9003-11-6 (generic)
Classification: Polyoxypropylene, polyoxyethylene block polymer
Formula: $HO(CHCH_3CH_2O)_x(CH_2CH_2O)_y(CH_2CHCH_3O)_z)H$, avg. x=18, y=6, z=18
Properties: Nonionic liq.
Uses: Surfactant used in creams

Meroxapol 252
CAS 9003-11-6 (generic)
Classification: Polyoxypropylene, polyoxyethylene block polymer
Formula: $HO(CHCH_3CH_2O)_x(CH_2CH_2O)_y(CH_2CHCH_3O)_z)H$, avg. x=18, y=14, z=18
Uses: Surfactant used in creams; lubricant base
Trade names: Macol® 40

Meroxapol 254
CAS 9003-11-6 (generic)
Classification: Polyoxypropylene, polyoxyethylene block polymer
Formula: $HO(CHCH_3CH_2O)_x(CH_2CH_2O)_y(CH_2CHCH_3O)_z)H$, avg. x=18, y=34, z=18
Uses: Surfactant used in creams

Meroxapol 258
CAS 9003-11-6 (generic)
Classification: Polyoxypropylene, polyoxyethylene block polymer
Formula: $HO(CHCH_3CH_2O)_x(CH_2CH_2O)_y(CH_2CHCH_3O)_z)H$, avg. x=18, y=163, z=18
Uses: Surfactant used in creams

Meroxapol 311

Meroxapol 311
  CAS 9003-11-6 (generic)
  Classification: Polyoxypropylene, polyoxyethylene block polymer
  Formula: HO(CHCH$_3$CH$_2$O)$_x$(CH$_2$CH$_2$O)$_y$(CH$_2$CHCH$_3$O)$_z$)H, avg. x=21, y=7, z=21
  Properties: Nonionic liq.
  Uses: Surfactant used in creams; lubricant base
  Trade names: Macol® 33

Merphenyl nitrate. *See* Phenylmercuric nitrate
Merthiolate. *See* Thimerosal

Metanilic acid
  CAS 121-47-1; EINECS 204-473-6
  Synonyms: m-Sulfanilic acid; m-Aminobenzenesulfonic acid; Aniline-3-sulfonic acid
  Empirical: C$_6$H$_7$NO$_3$S
  Formula: C$_6$H$_4$(NH$_2$)SO$_3$H
  Properties: Sm. colorless need.; sol. in water, alcohol, ether; sl. sol. in ethanol; m.w. 173.18
  Uses: Azo dye mfg. (sodium salt); sulfa drug synthesis
  Manuf./Distrib.: EniChem Am.; Konishi Chem. Ind.; Sanwa Kagaku Kogyo
  Manuf./Distrib. (pharm. & food): Aldrich; R.W. Greeff

Metaphosphoric acid potassium salt. *See* Potassium metaphosphate
Metaphosphoric acid trisodium salt. *See* Sodium trimetaphosphate

Methacrylic acid
  CAS 79-41-4; EINECS 201-204-4
  UN No. 2531 (inhibited)
  Synonyms: α-Methylacrylic acid (monomer); 2-Methylpropenoic acid
  Empirical: C$_4$H$_6$O$_2$
  Formula: H$_2$C:C(CH$_3$)COOH
  Properties: Colorless liq., acrid odor; sol. in warm water, alcohol, ether, most org. solvs.; m.w. 86.09; dens.
    1.015 (20 C); m.p. 15-16 C; b.p. 163 C; flash pt. (OC) 76 C
  Precaution: Combustible; corrosive
  Toxicology: Toxic material; strong irritant to skin; TLV 20 ppm
  Uses: Used in ophthalmics
  Regulatory: FDA approved for ophthalmics
  Manuf./Distrib.: Kuraray; Mitsubishi Gas Chem.; Rohm & Haas
  Manuf./Distrib. (pharm. & food): Aldrich

β-Methacrylic acid. *See* Crotonic acid

Methacrylic acid copolymer
  Definition: Fully polymerized copolymer of methacrylic acid and an acrylic or methacrylic ester; Type C may
    contain surfactants
  Properties: Wh. powd., faint char. odor; sol. in dil. alkali, buffer sol'ns. of pH ≥ 7, methanol, alcohol, IPA,
    acetone; insol. in water, dil. acids; visc. 50-200 cps
  Uses: Coating agent for pharmaceuticals
  Regulatory: USP/NF compliance
  Trade names: Eudragit® L 100-55

Methacrylic acid polymer with divinylbenzene, potassium salt. *See* Polacrilin potassium
Methallyl butyrate. *See* 2-Methylallyl butyrate
Methanal. *See* Formaldehyde
Methanecarboxylic acid. *See* Acetic acid
Methanedicarbonic acid. *See* Malonic acid
Methane dichloride. *See* Methylene chloride
Methane-, dichloro-. *See* Methylene chloride
Methanesulfinic acid, hydroxy-, monosodium salt. *See* Sodium formaldehyde sulfoxylate

Methanesulfonic acid
  CAS 75-75-2; EINECS 200-898-6
  UN No. 2584, 2586
  Synonyms: Sulfomethane; Methylsulfonic acid
  Classification: Aliphatic organic compd.
  Formula: CH$_3$SO$_3$H
  Properties: Colorless liq.; sol. in water, alcohol, ether; m.w. 96.10; dens. 1.481; m.p. 20 C; b.p. 167 C (10 mm);
    flash pt. > 230 F; ref. index 1.4300

Toxicology: Corrosive to tissue
Uses: Used in parenterals
Regulatory: FDA approved for parenterals; BP compliance
Manuf./Distrib.: Toyo Kasei Kogyo

Methane, trichloro-. *See* Chloroform
Methanol. *See* Methyl alcohol

Methenamine hippurate
Uses: Formaldehyde-releasing antimicrobial preservative, antibacterial; oral drug for urinary antisepsis

(±)-Methionine. *See* DL-Methionine

DL-Methionine
CAS 59-51-8; EINECS 200-432-1
FEMA 3301
Synonyms: 2-Amino-4-(methylthio)butyric acid; DL-2-Amino-4-methylthiobutanaoic acid; (±)-2-Amino-4-(methylmercapto)butyric acid; Acimetion; (±)-Methionine
Classification: Amino acid
Empirical: $C_5H_{11}NO_2S$
Formula: $CH_3SCH_2CH_2CH(NH_2)COOH$
Properties: Wh. cryst. platelets or powd., char. odor; sol. in water, dil. acids and alkalies; very sl. sol. in alcohol; ins. in ether; m.w. 149.21; m.p. approx. 280 C (dec.); pH 5.6-6.1 (1%)
Precaution: Light-sensitive
Toxicology: Mod. toxic by ingestion and other routes; experimental reproductive effects; heated to decomp., emits toxic fumes of SO_x and NO_x
Uses: Dietary supplement in pharmaceuticals
Regulatory: FDA 21CFR §172.320, 3.1% max., not for infant foods; FEMA GRAS; Japan approved; BP, Ph.Eur. compliance
Manuf./Distrib.: Am. Roland; Degussa; Penta Mfg.; Spectrum Chem. Mfg.; U.S. Biochemical
Manuf./Distrib. (pharm. & food): Aldrich; Am. Roland; R.W. Greeff; Ruger; Spectrum Chem. Mfg.

L-Methionine
CAS 63-68-3; EINECS 200-562-9
Synonyms: 2-Amino-4-(methylthio)butyric acid; (S)-2-Amino-4-(methylmercapto)butyric acid
Classification: Amino acid
Empirical: $C_5H_{11}NO_2S$
Formula: $CH_3SCH_2CH_2CH(NH_2)COOH$
Properties: Wh. cryst. powd. or platelets, sl. char. odor; sol. in water, dil. acids, alkalies; insol. in abs. alcohol, alcohol, benzene, acetone, ether; m.w. 149.21; dens. 1.340; m.p. 281 C (dec.)
Precaution: Light-sensitive
Toxicology: LD50 (oral, rat) 36 g/kg; mildly toxic by ingestion, intraperitoneal routes; human mutagenic data; experimental teratogen, reproductive effects; heated to decomp., emits very toxic fumes of NO_x and SO_x
Uses: Dietary supplement in pharmaceuticals; lipotropic
Regulatory: FDA 21CFR §172.320, limitation 3.1%; Japan approved; BP compliance
Manuf./Distrib.: Degussa; Penta Mfg.; Spectrum Chem. Mfg.; U.S. Biochemical
Manuf./Distrib. (pharm. & food): Aldrich; R.W. Greeff

Methocel. *See* Methylcellulose
4´-Methoxyacetophenone. *See* Acetanisole
p-Methoxyacetophenone. *See* Acetanisole
p-Methoxyallylbenzene. *See* Estragole
2-Methoxyaniline. *See* o-Anisidine
3-Methoxyaniline. *See* m-Anisidine
4-Methoxyaniline. *See* p-Anisidine
m-Methoxyaniline. *See* m-Anisidine
o-Methoxyaniline. *See* o-Anisidine
p-Methoxyaniline. *See* p-Anisidine
2-Methoxybenzaldehyde. *See* o-Methoxybenzaldehyde
4-Methoxybenzaldehyde. *See* p-Anisaldehyde

o-Methoxybenzaldehyde
CAS 135-02-4; EINECS 205-171-7
Synonyms: o-Anisaldehyde; Methyl salicylaldehyde; 2-Methoxybenzaldehyde; Salicylaldehyde methyl ether
Empirical: $C_8H_8O_2$
Properties: Colorless or cream-colored cryst., faint sweet floral odor, spice-like flavor; m.w. 136.15; dens.

p-Methoxybenzaldehyde

      1.1326; m.p. 35-37 C; b.p. 243-244 C; ref. index 1.560
      Uses: Sweet flavoring agent
      Regulatory: FDA 21CFR §172.515
      Manuf./Distrib. (pharm. & food): Aldrich

p-Methoxybenzaldehyde. *See* p-Anisaldehyde
4-Methoxybenzenemethanol. *See* Anisyl alcohol
p-Methoxybenzyl acetate. *See* Anisyl acetate
4-Methoxybenzyl alcohol. *See* Anisyl alcohol
p-Methoxybenzyl alcohol. *See* Anisyl alcohol
p-Methoxybenzyl formate. *See* Anisyl formate
p-Methoxybenzyl propionate. *See* Anisyl propionate

o-Methoxycinnamaldehyde
      CAS 1504-74-1
      FEMA 3181
      Synonyms: o-Cumaric aldehyde methyl ether
      Empirical: $C_{10}H_{10}O_2$
      Properties: Pale yel. cryst. flakes, spicy-floral odor; sol. in alcohol, ether, chloroform; sl. sol. in water; m.w. 162.18; m.p. 45-46 C; b.p. 295 C
      Uses: Sweet synthetic flavoring agent
      Regulatory: FDA 21CFR §172.515; FEMA GRAS
      Manuf./Distrib. (pharm. & food): Aldrich

2-Methoxy-p-cresol. *See* 2-Methoxy-4-methylphenol
2-Methoxyethyl ether. *See* Diethylene glycol dimethyl ether

2-Methoxy-4-methylphenol
      CAS 93-51-6; EINECS 202-252-9
      FEMA 2671
      Synonyms: 4-Methylguaiacol; Creosol; 4-Hydroxy-3-methyl-1-methylbenzene; 2-Methoxy-p-cresol; 2-Hydroxy-5-methylanisole
      Empirical: $C_8H_{10}O_2$
      Properties: Colorless to ylsh. liq., vanilla-like odor; sol. in alcohol, ether, benzene; m.w. 138.17; dens. 1.092 (20/4 C); m.p. 5 C; b.p. 221-222 C; flash pt. 99 C; ref. index 1.537 (20 C)
      Toxicology: Irritating to eyes, skin, respiratory system
      Uses: Sweet vanilla-like synthetic flavoring agent
      Regulatory: FDA 21CFR §172.515; FEMA GRAS
      Manuf./Distrib. (pharm. & food): Aldrich

2-Methoxy-2-methylpropane. *See* Methyl t-butyl ether
p-Methoxy-β-methylstyrene. *See* Anethole
2-Methoxyphenol. *See* Guaiacol
4-Methoxyphenol. *See* Hydroquinone monomethyl ether
o-Methoxyphenol. *See* Guaiacol
4-Methoxyphenylacetic acid. *See* p-Methoxyphenylacetic acid

p-Methoxyphenylacetic acid
      CAS 104-01-8; EINECS 203-166-4
      Synonyms: 4-Methoxyphenylacetic acid; Homoanisic acid; p-Methoxy-α-toluic acid
      Classification: Aromatic organic compd.
      Empirical: $C_9H_{10}O_3$
      Formula: $CH_3OC_6H_4CH_2COOH$
      Properties: Off-wh. to pale yel. flakes; sol. in methanol; m.w. 166.18; m.p. 86-88.5 C; b.p. 140 C (3 mm)
      Uses: Pharmaceuticals, other organic compds.
      Manuf./Distrib.: Penta Mfg.; Schweizerhall
      Manuf./Distrib. (pharm. & food): Aldrich; R.W. Greeff; Junsei Chem.; Midori Kagaku

4-p-Methoxyphenyl-2-butanone
      CAS 104-20-1
      FEMA 2672
      Synonyms: Anisyl acetone
      Empirical: $C_{11}H_{14}O_2$
      Properties: M.w. 178.23; dens. 1.045; m.p. 8 C; b.p. 152-153 C (15 mm); flash pt. > 230 F
      Uses: Sweet cherry, raspberry-like synthetic flavoring agent
      Regulatory: FDA 21CFR §172.515; FEMA GRAS
      Manuf./Distrib. (pharm. & food): Aldrich

1-(p-Methoxyphenyl)-2-propanone
CAS 122-84-9
FEMA 2674
Synonyms: Anisylmethyl ketone; Anisic ketone
Empirical: $C_{10}H_{12}O_2$
Properties: M.w. 164.20; dens. 1.067; b.p. 145 C (25 mm); flash pt. 215 F
Uses: Caramel, vanilla-like synthetic flavoring agent
Regulatory: FDA 21CFR §172.515; FEMA GRAS
Manuf./Distrib. (pharm. & food): Aldrich

Methoxy polyethylene glycol. *See* Polyethylene glycol monomethyl ether
1-Methoxy-4-propenylbenzene. *See* Anethole
1-Methoxy-4-(2-propenyl) benzene. *See* Estragole
p-Methoxypropenylbenzene. *See* Anethole
2-Methoxy-4-propenylphenol. *See* Isoeugenol
2-Methoxy-4-(2-propenyl) phenol. *See* Eugenol
2-Methoxy-4-propenylphenyl acetate. *See* Acetisoeugenol
2-Methoxy-4-propenylphenyl phenylacetate. *See* Isoeugenyl phenylacetate
Methoxypyrazine. *See* 2-Methoxypyrazine

2-Methoxypyrazine
CAS 3149-28-8
FEMA 3302
Synonyms: Methoxypyrazine
Empirical: $C_5H_6N_2O$
Properties: M.w. 110.12; dens. 1.110; b.p. 60-61 C (29 mm); flash pt. 114 F
Uses: Sweet, cocoa-like flavoring agent
Regulatory: FEMA GRAS
Manuf./Distrib. (pharm. & food): Aldrich

p-Methoxy-α-toluic acid. *See* p-Methoxyphenylacetic acid

2-Methoxy-4-vinylphenol
CAS 7786-61-0
FEMA 2675
Synonyms: p-Vinylguaiacol; 4-Hydroxy-3-methoxystyrene
Empirical: $C_9H_{10}O_2$
Properties: M.w. 150.18
Uses: Apple-like synthetic flavoring agent
Regulatory: FDA 21CFR §172.515; FEMA GRAS
Manuf./Distrib. (pharm. & food): Aldrich

Methylacetic acid. *See* Propionic acid

Methyl acetoacetate
CAS 105-45-3; EINECS 203-299-8
Synonyms: MAA
Classification: Aliphatic organic compd.
Empirical: $C_5H_8O_3$
Formula: $CH_3COCH_2COOCH_3$
Properties: M.w. 116.1; dens. 1.076 (20/4 C); b.p. 167-170 C; flash pt. 62 C
Toxicology: Eye irritant
Uses: Pharmaceutical intermediate
Manuf./Distrib.: Aceto; Eastman; Fluka; Lonza; Penta Mfg.
Manuf./Distrib. (pharm. & food): Aldrich

4´-Methyl acetophenone
CAS 122-00-9; EINECS 204-514-8
FEMA 2677
Synonyms: Methyl p-tolyl ketone; 1-Methyl-4-acetyl benzene; p-Methylacetophenone; p-Acetyl toluene
Empirical: $C_9H_{10}O$
Properties: Colorless liq., fruity-floral odor, strawberry-like flavor; insol. in water; m.w. 134.18; dens. 1.004 (20/ 4 C); m.p. -23 C; b.p. 220-223 C; flash pt. 82 C; ref. index 1.534 (20 C)
Uses: Fruity synthetic flavoring agent
Regulatory: FDA 21CFR §172.515; FEMA GRAS; Japan approved as flavoring
Manuf./Distrib. (pharm. & food): Aldrich

p-Methylacetophenone. *See* 4´-Methyl acetophenone
Methylacetopyronone. *See* Dehydroacetic acid
1-Methyl-4-acetyl benzene. *See* 4´-Methyl acetophenone

Methyl acrylate (monomer)
    CAS 96-33-3; EINECS 202-500-6
    UN No. 1919
    Synonyms: 2-Propenoic acid methyl ester; Acrylic acid methyl ester
    Classification: Aliphatic organic compd.
    Definition: Ester of methyl alcohol and acrylic acid
    Empirical: $C_4H_6O_2$
    Formula: CH_2:$CHCOOCH_3$
    Properties: Colorless volatile liq.; sl. sol. in water; m.w. 86.1; dens. 0.9574 (20/20 C); m.p. -76.5 C; b.p. 79-80 C; flash pt. (TOC) 25 F; ref. index 1.401 (20 C)
    Precaution: Flamm.; dangerous fire and explosion risk
    Toxicology: Toxic by inhalation, ingestion, and skin absorption; irritant to skin and eyes; TLV 10 ppm in air; LD50 (rat, oral) 0.3 g/kg
    Uses: Used in orals
    Regulatory: FDA approved for orals
    Manuf./Distrib.: Asahi Chem. Ind.; BASF; Hoechst Celanese; Mitsubishi Chem.; Showa Denko
    Manuf./Distrib. (pharm. & food): Aldrich

α-**Methylacrylic acid (monomer).** *See* Methacrylic acid

Methyl alcohol
    CAS 67-56-1; EINECS 200-659-6
    UN No. 1230
    Synonyms: Methanol; Wood alcohol; Wood naphtha; Wood spirit; Carbinol; Columbian spirits; Methyl hydroxide; Methylol
    Empirical: CH_4O
    Formula: CH_3OH
    Properties: Clear colorless liq., alcoholic odor (pure), pungent odor (crude); highly polar; misc. with water, alcohol, ether, benzene, ketones; m.w. 32.05; dens. 0.7924; m.p. -97.8 C; b.p. 64.5 C (760 mm); flash pt.(OC) 54 F; ref. index 1.3292 (20 C)
    Precaution: DOT: Flamm. liq.; dangerous fire risk; explosive limits 6.0-36.5% vol. in air; reacts vigorously with oxidizers; heated to decomp., emits acrid smoke and irritating fumes
    Toxicology: LD50 (oral, rat) 5628 mg/kg; toxic (causes blindness); poisonous by ingestion, inhalation, or percutaneous absorption; experimental teratogen, reproductive effects; eye and skin irritant; narcotic; usual fatal dose 100-250 ml; TLV 200 ppm in air
    Uses: Solvent, excipient; used in orals
    Regulatory: FDA 21CFR §172.560, 173.250, 173.385, 175.105, 176.180, 176.200, 176.210, 177.2420, 177.2460, 27CFR §21.115; FDA approved for orals; USP/NF, BP compliance
    Manuf./Distrib.: Air Prods.; Albright & Wilson; Ashland; Brown; Coyne; CPS; DuPont; Eastman; General Chem.; Hoechst Celanese; Mitsui Toatsu; Nissan Chem. Ind.; Norsk Hydro A/S; Quantum/USI; Veckridge
    Manuf./Distrib. (pharm. & food): Albright & Wilson; Aldrich; Eastman; Hoechst Celanese; Integra; Mallinckrodt; Ruger; Spectrum Chem. Mfg.
    Trade names containing: Filmex® A-2; Filmex® B; Filmex® C; Filmex® D-1; Filmex® D-2

2-Methylallyl butyrate
    FEMA 2678
    Synonyms: 2-Methyl-2-propenyl butyrate; Methallyl butyrate; Isopropenyl carbinyl-n-butyrate
    Definition: Ester of β-methylallyl alcohol and butyric acid
    Empirical: $C_8H_{14}O_2$
    Properties: Colorless liq., fruity ethereal odor; sol. in alcohol; insol. in water; m.w. 142.19; b.p. 168 C
    Uses: Synthetic flavoring agent
    Regulatory: FDA 21CFR §172.515; FEMA GRAS

Methylaminoacetic acid. *See* Sarcosine
Methyl 2-aminobenzoate. *See* Methyl anthranilate
Methyl-o-aminobenzoate. *See* Methyl anthranilate
1-Methylamino-1-deoxy-D-glucitol. *See* Meglumine
2-Methylamino methyl benzoate. *See* Dimethyl anthranilate

Methyl n-amyl ketone
    CAS 110-43-0; EINECS 203-767-1
    FEMA 2544

Synonyms: MAK; 2-Heptanone; Ketone C-7; n-Amyl methyl ketone; Methyl pentyl ketone
Empirical: $C_7H_{14}O$
Formula: $CH_3CH_2CH_2CH_2CH_2COCH_3$
Properties: Water-white liq., penetrating fruity odor; almost insol. in water; misc. with org. solvs.; m.w. 114.18; dens. 0.8166 (20/20 C); b.p. 150.6 C; flash pt. 49 C; ref. index 1.4110 (20 C)
Precaution: Combustible; moderate fire risk; reactive with oxidizing materials
Toxicology: LD50 (oral, rat) 1670 mg/kg; mod. toxic by ingestion; mildly toxic by inhalation, skin contact; skin irritant; narcotic in high concs.; TLV 50 ppm in air; heated to decomp., emits acrid smoke and fumes
Uses: Banana-like synthetic flavoring agent
Regulatory: FDA 21CFR §172.515; FEMA GRAS
Manuf./Distrib.: Aldrich; Ashland; Eastman; Union Carbide; Van Waters & Rogers
Manuf./Distrib. (pharm. & food): Aldrich; Ashland; Eastman

Methyl anthranilate
CAS 134-20-3; EINECS 205-132-4
FEMA 2682
Synonyms: Methyl-o-aminobenzoate; Methyl 2-anthranilate; Methyl 2-aminobenzoate; Neroli oil, artificial; Anthranilic acid methyl ester; 2-Aminobenzoic acid methyl ester
Classification: Aromatic organic compd.
Definition: Ester of methyl alcohol and 2-aminobenzoic acid
Empirical: $C_8H_9NO_2$
Formula: $H_2NC_6H_4CO_2CH_3$
Properties: Cryst. or pale yel. liq., bluish fluorescence, grape-like odor; sol. in fixed oils, propylene glycol; sl. sol. in water; insol. in glycerol; m.w. 151.18; dens. 1.167-1.175 (15 C); m.p. 23.8 C; b.p. 258-261 C; flash pt. 123 C; ref. index 1.583 (20 C)
Precaution: Light-sensitive
Toxicology: LD50 (oral, rat) 2910 mg/kg; poison by intravenous route; mod. toxic by ingestion; skin irritant; experimental tumorigen; heated to decomp., emits toxic fumes of NO_x
Uses: Intermediate for pharmaceuticals; flavoring agent (grape and berry); orange scent for ointments, sun tan oils
Regulatory: FDA 21CFR §182.60, GRAS; FEMA GRAS; Japan approved as flavoring
Manuf./Distrib.: Aldrich; BASF; Bell Flavors & Fragrances; Haarmann & Reimer; PMC Specialties; Spectrum Chem. Mfg.
Manuf./Distrib. (pharm. & food): Aldrich; Bell Flavors & Fragrances; Haarmann & Reimer; PMC Specialties

Methyl 2-anthranilate. *See* Methyl anthranilate
1-Methyl N-L-α-aspartyl-L-phenylalanine. *See* Aspartame
4-Methylbenzaldehyde. *See* p-Tolyl aldehyde
p-Methyl benzaldehyde. *See* p-Tolyl aldehyde
Methyl benzenecarboxylate. *See* Methyl benzoate
4-Methylbenzenesulfonic acid. *See* p-Toluene sulfonic acid
p-Methylbenzenesulfonic acid. *See* p-Toluene sulfonic acid

Methylbenzethonium chloride
CAS 25155-18-4; EINECS 246-675-7
Synonyms: Diisobutyl cresoxy ethoxy ethyl dimethyl benzyl ammonium chloride
Classification: Quaternary ammonium salt
Empirical: $C_{28}H_{44}NO_2 \cdot Cl$
Properties: Colorless to wh. cryst., odorless, bitter taste; hygroscopic; readily sol. in alcohol, hot benzene, Cellosolve, water; pract. insol. in chloroform; insol. in CCl_4, ether; m.w. 462.12; m.p. 161-163 C
Uses: Medicine; topical anti-infective; bactericide; sanitizer
Regulatory: USP/NF compliance
Manuf./Distrib.: Spectrum Chem. Mfg.
Trade names: Hyamine® 10X

Methyl benzoate
CAS 93-58-3; EINECS 202-259-7
FEMA 2683
Synonyms: Benzoic acid methyl ester; Niobe oil; Oil of niobe; Methyl benzenecarboxylate
Classification: Ester
Empirical: $C_8H_8O_2$
Formula: $C_6H_5COOCH_3$
Properties: Colorless liq., fragrant odor; sol. in alcohol, fixed oils, propylene glycol, water @ 30 C; misc. with alcohol, ether; insol. in glycerin; m.w. 136.15; dens. 1.082-1.088; m.p. -12.5 C; b.p. 199.6 C; flash pt. 181 F; ref. index 1.515

α-Methylbenzyl acetate

Precaution: Combustible; reactive with oxidizing materials
Toxicology: LD50 (oral, rat) 1350 mg/kg; mod. toxic by ingestion; mildly toxic by skin contact; skin and eye irritant; heated to decomp., emits acrid smoke and irritating fumes
Uses: Fruity synthetic flavoring agent
Regulatory: FDA 21CFR §172.515; FEMA GRAS
Manuf./Distrib.: Aldrich; Hüls AG; Morflex; Pentagon Chem. Ltd; Penta Mfg.; Schweizerhall; Sybron
Manuf./Distrib. (pharm. & food): Aldrich; Hüls AG

α-Methylbenzyl acetate
CAS 93-92-5
FEMA 2684
Synonyms: Styralyl acetate; Styrolene acetate; Gardenol; 1-Phenylethyl acetate; α-Phenylethyl acetate; Methyl phenylcarbinyl acetate
Empirical: $C_{10}H_{12}O_2$
Properties: Colorless liq., gardenia odor; sol. in fixed oils, glycerin; insol. in water; m.w. 164.20; dens. 1.023; b.p. 94-95 C (12 mm); flash pt. 196 F; ref. index 1.493-1.497
Precaution: Combustible liq.
Toxicology: Heated to decomp., emits acrid smoke and irritating fumes
Uses: Apple, apricot, pineapple, plum-like synthetic flavoring agent
Regulatory: FDA 21CFR §172.515; FEMA GRAS
Manuf./Distrib. (pharm. & food): Aldrich; Hüls AG

α-Methylbenzyl butyrate
CAS 3460-44-4
FEMA 2686
Synonyms: Styralyl butyrate; Methyl phenylcarbinyl butyrate
Empirical: $C_{12}H_{16}O_2$
Properties: M.w. 192.26; dens. 0.990; b.p. 83-84 C (3 mm); flash pt. 229 F
Uses: Fruity synthetic flavoring agent
Regulatory: FDA 21CFR §172.515; FEMA GRAS
Manuf./Distrib. (pharm. & food): Aldrich

3-Methyl-1,3-butadiene polymer with 2-methyl-1-propene. See Isobutylene/isoprene copolymer
2-Methylbutanal-1. See 2-Methylbutyraldehyde
3-Methylbutanal. See Isovaleraldehyde
3-Methyl-1,3-butanediol. See Isopentyldiol
3-Methylbutanoic acid ethyl ester. See Ethyl isovalerate
2-Methylbutanoic acid n-hexyl ester. See Hexyl 2-methylbutyrate
3-Methylbutanoic acid methyl ester. See Methyl isovalerate
2-Methyl-2-butanol. See t-Amyl alcohol
3-Methylbutanol. See Isoamyl alcohol
3-Methyl-1-butanol. See Isoamyl alcohol
3-Methyl-1-butanol acetate. See Isoamyl acetate

3-Methyl-2-buten-1-ol
CAS 556-82-1; EINECS 209-141-4
FEMA 3647
Synonyms: Prenol; 3,3-Dimethylallyl alcohol
Empirical: $C_5H_{10}O$
Formula: $(CH_3)_2C{:}CHCH_2OH$
Properties: M.w. 86.14; dens. 0.861 (20/4 C); b.p. 143-144 C; flash pt. 110 F; ref. index 1.443
Precaution: Flamm.
Toxicology: Harmful if swallowed; irritating to skin
Uses: Fruity flavoring agent
Regulatory: FEMA GRAS
Manuf./Distrib. (pharm. & food): Aldrich

2-Methylbutyl acetate
CAS 53496-15-4
FEMA 3644
Empirical: $C_7H_{14}O_2$
Properties: M.w. 130.19; dens. 0.876; b.p. 138 C (741 mm); flash pt. 95 F
Uses: Fruity banana-like flavoring agent
Regulatory: FEMA GRAS
Manuf./Distrib. (pharm. & food): Aldrich

β-Methylbutyl acetate. *See* Isoamyl acetate

Methyl t-butyl ether
CAS 1634-04-4; EINECS 216-653-1
UN No. 2398
Synonyms: MTBE; Methyl tertiary butyl ether; t-Butyl methyl ether; 2-Methoxy-2-methylpropane
Classification: Aliphatic ether
Empirical: $C_5H_{12}O$
Formula: $CH_3OC(CH_3)_3$
Properties: Clear liq., terpene-like odor; sl. sol. in water; misc. with all gasoline-type hydrocarbons; m.w. 88.15; dens. 0.7335; b.p. 91.1 C; f.p. -75 C; flash pt. -25.6 C
Precaution: Flamm.
Toxicology: Slight skin and eye irritant
Uses: Solvent, reaction medium in pharmaceuticals
Manuf./Distrib.: Allchem Ind.; Arco; Ashland; Fluka; Hüls Am.; Texas Petrochem.
Manuf./Distrib. (pharm. & food): Aldrich
Trade names: High Purity MTBE

2-Methylbutyl isovalerate
CAS 2445-77-4
FEMA 3506
Synonyms: 2-Methylbutyl-3-methylbutanoate
Empirical: $C_{10}H_{20}O_2$
Properties: M.w. 172.27; dens. 0.858; flash pt. 143 F
Uses: Apple-like flavoring agent
Regulatory: FDA 21CFR §172.515; FEMA GRAS
Manuf./Distrib. (pharm. & food): Aldrich

2-Methylbutyl-3-methylbutanoate. *See* 2-Methylbutyl isovalerate
3-Methylbutyl 2-methylpropanoate. *See* Isoamyl isobutyrate

Methyl butynol
CAS 115-19-5; EINECS 204-070-5
UN No. 1993
Synonyms: 2-Methyl-3-butyn-2-ol; Dimethyl ethynyl carbinol
Classification: Aliphatic organic compd.
Definition: Tertiary acetylenic alcohol
Empirical: C_5H_8O
Formula: $(CH_3)_2COHCCH$
Properties: Colorless liq., fragrant odor; misc. with water; sol. in most org. solvs.; m.w. 84.13; dens. 0.8672 (20/20 C); m.p. 2.6 C; b.p. 104-105 C; flash pt. (TOC) 25 C; ref. index 0.861 (20C)
Precaution: Flamm.
Toxicology: Moderately toxic by ingestion, intraperitoneal, subcutaneous routes
Uses: Reactive intermediate for pharmaceutical mfg.
Manuf./Distrib.: Air Prods.; BASF

2-Methyl-3-butyn-2-ol. *See* Methyl butynol

2-Methylbutyraldehyde
CAS 96-17-3; EINECS 202-485-6
FEMA 2691
Synonyms: Methyl ethyl acetaldehyde; 2-Methylbutanal-1
Empirical: $C_5H_{10}O$
Formula: $C_2H_5CH(CH_3)CHO$
Properties: Colorless liq.; sol. in alcohol; sl. sol. in water; m.w. 86.13; dens. 0.82 (20/4 C); b.p. 90-92 C; flash pt. 40 F
Precaution: Highly flamm.
Uses: Chocolate synthetic flavoring agent
Regulatory: FDA 21CFR §172.515; FEMA GRAS
Manuf./Distrib. (pharm. & food): Aldrich

3-Methylbutyraldehyde. *See* Isovaleraldehyde

2-Methylbutyric acid
CAS 600-07-7; EINECS 209-982-7
FEMA 2695
Synonyms: Carboxylic acid C_5

Methyl caproate

    Empirical: $C_5H_{10}O_2$
    Formula: $CH_3CH_2CH(CH_3)COOH$
    Properties: M.w. 102.14; dens. 0.934 (20/4 C); b.p. 173-176 C; flash pt. 83 C; ref. index 1.405
    Toxicology: Causes burns
    Uses: Fruity synthetic flavoring agent
    Regulatory: FDA 21CFR §172.515; FEMA GRAS
    Manuf./Distrib.: BASF
    Manuf./Distrib. (pharm. & food): Aldrich

Methyl caproate
    CAS 106-70-7; EINECS 203-425-1
    FEMA 2708
    Synonyms: Methyl hexanoate; Methyl 2-hexanoate
    Definition: Ester of methyl alcohol and caproic acid
    Empirical: $C_7H_{14}O_2$
    Formula: $CH_3(CH_2)_4COOCH_3$
    Properties: M.w. 130.19; dens. 0.884 (20/4 C); b.p. 150-151 C; flash pt. 43 C; ref. index 1.405
    Precaution: Flamm.
    Uses: Pineapple-like synthetic flavoring agent
    Regulatory: FDA 21CFR §172.515; FEMA GRAS
    Manuf./Distrib. (pharm. & food): Aldrich

Methyl caprylate
    CAS 111-11-5; EINECS 203-835-0
    FEMA 2728
    Synonyms: Methyl octanoate
    Definition: Ester of methyl alcohol and caprylic acid
    Empirical: $C_9H_{18}O_2$
    Formula: $CH_3(CH_2)_6COOCH_3$
    Properties: M.w. 158.24; dens. 0.875 (20/4 C); b.p. 193-194 C; flash pt. 69 C; ref. index 1.417 (20 C)
    Uses: Citrus synthetic flavoring agent
    Regulatory: FDA 21CFR §172.225, 172.515, 176.200, 176.210, 177.2800; FEMA GRAS
    Manuf./Distrib. (pharm. & food): Aldrich

Methylcatechol. *See* Guaiacol

Methylcellulose
    CAS 9004-67-5
    FEMA 2696
    Synonyms: MC; Cellulose methyl ether; Cologel; Methocel; Citrucel
    Definition: Methyl ether of cellulose
    Properties: Grayish-white fibrous powd., odorless, tasteless; aq. suspension swells in water to visc. colloidal sol'n.; sol. in cold water, glacial acetic acid, some org. solvs.; insol. in alcohol, ether, chloroform, warm water; m.w. 86,000-115,000
    Precaution: Combustible
    Toxicology: Nontoxic; nonallergenic; may cause immune responses; heated to decomp., emits acrid smoke and irritating fumes
    Uses: Thickener, suspending agent, stabilizer, emulsifier, dispersant, filler, tablet binder, coating agent; used in buccals, injectables, ophthalmics, orals, topicals, vaginals; placebo tablets and capsules; bulk laxative
    Regulatory: FDA 21CFR §150.141, 150.161, 175.105, 175.210, 175.300, 176.200, 182.1480, GRAS; USDA 9CFR §318.7, limitation 0.15% in meat and vegetable prods.; FEMA GRAS; Japan restricted (2% max.); Europe listed; UK approved; FDA approved for buccals, injectables, ophthalmics, orals, topicals, vaginals; USP/NF, BP, Ph.Eur. compliance
    Manuf./Distrib.: Aceto; Allchem Ind.; Aqualon; Ashland; Chemcentral; Courtaulds Water Soluble Polymers; Hoechst Celanese; Punda Mercantile; Shin-Etsu Chem.
    Manuf./Distrib. (pharm. & food): Aldrich; Am. Roland; Aqualon; Courtaulds; Croxton & Garry; Hercules; N I Ibrahim; Integra; Nordmann Rassmann; Penta Mfg.; Roeper; Ruger; Spectrum Chem. Mfg.; Van Waters & Rogers
    Trade names: Benecel® Methylcellulose; Methocel® A4C Premium; Methocel® A4M Premium; Methocel® A15C Premium; Methocel® A15-LV; Methocel® A15LV Premium; Methocel® A Premium
    Trade names containing: Mearlmaid® AA; Mearlmaid® TR

Methyl chavicol. *See* Estragole

Methylchloroisothiazolinone
    CAS 26172-55-4; EINECS 247-500-7

Synonyms: 5-Chloro-2-methyl-4-isothiazolin-3-one; 4-Isothiazolin-3-one, 5-chloro-2-methyl-; Chloro-methylisothiazolinone
Classification: Heterocyclic organic compd.
Empirical: C_4H_4CINOS
Uses: Antimicrobial preservative for topical drug prods.
Regulatory: FDA 21CFR §175.105, 176.170

α-Methylcinnamaldehyde
CAS 101-39-3
FEMA 2697
Empirical: $C_{10}H_{10}O$
Properties: M.w. 146.19; dens. 1.037; b.p. 148-149 C (27 mm); flash pt. 175 F
Uses: Cinnamon-like synthetic flavoring agent
Regulatory: FDA 21CFR §172.515; FEMA GRAS
Manuf./Distrib. (pharm. & food): Aldrich

Methyl cinnamate
CAS 103-26-4; EINECS 203-093-8
FEMA 2698
Synonyms: Methyl-3-phenyl propenoate; Methyl cinnamylate
Empirical: $C_{10}H_{10}O_2$
Formula: $C_6H_5CH:CHCOOCH_3$
Properties: Wh. to sl. yel. cryst., fruity odor; very sol. in alcohol, ether; sol. in fixed oils, glycerin, propylene glycol; insol. in water; m.w. 162.20; dens. 1.042 (36/0 C); m.p. 33.4 C; b.p. 263 C; flash pt. > 212 F
Precaution: Combustible
Toxicology: LD50 (oral, rat) 2610 mg/kg; mod. toxic by ingestion; heated to decomp., emits acrid smoke and irritating fumes
Uses: Strawberry-like synthetic flavoring agent
Regulatory: FDA 21CFR §172.515; FEMA GRAS; Japan approved as flavoring
Manuf./Distrib.: Aldrich; BASF
Manuf./Distrib. (pharm. & food): Aldrich

Methyl cinnamylate. *See* Methyl cinnamate
N-Methyl-N-(1-coconut alkyl) glycine. *See* Cocoyl sarcosine

6-Methylcoumarin
CAS 92-48-8
FEMA 2699
Empirical: $C_{10}H_8O_2$
Properties: Dry herbaceous coconut; m.w. 160.17; m.p. 73-76 C; b.p. 303 C (725 mm)
Uses: Coconut-like synthetic flavoring agent
Regulatory: FEMA GRAS
Manuf./Distrib. (pharm. & food): Aldrich

Methyl cyanide. *See* Acetonitrile

Methyl cyanoacetate
CAS 105-34-0; EINECS 203-288-8
Synonyms: Malonic methyl ester nitrile
Definition: Ester of cyanoacetic acid and methanol
Empirical: $C_4H_5NO_2$
Formula: $NCCH_2COOCH_3$
Properties: Colorless liq.; sol. in water, alcohol, ether; m.w. 99.09; dens. 1.123; m.p. -13 C; b.p. 204-207 C; flash pt. > 230 F; ref. index 1.4170
Toxicology: Irritant
Uses: Organic synthesis, pharmaceuticals
Manuf./Distrib.: R.W. Greeff; Hüls Am.; Lonza
Manuf./Distrib. (pharm. & food): Aldrich; Hüls Troisdorf Ag; Lonza Ltd

Methyl-α-cyclodextrin
Uses: Bioavailability enhancer; odor/taste masking; stabilizer
Trade names: Alpha W6 M1.8

Methyl-β-cyclodextrin
Uses: Bioavailability enhancer; odor/taste masking; stabilizer
Trade names: Beta W7 M1.8

Methyl-γ-cyclodextrin
Definition: Complex hosting guest molecule
Uses: Bioavailability enhancer; odor/taste masking; stabilizer
Trade names: Gamma W8 M1.8

3-Methyl-2-cyclohexen-1-one
CAS 1193-18-6
FEMA 3360
Empirical: $C_7H_{10}O$
Properties: M.w. 110.16; dens. 0.971; b.p. 199-200 C; flash pt. 155 F
Uses: Medicinal, mild cherry flavoring agent
Regulatory: FEMA GRAS
Manuf./Distrib. (pharm. & food): Aldrich

Methyl dimethylacetate. *See* Methyl isobutyrate
Methyl 2,4-dimethylphenyl ketone. *See* 2,4-Dimethylacetophenone
4-Methyl-1,3-dioxolan-2-one. *See* Propylene carbonate
Methyl dodecanoate. *See* Methyl laurate
Methyl enanthate. *See* Methyl heptanoate
N,N´´-Methylenebis[N´-[1-(hydroxymethyl)-2,5-dioxo-4-imidazolindinyl]urea]. *See* Imidazolidinyl urea
2,2´-Methylenebis (3,4,6-trichlorophenol). *See* Hexachlorophene

Methylene casein
Uses: Tablet disintegrant
Trade names: Plasvita® TSM

Methylene chloride
CAS 75-09-2; EINECS 200-838-9
UN No. 1593
Synonyms: DCM; Dichloromethane; Methylene dichloride; Methane dichloride; Methane-, dichloro-
Classification: Halogenated organic compd.
Empirical: CH_2Cl_2
Properties: Colorless clear volatile liq., penetrating ether-like odor; sol. in alcohol, ether; misc. with fixed and volatile oils; sl. sol. in water; m.w. 84.93; dens. 1.335 (15/4 C); f.p. -97 C; b.p. 40.1 C; ref. index 1.4244 (20 C)
Precaution: Nonflamm.; explosive as vapor exposed to heat or flame; contact with hot surfaces cause decomp., yielding toxic fumes; heated to decomp., emits highly toxic fumes of phosgene and Cl⁻
Toxicology: LD50 (oral, rat) 2136 mg/kg; poison by IV route; mod. toxic by ingestion, subcutaneous, IP routes; experimental carcinogen; human systemic effects; eye and severe skin irritant; human mutagenic data; narcotic in high concs.; ACGIH TLV:TWA 50 ppm
Uses: Solvent; anesthetic in medicine; used in orals
Regulatory: FDA 21CFR §73.1 (no residue), 173.255; FDA approved for orals; USP/NF compliance
Manuf./Distrib.: Ashland; R.E. Carroll; Chemcentral; Elf Atochem N. Am.; Farleyway Chem. Ltd; C.P. Hall; Harcros; Hüls Am.; ICI Specialties; Mallinckrodt; Mitsui Toatsu Chem.; Occidental; Samson; Spectrum Chem. Mfg.; Stanchem; TR-AMC; Van Waters & Rogers; Vulcan
Manuf./Distrib. (pharm. & food): Aldrich; Ashland; ICI Specialties; Integra; Spectrum Chem. Mfg.

Methylene dichloride. *See* Methylene chloride
3,4-Methylene dihydroxybenzaldehyde. *See* Heliotropine
3,4-Methylenedioxybenzaldehyde. *See* Heliotropine

1,2-Methylenedioxybenzene
CAS 274-09-9
Synonyms: MDB; 1,3-Benzodioxole; 1,3-Dioxaindane
Properties: Colorless liq.
Uses: Intermediate for mfg. of pharmaceuticals, flavors and fragrances; antibacterial compds.
Manuf./Distrib.: James River
Manuf./Distrib. (pharm. & food): Aldrich; James River

3,4-Methylenedioxybenzyl acetate. *See* Piperonyl acetate
3,4-Methylenedioxybenzyl isobutyrate. *See* Piperonyl isobutyrate
Methyl ethyl acetaldehyde. *See* 2-Methylbutyraldehyde
1-Methylethyl acetate. *See* Isopropyl acetate
4-(1-Methylethyl)benzaldehyde. *See* Cuminaldehyde
1-Methylethyl dodecanoate. *See* Isopropyl laurate
Methyl ethylene glycol. *See* Propylene glycol
1-Methylethyl hexandecanoate. *See* Isopropyl palmitate

1-Methylethyl-4-hydroxybenzoate. *See* Isopropylparaben
1-Methylethyl octadecanoate. *See* Isopropyl stearate
1-Methylethyl tetradecanoate. *See* Isopropyl myristate

Methyl 2-furoate
  CAS 611-13-2
  FEMA 2703
  Synonyms: Methyl pyromucate
  Empirical: $C_6H_6O_3$
  Properties: M.w. 126.11; dens. 1.179; b.p. 181 C; flash pt. 164 F
  Uses: Fruity flavoring agent
  Regulatory: FEMA GRAS
  Manuf./Distrib. (pharm. & food): Aldrich

N-Methylglucamine. *See* Meglumine

Methyl gluceth-10
  CAS 68239-42-9
  Synonyms: PEG-10 methyl glucose ether; POE (10) methyl glucose ether
  Definition: PEG ether of methyl glucose
  Formula: $CH_3 \cdot C_6H_{10}O_5 \cdot (OCH_2CH_2)_nOH$, avg. n = 10
  Uses: Solvent and solubilizer for topical pharmaceuticals
  Trade names: Glucam® E-10

Methyl gluceth-20
  CAS 68239-43-0
  Synonyms: PEG-20 methyl glucose ether; POE (20) methyl glucose ether
  Definition: PEG ether of methyl glucose
  Formula: $CH_3 \cdot C_6H_{10}O_5 \cdot (OCH_2CH_2)_nOH$, avg. n = 20
  Uses: Solvent and solubilizer for topical pharmaceuticals
  Trade names: Glucam® E-20

Methyl gluceth-20 distearate
  CAS 98073-10-0
  Uses: Emulsifier, emollient, lubricant for pharmaceuticals
  Trade names: Glucam® E-20 Distearate

N-Methylglycine. *See* Sarcosine
Methyl glycocoll. *See* Sarcosine
Methyl glycol. *See* Propylene glycol
Methylglyoxal. *See* Pyruvaldehyde
4-Methylguaiacol. *See* 2-Methoxy-4-methylphenol

Methyl heptanoate
  CAS 106-73-0; EINECS 203-428-8
  FEMA 2705
  Synonyms: Methyl enanthate; Heptanoic acid methyl ester
  Empirical: $C_8H_{16}O_2$
  Formula: $CH_3(CH_2)_5COOCH_3$
  Properties: Liq.; m.w. 144.22; dens. 0.881 (20/4 C); m.p. -55.8 C; b.p. 173.8 C; flash pt. 55 C; ref. index 1.412 (20 C)
  Precaution: Flamm.
  Uses: Berry-like synthetic flavoring agent
  Regulatory: FDA 21CFR §172.515; FEMA GRAS
  Manuf./Distrib. (pharm. & food): Aldrich

6-Methyl-5-heptene-2-one. *See* Methyl heptenone
Methyl-5-hepten-2-ol. *See* Methyl heptenone

Methyl heptenone
  CAS 110-93-0, 409-02-9; EINECS 203-816-7
  FEMA 2707
  Synonyms: 6-Methyl-5-heptene-2-one; Methyl-5-hepten-2-ol
  Empirical: $C_8H_{14}O$
  Formula: $(CH_3)_2C{:}CHCH_2CH_2COCH_3$
  Properties: Sl. yel. liq., citrus-lemongrass odor; misc. with alcohol, ether chloroform; insol. in water; m.w. 126.22; dens. 0.846-0.851; m.p. -67 C; b.p. 173-174 C; flash pt. 55 C; ref. index 1.438-1.442
  Precaution: Combustible

Methyl heptyl ketone

Toxicology: LD50 (oral, rat) 3500 mg/kg; mod. toxic by ingestion; skin irritant; heated to decomp., emits acrid smoke and irritating fumes
Uses: Synthetic flavoring agent
Regulatory: FDA 21CFR §172.515; FEMA GRAS
Manuf./Distrib.: BASF
Manuf./Distrib. (pharm. & food): Aldrich

Methyl heptyl ketone. *See* 2-Nonanone
Methyl hexanoate. *See* Methyl caproate
Methyl 2-hexanoate. *See* Methyl caproate

Methyl hexyl ketone
CAS 111-13-7; EINECS 203-837-1
FEMA 2802
Synonyms: 2-Octanone; Hexyl methyl ketone
Empirical: $C_8H_{16}O$
Formula: $CH_3(CH_2)_5COCH_3$
Properties: Liq., apple odor, camphor taste; misc. with alcohol, ether; insol. in water; m.w. 128.22; dens. 0.818 (20/4 C); m.p. -16 C; b.p. 170-172 C; flash pt. 56 C; ref. index 1.416 (20 C)
Precaution: Flamm.
Uses: Fruity synthetic flavoring agent
Regulatory: FDA 21CFR §172.515; FEMA GRAS
Manuf./Distrib.: Union Camp
Manuf./Distrib. (pharm. & food): Aldrich

Methyl hydrocinnamate. *See* Methyl 3-phenylpropionate
Methyl hydroxide. *See* Methyl alcohol
Methyl 2-hydroxybenzoate. *See* Methyl salicylate
Methyl 4-hydroxybenzoate. *See* Methylparaben
Methyl p-hydroxybenzoate. *See* Methylparaben

Methyl hydroxyethylcellulose
CAS 9032-42-2
Synonyms: Hydroxyethylmethylcellulose
Definition: Methyl ether of hydroxyethylcellulose
Uses: Thickener, dispersant, emulsifier, protective colloid; used in orals
Regulatory: FDA approved for orals; BP compliance
Trade names: Tylose® MH Grades; Tylose® MHB

Methyl hydroxypropyl cellulose. *See* Hydroxypropyl methylcellulose
Methyl isobutylacetate. *See* Methyl 4-methylvalerate

Methyl isobutyl ketone
CAS 108-10-1; EINECS 203-550-1
FEMA 2731; UN No. 1245
Synonyms: MIBK; 4-Methyl-2-pentanone; Hexone; Isopropylacetone; Isobutyl methyl ketone
Classification: Aliphatic ketone
Empirical: $C_6H_{12}O$
Formula: $CH_3COCH_2CH(CH_3)_2$
Properties: Colorless volatile liq., faint ketonic/camphoraceous odor; sl. sol. in water; misc. with alcohol, ether, benzene, most org. solvs.; m.w. 100.18; dens. 0.8042 (20/20 C); f.p. -85 C; b.p. 115.8 C; flash pt. 13 C; ref. index 1.396
Precaution: DOT: Flamm. liq.; dangerous fire risk; may form explosive peroxides on exposure to air; can react vigorously with reducing materials; explosive limits 1.4-7.5% in air
Toxicology: LD50 (oral, rat) 2080 mg/kg; poison by IP route; mod. toxic by ingestion; mildly toxic by inh.; very irritating to skin, eyes, mucous membranes; narcotic in high conc.; TLV 50 ppm in air
Uses: Alcohol denaturant, solvent for pharmaceuticals; fruity flavoring agent
Regulatory: FDA 21CFR §172.515; FEMA GRAS; USP/NF compliance
Manuf./Distrib.: Aldrich; Eastman; Elf Atochem SA; Exxon
Manuf./Distrib. (pharm. & food): Aldrich; Eastman
Trade names containing: Filmex® A-2; Filmex® B; Filmex® C; Filmex® D-1; Filmex® D-2

Methyl isobutyrate
CAS 547-63-7; EINECS 208-929-5
FEMA 2694
Synonyms: 2-Methylpropanoic acid methyl ester; Methyl dimethylacetate

Definition: Ester of methanol and isobutyric acid
Empirical: $C_5H_{10}O_2$
Formula: $(CH_3)_2CHCOOCH_3$
Properties: Colorless mobile liq.; sl. sol. in water; misc. with alcohol, ether; m.w. 102.14; dens. 0.891 (20/4 C); m.p. -84 to -85 C; b.p. 91-93 C; flash pt. 12 C; ref. index 1.384 (20 C)
Precaution: Highly flamm.
Uses: Fruity synthetic flavoring agent
Regulatory: FDA 21CFR §172.515; FEMA GRAS
Manuf./Distrib. (pharm. & food): Aldrich

Methyl isocaproate. *See* Methyl 4-methylvalerate
1-Methyl-4-isopropenyl cyclohexan-3-ol. *See* Isopulegol
6-Methyl-3-isopropenylcyclohexanol. *See* Dihydrocarveol
1-Methyl-4-isopropenyl-6-cyclohexen-2-ol. *See* Carveol
1-1-Methyl-4-isopropenyl-6-cyclohexen-2-one. *See* l-Carvone
6-Methyl-3-isopropenyl cyclohexyl acetate. *See* Dihydrocarvyl acetate
2-Methyl-5-isopropyl-1,3-cyclohexadiene. *See* α-Phellandrene
5-Methyl-2-isopropylcyclohexanol. *See* Menthol
1-Methyl-4-isopropyl-1-cyclohexen-8-ol. *See* α-Terpineol
1-Methyl-4-isopropyl-1-cyclohexen-3-one. *See* d-Piperitone
5-Methyl-2-isopropyl hexahydrophenol. *See* Menthol
1-Methyl-4-isopropylidene-3-cyclohexanone. *See* Pulegone
5-Methyl-2-isopropylphenol. *See* Thymol

Methylisothiazolinone
CAS 2682-20-4; EINECS 220-239-6
Synonyms: 2-Methyl-4-isothiazolin-3-one; 3(2H)-Isothiazolone, 2-methyl-; 2-Methyl-3(2H)-isothiazolone
Classification: Heterocyclic organic compd.
Empirical: C_4H_5NOS
Uses: Antimicrobial preservative; used in topical pharmaceuticals
Regulatory: FDA 21CFR §175.105, 176.170

2-Methyl-4-isothiazolin-3-one. *See* Methylisothiazolinone
2-Methyl-3(2H)-isothiazolone. *See* Methylisothiazolinone

Methyl isovalerate
CAS 556-24-1; EINECS 209-117-3
FEMA 2753
Synonyms: 3-Methylbutanoic acid methyl ester
Empirical: $C_6H_{12}O_2$
Formula: $(CH_3)_2CHCH_2COOCH_3$
Properties: Liq., valerian odor; sl. sol. in water; misc. with alcohol, ether; m.w. 116.16; dens. 0.880 (20/4 C); b.p. 115-117 C; flash pt. 16 C; ref. index 1.393 (20 C)
Precaution: Highly flamm.
Uses: Sweet apple-like synthetic flavoring agent
Regulatory: FDA 21CFR §172.515; FEMA GRAS
Manuf./Distrib. (pharm. & food): Aldrich

Methyl lardate
Uses: Pharmaceutical fermentation

Methyl laurate
CAS 111-82-0; 67762-40-7; EINECS 203-911-3
FEMA 2715
Synonyms: Methyl dodecanoate; Dodecanoic acid methyl ester
Definition: Ester of methyl alcohol and lauric acid
Empirical: $C_{13}H_{26}O_2$
Formula: $CH_3(CH_2)_{10}COOCH_3$
Properties: Water-white liq., fatty floral odor; insol. in water; m.w. 214.35; dens. 0.8702 (20/4 C); m.p. 4.8 C; b.p. 262 C (766 mm); flash pt. > 230 F; ref. index 1.4320
Precaution: Combustible; noncorrosive
Uses: Coconut-like synthetic flavoring agent
Regulatory: FDA 21CFR §172.225, 172.515, 176.200, 176.210, 177.2260, 177.2800; FEMA GRAS; BP compliance
Manuf./Distrib.: Aldrich; Henkel/Emery; Penta Mfg.; Procter & Gamble; Stepan
Manuf./Distrib. (pharm. & food): Aldrich; Procter & Gamble

Methyl β-methiopropionate

Methyl β-methiopropionate. *See* Methyl 3-methylthiopropionate
Methyl methylaminobenzoate. *See* Dimethyl anthranilate
N-Methyl methyl anthranilate. *See* Dimethyl anthranilate
Methyl 2-methylbutanoate. *See* Methyl 2-methylbutyrate

Methyl 2-methylbutyrate
 CAS 868-57-5; EINECS 212-778-0
 FEMA 2719
 Synonyms: Methyl 2-methylbutanoate
 Empirical: $C_6H_{12}O_2$
 Formula: $CH_3CH_2CH(CH_3)COOCH_3$
 Properties: M.w. 116.16; dens. 0.885 (20/4 C); b.p. 113-115 C; flash pt. 18 C; ref. index 1.394 (20 C)
 Precaution: Highly flamm.
 Uses: Apple-like synthetic flavoring agent
 Regulatory: FDA 21CFR §172.515; FEMA GRAS
 Manuf./Distrib. (pharm. & food): Aldrich

(-)-6-Methyl-2-(4-methyl-3-cyclohexen-1-yl)-5-hepten-2-ol. *See* Levomenol
7-Methyl-3-methylene-1,6-octadiene. *See* Myrcene
d-2-Methyl-5-(1-methylethenyl)-cyclohexanone. *See* d-Dihydrocarvone
2-Methyl-5-(1-methylethyl)-1,3-cyclohexadiene. *See* α-Phellandrene
5-Methyl-2-(1-methylethyl) cyclohexanol. *See* Menthol
5-Methyl-2(1-methylethyl)cyclohexanol-2-aminobenzoate. *See* Menthyl anthranilate
5-Methyl-2-(1-methylethylidene)cyclohexanone. *See* Pulegone
5-Methyl-2-(1-methylethyl) phenol. *See* Thymol
Methyl 3-(methylmercapto)propionate. *See* Methyl 3-methylthiopropionate
Methyl β-methyl mercaptopropionate. *See* Methyl 3-methylthiopropionate
Methyl 4-methylpentanoate. *See* Methyl 4-methylvalerate

Methyl 3-methylthiopropionate
 CAS 13532-18-8; EINECS 236-883-6
 FEMA 2720
 Synonyms: Methyl β-methyl mercaptopropionate; Methyl β-methiopropionate; Methyl 3-(methylmercapto) propionate
 Empirical: $C_5H_{10}O_2S$
 Formula: $CH_3SCH_2CH_2COOCH_3$
 Properties: Colorless to pale-yellow liq.; onion-like odor; m.w. 134.19; dens. 1.073 (20/4 C); b.p. 184-189 C; flash p t. 72 C; ref. index 1.465 (20 C)
 Uses: Fruity synthetic flavoring agent
 Regulatory: FDA 21CFR §172.515; FEMA GRAS
 Manuf./Distrib. (pharm. & food): Aldrich

Methyl 4-methylvalerate
 CAS 2412-80-8
 FEMA 2721
 Synonyms: Methyl 4-methylpentanoate; Methyl isocaproate; Methyl isobutylacetate
 Empirical: $C_7H_{14}O_2$
 Properties: M.w. 130.19; dens. 0.888; b.p. 139-140 C; flash pt. 103 F
 Uses: Sweet pineapple-like synthetic flavoring agent
 Regulatory: FDA 21CFR §172.515; FEMA GRAS
 Manuf./Distrib. (pharm. & food): Aldrich

4-Methyl morpholine. *See* p-Methyl morpholine

p-Methyl morpholine
 CAS 109-02-4; EINECS 203-640-0
 UN No. 2535
 Synonyms: 4-Methyl morpholine
 Empirical: $C_5H_{11}ON$
 Formula: $CH_2CH_2OCH_2CH_2NCH_3$
 Properties: Water-white liq., ammonia odor; forms constant-boiling mixture with 25% water and boiling at 97 C; misc. with benzene, water; m.w. 101.17; dens. 0.921; b.p. 115.4 C; f.p. -66 C; flash pt. (TOC) 75 F; ref. index 1.4349
 Precaution: Flamm.; dangerous fire risk
 Toxicology: Skin irritant
 Uses: Pharmaceuticals

Manuf./Distrib.: Aldrich
Manuf./Distrib. (pharm. & food): Aldrich

Methyl myristate
CAS 124-10-7; EINECS 204-680-1
FEMA 2722
Synonyms: Methyl tetradecanoate; Tetradecanoic acid, methyl ester
Definition: Ester of methyl alcohol and myristic acid
Empirical: $C_{15}H_{30}O_2$
Formula: $CH_3(CH_2)_{12}COOCH_3$
Properties: Colorless liq., honey and orris-like odor; insol. in water; m.w. 242.40; dens. 0.866 (20/4 C); m.p. 17.8 C; b.p. 186.8 C (30 mm); flash pt. > 112 C; ref. index 1.438 (20 C)
Precaution: Combustible
Uses: Honey-like synthetic flavoring agent
Regulatory: FDA 21CFR §172.225, 172.515, 176.200, 176.210, 177.2260, 177.2800; FEMA GRAS; BP compliance
Manuf./Distrib.: Aldrich; Henkel/Emery; Stepan
Manuf./Distrib. (pharm. & food): Aldrich

Methyl 2-naphthyl ketone. *See* 2'-Acetonaphthone
Methyl β-naphthyl ketone. *See* 2'-Acetonaphthone

Methyl nonanoate
CAS 1731-84-6; EINECS 217-052-7
FEMA 2724
Synonyms: Methyl pelargonate
Empirical: $C_{10}H_{20}O_2$
Formula: $CH_3(CH_2)_7COOCH_3$
Properties: M.w. 172.27; dens. 0.873 (20/4 C); b.p. 91-92 C (11 mm); flash pt. 87 C; ref. index 1.422 (20 C)
Uses: Coconut-like synthetic flavoring agent
Regulatory: FDA 21CFR §172.515; FEMA GRAS
Manuf./Distrib. (pharm. & food): Aldrich

Methyl nonyl ketone. *See* 2-Undecanone

Methyl 2-nonynoate
CAS 111-80-8
FEMA 2726
Synonyms: Methyloctyne carbonate
Empirical: $C_{10}H_{16}O_2$
Properties: M.w. 168.24; dens. 0.915; b.p. 121 C (20 mm); flash pt. 213 F
Uses: Peach-like synthetic flavoring agent
Regulatory: FDA 21CFR §172.515; FEMA GRAS
Manuf./Distrib. (pharm. & food): Aldrich

Methyl octadecanoate. *See* Methyl stearate
Methyl 9-octadecenoate. *See* Methyl oleate
Methyl octanoate. *See* Methyl caprylate
Methyloctyne carbonate. *See* Methyl 2-nonynoate
Methylol. *See* Methyl alcohol

Methyl oleate
CAS 112-62-9; 67762-38-3; EINECS 203-992-5; 267-015-4
Synonyms: Methyl 9-octadecenoate; 9-Octadecenoic acid, methyl ester
Definition: Ester of methyl alcohol and oleic acid
Empirical: $C_{19}H_{36}O_2$
Formula: $CH_3(CH_2)_7CH=CH(CH_2)_7COOCH_3$
Properties: Clear to amber liq., faint fatty odor; sol. in alcohols, most org. solvs.; insol. in water; dens. 0.8739 (20 C); f.p. -19.9 C; b.p. 218.5 C (20 mm); ref. index 1.4510 (26 C)
Precaution: Combustible
Toxicology: Low oral toxicity; mildly irritating to skin
Uses: Defoaming component in pharmaceutical fermentation
Regulatory: FDA 21CFR §172.225, 175.105, 176.200, 176.210, 177.2260, 177.2800; BP compliance
Manuf./Distrib.: Calgene; Ferro/Bedford; Henkel; Norman, Fox; Unichema; Union Camp; Witco/Oleo-Surf.
Manuf./Distrib. (pharm. & food): Aldrich
Trade names: Emery® Methyl Oleate

Methyl oxirane polymers. *See* Poloxamer 101
N-Methyl-N-(1-oxododecyl) glycine. *See* Lauroyl sarcosine
N-Methyl-N-(1-oxododecyl) glycine, sodium salt. *See* Sodium lauroyl sarcosinate

Methylparaben
CAS 99-76-3; EINECS 202-785-7
FEMA 2710
Synonyms: Methyl 4-hydroxybenzoate; Methyl parasept; 4-Hydroxybenzoic acid, methyl ester; Methyl p-hydroxybenzoate
Definition: Ester of methyl alcohol and p-hydroxybenzoic acid
Empirical: $C_8H_8O_3$
Formula: $CH_3OOCC_6H_4OH$
Properties: Colorless crystals or wh. cryst. powd., odorless or faint char. odor, sl. burning taste; sol. in alcohol, ether; sl. sol. in water, benzene, CCl_4; m.w. 152.14; m.p. 125-128 C; b.p. 270-280 C (dec.)
Precaution: Conc. dust may present an explosion hazard; incompat. with alkalies and strong oxidizing agents; burning may produce phenolic vapors and CO; heated to decomp., emits acrid smoke and fumes
Toxicology: LD50 (oral, dog) 3000 mg/kg; mod. toxic by ingestion, subcutaneous, and IP routes; mutagenic data; may cause skin and eye irritation, asthma, rashes, hyperactivity; may promote allergic sensitization in humans
Uses: Antimicrobial preservative, antifungal, antibacterial; used in injectables, parenterals, inhalants, intravenous, ophthalmics, orals, rectals, topicals; dental anesthetics; insulin preps.
Usage level: 0.05% (eye wash); 0.1-0.8% (drug extracts); 0.3% (cough syrups); 0.02-0.1% (tablets); 0.1% (ointment bases); 0.2% (suppositories)
Regulatory: FDA 21CFR §150.141, 150.161, 172.515, 181.22, 181.23, 184.1490, GRAS, limitation 0.1%, 556.390, zero limitation in milk; USA CIR approved, EPA reg.; FEMA GRAS; Japan listed; Europe listed; UK approved; FDA approved for injectables, parenterals, inhalants, intravenous, ophthalmics, orals, rectals, topicals; USP/NF, BP, Ph.Eur. compliance
Manuf./Distrib.: Aceto; Aldrich; Ashland; Int'l. Sourcing; Kraft; E. Merck; Napp; Nipa Labs; Sutton Labs
Manuf./Distrib. (pharm. & food): Aldrich; R.W. Greeff; Int'l. Sourcing; Ruger; Spectrum Chem. Mfg.; Tri-K Ind.
Trade names: Lexgard® M; Methyl Parasept® NF/FCC; Nipagin M
Trade names containing: Germaben® II; Nipaguard® BPX; Nipastat; Phenonip; Uniphen P-23

Methylparaben, potassium salt. *See* Potassium methylparaben
Methylparaben sodium. *See* Sodium methylparaben
Methylparaben sodium salt. *See* Sodium methylparaben
Methylparafynol. *See* Methyl pentynol
Methyl parasept. *See* Methylparaben
Methyl pelargonate. *See* Methyl nonanoate
2-Methyl-2,4-pentanediol. *See* Hexylene glycol
4-Methyl-2,4-pentanediol. *See* Hexylene glycol

3-Methylpentanoic acid
CAS 105-43-1
FEMA 3437
Empirical: $C_6H_{12}O_2$
Properties: M.w. 116.16; dens. 0.930; b.p. 196-198 C; flash pt. 185 F
Uses: Herbacous, sweet flavoring agent
Regulatory: FEMA GRAS
Manuf./Distrib. (pharm. & food): Aldrich

4-Methyl-2-pentanone. *See* Methyl isobutyl ketone

2-Methyl-2-pentenoic acid
CAS 16957-70-3
FEMA 3195
Synonyms: trans-2-Methyl-2-pentenoic acid
Empirical: $C_6H_{10}O_2$
Properties: M.w. 114.14; dens. 0.979; m.p. 24-26 C; b.p. 123-125 C (30 mm); flash pt. 226 F
Uses: Fruity flavoring agent
Regulatory: FEMA GRAS
Manuf./Distrib. (pharm. & food): Aldrich

trans-2-Methyl-2-pentenoic acid. *See* 2-Methyl-2-pentenoic acid
3-Methyl-2-(2-pentenyl)-2-cyclopenten-1-one. *See* cis-Jasmone
Methyl pentyl ketone. *See* Methyl n-amyl ketone

Methyl pentynol
CAS 77-75-8; EINECS 201-055-5
UN No. 1993
Synonyms: 3-Methyl-1-pentyn-3-ol; Methylparafynol; Meparfynol
Classification: Aliphatic organic compd.
Formula: CH₃CH₂CH₃COHCCH
Properties: Colorless liq.; moderately sol. in water; misc. with acetone, benzene, CCl₄, ethyl acetate; m.w.
98.16; dens. 0.8721 (20/20 C); b.p. 121.4 C; f.p. -30.6 C; flash pt. (TOC) 38.3 C; ref. index 1.4310
Precaution: Flamm.
Toxicology: Toxic by ingestion; moderately toxic by intraperitoneal and subcutaneous routes
Uses: Reactive intermediate in the mfg. of pharmaceuticals
Manuf./Distrib.: Air Prods.
Manuf./Distrib. (pharm. & food): Aldrich

3-Methyl-1-pentyn-3-ol. *See* Methyl pentynol
β-Methylphenethyl butyrate. *See* 2-Phenylpropyl butyrate
2-Methylphenol. *See* o-Cresol
3-Methylphenol. *See* m-Cresol
4-Methylphenol. *See* p-Cresol
Methyl phenylcarbinyl acetate. *See* α-Methylbenzyl acetate
Methyl phenylcarbinyl butyrate. *See* α-Methylbenzyl butyrate
3-Methyl-3-phenyl glycidic acid ethyl ester. *See* Ethyl methylphenylglycidate
Methyl phenyl ketone. *See* Acetophenone
4-Methyl-1-phenyl-2-pentanol. *See* α-Isobutylphenethyl alcohol

4-Methyl-1-phenyl-2-pentanone
CAS 5349-62-2
FEMA 2740
Synonyms: Benzyl isobutyl ketone
Empirical: C₁₂H₁₆O
Properties: M.w. 176.26; dens. 0.949; b.p. 250-251 C; flash pt. 221 F
Uses: Sweet synthetic flavoring agent
Regulatory: FDA 21CFR §172.515; FEMA GRAS
Manuf./Distrib. (pharm. & food): Aldrich

Methyl-3-phenyl propenoate. *See* Methyl cinnamate

Methyl 3-phenylpropionate
CAS 103-25-3
FEMA 2741
Synonyms: Methyl hydrocinnamate
Empirical: C₁₀H₁₂O₂
Properties: M.w. 164.20; dens. 1.043; b.p. 91-92 C (4 mm); flash pt. 212 F
Uses: Fruity synthetic flavoring agent
Regulatory: FDA 21CFR §172.515; FEMA GRAS
Manuf./Distrib. (pharm. & food): Aldrich

p-Methylphenylsulfonic acid. *See* p-Toluene sulfonic acid

2-Methylpropanal
CAS 78-84-2; EINECS 201-149-6
FEMA 2220
Synonyms: Isobutyraldehyde; 2-Methylpropionaldehyde; Isobutanal; Isobutyric aldehyde; Isobutyl aldehyde
Empirical: C₄H₈O
Formula: (CH₃)₂CHCHO
Properties: Colorless liq., pungent sharp odor; sol. 11 5/100 ml water; misc. with alcohol, ether, benzene,
carbon disulfide, acetone, toluene, chloroform; m.w. 72.12; dens. 0.7938 (20/4 C); m.p. -65 C; b.p. 64 C
(760 mm); flash pt. (CC) -40 F; ref. index 1.374
Precaution: Flamm.; dangerous fire hazard exposed to heat, flames, oxidizers; can react vigorously with
reducing materials; explosive limits 1.6-10.6%
Toxicology: LD50 (oral, rat) 2810 mg/kg; mod. toxic by ingestion; mildly toxic by skin contact, inh.; severe skin
and eye irritant; heated to decomp., emits acrid smoke and fumes
Uses: Banana-like synthetic flavoring agent
Regulatory: FDA 21CFR §172.515; FEMA GRAS
Manuf./Distrib.: Aldrich
Manuf./Distrib. (pharm. & food): Aldrich

2-Methylpropane. *See* Isobutane
Methyl propanoate. *See* Methyl propionate
2-Methylpropanoic acid ethyl ester. *See* Ethyl isobutyrate
2-Methylpropanoic acid methyl ester. *See* Methyl isobutyrate
2-Methylpropanoic acid 2-methylpropyl ester. *See* Isobutyl isobutyrate
2-Methylpropanol. *See* Isobutyl alcohol
2-Methyl-1-propanol. *See* Isobutyl alcohol
2-Methyl-2-propanol. *See* t-Butyl alcohol
2-Methyl propanyl butyrate. *See* Isobutyl butyrate
2-Methyl-1-propene, homopolymer. *See* Polyisobutene
2-Methylpropenoic acid. *See* Methacrylic acid
2-Methyl-2-propenyl butyrate. *See* 2-Methylallyl butyrate
2-Methylpropionaldehyde. *See* 2-Methylpropanal

Methyl propionate
>   CAS 554-12-1; EINECS 209-060-4
>   FEMA 2742
>   *Synonyms:* Propanoic acid methyl ester; Methyl propanoate
>   *Empirical:* $C_4H_8O_2$
>   *Formula:* $CH_3CH_2COOCH_3$
>   *Properties:* Colorless liq., fruity rum-like odor; sol. in 16 parts water; misc. with alcohol, ether; m.w. 88.11; dens. 0.915 (20/4 C); m.p. -87 C; b.p. 78-80 C; flash pt. -2 C; ref. index 1.377 (20 C)
>   *Precaution:* Highly flamm.
>   *Uses:* Apple, banana, strawberry-like synthetic flavoring agent
>   *Regulatory:* FDA 21CFR §172.515; FEMA GRAS
>   *Manuf./Distrib. (pharm. & food):* Aldrich

2-Methylpropyl acetate. *See* Isobutyl acetate
Methyl propyl diketone. *See* Acetyl butyryl
β-Methylpropyl ethanoate. *See* Isobutyl acetate

Methyl propyl ketone
>   CAS 107-87-9; EINECS 203-528-1
>   FEMA 2842
>   *Synonyms:* MPK; 2-Pentanone; Ethyl acetone; Methyl n-propyl ketone
>   *Empirical:* $C_5H_{10}O$
>   *Formula:* $CH_3COCH_2CH_2CH_3$
>   *Properties:* Water-wh. liq., fruity ethereal odor; sl. sol. in water; misc. with alcohol, ether; m.w. 86.14; dens. 0.801-0.806; m.p. -78 C; b.p. 216 F; flash pt. 45 F
>   *Precaution:* Highly flamm.; very dangerous fire hazard exposed to heat or flame; reacts vigorously with oxidizers; explosive limits 1.5-8.2%
>   *Toxicology:* ACGIH TLV:TWA 200 ppm; LD50 (oral, rat) 3730 mg/kg; mod. toxic by ingestion, IP; mildly toxic by skin contact, inh.; human systemic effects; skin irritant; mutagenic data; heated to decomp., emits acrid smoke and irritating fumes
>   *Uses:* Fruity synthetic flavoring agent
>   *Regulatory:* FDA 21CFR §172.515; FEMA GRAS
>   *Manuf./Distrib.:* Aldrich; Ashland; Eastman; Janssen Chimica; Penta Mfg.
>   *Manuf./Distrib. (pharm. & food):* Aldrich

Methyl n-propyl ketone. *See* Methyl propyl ketone
2-Methylpropyl octadecanoate. *See* Isobutyl stearate
Methylprotocatechualdehyde. *See* Vanillin
Methylprotocatechuic aldehyde. *See* Vanillin
2-Methylpyridine. *See* α-Picoline
3-Methylpyridine. *See* β-Picoline
4-Methylpyridine. *See* γ-Picoline
2-Methyl pyromeconic acid. *See* Maltol
Methyl pyromucate. *See* Methyl 2-furoate
1-Methyl-2-pyrrolidinone. *See* N-Methyl-2-pyrrolidone
N-Methylpyrrolidinone. *See* N-Methyl-2-pyrrolidone
N-Methyl-2-pyrrolidinone. *See* N-Methyl-2-pyrrolidone
Methylpyrrolidone. *See* N-Methyl-2-pyrrolidone
1-Methyl-2-pyrrolidone. *See* N-Methyl-2-pyrrolidone
N-Methylpyrrolidone. *See* N-Methyl-2-pyrrolidone

N-Methyl-2-pyrrolidone
CAS 872-50-4; EINECS 212-828-1
Synonyms: NMP; Methylpyrrolidone; N-Methylpyrrolidone; 1-Methyl-2-pyrrolidone; N-Methylpyrrolidinone; N-Methyl-2-pyrrolidinone; 1-Methyl-2-pyrrolidinone
Empirical: C_5H_9NO
Properties: Colorless liq., mild amine odor; misc. with water, org. solvs., castor oil; m.w. 99.13; dens. 1.032 (20/4 C); f.p. -24 C; b.p. 202 C; flash pt. 95 C; ref. index 1.470 (20 C)
Precaution: Combustible exposed to heat, open flame, powerful oxidizers; hygroscopic; photosensitive
Toxicology: LD50 (oral, rat) 7000 mg/kg; severely irritating to eyes, skin; mod. toxic by IP and IV routes; mildly toxic by ing., skin contact; experimental teratogen, reproductive effects; heated to decomp., emits toxic fumes of NO_x
Uses: Solvent; increases water sol. of therapeutic compds.; synthesis of vitamin E precursor; solubilizer for topicals; bioadhesive; spray bandages
Manuf./Distrib.: Allchem Ind.; Ashland; BASF; Coyne; Dynaloy; Fluka; ISP; Janssen Chimica; Spectrum Chem. Mfg.
Trade names: Pharmasolve™

2-Methylquinoline. *See* Quinaldine
α-Methylquinoline. *See* Quinaldine
Methyl salicylaldehyde. *See* o-Methoxybenzaldehyde

Methyl salicylate
CAS 119-36-8; EINECS 204-317-7
FEMA 2745; UN No. 3082
Synonyms: Methyl 2-hydroxybenzoate; Sweet birch oil; Wintergreen oil; Oil of wintergreen; Synthetic oil of wintergreen
Classification: Aromatic organic compd.
Definition: Ester of methyl alcohol and salicylic acid
Empirical: $C_8H_8O_3$
Formula: $C_6H_4OHCOOCH_3$
Properties: Colorless, yel., or red liq., wintergreen odor and taste; sol. in ether, glacial acetic acid; sl. sol. in water; m.w. 152.14; dens. 1.180-1.185 (25/25 C); m.p. -8.6 C; b.p. 222.2 C; flash pt. (CC) 101 C; ref. index 1.535-1.538 (20 C)
Precaution: Combustible when exposed to heat or flame; reactive with oxidizing materials; protect from light, alkaline, iron salts; heated to decomp., emits acrid smoke and irritating fumes
Toxicology: LD50 (oral, rat) 887 mg/kg; human poison by ing.; mod. toxic by ing., IP, IV, subcutaneous routes; lethal dose 30 cc in adults, 10 cc in children; experimental teratogen, reproductive effects; human systemic effects; severe skin/eye irritant
Uses: Sweet minty synthetic flavor, perfume, disinfectant, antiseptic; used in buccals, orals, topicals, dentifrices, analgesics; uv absorber in sunburn lotions; local anesthetic; relief of pain in lumbar and sciatic regions and for rheumatic conditions
Usage level: 0.5 mg/kg/day considered safe for ingestion
Regulatory: FDA 21CFR §175.105, 177.1010; 27CFR §21.65, 21.151; FEMA GRAS; Japan approved as flavoring; FDA approved for buccals, orals, topicals; USP/NF, BP, Ph.Eur. compliance
Manuf./Distrib.: Allchem Industries; R.W. Greeff; Nipa Hardwicke; Penta Mfg.; Quest Int'l.; Schweizerhall
Manuf./Distrib. (pharm. & food): Aldrich; Avrachem; R.W. Greeff; Int'l. Sourcing; Mallinckrodt; Nipa Hardwicke; Ruger; Spectrum Chem. Mfg.

Methyl stearate
CAS 112-61-8; 85586-21-6; EINECS 203-990-4; 287-824-6
Synonyms: Methyl octadecanoate; Octadecanoic acid, methyl ester
Definition: Ester of methyl alcohol and stearic acid
Empirical: $C_{19}H_{38}O_2$
Formula: $CH_3(CH_2)_{16}COOCH_3$
Properties: White crystals; insol. in water; sol. in ether, alcohol; m.w. 298.57; m.p. 37.8 C; b.p. 234.5 C (30 mm); flash pt. 307 F
Precaution: Combustible
Uses: Used in topicals
Regulatory: FDA 21CFR §172.225, 176.200, 176.210, 177.2260, 177.2800, 178.3910; FDA approved for topicals; BP compliance
Manuf./Distrib.: Ashland; Ferro/Bedford; Penta Mfg.; Sea-Land; Union Camp; Witco/Oleo-Surf.
Manuf./Distrib. (pharm. & food): Aldrich; Penta Mfg.

Methyl styryl ketone. *See* Benzylidene acetone
Methyl succinate. *See* Dimethyl succinate

Methylsulfonic acid

Methylsulfonic acid. *See* Methanesulfonic acid
Methyl sulfoxide. *See* Dimethyl sulfoxide
Methyl tertiary butyl ether. *See* Methyl t-butyl ether
Methyl tetradecanoate. *See* Methyl myristate
Methyltheobromine. *See* Caffeine
Methyl p-tolyl ketone. *See* 4´-Methyl acetophenone

Methyl valerate
CAS 624-24-8; EINECS 210-838-0
FEMA 2752
Synonyms: Methyl n-valerate
Empirical: $C_6H_{12}O_2$
Formula: $CH_3(CH_2)_3COOCH_3$
Properties: M.w. 116.16; dens. 0.889 (20/4 C); b.p. 126-128 C; flash pt. 27 C; ref. index 1.397 (20 C)
Precaution: Flamm.
Uses: Fruity synthetic flavoring agent
Regulatory: FDA 21CFR §172.515; FEMA GRAS
Manuf./Distrib. (pharm. & food): Aldrich

Methyl n-valerate. *See* Methyl valerate
Methyl vinyl ether/maleic anhydride copolymer. *See* PVM/MA copolymer
MHPC. *See* Hydroxypropyl methylcellulose
MIBK. *See* Methyl isobutyl ketone

Mica
CAS 12001-26-2
Synonyms: Muscovite mica; CI 77019
Classification: Silicate minerals
Properties: Colorless to sl. red, brown to greenish-yel. soft, translucent solid; dens. 2.6-3.2; Mohs hardness 2.8-3.2; heat resistant to 600 C
Precaution: Noncombustible
Toxicology: TLV:TWA 3 mg/m^3 (respirable dust); irritant by inhalation; nontoxic to skin
Uses: Color additive for external pharmaceuticals
Regulatory: FDA 21CFR §73.1496, 73.2496, 175.300, 177.1460, 177.2410, 177.2600; permanently listed
Manuf./Distrib.: Feldspar; Franklin Industrial Mins.; ISP Van Dyk; KMG Mins.; Mearl; Mykroy/Macalex Ceramics; Nyco Mins.; Spectrum Chem. Mfg.
Trade names containing: Flamenco® Interference Color Powds.; Flamenco® White Pearl Powds.; Timica®

Microcrystalline cellulose
CAS 9004-34-6
Synonyms: MCC; Cellulose gel
Definition: Isolated, colloidal crystalline portion of cellulose fibers; partially depolymerized acid hydrolysis prod. of purified wood cellulose
Properties: Wh. fine cryst. powd., odorless; insol. in water, dil. acids, and most org. solvs.; pH 5-7
Toxicology: LD50 (oral, rat) > 5 g/kg, no significant hazard; irritant by inhalation (dust); may be damaging to lungs
Uses: Tablet binder/disintegrant and lubricant; capsule and/or tablet diluent, filler; filtering aid; sorbent; suspending agent; visc.-increasing agent; adsorbs water-sol. ingreds. before compression; bulk laxative effect
Regulatory: FDA GRAS; Europe listed; UK approved; USP/NF, BP, Ph.Eur., JP compliance
Manuf./Distrib.: Asahi Chem.; Barrington; Fabrichem; Harrisons Trading; Howard Hall; Edw. Mendell; Schweizerhall
Manuf./Distrib. (pharm. & food): Asahi Chem.; Avrachem; Spectrum Chem. Mfg.
Trade names: Avicel® PH-101; Avicel® PH-102; Avicel® PH-103; Avicel® PH-105; Emcocel® 50M; Emcocel® 90M; Emcocel® LM; Vivacel® 10; Vivacel® 12; Vivacel® 20; Vivacel® 101; Vivacel® 102; Vivacel® 103; Vivacel® 105; Vivacel® 112; Vivacel® 200
Trade names containing: Os-Tab™ 4455
See also Cellulose

Microcrystalline wax
CAS 8063-08-9; 63231-60-7; 64742-42-3; EINECS 264-038-1
Synonyms: Petroleum wax, microcrystalline; Waxes, microcrystalline
Definition: Wax derived from petroleum and char. by fineness of crystals; consists of high m.w. saturated aliphatic hydrocarbons
Properties: Wh. or cream-colored waxy solid, odorless; sol. in chloroform, ether, volatile oils, most warm fixed

oils; insol. in water; very sl. sol. in dehydrated alcohol; m.p. 54-102 C
Toxicology: May be carcinogenic
Uses: Wax, coating agent, lubricant, protectant used in orals, topicals
Regulatory: FDA 21CFR §172.886, 173.340, 175.105, 175.320, 176.170, 176.200, 177.2600; Europe listed; UK approved for restricted use; FDA approved for orals, topicals; USP/NF compliance
Manuf./Distrib.: Astor Wax; Ferro; IGI; Koster Keunen; Mobil
Trade names: Koster Keunen Microcrystalline Waxes; Multiwax® 180-M; Multiwax® ML-445; Multiwax® W-445; Multiwax® W-835; Multiwax® X-145A
Trade names containing: Dehymuls® F; Ross Japan Wax Substitute 525

Milk acid. *See* Lactic acid
Milk, nonfat dry. *See* Nonfat dry milk
Milk of magnesia. *See* Magnesium hydroxide

Milk protein
CAS 9000-71-9; EINECS 232-555-1
Synonyms: Casein
Definition: Mixture of proteins obtained from cow's milk
Properties: Light-yel. powd.
Uses: Thickener for pharmaceutical prods.
Manuf./Distrib.: Meggle Marketing GmbH; Nat'l. Casein; U.S. Biochemical; Worthington Biochemical
Manuf./Distrib. (pharm. & food): Adams Food Ingreds.; Am. Casein; Am. Dairy Prods.; Byrton Dairy Prods.; Dena AG; Dutch Protein; EPI Bretagne; G Fiske; K&K Greeff; Kerry Foods; MD Foods; Meggle; New Zealand Milk Prods.; Sanofi France; Unilait France; Westin

Milk protein, casein. *See* Casein
Milk sugar. *See* Lactose

Mimosa bark extract
Definition: Extract of the bark of *Mimosa tenuiflora*
Uses: Protective agent in pharmaceutical lotions and creams
Trade names containing: Tepescohuite AMI Watersoluble; Tepescohuite HG; Tepescohuite HS; Tepescohuite LS

Mineral oil
CAS 8012-95-1; 8020-83-5 (wh.); 8042-47-5; EINECS 232-384-2; 232-455-8
Synonyms: Heavy mineral oil; Light mineral oil; White mineral oil; Paraffin oil; Liquid paraffin; Petrolatum liquid; Liquid petrolatum
Definition: Liq. mixture of hydrocarbons obtained from petroleum
Properties: Colorless transparent oily liq., odorless, tasteless; insol. in water, alcohol; sol. in benzene, chloroform, ether, petrol. ether, volatile oils; dens. 0.83-0.86 (light), 0.875-0.905 (heavy); flash pt. (OC) 444 F; surf. tens. < 35 dynes/cm
Precaution: Combustible
Toxicology: Eye irritant; human carcinogen and teratogen by inhalation; heated to decomp., emits acrid smoke and fumes
Uses: Oleaginous vehicle, filler, solv., lubricant, laxative; light min. oil as tablet/capsule lubricant; used in ophthalmic ointments or suspensions, oral tablets and capsules, topical creams, lotions, and ointments, suppositories
Regulatory: FDA 21CFR §172.878, 173.340 (limitation 0.008% in wash water for sliced potatoes, 150 ppm in yeast), 175.105, 175.210, 175.230, 175.300, 176.170, 176.200, 176.210, 177.1200, 177.2260, 177.2600, 177.2800, 178.3570, 178.3620, 178.3740, 178.3910, 179.45; 573.680; ADI not specified (FAO/WHO); FDA approved for ophthalmics, orals, topicals; USP/NF, BP, Ph.Eur. compliance
Manuf./Distrib.: Amoco/Lubricants; Chemisphere; Exxon; Magie Bros. Oil; Mobil; Penreco; Penta Mfg.; San Yuan; Sea-Land; Surco Prods.; Total Petrol.; Witco/Golden Bear, Petrol. Spec.
Manuf./Distrib. (pharm. & food): Aldrich; Penreco; Ruger; Spectrum Chem. Mfg.
Trade names: Benol®; Blandol®; Britol®; Britol® 6NF; Britol® 7NF; Britol® 9NF; Britol® 20USP; Britol® 35USP; Britol® 50USP; Carnation®; Crystosol USP 200; Crystosol USP 240; Crystosol USP 350; Drakeol® 5; Drakeol® 6; Drakeol® 7; Drakeol® 9; Drakeol® 13; Drakeol® 19; Drakeol® 21; Drakeol® 32; Drakeol® 34; Drakeol® 35; Gloria®; Hydrobrite 200PO; Hydrobrite 300PO; Hydrobrite 380PO; Hydrobrite 550PO; Kaydol®; Kaydol® S; Klearol®; Orzol®; PD-23; Protol®; Superla® No. 5; Superla® No. 6; Superla® No. 7; Superla® No. 9; Superla® No. 10; Superla® No. 13; Superla® No. 18; Superla® No. 21; Superla® No. 31; Superla® No. 35
Trade names containing: Aloe Vera Lipo-Quinone Extract™ Cosmetic Grade; Aloe Vera Lipo-Quinone Extract™ Low Odor (CG); Amerchol® BL; Amerchol L-101®; Amerchol® L-500; Argobase 125T; Argobase EU; Argobase EUC 2; Cremba; Crodarom Nut O; Dehymuls® K; Emery® 1732; Emery® 1740; Fancol LAO;

Mineral soap

Liquid Absorption Base Type A; Liquid Absorption Base Type T; Pionier® OEWA-II; Protegin®; Protegin® X; Ritachol®; Sebase

Mineral soap. *See* Bentonite
Mineral wax. *See* Ceresin; Ozokerite
Minkamidopropyl dimethyl 2-hydroxyethyl ammonium chloride. *See* Quaternium-26
Mint. *See* Spearmint
Mintlactone. *See* Menthalactone
MIPA. *See* Isopropanolamine
MKP. *See* Potassium phosphate
MMA. *See* Dimethyl anthranilate
Modified food starch. *See* Food starch, modified

Molasses
CAS 68476-78-8
Definition: Residue after sucrose has been removed from the mother liquor in sugar manufacture
Properties: Thick liq.
Uses: Colorant, sweetener for pharmaceutical tablets
Trade names containing: Mola-Tab®

Monoammonium glycyrrhizinate
CAS 1407-03-0
FEMA 2528
Synonyms: MAG; Ammonium glycyrrhizinate, pentahydrate; Ammonium glycyrrhizinate; Ammoniated glycyrrhizin
Definition: Obtained by extraction from ammoniated glycyrrhizin, derived from roots of *Glycyrrhiza glabra*
Empirical: $C_{42}H_{65}NO_{16} \cdot 5H_2O$
Properties: White powder; sweet taste; sol. in ammonia; insol. in glacial acetic acid; m.w. 839.91
Toxicology: Heated to decomp., emits acrid smoke and irritating fumes
Uses: Flavor enhancer, flavoring agent, surface-active agent; used in orals
Regulatory: FDA 21CFR §184.1408, GRAS; not permitted for use as nonnutritive sweetener in sugar substitutes; FEMA GRAS; FDA approved for orals
Manuf./Distrib. (pharm. & food): Am. Roland; R.W. Greeff
Trade names: Magnasweet®

Monoammonium phosphate. *See* Ammonium phosphate
Monobasic sodium phosphate. *See* Sodium phosphate
Mono-t-butyl hydroquinone. *See* t-Butyl hydroquinone
Monocalcium phosphate anhydrous. *See* Calcium phosphate monobasic anhydrous

Mono- and di-acetylated monoglycerides
Definition: Glycerin esterified with edible fat-forming fatty acids and acetic acid
Properties: Wh. to pale yel. waxy solid; sol. in ether, chloroform; sl. sol. in carbon disulfide; insol. in water; m.p. ≈ 45 C; acid no. 3 max.; sapon. no. 279-292; hyd. no. 133-152
Uses: Plasticizer for pharmaceuticals
Regulatory: USP/NF compliance

Mono- and diglycerides of fatty acids
CAS 67701-32-0; 67701-33-1; 68990-53-4
Definition: Mixt. of glycerol mono- and di-esters, with minor amts. of tri-esters, of fatty acids from edible oils
Properties: Yel. liqs. to ivory plastics to hard solids, bland odor and taste; sol. in alcohol, ethyl acetate, chloroform, other chlorinated hydrocarbons; insol. in water; acid no. 4 max.
Toxicology: Heated to decomp., emits acrid smoke and irritating fumes
Uses: Emulsifier for topical ointments; tableting aid
Regulatory: FDA 21CFR §172.863, 182.4505, 184.1505, GRAS; USDA 9CFR §318.7, 381.147; Europe listed; UK approved; USP/NF compliance
Manuf./Distrib. (pharm. & food): Browning
Trade names: Alphadim® 90SBK; BFP 64 O; BFP 74E
Trade names containing: Aldosperse® MO-50 FG; Descote® Pyridoxine Hydrochoride 33^1/$_3$%; Descote® Riboflavin 33^1/$_3$%; Descote® Thiamine Mononitrate 33^1/$_3$%; Dur-Em® 117; Dur-Em® 207-E; Rocoat® Niacinamide 33^1/$_3$% No. 69907; Rocoat® Pyridoxine Hydrochloride 33^1/$_3$% No. 60688; Rocoat® Riboflavin 25% No. 60289; Rocoat® Riboflavin 33^1/$_3$ No. 60288; Rocoat® Thiamine Mononitrate 33^1/$_3$% No. 60188

Monoethanolamine. *See* Ethanolamine

Monoglyceride citrate
Definition: Mixt. of glyceryl monooleate and its citric acid monoester

Properties: Wh. to ivory-colored soft waxy solid, bland odor/taste; sol. in most common fat solvs., alcohol; insol. in water
Regulatory: FDA limitation 200 ppm (cured meats); WHO limitation 100 ppm (fats, oils, margarine)

Monoglyme. *See* Ethylene glycol dimethyl ether
Monoisopropanolamine. *See* Isopropanolamine
Monolinolein. *See* Glyceryl linoleate
Monomyristin. *See* Glyceryl myristate
Monooctadecyl ether of glycerol. *See* Batyl alcohol
Monooctanoin. *See* Glyceryl caprylate
Monoolein. *See* Glyceryl oleate
Monopotassium carbonate. *See* Potassium bicarbonate
Monopotassium monosodium tartrate. *See* Potassium sodium tartrate anhyd.
Monopotassium monosodium tartrate tetrahydrate. *See* Potassium sodium tartrate tetrahydrate
Monopotassium orthophosphate. *See* Potassium phosphate
Monopotassium D(-)-pentahydroxy capronate. *See* Potassium D-gluconate
Monopotassium phosphate. *See* Potassium phosphate
Monopotassium L-(+)-tartrate. *See* Potassium acid tartrate
Monoricinolein. *See* Glyceryl ricinoleate
Monosodium ascorbate. *See* Sodium ascorbate
Monosodium L-ascorbate. *See* Sodium ascorbate
Monosodium carbonate. *See* Sodium bicarbonate
Monosodium citrate anhydrous. *See* Sodium citrate
Monosodium dihydrogen orthophosphate. *See* Sodium phosphate
Monosodium dihydrogen phosphate. *See* Sodium phosphate
Monosodium gluconate. *See* Sodium gluconate
Monosodium glutamate. *See* MSG
Monosodium L-glutamate monohydrate. *See* MSG
Monosodium hydroxymethane sulfinate. *See* Sodium formaldehyde sulfoxylate
Monosodium-2-hydroxypropane-1,2,3-tricarboxylate. *See* Sodium citrate
Monosodium D(-)-pentahydroxy capronate. *See* Sodium gluconate
Monostearin. *See* Glyceryl stearate
Monothioglycerol. *See* Thioglycerin
α-**Monothioglycerol.** *See* Thioglycerin

Montan acid wax
CAS 68476-03-9; EINECS 270-664-6
Synonyms: Fatty acids, montan wax; Waxes, montan fatty acids
Definition: Prod. obtained by the oxidation of montan wax
Uses: Retarding agent
Trade names: Hoechst Wax E Pharma

Morpholine
CAS 110-91-8; EINECS 203-815-1
UN No. 2054
Synonyms: Tetrahydro-1,4-oxazine; 1-Oxa-4-azacyclohexane; Tetrahydro-2H-1,4-oxazine; Diethylene oximide; Diethyleneimide oxide
Classification: Heterocyclic organic compd.
Empirical: C_4H_9NO
Formula: C_4H_8ONH
Properties: Colorless clear hygroscopic liq., amine-like odor; misc. with water, acetone, benzene, ether, castor oil, alcohol; m.w. 87.14; dens. 1.002 (20/20 C); b.p. 128.9 C; f.p. -4.9 C; flash pt. (OC) 37.7 C; autoignition temp. 590 F; ref. index 1.4540 (20 C)
Precaution: DOT: Flamm. liq.; dangerous fire hazard exposed to flame, heat or oxidizers; reactive with oxidizers; explosive with nitromethane
Toxicology: TLV:TWA 20 ppm; LD50 (oral, rat) 1050 mg/kg; mod. toxic by ing., inh., skin contact, IP; corrosive irritant to skin, eyes, mucous membranes; experimental neoplastigen; mutagenic data; kidney damage; heated to dec., emits highly toxic fumes of NO_x
Uses: Local anesthetic and antiseptic
Regulatory: FDA 21CFR §172.235, 173.310 (10 ppm max. in steam), 175.105, 176.210, 178.3300; BP compliance
Manuf./Distrib.: Air Prods.; Allchem Ind.; BASF; Coyne; Nippon Nyukazai; PMC Specialties; Texaco
Manuf./Distrib. (pharm. & food): Aldrich; PMC Specialties; Ruger

Morrhua oil. *See* Cod liver oil

Mossbunker oil

Mossbunker oil. *See* Menhaden oil
MPK. *See* Methyl propyl ketone

MSG
　　CAS 142-47-2; EINECS 205-538-1
　　FEMA 2756
　　Synonyms: Sodium glutamate; Monosodium glutamate; Sodium hydrogen L-glutamate; Glutamic acid
　　　　monosodium salt; Sodium L-glutamate; Monosodium L-glutamate monohydrate
　　Definition: Monosodium salt of L-form of glutamic acid
　　Empirical: $C_5H_8NO_4Na \cdot H_2O$
　　Formula: $HOOCCH_2CH_2CHNH_2COONa$
　　Properties: Wh. free-flowing cryst. or cryst. powd., sl. peptone-like odor, sl. sweet or sl. salty taste; very sol.
　　　　in water; sl. sol. in alcohol; m.w. 170.14; pH 6.7-7.2 (5%)
　　Toxicology: LD50 (oral, rat) 17 g/kg; mod. toxic by IV; mildly toxic by ingestion, etc.; experimental teratogen,
　　　　reproductive effects; human systemic effects by ingestion and IV; 'Chinese Restaurant Syndrome'; heated
　　　　to dec., emits toxic fumes of NO_x and Na_2O
　　Uses: Flavoring agent, perfume; used in one approved oral syrup
　　Regulatory: FDA 21CFR §145.131, 155.120, 155.130, 155.170, 155.200, 158.170, 161.190, 169.115,
　　　　169.140, 169.150, 172.320, 182.1, GRAS; USDA 9CFR §318.7, 381.147; not permitted for use in baby
　　　　foods in UK; FEMA GRAS; Japan approved; Europe listed; UK approved; USP/NF compliance
　　Manuf./Distrib.: Ajinomoto Co Inc; Allchem Industries; Asahi Chem Industry Co Ltd; Penta Mfg.; Schweizerhall
　　Manuf./Distrib. (pharm. & food): Able Prods.; ADM; Ajinomoto; Ashland; Browning; Calaga Food Ingreds.;
　　　　Cornelius; Croxton & Garry; Penta Mfg.; Scanchem; Spectrum Chem. Mfg.; Tesco; Todd's; Van Waters &
　　　　Rogers; E H Worlee GmbH

MSP. *See* Sodium phosphate
MTBE. *See* Methyl t-butyl ether

Mullein leaf
　　Uses: Used in orals
　　Regulatory: FDA approved for orals

Muriate of potash. *See* Potassium chloride
Muriatic acid. *See* Hydrochloric acid
Muscovite mica. *See* Mica
Mustard oil. *See* Allyl isothiocyanate
Mylase 100. *See* Amylase

Myrcene
　　CAS 123-35-3
　　FEMA 2762
　　Synonyms: 7-Methyl-3-methylene-1,6-octadiene
　　Empirical: $C_{10}H_{16}$
　　Properties: Oily liq., pleasant odor; sol. in alcohol, chloroform, ether; insol. in water; m.w. 136.23; dens. 0.791;
　　　　b.p. 167 C; flash pt. 103 F; ref. index 1.4650
　　Precaution: Combustible
　　Uses: Sweet synthetic flavoring agent
　　Regulatory: FDA 21CFR §172.515; FEMA GRAS
　　Manuf./Distrib. (pharm. & food): Aldrich

Myrcia oil. *See* Bay oil

Myreth-3 myristate
　　CAS 59599-55-2; 59686-68-9
　　Synonyms: PEG-3 myristyl ether myristate; POE (3) myristyl ether myristate
　　Definition: Ester of myreth-3 and myristic acid
　　Formula: $CH_3(CH_2)_{12}CO(OCH_2CH_2)_3OCH_2(CH_2)_{12}CH_3$
　　Uses: Emollient, thickener, carrier, base, emulsifier for pharmaceuticals
　　Trade names: Standamul® 1414-E

Myristaldehyde
　　CAS 124-25-4; EINECS 204-692-7
　　FEMA 2763
　　Synonyms: Tetradecanal; Tetradecyl aldehyde; Aldehyde C-14; Myristic aldehyde
　　Empirical: $C_{14}H_{28}O$
　　Formula: $CH_3(CH_2)_{12}CHO$
　　Properties: Colorless to sl. yel. liq., strong fatty orris-like odor; insol. in water; m.w. 212.38; dens. 0.825-0.835;

m.p. 23 C; b.p. 260 C; ref. index 1.43.80-1.4450
Uses: Citrus, fruity synthetic flavoring agent
Regulatory: FDA 21CFR §172.515; FEMA GRAS
Manuf./Distrib. (pharm. & food): Aldrich

Myristalkonium chloride
CAS 139-08-2; EINECS 205-352-0
Synonyms: N,N-Dimethyl-N-tetradecylbenzenemethanaminium chloride; Myristyl dimethyl benzyl ammonium chloride; Tetradecyl dimethyl benzyl ammonium chloride
Classification: Quaternary ammonium salt
Empirical: $C_{23}H_{42}N \cdot Cl$
Properties: M.w. 368.11
Toxicology: Skin and eye irritant; heated to decomp., emits very toxic fumes of NO_x, NH_3, and Cl^-
Uses: Antimicrobial preservative
Regulatory: FDA 21CFR §172.165 (limitation 3-12 ppm), 173.320 (limitation 0.6 ppm on wt. of raw sugar cane or raw beets), 175.105, 178.1010
Trade names: Catigene® DC 100

Myristamide DEA
CAS 7545-23-5; EINECS 231-426-7
Synonyms: Myristic diethanolamide; N,N-Bis(2-hydroxyethyl)myristamide; N,N-Bis(2-hydroxyethyl) tetradecanamide
Definition: Mixture of ethanolamides of myristic acid
Empirical: $C_{18}H_{37}NO_3$
Formula: $CH_3(CH_2)_{12}CON(CH_2CH_2OH)_2$
Toxicology: May produce contact sensitivity
Uses: Emulsifier for topical dermatological prods.
Regulatory: FDA 21CFR §175.105, 176.180, 176.210, 177.2260, 177.2800

Myristamide MEA
CAS 142-58-5; EINECS 205-546-5
Synonyms: Myristic monoethanolamide; N-(2-Hydroxyethyl)tetradecanamide; Myristoyl monoethanolamide
Definition: Mixture of ethanolamides of myristic acid
Empirical: $C_{16}H_{33}NO_2$
Formula: $CH_3(CH_2)_{12}CONHCH_2CH_2OH$
Uses: Emulsifier, thickener, opacifier, pearlescent in pharmaceutical formulations

Myristic acid
CAS 544-63-8; EINECS 208-875-2
FEMA 2764
Synonyms: Tetradecanoic acid; l-Tridecanecarboxylic acid; n-Tetradecoic acid
Classification: Organic acid
Empirical: $C_{14}H_{28}O_2$
Formula: $CH_3(CH_2)_{12}COOH$
Properties: Oily wh. cryst. solid; sol. in alcohol, ether, water; m.w. 228.36; dens. 0.8739 (80 C); m.p. 54.5 C; b.p. 326.2 C; flash pt. > 230 F
Precaution: Combustible
Toxicology: LD50 (IV, mouse) 43 mg/kg; poison by intravenous route; human skin irritant; mutagenic data; heated to decomp., emits acrid smoke and irritating fumes
Uses: Used in vaginals
Regulatory: FDA 21CFR §172.210, 172.860, 173.340, 175.105, 175.320, 176.170, 176.200, 176.210, 177.1010, 177.1200, 177.2260, 177.2600, 177.2800, 178.3570, 178.3910; FEMA GRAS; FDA approved for vaginals
Manuf./Distrib.: Akzo; Aldrich; Henkel/Emery; Mirachem Srl; Spectrum Chem. Mfg.; Unichema; Witco
Manuf./Distrib. (pharm. & food): Acme-Hardesty; Aldrich

Myristic acid isopropyl ester. *See* Isopropyl myristate
Myristic acid, 2-octyldodecyl ester. *See* Octyldodecyl myristate
Myristic aldehyde. *See* Myristaldehyde
Myristica oil. *See* Nutmeg oil
Myristic diethanolamide. *See* Myristamide DEA
Myristic monoethanolamide. *See* Myristamide MEA
Myristin. *See* Trimyristin
Myristoyl monoethanolamide. *See* Myristamide MEA

Myristyl alcohol

Myristyl alcohol
 CAS 112-72-1; EINECS 204-000-3
 Synonyms: 1-Tetradecanol
 Empirical: $C_{14}H_{30}O$
 Properties: Colorless to wh. waxy solid flakes, waxy odor; sol. in ether; sl. sol. in alcohol; insol. in water; m.w. 214.38; dens. 0.8355 (20/20 C); m.p. 38 C; b.p. 167 C; acid no. 2 max.; iodine no. 1 max.; hyd. no. 250-267; flash pt. 285 F
 Precaution: Combustible
 Toxicology: Nontoxic
 Uses: Oleaginous vehicle, consistency factor; used in orals; pharmaceutical raw material
 Regulatory: FDA 21CFR §172.864, 175.105, 175.300, 176.200, 176.210, 177.1010, 177.2800, 178.3480, 178.3910; FDA approved for orals; USP/NF compliance
 Manuf./Distrib.: Albemarle; Condor; R.W. Greeff; M. Michel; Schweizerhall; Spectrum Chem. Mfg.; Vista
 Manuf./Distrib. (pharm. & food): Aldrich; Ruger; Spectrum Chem. Mfg.
 Trade names: Dehydag® Wax 14; Lanette® 14; Nacol® 14-95; Nacol® 14-98; Unihydag Wax-14

Myristyl dimethyl benzyl ammonium chloride. *See* Myristalkonium chloride
Myristyl eicosanol. *See* Tetradecyleicosanol
Myristyleicosyl stearate. *See* Tetradecyleicosyl stearate

Myristyl lactate
 CAS 1323-03-1; EINECS 215-350-1
 Synonyms: 2-Hydroxypropanoic acid, tetradecyl ester; Tetradecyl 2-hydroxypropanoate
 Definition: Ester of myristyl alcohol and lactic acid
 Empirical: $C_{17}H_{34}O_3$
 Formula: $CH_3COHHCOOCH_2(CH_2)_{12}CH_3$
 Properties: Liq. or soft solid; sol. in ethanol, IPM, min. oil, oleyl alcohol, propylene glycol; insol. in water, glycerin; sp.gr. 0.892-0.904
 Toxicology: LD50 (rat, oral) 20 ml/kg; nonirritating to skin
 Uses: Pharmaceutical raw material; emollient, solubilizer, lubricant for pharmaceutical formulations
 Trade names: Cegesoft® C 17; Ceraphyl® 50; Pelemol® ML

Myristyl myristate
 CAS 3234-85-3; EINECS 221-787-9
 Synonyms: Tetradecyl tetradecanoate; Tetradecanoic acid, tetradecyl ester
 Definition: Ester of myristyl alcohol and myristic acid
 Empirical: $C_{28}H_{56}O_2$
 Formula: $CH_3(CH_2)_{12}COOCH_2(CH_2)_{12}CH_3$
 Properties: Waxy solid, bland char. odor; sol. in min. oil, IPM, oleyl alcohol; insol. in water, glycerin, propylene glycol; m.p. 36-39 C
 Toxicology: LD50 (rat, oral) 8.6 g/kg; minimal eye irritation, mild skin irritation
 Uses: Emollient for creams, lotions
 Trade names: Ceraphyl® 424; Cetiol® MM; Crodamol MM; Pelemol® MM

Myristyl stearate
 CAS 17661-50-6; EINECS 241-640-2
 Synonyms: Octadecanoic acid, tetradecyl ester
 Definition: Ester of myristyl alcohol and stearic acid
 Empirical: $C_{32}H_{64}O_2$
 Formula: $CH_3(CH_2)_{16}COOCH_2(CH_2)_{12}CH_3$
 Uses: Emollient, visc. builder used in pharmaceutical topicals
 Trade names: Kemester® 1418; Pelemol® MS

Myristyl trimethyl ammonium bromide. *See* Myrtrimonium bromide
Myroxylon pereirae oleoresin. *See* Balsam Peru

Myrtenol
 CAS 515-00-4
 FEMA 3439
 Synonyms: (1R)-(-)-Myrtenol
 Empirical: $C_{10}H_{16}O$
 Properties: M.w. 152.24; dens. 0.954; b.p. 221-22 C; flash pt. 193 F
 Uses: Medicinal flavoring agent
 Regulatory: FEMA GRAS
 Manuf./Distrib. (pharm. & food): Aldrich

(1R)-(-)-Myrtenol. *See* Myrtenol

Myrtrimonium bromide
CAS 1119-97-7; EINECS 214-291-9
Synonyms: Myristyl trimethyl ammonium bromide; Tetradecyltrimethylammonium bromide; N,N,N-Trimethyl-1-tetradecanaminium bromide; Tetradonium bromide
Classification: Quaternary ammonium salt
Empirical: $C_{17}H_{38}N \cdot Br$
Properties: White powd.; sol. in 5 parts water; m.w. 336.40; m.p. 245-250 C; pH 5-8 (1%)
Toxicology: Corrosive; LD50 (mice, IV) 12 mg/kg; can be toxic depending on dose and conc.; conc. sol'n. can irritate the skin and cause necrosis of the mucous membranes; conc. as low as 0.1% are irritating to eyes and mucous membranes
Uses: Disinfectant, sanitizer; used in dilute sol'ns. to sterilize the skin and mucous membranes; antiseptic creams; purification of heparin
Manuf./Distrib.: Spectrum Chem. Mfg.
Trade names: Pentonium 4Br40

NaDBS. *See* Sodium dodecylbenzenesulfonate
Naphthol red. *See* Amaranth
Naphthol yellow S. *See* D&C Yellow No. 8; Ext. D&C Yellow No. 7
Naphthylamine red. *See* Amaranth
Native calcium sulfate. *See* Calcium sulfate dihydrate
Natural brown 5. *See* CI 75130
Natural brown 10. *See* Caramel
Natural carotene. *See* CI 75130
Natural green 3. *See* CI 75810
Natural orange 4. *See* Annatto; Annatto extract; CI 75120
Natural pearl essence. *See* CI 75170; Guanine
Natural red 4. *See* Carmine; CI 75470
Natural white 1. *See* CI 75170; Guanine
Natural yellow 26. *See* Carotene; CI 75130
NDGA. *See* Nordihydroguairetic acid
(+)-Neomenthol. *See* d-Neomenthol

d-Neomenthol
CAS 2216-52-6; EINECS 218-691-4
FEMA 2666
Synonyms: 2-Isobutyl-5-methylcyclohexanol; (+)-Neomenthol; d-β-Pulegomenthol
Empirical: $C_{10}H_{20}O$
Properties: Liq., menthol-like odor; sol. in alcohol, acetone; insol. in water; m.w. 156.27; dens. 0.899 (20/4 C); m.p. -22 C; b.p. 209-210 C; flash pt. 83 C; ref. index 1.461 (20 C)
Uses: Synthetic flavoring agent
Regulatory: FDA 21CFR §172.515; FEMA GRAS
Manuf./Distrib. (pharm. & food): Aldrich

Neopentanoic acid, tridecyl ester. *See* Tridecyl neopentanoate

Neopentyl glycol dicaprylate/dicaprate
CAS 70693-32-2
Synonyms: Decanoic acid, mixed esters with neopentyl glycol and octanoic acid
Definition: Diester of a blend of caprylic and capric acids and neopentyl glycol
Uses: Dry-feel emollient for creams, lotions, antiperspirants

Nepheline syenite
CAS 37244-96-5
Synonyms: Nephylene syenite
Definition: Feldspathoid igneous rock primarily composed of the minerals microcline ($KAlSi_3O_8$), albite ($NaAlSi_3O_6$), and nepheline [$(Na,K)AlSiO_4$]
Properties: Wh. solid; sp.gr. 2.61; m.p. 1223 C
Toxicology: ACGIH TLV 10 mg/m^3; excessive/prolonged inh. of dust may harm respiratory system
Manuf./Distrib.: Hammill & Gillespie; D.N. Lukens; Unimin Canada Ltd; Jesse S. Young

Nephylene syenite. *See* Nepheline syenite

Neral

Neral. *See* Citral
Nerolidol. *See* Trimethyldodecatrieneol
Neroli oil, artificial. *See* Methyl anthranilate

Neryl acetate
CAS 141-12-8; EINECS 205-459-2
FEMA 2773
Synonyms: cis-3,7-Dimethyl-2,6-octadien-1-yl-acetate
Definition: Ester of nerol and acetic acid
Empirical: $C_{12}H_{20}O_2$
Formula: $(CH_3)_2C:CHCH_2CH_2C(CH_3):CHCH_2OCOCH_3$
Properties: Colorless to sl. yel. oily liq., sweet floral orange-blossom and rose-like odor, honey-like flavor; m.w. 196.29; dens. 0.912 (20/4 C); b.p. 234-236 C; flash pt. 210 F; ref. index 1.460 (20 C)
Uses: Sweet apple-like synthetic flavoring agent
Regulatory: FDA 21CFR §172.515; FEMA GRAS
Manuf./Distrib. (pharm. & food): Aldrich

Neryl butyrate
CAS 999-40-6
FEMA 2774
Empirical: $C_{12}H_{20}O_2$
Properties: M.w. 224.35; dens. 0.898; b.p. 240 C; flash pt. > 230 F
Uses: Sweet orange-like synthetic flavoring agent
Regulatory: FDA 21CFR §172.515; FEMA GRAS
Manuf./Distrib. (pharm. & food): Aldrich

Neryl isobutyrate
CAS 2345-24-6
FEMA 2775
Empirical: $C_{14}H_{24}O_2$
Properties: M.w. 224.35; dens. 0.895; b.p. 229 C; flash pt. > 230 F
Uses: Sweet orange-like synthetic flavoring agent
Regulatory: FDA 21CFR §172.515; FEMA GRAS
Manuf./Distrib. (pharm. & food): Aldrich

Neryl isovalerate
CAS 3915-83-1
FEMA 2778
Empirical: $C_{15}H_{26}O_2$
Properties: M.w. 238.37; dens. 0.890; b.p. 252 C; flash pt. > 230 F
Uses: Sweet synthetic flavoring agent
Regulatory: FDA 21CFR §172.515; FEMA GRAS
Manuf./Distrib. (pharm. & food): Aldrich

Neryl propionate
FEMA 2777
Definition: Ester of nerol and propionic acid
Empirical: $C_{13}H_{22}O_2$
Properties: Colorless oily liq., ether-like sweet intense fruity odor, plum-like taste; sol. in alcohol; sl. sol. in water; m.w. 210.31; b.p. 233 C; ref. index 1.4550
Uses: Synthetic flavoring agent
Regulatory: FDA 21CFR §172.515; FEMA GRAS

Niacinamide
CAS 98-92-0; EINECS 202-713-4
Synonyms: Nicotinamide; Vitamin B; 3-Pyridinecarboxamide; Nicotinic acid amide
Classification: Heterocyclic aromatic amide
Empirical: $C_6H_6N_2O$
Formula: $C_5H_4NCONH_2$
Properties: Colorless needles or wh. cryst. powd., odorless, bitter taste; sol. in water, ethanol, glycerin; m.w. 122.14; dens. 1.40; m.p. 129 C
Toxicology: Moderately toxic by ingestion, intravenous, intraperitoneal and subcutaneous routes; no known skin toxicity; mutagenic data; heated to decomp., emits toxic fumes of NO_x
Uses: Skin stimulant; dietary supplement to prevent pellagra
Regulatory: FDA 21CFR §182.5535, 184.1535, GRAS; BP, Ph.Eur. compliance
Manuf./Distrib.: Reilly Ind.

Manuf./Distrib. (pharm. & food): Aldrich; Am. Roland; R.W. Greeff; Reilly Ind.; Ruger; Spectrum Chem. Mfg.
Trade names: Niacinamide USP, FCC No. 69905; Niacinamide USP, FCC Fine Granular No. 69916
Trade names containing: Descote® Niacinamide $33^1/_3$%; Rocoat® Niacinamide $33^1/_3$% No. 69907; Rocoat® Niacinamide $33^1/_3$% Type S No. 69909

Niacin. *See* Nicotinic acid
Niconate. *See* Ferrous gluconate
Nicotinamide. *See* Niacinamide

Nicotinic acid
    CAS 59-67-6; EINECS 200-441-0
    Synonyms: Niacin; Vitamin B_3; 3-Picolinic acid; Pyridine-3-carboxylic acid; 3-Pyridinecarboxylic acid
    Classification: Heterocyclic aromatic compd.
    Empirical: $C_6H_5NO_2$
    Properties: Colorless needles or wh. cryst. powd., odorless to sl. odor, sour taste; nonhygroscopic; sol. in alcohol, 1.7 g/100 g water; insol. in most lipid solvs., ether; m.w. 123.12; dens. 1.473; m.p. 236 C, subl. above m.p.
    Toxicology: LD50 (oral, rat) 7000 mg/kg; poison by intraperitoneal route; moderately toxic by ingestion, intravenous and subcutaneous routes; megadoses may cause itching, nausea, headaches; experimental carcinogen; heated to decomp., emits toxic fumes of NO_x
    Uses: Dietary supplement; anti-pellagra vitamin
    Regulatory: FDA 21CFR §135.115, 137, 139, 182.5530, 184.1530, GRAS; Japan restricted; Europe listed; UK approved; BP, Ph.Eur. compliance
    Manuf./Distrib.: BASF; Degussa; R.W. Greeff; Lonza; Reilly Ind.; Schweizerhall
    Manuf./Distrib. (pharm. & food): Aldrich; Am. Roland; Avrachem; Mallinckrodt; Reilly Ind.; Ruger; Spectrum Chem. Mfg.
    Trade names: Niacin USP, FCC Fine Granular No. 69901; Niacin USP, FCC No. 69902

Nicotinic acid amide. *See* Niacinamide
Niobe oil. *See* Methyl benzoate
Nitratophenylmercury. *See* Phenylmercuric nitrate

Nitric acid
    CAS 7697-37-2; EINECS 231-714-2
    UN No. 2031
    Synonyms: Aqua fortis; Engraver's acid; Azotic acid
    Empirical: HNO_3
    Properties: Colorless or almost colorless fuming liq., char. highly irritating odor; misc. with water; m.w. 63.01; dens. 1.41; b.p. 120 C; flash pt. none; stains animal tissues yel.
    Precaution: DOT: Corrosive material
    Toxicology: Highly corrosive; rapidly destroys tissues; avoid contact
    Uses: Acidifying agent; used in inhalants, ophthalmics, topicals; corrosive agent for removing warts, tattoos
    Regulatory: FDA approved for inhalants, ophthalmics, topicals; USP/NF, BP compliance
    Manuf./Distrib.: Aceto; Air Prods.; Am. Cyanamid; ANGUS; Asahi Chem Industry Co Ltd; Bayer; DuPont; Monsanto; Nissan Chem. Ind.; Norsk Hydro A/S; Spectrum Chem. Mfg.
    Manuf./Distrib. (pharm. & food): Aldrich; Mallinckrodt; Spectrum Chem. Mfg.

Nitrile C₄. *See* Butyronitrile
2,2′,2″-Nitrilotris(ethanol). *See* Triethanolamine
1,1′,1″-Nitrilotris-2-propanol. *See* Triisopropanolamine
2-Nitrobenzaldehyde. *See* o-Nitrobenzaldehyde
4-Nitrobenzaldehyde. *See* p-Nitrobenzaldehyde

o-Nitrobenzaldehyde
    CAS 552-89-6; EINECS 209-025-3
    Synonyms: 2-Nitrobenzaldehyde
    Classification: Aromatic organic compd.
    Empirical: $C_7H_5NO_3$
    Formula: $O_2NC_6H_4CHO$
    Properties: Lt. yel. need.; sol. in alcohol, ether, chloroform; m.w. 151.12; m.p. 42-43 C; b.p. 153 C (23 mm); flash pt. > 230 F
    Toxicology: Irritant
    Uses: Used in the synthesis of pharmaceuticals
    Regulatory: BP compliance
    Manuf./Distrib.: Penta Mfg.; Schweizerhall; Spectrum Chem. Mfg.
    Manuf./Distrib. (pharm. & food): Sumitomo Seika Chems.

p-Nitrobenzaldehyde
CAS 555-16-8; EINECS 209-084-5
Synonyms: 4-Nitrobenzaldehyde
Classification: Aromatic organic compd.
Empirical: $C_7H_5NO_3$
Formula: $O_2NC_6H_4CHO$
Properties: Wh. to yel. cryst.; sol. in alcohol, benzene; sl. sol. in water, ether; m.w. 151.12; m.p. 106-107 C
Toxicology: Irritant
Uses: Used in the synthesis of pharmaceuticals
Manuf./Distrib.: Penta Mfg.; Schweizerhall; Spectrum Chem. Mfg.
Manuf./Distrib. (pharm. & food): Nippon Kayaku

5-Nitrobenzene-1,3-dicarboxylic acid. *See* 5-Nitroisophthalic acid

2-Nitro-1-butanol
CAS 609-31-4
Classification: Nitro alcohol
Formula: $CH_3CH_2CHNO_2CH_2OH$
Properties: Colorless liq.; sol. in water; m.w. 119.1; dens. 1.133; m.p. -48 C; b.p. 105 C (10 mm); ref. index
 1.4390
Precaution: Combustible
Uses: Pharmaceutical intermediate; deodorants

Nitrocarbol. *See* Nitromethane

Nitrocellulose
CAS 9004-70-0
UN No. 2059, 2555, 2556, 2557
Synonyms: Cellulose, nitrate; Cellulose tetranitrate; Celluloid; Pyroxylin; Nitrocotton; Collodion cotton;
 Guncotton; Soluble guncotton
Classification: Cellulose deriv.
Empirical: $C_{12}H_{16}O_{18}N_4$
Formula: $C_{12}H_{16}(ONO_2)_4O_6$
Properties: Colorless liq. or wh. amorphous solid; sol. in acetone, glac. acetic acid; insol. in water, ether-alcohol
 mixt.; m.w. 504.3; dens. 1.66; flash pt. 55 F
Precaution: Flamm. solid; highly dangerous exposed to heat, flame, strong oxidizers; ignites easily; explodes
Toxicology: No known toxicity
Uses: Pharmaceutic necessity used in creams
Regulatory: FDA 21CFR §175.105, 175.300, 176.170, 177.1200, 181.22, 181.30
Manuf./Distrib.: Aarbor Int'l.; Allchem Industries; Aqualon; Asahi Chem Industry Co Ltd; Bayer; Daicel Chem.
 Ind.; Hercules; Punda Mercantile; SNPE Chimie; Vanguard Chem. Int'l.
Manuf./Distrib. (pharm. & food): Allchem Industries; Asahi Chem Industry Co Ltd; Hercules

Nitrocotton. *See* Nitrocellulose

Nitroethane
CAS 79-24-3; EINECS 201-188-9
UN No. 2842
Classification: Aliphatic organic compd.; nitroparaffin
Empirical: $C_2H_5NO_2$
Formula: $CH_3CH_2NO_2$
Properties: Oily colorless liq., agreeable odor; sol. in water, acid, alkali; misc. with alcohol, chloroform, ether;
 m.w. 75.07; dens. 1.048 (20/4 C); m.p. -90 C; b.p. 112-116 C; flash pt. (OC) 106 F
Precaution: DOT: Flamm. liq.; explodes when heated
Toxicology: Poison by intraperitoneal route; moderately toxic by ingestion; irritating to eyes, mucous
 membranes; TLV 100 ppm in air; LD50 (rat, oral) 1100 mg/kg
Uses: Raw material for pharmaceutical synthesis, e.g., for α-methyldopa, a hypertensive drug, and for
 phenylpropanolamine used in bronchial decongestants and appetite suppressants
Regulatory: BP compliance
Manuf./Distrib.: ANGUS; Spectrum Chem. Mfg.
Manuf./Distrib. (pharm. & food): Aldrich
Trade names: NE™

2-Nitro-2-ethyl-1,3-propanediol
CAS 597-09-1
Classification: Nitro alcohol

Empirical: C$_4$H$_{13}$O$_4$N
Formula: HOCH$_2$C(CH$_2$H$_5$)(NO$_2$)CH$_2$OH
Properties: White crystals; sol. in water, org. solvs.; m.w. 149.14; m.p. 56-65 C
Uses: Pharmaceutical intermediate
Trade names: NEPD

Nitrogen
CAS 7727-37-9; EINECS 231-783-9
UN No. 1066 (compressed), 1977 (refrig. liq.)
Classification: Gaseous element
Definition: Gas that is 78% of the atmosphere by volume and essential to all living things
Empirical: N$_2$
Properties: Colorless gas, odorless, tasteless; sl. sol. in alcohol; sparingly sol. in water; at. wt. 14.0067; m.w. 28.01; m.p. -210 C; b.p. -195.79 C
Precaution: Nonflamm.; does not support combustion; combines with oxygen and hydrogen on sparking forming nitric oxide and ammonia resp.
Toxicology: Asphyxiant in high concs.; toxic conc. in humans is 90 ppm; in mice, 250 ppm
Uses: Propellant, diluent, air displacement in pharmaceuticals
Regulatory: FDA 21CFR §169.115, 169.140, 169.150, 184.1540, GRAS; Japan approved; USP/NF, BP compliance
Manuf./Distrib.: Aldrich
Manuf./Distrib. (pharm. & food): Aldrich

Nitrogen monoxide. *See* Nitrous oxide
Nitrogen oxide. *See* Nitrous oxide

5-Nitroisophthalic acid
CAS 75-52-5; 618-88-2; EINECS 200-876-6
Synonyms: 5-Nitrobenzene-1,3-dicarboxylic acid
Empirical: CH$_3$NO$_2$
Properties: M.w. 61.04; b.p. 259-261 C; dens. 1.13 (20 C); flash pt. >120 C
Uses: Pharmaceutical intermediate
Manuf./Distrib.: First; Pfister; Schweizerhall
Manuf./Distrib. (pharm. & food): Aldrich

Nitromethane
CAS 75-52-5; EINECS 200-876-6
UN No. 1261
Synonyms: Nitrocarbol
Classification: Nitroparaffin
Empirical: CH$_3$NO$_2$
Properties: Colorless oily liq., disagreeable odor; sol. in water, alcohol, ether; m.w. 61.04; dens. 1.139 (20/20 C); m.p. -29 C; b.p. 100-103 C; flash pt. 36 C (112 F)
Precaution: DOT: Flamm. liq.; dangerous fire and explosion risk; explosive limit 7.3% in air; reacts violently
Toxicology: Poison by ingestion, inhalation, intraperitoneal routes; TLV 100 ppm in air; LD50 (mice, oral) 1.44 g/kg
Uses: Raw material for syntesis of pharmaceutical actives, e.g., for 1,1-bis(metylthio)-2-nitroethane used to mfg. ranitidine, an anti-ulcer drug, or serinol, a raw material for iopamidol, an injectable radio-opaque x-ray contrast medium
Regulatory: BP compliance
Manuf./Distrib.: ANGUS; Spectrum Chem. Mfg.
Manuf./Distrib. (pharm. & food): Aldrich
Trade names: NM™

2-Nitro-2-methyl-1-propanol
CAS 76-39-1
Classification: Nitro alcohol
Empirical: C$_4$H$_9$O$_3$N
Formula: CH$_3$C(CH$_3$)(NO$_2$)CH$_2$OH
Properties: White crystals; sol. in water; m.w. 119.12; m.p. 90 C; b.p. 95 C (10 mm)
Uses: Pharmaceutical intermediate
Manuf./Distrib.: ANGUS
Trade names: NMP

Nitropropane
CAS 108-03-2; EINECS 203-544-9

1-Nitropropane

UN No. 2608
Synonyms: 1-Nitropropane
Classification: Nitroparaffin
Empirical: $C_3H_7NO_2$
Formula: $CH_3CH_2CH_2NO_2$
Properties: Colorless liq.; very sl. sol. in water; misc. with alcohol, ether; m.w. 89.09; dens. 1.003 (20/20 C); m.p. -108 C; b.p. 129-133 C; flash pt. (TOC) 93 F; ref. index 1.4018 (20 C)
Precaution: Flamm. liq.; reacts violently
Toxicology: Poison by intraperitoneal route and ingestion; irritating to mucous membranes; TLV 25 ppm in air
Uses: {Pharmaceutical intermediate
Manuf./Distrib.: ANGUS
Trade names: NiPar S-10™

1-Nitropropane. *See* Nitropropane

2-Nitropropane

CAS 79-46-9; EINECS 201-209-1
UN No. 2608
Synonyms: sec-Nitropropane
Classification: Nitroparaffin
Empirical: $C_3H_7NO_2$
Formula: $CH_3CH(NO_2)CH_3$
Properties: Colorless liq.; sl. sol. in water; misc. with many org. solvs.; m.w. 89.09; dens. 0.992 (20/20 C); m.p. -93 C; b.p. 119-122 C; flash pt. (TOC) 75 F
Precaution: Flamm. when exposed to heat, open flame, oxidizers; may explode on heating
Toxicology: TLV:CL 25 ppm in air; LD50 (oral, rat) 725 mg/kg; poison by ingestion, inhalation, and intraperitoneal routes (nausea, diarrhea, anorexia); suspected carcinogen; mutagenic
Uses: Pharmaceutical intermediate; used in beta blockers for treatment of cardiovascular disease and in anti-tumor drugs
Manuf./Distrib.: Aldrich; ANGUS; Ashland
Manuf./Distrib. (pharm. & food): ANGUS; Ashland
Trade names: NiPar S-20™

sec-Nitropropane. *See* 2-Nitropropane
Nitrous acid sodium salt. *See* Sodium nitrite

Nitrous oxide

CAS 10024-97-2; EINECS 233-032-0
FEMA 2779; UN No. 1070 (compressed), 2201 (refrig. liq.)
Synonyms: Nitrogen monoxide; Nitrogen oxide; Dinitrogen monoxide; Laughing gas
Classification: Gas
Empirical: N_2O
Properties: Colorless gas, sl. sweet odor, pract. tasteless; freely sol. in alcohol; sol. in ether, oils; m.w. 44.01; m.p. -91 C; b.p. -88 C
Precaution: Does not burn but will support combustion; oxidizer
Toxicology: Asphyxiant at high concs.
Uses: Propellant gas in aerosols; anesthetic in dentistry and surgery
Regulatory: FDA 21CFR §184.1545, GRAS; FEMA GRAS; BP, Ph.Eur. compliance
Manuf./Distrib.: Air Liquide Hellas SA; Air Prods.; Aldrich; Monsanto; Nissan Chem. Ind.; Showa Denko
Manuf./Distrib. (pharm. & food): Aldrich

NMP. *See* N-Methyl-2-pyrrolidone

γ-Nonalactone

CAS 104-61-0; EINECS 203-219-1
FEMA 2781
Synonyms: Coconut aldehyde; Aldehyde C-18; γ-N-Amylbutyrolactone; 4-Hydroxynonanoic acid, γ-lactone
Classification: Heterocyclic compd.
Empirical: $C_9H_{16}O_2$
Properties: Colorless to sl. yel. liq., coconut odor; sol. in alcohol, fixed oils, propylene glycol; insol. in water; m.w. 156.25; dens. 0.958-0.966; b.p. 243 C; flash pt. > 212 F; ref. index 1.446-1.450
Precaution: Combustible liq.
Toxicology: LD50 (oral, rat) 6600 mg/kg; mod. toxic by ingestion; skin irritant; heated to decomp., emits acrid smoke and irritating fumes
Uses: Coconut-like synthetic flavoring agent
Regulatory: FDA 21CFR §172.515; FEMA GRAS; Japan approved as flavoring
Manuf./Distrib. (pharm. & food): Aldrich

Nonalol. *See* Nonyl alcohol

Nonanal
CAS 124-19-6; EINECS 204-688-5
FEMA 2782
Synonyms: Aldehyde C-9; Nonanoic aldehyde; Pelargonic aldehyde; Pelargonaldehyde
Empirical: $C_9H_{18}O$
Formula: $CH_3(CH_2)_7CHO$
Properties: Colorless to lt. yel. liq., strong fatty odor; sol. in alcohol; insol. in water; m.w. 142.24; dens. 0.823 (20/4 C); b.p. 79-81 C (12 mm); flash pt. 63 C; ref. index 1.425 (20 C)
Precaution: Combustible
Toxicology: Skin and eye irritant
Uses: Citrus synthetic flavoring agent
Regulatory: FDA 21CFR §172.515; FEMA GRAS
Manuf./Distrib. (pharm. & food): Aldrich

Nonanoic acid ethyl ester. *See* Ethyl pelargonate
Nonanoic acid, 2-ethylhexyl ester. *See* Octyl pelargonate
Nonanoic acid, 1-methyl-1,2-ethanediyl ester. *See* Propylene glycol dipelargonate
Nonanoic aldehyde. *See* Nonanal
1-Nonanol. *See* Nonyl alcohol

2-Nonanol
CAS 628-99-9
FEMA 3315
Empirical: $C_9H_{20}O$
Properties: M.w. 144.26; dens. 0.827; b.p. 193-194 C; flash pt. 180 F
Uses: Melon-like flavoring agent
Regulatory: FEMA GRAS
Manuf./Distrib. (pharm. & food): Aldrich

2-Nonanone
CAS 821-55-6; EINECS 212-480-0
FEMA 2785
Synonyms: Methyl heptyl ketone; Heptyl methyl ketone
Empirical: $C_9H_{18}O$
Formula: $CH_3(CH_2)_6COCH_3$
Properties: Colorless oily liq., char. rue odor, rose tea-like flavor; sol. in alcohol; insol. in water; m.w. 142.24; dens. 0.82 (20/4 C); m.p. -21 C; b.p. 72-74 C (10 mm); flash pt. 68 C; ref. index 1.421 (20 C)
Uses: Fruity synthetic flavoring agent
Regulatory: FDA 21CFR §172.515; FEMA GRAS
Manuf./Distrib. (pharm. & food): Aldrich; Hüls AG

Nonate. *See* Isoamyl nonanoate
Noncarbinol. *See* n-Decyl alcohol

cis-6-Nonen-1-ol
CAS 35854-86-5
FEMA 3465
Empirical: $C_9H_{18}O$
Properties: Wh. to sl. yel. liq., powerful melon-like odor; insol. in water; m.w. 142.23; dens. 0.850-0.870; b.p. 115 C (20 mm); flash pt. 199 F; ref. index 1.448-1.450
Uses: Melon-like synthetic flavoring agent
Regulatory: FEMA GRAS
Manuf./Distrib. (pharm. & food): Aldrich

Nonfat dry milk
Synonyms: Milk, nonfat dry; Powdered skim milk; Nonfat milk
Definition: Solid residue from dehydration of defatted cow's milk
Uses: Ingred. in pharmaceuticals
Regulatory: FDA 21CFR §131.125
Manuf./Distrib. (pharm. & food): Blossom Farm Prods.; Browning
Trade names containing: Ches® 500

Nonfat milk. *See* Nonfat dry milk

Nonoxynol-1
CAS 26027-38-3 (generic); 37205-87-1 (generic); 27986-36-3; EINECS 248-762-5

Nonoxynol-2

Synonyms: Ethylene glycol nonyl phenyl ether; PEG-1 nonyl phenyl ether; 2-(Nonylphenoxy) ethanol
Classification: Ethoxylated alkyl phenol
Empirical: $C_{17}H_{28}O_2$
Formula: $C_9H_{19}C_6H_4OCH_2CH_2OH$
Properties: Yel. to almost colorless liq.; sol. in oil
Toxicology: Moderately toxic by ingestion, skin contact; severe eye and mild skin irritant in humans; heated to dec., emits acrid smoke and fumes
Uses: Emulsifier, solubilizer
Regulatory: FDA 21CFR §175.105, 176.180
Trade names: Synperonic NP1

Nonoxynol-2

CAS 26027-38-3 (generic); 37205-87-1 (generic); 27176-93-8 (generic); 9016-45-9 (generic); EINECS 248-291-5
Synonyms: PEG-2 nonyl phenyl ether; POE (2) nonyl phenyl ether; PEG 100 nonyl phenyl ether
Classification: Ethoxylated alkyl phenol
Empirical: $C_{19}H_{32}O_3$
Formula: $C_9H_{19}C_6H_4(OCH_2CH_2)_nOH$, avg. n = 2
Properties: Yel. to almost colorless liq.; sol. in oil
Toxicology: Moderately toxic by ingestion, skin contact; severe eye and mild skin irritant in humans; heated to dec., emits acrid smoke and fumes
Uses: Emulsifier, solubilizer
Regulatory: FDA 21CFR §176.105, 176.180, 176.210
Trade names: Synperonic NP2

Nonoxynol-4

CAS 7311-27-5; 9016-45-9 (generic); 26027-38-3 (generic); 37205-87-1 (generic); 27176-97-2;; EINECS 230-770-5
Synonyms: PEG-4 nonyl phenyl ether; POE (4) nonyl phenyl ether; PEG 200 nonyl phenyl ether
Classification: Ethoxylated alkyl phenol
Empirical: $C_{23}H_{40}O_5$
Formula: $C_9H_{19}C_6H_4(OCH_2CH_2)_nOH$, avg. n = 4
Properties: Yel. to almost colorless liq.; sol. in oil
Toxicology: Moderately toxic by ingestion, skin contact; severe eye and mild skin irritant in humans; heated to dec., emits acrid smoke and fumes
Uses: Nonionic surfactant, emulsifier, solubilizer; used in opthlamics, topicals, vaginals
Regulatory: FDA 21CFR §175.105, 176.180, 176.210, 178.3400; FDA approved for ophthalmics, topicals, vaginals
Trade names: Synperonic NP4

Nonoxynol-5

CAS 9016-45-9 (generic); 26027-38-3 (generic); 37205-87-1 (generic); 26264-02-8; 20636-48-0; EINECS 247-555-7
Synonyms: PEG-5 nonyl phenyl ether; POE (5) nonyl phenyl ether; 14-(Nonylphenoxy)-3,6,9,12-tetraoxatetradecan-1-ol
Classification: Ethoxylated alkyl phenol
Empirical: $C_{25}H_{44}O_6$
Formula: $C_9H_{19}C_6H_4(OCH_2CH_2)_nOH$, avg. n = 5
Properties: Yel. to almost colorless liq.; sol. in oil
Toxicology: Moderately toxic by ingestion, skin contact; severe eye and mild skin irritant in humans; heated to dec., emits acrid smoke and fumes
Uses: Emulsifier, solubilizer
Regulatory: FDA 21CFR §175.105, 176.180, 176.210, 178.3400
Trade names: Synperonic NP5; Synperonic NP5.5

Nonoxynol-6

CAS 9016-45-9 (generic); 26027-38-3 (generic); 37205-87-1 (generic); 27177-01-1; 27177-05-5
Synonyms: PEG-6 nonyl phenyl ether; POE (6) nonyl phenyl ether; PEG 300 nonyl phenyl ether
Classification: Ethoxylated alkyl phenol
Empirical: $C_{27}H_{48}O_7$
Formula: $C_9H_{19}C_6H_4(OCH_2CH_2)_nOH$, avg. n = 6
Properties: Yel. to almost colorless liq.
Toxicology: Moderately toxic by ingestion, skin contact; severe eye and mild skin irritant in humans; heated to dec., emits acrid smoke and fumes
Uses: Emulsifier, solubilizer

Regulatory: FDA 21CFR §175.105, 176.180, 176.210, 178.3400
Trade names: Synperonic NP6

Nonoxynol-7
CAS 9016-45-9 (generic); 26027-38-3 (generic); 27177-05-5; 37205-87-1 (generic); EINECS 248-292-0
Synonyms: PEG-7 nonyl phenyl ether; POE (7) nonyl phenyl ether
Classification: Ethoxylated alkyl phenol
Empirical: $C_{29}H_{52}O_8$
Formula: $C_9H_{19}C_6H_4(OCH_2CH_2)_nOH$, avg. n = 7
Properties: Yel. to almost colorless liq.
Toxicology: Moderately toxic by ingestion, skin contact; severe eye and mild skin irritant in humans; heated to dec., emits acrid smoke and fumes
Uses: Emulsifier, solubilizer
Regulatory: FDA 21CFR §175.105, 176.180, 176.210, 178.3400
Trade names: Synperonic NP7

Nonoxynol-8
CAS 9016-45-9 (generic); 26027-38-3 (generic); 37205-87-1 (generic); 26571-11-9; 27177-05-5; EINECS 248-293-6; 247-816-5
Synonyms: PEG-8 nonyl phenyl ether; POE (8) nonyl phenyl ether; PEG 400 nonyl phenyl ether
Classification: Ethoxylated alkyl phenol
Empirical: $C_{31}H_{56}O_9$
Formula: $C_9H_{19}C_6H_4(OCH_2CH_2)_nOH$, avg. n = 8
Properties: Yel. to almost colorless liq.
Toxicology: Moderately toxic by ingestion, skin contact; severe eye and mild skin irritant in humans; heated to dec., emits acrid smoke and fumes
Uses: Emulsifier, solubilizer
Regulatory: FDA 21CFR §175.105, 176.180, 176.210, 178.3400
Trade names: Synperonic NP8; Synperonic NP8.5; Synperonic NP8.75
Trade names containing: Simulsol® 5719

Nonoxynol-9
CAS 9016-45-9 (generic); 26027-38-3 (generic); 26571-11-9; 37205-87-1 (generic); 14409-72-4
Synonyms: PEG-9 nonyl phenyl ether; POE (9) nonyl phenyl ether; PEG 450 nonyl phenyl ether
Classification: Ethoxylated alkyl phenol
Empirical: $C_{33}H_{60}O_{10}$
Formula: $C_9H_{19}C_6H_4(OCH_2CH_2)_nOH$, avg. n = 9
Properties: Colorless to lt. yel. clear visc. liq.; sol. in water, ethanol, ethylene glycol, xylene, corn oil; m.w. 617; dens. 1.06 (25/4 C); solid. pt. 26 F; pour pt. 37 F; flash pt. 535-555 F; cloud pt. 126-133 F (1% aq.); visc. 175-250 cps
Toxicology: Moderately toxic by ingestion, skin contact; severe eye and mild skin irritant in humans; heated to dec., emits acrid smoke and fumes
Uses: Nonionic surfactant, wetting agent, solubilizer for pharmaceuticals; spermaticide
Regulatory: FDA 21CFR §175.105, 176.180, 176.210, 176.300, 178.3400; USP/NF compliance
Trade names: Igepal® CO-630 Special; Synperonic NP9; Synperonic NP9.5

Nonoxynol-10
CAS 9016-45-9 (generic); 26027-38-3 (generic); 27177-08-8; 37205-87-1 (generic); 27942-26-3; EINECS 248-294-1
Synonyms: PEG-10 nonyl phenyl ether; POE (10) nonyl phenyl ether; PEG 500 nonyl phenyl ether
Classification: Ethoxylated alkyl phenol
Empirical: $C_{35}H_{64}O_{11}$
Formula: $C_9H_{19}C_6H_4(OCH_2CH_2)_nOH$, avg. n = 10
Properties: Colorless to lt. amber visc. liq., aromatic odor; sol. in polar org.solvs., water; hyd. no. 81-97
Toxicology: Moderately toxic by ingestion, skin contact; severe eye and mild skin irritant in humans; heated to dec., emits acrid smoke and fumes
Uses: Wetting agent, emulsifier, solubilizer for pharmaceuticals
Regulatory: FDA 21CFR §175.105, 176.180, 176.210, 178.3400; USP/NF compliance
Trade names: Synperonic NP9.75; Synperonic NP10

Nonoxynol-12
CAS 9016-45-9 (generic); 26027-38-3 (generic); 37205-87-1 (generic)
Synonyms: PEG-12 nonyl phenyl ether; POE (12) nonyl phenyl ether; PEG 600 nonyl phenyl ether
Classification: Ethoxylated alkyl phenol
Formula: $C_9H_{19}C_6H_4(OCH_2CH_2)_nOH$, avg. n = 12

Nonoxynol-13

Properties: Yel. to almost colorless liq.
Toxicology: Moderately toxic by ingestion, skin contact; severe eye and mild skin irritant in humans; heated to dec., emits acrid smoke and fumes
Uses: Emulsifier, solubilizer
Regulatory: FDA 21CFR §175.105, 176.180, 176.210, 178.3400
Trade names: Synperonic NP12

Nonoxynol-13

CAS 9016-45-9 (generic); 26027-38-3 (generic); 37205-87-1 (generic)
Synonyms: PEG-13 nonyl phenyl ether; POE (13) nonyl phenyl ether
Classification: Ethoxylated alkyl phenol
Formula: $C_9H_{19}C_6H_4(OCH_2CH_2)_nOH$, avg. n = 13
Properties: Yel. to almost colorless liq.
Toxicology: Moderately toxic by ingestion, skin contact; severe eye and mild skin irritant in humans; heated to dec., emits acrid smoke and fumes
Uses: Emulsifier, solubilizer
Regulatory: FDA 21CFR §175.105, 176.180, 176.210, 178.3400
Trade names: Synperonic NP13

Nonoxynol-15

CAS 9106-45-9 (generic); 37205-87-1 (generic); 26027-38-3 (generic)
Classification: Ethoxylated alkyl phenol
Formula: $C_9H_{19}C_6H_4(OCH_2CH_2)_nOH$, avg. n = 15
Uses: Emulsifier, solubilizer
Regulatory: FDA 21CFR §175.105, 176.180, 176.210
Trade names: Synperonic NP15

Nonoxynol-17

Classification: Ethoxylated alkyl phenol
Formula: $C_9H_{19}C_6H_4(OCH_2CH_2)_nOH$, avg. n = 17
Toxicology: Moderately toxic by ingestion, skin contact; severe eye and mild skin irritant in humans; heated to dec., emits acrid smoke and fumes
Uses: Emulsifier, solubilizer
Trade names: Synperonic NP17

Nonoxynol-20

CAS 9016-45-9 (generic); 26027-38-3 (generic); 37205-87-1 (generic)
Synonyms: PEG-20 nonyl phenyl ether; POE (20) nonyl phenyl ether; PEG 1000 nonyl phenyl ether
Classification: Ethoxylated alkyl phenol
Formula: $C_9H_{19}C_6H_4(OCH_2CH_2)_nOH$, avg. n = 20
Properties: Pale yel. to off-white pastes or waxes
Toxicology: Moderately toxic by ingestion, skin contact; severe eye and mild skin irritant in humans; heated to dec., emits acrid smoke and fumes
Uses: Emulsifier, solubilizer
Regulatory: FDA 21CFR §175.105, 176.180
Trade names: Synperonic NP20

Nonoxynol-25

Classification: Ethoxylated alkyl phenol
Formula: $C_9H_{19}C_6H_4(OCH_2CH_2)_nOH$, avg. n = 25
Properties: Pale yel. to off-white pastes or waxes
Toxicology: Moderately toxic by ingestion, skin contact; severe eye and mild skin irritant in humans; heated to dec., emits acrid smoke and fumes
Uses: Emulsifier, solubilizer
Trade names: Synperonic NP25

Nonoxynol-30

CAS 9016-45-9 (generic); 26027-38-3 (generic); 37205-87-1 (generic)
Synonyms: PEG-30 nonyl phenyl ether; POE (30) nonyl phenyl ether
Classification: Ethoxylated alkyl phenol
Formula: $C_9H_{19}C_6H_4(OCH_2CH_2)_nOH$, avg. n = 30
Properties: Pale yel. to off-white pastes or waxes
Toxicology: Moderately toxic by ingestion, skin contact; severe eye and mild skin irritant in humans; heated to dec., emits acrid smoke and fumes
Uses: Nonionic surfactant, emulsifier, solubilizer; pharmaceutic aid
Regulatory: FDA 21CFR §175.105, 176.180, 178.3400
Trade names: Synperonic NP30; Synperonic NP30/70

Nonoxynol-35
Synonyms: PEG-35 nonyl phenyl ether; POE (35) nonyl phenyl ether
Classification: Ethoxylated alkyl phenol
Formula: $C_9H_{19}C_6H_4(OCH_2CH_2)_nOH$, avg. n = 35
Properties: Pale yel. to off-white pastes or waxes
Toxicology: Moderately toxic by ingestion, skin contact; severe eye and mild skin irritant in humans; heated to dec., emits acrid smoke and fumes
Uses: Emulsifier, solubilizer
Trade names: Synperonic NP35

Nonoxynol-40
CAS 9016-45-9 (generic); 26027-38-3 (generic); 37205-87-1 (generic)
Synonyms: PEG-40 nonyl phenyl ether; POE (40) nonyl phenyl ether; PEG 2000 nonyl phenyl ether
Classification: Ethoxylated alkyl phenol
Formula: $C_9H_{19}C_6H_4(OCH_2CH_2)_nOH$, avg. n = 40
Properties: Pale yel. to off-white pastes or waxes
Toxicology: Moderately toxic by ingestion, skin contact; severe eye and mild skin irritant in humans; heated to dec., emits acrid smoke and fumes
Uses: Emulsifier, solubilizer
Regulatory: FDA 21CFR §175.105, 176.180, 178.3400
Trade names: Synperonic NP40

Nonoxynol-50
CAS 9016-45-9 (generic); 26027-38-3 (generic); 37205-87-1 (generic)
Synonyms: PEG-50 nonyl phenyl ether; POE (50) nonyl phenyl ether
Classification: Ethoxylated alkyl phenol
Formula: $C_9H_{19}C_6H_4(OCH_2CH_2)_nOH$, avg. n = 50
Properties: Pale yel. to off-white pastes or waxes
Toxicology: Moderately toxic by ingestion, skin contact; severe eye and mild skin irritant in humans; heated to dec., emits acrid smoke and fumes
Uses: Emulsifier, solubilizer
Regulatory: FDA 21CFR §176.180, 178.3400
Trade names: Synperonic NP50

Nonoxynol iodine
Uses: Used in topicals
Regulatory: FDA approved for topicals

Nonpareil seed
Uses: Used in orals
Regulatory: FDA approved for orals

3-Nonyl acrolein. See 2-Dodecenal

Nonyl alcohol
CAS 143-08-8; EINECS 205-583-7
FEMA 2789
Synonyms: 1-Nonanol; Nonalol; Alcohol C-9; n-Nonyl alcohol
Empirical: $C_9H_{20}O$
Formula: $CH_3(CH_2)_8OH$
Properties: Colorless to ylsh. liq., citronella oil odor; misc. with alcohol, ether; pract. insol. in water; m.w. 144.26; dens. 0.8279 (20/4 C); m.p. -6 to -4 C; b.p. 210-213 C; flash pt. 98 C; ref. index 1.4338 (20 C)
Uses: Citrus synthetic flavoring agent
Regulatory: FDA 21CFR §172.515; FEMA GRAS
Manuf./Distrib. (pharm. & food): Aldrich

n-Nonyl alcohol. See Nonyl alcohol
Nonylcarbinol. See n-Decyl alcohol
2-(Nonylphenoxy) ethanol. See Nonoxynol-1
14-(Nonylphenoxy)-3,6,9,12-tetraoxatetradecan-1-ol. See Nonoxynol-5
Nopinene. See β-Pinene

Norbixin
Uses: Natural colorant
Trade names: Unibix CUS; Unibix ENC (Acid Proof)
Trade names containing: Red Soluble Powd. Natural Colorant; Unibix AP (Acid Proof)

Nordihydroguairetic acid

> CAS 500-38-9; EINECS 207-903-0
> *Synonyms:* NDGA; 4,4´-(2,3-Dimethyl-1,4-butanediyl)bis[1,2-benzenediol]; 4,4´-(2,3-Dimethyltetramethyl-ene) dipyrocatechol; 1,4-Bis(3,4-dihydroxyphenyl)-2,3-dimethylbutane
> *Classification:* Organic compd.
> *Empirical:* $C_{18}H_{22}O_4$
> *Properties:* Cryst.; sol. in lipids, ethanol, methanol, ether, acetone, glycerin, propylene glycol; sl. sol. in hot water, chloroform; sol. in dil. alkalies; m.w. 302.36; m.p. 184-185 C
> *Toxicology:* Irritant; harmful if swallowed
> *Uses:* Antioxidant for topical pharmaceuticals
> *Usage level:* 0.01-0.1%
> *Regulatory:* FDA 21CFR §175.300, 181.22, 181.24 (0.005% migrating from food pkg.), 189.165; Japan approved (0.1 g/kg max.)
> *Manuf./Distrib.:* Aldrich
> *Manuf./Distrib. (pharm. & food):* Aldrich

Norgine. *See* Alginic acid

Novatone. *See* Acetanisole

Novocaine. *See* Procaine

NT red. *See* FD&C Red No. 40

Nutmeg oil

> CAS 8008-45-5
> FEMA 2793
> *Synonyms:* Myristica oil; East Indian nutmeg oil
> *Definition:* Oil extracted from kernel of *Myristica fragrans*; consists of α- and β-pinene, camphene, myristicin, dipentene, sabanene
> *Properties:* Colorless to pale yel. liq., nutmeg odor and taste; very sol. in hot alcohol, chloroform, ether; sol. in fixed oils, min. oil; sl. sol. in cold alcohol; insol. in glycerin, propylene glycol, water; dens. 0.880-0.910; ref. index 1.474-1.488
> *Precaution:* Keep cool, well closed; light-sensitive
> *Toxicology:* LD50 (oral, rat) 2620 mg/kg; highly toxic-as little as 5 g can cause nausea, vomiting, and death; experimental reproductive effects; mutagenic data; skin irritant; heated to decomp., emits acrid smoke and irritating fumes
> *Uses:* Natural flavoring agent; carminative, stomachic
> *Regulatory:* FDA 21CFR §182.10, 182.20, GRAS; FEMA GRAS; Japan approved; Europe listed (< 1 to 15 ppm safrole); BP compliance
> *Manuf./Distrib. (pharm. & food):* Chart; Pierre Chauvet; Commodity Services; Florida Treatt; Ruger; Spectrum Chem. Mfg.

Nutmeg oil, expressed

> CAS 8007-12-3
> *Definition:* Oil from steam distillation of dried arillode of ripe seed of *Myristica fragrans*
> *Properties:* Colorless to pale yel. liq., nutmeg odor and taste; sol. in fixed oils, min. oil; very sol. in hot alcohol, chloroform, ether; E. Indian: dens. 0.880-0.930; ref. index 1.474-1.488; W. Indian: dens. 0.854-0.880; ref. index 1.469-1.480
> *Toxicology:* LD50 (oral, rat) 3640 mg/kg; mod. toxic by ing.; skin irritant; human ing. causes symptoms similar to volatile nutmeg oil, can cause flushing of skin, irregular heart rhythm, contact dermatitis; heated to decomp., emits acrid smoke/irritating fumes
> *Uses:* Natural flavoring agent; rubefacient; used in inhalants, orals
> *Regulatory:* FDA 21CFR §182.10, 182.20, GRAS; FDA approved for inhalants, orals

Nylon-6

> CAS 25038-54-4
> *Synonyms:* Poly[imino(1-oxo-1,6-hexanediyl)]; Poly(iminocarbonylpentamethylene)
> *Classification:* Polyamide
> *Empirical:* $(C_6H_{11}NO)_n$
> *Formula:* $[NH(CH_2)_5CO]_x$
> *Properties:* Dens. 1.14 (20/4 C); m.p. 223 C; resistant to most org. chem., dissolved by phenol, cresol, strong acids; immune to biological attack
> *Toxicology:* Moderately toxic by ingestion; mildly toxic by inhalation
> *Uses:* Raw material for pharmaceuticals; absorbent, carrier used in personal hygiene prods.
> *Regulatory:* FDA 21CFR §177.1500, 177.2260, 177.2470, 177.2480; BP compliance (sterile sutures)
> *Manuf./Distrib.:* Snia UK
> *Manuf./Distrib. (pharm. & food):* Aldrich
> *Trade names:* Orgasol 1002 D WHITE 5 COS

Nylon-12
  CAS 25038-74-8; 24937-16-4
  Synonyms: Azacyclotridecane-2-one polyamide; Poly(laurolactam); Azacyclotridecane-2-one, homopolymer
  Classification: Polyamide
  Definition: Polyamide derived from 12-aminododecanoic acid
  Empirical: $(C_{12}H_{23}NO)_n$
  Properties: Dens. 1.010
  Uses: Raw material for pharmaceuticals; absorbent, carrier used in personal hygiene prods.
  Regulatory: FDA 21CFR §177.1500, 177.2260
  Manuf./Distrib.: Elf Atochem SA; Daicel-Hüls; Hüls AG
  Manuf./Distrib. (pharm. & food): Aldrich
  Trade names: Orgasol 2002 D NAT COS; Orgasol 2002 EX D NAT COS; Orgasol 2002 UD NAT COS

Octacosanol
  CAS 557-61-9
  Synonyms: 1-Octacosanol; n-Octacosanol; Octacosyl alcohol
  Definition: Constituent of vegetable waxes
  Empirical: $C_{28}H_{58}O$
  Formula: $CH_3(CH_2)_{26}CH_2OH$
  Properties: Sol. in carbon disulfide, other fat solvs., oils; insol. in water; m.w. 410.74; m.p. 83.4 C
  Uses: Ingred. in pharmaceuticals and health food supplements
  Manuf./Distrib.: Spectrum Chem. Mfg.
  Trade names containing: Natural Octacosanol GF; Octacosanol GF

1-Octacosanol. *See* Octacosanol
n-Octacosanol. *See* Octacosanol
Octacosyl alcohol. *See* Octacosanol
9,12-Octadecadienoic acid. *See* Linoleic acid
(Z,Z)-9,12-Octadecadienoic acid. *See* Linoleic acid
9,12-Octadecadienoic acid, 2,3-dihydroxypropyl ester. *See* Glyceryl linoleate
9,12-Octadecadienoic acid ethyl ester. *See* Ethyl linoleate
9,12-Octadecadienoic acid, monoester with 1,2,3-propanetriol. *See* Glyceryl linoleate
n-Octadecanoic acid. *See* Stearic acid
Octadecanoic acid aluminum salt. *See* Aluminum stearate
Octadecanoic acid butyl ester. *See* Butyl stearate
Octadecanoic acid calcium salt. *See* Calcium stearate
Octadecanoic acid, 2-(1-carboxyethoxy)-1-methyl-2-oxoethyl ester, sodium salt. *See* Sodium stearoyl lactylate
Octadecanoic acid, decaester with decaglycerol. *See* Polyglyceryl-10 decastearate
Octadecanoic acid, diester with 1,2,3-propanetriol. *See* Glyceryl distearate
Octadecanoic acid, 2-(diethylamino) ethyl ester. *See* Diethylaminoethyl stearate
Octadecanoic acid, 1,2-ethanediyl ester. *See* Glycol distearate
Octadecanoic acid, 2-ethylhexyl ester. *See* Octyl stearate
Octadecanoic acid, magnesium salt. *See* Magnesium stearate
Octadecanoic acid, methyl ester. *See* Methyl stearate
Octadecanoic acid, 1-methylethyl ester. *See* Isopropyl stearate
Octadecanoic acid, monoester with decaglycerol. *See* Polyglyceryl-10 stearate
Octadecanoic acid, monoester with 1,2-propanediol. *See* Propylene glycol stearate
Octadecanoic acid, monoester with 1,2,3,-propanetriol. *See* Glyceryl stearate
Octadecanoic acid, octadecyl ester. *See* Stearyl stearate
Octadecanoic acid, 2-[(1-oxooctadecyl)amino]ethyl ester. *See* Stearamide MEA-stearate
Octadecanoic acid, potassium salt. *See* Potassium stearate
Octadecanoic acid, 1,2,3-propanetriyl ester. *See* Tristearin
Octadecanoic acid sodium salt. *See* Sodium stearate
Octadecanoic acid, tetradecyl ester. *See* Myristyl stearate
Octadecanoic acid, tridecyl ester. *See* Tridecyl stearate
Octadecanoic acid zinc salt. *See* Zinc stearate
1-Octadecanol. *See* Stearyl alcohol
n-Octadecanol. *See* Stearyl alcohol
6,9,12-Octadecatrienoic acid. *See* γ-Linolenic acid
9,12,15-Octadecatrienoic acid. *See* Linolenic acid

9-Octadecenoic acid. *See* Oleic acid
cis-9-Octadecenoic acid. *See* Oleic acid
9-Octadecenoic acid, diester with decaglycerol. *See* Polyglyceryl-10 dioleate
9-Octadecenoic acid, diester with oxybis [propanediol]. *See* Polyglyceryl-2 dioleate
9-Octadecenoic acid, diester with 1,2,3-propanetriol. *See* Glyceryl dioleate
9-Octadecenoic acid ethyl ester. *See* Ethyl oleate
9-Octadecenoic acid, 12-hydroxy-. *See* Ricinoleic acid
9-Octadecenoic acid, 12-hydroxy-, zinc salt. *See* Zinc ricinoleate
9-Octadecenoic acid, isodecyl ester. *See* Isodecyl oleate
9-Octadecenoic acid, methyl ester. *See* Methyl oleate
9-Octadecenoic acid, monoester with 1,2-propanediol. *See* Propylene glycol oleate
9-Octadecenoic acid, monoester with 1,2,3-propanetriol. *See* Glyceryl oleate
9-Octadecenoic acid, 9-octadecenyl ester. *See* Oleyl oleate
9-Octadecenoic acid, 1,2,3-propanetriyl ester. *See* Triolein
9-Octadecenoic acid, tetraester with decaglycerol. *See* Polyglyceryl-10 tetraoleate
9-Octadecen-1-ol. *See* Oleyl alcohol
cis-9-Octadecen-1-ol. *See* Oleyl alcohol
9-Octadecenyl 13-docosenoate. *See* Oleyl erucate
Octadecyl alcohol. *See* Stearyl alcohol
Octadecyl citrate. *See* Stearyl citrate
Octadecyl dimethyl benzyl ammonium chloride. *See* Stearalkonium chloride
Octadecyl 3-hydroxy-11-oxoolean-12-en-29-oate. *See* Stearyl glycyrrhetinate
3-(Octadecyloxy)-1,2-propanediol. *See* Batyl alcohol

γ-Octalactone
CAS 104-50-7
FEMA 2796
Synonyms: 4-Hydroxyoctanoic acid, γ-lactone; n-Octalactone
Empirical: $C_8H_{14}O_2$
Properties: Sl. yel. liq., strong fruity odor, sweet taste; m.w. 142.20; dens. 0.975; b.p. 234 C; flash pt. > 230 F
Uses: Coconut-like synthetic flavoring agent
Regulatory: FDA 21CFR §172.515; FEMA GRAS
Manuf./Distrib. (pharm. & food): Aldrich

n-Octalactone. *See* γ-Octalactone
1-Octanal. *See* n-Octanal

n-Octanal
CAS 124-13-0; EINECS 204-683-8
FEMA 2797
Synonyms: Aldehyde C-8; Caprylic aldehyde; Caprylaldehyde; 1-Octanal; n-Octyl aldehyde
Empirical: $C_8H_{16}O$
Formula: $CH_3(CH_2)_6CHO$
Properties: Colorless to lt. yel. liq., fatty-orange odor; sol. in alcohol, fixed oils, propylene glycol; insol. in glycerin; m.w. 128.24; dens. 0.821 (20/4 C); b.p. 163.4 C; flash pt. (CC) 125 F; ref. index 1.417-1.425
Precaution: Combustible exposed to heat or flame; can react with oxidizing materials
Toxicology: LD50 (oral, rat) 5630 mg/kg, (skin, rabbit) 6350 mg/kg; mildly toxic by ingestion and skin contact; skin and eye irritant
Uses: Synthetic flavoring agent
Regulatory: FDA 21CFR §172.515; FEMA GRAS; Japan approved as flavoring
Manuf./Distrib.: BASF
Manuf./Distrib. (pharm. & food): Aldrich; Florida Treatt

Octanedioic acid. *See* Suberic acid
Octanoic acid. *See* Caprylic acid
n-Octanoic acid. *See* Caprylic acid
Octanoic acid allyl ester. *See* Allyl octanoate
Octanoic acid ethyl ester. *See* Ethyl octanoate
Octanoic acid, monoester with 1,2,3-propanetriol. *See* Glyceryl caprylate
Octanoic acid, 1,3-propanediyl ester. *See* Propylene glycol dioctanoate
Octanoic acid, 1,2,3-propanetriol ester. *See* Trioctanoin
Octanoic acid sodium salt. *See* Sodium caprylate
Octanoic/decanoic acid triglyceride. *See* Caprylic/capric triglyceride
1-Octanol. *See* Caprylic alcohol
n-Octanol. *See* Caprylic alcohol

2-Octanone. *See* Methyl hexyl ketone

Octocrylene
   CAS 6197-30-4; EINECS 228-250-8
   Synonyms: 2-Ethylhexyl 2-cyano-3,3-diphenylacrylate; 2-Ethylhexyl 2-cyano-3,3-diphenyl-2-propenoate; UV
      Absorber-3
   Classification: Substituted acrylate
   Empirical: $C_{24}H_{27}NO_2$
   Formula: $(C_6H_5)_2C=C(CN)CO_2CH_2CH(C_2H_5)(CH_2)_3CH_3$
   Properties: Liq.; m.p. -10 C
   Uses: Active ingred. in OTC drug prods.; uv-B sunscreen
   Trade names: Escalol® 597

Octoic acid. *See* Caprylic acid

Octoxynol-1
   CAS 9002-93-1 (generic); 9036-19-5 (generic); 9004-87-9 (generic); 2315-67-5; EINECS 264-520-1
   Synonyms: Ethylene glycol octyl phenyl ether; PEG-1 octyl phenyl ether; 2-[p-(1,1,3,3-
      Tetramethylbutyl)phenoxy]ethanol
   Classification: Ethoxylated alkyl phenol
   Empirical: $C_{16}H_{26}O_2$
   Formula: $C_8H_{17}C_6H_4OCH_2CH_2OH$
   Uses: Used in topicals; spermaticide
   Regulatory: FDA 21CFR §172.710, 175.105, 176.180; FDA approved for topicals

Octoxynol-3
   CAS 9002-93-1 (generic); 9004-87-9 (generic); 9036-19-5 (generic); 2315-62-0; 27176-94-9
   Synonyms: 2-[2-[2-[p-(1,1,3,3-Tetramethylbutyl)phenoxy]ethoxy]ethoxy]ethanol; PEG-3 octyl phenyl ether;
      POE (3) octyl phenyl ether
   Classification: Ethoxylated alkyl phenol
   Empirical: $C_{20}H_{34}O_4$
   Formula: $C_8H_{17}C_6H_4(OCH_2CH_2)_nOH$, avg. n = 3
   Uses: Emulsifier, solubilizer
   Regulatory: FDA 21CFR §175.105, 176.180, 176.210
   Trade names: Synperonic OP3

Octoxynol-5
   CAS 9002-93-1 (generic); 9036-19-5 (generic); 9004-87-9 (generic); 2315-64-2; 27176-99-4
   Synonyms: PEG-5 octyl phenyl ether; POE (5) octyl phenyl ether; 14-(Octylphenoxy)-3,6,9,12-
      tetraoxatetradecan-1-ol
   Classification: Ethoxylated alkyl phenol
   Empirical: $C_{24}H_{42}O_6$
   Formula: $C_8H_{17}C_6H_4(OCH_2CH_2)_nOH$, avg. n = 5
   Uses: Emulsifier, solubilizer
   Regulatory: FDA 21CFR §172.710, 175.105, 176.180, 176.210, 178.3400
   Trade names: Synperonic OP4.5

Octoxynol-6
   Synonyms: PEG-6 octyl phenyl ether; POE (6) octyl phenyl ether
   Classification: Ethoxylated alkyl phenol
   Formula: $C_8H_{17}C_6H_4(OCH_2CH_2)_nOH$, avg. n = 6
   Uses: Emulsifier, solubilizer
   Trade names: Synperonic OP6

Octoxynol-8
   CAS 9004-87-9 (generic); 9036-19-5 (generic); 9002-93-1 (generic)
   Synonyms: PEG-8 octyl phenyl ether; PEG 400 octyl phenyl ether; POE (8) octyl phenyl ether
   Classification: Ethoxylated alkyl phenol
   Empirical: $C_{30}H_{54}O_9$
   Formula: $C_8H_{17}C_6H_4(OCH_2CH_2)_nOH$, avg. n = 8
   Uses: Emulsifier, solubilizer
   Regulatory: FDA 21CFR §172.710, 175.105, 176.180, 176.210, 178.3400
   Trade names: Synperonic OP7.5; Synperonic OP8

Octoxynol-9
   CAS 9002-93-1 (generic); 9004-87-9 (generic); 9010-43-9; 9036-19-5 (generic); 42173-90-0
   Synonyms: PEG-9 octyl phenyl ether; POE (9) octyl phenyl ether; PEG 450 octyl phenyl ether

Octoxynol-10

Classification: Ethoxylated alkyl phenol
Empirical: $C_{32}H_{58}O_{10}$
Formula: $C_8H_{17}C_6H_4(OCH_2CH_2)_nOH$, avg. n = 9
Properties: Pale yel. clear visc. liq., faint odor, bitter taste; sol. in benzene, toluene; misc. with water, alcohol, acetone; insol. in hexane; dens. 1.059-1.068; hyd. no. 85-101; cloud pt. 63-69 C; pH 6-8
Uses: Detergent, wetting agent, solubilizer, emulsifier, dispersant, spermaticide; used in topicals
Regulatory: FDA 21CFR §175.105, 176.180, 176.210, 178.3400; FDA approved for topicals
Trade names: Renex® 759

Octoxynol-10

CAS 9002-93-1 (generic); 9004-87-9 (generic); 9036-19-5 (generic); 2315-66-4; 27177-07-7
Synonyms: PEG-10 octyl phenyl ether; POE (10) octyl phenyl ether; PEG 500 octyl phenyl ether
Classification: Ethoxylated alkyl phenol
Empirical: $C_{34}H_{62}O_{11}$
Formula: $C_8H_{17}C_6H_4(OCH_2CH_2)_nOH$, avg. n = 10
Properties: Pale yel. visc. liq.; misc. with water, alcohol, acetone; sol. in benzene, toluene; m.w. 647; dens. 1.0595 (25/4 C)
Uses: Emulsifier, solubilizer
Regulatory: FDA 21CFR §172.710, 175.105, 176.180, 176.210, 178.3400
Trade names: Synperonic OP10; Synperonic OP10.5

Octoxynol-11

CAS 9004-87-9 (generic); 9036-19-5 (generic); 9002-93-1 (generic)
Synonyms: PEG-11 octyl phenyl ether; POE (11) octyl phenyl ether
Classification: Ethoxylated alkyl phenol
Formula: $C_8H_{17}C_6H_4(OCH_2CH_2)_nOH$, avg. n = 11
Uses: Emulsifier, solubilizer
Regulatory: FDA 21CFR §172.710, 175.105, 176.180, 176.210, 178.3400
Trade names: Synperonic OP11
Trade names containing: Solubilisant γ 2420; Solubilisant γ 2428

Octoxynol-13

CAS 9002-93-1 (generic); 9004-87-9 (generic); 9036-19-5 (generic)
Synonyms: PEG-13 octyl phenyl ether; POE (13) octyl phenyl ether
Classification: Ethoxylated alkyl phenol
Formula: $C_8H_{17}C_6H_4(OCH_2CH_2)_nOH$, avg. n = 13
Uses: Emulsifier, solubilizer
Regulatory: FDA 21CFR §172.710, 175.105, 176.180, 176.210, 178.3400
Trade names: Synperonic OP12.5

Octoxynol-16

CAS 9004-87-9 (generic); 9036-19-5 (generic); 9002-93-1 (generic)
Synonyms: PEG-16 octyl phenyl ether; POE (16) octyl phenyl ether
Classification: Ethoxylated alkyl phenol
Formula: $C_8H_{17}C_6H_4(OCH_2CH_2)_nOH$, avg. n = 16
Uses: Emulsifier, solubilizer
Regulatory: FDA 21CFR §175.105, 176.180
Trade names: Synperonic OP16; Synperonic OP16.5

Octoxynol-20

CAS 9002-93-1 (generic); 9036-19-5 (generic); 9004-87-9 (generic)
Synonyms: PEG-20 octyl phenyl ether; POE (20) octyl phenyl ether; PEG 1000 octyl phenyl ether
Classification: Ethoxylated alkyl phenol
Formula: $C_8H_{17}C_6H_4(OCH_2CH_2)_nOH$, avg. n = 20
Uses: Emulsifier, solubilizer
Regulatory: FDA 21CFR §175.105, 176.180
Trade names: Synperonic OP20

Octoxynol-25

CAS 9002-93-1 (generic); 9036-19-5 (generic); 9004-87-9 (generic)
Synonyms: PEG-25 octyl phenyl ether; POE (25) octyl phenyl ether
Classification: Ethoxylated alkyl phenol
Formula: $C_8H_{17}C_6H_4(OCH_2CH_2)_nOH$, avg. n = 25
Uses: Emulsifier, solubilizer
Regulatory: FDA 21CFR §175.105, 176.180
Trade names: Synperonic OP25

Octoxynol-30
CAS 9004-87-9 (generic); 9036-19-5 (generic); 9002-93-1 (generic)
Synonyms: PEG-30 octyl phenyl ether; POE (30) octyl phenyl ether
Classification: Ethoxylated alkyl phenol
Formula: $C_8H_{17}C_6H_4(OCH_2CH_2)_nOH$, avg. n = 30
Uses: Emulsifier, solubilizer
Regulatory: FDA 21CFR §172.710, 175.105, 176.180, 178.3400
Trade names: Synperonic OP30

Octoxynol-40
CAS 9002-93-1 (generic); 9004-87-9 (generic); 9036-19-5 (generic)
Synonyms: PEG-40 octyl phenyl ether; POE (40) octyl phenyl ether
Classification: Ethoxylated alkyl phenol
Formula: $C_8H_{17}C_6H_4(OCH_2CH_2)_nOH$, avg. n = 40
Uses: Emulsifier, solubilizer
Regulatory: FDA 21CFR §172.710, 175.105, 176.180, 178.3400
Trade names: Synperonic OP40; Synperonic OP40/70

Octyl acetate
CAS 112-14-1
FEMA 2806
Synonyms: 2-Ethylhexyl aceetate; Acetate C-8
Formula: $CH_3(CO_2(CH_2)_7CH_3$
Properties: M.w. 172.27; dens. 0.868; b.p. 211 C; flash pt. 86 C; ref. index 1.4180 (20 C)
Uses: Fruity synthetic flavoring agent
Regulatory: FDA 21CFR §172.515; FEMA GRAS
Manuf./Distrib. (pharm. & food): Aldrich

3-Octyl acetate
CAS 4864-61-3
FEMA 3583
Empirical: $C_{10}H_{20}O_2$
Properties: M.w. 172.27
Uses: Apple-like, minty synthetic flavoring agent
Regulatory: FDA 21CFR §172.515; FEMA GRAS
Manuf./Distrib. (pharm. & food): Aldrich

Octyl alcohol. *See* 2-Ethylhexanol
n-Octyl alcohol. *See* Caprylic alcohol
n-Octyl aldehyde. *See* n-Octanal

Octyl butyrate
CAS 110-39-4
FEMA 2807
Empirical: $C_{12}H_{24}O_2$
Properties: M.w. 200.32; dens. 0.862; m.p. -56 C; b.p. 224 C; flash pt. 218 F
Uses: Citrus synthetic flavoring agent
Regulatory: FDA 21CFR §172.515; FEMA GRAS
Manuf./Distrib. (pharm. & food): Aldrich

γ-Octyl-γ-butyrolactone. *See* γ-Dodecalactone
n-Octyldecyl alcohol. *See* Stearyl alcohol
Octyl dimethyl p-aminobenzoate. *See* Octyl dimethyl PABA
Octyl-p-(dimethylamino)benzoate. *See* Octyl dimethyl PABA

Octyl dimethyl PABA
CAS 21245-02-3; EINECS 244-289-3
Synonyms: Octyl dimethyl p-aminobenzoate; Octyl-p-(dimethylamino)benzoate; Padimate O; 2-Ethylhexyl-4(dimethylamino) benzoate; 2-Ethylhexyl p-dimethylaminobenzoate
Definition: Ester of 2-ethylhexyl alcohol and dimethyl p-aminobenzoic acid
Empirical: $C_{17}H_{27}NO_2$
Properties: M.w. 277.4; sp.gr. 0.99-1.00; ref. index 1.5390-1.5430
Toxicology: LD50 (rat, oral) 14.9 g/kg
Uses: uv-B absorber for topical sunscreens; active ingred. in OTC drug prods.
Manuf./Distrib.: First
Trade names: Escalol® 507

Octyldodecanol

Octyldodecanol
 CAS 5333-42-6; EINECS 226-242-9
 Synonyms: 2-Octyl dodecanol; 1-Dodecanol, 2-octyl-; Isoeicosyl alcohol
 Classification: Aliphatic alcohol
 Empirical: $C_{20}H_{42}O$
 Properties: Water-wh.clear liq.; sol. in alcohol, ether; insol. in water; m.w. 298; acid no. 0.5 max.; iodine no. 8 max.; sapon. no. 5 max.; hyd. no. 175-190; flash pt. (COC) 180 C
 Uses: Emollient, lubricant, oleaginous vehicle, carrier, solubilizer for pharmaceuticals; used in topicals, vaginal creams
 Regulatory: FDA approved for topicals, vaginal creams; USP/NF compliance
 Trade names: Eutanol® G; Isofol® 20
 Trade names containing: Amerchol® L-500; Argobase 125T

2-Octyl dodecanol. *See* Octyldodecanol
2-Octyldodecyl 13-docosenoate. *See* 2-Octyldodecyl erucate

2-Octyldodecyl erucate
 CAS 88103-59-7; 132208-25-4
 Synonyms: 2-Octyldodecyl 13-docosenoate; Erucic acid, 2-octyldodecyl ester; Eicosyl erucate
 Definition: Ester of octyldodecanol and erucic acid
 Empirical: $C_{42}H_{82}O_2$
 Uses: Emollient for pharmaceutical topicals
 Trade names: Pelemol® EE

Octyldodecyl myristate
 CAS 83826-43-1; 22766-83-2
 Synonyms: Myristic acid, 2-octyldodecyl ester; Tetradecanoic acid, 2-octyldodecyl ester
 Classification: Ester of octyldodecanol and myristic acid
 Empirical: $C_{34}H_{68}O_2$
 Uses: Emollient, plasticizer for pharmaceutical preps.
 Trade names: MOD; M.O.D. WL 2949; Pelemol® ODM; Wickenol® 142

Octyldodecyl stearate
 CAS 22766-82-1; EINECS 245-204-2
 Synonyms: Stearic acid, 2-octyldodecyl ester
 Definition: Ester of octyldodecanol and stearic acid
 Empirical: $C_{38}H_{76}O_2$
 Uses: Base, emollient
 Trade names: Standamul® 7063

Octyldodecyl stearoyl stearate
 CAS 58450-52-5; 90052-75-8; EINECS 289-991-0
 Synonyms: 12-[(1-Oxooctadecyl)oxy]octadecanoic acid, 2-octyldodecyl ester
 Classification: Ester
 Empirical: $C_{56}H_{110}O_4$
 Properties: Lt. to straw liq., char. mild odor; sol. in IPM, min. oil, oleyl alcohol, octyl palmitate; partly sol. in 95% ethanol, propylene glycol; insol. in water; sp.gr. 0.860-0.880; ref. index 1.447-1.467
 Toxicology: LD50 (rat, oral) > 20 g/kg; nonirritating to skin and eyes; possible sensitizer for allergic people
 Uses: Emollient, lubricant for topical pharmaceuticals, suppositories
 Trade names: Ceraphyl® 847

Octyl formate
 CAS 112-32-3
 FEMA 2809
 Empirical: $C_9H_{18}O_2$
 Properties: M.w. 158.24; dens. 0.877; b.p. 87-89 C (20 mm); flash pt. 171 F
 Uses: Orange-like synthetic flavoring agent
 Regulatory: FDA 21CFR §172.515; FEMA GRAS
 Manuf./Distrib. (pharm. & food): Aldrich

Octyl gallate
 CAS 1034-01-1; EINECS 213-853-0
 Empirical: $C_{15}H_{22}O_5$
 Formula: 3,4,5-$(HO)_3C_6H_2CO_2(CH_2)_7CH_3$
 Properties: More oil-sol. and less water-sol. than propyl gallate; m.w. 282.34; m.p. 101-104 C
 Toxicology: Nonirritant

Uses: Antioxidant for pharmaceuticals
Usage level: 0.01-0.1%
Regulatory: BP, Ph.Eur. compliance

Octyl hydroxystearate
CAS 29383-26-4; 29710-25-6
Synonyms: 2-Ethylhexyl oxystearate; 12-Hydroxyoctadecanoic acid, 2-ethylhexyl ester; 2-Ethylhexylhydroxy-stearate
Definition: Ester of 2-ethylhexyl alcohol and 12-hydroxystearic acid
Empirical: $C_{26}H_{52}O_3$
Formula: $CH_3(CH_2)_5COHH(CH_2)_{10}COOCH_2CCH_2CH_3H(CH_2)_3CH_3$
Uses: Emollient, moisturizer, pigment wetter/dispersant, counter-irritant, cosolv., solubilizer for topical pharmaceuticals
Trade names: Wickenol® 171

n-Octylic acid. *See* Caprylic acid

Octyl isononanoate
CAS 71566-49-9; EINECS 275-637-2
Synonyms: 2-Ethylhexyl isononanoate; Isononanoic acid, 2-ethylhexyl ester
Definition: Ester of 2-ethylhexyl alcohol and a branched chain nonanoic acid
Empirical: $C_{17}H_{34}O_2$
Formula: $CH_3(CH_3)_2CCH_2CH_3CHCH_2COOCH_2(CH_2CH_3)CH(CH_2)_3CH_3$
Properties: Clear water-white liq., typ. mild odor; sp.gr. 0.85; f.p. -34 C; b.p. 200 C; flash pt. (COC) 127 C
Precaution: Store away from strong oxidizing agents
Toxicology: Nontoxic
Uses: Emollient, lubricant, solv. for pharmaceutical topicals
Trade names: Pelemol® 89

Octyl isovalerate
CAS 7786-58-5
FEMA 2814
Empirical: $C_{13}H_{26}O_2$
Properties: M.w. 214.35; dens. 0.862; b.p. 249-251 C; flash pt. > 230 F
Uses: Honey-like synthetic flavoring agent
Regulatory: FDA 21CFR §172.515; FEMA GRAS
Manuf./Distrib. (pharm. & food): Aldrich

Octyl methoxycinnamate
CAS 5466-77-3; EINECS 226-775-7
Synonyms: 2-Ethylhexyl methoxycinnamate; 2-Ethylhexyl 3-(4-methoxyphenyl)-2-propenoate; Ethylhexyl p-methoxycinnamate
Definition: Ester of 2-ethylhexyl alcohol and methoxycinnamic acid
Empirical: $C_{18}H_{26}O_3$
Properties: M.w. 290.40; b.p. 185-195 C (1 mbar)
Toxicology: Minimal eye irritation, mild skin irritation
Uses: Active ingred. in OTC drug prods.; uv-B screening agent
Manuf./Distrib. (pharm. & food): R.W. Greeff
Trade names: Escalol® 557
Trade names containing: Unifilter U-41

Octyl palmitate
CAS 29806-73-3; EINECS 249-862-1
Synonyms: 2-Ethylhexyl palmitate; 2-Ethylhexyl hexadecanoate
Definition: Ester of 2-ethylhexyl alcohol and palmitic acid
Empirical: $C_{24}H_{48}O_2$
Formula: $CH_3(CH_2)_{14}COOCH_2(CH_2CH_3)CH(CH_2)_3CH_3$
Properties: Water-wh. liq.; sol. in min. oil, 95% ethanol, IPM, oleyl alcohol; insol. in water, glycerin, propylene glycol; sp.gr. 0.850-0.856; ref. index 1.4445-1.4465
Toxicology: LD50 (rat, oral) > 40 ml/kg; nonirritating to eyes; mild skin irritant
Uses: Emollient, spreading agent for topicals, sunscreens, antiperspirants; solubilizer for benzophenone-3
Manuf./Distrib.: Aquatec Quimica SA; Inolex; ISP Van Dyk; Union Camp
Manuf./Distrib. (pharm. & food): Ruger
Trade names: Cegesoft® C 24; Ceraphyl® 368; Lexol® EHP; Pelemol® OP; Wickenol® 155
Trade names containing: Wickenol® 161

Octyl pelargonate
CAS 59587-44-9; EINECS 261-819-9
Synonyms: 2-Ethylhexyl pelargonate; Nonanoic acid, 2-ethylhexyl ester
Definition: Ester of 2-ethylhexyl alcohol and pelargonic acid
Empirical: $C_{16}H_{34}O_2$
Formula: $CH_3(CH_2)_7COOCH_2(CH_2CH_2)CH(CH_2)_3CH_3$
Uses: Emollient, moisturizer, pigment wetter/dispersant; anticlogging agent in antiperspirants
Trade names: Wickenol® 160

Octylphenol polymethylene
Uses: Used in ophthalmics
Regulatory: FDA approved for ophthalmics

2-[2-[2-Octylphenoxy)ethoxy]ethoxy]ethanesulfonic acid, sodium salt. *See* Sodium octoxynol-2 ethane sulfonate

14-(Octylphenoxy)-3,6,9,12-tetraoxatetradecan-1-ol. *See* Octoxynol-5

Octyl salicylate
CAS 118-60-5; EINECS 204-263-4
Synonyms: 2-Ethylhexyl 2-hydroxybenzoate; 2-Ethylhexyl salicylate; 2-Hydroxybenzoic acid, 2-ethylhexyl ester
Definition: Ester of 2-ethylhexyl alcohol and salicylic acid
Empirical: $C_{15}H_{22}O_3$
Properties: Water-white liq., odorless; m.w. 250; sp.gr. 1.02; flash pt. (PMCC) > 200 F
Precaution: Store away from strong oxidizing agents; avoid excessive heat
Toxicology: May be mildy irritating to skin and eyes on prolonged contact
Uses: UV-B sunscreen; solubilizer for benzophenone-3
Trade names: Escalol® 587

Octyl stearate
CAS 22047-49-0; 26399-02-0; 91031-48-0; EINECS 244-754-0; 247-655-0
Synonyms: 2-Ethylhexyl stearate; 2-Ethylhexyl octadecanoate; Octadecanoic acid, 2-ethylhexyl ester
Definition: Ester of 2-ethylhexyl alcohol and stearic acid
Empirical: $C_{26}H_{52}O_2$
Formula: $CH_3(CH_2)_{16}COOCH_2(CH_2CH_3)CH(CH_2)_3CH_3$
Uses: Emollient, moisturizer, superfatting agent, pigment wetter/dispersant for topicals
Trade names: Cetiol® 868; Wickenol® 156
Trade names containing: Wickenol® 161

Octyl sulfate sodium salt. *See* Sodium octyl sulfate
Oenanthaldehyde. *See* Heptanal
Oenanthol. *See* Heptanal
Oenanthylidene acetone. *See* 3-Decen-2-one
Oil of grapes. *See* Ethyl heptanoate
Oil of niobe. *See* Methyl benzoate
Oil of Palma Christi. *See* Castor oil
Oils, jojoba. *See* Jojoba oil
Oils, lanolin. *See* Lanolin oil
Oils, linseed. *See* Linseed oil
Oils, menhaden. *See* Menhaden oil
Oils, orange roughy. *See* Orange roughy oil
Oils, palm. *See* Palm oil
Oils, palm, hydrogenated. *See* Hydrogenated palm oil
Oils, palm kernel, hydrogenated. *See* Hydrogenated palm kernel oil
Oils, rice bran. *See* Rice bran oil
Oils, soybean, maleated. *See* Maleated soybean oil
Oils, vegetable. *See* Vegetable oil
Oil of vitriol. *See* Sulfuric acid
Oil of wintergreen. *See* Methyl salicylate
OIPP. *See* o-Isopropylphenol
Okenite. *See* Calcium silicate
Olea europaea oil. *See* Olive oil

Oleic acid
CAS 112-80-1; EINECS 204-007-1
FEMA 2815

Synonyms: cis-9-Octadecenoic acid; Red oil; Elainic acid; 9-Octadecenoic acid
Classification: Aliphatic organic compd.; unsaturated fatty acid
Empirical: $C_{18}H_{34}O_2$
Formula: $CH_3(CH_2)_7CH:CH(CH_2)_7COOH$
Properties: Colorless liq., odorless; darkens when exposed to oxygen; insol. in water; sol. in alcohol, ether, benzene, chloroform, fixed/volatile oils; m.w. 282.47; dens. 0.895 (25/25 C); m.p. 6 C; b.p. 286 C (100 mm); acid no. 196-204; flash pt. 100 C; ref. index 1.463 (18 C)
Precaution: Combustible when exposed to heat or flame; incompat. with Al and perchloric acid; light-sensitive
Toxicology: LD50 (oral, rat) 74 g/kg; poison by intravenous route; mildly toxic by ingestion; experimental tumorigen; irritant to skin, mucous membranes; heated to decomp., emits acrid smoke and irritating fumes
Uses: Emulsifying/solubilizing agent, emulsion adjunct, pharmaceutic aid, solv.; used in inhalants, orals, topicals
Regulatory: FDA 21CFR §172.210, 172.860, 172.862, 173.315 (0.1 ppm max. in wash water), 173.340, 175.105, 175.320, 176.170, 176.200, 176.210, 177.1010, 177.1200, 177.2260, 177.2600, 177.2800, 178.3570, 178.3910, 182.70, 182.90; FEMA GRAS; FDA approved for inhalants, orals, topicals; USP/NF, BP compliance
Manuf./Distrib.: Akzo Nobel; Aldrich; Arizona; Brown; Henkel/Emery; Hercules; Schweizerhall; Unichema; Union Derivan SA; Witco/Oleo-Surf.
Manuf./Distrib. (pharm. & food): Aldrich; Hercules; Ruger; Spectrum Chem. Mfg.; Unichema
Trade names: Crossential Oleic; Emersol® 6313 NF; Emersol® 6321 NF; Emersol® 6333 NF
Trade names containing: Chroma-Seal™ 859027; Chroma-Seal™ 889031

Olein. *See* Triolein

Oleoresin capsicum Africanus. *See* Capsicum oleoresin

Oleostearine
Uses: Ingred. in pharmaceutical waxes
Trade names containing: Ross Japan Wax Substitute 525

Oleth-2
CAS 9004-98-2 (generic); 5274-65-7
Synonyms: PEG-2 oleyl ether; POE (2) oleyl ether; PEG 100 oleyl ether
Definition: PEG ether of oleyl alcohol
Formula: $CH_3(CH_2)_7CH=CH(CH_2)_7CH_2(OCH_2CH_2)_nOH$, avg. n = 2
Uses: Emulsifier
Trade names: Britex O 20

Oleth-3
CAS 9004-98-2 (generic); 5274-66-8
Synonyms: PEG-3 oleyl ether; POE (3) oleyl ether
Definition: PEG ether of oleyl alcohol
Formula: $CH_3(CH_2)_7CH=CH(CH_2)_7CH_2(OCH_2CH_2)_nOH$, avg. n = 3
Uses: Emulsifier, emollient, lubricant, solubilizer for topicals
Trade names: Volpo 3

Oleth-5
CAS 9004-98-2 (generic); 5353-27-5
Synonyms: PEG-5 oleyl ether; POE (5) oleyl ether; 3,6,9,12,15-Pentaoxatriacont-24-en-1-ol
Definition: PEG ether of oleyl alcohol
Empirical: $C_{28}H_{56}O_6$
Formula: $CH_3(CH_2)_7CH=CH(CH_2)_7CH_2(OCH_2CH_2)_nOH$, avg. n = 5
Uses: Emulsifier, lubricant, emollient, solubilizer
Trade names: Eumulgin® O5; Volpo 5

Oleth-10
CAS 9004-98-2 (generic); 24871-34-9
Synonyms: PEG-10 oleyl ether; Polyoxyl 10 oleyl ether; POE (10) oleyl ether; PEG 500 oleyl ether
Definition: PEG ether of oleyl alcohol
Empirical: $C_{38}H_{76}O_{11}$
Formula: $CH_3(CH_2)_7CH=CH(CH_2)_7CH_2(OCH_2CH_2)_nOH$, avg. n = 10
Properties: Wh. soft semisolid or pale yel. liq., bland odor; sol. in water, alcohol; disp. in min. oil, propylene glycol; acid no. 1.0 max.; iodine no. 23-40; sapon. no. 3 max.; hyd. no. 75-95
Uses: Emulsifier, solubilizer, wetting agent for pharmaceuticals
Regulatory: USP/NF compliance
Trade names: Britex O 100; Eumulgin® O10; Volpo 10

Oleth-12

CAS 9004-98-2 (generic)
Synonyms: PEG-12 oleyl ether; POE (12) oleyl ether; PEG 600 oleyl ether
Definition: PEG ether of oleyl alcohol
Formula: $CH_3(CH_2)_7CH=CH(CH_2)_7CH_2(OCH_2CH_2)_nOH$, avg. n = 12
Uses: Emulsfier for pharmaceuticals
Regulatory: FDA 21CFR §176.200, 177.2800
Trade names containing: Lanbritol Wax N21

Oleth-16

CAS 9004-98-2 (generic); 25190-05-0 (generic)
Synonyms: PEG-16 oleyl ether; POE (16) oleyl ether
Definition: PEG ether of oleyl alcohol
Formula: $CH_3(CH_2)_7CH=CH(CH_2)_7CH_2(OCH_2CH_2)_nOH$, avg. n = 16
Uses: Emulsifier for pharmaceuticals
Regulatory: FDA 21CFR §176.200, 177.2800

Oleth-20

CAS 9004-98-2 (generic)
Synonyms: PEG-20 oleyl ether; POE (20) oleyl ether; PEG 1000 oleyl ether
Definition: PEG ether of oleyl alcohol
Formula: $CH_3(CH_2)_7CH=CH(CH_2)_7CH_2(OCH_2CH_2)_nOH$, avg. n = 20
Uses: Emulsion stabilizer, emulsifier, solubilizer used in topicals
Regulatory: FDA 21CFR §175.105, 176.180, 176.200, 177.1210, 177.2800; FDA approved for topicals
Trade names: Britex O 200; Prox-onic OA-1/020; Prox-onic OA-2/020; Rhodasurf® ON-870; Rhodasurf® ON-877; Simulsol® 98; Volpo 20

Oleth-25

CAS 9004-98-2 (generic)
Synonyms: PEG-25 oleyl ether; POE (25) oleyl ether
Definition: PEG ether of oleyl alcohol
Formula: $CH_3(CH_2)_7CH=CH(CH_2)_7CH_2(OCH_2CH_2)_nOH$, avg. n = 25
Uses: Pharmaceutical emulsions
Regulatory: FDA 21CFR §176.180, 176.200, 177.2800
Trade names containing: Hydrolactol 70; Solulan® 25

Oleth-3 phosphate

CAS 39464-69-2 (generic)
Synonyms: PEG-3 oleyl ether phosphate; POE (3) oleyl ether phosphate; Oleyl triethoxy mono diphosphate
Definition: Complex mixture of esters of phosphoric acid and oleth-3
Uses: Surfactant, conditioner, emulsifier, gellant for pharmaceuticals
Trade names: Crodafos N-3 Acid; Hodag PE-1803

Oleth-10 phosphate

CAS 39464-69-2 (generic)
Synonyms: PEG-10 oleyl ether phosphate; POE (10) oleyl ether phosphate; PEG 200 oleyl ether phosphate
Definition: Complex mixture of esters of phosphoric acid and oleth-10
Uses: Surfactant, conditioner, emulsifier, gellant for pharmaceuticals
Trade names: Hodag PE-1810

Oleth-20 phosphate

CAS 39464-69-2 (generic)
Synonyms: PEG-20 oleyl ether phosphate; PEG 1000 oleyl ether phosphate; POE (20) oleyl ether phosphate
Definition: Complex mixture of esters of phosphoric acid and oleth-20
Uses: Surfactant
Trade names: Hodag PE-1820

Oleum Gossypii seminis. *See* Cottonseed oil
Oleum olivae. *See* Olive oil
Oleum papaveris. *See* Poppyseed oil
Oleum ricini. *See* Castor oil

Oleyl alcohol

CAS 143-28-2; EINECS 205-597-3
Synonyms: 9-Octadecen-1-ol; cis-9-Octadecen-1-ol
Classification: Unsaturated fatty alcohol
Empirical: $C_{18}H_{36}O$

Formula: $CH_3(CH_2)_7CH=CH(CH_2)_8OH$
Properties: Colorless to pale yel. oily visc. liq., faint char. odor, bland taste; insol. in water; sol. in alcohol, ether; m.w. 268.49; dens. 0.84; m.p. 13-19 C; b.p. 207 C (13 mm); acid no. 1 max.; iodine no. 85-95; hyd. no. 205-215; cloud pt. ≤ 10 C; flash pt. > 110 C; ref. index 1.4582 (27.5 C)
Precaution: Gives off acrid fumes when heated
Toxicology: Irritant
Uses: Emulsifying agent, emollient, lubricant, emulsion stabilizer, solubilizer; astringent in poison ivy/poison oak preps.; used in topicals
Regulatory: FDA 21CFR §176.170, 176.210, 177.1010, 177.1210, 177.2800, 178.3910; FDA approved for topicals; USP/NF compliance
Manuf./Distrib.: Croda; R.W. Greeff; Lanaetex; M. Michel; Ronsheim & Moore; Witco/Oleo-Surf.
Manuf./Distrib. (pharm. & food): Aldrich
Trade names: Adol® 90 NF; Fancol OA-95; Novol NF

Oleyl erucate
CAS 17673-56-2; EINECS 241-654-9
Synonyms: 9-Octadecenyl 13-docosenoate; Erucic acid, oleyl ester; 13-Docosenoic acid, 9-octadecenyl ester
Definition: Ester of oleyl alcohol and erucic acid
Empirical: $C_{40}H_{76}O_2$
Uses: Emollient, lubricant, dispersant, solubilizer, carrier/vehicle, solv. for topicals
Trade names: Dynacerin® 660

Oleyl 2-hydroxypropionate. *See* Oleyl lactate

Oleyl lactate
CAS 42175-36-0
Synonyms: Oleyl 2-hydroxypropionate
Definition: Ester of oleyl alcohol and lactic acid
Empirical: $C_{21}H_{40}O_3$
Formula: $CH_3CHOHCOOCH_2(CH_2)_7CH=CH(CH_2)_7CH_3$
Properties: Liq.; sol. in alcohol, hydroalcoholic sol'ns.
Uses: Softener, moisturizer for pharmaceutical topicals
Trade names: Pelemol® OL

Oleyl oleate
CAS 3687-45-4; EINECS 222-980-4
Synonyms: 9-Octadecenoic acid, 9-octadecenyl ester
Definition: Ester of oleyl alcohol and oleic acid
Empirical: $C_{36}H_{68}O_2$
Uses: Emollient, lubricant for pharmaceutical formulations; used in topicals
Regulatory: FDA approved for topicals
Trade names containing: Cetiol®

Oleyl triethoxy mono diphosphate. *See* Oleth-3 phosphate
Oleyl trimethyl ammonium chloride. *See* Oleyltrimonium chloride

Oleyltrimonium chloride
Synonyms: Oleyl trimethyl ammonium chloride
Uses: Additive for antibiotics mfg.
Trade names: Noramium MO 50

Olive oil
CAS 8001-25-0; EINECS 232-277-0
Synonyms: Olea europaea oil; Gomenoleo oil; Azeite; Oleum olivae
Definition: Fixed oil obtained from the ripe fruit of *Olea europaea*, contg. glycerides of oleic acid, palmitic acid, linoleic acid, stearic acid, and arachidic acid
Properties: Yel. to lt. grnsh. liq., pleasant odor, sl. char. taste; sl. sol. in alcohol; misc. with ether, chloroform, carbon disulfide; dens. 0.909-0.915 (25/25 C); m.p. -6 C; solid. pt. 17-26 C; iodine no. 79-88; sapon. no. 187-196; flash pt. (CC) 437 F; ref. index 1.466-1.468
Precaution: Photosensitive
Toxicology: Human skin irritant; devoid of side effects; heated to dec., emits acrid smoke and fumes
Uses: Oleaginous vehicle; lubricant, solv., and emollient for liniments, ointments, plasters, soaps, suspensions for injection; softener for ear wax, crusts of eczema and psoriasis; nutritive; FDA registered for one oral and one topical sol'n.
Regulatory: FDA 21CFR §175.105, 176.200, 176.210, GRAS; Japan approved (olive); USP/NF, BP, Ph.Eur., JP compliance

Olive oil PEG-6 esters

    Manuf./Distrib.: ABITEC; Arista Industries; Croda; Penta Mfg.; Reilly-Whiteman; Tri-K
    Manuf./Distrib. (pharm. & food): Aldrich; Anglia; Arista Industries; Croda; Penta Mfg.; Ruger; Spectrum Chem.
        Mfg.
    Trade names: EmCon Olive; Super Refined® Olive Oil

Olive oil PEG-6 esters
    CAS 103819-46-1
    Definition: Complex mixture formed from the transesterification of olive oil and PEG-6
    Uses: Hydrophilic oil for pharmaceutical formulations; amphiphilic agent improving drug delivery
    Trade names: Labrafil® M 1980 CS

Opalwax. *See* Hydrogenated castor oil
Opobalsam. *See* Balsam tolu
Optal. *See* n-Propyl alcohol
o- or 2-Aminobenzoic acid. *See* Anthranilic acid
Orange crystals. *See* 2′-Acetonaphthone

Orange extract
    CAS 84012-28-2
    Synonyms: Citrus sinensis extract
    Uses: Used in orals
    Regulatory: FDA approved for orals
    Manuf./Distrib.: Bio-Botanica

Orange II. *See* CI 15510; D&C Orange No. 4

Orange oil
    CAS 8008-57-9
    FEMA 2821
    Synonyms: Citrus sinensis oil; Orange oil, coldpressed; Sweet orange oil
    Definition: Volatile oil obtained by expression from the fresh peel of the ripe fruit *Citrus sinensis*
    Properties: Yel. to deep orange liq., char. orange odor and taste; sol. in 2 vols 90% alcohol, 1 vol glac. acetic
        acid; sl. sol. in water; misc. with abs. alcohol, carbon disulfide; dens. 0.842-0.846; ref. index 1.472 (20 C)
    Precaution: Keep well closed, cool, protected from light
    Toxicology: Experimental neoplastigen; skin irritant; inh. or frequent contact may cause headache, dizziness,
        shortness of breath, allergic reaction in hypersensitive persons; heated to decomp., emits acrid smoke and
        irritating fumes
    Uses: Natural flavoring agent; expectorant, tonic, stomachic, carminative; used in orals
    Regulatory: FDA 21CFR §182.20, GRAS; FEMA GRAS; Europe listed, no restrictions; FDA approved for orals;
        BP compliance
    Manuf./Distrib. (pharm. & food): Caminiti Foti & Co. Srl; Commodity Services; Florida Treatt; Chr. Hansen's;
        Ruger

Orange oil, coldpressed. *See* Orange oil

Orange roughy oil
    Synonyms: Oils, orange roughy
    Definition: Lipid derived from the subcutaneous fat of the deep sea fish Hoplostethus atlanticus
    Uses: Solubilizer
    Trade names: Super Refined® Orange Roughy Oil

Orange tincture
    Synonyms: Tincture of orange
    Uses: Flavoring agent; used in oral pharmaceuticals
    Usage level: 0.0075-0.9% (orals)

Orange wax
    CAS 144514-51-2
    Uses: Emollient, moisturizer, uv-A and -B absorber, natural antioxidant, mild antimicrobial, anti-inflammatory,
        analgesic (on burns)
    Trade names: Orange Wax; Orange Wax, Deodorized

Orange yellow S. *See* FD&C Yellow No. 6
o- or 2-Carboxyaniline. *See* Anthranilic acid
Organosiloxane. *See* Silicone
L-α-4(or 5)-Imidazolepropionic acid. *See* L-Histidine
γ-Orizanol. *See* Oryzanol
Orthoborato(1-)-o-phenylmercury. *See* Phenylmercuric borate

Orthoboric acid. *See* Boric acid
Orthophosphoric acid. *See* Phosphoric acid

Oryzanol
  CAS 11042-64-1
  Synonyms: γ-Orizanol
  Definition: Ester of ferulic acid and a terpene alcohol; derived from rice bran oil
  Empirical: $C_{40}H_{58}O_3$
  Uses: UV absorbent and antioxidant for drugs, sunscreens
  Trade names: Gamma Oryzanol

Ossein. *See* Collagen
Otto of rose. *See* Rose oil
1-Oxa-4-azacyclohexane. *See* Morpholine
1-Oxa-2-cyclohexadecanone. *See* Pentadecalactone
Oxacyclohexadecan-2-one. *See* Pentadecalactone
Oxacyclopropane. *See* Ethylene oxide
Oxane. *See* Ethylene oxide
Oxatone chromelin. *See* Dihydroxyacetone
Oxazolidine A. *See* Dimethyl oxazolidine
Oxidase, glucose. *See* Glucose oxidase

Oxidized cellulose
  Synonyms: Oxycellulose; Cellulose, oxidized
  Uses: For controlled-release pharmaceutical applics.; hemostatic agent, bioabsorbable surgical thread, drug
    carrier, kidney dialyzer membrane, surgical lubricant, enzyme carrier, blood reducing agent
  Regulatory: BP compliance
  Manuf./Distrib.: Eastman
  Trade names: Eastman® OC

Oxidoethane. *See* Ethylene oxide

Oxidronate sodium
  Uses: Used in intravenous
  Regulatory: FDA approved for intravenous

Oxine. *See* 8-Hydroxyquinoline
Oxine sulfate. *See* 8-Hydroxyquinoline sulfate
Oxirane. *See* Ethylene oxide
Oxirane, (phenoxymethyl)-. *See* Phenyl glycidyl ether
3-Oxobutanoic acid ethyl ester. *See* Ethylacetoacetate
3-Oxo-2,3-dihydro-1,2-benzisothiazole-1,1-dioxide. *See* Saccharin
2-[(1-Oxooctadecyl)amino]ethyl octadecanoate. *See* Stearamide MEA-stearate
12-[(1-Oxooctadecyl)oxy]octadecanoic acid, 2-octyldodecyl ester. *See* Octyldodecyl stearoyl stearate
4-Oxopentanoic acid. *See* Levulinic acid
4-Oxopentanoic acid ethyl ester. *See* Ethyl levulinate
5-Oxo-DL-proline, sodium salt. *See* Sodium PCA
2-Oxopropanal. *See* Pyruvaldehyde
4-Oxo-n-valeric acid. *See* Levulinic acid
Oxybenzone. *See* Benzophenone-3
2,2´-[Oxybis(2,1-ethanediyloxy)]bisethanol. *See* PEG-4
1,1´-[Oxybis(methylene)]bis[benzene]. *See* Benzyl ether
Oxycellulose. *See* Oxidized cellulose
Oxymethurea. *See* Diazolidinyl urea
Oxymethylene. *See* Formaldehyde
Oxyphenalon. *See* 4-(p-Hydroxyphenyl)-2-butanone
Oxypropylated cellulose. *See* Hydroxypropylcellulose
Oxyquinoline. *See* 8-Hydroxyquinoline
Oxyquinoline sulfate. *See* 8-Hydroxyquinoline sulfate

Oyster shell powder
  Uses: Carrier for pharmaceuticals
  Trade names: Oyster Shell Powd. 4402
  Trade names containing: Os-Tab™ 4455

Ozocerite. *See* Ozokerite

Ozokerite
CAS 8021-55-4; EINECS 265-134-6
Synonyms: Ozocerite; Ceresin; Mineral wax; Fossil wax
Classification: Hydrocarbon wax
Definition: Hydrocarbon wax derived from mineral or petroleum sources
Properties: Yel.-brown to black or green translucent (pure), noxious odor; sol. in lt. petrol. hydrocarbons, benzene, turpentine, kerosene, ether, carbon disulfide; sl. sol. in alcohol; insol. in water; dens. 0.85-0.95; m.p. 55-110 C (usually 70 C)
Precaution: Combustible
Toxicology: No known toxicity
Uses: Thickening agent used in orals, ointments
Regulatory: Japan approved; FDA approved for orals
Manuf./Distrib.: Eastman; ISP; Koster Keunen; Frank B. Ross; Strahl & Pitsch
Manuf./Distrib. (pharm. & food): Ruger
Trade names: Koster Keunen Ozokerite
Trade names containing: Argobase EUC 2; Protegin®; Protegin® W; Protegin® WX; Protegin® X

PAA. *See* Phenylacetaldehyde
PABA. *See* p-Aminobenzoic acid
Padimate O. *See* Octyl dimethyl PABA
Palm butter. *See* Palm oil

Palm glyceride
Synonyms: Palm oil glyceride
Definition: Monoglyceride derived from palm oil
Uses: Emulsifier, stabilizer, dispersant, opacifier for drug prods.
Trade names: Monomuls® 90-30

Palm glycerides
CAS 129521-59-1
Synonyms: Glycerides, palm oil mono-, di- and tri-
Definition: Mixt. of mono-, di-, and triglycerides derived from palm oil
Uses: Emulsifier, stabilizer, dispersant, opacifier for drugs
Trade names: Monomuls® 60-30
Trade names containing: Imwitor® 965

Palm grease. *See* Palm oil

Palmitic acid
CAS 57-10-3; EINECS 200-312-9
FEMA 2832
Synonyms: Hexadecanoic acid; Cetylic acid; Hexadecylic acid
Classification: Aliphatic organic compd.; saturated fatty acid
Definition: A mixt. of solid organic acids
Empirical: $C_{16}H_{32}O_2$
Formula: $CH_3(CH_2)_{14}COOH$
Properties: White cryst. scales, sl. char. odor/taste; insol. in water; sl. sol. in cold alcohol, petrol. ether; sol. in hot alcohol, ether, propyl alcohol, chloroform; m.w. 256.42; dens. 0.853 (62/4 C); m.p. 63-64 C; b.p. 215 C (15 mm); ref. index 1.4273 (80 C)
Precaution: Combustible
Toxicology: LD50 (IV, mouse) 57 mg/kg; acute poison by intravenous route; experimental neoplastigen; human skin irritant; heated to decomp., emits acrid smoke and fumes
Uses: Lubricant, emulsifier
Regulatory: FDA 21CFR §172.210, 172.860, 173.340, 175.105, 175.320, 176.170, 176.200, 176.210, 177.1010, 177.1200, 177.2260, 177.2600, 177.2800, 178.3570, 178.3910; must conform to FDA specs for fats or fatty acids derived from edible oils; FEMA GRAS; BP compliance
Manuf./Distrib.: Akzo; Aldrich; Ashland; Browning; Henkel/Emery; Unichema; Witco
Manuf./Distrib. (pharm. & food): Acme-Hardesty; Aldrich; Integra; Kao; New Japan Chem.; Ruger
Trade names: Hystrene® 9016
Trade names containing: Cutina® FS 25 Flakes; Cutina® FS 45 Flakes

Palmitic acid, hexadecyl ester. *See* Cetyl palmitate
Palmitin. *See* Tripalmitin

Palmitoyl animal collagen amino acids. *See* Palmitoyl collagen amino acids
Palmitoyl L-ascorbic acid. *See* Ascorbyl palmitate

Palmitoyl collagen amino acids
    Synonyms: Palmitoyl animal collagen amino acids
    Definition: Condensation prod. of palmitic acid chloride and collagen amino acids
    Uses: Anti-inflammatory, waterproofing agent for suncare prods., ointments, dermatologicals, anti-acne
      creams
    Trade names: Monteine PCO

Palmityl alcohol. *See* Cetyl alcohol
Palmityl trimethyl ammonium chloride. *See* Cetrimonium chloride

Palm kernelamide DEA
    CAS 68155-12-2; 73807-15-5
    Synonyms: Palm kernel oil acid diethanolamide; Diethanolamine palm kernel oil acid amide; N,N-Bis(2-
      hydroxyethyl)palm kernel oil acid amide
    Definition: Mixture of ethanolamides of fatty acids derived from palm kernel oil
    Formula: $RCO-N(CH_2CH_2OH)_2$, RCO- represents fatty acids derived from palm kernel oil
    Uses: Emulsifier, solubilizer, visc. builder, wetting agent for dermatologicals, germicidal liq. soaps
    Regulatory: FDA 21CFR §175.105
    Trade names: Accomid PK

Palm kernel oil
    CAS 8023-79-8; EINECS 232-425-4
    Definition: Oil obtained from seeds of *Elaeis guineensis*
    Properties: Fatty solid, char. sweet nutty flavor; iodine no. 14-19; sapon. no. 240-250
    Toxicology: Heated to decomp., emits acrid smoke and irritating fumes
    Uses: Ingred. in pharmaceutical waxes
    Regulatory: FDA 21CFR §175.105, 176.200, 176.210, GRAS; BP compliance (fractionated)
    Manuf./Distrib.: ABITEC; Alba Int'l.; Penta Mfg.; Stevenson Cooper
    Manuf./Distrib. (pharm. & food): ABITEC; Alba Int'l.; Penta Mfg.
    Trade names containing: Labrafil® M 2130 CS

Palm kernel oil acid diethanolamide. *See* Palm kernelamide DEA
Palm kernel oil, hydrogenated. *See* Hydrogenated palm kernel oil

Palm oil
    CAS 8002-75-3; EINECS 232-316-1
    Synonyms: Oils, palm; Palm butter; Palm grease
    Definition: Natural oil obtained from pulp of the fruit of *Elaeis guineensis*
    Properties: Yel.-brown buttery, edible solid at R.T.; sol. in alcohol, ether, chloroform, carbon disulfide; dens.
      0.952; m.p. 26-30 C; iodine no. ≈ 15; sapon. no. ≈ 247
    Precaution: Combustible
    Toxicology: Heated to decomp., emits acrid smoke and irritating fumes
    Uses: Ingred. in pharmaceutical waxes
    Regulatory: FDA 21CFR §175.105, 175.300, 176.200, 176.210, 177.2800, GRAS
    Manuf./Distrib.: ABITEC; Alba Int'l.; Penta Mfg.; Stevenson Cooper
    Manuf./Distrib. (pharm. & food): Aarhus Olie; ABITEC; Booths; British Arkady; Calgene; CanAmera Foods;
      Cargill; Croda Singapore; Enco Prods.; Penta Mfg.; J W Pike; Vamo-Fuji Specialities; Wensleydale Foods;
      Wynmouth Lehr
    Trade names containing: Labrafil® M 2130 CS

Palm oil glyceride. *See* Palm glyceride
Palm oil glyceride, hydrogenated. *See* Hydrogenated palm glyceride
Palm oil, hydrogenated. *See* Hydrogenated palm oil
Palygorskite. *See* Attapulgite

D-Panthenol
    CAS 81-13-0; EINECS 201-327-3
    Synonyms: Dexpanthenol; Pantothenol; 2,4-Dihydroxy-N-(3-hydroxypropyl)-3,3-dimethylbutanamide;
      Pantothenyl alcohol; Provitamin B_5
    Classification: Alcohol
    Empirical: $C_9H_{19}NO_4$
    Formula: $HOCH_2C(CH_3)_2CH(OH)CONH(CH_2)_2CH_2OH$
    Properties: Visc. liq., sl. bitter taste; hygroscopic; freely sol. in water, alcohol, methanol, ether; sl. sol. in
      glycerin; m.w. 205.29; dens. 1.2 (20/20 C); b.p. 118-120 C; easily dec. on distillation; ref. index 1.500 (20

DL-Panthenol

C); pH 9.5

Toxicology: LD50 (IP, mouse) 9 g/kg; mod. toxic by IV route; heated to decomp., emits toxic fumes of NO_x

Uses: Employed medicinally to aid digestion; anti-inflammatory; nutrient, humectant; promotes healing of skin irritated by minor wounds, sun, insect bites, allergic reactions

Regulatory: FDA 21CFR §182.5580, GRAS

Manuf./Distrib.: Hoffmann-LaRoche; RITA

Manuf./Distrib. (pharm. & food): Hoffmann-LaRoche; Ruger; Spectrum Chem. Mfg.

Trade names: Ritapan D

Trade names containing: Biophytex®

DL-Panthenol

CAS 16485-10-2

Synonyms: 2,4-Dihydroxy-N-(3-hydroxypropyl)-3,3-dimethylbutanamide; Pantothenol; Dexpanthenol; DL-Pantothenyl; Racemic pantothenyl alcohol; Pantothenyl alcohol; Provitamin B_5

Classification: Alcohol

Empirical: $C_9H_{19}NO_4$

Formula: $HOCH_2C(CH_3)_2CH(OH)CONH(CH_2)_2CH_2OH$

Properties: Visc. liq.; sol. in water and alcohol; m.w. 205.25; ref. index 1.497 (20 C)

Toxicology: No known toxicity

Uses: Nutrient, dietary supplement; anti-inflammatory, humectant, moisturizer; used to aid digestion, promote healing

Manuf./Distrib.: Hoffmann-LaRoche; RITA; Spectrum Chem. Mfg.

Manuf./Distrib. (pharm. & food): Hoffmann-LaRoche; Ruger

Trade names: d,l-Panthenol FCC Grade; DL-Panthenol USP, FCC No. 63915; Ritapan DL

Panthenyl triacetate

CAS 98133-47-2

Synonyms: D-Panthenyl triacetate

Definition: Triacetyl ester of panthenol

Empirical: $C_{15}H_{25}NO_7$

Formula: $CH_3COOCH_2C(CH_3)_2CHOCOCH_3CONH(CH_2)_2CH_2OCOCH_3$

Properties: Colorless liq.; oil-sol.

Uses: Nutrient, humectant; promotes healing

Usage level: 1-5%

Regulatory: USA and EEC permitted

Manuf./Distrib.: Induchem

Trade names: Ritapan TA

Trade names containing: Unitrienol T-27

D-Panthenyl triacetate. *See* Panthenyl triacetate

Pantothenol. *See* D-Panthenol; DL-Panthenol

DL-Pantothenyl. *See* DL-Panthenol

Pantothenyl alcohol. *See* D-Panthenol; DL-Panthenol

Papain

CAS 9001-73-4; EINECS 232-627-2

Synonyms: Vegetable pepsin; Papayotin

Definition: Proteolytic enzyme derived from latex of the green fruit and leaves of *Carica papaya*

Properties: Wh. to gray powd.; sl. hygroscopic; sol. in water, glycerin; insol. in other common org. solvs.; m.w. ≈ 21,000

Toxicology: Poison by intraperitoneal route; moderately toxic by ingestion; allergen; experimental teratogenic and reproductive effects; heated to decomp., emits toxic fumes of NO_x

Uses: Used medicinally to prevent adhesion; dissolves necrotic material due to protein digesting ability

Regulatory: FDA 21CFR §184.1585, GRAS; USDA 9CFR §318.7, 381.147; BATF 27CFR §240.1051, GRAS; Canada, UK, Japan approved

Manuf./Distrib.: EM Industries; Dr. Madis Labs; Meer; Spectrum Chem. Mfg.; Spice King; Stan Chem Int'l. Ltd

Manuf./Distrib. (pharm. & food): Am. Roland; Chart; Integra; Dr. Madis; Ruger

Papayotin. *See* Papain

Parachlorometacresol. *See* p-Chloro-m-cresol

Parachlorometaxylenol. *See* Chloroxylenol

Paraffin

CAS 8002-74-2; EINECS 232-315-6

FEMA 3216; UN No. 1223

Synonyms: Paraffin wax; Hard paraffin; Petroleum wax, crystalline

Classification: Aliphatic organic compd.; hydrocarbon
Definition: Solid mixture of hydrocarbons obtained from petroleum; characterized by relatively large crystals
Empirical: C_nH_{2n+2}
Properties: Colorless to white cryst. solid, odorless, tasteless; insol. in water, alcohol; sol. in benzene, chloroform, ether, carbon disulfide, oils; misc. with fats; dens. $\approx$ 0.9; m.p. 50-57 C; flash pt. 340 F
Precaution: Dangerous fire hazard
Toxicology: Anesthetic effect; ACGIH TLV:TWA 2 mg/m^3 (fume); experimental tumorigens by implantation; many paraffin waxes contain carcinogens
Uses: Stiffening agent, tablet coating agent; used in implants, orals, topicals, ointments
Regulatory: FDA 21CFR §133.181, 172.615, 173.3210, 175.105, 175.210, 175.250, 175.300, 175.320, 176.170, 176.200, 177.1200, 177.2420, 177.2600, 177.2800, 178.3710, 178.3800, 178.3910, 179.45; FEMA GRAS; Canada, Japan approved; FDA approved for implants, orals, topicals; USP/NF, BP compliance
Manuf./Distrib.: Astor Wax; EM Industries; Exxon; Humphrey; IGI; Jonk BV; Koster Keunen; Mobil; Penreco; Phillips; Frank B. Ross; Shell; Spectrum Chem. Mfg.; Stevenson Cooper; Texaco; Vista
Manuf./Distrib. (pharm. & food): Aldrich; Koster Keunen; Ruger
Trade names: Koster Keunen Paraffin Wax
Trade names containing: Argobase EU; Ross Beeswax Substitute 628/5; Ross Japan Wax Substitute 966

Paraffin oil. *See* Mineral oil
Paraffin wax. *See* Paraffin
Paraform. *See* Paraformaldehyde

Paraformaldehyde
CAS 30525-89-4; EINECS 200-001-8
Synonyms: p-Formaldehyde; Trioxylmethylene; Polyoxymethylene; Paraform
Classification: A polymer of formaldehyde in which n= 8-100
Formula: $HO(CH_2O)_nH$
Properties: M.w. $(30.03)_n$; m.p. 132-136 C
Toxicology: May cause allergic response
Uses: Formaldehyde-releasing preservative used in root canal filling pastes; hardener and waterproofing agent for gelatin contraceptive creams
Manuf./Distrib.: Andrulex Trading Ltd; Degussa; Hoechst Celanese; Mitsubishi Gas; Mitsui Toatsu Chem.

Pareth 25-12. *See* C12-15 pareth-12
Pareth-25-2 phosphate. *See* C12-15 pareth-2 phosphate

Patchouli oil
FEMA 2838
Synonyms: Patchouly oil
Definition: Oil derived from *Pogostemon cablin* and *P. heyneanus*
Properties: Yellowish to brownish
Toxicology: Sensitizer
Uses: Natural flavoring agent for pharmaceuticals
Regulatory: FEMA GRAS; Japan approved
Manuf./Distrib. (pharm. & food): Chart; Pierre Chauvet

Patchouly oil. *See* Patchouli oil
Patent Blue AC. *See* FD&C Blue No. 1
PCA-Na. *See* Sodium PCA
PCA Soda. *See* Sodium PCA
PCMC. *See* p-Chloro-m-cresol
PCMX. *See* Chloroxylenol
PDDB. *See* Domiphen bromide
PDMS. *See* Dimethicone
PE. *See* Polyethylene
Peach aldehyde. *See* γ-Undecalactone

Peach kernel oil
CAS 8023-98-1
Synonyms: Persic oil
Definition: Oil expressed from kernels of the peach, *Prunus persica*
Uses: Pharmaceutical excipient
Regulatory: FDA 21CFR §182.40, GRAS

Peanut oil
CAS 8002-03-7; EINECS 232-296-4

Peanut oil PEG-6 esters

Synonyms: Arachis oil; Groundnut oil; Katchung oil; Earthnut oil; Pecan shell powder
Classification: Fixed oil
Definition: Refined fixed oil obtained from seed kernels of one or more cultivated varieties of *Arachis hypogaea*
Properties: Pale yel. liq., nutty odor, bland taste; sol. in benzene, alcohol, ether, chloroform; insol. in alkalies; dens. 0.916-0.922; solid. pt. -5 C; iodine no. 84-100; sapon. no. 185-195; flash pt. 540 F; ref. index 1.466-1.470
Precaution: Combustible exposed to heat or flame; can react with oxidizing materials; light-sensitive
Toxicology: Experimental tumorigen; human skin irritant, mild allergen; mutagenic data; heated to decomp., emits acrid smoke and irritating fumes
Uses: Solvent for ointments and liniments; oleaginous vehicle for medicine; nutritive emulsions; softener for ear wax, enemas, in emollient creams; gall bladder evacuant; used in injectables, orals, vaginals, sunburn preps.
Regulatory: FDA 21CFR §175.105, 176.200, 176.210, 177.2800, 182.70; GRAS; FDA approved for injecables, orals, vaginals; USP/NF, BP compliance
Manuf./Distrib.: ABITEC; Arista Industries; Croda; Penta Mfg.; Tri-K
Manuf./Distrib. (pharm. & food): Arista Industries; S Black; Bunge Foods; Calgene; CanAmera Foods; Cargill; H E Daniel; Flavors of N. Am.; Edw. Gittens; MLG Enterprises; Penta Mfg.; Ruger; SKW Chemicals; Spectrum Chem. Mfg.; Vamo-Fuji Specialities; Van Den Bergh
Trade names: Super Refined® Peanut Oil
Trade names containing: Crodarom Nut O; Dry Beta Carotene Beadlets 10% CWS No. 65633; Dry Beta Carotene Beadlets 10% No. 65661; Dry Vitamin D$_3$ Beadlets Type 850 No. 652550401, 652550601; Palmabeads® Type 500 No. 65332; Palma-Sperse® Type 250A/50 D-S No. 65221

Peanut oil PEG-6 esters
Definition: Complex mixture obtained from transesterification of peanut oil and PEG-6
Uses: Hydrophilic oil for pharmaceuticals; amphiphilic agent improving drug delivery
Trade names: Labrafil® M 1969 CS

Pearl alum. *See* Aluminum sulfate
Pearl ash. *See* Potassium carbonate
Pearl essence. *See* CI 75170; Guanine
Pearl white. *See* Bismuth oxychloride
Pear oil. *See* Amyl acetate
Pecan shell powder. *See* Peanut oil

Pectin
CAS 9000-69-5; EINECS 232-553-0
Synonyms: Citrus pectin
Classification: Polysaccharide
Definition: Purified carbohydrate prod. obtained from the dilute acid extract of the inner portion of the rind of citrus fruits or from apple pomace
Properties: White powd. or syrupy conc., pract. odorless; sol. in water; insol. in alcohol, org. solvs.; m.w. 30,000-100,000
Toxicology: Nonallergenic; heated to decomp., emits acrid smoke and irritating fumes
Uses: Protective colloid, thickener, emulsifier, adsorbent; dentals; topicals; encapsulated drugs; diarrhea treatments; hemostatic formulations; blood plasma substitute; detoxication; dietary fiber fortification; cholesterol reduction; glucose metabolism
Regulatory: FDA 21CFR §135.140, 145, 150, 173.385, 184.1588, GRAS; Japan approved; Europe listed; UK approved; FDA approved for dentals, topicals; USP/NF compliance
Manuf./Distrib.: Herbstreith & Fox; Hercules; Penta Mfg.; Pomosin GmbH; Spice King; U.S. Biochemical
Manuf./Distrib. (pharm. & food): Am. Roland; Atomergic Chemetals; Copenhagen Pectin; Ellis & Everard; G Fiske; Grindsted; A C Hatrick; Herbstreith & Fox; Hercules; Ikeda; Lucas Meyer; Penta Mfg.; Pomosin GmbH; Rit-Chem; Ruger; Sanofi; Spectrum Chem. Mfg.; Spice King; TIC Gums
Trade names: Genu® HM USP 100; Genu® HM USP L200; Genu® Pectins; Genu® Pectin (citrus) type USP/100; Genu® Pectin (citrus) type USP/200; Genu® Pectin (citrus) type USP-H; Genu® Pectin (citrus) type USP-L/200; Mexpectin LA 100 Range; Mexpectin LC 700 Range; Mexpectin XSS 100 Range

Pectin sugar. *See* L-Arabinose
PEG. *See* Polyethylene glycol

PEG-4
CAS 25322-68-3 (generic); 112-60-7; EINECS 203-989-9
Synonyms: PEG 200; POE (4); 2,2´-[Oxybis(2,1-ethanediyloxy)]bisethanol
Definition: Polymer of ethylene oxide
Empirical: $C_8H_{18}O_5$

Formula: H(OCH$_2$CH$_2$)$_n$OH, avg. n = 4
Properties: Visc. liq., sl. char. odor; hygroscopic; m.w. 190-210; dens. 1.127 (25/25 C); visc. 4.3 cSt (210 F); supercools on freezing
Precaution: Solvent action on some plastics
Toxicology: LD50 (oral, rat) 28,900 mg/kg; mildly toxic by ingestion; heated to decomp., emits acrid smoke and irritating fumes
Uses: Solvent, vehicle for active ingreds. in soft gelatin capsules, oral liqs., parenterals; bulking agent; moisture and consistency regulator; used in topicals
Regulatory: FDA 21CFR §73.1, 172.210, 172.770, 172.820, 173.310, 173.340, 175.105, 175.300, 178.3750; FDA approved for topicals
Manuf./Distrib.: Ashland; C.P. Hall; Harwick; Henkel; Union Carbide
Trade names: Hodag PEG 200; Lipoxol® 200 MED; Macol® E-200; Poly-G® 200

PEG-6

CAS 25322-68-3 (generic); 2615-15-8; EINECS 220-045-1
Synonyms: Polyethylene glycol 300; PEG 300; Hexaethylene glycol; Macrogol 300
Definition: Polymer of ethylene oxide
Empirical: C$_{12}$H$_{26}$O$_7$
Formula: H(OCH$_2$CH$_2$)$_n$OH, avg. n = 6
Properties: Sp.gr. 1.124-1.127; visc. 5.4-6.4 cSt (99 C); pour pt. -15 to -8 C; flash pt. (COC) 196 C; ref. index 1.463-1.4641 (20 C); pH 4.5-7.5 (5%)
Toxicology: LD50 (oral, rat) 27,500 mg/kg; mildly toxic by ingestion; heated to decomp., emits acrid smoke and irritating fumes
Uses: Coating agent, plasticizer, suppository base, tablet/capsule lubricant; bulking agent; solvent for active ingreds. in soft gelatin capsules, oral liqs., parenterals; also in ophthalmics, topicals
Regulatory: FDA 21CFR §172.210, 172.770, 172.820, 173.310, 173.340, 175.105, 175.300, 178.3750, 178.3910; FDA approved for parenterals, ophthalmics, topicals; USP/NF, BP compliance
Manuf./Distrib.: Ashland; Harwick; Henkel; Union Carbide
Manuf./Distrib. (pharm. & food): Spectrum Chem. Mfg.
Trade names: Carbowax® PEG 300; Carbowax® Sentry® PEG 300; Dow E300 NF; Hodag PEG 300; Lipoxol® 300 MED; Macol® E-300; Renex® PEG 300; Rhodasurf® PEG 300; Teric PEG 300
Trade names containing: Carbowax® Sentry® PEG 540 Blend; Hodag PEG 540; Labrafil® M 2130 CS; Lipoxol® 550 MED

PEG-8

CAS 25322-68-3 (generic); 5117-19-1; EINECS 225-856-4
Synonyms: Macrogol 400; Polyethylene glycol 400; PEG 400; POE (8); 3,6,9,12,15,18,21-Heptaoxatricosane-1,23-diol
Definition: Polymer of ethylene oxide
Empirical: C$_{16}$H$_{34}$O$_9$
Formula: H(OCH$_2$CH$_2$)$_n$OH, avg. n = 8
Properties: Visc. liq., sl. char. odor, minimal taste; sl. hygroscopic; m.w. 380-420; dens. 1.128 (25/25 C); visc. 7.3 cSt (210 F); m.p. 4-8 C; pH 4.5-7.5 (5%)
Toxicology: LD50 (rat, oral) 30 ml/kg; low toxicity by ingestion, IV, IP routes; heated to decomp., emits acrid smoke and irritating fumes
Uses: Coating agent, plasticizer, suppository base, tablet/capsule lubricant; bulking agent; solvent for active ingreds. in soft gelatin capsules, oral liqs., parenterals
Regulatory: FDA 21CFR §172.210, 172.770, 172.820, 173.310, 173.340, 175.105, 175.300, 178.3750, 178.3910, 181.22, 181.30; USP/NF, BP, Ph.Eur. compliance
Manuf./Distrib.: Ashland; C.P. Hall; Harwick; Henkel; Union Carbide
Manuf./Distrib. (pharm. & food): Spectrum Chem. Mfg.
Trade names: Carbowax® Sentry® PEG 400; Dow E400 NF; Hodag PEG 400; Lipoxol® 400 MED; Macol® E-400; Pluracol® E400 NF; Renex® PEG 400; Teric PEG 400
Trade names containing: Docusate Sodium USP in Polyethylene Glycol 400 NF; Oxynex® K

PEG-9

CAS 25322-68-3 (generic); 3386-18-3; EINECS 222-206-1
Synonyms: PEG 450; POE (9)
Definition: Polymer of ethylene oxide
Empirical: C$_{18}$H$_{38}$O$_{10}$
Formula: H(OCH$_2$CH$_2$)$_n$OH, avg. n = 9
Uses: Solvent for active ingreds. in soft gelatin capsules, oral liqs., parenterals; bulking agent
Regulatory: FDA 21CFR §172.210, 172.770, 172.820, 173.310, 173.340, 175.105, 175.300, 178.3750, 178.3910

PEG-12

CAS 25322-68-3 (generic); 6790-09-6; EINECS 229-859-1

Synonyms: Polyethylene glycol 600; PEG 600; POE (12); Macrogol 600

Definition: Polymer of ethylene oxide

Empirical: $C_{24}H_{50}O_{13}$

Formula: $H(OCH_2CH_2)_nOH$, avg. n = 12

Properties: Visc. liq., char. odor; sl. hygroscopic; m.w. 570-630; dens. 1.128 (25/25 C); m.p. 20-25 C; visc. 10.5 cSt (210 F); pH 4.5-7.5 (5%)

Toxicology: LD50 (oral, rat) 38,100 mg/kg; low toxicity by ingestion; eye irritant; heated to decomp., emits acrid smoke and irritating fumes

Uses: Coating agent, plasticizer, suppository base, tablet/capsule lubricant; bulking agent; solvent for active ingreds. in soft gelatin capsules, oral liqs., parenterals

Regulatory: FDA 21CFR §172.210, 172.770, 172.820, 173.310, 173.340, 175.105, 175.300, 178.3750, 178.3910; USP/NF compliance

Manuf./Distrib.: Ashland; C.P. Hall; Harwick; Union Carbide

Manuf./Distrib. (pharm. & food): Spectrum Chem. Mfg.

Trade names: Carbowax® Sentry® PEG 600; Dow E600 NF; Hodag PEG 600; Lipoxol® 600 MED; Macol® E-600; Pluracol® E600 NF; Renex® PEG 600; Teric PEG 600

PEG-14

CAS 25322-68-3 (generic)

Synonyms: POE (14); PEG 700

Definition: Polymer of ethylene oxide

Empirical: $C_{28}H_{58}O_{15}$

Formula: $H(OCH_2CH_2)_nOH$, avg. n = 14

Properties: Visc. 11.5-13.0 cSt

Uses: Solvent for active ingreds. in soft gelatin capsules, oral liqs., parenterals; lubricant, binder, bulking agent

Regulatory: FDA 21CFR §172.210, 172.770, 172.820, 173.310, 173.340, 175.105, 175.300, 178.3750, 178.3910

Trade names: Rhodasurf® PEG 600

PEG-16

CAS 25322-68-3 (generic)

Synonyms: PEG 800; POE (16)

Definition: Polymer of ethylene oxide

Empirical: $C_{32}H_{66}O_{17}$

Formula: $H(OCH_2CH_2)_nOH$, avg. n = 16

Properties: Visc. 12.5-14.5 cSt

Uses: Solvent for active ingreds. in soft gelatin capsules, oral liqs., parenterals; moisture and consistency regulator, bulking agent

Regulatory: FDA 21CFR §172.210, 172.770, 172.820, 173.310, 173.340, 175.105, 175.300, 178.3750, 178.3910

Trade names: Lipoxol® 800 MED; Teric PEG 800

PEG-20

CAS 25322-68-3 (generic)

Synonyms: Polyethylene glycol 1000; PEG 1000; Macrogol 1000; POE (20)

Definition: Polymer of ethylene oxide

Empirical: $C_{40}H_{82}O_{21}$

Formula: $H(OCH_2CH_2)_nOH$, avg. n = 20

Properties: Solid; sp.gr. 1.085; visc. 16-19 cSt (99 C); pour pt. 37-40 C; flash pt. (COC) 265 C; pH 4.5-7.5 (5%)

Toxicology: LD50 (oral, rat) 42 g/kg; mod. toxic by IP, IV routes; mildly toxic by ingestion; experimental tumorigen; heated to decomp., emits acrid smoke and irritating fumes

Uses: Film coating agent, ointment base, tablet binder, tablet/capsule lubricant, plasticizer, solv., suppository base; bulking agent

Regulatory: FDA 21CFR §172.210, 172.770, 172.820, 173.310, 173.340, 175.105, 175.300, 178.3750, 178.3910; USP/NF, BP, Ph.Eur. compliance

Manuf./Distrib.: Ashland; Harwick; Union Carbide

Manuf./Distrib. (pharm. & food): Spectrum Chem. Mfg.

Trade names: Carbowax® Sentry® PEG 900; Carbowax® Sentry® PEG 1000; Dow E1000 NF; Hodag PEG 1000; Lipoxol® 1000 MED; Renex® PEG 1000

PEG-32

CAS 25322-68-3 (generic)

Synonyms: PEG 1540; Macrogol 1540; POE (32)

Definition: Polymer of ethylene oxide
Empirical: $C_{64}H_{130}O_{33}$
Formula: $H(OCH_2CH_2)_nOH$, avg. n = 32
Properties: Wh. powd.
Toxicology: LD50 (oral, rat) 44,200 mg/kg; mildly toxic by ingestion; human skin irritant; heated to decomp., emits acrid smoke and irritating fumes
Uses: Film coating agent, ointment base, tablet binder, lubricant; bulking agent; used in dentals, orals, rectals, topicals
Regulatory: FDA 21CFR §172.210, 172.770, 172.820, 173.310, 173.340, 175.105, 175.300, 178.3750, 178.3910; FDA approved for dentals, orals, rectals, topicals; BP compliance
Trade names: Carbowax® Sentry® PEG 1450; Dow E1450 NF; Hodag PEG 1450; Lipoxol® 1550 MED; Pluracol® E1450 NF; Renex® PEG 1500FL
Trade names containing: Carbowax® Sentry® PEG 540 Blend; Hodag PEG 540; Lipoxol® 550 MED

PEG-40
CAS 25322-68-3 (generic)
Synonyms: PEG 2000; POE (40)
Definition: Polymer of ethylene oxide
Empirical: $C_{80}H_{162}O_{41}$
Formula: $H(OCH_2CH_2)_nOH$, avg. n = 40
Properties: Solid; dens. 1.127; visc. 38-49 cSt; ref. index 1.4590 (20 C)
Uses: Film coating agent, ointment base, tablet binder, lubricant; bulking agent; used in parenterals
Regulatory: FDA 21CFR §172.210, 172.770, 172.820, 173.310, 173.340, 175.105, 175.300, 178.3750, 178.3910; FDA approved for parenterals
Manuf./Distrib.: Aldrich
Trade names: Lipoxol® 2000 MED

PEG-60
CAS 25322-68-3 (generic)
Synonyms: PEG 3000; POE (60)
Definition: Polymer of ethylene oxide
Formula: $H(OCH_2CH_2)_nOH$, avg. n = 60
Properties: Visc. 67-93 cSt
Uses: Moisture and consistency regulator, bulking agent
Trade names: Lipoxol® 3000 MED

PEG-75
CAS 25322-68-3 (generic)
Synonyms: Polyethylene glycol 3350; PEG 3350; POE (75)
Definition: Polymer of ethylene oxide
Empirical: $C_{150}H_{302}O_{76}$
Formula: $H(OCH_2CH_2)_nOH$, avg. n = 75
Properties: White powd. or creamy-white flakes; m.w. 3000-3700; dens. 1.212 (25/25 C); visc. 76-110 cSt (210 F); m.p. 54-58 C; pH 4.5-7.5 (5%)
Toxicology: LD50 (oral, rat) 50 g/kg; mildly toxic by ingestion; skin irritant; heated to decomp., emits acrid smoke and irritating fumes
Uses: Film coating agent, ointment and suppository base, solv., plasticizer, tablet binder, tablet/capsule lubricant; bulking agent; active ingred. in colonic lavage sol'ns.; used in injectables, orals, rectals, topicals, vaginals
Regulatory: FDA 21CFR §172.210, 172.770, 172.820, 173.310, 173.340, 175.105, 175.300, 178.3750, 178.3910; FDA approved for injectables, orals, rectals, topicals, vaginals; USP/NF compliance
Manuf./Distrib. (pharm. & food): Spectrum Chem. Mfg.
Trade names: Carbowax® Sentry® PEG 3350; Dow E3350 NF; Hodag PEG 3350; Lipoxol® 4000 MED; Renex® PEG 4000FL; Teric PEG 4000

PEG-100
CAS 25322-68-3 (generic)
Synonyms: PEG (100); POE (100)
Definition: Polymer of ethylene oxide
Empirical: $C_{200}H_{402}O_{101}$
Formula: $H(OCH_2CH_2)_nOH$, avg. n = 100
Uses: Film coating agent, ointment base, tablet binder, lubricant; bulking agent
Regulatory: FDA 21CFR §172.210, 172.770, 172.820, 173.310, 173.340, 175.105, 175.300, 178.3750, 178.3910
Trade names: Carbowax® Sentry® PEG 4600; Dow E4500 NF

PEG (100). *See* PEG-100

PEG-150
    CAS 25322-68-3 (generic)
    Synonyms: PEG 6000; Macrogol 6000; POE (150)
    Definition: Polymer of ethylene oxide
    Formula: $H(OCH_2CH_2)_nOH$, n = 150
    Properties: Powd. or creamy-white flakes; water-sol.; m.w. 7000-9000; dens. 1.21 (25/25 C); visc. 470-900 cSt (210 F); m.p. 56-63 C; flash pt. > 887 F
    Precaution: Combustible exposed to heat or flame
    Toxicology: LD50 (rat, oral) > 50 g/kg; mildly toxic by ingestion; mutagenic data; skin irritant; heated to decomp., emits acrid smoke and irritating fumes
    Uses: Film coating agent, ointment and suppository base, solv., plasticizer, tablet binder, tablet/capsule lubricant; bulking agent
    Regulatory: FDA 21CFR §172.210, 172.770, 172.820, 173.310, 173.340, 175.300, 177.2420, 178.3750, 178.3910
    Manuf./Distrib. (pharm. & food): Spectrum Chem. Mfg.
    Trade names: Carbowax® Sentry® PEG 8000; Dow E8000 NF; Hodag PEG 8000; Lipoxol® 6000 MED; Renex® PEG 6000FL; Teric PEG 6000

PEG-200
    CAS 25322-68-3 (generic)
    Synonyms: PEG 9000; POE (200)
    Definition: Polymer of ethylene oxide
    Formula: $H(OCH_2CH_2)_nOH$, avg. n = 200
    Properties: Solid
    Uses: Film coating agent, ointment base, tablet binder, lubricant; bulking agent; used in intramuscular injectables, orals, topicals
    Regulatory: FDA 21CFR §172.210, 172.770, 172.820, 173.310, 173.340, 175.300, 178.3750, 178.3910; FDA approved for intramuscular injectables, orals, topicals
    Manuf./Distrib. (pharm. & food): Ruger

PEG 200. *See* PEG-4
PEG 300. *See* PEG-6

PEG-350
    CAS 25322-68-3 (generic)
    Synonyms: PEG 20000; POE (350)
    Definition: Polymer of ethylene oxide
    Formula: $H(OCH_2CH_2)_nOH$, avg. n = 350
    Uses: Pharmaceutic aid
    Regulatory: FDA 21CFR §172.770, 173.310, 175.300, 178.3910

PEG-400
    CAS 9004-96-0
    Uses: Used in parenterals, ophthalmics, orals, rectals, topicals, vaginals
    Regulatory: FDA approved for parenterals, ophthalmics, orals, rectals, topicals, vaginals

PEG 400. *See* PEG-8
PEG 450. *See* PEG-9
PEG 600. *See* PEG-12
PEG 700. *See* PEG-14
PEG 800. *See* PEG-16

PEG-1000
    Uses: Used in orals, rectals, topicals, vaginals
    Regulatory: FDA approved for orals, rectals, topicals, vaginals

PEG 1000. *See* PEG-20

PEG-1500
    Uses: Used in dentals, orals, topicals
    Regulatory: FDA approved for dentals, orals, topicals

PEG 1540. *See* PEG-32
PEG 2000. *See* PEG-40
PEG-2000. *See* PEG-2M
PEG 3000. *See* PEG-60

PEG 3350. *See* PEG-75

PEG 3500
   Uses: Used in orals
   Regulatory: FDA approved for orals

PEG 4000. *See* PEG-4M
PEG-5000. *See* PEG-5M
PEG 6000. *See* PEG-150
PEG-6000. *See* PEG-6M
PEG-7000. *See* PEG-7M
PEG-8000. *See* PEG-8M
PEG 9000. *See* PEG-200
PEG-9000. *See* PEG-9M
PEG-14000. *See* PEG-14M
PEG 20000. *See* PEG-350
PEG-20000. *See* PEG-20M
PEG-23000. *See* PEG-23M
PEG-45000. *See* PEG-45M
PEG-90000. *See* PEG-90M
PEG-115000. *See* PEG-115M
PEG 300,000. *See* PEG-7M
PEG 600,000. *See* PEG-14M

PEG-2M
   CAS 25322-68-3 (generic)
   Synonyms: PEG-2000; Polyethylene glycol (2000); POE (2000)
   Definition: Polymer of ethylene oxide
   Formula: $H(OCH_2CH_2)_nOH$, avg. n = 2000
   Uses: Tablet coating; emulsifier; dispersant, antisetting agent in calamine lotion; lubricant for rubbing alcohol; controlled-release drugs; contact lens fluid
   Regulatory: FDA 21CFR §172.770, 173.310, 175.300, 178.3910
   Trade names: Polyox® WSR N-10; Prox-onic PEG-2000

PEG-4M
   Synonyms: PEG 4000; Macrogol 4000
   Uses: Used in dentals, injectables, orals, rectals, topicals, vaginals
   Regulatory: FDA approved for dentals, injectables, orals, rectals, topicals, vaginals; BP compliance

PEG-5M
   CAS 25322-68-3 (generic)
   Synonyms: PEG-5000; POE (5000)
   Definition: Polymer of ethylene oxide
   Formula: $H(OCH_2CH_2)_nOH$, avg. n = 5000
   Uses: Tablet coating; dispersant, antisetting agent in calamine lotion; lubricant for rubbing alcohol; controlled-release drugs; contact lens fluid
   Regulatory: FDA 21CFR §172.770, 173.310, 175.300, 178.3910
   Trade names: Polyox® WSR N-80

PEG-6M
   Synonyms: PEG-6000
   Uses: Used in orals, rectals, topicals, vaginals
   Regulatory: FDA approved for orals, rectals, topicals, vaginals

PEG-7M
   CAS 25322-68-3 (generic)
   Synonyms: PEG-7000; POE (7000); PEG 300,000
   Definition: Polymer of ethylene oxide
   Formula: $H(OCH_2CH_2)_nOH$, avg. n = 7000
   Uses: Tablet coating; dispersant, antisetting agent in calamine lotion; lubricant for rubbing alcohol; controlled-release drugs; contact lens fluid
   Regulatory: FDA 21CFR §172.770, 173.310, 175.300, 178.3910
   Trade names: Polyox® WSR N-750

PEG-8M
   CAS 25322-68-3 (generic)
   Synonyms: PEG-8000

PEG-9M

    Uses: Binder for capsules/pills; suppository base; used in ophthalmics, orals, rectals, topicals, vaginals
    Regulatory: FDA approved for ophthalmics, orals, rectals, topicals, vaginals
    Trade names: Teric PEG 8000

PEG-9M
    CAS 25322-68-3 (generic)
    Synonyms: PEG-9000; POE (9000)
    Definition: Polymer of ethylene oxide
    Formula: $H(OCH_2CH_2)_nOH$, avg. n = 9000
    Uses: Tablet coating; dispersant, antisetting agent in calamine lotion; lubricant for rubbing alcohol; controlled-release drugs; contact lens fluid
    Regulatory: FDA 21CFR §172.770, 173.310, 175.300, 178.3910
    Trade names: Polyox® WSR 3333

PEG-10M
    CAS 25322-68-3 (generic)
    Uses: Wetting agent, emulsifier
    Trade names: Prox-onic PEG-10,000

PEG-14M
    CAS 25322-68-3 (generic)
    Synonyms: PEG-14000; PEG 600,000; POE (14000)
    Definition: Polymer of ethylene oxide
    Formula: $H(OCH_2CH_2)_nOH$, avg. n = 14,000
    Uses: Tablet coating; dispersant, antisetting agent in calamine lotion; lubricant for rubbing alcohol; controlled-release drugs; contact lens fluid
    Regulatory: FDA 21CFR §172.770, 173.310, 175.300, 178.3910
    Trade names: Polyox® WSR 205; Polyox® WSR N-3000

PEG-20M
    CAS 25322-68-3 (generic)
    Synonyms: PEG-20000; POE (20000)
    Definition: Polymer of ethylene oxide
    Formula: $H(OCH_2CH_2)_nOH$, avg. n = 20,000
    Uses: Tablet coating; emulsifier, wetting agent; dispersant, antisetting agent in calamine lotion; lubricant for rubbing alcohol; controlled-release drugs; contact lens fluid
    Regulatory: FDA 21CFR §172.770, 173.310, 175.300, 178.3910; BP compliance
    Trade names: Polyox® WSR 1105; Prox-onic PEG-20,000

PEG-23M
    CAS 25322-68-3 (generic)
    Synonyms: PEG-23000; POE (23000)
    Definition: Polymer of ethylene oxide
    Formula: $H(OCH_2CH_2)_nOH$, avg. n = 23000
    Uses: Tablet coating; dispersant, antisetting agent in calamine lotion; lubricant for rubbing alcohol; controlled-release drugs; contact lens fluid
    Regulatory: FDA 21CFR §172.770, 173.310, 175.300, 178.3910
    Trade names: Polyox® WSR N-12K

PEG-35M
    CAS 25322-68-3 (generic)
    Uses: Wetting agent, emulsifier
    Trade names: Prox-onic PEG-35,000

PEG-45M
    CAS 25322-68-3 (generic)
    Synonyms: PEG-45000; POE (45000)
    Definition: Polymer of ethylene oxide
    Formula: $H(OCH_2CH_2)_nOH$, avg. n = 45,000
    Uses: Tablet coating; dispersant, antisetting agent in calamine lotion; lubricant for rubbing alcohol; controlled-release drugs; contact lens fluid
    Regulatory: FDA 21CFR §172.770, 173.310, 175.300, 178.3910
    Trade names: Polyox® WSR N-60K

PEG-90M
    CAS 25322-68-3 (generic)
    Synonyms: PEG-90000; POE (90000)

Definition: Polymer of ethylene oxide
Formula: $H(OCH_2CH_2)_nOH$, avg. n = 90000
Uses: Tablet coating; dispersant, antisetting agent in calamine lotion; lubricant for rubbing alcohol; controlled-release drugs; contact lens fluid
Regulatory: FDA 21CFR §172.770, 173.310, 175.300, 178.3910
Trade names: Polyox® WSR 301

PEG-115M

CAS 25322-68-3 (generic)
Synonyms: PEG-115000; POE (115000)
Definition: Polymer of ethylene oxide
Formula: $H(OCH_2CH_2)_nOH$, avg. n = 115,000
Uses: Tablet coating; dispersant, antisetting agent in calamine lotion; lubricant for rubbing alcohol; controlled-release drugs; contact lens fluid
Regulatory: FDA 21CFR §172.770, 173.310, 175.300, 178.3910
Trade names: Polyox® WSR Coagulant

PEG-20 almond glycerides

Synonyms: PEG 1000 almond glycerides; POE (20) almond glycerides
Definition: PEG deriv. of the mono and diglycerides from almond oil, avg. 20 moles EO
Uses: Emulsifier, wetting agent, solubilizer, dispersant, emollient
Trade names: Crovol A40

PEG-60 almond glycerides

Synonyms: PEG 3000 almond glycerides; POE (60) almond glycerides
Definition: PEG deriv. of the mono and diglycerides from almond oil, avg. 60 moles EO
Uses: Emulsifier, wetting agent, solubilizer, dispersant, emollient, counter-irritant
Trade names: Crovol A70

PEG 1000 almond glycerides. *See* PEG-20 almond glycerides
PEG 3000 almond glycerides. *See* PEG-60 almond glycerides

PEG-8 beeswax

Synonyms: PEG 400 beeswax; POE (8) beeswax
Definition: PEG deriv. of beeswax with avg. 8 moles ethylene oxide
Uses: Structural SE base for pharmaceutical o/w emulsions; stabilizer
Trade names: Apifil®

PEG 400 beeswax. *See* PEG-8 beeswax

PEG-8 behenate

Synonyms: PEG 400 behenate; POE (8) behenate
Definition: PEG ester of behenic acid
Formula: $CH_3(CH_2)_{20}CO(OCH_2CH_2)_nOH$, avg. n = 8
Uses: Ingred. in tableting
Trade names containing: Compritol HD5 ATO

PEG 400 behenate. *See* PEG-8 behenate
PEG-2-C12-15 alcohols phosphate. *See* C12-15 pareth-2 phosphate
PEG 400 caprylate/caprate glycerides. *See* PEG-8 caprylic/capric glycerides

PEG-6 caprylic/capric glycerides

CAS 52504-24-2
Synonyms: PEG 300 caprylic/capric glycerides; POE (6) caprylic/capric glycerides
Classification: Ethoxylated glyceride
Formula: $RCO\text{·}OCH_2COHHCH_2(OCH_2CH_2)_nOH$, $RCO\text{·}$ = mixt. of caprylic/capric radicals, avg. n=6
Properties: Oily liq.; sol. in water, acetone, ethyl acetate, butyl acetate; misc. with IPA, castor oil; sapon. no. 90-100
Uses: Emollient, refatting agent, solubilizer, wetting agent for pharmaceuticals
Trade names: Softigen® 767

PEG-8 caprylic/capric glycerides

CAS 57307-99-0; 85536-08-9
Synonyms: PEG 400 caprylate/caprate glycerides
Definition: PEG deriv. of a mixt. of mono, di, and triglycerides of caprylic and capric acids with an avg. of 8 moles of ethylene oxide
Uses: Hydrophilic oil; nonionic surfactant, solubilizer, bioavailability enhancer for drug delivery systems
Trade names: Labrafac® CM10; Labrasol; L.A.S.

667

PEG 300 caprylic/capric glycerides

PEG 300 caprylic/capric glycerides. *See* PEG-6 caprylic/capric glycerides

PEG-3 castor oil
CAS 61791-12-6 (generic); EINECS FDA 21CFR §175.300
Synonyms: POE (3) castor oil
Definition: PEG deriv. of castor oil with avg. 3 moles of ethylene oxide
Uses: Hydrotrope, emulsifier for pharmaceutical preps.
Trade names: Nikkol CO-3

PEG-5 castor oil
CAS 61791-12-6 (generic)
Synonyms: POE (5) castor oil
Definition: PEG deriv. of castor oil with avg. 5 moles of ethylene oxide
Uses: Emulsifier, dispersant, solubilizer, visc. control agent for pharmaceutical preps.
Regulatory: FDA 21CFR §175.105, 175.300
Trade names: Acconon CA-5

PEG-8 castor oil
CAS 61791-12-6 (generic)
Synonyms: POE (8) castor oil; PEG 400 castor oil
Definition: PEG deriv. of castor oil with avg. 8 moles of ethylene oxide
Uses: Emulsifier, dispersant, solubilizer, visc. control agent for pharmaceutical preps.
Regulatory: FDA 21CFR §175.105, 175.300, 176.210, 177.2800
Trade names: Acconon CA-8

PEG-9 castor oil
CAS 61791-12-6 (generic)
Synonyms: POE (9) castor oil; PEG 450 castor oil
Definition: PEG deriv. of castor oil with avg. 9 moles of ethylene oxide
Uses: Emulsifier, lubricant, dispersant, solubilizer, visc. control agent for pharmaceutical preps.
Regulatory: FDA 21CFR §175.105, 175.300, 177.2800
Trade names: Acconon CA-9

PEG-15 castor oil
CAS 61791-12-6 (generic)
Synonyms: POE (15) castor oil
Definition: PEG deriv. of castor oil with avg. 15 moles of ethylene oxide
Uses: Emulsifier, lubricant, dispersant, solubilizer, visc. control agent for pharmaceutical preps.
Regulatory: FDA 21CFR §175.105, 175.300, 176.210, 177.2800
Trade names: Acconon CA-15

PEG-17 castor oil
CAS 61791-12-6 (generic)
Synonyms: POE (17) castor oil
Definition: PEG deriv. of castor oil with avg. 17 moles of ethylene oxide
Uses: Used in phytopharmaceutical applics.
Trade names: Servirox OEG 45

PEG-20 castor oil
CAS 61791-12-6 (generic)
Synonyms: POE (20) castor oil; PEG 1000 castor oil
Definition: PEG deriv. of castor oil with avg. 20 moles of ethylene oxide
Properties: Pale yel. oil; HLB 9.0
Uses: Emulsifier, solubilizer, dispersant
Regulatory: FDA 21CFR §175.105, 175.300, 176.210, 177.2800
Trade names: Emalex C-20

PEG-26 castor oil
CAS 61791-12-6 (generic)
Synonyms: POE (26) castor oil
Definition: PEG deriv. of castor oil with avg. 26 moles of ethylene oxide
Uses: Used in phytopharmaceutical applics.
Trade names: Servirox OEG 55

PEG-30 castor oil
CAS 61791-12-6 (generic)
Synonyms: POE (30) castor oil
Definition: PEG deriv. of castor oil with avg. 30 moles of ethylene oxide

Uses: Emulsifier, wetting agent, pigment dispersant, lubricant, solubilizer
Regulatory: FDA 21CFR §175.105, 175.300, 177.2800
Trade names: Alkamuls® EL-620; Emalex C-30; Fancol CO-30

PEG-32 castor oil
CAS 61791-12-6 (generic)
Synonyms: POE (32) castor oil
Definition: PEG deriv. of castor oil with avg. 32 moles of ethylene oxide
Uses: Used in phytopharmaceutical applics.
Trade names: Servirox OEG 65

PEG-33 castor oil
CAS 61791-12-6 (generic)
Synonyms: POE (33) castor oil
Definition: PEG deriv. of castor oil with avg. 33 moles of ethylene oxide
Uses: Solvent, emulsifier
Regulatory: FDA 21CFR §175.105, 175.300, 1716.210, 177.2800
Trade names: Ricinion; Sellig R 3395

PEG-35 castor oil
CAS 61791-12-6 (generic)
Synonyms: POE (35) castor oil; Polyoxyl 35 castor oil
Definition: PEG deriv. of castor oil with avg. 35 moles of ethylene oxide
Properties: Yel. oily liq., faint char. odor, sl. bitter taste; very sol. in water; sol. in alcohol, ethyl acetate; insol. in min. oils; sp.gr. 1.105-1.06; visc. 650-850 cps; acid no. 2 max.; iodine no. 25-35; sapon. no. 60-76; hyd. no. 65-80
Toxicology: May cause a hepatitis-like reaction in large doses
Uses: Solubilizer, emulsifier, wetting agent for pharmaceuticals; solv. for intravenous steroid anesthetic and for miconazole
Regulatory: USP/NF compliance
Trade names: Cremophor® EL; Eumulgin® RO 35; Incrocas 35; Simulsol® 5817

PEG-36 castor oil
CAS 61791-12-6 (generic)
Synonyms: POE (36) castor oil; PEG 1800 castor oil
Definition: PEG deriv. of castor oil with avg. 36 moles of ethylene oxide
Properties: Liq.; sol. in water, xylene
Uses: Emulsifier, dispersant, solubilizer
Regulatory: FDA 21CFR §175.105, 175.300, 176.210, 177.2800
Trade names: Eumulgin® PRT 36
Trade names containing: Safester A 75 WS

PEG-40 castor oil
CAS 61791-12-6 (generic)
Synonyms: POE (40) castor oil; PEG 2000 castor oil
Definition: PEG deriv. of castor oil with avg. 40 moles of ethylene oxide
Uses: Emulsifier for vitamins and drugs; solubilizer, dispersant
Regulatory: FDA 21CFR §175.105, 175.300, 176.170, 176.180, 176.210, 177.2800
Trade names: Alkamuls® EL-719; Emalex C-40; Simulsol® OL 50
Trade names containing: Emulgade® F

PEG-50 castor oil
CAS 61791-12-6 (generic)
Synonyms: POE (50) castor oil
Definition: PEG deriv. of castor oil with avg. 50 moles of ethylene oxide
Uses: Emulsifier, solubilizer, dispersant
Regulatory: FDA 21CFR §175.105, 175.300, 177.2800
Trade names: Emalex C-50

PEG-56 castor oil
CAS 61791-12-6 (generic)
Uses: Emulsifier, dispersant, solubilizer
Trade names: Eumulgin® PRT 56

PEG-180 castor oil
CAS 61791-12-6 (generic)
Synonyms: POE (180) castor oil

PEG-200 castor oil

    Definition: PEG deriv. of castor oil with avg. 180 moles of ethylene oxide
    Uses: Used in phytopharmaceutical applics.
    Trade names: Servirox OEG 90/50

PEG-200 castor oil
    CAS 61791-12-6 (generic)
    Synonyms: POE (200) castor oil; PEG (200) castor oil
    Definition: PEG deriv. of castor oil with avg. 200 moles of ethylene oxide
    Uses: Emulsifier, dispersant, solubilizer
    Regulatory: FDA 21CFR §175.300
    Trade names: Eumulgin® PRT 200

PEG (200) castor oil. *See* PEG-200 castor oil
PEG 400 castor oil. *See* PEG-8 castor oil
PEG 450 castor oil. *See* PEG-9 castor oil
PEG 1000 castor oil. *See* PEG-20 castor oil
PEG 1800 castor oil. *See* PEG-36 castor oil
PEG 2000 castor oil. *See* PEG-40 castor oil
PEG-2 cetyl ether. *See* Ceteth-2
PEG-5 cetyl ether. *See* Ceteth-5
PEG-6 cetyl ether. *See* Ceteth-6
PEG-7 cetyl ether. *See* Ceteth-7
PEG-10 cetyl ether. *See* Ceteth-10
PEG-12 cetyl ether. *See* Ceteth-12
PEG-15 cetyl ether. *See* Ceteth-15
PEG-16 cetyl ether. *See* Ceteth-16
PEG-20 cetyl ether. *See* Ceteth-20
PEG-23 cetyl ether. *See* Ceteth-23
PEG-24 cetyl ether. *See* Ceteth-24
PEG-25 cetyl ether. *See* Ceteth-25
PEG-30 cetyl ether. *See* Ceteth-30
PEG-40 cetyl ether. *See* Ceteth-40
PEG 100 cetyl ether. *See* Ceteth-2
PEG 500 cetyl ether. *See* Ceteth-10
PEG 600 cetyl ether. *See* Ceteth-12
PEG-7 cetyl/stearyl ether. *See* Ceteareth-7
PEG-9 cetyl/stearyl ether. *See* Ceteareth-9
PEG-10 cetyl/stearyl ether. *See* Ceteareth-10
PEG-11 cetyl/stearyl ether. *See* Ceteareth-11
PEG-12 cetyl/stearyl ether. *See* Ceteareth-12
PEG-14 cetyl/stearyl ether. *See* Ceteareth-14
PEG-15 cetyl/stearyl ether. *See* Ceteareth-15
PEG-16 cetyl/stearyl ether. *See* Ceteareth-16
PEG-20 cetyl/stearyl ether. *See* Ceteareth-20
PEG-25 cetyl/stearyl ether. *See* Ceteareth-25
PEG-30 cetyl/stearyl ether. *See* Ceteareth-30
PEG-33 cetyl/stearyl ether. *See* Ceteareth-33
PEG (33) cetyl/stearyl ether. *See* Ceteareth-33
PEG-24 cholesteryl ether. *See* Choleth-24

PEG-3 cocamide MEA
    Uses: Foam builder/stabilizer for pharmaceutical shampoos; solubilizer
    Trade names: Mazamide® C-2

PEG-15 cocamine
    CAS 8051-52-3 (generic); 61791-14-8 (generic)
    Synonyms: POE (15) coconut amine
    Definition: PEG deriv. of cocamine
    Formula: $R\text{-}N(CH_2CH_2O)_xH(CH_2CH_2O)_yH$, R rep. alkyl groups from coconut oil, avg. $(x+y)=15$
    Uses: Emulsifier for topical pharmaceuticals
    Trade names: Ethomeen® C/25

PEG-20 corn glycerides
    Synonyms: PEG 1000 corn glycerides; POE (20) corn glycerides
    Definition: PEG deriv. of corn glycerides, avg. 20 moles EO

Uses: Emulsifier, wetting agent, solubilizer, dispersant, emollient
Regulatory: FDA 21CFR §175.300, 176.210
Trade names: Crovol M40

PEG-60 corn glycerides
Synonyms: PEG 3000 corn glycerides; POE (60) corn glycerides
Definition: PEG deriv. of corn glycerides, avg. 60 moles EO
Uses: Emulsifier, wetting agent, solubilizer, dispersant, emollient
Regulatory: FDA 21CFR §175.300, 176.210
Trade names: Crovol M70

PEG 1000 corn glycerides. *See* PEG-20 corn glycerides
PEG 3000 corn glycerides. *See* PEG-60 corn glycerides

PEG-4 dilaurate
CAS 9005-02-1 (generic)
Synonyms: PEG 200 dilaurate; POE (4) dilaurate
Definition: PEG diester of lauric acid
Empirical: $C_{32}H_{62}O_7$
Formula: $CH_3(CH_2)_{10}CO(OCH_2CH_2)_nOCO(CH_2)_{10}CH_3$, avg. n = 4
Uses: Emulsifier, dispersant, solubilizer, visc. control agent, lubricant, cosolvent for pharmaceuticals
Regulatory: FDA 21CFR §175.105, 175.300, 176.170, 176.180, 176.200, 176.210
Trade names: Hodag 22-L; Kessco® PEG 200 DL; Lexemul® PEG-200 DL; Mapeg® 200 DL

PEG-6 dilaurate
CAS 9005-02-1 (generic)
Synonyms: POE (6) dilaurate; PEG 300 dilaurate
Definition: PEG diester of lauric acid
Formula: $CH_3(CH_2)_{10}CO(OCH_2CH_2)_nOCO(CH_2)_{10}CH_3$, avg. n = 6
Uses: Surfactant, solubilizer, thickener, emollient, opacifier, spreading agent, wetting agent, dispersant for pharmaceuticals
Regulatory: FDA 21CFR §175.105, 175.300, 176.210
Trade names: Kessco® PEG 300 DL

PEG-8 dilaurate
CAS 9005-02-1 (generic)
Synonyms: POE (8) dilaurate; PEG 400 dilaurate
Definition: PEG diester of lauric acid
Empirical: $C_{40}H_{78}O_{11}$
Formula: $CH_3(CH_2)_{10}CO(OCH_2CH_2)_nOCO(CH_2)_{10}CH_3$, avg. n = 8
Properties: Sp.gr. 1.030; m.p. 15 C; flash pt. (COC) 249 C; ref. index 1.459
Uses: Emulsifier, wetting agent, plasticizer, thickener, solubilizer, emollient, dispersant
Regulatory: FDA 21CFR §175.105, 175.300, 176.210, 177.1210, 177.2260, 177.2800, 178.3520
Manuf./Distrib.: C.P. Hall; Inolex; Velsicol
Trade names: Hodag 42-L; Kessco® PEG 400 DL; Mapeg® 400 DL

PEG-12 dilaurate
CAS 9005-02-1 (generic)
Synonyms: POE (12) dilaurate; PEG 600 dilaurate
Definition: PEG diester of lauric acid
Empirical: $C_{48}H_{94}O_{15}$
Formula: $CH_3(CH_2)_{10}CO(OCH_2CH_2)_nOCO(CH_2)_{10}CH_3$, avg. n = 12
Uses: Dispersant, emulsifier, thickener, solubilizer, emollient for pharmaceuticals
Regulatory: FDA 21CFR §175.105, 175.300, 176.210, 177.2260, 177.2800
Trade names: Kessco® PEG 600 DL

PEG-20 dilaurate
CAS 9005-02-1 (generic)
Synonyms: POE (20) dilaurate; PEG 1000 dilaurate
Definition: PEG diester of lauric acid
Empirical: $C_{64}H_{126}O_{23}$
Formula: $CH_3(CH_2)_{10}CO(OCH_2CH_2)_nOCO(CH_2)_{10}CH_3$, avg. n = 20
Uses: Dispersant, emulsifier, wetting agent, cosolvent, solubilizer, thickener, emollient, opacifier, spreading agent for pharmaceuticals
Regulatory: FDA 21CFR §175.300, 176.210, 177.2260, 177.2800
Trade names: Kessco® PEG 1000 DL

PEG-32 dilaurate

PEG-32 dilaurate
CAS 9005-02-1 (generic)
Synonyms: POE (32) dilaurate; PEG 1540 dilaurate
Definition: PEG diester of lauric acid
Empirical: $C_{88}H_{174}O_{35}$
Formula: $CH_3(CH_2)_{10}CO(OCH_2CH_2)_nOCO(CH_2)_{10}CH_3$, avg. n = 32
Uses: Surfactant, solubilizer, thickener, emollient, opacifier, spreading agent, wetting agent, dispersant for pharmaceuticals
Regulatory: FDA 21CFR §175.300, 176.210, 177.2260, 177.2800
Trade names: Kessco® PEG 1540 DL

PEG-75 dilaurate
CAS 9005-02-1 (generic)
Synonyms: POE (75) dilaurate; PEG 4000 dilaurate
Definition: PEG diester of lauric acid
Formula: $CH_3(CH_2)_{10}CO(OCH_2CH_2)_nOCO(CH_2)_{10}CH_3$, avg. n = 75
Uses: Surfactant, solubilizer, thickener, emollient, opacifier, spreading agent, wetting agent, dispersant for pharmaceuticals
Regulatory: FDA 21CFR §175.300
Trade names: Kessco® PEG 4000 DL

PEG-150 dilaurate
CAS 9005-02-1 (generic)
Synonyms: POE (150) dilaurate; PEG 6000 dilaurate
Definition: PEG diester of lauric acid
Formula: $CH_3(CH_2)_{10}CO(OCH_2CH_2)_nOCO(CH_2)_{10}CH_3$, avg. n = 150
Uses: Surfactant, solubilizer, thickener, emollient, opacifier, spreading agent, wetting agent, dispersant for pharmaceuticals
Regulatory: FDA 21CFR §175.300
Trade names: Kessco® PEG 6000 DL

PEG 200 dilaurate. *See* PEG-4 dilaurate
PEG 300 dilaurate. *See* PEG-6 dilaurate
PEG 400 dilaurate. *See* PEG-8 dilaurate
PEG 600 dilaurate. *See* PEG-12 dilaurate
PEG 1000 dilaurate. *See* PEG-20 dilaurate
PEG 1540 dilaurate. *See* PEG-32 dilaurate
PEG 4000 dilaurate. *See* PEG-75 dilaurate
PEG 6000 dilaurate. *See* PEG-150 dilaurate

PEG-3 dimethyl ether
CAS 112-49-2; 24991-55-7
Synonyms: Triethylene glycol dimethyl ether
Uses: Solvent
Manuf./Distrib.: Brand-Nu Labs; Hoechst AG
Trade names: Triglyme

PEG-4 dimethyl ether
CAS 24991-55-7
Uses: Solvent, drug carrier, stabilizer
Trade names: Tetraglyme

PEG-4 dioleate
CAS 9005-07-6 (generic); 52688-97-0 (generic); 134141-38-1
Synonyms: POE (4) dioleate; PEG 200 dioleate
Definition: PEG diester of oleic acid
Uses: Emulsifier, thickener, solubilizer, emollient, spreading agent, wetting agent, dispersant
Regulatory: FDA 21CFR §173.340, 175.105, 175.300, 176.210
Trade names: Kessco® PEG 200 DO; Mapeg® 200 DO

PEG-6 dioleate
CAS 9005-07-6 (generic); 52688-97-0 (generic)
Synonyms: POE (6) dioleate; PEG 300 dioleate
Definition: PEG diester of oleic acid
Uses: Surfactant, solubilizer, thickener, emollient, opacifier, spreading agent, wetting agent, dispersant for pharmaceuticals

Regulatory: FDA 21CFR §175.105, 175.300, 176.210
Trade names: Kessco® PEG 300 DO

PEG-8 dioleate
CAS 9005-07-6 (generic); 52688-97-0 (generic)
Synonyms: POE (8) dioleate; PEG 400 dioleate
Definition: PEG diester of oleic acid
Uses: Emulsifier, solubilizer, lubricant, dispersant, wetting agent for pharmaceuticals
Regulatory: FDA 21CFR §173.340, 175.105, 175.300, 176.170, 176.200, 176.210, 177.1210, 177.2260, 177.2800
Trade names: Hodag 42-O; Kessco® PEG 400 DO; Mapeg® 400 DO

PEG-12 dioleate
CAS 9005-07-6 (generic); 52688-97-0 (generic); 85736-49-8; EINECS 288-459-5
Synonyms: POE (12) dioleate; PEG 600 dioleate
Definition: PEG diester of oleic acid
Uses: Emulsifier, wetting agent, plasticizer, thickener, solubilizer, emollient, spreading agent, dispersant
Regulatory: FDA 21CFR §173.340, 175.105, 175.300, 176.200, 176.210, 177.2260, 177.2800
Trade names: Hodag 62-O; Kessco® PEG 600 DO; Mapeg® 600 DO

PEG-20 dioleate
CAS 9005-07-6 (generic); 52688-97-0 (generic)
Synonyms: POE (20) dioleate; PEG 1000 dioleate
Definition: PEG diester of oleic acid
Uses: Surfactant, solubilizer, thickener, emollient, opacifier, spreading agent, wetting agent, dispersant for pharmaceuticals
Regulatory: FDA 21CFR §175.300, 176.210, 177.2260, 177.2800
Trade names: Kessco® PEG 1000 DO

PEG-32 dioleate
CAS 9005-07-6 (generic); 52688-97-0 (generic)
Synonyms: POE (32) dioleate; PEG 1540 dioleate
Definition: PEG diester of oleic acid
Uses: Surfactant, solubilizer, thickener, emollient, opacifier, spreading agent, wetting agent, dispersant for pharmaceuticals
Regulatory: FDA 21CFR §175.300, 176.210, 177.2260, 177.2800
Trade names: Kessco® PEG 1540 DO

PEG-75 dioleate
CAS 9005-07-6 (generic); 52688-97-0 (generic)
Synonyms: POE (75) dioleate; PEG 4000 dioleate
Definition: PEG diester of oleic acid
Uses: Surfactant, solubilizer, thickener, emollient, opacifier, spreading agent, wetting agent, dispersant for pharmaceuticals
Regulatory: FDA 21CFR §175.300
Trade names: Kessco® PEG 4000 DO

PEG-150 dioleate
CAS 9005-07-6 (generic); 52688-97-0 (generic)
Synonyms: POE (150) dioleate; PEG 6000 dioleate
Definition: PEG diester of oleic acid
Uses: Surfactant, solubilizer, thickener, emollient, opacifier, spreading agent, wetting agent, dispersant for pharmaceuticals
Regulatory: FDA 21CFR §175.300
Trade names: Kessco® PEG 6000 DO

PEG 200 dioleate. *See* PEG-4 dioleate
PEG 300 dioleate. *See* PEG-6 dioleate
PEG 400 dioleate. *See* PEG-8 dioleate
PEG 600 dioleate. *See* PEG-12 dioleate
PEG 1000 dioleate. *See* PEG-20 dioleate
PEG 1540 dioleate. *See* PEG-32 dioleate
PEG 4000 dioleate. *See* PEG-75 dioleate
PEG 6000 dioleate. *See* PEG-150 dioleate

PEG-4 distearate
CAS 9005-08-7 (generic); 52668-97-0; 142-20-1

PEG-6 distearate

Synonyms: POE (4) distearate; PEG 200 distearate
Definition: PEG diester of stearic acid
Formula: $CH_3(CH_2)_{16}CO(OCH_2CH_2)_nOCO(CH_2)_{16}CH_3$, avg. n = 4
Properties: M.p. 35-37 C; flash pt. > 110 C
Uses: Emulsifier, thickener, solubilizer, emollient, spreading agent, wetting agent, dispersant
Regulatory: FDA 21CFR §175.105, 175.300, 176.210
Trade names: Kessco® PEG 200 DS

PEG-6 distearate

CAS 9005-08-7 (generic); 52668-97-0
Synonyms: POE (6) distearate; PEG 300 distearate
Definition: PEG diester of stearic acid
Formula: $CH_3(CH_2)_{16}CO(OCH_2CH_2)_nOCO(CH_2)_{16}CH_3$, avg. n = 6
Properties: M.p. 35-37 C; flash pt. > 110 C
Uses: Surfactant, solubilizer, thickener, emollient, opacifier, spreading agent, wetting agent, dispersant for
   pharmaceuticals
Regulatory: FDA 21CFR §175.105, 175.300, 176.210
Trade names: Kessco® PEG 300 DS

PEG-8 distearate

CAS 9005-08-7 (generic); 52668-97-0
Synonyms: POE (8) distearate; PEG 400 distearate
Definition: PEG diester of stearic acid
Formula: $CH_3(CH_2)_{16}CO(OCH_2CH_2)_nOCO(CH_2)_{16}CH_3$, avg. n = 8
Properties: M.p. 35-37 C; flash pt. > 110 C
Uses: Surfactant, solubilizer, thickener, emollient, opacifier, spreading agent, wetting agent, dispersant for
   pharmaceuticals
Regulatory: FDA 21CFR §175.105, 175.300, 176.210, 177.1210, 177.2260, 177.2800
Trade names: Hodag 42-S; Kessco® PEG 400 DS; Mapeg® 400 DS

PEG-12 distearate

CAS 9005-08-7 (generic); 52668-97-0
Synonyms: POE (12) distearate; PEG 600 distearate
Definition: PEG diester of stearic acid
Formula: $CH_3(CH_2)_{16}CO(OCH_2CH_2)_nOCO(CH_2)_{16}CH_3$, avg. n = 12
Properties: M.p. 35-37 C; flash pt. > 110 C
Uses: Emulsifier, thickener, solubilizer, emollient, spreading agent, wetting agent, dispersant
Regulatory: FDA 21CFR §175.105, 175.300, 176.210, 177.2260, 177.2800
Trade names: Kessco® PEG 600 DS; Mapeg® 600 DS

PEG-20 distearate

CAS 9005-08-7 (generic); 52668-97-0
Synonyms: POE (20) distearate; PEG 1000 distearate
Definition: PEG diester of stearic acid
Formula: $CH_3(CH_2)_{16}CO(OCH_2CH_2)_nOCO(CH_2)_{16}CH_3$, avg. n = 20
Properties: M.p. 35-37 C; flash pt. > 110 C
Uses: Surfactant, solubilizer, thickener, emollient, opacifier, spreading agent, wetting agent, dispersant for
   pharmaceuticals
Regulatory: FDA 21CFR §175.300, 176.210, 177.2260, 177.2800
Trade names: Kessco® PEG 1000 DS

PEG-32 distearate

CAS 9005-08-7 (generic); 52668-97-0
Synonyms: POE (32) distearate; PEG 1540 distearate
Definition: PEG diester of stearic acid
Formula: $CH_3(CH_2)_{16}CO(OCH_2CH_2)_nOCO(CH_2)_{16}CH_3$, avg. n = 32
Properties: M.p. 35-37 C; flash pt. > 110 C
Uses: Surfactant, solubilizer, thickener, emollient, opacifier, spreading agent, wetting agent, dispersant for
   pharmaceuticals
Regulatory: FDA 21CFR §175.300, 176.210, 177.2260, 177.2800
Trade names: Kessco® PEG 1540 DS

PEG-75 distearate

CAS 9005-08-7 (generic); 52668-97-0
Synonyms: POE (75) distearate; PEG 4000 distearate
Definition: PEG diester of stearic acid

Formula: $CH_3(CH_2)_{16}CO(OCH_2CH_2)_nOCO(CH_2)_{16}CH_3$, avg. n = 75
Properties: M.p. 35-37 C; flash pt. > 110 C
Uses: Surfactant, solubilizer, thickener, emollient, opacifier, spreading agent, wetting agent, dispersant for pharmaceuticals
Regulatory: FDA 21CFR §175.300
Trade names: Kessco® PEG 4000 DS

PEG-150 distearate
CAS 9005-08-7 (generic); 52668-97-0
Synonyms: POE (150) distearate; PEG 6000 distearate
Definition: PEG diester of stearic acid
Formula: $CH_3(CH_2)_{16}CO(OCH_2CH_2)_nOCO(CH_2)_{16}CH_3$, avg. n = 150
Properties: M.p. 35-37 C; flash pt. > 110 C
Uses: Melting pt. control agent in suppositories; emulsifier, thickener, solubilizer, emollient, spreading agent, wetting agent, dispersant
Regulatory: FDA 21CFR §175.300
Trade names: Kessco® PEG 6000 DS; Mapeg® 6000 DS

PEG 200 distearate. *See* PEG-4 distearate
PEG 300 distearate. *See* PEG-6 distearate
PEG 400 distearate. *See* PEG-8 distearate
PEG 600 distearate. *See* PEG-12 distearate
PEG 1000 distearate. *See* PEG-20 distearate
PEG 1540 distearate. *See* PEG-32 distearate
PEG 4000 distearate. *See* PEG-75 distearate
PEG 6000 distearate. *See* PEG-150 distearate

PEG-8 ditallate
CAS 61791-01-3 (generic)
Synonyms: POE (8) ditallate; PEG 400 ditallate
Definition: PEG diester of tall oil acid
Formula: $RCO^-(OCH_2CH_2)_nOCOR$, RCO^- rep. tall oil fatty radicals, avg. n = 8
Uses: Emulsifier, dispersant
Regulatory: FDA 21CFR §175.105, 175.30, 176.210, 177.1210, 177.2800
Trade names: Mapeg® 400 DOT

PEG-12 ditallate
CAS 61791-01-3 (generic)
Synonyms: POE (12) ditallate; PEG 600 ditallate
Definition: PEG diester of tall oil acid
Formula: $RCO-(OCH_2CH_2)_nOCOR$, RCO- rep. tall oil fatty radicals, avg. n = 12
Uses: Emulsifier, dispersant
Regulatory: FDA 21CFR §175.105, 175.300, 176.210, 177.2800
Trade names: Mapeg® 600 DOT

PEG 400 ditallate. *See* PEG-8 ditallate
PEG 600 ditallate. *See* PEG-12 ditallate

PEG-7 glyceryl cocoate
CAS 66105-29-1; 68201-46-7 (generic)
Synonyms: POE (7) glyceryl monococoate; PEG (7) glyceryl monococoate
Definition: PEG ether of glyceryl cocoate
Formula: $RCO-OCH_2COHHCH_2(OCH_2CH_2)_nOH$, RCO- rep. fatty acids from coconut oil, avg. n=7
Uses: Emollient oil, superfatting agent, emulsifier, solubilizer, coupler for pharmaceuticals; dispersant for biologically act. ingreds.
Regulatory: FDA 21CFR §175.300
Trade names: Cetiol® HE; Mazol® 159; Standamul® HE
Trade names containing: Grillocin® AT Basis

PEG-26 glyceryl ether. *See* Glycereth-26
PEG-7 glyceryl ether benzoate. *See* Glycereth-7 benzoate
PEG-5 glyceryl ether lactate. *See* Glycereth-5 lactate
PEG-7 glyceryl ether triacetate. *See* Glycereth-7 triacetate

PEG-12 glyceryl laurate
CAS 59070-56-3 (generic); 51248-32-9
Synonyms: POE (12) glyceryl monolaurate; PEG 600 glyceryl monolaurate

PEG-20 glyceryl laurate

Definition: PEG ether of glyceryl laurate
Formula: $CH_3(CH_2)_{10}COOCH_2COHHCH_2(OCH_2CH_2)_nOH$, avg. n = 12
Uses: Emulsifier and solubilizer in pharmaceuticals
Regulatory: FDA 21CFR §175.300, 176.210, 177.2800
Trade names containing: Safester A 75 WS

PEG-20 glyceryl laurate

CAS 59070-56-3 (generic); 51248-32-9
Synonyms: POE (20) glyceryl monolaurate; PEG 1000 glyceryl monolaurate
Definition: PEG ether of glyceryl laurate
Formula: $CH_3(CH_2)_{10}COOCH_2COHHCH_2(OCH_2CH_2)_nOH$, avg. n = 20
Uses: Solubilizer, dispersant; prep. of pharmaceutical emulsions
Regulatory: FDA 21CFR §175.300, 176.210, 177.2800
Trade names: Tagat® L2

PEG (7) glyceryl monococoate. *See* PEG-7 glyceryl cocoate
PEG 600 glyceryl monolaurate. *See* PEG-12 glyceryl laurate
PEG 1000 glyceryl monolaurate. *See* PEG-20 glyceryl laurate
PEG 1000 glyceryl monooleate. *See* PEG-20 glyceryl oleate
PEG 1000 glyceryl monostearate. *See* PEG-20 glyceryl stearate

PEG-20 glyceryl oleate

CAS 68889-49-6 (generic); 51192-09-7
Synonyms: POE (20) glyceryl oleate; PEG 1000 glyceryl monooleate
Definition: PEG ether of glyceryl oleate
Formula: $CH_3[CH(CH_2)_7]_2COOCH_2CHOHCH_2(OCH_2CH_2)_nOH$, avg. n = 20
Uses: Prep. of pharmaceutical emulsions; solubilizer, dispersant
Regulatory: FDA 21CFR §175.300, 176.210, 177.2800
Trade names: Tagat® O2

PEG-1 glyceryl sorbitan isostearate

Uses: Emulsifier
Trade names: Tewax TC 82

PEG-5 glyceryl stearate

CAS 51158-08-8
Synonyms: POE (5) glyceryl monostearate
Definition: PEG ether of glyceryl stearate
Formula: $CH_3(CH_2)_{16}COOCH_2CHOHCH_2(OCH_2CH_2)_nOH$, avg. n = 5
Uses: Emulsifier
Regulatory: FDA 21CFR §175.300
Trade names: Tewax TC 83

PEG-20 glyceryl stearate

CAS 68153-76-4; 68553-11-7; 51158-08-8
Synonyms: PEG 1000 glyceryl monostearate; POE (20) glyceryl monostearate; Polyglycerate 60
Definition: PEG ether of glyceryl stearate
Formula: $CH_3(CH_2)_{16}COOCH_2COHHCH_2(OCH_2CH_2)_nOH$, avg. n = 20
Uses: Emulsifier, solubilizer, suspending and dispersing agent, wetting agent for pharmaceuticals
Trade names: Aldo® MS-20 KFG; Capmul® EMG; Tagat® S2

PEG-120 glyceryl stearate

Synonyms: POE (120) glyceryl monostearate
Definition: PEG ether of glyceryl stearate
Formula: $CH_3(CH_2)_{16}COOCH_2COHHCH_2(OCH_2CH_2)_nOH$, avg. n = 120
Uses: Ingred. in pharmaceuticals
Trade names containing: Drewmulse® 1128

PEG-5 hydrogenated castor oil

CAS 61788-85-0 (generic)
Synonyms: POE (5) hydrogenated castor oil; PEG (5) hydrogenated castor oil
Definition: PEG deriv. of hydrogenated castor oil with avg. 5 moles of ethylene oxide
Uses: Emulsifier, hydrotrope
Trade names: Cerex ELS 50; Nikkol HCO-5

PEG (5) hydrogenated castor oil. *See* PEG-5 hydrogenated castor oil

PEG-7 hydrogenated castor oil

CAS 61788-85-0 (generic)

Synonyms: POE (7) hydrogenated castor oil
Definition: PEG deriv. of hydrogenated castor oil with avg. 7 moles of ethylene oxide
Uses: Hydrotrope, emulsifier, softener used in pharmaceuticals
Trade names: Dehymuls® HRE 7; Nikkol HCO-7.5; Simulsol® 989

PEG-10 hydrogenated castor oil
CAS 61788-85-0 (generic)
Synonyms: POE (10) hydrogenated castor oil; PEG 500 hydrogenated castor oil
Definition: PEG deriv. of hydrogenated castor oil with avg. 10 moles of ethylene oxide
Uses: Emulsifier, hydrotrope
Trade names: Nikkol HCO-10

PEG-20 hydrogenated castor oil
CAS 61788-85-0 (generic)
Synonyms: POE (20) hydrogenated castor oil
Definition: PEG deriv. of hydrogenated castor oil with avg. 20 moles of ethylene oxide
Uses: Emulsifier, hydrotrope for pharmaceuticals
Regulatory: FDA 21CFR §177.2800
Trade names: Nikkol HCO-20

PEG-25 hydrogenated castor oil
CAS 61788-85-0 (generic)
Synonyms: POE (25) hydrogenated castor oil
Definition: PEG deriv. of hydrogenated castor oil with avg. 25 moles of ethylene oxide
Uses: Solubilizer, emulsifier
Regulatory: FDA 21CFR §177.2800
Trade names: Cerex ELS 250; Fancol HCO-25; Simulsol® 1292

PEG-30 hydrogenated castor oil
CAS 61788-85-0 (generic)
Synonyms: POE (30) hydrogenated castor oil
Definition: PEG deriv. of hydrogenated castor oil with avg. 30 moles of ethylene oxide
Uses: Emulsifier, hydrotrope
Regulatory: FDA 21CFR §177.2800
Trade names: Nikkol HCO-30

PEG-40 hydrogenated castor oil
CAS 61788-85-0 (generic)
Synonyms: POE (40) hydrogenated castor oil; Polyoxyl 40 hydrogenated castor oil
Definition: PEG deriv. of hydrogenated castor oil with avg. 40 moles of ethylene oxide
Properties: Wh. to ylsh. paste or pasty liq., faint odor, sl. taste; very sol. in water; sol. in alcohol, ethyl acetate; insol. in min. oils; congeal pt. 20-30 C; acid no. 2 max.; iodine no. 2 max.; sapon. no. 45-69; hyd. no. 60-80
Uses: Solubilizer, emulsifier, wetting agent, emollient for pharmaceuticals
Regulatory: FDA 21CFR §177.2800; USP/NF compliance
Trade names: Cerex ELS 400; Cremophor® RH 40; Cremophor® RH 410; Emalex HC-40; Eumulgin® HRE 40; Nikkol HCO-40; Nikkol HCO-40 Pharm; Simulsol® 1293; Tagat® R40
Trade names containing: Cremophor® RH 455; Solubilisant γ 2428

PEG-45 hydrogenated castor oil
CAS 61788-85-0 (generic)
Definition: PEG deriv. of hydrogenated castor oil with avg. 45 moles of ethylene oxide
Uses: Solubilizer
Regulatory: FDA 21CFR §177.2800
Trade names: Cerex ELS 450

PEG-50 hydrogenated castor oil
CAS 61788-85-0 (generic)
Synonyms: POE (50) hydrogenated castor oil
Definition: PEG deriv. of hydrogenated castor oil with avg. 50 moles of ethylene oxide
Uses: Solubilizer and emulsifier for pharmaceuticals
Regulatory: FDA 21CFR §177.2800
Trade names: Croduret 50; Nikkol HCO-50; Nikkol HCO-50 Pharm

PEG-60 hydrogenated castor oil
CAS 61788-85-0 (generic)
Synonyms: POE (60) hydrogenated castor oil

PEG-80 hydrogenated castor oil

Definition: PEG deriv. of hydrogenated castor oil with avg. 60 moles of ethylene oxide
Uses: Solubilizer, emulsifier, emollient for pharmaceuticals
Regulatory: FDA 21CFR §177.2800
Trade names: Eumulgin® HRE 60; Nikkol HCO-60; Nikkol HCO-60 Pharm; Tagat® R60
Trade names containing: Tagat® R63

PEG-80 hydrogenated castor oil
CAS 61788-85-0 (generic)
Synonyms: POE (80) hydrogenated castor oil
Definition: PEG deriv. of hydrogenated castor oil with avg. 80 moles of ethylene oxide
Uses: Hydrotrope, emulsifier used in pharmaceuticals
Trade names: Nikkol HCO-80

PEG-100 hydrogenated castor oil
CAS 61788-85-0 (generic)
Synonyms: POE (100) hydrogenated castor oil; PEG (100) hydrogenated castor oil
Definition: PEG deriv. of hydrogenated castor oil with avg. 100 moles of ethylene oxide
Uses: Solubilizer, emulsifier, emollient, hydrotrope for pharmaceuticals
Trade names: Nikkol HCO-100

PEG (100) hydrogenated castor oil. *See* PEG-100 hydrogenated castor oil
PEG 500 hydrogenated castor oil. *See* PEG-10 hydrogenated castor oil

PEG-20 hydrogenated lanolin
CAS 68648-27-1 (generic)
Synonyms: POE (20) hydrogenated lanolin; PEG 1000 hydrogenated lanolin
Definition: PEG deriv. of hydrogenated lanolin with avg. 20 moles of ethylene oxide
Uses: Solubilizer, emollient, superfatting agent, gellant, stabilizer, moisturizer
Trade names: Fancol HL-20; Lipolan 31-20; Super-Sat AWS-4

PEG-24 hydrogenated lanolin
CAS 68648-27-1 (generic)
Synonyms: POE (24) hydrogenated lanolin
Definition: PEG deriv. of hydrogenated lanolin with avg. 24 moles of ethylene oxide
Uses: Emollient, emulsifier, solubilizer for topical pharmaceuticals
Trade names: Fancol HL-24; Lipolan 31; Super-Sat AWS-24

PEG 1000 hydrogenated lanolin. *See* PEG-20 hydrogenated lanolin
PEG-20 isocetyl ether. *See* Isoceteth-20
PEG-30 isocetyl ether. *See* Isoceteth-30
PEG 1000 isocetyl ether. *See* Isoceteth-20

PEG-6 isostearate
CAS 56002-14-3 (generic)
Synonyms: PEG 300 monoisostearate; POE (6) monoisostearate
Definition: PEG ester of isostearic acid
Formula: $C_{17}H_{35}CO(OCH_2CH_2)_nOH$, avg. n = 6
Uses: Solvent, emulsifier
Trade names: Olepal ISO

PEG-27 lanolin
CAS 61790-81-6 (generic); 8051-81-8
Synonyms: POE (27) lanolin
Definition: PEG deriv. of lanolin with avg. 27 moles of ethylene oxide
Properties: Yel.-amber gel, faint, pleasant odor; disp. in water
Uses: Emollient, emulsifier, dispersant, wetting agent, solubilizer, foam stabilizer
Trade names: Lanogel® 21

PEG-30 lanolin
CAS 61790-81-6 (generic)
Synonyms: POE (30) lanolin
Definition: PEG deriv. of lanolin with avg. 30 moles of ethylene oxide
Uses: Solubilizer for pharmaceuticals
Trade names containing: Sebase

PEG-40 lanolin
CAS 8051-82-9; 61790-81-6 (generic)
Synonyms: POE (40) lanolin

Definition: PEG deriv. of lanolin with avg. 40 moles of ethylene oxide
Uses: Emollient, emulsifier, dispersant, wetting agent, solubilizer, foam stabilizer
Trade names: Lanogel® 31

PEG-60 lanolin
CAS 61790-81-6 (generic)
Synonyms: POE (60) lanolin
Definition: PEG deriv. of lanolin with avg. 60 moles of ethylene oxide
Uses: Solubilizer, superfatting agent, visc. enhancer, plasticizer, emollient, foam stabilizer, humectant
Trade names: Solan; Solan 50
Trade names containing: Ritachol® 3000; Ritachol® 4000

PEG-70 lanolin
CAS 61790-81-6 (generic)
Synonyms: POE (70) lanolin
Definition: PEG deriv. of lanolin with avg. 70 moles of ethylene oxide
Uses: Emollient, emulsifier, dispersant, solubilizer, superfatting agent for pharmaceuticals

PEG-75 lanolin
CAS 8039-09-6; 61790-81-6 (generic)
Synonyms: POE (75) lanolin; PEG 4000 lanolin
Definition: PEG deriv. of lanolin with avg. 75 moles of ethylene oxide
Uses: Emulsifier for pharmaceutical emulsions; emollient, superfatting agent, solubilizer
Trade names: Aqualose L75; Aqualose L75/50; Ethoxylan® 1685; Ethoxylan® 1686; Lan-Aqua-Sol 50; Lan-Aqua-Sol 100; Laneto 50; Laneto 100; Laneto 100-Flaked; Lanogel® 41; Super Solan Flaked

PEG-85 lanolin
CAS 61790-81-6 (generic)
Synonyms: POE (85) lanolin
Definition: PEG deriv. of lanolin with avg. 85 moles of ethylene oxide
Uses: Emollient, emulsifier, dispersant, wetting agent, solubilizer, foam stabilizer
Trade names: Lanogel® 61

PEG 4000 lanolin. *See* PEG-75 lanolin
PEG-5 lanolin alcohol. *See* Laneth-5
PEG-5 lanolin ether. *See* Laneth-5
PEG-10 lanolin ether. *See* Laneth-10
PEG-15 lanolin ether. *See* Laneth-15
PEG-16 lanolin ether. *See* Laneth-16
PEG-20 lanolin ether. *See* Laneth-20
PEG-25 lanolin ether. *See* Laneth-25
PEG-40 lanolin ether. *See* Laneth-40
PEG 500 lanolin ether. *See* Laneth-10
PEG 1000 lanolin ether. *See* Laneth-20
PEG 2000 lanolin ether. *See* Laneth-40
PEG 500 lanolin ether acetate. *See* Laneth-10 acetate
PEG-10 lanolin ether, acetylated. *See* Laneth-10 acetate
PEG-4 lanolin ether triphosphate. *See* Trilaneth-4 phosphate

PEG-6 lauramide DEA
Uses: Emulsifier, lubricant, foam builder, stabilizer, solubilizer
Trade names: Mazamide® L-5

PEG-4 laurate
CAS 9004-81-3 (generic); 10108-24-4
Synonyms: POE (4) monolaurate; PEG 200 monolaurate
Definition: PEG ester of lauric acid
Empirical: $C_{20}H_{40}O_6$
Formula: $CH_3(CH_2)_{10}CO(OCH_2CH_2)_nOH$, avg. n = 4
Uses: Emulsifier, wetting agent, solubilizer, dispersant, thickener, emollient, spreading agent
Regulatory: FDA 21CFR §175.105, 175.300, 176.210, 178.3910
Trade names: Algon LA 40; Crodet L4; Hodag 20-L; Kessco® PEG 200 ML; Mapeg® 200 ML

PEG-6 laurate
CAS 9004-81-3 (generic); 2370-64-1; EINECS 219-136-9
Synonyms: POE (6) monolaurate; PEG 300 monolaurate
Definition: PEG ester of lauric acid

PEG-8 laurate

    Empirical: $C_{24}H_{48}O_8$
    Formula: $CH_3(CH_2)_{10}CO(OCH_2CH_2)_nOH$, avg. n = 6
    Uses: Emulsifier, thickener, solubilizer, emollient, spreading and wetting agent, dispersant
    Regulatory: FDA 21CFR §175.105, 175.300, 176.210, 178.3910
    Trade names: Kessco® PEG 300 ML

PEG-8 laurate
    CAS 9004-81-3 (generic); 35179-86-3; 37318-14-2; EINECS 253-458-0
    Synonyms: POE (8) monolaurate; PEG 400 monolaurate
    Definition: PEG ester of lauric acid
    Empirical: $C_{28}H_{56}O_{10}$
    Formula: $CH_3(CH_2)_{10}CO(OCH_2CH_2)_nOH$, avg. n = 8
    Properties: Insol. in water
    Uses: Emulsifier, dispersant, solubilizer in creams and lotions
    Regulatory: FDA 21CFR §175.105, 175.300, 176.170, 176.210, 177.1200, 177.1210, 177.2260, 177.2800,
        178.3520, 178.3760, 178.3910
    Trade names: Acconon 400-ML; Algon LA 80; Crodet L8; Hodag 40-L; Kessco® PEG 400 ML; Mapeg® 400
        ML

PEG-12 laurate
    CAS 9004-81-3 (generic)
    Synonyms: POE (12) monolaurate; PEG 600 monolaurate
    Definition: PEG ester of lauric acid
    Formula: $CH_3(CH_2)_{10}CO(OCH_2CH_2)_nOH$, avg. n = 12
    Uses: Emulsifier, wetting agent, solubilizer, dispersant, emollient, thickener
    Regulatory: FDA 21CFR §175.105, 175.300, 176.170, 176.210, 177.1200, 177.2260, 177.2800, 178.3910
    Trade names: Crodet L12; Hodag 60-L; Kessco® PEG 600 ML

PEG-20 laurate
    CAS 9004-81-3 (generic)
    Synonyms: POE (20) monolaurate; PEG 1000 monolaurate
    Definition: PEG ester of lauric acid
    Formula: $CH_3(CH_2)_{10}CO(OCH_2CH_2)_nOH$, avg. n = 20
    Properties: Insol. in water
    Uses: Emulsifier, thickener, solubilizer, emollient, spreading and wetting agent, dispersant for pharmaceuti-
        cals
    Regulatory: FDA 21CFR §175.300, 176.210, 177.2260, 177.2800, 178.3910
    Trade names: Ethylan® L10; Kessco® PEG 1000 ML

PEG-24 laurate
    CAS 9004-81-3 (generic)
    Synonyms: POE (24) monolaurate
    Definition: PEG ester of lauric acid
    Properties: Insol. in water
    Uses: O/w emulsifier for pharmaceutical creams, lotions, ointments
    Trade names: Crodet L24

PEG-32 laurate
    CAS 9004-81-3 (generic)
    Synonyms: POE (32) monolaurate; PEG 1540 monolaurate
    Definition: PEG ester of lauric acid
    Formula: $CH_3(CH_2)_{10}CO(OCH_2CH_2)_nOH$, avg. n = 32
    Uses: Surfactant, solubilizer, thickener, emollient, opacifier, spreading agent, wetting agent, dispersant for
        pharmaceuticals
    Regulatory: FDA 21CFR §175.300, 176.210, 177.2260, 177.2800, 178.3910
    Trade names: Kessco® PEG 1540 ML

PEG-40 laurate
    CAS 9004-81-3 (generic)
    Synonyms: POE (40) monolaurate
    Definition: PEG ester of lauric acid
    Formula: $CH_3(CH_2)_{10}CO(OCH_2CH_2)_nOH$, avg. n = 40
    Properties: Insol. in water
    Uses: O/w emulsifier for pharmaceutical creams, lotions, and ointments
    Trade names: Crodet L40

PEG-75 laurate
CAS 9004-81-3 (generic)
Synonyms: POE (75) monolaurate; PEG 4000 monolaurate
Definition: PEG ester of lauric acid
Formula: $CH_3(CH_2)_{10}CO(OCH_2CH_2)_nOH$, avg. n = 75
Uses: Emulsifier, thickener, solubilizer, emollient, spreading agent, wetting agent, dispersant
Regulatory: FDA 21CFR §175.300, 178.3910
Trade names: Kessco® PEG 4000 ML

PEG-100 laurate
CAS 9004-81-3 (generic)
Synonyms: POE (100) monolaurate; PEG (100) monolaurate
Definition: PEG ester of lauric acid
Properties: Insol. in water
Uses: O/w emulsifier for pharmaceutical creams, lotions, and ointments
Trade names: Crodet L100

PEG-150 laurate
CAS 9004-81-3 (generic)
Synonyms: POE (150) monolaurate; PEG 6000 monolaurate
Definition: PEG ester of lauric acid
Formula: $CH_3(CH_2)_{10}CO(OCH_2CH_2)_nOH$, avg. n = 150
Uses: Emulsifier, thickener, solubilizer, emollient, spreading agent, wetting agent, dispersant
Regulatory: FDA 21CFR §175.300, 178.3910
Trade names: Kessco® PEG 6000 ML

PEG-2 lauryl ether. *See* Laureth-2
PEG-3 lauryl ether. *See* Laureth-3
PEG-4 lauryl ether. *See* Laureth-4
PEG-6 lauryl ether. *See* Laureth-6
PEG-7 lauryl ether. *See* Laureth-7
PEG-10 lauryl ether. *See* Laureth-10
PEG-12 lauryl ether. *See* Laureth-12
PEG-23 lauryl ether. *See* Laureth-23
PEG 200 lauryl ether. *See* Laureth-4
PEG 600 lauryl ether. *See* Laureth-12
PEG-2 lauryl ether acetate. *See* Laureth-2 acetate
PEG 100 lauryl ether acetate. *See* Laureth-2 acetate
PEG-5 lauryl ether carboxylic acid, sodium salt. *See* Sodium laureth-5 carboxylate
PEG (1-4) lauryl ether sulfate, sodium salt. *See* Sodium laureth sulfate

PEG-120 methyl glucose dioleate
Synonyms: POE (120) methyl glucose dioleate; Macrogol 120 methyl glucose dioleate
Definition: PEG ether of the diester of methyl glucose and oleic acid with avg. 120 moles of ethylene oxide

PEG-10 methyl glucose ether. *See* Methyl gluceth-10
PEG-20 methyl glucose ether. *See* Methyl gluceth-20
PEG 300 monoisostearate. *See* PEG-6 isostearate
PEG (100) monolaurate. *See* PEG-100 laurate
PEG 200 monolaurate. *See* PEG-4 laurate
PEG 300 monolaurate. *See* PEG-6 laurate
PEG 400 monolaurate. *See* PEG-8 laurate
PEG 600 monolaurate. *See* PEG-12 laurate
PEG 1000 monolaurate. *See* PEG-20 laurate
PEG 1540 monolaurate. *See* PEG-32 laurate
PEG 4000 monolaurate. *See* PEG-75 laurate
PEG 6000 monolaurate. *See* PEG-150 laurate
PEG 200 monooleate. *See* PEG-4 oleate
PEG 300 monooleate. *See* PEG-6 oleate
PEG 400 monooleate. *See* PEG-8 oleate
PEG 600 monooleate. *See* PEG-12 oleate
PEG 1000 monooleate. *See* PEG-20 oleate
PEG 1540 monooleate. *See* PEG-32 oleate
PEG 4000 monooleate. *See* PEG-75 oleate
PEG 6000 monooleate. *See* PEG-150 oleate

PEG 100 monostearate. *See* PEG-2 stearate
PEG (100) monostearate. *See* PEG-100 stearate
PEG 200 monostearate. *See* PEG-4 stearate
PEG 300 monostearate. *See* PEG-6 stearate
PEG 400 monostearate. *See* PEG-8 stearate
PEG 500 monostearate. *See* PEG-10 stearate
PEG 600 monostearate. *See* PEG-12 stearate
PEG 1000 monostearate. *See* PEG-20 stearate
PEG 1500 monostearate. *See* PEG-6-32 stearate
PEG 2000 monostearate. *See* PEG-40 stearate
PEG 4000 monostearate. *See* PEG-75 stearate
PEG 6000 monostearate. *See* PEG-150 stearate
PEG 200 monotallate. *See* PEG-4 tallate
PEG 400 monotallate. *See* PEG-8 tallate
PEG 600 monotallate. *See* PEG-12 tallate
PEG-3 myristyl ether myristate. *See* Myreth-3 myristate
PEG-1 nonyl phenyl ether. *See* Nonoxynol-1
PEG-2 nonyl phenyl ether. *See* Nonoxynol-2
PEG-4 nonyl phenyl ether. *See* Nonoxynol-4
PEG-5 nonyl phenyl ether. *See* Nonoxynol-5
PEG-6 nonyl phenyl ether. *See* Nonoxynol-6
PEG-7 nonyl phenyl ether. *See* Nonoxynol-7
PEG-8 nonyl phenyl ether. *See* Nonoxynol-8
PEG-9 nonyl phenyl ether. *See* Nonoxynol-9
PEG-10 nonyl phenyl ether. *See* Nonoxynol-10
PEG-12 nonyl phenyl ether. *See* Nonoxynol-12
PEG-13 nonyl phenyl ether. *See* Nonoxynol-13
PEG-20 nonyl phenyl ether. *See* Nonoxynol-20
PEG-30 nonyl phenyl ether. *See* Nonoxynol-30
PEG-35 nonyl phenyl ether. *See* Nonoxynol-35
PEG-40 nonyl phenyl ether. *See* Nonoxynol-40
PEG-50 nonyl phenyl ether. *See* Nonoxynol-50
PEG 100 nonyl phenyl ether. *See* Nonoxynol-2
PEG 200 nonyl phenyl ether. *See* Nonoxynol-4
PEG 300 nonyl phenyl ether. *See* Nonoxynol-6
PEG 400 nonyl phenyl ether. *See* Nonoxynol-8
PEG 450 nonyl phenyl ether. *See* Nonoxynol-9
PEG 500 nonyl phenyl ether. *See* Nonoxynol-10
PEG 600 nonyl phenyl ether. *See* Nonoxynol-12
PEG 1000 nonyl phenyl ether. *See* Nonoxynol-20
PEG 2000 nonyl phenyl ether. *See* Nonoxynol-40
PEG-1 octyl phenyl ether. *See* Octoxynol-1
PEG-3 octyl phenyl ether. *See* Octoxynol-3
PEG-5 octyl phenyl ether. *See* Octoxynol-5
PEG-6 octyl phenyl ether. *See* Octoxynol-6
PEG-8 octyl phenyl ether. *See* Octoxynol-8
PEG-9 octyl phenyl ether. *See* Octoxynol-9
PEG-10 octyl phenyl ether. *See* Octoxynol-10
PEG-11 octyl phenyl ether. *See* Octoxynol-11
PEG-13 octyl phenyl ether. *See* Octoxynol-13
PEG-16 octyl phenyl ether. *See* Octoxynol-16
PEG-20 octyl phenyl ether. *See* Octoxynol-20
PEG-25 octyl phenyl ether. *See* Octoxynol-25
PEG-30 octyl phenyl ether. *See* Octoxynol-30
PEG-40 octyl phenyl ether. *See* Octoxynol-40
PEG 400 octyl phenyl ether. *See* Octoxynol-8
PEG 450 octyl phenyl ether. *See* Octoxynol-9
PEG 500 octyl phenyl ether. *See* Octoxynol-10
PEG 1000 octyl phenyl ether. *See* Octoxynol-20

PEG-4 oleate
CAS 9004-96-0 (generic); 10108-25-5; EINECS 233-293-0
Synonyms: POE (4) monooleate; PEG 200 monooleate

Definition: PEG ester of oleic acid
Empirical: $C_{26}H_{50}O_6$
Formula: $CH_3(CH_2)_7CHCH(CH_2)_7CO(OCH_2CH_2)_nOH$, avg. n = 4
Uses: Emulsifier, thickener, solubilizer, emollient, spreading agent, wetting agent, dispersant
Regulatory: FDA 21CFR §175.105, 175.300, 176.210
Trade names: Kessco® PEG 200 MO; Mapeg® 200 MO

PEG-6 oleate

CAS 9004-96-0 (generic); 60344-26-5
Synonyms: POE (6) monooleate; PEG 300 monooleate
Definition: PEG ester of oleic acid
Empirical: $C_{30}H_{58}O_8$
Formula: $CH_3(CH_2)_7CHCH(CH_2)_7CO(OCH_2CH_2)_nOH$, avg. n = 6
Uses: Emulsifier, thickener, solubilizer, emollient, spreading agent, wetting agent, dispersant
Regulatory: FDA 21CFR §175.105, 175.300, 176.210
Trade names: Algon OL 60; Kessco® PEG 300 MO

PEG-7 oleate

CAS 9004-96-0 (generic)
Synonyms: POE (7) monooleate
Definition: PEG ester of oleic acid
Formula: $CH_3(CH_2)_7CHCH(CH_2)_7CO(OCH_2CH_2)_nOH$, avg. n = 7
Uses: Emulsifier
Regulatory: FDA 21CFR §175.300
Trade names: Algon OL 70

PEG-8 oleate

CAS 9004-96-0 (generic)
Synonyms: POE (8) monooleate; PEG 400 monooleate
Definition: PEG ester of oleic acid
Formula: $CH_3(CH_2)_7CHCH(CH_2)_7CO(OCH_2CH_2)_nOH$, avg. n = 8
Properties: Dk. red oil; sol. in alcohol; disp. in water; misc. with cottonseed oil
Uses: Emulsifier, dispersant, lubricant, chemical intermediate, solubilizer, visc. control agent for pharmaceuticals
Regulatory: FDA 21CFR §175.105, 175.300, 176.170, 176.200, 177.1200, 177.1210, 177.2260, 177.2800
Trade names: Acconon 400-MO; Hodag 40-O; Kessco® PEG 400 MO; Mapeg® 400 MO

PEG-12 oleate

CAS 9004-96-0 (generic)
Synonyms: POE (12) monooleate; PEG 600 monooleate
Definition: PEG ester of oleic acid
Formula: $CH_3(CH_2)_7CHCH(CH_2)_7CO(OCH_2CH_2)_nOH$, avg. n = 12
Uses: Emulsifier, thickener, solubilizer, emollient, spreading agent, wetting agent, dispersant
Regulatory: FDA 21CFR §175.105, 175.300, 176.170, 176.200, 177.1200, 177.2260, 177.2800
Trade names: Kessco® PEG 600 MO

PEG-20 oleate

CAS 9004-96-0 (generic)
Synonyms: POE (20) monooleate; PEG 1000 monooleate
Definition: PEG ester of oleic acid
Formula: $CH_3(CH_2)_7CHCH(CH_2)_7CO(OCH_2CH_2)_nOH$, avg. n = 20
Uses: Emulsifier, thickener, solubilizer, emollient, spreading agent, wetting agent, dispersant
Regulatory: FDA 21CFR §175.300, 176.200, 177.2260, 177.2800
Trade names: Kessco® PEG 1000 MO

PEG-32 oleate

CAS 9004-96-0 (generic)
Synonyms: POE (32) monooleate; PEG 1540 monooleate
Definition: PEG ester of oleic acid
Formula: $CH_3(CH_2)_7CHCH(CH_2)_7CO(OCH_2CH_2)_nOH$, avg. n = 32
Properties: Dk. red oil; sol. in alcohol; disp. in water; misc. with cottonseed oil
Uses: Surfactant, solubilizer, thickener, emollient, opacifier, spreading agent, wetting agent, dispersant for pharmaceuticals
Regulatory: FDA 21CFR §175.300, 176.200, 177.2261, 177.2800
Trade names: Kessco® PEG 1540 MO

PEG-75 oleate
CAS 9004-96-0 (generic)
Synonyms: POE (75) monooleate; PEG 4000 monooleate
Definition: PEG ester of oleic acid
Formula: $CH_3(CH_2)_7CHCH(CH_2)_7CO(OCH_2CH_2)_nOH$, avg. n = 75
Properties: Dk. red oil; sol. in alcohol; disp. in water; misc. with cottonseed oil
Uses: Surfactant, solubilizer, thickener, emollient, opacifier, spreading agent, wetting agent, dispersant for pharmaceuticals
Regulatory: FDA 21CFR §175.300, 176.200
Trade names: Kessco® PEG 4000 MO

PEG-150 oleate
CAS 9004-96-0 (generic)
Synonyms: POE (150) monooleate; PEG 6000 monooleate
Definition: PEG ester of oleic acid
Formula: $CH_3(CH_2)_7CHCH(CH_2)_7CO(OCH_2CH_2)_nOH$, avg. n = 150
Uses: Emulsifier, thickener, solubilizer, emollient, spreading agent, wetting agent, dispersant
Regulatory: FDA 21CFR §175.300, 176.200
Trade names: Kessco® PEG 6000 MO

PEG-300 oleate
Uses: Wetting aid, lubricant, opacifier, dispersant, o/w emulgent for pharmaceuticals

PEG-2 oleyl ether. *See* Oleth-2
PEG-3 oleyl ether. *See* Oleth-3
PEG-5 oleyl ether. *See* Oleth-5
PEG-10 oleyl ether. *See* Oleth-10
PEG-12 oleyl ether. *See* Oleth-12
PEG-16 oleyl ether. *See* Oleth-16
PEG-20 oleyl ether. *See* Oleth-20
PEG-25 oleyl ether. *See* Oleth-25
PEG 100 oleyl ether. *See* Oleth-2
PEG 500 oleyl ether. *See* Oleth-10
PEG 600 oleyl ether. *See* Oleth-12
PEG 1000 oleyl ether. *See* Oleth-20
PEG-3 oleyl ether phosphate. *See* Oleth-3 phosphate
PEG-10 oleyl ether phosphate. *See* Oleth-10 phosphate
PEG-20 oleyl ether phosphate. *See* Oleth-20 phosphate
PEG 200 oleyl ether phosphate. *See* Oleth-10 phosphate
PEG 1000 oleyl ether phosphate. *See* Oleth-20 phosphate

PEG-25 PABA
CAS 15716-30-0; 113010-52-9
Synonyms: POE (25) PABA; 4-Bis(polyethoxy)-p-aminobenzoic acid polyethoxyethyl ester
Definition: PEG deriv. of PABA
Uses: UV-B absorber for sunscreen prods.; stabilizer for light-sensitive prods.
Trade names: Unipabol U-17

PEG-8 palmitostearate
Uses: Solvent and emulsifier
Trade names: Stearate 400 WL 817

PEG-150 palmitostearate
Uses: Solvent and emulsifier
Trade names: Stearate 6000 WL 1644

PEG-5 phytosterol
Definition: PEG ether of phytosterol with an avg. ethoxylation value of 5
Uses: Emulsifier, solubilizer, dispersant, emollient, visc. modifier for pharmaceuticals
Trade names: Nikkol BPS-5

PEG-10 phytosterol
Definition: PEG ether of phytosterol with an avg. ethoxylation value of 10
Uses: Emulsifier, solubilizer, dispersant, emollient, visc. modifier for pharmaceuticals

PEG-15 phytosterol
Definition: PEG ether of phytosterol with an avg. ethoxylation value of 15
Uses: Emulsifier, solubilizer, dispersant, emollient, visc. modifier for pharmaceuticals

PEG-20 phytosterol
Definition: PEG ether of phytosterol with an avg. ethoxylation value of 20
Uses: Emulsifier, solubilizer, dispersant, emollient, visc. modifier for pharmaceuticals

PEG-25 phytosterol
Definition: PEG ether of phytosterol with an avg. ethoxylation value of 25
Uses: Emulsifier, solubilizer, dispersant, emollient, visc. modifier for pharmaceuticals

PEG-30 phytosterol
Definition: PEG ether of phytosterol with an avg. ethoxylation value of 30
Uses: Emulsifier, solubilizer, dispersant, emollient, visc. modifier for pharmaceuticals

PEG-10-PPG-10 glyceryl stearate
CAS 68783-63-1
Definition: Polyoxypropylene, polyoxyethylene ether of glyceryl stearate with avg. propoxylation value of 10 and avg. ethoxylation value of 10
Uses: Emulsifier, dispersant, solubilizer, visc. control agent, wetting agent for pharmaceutical dermatologicals
Trade names: Acconon TGH

PEG-10 propylene glycol
Synonyms: POE (10) propylene glycol; PEG 500 propylene glycol
Definition: PEG ether of propylene glycol
Formula: $CH_2(OCH_2CH_2)_xOHCH(OCH_2CH_2)_yOHCH_3$, avg. (x+y) = 10
Uses: Emulsifier, dispersant, solubilizer, visc. control agent for pharmaceuticals
Trade names containing: Acconon CON

PEG 500 propylene glycol. *See* PEG-10 propylene glycol

PEG-8 propylene glycol cocoate
Synonyms: POE (8) propylene glycol cocoate; PEG 400 propylene glycol cocoate
Definition: PEG ether of propylene glycol cocoate
Formula: $RCOOCH_2CHCH_3(OCH_2CH_2)_nOH$, RCO- rep. coconut fatty radical, avg. n = 8
Uses: Ingred. in pharmaceutical ointments
Trade names containing: Emulsynt® 1055

PEG 400 propylene glycol cocoate. *See* PEG-8 propylene glycol cocoate

PEG-6 propylene glycol dicaprylate/dicaprate
Uses: Surfactant, emollient, emulsifier, moisturizer for dermatologicals, microemulsions
Trade names: Captex® 200-E6

PEG-25 propylene glycol stearate
Synonyms: POE (25) propylene glycol monostearate
Definition: PEG ether of propylene glycol stearate
Formula: $CH_3(CH_2)_{16}COOCH_2CCH_3H(OCH_2CH_2)_nOH$, avg. n = 25
Uses: Emollient, visc. regulator
Trade names: Simulsol® PS20

PEG-120 propylene glycol stearate
Synonyms: POE (120) propylene glycol monostearate
Definition: PEG ether of propylene glycol stearate
Formula: $CH_3(CH_2)_{16}COOCH_2CCH_3H(OCH_2CH_2)_nOH$, avg. n = 120
Uses: Visc. builder in pharmaceutical ointments
Trade names containing: Drewmulse® 1128

PEG-8 ricinoleate
CAS 9004-97-1 (generic)
Synonyms: PEG 400 ricinoleate; POE (8) ricinoleate
Definition: PEG ester of ricinoleic acid
Uses: Emulsifier, wetting agent, plasticizer
Regulatory: FDA 21CFR §175.300, 176.210, 177.1210, 177.2800
Trade names: Hodag 40-R

PEG 400 ricinoleate. *See* PEG-8 ricinoleate

PEG-6 sorbitan beeswax
CAS 8051-15-8
Synonyms: PEG 300 sorbitan beeswax; POE (6) sorbitol beeswax
Definition: Ethoxylated sorbitol deriv. of beeswax with avg. 6 moles ethylene oxide
Uses: Emulsifier, emulsion stabilizer for pharmaceuticals
Trade names: Nikkol GBW-25

PEG-8 sorbitan beeswax
Synonyms: POE (8) sorbitol beeswax; PEG 400 sorbitan beeswax
Definition: Ethoxylated sorbitan deriv. of beeswax with avg. 8 moles ethylene oxide
Uses: Emulsifier
Trade names: Nikkol GBW-8

PEG-20 sorbitan beeswax
CAS 8051-73-8
Synonyms: POE (20) sorbitol beeswax; PEG 1000 sorbitan beeswax
Definition: Ethoxylated sorbitol deriv. of beeswax with avg. 20 moles ethylene oxide
Uses: Emulsifier, emulsion stabilizer
Trade names: Nikkol GBW-125

PEG 300 sorbitan beeswax. *See* PEG-6 sorbitan beeswax
PEG 400 sorbitan beeswax. *See* PEG-8 sorbitan beeswax
PEG 1000 sorbitan beeswax. *See* PEG-20 sorbitan beeswax

PEG-20 sorbitan isostearate
CAS 66794-58-9 (generic)
Synonyms: PEG 1000 sorbitan monoisostearate; POE (20) sorbitan monoisostearate; Polysorbate 120
Definition: Ethoxylated sorbitan monoester of isostearic acid with avg. 20 moles ethylene oxide
Uses: Emulsifier, solv., wetting agent for topical pharmaceuticals
Trade names: Crillet 6; Sorbilene ISM

PEG-40 sorbitan lanolate
CAS 8036-77-9
Synonyms: POE (40) sorbitol lanolate; PEG 2000 sorbitan lanolate
Definition: Ethoxylated sorbitan deriv. of lanolin acid with avg. 40 moles ethylene oxide
Uses: Emulsifier for pharmaceuticals
Trade names: G-1441

PEG 2000 sorbitan lanolate. *See* PEG-40 sorbitan lanolate
PEG-4 sorbitan laurate. *See* Polysorbate 21
PEG-20 sorbitan laurate. *See* Polysorbate 20

PEG-80 sorbitan laurate
CAS 9005-64-5 (generic)
Synonyms: POE (80) sorbitan monolaurate
Definition: Ethoxylated sorbitan monoester of lauric acid with avg. 80 moles ethylene oxide
Uses: Emulsifier, solubilizer, wetting agent, stabilizer, dispersant, visc. modifier
Regulatory: FDA 21CFR §175.300
Trade names: T-Maz® 28

PEG 1000 sorbitan monoisostearate. *See* PEG-20 sorbitan isostearate
PEG 300 sorbitan monooleate. *See* PEG-6 sorbitan oleate
PEG 300 sorbitan monostearate. *See* PEG-6 sorbitan stearate
PEG-5 sorbitan oleate. *See* Polysorbate 81

PEG-6 sorbitan oleate
CAS 9005-65-6 (generic)
Synonyms: POE (6) sorbitan oleate; PEG 300 sorbitan monooleate
Definition: Ethoxylated sorbitan ester of oleic acid with avg. 6 moles ethylene oxide
Toxicology: Moderately toxic by intravenous route; mildly toxic by ingestion
Uses: Emulsifier
Regulatory: FDA 21CFR §175.300, 176.210
Trade names: Nikkol TO-106

PEG-20 sorbitan oleate. *See* Polysorbate 80

PEG-40 sorbitan oleate
Uses: Emulsifier, solubilizer
Trade names: Emalex ET-8040

PEG-4 sorbitan stearate. *See* Polysorbate 61

PEG-6 sorbitan stearate
CAS 9005-67-8 (generic)
Synonyms: POE (6) sorbitan monostearate; PEG 300 sorbitan monostearate
Definition: Ethoxylated sorbitan ester of stearic acid with avg. 6 moles ethylene oxide

Uses: Emulsifier, solubilizer
Regulatory: FDA 21CFR §175.300, 176.210
Trade names: Nikkol TS-106

PEG-20 sorbitan stearate. *See* Polysorbate 60

PEG-30 sorbitan tetraoleate
Synonyms: POE (30) sorbitan tetraoleate
Definition: Tetraester of oleic acid and a PEG ether of sorbitol, avg. 30 moles ethylene oxide
Uses: Emulsifier, solubilizer, superfatting agent for drug prods.
Regulatory: FDA 21CFR §175.300
Trade names: Nikkol GO-430

PEG-40 sorbitan tetraoleate
CAS 9003-11-6
Synonyms: POE (40) sorbitan tetraoleate; PEG 2000 sorbitan tetraoleate
Definition: Tetraester of oleic acid and a PEG ether of sorbitol, avg. 40 moles ethylene oxide
Formula: $(C_3H_6O \cdot C_2H_4O)_x$
Toxicology: Moderately toxic by ingestion and intraperitoneal route
Uses: Emulsifier, solubilizer, superfatting agent for drug prods.
Regulatory: FDA 21CFR §175.300, 176.210
Trade names: Nikkol GO-440

PEG-60 sorbitan tetraoleate
Synonyms: POE (60) sorbitan tetraoleate
Definition: Tetraester of oleic acid and a PEG ether of sorbitol, avg. 60 moles ethylene oxide
Uses: Emulsifier, solubilizer, superfatting agent for drug prods.
Regulatory: FDA 21CFR §175.300
Trade names: Nikkol GO-460

PEG 2000 sorbitan tetraoleate. *See* PEG-40 sorbitan tetraoleate

PEG-17 sorbitan trioleate
CAS 9005-70-3
Definition: Triester of oleic acid and a PEG ether of sorbitol, avg. 17 moles ethylene oxide
Uses: Emulsifier for pharmaceuticals

PEG-20 sorbitan trioleate. *See* Polysorbate 85
PEG-20 sorbitan tristearate. *See* Polysorbate 65

PEG-20 sorbitan tritallate
Definition: Triester of tall oil acid and a PEG ether of sorbitol, avg. 20 moles ethylene oxide
Uses: Emulsifier, solubilizer, wetting agent, visc. modifier, stabilizer, dispersant used in drug prods.

PEG-20 sorbitol ether. *See* Sorbeth-20
PEG 1000 sorbitol ether. *See* Sorbeth-20

PEG-2 stearate
CAS 106-11-6; 9004-99-3 (generic); 85116-97-8; EINECS 203-363-5; 285-550-1
Synonyms: Diethylene glycol stearate; Diglycol stearate; PEG 100 monostearate
Definition: PEG ester of stearic acid
Empirical: $C_{22}H_{44}O_4$
Formula: $CH_3(CH_2)_{16}CO(OCH_2CH_2)_nOH$, avg. n = 2
Properties: Wh. wax-like solid, faint fatty odor; sol. in hot alcohol, oils
Precaution: Combustible
Toxicology: Poison by intravenous, intraperitoneal route; mildly toxic by ingestion
Uses: Thickening agent, emulsifier, solubilizer for pharmaceuticals
Regulatory: FDA 21CFR §175.300, 176.200, 176.210, 177.2800
Manuf./Distrib.: ABITEC; Henkel/Emery; Inolex; Lipo; Lonza; Stepan; Witco
Trade names: Hydrine; Nikkol MYS-2
Trade names containing: Sedefos 75®

PEG-4 stearate
CAS 106-07-0; 9004-99-3 (generic); EINECS 203-358-8
Synonyms: POE (4) stearate; PEG 200 monostearate
Definition: PEG ester of stearic acid
Empirical: $C_{26}H_{52}O_6$
Formula: $CH_3(CH_2)_{16}CO(OCH_2CH_2)_nOH$, avg. n = 4
Toxicology: Poison by intravenous, intraperitoneal route; mildly toxic by ingestion

PEG-5 stearate

    Uses: Emulsifier, dispersant, solubilizer, visc. control agent, wetting agent, spreading agent, emollient
    Regulatory: FDA 21CFR §175.105, 175.300, 176.210
    Trade names: Acconon 200-MS; Crodet S4; Kessco® PEG 200 MS; Nikkol MYS-4

PEG-5 stearate
    CAS 9004-99-3 (generic)
    Synonyms: POE (5) stearate
    Definition: PEG ester of stearic acid
    Formula: $CH_3(CH_2)_{16}CO(OCH_2CH_2)_nOH$, avg. n = 5
    Toxicology: Poison by intravenous, intraperitoneal route; mildly toxic by ingestion
    Uses: Emulsifier
    Regulatory: FDA 21CFR §173.340, 175.105, 175.300
    Trade names: Algon ST 50

PEG-6 stearate
    CAS 9004-99-3 (generic); 10108-28-8
    Synonyms: POE (6) stearate; PEG 300 monostearate
    Definition: PEG ester of stearic acid
    Empirical: $C_{30}H_{60}O_8$
    Formula: $CH_3(CH_2)_{16}CO(OCH_2CH_2)_nOH$, avg. n = 6
    Toxicology: Poison by intravenous, intraperitoneal route; mildly toxic by ingestion
    Uses: Emulsifier, thickener, solubilizer, emollient, spreading agent, wetting agent, dispersant
    Regulatory: FDA 21CFR §175.105, 175.300, 176.210
    Trade names: Kessco® PEG 300 MS; Superpolystate
    Trade names containing: Tefose® 2000; Tefose® 2561

PEG-6-32 stearate
    CAS 9004-99-3 (generic)
    Synonyms: PEG 1500 monostearate; POE 1500 monostearate
    Definition: PEG ester of stearic acid
    Toxicology: Poison by intravenous, intraperitoneal route; mildly toxic by ingestion
    Uses: Spreading agent, emulsifier, dispersant, lubricant for pharmaceuticals
    Trade names: Hodag 150-S; Tefose® 1500
    Trade names containing: Tefose® 63

PEG-8 stearate
    CAS 9004-99-3 (generic); 70802-40-3
    Synonyms: POE (8) stearate; PEG 400 monostearate
    Definition: PEG ester of stearic acid
    Empirical: $C_{34}H_{68}O_{10}$
    Formula: $CH_3(CH_2)_{16}CO(OCH_2CH_2)_nOH$, avg. n = 8
    Toxicology: Poison by intravenous, intraperitoneal route; mildly toxic by ingestion
    Uses: Emulsifier, dispersant, solubilizer, visc. control agent, emollient
    Regulatory: FDA 21CFR §175.105, 175.300, 176.170, 176.200, 176.210, 177.1200, 177.1210, 177.2260, 177.2800, 178.3910; Europe listed; UK approved
    Trade names: Acconon 400-MS; Algon ST 80; Cremophor® S 9; Crodet S8; Hodag 40-S; Kessco® PEG 400 MS; Mapeg® 400 MS; Myrj® 45

PEG-10 stearate
    CAS 9004-99-3 (generic)
    Synonyms: POE (10) stearate; PEG 500 monostearate
    Definition: PEG ester of stearic acid
    Formula: $CH_3(CH_2)_{16}CO(OCH_2CH_2)_nOH$, avg. n = 10
    Toxicology: Poison by intravenous, intraperitoneal route; mildly toxic by ingestion
    Uses: Emulsifier, solubilizer
    Regulatory: FDA 21CFR §175.105, 175.30, 177.2260, 177.2800
    Trade names: Algon ST 100; Nikkol MYS-10

PEG-12 stearate
    CAS 9004-99-3 (generic)
    Synonyms: POE (12) stearate; PEG 600 monostearate
    Definition: PEG ester of stearic acid
    Formula: $CH_3(CH_2)_{16}CO(OCH_2CH_2)_nOH$, avg. n = 12
    Toxicology: Poison by intravenous, intraperitoneal route; mildly toxic by ingestion
    Uses: Emulsifier, wetting agent, solubilizer, dispersant, emollient, spreading agent

Regulatory: FDA 21CFR §175.105, 175.300, 176.170, 176.210, 177.1200, 177.2260, 177.2800
Trade names: Crodet S12; Hodag 60-S; Kessco® PEG 600 MS; Mapeg® 600 MS

PEG-20 stearate
CAS 9004-99-3 (generic)
Synonyms: POE (20) stearate; PEG 1000 monostearate
Definition: PEG ester of stearic acid
Formula: $CH_3(CH_2)_{16}CO(OCH_2CH_2)_nOH$, avg. n = 20
Properties: Sol. in ethanol; partly sol. in propylene glycol; disp. in glycerin; insol. in water; m.p. 39.5-42.5 C; sapon. no. 40-50
Toxicology: Poison by intravenous, intraperitoneal route; mildly toxic by ingestion
Uses: Emulsifier, visc. builder, stabilizer, wetting agent, plasticizer, emollient, dispersant
Regulatory: FDA 21CFR §175.300, 176.210, 177.2260, 177.2800
Trade names: Algon ST 200; Cerasynt® 840; Hodag 100-S; Kessco® PEG 1000 MS; Mapeg® 1000 MS; Myrj® 49

PEG-24 stearate
CAS 9004-99-3 (generic)
Synonyms: POE (24) stearate
Definition: PEG ester of stearic acid
Formula: $CH_3(CH_2)_{16}CO(OCH_2CH_2)_nOH$, avg. n = 24
Uses: O/w emulsifier for pharmaceutical creams, lotions, and ointments; wetting agent, dispersant
Trade names: Crodet S24

PEG-25 stearate
CAS 9004-99-3 (generic)
Synonyms: POE (25) stearate
Definition: PEG ester of stearic acid
Formula: $CH_3(CH_2)_{16}CO(OCH_2CH_2)_nOH$, avg. n = 25
Toxicology: Poison by intravenous, intraperitoneal route; mildly toxic by ingestion
Uses: Emulsifier, solubilizer for pharmaceuticals
Regulatory: FDA 21CFR §175.300, 177.2260, 177.2800
Trade names: Nikkol MYS-25

PEG-30 stearate
CAS 9004-99-3 (generic)
Synonyms: POE (30) stearate
Definition: PEG ester of stearic acid
Formula: $CH_3(CH_2)_{16}CO(OCH_2CH_2)_nOH$, avg. n = 30
Toxicology: Poison by intravenous, intraperitoneal route; mildly toxic by ingestion
Uses: O/w emulsifier for pharmaceutical applics.
Regulatory: FDA 21CFR §175.300, 177.2260, 177.2800
Trade names: Myrj® 51

PEG-32 stearate
CAS 9004-99-3 (generic)
Synonyms: PEG 1540 stearate
Definition: PEG ester of stearic acid
Formula: $CH_3(CH_2)_{16}CO(OCH_2CH_2)_nOH$, avg. n = 32
Toxicology: Poison by intravenous, intraperitoneal route; mildly toxic by ingestion
Uses: Surfactant, solubilizer, thickener, emollient, opacifier, spreading agent, wetting agent, dispersant for pharmaceuticals
Regulatory: FDA 21CFR §175.300, 176.210, 177.2260, 177.2800
Trade names: Kessco® PEG 1540 MS

PEG-40 stearate
CAS 9004-99-3 (generic); 31791-00-2
Synonyms: POE (40) stearate; PEG 2000 monostearate; Polyoxyl 40 stearate
Definition: PEG ester of stearic acid
Formula: $CH_3(CH_2)_{16}CO(OCH_2CH_2)_nOH$, avg. n = 40
Properties: Wh. to cream waxy solid, nearly odorless, faint fatty odor; sol. in water, ether, alcohol, acetone; insol. in min. and veg. oils; m.p. 37-47 C; acid no. 2 max.; sapon. no. 25-35; hyd. no. 25-40
Toxicology: Poison by intravenous, intraperitoneal route; mildly toxic by ingestion
Uses: Solubilizer, emulsifier, wetting agent, stabilizer, antigellant, lubricant for creams, lotions; used in dentals, ophthalmics, orals, otics, topicals
Regulatory: FDA 21CFR §173.340, 175.105, 175.300, 176.200, 176.210, 177.2260, 177.2800; Europe listed;

PEG-45 stearate

UK approved; FDA approved for dentals, ophthalmics, orals, otics, topicals; USP/NF compliance
Manuf./Distrib. (pharm. & food): Spectrum Chem. Mfg.
Trade names: Algon ST 400; Crodet S40; Emerest® 2715; Mapeg® S-40K; Myrj® 52; Myrj® 52S; Nikkol MYS-40; Simulsol® M 52
Trade names containing: Drewmulse® HM-100

PEG-45 stearate
CAS 9004-99-3 (generic)
Synonyms: POE (45) stearate
Definition: PEG ester of stearic acid
Formula: $CH_3(CH_2)_{16}CO(OCH_2CH_2)_nOH$, avg. n = 45
Toxicology: Poison by intravenous, intraperitoneal route; mildly toxic by ingestion
Uses: Emulsifier, solubilizer for pharmaceuticals
Regulatory: FDA 21CFR §1175.300, 177.2260, 177.2800
Trade names: Nikkol MYS-45

PEG-50 stearate
CAS 9004-99-3 (generic)
Synonyms: POE (50) stearate; Polyoxyl 50 stearate
Definition: PEG ester of stearic acid
Formula: $CH_3(CH_2)_{16}CO(OCH_2CH_2)_nOH$, avg. n = 50
Properties: Cream-colored soft waxy solid, faint fatty odor; sol. in water, IPA; m.p. ≈ 45 C; acid no. 2 max.; sapon. no. 20-28; hyd. no. 23-35
Toxicology: Poison by intravenous, intraperitoneal route; mildly toxic by ingestion
Uses: Wetting and/or solublizing agent in pharmaceuticals
Regulatory: FDA 21CFR §175.300, 177.2260, 177.2800; USP/NF compliance
Manuf./Distrib. (pharm. & food): Spectrum Chem. Mfg.
Trade names: Algon ST 500; Myrj® 53

PEG-55 stearate
CAS 9004-99-3 (generic)
Synonyms: POE (55) stearate; Polyoxyl 50 stearate
Definition: PEG ester of stearic acid
Formula: $CH_3(CH_2)_{16}CO(OCH_2CH_2)_nOH$, avg. n = 55
Uses: Emulsifier, solubilizer, wetting agent for pharmaceuticals
Regulatory: USP/NF compliance
Trade names: Nikkol MYS-55

PEG-75 stearate
CAS 9004-99-3 (generic)
Synonyms: POE (75) stearate; PEG 4000 monostearate
Definition: PEG ester of stearic acid
Formula: $CH_3(CH_2)_{16}CO(OCH_2CH_2)_nOH$, avg. n = 75
Toxicology: Poison by intravenous, intraperitoneal route; mildly toxic by ingestion
Uses: Surfactant, solubilizer, thickener, emollient, opacifier, spreading agent, wetting agent, dispersant for pharmaceuticals
Regulatory: FDA 21CFR §175.300
Trade names: Kessco® PEG 4000 MS
Trade names containing: Gelot 64®

PEG-100 stearate
CAS 9004-99-3 (generic)
Synonyms: POE (100) stearate; PEG (100) monostearate
Definition: PEG ester of stearic acid
Formula: $CH_3(CH_2)_{16}CO(OCH_2CH_2)_nOH$, avg. n = 100
Toxicology: Poison by intravenous, intraperitoneal route; mildly toxic by ingestion
Uses: Surfactant, emulsifier, emollient for creams and lotions; solubilizer
Regulatory: FDA 21CFR §175.300, 176.210
Trade names: Algon ST 1000; Crodet S100; Myrj® 59
Trade names containing: Hodag GMS-A; Mazol® 165C; Simulsol® 165; Tewax TC 65

PEG-150 stearate
CAS 9004-99-3 (generic)
Synonyms: POE (150) stearate; PEG 6000 monostearate
Definition: PEG ester of stearic acid
Formula: $CH_3(CH_2)_{16}CO(OCH_2CH_2)_nOH$, avg. n = 150

Toxicology: Poison by intravenous, intraperitoneal route; mildly toxic by ingestion
Uses: Emulsifier, thickener, solubilizer, emollient, wetting agent, spreading agent, dispersant
Regulatory: FDA 21CFR §175.300
Trade names: Kessco® PEG 6000 MS
Trade names containing: Macol® CPS; Ritachol® 1000; Ritachol® 3000

PEG-300 stearate
Uses: Wetting aid, lubricant, opacifier, dispersant, o/w emulgent, visc. modifier for pharmaceuticals

PEG 1540 stearate. *See* PEG-32 stearate
PEG-2 stearyl ether. *See* Steareth-2
PEG-7 stearyl ether. *See* Steareth-7
PEG-10 stearyl ether. *See* Steareth-10
PEG-16 stearyl ether. *See* Steareth-16
PEG-20 stearyl ether. *See* Steareth-20
PEG-21 stearyl ether. *See* Steareth-21
PEG-25 stearyl ether. *See* Steareth-25
PEG 100 stearyl ether. *See* Steareth-2
PEG-100 stearyl ether. *See* Steareth-100
PEG 500 stearyl ether. *See* Steareth-10
PEG 1000 stearyl ether. *See* Steareth-20

PEG-4 tallate
CAS 61791-00-2 (generic)
Synonyms: POE (4) monotallate; PEG 200 monotallate
Definition: PEG ester of tall oil acid
Formula: $RCO-(OCH_2CH_2)_nOH$, RCO- rep. fatty acids from tall oil, avg. n = 4
Properties: Liq.
Uses: Nonionic detergent, emulsifier, lubricant, softener, wetting agent for pharmaceuticals
Regulatory: FDA 21CFR §175.105, 175.300, 176.210

PEG-8 tallate
CAS 61791-00-2 (generic)
Synonyms: POE (8) monotallate; PEG 400 monotallate
Definition: PEG ester of tall oil acid
Formula: $RCO-(OCH_2CH_2)_nOH$, RCO- rep. fatty acids from tall oil, avg. n = 8
Uses: Emulsifier, dispersant
Regulatory: FDA 21CFR §175.105, 175.300, 176.210, 177.1210, 177.2800
Trade names: Mapeg® 400 MOT

PEG-12 tallate
CAS 61791-00-2 (generic)
Synonyms: POE (12) monotallate; PEG 600 monotallate
Definition: PEG ester of tall oil acid
Formula: $RCO-(OCH_2CH_2)_nOH$, RCO- rep. fatty acids from tall oil, avg. n = 12
Uses: Emulsifier, dispersant
Regulatory: FDA 21CFR §175.105, 175.300, 176.170, 176.180, 176.210, 177.2800
Trade names: Mapeg® 600 MOT

PEG-660 tallate
Uses: Emulsifier for pharmaceutical formulations

PEG-10 tridecyl ether. *See* Trideceth-10
PEG-100 tridecyl ether. *See* Trideceth-100
PEG 500 tridecyl ether. *See* Trideceth-10
PEG-7 tridecyl ether carboxylic acid. *See* Trideceth-7 carboxylic acid

PEG vegetable oil
CAS 3051-35-2
Uses: Used in parenterals
Regulatory: FDA approved for parenterals

Pelargonaldehyde. *See* Nonanal
Pelargonic aldehyde. *See* Nonanal
Pelargonium oil. *See* Geranium oil

Pentadecalactone
CAS 106-02-5; EINECS 203-354-6

ω-Pentadecalactone

FEMA 2840
Synonyms: Oxacyclohexadecan-2-one; 1-Oxa-2-cyclohexadecanone; ω-Pentadecalactone; 15-Hydroxypentadecanoic acid, ω-lactone; Pentadecanolide; Angelica lactone; Cyclopentadecanolide; 14-Hydroxytetradecanoic acid
Definition: Lactone of 15-hydroxypentadecanoic acid
Empirical: $C_{15}H_{28}O_2$
Properties: Persistent musk-like odor; sol. in alcohol; insol. in water; m.w. 240.39; dens. 0.9447 (33 C); m.p. 34-36 C; b.p. 137 C (2 mm); flash pt. 62 C; ref. index 1.4669 (33 C)
Uses: Berry-like synthetic flavoring agent
Regulatory: FDA 21CFR §172.515; FEMA GRAS
Manuf./Distrib. (pharm. & food): Aldrich

ω-Pentadecalactone. *See* Pentadecalactone
Pentadecanolide. *See* Pentadecalactone

Pentaerythritylcocoate
Uses: Ingred. in pharmaceuticals
Trade names containing: Dehymuls® E

Pentaerythrityl tetracaprylate/caprate
CAS 68441-68-9; 69226-96-6; EINECS 270-474-3
Definition: Tetraester of pentaerythritol and a mixture of caprylic and capric acids
Properties: Sp.gr. 0.995 (16 C); flash pt. (COC) 232 C; ref. index 1.4355-1.4365 (16 C)
Uses: Lubricant, emollient for topicals (burn creams, acne creams/lotions, antibiotic ointments)
Manuf./Distrib.: Hatco; Henkel; Inolex
Trade names: Crodamol PTC

Pentaerythrityl tetraisostearate
Definition: Tetraester of isostearic acid and pentaerythritol
Empirical: $C_{77}H_{148}O_8$
Uses: Emollient, lubricant for topical pharmaceuticals
Trade names: Crodamol PTIS

Pentaerythrityl tetralaurate
CAS 13057-50-6; EINECS 235-946-5
Synonyms: Dodecanoic acid, 2,2-bis[[(1-oxododecyl)oxy]methyl-1,3-propanediyl ester
Definition: Tetraester of pentaerythritol and lauric acid
Empirical: $C_{53}H_{100}O_8$
Uses: Emulsifier, emollient for pharmaceutical topicals
Regulatory: FDA 21CFR §1176.210
Trade names: Pelemol® PTL

Pentahydroxycaproic acid. *See* D-Gluconic acid
1,2,3,4,5-Pentahydroxypentane. *See* Xylitol
3-Pentanecarboxylic acid. *See* Diethylacetic acid
Pentanedial. *See* Glutaral
2,4-Pentanedione. *See* Acetylacetone
1-Pentanol. *See* n-Amyl alcohol
Pentan-1-ol. *See* n-Amyl alcohol

3-Pentanol
CAS 584-02-1; EINECS 209-526-7
Synonyms: Diethyl carbinol; sec-n-Amyl alcohol
Empirical: $C_5H_{12}O$
Formula: $(C_2H_5)_2CHOH$
Properties: Liq., char. odor; sl. sol. in water; sol. in alcohol, ether; m.w. 88.15; dens. 0.819 (20/4 C); b.p. 114-116 C; flash pt. 34 C; ref. index 1.410
Precaution: Flamm.
Toxicology: LD50 (oral, rat) 1.87 g/kg; irritant to eyes, nose, and throat
Uses: Solvent; used in pharmaceuticals

t-Pentanol. *See* t-Amyl alcohol
2-Pentanone. *See* Methyl propyl ketone
3,6,9,12,15-Pentaoxahentriacontan-1-ol. *See* Ceteth-5
3,6,9,12,15-Pentaoxatriacont-24-en-1-ol. *See* Oleth-5
Pentasodium diethylene triamine pentaacetate. *See* Pentasodium pentetate
Pentasodium DTPA. *See* Pentasodium pentetate

Pentasodium pentetate
CAS 140-01-2; EINECS 205-391-3
Synonyms: DTPANa$_5$; Pentasodium diethylene triamine pentaacetate; Pentasodium DTPA; Pentetate pentasodium
Classification: Inorganic salt
Toxicology: Moderately irritating to skin and mucous membranes; ingestion can cause violent purging
Uses: Chelating agent; drug stabilization; antibiotic mfg.; used in intravenous
Regulatory: FDA 21CFR §175.105, 176.150; FDA approved for intravenous
Trade names: Cheelox® 80; Versenex 80

18-Pentatriacontanone. *See* Stearone

Pentetate calcium trisodium
CAS 12111-24-9
Synonyms: Calcium trisodium pentetate
Empirical: $C_{14}H_{18}CaN_3O_{10}$
Properties: Solid; sol. in water; insol. in alcohol; m.w. 497.36
Toxicology: LD50 (IP, rat) 3.8 g/kg
Uses: Used in injectables
Regulatory: FDA approved for injectables

Pentetate pentasodium. *See* Pentasodium pentetate

Pentosanpolysulfate sodium
Uses: Used in topicals
Regulatory: FDA approved for topicals

Pentyl acetate. *See* Amyl acetate
Pentyl alcohol. *See* n-Amyl alcohol
t-Pentyl alcohol. *See* t-Amyl alcohol

Pentylamine
CAS 110-58-7; EINECS 203-780-2
Synonyms: n-Amylamine; Amine C$_5$; 1-Aminopentane
Empirical: $C_5H_{13}N$
Formula: $CH_3(CH_2)_4NH_2$
Properties: Dens. 0.753 (20/4 C); b.p. 102-104 C; flash pt. -1 C; ref. index 1.412 (20 C)
Precaution: Highly flamm.; keep away from ignition sources
Toxicology: Irritating to eyes, skin, respiratory system
Uses: Used in topicals
Regulatory: FDA approved for topicals
Manuf./Distrib. (pharm. & food): Mallinckrodt

Pentyl butyrate. *See* Amyl butyrate
Pentylcarbinol. *See* Hexyl alcohol
α-**Pentylcinnamaldehyde.** *See* α-Amylcinnamaldehyde
α-**Pentylcinnamyl alcohol.** *See* α-Amylcinnamyl alcohol
Pentylformic acid. *See* Caproic acid

Pentyl 2-furyl ketone
CAS 14360-50-0
FEMA 3418
Empirical: $C_{10}H_{14}O_2$
Properties: M.w. 166.22; dens. 0.995; b.p. 65-67 C (0.5 mm); flash pt. 25 F
Uses: Apricot, peach-like flavoring agent
Regulatory: FEMA GRAS
Manuf./Distrib. (pharm. & food): Aldrich

Pentyl octanoate. *See* Amyl octanoate
Pepital. *See* Acetaldehyde phenethyl propyl acetal
Peppermint camphor. *See* Menthol

Peppermint leaves
FEMA 2847
Synonyms: Mentha piperita leaves
Definition: Dried leaves and tops of *Mentha piperita*
Properties: Aromatic char. odor, pungent taste producing a cooling sensation in the mouth
Uses: Flavoring agent for pharmaceuticals; stimulant, stomachic, carminative

Peppermint oil

    Regulatory: FDA 21CFR §182.10, GRAS; FEMA GRAS; Japan approved (peppermint); BP, Ph.Eur. compliance
    Manuf./Distrib. (pharm. & food): Chr. Hansen's; Ruger

Peppermint oil
    CAS 8006-90-4
    FEMA 2848
    Synonyms: Mentha piperita oil
    Definition: Volatile oil from steam distillation of *Mentha piperita*
    Properties: Colorless to pale yel. liq., strong penetrating peppermint odor, pungent taste producing sensation of cold when air is drawn into mouth; sol. in 4 vols 90% alcohol; very sl. sol. in water; dens. 0.896-0.908; ref. index 1.460-1.471 (20 C)
    Precaution: Light-sensitive
    Toxicology: LD50 (oral, rat) 2426 mg/kg; mod. toxic by ingestion and IP routes; can cause allergic reactions, hay fever, skin rash; mutagenic data; heated to decomp., emits acrid smoke and irritating fumes
    Uses: Natural flavoring agent, perfume; carminative; used in buccals, orals, toothpaste, tooth powds., eye lotions; peppermint water as vehicle
    Regulatory: FDA 21CFR §182.10, 182.20, GRAS; 27CFR §21.65, 21.151; FEMA GRAS; Europe listed (pulegone levels: 25 ppm in food to 350 ppm in mint confectionery); FDA approved for buccals, orals; USP/ NF, BP, Ph.Eur. compliance
    Manuf./Distrib. (pharm. & food): Acme-Hardesty; Chart; Commodity Services; Florida Treatt; Ruger; Spectrum Chem. Mfg.

Peppermint spirit
    CAS 8030-00-0
    UN No. 1170
    Definition: Contains peppermint oil and alcohol
    Precaution: DOT: Flamm. liq.; light-sensitive
    Uses: Flavoring agent, perfume for pharmaceuticals
    Regulatory: USP/NF compliance; BP compliance
    Manuf./Distrib. (pharm. & food): Spectrum Chem. Mfg.

Pepsin
    CAS 9001-75-6; EINECS 232-629-3
    Synonyms: Pepsinum
    Definition: A digestive enzyme of gastric juice which hydrolyzes certain linkages of proteins to produce peptones
    Properties: Wh. or ylsh. wh. powd. or lustrous transparent or translucent scales, odorless; sol. in water; insol. in alcohol, chloroform, ether; m.w. ≈ 36,000
    Uses: Proteolytic enzyme
    Regulatory: FDA GRAS; Canada, Japan approved; BP, Ph.Eur. compliance
    Manuf./Distrib.: Am. Biorganics; EM Industries; G Fiske & Co Ltd; R.W. Greeff; Worthington Biochemical
    Manuf./Distrib. (pharm. & food): G Fiske & Co Ltd
    Trade names: Pepsin 1:3000 NF XII Powd.; Pepsin 1:10,000 Powd. or Gran.; Pepsin 1:15,000 Powd.

Pepsinum. *See* Pepsin
Perhydrosqualene. *See* Squalane
Periclase. *See* Magnesium oxide

Perillaldehyde
    CAS 18031-40-8
    FEMA 3557
    Synonyms: 4-Isopropenyl-1-cyclohexene-1-carboxaldehyde; p-Mentha-1,8-dien-7-al
    Empirical: $C_{10}H_{14}O$
    Properties: Green oily fatty cherry odor; m.w. 150.22; dens. 0.965; b.p. 104-105 C (10 mm); flash pt. 204 F; ref. index 1.5072
    Toxicology: Irritant
    Uses: Cherry-like synthetic flavoring agent
    Regulatory: FDA 21CFR §172.515; FEMA GRAS; Japan approved as flavoring
    Manuf./Distrib. (pharm. & food): Aldrich

Permanent orange. *See* D&C Orange No. 17
Permatone orange. *See* D&C Orange No. 17
Peroxydisulfuric acid dipotassium salt. *See* Potassium persulfate
Persic oil. *See* Apricot kernel oil; Peach kernel oil
Peruvian balsam. *See* Balsam Peru

Peruviol. *See* Trimethyldodecatrieneol
Petrohol. *See* Isopropyl alcohol

Petrolatum
CAS 8009-03-8 (NF); 8027-32-5 (USP); EINECS 232-373-2
Synonyms: Petroleum jelly; White soft paraffin; Petrolatum amber; Vaseline; Petrolatum white; White petrolatum
Classification: Petroleum hydrocarbons
Definition: Semisolid mixture of hydrocarbons obtained from petroleum
Properties: Yellowish to lt. amber or white semisolid, unctuous mass; pract. odorless and tasteless; sol. in benzene, chloroform, ether, petrol. ether, oils; pract. insol. in water; dens. 0.820-0.865 (60/25 C); m.p. 38-54 C; ref. index 1.460-1.474 (60 C)
Toxicology: Can cause allergic skin reactions in hypersensitive persons; generally nontoxic; heated to decomp., emits acrid smoke and irritating fumes
Uses: Ointment base, filler, emollient; used in topical prescription pharmaceuticals, ophthalmics, orals, otics, suppositories; protects skin from irritation
Regulatory: FDA 21CFR §172.880, 172.884, 173.340, 175.105, 175.125, 175.176, 175.300, 176.170, 176.200, 176.210, 177.2600, 177.2800, 1787.3570, 178.3700, 178.3910, 573.720; FDA approved for ophthalmics, orals, topicals, otics; USP/NF, BP compliance
Manuf./Distrib.: Exxon; Harcros; Magie Bros. Oil; Mobil; Penreco; Stevenson Cooper; Witco/Petrol. Spec.
Manuf./Distrib. (pharm. & food): Aldrich; Ruger; Spectrum Chem. Mfg.
Trade names: Fonoline® White; Fonoline® Yellow; Mineral Jelly No. 10; Mineral Jelly No. 14; Mineral Jelly No. 17; Ointment Base No. 3; Ointment Base No. 4; Ointment Base No. 6; Penreco Amber; Penreco Blond; Penreco Cream; Penreco Lily; Penreco Regent; Penreco Royal; Penreco Snow; Penreco Super; Penreco Ultima; Perfecta® USP; Protopet® Alba; Protopet® White 1S; Protopet® White 2L; Protopet® White 3C; Protopet® Yellow 2A; Protopet® Yellow 3C; Protopet® Yellow A; Sonojell® No. 4; Sonojell® No. 9; Super White Fonoline®; Super White Protopet®
Trade names containing: Alcolan®; Alcolan® 36W; Alcolan® 40; Amerchol® 400; Amerchol® C; Amerchol® CAB; Amerchol® H-9; Argobase EU; Argobase EUC 2; Cremba; Dehymuls® K; Emery® 1740; Emery® 1747; Fancol CAB; Lexate® PX; Protegin®; Protegin® W; Protegin® WX; Protegin® X

Petrolatum amber. *See* Petrolatum
Petrolatum liquid. *See* Mineral oil
Petrolatum white. *See* Petrolatum
Petroleum jelly. *See* Petrolatum
Petroleum wax, crystalline. *See* Paraffin
Petroleum wax, microcrystalline. *See* Microcrystalline wax
PGE. *See* Phenyl glycidyl ether

Pharmaceutical glaze
Synonyms: Glaze, pharmaceutical
Definition: Denatured alcohol sol'n. contg. 20-57% of anhydrous shellac
Uses: Coating agent used in orals
Regulatory: FDA approved for orals; USP/NF compliance

α-Phellandrene
CAS 99-83-2
FEMA 2856
Synonyms: p-Mentha-1,5-diene; 2-Methyl-5-isopropyl-1,3-cyclohexadiene; 2-Methyl-5-(1-methylethyl)-1,3-cyclohexadiene; 5-Isopropyl-2-methyl-1,3-cyclohexadiene
Empirical: $C_{10}H_{16}$
Properties: Colorless mobile oil, minty herbaceous odor; sol. in ether; insol. in water; m.w. 136.23; dens. 0.850; flash pt. 117 F
Toxicology: Ingestion can cause vomiting, diarrhea; can be irritating to, and absorbed through, skin
Uses: Minty synthetic flavoring agent
Regulatory: FDA 21CFR §172.515; FEMA GRAS
Manuf./Distrib. (pharm. & food): Aldrich

Phemerol chloride. *See* Benzethonium chloride
Phenacyl chloride. *See* Chloroacetophenone
Phenazone. *See* Antipyrine
β-Phenethanol. *See* Phenethyl alcohol
Phenethyl acetate. *See* 2-Phenylethyl acetate
2-Phenethyl acetate. *See* 2-Phenylethyl acetate
β-Phenethyl acetate. *See* 2-Phenylethyl acetate

Phenethyl alcohol
CAS 60-12-8; EINECS 200-456-2
FEMA 2858
Synonyms: Benzeneethanol; Benzyl carbinol; 2-Phenylethanol; β-Phenethanol; 2-Phenylethyl alcohol; Phenylethyl alcohol; β-Phenylethyl alcohol
Classification: Aromatic alcohol
Empirical: $C_8H_{10}O$
Formula: $C_6H_5CH_2CH_2OH$
Properties: Colorless liq., floral rose odor, burning taste; misc. with alcohol, ether; sol. in fixed oils, glycerin, propylene glycol; sl. sol. in water; m.w. 122.18; dens. 1.0245 (15 C); m.p. -27 C; b.p. 220 C; flash pt. 102 C; ref. index 1.532 (20 C)
Precaution: Combustible when exposed to heat or flame; reactive with oxidizing materials
Toxicology: LD50 (oral, rat) 1790 mg/kg; poison by ingestion, IP routes; mod. toxic by skin contact; skin and eye irritant; experimental teratogenic effects; severe CNS injury; heated to decomp., emits acrid smoke and irritating fumes
Uses: Antimicrobial preservative; antiseptic for topical use; solvent; honey-like flavoring and fragrance; used in ophthalmics, otics, topicals, vaginals
Regulatory: FDA 21CFR §172.515, CIR approved, EPA reg.; FEMA GRAS; JSCI listed; FDA approved for ophthalmics, otics, topicals, vaginals; USP/NF compliance
Manuf./Distrib.: Aldrich; Arco; BASF
Manuf./Distrib. (pharm. & food): Aldrich; Chr. Hansen's; Mallinckrodt; Spectrum Chem. Mfg.

Phenethyl anthranilate
CAS 133-18-6
FEMA 2859
Synonyms: Benzyl carbinyl anthranilate; β-Phenylethyl-o-aminobenzoate; 2-Phenylethyl anthranilate
Definition: Ester of anthranilic acid and phenylethyl alcohol
Empirical: $C_{15}H_{15}NO_2$
Properties: Wh. colorless cryst. mass; insol. in water; m.w. 241.29; m.p. 39-44 C; b.p. 226 C; flash pt. > 230 F
Uses: Honey-like, fruity synthetic flavoring agent
Regulatory: FDA 21CFR §172.515; FEMA GRAS
Manuf./Distrib. (pharm. & food): Aldrich

Phenethyl benzoate
CAS 94-47-3
FEMA 2860
Synonyms: 2-Phenylethyl benzoate
Empirical: $C_{15}H_{14}O_2$
Properties: Colorless to ylsh. oily liq., rose honey-like odor; insol. in water; m.w. 226.28; flash pt. > 100 C; ref. index 1.558-1.562
Uses: Honey-like synthetic flavoring agent
Regulatory: FDA 21CFR §172.515; FEMA GRAS
Manuf./Distrib. (pharm. & food): Aldrich

β-Phenethyl-n-butanoate. *See* Phenethyl butyrate

Phenethyl butyrate
CAS 103-52-6
FEMA 2861
Synonyms: β-Phenethyl-n-butanoate; 2-Phenylethyl butyrate
Definition: Ester of phenylethyl alcohol and n-butyric acid
Empirical: $C_{12}H_{16}O_2$
Properties: Colorless liq., rose-like odor, sweet honey-like taste; insol. in water; m.w. 192.26; dens. 0.994; b.p. 260 C; flash pt. > 230 F; ref. index 1.488-1.492
Uses: Sweet grape, strawberry-like synthetic flavoring agent
Regulatory: FDA 21CFR §172.515; FEMA GRAS
Manuf./Distrib. (pharm. & food): Aldrich

Phenethyl hexanoate
CAS 6290-37-5
FEMA 3221
Empirical: $C_{14}H_{20}O_2$
Properties: M.w. 220.31; dens. 0.971; flash pt. > 230 F
Uses: Fruity banana, pineapple-like flavoring agent
Regulatory: FEMA GRAS
Manuf./Distrib. (pharm. & food): Aldrich

Phenethyl isobutyrate
CAS 103-48-0
FEMA 2862
Synonyms: 2-Phenylethyl isobutyrate
Empirical: $C_{12}H_{16}O_2$
Properties: M.w. 192.26; dens. 0.988; b.p. 250 C; flash pt. 227 F
Uses: Fruity synthetic flavoring agent
Regulatory: FDA 21CFR §172.515; FEMA GRAS
Manuf./Distrib. (pharm. & food): Aldrich

Phenethyl isovalerate
CAS 140-26-1
FEMA 2871
Synonyms: 2-Phenylethyl isovalerate; Phenethyl 3-methylbutyrate
Empirical: $C_{13}H_{18}O_2$
Properties: M.w. 206.29; dens. 0.974; b.p. 268 C; flash pt. > 230 F
Uses: Fruity synthetic flavoring agent
Regulatory: FDA 21CFR §172.515; FEMA GRAS
Manuf./Distrib. (pharm. & food): Aldrich

Phenethyl 2-methylbutyrate
CAS 24817-51-4
FEMA 3632
Empirical: $C_{13}H_{18}O_2$
Properties: M.w. 206.29; dens. 0.975; flash pt. > 230 F
Uses: Fruity synthetic flavoring agent
Regulatory: FDA 21CFR §172.515; FEMA GRAS
Manuf./Distrib. (pharm. & food): Aldrich

Phenethyl 3-methylbutyrate. *See* Phenethyl isovalerate
Phenododecinium bromide. *See* Domiphen bromide

Phenol
CAS 108-95-2; EINECS 203-632-7
FEMA 3223; UN No. 1671 (solid), 2312 (fused), 2821 (sol'n.)
Classification: Aromatic organic compd.; carbolic acid
Empirical: C_6H_6O
Formula: C_6H_5OH
Properties: Colorless to lt. pink needle-shaped cryst., char. odor of coal tar and wood; sol. in alcohol, glycerin, chloroform, ether, water; sl. sol. in min. oil; m.w. 94.11; dens. 1.07; m.p. 40-42 C; b.p. 182 C; flash pt. 175 F; darkens on exposure to lt., air
Precaution: Vapor is flamm.; avoid contact with skin; DOT: poisonous material; moisture- and light-sensitive
Toxicology: Ingestion of even sm. amts. may cause vomiting, circulatory collapse, paralysis, convulsions, coma, grnsh. urine, necrosis of mouth and gastrointestinal tract; death results from respiratory failure; may cause serious skin burns; possible carcinogen
Uses: Antimicrobial preservative for topical pharmaceuticals, parenteral drug prods., injectables, insulin prods.; disinfectant anesthetic for skin; active ingred. in deodorant soaps and mouthwashes
Usage level: 0.5% (topicals), 0.2-5% (parenterals)
Regulatory: FEMA GRAS; FDA approved for injectables, parenterals, topicals; USP/NF, BP, Ph.Eur. compliance
Manuf./Distrib.: Allied-Signal; Aristech; Ashland; J.T. Baker; PMC Spec.; Royale Pigments & Chems.; Shell; Texaco; Van Waters & Rogers
Manuf./Distrib. (pharm. & food): Aldrich; R.W. Greeff; Integra; Ruger; Spectrum Chem. Mfg.

Phenol, 5-methyl-2-(1-methylethyl)-. *See* Thymol

Phenol sulfonic acid
CAS 98-67-9; 1333-39-7' 74665-14-8; EINECS 202-691-6; 215-587-0; 277-962-5
UN No. 1803
Synonyms: p-Phenolsulfonic acid; Phenol-4-sulfonic acid; 4-Hydroxybenzenesulfonic acid; Sulfocarbolic acid
Classification: Aromatic organic compd.
Empirical: $C_6H_6O_4S$
Formula: $HOC_6H_4SO_3H$
Properties: Yellowish liq. (brown in air); sol. in water, alcohol; m.w. 174.18; dens. 1.34 (20/4 C, 65% aq.)
Precaution: DOT: Corrosive material
Toxicology: Irritant to skin and tissues; causes burns

Phenol-4-sulfonic acid

Uses: Mfg. of pharmaceuticals
Manuf./Distrib.: Fluka; A J & J O Pilar; Sloss Ind.; Spectrum Chem. Mfg.
Manuf./Distrib. (pharm. & food): Kishida Chems.
Trade names: Eltesol® PA 65; Eltesol® PSA 65

Phenol-4-sulfonic acid. *See* Phenol sulfonic acid
p-Phenolsulfonic acid. *See* Phenol sulfonic acid
Phenol, 4-(1,1,3,3-tetramethylbutyl)-, polymer with formaldehyde and oxirane. *See* Tyloxapol
Phenomerborum. *See* Phenylmercuric borate

Phenoxyacetic acid
CAS 122-59-8; EINECS 204-556-7
FEMA 2872
Synonyms: Phenylium; o-Phenylglycolic acid; Phenoxyethanoic acid; Glycolic acid phenyl ether
Empirical: $C_8H_8O_3$
Formula: $C_6H_5OCH2COOH$
Properties: Cryst. solid, sour odor, honey-like taste; readily sol. in alcohol, ether, benzene, CS_2, glac. acetic acid; sl. sol. in water; m.w. 152.14; m.p. 95 C; b.p 285 C (some decomp.)
Toxicology: Mild irritant
Uses: Intermediate for pharmaceuticals (keratin exfoliative to soften calluses, corns); precursor in antibiotic fermentations esp. penicillin V; synthetic flavoring agent
Regulatory: FDA 21CFR §172.515; FEMA GRAS; BP compliance
Manuf./Distrib.: Aldrich; Chemie Linz UK; Great Lakes; Penta Mfg.; Schweizerhall; Spectrum Chem. Mfg.
Manuf./Distrib. (pharm. & food): Aldrich; Mikuni Pharmaceutical; Penta Mfg.

Phenoxyethanoic acid. *See* Phenoxyacetic acid

Phenoxyethanol
CAS 122-99-6; EINECS 204-589-7
Synonyms: 2-Phenoxyethanol; Ethylene glycol monophenyl ether; Ethylene glycol phenyl ether; Phenoxytol
Classification: Aromatic ether alcohol
Definition: Phenol polyglycol ether
Empirical: $C_8H_{10}O_2$
Properties: Clear liq., faint aromatic odor, burning taste; sl. sol. in water; sol. in alcohol, ether, NaOH sol'ns.; m.w. 138.18; dens. 1.1094 (20/20 C); m.p. 14 C; b.p. 242 C; flash pt. 121 C; ref. index 1.534 (20 C)
Toxicology: Moderately toxic by ingestion and skin contact; skin and severe eye irritant; LD50 (rat, oral) 1.26 g/kg
Uses: Antimicrobial preservative
Regulatory: FDA 21CFR §175.105; CIR approved, EPA reg.; JSCI listed 1.0% max.; Europe listed 1% max.; BP, Ph.Eur. compliance
Manuf./Distrib.: Amber Syn.; Jan Dekker; Hüls AG; Penta Mfg.; Tri-K
Trade names: Phenoxetol
Trade names containing: Nipaguard® BPX; Phenonip; Uniphen P-23

2-Phenoxyethanol. *See* Phenoxyethanol

Phenoxyethyl isobutyrate
CAS 103-60-6
FEMA 2873
Synonyms: 2-Phenoxyethyl 2-methylpropionate; 2-Phenoxyethyl isobutyrate
Empirical: $C_{12}H_{16}O_3$
Properties: Colorless liq., honey rose-like odor, sweet peach-like taste; misc. in alcohol, chloroform, ether; insol. in water; m.w. 208.26; dens. 1.044; b.p. 265 C; flash pt. > 212 F; ref. index 1.492
Precaution: Combustible
Toxicology: Heated to decomp., emits acrid smoke and irritating fumes
Uses: Honey-like synthetic flavoring agent
Regulatory: FDA 21CFR §172.515; FEMA GRAS
Manuf./Distrib.: Hüls
Manuf./Distrib. (pharm. & food): Aldrich; Hüls AG

2-Phenoxyethyl isobutyrate. *See* Phenoxyethyl isobutyrate
2-Phenoxyethyl 2-methylpropionate. *See* Phenoxyethyl isobutyrate

Phenoxyisopropanol
CAS 4169-04-4; EINECS 224-027-4
Synonyms: 1-Phenoxy-2-propanol; 1-Phenoxypropan-2-ol
Classification: Aromatic ether alcohol

Empirical: $C_9H_{12}O_2$
Uses: Antiseptic for skin care
Trade names: Propylene Phenoxetol
Trade names containing: Phenosept

1-Phenoxy-2-propanol. *See* Phenoxyisopropanol
1-Phenoxypropan-2-ol. *See* Phenoxyisopropanol
Phenoxytol. *See* Phenoxyethanol

Phenylacetaldehyde
CAS 122-78-1; EINECS 204-574-5
FEMA 2874
Synonyms: PAA; Benzeneacetaldehyde; Hyacinthin; α-Tolualdehyde; α-Toluic aldehyde; Phenylacetic aldehyde; Phenylethanal
Empirical: C_8H_8O
Formula: $C_5H_5CH_2CHO$
Properties: Colorless oily liq., becomes more visc. on standing, hyacinth, lilac odor; sol. in alcohol, ether, propylene glycol; sl. sol. in water; m.w. 120.16; dens. 1.0123-1.030; m.p. 33-34 C; b.p. 78 C (10 mm); flash pt. 68 C; ref. index 1.525-1.545
Precaution: Combustible liq.
Toxicology: LD50 (oral, rat) 1550 mg/kg; mod. toxic by ingestion; human skin irritant; heated to decomp., emits acrid smoke and irritating fumes
Uses: Apricot, berry-like flavoring and fragrance in medicinal preps.
Regulatory: FDA 21CFR §172.515; FEMA GRAS
Manuf./Distrib.: BASF
Manuf./Distrib. (pharm. & food): Aldrich; BASF

Phenylacetaldehyde 2,3-butylene glycol acetal
FEMA 2875
Synonyms: 4,5-Dimethyl-2-benzyl-1,3-dioxolan
Empirical: $C_{12}H_{16}O_2$
Properties: Colorless visc. liq., earthy fragrance, fruity flavor; sol. in alcohol; insol. in water; m.w. 192.26
Uses: Synthetic flavoring agent
Regulatory: FDA 21CFR §172.515; FEMA GRAS

Phenylacetic acid
CAS 103-82-2; EINECS 203-148-6
FEMA 2878
Synonyms: α-Toluic acid; Benzeneacetic acid; α-Tolylic acid
Classification: Aromatic organic compd.
Empirical: $C_8H_8O_2$
Formula: $C_6H_5CH_2COOH$
Properties: Wh. crystals, disagreeable geranium odor; sol. in alcohol, ether, hot water; m.w. 136.16; dens. 1.0809; m.p. 77-78 C; b.p. 265.5 C; flash pt. > 212 F
Precaution: Combustible
Toxicology: LD50 (oral, rat) 2250 mg/kg; mod. toxic by ingestion, subcutaneous, IP routes; experimental teratogen; heated to decomp., emits acrid smoke and irritating fumes
Uses: Precursor in mfg. of penicillin G; honey-like synthetic flavoring agent
Regulatory: FDA 21CFR §172.515; FEMA GRAS
Manuf./Distrib.: Aldrich; Penta Mfg.; Schweizerhall; Spectrum Chem. Mfg.
Manuf./Distrib. (pharm. & food): Aldrich; Mikuni Pharmaceutical

Phenylacetic aldehyde. *See* Phenylacetaldehyde
Phenylacrolein. *See* Cinnamal
β-Phenylacrylic acid. *See* Cinnamic acid
trans-3-Phenylacrylic acid. *See* Cinnamic acid
γ-Phenylallyl alcohol. *See* Cinnamyl alcohol
γ-Phenylallyl propionate. *See* Cinnamyl propionate
1-[[4-(Phenylazo)phenyl]azo]-2-naphthalenol. *See* CI 26100; D&C Red No. 17
N-Phenyl-1,4-benzenediamine. *See* N-Phenyl-p-phenylenediamine

Phenylbenzimidazole sulfonic acid
CAS 27503-81-7
Synonyms: 2-Phenylbenzimidazole-5-sulfonic acid
Classification: Aromatic organic compd.
Empirical: $C_{13}H_{10}N_2O_3S$

2-Phenylbenzimidazole-5-sulfonic acid

> *Properties:* Cryst. powd.; m.w. 274.30
> *Uses:* UV-B filter for sunscreens

2-Phenylbenzimidazole-5-sulfonic acid. *See* Phenylbenzimidazole sulfonic acid
4-Phenyl-3-buten-2-one. *See* Benzylidene acetone
trans-4-Phenyl-3-buten-2-one. *See* Benzylidene acetone
Phenylcarbinol. *See* Benzyl alcohol
Phenylcarboxylic acid. *See* Benzoic acid

Phenyl dichlorophosphate
> CAS 770-12-7
> *Uses:* Intermediate
> *Manuf./Distrib.:* Albright & Wilson
> *Manuf./Distrib. (pharm. & food):* Aldrich
> *Trade names:* PDCP

Phenyldimethyl carbinyl isobutyrate. *See* α,α-Dimethylbenzyl isobutyrate
Phenylethanal. *See* Phenylacetaldehyde
2-Phenylethanol. *See* Phenethyl alcohol
1-Phenylethanone. *See* Acetophenone
1-Phenylethyl acetate. *See* α-Methylbenzyl acetate

2-Phenylethyl acetate
> CAS 103-45-7; EINECS 203-113-5
> FEMA 2857
> *Synonyms:* Phenethyl acetate; 2-Phenethyl acetate; β-Phenethyl acetate; Acetic acid 2-phenylethyl ester;
> Benzylcarbinyl acetate
> *Definition:* Ester of phenethyl alcohol and acetic acid
> *Empirical:* $C_{10}H_{12}O_2$
> *Formula:* $CH_3COOCH_2CH_2C_6H_5$
> *Properties:* Colorless liq., sweet rosy honey odor; sol. in alcohol, fixed oils, propylene glycol; insol. in water,
> glycerin; m.w. 164.21; dens. 1.033 (20/4 C); m.p. 164 C; b.p. 232-234 C; flash pt. ≈ 105 C; ref. index 1.498
> (20 C)
> *Precaution:* Combustible exposed to heat or flame; can react vigorously with oxidizing agents
> *Toxicology:* LD50 (oral, rat) 3670 mg/kg; mod. toxic by ingestion; mildly toxic by skin contact; heated to
> decomp., emits acrid smoke and irritating fumes
> *Uses:* Apple, apricot, honey-like synthetic flavoring agent
> *Regulatory:* FDA 21CFR §172.515; FEMA GRAS; Japan approved as flavoring
> *Manuf./Distrib. (pharm. & food):* Aldrich

α-Phenylethyl acetate. *See* α-Methylbenzyl acetate
Phenylethyl alcohol. *See* Phenethyl alcohol
2-Phenylethyl alcohol. *See* Phenethyl alcohol
β-Phenylethyl alcohol. *See* Phenethyl alcohol
β-Phenylethyl-o-aminobenzoate. *See* Phenethyl anthranilate
2-Phenylethyl anthranilate. *See* Phenethyl anthranilate
2-Phenylethyl benzoate. *See* Phenethyl benzoate
2-Phenylethyl butyrate. *See* Phenethyl butyrate
Phenylethylene. *See* Styrene
2-Phenylethyl isobutyrate. *See* Phenethyl isobutyrate
2-Phenylethyl isovalerate. *See* Phenethyl isovalerate
Phenylformic acid. *See* Benzoic acid

Phenyl glycidyl ether
> CAS 122-60-1; EINECS 204-557-2
> *Synonyms:* PGE; 1,2-Epoxy-3-phenoxypropane; Oxirane, (phenoxymethyl)-
> *Classification:* Aromatic organic compd.
> *Empirical:* $C_9H_{10}O_2$
> *Formula:* $H_2COCHCH_2OC_6H_5$
> *Properties:* Colorless liq.; sol. in ethanol; m.w. 150.19; dens. 1.113 (20/4 C); m.p. 3.5 C; b.p. 245 C
> *Precaution:* Incompat. with acids, alkalies, amines, oxidizing agents; hazardous decomp. prods.: CO,
> hydrocarbons
> *Toxicology:* LD50 (oral, rat) 2150-3850 mg/kg, (dermal, rabbit) 1500 mg/kg; moderately toxic by ingestion, skin
> contact, subcutaneous routes; severe eye and skin irritant; TLV 1 ppm in air; may cause sensitization by
> skin contact; may cause cancer

Uses: Chemical intermediate for pharmaceuticals
Manuf./Distrib.: Monomer-Polymer & Dajac; Raschig; Richman

o-Phenylglycolic acid. *See* Phenoxyacetic acid
Phenyl-2-hydroxybenzoate. *See* Phenyl salicylate
Phenylium. *See* Phenoxyacetic acid
Phenyl mercaptan. *See* Thiophenol
Phenylmercuriborate. *See* Phenylmercuric borate

Phenylmercuric acetate
CAS 62-38-2; EINECS 200-532-5
UN No. 1674
Synonyms: PMAC; Phenylmercury acetate; (Acetato)phenylmercury; Acetoxyphenylmercury
Classification: Metallo-organic compd.
Empirical: $C_8H_8HgO_2$
Formula: $C_6H_5HgOCOCH_3$
Properties: White to cream prisms, odorless; sol. in 600 parts water; sol. in alcohol, benzene, acetone, glacial acetic acid; m.w. 336.75; m.p. 148-150 C
Precaution: Inactivated by sulfides, thioglycollates; light-sensitive
Toxicology: Toxic by ingestion, inhalation, skin absorption; strong irritant; LD50 (rat, oral) 22 mg/kg
Uses: Antimicrobial preservative, antibacterial, antifungal; used in parenteral prods., ophthalmics, nasal sprays, ointments, eye drops; spermacide
Usage level: 0.0065%; 0.001% (parenterals); 0.002-0.004% (ophthalmics)
Regulatory: USA EPA reg., limited to eye cosmetics/pharmaceuticals; Europe listed; USP/NF compliance
Manuf./Distrib.: Allchem Industries; Aldrich; Atomergic Chemetals; W.A. Cleary; EM Industries
Manuf./Distrib. (pharm. & food): Spectrum Chem. Mfg.

Phenylmercuric borate
CAS 102-98-7
UN No. 2026
Synonyms: Phenomerborum; Phenylmercuriborate; Phenylmercury borate; Orthoborato(1-)-o-phenylmercury
Classification: Phenylmercuric salt
Empirical: $C_6H_7BHgO_3$
Formula: $C_6H_5HgOB(OH)_2$
Properties: Wh. cryst. powd.; sol. in alcohol; sl. sol. in water; m.w. 3383.56; m.p. 120-130 C
Precaution: Light-sensitive
Toxicology: Toxic by ingestion, inhalation, and skin absorption
Uses: Antimicrobial preservative for parenterals, ophthalmics
Usage level: 0.001% (parenterals), 0.002-0.004% (ophthalmics)
Regulatory: BP, Ph.Eur. compliance
Manuf./Distrib.: Spectrum Chem. Mfg.

Phenylmercuric nitrate
CAS 55-68-5; 8003-05-2
UN No. 1895
Synonyms: PMN; Merphenyl nitrate; Nitratophenylmercury; Phenylmercury nitrate
Formula: $C_6H_5HgNO_3HOHgC_6H_5$
Properties: Wh. fine cryst.; sl. sol. in alcohol, glycerin; very sl. sol. in water; insol. in ether; m.w. 634.41; m.p. 176-186 C dec.
Precaution: Light-sensitive
Toxicology: Irritant; toxic by ingestion, inhalation, and skin absorption; causes burns; irritating to respiratory system
Uses: Antimicrobial preservative, antibacterial, antifungal for parenterals, ophthalmics, intramuscular injectables; spermicide; its use in topical eye preps. and as an intravaginal contraceptive may cause concerns of mercurial poisoning
Usage level: 0.001% (parenterals); 0.002-0.004% (ophthalmics)
Regulatory: FDA approved for intramuscular injectables; USP/NF, BP, Ph.Eur. compliance
Manuf./Distrib.: Fluka
Manuf./Distrib. (pharm. & food): Aldrich; Spectrum Chem. Mfg.

Phenylmercury acetate. *See* Phenylmercuric acetate
Phenylmercury borate. *See* Phenylmercuric borate
Phenylmercury nitrate. *See* Phenylmercuric nitrate
Phenylmethanol. *See* Benzyl alcohol

Phenylmethyl acetate. *See* Benzyl acetate
Phenylmethyl benzoate. *See* Benzyl benzoate
Phenylmethyl 2-hydroxybenzoate. *See* Benzylsalicylate
Phenylmethyl 4-hydroxybenzoate. *See* Benzylparaben
Phenylmethyl 3-phenyl-2-propenoate. *See* Benzyl cinnamate
1-Phenyl-2-pentanol. *See* α-Propylphenethyl alcohol

5-Phenyl-1-pentanol
  CAS 10521-91-2
  FEMA 3618
  Empirical: $C_{11}H_{16}O$
  Properties: M.w. 164.25; dens. 0.975; b.p. 155 C (20 mm); flash pt. > 230 F
  Uses: Medicinal flavoring agent
  Regulatory: FEMA GRAS
  Manuf./Distrib. (pharm. & food): Aldrich

N-Phenyl-p-phenylenediamine
  CAS 101-54-2; EINECS 202-951-9
  Synonyms: 4-Aminodiphenylamine; p-Aminodiphenylamine; N-Phenylphenylene-p-diamine; N-Phenyl-1,4-
    benzenediamine
  Classification: Aromatic amine salt
  Empirical: $C_{12}H_{12}N_2$
  Formula: $NH_2C_6H_4NHC_6H_5$
  Properties: Purple powd.; insol. in water; sol. in alcohol, acetone; m.w. 184.11; m.p. 75 C
  Toxicology: Moderately toxic by ingestion; severe eye irritant; heated to dec., emits toxic fumes of NO_x
  Uses: Intermediate for pharmaceuticals
  Manuf./Distrib.: Fluka
  Manuf./Distrib. (pharm. & food): Aldrich

N-Phenylphenylene-p-diamine. *See* N-Phenyl-p-phenylenediamine
3-Phenylpropanal. *See* Hydrocinnamaldehyde

1-Phenyl-1,2-propanedione
  CAS 579-07-7
  FEMA 3226
  Empirical: $C_9H_8O_2$
  Properties: M.w. 148.16; dens. 1.101; b.p. 103-105 C (14 mm); flash pt. 184 F
  Uses: Medicinal flavoring agent
  Regulatory: FEMA GRAS
  Manuf./Distrib. (pharm. & food): Aldrich

2-Phenylpropan-2-yl isobutyrate. *See* α,α-Dimethylbenzyl isobutyrate
3-Phenylpropenal. *See* Cinnamal
3-Phenyl-2-propenal. *See* Cinnamal
3-Phenylpropenoic acid. *See* Cinnamic acid
3-Phenyl-2-propen-1-ol. *See* Cinnamyl alcohol
Phenyl propenyl-n-butyrate. *See* Cinnamyl butyrate
3-Phenyl-2-propenyl propanoate. *See* Cinnamyl propionate
3-Phenylpropionaldehyde. *See* Hydrocinnamaldehyde
3-Phenylpropionic acid. *See* Hydrocinnamic acid
α-Phenylpropyl alcohol butyric ester. *See* 2-Phenylpropyl butyrate
α-Phenylpropyl alcohol isobutyric ester. *See* 2-Phenylpropyl isobutyrate

2-Phenylpropyl butyrate
  CAS 80866-83-7
  FEMA 2891
  Synonyms: β-Methylphenethyl butyrate; Hydratropyl butyrate; α-Phenylpropyl alcohol butyric ester
  Empirical: $C_{13}H_{18}O_2$
  Properties: M.w. 206.29; dens. 0.991; flash pt. > 230 F
  Uses: Sweet apricot-like synthetic flavoring agent
  Regulatory: FDA 21CFR §172.515; FEMA GRAS
  Manuf./Distrib. (pharm. & food): Aldrich

α-Phenylpropyl butyrate. *See* α-Ethylbenzyl butyrate

2-Phenylpropyl isobutyrate
  CAS 65813-53-8

FEMA 2892
Synonyms: Hydratropyl isobutyrate; α-Phenylpropyl alcohol isobutyric ester
Empirical: $C_{13}H_{18}O_2$
Properties: M.w. 206.29; dens. 0.973; flash pt. > 230 F
Uses: Fruity synthetic flavoring agent
Regulatory: FDA 21CFR §172.515; FEMA GRAS
Manuf./Distrib. (pharm. & food): Aldrich

3-Phenylpropyl isobutyrate
CAS 103-58-2
FEMA 2893
Synonyms: 3-Phenylpropyl 2-methylpropionate; Hydrocinnamic isobutyrate; Hydrocinnamyl isobutyrate
Empirical: $C_{13}H_{18}O_2$
Properties: M.w. 206.29; dens. 0.979; b.p. 282 C; flash pt. > 230 F
Uses: Fruity synthetic flavoring agent
Regulatory: FDA 21CFR §172.515; FEMA GRAS
Manuf./Distrib. (pharm. & food): Aldrich; Hüls AG

3-Phenylpropyl isovalerate
CAS 5452-07-3
FEMA 2899
Synonyms: Hydrocinnamyl isovalerate
Empirical: $C_{14}H_{20}O_2$
Properties: M.w. 220.31; dens. 0.980; b.p. 285 C; flash pt. > 230 F
Uses: Plum, raspberry, strawberry-like synthetic flavoring agent
Regulatory: FDA 21CFR §172.515; FEMA GRAS
Manuf./Distrib. (pharm. & food): Aldrich

3-Phenylpropyl 2-methylpropionate. *See* 3-Phenylpropyl isobutyrate

Phenyl salicylate
CAS 118-55-8; EINECS 204-259-2
Synonyms: Phenyl-2-hydroxybenzoate; Salol
Formula: $2\text{-}(HO)C_6H_4CO_2C_6H_5$
Properties: Solid; m.w. 214.22; m.p. 62 C; b.p. 172-173 C (12 mm); flash pt. > 110 C
Uses: Fruity flavoring agent
Regulatory: FDA 21CFR §177.1010, 27CFR §21.65, 21.151
Manuf./Distrib.: AC Ind.; Aldrich; Eastman; Spectrum Chem. Mfg.
Manuf./Distrib. (pharm. & food): Aldrich

Phloroglucine. *See* 1,3,5-Trihydroxybenzene
Phloroglucinol. *See* 1,3,5-Trihydroxybenzene
Phloxine B. *See* D&C Red No. 28
Phosphate cross-linked starch. *See* Distarch phosphate

Phosphatidylcholine
CAS 97281-47-5
Definition: Purified grade of lecithin containing no less than 95% of the phospholipid
Uses: Emulsifier and dispersant for pharmaceuticals and liposomes; choline enrichment, carrier for dietetics, pharmaceuticals, encapsulation
Trade names containing: Phosal® 50 PG

Phosphinic acid. *See* Hypophosphorous acid

Phosphoric acid
CAS 7664-38-2; EINECS 231-633-2
FEMA 2900; UN No. 1805
Synonyms: Orthophosphoric acid
Classification: Inorganic acid
Empirical: H_3O_4P
Formula: H_3PO_4
Properties: Colorless liq. or rhombic crystals, odorless; sol. in water, alcohol; m.w. 98.00; dens. 1.70 (20/4 C); m.p. 42.4 C; b.p. 158 C
Precaution: DOT: Corrosive material; mixts. with nitromethane are explosive
Toxicology: LD50 (oral, rat) 1530 mg/kg; mod. toxic by ingestion and skin contact; conc. sol'ns. irritating to skin, mucous membranes; corrosive irritant to eyes; TLV:TWA 1 mg/m^3 of air; heated to decomp., emits toxic fumes of PO_x

Phosphoric acid, aluminum salt (1:1)

Uses: Pharmaceutic aid, acidifying agent, buffering agent; used in parenterals, intramuscular injectables, orals, topicals, vaginals; in dental cements and etchants; dil. as tonic, for management of nausea, vomiting
Regulatory: FDA 21CFR §131.144, 133, 175.300,177.2260, 178.3520, 182.1073, GRAS; USDA 9CFR §318.7, 381.147 (0.01% max. in lard, shortening, poultry fat); FEMA GRAS; Japan approved; Europe listed; UK approved; FDA approved for parenterals, intramuscular injectables, orals, topicals, vaginals; USP/NF, BP, Ph.Eur. compliance
Manuf./Distrib.: Albright & Wilson; Ashland; Farleyway Chem. Ltd; FMC; Mallinckrodt; Mitsui Toatsu Chem.; Monsanto; Rasa Ind.; Rhone-Poulenc Food Ingreds.
Manuf./Distrib. (pharm. & food): Albright & Wilson Am.; Browning; FMC; Rhone-Poulenc Food Ingreds.; Ruger; Spectrum Chem. Mfg.

Phosphoric acid, aluminum salt (1:1). *See* Aluminum orthophosphate
Phosphoric acid calcium salt (1:1). *See* Calcium phosphate dibasic
Phosphoric acid calcium salt (2:1). *See* Calcium phosphate monobasic anhydrous
Phosphoric acid, cetyl ester, potassium salt. *See* Potassium cetyl phosphate
Phosphoric acid diammonium salt. *See* Ammonium phosphate, dibasic
Phosphoric acid dipotassium salt. *See* Potassium phosphate dibasic
Phosphoric acid, hydroxycetyl ester. *See* Hydroxycetyl phosphate
Phosphoric acid monopotassium salt. *See* Potassium phosphate

Phosphorus oxychloride
CAS 10025-87-3; EINECS 233-046-7
UN No. 1810
Synonyms: Phosphoryl chloride
Empirical: Cl_3OP
Formula: $POCl_3$
Properties: Colorless fuming liq., pungent odor; dec. by water and alcohol with evolution of heat; m.w. 153.35; dens. 1.675 (20/20 C); m.p. 1.2 C; b.p. 107.2 C; dens. 1.675 (20C); ref. index 1.461 (20C)
Precaution: DOT: Corrosive material; moisture-sensitive
Toxicology: Toxic by ingestion and inhalation; strong irritant to skin and tissue
Uses: Mfg. of pharmaceuticals
Manuf./Distrib.: Albright & Wilson; Aldrich; Cerac; FMC; Hoechst Celanese; Rhone-Poulenc Basic; Spectrum Chem. Mfg.

Phosphoryl chloride. *See* Phosphorus oxychloride
Phthalic acid, diethyl ester. *See* Diethyl phthalate
Phthalocyanine blue. *See* Copper phthalocyanine blue
Phylloquinone. *See* Vitamin K_1
Phytodione. *See* Vitamin K_1
Phytomenadione. *See* Vitamin K_1
Phytonadione. *See* Vitamin K_1
PIB. *See* Polybutene; Polyisobutene
2-Picoline. *See* α-Picoline
3-Picoline. *See* β-Picoline
4-Picoline. *See* γ-Picoline

α-Picoline
CAS 109-06-8; EINECS 203-643-7
Synonyms: 2-Methylpyridine; 2-Picoline
Empirical: C_6H_7N
Formula: $C_5H_4N(CH_3)$
Properties: Colorless liq., strong unpleasant odor; misc. with water and alcohol; m.w. 93.13; dens. 0.943; m.p. -70 C; b.p. 128-129 C; flash pt. 26 C; ref. index 1.500
Precaution: Flamm.
Toxicology: Irritant
Uses: Organic intermediate for pharmaceuticals
Manuf./Distrib.: Lonza; Nepera; Raschig; Reilly Ind.; Schweizerhall
Manuf./Distrib. (pharm. & food): Aldrich

β-Picoline
CAS 108-99-6; EINECS 203-636-9
Synonyms: 3-Picoline; 3-Methylpyridine
Empirical: C_6H_7N
Properties: Colorless liq., unpleasant odor; sol. in water, alcohol, ether; m.w. 93.13; dens. 0.957; f.p. -18 C; b.p. 144 C; flash pt. 36 C; ref. index 1.5050

Precaution: Moderate fire risk
Toxicology: Irritant
Uses: Solvent in synthesis of pharmaceuticals
Manuf./Distrib.: Nepera; Raschig; Reilly Ind.; Schweizerhall
Manuf./Distrib. (pharm. & food): Aldrich

γ-**Picoline**
CAS 108-89-4; EINECS 203-626-4
Synonyms: 4-Methylpyridine; 4-Picoline
Empirical: C₆H₇N
Formula: NCHCHC(CH₃)CHCH
Properties: Colorless, moderately volatile liq.; sol. in water, alcohol, ether; m.w. 93.13; dens. 0.957; m.p. 2.4
    C; b.p. 145 C; flash pt. 56 C; ref. index 1.5050
Toxicology: Irritant
Uses: Solvent in synthesis of pharmaceuticals
Manuf./Distrib.: Lonza; Raschig; Reilly Ind.; Schweizerhall
Manuf./Distrib. (pharm. & food): Aldrich

3-Picolinic acid. *See* Nicotinic acid
Pigment black 11. *See* CI 77499
Pigment blue 15. *See* Copper phthalocyanine blue
Pigment blue 27. *See* CI 77510; Ferric ferrocyanide
Pigment brown 6. *See* CI 77491; CI 77492; CI 77499
Pigment brown 7. *See* CI 77491; CI 77492; CI 77499
Pigment green 17. *See* Chromium oxide greens; CI 77288
Pigment green 18. *See* Chromium hydroxide green; CI 77289
Pigment metal 1. *See* CI 77000
Pigment metal 2. *See* CI 77400
Pigment orange 5. *See* D&C Orange No. 17
Pigment red 4. *See* CI 12085; D&C Red No. 36
Pigment red 53. *See* D&C Red No. 8
Pigment red 53:1. *See* D&C Red No. 9
Pigment red 57. *See* CI 15850; D&C Red No. 6
Pigment red 57:1. *See* D&C Red No. 7
Pigment red 63:1. *See* D&C Red No. 34
Pigment red 64:1. *See* D&C Red No. 31
Pigment red 100. *See* D&C Red No. 39
Pigment red 101. *See* CI 77491
Pigment red 102. *See* CI 77491
Pigment white 4. *See* CI 77947; Zinc oxide
Pigment white 6. *See* CI 77891; Titanium dioxide
Pigment white 14. *See* Bismuth oxychloride; CI 77163
Pigment white 18. *See* CI 77220
Pigment white 24. *See* CI 77002
Pigment white 26. *See* Talc
Pigment yellow 42. *See* CI 77492
Pigment yellow 43. *See* CI 77492
Pimpinella anisum oil. *See* Anise oil

Pineapple juice
Definition: Liq. obtained from the fruit of the pineapple, *Ananas comosus*
Uses: Flavoring

2-Pinene. *See* α-Pinene
2(10)-Pinene. *See* β-Pinene

α-**Pinene**
CAS 80-56-8; 7785-26-4 (-); 7785-70-8 (+); EINECS 232-077-3 (-); 232-087-8 (+)
FEMA 2902; UN No. 2368
Synonyms: 2-Pinene; 2,6,6-Trimethylbicyclo(3.1.1)-2-hept-2-ene; 2,6,6-Trimethylbicyclo(3.1.1)-2-heptene
Classification: Terpene hydrocarbon
Empirical: C₁₀H₁₆
Properties: Colorless liq., turpentine odor; insol. in water; sol. in alcohol, chloroform, ether, glacial acetic acid;

β-Pinene

m.w. 136.26; dens. 0.8592 (20/4 C); m.p. -55 C; b.p. 155 C; flash pt. 91 F; ref. index 1.464-1.468
Precaution: DOT: Flamm. liq.; dangerous fire hazard exposed to heat, flame, oxidizers; explodes on contact with nitrosyl perchlorate
Toxicology: LD50 (oral, rat) 3700mg/kg; deadly poison by inh.; mod. toxic by ingestion; eye, mucous membrane, and severe skin irritant; toxic effects similar to turpentine
Uses: Synthetic flavoring agent
Regulatory: FDA 21CFR §172.515; FEMA GRAS
Manuf./Distrib.: Aldrich; Arizona; Hercules; SCM Glidco Organics; Spectrum Chem. Mfg.; Veitsiluoto Oy
Manuf./Distrib. (pharm. & food): Aldrich
Trade names: alpha-Pinene P&F, FCC

β-Pinene

CAS 127-91-3; 18172-67-3 (-); EINECS 242-060-2 (-)
FEMA 2903
Synonyms: 6,6-Dimethyl-2-methylenebicyclo[3.1.1]heptane; Nopinene; 2(10)-Pinene; Pseudopinene
Classification: Terpene hydrocarbon
Empirical: $C_{10}H_{16}$
Properties: Colorless liq., terpene odor; insol. in water; sol. in alcohol, chloroform, ether; m.w. 136.24; dens. 0.859; m.p. -61 C; b.p. 165-167 C; soften. pt. 112-118 C; flash pt. 32 C
Precaution: Flamm.; fire risk
Toxicology: LD50 (oral, rat) 4700 mg/kg; mildly toxic by ingestion; irritating to eyes, skin, respiratory system; heated to decomp., emits acrid smoke and irritating fumes
Uses: Synthetic flavoring agent; moisture barrier on soft gelatin capsules and on powders of ascorbic acid or its salts
Regulatory: FDA 21CFR §172.280, 172.515; FEMA GRAS
Manuf./Distrib.: Aldrich; Arizona; Penta Mfg.; SCM Glidco Organics
Manuf./Distrib. (pharm. & food): Aldrich; SCM Glidco Organics
Trade names: beta-Pinene P&F

Pine needle oil

CAS 8000-26-8
FEMA 2905
Synonyms: Siberian fir oil
Definition: Oil derived from *Abies* spp.
Properties: Sp.gr. 0.916; ref. index 1.465 ± 0.01 (20 C)
Precaution: Combustible
Uses: Natural flavoring/fragrance; used in topicals
Regulatory: FEMA GRAS; FDA approved for topicals
Manuf./Distrib.: Spectrum Chem. Mfg.

PIP. *See* Piperazine
Piperazidine. *See* Piperazine

Piperazine

CAS 110-85-0; EINECS 203-808-3
UN No. 2579
Synonyms: PIP; Piperazine anhydrous; Diethylene diamine; Pyrazine hexahydride; Piperazidine
Empirical: $C_4H_{10}N_2$
Properties: Wh. to sl. off-wh. lumps or flakes, ammoniacal odor; hygroscopic; sol. in water, alcohol; insol. in ether; m.w. 86.14; sp.gr. 0.97; m.p. 109.6 C; b.p. 148.5 C (760 mm); flash pt. (TCC) 229 F
Precaution: DOT: Corrosive material; light-sensitive
Toxicology: Adverse reactions incl. incoordination, numbness, seizures, memory problems, headache, dizziness, eye problems, nausea, vomiting, diarrhea, abdominal cramps, hives, skin rashes, joint pain, bronchospasm, anemia
Uses: Mfg. of antihistamines, tranquilizers, analgesics, sedatives, hormones, therapeutics; treatment of burns, shock, hypertension; anticonvulsant; antitumor drugs; anthelmintic agent which paralyzes worms, causing their expulsion
Manuf./Distrib.: Akzo Nobel; Alfa; Allchem Industries; BASF; Janssen Chimica; Texaco; Tosoh
Manuf./Distrib. (pharm. & food): Aldrich; Spectrum Chem. Mfg.; Texaco

Piperazine anhydrous. *See* Piperazine
2-Piperazinoethylamione. *See* Aminoethylpiperazine

Piperidine

CAS 110-89-4; EINECS 203-813-0
FEMA 2908; UN No. 2401

Synonyms: Hexahydropyridine; Hexazane
Empirical: $C_5H_{11}N$
Properties: Liq., char. heavy sweet animal-like odor; hygroscopic; sol. in alcohol, benzene, chloroform; misc. with water; m.w. 85.15; dens. 0.862 (20/4 C); m.p. -11 to -9 C; b.p. 104-106 C; flash pt. 16 C; ref. index 1.453 (20 C)
Precaution: Highly flamm.
Toxicology: LD50 (oral, rat) 0.52 ml/kg; toxic by inhalation and skin contact; causes burns
Uses: Sweet synthetic flavoring agent
Regulatory: FDA 21CFR §172.515; FEMA GRAS
Manuf./Distrib.: Aldrich; Janssen Chimica; Nepera; Raschig; Reilly Ind.; Schweizerhall
Manuf./Distrib. (pharm. & food): Aldrich

d-Piperitone
FEMA 2910
Synonyms: p-Menth-1-en-3-one; 1-Methyl-4-isopropyl-1-cyclohexen-3-one
Empirical: $C_{10}H_{16}O$
Properties: Colorless liq., camphor-like odor, sharp minty flavor; sol. in alcohol; insol. in water; m.w. 152.23
Uses: Synthetic flavoring agent
Regulatory: FDA 21CFR §172.515; FEMA GRAS

Piperonal. See Heliotropine

Piperonyl acetate
CAS 326-61-4
FEMA 2912
Synonyms: Heliotropyl acetate; 3,4-Methylenedioxybenzyl acetate
Empirical: $C_{10}H_{10}O_4$
Properties: Colorless to lt. yel. liq., cherry/strawberry/heliotrope odor; sol. in alcohol; almost insol. in water; m.w. 194.19; dens. 1.227; b.p. 150-151 C (10 mm); flash pt. > 230 F
Toxicology: LD50 (oral, rat) 2100 mg/kg; mod. toxic by ingestion; skin irritant; heated to decomp., emits acrid smoke and irritating fumes
Uses: Cherry, strawberry-like synthetic flavoring agent
Regulatory: FDA 21CFR §172.515; FEMA GRAS
Manuf./Distrib. (pharm. & food): Aldrich

Piperonyl aldehyde. See Heliotropine

Piperonyl isobutyrate
CAS 5461-08-5
FEMA 2913
Synonyms: Helioptropyl isobutyrate; 3,4-Methylenedioxybenzyl isobutyrate
Empirical: $C_{12}H_{14}O_4$
Properties: Colorless oily liq., fruity berry odor; sol. in alcohol; insol. in water; m.w. 222.24; dens. 1.154; b.p. 91-92 C (0.005 mm); flash pt. > 230 F
Uses: Berry, jam-like synthetic flavoring agent
Regulatory: FDA 21CFR §172.515; FEMA GRAS
Manuf./Distrib. (pharm. & food): Aldrich

PIPP. See p-Isopropylphenol

Pivaloyl chloride
CAS 3282-30-2; EINECS 221-921-6
Synonyms: Trimethylacetyl chloride
Formula: $(CH_3)_3CCOCl$
Properties: M.w. 120.58; dens. 0.979; b.p. 105-106 C; flash pt. 19 C; ref. index 1.4120
Precaution: Flamm.; corrosive
Uses: Intermediate; coupling agent in mfg. of antibiotics
Manuf./Distrib.: Aldrich; Elf Atochem
Manuf./Distrib. (pharm. & food): Aldrich; R.W. Greeff

PLA. See Poly (DL-lactic acid)
Plaster of Paris. See Calcium sulfate; Calcium sulfate hemihydrate
Platy talc. See Talc
PMAC. See Phenylmercuric acetate
PMN. See Phenylmercuric nitrate
POE (4). See PEG-4
POE (8). See PEG-8

POE (9). *See* PEG-9
POE (12). *See* PEG-12
POE (14). *See* PEG-14
POE (16). *See* PEG-16
POE (20). *See* PEG-20
POE (32). *See* PEG-32
POE (40). *See* PEG-40
POE (60). *See* PEG-60
POE (75). *See* PEG-75
POE (100). *See* PEG-100
POE (150). *See* PEG-150
POE (200). *See* PEG-200
POE (350). *See* PEG-350
POE (2000). *See* PEG-2M
POE (5000). *See* PEG-5M
POE (7000). *See* PEG-7M
POE (9000). *See* PEG-9M
POE (14000). *See* PEG-14M
POE (20000). *See* PEG-20M
POE (23000). *See* PEG-23M
POE (45000). *See* PEG-45M
POE (90000). *See* PEG-90M
POE (115000). *See* PEG-115M
POE (20) almond glycerides. *See* PEG-20 almond glycerides
POE (60) almond glycerides. *See* PEG-60 almond glycerides
POE (8) beeswax. *See* PEG-8 beeswax
POE (8) behenate. *See* PEG-8 behenate
POE (6) caprylic/capric glycerides. *See* PEG-6 caprylic/capric glycerides
POE (3) castor oil. *See* PEG-3 castor oil
POE (5) castor oil. *See* PEG-5 castor oil
POE (8) castor oil. *See* PEG-8 castor oil
POE (9) castor oil. *See* PEG-9 castor oil
POE (15) castor oil. *See* PEG-15 castor oil
POE (17) castor oil. *See* PEG-17 castor oil
POE (20) castor oil. *See* PEG-20 castor oil
POE (26) castor oil. *See* PEG-26 castor oil
POE (30) castor oil. *See* PEG-30 castor oil
POE (32) castor oil. *See* PEG-32 castor oil
POE (33) castor oil. *See* PEG-33 castor oil
POE (35) castor oil. *See* PEG-35 castor oil
POE (36) castor oil. *See* PEG-36 castor oil
POE (40) castor oil. *See* PEG-40 castor oil
POE (50) castor oil. *See* PEG-50 castor oil
POE (180) castor oil. *See* PEG-180 castor oil
POE (200) castor oil. *See* PEG-200 castor oil
POE (2) cetyl ether. *See* Ceteth-2
POE (5) cetyl ether. *See* Ceteth-5
POE (6) cetyl ether. *See* Ceteth-6
POE (7) cetyl ether. *See* Ceteth-7
POE (10) cetyl ether. *See* Ceteth-10
POE (12) cetyl ether. *See* Ceteth-12
POE (15) cetyl ether. *See* Ceteth-15
POE (16) cetyl ether. *See* Ceteth-16
POE (20) cetyl ether. *See* Ceteth-20
POE (23) cetyl ether. *See* Ceteth-23
POE (24) cetyl ether. *See* Ceteth-24
POE (25) cetyl ether. *See* Ceteth-25
POE (30) cetyl ether. *See* Ceteth-30
POE (40) cetyl ether. *See* Ceteth-40
POE (9) cetyl/stearyl ether. *See* Ceteareth-9
POE (10) cetyl/stearyl ether. *See* Ceteareth-10
POE (11) cetyl/stearyl ether. *See* Ceteareth-11

POE (12) cetyl/stearyl ether. *See* Ceteareth-12
POE (14) cetyl/stearyl ether. *See* Ceteareth-14
POE (15) cetyl/stearyl ether. *See* Ceteareth-15
POE (16) cetyl/stearyl ether. *See* Ceteareth-16
POE (20) cetyl/stearyl ether. *See* Ceteareth-20
POE (25) cetyl/stearyl ether. *See* Ceteareth-25
POE (30) cetyl/stearyl ether. *See* Ceteareth-30
POE (33) cetyl/stearyl ether. *See* Ceteareth-33
POE (15) coconut amine. *See* PEG-15 cocamine
POE (20) corn glycerides. *See* PEG-20 corn glycerides
POE (60) corn glycerides. *See* PEG-60 corn glycerides
POE (4) dilaurate. *See* PEG-4 dilaurate
POE (6) dilaurate. *See* PEG-6 dilaurate
POE (8) dilaurate. *See* PEG-8 dilaurate
POE (12) dilaurate. *See* PEG-12 dilaurate
POE (20) dilaurate. *See* PEG-20 dilaurate
POE (32) dilaurate. *See* PEG-32 dilaurate
POE (75) dilaurate. *See* PEG-75 dilaurate
POE (150) dilaurate. *See* PEG-150 dilaurate
POE (4) dioleate. *See* PEG-4 dioleate
POE (6) dioleate. *See* PEG-6 dioleate
POE (8) dioleate. *See* PEG-8 dioleate
POE (12) dioleate. *See* PEG-12 dioleate
POE (20) dioleate. *See* PEG-20 dioleate
POE (32) dioleate. *See* PEG-32 dioleate
POE (75) dioleate. *See* PEG-75 dioleate
POE (150) dioleate. *See* PEG-150 dioleate
POE (4) distearate. *See* PEG-4 distearate
POE (6) distearate. *See* PEG-6 distearate
POE (8) distearate. *See* PEG-8 distearate
POE (12) distearate. *See* PEG-12 distearate
POE (20) distearate. *See* PEG-20 distearate
POE (32) distearate. *See* PEG-32 distearate
POE (75) distearate. *See* PEG-75 distearate
POE (150) distearate. *See* PEG-150 distearate
POE (8) ditallate. *See* PEG-8 ditallate
POE (12) ditallate. *See* PEG-12 ditallate
POE (26) glyceryl ether. *See* Glycereth-26
POE (7) glyceryl ether benzoate. *See* Glycereth-7 benzoate
POE (5) glyceryl ether lactate. *See* Glycereth-5 lactate
POE (7) glyceryl ether triacetate. *See* Glycereth-7 triacetate
POE (7) glyceryl monococoate. *See* PEG-7 glyceryl cocoate
POE (12) glyceryl monolaurate. *See* PEG-12 glyceryl laurate
POE (20) glyceryl monolaurate. *See* PEG-20 glyceryl laurate
POE (5) glyceryl monostearate. *See* PEG-5 glyceryl stearate
POE (20) glyceryl monostearate. *See* PEG-20 glyceryl stearate
POE (120) glyceryl monostearate. *See* PEG-120 glyceryl stearate
POE (20) glyceryl oleate. *See* PEG-20 glyceryl oleate
POE (5) hydrogenated castor oil. *See* PEG-5 hydrogenated castor oil
POE (7) hydrogenated castor oil. *See* PEG-7 hydrogenated castor oil
POE (10) hydrogenated castor oil. *See* PEG-10 hydrogenated castor oil
POE (20) hydrogenated castor oil. *See* PEG-20 hydrogenated castor oil
POE (25) hydrogenated castor oil. *See* PEG-25 hydrogenated castor oil
POE (30) hydrogenated castor oil. *See* PEG-30 hydrogenated castor oil
POE (40) hydrogenated castor oil. *See* PEG-40 hydrogenated castor oil
POE (50) hydrogenated castor oil. *See* PEG-50 hydrogenated castor oil
POE (60) hydrogenated castor oil. *See* PEG-60 hydrogenated castor oil
POE (80) hydrogenated castor oil. *See* PEG-80 hydrogenated castor oil
POE (100) hydrogenated castor oil. *See* PEG-100 hydrogenated castor oil
POE (20) hydrogenated lanolin. *See* PEG-20 hydrogenated lanolin
POE (24) hydrogenated lanolin. *See* PEG-24 hydrogenated lanolin
POE (30) isocetyl ether. *See* Isoceteth-30

POE (20) isohexadecyl ether. *See* Isoceteth-20
POE (27) lanolin. *See* PEG-27 lanolin
POE (30) lanolin. *See* PEG-30 lanolin
POE (40) lanolin. *See* PEG-40 lanolin
POE (60) lanolin. *See* PEG-60 lanolin
POE (70) lanolin. *See* PEG-70 lanolin
POE (75) lanolin. *See* PEG-75 lanolin
POE (85) lanolin. *See* PEG-85 lanolin
POE (5) lanolin ether. *See* Laneth-5
POE (10) lanolin ether. *See* Laneth-10
POE (15) lanolin ether. *See* Laneth-15
POE (16) lanolin ether. *See* Laneth-16
POE (20) lanolin ether. *See* Laneth-20
POE (25) lanolin ether. *See* Laneth-25
POE (40) lanolin ether. *See* Laneth-40
POE (6) lauryl ether. *See* Laureth-6
POE (7) lauryl ether. *See* Laureth-7
POE (10) lauryl ether. *See* Laureth-10
POE (12) lauryl ether. *See* Laureth-12
POE (23) lauryl ether. *See* Laureth-23
POE (2) lauryl ether acetate. *See* Laureth-2 acetate
POE (120) methyl glucose dioleate. *See* PEG-120 methyl glucose dioleate
POE (10) methyl glucose ether. *See* Methyl gluceth-10
POE (20) methyl glucose ether. *See* Methyl gluceth-20
POE (6) monoisostearate. *See* PEG-6 isostearate
POE (4) monolaurate. *See* PEG-4 laurate
POE (6) monolaurate. *See* PEG-6 laurate
POE (8) monolaurate. *See* PEG-8 laurate
POE (12) monolaurate. *See* PEG-12 laurate
POE (20) monolaurate. *See* PEG-20 laurate
POE (24) monolaurate. *See* PEG-24 laurate
POE (32) monolaurate. *See* PEG-32 laurate
POE (40) monolaurate. *See* PEG-40 laurate
POE (75) monolaurate. *See* PEG-75 laurate
POE (100) monolaurate. *See* PEG-100 laurate
POE (150) monolaurate. *See* PEG-150 laurate
POE (4) monooleate. *See* PEG-4 oleate
POE (6) monooleate. *See* PEG-6 oleate
POE (7) monooleate. *See* PEG-7 oleate
POE (8) monooleate. *See* PEG-8 oleate
POE (12) monooleate. *See* PEG-12 oleate
POE (20) monooleate. *See* PEG-20 oleate
POE (32) monooleate. *See* PEG-32 oleate
POE (75) monooleate. *See* PEG-75 oleate
POE (150) monooleate. *See* PEG-150 oleate
POE 1500 monostearate. *See* PEG-6-32 stearate
POE (4) monotallate. *See* PEG-4 tallate
POE (8) monotallate. *See* PEG-8 tallate
POE (12) monotallate. *See* PEG-12 tallate
POE (3) myristyl ether myristate. *See* Myreth-3 myristate
POE (2) nonyl phenyl ether. *See* Nonoxynol-2
POE (4) nonyl phenyl ether. *See* Nonoxynol-4
POE (5) nonyl phenyl ether. *See* Nonoxynol-5
POE (6) nonyl phenyl ether. *See* Nonoxynol-6
POE (7) nonyl phenyl ether. *See* Nonoxynol-7
POE (8) nonyl phenyl ether. *See* Nonoxynol-8
POE (9) nonyl phenyl ether. *See* Nonoxynol-9
POE (10) nonyl phenyl ether. *See* Nonoxynol-10
POE (12) nonyl phenyl ether. *See* Nonoxynol-12
POE (13) nonyl phenyl ether. *See* Nonoxynol-13
POE (20) nonyl phenyl ether. *See* Nonoxynol-20
POE (30) nonyl phenyl ether. *See* Nonoxynol-30

POE (35) nonyl phenyl ether. *See* Nonoxynol-35
POE (40) nonyl phenyl ether. *See* Nonoxynol-40
POE (50) nonyl phenyl ether. *See* Nonoxynol-50
POE (3) octyl phenyl ether. *See* Octoxynol-3
POE (5) octyl phenyl ether. *See* Octoxynol-5
POE (6) octyl phenyl ether. *See* Octoxynol-6
POE (8) octyl phenyl ether. *See* Octoxynol-8
POE (9) octyl phenyl ether. *See* Octoxynol-9
POE (10) octyl phenyl ether. *See* Octoxynol-10
POE (11) octyl phenyl ether. *See* Octoxynol-11
POE (13) octyl phenyl ether. *See* Octoxynol-13
POE (16) octyl phenyl ether. *See* Octoxynol-16
POE (20) octyl phenyl ether. *See* Octoxynol-20
POE (25) octyl phenyl ether. *See* Octoxynol-25
POE (30) octyl phenyl ether. *See* Octoxynol-30
POE (40) octyl phenyl ether. *See* Octoxynol-40
POE (2) oleyl ether. *See* Oleth-2
POE (3) oleyl ether. *See* Oleth-3
POE (5) oleyl ether. *See* Oleth-5
POE (10) oleyl ether. *See* Oleth-10
POE (12) oleyl ether. *See* Oleth-12
POE (16) oleyl ether. *See* Oleth-16
POE (20) oleyl ether. *See* Oleth-20
POE (25) oleyl ether. *See* Oleth-25
POE (3) oleyl ether phosphate. *See* Oleth-3 phosphate
POE (10) oleyl ether phosphate. *See* Oleth-10 phosphate
POE (20) oleyl ether phosphate. *See* Oleth-20 phosphate
POE (25) PABA. *See* PEG-25 PABA
POE (1) POP (4) cetyl ether. *See* PPG-4 ceteth-1
POE (1) POP (8) cetyl ether. *See* PPG-8-ceteth-1
POE (10) POP (4) cetyl ether. *See* PPG-4-ceteth-10
POE (20) POP (4) cetyl ether. *See* PPG-4-ceteth-20
POE (10) POP (5) cetyl ether phosphate. *See* PPG-5 ceteth-10 phosphate
POE (9) POP (2) cetyl/stearyl ether. *See* PPG-2-ceteareth-9
POE (50) POP (12) lanolin. *See* PPG-12-PEG-50 lanolin
POE (65) POP (12) lanolin oil. *See* PPG-12-PEG-65 lanolin oil
POE (5) POP (5) lauryl ether. *See* PPG-5-laureth-5
POE (9) POP (3) lauryl ether. *See* PPG-3-laureth-9
POE (16) POP (12) monobutyl ether. *See* PPG-12-buteth-16
POE (10) propylene glycol. *See* PEG-10 propylene glycol
POE (8) propylene glycol cocoate. *See* PEG-8 propylene glycol cocoate
POE (25) propylene glycol monostearate. *See* PEG-25 propylene glycol stearate
POE (120) propylene glycol monostearate. *See* PEG-120 propylene glycol stearate
POE (8) ricinoleate. *See* PEG-8 ricinoleate
POE (20) sorbitan monoisostearate. *See* PEG-20 sorbitan isostearate
POE (4) sorbitan monolaurate. *See* Polysorbate 21
POE (20) sorbitan monolaurate. *See* Polysorbate 20
POE (80) sorbitan monolaurate. *See* PEG-80 sorbitan laurate
POE (5) sorbitan monooleate. *See* Polysorbate 81
POE (20) sorbitan monooleate. *See* Polysorbate 80
POE (20) sorbitan monooleate acetate. *See* Polysorbate 80 acetate
POE (20) sorbitan monopalmitate. *See* Polysorbate 40
POE (4) sorbitan monostearate. *See* Polysorbate 61
POE (6) sorbitan monostearate. *See* PEG-6 sorbitan stearate
POE (20) sorbitan monostearate. *See* Polysorbate 60
POE (6) sorbitan oleate. *See* PEG-6 sorbitan oleate
POE (30) sorbitan tetraoleate. *See* PEG-30 sorbitan tetraoleate
POE (40) sorbitan tetraoleate. *See* PEG-40 sorbitan tetraoleate
POE (60) sorbitan tetraoleate. *See* PEG-60 sorbitan tetraoleate
POE (20) sorbitan trioleate. *See* Polysorbate 85
POE (20) sorbitan tristearate. *See* Polysorbate 65
POE (6) sorbitol beeswax. *See* PEG-6 sorbitan beeswax

POE (8) sorbitol beeswax. *See* PEG-8 sorbitan beeswax
POE (20) sorbitol beeswax. *See* PEG-20 sorbitan beeswax
POE (20) sorbitol ether. *See* Sorbeth-20
POE (40) sorbitol lanolate. *See* PEG-40 sorbitan lanolate
POE (4) stearate. *See* PEG-4 stearate
POE (5) stearate. *See* PEG-5 stearate
POE (6) stearate. *See* PEG-6 stearate
POE (8) stearate. *See* PEG-8 stearate
POE (10) stearate. *See* PEG-10 stearate
POE (12) stearate. *See* PEG-12 stearate
POE (20) stearate. *See* PEG-20 stearate
POE (24) stearate. *See* PEG-24 stearate
POE (25) stearate. *See* PEG-25 stearate
POE (30) stearate. *See* PEG-30 stearate
POE (40) stearate. *See* PEG-40 stearate
POE (45) stearate. *See* PEG-45 stearate
POE (50) stearate. *See* PEG-50 stearate
POE (55) stearate. *See* PEG-55 stearate
POE (75) stearate. *See* PEG-75 stearate
POE (100) stearate. *See* PEG-100 stearate
POE (150) stearate. *See* PEG-150 stearate
POE (2) stearyl ether. *See* Steareth-2
POE (7) stearyl ether. *See* Steareth-7
POE (10) stearyl ether. *See* Steareth-10
POE (16) stearyl ether. *See* Steareth-16
POE (20) stearyl ether. *See* Steareth-20
POE (21) stearyl ether. *See* Steareth-21
POE (25) stearyl ether. *See* Steareth-25
POE (100) stearyl ether. *See* Steareth-100
POE (10) tridecyl ether. *See* Trideceth-10
POE (100) tridecyl ether. *See* Trideceth-100
POE (7) tridecyl ether carboxylic acid. *See* Trideceth-7 carboxylic acid
Pogy oil. *See* Menhaden oil

Polacrilin potassium
CAS 39394-76-5
Synonyms: Methacrylic acid polymer with divinylbenzene, potassium salt
Definition: Potassium salt of a low crosslinked carboxylic cation-exchange resin prepared from methacrylic acid and divinylbenzene
Properties: Wh. to off-wh. free-flowing powd., odorless to faint odor, tasteless; pract. insol. in water and in most liqs.
Uses: Tablet disintegrant; used in orals
Regulatory: FDA approved for orals; USP/NF compliance

Poloxalene. *See* Poloxamer 188

Poloxamer 101
CAS 9003-11-6 (generic)
Synonyms: Methyl oxirane polymers (generic); Polyethylenepolypropylene glycols, polymers (generic)
Classification: Polyoxyethylene, polyoxypropylene block polymer
Formula: $HO(CH_2CH_2O)_x(CH(CH_3)CH_2O)_y(CH_2CH_2O)_zH$, avg. x=2, y=16, z=2
Toxicology: Moderately toxic by ingestion, intraperitoneal route
Uses: Nonionic surfactant, wetting agent, emulsifier and/or solubilizer
Regulatory: FDA 21CFR §176.210; USP/NF compliance

Poloxamer 105
CAS 9003-11-6 (generic)
Classification: Polyoxyethylene, polyoxypropylene block polymer
Formula: $HO(CH_2CH_2O)_x(CCH_3HCH_2O)_y(CH_2CH_2O)_zH$, avg. x=11, y=16, z=11
Toxicology: Moderately toxic by ingestion, intraperitoneal route
Uses: Emulsifier, wetting agent, solubilizer, stabilizer in flavor concs.
Regulatory: FDA 21CFR §172.808, 173.340, 175.105, 176.180, 176.200, 176.210, 177.1200

Poloxamer 108
CAS 9003-11-6 (generic)

Classification: Polyoxyethylene, polyoxypropylene block polymer
Formula: $HO(CH_2CH_2O)_x(CCH_3HCH_2O)_y(CH_2CH_2O)_zH$, avg. x=46, y=16, z=46
Toxicology: Moderately toxic by ingestion, intraperitoneal route
Uses: Emulsifier, wetting agent, solubilizer
Regulatory: FDA 21CFR §172.808, 173.340, 175.105, 176.180, 176.200, 176.210, 177.1200, 177.1210

Poloxamer 123
CAS 9003-11-6 (generic)
Classification: Polyoxyethylene, polyoxypropylene block polymer
Formula: $HO(CH_2CH_2O)_x(CCH_3HCH_2O)_y(CH_2CH_2O)_zH$, avg. x=7, y=21, z=7
Toxicology: Moderately toxic by ingestion, intraperitoneal route
Uses: Emulsifier, wetting agent, solubilizer, stabilizer in flavor concs.
Regulatory: FDA 21CFR §172.808, 173.340, 175.105, 176.180, 176.200, 176.210, 177.1200

Poloxamer 124
CAS 9003-11-6 (generic)
Classification: Polyoxyethylene, polyoxypropylene block polymer
Formula: $HO(CH_2CH_2O)_x(CCH_3HCH_2O)_y(CH_2CH_2O)_zH$, avg. x=11, y=21, z=11
Properties: Colorless liq., mild odor; sol. in water, alcohol, IPA, propylene glycol, xylene; m.w. 2090-2360; m.p. 16 C; pH 5.0-7.5 (1 in 40)
Toxicology: Moderately toxic by ingestion, intraperitoneal route
Uses: Nonionic surfactant, emulsifier, wetting agent
Regulatory: FDA 21CFR §172.808, 173.340, 175.105, 176.180, 176.200, 176.210, 177.1200
Trade names: Pluronic® L44NF

Poloxamer 181
CAS 9003-11-6 (generic); 53637-25-5
Classification: Polyoxyethylene, polyoxypropylene block polymer
Formula: $HO(CH_2CH_2O)_x(CCH_3HCH_2O)_y(CH_2CH_2O)_zH$, avg. x=3, y=30, z=3
Toxicology: Moderately toxic by ingestion, intraperitoneal route
Uses: Emulsifier, solubilizer, wetting agent, stabilizer in flavor concs.
Regulatory: FDA 21CFR §172.808, 173.340, 175.105, 176.180, 176.200, 176.210, 177.1200
Trade names: Macol® 1

Poloxamer 182
CAS 9003-11-6 (generic)
Classification: Polyoxyethylene, polyoxypropylene block polymer
Formula: $HO(CH_2CH_2O)_x(CCH_3HCH_2O)_y(CH_2CH_2O)_zH$, avg. x=8, y=30, z=8
Properties: Dens. 1.018; flash pt. > 110 C
Toxicology: Moderately toxic by ingestion, intraperitoneal route
Uses: Emulsifier, solubilizer, wetting agent
Regulatory: FDA 21CFR §172.808, 173.340, 175.105, 176.180, 176.200, 176.210, 177.1200
Manuf./Distrib.: Aldrich

Poloxamer 184
CAS 9003-11-6 (generic)
Classification: Polyoxyethylene, polyoxypropylene block polymer
Formula: $HO(CH_2CH_2O)_x(CCH_3HCH_2O)_y(CH_2CH_2O)_zH$, avg. x=13, y=30, z=13
Properties: Dens. 1.018; flash pt. > 110 C
Toxicology: Moderately toxic by ingestion, intraperitoneal route
Uses: Emulsifier, solubilizer, wetting agent
Regulatory: FDA 21CFR §172.808, 173.340, 175.105, 176.180, 176.200, 176.210, 177.1200, 177.1210
Manuf./Distrib.: Aldrich

Poloxamer 185
CAS 9003-11-6 (generic)
Classification: Polyoxyethylene, polyoxypropylene block polymer
Formula: $HO(CH_2CH_2O)_x(CCH_3HCH_2O)_y(CH_2CH_2O)_zH$, avg. x=19, y=30, z=19
Toxicology: Moderately toxic by ingestion, intraperitoneal route
Uses: Emulsifier, solubilizer, wetting agent
Regulatory: FDA 21CFR §172.808, 173.340, 175.105, 176.180, 176.200, 176.210, 177.1200, 177.1210

Poloxamer 188
CAS 9003-11-6 (generic)
Synonyms: Poloxalene
Classification: Polyoxyethylene, polyoxypropylene block polymer

Poloxamer 217

Formula: HO(CH$_2$CH$_2$O)$_x$(CCH$_3$HCH$_2$O)$_y$(CH$_2$CH$_2$O)$_z$H, avg. x=75, y=30, z=75
Properties: Wh. flakeable solid, nearly odorless; sol. in water, alcohol; m.w. 7680-9510; m.p. 50 C min.; cloud pt. > 100 C (10% aq.); pH 5.0-7.5 (1 in 40)
Toxicology: Moderately toxic by ingestion, intraperitoneal route
Uses: Nonionic surfactant; emulsifier, solubilizer, wetting agent, stabilizer; used in intravenous, orals
Regulatory: FDA 21CFR §172.808, 173.340, 175.105, 176.180, 176.200, 176.210, 177.1200, 177.1210; FDA approved for intravenous, orals; BP compliance
Manuf./Distrib. (pharm. & food): Spectrum Chem. Mfg.
Trade names: Pluronic® F68NF

Poloxamer 217
CAS 9003-11-6 (generic)
Classification: Polyoxyethylene, polyoxypropylene block polymer
Formula: HO(CH$_2$CH$_2$O)$_x$(CCH$_3$HCH$_2$O)$_y$(CH$_2$CH$_2$O)$_z$H, avg. x=52, y=35, z=52
Toxicology: Moderately toxic by ingestion, intraperitoneal route
Uses: Emulsifier, solubilizer, wetting agent
Regulatory: FDA 21CFR §172.808, 173.340, 175.105, 176.180, 176.200, 176.210, 177.1200, 177.1210

Poloxamer 231
CAS 9003-11-6 (generic)
Classification: Polyoxyethylene, polyoxypropylene block polymer
Formula: HO(CH$_2$CH$_2$O)$_x$(CCH$_3$HCH$_2$O)$_y$(CH$_2$CH$_2$O)$_z$H, avg. x=6, y=39, z=6
Toxicology: Moderately toxic by ingestion, intraperitoneal route
Uses: Emulsifier, solubilizer, wetting agent
Regulatory: FDA 21CFR §172.808, 173.340, 175.105, 176.180, 176.200, 176.210, 177.1200, 177.1210

Poloxamer 234
CAS 9003-11-6 (generic)
Classification: Polyoxyethylene, polyoxypropylene block polymer
Formula: HO(CH$_2$CH$_2$O)$_x$(CCH$_3$HCH$_2$O)$_y$(CH$_2$CH$_2$O)$_z$H, avg. x=22, y=39, z=22
Toxicology: Moderately toxic by ingestion, intraperitoneal route
Uses: Emulsifier, solubilizer, wetting agent
Regulatory: FDA 21CFR §172.808, 173.340, 175.105, 176.180, 176.200, 176.210, 177.1200, 177.1210

Poloxamer 235
CAS 9003-11-6 (generic)
Classification: Polyoxyethylene, polyoxypropylene block polymer
Formula: HO(CH$_2$CH$_2$O)$_x$(CCH$_3$HCH$_2$O)$_y$(CH$_2$CH$_2$O)$_z$H, avg. x=27, y=39, z=27
Toxicology: Moderately toxic by ingestion, intraperitoneal route
Uses: Emulsifier, solubilizer, wetting agent
Regulatory: FDA 21CFR §172.808, 173.340, 175.105, 176.180, 176.200, 1876.210, 177.1200, 177.1210

Poloxamer 237
CAS 9003-11-6 (generic)
Classification: Polyoxyethylene, polyoxypropylene block polymer
Formula: HO(CH$_2$CH$_2$O)$_x$(CCH$_3$HCH$_2$O)$_y$(CH$_2$CH$_2$O)$_z$H, avg. x=62, y=39, z=62
Properties: Wh. prilled or cast solid, odorless to mild odor; sol. in water, alcohol; sparingly sol. in IPA, xylene; m.w. 6840-8830; m.p. 49 C; pH 5.0-7.5 (1 in 40)
Toxicology: Moderately toxic by ingestion, intraperitoneal route
Uses: Emulsifier, solubilizer, wetting agent for pharmaceuticals; stabilizer in flavor concs.
Regulatory: FDA 21CFR §172.808, 173.340, 175.105, 176.180, 176.200, 176.210, 177.1200, 177.1210
Manuf./Distrib. (pharm. & food): Spectrum Chem. Mfg.
Trade names: Pluronic® F87NF

Poloxamer 238
CAS 9003-11-6 (generic)
Classification: Polyoxyethylene, polyoxypropylene block polymer
Formula: HO(CH$_2$CH$_2$O)$_x$(CCH$_3$HCH$_2$O)$_y$(CH$_2$CH$_2$O)$_z$H, avg. x=97, y=39, z=97
Properties: Dens. 1.018; flash pt. > 110 C
Toxicology: Moderately toxic by ingestion, intraperitoneal route
Uses: Emulsifier, solubilizer, wetting agent, stabilizer in flavor concs.
Regulatory: FDA 21CFR §172.808, 173.340, 175.105, 176.180, 176.200, 176.210, 177.1200, 177.1210

Poloxamer 282
CAS 9003-11-6 (generic)
Classification: Polyoxyethylene, polyoxypropylene block polymer

Formula: HO(CH$_2$CH$_2$O)$_x$(CCH$_3$HCH$_2$O)$_y$(CH$_2$CH$_2$O)$_z$H, avg. x=10, y=47, z=10
Toxicology: Moderately toxic by ingestion, intraperitoneal route
Uses: Emulsifier, solubilizer, wetting agent
Regulatory: FDA 21CFR §172.808, 173.340, 175.105, 176.180, 176.200, 176.210, 177.1200, 177.1210

Poloxamer 284
CAS 9003-11-6 (generic)
Classification: Polyoxyethylene, polyoxypropylene block polymer
Formula: HO(CH$_2$CH$_2$O)$_x$(CCH$_3$HCH$_2$O)$_y$(CH$_2$CH$_2$O)$_z$H, avg. x=21, y=47, z=21
Toxicology: Moderately toxic by ingestion, intraperitoneal route
Uses: Emulsifier, solubilizer, wetting agent
Regulatory: FDA 21CFR §172.808, 173.340, 175.105, 176.180, 176.200, 176.210, 177.1200, 177.1210

Poloxamer 288
CAS 9003-11-6 (generic)
Classification: Polyoxyethylene, polyoxypropylene block polymer
Formula: HO(CH$_2$CH$_2$O)$_x$(CCH$_3$HCH$_2$O)$_y$(CH$_2$CH$_2$O)$_z$H, avg. x=122, y=47, z=122
Toxicology: Moderately toxic by ingestion, intraperitoneal route
Uses: Emulsifier, solubilizer, wetting agent, stabilizer in flavor concs.
Regulatory: FDA 21CFR §172.808, 173.340, 175.105, 176.180, 176.200, 176.210, 177.1200, 177.1210

Poloxamer 331
CAS 9003-11-6 (generic)
Classification: Polyoxyethylene, polyoxypropylene block polymer
Formula: HO(CH$_2$CH$_2$O)$_x$(CCH$_3$HCH$_2$O)$_y$(CH$_2$CH$_2$O)$_z$H, avg. x=7, y=54, z=7
Properties: Colorless liq.; sol. in alcohol; very sl. sol. in water; m.w. 3800; dens. 1.018 (25/25 C); visc. 756 cp; cloud pt. 11 C (10% aq.)
Toxicology: Moderately toxic by ingestion, intraperitoneal route; heated to decomp., emits acrid smoke and irritating fumes
Uses: Nonionic surfactant; emulsifier, solubilizer, wetting agent, and stabilizer; used in orals
Regulatory: FDA 21CFR §172.808, 173.340, 175.105, 176.180, 176.200, 176.210, 177.1200, 177.1210; 9CFR §381.147; FDA approved for orals

Poloxamer 333
CAS 9003-11-6 (generic)
Classification: Polyoxyethylene, polyoxypropylene block polymer
Formula: HO(CH$_2$CH$_2$O)$_x$(CCH$_3$HCH$_2$O)$_y$(CH$_2$CH$_2$O)$_z$H, avg. x=20, y=54, z=20
Toxicology: Moderately toxic by ingestion, intraperitoneal route
Uses: Emulsifier, solubilizer, wetting agent
Regulatory: FDA 21CFR §172.808, 173.340, 175.105, 176.180, 176.200, 176.210, 177.1200, 177.1210

Poloxamer 334
CAS 9003-11-6 (generic)
Classification: Polyoxyethylene, polyoxypropylene block polymer
Formula: HO(CH$_2$CH$_2$O)$_x$(CCH$_3$HCH$_2$O)$_y$(CH$_2$CH$_2$O)$_z$H, avg. x=31, y=54, z=31
Toxicology: Moderately toxic by ingestion, intraperitoneal route
Uses: Emulsifier, solubilizer, wetting agent
Regulatory: FDA 21CFR §172.808, 173.340, 175.105, 176.180, 176.200, 176.210, 177.1200, 177.1210

Poloxamer 335
CAS 9003-11-6 (generic)
Classification: Polyoxyethylene, polyoxypropylene block polymer
Formula: HO(CH$_2$CH$_2$O)$_x$(CCH$_3$HCH$_2$O)$_y$(CH$_2$CH$_2$O)$_z$H, avg. x=38, y=54, z=38
Toxicology: Moderately toxic by ingestion, intraperitoneal route
Uses: Emulsifier, solubilizer, wetting agent
Regulatory: FDA 21CFR §172.808, 173.340, 175.105, 176.180, 176.200, 176.210, 177.1200, 177.1210

Poloxamer 338
CAS 9003-11-6 (generic)
Classification: Polyoxyethylene, polyoxypropylene block polymer
Formula: HO(CH$_2$CH$_2$O)$_x$(CCH$_3$HCH$_2$O)$_y$(CH$_2$CH$_2$O)$_z$H, avg. x=128, y=54, z=128
Properties: Wh. prilled or cast solid, odorless to mild odor; sol. in water, alcohol; sparingly sol. in propylene glycol; m.w. 12,700-17,400; m.p. 57 C; pH 5.0-7.5 (1 in 40)
Toxicology: Moderately toxic by ingestion, intraperitoneal route
Uses: Emulsifier, solubilizer, wetting agent for pharmaceuticals
Regulatory: FDA 21CFR §172.808, 173.340, 175.105, 176.180, 176.200, 176.210, 177.1200, 177.1210

Poloxamer 401

Manuf./Distrib. (pharm. & food): Spectrum Chem. Mfg.
Trade names: Pluronic® F108NF

Poloxamer 401
CAS 9003-11-6 (generic)
Classification: Polyoxyethylene, polyoxypropylene block polymer
Formula: $HO(CH_2CH_2O)_x(CCH_3HCH_2O)_y(CH_2CH_2O)_zH$, avg. x=6, y=67, z=6
Toxicology: Moderately toxic by ingestion, intraperitoneal route
Uses: Emulsifier, solubilizer, wetting agent
Regulatory: FDA 21CFR §172.808, 173.340, 175.105, 176.180, 176.200, 176.210, 177.1200, 177.1210

Poloxamer 402
CAS 9003-11-6 (generic)
Classification: Polyoxyethylene, polyoxypropylene block polymer
Formula: $HO(CH_2CH_2O)_x(CCH_3HCH_2O)_y(CH_2CH_2O)_zH$, avg. x=13, y=67, z=13
Toxicology: Moderately toxic by ingestion, intraperitoneal route
Uses: Emulsifier, solubilizer, wetting agent
Regulatory: FDA 21CFR §172.808, 173.340, 175.105, 176.180, 176.200, 176.210, 177.1200, 177.1210

Poloxamer 403
CAS 9003-11-6 (generic)
Classification: Polyoxyethylene, polyoxypropylene block polymer
Formula: $HO(CH_2CH_2O)_x(CCH_3HCH_2O)_y(CH_2CH_2O)_zH$, avg. x=21, y=67, z=21
Toxicology: Moderately toxic by ingestion, intraperitoneal route
Uses: Emulsifier, solubilizer, wetting agent
Regulatory: FDA 21CFR §172.808, 173.340, 175.105, 176.180, 176.200, 176.210, 177.1200, 177.1210

Poloxamer 407
CAS 9003-11-6 (generic)
Classification: Polyoxyethylene, polyoxypropylene block polymer
Formula: $HO(CH_2CH_2O)_x(CCH_3HCH_2O)_y(CH_2CH_2O)_zH$, avg. x=98, y=67, z=98
Properties: Wh. prilled or cast solid, odorless to mild odor; sol. in water and alcohol; m.w. 9840-14,600; m.p. ≈ 56 C; pH 5.0-7.5 (1 in 40)
Toxicology: Moderately toxic by ingestion, intraperitoneal route
Uses: Nonionic surfactant; emulsifier, solubilizer, wetting agent, stabilizer for pharmaceuticals
Regulatory: FDA 21CFR §172.808, 173.340, 175.105, 176.180, 176.200, 176.210, 177.1200, 177.1210
Manuf./Distrib. (pharm. & food): Ruger; Spectrum Chem. Mfg.
Trade names: Pluronic® F127NF

Poloxamine 304
CAS 11111-34-5 (generic)
Definition: Polyoxyethylene, polyoxypropylene block polymer of ethylene diamine
Uses: Emulsifier, thickener, wetting agent, dispersant, solubilizer, stabilizer for pharmaceuticals
Trade names: Tetronic® 304

Poloxamine 504
CAS 11111-34-5 (generic)
Definition: Polyoxyethylene, polyoxypropylene block polymer of ethylene diamine
Uses: Emulsifier, thickener, wetting agent, dispersant, solubilizer, stabilizer for pharmaceuticals

Poloxamine 701
CAS 11111-34-5 (generic)
Definition: Polyoxyethylene, polyoxypropylene block polymer of ethylene diamine
Uses: Emulsifier, thickener, wetting agent, dispersant, solubilizer, stabilizer for pharmaceuticals

Poloxamine 702
CAS 11111-34-5 (generic)
Definition: Polyoxyethylene, polyoxypropylene block polymer of ethylene diamine
Uses: Emulsifier, thickener, wetting agent, dispersant, solubilizer, stabilizer for pharmaceuticals

Poloxamine 704
CAS 11111-34-5 (generic)
Definition: Polyoxyethylene, polyoxypropylene block polymer of ethylene diamine
Uses: Emulsifier, thickener, wetting agent, dispersant, solubilizer, stabilizer for pharmaceuticals

Poloxamine 707
CAS 11111-34-5 (generic)

Definition: Polyoxyethylene, polyoxypropylene block polymer of ethylene diamine
Uses: Emulsifier, thickener, wetting agent, dispersant, solubilizer, stabilizer for pharmaceuticals

Poloxamine 901
CAS 11111-34-5 (generic)
Definition: Polyoxyethylene, polyoxypropylene block polymer of ethylene diamine
Uses: Emulsifier, thickener, wetting agent, dispersant, solubilizer, stabilizer for pharmaceuticals

Poloxamine 904
CAS 11111-34-5 (generic)
Definition: Polyoxyethylene, polyoxypropylene block polymer of ethylene diamine
Uses: Emulsifier, thickener, wetting agent, dispersant, solubilizer, stabilizer for pharmaceuticals

Poloxamine 908
CAS 11111-34-5 (generic)
Definition: Polyoxyethylene, polyoxypropylene block polymer of ethylene diamine
Uses: Emulsifier, thickener, wetting agent, dispersant, solubilizer, stabilizer for pharmaceuticals

Poloxamine 1101
CAS 11111-34-5 (generic)
Definition: Polyoxyethylene, polyoxypropylene block polymer of ethylene diamine
Uses: Emulsifier, thickener, wetting agent, dispersant, solubilizer, stabilizer for pharmaceuticals

Poloxamine 1102
CAS 11111-34-5 (generic)
Definition: Polyoxyethylene, polyoxypropylene block polymer of ethylene diamine
Uses: Emulsifier, thickener, wetting agent, dispersant, solubilizer, stabilizer for pharmaceuticals

Poloxamine 1104
CAS 11111-34-5 (generic)
Definition: Polyoxyethylene, polyoxypropylene block polymer of ethylene diamine
Uses: Emulsifier, thickener, wetting agent, dispersant, solubilizer, stabilizer for pharmaceuticals

Poloxamine 1107
CAS 11111-34-5 (generic)
Definition: Polyoxyethylene, polyoxypropylene block polymer of ethylene diamine
Uses: Emulsifier, thickener, wetting agent, dispersant, solubilizer, stabilizer for pharmaceuticals

Poloxamine 1301
CAS 11111-34-5 (generic)
Definition: Polyoxyethylene, polyoxypropylene block polymer of ethylene diamine
Uses: Emulsifier, thickener, wetting agent, dispersant, solubilizer, stabilizer for pharmaceuticals

Poloxamine 1302
CAS 11111-34-5 (generic)
Definition: Polyoxyethylene, polyoxypropylene block polymer of ethylene diamine
Uses: Emulsifier, thickener, wetting agent, dispersant, solubilizer, stabilizer for pharmaceuticals

Poloxamine 1304
CAS 11111-34-5 (generic)
Definition: Polyoxyethylene, polyoxypropylene block polymer of ethylene diamine
Uses: Emulsifier, thickener, wetting agent, dispersant, solubilizer, stabilizer for pharmaceuticals

Poloxamine 1307
CAS 11111-34-5 (generic)
Definition: Polyoxyethylene, polyoxypropylene block polymer of ethylene diamine
Uses: Emulsifier, thickener, wetting agent, dispersant, solubilizer, stabilizer for pharmaceuticals

Poloxamine 1501
CAS 11111-34-5 (generic)
Definition: Polyoxyethylene, polyoxypropylene block polymer of ethylene diamine
Uses: Emulsifier, thickener, wetting agent, dispersant, solubilizer, stabilizer for pharmaceuticals

Poloxamine 1502
CAS 11111-34-5 (generic)
Definition: Polyoxyethylene, polyoxypropylene block polymer of ethylene diamine
Uses: Emulsifier, thickener, wetting agent, dispersant, solubilizer, stabilizer for pharmaceuticals

Poloxamine 1504
CAS 11111-34-5 (generic)

Poloxamine 1508

Definition: Polyoxyethylene, polyoxypropylene block polymer of ethylene diamine
Uses: Emulsifier, thickener, wetting agent, dispersant, solubilizer, stabilizer for pharmaceuticals

Poloxamine 1508
CAS 11111-34-5 (generic)
Definition: Polyoxyethylene, polyoxypropylene block polymer of ethylene diamine
Uses: Emulsifier, thickener, wetting agent, dispersant, solubilizer, stabilizer for pharmaceuticals

Polyacetal. *See* Acetal

Polyacrylamide
CAS 9003-05-8
Synonyms: 2-Propenamide, homopolymer
Definition: Polyamide of acrylic monomers
Empirical: $(C_3H_5NO)_x$
Formula: $[CH_2CHCONH_2]_x$
Properties: Wh. solid; water-sol. high polymer; m.w. 10,000-18,000,000; dens. 1.302
Toxicology: LD50 (mouse, IP) 170 mg/kg (monomer); heated to decomp., emits acrid smoke and irritating fumes
Uses: Ingred. in antibiotic gels
Regulatory: FDA 21CFR §172.255, 173.10, 173.315 (10 ppm in wash water), 175.105, 176.180; BP compliance (gel)
Manuf./Distrib.: Aldrich; Allchem Ind.; Allied Colloids; Allied Colloids; AMRESCO; Calgon; Cyanamid BV; Cytec; Rhone-Poulenc Water Treatment
Trade names containing: Sepigel 305

Polyacrylate. *See* Polyacrylic acid

Polyacrylic acid
CAS 9003-01-4
Synonyms: 2-Propenoic acid, homopolymer; Acrylic acid polymers; Polyacrylate
Definition: Polymer of acrylic acid
Empirical: $(C_3H_4O_2)_x$
Formula: $[CH_2CHCOOH]_x$
Properties: M.w. 168.06
Toxicology: Possible carcinogen
Uses: Emulsifier, thickener, stabilizer, suspending agent, lubricant for topical pharmaceuticals
Regulatory: FDA 21CFR §175.105, 175.300, 175.320, 176.180
Manuf./Distrib.: Alco; Aldrich; Anedco; CPS; BFGoodrich; Rhone-Poulenc
Trade names: Carbopol® 907

Polyaluminum chloride. *See* Aluminum chloride basic

Polyaminopropyl biguanide
CAS 27083-27-8
Classification: Organic compd.
Uses: Preservative in hard/rigid gas-permeable lens prods.
Regulatory: USA not restricted; Europe listed

Polybutene
CAS 9003-28-5
Synonyms: PIB; Polybutylene; 1-Butene, homopolymer
Definition: Polymer formed by polymerization of a mixture of iso- and normal butenes
Empirical: $(C_4H_8)_x$
Formula: $[CH_2CH(C_2H_5)]_n$
Properties: Liq.; m.w. 500-75,000; dens. 0.910
Toxicology: May asphyxiate
Uses: Plasticizer
Regulatory: FDA 21CFR §175.105, 175.125, 177.1570, 177.2600,178.3750
Manuf./Distrib.: Amoco; Ashland; BP Chem. Ltd; Chemcentral; Harcros; Monomer-Polymer & Dajac; Nat'l. Chem.; NOF; Punda Mercantile; H.M. Royal; Stanchem; Van Waters & Rogers
Manuf./Distrib. (pharm. & food): Aldrich

Polybutilate
CAS 24936-97-8
Uses: Used in implants
Regulatory: FDA approved for implants

Polybutylene. *See* Polybutene

Polycarbophil
CAS 9003-01-4
Definition: Acrylic acid polymer crosslinked with divinyl glycol
Properties: Wh. to creamy wh. gran., char. ester-like odor; swells in water; insol. in water, dil. acids, dil. alkalies, common org. solvs.
Uses: Rheology control agent, tablet binder, moisture enhancer; bioadhesive; drug delivery matrix; adsorbent in antidiarrheal prods.
Trade names: Noveon® AA-1

Polydimethylsiloxane. *See* Dimethicone
Poly(dimethylsiloxy)stearoxysiloxane. *See* Stearoxy dimethicone

Polyester adipate
Uses: Plasticizer; skin patch drug delivery
Manuf./Distrib.: C.P. Hall; Hüls
Trade names: Admex® 760

Polyether glycol. *See* Polyethylene glycol

Polyethylene
CAS 9002-88-4; EINECS 200-815-3
Synonyms: PE; Ethene, homopolymer; Ethene polymer; Ethylene homopolymer; Ethylene polymers
Definition: Polymer of ethylene monomers
Empirical: $(C_2H_4)_x$
Formula: $[CH_2CH_2]_x$
Properties: Wh. translucent partially cryst./partially amorphous plastic solid, odorless; sol. in hot benzene; insol. in water; m.w. 1500-100,000; dens. 0.92 (20/4 C); m.p. 85-110 C
Precaution: Combustible; store in well closed containers; reacts violently with F_2
Toxicology: No known skin toxicity; ingestion of lg. oral doses has produced kidney and liver damage; suspected carcinogen and tumorigen by implants; heated to decomp., emits acrid smoke and irritating fumes
Uses: Excipient; thickener for gels; emollient, moisture control; film-former; nonirritating abrasive; used in dentals, ophthalmics, orals, topicals, vaginals
Regulatory: FDA 21CFR §172.260, 172.615 (m.w. 2000-21,000), 173.20, 175.105, 175.300, 176.180, 176.200, 176.210, 177.1200, 177.1520, 177.2600, 178.3570, 178.3850; FDA approved for dentals, ophthalmics, orals, topicals, vaginals
Manuf./Distrib.: Asahi Chem Industry Co Ltd; Ashland; Eastman; Elf Atochem SA; Exxon; Henkel; LNP; Mitsubishi Petrochem.; Quantum/USI; Rohm & Haas; Zinchem
Manuf./Distrib. (pharm. & food): Aldrich; Asahi Chem Industry Co Ltd; Eastman
Trade names: A-C® 617, 617A

Polyethylene glycol
CAS 25322-68-3; EINECS 203-473-3
Synonyms: PEG; α-Hydroxy-ω-hydroxy poly(oxy-1,2-ethanediyl); Polyglycol; Poly(ethylene oxide); Polyether glycol
Classification: Aliphatic organic compd.
Definition: Condensation polymer of ethylene glycol
Formula: $H(OC_2H_4)_nOH, n \geq 4$
Properties: Clear liq. or wh. solid; sol. in org. solvs., aromatic hydrocarbons; dens. 1.110-1.140 (20 C); m.p. 4-10 C; flash pt. 471 F; ref. index 1.4590
Precaution: Combustible liq.
Toxicology: LD50 (oral, rat) 33,750 mg/kg; sl. toxic by ingestion; skin and eye irritant; contact dermatitis sensitization; may cause hives; heated to decomp., emits acrid smoke and irritating fumes
Uses: Ointment base, suppository base, coating agent, plasticizer, solvent, tablet or capsule lubricant; used in orals, topicals, ophthalmics; improves resist. to moisture and oxidation
Regulatory: FDA 21CFR §172.210, 172.820, 173.340; FDA approved for orals, topicals; USP/NF compliance
Manuf./Distrib.: BASF; BP Chem. Ltd; Calgene; Dow; DuPont; Harcros; Henkel; Hüls; Inolex; Olin; Rhone-Poulenc Surf.; Texaco; Union Carbide
Manuf./Distrib. (pharm. & food): Aldrich; Calgene
Trade names containing: Chroma-Seal™ 859027; Chroma-Seal™ 889031
See also PEG...

Polyethylene glycol 300. *See* PEG-6
Polyethylene glycol 400. *See* PEG-8

Polyethylene glycol 600. *See* PEG-12
Polyethylene glycol 1000. *See* PEG-20
Polyethylene glycol (2000). *See* PEG-2M
Polyethylene glycol 3350. *See* PEG-75

Polyethylene glycol t-dodecylthioether
Uses: Used in orals
Regulatory: FDA approved for orals

Polyethylene glycol monomethyl ether
CAS 9004-74-4
Synonyms: Methoxy polyethylene glycol
Definition: Addition polymer of ethylene oxide and methanol
Formula: $CH_3(OCH_2CH_2)_nOH$, n = no. of oxyethylene groups
Properties: Liq. grades: Colorless or pract. colorless clear to sl. hazy sl. hygroscopic visc. liqs., sl. char. odor; sol. in acetone, alcohol, chloroform, ethyl acetate, toluene; misc. with water; sp.gr. 1.09-1.10;; Solid grades: wh. waxy plastic, flakes, beads, or powds., pract. odorless and tasteless; sol. in water, acetone, alcohol, chloroform, ethyl acetate, toluene
Uses: Ointment base; solvent; plasticizer for pharmaceuticals

Polyethylene oxide
Classification: Polyether
Definition: Nonionic homopolymer of ethylene oxide
Formula: $(-O-CH_2CH_2.)_n$, n varies from about 2000 to > 100,000
Properties: Wh. to off-wh. powd. or gran.; sol. in water, acetonitrile, ethylene dichloride, trichloroethylene, methylene chloride; insol. in aliphatic HC, ethylene glycol, diethylene glycol, glycerol
Uses: Coating for tablets, dispersant, antisettling agent in calamine lotion, lubricant, evaporation inhibitor for rubbing alcohol, controlled-release drugs, contact lens fluid

Poly(ethylene oxide). *See* Polyethylene glycol
Polyethylenepolypropylene glycols, polymers (generic). *See* Poloxamer 101

Polyethylene wax
CAS 9002-88-4; EINECS 200-815-3
Formula: $(-CH_2CH_2.)_n$
Uses: Thickener for pharmaceutical gels
Manuf./Distrib.: AlliedSignal; Hoechst Celanese; Hüls AG; IGI; Sartomer; Stevenson Cooper; Syn. Prods.
Trade names: A-C® 7, 7A

Polyglycerate 60. *See* PEG-20 glyceryl stearate

Polyglyceryl-10 decaoleate
CAS 11094-60-3; EINECS 234-316-7
Synonyms: Decaglycerol decaoleate; Decaglyceryl decaoleate
Definition: Decaester of oleic acid and a glycerin polymer containing an avg. 10 glycerin units
Empirical: $C_{210}H_{382}O_{31}$
Uses: Dispersant, emollient, emulsifier, lubricant, solubilizer for delivery/absorp. enhancement, dermatologicals, suppositories
Regulatory: FDA 21CFR §172.854
Trade names: Caprol® 10G10O; Drewmulse® 10-10-O; Drewpol® 10-10-O

Polyglyceryl-10 decastearate
CAS 39529-26-5; EINECS 254-495-5
Synonyms: Decaglycerol decastearate; Decaglyceryl decastearate; Octadecanoic acid, decaester with decaglycerol
Definition: Decaester of stearic acid and a glycerin polymer containing an avg. 10 glycerin units
Empirical: $C_{210}H_{402}O_{31}$
Uses: Emulsifier, solubilizer, dispersant
Regulatory: FDA 21CFR §172.854
Trade names: Drewmulse® 10-10-S

Polyglyceryl-3 diisostearate
CAS 66082-42-6; 85404-84-8; EINECS 291-548-1
Synonyms: Triglyceryl diisostearate; Isooctadecanoic acid, diester with triglycerol
Definition: Diester of isostearic acid and a glycerin polymer with avg. 3 glycerin units
Uses: Emollient, thickener, solvent used for creams, lotions
Trade names: Lameform® TGI; Plurol® Diisostearique

Polyglyceryl-2 dioleate
CAS 67965-56-4; 60219-68-3
Synonyms: Diglyceryl dioleate; 9-Octadecenoic acid, diester with oxybis [propanediol]
Definition: Diester of oleic acid and a glycerin polymer with avg. 2 glycerin units
Uses: W/o emulsifier for pharmaceuticals
Trade names: Nikkol DGDO

Polyglyceryl-6 dioleate
CAS 9007-48-1; 76009-37-5
Synonyms: Hexaglycerol dioleate; Hexaglyceryl dioleate
Definition: Diester of oleic acid and a glycerin polymer containing an avg. of 6 glycerin units
Empirical: $C_{54}H_{102}O_{15}$
Uses: Dispersant, emollient, emulsifier, solubilizer, humectant, wetting agent for delivery/absorp. enhance-
   ment, dermatologicals, suppositories
Regulatory: FDA 21CFR §172.854
Trade names: Caprol® 6G2O; Plurol® Oleique WL 1173

Polyglyceryl-10 dioleate
CAS 9009-48-1; 33940-99-7
Synonyms: Decaglycerol dioleate; 9-Octadecenoic acid, diester with decaglycerol; Decaglycerin dioleate;
   Decaglyceryl dioleate
Definition: Diester of oleic acid and a glycerin polymer containing an avg. 10 glycerin units
Empirical: $C_{66}H_{126}O_{23}$
Uses: O/w emulsifier, humectant, lubricant for pharmaceuticals
Trade names: Nikkol Decaglyn 2-O

Polyglyceryl-6 distearate
CAS 34424-97-0; 61725-93-7
Synonyms: Hexaglycerol distearate; Hexaglyceryl distearate
Definition: Diester of stearic acid and a glycerin polymer containing an avg. 6 glycerin units
Empirical: $C_{54}H_{106}O_{15}$
Uses: Coupling agent, bodying agent, emulsifier, visc. modifier for delivery/absorp. enhancement, dermato-
   logicals, suppositories
Regulatory: FDA 21CFR §172.854
Trade names: Caprol® 6G2S; Drewmulse® 6-2-S

Polyglyceryl-10 distearate
CAS 12764-60-2
Synonyms: Decaglycerin distearate; Decaglyceryl distearate
Definition: Diester of stearic acid and a glycerin polymer containing an avg. 10 glycerin units
Empirical: $C_{66}H_{130}O_{23}$
Uses: O/w emulsifier for pharmaceuticals
Regulatory: FDA 21CFR §172.854
Trade names: Nikkol Decaglyn 2-S

Polyglyceryl-10 hexaoleate
Synonyms: Decaglyceryl hexaoleate
Definition: Hexaester of oleic acid and a glycerin polymer containing an avg. 10 glycerin units
Uses: W/o and o/w emulsifier, emollient, and lubricant for pharmaceuticals
Trade names: Emulsifier D-1; Polyaldo® DGHO

Polyglyceryl-4 isostearate
CAS 91824-88-3
Synonyms: Tetraglyceryl monoisostearate; Isooctanoic acid, monoester with tetraglycerol
Definition: Ester of isostearic acid and a glycerin polymer containing an avg. 4 glycerin units
Empirical: $C_{30}H_{60}O_{10}$
Uses: Dispersant in pharmaceutical lotions
Trade names containing: Abil® WE 09

Polyglyceryl-6 isostearate
CAS 126928-07-2
Definition: Ester of isostearic acid and a glycerin polymer containing an avg. of 6 glycerin units
Uses: Cosurfactant, emulsifier
Trade names: Plurol® Isostearique

Polyglyceryl-10 isostearate
CAS 133738-23-5

Polyglyceryl isostearostearate

Synonyms: Decaglycerin monoisostearate; Decaglyceryl monoisostearate
Definition: Ester of isostearic acid and a glycerin polymer containing an avg. 10 glycerin units
Empirical: $C_{48}H_{96}O_{22}$
Uses: Emulsifier, solubilizer, dispersant for pharmaceuticals
Trade names: Nikkol Decaglyn 1-IS

Polyglyceryl isostearostearate
Uses: Superfatting agent
Trade names: Lafil WL 3254

Polyglyceryl-10 laurate
CAS 34406-66-1
Synonyms: Decaglycerin monolaurate; Decaglyceryl monolaurate
Definition: Ester of lauric acid and a glycerin polymer containing an avg. 10 glycerin units
Empirical: $C_{42}H_{84}O_{22}$
Uses: Emulsifier, solubilizer, dispersant for pharmaceuticals
Regulatory: FDA 21CFR §172.854
Trade names: Nikkol Decaglyn 1-L

Polyglyceryl-10 linoleate
Synonyms: Decaglycerin monolinoleate
Definition: Ester of linoleic acid and a glycerin polymer containing an avg. 10 glycerin units
Uses: Emulsifier, solubilizer, dispersant for pharmaceuticals
Trade names: Nikkol Decaglyn 1-LN

Polyglyceryl-10 myristate
CAS 87390-32-7
Synonyms: Decaglycerin monomyristate
Definition: Ester of myristic acid and a glycerin polymer containing an avg. 10 glycerin units
Empirical: $C_{44}H_{88}O_{22}$
Uses: Emulsifier, solubilizer, dispersant for pharmaceuticals
Regulatory: FDA 21CFR §172.854
Trade names: Nikkol Decaglyn 1-M

Polyglyceryl-10 octaoleate
Synonyms: Decaglycerol octaoleate; Decaglyceryl octaoleate
Definition: Octaester of oleic acid and a glycerin polymer containing an avg. 10 glycerin units
Uses: Emulsifier, solubilizer, dispersant for pharmaceuticals (w/o and o/w emulsions, creams, lotions, internal use)
Regulatory: FDA 21CFR §172.854
Trade names: Drewmulse® 10-8-O

Polyglyceryl-2 oleate
CAS 9007-48-1 (generic); 49553-76-6
Synonyms: Diglyceryl monooleate
Definition: Ester of oleic acid and a dimer of glycerin
Empirical: $C_{24}H_{46}O_6$
Uses: W/o emulsifier for pharmaceuticals
Regulatory: FDA 21CFR §172.854
Trade names: Nikkol DGMO-C

Polyglyceryl-3 oleate
CAS 9007-48-1 (generic); 33940-98-6
Synonyms: Triglyceryl oleate
Definition: Ester of oleic acid and a glycerin polymer containing an avg. 3 glycerin units
Empirical: $C_{27}H_{52}O_8$
Uses: Emulsifier, solubilizer, dispersant for pharmaceuticals (w/o and o/w emulsions, creams, lotions, internal use)
Regulatory: FDA 21CFR §172.854
Trade names: Caprol® 3GO; Drewmulse® 3-1-O; Drewpol® 3-1-O; Mazol® PGO-31 K
Trade names containing: Protegin® W; Protegin® WX

Polyglyceryl-4 oleate
CAS 9007-48-1 (generic); 71012-10-7
Synonyms: Tetraglyceryl monooleate
Definition: Ester of oleic acid and a glycerin polymer containing an avg. 4 glycerin units
Empirical: $C_{30}H_{58}O_{10}$

Uses: Emulsifier in pharmaceutical ointments
Regulatory: FDA 21CFR §172.854
Trade names containing: Emulsynt® 1055

Polyglyceryl-6 oleate
CAS 9007-48-1 (generic); 79665-92-2
Synonyms: Hexaglycerin monooleate; Hexaglyceryl oleate
Definition: Ester of oleic acid and a glycerin polymer containing an avg. 6 glycerin units
Empirical: $C_{36}H_{70}O_{14}$
Uses: Emulsifier
Regulatory: FDA 21CFR §172.854
Trade names: Drewpol® 6-1-O

Polyglyceryl-10 oleate
CAS 9007-48-1 (generic); 67784-82-1; 79665-93-3
Synonyms: Decaglycerin monooleate; Decaglyceryl monooleate
Definition: Ester of oleic acid and a glycerin polymer containing an avg. 10 glycerin units
Empirical: $C_{48}H_{94}O_{22}$
Uses: Emulsifier, solubilizer, dispersant for pharmaceuticals
Regulatory: FDA 21CFR §172.854
Trade names: Nikkol Decaglyn 1-O

Polyglyceryl-2-PEG-4 stearate
Synonyms: Diglyceryl PEG-4 stearate
Definition: Ether of PEG-4 stearate and a glycerin polymer containing an avg. of 2 glycerin units
Uses: Emulsifier for pharmaceuticals

Polyglyceryl-2 sesquiisostearate
Synonyms: Diglyceryl sesquiisostearate
Definition: Mixture of mono and diesters of isostearic acid and a dimer of glycerin
Uses: Emulsifier for pharmaceuticals

Polyglyceryl-2 sesquioleate
Synonyms: Diglyceryl sesquioleate
Definition: Mixture of mono and diesters of oleic acid and a dimer of glycerin
Uses: Emulsifier for pharmaceuticals
Regulatory: FDA 21CFR §172.854

Polyglyceryl-2 stearate
CAS 12694-22-3; EINECS 235-777-7
Synonyms: Diglyceryl monostearate
Definition: Ester of stearic acid and a dimer of glycerin
Empirical: $C_{24}H_{48}O_6$
Uses: W/o emulsifier for pharmaceuticals
Trade names: Nikkol DGMS

Polyglyceryl-3 stearate
CAS 37349-34-1 (generic); 27321-72-8; 26855-43-6; 61790-95-2; EINECS 248-403-2
Synonyms: Triglyceryl stearate
Definition: Ester of stearic acid and a glycerin polymer containing an avg. 3 glycerin units
Uses: Bodying agent, solubilizer, dispersant, emulsifier, visc. modifier for delivery/absorp. enhancement, dermatologicals, suppositories
Regulatory: FDA 21CFR §172.854
Trade names: Caprol® 3GS; Drewmulse® 3-1-S

Polyglyceryl-10 stearate
CAS 79777-30-3
Synonyms: Decaglycerin monostearate; Decaglyceryl monostearate; Octadecanoic acid, monoester with decaglycerol
Definition: Ester of stearic acid and a glycerin polymer containing an avg. 10 glycerin units
Empirical: $C_{48}H_{96}O_{22}$
Uses: Emulsifier, solubilizer, dispersant for pharmaceuticals
Regulatory: FDA 21CFR §172.854
Trade names: Nikkol Decaglyn 1-S

Polyglyceryl-10 tetralinoleate
Synonyms: Decaglycerol tetralinoleate

Polyglyceryl-10 tetraoleate

Uses: Used in orals
Regulatory: FDA approved for orals

Polyglyceryl-10 tetraoleate
CAS 34424-98-1; EINECS 252-011-7
Synonyms: Decaglycerol tetraoleate; Decaglyceryl tetraoleate; 9-Octadecenoic acid, tetraester with decaglycerol
Definition: Tetraester of oleic acid and a glycerin polymer containing an avg. 10 glycerin units
Empirical: $C_{102}H_{190}O_{25}$
Toxicology: No known toxicity
Uses: Emulsifier, lubricant, gelling agent, plasticizer, and dispersant for drugs
Regulatory: FDA 21CFR §172.854
Trade names: Caprol® 10G4O; Drewmulse® 10-4-O; Drewpol® 10-4-O; Mazol® PGO-104

Polyglycol. *See* Polyethylene glycol
Poly(iminocarbonylpentamethylene). *See* Nylon-6
Poly[imino(1-oxo-1,6-hexanediyl)]. *See* Nylon-6
Polyisobutane. *See* Hydrogenated polyisobutene

Polyisobutene
CAS 9003-27-4
Synonyms: PIB; Polyisobutylene; 2-Methyl-1-propene, homopolymer
Definition: Homopolymer of isobutylene
Empirical: $(C_4H_8)_x$
Formula: $[CH_2C(CH_3)HCH_2]_x$
Uses: Used in injectables
Regulatory: FDA 21CFR §172.615 (min. m.w. 37,000), 175.105, 175.125, 175.300, 176.180, 177.1200, 177.1210, 177.1420, 178.3570, 178.3740, 178.3910; Japan approved; FDA approved for injectables
Manuf./Distrib.: BASF; Monomer-Polymer & Dajac; Rit-Chem
Trade names containing: Fancorsil P

Polyisobutylene. *See* Polyisobutene
trans-Polyisoprene. *See* Gutta percha

Poly (DL-lactic acid)
Synonyms: PLA
Classification: Aliphatic polyester polymer
Uses: Biocompatible polymer for use in medicine, controlled-release implantation systems, microspheres, microcapsules, sustained-release coatings; sterilizable, biodeg.
Manuf./Distrib. (pharm. & food): DuPont; FMC; Boehringer Ingelheim

Poly(laurolactam). *See* Nylon-12

Polylysine
Synonyms: Poly-l-lysine
Classification: Polyamide
Toxicology: May cause allergic skin sensitivity reactions; may have histamine-releasing props. under certain conditions
Uses: Coating material for pharmaceuticals

Poly-l-lysine. *See* Polylysine
Polymannuronic acid. *See* Alginic acid
Poly(methylvinyl ether/maleic acid) butyl ester. *See* PVM/MA copolymer, butyl ester
Poly(methylvinyl ether/maleic acid) isopropyl ester. *See* PVM/MA copolymer, isopropyl ester
Poly(methyl vinyl ether/maleic anhydride). *See* PVM/MA copolymer

Polyols
Classification: Polyhydric alcohol
Formula: $CH_2OH(CHOH)_nCH_2OH$
Properties: Solid (m.w. > 1000), liq. (m.w. < 600)
Toxicology: Low toxicity; high doses can cause kidney damage
Uses: Used in dentals; absorbs moisture
Regulatory: FDA approved for dentals

Polyox
CAS 8050-62-2
Uses: Used in orals, topicals
Regulatory: FDA approved for orals, topicals

Polyoxyl 35 castor oil. *See* PEG-35 castor oil
Polyoxyl 20 cetostearyl ether. *See* Ceteareth-20
Polyoxyl 40 hydrogenated castor oil. *See* PEG-40 hydrogenated castor oil
Polyoxyl 10 oleyl ether. *See* Oleth-10
Polyoxyl 40 stearate. *See* PEG-40 stearate
Polyoxyl 50 stearate. *See* PEG-50 stearate
Polyoxymethylene. *See* Paraformaldehyde
Polypropene. *See* Polypropylene

Polypropylene
CAS 9003-07-0; 9010-79-1 (nucleated)
Synonyms: PP; 1-Propene, homopolymer; Propene polymer; Propylene polymer; Polypropene
Definition: Polymer of propylene monomers; three forms: isotactic (fiber-forming), syndiotactic, atactic
(amorphous)
Empirical: $(C_3H_6)_x$
Formula: $[CH_2(CH_3)CH]_x$
Properties: Wh. translucent solid; m.w. > 40,000; dens. 0.90; m.p. 168-171 c; Isotactic: solid; pract. insol. in
cold org. solvs.; sol. in hot decalin, hot tetralin, boiling tetrachloroethane; dens. 0.090-0.92; m.p. 165 C
Precaution: Combustible
Uses: Excipient; used in injectables
Regulatory: FDA 21CFR §175.105, 175.300, 177.1200, 177.1520, 179.45; FDA approved for injectables; BP
compliance (stockinette)
Manuf./Distrib.: Amoco; Aristech; Ashland; Chisso; Cray Valley; Eastman; Exxon; Fina; Hüls Am.; LNP;
Mitsubishi Petrochem.; Mitsui Toatsu; Nat'l. Chem.; Neste UK; Quantum/USI; Shell; Solvay Polymers;
Stanchem
Manuf./Distrib. (pharm. & food): Aldrich

Polypropylene glycol
CAS 25322-69-4; EINECS 200-338-0
Synonyms: PPG
Classification: Aliphatic organic compd.
Empirical: $(C_3H_8O_2)_n$
Formula: $HO(C_3H_6O)_nH$
Properties: Colorless clear visc. liq., sl. bitter taste; sol. in water, aliphatic ketones, alcohol; insol. in ether,
aliphatic hydrocarbons; m.w. 400-2000; dens. 1.001-1.007; m.p. does not cryst.; flash pt. > 390 F
Precaution: Combustible exposed to heat or flame; reactive with oxidizers
Toxicology: LD50 (oral, rat) 4190 mg/kg; mildly toxic by ingestion; skin and eye irritant; linked to sensitive
reactions; heated to decomp., emits acrid smoke and irritating fumes
Uses: Absorbs moisture and acts as a solv. for fats, oils, waxes, resins; used in ophthalmics, orals, topicals
Regulatory: FDA 21CFR §173.340; FDA approved for ophthalmics, orals, topicals
Manuf./Distrib.: Aldrich; Arco; Ashland; BASF; Bayer; BP Chem. Ltd; Calgene; Dow; Harcros; Hüls AG; Olin;
PPG Industries; Rhone-Poulenc Surf.; Texaco; Witco/Oleo-Surf.
Manuf./Distrib. (pharm. & food): Ashland; Calgene
See also PPG...

Polyquaternium-1
CAS 68518-54-7
Classification: Polymeric quaternary ammonium salt
Uses: Antistatic agent, film-former; preservative in soft lens prods.

Polysorbate 20
CAS 9005-64-5 (generic)
FEMA 2915
Synonyms: Sorbitan, monodecanoate, poly(oxy-1,2-ethanediyl) derivs.; POE (20) sorbitan monolaurate;
PEG-20 sorbitan laurate; Sorbimacrogol laurate 300
Definition: Mixture of laurate esters of sorbitol and sorbitol anhydrides, with ≈ 20 moles ethylene oxide
Properties: Lemon to amber liq., char. odor, bitter taste; sol. in water, alcohol, ethyl acetate, methanol, dioxane;
insol. in min. oil, min. spirits; acid no. 2.2 max.; sapon. no. 40-50; hyd. no. 96-108
Toxicology: LD50 (oral, rat) 37 g/kg; mod. toxic by intraperitoneal, intravenous routes; mildly toxic by ingestion;
human skin irritant; heated to decomp., emits acrid smoke and irritating fumes
Uses: Emulsifying agent, solubilizer, wetting agent; used in intravenous, parenterals, ophthalmics, orals,
topicals, vaginals
Usage level: 1-15% (emulsifier for pharmaceuticals)
Regulatory: FDA 21CFR §172.515, 175.105, 175.300, 178.3400; FEMA GRAS; Europe listed; FDA approved
for intravenous, parenterals, ophthalmics, orals, topicals, vaginals; USP/NF, BP, Ph.Eur. compliance

Polysorbate 21

Manuf./Distrib. (pharm. & food): Spectrum Chem. Mfg.
Trade names: Alkamuls® PSML-20; Capmul® POE-L; Crillet 1; Drewmulse® POE-SML; Emalex ET-2020; Eumulgin® SML 20; Glycosperse® L-20; Montanox® 20; Montanox® 20 DF; Nikkol TL-10, TL-10EX; Nissan Nonion LT-221; Sorbilene L; Sorbilene LH; T-Maz® 20
Trade names containing: Solubilisant γ 2420; Solubilisant γ 2428

Polysorbate 21
CAS 9005-64-5 (generic)
Synonyms: POE (4) sorbitan monolaurate; PEG-4 sorbitan laurate
Definition: Mixture of laurate esters of sorbitol and sorbitol anhydrides, with ≈ 4 moles ethylene oxide
Toxicology: Moderately toxic by intraperitoneal, intravenous routes; midly toxic by ingestion; skin irritant
Uses: Emulsifier, solubilizer, wetting agent
Regulatory: FDA 21CFR §175.300
Trade names: Crillet 11; Sorbilene L 4

Polysorbate 40
CAS 9005-66-7
Synonyms: POE (20) sorbitan monopalmitate; Sorbitan, monohexadecanoate, poly(oxy-1,2-ethaneidyl) derivs.; Sorbimacrogol palmitate 300
Definition: Mixture of palmitate esters of sorbitol and sorbitol anhydrides, with ≈ 20 moles of ethylene oxide
Properties: Yel. liq., faint char. odor; sol. in water, alcohol; insol. in min. and veg. oils; acid no. 2.2 max.; sapon. no. 41-52; hyd. no. 89-105
Toxicology: Moderately toxic by intravenous route
Uses: O/w emulsifier, solubilizer, wetting agent; used in parenterals, intramuscular injectables, orals, topicals
Regulatory: FDA 21CFR §175.105, 175.300, 178.3400; Europe listed; UK approved; FDA approved for parenterals, intramuscular injectables, orals, topicals; USP/NF compliance
Manuf./Distrib. (pharm. & food): Spectrum Chem. Mfg.
Trade names: Crillet 2; Glycosperse® P-20; Montanox® 40; Montanox® 40 DF; Sorbilene P

Polysorbate 60
CAS 9005-67-8 (generic)
FEMA 2916
Synonyms: POE (20) sorbitan monostearate; PEG-20 sorbitan stearate; Sorbimacrogol stearate 300
Definition: Mixture of stearate esters of sorbitol and sorbitol anhydrides, with ≈ 20 moles ethylene oxide
Empirical: $C_{64}H_{126}O_{26}$
Properties: Lemon to orange oily liq., faint char. odor, bitter taste; sol. in water, aniline, ethyl acetate, toluene; insol. in min. and veg. oils; m.w. 1311.90; acid no. 2 max.; sapon. no. 45-55; hyd. no. 81-96
Toxicology: LD50 (IV, rat) 1220 mg/kg; moderately toxic by intravenous route; experimental tumorigen, reproductive effects; heated to decomp., emits acrid smoke and irritating fumes
Uses: Emulsifier, solubilizer, wetting agent; used in orals, rectals, topicals, vaginals, suntan lotions
Regulatory: FDA 21CFR §73.1001, 172.515, 172.836, 172.878, 172.886, 173.340, 175.105, 175.300, 178.3400; USDA CFR9 §318.7, 381.147 (limitation 1% max., 1% total combined with polysorbate 80, 0.0175% in scald water); FEMA GRAS; Europe listed; UK approved; FDA approved for orals, rectals, topicals, vaginals; USP/NF, BP, Ph.Eur. compliance
Manuf./Distrib. (pharm. & food): Am. Ingreds.; Spectrum Chem. Mfg.
Trade names: Capmul® POE-S; Crillet 3; Drewmulse® POE-SMS; Eumulgin® SMS 20; Glycosperse® S-20; Montanox® 60; Montanox® 60 DF; Nikkol TS-10; Sorbilene S; T-Maz® 60K
Trade names containing: Macol® CPS; Mazawax® 163R; Mazawax® 163SS; Ritachol® 1000; Ritachol® 2000; Ritachol® 3000

Polysorbate 61
CAS 9005-67-8 (generic)
Synonyms: POE (4) sorbitan monostearate; PEG-4 sorbitan stearate
Definition: Mixture of stearate esters of sorbitol and sorbitol anhydrides, with ≈ 4 moles ethylene oxide
Properties: M.w. 1311.70; dens. 1.044; flash pt. > 110 C
Toxicology: Moderately toxic by intravenous route
Uses: Emulsifier, solubilizer, lubricant for suppositories in pharmaceuticals
Regulatory: FDA 21CFR §175.300
Trade names: Alkamuls® PSMS-4; Crillet 31; Sorbilene S 4; T-Maz® 61

Polysorbate 65
CAS 9005-71-4
Synonyms: POE (20) sorbitan tristearate; PEG-20 sorbitan tristearate; Sorbimacrogol tristearate 300
Definition: Mixture of stearate esters of sorbitol and sorbitol anhydrides, with ≈ 20 moles ethylene oxide
Properties: Tan waxy solid, faint odor, bitter taste; sol. in min. and veg. oils, min. spirits, acetone, ether, dioxane,

alcohol, methanol; disp. in water, CCl₄; acid no. 2 max.; sapon. no. 88-98; hyd. no. 44-60
Toxicology: Heated to decomp., emits acrid smoke and irritating fumes
Uses: Emulsifier, solubilizer, wetting agent
Regulatory: FDA 21CFR §73.1001, 172.838, 173.340, 175.300, 178.3400; Europe listed; UK approved
Trade names: Crillet 35; Drewmulse® POE-STS; Glycosperse® TS-20; Montanox® 65; Nikkol TS-30; Sorbilene TS; T-Maz® 65K

Polysorbate 80
CAS 9005-65-6 (generic); 37200-49-0; 61790-86-1; EINECS 215-665-4; 200-849-9
FEMA 2917
Synonyms: POE (20) sorbitan monooleate; PEG-20 sorbitan oleate; Sorbimacrogol oleate 300
Definition: Mixture of oleate esters of sorbitol and sorbitol anhydrides, with ≈ 20 moles ethylene oxide
Properties: Amber visc. liq.; nonionic; very sol. in water; sol. in alcohol, cottonseed oil, corn oil, ethyl acetate, methanol, toluene; insol. in min. oil; dens. 1.06-1.10; visc. 270-430 cSt; acid no. 2 max.; sapon. no. 45-55; hyd. no. 65-80; pH 5-7 (5% aq.)
Toxicology: LD50 (oral, mouse) 25 g/kg; mod. toxic by intravenous route; mildly toxic by ingestion; eye irritant; experimental tumorigen, reproductive effects; mutagenic data; heated to decomp., emits acrid smoke and irritating fumes
Uses: Pharmaceutic aid, surfactant, emulsifier, solubilizer, wetting agent, dispersant; used in buccals, intramuscular injectables, intravenous, parenterals, ophthalmics, orals, otics, rectals, topicals, vaginals
Regulatory: FDA 21CFR §73.1, 73.1001, 172.515, 172.840, 173.340, 175.105, 175.300, 178.3400; USDA 9CFR §318.7, 381.147 (limitation 1% alone, 1% total combined with polysorbate 60); FEMA GRAS; Europe listed; UK approved; FDA approved for buccals, intramuscular injectables, intravenous, parenterals, ophthalmics, orals, otics, rectals, topicals, vaginals; USP/NF, BP, Ph.Eur. compliance
Manuf./Distrib. (pharm. & food): Spectrum Chem. Mfg.
Trade names: Crillet 4; Drewmulse® POE-SMO; Emalex ET-8020; Ethylan® GEO8; Eumulgin® SMO 20; Glycosperse® O-20; Glycosperse® O-20 FG; Glycosperse® O-20 KFG; Montanox® 80; Montanox® 80 DF; Nikkol TO-10; Sorbilene O; T-Maz® 80; T-Maz® 80K; T-Maz® 80KLM
Trade names containing: Aldosperse® MO-50 FG; Aldosperse® O-20 KFG; Crodalan AWS; Drewmulse® 700K; Fancol ALA-10; Ritawax AEO; Solulan® 98; Unibix AP (Acid Proof)

Polysorbate 81
CAS 9005-65-5 (generic)
Synonyms: POE (5) sorbitan monooleate; PEG-5 sorbitan oleate
Definition: Mixture of oleate esters of sorbitol and sorbitol anhydrides, with ≈ 5 moles ethylene oxide
Uses: Emulsifier, solubilizer, wetting agent, dispersant, suspending agent, visc. modifier
Regulatory: FDA 21CFR §175.300
Trade names: Crillet 41; Glycosperse® O-5; Sorbilene O 5; T-Maz® 81; T-Maz® 81K
Trade names containing: Alcolan® 40

Polysorbate 85
CAS 9005-70-3
Synonyms: POE (20) sorbitan trioleate; PEG-20 sorbitan trioleate; Sorbimacrogol trioleate 300
Definition: Mixture of oleate esters of sorbitol and sorbitol anhydrides, with ≈ 20 moles ethylene oxide
Toxicology: Skin irritant
Uses: Surfactant, emulsifier, solubilizer used in tanning lotions
Regulatory: FDA 21CFR §175.300, 178.3400
Manuf./Distrib.: Spectrum Chem. Mfg.
Trade names: Crillet 45; Glycosperse® TO-20; Montanox® 85; Nikkol TO-30; Sorbilene TO; T-Maz® 85

Polysorbate 120. *See* PEG-20 sorbitan isostearate

Polysorbate 80 acetate
Synonyms: POE (20) sorbitan monooleate acetate
Definition: Acetyl ester of polysorbate 80
Uses: Used in pharmaceuticals
Trade names containing: Solulan® 97

Polystyrene
CAS 9003-53-6
Synonyms: PS; Styrene polymer; Ethenylbenzene, homopolymer; Benzene, ethenyl-, homopolymer
Classification: Polymer
Definition: Grades: crystal, impact, expandable
Empirical: $(C_8H_8)_x$
Properties: Colorless to ylsh. oily liq., penetrating odor; sol. in alcohol; sl. sol. in water; m.w. 2500-250,000
Toxicology: May cause irritation to eyes and mucous membranes; can be narcotic in high concs.; experimental

Polyurethane prepolymer

        tumorigen by implant
    Uses: Excipient
    Regulatory: FDA 21CFR §175.105, 175.125, 175.300, 175.320, 176.180, 177.1200, 177.1640, 177.2600
    Manuf./Distrib.: Amoco; Asahi Chem Industry Co Ltd; Ashland; BASF; Chevron; Elf Atochem SA; Fina; BFGoodrich; Hüls AG; LNP; Mitsubishi Petrochem.; Mitsui Toatsu; Reichhold; Scott Bader; Westlake Plastics; Zinchem
    Manuf./Distrib. (pharm. & food): Aldrich

Polyurethane prepolymer
    Uses: Foamable hydrophilic prepolymer for wound dressings, biocompat. coatings, drug delivery vehicles
    Manuf./Distrib.: Air Prods.; Bayer; CasChem; Conap; BFGoodrich; Hampshire; ICI Polyurethanes; Polyurethane Corp. of Am.; Polyurethane Spec.; Soluol; Uniroyal; Zeneca Resins
    Trade names: Hypol® 2002

Polyvidone. *See* PVP
Polyvidonum. *See* PVP
Polyvidonum insoluble, crosslinked. *See* Crospovidone

Polyvinyl acetate (homopolymer)
    CAS 9003-20-7
    Synonyms: PVAc; Acetic acid, ethenyl ester, homopolymer; Acetic acid vinyl ester polymers; Ethenyl acetate, homopolymer
    Classification: Homopolymer
    Definition: Homopolymer of vinyl acetate
    Empirical: $(C_4H_6O_2)_x$
    Formula: $[CH_2CHOOCOCH_3]_x$
    Properties: Water-wh. clear solid resin; sol. in benzene, acetone; insol. in water
    Toxicology: Heated to decomp., emits acrid smoke and irritating fumes
    Uses: Binder, emulsion stabilizer, film-former used in orals
    Regulatory: FDA 21CFR §73.1, 172.615 (m.w. 2000 min.), 175.105, 175.300, 175.320, 176.170, 176.180, 177.1200, 177.2800, 181.22, 181.30; Japan approved; FDA approved for orals
    Manuf./Distrib.: Air Prods.; Aldrich; Ashland; H.B. Fuller; General Latex & Chem.; Hampshire; Lenape Ind.; Monsanto; Nat'l. Starch & Chem.; Reichhold; Rhone-Poulenc; Rohm & Haas; StanChem; Union Carbide; VYN-AC; Wacker-Chemie GmbH
    Manuf./Distrib. (pharm. & food): Nat'l. Starch & Chem.

Polyvinyl acetate phthalate
    Synonyms: PVAP
    Definition: Reaction prod. of phthalic anhydride and a partially hydrolyzed polyvinyl acetate
    Properties: Wh. free-flowing powd., sl. acetic acid odor; sol. in methanol, alcohol; insol. in water, methylene chloride, chloroform; visc. 7-11 cps
    Uses: Enteric film-former; coating agent, visc. modifier for pharmaceutical tablets
    Regulatory: USP/NF compliance
    Trade names: Opaseal®; pHthalavin™
    Trade names containing: Sureteric™

Polyvinyl alcohol
    CAS 9002-89-5 (super and fully hydrolyzed); EINECS 209-183-3
    Synonyms: PVA; PVAL; Ethenol homopolymer; PVOH; Poval; Vinyl alcohol polymer
    Classification: Water-sol. synthetic polymer; aliphatic organic compd.
    Empirical: $(C_2H_4O)_x$, avg. x = 500-5000
    Formula: $[CH_2CHOH]_x$
    Properties: Wh. to cream amorphous powd. or gran., odorless; sol. in water; insol. in petrol. solvs.; m.w. $(44.05)_x$, avg. 120,000; dens. 1.329; softens at 200 C with dec.; flash pt. (OC) 175 F; ref. index 1.49-1.53; pH 5-8 (4%)
    Precaution: Flamm. exposed to heat or flame; reactive with oxidizers; dust exposed to flame presents sl. explosion hazard
    Toxicology: Experimental carcinogen and tumorigen; heated to decomp., emits acrid smoke and irritating fumes
    Uses: Suspending agent, visc.-increasing agent; pharmaceutical finishing; ophthalmic lubricant; emulsifier; hydrogel for controlled-drug delivery; used in ophthalmics, orals, injectables, topicals, vaginals; artificial tear prods.
    Regulatory: FDA 21CFR §73.1, 175.105, 175.300, 175.320, 176.170, 176.180, 177.1200, 177.1670, 177.2260, 177.2800, 178.3910, 181.22, 181.30; FDA approved for ophthalmics, orals, injectables, topicals, vaginals; USP/NF compliance

Manuf./Distrib.: Air Prods.; Allchem Ind.; British Traders & Shippers; GCA; Hoechst Celanese; Honeywill & Stein Ltd; Hunt; Itochu Spec.; Monomer-Polymer & Dajac; Polysciences; Rhone-Poulenc; San Yuan; Shin-Etsu; Spectrum Chem. Mfg.; Wacker-Chemie GmbH

Manuf./Distrib. (pharm. & food): Aldrich; Ruger; Spectrum Chem. Mfg.

Poly (n-vinylbutyrolactam). *See* PVP

Polyvinyl chloride
CAS 9002-86-2; EINECS 208-750-2
Synonyms: PVC; Chloroethene homopolymer; Chloroethylene polymer; Poly(vinyl chloride)
Classification: Synthetic thermoplastic high polymer
Empirical: $(C_2H_3Cl)_n$
Formula: $[CH_2CHClCH_2CHCl]_n$
Properties: Wh. powd. or colorless gran.; m.w. 60,000-150,000; dens. 1.406; ref. index 1.54
Toxicology: Suspected tumorigen by ingestion and implantation; chronic inhalation health problems; may cause necrotizing or contact dermatitis
Uses: Excipient; used in parenterals, topicals, dialysis
Regulatory: FDA approved for parenterals
Manuf./Distrib.: Air Prods.; Aldrich; Asahi Glass; Ashland; Chisso; Elf Atochem SA; Georgia Gulf; BFGoodrich; Goodyear; Hüls Am.; Mitsui Toatsu; Nat'l. Starch & Chem.; Nippon Zeon; Norsk Hydro AS; Occidental; Shin-Etsu; Teknor Apex; Vista; Wacker-Chemie GmbH

Poly(vinyl chloride). *See* Polyvinyl chloride

Polyvinylpolypyrrolidone
CAS 9003-39-8
Synonyms: PVPP
Definition: Insoluble homopolymer of purified vinylpyrrolidone
Properties: Wh. powd., faint bland odor; hygroscopic; insol. in water
Toxicology: Heated to decomp., emits acrid smoke and irritating fumes
Uses: Binder/disintegrant in pharmaceutical tablets; suspension aid
Regulatory: FDA 21CFR §173.50 (must be removed by filtration); BATF 27CFR §240.1051 (limitation 6 lb/1000 gal in wine)
Manuf./Distrib. (pharm. & food): Aldrich

Poly(vinylpolypyrrolidone). *See* Crospovidone
Polyvinylpyrrolidone. *See* PVP
Polyvinylpyrrolidone/hexadecene copolymer. *See* PVP/hexadecene copolymer
Polyvinylpyrrolidone-iodine complex. *See* PVP-iodine
Polyvinylpyrrolidone/vinyl acetate copolymer. *See* PVP/VA copolymer
Ponceau SX. *See* CI 14700
Ponceau SX. *See* FD&C Red No. 4
POP (30) cetyl ether. *See* PPG-30 cetyl ether
POP (2) lanolin ether. *See* PPG-2 lanolin alcohol ether
POP (5) lanolin ether. *See* PPG-5 lanolin alcohol ether
POP (10) lanolin ether. *See* PPG-10 lanolin alcohol ether
POP (20) lanolin ether. *See* PPG-20 lanolin alcohol ether
POP (10) methyl glucose ether. *See* PPG-10 methyl glucose ether
POP (20) methyl glucose ether. *See* PPG-20 methyl glucose ether
POP (20) methyl glucose ether distearate. *See* PPG-20 methyl glucose ether distearate
POP (26) monooleate. *See* PPG-26 oleate
POP (2) monosalicylate. *See* Dipropylene glycol salicylate
POP (2) myristyl ether propionate. *See* PPG-2 myristyl ether propionate
POP (4) POE (1) cetyl ether. *See* PPG-4 ceteth-1
POP (4) POE (10) cetyl ether. *See* PPG-4-ceteth-10
POP (8) POE (1) cetyl ether. *See* PPG-8-ceteth-1
POP (5) POE (10) cetyl ether phosphate. *See* PPG-5 ceteth-10 phosphate
POP (2) POE (9) cetyl/stearyl ether. *See* PPG-2-ceteareth-9
POP (12) POE (50) lanolin. *See* PPG-12-PEG-50 lanolin
POP (12) POE (65) lanolin oil. *See* PPG-12-PEG-65 lanolin oil
POP (3) POE (9) lauryl ether. *See* PPG-3-laureth-9
POP (5) POE (5) lauryl ether. *See* PPG-5-laureth-5
POP (12) POE (16) monobutyl ether. *See* PPG-12-buteth-16

Poppyseed oil
Synonyms: Maw oil; Oleum papaveris

POP (15) stearyl ether

Definition: Fixed oil derived from ripe seeds of the opium poppy, *Papaver somniferum*
Uses: Substitute for olive oil in pharmaceuticals; prep. of iodized oil fluid injection

POP (15) stearyl ether. *See* PPG-15 stearyl ether
Potash. *See* Potassium carbonate
Potash alum. *See* Potassium alum dodecahydrate
Potash lye. *See* Potassium hydroxide
Potash sulfurated. *See* Sulfurated potash
Potassa. *See* Potassium hydroxide
Potassium acesulfame. *See* Acesulfame potassium

Potassium acetate
CAS 127-08-2; EINECS 204-822-2
FEMA 2920
Synonyms: Acetic acid potassium salt
Classification: Aliphatic organic compd.
Empirical: $C_2H_3KO_2$
Formula: CH_3COOK
Properties: Colorless lustrous cryst. or wh. cryst. powd. or flakes, odorless or faint acetous odor, saline taste; deliq.; sol. in water, alcohol; insol. in ether; m.w. 98.14; dens. 1.57; m.p. 292 C
Precaution: Keep tightly closed
Toxicology: LD50 (oral, rat) 3.25 g/kg
Uses: Raw material for pharmaceuticals; synthetic flavoring agent; used in ophthalmics, rectals
Regulatory: FDA 21CFR §172.515; FEMA GRAS; Europe listed; FDA approved for ophthalmics, rectals; BP compliance
Manuf./Distrib.: Am. Int'l. Chem.; EM Ind.; General Chem.; Heico; Hoechst AG; Honeywill & Stein Ltd; Ikoma Fine Chem.; Lohmann; Niacet; Poly Research; Schaefer Salt & Chem.; Spectrum Chem. Mfg.
Manuf./Distrib. (pharm. & food): Aldrich; Heico; Honeywill & Stein Ltd; Integra; Lohmann; Mallinckrodt; Niacet; Ruger; Spectrum Chem. Mfg.

Potassium acid tartrate
CAS 868-14-4; EINECS 212-769-1
Synonyms: Potassium bitartrate; Monopotassium L-(+)-tartrate; Potassium hydrogen tartrate; Cream of tartar; L-Tartaric acid monopotassium salt; Acid potassium tartrate; Dipotassium L-(+)-tartrate
Definition: Salt of L(+)-tartaric acid
Empirical: $C_4H_5KO_6$
Formula: $KHC_4H_4O_6$
Properties: Colorless or sl. opaque cryst. or wh. cryst. powd., pleasant acid taste; sol. in water, sl. sol. in alcohol; m.w. 188.18; dens. 1.984
Toxicology: Heated to decomp., emits acrid smoke and irritating fumes
Uses: Cathartic
Regulatory: FDA 21CFR §184.1077, GRAS; USDA 9CFR §318.7; BATF 27CFR §240.1051 (limitation 25 lb/1000 gal grape wine); Europe listed; UK approved; Japan approved
Manuf./Distrib.: Lohmann; Penta Mfg.; Spectrum Chem. Mfg.
Manuf./Distrib. (pharm. & food): AB Tech.; Ashland; British Pepper & Spice; Browning; Calaga Food Ingreds.; Ellis & Everard; Int'l. Sourcing; Jungbunzlauer; Lohmann; New England Spice; Pacific Foods; Penta Mfg.; Siber Hegner; Spectrum Chem. Mfg.; Spice King; Van Waters & Rogers

Potassium alginate
CAS 9005-36-1
Synonyms: Potassium polymannuronate; Alginic acid, potassium salt
Definition: Potassium salt of alginic acid
Empirical: $(C_6H_7O_6K)_x$
Properties: Wh. gran., odorless, tasteless; sol. in water; insol. in alcohol, chloroform, ether; m.w. 214.22
Toxicology: Heated to decomp., emits acrid smoke and irritating fumes
Uses: Gellant, thickener, suspending agent in creams, tablets, dental impression compds.
Regulatory: FDA 21CFR §184.1610, GRAS; Europe listed; UK approved
Manuf./Distrib.: Atomergic Chemetals; Kelco Int'l.
Manuf./Distrib. (pharm. & food): Atomergic Chemetals; Kelco Int'l.; Spectrum Chem. Mfg.
Trade names: KELMAR®; KELMAR® CR; KELMAR® Improved; Protanal KF 200; Protanal KF 200 RBS; Protanal KF 200 S; Sobalg FD 200 Range

Potassium alum. *See* Potassium alum dodecahydrate

Potassium alum dodecahydrate
CAS 7784-24-9; EINECS 233-141-3

Synonyms: Aluminum potassium sulfate; Potash alum; Alum; Alum, potassium; Potassium alum; Potassium aluminum sulfate; Kalinite
Classification: Inorganic salt
Formula: $KAl(SO_4)_2 \cdot 12H_2O$ (dodecahydrate)
Properties: Dodecahydrate: Transparent cryst. or wh. cryst. powd., odorless, sweetish astringent taste; sol. glycerin; sol. 1 g/7.2 ml water; insol. in alcohol; m.w. 474.38; dens. 1.725; m.p. 92.5 C
Toxicology: Nuisance dust
Uses: Active ingred. in OTC drug prods.; astringent
Regulatory: FDA 21CFR §133.102, 133.106, 133.111, 133.141, 133.165, 133.181, 133.183, 133.195, 137.105, 137.155, 137.160, 137.165, 137.170, 137.175, 137.180, 137. 185. 178.3120, 182.90, 182.1129, GRAS; Japan approved except for miso; BP, Ph.Eur. compliance

Potassium aluminum sulfate. *See* Potassium alum dodecahydrate

Potassium benzoate
CAS 582-25-2 (anhyd.); EINECS 209-481-3
Synonyms: Benzoic acid potassium salt
Empirical: $C_7H_5KO_2$
Formula: C_6H_5COOK
Properties: Wh. gran. or cryst. powd., odorless or pract. odorless; hygroscopic; sol. in water; sparingly sol. in alcohol; m.w.160.22; m.p. > 300 C; stable in air
Toxicology: Mild irritant to skin, eyes, and mucous membranes
Uses: Antimicrobial preservative, lubricant for pharmaceutical tabletting
Regulatory: USDA 9CFR §318.7 (limitation 0.1%), BATF 27CFR §240.1051 (limitation 0.1% in wine); Europe listed; USP/NF compliance
Manuf./Distrib.: Am. Biorganics; Lohmann; Mallinckrodt; Pentagon Chems. Ltd; Pfizer Food Science; Schweizerhall; Verdugt BV
Manuf./Distrib. (pharm. & food): Aldrich; Integra; Lohmann; Pentagon Chems. Ltd; Pfizer Food Science; Ruger; Spectrum Chem. Mfg.

Potassium bicarbonate
CAS 298-14-6; EINECS 206-059-0
Synonyms: Carbonic acid monopotassium salt; Potassium hydrogen carbonate; Monopotassium carbonate
Classification: Inorganic salt
Empirical: $CH_2O_3 \cdot K$
Formula: $KHCO_3$
Properties: Colorless prisms or wh. gran. powd., odorless; hygroscopic; sol. in water; insol. in alcohol; m.w. 100.12; stable in air
Toxicology: Nuisance dust
Uses: pH adjustor; used in effervescent tablets
Regulatory: FDA 21CFR §163.110, 184.1613, GRAS; USDA 9CFR §318.7; BATF 27CFR §240.1051
Manuf./Distrib.: Hüls AG; Lohmann
Manuf./Distrib. (pharm. & food): Aldrich; Browning; Church & Dwight; Hays; Hüls AG; Integra; Lohmann; Mallinckrodt; Penta Mfg.; Ruger; Spectrum Chem. Mfg.; Van Waters & Rogers

Potassium biphosphate. *See* Potassium phosphate

Potassium bisulfite
CAS 7773-03-7
Toxicology: May cause allergic reactions incl. anaphylaxis
Uses: Antioxidant, preservative for nebulizer sol'ns., parenterals, peritoneal dialysis sol'ns.
Regulatory: FDA 21CFR §182.3616 (not for use in meats), GRAS

Potassium bitartrate. *See* Potassium acid tartrate

Potassium bromide
CAS 7758-02-3; EINECS 231-830-3
Empirical: BrK
Formula: KBr
Properties: Colorless cubic cryst.; sl. hygroscopic; sol. in water, glycerol, ether; sl. sol. in alcohol; m.w. 119.01; dens. 2.75; m.p. 730 C; b.p. 1380 C; pH 5.5-8.5 (5%, 20 C)
Precaution: Violent reaction with BrF_3
Toxicology: Large doses can cause CNS depression; prolonged inh. can cause skin eruptions; mutagenic data; heated to decomp., emits toxic fumes of K_2O and Br.
Uses: Raw material for pharmaceutical (sedative)
Regulatory: FDA 21CFR §173.315; BP, Ph.Eur. compliance

Potassium butyl paraben

> *Manuf./Distrib.:* Aldrich; Great Lakes; Mallinckrodt; Morton Int'l.; Spectrum Chem. Mfg.
> *Manuf./Distrib. (pharm. & food):* Integra; Mallinckrodt; Ruger

Potassium butyl paraben
> CAS 38566-94-8
> *Synonyms:* Butylparaben, potassium salt; n-Butyl-4-hydroxybenzoate potassium salt
> *Definition:* Potassium salt of butylparaben
> *Empirical:* $C_{11}H_{14}O$ • K
> *Uses:* Preservative, bactericide, fungicide
> *Trade names:* Nipabutyl Potassium

Potassium carbonate
> CAS 584-08-7; EINECS 209-529-3
> *Synonyms:* Carbonic acid dipotassium salt; Dipotassium carbonate; Pearl ash; Potash; Salt of tartar; American ash
> *Classification:* Inorganic salt
> *Empirical:* CO_3 • 2K
> *Formula:* K_2CO_3
> *Properties:* White deliq. gran., translucent powd., odorless; deliq., hygroscopic; alkaline reaction; sol. in water; insol. in alcohol, glycerol; m.w. 138.20; dens. 2.428 (19 C); m.p. 891 C
> *Precaution:* Noncombustible; incompatible with KCO, magnesium
> *Toxicology:* LD50 (oral, rat) 1870 mg/kg; poison by ingestion; solutions irritating to tissue; strong caustic; heated to decomp., emits toxic fumes of K_2O
> *Uses:* Used in orals, topicals
> *Regulatory:* FDA 21CFR §163.110, 172.560, 173.310, 184.1619, GRAS; USDA 9CFR §318.7; BATF 27CFR §240.1051; Japan approved; Europe listed; UK approved; FDA approved for orals, topicals; BP compliance
> *Manuf./Distrib.:* Asahi Glass; Hüls; Lohmann; Mallinckrodt; Nippon Soda; Occidental
> *Manuf./Distrib. (pharm. & food):* Aldrich; Browning; Church & Dwight; Hays; Hüls AG; Integra; Lohmann; Mallinckrodt; Penta Mfg.; Ruger; Spectrum Chem. Mfg.; Van Waters & Rogers; Peter Whiting

Potassium cetyl phosphate
> CAS 19035-79-1; EINECS 242-769-1
> *Synonyms:* Phosphoric acid, cetyl ester, potassium salt
> *Definition:* Potassium salt of a complex mixture of esters of phosphoric acid and cetyl alcohol
> *Uses:* Emulsifier, stabilizer
> *Trade names:* Amphisol® K

Potassium chloride
> CAS 7447-40-7; EINECS 231-211-8
> *Synonyms:* Dipotassium dichloride; Potassium monochloride; Muriate of potash
> *Classification:* Inorganic salt
> *Empirical:* ClK
> *Formula:* KCl
> *Properties:* Colorless to wh. crystals or powd., odorless, saline taste at low concs.; hygroscopic; sol. in water, glycerin; sl. sol. in alcohol; insol. in abs. alcohol, ether, acetone; m.w. 74.55; dens. 1.987; m.p. 773 C (sublimes 1500 C); pH 7
> *Precaution:* Explosive reaction with BrF_3
> *Toxicology:* LD50 (oral, rat) 2600 mg/kg; human poison by ingestion; moderately toxic by subcutaneous route; eye irritant; human systemic effects; mutagenic data; heated to decomp., emits toxic fumes of K_2O and Cl⁻
> *Uses:* Tonicity agent; sodium reduction; flavoring agent; nutrient replacement; used in injectables, parenterals, ophthalmics, orals, extended-release capsules
> *Regulatory:* FDA 21CFR §150.141, 150.161, 166.110, 182.5622, 184.1622, GRAS, 201.306; USDA 9CFR §318.7, 381.147 (limitation ≤ 3% of 2 molar sol'n.); Japan approved; Europe listed; UK approved; FDA approved for injectables, parenterals, ophthalmics, orals; USP/NF, BP, Ph.Eur. compliance
> *Manuf./Distrib.:* Aldrich; Heico; Lohmann; Mallinckrodt; Morton Int'l.; Otsuka Chem.; Reheis
> *Manuf./Distrib. (pharm. & food):* Browning; R.W. Greeff; Integra; Mallinckrodt; Reheis; Ruger; Spectrum Chem. Mfg.
> *Trade names:* Controlled Particle Size KCl; Free-flowing KCl; Standard KCl; Superfine KCl; Wholecut KCl
> *Trade names containing:* Cap-Shure® KCL-140-50; Cap-Shure® KCL-165-70; Durkote Potassium Chloride/Hydrog. Veg. Oil

Potassium citrate
> CAS 866-84-2 (anhyd.); 6100-05-6 (monohydrate); EINECS 212-755-5, 231-905-0 (monohydrate)
> *Synonyms:* Citric acid tripotassium salt; 1,2,3-Propanetricarboxylic acid, 2-hydroxy, tripotassium salt; Tripotassium citrate monohydrate; Potassium citrate tertiary

Empirical: C$_6$H$_5$O$_7$ • 3K (anhyd.), C$_6$H$_5$K$_3$O$_7$ • H$_2$O (monohydrate)
Properties: Colorless or wh. cryst. or powd., odorless, cooling saline taste; deliq.; sol. in water, glycerol; insol. in alcohol; m.w. 306.41 (anhyd.), 324.42 (monohydrate); dens. 1.98; dec. 230 C; pH 8.5
Toxicology: LD50 (IV, dog) 167 mg/kg; poison by intravenous routes; heated to decomp., emits toxic fumes of K$_2$O, acrid smoke and irritating fumes
Uses: Potassium and citrate source in pharmaceuticals; buffering agent; antiurolithic; antacid; used in orals, extended-release tablets
Regulatory: FDA 21CFR §181.29, 182.1625, 182.6625, GRAS; USDA 9CFR §318.7; BATF 27CFR §240.1051 (limitation 25 lb/1000 gal wine); Japan approved; Europe listed; UK approved; FDA approved for orals; USP/NF, BP, Ph.Eur. compliance
Manuf./Distrib.: Haarmann & Reimer; Lohmann; Mallinckrodt; Pfizer SA; Schweizerhall
Manuf./Distrib. (pharm. & food): ADM; Aldrich; Browning; Integra; Jungbunzlauer; Lohmann; Ruger; Spectrum Chem. Mfg.

Potassium citrate tertiary. *See* Potassium citrate

Potassium cocoate
CAS 61789-30-8; EINECS 263-049-9
Synonyms: Potassium coconate; Coconut acid, potassium salt; Fatty acids, coconut oil, potassium salts
Definition: Potassium salt of coconut acid
Uses: Used in medicinal soaps
Regulatory: FDA 21CFR §175.105, 176.170, 176.200, 176.210, 177.1200, 177.2600, 177.2800, 178.3910
Trade names containing: Kelisema Collagen-CCK Complex

Potassium coconate. *See* Potassium cocoate
Potassium dihydrogen orthophosphate. *See* Potassium phosphate
Potassium dihydrogen phosphate. *See* Potassium phosphate

Potassium dimethicone copolyol phosphate
CAS 150522-09-1
Definition: Potassium salt of dimethicone copolyol phosphate
Uses: O/w emulsifier for topical pharmaceuticals, sunscreens
Trade names: Pecosil® PS-100K

Potassium disulfite. *See* Potassium metabisulfite

Potassium ethylparaben
CAS 36457-19-9
Synonyms: Ethylparaben, potassium salt; Ethyl-4-hydroxybenzoate potassium salt
Definition: Potassium salt of ethylparaben
Empirical: C$_9$H$_{10}$O$_3$•K
Uses: Preservative, bactericide, fungicide
Trade names: Nipagin A Potassium

Potassium D-gluconate
CAS 299-27-4; EINECS 206-074-2
Synonyms: D-Gluconic acid potassium salt; Monopotassium D(-)-pentahydroxy capronate; D-Gluconic acid monopotassium salt
Empirical: C$_6$H$_{11}$O$_7$K
Properties: Wh. or ylsh. fine powd., odorless, sl. bitter taste; sol. in water, glycerin; insol. in alcohol, ether, chloroform, benzene; m.w. 234.3; m.p. 180 C (dec.)
Precaution: Avoid dust formation
Toxicology: LD50 (oral, rat) 10,380 mg/kg; mod. toxic by IP route; mildly toxic by ingestion; heated to decomp., emits toxic fumes of K$_2$O
Uses: Mineral source for pharmaceutical prods.
Regulatory: USDA 9CFR §318.7; Europe listed; UK approved
Manuf./Distrib.: Akzo; R.W. Greeff; Lohmann
Manuf./Distrib. (pharm. & food): Am. Roland; R.W. Greeff; Jungbunzlauer; Lohmann; Spectrum Chem. Mfg.
Trade names: Gluconal® K

Potassium 2,4-hexadienoate. *See* Potassium sorbate
Potassium hydrate. *See* Potassium hydroxide
Potassium hydrogen carbonate. *See* Potassium bicarbonate
Potassium hydrogen tartrate. *See* Potassium acid tartrate

Potassium hydroxide
CAS 1310-58-3; EINECS 215-181-3
UN No. 1813

Potassium-L-2-hydroxypropionate

Synonyms: Caustic potash; Potassium hydrate; Lye; Potash lye; Potassa
Classification: Inorganic base
Empirical: HKO
Formula: KOH
Properties: Wh. flakes, lumps or pellets, highly deliq.; hygroscopic; sol. in water, alcohol, glycerol; sl. sol. in ether; m.w. 56.11; dens. 2.044; m.p. 405 C; b.p. 1320 C
Precaution: DOT: Corrosive material
Toxicology: LD50 (oral, rat) 365 mg/kg; toxic by ingestion, inh.; strong caustic; eye and severe skin irritant; mutagenic data; TLV 2 mg/m^3 of air (ACGIH); heated to dec., emits toxic fumes of K_2O; above 84 C reacts with reducing sugars to form CO
Uses: Alkalizing agent; used in intravenous, parenterals, orals, topicals; caustic for wart removal; cuticle solv.; in escharotic preps.
Regulatory: FDA 21CFR §163.110, 175.210, 184.1631, GRAS; USDA 9CFR §381.147; Europe listed; UK approved; FDA approved for intravenous, parenterals, orals, topicals; USP/NF, BP, JP compliance
Manuf./Distrib.: Hüls Am.; ICI Specialties; Occidental; Olin
Manuf./Distrib. (pharm. & food): Aldrich; Avrachem; Mallinckrodt; Ruger; Spectrum Chem. Mfg.
Trade names containing: Annatto OS #2894; Annatto OS #2922; Annatto OS #2923; Annatto Liq. #3968, Acid Proof

Potassium-L-2-hydroxypropionate. *See* Potassium lactate

Potassium iodide
CAS 7681-11-0; EINECS 231-659-4
Classification: Inorganic salt
Definition: Potassium salt of hydriodic acid
Formula: KI
Properties: Colorless to wh. cryst. granules or powd., strong bitter saline taste; sl. hygroscopic; sol. in water, alcohol, acetone, glycerol; m.w. 166.02; dens. 3.123; b.p. 1420 C; m.p. 723 C
Precaution: Moisture- and light-sensitive; explosive reaction with charcoal + ozone; incompat. with oxidants, BrF_3, FCIO, metallic salts
Toxicology: Irritant; poison by intravenous route; mod. toxic by ing. and IP routes; may cause allergic reactions; human teratogenic effects; experimental reproductive effects; mutagenic data; heated to decomp., emits very toxic fumes of K_2O and I
Uses: Source of dietary iodine; dye remover; antiseptic
Regulatory: FDA 21CFR §172.375, 178.1010, 184.1634, GRAS; BP, Ph.Eur. compliance
Manuf./Distrib.: Aldrich; Atomergic Chemetals; R.W. Greeff; Mitsui Toatsu
Manuf./Distrib. (pharm. & food): Atomergic Chemetals; Avrachem; R.W. Greeff; Integra; Mallinckrodt; Ruger; Spectrum Chem. Mfg.

Potassium Kurrol's salt. *See* Potassium metaphosphate; Potassium polymetaphosphate

Potassium lactate
CAS 996-31-6; EINECS 213-631-3
Synonyms: Potassium-L-2-hydroxypropionate; Propanoic acid, 2-hydroxy-, monopotassium salt
Definition: Potassium salt of lactic acid
Empirical: $C_3H_5KO_3$
Formula: $CH_3CHOHCOOK$
Properties: Wh. solid, odorless; hygroscopic; m.w. 128.17
Toxicology: Heated to decomp., emits acrid smoke and irritating fumes
Uses: Humectant, antimicrobial preservative for pharmaceuticals
Regulatory: FDA 21CFR §184.1639, GRAS; not authorized for infant formulas; Europe listed; UK approved
Manuf./Distrib.: Lohmann
Manuf./Distrib. (pharm. & food): Lohmann
Trade names: Purasal® P/HQ 60; Purasal® P/USP 60

Potassium metabisulfite
CAS 16731-55-8; EINECS 240-795-3
Synonyms: Disulfurous acid dipotassium salt; Potassium pyrosulfite; Dipotassium pyrosulfite; Potassium disulfite; Dipotassium disulfite
Classification: Inorganic salt
Empirical: $K_2O_5S_2$
Formula: $K_2S_2O_5$
Properties: Colorless to wh. gran. or powd., pungent sharp odor; sol. in water, insol. in alcohol; m.w. 222.32; dens. 2.3; m.p. > 300 C; dec. at 150-190 C; oxidizes in air and moisture to sulfate
Precaution: Moisture sensitive; keep dry and well closed

Toxicology: Low toxicity; irritant; experimental tumorigen, reproductive effects; heated to decomp., emits toxic fumes of SO$_x$ and K$_2$O
Uses: Antiseptic, preservative, antioxidant used in injectables, parenterals, intravenous, otics, rectals
Regulatory: FDA 21CFR §182.3637, GRAS; BATF 27CFR §240.1051; Europe listed; FDA approved for injectables, parenterals, intravenous, otics, rectals; USP/NF compliance
Manuf./Distrib.: Allchem Industries; Farleyway Chem. Ltd; Mallinckrodt
Manuf./Distrib. (pharm. & food): Aldrich; Allchem Industries; Integra; Mallinckrodt; Ruger; Spectrum Chem. Mfg.

Potassium metaphosphate
CAS 7790-53-6
Synonyms: Metaphosphoric acid potassium salt; Potassium Kurrol's salt; Potassium polymetaphosphate
Classification: Straight-chain polyphosphate
Empirical: KPO$_3$
Properties: Wh. powd., odorless; sol. in dil. sodium salt sol'ns.; pract. insol. in water; m.w. 118.07
Uses: Buffering agent; used in orals
Regulatory: FDA approved for orals; USP/NF compliance
See also Potassium polymetaphosphate

Potassium 6-methyl-1,2,3-oxathiazine-4(3H)-1,2,2-dioxide. *See* Acesulfame potassium

Potassium methylparaben
CAS 26112-07-2; EINECS 247-464-2
Synonyms: 4-Hydroxybenzoic acid, methyl ester, potassium salt; Methylparaben, potassium salt
Definition: Potassium salt of methylparaben
Empirical: C$_8$H$_8$O$_3$•K
Uses: Preservative, bactericide, fungicide
Trade names: Nipagin M Potassium

Potassium monochloride. *See* Potassium chloride
Potassium peroxodisulfate. *See* Potassium persulfate
Potassium peroxydisulfate. *See* Potassium persulfate

Potassium persulfate
CAS 7727-21-1; EINECS 231-781-8
UN No. 1492
Synonyms: Peroxydisulfuric acid dipotassium salt; Potassium peroxydisulfate; Potassium peroxodisulfate; Dipotassium persulfate
Empirical: K$_2$O$_8$S$_2$
Formula: K$_2$S$_2$O$_8$
Properties: Colorless or wh. cryst., odorless; sol. in 50 parts water; insol. in alcohol; m.w. 270.33; dens. 2.477; m.p. 100 C (dec.)
Precaution: Powerful oxidizer; flamm. when exposed to heat or by chemical reaction; reactive with reducing materials; liberates oxygen above 100 C (dry), 50 C (sol'n.); keep well closed in cool place
Toxicology: TLV:TWA 5 mg(S$_2$O$_8$)/m^3; mod. toxic; irritant; allergen; heated to decomp., emits highly toxic fumes of SO$_x$ and K$_2$O
Uses: Pharmaceuticals
Regulatory: FDA 21CFR §172.210, 175.105, 175.210, 176.170, 177.1210, 177.2600; USDA 9CFR §381.147; BP compliance
Manuf./Distrib.: Allchem Industries; DuPont; FMC; Mallinckrodt; Mitsubishi Gas Chem.; San Yuan Chem. Co. Ltd.; Spectrum Chem. Mfg.; Transol Chem. UK Ltd
Manuf./Distrib. (pharm. & food): Aldrich; Allchem Industries; FMC; Mallinckrodt

Potassium phosphate
CAS 7778-77-0; EINECS 231-913-4
Synonyms: MKP; Potassium phosphate monobasic; Monopotassium phosphate; Potassium phosphate primary; Phosphoric acid monopotassium salt; Potassium dihydrogen orthophosphate; Potassium dihydrogen phosphate; Monopotassium orthophosphate; Potassium biphosphate
Classification: Inorganic salt
Empirical: KH$_2$PO$_4$
Formula: H$_3$O$_4$P • K
Properties: Colorless cryst. or wh. cryst. powd., odorless; hygroscopic; acid in reaction; sol. in water; insol. in alcohol; m.w. 136.09; dens. 2.338; m.p. 253 C; pH 4.5 (1%); stable in air
Toxicology: No known toxicity; nuisance dust
Uses: Buffering agent, sequestrant; used in injectables, parenterals, intravenous, ophthalmics, orals, otics; used as a urinary acidifier

Potassium phosphate dibasic

   Regulatory: FDA 21CFR §160.110, 175.105; USDA 9CFR §318.7, 381.147; Japan approved; Europe listed; UK approved; FDA approved for injectables, parenterals, intravenous, ophthalmics, orals, otics; USP/NF, BP, Ph.Eur. compliance
   Manuf./Distrib.: Albright & Wilson; Aldrich; FMC; Heico; Lohmann; Monsanto; Spectrum Chem. Mfg.
   Manuf./Distrib. (pharm. & food): Albright & Wilson Am.; Browning; FMC; Lohmann; Ruger; Spectrum Chem. Mfg.

Potassium phosphate dibasic

   CAS 7758-11-4; EINECS 231-834-5
   Synonyms: DKP; Dipotassium phosphate; Phosphoric acid dipotassium salt; Dibasic potassium phosphate; Dipotassium hydrogen orthophosphate; Dipotassium hydrogen phosphate; Dipotassium orthophosphate
   Classification: Inorganic salt
   Empirical: K_2HPO_4
   Properties: Colorless or wh. cryst. or powd.; deliq., hygroscopic; sol. in water; insol. in alcohol; m.w. 174.18; pH 8.5-9.6 (5%)
   Toxicology: No known toxicity; nuisance dust
   Uses: Buffer, urinary acidifier; used in intramuscular injectables, orals
   Regulatory: FDA 21CFR §133.169, 133.173, 133.179, 175.105, 182.6285, GRAS; USDA 9CFR §318.7, 381.147; FDA approved for intramuscular injectables, orals; Europe listed; UK approved; Japan approved
   Manuf./Distrib.: Albright & Wilson; Aldrich; FMC; Heico; Monsanto; Rhone-Poulenc Food Ingreds.; Spectrum Chem. Mfg.; U.S. Biochemical
   Manuf./Distrib. (pharm. & food): Albright & Wilson Am.; Browning; FMC; Rhone-Poulenc Food Ingreds.; Mallinckrodt; Ruger; Spectrum Chem. Mfg.

Potassium phosphate monobasic. *See* Potassium phosphate
Potassium phosphate primary. *See* Potassium phosphate
Potassium polymannuronate. *See* Potassium alginate

Potassium polymetaphosphate

   Synonyms: Potassium metaphosphate; Potassium Kurrol's salt
   Definition: Straight-chain polyphosphate
   Empirical: $(KPO_3)_x$
   Properties: Wh. powd., odorless; insol. in water
   Regulatory: Japan approved
   See also Potassium metaphosphate

Potassium propylparaben

   CAS 84930-16-5
   Synonyms: Propylparaben, potassium salt; n-Propyl-4-hydroxybenzoate potassium salt
   Definition: Potassium salt of propylparaben
   Empirical: $C_{10}H_{12}O_3 \cdot K$
   Uses: Preservative, bactericide, fungicide
   Trade names: Nipasol M Potassium

Potassium pyrosulfite. *See* Potassium metabisulfite
Potassium rhodanide. *See* Potassium thiocyanate
Potassium sodium copper chlorophyllin. *See* Chlorophyllin-copper complex; CI 75810
Potassium sodium L-(+)-tartrate. *See* Potassium sodium tartrate anhyd.

Potassium sodium tartrate anhyd.

   CAS 304-59-6; EINECS 206-156-8
   Synonyms: Rochelle salt; Sodium potassium tartrate; Potassium sodium L-(+)-tartrate; Seignette salt; Monopotassium monosodium tartrate; 2,3-Dihydroxybutanedioic acid, monopotassium monosodium salt
   Classification: Organic salt
   Definition: Sodium potassium salt of L-tartaric acid
   Empirical: $C_4H_4KNaO_6$
   Properties: Colorless cryst. or wh. cryst. powd., cooling saline taste; freely sol. in water; pract. insol. in alcohol; m.w. 210.16
   Uses: Cathartic
   Regulatory: FDA 21CFR §133.169, 133.173, 133.179, 150.141, 150.161, 184.1804; Europe listed; UK approved; BP compliance
   Manuf./Distrib.: Lohmann
   Manuf./Distrib. (pharm. & food): Browning; Int'l. Sourcing; Jungbunzlauer

Potassium sodium tartrate tetrahydrate

   CAS 6100-16-9; 6381-59-5; EINECS 205-698-2, 206-156-8

Synonyms: Sodium potassium tartrate; Monopotassium monosodium tartrate tetrahydrate; Rochelle salt; Seignette salt
Empirical: $C_4H_4KNaO_6 \cdot 4H_2O$
Formula: $KOCOCH(OH)CH(OH)COONa \cdot 4H_2O$
Properties: Colorless cryst. or wh. cryst. powd., cooling saline taste; sol. in 0.9 part water; almost insol. in alcohol; m.w. 282.23; dens. 1.79; m.p. 70-80 C; loses $3 H_2O$ @ 100 C, becomes anhyd. @ 130-140 C, dec. @ 220 C; pH 7-8
Precaution: Incompat. with acids, calcium or lead salts, magnesium sulfate, silver nitrate
Toxicology: Heated to decomp., emits acrid smoke and irritating fumes
Uses: Cathartic
Regulatory: FDA 21CFR §184.1804, GRAS; USDA 9CFR §318.7
Manuf./Distrib.: Aldrich; EM Industries; Mallinckrodt; Pfizer Spec. Chem.
Manuf./Distrib. (pharm. & food): Lohmann; Pfizer Spec. Chem.; Spectrum Chem. Mfg.

Potassium sorbate
CAS 590-00-1; 24634-61-5; EINECS 246-376-1
FEMA 2921
Synonyms: 2,4-Hexadienoic acid potassium salt; Potassium (E,E)-sorbate; Sorbic acid potassium salt; Potassium 2,4-hexadienoate
Empirical: $C_6H_7O_2 \cdot K$
Formula: $CH_3CH=CHCH=CHCOOK$
Properties: Wh. cryst., powd., or pellets, char. odor; sol. 58.2% in water @ 20 C, 6.5% in alcohol @ 20 C; m.w. 150.23; dens. 1.363 (25/20 C); m.p. 270 C (dec.)
Precaution: Light-sensitive
Toxicology: LD50 (oral, rat) 4920 mg/kg; moderately toxic by intraperitoneal route; mildly toxic by ingestion; skin irritant; mutagenic data; heated to decomp., emits toxic fumes of K_2O
Uses: Mold and yeast inhibitor in aq. sol'ns.; antimicrobial preservative; used in orals, topicals, hard/rigid gas-permeable lens prods.
Regulatory: FDA 21CFR §133, 150.141. 150.161, 166.110, 182.90, 182.3640, GRAS; USDA 9CFR §318.7; BATF 27CFR §240.1051; FEMA GRAS, CIR approved; Japan approved with limitations; JSCI approved 0.5% max.; Europe listed 0.8% max.; FDA approved for orals, topicals; USP/NF, BP, Ph.Eur. compliance
Manuf./Distrib.: Chisso Am.; Eastman; Gist-brocades Food Ingreds.; Hoechst Celanese; Int'l. Sourcing; Kraft; Pfizer Spec. Chem.; Protameen; Tri-K
Manuf./Distrib. (pharm. & food): Browning; Consolidated Flavor; Daicel; Gist-brocades Food Ingreds.; Integra; Int'l. Sourcing; Jungbunzlauer; Ruger; Spectrum Chem. Mfg.; Ueno

Potassium (E,E)-sorbate. *See* Potassium sorbate

Potassium stearate
CAS 593-29-3; EINECS 209-786-1
Synonyms: Octadecanoic acid, potassium salt; Stearic acid, potassium salt
Definition: Potassium salt of stearic acid
Empirical: $C_{18}H_{35}O_2 \cdot K$
Formula: $CH_3(CH_2)_{16}COOK$
Properties: White powd., sl. fatty odor; slowly sol. in cold water; readily sol. in hot water, alcohol; m.w. 322.57
Toxicology: Heated to decomp., emits acrid smoke and irritating fumes
Uses: Emulsifier in pharmaceutical ointments
Regulatory: FDA 21CFR §172.615, 172.863, 173.340, 175.105, 175.300, 176.170, 176.200, 176.210, 177.1200, 177.2260, 177.2600, 177.2800, 178.3910, 179.45, 181.22, 181.29
Manuf./Distrib.: Original Bradford Soap Works; RTD; Witco/Oleo-Surf.
Trade names containing: Cutina® KD16; Imwitor® 965

Potassium sulfocyanate. *See* Potassium thiocyanate

Potassium thiocyanate
CAS 333-20-0; EINECS 206-370-1
Synonyms: Thiocyanic acid potassium salt; Potassium rhodanide; Potassium sulfocyanate
Classification: Inorganic salt
Formula: KSCN
Properties: Colorless to wh. transparent cryst. powd., odorless; deliq.; sol. in cold water, acetone, ethanol, amyl alcohol; m.w. 97.19; dens. 1.886; m.p. 173 C; dec. 500 C; pH 5.3-8.7 (5%)
Precaution: Moisture-sensitive
Toxicology: Toxic by ingestion
Uses: Intermediate for pharmaceuticals
Regulatory: BP compliance

Potato starch

Manuf./Distrib.: Katayama Chem. Ind.; Spectrum Chem. Mfg.; Toyo Kasei Kogyo; Witco/PAG
Manuf./Distrib. (pharm. & food): Aldrich; Integra; Witco

Potato starch
CAS 9005-25-8
Definition: Natural substance obtained from potatoes, Solanum tuberosum, contg. amylose and amylopectin
Formula: $(C_6H_{10}O_5)_n$
Properties: Irreg. ovoid or spherical gran.; swells in hot water to form a gel on cooling
Toxicology: May cause allergic reactions and stuffy nose in hypersensitive persons
Uses: Used with glycerin to form a soothing, protective applic. for eczema, skin rash, and chapped skin
Regulatory: FDA 21CFR §175.105, 178.3520, 182.70; BP, Ph.Eur. compliance
Manuf./Distrib.: Spectrum Chem. Mfg.

Poval. See Polyvinyl alcohol
Povidone. See PVP
Povidone-iodine. See PVP-iodine
Powdered cellulose. See Cellulose
Powdered skim milk. See Nonfat dry milk
PP. See Polypropylene
PPG. See Polypropylene glycol

PPG-400
Uses: Intermediate; lubricant, defoaming agent for pharmaceuticals
Trade names: Jeffox PPG-400

PPG-2000
Uses: Intermediate; lubricant, defoaming agent for pharmaceuticals
Trade names: Jeffox PPG-2000

PPG-10 butanediol
Definition: POP ether of butanediol
Formula: $HO(CH_2CHCH_3O)_xCH_2CH_2CH_2CH_2(OCHCH_3CH_2)_yOH$, avg. (x+y)=10
Uses: Emollient for antiperspirants; solv. for sunscreen actives; crystal growth inhibitor
Trade names: Macol® 57

PPG-12-buteth-16
CAS 9038-95-3 (generic); 9065-63-8 (generic); 74623-31-7
Synonyms: POE (16) POP (12) monobutyl ether; POP (12) POE (16) monobutyl ether
Definition: Polyoxypropylene, polyoxyethylene ether of butyl alcohol
Empirical: $(C_7H_{14}O_2 \cdot C_6H_{12}O_2)_x$
Formula: $C_4H_9(OCH_3CHCH_2)_x(OCH_2CH_2)_yOH$, avg. x = 12, avg. y = 16
Regulatory: FDA 21CFR §173.310, 175.105, 176.210, 178.3570

PPG-2-ceteareth-9
Synonyms: POE (9) POP (2) cetyl/stearyl ether; POP (2) POE (9) cetyl/stearyl ether
Definition: Polyoxypropylene, polyoxyethylene ether of cetearyl alcohol
Formula: $R(OCHCH_3CH_2)_x(OCH_2CH_2)_yOH$, R rep. cetyl/stearyl radicals, avg. x=2, avg. y=9
Uses: Solubilizer
Trade names: Eumulgin® L

PPG-4 ceteth-1
CAS 9087-53-0 (generic); 37311-01-6 (generic)
Synonyms: POE (1) POP (4) cetyl ether; POP (4) POE (1) cetyl ether
Definition: Polyoxypropylene, polyoxyethylene ether of cetyl alcohol
Formula: $CH_3(CH_2)_{14}CH_2(OCH_3CHCH_2)_x(OCH_2CH_2)_yOH$, avg. x = 4, avg. y = 1
Uses: Emulsifier, solubilizer, dispersant used in pharmaceuticals
Trade names: Nikkol PBC-31

PPG-4-ceteth-10
CAS 9087-53-0 (generic); 37311-01-6 (generic)
Synonyms: POE (10) POP (4) cetyl ether; POP (4) POE (10) cetyl ether
Definition: Polyoxypropylene, polyoxyethylene ether of cetyl alcohol
Formula: $CH_3(CH_2)_{14}CH_2(OCH_3CHCH_2)_x(OCH_2CH_2)_yOH$, avg. x = 4, avg. y = 10
Uses: Emulsifier, solubilizer, dispersant used in pharmaceuticals

PPG-4-ceteth-20
CAS 9087-53-0 (generic); 37311-01-6 (generic)
Synonyms: POE (20) POP (4) cetyl ether

Definition: Polyoxypropylene, polyoxyethylene ether of cetyl alcohol
Formula: $CH_3(CH_2)_{14}CH_2(OCH_3CHCH_2)_x(OCH_2CH_2)_yOH$, avg. x = 4, avg. y = 20
Uses: Emulsifier, solubilizer, dispersant used in pharmaceuticals

PPG-8-ceteth-1
CAS 9087-53-0 (generic); 37311-01-6 (generic)
Synonyms: POE (1) POP (8) cetyl ether; POP (8) POE (1) cetyl ether
Definition: Polyoxypropylene, polyoxyethylene ether of cetyl alcohol
Formula: $CH_3(CH_2)_{14}CH_2(OCH_3CHCH_2)_x(OCH_2CH_2)_yOH$, avg. x = 8, avg. y = 1
Uses: Emulsifier, solubilizer, dispersant used in pharmaceuticals

PPG-5 ceteth-10 phosphate
CAS 50643-20-4
Synonyms: POE (10) POP (5) cetyl ether phosphate; POP (5) POE (10) cetyl ether phosphate
Definition: Mixture of esters of phosphoric acid and the polyoxypropylene, polyoxyethylene ether of cetyl alcohol
Uses: Surfactant, emulsifier, gellant for pharmaceuticals

PPG-30 cetyl ether
CAS 9035-85-2 (generic)
Synonyms: POP (30) cetyl ether; PPG (30) cetyl ether
Definition: Polypropylene glycol ether of cetyl alcohol
Formula: $CH_3(CH_2)_{14}CH_2(OCH_3CHCH_2)_nOH$, avg. n = 30
Properties: Liq.; sol. in oils, alcohol; insol. in water
Toxicology: No known toxicity
Uses: Emollient, moisturizer in pharmaceuticals
Trade names: Macol® CA 30P

PPG (30) cetyl ether. *See* PPG-30 cetyl ether

PPG-2 lanolin alcohol ether
CAS 68439-53-2 (generic)
Synonyms: POP (2) lanolin ether; PPG (2) lanolin ether; PPG-2 lanolin ether
Definition: Polypropylene glycol ether of lanolin alcohol with avg. propoxylation value of 2
Properties: Semisolid; sol. in isopropyl esters, veg. oils, ethanol
Uses: Conditioner, spreading agent, dispersant, plasticizer, emollient for pharmaceuticals; dermatological vehicles
Trade names: Solulan® PB-2

PPG-5 lanolin alcohol ether
CAS 68439-53-2 (generic)
Synonyms: POP (5) lanolin ether; PPG (5) lanolin ether; PPG-5 lanolin ether
Definition: Polypropylene glycol ether of lanolin alcohol with avg. propoxylation value of 5
Properties: Liq.; sol. in isopropyl esters, veg. oils, ethanol
Uses: Spreading agent, dispersant, plasticizer, emollient for pharmaceuticals
Trade names: Solulan® PB-5

PPG-10 lanolin alcohol ether
CAS 68439-53-2 (generic)
Synonyms: POP (10) lanolin ether; PPG (10) lanolin ether; PPG-10 lanolin ether
Definition: Polypropylene glycol ether of lanolin alcohol with avg. propoxylation value of 10
Uses: Emollient and conditioner for pharmaceuticals
Trade names: Solulan® PB-10

PPG-20 lanolin alcohol ether
CAS 68439-53-2 (generic)
Synonyms: POP (20) lanolin ether; PPG (20) lanolin ether; PPG-20 lanolin ether
Definition: Polypropylene glycol ether of lanolin alcohol with avg. propoxylation value of 20
Uses: Emollient and conditioner for pharmaceuticals
Trade names: Solulan® PB-20

PPG (2) lanolin ether. *See* PPG-2 lanolin alcohol ether
PPG-2 lanolin ether. *See* PPG-2 lanolin alcohol ether
PPG (5) lanolin ether. *See* PPG-5 lanolin alcohol ether
PPG-5 lanolin ether. *See* PPG-5 lanolin alcohol ether
PPG (10) lanolin ether. *See* PPG-10 lanolin alcohol ether
PPG-10 lanolin ether. *See* PPG-10 lanolin alcohol ether
PPG (20) lanolin ether. *See* PPG-20 lanolin alcohol ether

PPG-20 lanolin ether. *See* PPG-20 lanolin alcohol ether

PPG-3-laureth-9
CAS 9004-94-3
Synonyms: POE (9) POP (3) lauryl ether; POP (3) POE (9) lauryl ether
Definition: Polyoxypropylene, polyoxyethylene ether of lauryl alcohol
Formula: $CH_3(CH_2)_{10}CH_2(OCH_3CHCH_2)_x(OCH_2CH_2)_yOH$, avg. x = 3, avg. y = 9
Uses: Surfactant, emulsifier, dispersant, solubilizer, visc. control agent for pharmaceuticals
Trade names: Acconon 1300 MS

PPG-5-laureth-5
CAS 68439-51-0
Synonyms: POE (5) POP (5) lauryl ether; POP (5) POE (5) lauryl ether
Definition: Polyoxypropylene, polyoxyethylene ether of lauryl alcohol
Formula: $CH_3(CH_2)_{10}CH_2(OCH_3CHCH_2)_x(OCH_2CH_2)_yOH$, avg. x = 5, avg. y = 5
Uses: Superfatting agent, emollient
Trade names: Aethoxal® B

PPG-10 methyl glucose ether
CAS 61849-72-7
Synonyms: POP (10) methyl glucose ether; PPG (10) methyl glucose ether
Definition: PPG ether of methyl glucose
Formula: $CH_3(CH_6H_{10}O_5)(OCH_3CHCH_2)_nOH$, avg. n = 10
Uses: Solvent and solubilizer for topical pharmaceuticals
Trade names: Glucam® P-10

PPG (10) methyl glucose ether. *See* PPG-10 methyl glucose ether

PPG-20 methyl glucose ether
CAS 61849-72-7
Synonyms: POP (20) methyl glucose ether; PPG (20) methyl glucose ether
Definition: PPG ether of methyl glucose
Formula: $CH_3(CH_6H_{10}O_5)(OCH_3CHCH_2)_nOH$, avg. n = 20
Uses: Solvent and solubilizer for topical pharmaceuticals
Trade names: Glucam® P-20

PPG (20) methyl glucose ether. *See* PPG-20 methyl glucose ether

PPG-20 methyl glucose ether distearate
Synonyms: PPG-20 methyl glucoside distearate; POP (20) methyl glucose ether distearate; PPG (20) methyl
glucose ether distearate
Classification: Diester of PPG-20 methyl glucose ether and stearic acid
Uses: Conditioner, emollient for pharmaceuticals
Trade names: Glucam® P-20 Distearate

PPG (20) methyl glucose ether distearate. *See* PPG-20 methyl glucose ether distearate
PPG-20 methyl glucoside distearate. *See* PPG-20 methyl glucose ether distearate
PPG (26) monooleate. *See* PPG-26 oleate
PPG (2) monosalicylate. *See* Dipropylene glycol salicylate

PPG-2 myristyl ether propionate
Synonyms: POP (2) myristyl ether propionate; PPG (2) myristyl ether propionate
Definition: Ester of propionic acid and the PPG ether of myristyl alcohol
Formula: $CH_3(CH_2)_{12}CH_2(OCH_3CHCH_2)_2OCOCH_2CH_3$
Uses: Emollient, emulsion stabilizer, spreading agent; reduces tackiness
Trade names: Crodamol PMP

PPG (2) myristyl ether propionate. *See* PPG-2 myristyl ether propionate

PPG-26 oleate
CAS 31394-71-5 (generic)
Synonyms: POP (26) monooleate; PPG (26) monooleate
Definition: PPG ester of oleic acid
Formula: $CH_3(CH_2)_7CH=CH(CH_2)_7CO(OCH_3CHCH_2)_nOH$, avg. n = 26
Uses: Used in topicals
Regulatory: FDA approved for topicals

PPG-12-PEG-50 lanolin
CAS 68458-88-8 (generic)

Synonyms: POE (50) POP (12) lanolin; POP (12) POE (50) lanolin
Definition: Polyoxypropylene, polyoxyethylene deriv. of lanolin
Formula: $R(OCH_3CHCH_2)_x(OCH_2CH_2)_yOH$, R rep. lanolin radicals, avg. x=12, avg. y=50
Toxicology: LD50 (rat, oral) 32 g/kg
Uses: Emollient, emulsifier, solubilizer for topicals
Trade names: Laneto AWS; Lanexol AWS

PPG-12-PEG-65 lanolin oil
CAS 68458-58-8 (generic)
Synonyms: POE (65) POP (12) lanolin oil; POP (12) POE (65) lanolin oil
Definition: Polyoxypropylene, polyoxyethylene deriv. of lanolin oil
Formula: $R(OCH_3CHCH_2)_x(OCH_2CH_2)_yOH$, R rep. lanolin radical, avg. x=12, avg. y=65
Properties: Liq.; sol. in water and alcohol
Toxicology: LD50 (rat, oral) > 5 g/kg
Uses: Nonionic emulsifier, emollient, penetrant for pharmaceuticals
Trade names: Fluilan AWS; Ritalan® AWS; Vigilan AWS
Trade names containing: Lanotein AWS 30

PPG-2 salicylate. *See* Dipropylene glycol salicylate

PPG-15 stearyl ether
CAS 25231-21-4 (generic)
Synonyms: POP (15) stearyl ether; PPG (15) stearyl ether
Definition: PPG ether of stearyl alcohol
Formula: $CH_3(CH_2)_{16}CH_2(OCH_3CHCH_2)_nOH$, avg. n = 15
Uses: Emulsifier, dispersant, solubilizer, visc. control agent, emollient, solvent, lubricant; used in topical pharmaceuticals
Regulatory: FDA approved for topicals
Trade names: Acconon E

PPG (15) stearyl ether. *See* PPG-15 stearyl ether
Precipitated barium sulfate. *See* Barium sulfate
Precipitated calcium carbonate. *See* Calcium carbonate
Precipitated calcium phosphate. *See* Calcium phosphate tribasic
Precipitated calcium sulfate. *See* Calcium sulfate dihydrate
Precipitated chalk. *See* Calcium carbonate
Precipitated silica. *See* Silica, hydrated
Prenol. *See* 3-Methyl-2-buten-1-ol
pri-Heptyl alcohol. *See* Heptyl alcohol
Primary ammonium phosphate. *See* Ammonium phosphate
pri-Octyl alcohhol. *See* Caprylic alcohol

Procaine
CAS 59-46-1
Synonyms: Novocaine
Empirical: $C_{13}H_{20}N_2O_2$
Properties: Hygroscopic; m.w. 236.32; m.p. 61-62 C
Toxicology: Potential adverse reactions incl. skin reactions, swelling, continuous asthma attacks, severe allergic reactions, anxiety, nervousness, respiratory arrest
Uses: Local anesthetic; used in intramuscular injectables
Regulatory: FDA approved for intramuscular injectables
Manuf./Distrib.: Spectrum Chem. Mfg.
Manuf./Distrib. (pharm. & food): Aldrich

Procaine hydrochloride. *See* Benzocaine
1-Propanaminium, 3-(D-gluconoylamino)-N-(2-hydroxyethyl)-N,N-dimethyl-, chloride. *See* Quaternium-22

Propane
CAS 74-98-6; EINECS 200-827-9
UN No. 1978
Synonyms: Dimethylmethane; Propyl hydride
Classification: Hydrocarbon
Empirical: C_3H_8
Formula: $CH_3CH_2CH_3$
Properties: Colorless gas, nat. gas odor; easily liquefied under pressure at R.T.; noncorrosive; sol. in ether, alcohol; sl. sol. in water; m.w. 44.09; dens. 0.513 (0 C, as liq.), 1.56 (0 C, as vapor); m.p. -188 C; b.p. -42.5

Propanedioic acid

C; f.p. -189.9 C; flash pt. -156 C
Precaution: Flamm.; autoignit. temp. 467 C; dangerous fire risk; explosive limits in air 2.4-9.5%; reactive with
oxidizers
Toxicology: Asphyxiant; narcotic in high concs.; TWA 1000 ppm; heated to decomp., emits acrid smoke and
irritating fumes
Uses: Aerosol propellant used in topicals
Regulatory: FDA 21CFR §173.350, 184.1655, GRAS; FDA approved for topicals; USP/NF compliance
Manuf./Distrib.: Air Prods.; Aldrich; Exxon; Fina; Phillips 66; Stanchem
Manuf./Distrib. (pharm. & food): Aldrich

Propanedioic acid. *See* Malonic acid
Propanedioic acid diethyl ester. *See* Diethyl malonate
1,2-Propanediol. *See* Propylene glycol
Propane-1,2-diol. *See* Propylene glycol
Propane-1,2-diol alginate. *See* Propylene glycol alginate
1,3-Propanediol, 2-bromo-2-nitro. *See* 2-Bromo-2-nitropropane-1,3-diol
1,2-Propanediol monostearate. *See* Propylene glycol stearate

Propane phosphonic acid anhydride
Empirical: $(C_3H_7O_2P)_n$, n > 3
Uses: Coupling reagent for peptide/amide synthesis for pharmaceuticals
Trade names containing: PPA

1,2,3-Propanetricarboxylic acid, 2-hydroxy, tripotassium salt. *See* Potassium citrate
1,2,3-Propanetriol. *See* Glycerin
Propane-1,2,3-triol. *See* Glycerin
1,2,3-Propanetriol octadecanoate. *See* Glyceryl stearate
1,2,3-Propanetriol triacetate. *See* Triacetin
1,2,3-Propanetriol tridocosanoate. *See* Tribehenin
1,2,3-Propanetriol tridodecanoate. *See* Trilaurin
1,2,3-Propanetriol trioctadecanoate. *See* Tristearin
1,2,3-Propanetriol trioctanoate. *See* Tricaprylin
1,2,3-Propanetriol tritetradecanoate. *See* Trimyristin
Propanoic acid. *See* Propionic acid
Propanoic acid butyl ester. *See* n-Butyl propionate
Propanoic acid, calcium salt. *See* Calcium propionate
Propanoic acid ethyl ester. *See* Ethyl propionate
Propanoic acid, 2-hydroxy-, monopotassium salt. *See* Potassium lactate
Propanoic acid methyl ester. *See* Methyl propionate
Propanoic acid propyl ester. *See* Propyl propionate
Propanoic acid sodium salt. *See* Sodium propionate
Propanoic acid, 3,3´-thiobis-, ditetradecyl ester. *See* Dimyristyl thiodipropionate
1-Propanol. *See* n-Propyl alcohol
Propan-1-ol. *See* n-Propyl alcohol
2-Propanol. *See* Isopropyl alcohol
n-Propanol. *See* n-Propyl alcohol
2-Propanol, 2-methyl-. *See* t-Butyl alcohol
2-Propanone. *See* Acetone
2-Propenamide, homopolymer. *See* Polyacrylamide
2-Propenamide, polymer with 2-propenoic acid, sodium salt. *See* Acrylamide/sodium acrylate copolymer
1-Propene, homopolymer. *See* Polypropylene
Propene polymer. *See* Polypropylene
1-Propene-1,2,3-tricarboxylic acid. *See* Aconitic acid
1,2,3-Propenetricarboxylic acid. *See* Aconitic acid
2-Propenoic acid, homopolymer. *See* Polyacrylic acid
2-Propenoic acid, 2-methyl-, 2-(dimethylamino)ethyl ester, polymer with 1-ethenyl-2-pyrrolidinone. *See*
PVP/dimethylaminoethylmethacrylate copolymer
2-Propenoic acid methyl ester. *See* Methyl acrylate (monomer)
2-Propenoic acid, sodium salt, polymer with 2-propenamide. *See* Acrylamide/sodium acrylate copolymer
2-Propenylacrylic acid. *See* Sorbic acid
p-Propenylanisole. *See* Anethole
Propenyl cinnamate. *See* Allyl cinnamate
2-Propenyl-6-ethoxyphenol. *See* Propenylguaethol

Propenylguaethol
CAS 94-86-0
FEMA 2922
Synonyms: Isosafroeugenol; Hydroxymethyl anethole; 2-Propenyl-6-ethoxyphenol; 6-Ethoxy-m-anol; 1-Ethoxy-2-hydroxy-4-propenylbenzene
Empirical: $C_{11}H_{14}O_2$
Properties: Wh. cryst. powd., vanilla odor; sol. in fixed oils; insol. in water; m.w. 178.25; m.p. 85-86 C; flash pt. > 212 F
Precaution: Combustible liq.
Toxicology: LD50 (oral, rat) 2400 mg/kg; mod. toxic by ingestion; heated to decomp, emits acrid smoke and fumes
Uses: Sweet vanilla-like or medicinal synthetic flavoring agent
Regulatory: FDA 21CFR §172.515; FEMA GRAS
Manuf./Distrib. (pharm. & food): Aldrich; Chart

4-Propenylguaiacol. *See* Isoeugenol
2-Propenyl heptanoate. *See* Allyl heptanoate
2-Propenyl hexanoate. *See* Allyl caproate
2-Propenyl isovalerate. *See* Allyl isovalerate
2-Propenyl 3-methylbutanoate. *See* Allyl isovalerate

Propionic acid
CAS 79-09-4; EINECS 201-176-3
FEMA 2924; UN No. 1848
Synonyms: Methylacetic acid; Propanoic acid; Ethylformic acid
Classification: Acid
Empirical: $C_3H_6O_2$
Formula: C_2H_5COOH
Properties: Oily liq., sl. pungent rancid odor; misc. in water, alcohol, ether, chloroform; m.w. 74.09; dens. 0.998 (15/4 C); visc. 1.020 cp (15 C); m.p. -21.5 C; b.p. 141. C (760 mm); flash pt. (OC) 58 C; ref. index 1.3862; surf. tension 27.21 dynes/cm (15 C)
Precaution: DOT: Corrosive material; highly flamm. exposed to heat, flame, oxidizers; incompat. with $CaCl_2$; dec. at high temp.
Toxicology: TLV:TWA 10 ppm; LD50 (oral, rat) 3500 mg/kg; poison by intraperitoneal route; mod. toxic by ingestion, skin contact, IV route; irritant to eye, skin; lethal to rats in lg. doses; heated to decomp., emits acrid smoke and irritating fumes
Uses: Acidifying agent, antioxidant, preservative, mold inhibitor; used in orals, topicals
Regulatory: FDA 21CFR §172.515, 184.1081, GRAS; FEMA GRAS; EPA reg.; Japan restricted to flavoring use, limitation with sorbic acid 3 g/kg total; Europe listed; UK approved; FDA approved for orals, topicals; USP/NF compliance
Manuf./Distrib.: Aldrich F&F; BASF; BP Chem.; Eastman; Great Western; Hoechst Celanese; Lohmann; Penta Mfg.; Union Carbide
Manuf./Distrib. (pharm. & food): Aldrich; Eastman; Hays; Honeywill & Stein; Lohmann; Penta Mfg.; Ruger; Spectrum Chem. Mfg.; Tournay; Unipex; Van Waters & Rogers

Propionic acid, calcium salt. *See* Calcium propionate
Propionic acid sodium salt. *See* Sodium propionate

Propyl acetate
CAS 109-60-4; EINECS 203-686-1
FEMA 2925
Synonyms: Acetic acid n-propyl ester; n-Propyl acetate
Definition: Ester of propyl alcohol and acetic acid
Empirical: $C_5H_{10}O_2$
Formula: $CH_3COOCH_2CH_2CH_3$
Properties: Liq., pear-like odor; misc. with alcohol, ether; m.w. 102.14; dens. 0.887 (20/20 C); m.p. -92 C; b.p. 99-102 C; flash pt. (CC) 14 C; ref. index 1.384 (20 C)
Precaution: Highly flamm.
Toxicology: LD50 (oral, rat) 9370 mg/kg; may be irritating to skin, mucous membranes; narcotic in high concs.
Uses: Synthetic flavoring agent
Regulatory: FDA 21CFR §172.515, 177.1200; FEMA GRAS
Manuf./Distrib.: Aldrich; BASF; BP Chem. Ltd; Eastman; Hoechst Celanese; Union Carbide
Manuf./Distrib. (pharm. & food): Aldrich

2-Propyl acetate. *See* Isopropyl acetate

n-Propyl acetate. *See* Propyl acetate
β-Propyl acrolein. *See* 2-Hexenal
Propyl alcohol. *See* n-Propyl alcohol

n-Propyl alcohol
CAS 71-23-8; EINECS 200-746-9
FEMA 2928; UN No. 1274
Synonyms: 1-Propanol; Propan-1-ol; n-Propanol; Propylic alcohol; Albacol; Optal; Propyl alcohol; Ethyl carbinol; Alcohol C-3
Classification: Aliphatic alcohol
Empirical: C_3H_8O
Formula: $CH_3CH_2CH_2OH$
Properties: Colorless liq., alcoholic and sl. stupefying odor; misc. with water, alcohol, ether; dissolves fat; m.w. 60.10; dens. 0.804 (20/4 C); m.p. -127 C; b.p. 97-98 C; flash pt. (TCC) 23 C; ref. index 1.385 (20 C)
Precaution: Highly flamm.; dangerous fire risk; explosive limits in air 2-13%
Toxicology: LD50 (oral, rat) 1.87 g/kg; TLV 200 ppm in air; toxic by skin absorption; drying effect on skin may lead to cracking, fissuring, and infections; mildly irritating to eyes, mucous membranes; depressant action
Uses: Sweet synthetic flavoring agent ; used in topicals, liniments, mouthwashes, gargles
Regulatory: FDA 21CFR §172.515, 175.105, 177.1200, 573.880; FEMA GRAS; FDA approved for topicals; BP compliance
Manuf./Distrib.: Arco; Eastman; Hoechst Celanese; Mallinckrodt; Spectrum Chem. Mfg.; Union Carbide
Manuf./Distrib. (pharm. & food): Aldrich; Ruger

γ-Propylallyl alcohol. *See* 2-Hexenol

Propyl benzoate
CAS 2315-68-6
FEMA 2931
Synonyms: n-Propyl benzoate
Empirical: $C_{10}H_{12}O_2$
Properties: Colorless oily liq., balsamic nutty odor, sweet fruity nut-like taste; sol. in alcohol; insol. in water; m.w. 164.21; dens. 1.026; b.p. 230-231 C; m.p. -51 to -52 C; flash pt. 98 C; ref. index 1.5100
Uses: Synthetic flavoring agent
Regulatory: FDA 21CFR §172.515; FEMA GRAS

n-Propyl benzoate. *See* Propyl benzoate
Propyl carbinol. *See* Butyl alcohol
Propyl cyanide. *See* Butyronitrile

Propylene carbonate
CAS 108-32-7; EINECS 203-572-1
Synonyms: 1,3-Dioxolan-2-one, 4-methyl; 4-Methyl-1,3-dioxolan-2-one; Carbonic acid, 1,2-propylene glycol ester
Classification: Organic compd.
Empirical: $C_4H_6O_3$
Properties: Clear liq.; m.w. 102.10; dens. 1.2069 (20/20 C); m.p. -48.8 C; b.p. 242.1 C; flash pt. (OC) 275 F
Toxicology: Mildly toxic by ingestion; human skin and eye irritant
Uses: Medicinal, minty flavoring agent; used in topicals
Regulatory: FDA 21CFR §175.105; FDA approved for topicals
Manuf./Distrib.: Allchem Ind.; Ashland; Great Western; Hüls AG; Spectrum Chem. Mfg.
Manuf./Distrib. (pharm. & food): Aldrich; Ruger
Trade names containing: Miglyol® 840 Gel B; Miglyol® Gel B; Miglyol® Gel T

Propylene glycol
CAS 57-55-6; 4254-15-3 (+); 4254-14-2 (-); 4254-16-4 (±); EINECS 200-338-0
FEMA 2940
Synonyms: 1,2-Propanediol; Propane-1,2-diol; 1,2-Dihydroxypropane; Methyl glycol; Methyl ethylene glycol
Classification: Aliphatic alcohol
Empirical: $C_3H_8O_2$
Formula: $CH_3CHOHCH_2OH$
Properties: Colorless clear visc. liq., odorless, sl. acrid taste; hygroscopic; sol. in essential oils; misc. with water, acetone, chloroform; m.w. 76.11; dens. 1.0362; b.p. 188.2 C; flash pt. (OC) 210 F
Precaution: Combustible exposed to heat or flame; reactive with oxidizers; explosive limits 2.6-12.6%
Toxicology: LD50 (oral, rat) 25 ml/kg; eye/human skin irritant; sl. toxic by ingestion, IP,IV, subcutaneous routes; human systemic effects; experimental teratogenic, reproductive effects; mutagenic data; heated to decomp., emits acrid smoke and irritating fumes

Uses: Solvent, vehicle, humectant, preservative, plasticizer; stabilizer in vitamin preps.; protectant in hemorrhoidal prods.; used in orals, otics, parenterals, vaginals, topical prods.

Usage level: 10-25% (oral sol'ns.), 10-80% (parenterals), 5-80% (topicals)

Regulatory: FDA 21CFR §169.175, 169.176, 169.177, 169.178, 169.180, 169.181, 175.300, 177.2600, 178.3300, 184.1666, 582.4666, GRAS; USDA 9CFR §318.7, 381.147; BATF 27CFR §240.1051; EPA reg., approved for some drugs; Japan approved with limitations; Europe listed; FEMA GRAS; FDA approved for orals, parenterals, topicals; USP/NF, BP, Ph.Eur., JP compliance

Manuf./Distrib.: Aldrich; Arco; Asahi Denka Kogyo; Ashland; BP Chem. Ltd; Eastman; Hüls AG; Olin; Primachem; Seeler Ind.; Texaco; Veckridge; Westco

Manuf./Distrib. (pharm. & food): Aldrich; Ashland; Crompton & Knowles; Ellis & Everard; K&K Greeff; Hays; Honeywill & Stein; Integra; Mallinckrodt; Meer; Nisso Petrochem. Ind.; Norman Fox; Penta Mfg.; Ruger; Showa Denko; Spectrum Chem. Mfg.; Texaco; Todd's; R C Treatt; Van Waters & Rogers

Trade names: Adeka Propylene Glycol (P); Propylene Glycol USP/FCC Ultra Grade

Trade names containing: Aloe-Moist™; Aloe-Moist™ A; Annatto OS #2894; Annatto OS #2922; Annatto OS #2923; Annatto Liq. #3968, Acid Proof; Arlacel® 186; Biophytex®; Carmine AS; Cremophor® RH 455; Crodarom Nut A; Dehymuls® F; Germaben® II; Grillocin® AT Basis; Lanotein AWS 30; Lipo PE Base GP-55; Lubrajel® CG; Lubrajel® DV; Lubrajel® MS; Lubrajel® TW; Monawet MO-70R; Natipide® II PG; Oxynex® 2004; Phosal® 50 PG; Phosal® 60 PG; Phosal® NAT-50-PG; Reach® AZP-908PG; Reach® AZZ-908PG; Rezal® 36GPG; Tagat® R63; Tepescohuite AMI Watersoluble; Tepescohuite HG; Tepescohuite HS; Unibix AP (Acid Proof); Westchlor® A2Z 8106

Propylene glycol alginate
CAS 9005-37-2
FEMA 2941

Synonyms: Hydroxypropyl alginate; Alginic acid, ester with 1,2-propanediol; Propane-1,2-diol alginate

Definition: Mixture of propylene glycol esters of alginic acid

Empirical: $(C_9H_{14}O_7)_8$

Properties: Wh. to ylsh. fibrous or gran. powd., pract. odorless and tasteless; sol. in water, dil. organic acids, hydroalcoholic mixts.; m.w. 1873.6

Toxicology: LD50 (oral, rat) 7200 mg/kg; mildly toxic by ingestion; heated to decomp., emits acrid smoke and irritating fumes

Uses: Flavoring adjuvant; suspending agent, thickener, gellant, film-former, emulsifier, formulation aid, stabilizer, solvent, defoamer; used in orals

Regulatory: FDA 21CFR §133.133, 133.134, 133.162, 133.178. 133.179, 172.210, 172.820, 172.858, 173.340, 176.170, GRAS; FEMA GRAS; Japan approved (1% max.); Europe listed; UK approved; FDA approved for orals; USP/NF compliance

Manuf./Distrib.: Kelco Int'l.; Meer

Manuf./Distrib. (pharm. & food): Kelco Int'l.; Meer; Pronova; Spectrum Chem. Mfg.

Trade names: Colloid 602; KELCOLOID® D; KELCOLOID® DH; KELCOLOID® DSF; KELCOLOID® HVF; KELCOLOID® LVF; KELCOLOID® S; Kimiloid HV; Kimiloid NLS-K

Trade names containing: Ches® 500

Propylene glycol diacetate
CAS 623-84-7; EINECS 210-817-6

Synonyms: 1,2-Diacetoxypropane

Empirical: $C_7H_{12}O_4$

Properties: Transparent liq., fruit-like odor; sol. in water; m.w. 160.10; sp.gr. 1.040-1.060; flash pt. 87 C; ref. index 1.413-1.415 (20 C); pH 4-6 (5%)

Uses: Emulsifier, solubilizer; used in otics

Regulatory: FDA approved for otics; USP/NF compliance

Propylene glycol dicaprylate/dicaprate
CAS 9062-04-8; 58748-27-9; 68583-51-7; 68988-72-7

Synonyms: Decanoic acid, 1-methyl-1,2-ethanediyl ester mixed with 1-methyl-1,2-ethanediyl dioctanoate

Definition: Mixture of the propylene glycol diesters of caprylic and capric acids

Uses: Gel used in emollients; carrier, coupler, solv. for flavors, sol. colorants, vitamins, medicinals

Regulatory: FDA 21CFR §172.856, 173.340, 175.300, 176.170, 176.210, 177.2800

Trade names: Calgene CC-22; Calgene CC-22-S; Captex® 200; Lexol® PG-865; Miglyol® 840; Myritol® PC; Neobee® 1054; Neobee® M-20; Pelemol® PDD; Standamul® 302

Trade names containing: Miglyol® 840 Gel B

Propylene glycol dinonanoate. *See* Propylene glycol dipelargonate

Propylene glycol dioctanoate
CAS 7384-98-7; 56519-71-1

Propylene glycol dipelargonate

Synonyms: 2-Ethylhexanoic acid, 1-methyl-1,2-ethanediyl ester; Octanoic acid, 1,3-propanediyl ester
Definition: Diester of propylene glycol and 2-ethylhexanoic acid
Empirical: $C_{19}H_{36}O_4$
Formula: $CH_3(CH_2)_3CHCH_3CH_2COOCH_2CHCH_3OCOCHCH_2CH_3(CH_2)_3CH_3$
Properties: Sol. in alcohol, min. oil; sp.gr. 0.921; flash pt. (COC) 159 C; ref. index 1.4350
Uses: Emollient, moisturizer, lubricant, penetration aid; humectant in dry skin prods.; carrier/vehicle; for dermatologicals, suppositories
Manuf./Distrib.: Inolex
Trade names: Captex® 800; Lexol® PG-800

Propylene glycol dipelargonate
CAS 41395-83-9; EINECS 255-350-9
Synonyms: Propylene glycol dinonanoate; Nonanoic acid, 1-methyl-1,2-ethanediyl ester
Definition: Diester of propylene glycol and pelargonic acid
Empirical: $C_{21}H_{40}O_4$
Formula: $CH_3(CH_2)_7COOCH_2CHCH_3OCO(CH_2)_7CH_3$
Properties: Sp.gr. 0.918; flash pt. (COC) 197 C; ref. index 1.4404
Uses: Emollient, lubricant for pharmaceuticals
Manuf./Distrib.: Henkel; Inolex
Trade names: D.P.P.G.

Propylene glycol isostearate
CAS 68171-38-0; EINECS 269-027-5
Synonyms: Propylene glycol monoisostearate; Isooctadecanoic acid, monoester with 1,2-propanediol
Definition: Ester of propylene glycol and isostearic acid
Empirical: $C_{21}H_{42}O_3$
Uses: Superfatting agent
Trade names: Hydrophilol ISO
Trade names containing: Hydrolactol 70

Propylene glycol laurate
CAS 142-55-2; 27194-74-7; EINECS 205-542-3
Synonyms: Dodecanoic acid, 2-hydroxypropyl ester; Dodecanoic acid, monoester with 1,2-propanediol; Propylene glycol monolaurate
Definition: Ester of propylene glycol and lauric acid
Empirical: $C_{15}H_{30}O_3$
Formula: $CH_3(CH_2)_{10}COOCH_2CHCH_3OH$
Properties: Sp.gr. 0.911; m.p. 0-12 C; flash pt. (COC) 188 C
Toxicology: Nontoxic but can cause allergic reactions in hypersensitive persons
Uses: Emulsifier, coemulsifier, stabilizer, lubricant, emollient, solvent; used in pharmaceuticals
Regulatory: FDA 21CFR §172.856, 173.340, 175.105, 175.300, 176.170, 176.210, 177.2800
Manuf./Distrib.: Inolex; Velsicol
Trade names: Cithrol PGML N/E; Lauroglycol

Propylene glycol laurate SE
Uses: Emulsifier, coemulsifier, stabilizer, wetting agent, lubricant; used in pharmaceuticals

Propylene glycol monoisostearate. See Propylene glycol isostearate
Propylene glycol monolaurate. See Propylene glycol laurate
Propylene glycol monomyristate. See Propylene glycol myristate
Propylene glycol monoricinoleate. See Propylene glycol ricinoleate
Propylene glycol monostearate. See Propylene glycol stearate

Propylene glycol myristate
CAS 29059-24-3; EINECS 249-395-3
Synonyms: Propylene glycol monomyristate; Tetradecanoic acid, monoester with 1,2-propanediol
Definition: Ester of propylene glycol and myristic acid
Empirical: $C_{17}H_{34}O_3$
Formula: $CH_3(CH_2)_{12}COOCH_2CHCH_3OH$
Uses: Wetting aid, lubricant, opacifier, dispersant, w/o emulgent; used in pharmaceuticals
Regulatory: FDA 21CFR §172.856, 173.340, 175.300, 176.170, 176.210, 177.2800

Propylene glycol octadecanoate. See Propylene glycol stearate

Propylene glycol oleate
CAS 1330-80-9; EINECS 215-549-3
Synonyms: 9-Octadecenoic acid, monoester with 1,2-propanediol

Definition: Ester of propylene glycol and oleic acid
Empirical: $C_{21}H_{40}O_3$
Formula: $CH_3(CH_2)_7CH=CH(CH_2)_7COOCH_2CHCH_3OH$
Uses: Emulsifier, coemulsifier, stabilizer, wetting agent, lubricant; used in pharmaceuticals
Regulatory: FDA 21CFR §172.856, 173.340, 175.300, 176.210, 177.2800
Trade names: Cithrol PGMO N/E

Propylene glycol oleate SE
Definition: Self-emulsifying grade of propylene glycol oleate that contains some sodium and/or potassium oleate
Uses: Emulsifier, coemulsifier, stabilizer, wetting agent, lubricant; used in pharmaceuticals

Propylene glycol palmito/stearate
Uses: Emulsifier, stabilizer
Trade names: Monosteol

Propylene glycol ricinoleate
CAS 26402-31-3; EINECS 247-669-7
Synonyms: 12-Hydroxy-9-octadecenoic acid, monoester with 1,2-propanediol; Propylene glycol monoricinoleate
Definition: Ester of propylene glycol and ricinoleic acid
Empirical: $C_{21}H_{40}O_4$
Properties: Sp.gr. 0.960; m.p. < -16 C; flash pt. (COC) 221 C; ref. index 1.469
Uses: Emulsifier, coemulsifier, stabilizer, wetting agent, lubricant, emollient; used in pharmaceuticals
Manuf./Distrib.: CasChem
Trade names: Cithrol PGMR N/E

Propylene glycol ricinoleate SE
Uses: Emulsifier, coemulsifier, stabilizer, wetting agent, lubricant; used in pharmaceuticals

Propylene glycol stearate
CAS 1323-39-3; EINECS 215-354-3
FEMA 2942
Synonyms: Propylene glycol monostearate; Propylene glycol octadecanoate; Octadecanoic acid, monoester with 1,2-propanediol; 1,2-Propanediol monostearate
Definition: Ester of propylene glycol and stearic acid
Empirical: $C_{21}H_{42}O_3$
Formula: $CH_3(CH_2)_{16}COOCH_2CHCH_3OH$
Properties: Wh. to cream flakes, bland typ. fatty odor and taste; sol. in min. oil, IPM, oleyl alcohol; insol. in water, glycerin, propylene glycol; m.p. 35-38 C; acid no. 4 max.; iodine no. 3 max.; sapon. no. 155-165; hyd. no. 160-175
Toxicology: Poison by intraperitoneal route
Uses: Surfactant, dispersant; emulsifier, solubilizer, lubricant in creams and lotions; humectant in dry skin prods.; used in rectals, vaginals
Regulatory: FDA 21CFR §172.856, 172.860, 172.862, 173.340, 175.105, 175.300, 176.170, 176.210, 177.2800; USDA 9CFR §318.7, 381.147; FEMA GRAS; FDA approved for rectals, vaginals; USP/NF compliance
Manuf./Distrib.: ABITEC; Aquatec Quimica SA; Eastman; Grindsted; Inolex; ISP Van Dyk; Lipo; Lonza; Witco/PAG
Trade names: Aldo® PGHMS; Cerasynt® PA; Cithrol PGMS N/E; Kessco PGMS; Nikkol PMS-1C
Trade names containing: Hydrolactol 70; Myvatex® TL

Propylene glycol stearate SE
Definition: Self-emulsifying grade of propylene glycol stearate containing some sodium and/or potassium stearate
Uses: Emulsifier, coemulsifier, stabilizer, wetting agent, lubricant, pearlescent, spreading agent; used in pharmaceuticals
Trade names: Cithrol PGMS S/E; Nikkol PMS-1CSE; Tegin® P; Tesal

Propylene polymer. *See* Polypropylene

Propyl formate
CAS 110-74-7; EINECS 203-798-0
FEMA 2943
Synonyms: Formic acid propyl ester; n-Propyl formate; n-Propyl methanoate
Empirical: $C_4H_8O_2$
Formula: $HCOOC_3H_7$

n-Propyl formate

    Properties: Colorless liq., pleasant odor, bittersweet flavor; sol. in 45 parts water; misc. with alcohol, ether; m.w.
      88.10; dens. 0.901 (20 C); m.p. -93 C; b.p. 81-82 C; flash pt. (CC) -3 C; ref. index 1.3771 (20 C)
    Toxicology: LD50 (oral, rat) 3980 mg/kg
    Uses: Sweet berry-like synthetic flavoring agent
    Regulatory: FDA 21CFR §172.515; FEMA GRAS
    Manuf./Distrib. (pharm. & food): Aldrich

n-Propyl formate. *See* Propyl formate

Propyl 2-furanacrylate
    FEMA 2945
    Synonyms: Propyl β-furylacrylate; Propyl-3-furylpropenoate; Propyl 3-(2-furyl) acrylate
    Definition: Ester of n-propanol and furanacrylic acid
    Empirical: $C_{10}H_{12}O_3$
    Properties: Colorless liq., lt. strawberry apple-/pear-like odor; sol. in alcohol; insol. in water; m.w. 180.21; dens.
      1.0744; b.p. 236 C; ref. index 1.5229
    Uses: Synthetic flavoring agent
    Regulatory: FDA 21CFR §172.515; FEMA GRAS

Propyl 3-(2-furyl) acrylate. *See* Propyl 2-furanacrylate
Propyl β-furylacrylate. *See* Propyl 2-furanacrylate
Propyl-3-furylpropenoate. *See* Propyl 2-furanacrylate

Propyl gallate
    CAS 121-79-9; EINECS 204-498-2
    FEMA 2947
    Synonyms: 3,4,5-Trihydroxybenzoic acid, n-propyl ester; n-Propyl 3,4,5-trihydroxybenzoate; Gallic acid
      propyl ester
    Classification: Aromatic ester
    Definition: Aromatic ester of propyl alcohol and gallic acid
    Empirical: $C_{10}H_{12}O_5$
    Formula: $(HO)_3C_6H_2COOCH_2CH_2CH_3$
    Properties: Ivory fine powd. or crystals, odorless, sl. bitter taste; sl. sol. in water; sol. in alcohol, oils; m.w.
      212.22; m.p. 147-149 C; b.p. dec. > 148 C
    Precaution: Combustible exposed to heat or flame; reactive with oxidizers
    Toxicology: LD50 (oral, rat) 3.8 g/kg; poison by ingestion and intraperitoneal route; a sensitizer but not a
      primary irritant; experimental tumorigen, reproductive effects; mutagenic data; heated to decomp., emits
      acrid smoke and irritating fumes
    Uses: Antioxidant and preservative; used in topical and parenteral pharmaceuticals, intramuscular injectables
    Usage level: 0.01-0.1%
    Regulatory: FDA 21CFR §172.615, 175.125, 175.300, 181.22, 181.24 (0.005% migrating from food pkg.),
      184.1660 (0.02% max. of fat or oil), GRAS; USDA 9CFR §318.7, 381.147; FEMA GRAS; Japan approved
      (0.1 g/kg max.); Europe listed; UK approved; FDA approved for intramuscular injectables, topicals; USP/
      NF, BP compliance
    Manuf./Distrib.: Aceto; Eastman; Nipa Labs; Penta Mfg.; Spectrum Chem. Mfg.; UOP
    Manuf./Distrib. (pharm. & food): Aceto; Aldrich; Eastman; Nipa Labs; Spectrum Chem. Mfg.; UOP

Propyl heptanoate
    CAS 7778-87-2
    FEMA 2948
    Empirical: $C_{10}H_{20}O_2$
    Properties: M.w. 172.27; dens. 0.869; m.p. -64 C; b.p. 208 C; flash pt. 170 F
    Uses: Fruity synthetic flavoring agent
    Regulatory: FDA 21CFR §172.515; FEMA GRAS
    Manuf./Distrib. (pharm. & food): Aldrich

Propyl hydride. *See* Propane
Propyl 4-hydroxybenzoate. *See* Propylparaben
Propyl p-hydroxybenzoate. *See* Propylparaben
n-Propyl-4-hydroxybenzoate potassium salt. *See* Potassium propylparaben
Propyl-4-hydroxybenzoate, sodium salt. *See* Sodium propylparaben
Propylic alcohol. *See* n-Propyl alcohol

3-Propylidenephthalide
    CAS 17369-59-4
    FEMA 2952

Empirical: $C_{11}H_{10}O_2$
Properties: M.w. 174.20; dens. 1.122; m.p. 5 C; b.p. 170 C (12 mm); flash pt. > 230 F
Uses: Sweet synthetic flavoring agent
Regulatory: FDA 21CFR §172.515; FEMA GRAS
Manuf./Distrib. (pharm. & food): Aldrich

Propyl isobutyrate
CAS 644-49-5
FEMA 2936
Empirical: $C_7H_{14}O_2$
Properties: M.w. 130.19
Uses: Pineapple-like synthetic flavoring agent
Regulatory: FDA 21CFR §172.515; FEMA GRAS
Manuf./Distrib. (pharm. & food): Aldrich

n-Propyl methanoate. *See* Propyl formate

Propylparaben
CAS 94-13-3; EINECS 202-307-7
FEMA 2951
Synonyms: Propyl p-hydroxybenzoate; Propyl 4-hydroxybenzoate; Propyl parasept; 4-Hydroxybenzoic acid, propyl ester; Propyl parahydroxybenzoate
Classification: Organic ester
Definition: Ester of n-propyl alcohol and p-hydroxybenzoic acid
Empirical: $C_{10}H_{12}O_3$
Properties: Colorless cryst. or wh. powd., sl. char. odor; sl. sol. in boiling water; sol. in alcohol, ether, acetone; m.w. 180.22; m.p. 95-98 C
Precaution: Conc. dust may present an explosion hazard; incompat. with alkalies and strong oxidizing agents; burning may produce phenolic vapors and CO
Toxicology: Poison by intraperitoneal route; moderately toxic by subcutaneous route; mildly toxic by ingestion; inh. of powd. may cause respiratory irritation; may cause asthma, rashes, hyperactivity, eye and skin irritation, contact dermatitis
Uses: Antimicrobial preservative, antifungal, antibacterial; used in injectables, parenterals, intravenous, ophthalmics, orals, rectals, topicals, vaginals; dental anesthetics
Usage level: 0.003-1%; 0.03% (eye wash); 0.003-0.05% (drug extracts); 0.05% (tablets); 0.04% (ointment bases); 0.1% (suppositories)
Regulatory: FDA 21CFR §150.141, 150.161, 172.515, 181.22, 181.23, 184.1670; FEMA GRAS; USA CIR approved, EPA reg.; Japan listed; Europe listed; UK approved; FDA approved for injectables, parenterals, intravenous, ophthalmics, orals, rectals, topicals, vaginals; USP/NF, BP, Ph.Eur. compliance
Manuf./Distrib.: Aceto; Allchem Industries; Ashland; R.W. Greeff; Int'l. Sourcing; Kraft; E. Merck; Napp; Nipa Labs; Penta Mfg.; Sutton Labs
Manuf./Distrib. (pharm. & food): Aceto; Aldrich; Allchem Industries; Ashland; R.W. Greeff; Int'l. Sourcing; Kraft; E. Merck; Nipa Labs; Penta Mfg.; Spectrum Chem. Mfg.; Tri-K Ind.
Trade names: Lexgard® P; Nipasol M; Propyl Parasept® NF/FCC
Trade names containing: Germaben® II; Nipaguard® BPX; Nipastat; Phenonip; Uniphen P-23

Propylparaben, potassium salt. *See* Potassium propylparaben
Propylparaben sodium. *See* Sodium propylparaben
Propylparaben sodium salt. *See* Sodium propylparaben
Propyl parahydroxybenzoate. *See* Propylparaben
Propyl parasept. *See* Propylparaben
Propyl phenethyl acetal. *See* Acetaldehyde phenethyl propyl acetal

α-Propylphenethyl alcohol
CAS 705-73-7
FEMA 2953
Synonyms: Benzylbutyl alcohol; Benzyl-n-propyl carbinol; Benzylpropyl carbinol; 1-Phenyl-2-pentanol
Empirical: $C_{11}H_{16}O$
Properties: Colorless oily liq., mild green sweet odor; sol. in alcohol; almost insol. in water; m.w. 164.25; dens. 0.98; b.p. 247 C; flash pt. 221 F
Uses: Sweet synthetic flavoring agent
Regulatory: FDA 21CFR §172.515; FEMA GRAS
Manuf./Distrib. (pharm. & food): Aldrich

4-Propylphenol
CAS 645-56-7

p-Propylphenol

FEMA 3649
Synonyms: p-Propylphenol
Empirical: $C_9H_{12}O$
Properties: M.w. 136.19; dens. 0.983; b.p. 232 C; flash pt. 232 F
Uses: Medicinal flavoring agent
Regulatory: FEMA GRAS
Manuf./Distrib. (pharm. & food): Aldrich

p-Propylphenol. *See* 4-Propylphenol

Propyl phenylacetate

CAS 4606-15-9
FEMA 2955
Synonyms: n-Propyl-α-toluate
Definition: Ester of n-propanol and phenylacetic acid
Empirical: $C_{11}H_{14}O_2$
Properties: Colorless liq., honey-like apricot-rose odor, sweet honey-like taste; sol. in alcohol; almost insol. in water; m.w. 178.23; dens. 0.990 (15.5 C); b.p. 253 C; ref. index 1.4955
Uses: Apricot, honey-like synthetic flavoring agent
Regulatory: FDA 21CFR §172.515; FEMA GRAS
Manuf./Distrib. (pharm. & food): Aldrich

Propyl propionate

CAS 106-36-5; EINECS 203-389-7
FEMA 2958
Synonyms: Propanoic acid propyl ester; n-Propyl propionate
Empirical: $C_6H_{12}O_2$
Formula: $CH_3CH_2COOCH_2CH_2CH_3$
Properties: Liq., complex fruity odor; sol. in 200 parts water; misc. with alcohol, ether; m.w. 116.16; dens. 0.881 (20/4 C); m.p. -76 C; b.p. 120-122 C; flash pt. 22 C; ref. index 1.3935 (20 C)
Precaution: Flamm.
Uses: Fruity synthetic flavoring agent
Regulatory: FDA 21CFR §172.515; FEMA GRAS
Manuf./Distrib.: Union Carbide
Manuf./Distrib. (pharm. & food): Aldrich

n-Propyl propionate. *See* Propyl propionate

Propyl tiglate

CAS 61692-83-9
Empirical: $C_8H_{14}O_2$
Properties: M.w. 142.20; dens. 0.904; flash pt. 137 F
Uses: Apple, fruity flavoring agent
Manuf./Distrib. (pharm. & food): Aldrich

n-Propyl-α-toluate. *See* Propyl phenylacetate
n-Propyl 3,4,5-trihydroxybenzoate. *See* Propyl gallate

Protamine sulfate

CAS 9009-65-8; 53597-25-4
Synonyms: Salmine sulfate
Definition: Mixt. of simple proteins obtained from the sperm or testes of certain species of fish; has property of neutralizing heparin
Uses: Used in parenterals, injectables
Regulatory: FDA approved for parenterals; BP, Ph.Eur. compliance
Manuf./Distrib.: Spectrum Chem. Mfg.

Protease

CAS 9014-01-1; EINECS 232-752-2
Classification: Enzyme
Properties: Sol. in water; m.w. $\approx$ 27,000
Toxicology: Irritant
Uses: Enzyme for hydrolysis of proteins; digestive aids; wound debriding agent; blood typing aid
Regulatory: Canada, Japan approved
Manuf./Distrib.: Aldrich; Am. Biorganics; PMP Fermentation Prods.; Schweizerhall; U.S. Biochemical
Manuf./Distrib. (pharm. & food): PMP Fermentation Prods.; Solvay Enzymes
Trade names: Bromelain 1:10; Bromelain Conc.; Fungal Protease 31,000; Fungal Protease 60,000; Fungal

Protease 500,000; Fungal Protease Conc.; Papain 16,000; Papain 30,000; Papain Conc.; Prolase® 300
Trade names containing: Pancreatin 3X USP Powd.; Pancreatin 4X USP Powd.; Pancreatin 5X USP Powd.;
Pancreatin 6X USP Powd.; Pancreatin 8X USP Powd.; Pancreatin USP Powd.; Pancrelipase USP; SPL
High Lipase Pancreatic Enzyme Conc. (PEC); SPL Pancreatin 3X USP; SPL Pancreatin 4X USP; SPL
Pancreatin 5X USP; SPL Pancreatin 6X USP; SPL Pancreatin 7X USP; SPL Pancreatin 8X USP; SPL
Pancreatin USP; SPL Pancrelipase USP; SPL Undiluted Pancreatic Enzyme Conc. (PEC)

Protein hydrolysate. *See* Hydrolyzed collagen
Proteins, collagen, hydrolysate. *See* Hydrolyzed collagen
Proteins, hydrolysates, reaction prods. with abietoyl chloride, compd. with triethanolamine. *See* TEA-abietoyl hydrolyzed collagen
Proteins, milk, hydrolysate. *See* Hydrolyzed milk protein
Proteins, vegetable, hydrolysate. *See* Hydrolyzed vegetable protein
Protocatechualdehyde dimethyl ether. *See* Veratraldehyde
Protovanol. *See* Vanilla
Provitamin A. *See* Carotene
Provitamin B₅. *See* D-Panthenol; DL-Panthenol
Prunus armeniaca. *See* Apricot kernel oil
Prussian blue. *See* CI 77510; Ferric ferrocyanide
PS. *See* Polystyrene
Pseudopinene. *See* β-Pinene
Pteroylglutamic acid. *See* Folic acid
d-β-Pulegomenthol. *See* d-Neomenthol

Pulegone
CAS 89-82-7; EINECS 201-943-2
FEMA 2963
Synonyms: p-Menth-4(8)-en-3-one; R-(+)-p-menth-4(8)-en-3-one; 1-Methyl-4-isopropylidene-3-cyclohexanone; (R)-2-Isopropylidene-5-methylcyclohexanone;; 5-Methyl-2-(1-methylethylidene)cyclohexanone
Classification: Ketone
Empirical: $C_{10}H_{16}O$
Properties: Oil, pleasant odor of peppermint/camphor; misc. with alcohol, ether, chloroform; pract. insol. in water; m.w. 152.24; dens. 0.936 (20/4 C); b.p. 223-224 C; flash pt. 55 C; ref. index 1.487 (20 C)
Precaution: Flamm.
Uses: Minty synthetic flavoring agent
Regulatory: FDA 21CFR §172.515; FEMA GRAS
Manuf./Distrib. (pharm. & food): Aldrich

Purified gum spirits. *See* Turpentine oil
Purple medick extract. *See* Alfalfa extract
PVA. *See* Polyvinyl alcohol
PVAc. *See* Polyvinyl acetate (homopolymer)
PVAL. *See* Polyvinyl alcohol
PVAP. *See* Polyvinyl acetate phthalate
PVC. *See* Polyvinyl chloride

PVM/MA copolymer
CAS 9011-16-9; 52229-50-2
Synonyms: Methyl vinyl ether/maleic anhydride copolymer; Poly(methyl vinyl ether/maleic anhydride); 2,5-Furandione, polymer with methoxyethylene
Definition: Copolymer of methyl vinyl ether and maleic anhydride
Empirical: $(C_4H_2O_3 \cdot C_3H_6O)_x$
Uses: Dispersant, coupling agent, stabilizer; film-former in spray bandages; complexing agent for sustained-release iron preps.; bioadhesives; dentifrices; thickener
Trade names: Gantrez® AN-119; Gantrez® AN-139; Gantrez® AN-139 BF; Gantrez® AN-149; Gantrez® AN-169; Gantrez® S-95; Gantrez® S-97; Luviform® FA 119

PVM/MA copolymer, butyl ester
CAS 54018-18-7; 54578-91-5; 53200-28-5
Synonyms: Poly(methylvinyl ether/maleic acid) butyl ester; Butyl ester of PVM/MA copolymer; 2-Butenedioic acid, polymer with methoxyethene, butyl ester
Definition: Polymer consisting of partial butyl ester of the polycarboxylic acid formed from vinyl methyl ether and maleic anhydride
Empirical: $(C_{11}H_{18}O_5)_n$
Formula: $-[CH_2CHOCH_3CHOCOHCHCOOC_4H_9]_n-$

PVM/MA copolymer, ethyl ester

Uses: Ingred. in sustained- or controlled-release coatings for tablets
Trade names containing: Gantrez® ES-425; Gantrez® ES-435

PVM/MA copolymer, ethyl ester
CAS 50935-57-4; 67724-93-0; 54578-90-4
Synonyms: Ethyl ester of PVM/MA copolymer
Trade names containing: Gantrez® ES-225

PVM/MA copolymer, isopropyl ester
CAS 54578-88-0; 54077-45-1; 56091-51-1
Synonyms: Poly(methylvinyl ether/maleic acid) isopropyl ester; 2-Butenedioic acid, polymer with methoxyethene, 1-methylethyl ester; Isopropyl ester of PVM/MA copolymer
Trade names containing: Gantrez® ES-335

PVOH. *See* Polyvinyl alcohol

PVP
CAS 9003-39-8; EINECS 201-800-4
Synonyms: Polyvinylpyrrolidone; Poly (n-vinylbutyrolactam); Polyvidonum; Polyvidone; Povidone; 1-Vinyl-2-pyrrolidinone polymer; 1-Ethenyl-2-pyrrolidinone homopolymer
Classification: Synthetic linear polymer
Definition: Polymer of 1-vinyl-2-pyrrolidone monomers
Empirical: $(C_6H_9NO)_x$
Properties: Wh. amorphous powd., odorless; hygroscopic; sol. in water, chlorinated hydrocarbons, alcohol, amines, nitroparaffins, lower m.w. fatty acids; m.w. $\approx$ 10,000, $\approx$ 24,000, $\approx$ 40,000 (food use), $\approx$ 160,000, $\approx$ 360,000 (beer); dens. 1.23-1.29; pH 3.0-7.0 (5%)
Toxicology: LD50 (IP, mouse) 12 g/kg; mildly toxic by IP and IV routes; potent histamine-releasing agent in animals; heated to decomp., emits toxic fumes of NO_x
Uses: Dispersing and suspending agent; visc.-increasing agent; tablet binder; used in parenterals, intramuscular injectables, orals, topicals; multivitamin chewable tablets; artificial tear prods.
Usage level: 3-5%; 0.03-0.9% (injectable drug prods.); 1-50 mg (oral dosage forms)
Regulatory: FDA 21CFR §73.1, 73.1001, 172.210, 173.50, 173.55, 175.105, 175.300, 176.170, 176.180, 176.210; BATF 27CFR §240.1051; FDA approved for parenterals, intramuscular injectables, orals, topicals; USP/NF, BP, Ph.Eur. compliance
Manuf./Distrib.: Allchem Ind.; BASF; Great Western; Hickson Danchem; ISP; Jarchem Ind.; Monomer-Polymer & Dajac
Manuf./Distrib. (pharm. & food): Allchem Industries; Aldrich; ISP; Ruger; Spectrum Chem. Mfg.
Trade names: Iodasept; Kollidon®; Kollidon® USP; Plasdone® C-15; Plasdone® C-30; Plasdone® K-25; Plasdone® K-29/32; Plasdone® K-90; Plasdone® K-90D; Plasdone® K-90M
Trade names containing: Chroma-Seal™ 889031

PVP/dimethiconylacrylate/polycarbamyl/polyglycol ester
Definition: Copolymer of vinylpyrrolidone, acrylated dimethiconol, and polyurethane
Uses: Film-former for sunscreens, pharmaceutical topicals
Trade names: Pecogel® S-1120

PVP/dimethylaminoethylmethacrylate copolymer
CAS 30581-59-0
Synonyms: 2-Propenoic acid, 2-methyl-, 2-(dimethylamino)ethyl ester, polymer with 1-ethenyl-2-pyrrolidinone; Vinylpyrrolidone/dimethylaminoethyl methacrylate copolymer
Definition: Polymer from vinylpyrrolidone and dimethylaminoethylmethacrylate monomers
Uses: Film-forming resin for topical pharmaceuticals

PVP/dimethylaminoethyl methacrylate/polycarbamyl polyglycol ester
Definition: Copolymer of PVP, dimethylaminoethylmethacrylate, and polyurethane
Uses: Film-former in pharmaceutical topicals
Trade names: Pecogel® GC-310; Pecogel® GC-1110

PVP/hexadecene copolymer
CAS 32440-50-9
Synonyms: Polyvinylpyrrolidone/hexadecene copolymer
Definition: Polymer of hexadecene and vinylpyrrolidone monomers

PVP-iodine
CAS 25655-41-8
Synonyms: Polyvinylpyrrolidone-iodine complex; Povidone-iodine; 2-Pyrrolidinone, 1-ethenyl-, homopolymer, compd. with iodine
Definition: Complex of polyvinylpyrrolidone and iodine

Empirical: $(C_6H_9NO)_x \cdot xI_2$
Properties: Ylsh. brn. amorphous powd., sl. char. odor; sol. in water, alcohol; pract. insol. in chloroform, CCl_4, ether, hexane, acetone
Precaution: Moisture-sensitive
Uses: Active ingred. in OTC microbiocidally active drug prods., gels, ointments, soaps, solutions, aerosols, antiseptics
Regulatory: USP/NF, BP compliance
Manuf./Distrib.: BASF
Manuf./Distrib. (pharm. & food): Spectrum Chem. Mfg.
Trade names: PVP-Iodine 17/12, 30/06

PVPP. *See* Polyvinylpolypyrrolidone

PVP/polycarbamyl polyglycol ester
Definition: Copolymer of PVP and polyurethane
Uses: Film-former for pharmaceutical topicals
Trade names: Pecogel® H-12; Pecogel® H-115; Pecogel® H-1220

PVP/VA copolymer
CAS 25086-89-9
Synonyms: 1-Ethenyl-2-pyrrolidinone, polymer with acetic acid ethenyl ester; Polyvinylpyrrolidone/vinyl acetate copolymer; Vinylpyrrolidone/vinyl acetate copolymer
Definition: Copolymer of vinyl acetate and vinylpyrrolidone monomers
Empirical: $(C_6H_9NO \cdot C_4H_6O_2)_x$
Uses: Film-former for antiseptic/anesthetic spray bandages, antibiotic sprays, spray gloves/masks; solubilizer; visc. modifier/stabilizer; tablet binder/coating
Trade names: PVP/VA S-630
Trade names containing: PVP/VA E-335; PVP/VA E-535; PVP/VA E-635; PVP/VA E-735; PVP/VA I-235; PVP/VA I-335; PVP/VA I-535; PVP/VA I-735

2H-Pyran-2,4(3H)-dione, 3-acetyl-6-methyl-, monosodium salt. *See* Sodium dehydroacetate
Pyranine conc. *See* D&C Green No. 8

Pyrazine
CAS 290-37-9
Empirical: $C_4H_4N_2$
Properties: M.w. 80.09; m.p. 53-56 C; b.p. 115-116 C; flash pt. 132 F
Uses: Sweet flavoring agent
Manuf./Distrib. (pharm. & food): Aldrich

Pyrazine hexahydride. *See* Piperazine

Pyridine
CAS 110-86-1; EINECS 203-809-9
FEMA 2966; UN No. 1282
Empirical: C_5H_5N
Properties: Colorless liq., char. disagreeable odor, sharp taste; misc. with water, alcohol, ether, petroleum ether, oils, other org. liqs.; m.w. 79.10; dens. 0.98272 (20/4 C); m.p. -41.6 C; b.p. 115-116 C; flash pt. (CC) 20 C; ref. index 1.510 (20 C)
Precaution: DOT: Flamm. liq.; highly flamm.; volatile with steam
Toxicology: LD50 (oral, rat) 1.58 g/kg; may cause human CNS depression, irritation of skin and respiratory tract; large does may produce GI disturbances, kidney and liver damage
Uses: Synthetic flavoring agent; pharmaceuticals, sedative; acid scavenger; chem. intermediate
Regulatory: FDA 21CFR §172.515; FEMA GRAS; BP compliance
Manuf./Distrib.: Aldrich; Allchem Ind.; Berje; Daicel; Koei; Nepera; Penta Mfg.; Raschig; Reilly Ind.; Schweizerhall; Spectrum Chem. Mfg.
Manuf./Distrib. (pharm. & food): Aldrich; Ruger
Trade names: Pyridine 1°

3-Pyridinecarboxamide. *See* Niacinamide
Pyridine-3-carboxylic acid. *See* Nicotinic acid
3-Pyridinecarboxylic acid. *See* Nicotinic acid

Pyridoxine HCl
CAS 58-56-0; EINECS 200-386-2
Synonyms: 5-Hydroxy-6-methyl-3,4-pyridinedimethanol hydrochloride; 3-Hydroxy-4,5-dihydroxymethyl-2-methylpyridine HCl; Vitamin B_6 hydrochloride; Adermine hydrochloride; Pyridoxine hydrochloride; Pyridoxol hydrochloride

Pyridoxine hydrochloride

Classification: Substituted aromatic compd.
Empirical: $C_8H_{11}NO_3$ • HCl
Properties: Colorless to wh. platelets or cryst. powd., odorless; sol. in water, alcohol, acetone, propylene glycol; sl. sol. in other org. solvs.; insol. in ether, chloroform; m.w. 205.66; m.p. 204-206 C (dec.); pH 2.0-3.5 (5% aq.)
Toxicology: LD50 (oral, rat) 4000 mg/kg; poison by IV route; mod. toxic by ingestion; prolonged high doses may cause ataxia; human reproductive effects; experimental teratogen; human mutagenic data; heated to decomp., emits very toxic fumes of NO_x and HCl
Uses: Dietary supplement
Regulatory: FDA 21CFR §182.5676, 184.1676, GRAS; Japan approved; BP compliance
Manuf./Distrib. (pharm. & food): Am. Roland; Daiichi Pharmaceutical; Unipex
Trade names: Pyridoxine Hydrochloride USP, FCC Fine Powd. No. 60650
Trade names containing: Descote® Pyridoxine Hydrochoride $33^1/_3$%; Rocoat® Pyridoxine Hydrochloride $33^1/_3$% No. 60688

Pyridoxine hydrochloride. See Pyridoxine HCl
Pyridoxol hydrochloride. See Pyridoxine HCl
Pyrithione zinc. See Zinc pyrithione

Pyrithyldione
CAS 77-04-3
Synonyms: 3,3-Diethyl-2,4(1H,3H)-pyridinedione
Properties: M.w. 167.21; b.p. 187-189 C (14 mm)
Uses: Used in topicals
Regulatory: FDA approved for topicals
Manuf./Distrib. (pharm. & food): Aldrich

Pyroacetic ether. See Acetone
Pyrocatechin. See Pyrocatechol

Pyrocatechol
CAS 120-80-9; EINECS 204-427-5
Synonyms: 1,2-Benzenediol; Catechol; Pyrocatechin; 1,2-Dihydroxybenzene; o-Dihydroxybenzene
Classification: Phenol
Empirical: $C_6H_6O_2$
Formula: $C_6H_4(OH)_2$
Properties: Colorless monocl. leaflets; sol. in water, alcohol, benzene, ether; m.w. 110.11; dens. 1.371 (15 C); m.p. 105 C; b.p. 240 C
Precaution: Oxygen- and light-sensitive
Toxicology: Skin irritant, corrosive, toxic
Uses: Synthesis of pharmaceuticals
Regulatory: BP compliance
Manuf./Distrib.: Aldrich; Coalite Chem. Div.; James River; Spectrum Chem. Mfg.
Manuf./Distrib. (pharm. & food): James River
Trade names: Catechol XP

Pyrocatechol methyl ether. See Guaiacol
Pyrogallic acid. See Pyrogallol

Pyrogallol
CAS 87-66-1; EINECS 201-762-9
Synonyms: 1,2,3-Benzenetriol; Pyrogallic acid; CI 76515; 1,2,3-Trihydroxybenzene
Classification: Phenol
Definition: An aromatic alcohol of pyrogallic acid
Empirical: $C_6H_6O_3$
Formula: $C_6H_3(OH)_3$
Properties: White lustrous cryst.; sol. in water, alcohol, ether; sl. sol. in benzene, chloroform; m.w. 126.12; dens. 1.453 (4/4 C); m.p. 131-133 C; b.p. 309 C
Precaution: Light-sensitive
Toxicology: Human poison by ing., subcutaneous routes; ing. causes severe gastrointestinal irritation, kidney/liver damage, circulatory collapse, death; experimental poison by ing., subcutaneous, IV, IP; severe skin/eye irritant
Uses: Intermediate, synthetic drugs, medicine; colorant with ferric ammonium citrate in sutures for general and ophthalmic surgery; external antimicrobial; soothes irritated skin
Usage level: 3% max. (sutures)
Regulatory: FDA 21CFR §73.1375; BP compliance

Quaternary ammonium compds., (hydroxyethyl)dimethyl(3-mink oil amidopropyl), chlorides

Manuf./Distrib.: Burlington Bio-Medical; Dainippon Pharmaceutical; Fuji Chem. Ind.; Hoechst Celanese; Mallinckrodt; Spectrum Chem. Mfg.
Manuf./Distrib. (pharm. & food): Aldrich; Dainippon Pharmaceutical

Pyroligneus acid. *See* Acetic acid
Pyromucic acid. *See* 2-Furoic acid

Pyrophyllite
CAS 12269-78-2
Synonyms: Hydrated aluminum silicate; Agalmatolite
Definition: Naturally occurring mineral substance consisting predominantly of hydrous aluminum silicate
Empirical: $Al_2O_3 \cdot 4SiO_2 \cdot H_2O$
Formula: $Al_2Si_4O_{10}(OH)$
Properties: Colorless, white, green, gray, brown; dens. 2.8-2.9
Uses: Color additive for external pharmaceuticals; diluent, carrier
Regulatory: FDA 21CFR §73.1400, 73.2400; permanently listed
Manuf./Distrib.: Chem-Materials; D.N. Lukens; R.T. Vanderbilt; Whittaker, Clark & Daniels
Trade names: Pyrax® ABB; Pyrax® B
See also Aluminum silicate

Pyroxylin. *See* Nitrocellulose
2-Pyrrolidinone, 1-ethenyl-, homopolymer. *See* Crospovidone
2-Pyrrolidinone, 1-ethenyl-, homopolymer, compd. with iodine. *See* PVP-iodine
Pyrrolidone-2. *See* 2-Pyrrolidone

2-Pyrrolidone
CAS 616-45-5; EINECS 204-648-7
Synonyms: Butyrolactam; Pyrrolidone-2
Empirical: C_4H_7NO
Formula: $CH_2CH_2CH_2C(O)NH$
Properties: Lt. yel. liq.; sol. in water, ethanol, ethyl ether, chloroform, benzene, ethyl acetate, carbon disulfide; m.w. 85.12; dens. 1.1; b.p. 245 C; flash pt. 265 F
Toxicology: Mildly toxic by ingestion, subcutaneous route
Uses: Solv., solubilizer; synthesis of piracetam; treatment of cerebral distress; intermediate
Manuf./Distrib.: Allchem Ind.; BASF; ISP; UCB SA; Unitex
Trade names: 2-Pyrol®

Pyruvaldehyde
CAS 78-98-8; EINECS 201-164-8
FEMA 2969
Synonyms: Methylglyoxal; 2-Oxopropanal; 2-Ketopropopnaldehyde; Pyruvic aldehyde; Acetyl formaldehyde
Empirical: $C_3H_4O_2$
Formula: CH_3COCHO
Properties: Yel. mobile liq., pungent stinging odor, caramellic sweet odor; hygroscopic; sol. in alcohol, ether; m.w. 72.06; dens. 1.178; b.p. 72 C; ref. index 1.4002 (17.5 C)
Toxicology: Irritant
Uses: Caramel synthetic flavoring agent
Regulatory: FDA 21CFR §172.515; FEMA GRAS
Manuf./Distrib. (pharm. & food): Aldrich

Pyruvic aldehyde. *See* Pyruvaldehyde

Quassia
Synonyms: Bitter wood; Bitter ash
Definition: Wood of *Picrasma excelsa* or *Quassia amara*, contg. bitter principle quassin
Properties: Ylsh-wh. to bright yel. chips or fibrous coarse grains, sl. odor, very bitter taste
Uses: Natural flavoring; anthelmintic, tonic, bitter
Regulatory: FDA 21CFR §172.510; Japan approved
Manuf./Distrib. (pharm. & food): Bio-Botanica; Chart

Quat. ammonium compds., carboxymethyl (coco alkyl) dimethyl hydroxides, inner salts. *See* Coco-betaine
Quaternary ammonium compds., (hydroxyethyl)dimethyl(3-mink oil amidopropyl), chlorides. *See* Quaternium-26

Quaternary ammonium compds., tallow alkyl trimethyl, chlorides

Quaternary ammonium compds., tallow alkyl trimethyl, chlorides. *See* Tallowtrimonium chloride
Quaternary ammonium compounds, bis(hydrog. tallow alkyl) dimethyl, chlorides, reaction products with hectorite. *See* Quaternium-18 hectorite
Quaternium-5. *See* Distearyldimonium chloride

Quaternium-14
CAS 27479-28-3; EINECS 248-486-5
Synonyms: Dodecyl dimethyl ethylbenzyl ammonium chloride; N-Dodecyl-*ar*-ethyl-N,N-dimethylbenzene-methanaminium chloride
Classification: Quaternary ammonium salt
Empirical: $C_{23}H_{42}N \cdot Cl$
Properties: Water-sol.
Toxicology: Causes dermatitis
Uses: Antimicrobial active against bacteria but not yeast
Regulatory: FDA 21CFR §172.165, 173.320

Quaternium-15
CAS 51229-78-8; 4080-31-3; EINECS 223-805-0
Synonyms: 1-(3-Chloroallyl)-3,5,7-triaza-1-azoniaadamantane chloride; N-(3-Chloroallyl)hexaminium chloride; Chlorallyl methenamine chloride
Classification: Quaternary ammonium salt
Empirical: $C_9H_{16}ClN_4 \cdot Cl$
Formula: $C_6H_{12}N_4(CH_2CHCHCl)Cl$
Uses: Formaldehyde-releasing antimicrobial preservative for topical pharmaceuticals, esp. water-sol. creams and lotions, eyewashes
Usage level: 0.02-03%; 0.02% (topicals)
Regulatory: FDA 21CFR §175.105, 176.170; CIR approved; Europe listed; Japan not approved; FDA approved for topicals

Quaternium-22
CAS 51812-80-7; 82970-95-4; EINECS 257-440-3
Synonyms: 1-Propanaminium, 3-(D-gluconoylamino)-N-(2-hydroxyethyl)-N,N-dimethyl-, chloride; γ-Gluconamidopropyl dimethyl 2-hydroxyethyl ammonium chloride
Classification: Quaternary ammonium salt
Empirical: $C_{13}H_{29}N_2O_7 \cdot Cl$
Properties: Lt. amber liq.; sol. in water, 70% ethanol, glycerin, propylene glycol; insol. in IPM, min. oil; sp.gr. 1.170-1.210
Toxicology: Nonirritating to skin and eyes
Uses: Cationic surfactant, emollient, humectant, antistatic

Quaternium-26
CAS 68953-64-0; EINECS 273-222-0
Synonyms: Quaternary ammonium compds., (hydroxyethyl)dimethyl(3-mink oil amidopropyl), chlorides; Minkamidopropyl dimethyl 2-hydroxyethyl ammonium chloride
Classification: Quaternary ammonium salt
Formula: $[RCO-NH(CH_2)_3N(CH_3)_2CH_2CH_2OH]^+Cl^-$, RCO- rep. fatty acid groups from mink oil
Properties: Clear amber liq.; sol. in water, 70% ethanol, glycerin, propylene glycol; insol. in min. oil, IPM
Toxicology: Mild eye irritant, nonirritating to skin
Uses: Cationic surfactant, emulsifier, emollient, antistatic

Quaternium-18 hectorite
CAS 12001-31-9; 71011-27-3; EINECS 234-406-6
Synonyms: Quaternary ammonium compounds, bis(hydrog. tallow alkyl) dimethyl, chlorides, reaction products with hectorite
Definition: Reaction prod. of hectorite and quaternium-18

Quicklime. *See* Calcium oxide
Quicksilver. *See* Mercury

Quinaldine
CAS 91-63-4; EINECS 202-085-1
Synonyms: Chinaldine; α-Methylquinoline; 2-Methylquinoline
Empirical: $C_{10}H_9N$
Formula: $C_9H_6NCH_3$
Properties: Colorless oily liq.; sol. in alcohol, ether, chloroform; insol. in water; m.w. 143.19; dens. 1.058; m.p. -2 C; b.p. 248 C; flash pt. 79 C; ref. index 1.6120

Toxicology: Irritant
Uses: Mfg. of pharmaceuticals
Manuf./Distrib.: Aldrich; Allchem Industries; Sumikin Chem.
Manuf./Distrib. (pharm. & food): Aldrich; Mallinckrodt

Quince seed
Synonyms: Cydonia oblonga seed
Definition: Dried seeds of Cydonia oblonga
Properties: Thick jelly produced by soaking seeds in water
Toxicology: May cause allergic reaction
Uses: Natural flavoring; used as suspension in creams and lotions; medicinally as demulcent
Regulatory: FDA 21CFR §182.40; Japan approved
Manuf./Distrib. (pharm. & food): Bio-Botanica

Quinine sulfate dihydrate
CAS 6119-70-6; EINECS 212-359-2
FEMA 2977, 3088
Empirical: $C_{40}H_{50}N_4O_8S \cdot 2H_2O$
Formula: $(C_{20}H_{24}N_2O_2)_2 \cdot H_2SO_4 \cdot 2H_2O$
Properties: Dull needles or rods; sl. sol. in chloroform and ether; m.w. 782.96
Precaution: Keep well closed, protect from light; incompat. with ammonia, alkalies, tannic acid, iodine, citrates, tartrates, benzoates, salicylates
Uses: Used as an antimalarial drug and a muscle relaxant
Regulatory: BP, Ph.Eur. compliance
Manuf./Distrib.: Atomergic Chemetals; Monomer-Polymer & Dajac; R.W. Greeff
Manuf./Distrib. (pharm. & food): Integra; Spectrum Chem. Mfg.

Quinizarin green SS. See D&C Green No. 6
Quinoline yellow. See CI 47005; D&C Yellow No. 10
Quinoline yellow spirit soluble. See D&C Yellow No. 11
Quinoline yellow SS. See D&C Yellow No. 11
Quinoline yellow WS. See D&C Yellow No. 10
8-Quinolinol. See 8-Hydroxyquinoline
8-Quinolinol hydrogen sulfate (2:1). See 8-Hydroxyquinoline sulfate
8-Quinolinol sulfate. See 8-Hydroxyquinoline sulfate
8-Quinolinol sulfate (2:1) (salt). See 8-Hydroxyquinoline sulfate
2-(2-Quinolyl)-1,3-indandione. See CI 47000; D&C Yellow No. 11

Racemic menthol. See Menthol
Racemic pantothenyl alcohol. See DL-Panthenol
Rapeseed. See Canola oil

Rapeseed oil
CAS 8002-13-9; EINECS 232-299-0
Synonyms: Brassica campestris oil; Colza oil; Canola oil (low erucic acid rapeseed oil)
Definition: Vegetable oil expressed from seeds of Brassica campestris
Properties: Brn. viscous liq., yel. when refined, noxious odor; sol. in chloroform, ether, CS_2; dens. 0.913-0.916; m.p. 17-22 C; solidifies at 0 C; flash pt. 325 F; iodine no. 97-105; sapon. no. 170-177 C; ref. index 1.4720-1.4752
Precaution: Subject to spontaneous heating
Toxicology: Toxic-allergic potential; can cause acne-like skin eruptions
Uses: Excipient used in orals
Regulatory: FDA 21CFR §175.105, 176.210, 177.1200, 177.2800, 184.1555; Japan approved (extract); FDA approved for orals; BP compliance
Manuf./Distrib.: ABITEC; Arista Industries; Climax Performance; Penta Mfg.; Reilly-Whiteman; Werner G. Smith; Witco/Oleo-Surf.
Manuf./Distrib. (pharm. & food): Arista Industries; Penta Mfg.
See also Canola oil

Raspberry ketone. See 4-(p-Hydroxyphenyl)-2-butanone
Raw linseed oil. See Linseed oil
(R)-2,3-Dihydroxybutanedioic acid diethyl ester. See Diethyl tartrate
Red dye No. 2. See Amaranth

Red iron oxide

Red iron oxide. *See* Ferric oxide
Red iron trioxide. *See* Ferric oxide
Red oil. *See* Oleic acid
Red pepper. *See* Capsicum
Red precipitate. *See* Mercury oxide (ic), red and yellow
Red sage. *See* Sage
Red thyme oil. *See* Thyme oil
Resin. *See* Rosin
Resin tolu. *See* Balsam tolu
Resorcin. *See* Resorcinol

Resorcinol
CAS 108-46-3; EINECS 203-585-2
FEMA 3589
Synonyms: 1,3-Benzenediol; m-Dihydroxybenzene; Resorcin
Classification: Phenol
Empirical: $C_6H_6O_2$
Formula: $C_6H_4(OH)_2$
Properties: White crystals, unpleasant sweet taste; very sol. in alcohol, ether, glycerol; sl. sol. in chloroform; sol. in water; m.w. 110.12; dens. 1.285 (15 C); m.p. 110 C; b.p. 280.5 C; flash pt. (CC) 261 F
Precaution: Protect from light
Toxicology: TLV:TWA 10 ppm; moderately toxic by skin contact and intravenous route; poison by ingestion; skin and severe eye irritant
Uses: Flavoring agent; antimicrobial in vaginal creams
Regulatory: FDA 21CFR §177.1210; FEMA GRAS
Manuf./Distrib.: Allchem Ind.; J.T. Baker; Cardolite; Fairmount; R.W. Greeff; Hoechst Celanese; Indspec; Janssen Chimica; Napp Tech.; Penta Mfg.; Richman
Manuf./Distrib. (pharm. & food): Aldrich

Resorcinol dimethyl ether. *See* m-Dimethoxybenzene
Resorcinolphthalein. *See* Fluorescein
Retinol, hexadecanoate. *See* Retinyl palmitate

Retinyl palmitate
CAS 79-81-2; EINECS 201-228-5
Synonyms: Retinol, hexadecanoate; Vitamin A palmitate
Definition: Ester of retinol and palmitic acid
Empirical: $C_{36}H_{60}O_2$
Properties: Amorphous or cryst.; m.w. 524.88; m.p. 28-29 C
Toxicology: LD50 (oral, rat, 10 day) 7910 mg/kg; mildly toxic by ingestion; heated to dec., emits acrid smoke and irritating fumes
Uses: Antikeratinizing agent, moisturizer for skin and after-sun care prods.; in gelatin capsules, multivitamins
Regulatory: FDA 21CFR §182.5936, 184.1930, GRAS
Trade names: Vitamin A Palmitate Type PIMO/BH No. 638280100; Vitamin A Palmitate USP, FCC Type P1.7/E No. 63699; Vitamin A Palmitate USP, FCC Type P1.7 No. 262090000
Trade names containing: Dry Vitamin A Palmitate Type 250-SD No. 65378; Palmabeads® Type 500 No. 65332; Palma-Sperse® Type 250-S No. 65322; Palma-Sperse® Type 250A/50 D-S No. 65221; Vitamin A Palmitate Type 250-CWS No. 65312; Vitamin A Palmitate USP, FCC Type P1.7/BHT No. 63693

Rhamnose
CAS 3615-41-6
FEMA 3730
Synonyms: 6-Deoxy-L-mannose; L-Rhamnose; L-Mannomethylose; Isodulcit
Empirical: $C_6H_{12}O_5$
Properties: Wh. cryst.; sol. in water, methanol; m.w. 164.16; m.p. 82-92 C
Uses: Synthetic sweetener
Regulatory: FEMA GRAS; Japan approved; BP compliance
Manuf./Distrib.: Penta Mfg.; Pfanstiehl Labs; U.S. Biochemical
Manuf./Distrib. (pharm. & food): Penta Mfg.

L-Rhamnose. *See* Rhamnose
Rhamnus purshiana extract. *See* Cascara extract
Rhodamine B. *See* D&C Red No. 19
Rhodamine B stearate. *See* D&C Red No. 37
Rhodinal. *See* Citronellal

Rhodinyl butyrate
FEMA 2982
Synonyms: Citronellyl butyrate
Empirical: $C_{14}H_{26}O_2$
Properties: Colorless to ylsh. or greenish liq., fruity sweet odor; m.w. 226.36; b.p. 137 C (13 mm); flash pt. > 100 C; ref. index 1.451-1.455
Uses: Synthetic flavoring agent
Regulatory: FDA 21CFR §172.515; FEMA GRAS

Rhus succedanea wax. *See* Japan wax

Riboflavin
CAS 83-88-5; EINECS 201-507-1
Synonyms: Vitamin B_2; 6,7-Dimethyl-9-d-ribitylisoalloxazine; 7,8-Dimethyl-10-(d-ribityl) isoalloxazine; Flavaxin; Lactoflavin; Vitamin G
Classification: Organic compd.
Empirical: $C_{17}H_{20}N_4O_6$
Properties: Orange to yel. cryst., sl. odor, bitter taste; sl. sol. in water, alcohol; insol. in ether, chloroform; m.w. 376.41; m.p. 282 C (dec.)
Toxicology: LD50 (IP, rat) 560 mg/kg; poison by intravenous route; moderately toxic by intraperitoneal and subcutaneous routes; mutagenic adata; heated to decomp., emits fumes of NO_x
Uses: Dietary supplement; colorant; used in emollients, for building and maintaining healthy human tissue; protects eyes from sensitivity to light
Regulatory: FDA 21CFR §73.450, 136.115, 137, 139, 182.5695, 184.1695, GRAS; Europe listed; UK, Japan approved; BP, Ph.Eur. compliance
Manuf./Distrib.: Am. Biorganics; BASF; Bio-Rad Labs; EM Industries; Hoffmann-La Roche; Honeywill & Stein Ltd; Takeda USA
Manuf./Distrib. (pharm. & food): ADM; Aldrich; Am. Roland; Browne & Dureau Int'l.; Crompton & Knowles; CSR Food Ingreds.; Food Additives & Ingreds.; Forum; R.W. Greeff; Hoffmann-La Roche; LaMonde; E Merck; Penta Mfg.; Produits Roche; Roche; Ruger; Scanchem; SCI; Spectrum Chem. Mfg.; Takeda Europe
Trade names: Riboflavin USP, FCC 184045; Riboflavin USP, FCC No. 602940002; Riboflavin USP, FCC Type S
Trade names containing: Descote® Riboflavin $33^1/_3$%; Descote® Thiamine Mononitrate $33^1/_3$%; Rocoat® Riboflavin 25% No. 60289; Rocoat® Riboflavin $33^1/_3$ No. 60288; Unipertan P-24; Unipertan P-2002; Unipertan VEG 24

Riboflavin 5´-monophosphate sodium salt dihydrate. *See* Riboflavin-5´-phosphate sodium
Riboflavin 5´-phosphate ester monosodium salt. *See* Riboflavin-5´-phosphate sodium

Riboflavin-5´-phosphate sodium
CAS 130-40-5; EINECS 204-988-6
Synonyms: Riboflavin 5´-monophosphate sodium salt dihydrate; Riboflavin sodium phosphate; Vitamin B_2 phosphate sodium; Riboflavin 5´-phosphate ester monosodium salt
Formula: $C_{17}H_{20}N_4O_9PNa \cdot 2H_2O$
Properties: Yel. to orange-yel. cryst. powd., sl. odor; hygroscopic; sol. in water; m.w. 514.36
Precaution: Decomposed by light when in sol'n.
Toxicology: Heated to decomp., emits toxic fumes of NO_x and NaO_2
Uses: Dietary supplement; enzyme cofactor vitamin
Regulatory: FDA 21CFR §182.5697, 184.1697, GRAS; Europe listed; UK, Japan approved; BP, Ph.Eur. compliance
Manuf./Distrib.: Spectrum Chem. Mfg.
Manuf./Distrib. (pharm. & food): Spectrum Chem. Mfg.
Trade names: Riboflavin-5´-Phosphate Sodium USP, FCC No. 60296

Riboflavin sodium phosphate. *See* Riboflavin-5´-phosphate sodium

Rice bran oil
CAS 68553-81-1; 84696-37-7; EINECS 271-397-8
Synonyms: Oils, rice bran; Rice oil
Definition: Oil expressed from rice bran
Properties: Golden yel. oil; misc. with hexane and other fat solvs.; dens. 0.916-0.921; cloud pt. < -7 C; acid no. < 0.1; iodine no. 92-115; sapon. no. 181-189; ref. index 1.470-1.473
Uses: Solvent for ointments; edible oil suitable for pharmaceuticals
Regulatory: FDA 21CFR §175.105, 176.200, 176.210, 177.2260, 177.2800
Manuf./Distrib.: Arista Industries; Tri-K

Rice oil

Manuf./Distrib. (pharm. & food): Arista Industries
Trade names: EmCon Rice Bran

Rice oil. *See* Rice bran oil

Rice starch
CAS 9005-25-8
Definition: Finely pulverized grains of the rice plant
Formula: $(C_6H_{10}O_5)_n$
Toxicology: May cause mechanical irritation by blocking pores and putrefying; may cause allergic reaction
Uses: Demulcent and emollient forming a soothing and protective film when applied
Regulatory: BP compliance
Manuf./Distrib.: Spectrum Chem. Mfg.
Manuf./Distrib. (pharm. & food): Ruger

Ricini oleum. *See* Castor oil

Ricinoleic acid
CAS 141-22-0; EINECS 205-470-2
Synonyms: 12-Hydroxy-9-octadecenoic acid; 9-Octadecenoic acid, 12-hydroxy-; d-12-Hydroxyoleic acid
Classification: Unsaturated fatty acid
Empirical: $C_{18}H_{34}O_3$
Formula: $CH_3(CH_2)_5CH(OH)CH_2CH=CH(CH_2)_7COOH$
Properties: Liq.; sol. in alcohol, acetone, ether, chloroform; m.w. 298.45; dens. 0.940 (27.4/4 C); m.p. 5.5 C; b.p. 245 C (10 mm); ref. index 1.4716 (20 C)
Uses: Ingred. in vaginal jellies to maintain or restore normal vaginal acidity
Manuf./Distrib.: CasChem

Ricinus oil. *See* Castor oil
(R)-4-Isopropenyl-1-methyl-1-cyclohexene. *See* d-Limonene
(R)-2-Isopropylidene-5-methylcyclohexanone. *See* Pulegone
R(+)-Limonene. *See* d-Limonene
R-(+)-p-menth-4(8)-en-3-one. *See* Pulegone
Robane. *See* Squalane
Rochelle salt. *See* Potassium sodium tartrate anhyd.; Potassium sodium tartrate tetrahydrate
Rock salt. *See* Sodium chloride
Rose geranium oil Algerian. *See* Geranium oil

Rosemary oil
CAS 8000-25-7
FEMA 2992
Definition: Volatile oil obtained from flowering tops of *Rosmarinus officinalis*
Properties: Colorless to pale yel. liq., rosemary odor, camphoraceous taste; sol. in 10 vols 80% alcohol; pract. insol. in water; dens. 0.894-0.912 (25/25 C); ref. index 1.464-1.476 (20 C)
Precaution: Keep cool, well closed; protect from light
Toxicology: LD50 (oral, rat) 5000 mg/kg; mildly toxic by ingestion; skin irritant; heated to decomp., emits acrid smoke and irritating fumes
Uses: Natural flavoring agent, carminative; in perfumery, liniments
Regulatory: FDA 21CFR §182.10, 182.20, GRAS; 27CFR 21.151; FEMA GRAS; Japan approved (rosemary); Europe listed, no restrictions
Manuf./Distrib. (pharm. & food): Chart; Pierre Chauvet; Florida Treatt

Rose oil
CAS 8001-01-0; 8007-01-0; 84603-93-0
FEMA 2989
Synonyms: Otto of rose; Bulgarian rose oil; Essence of rose; Attar of rose
Definition: Volatile oil obtained from the flowers of *Rosa spp.*, contg. geraniol, citronellol
Properties: Colorless to pale yel. visc. liq., char. rose odor and taste; congeals @ 18-22 C to a translucent cryst. mass; sol. in fatty oils, chloroform; sparingly sol. in alcohol; very sl. sol. in water; dens. 0.848-0.863 (30/15 C); ref. index 1.457-1.463 (30 C)
Precaution: Keep cool, well closed; protect from light
Toxicology: Sensitizer
Uses: Natural flavoring for pharmaceuticals; used in lozenges, dental and topical formulations, commonly in the form of rose water
Regulatory: FDA 21CFR §182.20, GRAS; FEMA GRAS; Europe listed, no restrictions; USP/NF compliance
Manuf./Distrib. (pharm. & food): C.A.L.-Pfizer; Pierre Chauvet; Florida Treatt; Integra; Spectrum Chem. Mfg.

Rose water
FEMA 2993
Definition: Saturated aq. sol'n. of the odoriferous principles of flowers or *Rosa centifloia*
Uses: Natural flavoring agent for pharmaceuticals; ointment base
Regulatory: FDA 21CFR §182.20, GRAS; FEMA GRAS; USP/NF compliance
Manuf./Distrib.: Spectrum Chem. Mfg.

Rosin
CAS 8050-09-7; 8052-10-6; EINECS 232-475-7
Synonyms: Colophony; Colophane; Colophonium; Gum rosin; Yellow pine rosin; Rosin gum; Resin
Definition: Residue from distilling off the volatile oil from the oleoresin obtained from *Pinus palustris* and other species of *Pinaceae*
Properties: Pale yel. to amber translucent, sl. turpentine odor and taste; insol. in water; sol. in alcohol, benzene, ether, glacial acetic acid, oils, carbon disulfide; dens. 1.07-1.09; m.p. 100-150 C; flash pt. 187 C
Precaution: Combustible
Toxicology: May cause contact dermatitis
Uses: Stiffening agent; used in coated and sustained-action tablets, orals, ointments
Regulatory: FDA 21CFR §73.1, 172.210, 172.510, 172.615, 175.105, 175.125, 175.300, 176.170, 176.200, 176.210, 177.1200, 177.1210, 177.2600, 178.3120, 178.3800, 178.3870; Japan approved; FDA approved for orals
Manuf./Distrib.: Akzo; Arakawa; Arizona; Browning; Chemcentral; Cytec; Focus; Georgia-Pacific; Hercules BV; Meer; Natrochem; Punda Mercantile; Spectrum Chem. Mfg.; Veitsiluoto Oy; Westvaco
Manuf./Distrib. (pharm. & food): Meer

Rosin gum. *See* Rosin
RRR-γ-Tocopherol. *See* (+)-γ-Tocopherol
Rusco extract. *See* Butcherbroom extract
Ruscus aculeatus extract. *See* Butcherbroom extract

Saccharin
CAS 81-07-2; EINECS 201-321-0; 220-120-9
Synonyms: Saccharin insoluble; o-Benzoic acid sulfimide; 3-Oxo-2,3-dihydro-1,2-benzisothiazole-1,1-diox-ide; 1,2-Benzisothiazolin-3-one 1,1-dioxide; 2 3-Dihydroxy-1,2-benzothiazolin-3-one-1,1-dioxide; o-Sulfobenzimide; Saccharin acid form
Classification: Organic compd.; o-toluene sulfonamide
Definition: Sodium salt of orthosulfobenzimide; artificial sweetener, 300 times as sweet as natural sugar
Empirical: $C_7H_5NO_3S$
Properties: Wh. cryst., odorless, bitter metallic aftertaste; sol. in boiling water, alcohol, benzene, amyl acetate, ethyl acetate; sl. sol. in water, ether, chloroform; m.w. 183.18; dens. 0.828; m.p. 226-230 C
Toxicology: May cause allergic reactions incl. urticaria, nausea, vomiting, diarrhea; has been linked to bladder cancer in test animals; not considered human carcinogen by recent findings
Uses: Noncaloric sweetener, pharmaceutic aid; used in inhalants, orals, rectals, topicals
Usage level: 1 g/day for 150 lb person
Regulatory: FDA 21CFR §145.116, 145.126, 145.131, 145.136, 145.171, 145.181, 150.141, 150.161, 180.37; FEMA GRAS; Japan approved (0.05 g/kg max. in chewing gum); FDA approved for inhalants, orals, rectals, topicals; USP/NF, BP compliance
Manuf./Distrib.: Aldrich; Aisan Chem Co Ltd; R.W. Greeff; Maruzen Fine Chem.; PMC Specialties; Rit-Chem; Spice King
Manuf./Distrib. (pharm. & food): Atomergic Chemetals; Boots; Cornelius; Ellis & Everard; K&K Greeff; R.W. Greeff; Hays; Hilton Davis; Integra; Int'l. Sourcing; Jungbunzlauer; Maruzen; Penta Mfg.; PMC Specialties; Quimdis; Rit-Chem; Ruger; Scanchem; Spectrum Chem. Mfg.; Spice King
Trade names: Syncal® SDI; Unisweet SAC

Saccharin acid form. *See* Saccharin
Saccharin calcium. *See* Calcium saccharin
Saccharine soluble. *See* Saccharin sodium
Saccharin insoluble. *See* Saccharin

Saccharin sodium
CAS 128-44-9 (anhyd.); 6155-57-3 (dihydrate); EINECS 204-886-1
FEMA 2997
Synonyms: Saccharin soluble; Saccharine soluble; Sodium saccharide; Sodium saccharin; 1,1-Dioxide-1,2-

benzisothiazol-3(2H)-one sodium salt; Sodium 2,3-dihydro-1,2-benzisothiazolin-3-one-1,1-dioxide; Sodium o-benzosulfimide; Sodium benzosulfimide

Classification: Organic compd.

Definition: Sodium salt of saccharin

Empirical: $C_7H_4NO_3S \cdot Na$ or $C_7H_4NNaO_3S \cdot 2H_2O$

Properties: Wh. cryst. or cryst. powd., odorless or faint aromatic odor, very sweet taste; very sol. in water, sl. sol. in alcohol; m.w. 205.17 (anhyd.), 241.20 (dihydrate)

Toxicology: LD50 (oral, rat) 14,200 mg/kg; mod. toxic by ingestion and IP routes; experimental carcinogen, neoplastigen, tumorigen, teratogen, reproductive effects; human mutagenic data; heated to decomp., emits very toxic fumes of SO_x, Na_2O, and NO_x

Uses: Sweetener; used in buccals, dentals, parenterals, inhalants, orals, rectals

Regulatory: FDA 21CFR §145.126, 145.131, 145.136, 145.171, 145.181, 150.141, 150.161, 180.37, GRAS; USDA 9CFR §318.7; FEMA GRAS; Japan approved (0.1-2 g/kg residual); FDA approved for buccals, dentals, parenterals, inhalants, orals, rectals; USP/NF, BP, Ph.Eur. compliance

Manuf./Distrib. (pharm. & food): Aldrich; Boots; R.W. Greeff; Int'l. Sourcing; Jungbunzlauer; Spectrum Chem. Mfg.

Trade names: Syncal® GS; Syncal® GSD; Syncal® S; Syncal® SDS; Syncal® US; Unisweet SOSAC

Saccharin soluble. *See* Saccharin sodium

Saccharose. *See* Sucrose

Saccharose distearate. *See* Sucrose distearate

Saccharose mono/distearate. *See* Sucrose polystearate

Saccharose palmitate. *See* Sucrose palmitate

Saccharum lactis. *See* Lactose

Safflower oil

CAS 8001-23-8; EINECS 232-276-5

Synonyms: Carthanus tinctorious oil

Definition: Oily liq. obtained from seeds of *Carthanus tinctorius* consisting principally of triglycerides of linoleic acid

Properties: Lt. yel. oil; sol. in oil and fat solvs.; insol. in water; misc. with ether, chloroform; dens. 0.9211-0.9215 (25/25 C); iodine no. 135-150; sapon. no. 188-194; ref. index 1.472-1.475

Precaution: Light-sensitive; becomes rancid on exposure to air

Toxicology: Human skin irritant; ingestion in large volumes produces vomiting; heated to decomp., emits acrid smoke and irritating fumes

Uses: Emollient, oleaginous vehicle for creams, lotions, oral and topical pharmaceuticals; laxative, diaphoretic

Regulatory: FDA 21CFR §175.105, 175.300, 176.200, 176.210, GRAS; Japan approved (safflower); USP/NF compliance

Manuf./Distrib.: ABITEC; Arista Industries; Calgene; Croda; Lipo; Tri-K

Manuf./Distrib. (pharm. & food): Anglia; Arista Industries; Croda; Lipo; Ruger; Spectrum Chem. Mfg.

Trade names: Neobee® 18; Super Refined® Safflower Oil

Trade names containing: Phosal® 50 SA; Phosal® 75 SA

Safflower oil, hybrid. *See* Hybrid safflower oil

Sage

FEMA 3000

Synonyms: Salvia; Garden sage; Red sage

Definition: Salvia officinalis

Properties: Warm spicy odor, flavor

Toxicology: No known toxicity

Uses: Natural flavoring agent, aromatic, astringent; in gargles for throat, tonsils, for ulceration of mouth and throat

Regulatory: FDA 21CFR §182.10, 182.20, GRAS; FEMA GRAS; Japan approved

Manuf./Distrib. (pharm. & food): Bio-Botanica; C.A.L.-Pfizer; Chart

SAIB. *See* Sucrose acetate isobutyrate

Saigon cinnamon. *See* Cinnamon oil

Sal chalybis. *See* Ferrous sulfate

Sal ethyl. *See* Ethyl salicylate

Salicylaldehyde methyl ether. *See* o-Methoxybenzaldehyde

Salicylic acid

CAS 69-72-7; EINECS 200-712-3

Synonyms: 2-Hydroxybenzoic acid; o-Hydroxybenzoic acid

Classification: Aromatic acid

Empirical: $C_7H_6O_3$
Formula: HOC_6H_4COOH
Properties: Wh. cryst. or cryst. powd., sweetish to acrid taste; sol. in alcohol, ether; sl. sol. in water, benzene, chloroform; m.w. 138.12; dens. 1.443 (20/4 C); m.p. 157-159 C; b.p. 211 C (20 mm) sublimes at 76 C; stable in air
Precaution: Light- and moisture-sensitive
Toxicology: LD50 (oral, rat) 891 mg/kg, (IV, mouse) 500 mg/kg; poison by ing., IV, IP routes; mod. toxic by subcutaneous route; skin/severe eye irritant; experimental teratogen, reproductive effects; mutagenic data; heated to decomp., emits acrid smoke
Uses: Preservative; mfg. of methyl salicylate; topical keratolytic agent; OTC drug active ingred.; antiseptic in oral rinse prods.; with resorcinol for acne prods.
Regulatory: FDA 21CFR §175.105, 175.300, 177.2600, 556.590; BP, Ph.Eur. compliance
Manuf./Distrib.: Allchem Ind.; EM Ind.; Hilton Davis; Great Western; R.W. Greeff; Janssen Chimica; Mitsui Toatsu; PMC Specialties; Rhone-Poulenc Santé SA
Manuf./Distrib. (pharm. & food): Aldrich; Allchem Industries; R.W. Greeff; Hilton Davis; Integra; PMC Specialties; Ruger; Spectrum Chem. Mfg.

Salicylic acid sodium salt. *See* Sodium salicylate
Salicylic ether. *See* Ethyl salicylate
Salicylic ethyl ester. *See* Ethyl salicylate
Salmine sulfate. *See* Protamine sulfate
Salol. *See* Phenyl salicylate
Salt. *See* Sodium chloride
Sal tartar. *See* Sodium tartrate
Salt cake. *See* Sodium sulfate
Salt of tartar. *See* Potassium carbonate
Salt of tin. *See* Stannous pyrophosphate
Salvia. *See* Sage

Sambucus oil
CAS 68916-55-2
Definition: Volatile oil obtained from *Sambucus nigra* and other species of *Sambucus*
Uses: Natural flavoring agent; used in skin and eye lotions; mild astringent used in salves to treat burns, rashes, minor skin ailments
Regulatory: FDA 21CFR §172.510, 182.20

Sandalwood oil
CAS 8006-87-9
FEMA 3005
Synonyms: Santalum album oil; Santal oil; Arheol; East Indian sandalwood oil
Definition: Volatile oil obtained from heartwood of *Santalum album*
Properties: Pale yel. liq., char. sandalwood odor and taste; sol. in 5 vols 70% alcohol; very sl. sol. in water; dens. 0.965-0.980 (25/25 C); ref. index 1.500-1.510 (20 C)
Precaution: Keep cool, well closed; protect from light
Toxicology: Sensitizer
Uses: Natural flavoring agent for pharmaceuticals
Regulatory: FDA 21CFR §172.510; FEMA GRAS
Manuf./Distrib. (pharm. & food): Chart; Pierre Chauvet; Florida Treatt

Santal oil. *See* Sandalwood oil
Santalum album oil. *See* Sandalwood oil

Sarcosine
CAS 107-97-1; EINECS 203-538-6
Synonyms: N-Methylglycine; Methyl glycocoll; Methylaminoacetic acid
Empirical: $C_3H_7NO_2$
Formula: CH_3NHCH_2COOH
Properties: Cryst., sweet taste; deliq.; hygroscopic; sol. in water; m.w. 89.09; m.p. 208 C (dec.)
Precaution: Combustible
Toxicology: No known toxicity
Uses: Synthesis of foaming antienzyme compds. for pharmaceuticals
Manuf./Distrib.: BASF; Hampshire; Schweizerhall; SWS Oilchemicals BV
Manuf./Distrib. (pharm. & food): Aldrich

Sarsaparilla
Synonyms: Sarsaparilla root

Sarsaparilla root

Definition: Dried root of *Smilax* spp.
Uses: Vehicle and flavoring agent for medicaments; in herbal and homeopathic preps.; usually as decoction or extract
Regulatory: JP compliance (S. glabra)

Sarsaparilla root. See Sarsaparilla
Schardinger α-dextrin. See Cyclodextrin
Schardinger β-dextrin. See β-Cyclodextrin

SD alcohol 3A

Definition: Ethyl alcohol denatured with methyl alcohol
Uses: Solv. used in coating systems for pharmaceutical tablets
Regulatory: FDA 27CFR §20.11, 21.35

SD alcohol 40

Definition: Ethyl alcohol denatured with brucine (alkaloid), brucine sulfate, or quassin, and t-butyl alcohol, etc.
Uses: Thickener, solidifier, liquefier
Regulatory: FDA 27CFR §20.11, 21.74

SD alcohol 40-B

Definition: Ethyl alcohol denatured with denatonium benzoate and t-butyl alcohol
Uses: Thickener, solidifier, liquefier
Regulatory: FDA 27CFR §20.11, 21.76

SDBS. See Sodium dodecylbenzenesulfonate
SDS. See Sodium lauryl sulfate
9,10-seco(5Z,7E)-5,7,10(19)-Cholestatrien-3-ol. See Cholecalciferol
Secondary ammonium phosphate. See Ammonium phosphate, dibasic
Seignette salt. See Potassium sodium tartrate anhyd.; Potassium sodium tartrate tetrahydrate

Senna extract

CAS 85085-71-8
Definition: Extract of leaves of *Cassia obovata*
Uses: Natural flavoring; cathartic, laxative; stimulant in laxative prods.
Regulatory: FDA 21CFR §172.510; BP compliance
Manuf./Distrib.: Bio-Botanica
Manuf./Distrib. (pharm. & food): Chart

L-Serine

CAS 56-45-1; EINECS 200-274-3
Synonyms: 2-Amino-3-hydroxypropionic acid
Classification: Amino acid
Empirical: $C_3H_7NO_3$
Formula: $HOCH_2CH(NH_2)COOH$
Properties: Wh. cryst. or cryst. powd., odorless, sweet taste; sol. in water; insol. in alcohol, ether; m.w. 105.10; m.p. 228 C (dec.)
Uses: Dietary supplement
Regulatory: FDA 21CFR §172.320, 8.4% max.; Japan approved; BP compliance
Manuf./Distrib.: Degussa; Janssen Chimica; Mitsui Toatsu Chem.; Nippon Rikagakuyakuhin; U.S. Biochemical
Manuf./Distrib. (pharm. & food): Degussa; R.W. Greeff; Nippon Rikagakuyakuhin; Spectrum Chem. Mfg.

Serpentaria extract

CAS 84775-44-0; EINECS 283-873-2
Synonyms: Birthwort extract; Aritolochia extract; Snakeroot; Snakeweed
Definition: Extract of rhizomes of *Aristolochia clematitis*
Properties: Yel. rods turn red on drying
Toxicology: No known toxicity when applied to the skin; can affect heart and blood pressure when ingested
Uses: Natural flavoring
Regulatory: FDA 21CFR §172.510

Sesame oil

CAS 8008-74-0; EINECS 232-370-6
Synonyms: Gingilli oil; Gingelly oil; Teel oil; Sesame seed oil; Benne oil
Definition: Refined fixed oil obtained from the seeds of *Sesamum indicum*
Properties: Bland ylsh. oily liq., pract. odorless, bland taste; sl. sol. in alcohol; misc. with ether, chloroform, hexane, carbon disulfide; dens. 0.916-0.921; iodine no. 103-116; sapon. no. 188-195; flash pt. 491 F; ref. index 1.4575-1.4598 (60 C)

Precaution: Light-sensitive
Toxicology: Poison by intravenous route; human skin irritant; may cause allergic reactions, primarily contact dermatitis
Uses: Solvent, oleaginous vehicle, lubricant, emollient; keratin softener for dry skin prods.; used in parenteral, oral, and topical pharmaceuticals; in liniments, plasters, ointments, soaps; as solv. for steroids
Regulatory: FDA 21CFR §175.105, 175.300, 176.200, 176.210; FDA approved for parenterals, orals, topicals; USP/NF, BP, Ph.Eur., JP compliance
Manuf./Distrib.: Arista Industries; Tri-K
Manuf./Distrib. (pharm. & food): Anglia; Arista Industries; Ruger; Spectrum Chem. Mfg.; Vitamins Inc.
Trade names: Lipovol SES; Sesame Oil USP/NF 16; Super Refined® Sesame Oil
Trade names containing: Lipovol SES-S

Sesame seed oil. *See* Sesame oil

Shark liver oil
CAS 68990-63-6; EINECS 273-616-2
Definition: Oil expressed from fresh livers of sharks and other *Elasmobranchii* species
Properties: Yel.-red-brown liq., strong odor; sol. in ether, chloroform, benzene, carbon disulfide; dens. 0.917-0.928; iodine no. 125-155; sapon. no. 170-187; ref. index 1.4784 (20 C); sapon. no. 140-146
Uses: Skin protectant; used for topical hemorrhoidal preps.
Regulatory: FDA CFR §175.105, 176.210, 177.2800
Manuf./Distrib.: Arista Industries
Manuf./Distrib. (pharm. & food): Am. Roland; Arista Industries
Trade names: Super Refined® Shark Liver Oil

Shea butter
CAS 68424-60-2; 977026-99-5
Definition: Natural fat obtained from fruit of the Karite tree, *Butyrospermum parkii*
Properties: Iodine no. 53-65; sapon. no.178-190
Uses: Emollient, consistency agent, lubricant, moisturizer, vehicle/carrier, visc. modifier, skin protectant oil; for coating, dermatologicals, suppositories
Manuf./Distrib.: ABITEC
Trade names: Akoext SB; Cetiol® SB45; Kelisema Natural Pure Shea Butter; Lipex 102; Lipex 202

Shea butter extract
CAS 68424-59-9
Definition: Extract of shea butter
Uses: Emollient, spreading agent for suntan preps., ointments, suppositories
Trade names: Fancol Karite Extract
Trade names containing: Fancol VB

Shellac
CAS 9000-59-3; EINECS 232-549-9
Synonyms: White shellac; Bleached shellac; Button lac; Lacca
Classification: Fatty acid
Definition: Waxy amorphous protein which is the resinous secretion of the insect *Laccifer (Tachardia) lacca*
Properties: Off-wh. amorphous gran. solid, very little odor; slowly sol. in alcohol; sl. sol. in acetone, ether, benzene, petrol. ether; insol. in water; acid no. 73-89 (reg.), 75-91 (refined)
Toxicology: Nonallergenic; may cause contact dermatitis; heated to decomp., emits acrid smoke and irritating fumes
Uses: Enteric coating agent for slow-release tablets; used in solid oral dosage forms, microencapsulation preps., dental impression compds.; improves tablet stability
Regulatory: FDA 21CFR §73.1, 175.105, 175.300, 175.380, 175.390, 182.99; 27CFR §21.126, 212.61, 212.90; 40CFR §180.1001; Japan approved; Europe listed; UK approved; FDA approved for orals; USP/NF compliance; JP compliance (purified shellac and white shellac)
Manuf./Distrib.: Mantrose-Haeuser; Punda Mercantile
Manuf./Distrib. (pharm. & food): Classic Flavors; H E Daniel; Deutsche Nichimen; Ikeda; Mantrose-Haeuser; Roeper; Ruger; Thew Arnott; Wm. Vinsser; Alfred L Wolff; E H Worlee GmbH
Trade names containing: Opaglos®

SHMP. *See* Sodium hexametaphosphate

Shorea butter
Definition: Natural fat obtained from *Shorea stenoptera*
Uses: Natural oil for pharmaceutical formulations
Trade names: Lipex 106

Siam benzoin. *See* Gum benzoin
Siberian fir oil. *See* Pine needle oil

Silica
CAS 7631-86-9 (colloidal); 112945-52-5 (fumed); 60676-86-0; EINECS 231-545-4
Synonyms: Silicon dioxide, fumed; Colloidal silicon dioxide; Silicon dioxide; Fumed silica; Silicic anhydride
Classification: Inorganic oxide
Definition: Occurs in nature as agate, amethyst, chalcedony, cristobalite, flint, quartz, sand, tridymite
Empirical: O_2Si
Formula: SiO_2
Properties: Transparent crystals or amorphous very fine powd.; hygroscopic; pract. insol. in water, alc., and acids except hydrofluoric; m.w. 60.09; dens. 2.2 (amorphous), 2.65 (quartz, 0 C); lowest coeff. of heat expansion; melts to a glass; pH 3.5-4.4
Toxicology: LD50 (oral, rat) 3160 mg/kg; poison by intraperitoneal, intravenous, intratracheal routes; moderately toxic by ingestion; prolonged inhalation of dust can cause silicosis
Uses: Suspending and/or visc.-increasing agent; glidant, anticaking agent, thickener, tablet binder/disintegrant, oil adsorbent, stabilizer; carrier in water-sol. drugs; abrasive in dentifrices; used in orals, rectals, vaginals
Regulatory: FDA 21CFR §73.1, 172.230, 172.480 (limitation 2%), 173.340, 175.105, 175.300, 176.200, 176.210, 177.1200, 177.1460, 177.2420, 177.2600, 182.90, 182.1711, GRAS; USDA 9CFR §318.7; Japan approved (2% max. as anticaking), other restrictions; Europe listed; UK approved; FDA approved for orals, rectals, vaginals; USP/NF, BP, Ph.Eur. compliance
Manuf./Distrib.: Akzo Nobel; BYK-Chemie; Cabot Carbon Ltd; Catalysts & Chemicals Industries; Chisso Am.; Degussa; DuPont; Geltech; J.M. Huber; Nippon Silica Ind.; Nissan Chem. Ind.; PPG Industries; PQ; Spectrum Chem. Mfg.; Unimin
Manuf./Distrib. (pharm. & food): Aldrich; Cabot Carbon Ltd; Degussa; Nippon Aerosil Co. Ltd.
Trade names: Aerosil® 200; Aerosil® 300; Aerosil® 380; Aerosil® R812; Aerosil® R972; A.F.S.; Cab-O-Sil® EH-5; Cab-O-Sil® H-5; Cab-O-Sil® HS-5; Cab-O-Sil® L-90; Cab-O-Sil® LM-150; Cab-O-Sil® M-5; Cab-O-Sil® MS-55; Cab-O-Sil® PTG; Hi-Sil® T-600; Koraid PSM; Sident® 15; Sident® 22LS; Sident® 22S; Wacker HDK® H20; Wacker HDK® N20; Wacker HDK® V15
Trade names containing: Aerosil® COK 84; Cab-O-Sil® TS-530; Descote® Niacinamide $33^1/_3$%; Dry Phytonadione 1% SD No. 61748; Dry Vitamin A Palmitate Type 250-SD No. 65378; Dry Vitamin E Acetate 50% SD No. 65356; DSS Tablet Grade; Myvatex® TL; Niacinamide Free Flowing No. 69914; Rocoat® Niacinamide $33^1/_3$% No. 69907; Rocoat® Niacinamide $33^1/_3$% Type S No. 69909; Vitamin B_{12} 0.1% SD No. 65354; Vitamin B_{12} 1.0% SD No. 65305

Silica aerogel
CAS 7631-86-9; 112926-00-8 (silica gel)
Synonyms: Silica amorphous hydrated; Silica gel; Silicic acid
Definition: Fine powd. microcellular silica foam, 89.5% min. silica content
Empirical: O_2Si
Properties: M.w. 60.09
Toxicology: TLV:TWA 10 mg/m³; pure unaltered form considered nontoxic; some deposits are fibrogenic
Uses: Component for antifoaming agents used in buccals, dentals, orals
Regulatory: FDA 21CFR §182.1711, GRAS; BATF 27CFR §240.1051; FDA approved for buccals, dentals, orals; BP compliance

Silica amorphous hydrated. *See* Silica aerogel
Silica gel. *See* Silica aerogel; Silica, hydrated
Silica hydrate. *See* Silica, hydrated

Silica, hydrated
CAS 1343-98-2 (silicic acid); 112926-00-8; EINECS 215-683-2
Synonyms: Silicic acid; Silica hydrate; Silica gel; Precipitated silica
Classification: Inorganic oxide
Definition: Occurs in nature as opal
Formula: $SiO_2 \cdot xH_2O$, x varies with method of precipitation and extent of drying
Properties: White amorphous powd.; insol. in water or acids except hydrofluoric; m.w. 60.08 + water
Toxicology: Eye irritant; poison by intravenous route; TLV:TWA 10 mg/m³ (total dust)
Uses: Adsorbent in skin protectants; abrasive in dentifrices; carrier; filler; rheology control agent; free-flow aid; thickener
Regulatory: FDA 21CFR §73.1, 160.105, 160.185, 172.480, 173.340, 175.105, 175.300, 176.170, 176.180, 176.200, 176.210, 177.1200, 177.2420, 177.2600, 182.90, 573.940
Manuf./Distrib.: Crosfield; J.M. Huber; MEI (Magnesium Elektron); Osram Sylvania; PPG Ind.; PQ; Spectrum Chem. Mfg.

Trade names: FK 500LS; Sipernat® 22LS; Sipernat® 22S; Tixosil 311; Tixosil 321; Tixosil 331; Tixosil 333, 343; Tixosil 375; Tullanox HM-100; Tullanox HM-150; Tullanox HM-250

Siliceous earth. *See* Diatomaceous earth
Silicic acid. *See* Silica aerogel; Silica, hydrated
Silicic acid, calcium salt. *See* Calcium silicate
Silicic acid, magnesium salt (1:1). *See* Magnesium silicate
Silicic acid, magnesium salt (1:2). *See* Magnesium trisilicate
Silicic anhydride. *See* Silica

Silicon
CAS 7440-21-3; EINECS 231-130-8
UN No. 1346
Classification: Nonmetallic element
Empirical: Si
Precaution: DOT: Flamm. solid
Uses: Used in orals, topicals
Regulatory: FDA approved for orals, topicals
Manuf./Distrib.: Atomergic Chemetals; Cerac; Dow Corning; Eagle-Picher; Pechiney Electrométallurgie; Shin-Etsu Chem.; Spectrum Chem. Mfg.
Manuf./Distrib. (pharm. & food): Aldrich

Silicon dioxide. *See* Silica
Silicon dioxide, fumed. *See* Silica

Silicone
Synonyms: Organosiloxane
Classification: Siloxane polymers
Properties: Liq., semisolid, or solid; cis 1->1,000,000 cs; water repellant; sol. in most organic solvents
Precaution: Unhalogenated types combustible
Toxicology: Silicone-related diseases can occur, e.g., silicone-induced synovitis and lymphadenopathy, acute and chronic pneumonitis from 'bleeding' from ruptured bag-gel breast implants, pulmonary lesions, granulomatous reactions
Uses: Biomaterial for medicine (implants, prosthetic devices); defoamer
Manuf./Distrib.: Ashland; Bayer; Chemcentral; Crucible; Dow Corning; GE Silicones; Genesee Polymers; Goldschmidt; Harcros; Hüls Am.; D.N. Lukens; Reichhold; Rhone-Poulenc; Sandoz; Seegott; Shin-Etsu Chem.; Tego Chemie
Trade names: Foamkill® 830
See also Dimethicone; Cyclomethicone; Simethicone

Silicone emulsions
Classification: Organosiloxane
Toxicology: No known toxicity
Uses: Desiccant, water repellent, defoamer; film-former for tablets and microencapsulations; used in orals, topicals
Regulatory: FDA approved for orals, topicals; USP/NF compliance
Manuf./Distrib.: CNC Int'l.; Crucible; Dow Corning; Genesee Polymers; Great Western; Hüls Am.; OSi Spec.; Ross Chem.; Sandoz; Soluol; Wacker Silicones; Wacker-Chemie GmbH
Manuf./Distrib. (pharm. & food): Ruger
Trade names: Foam Blast 106; Foam Blast 150 Kosher; Foamkill® MS Conc.; Hodag Antifoam FD-62; Hodag Antifoam FD-82
See also Dimethicone; Cyclomethicone; Simethicone

Siloxanes and silicones, 3-[(2-aminoethyl amino]propyl, methyl, dimethyl, docosanoates. *See* Dimethicone propylethylenediamine behenate

Silver
CAS 7440-22-4; EINECS 231-131-3
Synonyms: Silver, colloidal; CI 77820
Classification: Metallic element
Empirical: Ag
Properties: Soft ductile malleable lustrous wh. metal; sol. in fused alkali hydroxides in presence of air, in fused alkali peroxides; not attacked by water or atmospheric oxygen; inert to most acids; at.wt. 107.868; dens. 10.50 (15 C); m.p. 961.93 C; b.p. 2212 C
Toxicology: TLV:TWA 0.1mg/m^3 (metal); nontoxic but prolonged absorption of compds. can cause grayish discoloration of skin (argyria); avoid inhalation of dust

Silver, colloidal

Uses: Antibacterial; used topically as the metal or as silver salts; ingred. in dental alloys
Regulatory: FDA 21CFR §73.2500
Manuf./Distrib.: Aldrich; Asarco; Cerac; Degussa; Handy & Harman; Mariovilla SpA
Manuf./Distrib. (pharm. & food): Degussa

Silver, colloidal. See Silver

Simethicone
CAS 8050-81-5
Synonyms: α-(Trimethylsilyl)-ω-methylpoly[oxy(dimethylsilylene)], mixt. with silicon dioxide
Definition: Mixture of dimethicone with an avg. chain length of 200-350 dimethylsiloxane units and silica gel
Formula: $(CH_3)_3SiO[Si(CH_3)_2O]_nSi(CH_3)_3$, n = 200-350
Properties: Hazy translucent visc. fluid; sol. in chloroform, ether; insol. in water and alcohol
Toxicology: No known toxicity
Uses: Coating agent used in orals, rectals, topicals, emulsions, oral suspensions, capsules; ointment base
    ingred.; antifoaming agent; water repelling agent; anti-flatulence oral dosages
Regulatory: Europe listed; UK approved; FDA approved for orals, rectals, topicals; USP/NF compliance
Manuf./Distrib.: PPG Ind.
Manuf./Distrib. (pharm. & food): Aldrich; Ruger
Trade names: Dow Corning® Q7-2243 LVA; Hodag Antifoam F-1; Mazu® DF 200SP; Wacker Silicone
    Antifoam Emulsion SE 9
Trade names containing: Dow Corning® Q7-2587; Dow Corning® Medical Antifoam AF Emulsion

Slaked lime. See Calcium hydroxide
SLS. See Sodium lauryl sulfate
SMO. See Sorbitan oleate
SMS. See Sorbitan stearate
Snakeroot. See Serpentaria extract
Snakeweed. See Serpentaria extract
(3-sn-Phosphatidyl)choline, soya, hydrogenated. See Hydrogenated lecithin
Soap clay. See Bentonite
Soda ash. See Sodium carbonate
Soda calcined. See Sodium carbonate

Soda lime
CAS 8006-28-8
Synonyms: Cal sodada; Calcaria absorbens; Calx sodica
Definition: Mixt. of calcium hydroxide and sodium and/or potassium hydroxide
Properties: Wh. or grayish wh. gran.; partly sol. in water; almost completely sol. in 1M acetic acid
Precaution: Incompat. with trichloroethylene which is decomposed by warm alkali to produce a toxic end prod.
Uses: Sorbent for carbon dioxide for pharmaceuticals, in closed-circuit anesthetic apparatus, determining
    basal metabolic rate
Regulatory: USP/NF, BP compliance
Manuf./Distrib. (pharm. & food): Aldrich

Soda lye. See Sodium hydroxide
Soda niter. See Sodium nitrate
Sodium acetate. See Sodium acetate anhydrous

Sodium acetate anhydrous
CAS 127-09-3; EINECS 204-823-8
FEMA 3024
Synonyms: Sodium acetate; Acetic acid sodium salt anhydrous
Classification: Aliphatic organic compd.
Empirical: $C_2H_3NaO_2$
Formula: CH_3COONa
Properties: Colorless to wh. cryst., gran. powd., or flakes, odorless or faint acetous odor, sl. bitter saline taste;
    hygroscopic; sol. in water, alcohol; m.w. 82.04; dens. 1.45; m.p. 58 C; pH 7.5-9.2 (3%)
Toxicology: LD50 (oral, rat) 3530 mg/kg; poison by IV route; mod. toxic by ingestion; skin and eye irritant;
    heated to decomp., emits toxic fumes of Na_2O
Uses: Buffering agent; used medicinally as alkalizer and as diuretic to reduce body water; used in parenterals,
    ophthalmics, orals, topicals, eyewashes
Regulatory: FDA 21CFR §173.310, 182.70, 184.1721, GRAS; FEMA GRAS; Japan approved; Europe listed;
    UK approved; FDA approved for parenterals, ophthalmics, orals, topicals; USP/NF, BP, Ph.Eur. compli-
    ance

Manuf./Distrib.: Aldrich; EM Industries; General Chem.; Heico; Honeywill & Stein Ltd; Lohmann; Lonza; Niacet; Verdugt BV
Manuf./Distrib. (pharm. & food): Daito Chem. Ind.; Int'l. Sourcing; Lohmann; Mallinckrodt; Spectrum Chem. Mfg.

Sodium acetate trihydrate
CAS 6131-90-4; EINECS 204-823-8
Synonyms: Acetic acid sodium salt trihydrate
Classification: Aliphatic organic compd.
Empirical: $C_2H_3NaO_2 \cdot 3H_2O$
Formula: $CH_3COONa \cdot 3H_2O$
Properties: M.w. 136.08; pH 7.5-9.2 (3%)
Uses: Buffering agent used in parenterals, orals
Regulatory: FDA 21CFR §184.1721, GRAS; FDA approved for parenterals, orals, injectabless
Manuf./Distrib. (pharm. & food): Daito Chem. Ind.; Lohmann; Ruger; Spectrum Chem. Mfg.

Sodium acetone bisulfite. *See* Acetone sodium bisulfite
Sodium acid phosphate. *See* Sodium phosphate
Sodium acid sulfate. *See* Sodium bisulfate
Sodium acid sulfite. *See* Sodium bisulfite
Sodium alginate. *See* Algin

Sodium alkyl sulfate
CAS 8036-54-2
Uses: Used in dentals, topicals
Regulatory: FDA approved for dentals, topicals

Sodium aluminosilicate. *See* Sodium silicoaluminate

Sodium aluminum chlorohydroxy lactate
CAS 8038-93-5
Definition: Sodium salt of a complex of lactic acid and aluminum chlorohydrate
Uses: Deodorant
Manuf./Distrib.: Reheis
Trade names: Chloracel® 40% Sol'n.; Chloracel® Solid

Sodium aluminum silicate. *See* Sodium silicoaluminate

Sodium aminobenzoate
CAS 555-06-6
Uses: Used in orals
Regulatory: FDA approved for orals

Sodium ascorbate
CAS 134-03-2; EINECS 205-126-1
Synonyms: L(+)-Ascorbic acid sodium salt; L-Ascorbic acid monosodium salt; Vitamin C sodium salt; Monosodium ascorbate; Monosodium L-ascorbate
Empirical: $C_6H_7NaO_6$
Properties: Wh. to yel. cryst. or cryst. powd., odorless; sol. in water; very sl. sol. in alcohol; insol. in chloroform, ether; m.w. 198.11; dec. 218 C; pH 7-8 (10%); relatively stable in air
Precaution: Combustible; light-sensitive; darkens on exposure to light
Toxicology: Human mutagenic data; heated to decomp., emits toxic fumes of Na_2O
Uses: Antioxidant, preservative; used in parenterals
Regulatory: FDA 21CFR §182.3731, GRAS; USDA 9CFR §318.7; Japan approved; Europe listed; UK approved; FDA approved for parenterals; BP compliance (sol'n.)
Manuf./Distrib.: BASF; EM Industries; Hoffmann-La Roche; Pfizer Spec. Chem.; Spice King; Takeda USA
Manuf./Distrib. (pharm. & food): Aldrich; Browning; Ruger; Spectrum Chem. Mfg.; Spice King
Trade names: Descote® Sodium Ascorbate 50%; Sodium Ascorbate USP, FCC Fine Gran. No. 6047709; Sodium Ascorbate USP, FCC Fine Powd. No. 6047708; Sodium Ascorbate USP, FCC Type AG No. 6047710

Sodium bentonite
Uses: Suspending agent, gellant, binder
Trade names: Volclay® NF-BC; Volclay® NF-ID

Sodium benzoate
CAS 532-32-1; EINECS 208-534-8
FEMA 3025

Sodium benzosulfimide

Synonyms: Benzoic acid sodium salt; Benzoate of soda; Benzoate sodium
Definition: Sodium salt of benzoic acid
Empirical: $C_7H_5NaO_2$
Formula: C_6H_5COONa
Properties: Wh. gran. or cryst. powd., odorless, sweetish astringent taste; hygroscopic; sol. in water; sparingly sol. in alcohol; m.w. 144.11; pH ≈ 8; stable in air
Precaution: Combustible when exposed to heat or flame; incompat. with acids, ferric salts; heated to decomp., emits toxic fumes of Na_2O
Toxicology: LD50 (oral, rat) 4.07 g/kg; poison by subcutaneous, IV routes; mod. toxic by ingestion, IP routes; may cause human intolerance reaction, asthma, rashes, hyperactivity; experimental teratogen, reproductive effects; mutagenic data
Uses: Antimicrobial preservative, antifungal; used in orals, parenterals, dentifrices, injectables, topicals
Usage level: 0.1% (parenterals), 0.08% (dentifrices), 4.75-5% (injectables), 0.02-0.5% (orals)
Regulatory: FDA 21CFR §146.152, 146.154, 150.141, 150.161, 166.40, 166.110, 181.22, 181.23, 184.1733; GRAS; USDA 9CFR §318.7; BATF 27CFR §240.1051; EPA reg.; FEMA GRAS; Japan approved with limitations; Europe listed 0.5% as acid; FDA approved for dentals, orals, rectals, topicals; USP/NF, BP, Ph.Eur. compliance
Manuf./Distrib.: Aceto; Aldrich; Allchem Ind.; Jan Dekker; R.W. Greeff; Haarmann & Reimer; Int'l. Sourcing; Lohmann; Mallinckrodt; E. Merck; Pfizer Food Science; San Yuan; Tri-K
Manuf./Distrib. (pharm. & food): Aldrich; Ashland; Avrachem; Browning; Consolidated Flavor; R.W. Greeff; Integra; Int'l. Sourcing; Jungbunzlauer; Lohmann; Mallinckrodt; Pfizer; Ruger; Spectrum Chem. Mfg.
Trade names: Sodium Benzoate BP88
Trade names containing: Cal-O-Vera 1:1; Cal-O-Vera 10:1; Cal-O-Vera 40:1; Dry Vitamin A Palmitate Type 250-SD No. 65378; DSS Granular; Nipacombin A; Vitamin B_{12} 0.1% SD No. 65354; Vitamin B_{12} 1.0% SD No. 65305

Sodium benzosulfimide. See Saccharin sodium
Sodium o-benzosulfimide. See Saccharin sodium
Sodium biborate decahydrate. See Sodium borate decahydrate

Sodium bicarbonate
CAS 144-55-8; EINECS 205-633-8
Synonyms: Baking soda; Sodium hydrogen carbonate; Bicarbonate of soda; Carbonic acid monosodium salt; Monosodium carbonate
Classification: Inorganic salt
Empirical: $CHNaO_3$
Formula: $NaHCO_3$
Properties: Wh. powd. or cryst. lumps, sl. alkaline taste; sol. in water; insol. in alcohol; m.w. 84.01; dens. 2.159; stable in dry air, slowly decomp. in moist air
Precaution: Moisture-sensitive
Toxicology: Harmless to the skin; leaves an alkaline residue that may cause irritation; nuisance dust; excessive ingestion of sodium may be detrimental to certain persons
Uses: Alkalizing agent, pH adjustor; antibiotic mfg., antacids; abrasive in dentifrices; used in effervescent tablets, injectables, parenterals, ophthalmics, orals; OTC drug active
Regulatory: FDA 21CFR §137.180, 137.270, 163.110, 173.385, 182.1736, 184.1736, GRAS; USDA 9CFR §318.7, 381.147; Japan approved; Europe listed; FDA approved for injectables, parenterals, ophthalmics, orals; USP/NF, BP, Ph.Eur. compliance
Manuf./Distrib.: Allchem Ind.; Balchem; Captree; Church & Dwight; Coyne; EM Ind.; Farleyway Chem. Ltd; FMC; ICI Spec.; Kraft; Lohmann; Rhone-Poulenc Basic
Manuf./Distrib. (pharm. & food): Aldrich; Browning; FMC; Integra; Mallinckrodt; Rhone-Poulenc Food Ingreds.; Ruger; Spectrum Chem. Mfg.
Trade names: Sodium Bicarbonate USP No. 1 Powd.; Sodium Bicarbonate USP No. 2 Fine Gran.; Sodium Bicarbonate USP No. 3 Extra Fine Powd.; Sodium Bicarbonate USP No. 5 Coarse Gran.

Sodium biphosphate. See Sodium phosphate
Sodium 1,4-bis(2-ethylhexyl) sulfosuccinate. See Dioctyl sodium sulfosuccinate

Sodium bisulfate
CAS 7681-38-1; EINECS 231-665-7
UN No. 1821 (solid), 2837 (sol'n.)
Synonyms: Sulfuric acid monosodium salt; Sodium acid sulfate; Sodium hydrogen sulfate; Sodium pyrosulfate
Empirical: $HNaO_4S$
Formula: $NaHSO_4$
Properties: Colorless cryst. or wh. fused lumps; hygroscopic; sol. in water; m.w. 120.07
Toxicology: Causes burns; irritating to respiratory system

Uses: Used in inhalants, ophthalmics, orals
Regulatory: FDA 21CFR §175.105; FDA approved for inhalants, ophthalmics, orals
Manuf./Distrib.: AMRESCO; Ashland; Harcros; Kraft; Lowenstein; Penta Mfg.; Ruger; Spectrum Chem. Mfg.
Manuf./Distrib. (pharm. & food): Aldrich; Integra; Mallinckrodt; Ruger

Sodium bisulfate acetone
CAS 7546-12-5
Uses: Used in injectables, dentals
Regulatory: FDA approved for injectables, dentals

Sodium bisulfite
CAS 7631-90-5; EINECS 231-548-0
UN No. 2693 (sol'n.)
Synonyms: Sodium acid sulfite; Acid sodium sulfite; Sodium bisulfite (1:1); Sulfurous acid monosodium salt; Sodium hydrogen sulfite; Sodium sulhydrate
Classification: Inorganic salt
Empirical: $HO_3S \cdot Na$
Formula: $NaHSO_3$
Properties: Wh. cryst. powd., SO_2 odor, diasgreeable taste; sol. in water; sl. sol. in alcohol; m.w. 104.06; dens. 1.48; m.p. 315 C
Precaution: Corrosive
Toxicology: LD50 (oral, rat) 2000 mg/kg; poison by intravenous and intraperitoneal routes; mod. toxic by ingestion; corrosive irritant to skin, eyes, mucous membranes; mutagenic data; allergen; heated to decomp., emits toxic fumes of SO_x and Na_2O
Uses: Antioxidant, stabilizer; used primarily in sympathomimetic and aminoglycoside medications; also used in parenterals, inhalants, ophthalmics, orals, topicals
Usage level: 0.3-0.75% (sympathomimetic/aminoglycoside medications)
Regulatory: FDA 21CFR §161.173, 173.310, 182.3739, GRAS; Europe listed; FDA approved for parenterals, inhalants, ophthalmics, orals, topicals
Manuf./Distrib.: Aldrich; Ashland; BASF; Browning; DuPont; Harcros; Hoechst Celanese; Hüls AG; Penreco; Penta Mfg.; Rhone-Poulenc Basic; Ruger; Spectrum Chem. Mfg.; Universal Preserv-A-Chem
Manuf./Distrib. (pharm. & food): Hoechst Celanese; Integra; Mallinckrodt; Penreco
See also Sodium metabisulfite

Sodium bisulfite (1:1). *See* Sodium bisulfite

Sodium borate
CAS 1330-43-4 (anhyd.); EINECS 215-540-4
Synonyms: Sodium tetraborate anhyd.; Sodium pyroborate anhyd.; Borax, fused
Classification: Inorganic salt
Empirical: $B_4Na_2O_7$
Formula: $Na_2B_4O_7$
Properties: Colorless to wh. cryst. or powd., odorless; hygroscopic; sol. in water, glycerol; insol. in alcohol; m.w. 201.22; dens. 1.730
Toxicology: Irritant
Uses: Alkalizing agent, preservative and emulsifier; used in ophthalmics, foot preps., scalp lotions
Regulatory: FDA 21CFR §175.105, 175.210, 176.180, 177.2800, 181.22, 181.30; FDA approved for ophthalmics; USP/NF, BP compliance
Manuf./Distrib.: Aldrich; Spectrum Chem. Mfg.; U.S. Borax & Chem.
Manuf./Distrib. (pharm. & food): Aldrich; Integra; Mallinckrodt; Ruger

Sodium borate decahydrate
CAS 1303-96-4; EINECS 215-540-4
Synonyms: Borax; Sodium tetraborate decahydrate; Sodium biborate decahydrate; Boric acid disodium salt
Classification: Inorganic salt
Empirical: $B_4Na_2O_7 \cdot 10H_2O$
Formula: $Na_2B_4O_7 \cdot 10H_2O$
Properties: White hard crystals, granules, or crystalline powd., odorless; efflorescent; sol. 1 g/16 ml water, 1 ml glycerol; insol. in alcohol; m.w. 381.37; dens. 1.73; becomes anhyd. at 320 C; pH ≈ 9.5
Precaution: Incompatible with acids, alkaloidal and metallic salts
Toxicology: Irritant; moderately toxic by ingestion, intravenous, intraperitoneal routes; heated to dec., emits toxic fumes of Na_2O; LD50 (rat, oral) 5.66 g/kg
Uses: Alkalizing agent, preservative and emulsifier; used in ophthalmics, foot preps., scalp lotions
Regulatory: FDA 21CFR §175.105, 175.210, 176.180, 177.2800, 181.22, 181.30; BP, Ph.Eur. compliance

Sodium n-butyl-4-hydroxybenzoate

    Manuf./Distrib.: Fluka; Spectrum Chem. Mfg.
    Manuf./Distrib. (pharm. & food): Spectrum Chem. Mfg.

Sodium n-butyl-4-hydroxybenzoate. *See* Sodium butylparaben
Sodium butyl-p-hydroxybenzoate. *See* Sodium butylparaben

Sodium butylparaben
    CAS 36457-20-2
    Synonyms: Butylparaben, sodium salt; Sodium n-butyl-4-hydroxybenzoate; Sodium butyl-p-hydroxybenzoate
    Definition: Sodium salt of butylparaben
    Empirical: $C_{11}H_{14}O_3 \cdot Na$
    Uses: Preservative, bactericide, fungicide for pharmaceuticals, medicinals, soft gelatin capsules
    Regulatory: BP compliance
    Trade names: Nipabutyl Sodium

Sodium C12-15 alcohols sulfate. *See* Sodium C12-15 alkyl sulfate
Sodium C12-18 alcohols sulfate. *See* Sodium C12-18 alkyl sulfate

Sodium C12-15 alkyl sulfate
    Synonyms: Sodium C12-15 alcohols sulfate
    Definition: Sodium salt of the sulfate of C12-15 alcohols
    Uses: Used in pharmaceutical preps., creams, ointments, and lotions
    Trade names containing: Lanette® Wax SX, SXBP

Sodium C12-18 alkyl sulfate
    Synonyms: Sodium C12-18 alcohols sulfate
    Definition: Sodium salt of the sulfate of a mixture of synthetic fatty alcohols with 12-18 carbons in alkyl chain
    Uses: Pharmaceutical raw material in creams, lotions, ointments, and liniments
    Trade names containing: Galenol® 1618 KS

Sodium caprylate
    CAS 1984-06-1; EINECS 217-850-5
    Synonyms: Caprylic acid sodium salt; Octanoic acid sodium salt
    Empirical: $C_8H_{15}NaO_2$
    Formula: $CH_3(CH_2)_6COONa$
    Properties: Clear; sol. in water; m.w. 166.20; m.p. ≈ 245 C
    Toxicology: No known toxicity
    Uses: Used in ointments
    Manuf./Distrib.: Aldrich; Hart Prod. Corp.; Penta Mfg.; Spectrum Chem. Mfg.
    Manuf./Distrib. (pharm. & food): Ruger

Sodium capryl sulfate. *See* Sodium octyl sulfate

Sodium carbonate
    CAS 497-19-8 (anhyd.); 5968-11-6 (monohydrate); 6132-02-1 (decahydrate); EINECS 207-838-8
    Synonyms: Soda ash; Soda calcined; Carbonic acid disodium salt; Disodium carbonate
    Classification: Inorganic salt
    Empirical: $CO_3 \cdot 2Na$
    Formula: Na_2CO_3
    Properties: Colorless to wh. cryst. or cryst. powd., odorless, alkaline taste; hygroscopic; sol. in water, glycerol; insol. in alcohol; m.w. 105.99 (anhyd.), 124.00 (monohydrate); dens. 2.509 (0 C); m.p. 109 C (loses water 851 C)
    Toxicology: LD50 (oral, rat) 4090 mg/kg; skin and eye irritant; poison by intraperitoneal route; moderately toxic by inhalation and subcutaneous routes; mildly toxic by ingestion; experimental reproductive effects; heated to decomp., emits toxic fumes of Na_2O
    Uses: Alkalizing agent, antacid, reagent; used in injectables, parenterals, ophthalmics, orals, rectals, mouthwashes, foot preps., vaginal douches
    Regulatory: FDA 21CFR §173.310, 184.1742, GRAS; USDA 9CFR §318.7, 381.147; Japan approved; Europe listed; FDA approved for injectables, parenterals, ophthalmics, orals, rectals; USP/NF, BP, Ph.Eur., JP compliance
    Manuf./Distrib.: Albright & Wilson; EM Industries; FMC; General Chem.; Lohmann; Mallinckrodt; Norsk Hydro A/S; Rhone-Poulenc Basic; Solvay SA; Spectrum Chem. Mfg.; Texasgulf
    Manuf./Distrib. (pharm. & food): Aldrich; Integra; Lohmann; Ruger; Solvay Minerals; Spectrum Chem. Mfg.

Sodium carboxymethylcellulose. *See* Carboxymethylcellulose sodium
Sodium carboxymethyl starch. *See* Sodium starch glycolate

Sodium cellulose
Uses: Used in orals
Regulatory: FDA approved for orals

Sodium cetearyl sulfate
CAS 59186-41-3; 68955-20-4
Synonyms: Sodium cetostearyl sulfate; Sodium cetyl/stearyl sulfate
Definition: Sodium salt of a mixture of cetyl and stearyl sulfate
Formula: $CH_3(CH_2)_nCH_2OSO_3Na$, n = 14 and 16
Toxicology: No known toxicity
Uses: Wax used as surface-active agent, emulsifier, wetting agent
Regulatory: BP, Ph.Eur. compliance
Trade names: Dehydag® Wax E; Lanette® E
Trade names containing: Emulgade® F; Galenol® 1618 CS; Lanette® N

Sodium cetostearyl sulfate. *See* Sodium cetearyl sulfate
Sodium cetyl/stearyl sulfate. *See* Sodium cetearyl sulfate

Sodium chlorate
CAS 7775-09-9; EINECS 231-887-4
UN No. 1495
Synonyms: Chlorate of soda
Empirical: $ClNaO_3$
Formula: $NaClO_3$
Properties: Colorless cryst., odorless, saline taste; sol. in water, alcohol; m.w. 106.45; dens. 2.490; m.p. 248-261 C; b.p. dec.
Precaution: DOT: Oxidizer; dangerous fire risk; corrosive
Toxicology: Human poison by unspecified routes; moderately toxic by ingestion and intraperitoneal routes
Uses: Astringent; used in injectables
Regulatory: FDA approved for injectables
Manuf./Distrib.: Albright & Wilson; Aldrich; Eka Nobel AB; Elf Atochem; Georgia Gulf; Kerr-McGee; Occidental; PPG Industries; Spectrum Chem. Mfg.
Manuf./Distrib. (pharm. & food): Aldrich

Sodium chloride
CAS 7647-14-5; EINECS 231-598-3
Synonyms: Rock salt; Salt; Table salt; Common salt
Classification: Inorganic salt
Definition: Occurs in nature as the mineral halite
Empirical: ClNa
Formula: NaCl
Properties: Colorless transparent cryst. or wh. cryst. powd., saline taste; hygroscopic; sol. 1 g/2.8 ml water; sol. in glycerin; very sl. sol. in alcohol; m.w. 58.45; dens. 2.17; m.p. 804 C; f.p. -20.5 C (23% aq.); pH 6.7-7.3
Precaution: Heated to decomp., emits toxic fumes of Cl^- and Na_2O
Toxicology: LD50 (oral, rat) 3.75 g/kg; mod. toxic by ingestion, IV, subcutaneous routes; experimental teratogen; human systemic effects (blood pressure increase); terminates human pregnancy by intraplacental route; human mutagenic data; skin/eye irritant
Uses: Preservative, flavoring agent, tonicity agent; used in injectables, dentals, parenterals, inhalants, ophthalmics, orals, rectals, topicals (FDA approved)
Regulatory: FDA 2CFR §163.153; 21CFR §131.111, 131.112, 131.136, 131.138, 131.144, 131.146, 131.162, 131.170, 131.185, 131.187, 133.123, 133.124, 133.169, 133.173, 133.179, 133.187, 133.188, 133.189, 133.190, 133.195, 136.110, 136.115, 136.130, 136.160, 136.180; 145.110, 145.130, 155, 156, 158, 161.170, 161.173, 161.190, 163.111, 163.112, 163.113, 163.114, 163.117, 163.123, 163.130, 163.135, 163.140, 163.145, 163.150, 163.155, 166.110, 169.115, 169.140, 169.150, 182.1, 182.70, 182.90; 9CFR §381.147; BP, Ph.Eur.
Manuf./Distrib.: Akzo Salt; EM Industries; Heico; Morton Salt; Spectrum Chem. Mfg.; Stan Chem Int'l. Ltd; Spectrum Chem. Mfg.
Manuf./Distrib. (pharm. & food): Akzo Salt; Aldrich; Heico; Mallinckrodt; Morton Salt; Ruger; Spectrum Chem. Mfg.
Trade names: Sterling® Purified USP Salt
Trade names containing: Amino Gluten MG; Durkote Calcium Carbonate/Starch, Acacia Gum

Sodium citrate
CAS 18996-35-5; EINECS 242-734-6

Sodium citrate primary

Synonyms: Citric acid monosodium salt; Monosodium citrate anhydrous; Monosodium-2-hydroxypropane-1,2,3-tricarboxylate; Sodium dihydrogen citrate; Sodium citrate primary
Empirical: $C_6H_7NaO_7$
Formula: $HO_2CCH_2C(OH)(CO_2H)CH_2CO_2Na$
Properties: Hygroscopic; m.w. 214.11; m.p. 212 C
Precaution: Combustible; avoid dust formation
Toxicology: LD50 (IP, rat) 1348 mg/kg; (IV, mouse) 49 mg/kg; poison by IV route; mod. toxic by IP route; heated to decomp., emits toxic fumes of Na_2O
Uses: Sequestrant, buffering agent; used in injectables, parenterals, inhalants, ophthalmics, orals, rectals, topicals, vaginals
Regulatory: FDA 21CFR §181.29, GRAS; Europe listed; UK approved; FDA approved for injectables, parenterals, inhalants, ophthalmics, orals, rectals, topicals, vaginals; USP/NF, BP, Ph.Eur. compliance
Manuf./Distrib.: Cargill; Haarmann & Reimer; Hoffmann-La Roche; Lohmann; Mallinckrodt; Tanabe USA; Whiting, Peter Ltd
Manuf./Distrib. (pharm. & food): ADM; Aldrich; Ashland; Browning; Cargill; Cheil Foods; Haarmann & Reimer; Hays; N I Ibrahim; Integra; Int'l. Sourcing; Jungbunzlauer; Lohmann; Penta Mfg.; Produits Roche; Quimdis; Roche; Ruger; SAPA; Tesco; Van Waters & Rogers
Trade names: Sodium Citrate USP, FCC Dihydrate Gran. No. 69976; Sodium Citrate USP, FCC Dihydrate Fine Gran. No. 69975
Trade names containing: Palma-Sperse® Type 250-S No. 65322; Palma-Sperse® Type 250A/50 D-S No. 65221; Uninontan U 34; Vitamin B_{12} 0.1% SD No. 65354; Vitamin B_{12} 1.0% SD No. 65305
See also Trisodium citrate

Sodium citrate primary. *See* Sodium citrate
Sodium citrate tertiary. *See* Trisodium citrate
Sodium CMC. *See* Carboxymethylcellulose sodium

Sodium cocoate
CAS 61789-31-9; EINECS 263-050-4
Synonyms: Coconut oil fatty acid, sodium salt; Fatty acids, coconut oil, sodium salts; Sodium coconut oil soap
Definition: Sodium salt of coconut acid
Toxicology: May cause allergic skin rash
Uses: Ointment base
Regulatory: FDA 21CFR §175.105, 175.320, 176.170, 176.200, 176.210, 177.1200, 177.2260, 177.2600, 177.2800, 178.3910

Sodium cocomonoglyceride sulfonate
Synonyms: Sodium coconut monoglyceride sulfonate
Formula: $RCO-OCH_2CHOHCH_2SO_3Na$, RCO- rep. fatty acids from coconut oil
Uses: Used in dentals
Regulatory: FDA approved for dentals

Sodium coconut monoglyceride sulfonate. *See* Sodium cocomonoglyceride sulfonate
Sodium coconut oil soap. *See* Sodium cocoate

Sodium cocoyl isethionate
CAS 61789-32-0; 58969-27-0; EINECS 263-052-5
Synonyms: Fatty acids, coconut oil, sulfoethyl esters, sodium salts; Cocoyl sodium isethionate
Definition: Sodium salt of the coconut fatty acid ester of isethionic acid
Formula: $RCO-OCH_2CH_2SO_3Na$, RCO- rep. fatty acids derived from coconut oil
Uses: Used in topicals
Regulatory: Approved for topicals

Sodium cocoyl methyl taurate. *See* Sodium methyl cocoyl taurate
Sodium N-cocoyl-N-methyl taurate. *See* Sodium methyl cocoyl taurate

Sodium C14-16 olefin sulfonate
CAS 68439-57-6; EINECS 270-407-8
Definition: Mixt. of long chain sulfonate salts from sulfonation of C14-16 alpha olefins; consists of sodium alkene sulfonates and sodium hydroxyalkane sulfonates
Regulatory: FDA 21CFR §175.105, 178.3406

Sodium dehydroacetate
CAS 4418-26-2; EINECS 224-580-1
Synonyms: 3-(1-Hydroxyethylidene)-6-methyl-2H-pyran-2,4(3H)-dione sodium salt; 2H-Pyran-2,4(3H)-dione, 3-acetyl-6-methyl-, monosodium salt; Sodium dehydroacetic acid
Classification: Heterocyclic compd.

Empirical: $C_8H_7O_4 \cdot Na$
Properties: Wh. powd., odorless, sl. char. taste; sol. in water, propylene glycol, glycerin; insol. in most org. solvs.; heat stable to 120 C; m.w. 190.14; m.p. 109-111 C
Toxicology: LD50 (oral, mouse) 1175 mg/kg; poison by IV route; mod. toxic by ingestion; experimental teratogen, reproductive effects; mutagenic data; heated to decomp., emits toxic fumes of Na_2O
Uses: Antimicrobial preservative in pharmaceuticals
Regulatory: FDA 21CFR §172.130, 175.105; CIR approved; Japan approved (0.5 g/kg as dehydroacetic acid); Europe listed 0.6% max. (acid); USP/NF compliance
Manuf./Distrib.: Int'l. Sourcing; Spectrum Chem. Mfg.; Tri-K
Manuf./Distrib. (pharm. & food): Int'l. Sourcing; Ruger

Sodium dehydroacetic acid. *See* Sodium dehydroacetate
Sodium deoxycholate. *See* Sodium desoxycholate

Sodium desoxycholate
CAS 302-95-4; EINECS 206-132-7
Synonyms: Sodium deoxycholate; 7-Deoxycholic acid sodium salt
Empirical: $C_{24}H_{39}NaO_4$
Properties: M.w. 414.56; hygroscopic
Uses: Used in parenterals
Regulatory: FDA approved for parenterals; BP compliance
Manuf./Distrib.: Spectrum Chem. Mfg.

Sodium di(2-ethylhexyl) sulfosuccinate. *See* Dioctyl sodium sulfosuccinate
Sodium 2,3-dihydro-1,2-benzisothiazolin-3-one-1,1-dioxide. *See* Saccharin sodium
Sodium dihydrogen citrate. *See* Sodium citrate
Sodium dihydrogen phosphate. *See* Sodium phosphate

Sodium 1,2-dimyristoyl-sn-glycero(3)phosphatidylcholine
CAS 6732-80-8; 116870-30-5
Synonyms: 1,2-Dimyristoyl-sn-glycero(3)phosphoglycerol sodium salt
Uses: For mfg. of liposomes and mixed micelles
Trade names: Phospholipon® MG Na

Sodium dioctyl sulfosuccinate. *See* Dioctyl sodium sulfosuccinate

Sodium dioleth-8 phosphate
Definition: Sodium salt of a complex mixture of phosphate diesters of oleth-8
Uses: Solubilizer
Trade names: Nikkol DOP-8N

Sodium 1,2-dipalmitoyl-sn-glycero(3)phosphatidylcholine
CAS 116870-31-6
Synonyms: L-α-1,2-Dipalmitoyl-sn-phosphatidylglycerol sodium salt
Uses: Emulsifier, solubilizer for dermatology; mfg. of liposomes and mixed micelles
Trade names: Phospholipon® PG Na

Sodium 1,2-distearoyl-sn-glycero(3)phosphatidylcholine
Synonyms: 1,2-Distearoyl-sn-glycero(3)phosphoglycerol sodium salt
Uses: Emulsifier, solubilizer for dermatology; mfg. of liposomes and mixed micelles
Trade names: Phospholipon® SG Na

Sodium dithionite
CAS 7775-14-6 (anhyd.); EINECS 231-890-0
UN No. 1384
Synonyms: Sodium hydrosulfite; Sodium hyposulfite; Sodium sulfoxylate
Empirical: $Na_2S_2O_4$
Properties: Light lemon-colored powd. or flake, bitter taste; sl. sol. in water; insol. in alcohol; m.w. 174.10; m.p. 55 C (dec.)
Precaution: DOT: Spontaneously combustible material; flamm.; fire risk; moisture-sensitive
Toxicology: Toxic; irritant to skin; allergen
Uses: Reducing agent; used in pharmaceuticals (salvarsan), parenterals, urine tests for detection of paraquat poisoning
Regulatory: FDA approved for parenterals; BP compliance
Manuf./Distrib.: Mitsubishi Gas Chem.; Mitsui Toatsu; Nippon Soda; Spectrum Chem. Mfg.; Sumitomo Chem.
Manuf./Distrib. (pharm. & food): Aldrich

Sodium-N-dodecanoyl-N-methylglycinate. *See* Sodium lauroyl sarcosinate

Sodium dodecylbenzenesulfonate

Sodium dodecylbenzenesulfonate
CAS 25155-30-0; 68081-81-2; 85117-50-6; EINECS 246-680-4
Synonyms: SDBS; NaDBS; Sodium lauryl benzene sulfonate; Dodecylbenzenesulfonic acid sodium salt; Dodecylbenzene sodium sulfonate
Classification: Substituted aromatic compd.
Empirical: $C_{18}H_{29}O_3S \cdot Na$
Properties: White to lt. yel. flakes, granules, or powd.; m.w. 348.52
Precaution: Combustible
Toxicology: LD50 (oral, rat) 1260 mg/kg, (oral, mouse) 2 g/kg, (IV, mouse) 105 mg/kg; poison by intravenous route; moderately toxic by ingestion; skin and severe eye irritant; heated to decomp., emits toxic fumes of Na_2O
Uses: Surfactant; used in topicals
Regulatory: FDA 21CFR §173.315, 175.105, 175.300, 175.320, 176.210, 177.1010, 177.1200, 177.1630, 177.2600, 177.2800, 178.3120, 178.3130, 178.3400; USDA 9CFR §318.7, 381.147; FDA approved for topicals
Manuf./Distrib.: Albright & Wilson; DuPont; Emkay; Fluka; Norman, Fox; Pilot; Rhone-Poulenc Spec.; Spectrum Chem. Mfg.; Stepan; Tokyo Kasei Kogyo Ltd; Unger Fabrikker AS; Witco/Oleo-Surf.

Sodium dodecyl sulfate. *See* Sodium lauryl sulfate
Sodium 2-ethylhexyl sulfate. *See* Sodium octyl sulfate
Sodium ethyl 4-hyroxybenzoate. *See* Sodium ethylparaben
Sodium ethylmercurithiosalicylate. *See* Thimerosal

Sodium ethylparaben
CAS 35285-68-8; EINECS 252-487-6
Synonyms: 4-Hydroxybenzoic acid, ethyl ester, sodium salt; Ethylparaben, sodium salt; Sodium ethyl 4-hyroxybenzoate
Definition: Sodium salt of ethylparaben
Empirical: $C_9H_{10}O_3 \cdot Na$
Toxicology: May cause asthma, rashes, hyperactivity
Uses: Antimicrobial preservative; used in orals
Regulatory: FDA approved for orals
Trade names: Nipagin A Sodium
Trade names containing: Nipacombin A; Nipasept Sodium

Sodium fluorescein. *See* CI 45350; D&C Yellow No. 8

Sodium formaldehyde sulfoxylate
CAS 149-44-0; 6035-47-8 (dihydrate)
Synonyms: Methanesulfinic acid, hydroxy-, monosodium salt; Monosodium hydroxymethane sulfinate
Empirical: CH_3NaO_3S
Formula: $HOCH_2SOONa$
Properties: Wh. cryst., garlic odor; sol. in water; sl. sol. in alcohol, ether, chloroform, benzene; m.w. 118.09 (anhyd.), 154.11 (dihydrate); pH 9.5-10.5 (2%)
Uses: Antioxidant; used in parenterals, topicals
Regulatory: FDA approved for parenterals, topicals; USP/NF compliance
Manuf./Distrib.: Aceto; Henkel/Coatings & Inks; Passaic Color & Chem.; Phibrochem; Royce Assoc.
Manuf./Distrib. (pharm. & food): Ruger

Sodium gluconate
CAS 527-07-1; EINECS 208-407-7
Synonyms: D-Gluconic acid monosodium salt; Monosodium D(-)-pentahydroxy capronate; Gluconic acid sodium salt; Monosodium gluconate; Sodium d-gluconate
Definition: Sodium salt of gluconic acid
Empirical: $C_6H_{12}NaO_7$
Formula: $HOCH_2CHOHCHOHCHOHCHOHCOONa$
Properties: Wh. to ylsh. cryst. powd., pleasant odor; sol. 59 g/100 ml water; sl. sol. in alcohol; insol. in ether; m.w. 219.17
Precaution: Avoid dust formation
Toxicology: Low toxicity by IV route; heated to decomp., emits acrid smoke and irritating fumes
Uses: Mineral source for pharmaceuticals; used in orals
Regulatory: FDA 21CFR §182.6757, GRAS; Europe listed; UK approved; FDA approved for orals
Manuf./Distrib.: Akzo; Albright & Wilson; Lohmann; Pfizer Spec. Chem.; PMP Fermentation Prods.; Rit-Chem.

Manuf./Distrib. (pharm. & food): ADM; Aldrich; Ashland; Hays; Integra; Jungbunzlauer; Pfaltz & Bauer; PMP Fermentation Prods.; Ruger; Spectrum Chem. Mfg.
Trade names: Gluconal® NA

Sodium d-gluconate. *See* Sodium gluconate
Sodium L-glutamate. *See* MSG
Sodium glutamate. *See* MSG

Sodium glyceryl oleate phosphate
Definition: Sodium salt of a complex mixture of phosphate esters of glyceryl monooleate
Uses: Emulsifier for pharmaceuticals
Trade names containing: Ches® 500

Sodium guanosine-5´-monophosphate. *See* Disodium guanylate
Sodium guanylate. *See* Disodium guanylate

Sodium hectorite
Uses: Viscosifier, suspension agent, binder
Trade names: Hectalite® 200

Sodium hexametaphosphate
CAS 10124-56-8, 68915-31-1; EINECS 233-343-1
FEMA 3027
Synonyms: SHMP; Sodium polyphosphates glassy; Sodium tetrapolyphosphate; Graham's salt; Amorphous sodium polyphosphate; Sodium phosphate glass; Sodium metaphosphate
Classification: Inorganic salt
Empirical: $H_6O_{18}P_6$ • 6Na
Formula: $(NaPO_3)_6$
Properties: White powd. or flakes; sol. in water; m.w. 101.98
Toxicology: LD50 (oral, mouse) 7250 mg/kg, (IP, mouse) 870 mg/kg; poison by intravenous route; moderately toxic by intraperitoneal, subcutaneous routes; mildly toxic by ingestion; heated to decomp., emits toxic fumes of PO_x and Na_2O
Uses: Used in buccals
Regulatory: FDA 21CFR §173.310, 182.90, 182.6760, 182.6769, GRAS; USDA 9CFR §318.7, 381.147; FEMA GRAS; FDA approved for buccals
Manuf./Distrib.: Albright & Wilson; Calgon; Farleyway Chem. Ltd; FMC; Monsanto; Rhone-Poulenc Basic
Manuf./Distrib. (pharm. & food): Albright & Wilson Am.; Browning

Sodium hyaluronate
CAS 9067-32-7
Definition: Sodium salt of hyaluronic acid; found naturally in eye fluids
Properties: Wh. powd.
Toxicology: Moderately toxic by intraperitoneal route; heated to dec., emits toxic fumes of Na_2O
Uses: Gelling agent
Manuf./Distrib.: Nikko Chem. Co. Ltd.
Trade names: Hyaluronic Acid FCH; Kelisema Sodium Hyaluronate Bio; Pronova™

Sodium hydrate. *See* Sodium hydroxide
Sodium hydrogen carbonate. *See* Sodium bicarbonate
Sodium hydrogen L-glutamate. *See* MSG
Sodium hydrogen sulfate. *See* Sodium bisulfate
Sodium hydrogen sulfite. *See* Sodium bisulfite
Sodium hydrosulfite. *See* Sodium dithionite

Sodium hydroxide
CAS 1310-73-2; EINECS 215-185-5
UN No. 1823
Synonyms: Caustic soda; Sodium hydrate; White caustic; Soda lye; Lye
Classification: Inorganic base
Empirical: HNaO
Formula: NaOH
Properties: White deliq. solid beads or pellets; deliq.; absorbs water and CO_2 from air; sol. in water, alcohol, glycerin; m.w. 40; dens. 2.12 (20/4 C); m.p. 318 C; b.p. 1390 C
Precaution: DOT: Corrosive material; strong base; may ignite or react violently with many org. compds.; dangerous material to handle
Toxicology: TLV:Cl 2 mg/m³ of air; LD50 (IP, mouse) 40 mg/kg; poison by IP route; mod. toxic by ingestion; mutagenic data; corrosive irritant to eye, skin, mucous membrane; mists and dusts cause small burns;

Sodium-L-2-hydroxypropionate

heated to decomp., emits toxic fumes of Na_2O

Uses: Alkalizing agent, buffering agent; used in injectables, dentals, parenterals, inhalants, ophthalmics, orals, rectals, topicals, vaginals; eyewashes

Regulatory: FDA 21CFR §163.110, 172.560, 172.814, 172.892, 173.310, 184.1763, GRAS; USDA 9CFR §318.7, 381.147; BATF 27CFR §21.101, 240.1051a; Japan restricted; Europe listed; UK approved; FDA approved for injectables, dentals, parenterals, inhalants, ophthalmics, orals, rectals, topicals, vaginals; USP/NF, BP, Ph.Eur. compliance

Manuf./Distrib.: Akzo; Asahi Chem Industry Co Ltd; Asahi Denka Kogyo; Elf Atochem N. Am.; Georgia Gulf; Georgia-Pacific; Hüls AG; ICI Spec.; Nissan Chem. Ind.; Norsk Hydro A/S; Occidental; Olin; PPG Industries; Rasa Ind.; Spectrum Chem. Mfg.

Manuf./Distrib. (pharm. & food): Aldrich; Asahi Chem Industry Co Ltd; Avrachem; Hüls AG; Integra; Mallinckrodt; Ruger; Spectrum Chem. Mfg.

Sodium-L-2-hydroxypropionate. *See* Sodium lactate

Sodium hypochlorite

CAS 7681-52-9; EINECS 231-668-3

UN No. 1791 (sol'n.)

Synonyms: Dakins sol'n.; Bleaching sol'n.; Labarrque's sol'n.

Empirical: NaClO

Formula: NaOCl • 5HOH

Properties: Pale greenish liq., disagreeable chlorine odor; sol. in cold water; dec. by hot water; m.w. 74.45 (anhyd.); m.p. 18 C

Precaution: Anhyd.: highly explosive, sensitive to heat or friction; forms explosive prods. with amines; unstable in air; fire risk; exposure limits: none

Toxicology: Toxic by ingestion; strong irritant to tissue; eye irritant; human mutagenic data; heated to decomp., emits toxic fumes of Na_2O and Cl^-

Uses: Antiseptic for wounds in medicine

Regulatory: FDA 21CFR §173.315; Japan approved as bleaching agent, restricted as sterilizing agent; BP compliance (sol'n.)

Manuf./Distrib.: Ajinomoto; Asahi Denka Kogyo; Hüls AG; George Mann; Mitsubishi Chem.; Mitsui Toatsu; Norsk Hydro A/S; Occidental; Olin; Showa Denko; Spectrum Chem. Mfg.

Manuf./Distrib. (pharm. & food): Aldrich; Hüls AG; Integra; Ruger; Spectrum Chem. Mfg.

Sodium hyposulfite. *See* Sodium dithionite; Sodium thiosulfate anhydrous
Sodium inosinate. *See* Disodium inosinate
Sodium 5´-inosinate. *See* Disodium inosinate

Sodium iodide

CAS 7681-82-5; EINECS 231-679-3

Empirical: INa

Formula: NaI

Properties: Wh. or colorless cryst. or powd.; deliq.; hygroscopic; very sol. in water; sol. in alcohol and glycerin; m.w. 149.89; dens. 3.667; m.p. 661 C

Toxicology: Irritant

Uses: Antiseptic in topical anti-infective prods.; also used in parenterals, vaginals

Regulatory: FDA approved for parenterals, topicals, vaginals; USP/NF, BP, Ph.Eur. compliance

Manuf./Distrib.: Aldrich; EM Industries; Mallinckrodt; Spectrum Chem. Mfg.

Manuf./Distrib. (pharm. & food): Aldrich; R.W. Greeff; Integra; Mallinckrodt; Ruger; Spectrum Chem. Mfg.

Sodium lactate

CAS 72-17-3; EINECS 200-772-0

Synonyms: 2-Hydroxypropanoic acid monosodium salt; Lacolin; Sodium-L-2-hydroxypropionate

Definition: Sodium salt of lactic acid

Empirical: $C_3H_5O_3$ • Na

Formula: $CH_3CHOHCOONa$

Properties: Colorless or ylsh. syrupy liq., odorless to sl. odor, sl. salt taste; very hygroscopic; misc. in water, alcohol; m.w. 112.07; m.p. 17 C; dec. 140 C

Precaution: Combustible

Toxicology: LD50 (IP, rat) 2000 mg/kg; moderately toxic by intraperitoneal; eye irritant; heated to decomp., emits toxic fumes of Na_2O

Uses: Buffering agent, humectant, antimicrobial preservative used in parenterals, orals; intermediate

Regulatory: FDA 21CFR §184.1768, GRAS (not for infant formulas); USDA 9CFR §318.7; Japan approved; Europe listed; UK approved; FDA approved for parenterals, orals; USP/NF compliance (sol'n.); BP compliance

Manuf./Distrib.: Am. Biorganics; Am. Ingreds.; EM Industries; R.W. Greeff; Lohmann; RITA; Verdugt BV
Manuf./Distrib. (pharm. & food): Am. Ingreds.; Integra; Lohmann; Ruger; Spectrum Chem. Mfg.
Trade names: Patlac® NAL; Purasal® S/HQ 60; Purasal® S/PF 60; Purasal® S Powd.

Sodium L-lactate
CAS 867-56-1; EINECS 212-762-3
Synonyms: (S)-2-Hydroxypropionic acid sodium salt; L-Lactic acid sodium salt
Empirical: $C_3H_5NaO_3$
Formula: $CH_3CH(OH)COONa$
Properties: Hygroscopic; m.w. 112.06
Uses: Used in injectables, parenterals
Regulatory: FDA approved for injectables, parenterals

Sodium laureth-5 carboxylate
CAS 33939-64-9 (generic); 38975-03-0
Synonyms: PEG-5 lauryl ether carboxylic acid, sodium salt; Sodium POE (5) lauryl ether carboxylate; Laureth-5 carboxylic acid, sodium salt
Definition: Sodium salt of the carboxylic acid derived from laureth-5
Empirical: $C_{32}H_{43}O_7Na$
Formula: $CH_3(CH_2)_{10}CH_2(OCH_2CH_2)_nOCH_2COONa$, avg. n = 4
Uses: Mild surfactant for medicated soaps and shampoos
Trade names: Sandopan® LA-8-HC

Sodium laureth sulfate
CAS 1335-72-4; 3088-31-1; 9004-82-4 (generic); 13150-00-0; 15826-16-1; 68891-38-3; 68585-34-2; EINECS 221-416-0
Synonyms: Sodium lauryl ether sulfate (n=1-4); PEG (1-4) lauryl ether sulfate, sodium salt
Definition: Sodium salt of sulfated ethoxylated lauryl alcohol
Formula: $CH_3(CH_2)_{10}CH_2(OCH_2CH_2)_nOSO_3Na$, avg. n = 1-4
Uses: Used in topicals
Regulatory: FDA approved for topicals
Manuf./Distrib.: Aquatec Quimica SA; Chemron; Lonza; Norman, Fox; Pilot; Rhone-Poulenc Spec.; Sandoz; Sea-Land; Stepan; Unger Fabrikker AS; U.S. Synthetics; Vista

Sodium lauroyl sarcosinate
CAS 137-16-6; EINECS 205-281-5
Synonyms: N-Methyl-N-(1-oxododecyl)glycine, sodium salt; N-Lauroylsarcosine sodium salt; Sodium-N-dodecanoyl-N-methylglycinate
Definition: Sodium salt of lauroyl sarcosine
Empirical: $C_{15}H_{29}NO_3 \cdot Na$
Formula: $CH_3(CH_2)_{10}CONCH_3CH_2COONa$
Properties: M.w. 293.39
Uses: Mild surfactant, foamer, wetting agent, bacteriostat, enzyme inhibitor used in orals, topicals, dental care preps., surgical scrubs
Regulatory: FDA approved for orals, topicals
Manuf./Distrib.: Hampshire; R.T. Vanderbilt
Trade names: Crodasinic LS30; Crodasinic LS35; Hamposyl® L-30; Oramix® L30

Sodium lauryl benzene sulfonate. *See* Sodium dodecylbenzenesulfonate
Sodium lauryl ether sulfate (n=1-4). *See* Sodium laureth sulfate

Sodium lauryl sulfate
CAS 151-21-3; 68585-47-7; 68955-19-1; EINECS 205-788-1; 271-557-7; 273-257-1
Synonyms: SDS; SLS; Sulfuric acid monododecyl ester sodium salt; Sodium monododecyl sulfate; Sodium dodecyl sulfate; Dodecyl sodium sulfate; Dodecylsulfate sodium salt
Definition: Sodium salt of lauryl sulfate
Empirical: $C_{12}H_{25}O_4S \cdot Na$
Formula: $CH_3(CH_2)_{10}CH_2OSO_3Na$
Properties: Wh. to cream crystals, flakes, or powd., faint fatty odor; sol. in water; m.w. 288.38; m.p. 204-207 C
Precaution: Heated to decomp., emits toxic fumes of SO_x and Na_2O
Toxicology: LD50 (oral, rat) 1288 mg/kg; poison by IV, IP routes; mod. toxic by ingestion; human skin irritant; experimental eye, severe skin irritant; mild allergen; mutagenic data; experimental teratogen, reproductive effects
Uses: Emulsifier, wetting agent, solubilizer; used in oral liqs. and solids, topicals, dentals, vaginals
Usage level: 0.004-0.6 mg (oral solids); 0.01-0.02% (oral liqs.); 0.1-12.7% (topical pharmaceuticals)
Regulatory: FDA 21CFR §172.210, 172.822, 175.105, 175.300, 175.320, 176.170, 176.210, 177.1200,

Sodium lauryl sulfoacetate

177.1210, 177.1630, 177.2600, 177.2800, 178.1010, 178.3400; USDA 9CFR §318.7, 381.147; FDA approved for dentals, orals, topicals, vaginals; USP/NF, BP, Ph.Eur. compliance
Manuf./Distrib.: Albright & Wilson Ltd; Chemron; DuPont; Lonza; Norman, Fox; Monomer-Polymer & Dajac; Pilot; Sandoz; Spectrum Chem. Mfg.; Stepan; Unger Fabrikker AS; Witco
Manuf./Distrib. (pharm. & food): Albright & Wilson Ltd; Aldrich; Integra; Ruger; Spectrum Chem. Mfg.
Trade names: Empicol® 0185; Empicol® 0303; Empicol® 0303VA; Empicol® LX; Empicol® LX100; Empicol® LXS95; Empicol® LXV100; Empicol® LXV/D; Empicol® LZ; Empicol® LZ/D; Empicol® LZV/D; Naxolate™ WA-97; Naxolate™ WAG; Polystep® B-3; Stepanol® ME Dry; Stepanol® WA-100; Stepanol® WAC; Stepanol® WA Extra; Stepanol® WA Paste; Stepanol® WAQ; Stepanol® WA Special; Supralate® C; Texapon® K-12 Needles; Texapon® K-12 Powd.; Texapon® K-12 USP; Texapon® K-1296 Needles; Texapon® K-1296 Powd.; Texapon® K-1296 USP; Texapon® Z; Texapon® Z Highly Conc. Needles; Texapon® Z Highly Conc. Powder; Zoharpon LAS; Zoharpon LAS Spray Dried
Trade names containing: Cerasynt® WM; Crodex A; Empiwax SK; Empiwax SK/BP; Galenol® 1618 DSN; Lanette® W; Lexemul® AS

Sodium lauryl sulfoacetate
CAS 1847-58-1; EINECS 217-431-7
Synonyms: Acetic acid, sulfo-, 1-dodecyl ester, sodium salt; Sulfoacetic acid, 1-dodecyl ester, sodium salt
Classification: Organic salt
Empirical: $C_{14}H_{28}O_5S \cdot Na$
Formula: $CH_3(CH_2)_{10}CH_2OCOCH_2SO_3Na$
Uses: Used in topicals
Regulatory: FDA approved for topicals

Sodium magnesium silicate
CAS 53320-86-8; EINECS 258-476-2
Definition: Synthetic silicate clay composed mainly of magnesium and sodium silicate
Uses: Thickener for toothpastes
Trade names: Laponite® D

Sodium mercaptoacetate. *See* Sodium thioglycolate

Sodium metabisulfite
CAS 7681-57-4; EINECS 231-673-0
Synonyms: Disulfurous acid disodium salt; Sodium pyrosulfite; Disodium pyrosulfite; Disodium disulfite; Sodium bisulfite
Classification: Inorganic salt
Empirical: $O_5S_2 \cdot 2Na$
Formula: $Na_2S_2O_5$
Properties: Colorless cryst. or wh. to ylsh. powd., SO_2 odor; sol. in water, glycerin; sl. sol. in alcohol; m.w. 190.10; dens. 1.480
Precaution: Moisture-sensitive
Toxicology: TWA 5 mg/m³; LD50 (IV, rat) 115 mg/kg; poison by intravenous route; moderately toxic by parenteral route; experimental reproductive effects; mutagenic data; heated to decomp., emits toxic fumes of SO_x and Na_2O
Uses: Antioxidant; used primarily in sympathomimetic and aminoglycoside medications; also for ophthalmics, orals, inhalants, injectables, parenterals
Usage level: 0.3-0.75% (sympathomimetic/aminoglycoside medications)
Regulatory: FDA 21CFR §173.310, 177.1200, 182.3766, GRAS; Europe listed; FDA approved for inhalants, injectables, parenterals, ophthalmics, orals; USP/NF, BP compliance
Manuf./Distrib.: BASF; Blythe, William Ltd; EM Industries; General Chem.; Mallinckrodt; Spectrum Chem. Mfg.
Manuf./Distrib. (pharm. & food): Aldrich; Browning; Ruger; Spectrum Chem. Mfg.

Sodium metaphosphate. *See* Sodium hexametaphosphate

Sodium methyl cocoyl taurate
CAS 12765-39-8; 61791-42-2
Synonyms: Sodium cocoyl methyl taurate; Sodium N-cocoyl-N-methyl taurate; Sodium N-methyl-N-cocoyl taurate
Definition: Sodium salt of the coconut fatty acid amide of N-methyltaurine
Formula: $RCO-NCH_3CH_2CH_2SO_3Na$, RCO- rep. coconut acid radical
Uses: Detergent, foamer, dispersant, emulsifier in pharmaceuticals, dentifrice prods.
Trade names: Adinol CT95; Tauranol WS H.P.

Sodium N-methyl-N-cocoyl taurate. *See* Sodium methyl cocoyl taurate
Sodium methyl 4-hyroxybenzoate. *See* Sodium methylparaben

Sodium methylparaben
CAS 5026-62-0; EINECS 225-714-1
Synonyms: 4-Hydroxybenzoic acid, methyl ester, sodium salt; Methylparaben sodium salt; Sodium methyl 4-hyroxybenzoate; Methylparaben sodium
Definition: Sodium salt of methylparaben
Empirical: $C_8H_7NaO_3$
Properties: Wh. powd.; hygroscopic; freely sol. in water; sparingly sol. in alcohol; insol. in fixed oils; m.w. 174.14; pH 9.5-10.5 (1 in 1000)
Uses: Antimicrobial preservative; used in orals
Regulatory: FDA approved for orals; USP/NF, BP compliance
Manuf./Distrib. (pharm. & food): Spectrum Chem. Mfg.
Trade names: Nipagin M Sodium
Trade names containing: Nipacombin A; Nipasept Sodium

Sodium monododecyl sulfate. *See* Sodium lauryl sulfate

Sodium myristyl sulfate
CAS 1191-50-0; 139-88-8; EINECS 214-737-2
Synonyms: Sodium tetradecyl sulfate; Sulfuric acid, monotetradecyl ester, sodium salt; 1-Tetradecanol, hydrogen sulfate, sodium salt
Definition: Sodium salt of myristyl sulfate
Empirical: $C_{14}H_{30}O_4S \cdot Na$
Formula: $CH_3(CH_2)_{12}CH_2OSO_3Na$
Properties: M.w. 316.48
Toxicology: Poison by intraperitoneal, intravenous routes
Uses: Wetting agent, penetrant, emulsifier
Regulatory: FDA 21CFR §175.105, 177.1210, 177.2800
Trade names: Niaproof® Anionic Surfactant 4

Sodium nitrate
CAS 7631-99-4; EINECS 231-554-3
UN No. 1498
Synonyms: Soda niter; Cubic niter; Chile saltpeter
Empirical: $NNaO_3$
Formula: $NaNO_3$
Properties: Colorless transparent crystals, odorless, saline sl. bitter taste; deliq.; sol. in water, glycerol; sl. sol. in alcohol; m.w. 85.01; dens. 2.267; m.p. 308 C; dec. @ 380 C; pH 5.5-8.3 (5%)
Precaution: Strong oxidizer; ignites with heat or friction; explodes @ 537 C
Toxicology: LD50 (oral, rabbit) 2680 mg/kg; poison by intavenous route; moderately toxic by ingestion; can produce nitrosamines associated with cancers; can reduce blood oxygen levels; human mutagenic data; heated to decomp., emits toxic fumes of NO_x and Na_2O
Uses: Used in ophthalmics, orals
Regulatory: FDA 21CFR §171.170, 172.170, 172.177, 173.310, 181.33; USDA 9CFR §318.7, 381.147; Japan approved with limitations; Europe listed; UK approved; FDA approved for ophthalmics, orals; BP compliance
Manuf./Distrib.: Aldrich; BASF; Faesy & Besthoff; Farleyway Chem. Ltd; Mallinckrodt; Mitsubishi Chem.; Nissan Chem. Ind.; Spectrum Chem. Mfg.; Spice King; Sumitomo Chem.; Ube Ind.
Manuf./Distrib. (pharm. & food): Integra; Lohmann; Mallinckrodt; Spectrum Chem. Mfg.; Spice King

Sodium nitrite
CAS 7632-00-0; EINECS 231-555-9
UN No. 1500
Synonyms: Nitrous acid sodium salt
Empirical: $NNaO_2$
Formula: $NaNO_2$
Properties: Sl. ylsh. or wh. cryst. or powd., bitter sl. saline taste; deliq. in air; sol. in water, sl. sol. in alcohol, ether; m.w. 69.00; dens. 2.168; m.p. 271 C; b.p. dec. @ 320 C
Precaution: Strong oxidizing agent; oxygen-sensitive; flamm.; ignites by friction in contact with organic matter; heated to decomp., emits toxic fumes of NO_x and Na_2O
Toxicology: LD50 (oral, rat) 85 mg/kg; human poison by ingestion; experimental neoplastigen, tumorigen, teratogen; human systemic effects; human mutagenic data; eye irritant; can produce nitrosamines associated with cancers; can reduce blood oxygen levels
Uses: Pharmaceuticals
Regulatory: FDA 21CFR §172.175, 172.177, 181.34; USDA 9CFR §318.79, 381.147; Japan approved (0.005-0.07 g/kg); Europe listed; UK approved; BP compliance

Sodium octadecanoate

  Manuf./Distrib.: Aldrich; BASF; DuPont; EM Industries; Farleyway Chem. Ltd; General Chem.; ICI Spec.; Mitsubishi Chem.; PMC Spec.; Tomiyama Pure Chem. Ind.; Ube Ind.
  Manuf./Distrib. (pharm. & food): Browning; Integra; Mallinckrodt; Ruger; Spectrum Chem. Mfg.

Sodium octadecanoate. *See* Sodium stearate

Sodium octoxynol-2 ethane sulfonate
  CAS 2917-94-4; 67923-87-9; EINECS 267-791-4; 220-851-3
  Synonyms: 2-[2-[2-Octylphenoxy)ethoxy]ethoxy]ethanesulfonic acid, sodium salt; Entsufon; Entsufon sodium
  Classification: Organic compd.
  Empirical: $C_{20}H_{34}O_6S \cdot Na$
  Formula: $C_8H_{17}C_6H_4O(CH_2CH_2O)_2CH_2CH_2SO_3Na$
  Properties: M.w. 425.54
  Uses: Used in topicals
  Regulatory: FDA 21CFR §176.180; FDA approved for topicals

Sodium octyl sulfate
  CAS 126-92-1; 142-31-4; EINECS 204-812-8
  Synonyms: Sodium 2-ethylhexyl sulfate; Sodium capryl sulfate; Sulfuric acid, mono (2-ethylhexyl) ester sodium salt; Octyl sulfate sodium salt
  Definition: Sodium salt of 2-ethylhexyl sulfate
  Empirical: $C_8H_{18}O_4S \cdot Na$
  Formula: $CH_3(CH_2)_3CHCH_3CH_2CH_2OSO_3Na$
  Properties: M.w. 233.31; m.p. 195 C
  Toxicology: LD50 (oral, mouse) 1550 mg/kg; poison by intraperitoneal route; moderately toxic by ingestion, skin contact; skin and eye irritant; heated to decomp., emits very toxic fumes of SO_x and Na_2O
  Uses: Wetting agent, penetrant, emulsifier
  Regulatory: FDA 21CFR §173.315, 175.105, 176.170; USDA 9CFR §381.147; BP compliance
  Manuf./Distrib.: Aldrich
  Manuf./Distrib. (pharm. & food): Aldrich
  Trade names: Niaproof® Anionic Surfactant 08

Sodium N-oleoyl sarcosinate
  Uses: Wetting agent, lubricant, bacteriostat, penetrant used in dental, pharmaceutical applics.

Sodium PCA
  CAS 28874-51-3; 54571-67-4; EINECS 249-277-1
  Synonyms: PCA-Na; PCA Soda; 5-Oxo-DL-proline, sodium salt; Sodium pyroglutamate
  Definition: Sodium salt of pyroglutamic acid
  Empirical: $C_5H_7NO_3 \cdot Na$
  Properties: Colorless liq., odorless, sl. salty taste; extremely hygroscopic; m.w. 151.1
  Toxicology: No known toxicity; nonirritant to skin, eye mucosa
  Uses: Humectant for dermatological soap, nutritive creams and lotions

Sodium phenoxy acetate
  CAS 3598-16-1
  Definition: Reaction prod. of sodium phenolate and sodium chloro acetate
  Uses: For fermentation of penicillin V, esters of cortical hormones
  Trade names: Niacet Sodium Phenoxy Acetate

Sodium phosphate
  CAS 7558-80-7 (anhyd.); 10049-21-5 (monohydrate); 13472-35-0 (dihydrate); EINECS 231-449-2
  Synonyms: MSP; Sodium phosphate monobasic; Sodium acid phosphate; Monobasic sodium phosphate; Sodium dihydrogen phosphate; Monosodium dihydrogen phosphate; Monosodium dihydrogen orthophosphate; Sodium biphosphate; Sodium phosphate primary
  Classification: Inorganic salt
  Empirical: H_2NaO_4P
  Formula: NaH_2PO_4
  Properties: Colorless to wh. cryst. powd., gran., odorless; hygroscopic; sl. deliq.; sol. 87 g/100 g water; pract. insol. in alcohol; m.w. 119.98 (anhyd.), 137.99 (monohydrate), 156.01 (dihydrate); pH 4.1-4.5
  Toxicology: LD50 (oral, rat) 8290 mg/kg; poison by intramuscular route; mildly toxic by ingestion; eye irritant; heated to decomp., emits toxic fumes of PO_x and Na_2O
  Uses: Medical precipitation agent, buffering agent, laxative, effervescent; used in buccals, parenterals, ophthalmics, orals, topicals, vaginals
  Regulatory: FDA 21CFR §133, 150, 160, 163.123, 163.130, 163.135, 163.140, 163.145, 163.150, 163.153, 163.155, 172.892, 173.310, 182.1778, 182.5778, 182.6085, 182.6778, 182.8778, GRAS; USDA 9CFR

§318.7, 381.147; Japan approved; FDA approved for buccals, parenterals, ophthalmics, orals, topicals, vaginals; USP/NF, BP compliance

Manuf./Distrib.: Albright & Wilson; Aldrich; BritAg Industries Ltd; FMC; Lohmann; Rhone-Poulenc Food Ingreds.; Spectrum Chem. Mfg.

Manuf./Distrib. (pharm. & food): Albright & Wilson Am.; Browning; FMC; Lohmann; Mallinckrodt; Rhone-Poulenc Food Ingreds.; Spectrum Chem. Mfg.

Sodium phosphate dibasic anhydrous

CAS 7558-79-4; EINECS 231-448-7

FEMA 2398

Synonyms: DSP-0; Disodium phosphate; Dibasic sodium phosphate; Disodium hydrogen phosphate; Disodium monohydrogen orthophosphate; Disodium orthophosphate

Classification: Inorganic salt

Definition: Phosphoric acid, disodium salt

Empirical: $HO_4P \cdot 2Na$

Formula: Na_2HPO_4

Properties: Colorless translucent cryst. or wh. powd., saline taste; hygroscopic; sol. in water; very sol. in alcohol; m.w. 141.97 (anhyd.), 177.99 (dihydrate); dens. 1.5235; m.p. 35 C, loses water at 92.5 C

Toxicology: LD50 (oral, rat) 17 g/kg; skin and eye irritant; poison by intravenous route, moderately toxic by intraperitoneal, subcutaneous route; mildly toxic by ingestion; when heated to decomp., emits toxic fumes of PO_x and Na_2O

Uses: Buffering agent; used in buccals, parenterals, ophthalmics, vaginals

Regulatory: FDA 21CFR §133.169, 133.173, 133.179, 135.110, 137.305, 139.110, 139.115, 139.117, 139.135, 150.141, 150.161, 173.310, 175.210, 175.300, 181.22, 181.29, 182.1778, 182.5778, 182.6290, 182.6778, 182.8778, 182.8890, GRAS; USDA 9CFR 318.7, 381.147; Japan approved; FDA approved for buccals, parenterals, ophthalmics, vaginals; USP/NF, BP, Ph.Eur. compliance

Manuf./Distrib.: Albright & Wilson; FMC; Monsanto; Rhone-Poulenc Food Ingreds.; Spectrum Chem. Mfg.; U.S. Biochemical; Whiting, Peter Ltd

Manuf./Distrib. (pharm. & food): Albright & Wilson Am.; FMC; Integra; Lohmann; Monsanto; Rhone-Poulenc Food Ingreds.; Ruger; Spectrum Chem. Mfg.

Sodium phosphate dibasic heptahydrate

CAS 7782-85-6; EINECS 231-448-7

Synonyms: DSP-7; Disodium phosphate heptahydrate; Dibasic sodium phosphate heptahydrate; Disodium hydrogen phosphate heptahydrate; Disodium orthophosphate heptahydrate

Classification: Inorganic salt

Definition: Phosphoric acid, disodium salt

Empirical: $HNa_2O_4P \cdot 7H_2O$

Formula: $Na_2HPO_4 \cdot 7H_2O$

Properties: Colorless or wh. gran.; effloresces in warm dry air; sol. in water; very sl. sol. in alcohol; m.w. 268.07; dens. 1.679

Uses: Buffering agent for pharmaceuticals

Regulatory: USP/NF compliance

Manuf./Distrib.: Aldrich; Fluka; Spectrum Chem. Mfg.

Manuf./Distrib. (pharm. & food): Albright & Wilson Am.; Aldrich; FMC; Lohmann; Monsanto; Rhone-Poulenc Food Ingreds.; Spectrum Chem. Mfg.

Sodium phosphate glass. *See* Sodium hexametaphosphate
Sodium phosphate monobasic. *See* Sodium phosphate
Sodium phosphate primary. *See* Sodium phosphate
Sodium POE (5) lauryl ether carboxylate. *See* Sodium laureth-5 carboxylate
Sodium polymannuronate. *See* Algin
Sodium polyphosphates glassy. *See* Sodium hexametaphosphate
Sodium potassium tartrate. *See* Potassium sodium tartrate anhyd.; Potassium sodium tartrate tetrahydrate

Sodium propionate

CAS 137-40-6 (anhyd.); 6700-17-0 (hydrate); EINECS 205-290-4

Synonyms: Propanoic acid sodium salt; Propionic acid sodium salt

Definition: Sodium salt of propionic acid

Empirical: $C_3H_5O_2 \cdot Na$ or $C_3H_5NaO_2 \cdot xH_2O$

Formula: CH_3CH_2COONa

Properties: Transparent cryst. or gran., nearly odorless; hygroscopic; deliq. in moist air; very sol. in water; sl. sol. in alcohol; m.w. 96.07 (anhyd.); m.p. 287-289 C

Precaution: Combustible

Toxicology: LD50 (skin, rabbit) 1640 mg/kg; moderately toxic by skin contact and subcutaneous route; can

Sodium propyl 4-hydroxybenzoate

cause allergic reactions
Uses: Antimicrobial preservative; used in orals and to treat fungal infections of the skin
Regulatory: FDA 21CFR §133.123, 133.124, 133.169, 133.173, 133.179, 150.141, 150.161, 179.45, 181.22, 181.23, 184.1784, GRAS; USDA 9CFR §318.7, 381.147; Japan approved with limitations; Europe listed; FDA approved for orals; USP/NF compliance
Manuf./Distrib.: Gist-brocades Food Ingreds.; Lohmann; Niacet; Spectrum Chem. Mfg.; Verdugt BV
Manuf./Distrib. (pharm. & food): Aldrich; Browning; Gist-brocades Food Ingreds.; Lohmann; Ruger; Spectrum Chem. Mfg.

Sodium propyl 4-hydroxybenzoate. *See* Sodium propylparaben

Sodium propylparaben
CAS 35285-69-9; EINECS 252-488-1
Synonyms: 4-Hydroxybenzoic acid, propyl ester, sodium salt; Sodium propyl 4-hydroxybenzoate; Propyl-4-hydroxybenzoate, sodium salt; Propylparaben sodium; Propylparaben sodium salt
Definition: Sodium salt of propylparaben
Empirical: $C_{10}H_{11}O_3 \cdot Na$
Properties: Wh. powd., odorless; hygroscopic; sol. in water; sparingly sol. in alcohol; insol. in fixed oils; m.w. 202.00; pH 9.5-10.5 (1 in 1000)
Toxicology: May cause asthma, rashes, hyperactivity
Uses: Antimicrobial preservative; used in orals
Regulatory: FDA approved for orals; USP/NF, BP compliance
Manuf./Distrib. (pharm. & food): Spectrum Chem. Mfg.
Trade names: Nipasol M Sodium
Trade names containing: Nipacombin A; Nipasept Sodium

Sodium pyroborate anhyd. *See* Sodium borate
Sodium pyroglutamate. *See* Sodium PCA
Sodium pyrophosphate. *See* Tetrasodium pyrophosphate
n-Sodium pyrophosphate. *See* Tetrasodium pyrophosphate
Sodium pyrosulfate. *See* Sodium bisulfate
Sodium pyrosulfite. *See* Sodium metabisulfite

Sodium pyrrolidone carboxylate
Uses: Used in topicals
Regulatory: FDA approved for topicals

Sodium rhodanide. *See* Sodium thiocyanate
Sodium saccharide. *See* Saccharin sodium
Sodium saccharin. *See* Saccharin sodium

Sodium salicylate
CAS 54-21-7; EINECS 200-198-0
Synonyms: Salicylic acid sodium salt
Empirical: $C_7H_5NaO_3$
Formula: HOC_6H_4COONa
Properties: Wh. lustrous cryst. scales or amorphous powd., odorless or faint odor, saline taste; becomes pinkish on long exposure to light; hygroscopic; sol. in water, glycerin; slowly sol. in alcohol; m.w. 160.11
Precaution: Combustible; light-sensitive
Toxicology: May cause nasal allergy
Uses: Mild antiseptic, analgesic, and preservative; used in orals, sunscreen lotions; used to lower fever and kill pain in animals
Regulatory: FDA approved for orals; BP, Ph.Eur. compliance
Manuf./Distrib.: Spectrum Chem. Mfg.
Manuf./Distrib. (pharm. & food): Aldrich; Integra; Mallinckrodt; Ruger; Spectrum Chem. Mfg.

Sodium silicoaluminate
CAS 1318-02-1; 1344-00-9; EINECS 215-684-8
Synonyms: Sodium aluminosilicate; Sodium aluminum silicate; Aluminum sodium silicate
Definition: Series of hydrated sodium aluminum silicates
Empirical: $Na_2O : Al_2O_3 : SiO_2$ with mole ratio $\approx$ 1:1:13.2
Properties: Fine white amorphous powd. or beads, odorless and tasteless; insol. in water, alcohol, org. solvs.; partly sol. in strong acids and alkali hydroxides @ 80-100 C; pH 6.5-10.5 (20% slurry)
Precaution: Noncombustible
Toxicology: Irritant to skin, eyes, mucous membranes; heated to decomp., emits toxic fumes of Na_2O
Uses: Used in orals

Regulatory: FDA 21CFR §133.146, 160.105, 160.185, 182.2727 (2% max.), 582.2727, GRAS; Europe listed; UK approved; FDA approved for orals
Manuf./Distrib.: Spectrum Chem. Mfg.
See also Zeolite

Sodium stannate
CAS 12058-66-1; EINECS 235-030-5
Classification: Inorganic salt
Formula: $Na_2SnO_3 \cdot 3H_2O$ or $Na_2Sn(OH)_6$
Properties: Wh. hexagonal cryst.; hygroscopic; sol. in water; insol. in alcohol, acetone; m.w. 266.71
Toxicology: No known toxicity
Uses: Used in orals
Regulatory: FDA approved for orals
Manuf./Distrib.: Blythe, William Ltd; Elf Atochem N. Am.; Showa Denko; Spectrum Chem. Mfg.
Manuf./Distrib. (pharm. & food): Integra; Ruger

Sodium starch glycolate
CAS 9063-38-1
Synonyms: Sodium carboxymethyl starch; Starch carboxymethyl ether sodium salt; Carboxymethyl starch sodium salt
Definition: Sodium salt of a carboxymethyl ether of starch
Formula: $(C_6H_9O_4 \cdot O \cdot CH_2 \cdot COONa)_n$
Properties: Wh. powd., odorless, tasteless; hygroscopic; pH 3-5 or 5.5-7.5 (1 g/30 ml aq. susp.)
Uses: Tablet disintegrant for pharmaceuticals; used in buccals, orals
Regulatory: FDA approved for buccals, orals; USP/NF, BP compliance
Manuf./Distrib.: Matsutani Chem. Ind.; Nippon Starch Chem.
Manuf./Distrib. (pharm. & food): Avrachem
Trade names: Explotab®; Primojel®

Sodium stearate
CAS 822-16-2; EINECS 212-490-5
Synonyms: Sodium octadecanoate; Octadecanoic acid sodium salt; Stearic acid sodium salt
Definition: Sodium salt of stearic acid
Empirical: $C_{18}H_{36}O_2 \cdot Na$
Formula: $CH_3(CH_2)_{16}COONa$
Properties: Wh. fine powd., fatty odor; sol. in hot water and hot alcohol; slowly sol. in cold water and cold alcohol; insol. in many org. solvs.; m.w. 306.52
Precaution: Light-sensitive
Toxicology: Poison by intravenous and other routes; nonirritating to skin; heated to decomp., emits toxic fumes of Na_2O
Uses: Emulsifier, solubilizer, and stiffener in pharmaceuticals; metal soap stabilizer; glycerol suppositories; used in orals, topicals; used to treat skin diseases
Regulatory: FDA 21CFR §172.615, 172.863, 175.105, 175.300, 175.320, 176.170, 176.200, 176.210, 177.1200, 177.2260, 177.2600, 177.2800, 178.3910, 179.45, 181.22, 181.29; FDA approved for orals, topicals; USP/NF compliance
Manuf./Distrib.: Cometals; Elf Atochem N. Am.; Magnesia GmbH; Norman, Fox; Original Bradford Soap Works; Spectrum Chem. Mfg.; Witco/Oleo-Surf.
Manuf./Distrib. (pharm. & food): Integra; Ruger; Spectrum Chem. Mfg.
Trade names: Haro® Chem NG
Trade names containing: Monomuls® 60-25/2; Monomuls® 90-25/2; Monomuls® 90-25/5

Sodium stearoyl fumarate. *See* Sodium stearyl fumarate

Sodium stearoyl lactylate
CAS 25383-99-7; EINECS 246-929-7
Synonyms: Octadecanoic acid, 2-(1-carboxyethoxy)-1-methyl-2-oxoethyl ester, sodium salt; Sodium stearyl-2-lactylate
Definition: Sodium salt of the stearic acid ester of lactyl lactate
Empirical: $C_{24}H_{44}O_6 \cdot Na$
Formula: $CH_3(CH_2)_{16}COOCHCH_3COOCHCH_3COONa$
Properties: White or cream-colored powd., caramel odor; sol. in hot oil or fat; disp. in warm water; m.p. 46-52 C; HLB 10-12
Toxicology: Heated to decomp., emits acrid smoke and irritating fumes
Uses: Emulsifier
Regulatory: FDA 21CFR §172.846, 177.1200; Europe listed; UK approved

Sodium stearyl fumarate

    Trade names: Lamegin® NSL
    Trade names containing: Myvatex® TL

Sodium stearyl fumarate
    CAS 4070-80-8
    Synonyms: Sodium stearoyl fumarate
    Empirical: $C_{22}H_{39}NaO_4$
    Properties: Wh. fine powd.; sl. sol. in methanol; pract. insol. in water; m.w. 390.54; sapon. no. 142-146
    Toxicology: Heated to decomp., emits toxic fumes of Na_2O
    Uses: Inert hydrophilic tablet/capsule lubricant
    Regulatory: FDA 21CFR §172.826; USP/NF compliance
    Manuf./Distrib. (pharm. & food): Spectrum Chem. Mfg.
    Trade names: Pruv™

Sodium stearyl-2-lactylate. *See* Sodium stearoyl lactylate

Sodium p-styrenesulfonate
    CAS 2695-37-6; EINECS 220-266-3
    Synonyms: p-Sodium styrenesulfonate
    Empirical: $C_8H_7SO_3Na$
    Formula: $CH:CH_2C_6H_4SO_3Na$
    Properties: Wh. to pale yel. cryst. powd., odorless; sol. in water; insol. in aromatics, high alcohols; m.w. 206.20; sp.gr. 5.5; m.p. 330 C
    Uses: Pharmaceutical ingred.
    Manuf./Distrib.: Aceto; Monomer-Polymer & Dajac; Polysciences; Tosoh; Wako Pure Chem. Ind.
    Trade names: Spinomar NaSS

p-Sodium styrenesulfonate. *See* Sodium p-styrenesulfonate
Sodium subsulfite. *See* Sodium thiosulfate anhydrous

Sodium succinate
    CAS 150-90-3 (hexahydrate)
    FEMA 3277
    Synonyms: Succinic acid sodium salt; Disodium succinate; Soduxin
    Empirical: $C_4H_4Na_2O_4$
    Formula: $(CH_2COONa)_2 \cdot 6H_2O$ (hexahydrate)
    Properties: Hexahydrate gran. or cryst. powd.; hygroscopic; sol. in 5 parts water; insol. in alcohol; m.w. 162.05, 270.15 (hexahydrate)
    Toxicology: LD50 (IV, mouse) 4.5 g/kg
    Uses: Used in orals
    Regulatory: FDA approved for orals
    Manuf./Distrib.: Lohmann; Spectrum Chem. Mfg.
    Manuf./Distrib. (pharm. & food): Aldrich; Integra; Mallinckrodt; Ruger

Sodium sulfate
    CAS 7757-82-6 (anhyd.); 7727-73-3 (decahydrate); EINECS 231-820-9
    Synonyms: Sodium sulfate anhydrous; Sodium sulfate (2:1); Glauber's salt; Salt cake; Disodium sulfate
    Classification: Inorganic salt
    Empirical: Na_2O_4S
    Formula: Na_2SO_4
    Properties: Wh. cryst. or powd., odorless, bitter saline taste; hygroscopic; sol. in water, glycerol; insol. in alcohol; m.w. 142.04, 322.20 (decahydrate); dens. 2.671; m.p. 888 C
    Toxicology: LD50 (oral, mouse) 5989 mg/kg; moderately toxic by intravenous route; mildly toxic by ingestion; experimental teratogen, reproductive effects; heated to decomp., emits toxic fumes of SO_x and Na_2O
    Uses: Used in parenterals, ophthalmics, orals, topicals; used to reduce body water
    Regulatory: FDA 21CFR §172.615, 173.310, 177.1200, 186.1797, GRAS as indirect food additive; USDA 9CFR §318.7, 381.147; Japan approved; Europe listed; UK approved; FDA approved for parenterals, ophthalmics, orals, topicals; BP, Ph.Eur. compliance
    Manuf./Distrib.: Akzo Salt; Elf Atochem N. Am.; Kemira Kemi AB; Lenzing AG; Lohmann; Occidental; Spectrum Chem. Mfg.
    Manuf./Distrib. (pharm. & food): Aldrich; Integra; Mallinckrodt; Ruger; Spectrum Chem. Mfg.

Sodium sulfate (2:1). *See* Sodium sulfate
Sodium sulfate anhydrous. *See* Sodium sulfate

Sodium sulfite
    CAS 7757-83-7; EINECS 231-821-4

Synonyms: Sulfurous acid sodium salt (1:2); Sulfurous acid disodium salt; Sodium sulfite (2:1); Sodium sulfite anhydrous
Classification: Inorganic salt
Empirical: $O_3S \cdot 2Na$
Formula: Na_2SO_3
Properties: Wh. to tan or pink powd. or hexagonal crystals, odorless, salty sulfurous taste; sol. in 3.2 parts water; sol. in glycerol; pract. insol. in alcohol; m.w. 126.04; dens. 2.633 (15.4 C); b.p. dec.; pH ≈ 9
Precaution: Reducing agent; moisture-sensitive
Toxicology: LD50 (IV, rat) 115 mg/kg; poison by intravenous, subcutaneous routes; mod. toxic by ingestion, intraperitoneal routes; human mutagenic data; may provoke asthma; destroys vitamin B_1; heated to decomp., emits very toxic fumes of Na_2O and SO_x
Uses: Antioxidant, antiseptic, preservative, topical antifungal agent; used primarily in symphathomimetic and aminoglycoside medications; also for injectables, inhalants, orals, topicals
Usage level: 0.3-0.75% (symphathomimetic/aminoglycoside medications)
Regulatory: FDA 21CFR §172.615, 173.310, 177.1200, 182.3798, GRAS; Japan approved (0.03-5 g/kg max. residual as sulfur dioxide); Europe listed; FDA approved for injectables, inhalants, orals, topicals; BP, Ph.Eur. compliance
Manuf./Distrib.: BASF; Blythe, William Ltd; EM Industries; Ferro/Grant; Indspec; Nissan Chem. Ind.; Rhone-Poulenc Basic
Manuf./Distrib. (pharm. & food): Aldrich; Browning; General Chem.; Integra; Mallinckrodt; Ruger; Spectrum Chem. Mfg.

Sodium sulfite (2:1). *See* Sodium sulfite
Sodium sulfite anhydrous. *See* Sodium sulfite
Sodium sulfocyanate. *See* Sodium thiocyanate
Sodium sulfocyanide. *See* Sodium thiocyanate
Sodium sulfoxylate. *See* Sodium dithionite
Sodium sulhydrate. *See* Sodium bisulfite

Sodium tallowate
CAS 8052-48-0; EINECS 232-491-4
Synonyms: Tallow, sodium salt
Definition: Sodium salt of tallow acid
Uses: Used in topicals
Regulatory: FDA 21CFR §175.105, 175.320, 176.170, 176.200, 177.2600, 177.2800, 178.3910; FDA approved for topicals

Sodium tartrate
CAS 868-18-8 (anhyd.); EINECS 212-773-3
Synonyms: Sal tartar; Disodium tartrate; Disodium L-(+)-tartrate; Bisodium tartrate; L-Tartaric acid disodium salt
Definition: Disodium salt of L(+)-tartaric acid
Empirical: $C_4H_4Na_2O_6$
Properties: Colorless transparent cryst., odorless; sol. in water; m.w. 194.05
Toxicology: Mod. toxic by ingestion; heated to decomp., emits acrid smoke and irritating fumes
Uses: Used in parenterals
Regulatory: FDA 21CFR §184.1801, GRAS; USDA 9CFR §318.7; Europe listed; UK approved; FDA approved for parenterals; BP compliance
Manuf./Distrib.: Lohmann; Novarina Srl; Schweizerhall
Manuf./Distrib. (pharm. & food): Aldrich; Integra; Lohmann; Mallinckrodt

Sodium/TEA-undecenoyl collagen amino acids
Synonyms: Sodium/TEA-undecylenoyl animal collagen amino acids
Definition: Mixture of sodium and triethanolamine salts of the condensation prod. of undecylenic acid chloride and collagen amino acids
Uses: Foaming lipoprotein, fungistat for antidandruff shampoos
Trade names: Proteol UCO

Sodium/TEA-undecylenoyl animal collagen amino acids. *See* Sodium/TEA-undecenoyl collagen amino acids
Sodium tetraborate anhyd. *See* Sodium borate
Sodium tetraborate decahydrate. *See* Sodium borate decahydrate
Sodium tetradecyl sulfate. *See* Sodium myristyl sulfate
Sodium tetrapolyphosphate. *See* Sodium hexametaphosphate

Sodium thiocyanate

Sodium thiocyanate
CAS 540-72-7; EINECS 208-754-4
Synonyms: Sodium rhodanide; Sodium sulfocyanate; Sodium sulfocyanide
Classification: Inorganic compd.
Empirical: CNNaS
Formula: NaSCN
Properties: Colorless cryst.; hygroscopic; deliq.; sol. in water, alcohol; m.w. 81.07; m.p. 287 C
Precaution: Light-sensitive
Toxicology: Irritant
Uses: Intermediate for pharmaceuticals
Manuf./Distrib.: Witco/PAG; Sanko Kagaku; Spectrum Chem. Mfg.; Toyo Kasei Kogyo
Manuf./Distrib. (pharm. & food): Aldrich; Integra; Witco

Sodium thioglycolate
CAS 367-51-1; EINECS 206-696-4
Synonyms: Sodium mercaptoacetate; Mercaptoacetic acid sodium salt; Thioglycolic acid sodium salt
Definition: Sodium salt of thioglycolic acid
Empirical: $C_2H_3NaO_2S$
Formula: $HSCH_2COONa$
Properties: Wh. cryst. powd.; hygroscopic; sol. in water; sl. sol. in alcohol; m.w. 114.10
Precaution: Combustible; oxygen-sensitive; refrigerate
Toxicology: Irritating to skin, respiratory system
Uses: Reducing agent
Regulatory: BP compliance
Manuf./Distrib.: Evans Chemetics; Fluka; Spectrum Chem. Mfg.
Manuf./Distrib. (pharm. & food): Aldrich; Ruger

Sodium thiomalate
CAS 30245-51-3
Uses: Used in parenterals
Regulatory: FDA approved for parenterals

Sodium thiosulfate anhydrous
CAS 7772-98-7; EINECS 231-867-5
Synonyms: Sodium hyposulfite; Hypo; Disodium thiosulfate; Sodium subsulfite; Thiosulfuric acid disodium salt
Classification: Inorganic salt
Empirical: $Na_2O_3S_2$
Formula: $Na_2S_2O_3$
Properties: Colorless cryst. or cryst. powd.; hygroscopic; deliq. in moist air; sol. in water; pract. insol. in alcohol; m.w. 158.11; dens. 1.667
Precaution: Incompat. with metal nitrates, sodium nitrite
Toxicology: Irritant; mod. toxic by subcutaneous route; heated to decomp., emits very toxic fumes of Na_2O and SO_x
Uses: Antioxidant; used in intravenous, ophthalmics, orals; antidote for cyanide poisoning
Regulatory: FDA 21CFR §184.1807, GRAS; FDA approved for intravenous, ophthalmics, orals; USP/NF, BP, Ph.Eur. compliance
Manuf./Distrib.: Aldrich; Blythe, William Ltd; Ferro/Grant; General Chem.; Nissan Chem. Ind.; Spectrum Chem. Mfg.
Manuf./Distrib. (pharm. & food): Integra; Ruger; Spectrum Chem. Mfg.

Sodium trimetaphosphate
CAS 7785-84-4; EINECS 232-088-3
Synonyms: Trimetaphosphate sodium; Metaphosphoric acid trisodium salt
Classification: Inorganic salt
Empirical: $O_9P_3 \cdot 3Na$
Formula: $(NaPO_3)_3$
Properties: Wh. cryst. or wh. cryst. powd.; sol. in water; m.w. 305.88
Toxicology: LD50 (IP, rat) 3650 mg/kg; poison by IV route; mod. toxic by intraperitoneal route; heated to decomp., emits toxic fumes of PO_x and Na_2O
Uses: Used in intravenous
Regulatory: GRAS; FDA approved for intravenous
Manuf./Distrib.: Spectrum Chem. Mfg.
Manuf./Distrib. (pharm. & food): Spectrum Chem. Mfg.

Sodium undecylenate
  CAS 3398-33-2; EINECS 222-264-8
  Synonyms: 10-Undecenoic acid, sodium salt
  Definition: Sodium salt of undecylenic acid
  Empirical: $C_{11}H_{20}O_2$ • Na
  Formula: $CH_2=CH(CH_2)_8COONa$
  Properties: Wh. powd., sweaty odor; limited sol. in most org. solvs.; sol. in water; dec. above 200 C
  Precaution: Combustible
  Uses: Bacteriostat and fungistat for topical pharmaceuticals
  Regulatory: USA not restricted; Europe listed 0.2% max. as acid
  Manuf./Distrib.: Elf Atochem N. Am.

Sodium xylenesulfonate
  CAS 1300-72-7; EINECS 215-090-9
  Synonyms: Dimethylbenzene sulfonic acid, sodium salt
  Definition: Sodium salt of ring sulfonated mixed xylene isomers
  Empirical: $C_8H_{10}O_3S$ • Na
  Formula: $(CH_3)_2C_6H_3SO_3Na$
  Properties: M.w. 208.21
  Toxicology: No known toxicity; irritant
  Uses: Solubilizer used in topicals
  Regulatory: FDA approved for topicals
  Manuf./Distrib.: Mitsubishi Gas; Pilot; Ruetgers-Nease; Stepan; Witco
  Manuf./Distrib. (pharm. & food): Aldrich; R.W. Greeff

Soduxin. *See* Sodium succinate
Soluble animal collagen. *See* Soluble collagen

Soluble collagen
  CAS 9007-34-5; EINECS 232-697-4
  Synonyms: Soluble animal collagen; Soluble native collagen
  Definition: Nonhydrolyzed, native protein derived from connective tissue of young animals
  Properties: M.w. 285,000
  Uses: Base in medicinal soaps
  Manuf./Distrib.: Henkel/Cospha
  Trade names containing: Kelisema Collagen-CCK Complex

Soluble guncotton. *See* Nitrocellulose
Soluble native collagen. *See* Soluble collagen
Soluble sulfur. *See* Sulfur
Solvent green 3. *See* CI 61565; D&C Green No. 6
Solvent green 7. *See* CI 59040; D&C Green No. 8
Solvent red 23. *See* CI 26100; D&C Red No. 17
Solvent red 43. *See* D&C Red No. 21
Solvent red 48. *See* D&C Red No. 27
Solvent red 72. *See* D&C Orange No. 5
Solvent red 73. *See* D&C Orange No. 10
Solvent violet 13. *See* CI 60725; D&C Violet No. 2
Solvent yellow 33. *See* CI 47000; D&C Yellow No. 11
Solvent yellow 94. *See* D&C Yellow No. 7

Sorbeth-20
  CAS 53694-15-8
  Synonyms: PEG-20 sorbitol ether; POE (20) sorbitol ether; PEG 1000 sorbitol ether
  Definition: PEG ether of sorbitol with an avg. 20 moles ethylene oxide
  Uses: Emulsifier, humectant for pharmaceutical uses
  Trade names: Ethosperse® SL-20

Sorbic acid
  CAS 110-44-1; 22500-92-1; EINECS 203-768-7
  Synonyms: 2,4-Hexadienoic acid; Hexadienic acid; (2-Butenylidene) acetic acid; 2-Propenylacrylic acid
  Classification: Organic acid
  Empirical: $C_6H_8O_2$
  Formula: $CH_3CH=CHCH=CHCOOH$
  Properties: Colorless needles or wh. powd., char. odor, almost tasteless; sol. in hot water; very sol. in alcohol, ether; m.w. 112.14; m.p. 134.5 C; b.p. 228 C (dec.); flash pt. (OC) 260 F

Sorbic acid ethyl ester

Precaution: Combustible exposed to heat or flame; reactive with oxidizers; light-sensitive
Toxicology: LD50 (oral, rat) 7360 mg/kg; mod. toxic by IP, subcut. routes; mildly toxic by ingestion; severe human skin irritant; eye irritant; experimental tumorigen, reproductive effects; mutagenic data; heated to decomp., emits acrid smoke, irritating fumes
Uses: Antimicrobial preservative, antibacterial, antifungal for orals, ophthalmics, topical dermatologicals incl. corticosteroid creams
Usage level: 0.05-0.5%; 0.1-0.13% (ophthalmics); 0.3% (oral enzyme prods., gelatin capsules)
Regulatory: FDA 21CFR §133, 146.115, 146.152, 146.154, 150.141, 150.161, 166.110, 181.22, 181.23, 182.3089, GRAS; USDA 9CFR §318.7; BATF 27CFR §240.1051; USA CIR approved, EPA reg.; JSCI approved 0.5% max.; Europe listed 0.6% max.; Japan approved with limitations; Europe listed; UK approved; FDA approved for orals, topicals; USP/NF, BP, Ph.Eur. compliance
Manuf./Distrib.: Allchem Industries; Ashland; Chisso; Eastman; Hoechst Celanese; Honeywill & Stein Ltd; Int'l. Sourcing; E. Merck; Penta Mfg.; Spectrum Chem. Mfg.; Spice King; Tri-K; Ueno Fine Chem. Ind.
Manuf./Distrib. (pharm. & food): Aldrich; Ashland; Daicel; Daiichi Pharmaceutical; Dainippon Pharmaceutical; Eastman; Ellis & Everard; Hoechst AG; Honeywill & Stein; Integra; Int'l. Sourcing; Jungbunzlauer; E Merck; Penta Mfg.; Quimdis; Robt. Bryce; Ruger; Sanofi; Siber Hegner; Spectrum Chem. Mfg.; Tesco; Ueno; Unipex; Van Waters & Rogers
Trade names containing: Dow Corning® Q7-2587; Dow Corning® Medical Antifoam AF Emulsion; Dry Vitamin A Palmitate Type 250-SD No. 65378; Vitamin B_{12} 0.1% SD No. 65354; Vitamin B_{12} 1.0% SD No. 65305

Sorbic acid ethyl ester. *See* Ethyl sorbate
Sorbic acid potassium salt. *See* Potassium sorbate
Sorbimacrogol laurate 300. *See* Polysorbate 20
Sorbimacrogol oleate 300. *See* Polysorbate 80
Sorbimacrogol palmitate 300. *See* Polysorbate 40
Sorbimacrogol stearate 300. *See* Polysorbate 60
Sorbimacrogol trioleate 300. *See* Polysorbate 85
Sorbimacrogol tristearate 300. *See* Polysorbate 65
Sorbit. *See* Sorbitol

Sorbitan caprylate
Uses: Emulsifier for pharmaceutical applics.
Trade names: Nissan Nonion CP-08R

Sorbitan, esters, monododecanoate. *See* Sorbitan laurate
Sorbitan, esters, monohexadecanoate. *See* Sorbitan palmitate
Sorbitan, esters, monooctadecanoate. *See* Sorbitan stearate

Sorbitan isostearate
CAS 54392-26-6; 71902-01-7
Synonyms: Anhydrosorbitol monoisostearate; 1,4-Anhydro-D-glucitol, 6-isooctadecanoate; Sorbitan monoisooctadecanoate
Definition: Monoester of isostearic acid and hexitol anhydrides derived from sorbitol
Empirical: $C_{24}H_{46}O_6$
Properties: M.w. 346.52
Toxicology: Experimental neoplastigen
Uses: Emulsifier, solubilizer, wetting agent for pharmaceuticals
Trade names: Crill 6; Nikkol SI-10R; Nikkol SI-10T; Nikkol SI-15T; Sorbirol ISM

Sorbitan laurate
CAS 1338-39-2; 5959-89-7; EINECS 215-663-3; 227-729-9
Synonyms: Sorbitan monolaurate; Sorbitan, esters, monododecanoate; Anhydrosorbitol monolaurate; Sorbitan monododecanoate
Definition: Monoester of lauric acid and hexitol anhydrides derived from sorbitol
Empirical: $C_{18}H_{34}O_6$
Properties: Yel. to amber oily liq., bland char. odor; sol. in methanol, alcohol, min. oil; sl. sol. in cottonseed oil, ethyl acetate; insol. in water; m.w. 346.47; dens. 1.032; acid no. 8 max.; sapon. no. 158-170; hyd. no. 330-358; flash pt. > 230 F;; ref. index 1.4740
Toxicology: Experimental neoplastigen
Uses: Emulsifier, solubilizer, wetting agent, surfactant; used in ophthalmics, orals
Regulatory: FDA 21CFR §175.320, 178.3400; Europe listed; UK approved; FDA approved for ophthalmics, orals; USP/NF, BP compliance
Manuf./Distrib.: Spectrum Chem. Mfg.

Trade names: Ablunol S-20; Arlacel® 20; Crill 1; Dehymuls® SML; Drewmulse® SML; Ethylan® GL20; Glycomul® L; Kemester® S20; Montane® 20; Nissan Nonion LP-20R, LP-20RS; Sorbitol L; Sorgen 90; Span® 20

Sorbitan, monodecanoate, poly(oxy-1,2-ethanediyl) derivs. *See* Polysorbate 20
Sorbitan monododecanoate. *See* Sorbitan laurate
Sorbitan, monohexadecanoate. *See* Sorbitan sesquiisostearate
Sorbitan, monohexadecanoate, poly(oxy-1,2-ethaneidyl) derivs. *See* Polysorbate 40
Sorbitan monoisooctadecanoate. *See* Sorbitan isostearate
Sorbitan monolaurate. *See* Sorbitan laurate
Sorbitan monooctadecanoate. *See* Sorbitan stearate
Sorbitan mono-9-octadecenoate. *See* Sorbitan oleate
Sorbitan monooleate. *See* Sorbitan oleate
Sorbitan monopalmitate. *See* Sorbitan palmitate
Sorbitan monostearate. *See* Sorbitan stearate

Sorbitan myristate
Definition: Monoester of myristic acid and hexitol anhydrides derived from sorbitol
Uses: Emulsifier for pharmaceutical applics.
Trade names: Nissan Nonion MP-30R

Sorbitan, 9-octadecenoate (2:3). *See* Sorbitan sesquioleate

Sorbitan oleate
CAS 1338-43-8; 5938-38-5; EINECS 215-665-4
Synonyms: SMO; Sorbitan monooleate; Sorbitan mono-9-octadecenoate; Anhydrosorbitol monooleate
Definition: Monoester of oleic acid and hexitol anhydrides derived from sorbitol
Empirical: $C_{24}H_{44}O_6$
Properties: Yel. to amber visc. liq., char. bland odor; misc. with min. and veg. oils; sl. sol. in ether; insol. in water, acetone, propylene glycol; m.w. 428.62; dens. 0.986; acid no. 8 max.; iodine no. 62-76; sapon. no. 145-160; hyd. no. 193-210; flash pt. > 230 F; ref. index 1.4800
Toxicology: Heated to decomp., emits acrid smoke and irritating fumes
Uses: Emulsifier, solubilizer, wetting agent, surfactant; used in orals, topicals
Regulatory: FDA 21CFR §73.1001, 173.75, 175.105, 175.320, 178.3400; Europe listed; UK approved; FDA approved for orals, topicals; USP/NF, BP compliance
Manuf./Distrib.: ABITEC; Heterene; ICI Surf.; Lonza; Norman, Fox; Spectrum Chem. Mfg.; Witco/Oleo-Surf.
Manuf./Distrib. (pharm. & food): Spectrum Chem. Mfg.
Trade names: Ablunol S-80; Arlacel® 80; Armotan® MO; Crill 4; Crill 50; Dehymuls® SMO; Drewmulse® SMO; Ethylan® GO80; Glycomul® O; Kemester® S80; Montane® 80; Nissan Nonion OP-80R; Rheodol AO-10; Sorbirol O; Sorgen 40
Trade names containing: Montane® 481

Sorbitan palmitate
CAS 26266-57-9; EINECS 247-568-8
Synonyms: Sorbitan monopalmitate; 1,4-Anhydro-D-glucitol, 6-hexadecanoate; Sorbitan, esters, monohexadecanoate
Definition: Partial ester of palmitic acid with sorbitol mono- and dianhydrides
Empirical: $C_{22}H_{42}O_6$
Properties: Tan gran. waxy solid, faint tallow-like odor; sol. in ethyl acetate, warm abs. alcohol; sol. hazy in warm peanut or min. oil; insol. in water; m.w. 1109.59; dens. 0.989; acid no. 8 max.; sapon. no. 140-150; hyd. no. 275-305; flash pt. > 230 F; ref. index 1.4780
Toxicology: No known toxicity; irritant
Uses: Nonionic surfactant, emulsifier, solubilizer, wetting agent; used in intramuscular injectables
Regulatory: FDA 21CFR §175.320, 178.3400; Europe listed; UK approved; FDA approved for intramuscular injectables; USP/NF compliance
Manuf./Distrib.: Spectrum Chem. Mfg.
Manuf./Distrib. (pharm. & food): Spectrum Chem. Mfg.
Trade names: Ablunol S-40; Arlacel® 40; Glycomul® P; Kemester® S40; Montane® 40; Nissan Nonion PP-40R; Sorbirol P; Span® 40

Sorbitan sesquiisostearate
Synonyms: Sorbitan, monohexadecanoate
Definition: Mixture of mono and diesters of isostearic acid and hexitol anhydrides derived from sorbitol
Uses: W/o emulsifier for pharmaceuticals
Trade names: Nikkol SI-15R

Sorbitan sesquioleate

Sorbitan sesquioleate
 CAS 8007-43-0; EINECS 232-360-1
 Synonyms: Anhydrosorbitol sesquioleate; Anhydrohexitol sesquioleate; Sorbitan, 9-octadecenoate (2:3)
 Definition: Mixture of mono and diesters of oleic acid and hexitol anhydrides derived from sorbitol
 Properties: Yel. to amber thick oily liq.; sol. in alcohol, IPA, min. oil, cottonseed oil; insol. in water, propylene glycol; acid no. 14 max.; iodine no. 65-75; sapon. no. 143-165; hyd. no. 182-220
 Uses: W/o emulsifier, solubilizer, antifoam; used in topicals
 Regulatory: FDA 21CFR §175.320; FDA approved for topicals
 Manuf./Distrib.: Spectrum Chem. Mfg.
 Manuf./Distrib. (pharm. & food): Aldrich
 Trade names: Arlacel® 83; Crill 43; Dehymuls® SSO; Glycomul® SOC; Montane® 83; Nissan Nonion OP-83RAT; Rheodol AO-15; Sorbirol SQ; Sorgen 30
 Trade names containing: Alcolan®; Alcolan® 36W; Alcolan® 40; Dehymuls® E; Dehymuls® K

Sorbitan stearate
 CAS 1338-41-6; 69005-67-8; EINECS 215-664-9
 FEMA 3028
 Synonyms: SMS; Sorbitan monostearate; Sorbitan monooctadecanoate; Sorbitan, esters, monooctadecanoate; Anhydrosorbitol monostearate
 Definition: Monoester of stearic acid and hexitol anhydrides derived from sorbitol
 Empirical: $C_{24}H_{46}O_6$
 Properties: Cream to tan beads, bland odor and taste; sol. in veg. and min. oils; insol. in water, acetone, alcohol, propylene glycol; m.w. 430.70; acid no. 5-10; sapon. no. 147-157; hyd. no. 235-260
 Toxicology: LD50 (oral, rat) 31 g/kg; very mildly toxic by ingestion; experimental reproductive effects; heated to decomp., emits acrid smoke and irritating fumes
 Uses: Emulsifier, solubilizer, wetting agent, surfactant; used in topicals, vaginals, orals, suntan creams
 Regulatory: FDA 21CFR §73.1001, 163.123, 163.130, 163.135, 163.140, 163.145, 163.150, 163.153, 163.155, 172.515, 172.842, 173.340, 175.105, 175.320, 178.3400, 573.960; FEMA GRAS; Europe listed; UK approved; FDA approved for topicals, vaginals, orals; USP/NF, BP compliance
 Manuf./Distrib.: Aldrich; Aquatec Quimica SA; Spectrum Chem. Mfg.
 Manuf./Distrib. (pharm. & food): Aldrich; Spectrum Chem. Mfg.
 Trade names: Ablunol S-60; Arlacel® 60; Capmul® S; Crill 3; Dehymuls® SMS; Drewmulse® SMS; Ethylan® GS60; Glycomul® S; Kemester® S60; Montane® 60; Nissan Nonion SP-60R; Rheodol AS-10; S-Maz® 60K; Sorbirol S; Sorgen 50; Span® 60; Span® 60K; Span® 60 VS

Sorbitan trioctadecanoate. *See* Sorbitan tristearate
Sorbitan tri-9-octadecenoate. *See* Sorbitan trioleate

Sorbitan trioleate
 CAS 26266-58-0; 85186-88-5; EINECS 247-569-3; 286-074-7
 Synonyms: STO; Anhydrosorbitol trioleate; Sorbitan tri-9-octadecenoate
 Definition: Triester of oleic acid and hexitol anhydrides derived from sorbitol
 Empirical: $C_{60}H_{108}O_8$
 Properties: Yel. to amber oily liq.; sol. in alcohol, veg. oil, min. oil; insol. in water, ethylene glycol, propylene glycol; m.w. 957.52; dens. 0.956; acid no. 17 max.; iodine no. 77-85; sapon. no. 170-190; hyd. no. 50-75; flash pt. > 230 F; ref. index 1.4760
 Toxicology: Irritant
 Uses: Emulsifier, surfactant, solubilizer; used in inhalants, orals, topicals
 Regulatory: FDA 21CFR §175.320, 178.3400; FDA approved for inhalants, orals, topicals
 Manuf./Distrib.: Spectrum Chem. Mfg.
 Manuf./Distrib. (pharm. & food): Aldrich
 Trade names: Ablunol S-85; Arlacel® 85; Crill 45; Ethylan® GT85; Glycomul® TO; Kemester® S85; Montane® 85; Nissan Nonion OP-85R; Sorbirol TO; Span® 85

Sorbitan tristearate
 CAS 26658-19-5; 72869-62-6; EINECS 247-891-4; 276-951-2
 Synonyms: STS; Anhydrosorbitol tristearate; Sorbitan trioctadecanoate
 Definition: Triester of stearic acid and hexitol anhydrides derived from sorbitol
 Empirical: $C_{60}H_{114}O_8$
 Properties: Tan waxy beads; sol. in IPA; insol. in water; m.w. 963.56; acid no. 12-15; sapon. no. 176-188
 Toxicology: No known toxicity
 Uses: Surfactant, emulsifier, lubricant, stabilizer, solubilizer, dispersant, wetting agent, visc. control agent
 Regulatory: FDA 21CFR §175.320, 178.3400; Europe listed; UK approved
 Manuf./Distrib.: Henkel/Emery; ICI Surf.; Lonza; Spectrum Chem. Mfg.
 Manuf./Distrib. (pharm. & food): ICI Spec.

Trade names: Crill 35; Drewmulse® STS; Glycomul® TS; Kemester® S65; Montane® 65; Sorbirol TS; Span® 65; Span® 65K

D-Sorbite. *See* Sorbitol

Sorbitol

CAS 50-70-4; EINECS 200-061-5
FEMA 3029
Synonyms: D-Glucitol; Sorbit; Sorbol; Sorbo; D-Sorbitol; D-Sorbite; 1,2,3,4,5,6-Hexanehexol
Classification: Hexahydric alcohol
Empirical: $C_6H_{14}O_6$
Formula: $CH_2OHHCOHHOCHHCOHHCOHCH_2OH$
Properties: White cryst. powd., gran. or flakes, odorless, sweet taste; hygroscopic; sol. in water; sol. in hot alcohol, methanol, IPA, DMF, acetic acid, phenol, acetamide sol'ns.; m.w. 182.20; dens. 1.47 (-5 C); m.p. 93-97.5 C; b.p. 105 C; pH ≈ 7.0
Toxicology: LD50 (oral, rat) 17.5 mg/kg; mildly toxic by ingestion; excess consumption may have laxative effect; intolerance manifested by abdominal pain, bloating, diarrhea; no known toxicity if used externally
Uses: Humectant, plasticizer, nutritive sweetener, oleaginous vehicle; tablet diluent; used in suspensions, sol'ns., syrups, elixirs, dentals, intramuscular injectables, rectals, dentifrices, deodorants, antiperspirants; increases absorp. of vitamins
Usage level: 70-72% (suspensions); 6-35% (sol'ns.); 5-25% (syrups); 5-20% (elixirs)
Regulatory: FDA 21CFR §175.300, 182.90, 184.1835, GRAS; FEMA GRAS; Japan approved; Europe listed; UK approved; FDA approved for dentals, intramuscular injectables, orals, rectals; USP/NF, BP, Ph.Eur. compliance
Manuf./Distrib.: Aldrich; Cerestar UK; EM Industries; Fanning; ICI Spec.; Lipo; Lonza; Pfizer Food Science
Manuf./Distrib. (pharm. & food): ADM; Aldrich; Am. Roland; Am. Xyrofin; Ashland; Browning; Calaga Food Ingreds.; Cerestar Int'l.; Cheil Foods; Ellis & Everard; ICI Atkemix; Integra; Int'l. Sourcing; E Merck; Penta Mfg.; Pfizer Food Science; Regency Mowbray; Ruger; Spectrum Chem. Mfg.
Trade names: A-641; Arlex; Fancol SORB; Hydex® 100 Coarse Powd.; Hydex® 100 Coarse Powd. 35; Hydex® 100 Gran. 206; Hydex® 100 Powd. 60; Hydex® Tablet Grade; Liponic 70-NC; Liponic 76-NC; Liponic 83-NC; Liponic Sorbitol Sol'n. 70% USP; Liposorb 70; Sorbelite™ C; Sorbelite™ FG; Unisweet 70; Unisweet 70/CONC; Unisweet CONC
Trade names containing: Palma-Sperse® Type 250-S No. 65322; Palma-Sperse® Type 250A/50 D-S No. 65221

D-Sorbitol. *See* Sorbitol

Sorbitol sol'n.

CAS 50-70-4; 3959-43-3
FEMA 3029
Definition: Water-based sol'n. contg. no less than 64% D-sorbitol
Properties: Colorless clear syrupy liq., no char. odor, sweet taste; dens. ≥ 1.285; ref. index 1.455-1.465 (20 C); neutral pH
Uses: Sweetening agent, vehicle; used in intramuscular injectables, rectals, topicals
Regulatory: FDA approved for intramuscular injectables, rectals, topicals; USP/NF, BP compliance
Manuf./Distrib. (pharm. & food): Spectrum Chem. Mfg.

Sorbo. *See* Sorbitol
Sorbol. *See* Sorbitol
Soya bean oil. *See* Soybean oil
Soya flour. *See* Soy flour
Soya lecithin. *See* Lecithin
Soya oil. *See* Soybean oil

Soybean oil

CAS 8001-22-7; EINECS 232-274-4
Synonyms: Soya oil; Soya bean oil; Chinese bean oil
Classification: Fixed oil
Definition: Oil obtained from seeds of soya plant, *Glycine soja*, by extraction or expression; consists of triglycerides of oleic, linoleic, linolenic, and saturated acids
Properties: Pale yel. to brnsh. yel. oil, sl. char. odor and taste; sol. in alcohol, ether, chloroform, carbon disulfide; insol. in water; dens. 0.924-0.929; visc. 50.09 cps; m.p. 22-31 C; iodine no. 120-141; sapon. no. 189-195; flash pt. 540 F; ref. index 1.471
Precaution: Combustible; light-sensitive
Toxicology: May cause allergic reactions incl. hair damage and acne-like pimples; heated to decomp., emits acrid smoke and irritating fumes

Soybean oil hydrogenated

Uses: Oleaginous vehicle; used in parenteral pharmaceuticals, orals, topicals
Regulatory: FDA 21CFR §175.105, 175.300, 176.200, 176.210, 177.2800, GRAS; FDA approved for orals, topicals; USP/NF, BP compliance
Manuf./Distrib.: ABITEC; Arista Industries; Tri-K
Manuf./Distrib. (pharm. & food): Aarhus Olie; ABITEC; Aldrich; Amcan France; Am. Ingreds.; Am. Roland; Arista Industries; S Black; Calgene; CanAmera Foods; Cargill; Central Soya; Penta Mfg.; Riceland Foods; Ruger; Soya Mainz; Spectrum Chem. Mfg.; Spectrum Naturals; Vamo-Fuji Specialities
Trade names: Super Refined® Soybean Oil USP
Trade names containing: Aloe Vera Lipo-Quinone Extract™ Food Grade; Neobee® SL-110; Neobee® SL-140

Soybean oil hydrogenated. *See* Hydrogenated soybean oil
Soybean oil, maleated. *See* Maleated soybean oil

Soy flour
CAS 68513-95-1
Synonyms: Flour, soy; Soya flour
Definition: Powd. prepared from fine grinding of soybean, *Glycine max.*
Uses: Tablet disintegrant
Trade names: Emcosoy®

Spearmint
Synonyms: Mentha viridis; Mint
Definition: Dried leaves and flowering tops of *Mentha spicata*
Uses: Natural flavoroing agent; carminative

Spearmint oil
CAS 8008-79-5
FEMA 3032
Synonyms: Mentha spicata oil; Crispmint oil; Curled mint oil
Definition: Volatile oil obtained from the dried tops and leaves of *Mentha spicata*, contg. chiefly carvone
Properties: Colorless or greenish-yel. liq., spearmint odor and taste; sol. in equal vol 80% alcohol; very sl. sol. in water; dens. 0.917-0.934 (25/25 C); ref. index 1.4820-1.4900 (20 C)
Precaution: Keep cool, well closed; protect from light
Toxicology: LD50 (oral, rat) 5 g/kg; mildly toxic by ingestion; mutagenic data; skin irritant; allergen causing skin rash; heated to decomp., emits acrid smoke and irritating fumes
Uses: Natural flavoring agent; used in buccals, orals, toothpaste; stimulant, carminative, antispasmodic
Regulatory: FDA 21CFR §182.10, 182.20, GRAS; 27CFR §21.65, 12.128, 21.151; FEMA GRAS; Japan approved (spearmint); Europe listed, no restrictions; FDA approved for buccals, orals; BP compliance
Manuf./Distrib. (pharm. & food): Acme-Hardesty; Florida Treatt; Ruger; Spectrum Chem. Mfg.

Spinacane. *See* Squalane
Spinacene. *See* Squalene
Spirit of Hartshorn. *See* Ammonium hydroxide
Spirit of salt. *See* Hydrochloric acid

Squalane
CAS 111-01-3; EINECS 203-825-6
Synonyms: Cosbiol; Dodecahydrosqualene; Spinacane; 2,6,10,15,19,23-Hexamethyltetracosane; Perhydrosqualene; Robane
Classification: Saturated hydrocarbon
Definition: Saturated branched chain hydrocarbon obtained by hydrogenation of shark liver oil or other natural oils
Empirical: $C_{30}H_{62}$
Formula: $[(CH_3)_2CHCH_2CH_2CH_2CH(CH_3)CH_2CH_2CH_2CH(CH_3)CH_2CH_2.]_2$
Properties: Colorless liq., odorless, tasteless; sol. in ether, gasoline; misc. with veg. and min. oils, org. solvs., lipophilic substances; m.w. 422.83; dens. 0.805-0.812 (20 C); m.p. -38 C; b.p. 350 C (760 mm); acid no. 0.2 max.; iodine no. 4 max.; sapon. no. 2 max.; flash pt. 218 C; ref. index 1.4530 (15 C)
Precaution: Combustible
Toxicology: No known toxicity
Uses: Bactericide, oleaginous vehicle, lubricant in topical pharmaceuticals; carrier of lipid-sol. drugs in suppositories; ointment base
Regulatory: FDA approved for topicals; USP/NF, BP compliance
Manuf./Distrib.: Arista Industries; Kishimoto Sangyo; Kuraray; Nikko Chem.; Robeco
Manuf./Distrib. (pharm. & food): Aldrich; Kishimoto Sangyo; Kuraray; Ruger
Trade names: Robane®

Squalene
CAS 111-02-4; EINECS 203-826-1
Synonyms: 2,6,10,15,19,23-Hexamethyl-2,6,10,14,18,22-tetracosahexaene; Spinacene
Empirical: $C_{30}H_{50}$
Properties: Oil, faint odor; insol. in water; sl. sol. in alcohol; sol. in lipids, org. solvs.; m.w. 410.73; dens. 0.858-0.860 (20 C); m.p. -75 C; b.p. 285 C (25 mm); ref. index 1.4965 (20 C); visc. 12 cps (25 C); flash pt. 200 C; ref. index 1.496 (20 C)
Precaution: Combustible; photosensitive
Uses: Chemical intermediate for mfg. of pharmaceuticals; pharmaceutical research; emollient, protectant, vehicle used in topicals
Regulatory: FDA approved for topicals
Manuf./Distrib.: Arista Industries; Robeco
Manuf./Distrib. (pharm. & food): Aldrich; Ruger
Trade names: Supraene®

Stannous chloride anhyd.
CAS 7772-99-8; EINECS 231-868-0
UN No. 1759 (solid)
Synonyms: Tin (II) chloride anhydrous; Tin crystals; Tin (II) chloride (1:2); Tin salt; Tin dichloride; Tin protochloride
Definition: Chloride salt of metallic tin
Empirical: Cl_2Sn
Formula: $SnCl_2$
Properties: Colorless orthorhombic cryst. mass or flakes, fatty appearance; sol. in water, ethanol, acetone, ether, methyl acetate, MEK, isobutyl alcohol; pract. insol. in min. spirits, xylene; m.w. 189.60; dens. 3.95; m.p. 246.8 C; b.p. 652 C
Precaution: Potentially explosive reaction with metal nitrates; violent reactions with hydrogen peroxide, ethylene oxide, nitrates, K, Na; moisture-sensitive
Toxicology: TLV:TWA 2 mg(Sn)/m^3; LD50 (oral, rat) 700 mg/kg, (IP, mouse) 66 mg/kg; poison by ingestion, IP, IV, subcutaneous routes; experimental reproductive effects; human mutagenic data; heated to decomp., emits toxic fumes of Cl⁻
Uses: Antioxidant used in intravenous, parenterals
Regulatory: FDA 21CFR §155.200, 172.180, 175.300, 177.2600, 184.1845, GRAS; FDA approved for intravenous, parenterals
Manuf./Distrib.: Aldrich; Blythe, William Ltd; Cerac; Elf Atochem N. Am.; Noah Chem.; Spectrum Chem. Mfg.
Manuf./Distrib. (pharm. & food): Integra

Stannous fluoride
CAS 7783-47-3 (anhyd.); EINECS 231-999-3
Synonyms: Tin fluoride; Tin difluoride
Empirical: F_2Sn
Formula: SnF_2
Properties: Wh. lustrous cryst. powd., bitter salty taste; hygroscopic; sol. in water; almost insol. in ether, chloroform, alcohol; m.w. 156.69; m.p. 212-214 C; pH 2.8-3.5 (0.4%)
Toxicology: Toxic by inhalation, skin contact, ingestion; causes burns
Uses: Decay preventative in dentifrices, mouthwashes; also in intravenous
Regulatory: FDA approved for intravenous; USP compliance
Manuf./Distrib.: Spectrum Chem. Mfg.
Manuf./Distrib. (pharm. & food): Integra; Ruger; Spectrum Chem. Mfg.

Stannous pyrophosphate
CAS 15578-26-4; EINECS 239-635-5
Synonyms: Diphosphoric acid tin (2+) salt; Ditin diphosphate; Salt of tin
Formula: $Sn_2P_2O_7$
Properties: Wh. powd.; insol. in water; sol. in HCl, aq. ammonia, alkaline pyrophosphate sol'n.; m.w. 411.32
Toxicology: Relatively nontoxic when used externally
Uses: Used in dentals
Regulatory: FDA approved for dentals
Manuf./Distrib.: Nihon Kagaku Sangyo

Stannous tartrate
CAS 815-85-0
Uses: Used in intravenous
Regulatory: FDA approved for intravenous

Stannum

Stannum. *See* Tin

Star anise
FEMA 2095
Definition: Derived from *Illicium verum*
Uses: Natural flavoring agent; used in oral hygiene
Regulatory: FDA 21CFR §182.10, GRAS; FEMA GRAS; Japan approved; Europe listed, no restrictions (oil)

Star anise oil. *See* Anise oil

Starch
CAS 9005-25-8; 9005-84-9; EINECS 232-686-4
Classification: Carbohydrate polymer
Definition: Complex polysaccharide composed of units of glucose consisting of about one quarter amylose and three quarters amylopectin; derived from corn, wheat, potatoes, or tapioca
Empirical: $(C_6H_{10}O_5)_n$
Properties: White amorphous powd. or gran., odorless, sl. char. taste; insol. in cold water, alcohol; forms gels in hot water; m.w. 162.14_n
Toxicology: May cause contact dermatitis, peritonitis
Uses: Filler, binder, disintegrant, adsorbent, diluent, carrier for tablets; used in buccals, parenterals, orals, rectals, topicals, vaginals; rubber glove powd.
Regulatory: FDA 21CFR §182.90, GRAS; FDA approved for buccals, parenterals, orals, rectals, topicals, vaginals; USP/NF, BP compliance
Manuf./Distrib.: Nat'l. Starch & Chem.
Manuf./Distrib. (pharm. & food): Aldrich; Spectrum Chem. Mfg.
Trade names containing: Colored Nu-Pareil® PG 14/18; Colored Nu-Pareil® PG 16/20; Colored Nu-Pareil® PG 18/20; Colored Nu-Pareil® PG 20/25; Colored Nu-Pareil® PG 25/30; Colored Nu-Pareil® PG 30/35; Destab™ Calcium Carbonate 90; Destab™ Calcium Carbonate 95; Durkote Calcium Carbonate/Starch, Acacia Gum; Nu-Core® 35/45; Nu-Core® 40/50; Nu-Core® 45/60; Nu-Pareil® PG 14/18; Nu-Pareil® PG 16/20; Nu-Pareil® PG 18/20; Nu-Pareil® PG 20/25; Nu-Pareil® PG 25/30; Nu-Pareil® PG 30/35; Rocoat® Riboflavin 25% No. 60289

Starch carboxymethyl ether sodium salt. *See* Sodium starch glycolate
Starch, corn. *See* Corn starch

Starch glycerin
Synonyms: Starch glycerite
Uses: Emollient; pill excipient

Starch glycerite. *See* Starch glycerin
Starch gum. *See* Dextrin

Starch, pregelatinized
Classification: Carbohydrate polymer
Definition: Starch that has been chemically or mechanically processed to rupture all or part of the gran. in the presence of water, and then dried
Properties: Wh. to off-wh. fine to coarse powd., odorless, sl. char. taste; sl. sol. to sol. in cold water; insol. in alcohol; pH 4.5-7
Uses: Tablet/capsule binder, diluent, disintegrant
Regulatory: USP/NF compliance
Trade names containing: Cal-Carb® 4457; Cal-Carb® 4462

Starch syrup. *See* Glucose, liquid

Stearalkonium bentonite
Definition: Reaction prod. of bentonite and stearalkonium chloride
Uses: Ingred. in pharmaceutical ointments and creams
Trade names containing: Miglyol® Gel T

Stearalkonium chloride
CAS 122-19-0; EINECS 204-527-9
UN No. 1993
Synonyms: Stearyl dimethyl benzyl ammonium chloride; Dimethyloctadecylbenzyl ammonium chloride; Octadecyl dimethyl benzyl ammonium chloride; N,N-Dimethyl-N-octadecylbenzenemethanaminium chloride
Classification: Quaternary ammonium salt
Empirical: $C_{27}H_{50}N \cdot Cl$
Properties: M.w. 424.23

Precaution: DOT: Flamm. liq.
Toxicology: LD50 (oral, rat) 125 mg/kg; poison by intraperitoneal route; moderately toxic by ingestion; human skin and severe eye irritant; heated to decomp., emits very toxic fumes of NO_x, NH_3, and Cl^-
Uses: Antimicrobial, emulsifier; used in topicals
Regulatory: FDA 21CFR §172.165 (limitation 1.5-6 ppm), 173.320 (limitation 0.05 ppm raw sugarcane or raw beets), 175.105; FDA approved for topicals
Manuf./Distrib.: Ferrosan Fine Chem. A/S; Lonza; Mason; McIntyre; Witco
Trade names: Arquad® DM18B-90

Stearalkonium hectorite
CAS 94891-33-5; 12691-60-0
Definition: Reaction prod. of hectorite and stearalkonium chloride
Uses: Thixotrope, gellant, thickener; used in topicals
Regulatory: FDA approved for topicals
Trade names containing: Miglyol® 840 Gel B; Miglyol® Gel B

Stearamide DEA
CAS 93-82-3; EINECS 202-280-1
Synonyms: Stearic acid diethanolamide; Stearoyl diethanolamide; Diethanolamine stearic acid amide; N,N-Bis(2-hydroxyethyl) stearamide; N,N-Bis(2-hydroxyethyl) octadecanamide
Definition: Mixture of ethanolamides of stearic acid
Empirical: $C_{22}H_{45}NO_3$
Formula: $CH_3(CH_2)_{16}CON(CH_2CH_2OH)_2$
Uses: Used in dermatologicals
Regulatory: FDA 21CFR §175.105, 176.180, 177.2260, 177.2800
Trade names containing: Cetina

Stearamide MEA-stearate
CAS 14351-40-7; EINECS 238-310-5
Synonyms: Octadecanoic acid, 2-[(1-oxooctadecyl)amino]ethyl ester; Stearic monoethanolamide stearate; 2-[(1-Oxooctadecyl)amino]ethyl octadecanoate
Classification: Substituted ethanolamide
Properties: Flakes; insol. in water; gels in min. oil, IPM; m.p. 76-82 C; sapon. no. 97-107
Toxicology: No known toxicity
Uses: Emulsifier
Trade names: Cerasynt® D

Stearamidoethyl diethylamine
CAS 16889-14-8; EINECS 240-924-3
Synonyms: Diethylaminoethyl stearamide; N-[2-Diethylamino)ethyl]octadecanamide
Classification: Amidoamine
Empirical: $C_{24}H_{50}N_2O$
Formula: $CH_3(CH_2)_{16}CONH(CH_2)_2N(CH_2CH_3)_2$
Uses: Emulsifier for topical pharmaceuticals
Trade names containing: Lexemul® AR

Stearamidopropyl dimethylamine
CAS 7651-02-7; EINECS 231-609-1
Synonyms: Dimethylaminopropyl stearamide; N-[3-(Dimethylamino)propyl]octadecanamide
Classification: Amidoamine
Empirical: $C_{23}H_{48}N_2O$
Formula: $CH_3(CH_2)_{16}CONH(CH_2)_3N(CH_3)_2$
Uses: Raw material for pharmaceuticals
Trade names: Lipamine SPA

Steareth-2
CAS 9005-00-9 (generic); 16057-43-5
Synonyms: PEG-2 stearyl ether; POE (2) stearyl ether; PEG 100 stearyl ether
Definition: PEG ether of stearyl alcohol
Empirical: $C_{22}H_{46}O_3$
Formula: $CH_3(CH_2)_{16}CH_2(OCH_2CH_2)_nOH$, avg. n = 2
Properties: Oily liq.
Toxicology: Moderately toxic by ingestion
Uses: Surfactant and emulsifier used in topicals
Regulatory: FDA approved for topicals
Trade names: Acconon SA-2; Britex S 20; Volpo S-2

Steareth-7

CAS 9005-00-9 (generic); 66146-84-7
Synonyms: PEG-7 stearyl ether; POE (7) stearyl ether; 3,6,9,12,15,18,21-Heptaoxanonatriacontan-1-ol
Definition: PEG ether of stearyl alcohol
Empirical: $C_{32}H_{66}O_8$
Formula: $CH_3(CH_2)_{16}CH_2(OCH_2CH_2)_nOH$, avg. n = 7
Uses: Emulsifier for pharmaceuticals
Trade names containing: Emulgator E 2149; Emulgator E 2155

Steareth-8

CAS 9005-00-9 (generic)
Uses: Emulsifier
Trade names: Tewax TC 72

Steareth-10

CAS 9005-00-9 (generic); 13149-86-5
Synonyms: PEG-10 stearyl ether; POE (10) stearyl ether; PEG 500 stearyl ether
Definition: PEG ether of stearyl alcohol
Empirical: $C_{38}H_{78}O_{11}$
Formula: $CH_3(CH_2)_{16}CH_2(OCH_2CH_2)_nOH$, avg. n = 10
Uses: Surfactant and emulsifying agent used in rectals, topicals
Regulatory: FDA approved for rectals, topicals
Trade names: Britex S 100; Volpo S-10
Trade names containing: Cosmowax; Emulgator E 2155

Steareth-16

CAS 9005-00-9 (generic)
Synonyms: PEG-16 stearyl ether; POE (16) stearyl ether
Definition: PEG ether of stearyl alcohol
Empirical: $C_{50}H_{102}O_{17}$
Formula: $CH_3(CH_2)_{16}CH_2(OCH_2CH_2)_nOH$, avg. n = 16
Uses: Surfactant, emulsifying agent
Regulatory: FDA 21CFR §177.2800

Steareth-20

CAS 9005-00-9 (generic)
Synonyms: PEG-20 stearyl ether; POE (20) stearyl ether; PEG 1000 stearyl ether
Definition: PEG ether of stearyl alcohol
Empirical: $C_{58}H_{118}O_{21}$
Formula: $CH_3(CH_2)_{16}CH_2(OCH_2CH_2)_nOH$, avg. n = 20
Uses: Emulsifier, gellant, stabilizer, wetting agent, dispersant, solubilizer
Regulatory: FDA 21CFR §177.2800
Trade names: Britex S 200; Simulsol® 78; Volpo S-20
Trade names containing: Cosmowax; Macol® CPS; Ritachol® 1000; Ritachol® 3000; Ritachol® 4000; Tefose® 2000

Steareth-21

CAS 9005-00-9 (generic)
Synonyms: PEG-21 stearyl ether; POE (21) stearyl ether
Definition: PEG ether of stearyl alcohol
Empirical: $C_{60}H_{122}O_{22}$
Formula: $CH_3(CH_2)_{16}CH_2(OCH_2CH_2)_nOH$, avg. n = 21
Uses: Surfactant and emulsifying agent used in topicals
Regulatory: FDA approved for topicals

Steareth-25

CAS 9005-00-9 (generic)
Synonyms: PEG-25 stearyl ether; POE (25) stearyl ether
Definition: PEG ether of stearyl alcohol
Empirical: $C_{68}H_{138}O_{26}$
Formula: $CH_3(CH_2)_{16}CH_2(OCH_2CH_2)_nOH$, avg. n = 25
Uses: Ingred. in pharmaceuticals
Regulatory: FDA 21CFR §177.2800
Trade names containing: Solulan® 25

Steareth-100

CAS 9005-00-9 (generic)

Synonyms: PEG-100 stearyl ether; POE (100) stearyl ether
Definition: PEG ether of stearyl alcohol
Empirical: $C_{218}H_{438}O_{101}$
Formula: $CH_3(CH_2)_{16}CH_2(OCH_2CH_2)_nOH$, avg. n = 100
Uses: Emulsifier for pharmaceuticals
Trade names: Brij® 700

Stearic acid

CAS 57-11-4; EINECS 200-313-4
FEMA 3035
Synonyms: n-Octadecanoic acid; Carboxylic acid C_{18}
Classification: Fatty acid
Empirical: $C_{18}H_{36}O_2$
Formula: $CH_3(CH_2)_{16}COOH_9$
Properties: White to ylsh.-wh. amorphous solid, tallow-like odor and taste; very sl. sol. in water; sol. in alcohol, ether, acetone, CCl_4; m.w. 284.47; dens. 0.847 (70 C); m.p. 69.3 C; b.p. 383 C; acid no. 195-200; iodine no. 4 max.; flash pt. (CC) 385 F; ref. index 1.4299 (80 C)
Precaution: Combustible when exposed to heat or flame; heats spontaneously
Toxicology: LD50 (IV, rat) 21.5 ± 1.8 mg/kg; poison by intravenous route; experimental tumorigen; human skin irritant; possible sensitizer for allergic persons; heated to decomp., emits acrid smoke and irritating fumes
Uses: Tablet/capsule lubricant; lubricant/softener in suppositories, ointments; emulsifier, solubilizer; used in buccals, implants, orals, topicals, vaginals; sunscreens; stearates as pharmaceutical aids
Regulatory: FDA 21CFR §172.210, 172.615, 172.860, 175.105, 175.300, 175.320, 176.170, 176.200, 176.210, 177.1010, 177.1200, 177.2260, 177.2600, 177.2800, 178.3570, 178.3910, 184.1090, GRAS; FEMA GRAS; Europe listed; FDA approved for buccals, implants, orals, topicals, vaginals; USP/NF, BP, JP compliance
Manuf./Distrib.: Akrochem; Akzo Nobel; Allchem Ind.; Condor; Cookson Spec.; Great Western; Henkel/Emery; Lonza; Penta Mfg.; Syn. Prods.; Unichema; Witco/Oleo-Surf.
Manuf./Distrib. (pharm. & food): Acme-Hardesty; Aldrich; Integra; Ruger; Spectrum Chem. Mfg.
Trade names: Emersol® 6332 NF; Hystrene® 4516; Hystrene® 5016 NF; Hystrene® 9718 NF
Trade names containing: Cutina® FS 25 Flakes; Cutina® FS 45 Flakes; Descote® Niacinamide 33$^1/_3$%; Montane® 481; Rocoat® Niacinamide 33$^1/_3$% Type S No. 69909; Ross Beeswax Substitute 628/5

Stearic acid aluminum dihydroxide salt. *See* Aluminum stearate
Stearic acid calcium salt. *See* Calcium stearate
Stearic acid diethanolamide. *See* Stearamide DEA
Stearic acid, 2-methylpropyl ester. *See* Isobutyl stearate
Stearic acid, 2-octyldodecyl ester. *See* Octyldodecyl stearate
Stearic acid, potassium salt. *See* Potassium stearate
Stearic acid sodium salt. *See* Sodium stearate
Stearic monoethanolamide stearate. *See* Stearamide MEA-stearate
Stearin. *See* Tristearin

Stearone

CAS 504-53-0; EINECS 207-993-1
Synonyms: Diheptadecyl ketone; 18-Pentatriacontanone
Classification: Aliphatic ketone
Empirical: $C_{35}H_{70}O$
Formula: $CH_3(CH_2)_{16}CO(CH_2)_{16}CH_3$
Uses: Used in pharmaceutical systems
Trade names containing: Amerchol® 400

Stearoxy dimethicone

CAS 68554-53-0
Synonyms: Dimethyl siloxy stearoxy siloxane polymer; Poly(dimethylsiloxy)stearoxysiloxane
Definition: Polymer of dimethylpolysiloxane endblocked with stearoxy groups
Uses: Spreading agent, emollient for antiperspirants, sunscreens
Trade names: Abil®-Wax 2434

Stearoyl diethanolamide. *See* Stearamide DEA

Stearyl alcohol

CAS 112-92-5; EINECS 204-017-6
Synonyms: n-Octadecanol; Octadecyl alcohol; Stenol; 1-Octadecanol; n-Octyldecyl alcohol; C18 linear alcohol; Decyl octyl alcohol
Classification: Fatty alcohol

Stearyl citrate

Empirical: $C_{18}H_{38}O$
Formula: $CH_3(CH_2)_{16}CH_2OH$
Properties: Wh. unctuous flakes or gran., faint odor, bland taste; sol. in alcohol, acetone, ether; insol. in water; m.w. 270.56; dens. 0.8124 (59/4 C); m.p. 55-60 C; b.p. 210.5 C (15 mm); acid no. 2 max.; iodine no. 2 max.; hyd. no. 195-220
Precaution: Flamm. when exposed to heat or flame; can react with oxidizers
Toxicology: LD50 (oral, rat) 20 g/kg; mildly toxic by ingestion; may cause skin sensitivity; nonallergenic; experimental neoplastigen; heated to decomp., emits acrid smoke and irritating fumes
Uses: Surface-active agent used to stabilize emulsions; emollient, emulsifier; stiffening agent; astringent in anti-itch preps.; used in orals, topicals, vaginals
Regulatory: FDA 21CFR §172.755, 172.864, 175.105, 175.300, 176.200, 176.210, 177.1010, 177.1200, 177.2800, 178.3480, 178.3910; FDA approved for orals, topicals, vaginals; USP/NF, BP, Ph.Eur. compliance
Manuf./Distrib.: Aarhus Oliefabrik A/S; Albemarle; Amerchol; Chemron; Croda; Kraft; Lipo; Lonza; M. Michel; Procter & Gamble; Vista
Manuf./Distrib. (pharm. & food): Aarhus Oliefabrik A/S; Aldrich; Croda; Integra; Procter & Gamble; Ruger; Spectrum Chem. Mfg.
Trade names: Adol® 61 NF; Cachalot® S-56; Crodacol S-95NF; Dehydag® Wax 18; Epal® 18NF; Hyfatol 18-95; Hyfatol 18-98; Lanette® 18; Lanette® 18 DEO; Mackol 18; Nacol® 18-94; Nacol® 18-98; Steraffine; Unihydag Wax-18
Trade names containing: Brookswax™ G; Cerasynt® WM; Cosmowax; Cosmowax K; Emulgator E 2149; Emulgator E 2155; Macol® 125; Pionier® OEWA-II; Promulgen® G

Stearyl citrate
CAS 1337-33-3; EINECS 215-654-4
Synonyms: 2-Hydroxy-1,2,3-propanetricarboxylic acid, monooctadecyl ester; Octadecyl citrate; Citric acid, octadecyl ester
Definition: Ester of stearyl alcohol and citric acid
Empirical: $C_{24}H_{44}O_7$
Formula: $HOCH_2COOHCCOOHCH_2COOCH_2(CH_2)_{16}CH_3$
Precaution: Moisture-sensitive
Toxicology: Heated to decomp., emits acrid smoke and irritating fumes
Uses: Used in pharmaceutical ointments and creams
Regulatory: FDA 21CFR §166.40, 166.110, 175.300, 178.3910, 181.22, 181.27, 182.6851 (0.15% max. as sequestrant), GRAS, 582.6851
Trade names containing: Dehymuls® E

Stearyl dimethyl benzyl ammonium chloride. *See* Stearalkonium chloride
Stearyl glyceryl ether. *See* Batyl alcohol

Stearyl glycyrrhetinate
CAS 13832-70-7
Synonyms: Octadecyl 3-hydroxy-11-oxoolean-12-en-29-oate
Definition: Ester of stearyl alcohol and glycyrrhetinic acid
Empirical: $C_{48}H_{82}O_4$
Properties: Wh. to pale yel. cryst. powd.; oil-sol.
Uses: Anti-inflammatory; anti-allergenic
Manuf./Distrib.: Nikko Chem. Co. Ltd.
Trade names: Co-Grhetinol; Nikkol Stearyl Glycyrrhetinate

Stearyl heptanoate
CAS 66009-41-4
Synonyms: Heptanoic acid, octadecyl ester
Definition: Ester of stearyl alcohol and heptanoic acid
Empirical: $C_{25}H_{50}O_2$
Formula: $CH_3(CH_2)_5COOCH_2(CH_2)_{16}CH_3$
Uses: Emollient and water repellent
Trade names: Crodamol W

Stearyl stearate
CAS 2778-96-3; 85536-04-5; EINECS 220-476-5; 287-484-9
Synonyms: Octadecanoic acid, octadecyl ester
Definition: Ester of stearyl alcohol and stearic acid
Empirical: $C_{36}H_{72}O_2$
Formula: $CH_3(CH_2)_{16}COOCH_2(CH_2)_{16}CH_3$

Properties: M.w. 537.00; m.p. 56 C; flash pt. (COC) 242 C
Uses: Raw material for pharmaceuticals
Regulatory: FDA 21CFR §178.3910
Manuf./Distrib.: Inolex
Trade names: Ritachol® SS

Stearyl trihydroxyethyl propylenediamine dihydrofluoride
CAS 6818-37-7
Uses: Pharmaceutical ingred. for caries prophylaxis in toothpaste, gels, mouthwashes
Trade names: Unifluorid D 401

Stenol. *See* Stearyl alcohol
Sterculia gum. *See* Karaya gum
Sterculia urens gum. *See* Karaya gum
St. John's bread. *See* Locust bean gum
STO. *See* Sorbitan trioleate

Storax
CAS 8023-62-9; 8046-19-3
FEMA 3036
Synonyms: Styrax; Liquid storax; Storax gum; Sweet oriental gum; Sweet gum
Definition: Balsam obtained from trunk of *Liquidambar orientalis*
Properties: Grayish-brn. semiliq. to semisolid, char. odor and taste; sol. in 1 part warm alcohol; sol. in ether, acetone, CS_2; insol. in water
Toxicology: Mod. toxic when ingested; can cause urinary problems when absorbed thru skin; can cause skin irritation, welts, and discomfort when applied topically; common allergen
Uses: Expectorant, weak antiseptic, stimulant; topical protectant; formerly applied as ointment in treatment of parasitic skin diseases
Regulatory: FDA 21CFR §172.510; FEMA GRAS
Manuf./Distrib.: Bio-Botanica
Manuf./Distrib. (pharm. & food): Spectrum Chem. Mfg.

Storax gum. *See* Storax
Strained honey. *See* Honey
Strawberry aldehyde. *See* Ethyl methylphenylglycidate
Strong ammonia solution. *See* Ammonium hydroxide
STS. *See* Sorbitan tristearate
Styralyl acetate. *See* α-Methylbenzyl acetate
Styralyl butyrate. *See* α-Methylbenzyl butyrate
Styrax. *See* Storax

Styrene
CAS 100-42-5; EINECS 202-851-5
FEMA 3233
Synonyms: Phenylethylene; Ethenylbenzene; Styrol; Styrolene; Vinylbenzene; Cinnamene; Cinnamol
Empirical: C_8H_8
Formula: $C_6H_5CH:CH_2$
Properties: Colorless to ylsh. oily liq., penetrating odor; sol. in alcohol, ether, methanol, acetone, CS_2; sparingly sol. in water; m.w. 104.15; dens. 0.906 (20/4 C); m.p. -30.6 C; b.p. 145-146 C; flash pt. (CC) 31 C; ref. index 1.546 (20 C)
Precaution: Flamm.; slowly undergoes polymerization and oxidation on exposure to light and air, yielding peroxides, etc.
Toxicology: LD50 (IV, mouse) 90 ± 5.2 mg/kg, (IP, mouse) 660 ±44.3 mg/kg; may be irritating to eyes, mucous membranes; narcotic in high concs.
Uses: Medicinal synthetic flavoring agent
Regulatory: FDA 21CFR §172.515; FEMA GRAS
Manuf./Distrib. (pharm. & food): Aldrich

Styrene/acrylate copolymer. *See* Styrene/acrylates copolymer

Styrene/acrylates copolymer
Synonyms: Styrene/acrylate copolymer; Styrene-acrylic
Definition: Polymer of styrene and a monomer consisting of acrylic acid, methacrylic acid, or their simple esters
Empirical: $(C_6H_8 \cdot C_3H_5NO)_x$
Toxicology: Strong irritant
Uses: Opacifier

Styrene-acrylic

Regulatory: FDA 21CFR §175.300, 175.320, 176.170, 177.1010, 177.1830
Manuf./Distrib.: Goodyear Tire & Rubber; Polysat; Reichhold; Seegott

Styrene-acrylic. See Styrene/acrylates copolymer
Styrene polymer. See Polystyrene
Styroen. See Cinnamyl alcohol
Styrol. See Styrene
Styrolene acetate. See α-Methylbenzyl acetate
Styryl carbinol. See Cinnamyl alcohol
2-Styryl-1,3-dioxolane. See Cinnamaldehyde ethylene glycol acetal
2-Styryl-m-dioxolane. See Cinnamaldehyde ethylene glycol acetal

Suberic acid
CAS 505-48-6; EINECS 208-010-9
Synonyms: Dicarboxylic acid C_8; Octanedioic acid
Empirical: $C_8H_{14}O_4$
Formula: $HOOC(CH_2)_6COOH$
Properties: M.w. 174.20; m.p. 142-144 C; b.p. 230 C (15 mm)
Uses: Intermediate for synthesis of drugs
Manuf./Distrib.: BASF; Hüls AG; Penta Mfg.
Manuf./Distrib. (pharm. & food): Aldrich

Substituted hexa hydropyrimidine. See Hexetidine

Succinic acid
CAS 110-15-6; EINECS 203-740-4
Synonyms: 1,4-Butanedioic acid; Amber; Amber acid; 1,2-Ethanedicarboxylic acid; Ethylenesuccinic acid
Classification: Dicarboxylic acid
Empirical: $C_4H_6O_4$
Formula: $HOOCCH_2CH_2COOH$
Properties: Colorless monoclinic prisms, odorless, sour acid taste; very sol. in alcohol, ether, acetone, glycerin; sol. in water; m.w. 118.09; dens. 1.552; m.p. 185 C; b.p. 235 C
Precaution: Combustible
Toxicology: LD50 (oral, rat) 2260 mg/kg; moderately toxic by subcutaneous route; severe eye irritant; heated to decomp., emits acrid smoke and irritating fumes
Uses: Germicide, buffer, neutralizing agent, laxative; used in parenterals, orals, mouthwashes
Regulatory: FDA 21CFR §131.144, 184.1091, GRAS; Japan approved; Europe listed; UK approved; FDA approved for parenterals, orals
Manuf./Distrib.: Am. Biorganics; J.T. Baker; DuPont; General Chem.; Hüls AG; Hayashi Pure Chem. Ind.; Mallinckrodt; Mitsubishi Chem.; Nippon Shokubai; Riken; Schweizerhall; Takeda Chem. Ind.; Ueno Fine Chem. Ind.
Manuf./Distrib. (pharm. & food): Aldrich; Fujisawa Pharmaceutical; Integra; Spectrum Chem. Mfg.

Succinic acid anhydride. See Succinic anhydride
Succinic acid sodium salt. See Sodium succinate

Succinic anhydride
CAS 108-30-5; EINECS 203-570-0
Synonyms: Dihydro-2,5-furandione; Butanedioic anhydride; 2,5-Diketotetrahydrofuran; Succinic acid anhydride; Succinyl oxide
Empirical: $C_4H_4O_3$
Formula: $OCCH_2CH_2COO$
Properties: Orthorhombic prisms; sol. in chloroform, CCl_4, alcohol; very sl. sol. in ether, water; m.w. 100.08; dens. 1.503; m.p. 119-120 C; b.p. 261 C (760 mm); sublimes @ 115 C and 5 mm pressure
Precaution: Moisture-sensitive
Toxicology: Irritating to eyes, respiratory system
Uses: Mfg. of pharmaceuticals
Regulatory: FDA
Manuf./Distrib.: J.T. Baker; Cambridge Ind. of Am.; Hüls AG; Humphrey; Lubrizol; Penta Mfg.; Punda Mercantile; Schweizerhall; Spectrum Chem. Mfg.
Manuf./Distrib. (pharm. & food): Aldrich

Succinyl oxide. See Succinic anhydride

Sucrose
CAS 57-50-1; EINECS 200-334-9
Synonyms: β-D-Fructofuranosyl-α-D-glucopyranoside; Saccharose; Granulated sugar; Table sugar; Sugar;

Beet sugar; Cane sugar; Confectioner's sugar
Classification: Disaccharide
Definition: Sugar obtained from *Saccharum officinarum, Beta vulgaris* andother sources; molecule of glucose linked to one of fructose
Empirical: $C_{12}H_{22}O_{11}$
Properties: Wh. crystals or powd., sweet taste; sol. in water, alcohol; insol. in ether; m.w. 342.30; dens. 1.587 (25/4 C); m.p. 160-186 C (dec.); ref. index 1.34783 (10%, 20 C)
Precaution: Vigorous reaction with nitric acid or sulfuric acid
Toxicology: TLV:TWA 10 mg/m^3; LD50 (oral, rat) 29,700 mg/kg; mildly toxic by ingestion; experimental teratogen, reproductive effects; mutagenic data; heated to decomp., emits acrid smoke and irritating fumes
Uses: Coating agent, tablet and capsule diluent, sweetener; used in buccals, orals, rectals, topicals, medicinal syrups
Regulatory: FDA 21CFR §184.1854, GRAS; USDA 9CFR §318.7, 381.147; cleared by MID to flavor sausage, ham, misc. meat prods.; FDA approved for buccals, orals, rectals, topicals; USP/NF, BP, Ph.Eur. compliance
Manuf./Distrib.: Am. Biorganics; Mallinckrodt; Mendell; Pfanstiehl Labs; Vista
Manuf./Distrib. (pharm. & food): Aldrich; Integra; Mallinckrodt; Ruger; Spectrum Chem. Mfg.
Trade names containing: Canthaxanthin Beadlets 10%; Colored Nu-Pareil® PG 14/18; Colored Nu-Pareil® PG 16/20; Colored Nu-Pareil® PG 18/20; Colored Nu-Pareil® PG 20/25; Colored Nu-Pareil® PG 25/30; Colored Nu-Pareil® PG 30/35; Dry Beta Carotene Beadlets 10% CWS No. 65633; Dry Beta Carotene Beadlets 10% No. 65661; Dry Vitamin D$_3$ Beadlets Type 850 No. 652550401, 652550601; Dry Vitamin D$_3$ Type 100 CWS No. 65242; Nu-Core® 35/45; Nu-Core® 40/50; Nu-Core® 45/60; Nu-Pareil® PG 14/18; Nu-Pareil® PG 16/20; Nu-Pareil® PG 18/20; Nu-Pareil® PG 20/25; Nu-Pareil® PG 25/30; Nu-Pareil® PG 30/35; Nu-Tab®; Palmabeads® Type 500 No. 65332; Palma-Sperse® Type 250-S No. 65322; Palma-Sperse® Type 250A/50 D-S No. 65221; Sugartab®; Vitamin A Palmitate Type 250-CWS No. 65312

Sucrose acetate isobutyrate
CAS 126-13-6; EINECS 204-771-6
Synonyms: SAIB
Classification: Sucrose derivative
Definition: Mixed ester of sucrose and acetic and isobutyric acids
Empirical: $C_{40}H_{62}O_{19}$
Formula: $(CH_3COO)_2C_{12}H_{14}O_3[OOCCH(CH_3)_2]_6$
Properties: Clear semisolid or sol'n.; m.w. 847.02; sp.gr. 1.146; flash pt. (COC) 260 C; ref. index 1.4540
Precaution: Combustible
Uses: Emulsion stabilizer; clouding agent; modifying extender for film-forming polymers
Regulatory: FDA 21CFR §175.105
Manuf./Distrib.: Ashland; Eastman; Technical Chems. & Prods.
Trade names: Eastman® SAIB-SG

Sucrose cocoate
CAS 91031-88-8
Definition: Mixture of sucrose esters of coconut acid; consists mainly of monoester
Uses: Dispersant, emulsifier, wetting agent, solubilizer for pharmaceuticals
Trade names: Crodesta SL-40

Sucrose dilaurate
Definition: Diester of lauric acid and sucrose
Uses: Emulsifier, solubilizer, stabilizer; tablet lubricant/disintegrant/binder/filler
Trade names: Ryoto Sugar Ester L-595

Sucrose distearate
CAS 27195-16-0; EINECS 248-317-5
Synonyms: α-D-Glucopyranoside, β-D-fructofuranosyl, dioctadecanoate; Saccharose distearate
Definition: Mixture of sucrose esters of stearic acid; consists mainly of the diester
Empirical: $C_{48}H_{90}O_{13}$
Uses: Dispersant, emulsifier, wetting agent, solubilizer for pharmaceuticals
Trade names: Crodesta F-10; Crodesta F-50; Ryoto Sugar Ester S-570; Ryoto Sugar Ester S-770; Ryoto Sugar Ester S-970; Sucro Ester 7
Trade names containing: Crodesta F-110

Sucrose laurate
CAS 25339-99-5; EINECS 246-873-3
Synonyms: α-D-Glucopyranoside, β-D-fructofuranosyl, monododecanoate
Definition: Mixture of sucrose esters of lauric acid; consists mainly of monoester

Sucrose mono/distearate

Empirical: $C_{24}H_{44}O_{12}$
Uses: Emulsifier, solubilizer, stabilizer; tablet lubricant, disintegrant, binder, filler
Trade names: Ryoto Sugar Ester L-1570; Ryoto Sugar Ester L-1695; Ryoto Sugar Ester LWA-1570

Sucrose mono/distearate. See Sucrose polystearate

Sucrose mono/disterarate
Uses: Emulsifier; tableting agent and lipophilic matrix
Trade names: Sucro Ester 11

Sucrose myristate
Definition: Monoester of myristic acid and sucrose
Empirical: $C_{26}H_{48}O_{12}$
Uses: Emulsifier, solubilizer, stabilizer; tablet lubricant, disintegrant, binder, filler
Trade names: Ryoto Sugar Ester M-1695

Sucrose octaacetate
CAS 126-14-7; EINECS 204-772-1
FEMA 3038
Synonyms: α-D-Glucopyranoside, 1,3,4,6-tetra-O-acetyl-β-D-fructofuranosyl, tetraacetate; D-(+)-Sucrose octaacetate
Empirical: $C_{28}H_{38}O_{19}$
Properties: Wh. need., pract. odorless, intensely bitter taste; hygroscopic; sol. in ether, methanol, chloroform, 1100 parts water, 11 parts alcohol, 22 parts CCl_4; m.w. 678.60; m.p. 82-85 C; dec. above 285 C; b.p. 260 C (1 mm); ref. index 1.4660
Precaution: Combustible
Uses: Alcohol denaturant; in preps. intended to deter nail biting
Regulatory: FDA 21CFR §172.515; FEMA GRAS; USP/NF compliance
Manuf./Distrib. (pharm. & food): Aldrich; Ruger; Spectrum Chem. Mfg.

D-(+)-Sucrose octaacetate. See Sucrose octaacetate

Sucrose oleate
Definition: Monoester of oleic acid and sucrose
Uses: Emulsifier, solubilizer, stabilizer; tablet lubricant, disintegrant, binder, filler
Regulatory: FDA 21CFR §172.859
Trade names: Ryoto Sugar Ester O-1570; Ryoto Sugar Ester OWA-1570

Sucrose palmitate
CAS 26446-38-8; EINECS 247-706-7
Synonyms: Saccharose palmitate
Definition: Monoester of palmitic acid and sucrose
Uses: Emulsifier, solubilizer, stabilizer; tablet lubricant, disintegrant, binder, filler
Regulatory: FDA 21CFR §172.859
Trade names: Ryoto Sugar Ester P-1570; Ryoto Sugar Ester P-1570S; Ryoto Sugar Ester P-1670; Sucro Ester 15

Sucrose polylaurate
Definition: Mixture of esters of lauric acid and sucrose
Uses: Emulsifier
Trade names: Ryoto Sugar Ester L-195

Sucrose polylinoleate
Definition: Mixture of esters of linoleic acid and sucrose
Uses: Emulsifier
Trade names: Ryoto Sugar Ester LN-195

Sucrose polyoleate
Definition: Mixture of esters of oleic acid and sucrose
Uses: Emulsifier
Trade names: Ryoto Sugar Ester O-170

Sucrose polystearate
Synonyms: Sucrose mono/distearate; Saccharose mono/distearate
Definition: Mixture of esters of stearic acid and sucrose
Uses: Emulsifier, solubilizer, stabilizer; tablet lubricant, disintegrant, binder, filler
Trade names: Ryoto Sugar Ester S-070; Ryoto Sugar Ester S-170; Ryoto Sugar Ester S-270

Sucrose stearate
CAS 25168-73-4; EINECS 246-705-9

Synonyms: α-D-Glucopyranoside, β-D-fructofuranoysl, monooctadecanoate
Definition: Monoester of stearic acid and sucrose
Empirical: $C_{30}H_{56}O_{12}$
Uses: Thickener, suspending agent, dispersant, emulsifier, wetting agent, solubilizer for pharmaceuticals; tablet lubricant, disintegrant, binder, filler
Trade names: Crodesta F-160; Ryoto Sugar Ester S-1170; Ryoto Sugar Ester S-1170S; Ryoto Sugar Ester S-1570; Ryoto Sugar Ester S-1670; Ryoto Sugar Ester S-1670S
Trade names containing: Crodesta F-110

Sucrose tetrastearate triacetate
Definition: Mixt. of esters of stearic acid, acetic acid, and sucrose
Uses: Emulsifier
Trade names: Ryoto Sugar Ester S-170 Ac

Sucrose tribehenate
Definition: Triester of behenic acid and sucrose
Empirical: $C_{66}H_{124}O_{14}$
Uses: Emulsifier; solubilizer, stabilizer for fat-sol. vitamins and antibiotics; tablet lubricant, disintegrator, binder, and filler
Trade names: Ryoto Sugar Ester B-370

Sucrose tristearate
Definition: Triester of stearic acid and sucrose
Uses: Emulsifier, solubilizer, stabilizer; tablet lubricant, disintegrant, binder, filler
Regulatory: FDA 21CFR §172.859
Trade names: Ryoto Sugar Ester S-370; Ryoto Sugar Ester S-370F

Sudan gum. *See* Acacia
Sudan III. *See* CI 26100; D&C Red No. 17
Sugar. *See* Sucrose

Sugar, compressible
Definition: Dried at 105 C for 4 h, contains 95-98% sucrose; may also contain starch, maltodextrin, invert sugar, and a lubricant
Properties: Pract. wh. cryst. powd., odorless, sweet taste; sucrose portion is very sol. in water; stable in air
Uses: Sweetening agent; tablet/capsule diluent
Regulatory: USP/NF compliance

Sugar, confectioner's
Definition: Sucrose gorund with corn starch to a fine powd. and contg. ≥ 95% sucrose
Properties: Wh. fine powd., odorless, sweet taste; freely sol. in boiling water; sucrose portion is sol. in cold water; stable in air
Uses: Sweetening agent; tablet/capsule diluent
Regulatory: USP/NF compliance

Sugar spheres
Definition: Contains 62.5-91.5% sucrose and starch; may contain FDA approved color additives for use in drugs
Properties: Wh. or colored hard brittle free-flowing spherical particles, 10-60 mesh; sol. in water varies
Uses: Sweetening agent; tablet/capsule diluent; solid carrier/vehicle for pharmaceuticals
Regulatory: USP/NF compliance

m-Sulfanilic acid. *See* Metanilic acid

Sulfated castor oil
CAS 72-48-0; 8002-33-3; EINECS 232-306-7
Synonyms: Castor oil sulfated; Sulfonated castor oil; Turkey-red oil
Definition: Oil consisting primarily of sodium salt of the sulfated triglyceride of ricinoleic acid
Uses: Surface-active agent
Regulatory: FDA 21CFR §175.105, 176.170, 176.200, 177.1200
Manuf./Distrib.: Graden; Spectrum Chem. Mfg.

Sulfinylbis (methane). *See* Dimethyl sulfoxide
Sulfoacetic acid, 1-dodecyl ester, sodium salt. *See* Sodium lauryl sulfoacetate
o-Sulfobenzimide. *See* Saccharin
Sulfobutanedioic acid, 1-dodecyl ester, disodium salt. *See* Disodium lauryl sulfosuccinate
Sulfobutanedioic acid, 4-[2-[2-[2-(dodecyloxy)ethoxy]ethoxy]ethyl]ester, disodium salt. *See* Disodium laureth sulfosuccinate

Sulfocarbolic acid. *See* Phenol sulfonic acid
Sulfomethane. *See* Methanesulfonic acid
Sulfonated castor oil. *See* Sulfated castor oil

5-Sulfosalicylic acid
CAS 97-05-2; 5965-83-3 (dihydrate); EINECS 202-555-6
UN No. 1759
Synonyms: 2-Hydroxy-5-sulfobenzoic acid
Classification: Aromatic organic compd.
Empirical: $C_7H_6O_6S \cdot 2H_2O$ (dihydrate)
Formula: $HOC_6H_3(COOH)SO_3H \cdot 2H_2O$ (dihydrate)
Properties: Wh. cryst. solid; sol. in water, ethanol; m.w. 254.22 (dihydrate); m.p. 113 C
Precaution: DOT: Corrosive material; light-sensitive
Uses: In urine testing for bilirubin; solubilizer for vitamin B_2; mfg. of antibiotics
Regulatory: BP compliance
Manuf./Distrib.: Croda Colloids Ltd
Manuf./Distrib. (pharm. & food): Aldrich; Croda Colloids Ltd; Kishida Chem.; Konishi Chem. Ind.; Ruger

Sulfourea. *See* Thiourea

Sulfur
CAS 7704-34-9; EINECS 231-722-6
Synonyms: Brimstone; Sulphur; Soluble sulfur; Sulfur soluble
Classification: Nonmetallic element
Empirical: S
Properties: Insol. in water; sl. sol. in alcohol, ether; sol. in carbon disulfide, CCl_4, benzene; at.wt. 32.064; α: rhombic yel. crystals; dens. 2.06; β: monoclinic pale yel. crystals; dens. 1.96; m.p. 119 C; b.p. 444.6 C; flash pt. 405 F
Precaution: Combustible
Toxicology: Skin, eye, mucous membranes irritant; poison by ingestion, intravenous, intraperitoneal routes
Uses: Keratolytic in dermatitis and psoriasis prods.
Regulatory: FDA 21CFR §175.105, 177.1210, 177.2600
Manuf./Distrib.: Akrochem; Ashland; Kraft; Lohmann; Norsk Hydro A/S; San Yuan; Shell; Solvay GmbH; Texaco BV; Wilbur-Ellis

Sulfurated potash
CAS 39365-88-3
Synonyms: Liver of sulfur; Potash sulfurated
Definition: Mixt. of potassium polysulfides and potassium thiosulfate
Formula: K_2S_x
Properties: Liver-brn. to grnsh.-yel. irregular pieces, hydrogen sulfide odor, bitter acrid alkaline taste; hygroscopic; sol. in water
Precaution: Decomposes on exposure to air
Uses: Dermatologic pharmaceuticals
Regulatory: USP/NF compliance
Manuf./Distrib.: Spectrum Chem. Mfg.
Manuf./Distrib. (pharm. & food): Spectrum Chem. Mfg.

Sulfur dioxide
CAS 7446-09-5; EINECS 231-195-2
FEMA 3039; UN No. 1079
Synonyms: Sulfurous anhydride; Sulfurous oxide
Empirical: O_2S
Formula: SO_2
Properties: Colorless gas, strong suffocating odor; condenses @ -10 C to colorless liq.; sol. 8.5% in water, 25% in alcohol, 32% in methanol; sol. in ether, chloroform; m.w. 64.06; dens. 1.5 (liq.); m.p. -72 C; b.p. -10 C (liq.)
Precaution: Nonflamm.; reacts with water or steam to produce toxic and corrosive fumes
Toxicology: TLV:TWA 2 ppm; poison gas; mildly toxic to humans by inh.; corrosive irritant to eyes, respiratory tract; destroys vitamin B_1; experimental tumorigen, teratogen, reproductive effects; human mutagenic data; heated to dec., emits toxic fumes of SO_x
Uses: Antioxidant, preservative for pharmaceuticals
Regulatory: FDA 21CFR §182.3862, GRAS; BATF 27CFR §240.1051; FEMA GRAS; Japan approved (0.03-5 g/kg); Europe listed; UK approved; USP/NF, BP compliance
Manuf./Distrib.: Air Prods.; Boliden Intertrade; Hoechst Celanese; Outokumpu Oy; Rhone-Poulenc Basic;

Schweizerhall
Manuf./Distrib. (pharm. & food): Aldrich; Pfizer Food Science

Sulfur dioxide sol'n. *See* Sulfurous acid
Sulfuri acid, monododecyl ester, magnesium salt. *See* Magnesium lauryl sulfate

Sulfuric acid
CAS 7664-93-9; EINECS 231-639-5
UN No. 1830
Synonyms: Hydrogen sulfate; Battery acid; Electrolyte acid; Oil of vitriol
Classification: Inorganic acid
Empirical: H_2O_4S
Formula: H_2SO_4
Properties: Colorless to dk. brn. dense oily liq.; misc. with water and alcohol; m.w. 98.08; dens. 1.84; m.p. 10.4 C; b.p. 290 C; dec. 340 C
Precaution: Caustic; corrosive; powerful acidic oxidizer; ignites or explodes on contact with many materials; reacts with water to produce heat; reactive with oxidizing/reducing materials
Toxicology: TLV 1 mg/m^3 of air; LD50 (oral, rat) 2.14 g/kg; human poison; mod. toxic by ingestion; strongly corrosive; strong irritant to tissue; can cause severe burns, chronic bronchitis; heated to decomp., emits toxic fumes of SO_x
Uses: Acidifying agent; used in parenterals, inhalants, intramuscular injectables, ophthalmics, orals; astringent in diarrhea; in mixts. to stimulate appetite
Regulatory: FDA 21CFR §172.560, 172.892, 173.385, 178.1010, 184.1095, GRAS; BATF 27CFR §240.1051a; Japan restricted; Europe listed; UK approved; FDA approved for parenterals, inhalants, injectables, ophthalmics, orals; USP/NF, BP compliance
Manuf./Distrib.: Akzo Nobel; Amax; Am. Cyanamid; Boliden Intertrade; DuPont; Metallgesellschaft AG; Nissan Chem. Ind.; Occidental; Olin; Pasminco Europe; Rasa Ind.; Rhone-Poulenc Basic; Spectrum Chem. Mfg.
Manuf./Distrib. (pharm. & food): Aldrich; Integra; Rhone-Poulenc; Ruger; Spectrum Chem. Mfg.

Sulfuric acid barium salt (1:1). *See* Barium sulfate
Sulfuric acid magnesium salt (1:1). *See* Magnesium sulfate anhyd.
Sulfuric acid, monododecyl ester, ammonium salt. *See* Ammonium lauryl sulfate
Sulfuric acid, monododecyl ester, compd. with 2,2´-iminodiethanol (1:1). *See* DEA-lauryl sulfate
Sulfuric acid, monododecyl ester, compd. with 2,2´,2´´-nitrilotris[ethanol] (1:1). *See* TEA-lauryl sulfate
Sulfuric acid monododecyl ester sodium salt. *See* Sodium lauryl sulfate
Sulfuric acid, mono (2-ethylhexyl) ester sodium salt. *See* Sodium octyl sulfate
Sulfuric acid monosodium salt. *See* Sodium bisulfate
Sulfuric acid, monotetradecyl ester, sodium salt. *See* Sodium myristyl sulfate
Sulfuric acid zinc salt (1:1). *See* Zinc sulfate

Sulfurous acid
CAS 7782-99-2
UN No. 1833
Synonyms: Sulfur dioxide sol'n.
Definition: A sol'n. of sulfur dioxide in water
Properties: Colorless liq., suffocating sulfur odor; sol. in water; dens. 1.03; unstable
Precaution: DOT: Corrosive material
Toxicology: Toxic by ingestion and inhalation; strong tissue irritant
Uses: Used in injectables
Regulatory: FDA approved for injectables; BP compliance
Manuf./Distrib.: Spectrum Chem. Mfg.
Manuf./Distrib. (pharm. & food): Aldrich; Integra; Mallinckrodt

Sulfurous acid disodium salt. *See* Sodium sulfite
Sulfurous acid monosodium salt. *See* Sodium bisulfite
Sulfurous acid sodium salt (1:2). *See* Sodium sulfite
Sulfurous anhydride. *See* Sulfur dioxide
Sulfurous oxide. *See* Sulfur dioxide
Sulfur soluble. *See* Sulfur
Sulisobenzone. *See* Benzophenone-4
Sulphur. *See* Sulfur
Sumac wax. *See* Japan wax
Sumatra benzoin. *See* Gum benzoin
Sunflower oil. *See* Sunflower seed oil
Sunflower seed mono-, di- and tri-glycerides. *See* Sunflower seed oil glycerides

Sunflower seed oil

Sunflower seed oil
CAS 8001-21-6; EINECS 232-273-9
Synonyms: Sunflower oil
Definition: Oil expressed from seeds of the sunflower, *Helianthus annuus*
Properties: Amber liq., pleasant odor, mild taste; sol. in alcohol, ether, chloroform, CS_2; dens. 0.924-0.926; iodine no. 125-140; sapon. no.188-194; ref. index 1.4611
Precaution: Combustible
Toxicology: No known toxicity; heated to decomp., emits acrid smoke and irritating fumes
Uses: Raw material for pharmaceuticals; diluent, carrier, emulsifier, emollient, tablet binder, nutritional supplement; diuretic, expectorant
Regulatory: FDA 21CFR §175.300, 176.200, GRAS; BP compliance
Manuf./Distrib.: ABITEC; Arista Ind.; Charkit; Lipo; Penta Mfg.; Tri-K; Welch, Holme & Clark
Manuf./Distrib. (pharm. & food): Arista Industries; Penta Mfg.
Trade names: GTO 80; GTO 90; GTO 90E; NS-20; Sunyl® 80; Sunyl® 80 RBD; Sunyl® 80 RBD ES; Sunyl® 80 RBWD; Sunyl® 80 RBWD ES; Sunyl® 90; Sunyl® 90 RBD; Sunyl® 90 RBWD; Sunyl® 90E RBWD; Sunyl® 90E RBWD ES 1016; Sunyl® HS 500
Trade names containing: Neobee® SL-130; Tepescohuite LS

Sunflower seed oil glyceride
Synonyms: Glycerides, sunflower seed mono-
Definition: Monoglyceride derived from sunflower seed oil
Toxicology: No known toxicity
Uses: Emulsifier, stabilizer, dispersant
Trade names: Monomuls® 90-40

Sunflower seed oil glycerides
Synonyms: Sunflower seed mono-, di- and tri-glycerides; Glycerides, sunflower seed mono-, di- and tri-
Definition: Mixture of mono, di and triglycerides derived from sunflower seed oil
Uses: Emulsifier, stabilizer, dispersant, opacifier for drug prods.
Trade names: Monomuls® 60-40

Sunnette. *See* Acesulfame potassium
Sunset yellow. *See* CI 15985
Sunset yellow. *See* FD&C Yellow No. 6

Sweet almond oil
CAS 8007-69-0
Synonyms: Almond oil, sweet; Almond oil
Definition: Fixed oil obtained from the ripe seed kernel of *Prunus amygdalus*, contg. chiefly glyceryl oleate
Properties: Colorless or pale yel. oily liq., almost odorless, bland taste; sl. sol. in alcohol; misc. with benzene, chloroform, ether, petrol. ether; insol. in water; dens. 0.910-0.915; iodine no. 93-100; sapon. no. 191-200; ref. index 1.4593-1.4646 (40 C)
Precaution: Keep cool, well closed; protect from light
Uses: Oleaginous vehicle, solv., flavoring agent for pharmaceuticals; component of rose water ointment USP; nutritive, demulcent; emollient; softener for ear wax
Regulatory: USP/NF, BP compliance
Manuf./Distrib.: Arista Industries; Tri-K
Manuf./Distrib. (pharm. & food): Arista Industries; Spectrum Chem. Mfg.
Trade names: Super Refined® Almond Oil

Sweet birch oil. *See* Methyl salicylate
Sweet fennel. *See* Fennel
Sweet fennel oil. *See* Fennel oil
Sweet gum. *See* Storax
Sweet orange oil. *See* Orange oil
Sweet oriental gum. *See* Storax
sym-Dichlorotetrafluoroethane. *See* Dichlorotetrafluoroethane
sym-Diphenylthiourea. *See* N,N´-Diphenylthiourea

Synchron oral carrier
Uses: Used in buccals, orals
Regulatory: FDA approved for buccals, orals

Synthetic beeswax
CAS 71243-51-1; 97026-94-0; EINECS 275-286-5
Synonyms: Beeswax, synthetic

Definition: Synthetic wax with composition and properties generally indistinguishable from natural beeswax
Uses: Raw material for pharmaceuticals
Trade names: Lipobee 102

Synthetic carotene. *See* CI 40800
Synthetic oil of wintergreen. *See* Methyl salicylate
Synthetic pearl. *See* Bismuth oxychloride
Synthetic spermaceti. *See* Cetyl esters
Synthetic spermaceti wax. *See* Cetyl esters

Syrup
CAS 8027-47-2
Definition: Solution of sucrose in purified water; may contain a preservative
Properties: Sol'n.; sp.gr. 1.3 min.
Uses: Sweetening agent, tablet binder, flavored and/or sweetened vehicle; used in orals
Regulatory: FDA approved for orals; USP/NF, BP compliance
Manuf./Distrib. (pharm. & food): Spectrum Chem. Mfg.

Table salt. *See* Sodium chloride
Table sugar. *See* Sucrose
Tabular alumina. *See* Alumina
Tailed pepper. *See* Cubeb oil

Talc
CAS 14807-96-6; EINECS 238-877-9
Synonyms: Hydrous magnesium silicate; Magnesium hydrogen metasilicate; Hydrous magnesium calcium silicate; Industrial talc; Cosmetic talc; Platy talc; French chalk; Talcum; Pigment white 26; CI 77019
Definition: Native, hydrous magnesium silicate sometimes containing small portion of aluminum silicate
Formula: $Mg_3Si_4O_{10}(OH)_2$ or $3MgO \cdot 4SiO_2 \cdot HOH$
Properties: Wh., apple green, gray powd., pearly or greasy luster, greasy feel; insol. in water, cold acids or in alkalies; m.w. 379.29; dens. 2.7-2.8
Toxicology: TLV:TWA 2 mg/m^3, respirable dust; toxic by inhalation; talc with < 1% asbestos is nuisance dust; experimental tumorigen; human skin irritant; prolonged/repeated exposure can produce talc pneumoconiosis; talc-based powds. linked to ovarian cancer
Uses: Glidant, anticaking agent, tablet and capsule lubricant, color additive, dusting powd. and filler; used in oral solid dosage forms, topicals, rectals; lubricant on surgical gloves
Usage level: 0.003-220.4 mg (oral solids)
Regulatory: FDA 21CFR §73.1550, 175.300, 175.380, 175.390, 176.170, 177.1210, 177.1350, 177.1460, 182.70, 182.90; GRAS; Japan restricted (5000 ppm); Europe listed; UK approved; FDA approved for orals, rectals, topicals; USP/NF, BP, Ph.Eur. compliance
Manuf./Distrib.: Aldrich; Luzenac Am.; Minerals Tech.; Pfizer; L.A. Salomon; R.T. Vanderbilt; Whittaker, Clark & Daniels
Manuf./Distrib. (pharm. & food): Integra; Pfizer; Ruger; Spectrum Chem. Mfg.
Trade names: Act II 500 USP; Alphafil 500 USP; Alpine Talc USP BC 127; Altalc 200 USP; Altalc 300 USP; Altalc 400 USP; Altalc 500 USP; Brillante; Dover 50 A; Purtalc USP; SteriLine 200; Supra A; Supra EF A; Suprafino A; Supreme USP; Ultrafino

Talcum. *See* Talc

Tall oil
CAS 8002-26-4; EINECS 232-304-6
Synonyms: Liquid rosin; Tallol
Definition: Byprod. of wood pulp contg. rosin acids, oleic and linoleic acids, and long chain alcohols
Properties: Dk. brn. liq., acrid odor; dens. 0.95; acid no. 178 min.; flash pt. 360 F
Precaution: Combustible when exposed to heat or flame; can react with oxidizing materials
Toxicology: Mild allergen; heated to decomp., emits acrid smoke and irritating fumes
Uses: Fungicide used in topicals
Regulatory: FDA 21CFR §175.105, 175.300, 176.200, 176.210, 177.2600, 177.2800, 181.22, 181.26, 182.70, 186.1557, GRAS as indirect food additive; FDA approved for topicals
Manuf./Distrib.: Spectrum Chem. Mfg.

Tallol. *See* Tall oil

Tallow acid
CAS 61790-37-2; 67701-06-8; EINECS 263-129-3

Tallowalkonium chloride

    Synonyms: Fatty acids, tallow; Acids, tallow
    Definition: Mixture of fatty acids derived from tallow
    Uses: Used in pharmaceutical pastes
    Regulatory: FDA 21CFR §175.105, 175.320, 176.200, 176.210, 177.2260, 177.2800, 178.3570, 178.3910
    Manuf./Distrib.: Norman, Fox; Witco/Oleo-Surf.
    Trade names containing: Hystrene® 1835

Tallowalkonium chloride
    CAS 61789-75-1; EINECS 263-085-5
    Synonyms: Tallow dimethyl benzyl ammonium chloride; Dimethyl benzyl tallow ammonium chloride
    Classification: Quaternary ammonium salt
    Uses: Additive for antibiotics mfg.
    Trade names: Noramium S 75

Tallow dimethyl benzyl ammonium chloride. *See* Tallowalkonium chloride

Tallow glyceride
    CAS 61789-13-7; EINECS 263-035-2
    Synonyms: Tallow monoglyceride; Glycerides, tallow mono-
    Definition: Monoglyceride derived from tallow
    Uses: Emulsifier, stabilizer, dispersant
    Regulatory: FDA 21CFR §175.105, 176.210
    Trade names: Monomuls® 90-20

Tallow glycerides
    CAS 67701-27-3
    Synonyms: Tallow mono, di and tri glycerides; Glycerides, tallow mono-, di- and tri-
    Definition: Mixture of mono, di and triglycerides derived from tallow
    Uses: Emulsifier, stabilizer, dispersant for drug prods.
    Regulatory: FDA 21CFR §175.105, 176.210
    Trade names: Monomuls® 60-20
    Trade names containing: Ross Japan Wax Substitute 525

Tallow, hydrogenated. *See* Hydrogenated tallow
Tallow mono, di and tri glycerides. *See* Tallow glycerides
Tallow monoglyceride. *See* Tallow glyceride
Tallow, sodium salt. *See* Sodium tallowate
Tallow trimethyl ammonium chloride. *See* Tallowtrimonium chloride

Tallowtrimonium chloride
    CAS 8030-78-2; 7491-05-2; 68002-61-9; EINECS 232-447-4
    Synonyms: Quaternary ammonium compds., tallow alkyl trimethyl, chlorides; Tallow trimethyl ammonium chloride
    Classification: Quaternary ammonium salt
    Formula: $[R-N(CH_3)_3]^+Cl^-$, R rep. alkyl groups derived from tallow
    Uses: Emulsifier
    Trade names: Noramium MS 50

Tangantangan oil. *See* Castor oil

Tannic acid
    CAS 1401-55-4; EINECS 276-638-0, 215-753-2
    FEMA 3042
    Synonyms: Glycerite; Tannin; Gallotannic acid; Gallotannin
    Classification: Organic acids, mixture
    Definition: Occurs in the bark and fruit of many plants, e.g., oak species, sumac
    Empirical: $C_{76}H_{52}O_{46}$
    Properties: Yellowish-white to lt. brown powd. or flakes, faint char. odor, strongly astringent taste; very sol. in alcohol, acetone; pract. insol. in benzene, chloroform, ether, petrol. ether, carbon disulfide, CCl_4; m.w. 1701.23; dec. 210-215 C
    Precaution: Combustible exposed to heat or flame; keep well closed, protect from light; incompat. with salts of heavy metals, alkaloids, gelatin, starch, oxidizers
    Toxicology: LD50 (oral, rat) 2260 mg/kg; poison by ingestion, IV, subcutaneous routes; experimental carcinogen, tumorigen, reproductive effects; mutagenic data; may cause liver damage; heated to decomp., emits acrid smoke and irritating fumes
    Uses: Used in rectals, sunscreen preps., eye lotions, antiperspirants
    Regulatory: FDA 21CFR §173.310, 184.1097, GRAS; 9CFR §318.7; BATF 27CFR §240.1051; FEMA GRAS;

FDA approved for rectals; BP compliance

Manuf./Distrib.: Aceto; Burlington Bio-Medical; Crompton & Knowles; Fuji Chem. Ind.; Mallinckrodt; Spectrum Chem. Mfg.

Manuf./Distrib. (pharm. & food): Aceto; Aldrich; Burlington Bio-Medical; Crompton & Knowles; R.W. Greeff; Integra; Mallinckrodt; Ruger; Spectrum Chem. Mfg.

Tannin. *See* Tannic acid

Tapioca. *See* Dextrin

Tapioca starch
CAS 9005-25-8
Synonyms: Cassava starch
Definition: Granules obtained from tapioca *Manihot utilissima*
Properties: Spherical gran.
Uses: Tablet diluent and disintegrating agent; nutritive; demulcent
Regulatory: FDA 21CFR §182.70; BP compliance

Tartaric acid
CAS 87-69-4 (L-); 526-83-0 (L-); 147-71-7 (D-); 133-37-9 (DL-α); 147-73-9 (m-); EINECS 201-766-0 (L-); 205-695-6 (D-); 205-105-7 (DL-); 205-696-1 (m-)
FEMA 3044
Synonyms: DL-Tartaric acid anhydrous; Dihydroxysuccinic acid; α,β-Dihydroxysuccinic acid; 2,3-Dihydroxybutanedioic acid
Classification: Acid
Empirical: $C_4H_6O_6$
Formula: $HOOC(CHOH)_2COOH$
Properties: Colorless lg. translucent cryst., odorless, acid taste; effervescent; sol. in water, methanol; partly sol. in ether; m.w. 150.09; m.p. 169-170 C; flash pt. (OC) 210 C
Toxicology: May be mildly irritating to skin
Uses: Acidifying agent; buffering agent; used in parenterals, intravenous, orals, rectals, vaginals, denture powds., effervescent powds., grans., and tablets; ingred. in cooling drinks; saline purgative
Regulatory: FDA 21CFR §184.1099, GRAS; FEMA GRAS; FDA approved for parenterals, intravenous, orals, rectals, vaginals; USP/NF, BP, Ph.Eur., JP compliance
Manuf./Distrib.: Aldrich; R.W. Greeff; Lohmann; Mallinckrodt; Penta Mfg.; Rit-Chem.; Spectrum Chem. Mfg.
Manuf./Distrib. (pharm. & food): Aldrich; Dainippon Pharmaceutical; R.W. Greeff; Ruger; Spectrum Chem. Mfg.

DL-Tartaric acid anhydrous. *See* Tartaric acid
L-Tartaric acid disodium salt. *See* Sodium tartrate
L-Tartaric acid monopotassium salt. *See* Potassium acid tartrate

Tartrazine
CAS 1934-21-0; EINECS 217-699-5
Synonyms: CI 19140; FD&C Yellow No. 5; Acid yellow 23
Classification: Pyrazole color
Empirical: $C_{16}H9N_4Na_3O_9S_2$
Properties: Bright orange-yel. powd.; hygroscopic; sol. in water; m.w. 534.37
Toxicology: Allergen; those allergic to aspirin are often allergic to tartrazine; may cause urticaria, anaphylactoid reactions, angioedema, rhinitis, bronchial asthma, contact dermatitis, etc.
Uses: Colorant; used in buccals, orals, nasals, topicals, vaginals, antiallergic and antiasthmatic medications
Regulatory: Europe listed; UK approved; FDA approved for buccals, orals, topicals, vaginals
Manuf./Distrib.: Spectrum Chem. Mfg.
Manuf./Distrib. (pharm. & food): Aldrich
See also FD&C Yellow No. 5; CI 19140

Taurine
CAS 107-35-7; EINECS 203-483-8
Synonyms: 2-Aminoethanesulfonic acid
Classification: Amino acid
Empirical: $C_2H_7NO_3S$
Formula: $NH_2CH_2CH_2SO_3H$
Properties: Solid; sol. in water; insol. in alcohol; m.w. 125.15; m.p. > 300 C
Uses: Used in parenteral nutritive preps. for low-birth-weight infants and in infant formulas; in treatment of hypercholesterolemia and metabolic disorders
Manuf./Distrib.: Chemisphere Ltd; Mitsui Toatsu Chem.; Penta Mfg.; Schweizerhall; Spectrum Chem. Mfg.; Tanabe USA
Manuf./Distrib. (pharm. & food): Aldrich; Ruger

TBA. *See* t-Butyl alcohol
TBC. *See* Tributyl citrate
TBHQ. *See* t-Butyl hydroquinone
TCE. *See* Trichloroethylene
TCP. *See* Calcium phosphate tribasic
TEA. *See* Triethanolamine
TEA-abietoyl hydrolyzed animal protein. *See* TEA-abietoyl hydrolyzed collagen

TEA-abietoyl hydrolyzed collagen
CAS 68918-77-4
Synonyms: Proteins, hydrolysates, reaction prods. with abietoyl chloride, compd. with triethanolamine; Triethanolamine abietoyl hydrolyzed animal protein; TEA-abietoyl hydrolyzed animal protein
Definition: Triethanolamine salt of the condensation prod. of abietic acid chloride and hydrolyzed collagen
Uses: Sebum control additive for shampoos

TEA-alginate
Synonyms: Triethanolamine alginate
Uses: Gellant for dental impression materials
Trade names: Protanal TA 250; Protanal TA 375

TEA alkyl sulfate
Synonyms: Trolamine alkyl sulfate
Uses: Used in topicals
Regulatory: FDA approved for topicals

TEA-lauryl sulfate
CAS 139-96-8; EINECS 205-388-7
Synonyms: Sulfuric acid, monododecyl ester, compd. with 2,2′,2′′-nitrilotris[ethanol] (1:1); Triethanolammonium lauryl sulfate; Trolamine lauryl sulfate; Triethanolamine lauryl sulfate
Definition: Triethanolamine salt of lauryl sulfuric acid
Empirical: $C_{12}H_{26}O_4S \cdot C_6H_{15}NO_3$
Formula: $CH_3(CH_2)_{10}CH_2OSO_3H \cdot N(CH_2CH_2OH)_3$
Properties: Liq. or paste; m.w. 415.66
Uses: Cleansing agent, emulsifier, foamer; used in topicals
Regulatory: FDA approved for topicals
Manuf./Distrib.: Chemron; Lonza; Norman, Fox; Sandoz; Stepan
Trade names: Stepanol® WAT
Trade names containing: Mearlmaid® TR

TEA-stearate
CAS 4568-28-9; EINECS 224-945-5
Synonyms: Triethanolamine stearate
Uses: Emulsifier, solubilizer for pharmaceutical formulations
Regulatory: FDA 21CFR §176.210, 177.2260

Tea tree. *See* Cajeput oil

Tea tree oil
CAS 68647-73-4
Classification: Essential oil
Definition: Oil distilled from leaves of *Melaleuca alternifolia*
Properties: Lt. yel.
Toxicology: No known toxicity
Uses: Antimicrobial for pharmaceutical ointments; penetrates the skin readily; accelerates the healing of skin disorders
Manuf./Distrib.: Tri-K
Trade names: EmCon Tea Tree

TEC. *See* Triethyl citrate
Teel oil. *See* Sesame oil

Tellurium
CAS 13494-80-9; EINECS 236-813-4
Classification: Nonmetallic element
Empirical: Te
Properties: Silvery-white lustrous solid; sol. in sulfuric acid, nitric acid, KOH, KCN sol'n.; insol. in water; at.wt. 127.60; dens. 6.24 (30 C); m.p. 450 C; b.p. 990 C
Precaution: Flamm.

Toxicology: Toxic by inhalation; causes nausea, vomiting, CNS depression; TLV 0.1 mg/m^3 of air
Uses: Used in orals
Regulatory: FDA approved for orals
Manuf./Distrib.: All Chemie Ltd; Asarco; Atomergic Chemetals; Cabot; Cerac; Johnson Matthey; Mitsui Mining & Smelting; Noah; Sumitomo Metal Mining; R.T. Vanderbilt
Manuf./Distrib. (pharm. & food): Aldrich

Terpene resin, natural
CAS 9003-74-1
Classification: Unsat. hydrocarbon
Toxicology: No known toxicity; heated to decomp., emits acrid smoke and irritating fumes
Uses: Antiseptic; used in orals
Usage level: Limitation 0.07% (of wt. of capsule) 7% (of ascorbic acid and salts)
Regulatory: FDA 21CFR §73.1, 172.280, 172.615, 178.3930; FDA approved for orals
Manuf./Distrib.: Arizona; Cardolite; Hercules; Langley Smith Ltd
Manuf./Distrib. (pharm. & food): Hercules
See also Dipentene, Pinene

α-Terpinene
CAS 99-86-5
FEMA 3558
Synonyms: p-Mentha-1,3-diene; Tirpilene
Empirical: $C_{10}H_{16}$
Properties: M.w. 136.24; flash pt. 115 F
Uses: Lemon flavoring agent
Regulatory: FEMA GRAS
Manuf./Distrib. (pharm. & food): Aldrich

γ-Terpinene
CAS 99-85-4; EINECS 202-794-6
FEMA 3559
Synonyms: 1-Isopropyl-4-methyl-1,4-cyclohexadiene; p-Mentha-1,4-diene
Empirical: $C_{10}H_{16}$
Properties: Oil, herbaceous citrus odor; sol. in alcohol; insol. in water; m.w. 136.24; dens. 0.848 (20/4 C); b.p. 183-186 C; flash pt. 50 C; ref. index 1.474 (20 C)
Precaution: Flamm.
Uses: Citrus synthetic flavoring agent
Regulatory: FDA 21CFR §172.515; FEMA GRAS
Manuf./Distrib. (pharm. & food): Aldrich; Florida Treatt

α-Terpineol
CAS 98-55-5; 8000-41-7 (mixt.)
FEMA 3045
Synonyms: α,α,4-Trimethyl-3-cyclohexene-1-methanol; 1-Methyl-4-isopropyl-1-cyclohexen-8-ol; p-Menth-1-en-8-ol; p-Menthen-1-en-8-ol
Empirical: $C_{10}H_{18}O$
Formula: $C_{10}H_{17}OH$
Properties: Colorless visc. liq., lilac-like odor; sol. in propylene glycol; very sl. sol. in water; insol. in min. oil; m.w. 154.24; dens. 0.930; m.p. 40-41 C; f.p. 193 F; b.p. 214-224 C
Precaution: Combustible
Toxicology: Can be a sensitizer
Uses: Synthetic flavoring agent, denaturant, antiseptic, disinfectant, solv.; used in topicals, preps. for respiratory tract disorders
Regulatory: FDA 21CFR §172.515; FEMA GRAS; FDA approved for topicals; BP compliance
Manuf./Distrib.: Aldrich; Arakawa Chem. Ind.; Hercules; Quest Int'l.; SCM Glidco Organics; Soda Aromatic; Spectrum Chem. Mfg.; Toyotama Perfumery
Manuf./Distrib. (pharm. & food): Aldrich; Hercules; Quest Int'l.

Terpinyl formate
CAS 2153-26-6
FEMA 3052
Synonyms: p-Menth-1-en-8-yl formate
Empirical: $C_{11}H_{18}O_2$
Properties: M.w. 182.27
Uses: Sweet, citrus-like synthetic flavoring agent

TETA

Regulatory: FDA 21CFR §172.515; FEMA GRAS
Manuf./Distrib. (pharm. & food): Aldrich

TETA. *See* Triethylenetetramine

Tetraammonium EDTA
Uses: Chelating agent; drug stabilization; heavy metal poisoning treatment
Trade names: Versene Tetraammonium EDTA

2´,4´,5´,7´-Tetrabromo-3´,6´-dihydroxyspiro[isobenzofuran-1(3H),9´-[9H]xanthen]-3-one. *See* D&C Red No. 21

2´,4´,5´,7´-Tetrabromo-3´,6´-dihydroxyspiro[isobenzofuran-1(3H),9´-[9H]xanthen]-3-one disodium salt. *See* CI 45380; D&C Red No. 22

Tetrabromofluorescein. *See* D&C Red No. 21; D&C Red No. 22

2´,4´,5´,7´-Tetrabromo-4,5,6,7-tetrachloro-3´,6´-dihydroxyspiro[isobenzofuran-1(3H),9´-[9H]xanthen]-3-one. *See* D&C Red No. 27

2´,4´,5´,7´-Tetrabromo-4,5,6,7-tetrachloro-3´,6´-dihydroxyspiro[isobenzofuran-1(3H),9´-[9H]xanthen]-3-one disodium salt. *See* CI 45410; D&C Red No. 28

Tetrabromotetrachlorofluorescein. *See* D&C Red No. 27

Tetrachlorotetrabromofluorescein. *See* D&C Red No. 27

Tetradecanal. *See* Myristaldehyde

Tetradecanoic acid. *See* Myristic acid

Tetradecanoic acid, methyl ester. *See* Methyl myristate

Tetradecanoic acid, 1-methylethyl ester. *See* Isopropyl myristate

Tetradecanoic acid, monoester with 1,2-propanediol. *See* Propylene glycol myristate

Tetradecanoic acid, monoester with 1,2,3-propanetriol. *See* Glyceryl myristate

Tetradecanoic acid, 2-octyldodecyl ester. *See* Octyldodecyl myristate

Tetradecanoic acid, tetradecyl ester. *See* Myristyl myristate

1-Tetradecanol. *See* Myristyl alcohol

1-Tetradecanol, hydrogen sulfate, sodium salt. *See* Sodium myristyl sulfate

n-Tetradecoic acid. *See* Myristic acid

Tetradecyl aldehyde. *See* Myristaldehyde

Tetradecyl dimethyl benzyl ammonium chloride. *See* Myristalkonium chloride

Tetradecyleicosanol
Synonyms: Myristyl eicosanol
Classification: Aliphatic alcohol
Empirical: $C_{34}H_{70}O$
Properties: Lt. colored soft wax; sol. in min. oil, isopropyl myristate, oleyl alcohol, castor oil; m.p. 33-40 C
Uses: Emollient wax for pharmaceutical topical preps.
Trade names: Standamul® G-32/36

Tetradecyleicosyl stearate
Synonyms: Myristyleicosyl stearate
Classification: Ester
Definition: Ester of myristyleicosanol and stearic acid
Empirical: $C_{52}H_{104}O_2$
Uses: Stabilizer, base, lubricant, emollient for pharmaceutical prods.
Trade names: Standamul® G-32/36 Stearate

Tetradecyl 2-hydroxypropanoate. *See* Myristyl lactate

Tetradecyl tetradecanoate. *See* Myristyl myristate

Tetradecyltrimethylammonium bromide. *See* Myrtrimonium bromide

Tetradonium bromide. *See* Myrtrimonium bromide

Tetrafluorodichloroethane. *See* Dichlorotetrafluoroethane

Tetrafluorodichloromethane. *See* Dichlorotetrafluoromethane

Tetraglyceryl monoisostearate. *See* Polyglyceryl-4 isostearate

Tetraglyceryl monooleate. *See* Polyglyceryl-4 oleate

3,6-Dimethyl5,6,7,7a-tetrahydro-2(4H)-benzofuranone. *See* Menthalactone

4,5,6,7-Tetrahydro-3,6-dimethylbenzofuran
CAS 494-90-6
FEMA 3235
Synonyms: Menthofuran
Empirical: $C_{10}H_{14}O$
Properties: M.w. 150.22; dens. 0.970; b.p. 80-82 C (13 mm); flash pt. 168 F

2-[2-[2-[p-(1,1,3,3-Tetramethylbutyl)phenoxy]ethoxy]ethoxy]ethanol

Uses: Medicinal flavoring agent
Regulatory: FEMA GRAS
Manuf./Distrib. (pharm. & food): Aldrich

Tetrahydrofuran
CAS 109-99-9; EINECS 203-726-8
UN No. 2056
Synonyms: THF
Empirical: C_4H_8O
Formula: $CH_2CH_2CH_2CH_2O$
Properties: Water-wh. liq., ethereal odor; sol. in water and org. solvs.; m.w. 72.11; dens. 0.888 (20 C); f.p. -65 C; b.p. 66 C; flash pt. (OC) -15 C; ref. index 1.4070
Precaution: Flamm. limits in air 2-11.8%
Toxicology: Toxic by ingestion and inhalation; TLV 200 ppm in air
Uses: pharmaceutical intermediate; extraction solv.; steroid hormone prod. for use in birth control pills; solv. for Grignard reactions
Regulatory: BP compliance
Manuf./Distrib.: Allchem Ind.; Arco Europe; Ashland; BASF; J.T. Baker; Chemcentral; DuPont; Great Lakes; Harcros; Hüls UK; ISP; Janssen Chimica; QO; Richman; Stanchem; Van Waters & Rogers

Tetrahydrofurfuryl butyrate
CAS 92345-48-7
FEMA 3057
Empirical: $C_9H_{16}O_3$
Properties: M.w. 172.22; dens. 1.012; b.p. 225-227 C (759 mm); flash pt. 210 F
Uses: Fruity synthetic flavoring agent
Regulatory: FDA 21CFR §172.515; FEMA GRAS
Manuf./Distrib. (pharm. & food): Aldrich

Tetrahydrofurfuryl propionate
CAS 637-65-0
FEMA 3058
Empirical: $C_8H_{14}O_3$
Properties: M.w. 158.20; dens. 1.040; b.p. 207 C; flash pt. 198 F
Uses: Fruity, medicinal synthetic flavoring agent
Regulatory: FDA 21CFR §172.515; FEMA GRAS
Manuf./Distrib. (pharm. & food): Aldrich

Tetrahydrogeraniol. *See* 3,7-Dimethyl-1-octanol
Tetrahydro-1,4-oxazine. *See* Morpholine
Tetrahydro-2H-1,4-oxazine. *See* Morpholine

Tetrahydroxypropyl ethylenediamine
CAS 102-60-3; EINECS 203-041-4
Synonyms: N,N,N´,N´-Tetrakis(2-hydroxypropyl) ethylenediamine; Ethylenedinitrilotetra-2-propanol
Classification: Substituted amine
Empirical: $C_{14}H_{32}N_2O_4$
Formula: $(HOC_3H_6)_2NCH_2CH_2N(C_3H_6OH)$
Properties: Water-wh. visc. liq.; sol. in ethanol, toluene, ethylene glycol; misc. with water; m.w. 292.42; dens. 1.013; b.p. 175-181 C (0.8 mm); flash pt. > 230 F; ref. index 1.4812
Precaution: Combustible
Toxicology: May be irritating to skin and mucous membranes; may cause skin sensitization
Uses: Solvent, preservative, chelating agent, intermediate, emulsifier for pharmaceuticals
Trade names: Quadrol®

Tetraiodofluorescein sodium salt. *See* FD&C Red No. 3

Tetraisopropyl methylenediphosphonate
CAS 11660-95-3
Uses: Intermediate; reagent
Manuf./Distrib.: Albright & Wilson
Trade names: TIPMDP

N,N,N´,N´-Tetrakis(2-hydroxypropyl) ethylenediamine. *See* Tetrahydroxypropyl ethylenediamine
p-(1,1,3,3-Tetramethylbutyl) phenol polymer with ethylene oxide and formaldehyde. *See* Tyloxapol
2-[p-(1,1,3,3-Tetramethylbutyl)phenoxy]ethanol. *See* Octoxynol-1
2-[2-[2-[p-(1,1,3,3-Tetramethylbutyl)phenoxy]ethoxy]ethoxy]ethanol. *See* Octoxynol-3

2,6,10,10-Tetramethyl-1-oxaspiro[4.5]dec-6-ene

2,6,10,10-Tetramethyl-1-oxaspiro[4.5]dec-6-ene. *See* Theaspirane

2,3,5,6-Tetramethylpyrazine
CAS 1124-11-4
FEMA 3237
Empirical: $C_8H_{12}N_2$
Properties: White crystals or powder
Uses: Chocolate flavoring agent
Regulatory: FEMA GRAS
Manuf./Distrib. (pharm. & food): Aldrich

Tetramethylthioperoxydicarbonic diamide. *See* Tetramethylthiuram disulfide

Tetramethylthiuram disulfide
CAS 137-26-8; EINECS 205-286-2
Synonyms: TMTD; Thiram; Tetramethylthioperoxydicarbonic diamide; Thiuram disulfide; Bis(dimethylthio-carbamyl) disulfide
Classification: Organic compd.
Empirical: $C_6H_{12}N_2S_4$
Formula: $[(CH_3)_2NCH]_2S_2$
Properties: White crystalline powd. with odor; sol. in alcohol, benzene, chloroform, carbon disulfide; insol. in water, dilute alkali, gasoline; m.w. 240.44; dens. 1.29 (20 C); m.p. 155-156 C
Toxicology: Toxic by ingestion and inhalation; irritant to skin and eyes; TLV 5 mg/m³ of air; LD50 (rat, oral) 640 mg/kg
Uses: Antibacterial, antifungal; applied topically as an aerosol in treatment of wounds and other skin disorders
Manuf./Distrib.: Complex Quimica SA; R.T. Vanderbilt

2,5,7,8-Tetramethyl-2-(4′,8′,12′-trimethyltridecyl)-6-chromanol. *See* D-α-Tocopherol
2,5,7,8-Tetramethyl-2-(4′,8′,12′-trimethyltridecyl)-6-chromanol acetate. *See* d-α-Tocopheryl acetate
2,5,7,8-Tetramethyl-2-(4,8,12-trimethyltridecyl)-6-chromanol acetate. *See* dl-α-Tocopheryl acetate
2,5,7,8-Tetramethyl-2-(4′,8′,12′-trimethyltridecyl)-6-chromanol-3-carboxypyridine. *See* d-α-Tocopheryl nicotinate
3,6,9,12-Tetraoxatetracosan-1-ol. *See* Laureth-4
Tetrasodium diphosphate. *See* Tetrasodium pyrophosphate
Tetrasodium edetate. *See* Tetrasodium EDTA

Tetrasodium EDTA
CAS 64-02-8; EINECS 200-573-9
Synonyms: EDTA Na₄; Edetate sodium; Tetrasodium edetate; Ethylene diamine tetraacetic acid, sodium salt
Classification: Substituted amine
Definition: Powdered sodium salt that reacts with metals
Empirical: $C_{10}H_{12}N_2O_8$ • 4Na
Formula: $(NaOOCCH_2)_2NCH_2CH_2N(CH_2COONa)_2$
Properties: White powd.; freely sol. in water; m.w. 380.20; dens. 6.9 lb/gal; m.p. > 300 C
Toxicology: LD50 (IP, mouse) 330 mg/kg; poison by IP route; skin and eye irritant; can deplete the body of calcium if taken internally; heated to decomp., emits toxic fumes of NO_x and Na_2O
Uses: Chelating agent used in injectables (IM, IV), inhalants, ophthalmics, orals, topicals; drug stabilization; heavy metal poisoning treatment
Regulatory: FDA 21CFR §173.310, 173.315, 175.105, 175.125, 175.300, 176.150, 176.170, 176.210, 177.2800, 178.3120, 178.3910; USDA 9CFR §381.147; FDA approved for injectables (IM, IV), inhalants, ophthalmics, orals, topicals
Manuf./Distrib.: Akzo Nobel; Chemplex; Complex Quimica SA; GFS; Great Western; Hampshire; Rhone-Poulenc Basic; Spectrum Chem. Mfg.
Manuf./Distrib. (pharm. & food): Rhone-Poulenc
Trade names: Versene 100; Versene 100 EP; Versene 100 LS; Versene 100 SRG; Versene 100 XL; Versene 220

Tetrasodium etidronate
CAS 3794-83-0; EINECS 223-267-7
Synonyms: Tetrasodium 1-hydroxyethane-1,1-diphosphonate; (1-Hydroxyethylidene)bisphosphonic acid, tetrasodium salt
Classification: Diphosphonic acid deriv.
Empirical: $C_2H_8O_2P_2$•4Na
Uses: Chelating agent; stabilizer for pharmaceutical topical preps.
Regulatory: FDA 21CFR §173.310
Trade names: Turpinal® 4 NL

Tetrasodium 1-hydroxyethane-1,1-diphosphonate. *See* Tetrasodium etidronate

Tetrasodium pyrophosphate
CAS 7722-88-5; EINECS 231-767-1
Synonyms: TSPP; Tetrasodium diphosphate; n-Sodium pyrophosphate; Diphosphoric acid tetrasodium salt; Sodium pyrophosphate
Classification: Inorganic salt
Empirical: $Na_4P_2O_7$
Properties: Wh. cryst. powd., gran.; sol. 8 g/100 g water; insol. in alcohol; m.w. 265.91; dens. 2.534; m.p. 988 C
Toxicology: TLV:TWA 5 mg/m³; LD50 (oral, rat) 4000 mg/kg; poison by ingestion, IP, IV, subcutaneous routes; heated to decomp., emits toxic fumes of PO_x and Na_2O; not a cholinesterase inhibitor
Uses: Used in buccals, dentals
Regulatory: FDA 21CFR §133.169, 133.173, 133.179, 173.310, 175.210, 175.300, 181.22, 181.29, 182.70, 182.6787, 182.6789, GRAS; Japan approved; Europe listed; UK approved; FDA approved for buccals, dentals
Manuf./Distrib.: Albright & Wilson; Farleyway Chem. Ltd; FMC; Lohmann; Mitsui Toatsu Chem.; Monsanto; Nippon Chem. Ind.; Rhone-Poulenc Food Ingreds.; Spectrum Chem. Mfg.; Yoneyama Chem. Ind.
Manuf./Distrib. (pharm. & food): Albright & Wilson Am.; Browning; FMC; Lohmann; Rhone-Poulenc Food Ingreds.

Tetryl formate. *See* Isobutyl formate
THAM. *See* Tris (hydroxymethyl) aminomethane

Theaspirane
CAS 36431-72-8
FEMA 3774
Synonyms: 2,6,10,10-Tetramethyl-1-oxaspiro[4.5]dec-6-ene
Empirical: $C_{13}H_{22}O$
Properties: M.w. 194.32; dens. 0.931; b.p. 68-72 C (3 mm); flash pt. 95 F
Uses: Medicinal flavoring agent
Regulatory: FEMA GRAS
Manuf./Distrib. (pharm. & food): Aldrich

Theine. *See* Caffeine
Theobroma oil. *See* Cocoa butter
THF. *See* Tetrahydrofuran
Thiamin chloride. *See* Thiamine HCl
Thiamine dichloride. *See* Thiamine HCl

Thiamine HCl
CAS 67-03-8; EINECS 200-641-8
FEMA 3322
Synonyms: Thiamine dichloride; Thiamin chloride; Vitamin B_1 hydrochloride; Aneurine hydrochloride; Thiamine hydrochloride
Definition: Chloride-hydrochloride salt of thiamine
Empirical: $C_{12}H_{18}N_4OSCl_2$
Formula: $C_{12}H_{17}ClN_4OS \cdot HCl$
Properties: Small white cryst. or cryst. powd., nut-like odor, hygroscopic; sol. in water, glycerol; sl. sol. in alcohol; insol. in ether, benzene; m.w. 337.30; m.p. 248 C (dec.)
Toxicology: LD50 (oral, mouse) 8224 mg/kg; poison by intravenous, intraperitoneal routes; mildly toxic by ingestion; heated to decomp., emits very toxic fumes of HCl, Cl⁻, SO_x, NO_x
Uses: Nutrient, thiamine source
Regulatory: FDA 21CFR §182.5875, 184.1875, GRAS; BATF 27CFR §240.1051; FEMA GRAS; Japan approved; BP, Ph.Eur. compliance
Manuf./Distrib.: Aldrich; BASF; EM Industries; Hoffmann-La Roche; Takeda USA
Manuf./Distrib. (pharm. & food): Aldrich; Am. Roland
Trade names: Thiamine Hydrochloride USP, FCC Regular Type No. 601160

Thiamine hydrochloride. *See* Thiamine HCl
Thiamine mononitrate. *See* Thiamine nitrate

Thiamine nitrate
CAS 532-43-4; EINECS 208-537-4
Synonyms: 3-[(4-Amino-2-methyl-5-pyrimidinyl)methyl]-4-(2-hydroxyethyl)-4-methylthiazolium nitrate (salt); Thiamine mononitrate; Thiamin nitrate; Vitamin B_1 nitrate; Aneurine mononitrate
Classification: Organic compd.

Thiamin nitrate

Definition: Mononitrate salt of thiamine
Empirical: $C_{12}H_{17}N_5O_4S$
Formula: $C_{12}H_{17}N_4OS \cdot NO_3$
Properties: Wh. cryst. or cryst. powd., sl. char. odor; pract. nonhygroscopic; sol. 2.7 g/100 ml water; sl. sol. in alcohol, chloroform; m.w. 327.36; m.p. 196-200 C (dec.); pH 6.5-7.1 (2% aq.)
Precaution: Powerful oxidizer
Toxicology: LD50 (IV, rabbit) 113 mg/kg; poison by IV and IP routes; heated to decomp., emits very toxic fumes of NO_x and SO_x
Uses: Nutrient, thiamine source
Regulatory: FDA 21CFR §182.5878, 184.1878, GRAS; Japan approved; BP, Ph.Eur. compliance
Manuf./Distrib. (pharm. & food): Am. Roland
Trade names: Thiamine Mononitrate USP, FCC Fine Powd. No. 601340
Trade names containing: Rocoat® Thiamine Mononitrate $33^1/_3$% No. 60188

Thiamin nitrate. *See* Thiamine nitrate

Thiazoximic acid
Uses: Used in parenterals
Regulatory: FDA approved for parenterals

Thimerosal
CAS 54-64-8; EINECS 200-210-4
UN No. 2025
Synonyms: Mercury, ethyl(2-mercaptobenzoato-S)-, sodium salt; 2-(Ethylmercuriomercapto)benzoic acid sodium salt; Ethyl (sodium o-mercaptobenzoato) mercury; Merthiolate; Thiomersal; Sodium ethylmercurithiosalicylate
Classification: Metallo-organic compd.
Empirical: $C_9H_9HgNaO_2S$
Formula: $COONaC_6H_4SHgCH_2CH_3$
Properties: Lt. cream-colored cryst. powd., sl. char. odor; freely sol. in water; sol. in alcohol; pract. insol. in ether; m.w. 404.81; m.p. 234-237 C (dec.); flash pt. > 250 C; pH 6.7 (1%)
Precaution: Photosensitive
Toxicology: DOT: Poisonous material; high potential for causing allergic reactions incl. eczematous contact allergy
Uses: Antimicrobial preservative, bacteriostat, fungistat in pharmaceuticals; used in topicals, tinctures, wound antiseptics, vaccines, skin test sol'ns., immunoglobulin preps., eye/ear drops, saline soft lens sol'ns.; treatment for minor skin injuries
Usage level: 0.002-0.01% (ophthalmics, topicals, parenterals)
Regulatory: FDA approved for parenterals, ophthalmics, topicals; USP/NF, BP compliance
Manuf./Distrib.: Fluka
Manuf./Distrib. (pharm. & food): Aldrich; Avrachem; Ruger; Spectrum Chem. Mfg.

Thiobis(dodecyl propionate). *See* Dilauryl thiodipropionate
3,3´-Thiobispropanoic acid, dioctadecyl ester. *See* Distearyl thiodipropionate
3,3´-Thiobispropanoic acid, ditridecyl ester. *See* Ditridecyl thiodipropionate
Thiocarbamide. *See* Thiourea
Thiocarbanilide. *See* N,N´-Diphenylthiourea
Thiocyanic acid potassium salt. *See* Potassium thiocyanate
Thiodipropionic acid dilauryl ester. *See* Dilauryl thiodipropionate
Thiodipropionic acid, distearyl ester. *See* Distearyl thiodipropionate
Thioethylene glycol. *See* 2-Mercaptoethanol
Thiofuran. *See* Thiophene

Thioglycerin
CAS 96-27-5; EINECS 202-495-0
Synonyms: 3-Mercapto-1,2-propanediol; Monothioglycerol; α-Monothioglycerol; Thioglycerol; 1-Thioglycerol
Classification: Polyhydric alcohol
Empirical: $C_3H_8O_2S$
Formula: $HOCH_2CHOHCH_2SH$
Properties: Colorless to pale ylsh. visc. liq., sl. sulfidic odor; hygroscopic; sl. sol. in water; misc. with alcohol; insol. in ether; m.w. 108.16; dens. 1.295; b.p. 118 C (5 mm); flash pt. > 230 F; ref. index 1.5260; pH 3.5-7.0 (10%)
Toxicology: Irritant
Uses: Antioxidant, preservative; stabilizer; pharmaceutical intermediate; in wound healing; used in injectables, buccals, parenterals

Regulatory: FDA approved for injectables, buccals, parenterals; USP/NF compliance
Manuf./Distrib.: Asahi Chem.; Evans Chemetics; NOF; SAF Bulk; Schweizerhall
Manuf./Distrib. (pharm. & food): Spectrum Chem. Mfg.
Trade names: Thiovanol®

Thioglycerol. *See* Thioglycerin
1-Thioglycerol. *See* Thioglycerin
Thioglycol. *See* 2-Mercaptoethanol
Thioglycolic acid sodium salt. *See* Sodium thioglycolate
Thioindigoid pink R. *See* D&C Red No. 30 aluminum lake
Thiomersal. *See* Thimerosal

Thiophene
CAS 110-02-1; EINECS 203-729-4
UN No. 2414
Synonyms: Thiofuran
Empirical: C_4H_4S
Properties: Colorless liq.; sol. in alcohol, ether; insol. in water; m.w. 84.14; dens. 1.051; m.p. -38 C; b.p. 84 C; ref. index 1.5270
Precaution: DOT: Flamm. liq.
Uses: Organic synthesis, pharmaceutical mfg.
Manuf./Distrib.: Elf Atochem N. Am.; Penta Mfg.; Spectrum Chem. Mfg.
Manuf./Distrib. (pharm. & food): Aldrich

Thiophenol
CAS 108-98-5; EINECS 203-635-3
FEMA 3616; UN No. 2337
Synonyms: Phenyl mercaptan; Benzenethiol
Classification: Aromatic organic compd.
Empirical: C_6H_6S
Formula: C_6H_5SH
Properties: Water-wh. liq., repulsive penetrating garlic-like odor; very sol. in alcohol; misc. with ether, benzene, CS_2; insol. in water; m.w. 110.04; dens. 1.078 (20/4 C); m.p. 70 C; b.p. 169.5 C; flash pt. 55 C; ref. index 1.5931 (14 C)
Precaution: Combustible; oxidizes in air
Toxicology: Toxic by inhalation, skin contact, ingestion; causes burns
Uses: Pharmaceutical synthesis
Regulatory: FDA 21CFR §172.515
Manuf./Distrib.: Aldrich; ICI Am.; Janssen Chimica; Schweizerhall; Sumitomo Seika Chem.
Manuf./Distrib. (pharm. & food): Aldrich; Sumitomo Seika Chems.

Thiosulfuric acid disodium salt. *See* Sodium thiosulfate anhydrous

Thiourea
CAS 62-56-6; EINECS 200-543-5
UN No. 2811
Synonyms: Sulfourea; Thiocarbamide
Empirical: CH_4N_2S
Formula: NH_2CSNH_2
Properties: Wh. cryst., bitter taste; sol. in water, alcohol; m.w. 76.12; sp.gr. 1.406; m.p. 180 C
Toxicology: DOT: Poisonous material; skin irritant, allergenic; carcinogenic
Uses: Pharmaceutical synthesis
Regulatory: FDA 21CFR §189.190 (prohibited from direct addition or use in human food); BP compliance
Manuf./Distrib.: Allchem Industries; Fairmount; R.W. Greeff; Mitsui Toatsu; Monomer-Polymer & Dajac; Sakai Chem. Ind.; Nippon Chem. Ind.
Manuf./Distrib. (pharm. & food): Aldrich; Ruger

Thiram. *See* Tetramethylthiuram disulfide
Thiuram disulfide. *See* Tetramethylthiuram disulfide
Thomas balsam. *See* Balsam tolu

Thyme
Synonyms: Common thyme; Garden thyme
Definition: Dried leaves and flowering tops of *Thymus vulgaris*
Uses: Natural flavoring agent; carminative, antitussive, expectorant; in preps. for respiratory disorders

Thyme camphor. *See* Thymol

Thyme extract
CAS 84929-51-1
Synonyms: Thymus vulgaris extract
Definition: Extract of the leaves and flowers of *Thymus vulgaris*
Toxicology: May cause contact dermatitis and hay fever
Uses: Natural flavoring agent in toothpastes and cough medicines
Regulatory: FDA 21CFR §172.510, 182.20, GRAS
Manuf./Distrib. (pharm. & food): Bio-Botanica; C.A.L.-Pfizer; Chart; Pierre Chauvet

Thyme oil
CAS 8007-46-3
FEMA 3064
Synonyms: Thymus vulgaris oil; Red thyme oil; Thyme oil, red
Definition: Volatile oil from distillation of flowering plant *Thymus vulgaris*, contg. thymol, carvacrol, cymene, pinene, linalool, bornyl acetate
Properties: Colorless to reddish-brn. liq., pleasant thymol odor, sharp taste; sol. in 2 vols 80% alcohol; very sl. sol. in water; dens. 0.894-0.930; ref. index 1.4830-1.5100 (20 C)
Precaution: Combustible when exposed to heat or flame; keep cool, well closed; protect from light
Toxicology: LD50 (oral, rat) 2840 mg/kg; mod. toxic by ingestion; mutagenic data; allergen; irritant; heated to decomp., emits acrid smoke and irritating fumes
Uses: Natural flavoring agent; carminative, antitussive, expectorant; in preps. for respiratory disorders
Regulatory: FDA 21CFR §182.10, 182.20, GRAS; 27CFR §21.65, 21.151; FEMA GRAS
Manuf./Distrib.: Spectrum Chem. Mfg.
Manuf./Distrib. (pharm. & food): Chart; Pierre Chauvet; Commodity Services

Thyme oil, red. *See* Thyme oil

Thymol
CAS 89-83-8; EINECS 201-944-8
FEMA 3066
Synonyms: 5-Methyl-2-(1-methylethyl) phenol; 3-p-Cymenol; p-Cymen-3-ol; Isopropyl metacresol; Thyme camphor; 6-Isopropyl-m-cresol; 3-Hydroxy-p-cymene; Phenol, 5-methyl-2-(1-methylethyl)-; 2-Isopropyl-5-methylphenol; 5-Methyl-2-isopropylphenol
Classification: Aromatic organic compd.; substituted phenol
Empirical: $C_{10}H_{14}O$
Formula: $(CH_3)_2CHC_6H_3(CH_3)OH$
Properties: Colorless translucent cryst., pungent caustic taste; sol. in water, alkali, glac. acetic acid, fixed/volatile oils; very sol. in alcohol, ether, chloroform, olive oil; m.w. 150.24; dens. 0.972; m.p. 51 C; b.p. 233 C; flash pt. 216 F; ref. index 1.523
Precaution: Combustible; affected by light
Toxicology: Poison by ingestion, intravenous, intraperitoneal, subcutaneous routes; local irritant; allergen; accumulation of toxic levels causes pulmonary edema
Uses: Medicinal synthetic flavoring agent, perfume, antimicrobial preservative, disinfectant, deodorant; used in buccals, inhalants, mouthwashes; preservative in insulin preps.; destroys mold, preserves anatomical specimens; topical angifungal agent
Regulatory: FDA 21CFR §172.515, 175.105; 27CFR §21.65, 21.151; FEMA GRAS; FDA approved for buccals, inhalants; USP/NF, BP, Ph.Eur. compliance
Manuf./Distrib.: Aldrich; Haarmann & Reimer; Janssen Chimica; Kishida Chem.; Quest Int'l.
Manuf./Distrib. (pharm. & food): Aldrich; Integra; Kishida Chem.; Mallinckrodt; Ruger; Spectrum Chem. Mfg.

Thymus vulgaris extract. *See* Thyme extract
Thymus vulgaris oil. *See* Thyme oil
Tiger orange. *See* D&C Red No. 36
Tilia cordata extract. *See* Linden extract

Tin
CAS 7440-31-5; EINECS 231-141-8
Synonyms: Stannum
Classification: Element
Empirical: Sn
Properties: Silver-white ductile solid; sol. in acids, hot KOH sol'ns.; insol. in water; at.wt. 118.69; dens. 7.29 (20 C); m.p. 232 C; b.p. 2260 C
Toxicology: TLV 2 mg/m³ of air (inorg. compds.), TLV 0.1 mg/m³ of air (org. compds.)
Uses: Ingred. in dental amalgam; formerly used for treatment of tapeworm
Regulatory: BP compliance
Manuf./Distrib.: Aldrich; Atomergic Chemetals; Cerac; Noah

Tin crystals. *See* Stannous chloride anhyd.
Tincture of orange. *See* Orange tincture
Tin dichloride. *See* Stannous chloride anhyd.
Tin difluoride. *See* Stannous fluoride
Tin fluoride. *See* Stannous fluoride
Tin (II) chloride (1:2). *See* Stannous chloride anhyd.
Tin (II) chloride anhydrous. *See* Stannous chloride anhyd.
Tin protochloride. *See* Stannous chloride anhyd.
Tin salt. *See* Stannous chloride anhyd.
TIPA. *See* Triisopropanolamine
Tirpilene. *See* α-Terpinene
Titanic acid anhydride. *See* Titanium dioxide
Titanic anhydride. *See* Titanium dioxide
Titanic earth. *See* Titanium dioxide
Titanic oxide. *See* Titanium dioxide

Titanium dioxide
CAS 1317-80-2; 13463-67-7; EINECS 236-675-5
Synonyms: Titanic anhydride; Titanic earth; Titanic oxide; Titanic acid anhydride; Titanium oxide; Titanium white; Pigment white 6; CI 77891
Classification: Inorganic oxide
Empirical: TiO_2
Properties: Wh. amorphous powd., odorless, tasteless; insol. in water, HCl, HNO_3, dil. H_2SO_4; sol. in HF, hot conc. H_2SO_4; m.w. 79.90; Anatase: dens. 3.90; Rutile: dens. 4.23
Precaution: Violent or incandescent reaction with metals (e.g., aluminum, calcium, magnesium, potassium, sodium, zinc, lithium)
Toxicology: TLV:TWA 10 mg/m^3 of total dust; experimental carcinogen, neoplastigen, tumorigen; human skin irritant; nuisance dust
Uses: Opacifying agent, color additive, coating agent; sunscreen agent; used in ophthalmics, orals, topicals, tableted drugs, protective creams, antiperspirants
Regulatory: FDA 21CFR §73.575, 73.1575, 73.2575, 175.105, 175.210, 175.300, 175.380, 175.390, 176.170, 177.1200, 177.1210, 177.1350, 177.1400, 177.1460, 177.1650, 177.2260, 177.2600, 177.2800, 181.22, 181.30; USDA 9CFR §318.7, 381.147; Japan restricted as colorant; Europe listed; UK approved; prohibited in Germany; FDA approved for ophthalmics, orals, topicals; USP/NF, BP, Ph.Eur. compliance
Manuf./Distrib.: Aceto; Ashland; J.T. Baker; Bayer NV; British Traders & Shippers; Chemcentral; The Chemical Co.; Degussa; DuPont; Engelhard; Ferro/Transelco; Fuji Titanium Ind.; Furukawa; Harcros; Hilton Davis; Hitox; Kemira; Kerr-McGee; Landers-Segal Color; Lenape Ind.; D.N. Lukens; Ore & Chem.; Royale Pigments & Chems.; Sachtleben Chemie GmbH; SCM; Seegott; Tioxide Am.; Titan Kogyo; Tricon Colors; Van Waters & Rogers; Whittaker, Clark & Daniels
Manuf./Distrib. (pharm. & food): Aldrich; Degussa; R.W. Greeff; Integra; Spectrum Chem. Mfg.
Trade names: Hilton Davis Titanium Dioxide
Trade names containing: Flamenco® Interference Color Powds.; Flamenco® White Pearl Powds.; Opacode®; Opacode® WB; Opalux®; Opaspray®; Timica®
See also CI 77891

Titanium oxide. *See* Titanium dioxide
Titanium white. *See* Titanium dioxide
TMTD. *See* Tetramethylthiuram disulfide

Tocopherol
CAS 1406-18-4; 59-02-9 (d-α); 10191-41-0 (dl-α); EINECS 215-798-8; 200-412-2
Synonyms: Vitamin E; D-α Tocopherol; DL-α Tocopherol
Empirical: $C_{29}H_{50}O_2$
Properties: Visc. oil; sol. in fats; insol. in water
Uses: Antioxidant, dietary supplement for medicine, nutrition
Regulatory: FDA 21CFR §182.3890, 182.5890, 182.8890, 184.1890, GRAS; EC E306; USP/NF, BP, Ph.Eur. compliance
Manuf./Distrib. (pharm. & food): ADM; Aldrich; Eastman; Ruger
Trade names: Vitamin E USP Tocopherol
Trade names containing: Copherol® 950LC; Oxynex® K; Oxynex® LM

2R,4′R,8′R-α-Tocopherol. *See* D-α-Tocopherol

D-α-Tocopherol
CAS 59-02-9; EINECS 200-412-2

DL-α Tocopherol

Synonyms: 2,5,7,8-Tetramethyl-2-(4´,8´,12´-trimethyltridecyl)-6-chromanol; 5,7,8-Trimethyltocol; 2R,4´R,8´R-α-Tocopherol; Vitamin E

Classification: Antioxidant fat-soluble compd.

Empirical: $C_{29}H_{50}O_2$

Properties: Red visc. oil, nearly odorless; freely sol. in oils, fats, acetone, alcohol, chloroform, ether; pract. insol. in water; m.w. 430.72; dens. 0.950 (25/4 C); m.p. 2.5-3.5 C

Toxicology: Experimental reproductive effects; mutagenic data; heated to decomp., emits acrid smoke and irritating fumes

Uses: Nutrient, antioxidant for fats, dietary supplement, preservative

Regulatory: FDA 21CFR §182.3890, 182.5890, 182.8890, 184.1890, GRAS; USDA 9CFR §318.7, 381.147; Japan approved; Europe listed; UK approved

Manuf./Distrib. (pharm. & food): ADM; Am. Roland

Trade names: Copherol® F-1300

See also Tocopherol

DL-α-Tocopherol

CAS 10191-41-0; EINECS 233-466-0

Synonyms: all-rac-α-Tocopherol; Vitamin E

Classification: Antioxidant fat-soluble compd.

Empirical: $C_{29}H_{50}O_2$

Properties: Pale yel. visc. oil; m.w. 430.72; dens. 0.947-0.958 (25/25 C); b.p. 200-220 C (0.1 mm); ref. index 1.5030-1.5070

Precaution: Light-sensitive, refrigerate

Uses: Antioxidant for pharmaceuticals; medicine, nutrition

Regulatory: FDA 21CFR §182.3890, 182.5890, 182.8890, 184.1890, GRAS; Japan restricted for purpose of antioxidation; UK approved

Manuf./Distrib.: Spectrum Chem. Mfg.

Manuf./Distrib. (pharm. & food): Am. Roland; Spectrum Chem. Mfg.

Trade names containing: 24% Beta Carotene HS-E in Veg. Oil No. 65671; Canthaxanthin Beadlets 10%; Dry Beta Carotene Beadlets 10% CWS No. 65633; Dry Beta Carotene Beadlets 10% No. 65661; Dry Vitamin D_3 Type 100 CWS No. 65242; Palma-Sperse® Type 250-S No. 65322; Palma-Sperse® Type 250A/50 D-S No. 65221; Vitamin A Palmitate Type 250-CWS No. 65312

See also Tocopherol

(+)-γ-Tocopherol

CAS 54-28-4; EINECS 200-201-5

Synonyms: 7,8-Dimethyltocol; RRR-γ-Tocopherol

Empirical: $C_{28}H_{48}O_2$

Properties: M.w. 416.69

Tocopheryl acetate

CAS 1406-70-8; EINECS 231-710-0

Synonyms: D-α Tocopheryl acetate; DL-α Tocopheryl acetate; Vitamin E acetate

Definition: Ester of tocopherol and acetic acid

Empirical: $C_{31}H_{52}O_3$

Uses: Antioxidant; vitamin E source for pharmaceutical capsules and liqs.

Regulatory: FDA 21CFR §182.5892, 182.5915, 182.8892, GRAS; BP, Ph.Eur. compliance

Trade names: Vitamin E Acetate USP Oil; Vitamin E USP, FCC No. 60525; Vitamin E USP, FCC No. 60526; Vitinc® dl-alpha Tocopheryl Acetate USP XXII

2R,4´R,8´R-α-Tocopheryl acetate. *See* d-α-Tocopheryl acetate

d-α-Tocopheryl acetate

CAS 58-95-7

Synonyms: 2R,4´R,8´R-α-Tocopheryl acetate; 2,5,7,8-Tetramethyl-2-(4´,8´,12´-trimethyltridecyl)-6-chromanol acetate; Vitamin E acetate

Definition: Obtained from vacuum steam distillation and acetylation of edible vegetable oil prods.

Empirical: $C_{31}H_{52}O_3$

Properties: Cryst., odorless; sol. in alcohol; misc. with acetone, chloroform, ether, vegetable oil; insol. in water; m.w. 472.75; m.p. 25 C

Toxicology: Heated to decomp., emits acrid smoke and irritating fumes

Uses: Antioxidant, vitamin E source; used in topicals

Regulatory: FDA 21CFR §182.5892, 182.8892, GRAS; FDA approved for topicals

Trade names: Copherol® 1250

See also Tocopheryl acetate

D-α Tocopheryl acetate. *See* Tocopheryl acetate

dl-α-Tocopheryl acetate
　　CAS 7695-91-2; EINECS 231-710-0
　　Synonyms: 2,5,7,8-Tetramethyl-2-(4,8,12-trimethyltridecyl)-6-chromanol acetate
　　Definition: Obtained from vacuum steam distillation and acetylation of edible vegetable oil prods.
　　Empirical: $C_{31}H_{52}O_3$
　　Properties: Colorless to yel. visc. oil, odorless; sol. in alcohol; misc. with acetone, chloroform, ether, vegetable
　　　　oil; insol. in water; m.w. 472.75; dens. 0.9533 (21.3/4 C); m.p. -27.5 C; b.p. 184 C (0.01 mm); flash pt. >
　　　　230 F; ref. index 1.4950-1.4972
　　Precaution: Light-sensitive
　　Toxicology: Heated to decomp., emits acrid smoke and irritating fumes
　　Uses: Antioxidant
　　Regulatory: FDA 21CFR §182.5892, 182.8892, GRAS
　　Manuf./Distrib.: Spectrum Chem. Mfg.
　　Manuf./Distrib. (pharm. & food): Eisai USA; Spectrum Chem. Mfg.
　　Trade names: Tri-K Vitamin E Acetate
　　Trade names containing: Dry Vitamin E Acetate 50% SD No. 65356; Dry Vitamin E Acetate 50% Type CWS/
　　　　F No. 652530001
　　See also Tocopheryl acetate

DL-α Tocopheryl acetate. *See* Tocopheryl acetate
2R,4′R,8′R-α-Tocopheryl nicotinate. *See* d-α-Tocopheryl nicotinate

d-α-Tocopheryl nicotinate
　　Synonyms: 2,5,7,8-Tetramethyl-2-(4′,8′,12′-trimethyltridecyl)-6-chromanol-3-carboxypyridine; Vitamin E
　　　　nicotinate; 2R,4′R,8′R-α-Tocopheryl nicotinate
　　Definition: Ester of tocopherol and nicotinic acid
　　Empirical: $C_{35}H_{53}NO_3$
　　Properties: Lt. yel. waxy solid; m.w. 535.82; m.p. 42-48 C
　　Uses: Pharmaceutical topicals ingred.
　　Trade names: Nicopherol®

α-Tolualdehyde. *See* Phenylacetaldehyde
p-Tolualdehyde. *See* p-Tolyl aldehyde
Tolu balsam. *See* Balsam tolu
4-Toluenesulfonic acid. *See* p-Toluene sulfonic acid

p-Toluene sulfonic acid
　　CAS 104-15-4; EINECS 203-180-0
　　UN No. 2585
　　Synonyms: 4-Methylbenzenesulfonic acid; 4-Toluenesulfonic acid; p-Methylbenzenesulfonic acid; Toluene-
　　　　p-sulfonic acid; p-Methylphenylsulfonic acid; Tosic acid
　　Classification: Substituted aromatic acid
　　Empirical: $C_7H_8O_3S$
　　Formula: $C_6H_4(SO_3H)(CH_3)$
　　Properties: Colorless leaflets; sol. in alcohol, ether, water; m.w. 172.21; m.p. 107 C; b.p. 140 C (20 mm)
　　Precaution: DOT: Corrosive material; combustible; potentially explosive reaction with acetic anhydride +
　　　　water; heated to decomp., emits toxic fumes of SO_x
　　Toxicology: LD50 (oral, rat) 2480 mg/kg; poison by ingestion; skin and mucous membrane irritant
　　Uses: Intermediate for pharmaceutical chemicals
　　Regulatory: BP compliance
　　Manuf./Distrib.: Bayer; Boliden Intertrade; BYK-Chemie; Eastman; Ferro/Grant; Nissan Chem. Ind.; PMC
　　　　Spec.; Ruetgers-Nease; Spectrum Chem. Mfg.; Witco/Oleo-Surf.
　　Manuf./Distrib. (pharm. & food): Aldrich
　　Trade names: Eltesol® TSX; Eltesol® TSX/A; Eltesol® TSX/SF

Toluene-p-sulfonic acid. *See* p-Toluene sulfonic acid
α-Toluic acid. *See* Phenylacetic acid
α-Toluic acid ethyl ester. *See* Ethyl phenylacetate
α-Toluic aldehyde. *See* Phenylacetaldehyde
Toluifera balsamam resin. *See* Balsam tolu
Tolu resin. *See* Balsam tolu
p-Toluylaldehyde. *See* p-Tolyl aldehyde

p-Tolyl aldehyde

p-Tolyl aldehyde
CAS 104-87-0; 1334-78-7; EINECS 203-246-9
Synonyms: p-Methyl benzaldehyde; 4-Methylbenzaldehyde; p-Toluylaldehyde; p-Tolualdehyde
Empirical: C_8H_8O
Formula: $CH_3C_6H_4CHO$
Properties: Colorless to yel. liq., aromatic odor; sol. in alcohol, ether; sl. sol. in water; m.w. 120.15; dens. 1.016 (20/4 C); b.p. 82-85 C (11 mm); flash pt. 85 C; ref. index 1.545 (20 C)
Precaution: Combustible
Toxicology: LD50 (oral, rat) 1000 mg/kg; eye and skin irritant
Uses: Synthetic flavoring agent; pharmaceutical intermediate
Manuf./Distrib.: BASF; Fabrichem; Mallinckrodt; Mitsubishi Gas; Penta Mfg.
Manuf./Distrib. (pharm. & food): Aldrich

α-Tolylic acid. *See* Phenylacetic acid

o-Tolyl isobutyrate
CAS 36438-54-7
FEMA 3753
Synonyms: o-Tolyl 2-methylpropanoate
Empirical: $C_{11}H_{14}O_2$
Properties: M.w. 178.23; dens. 1.004; b.p. 107-108 C (8 mm); flash pt. 203 F
Uses: Berry, medicinal flavoring agent
Regulatory: FEMA GRAS
Manuf./Distrib. (pharm. & food): Aldrich

o-Tolyl 2-methylpropanoate. *See* o-Tolyl isobutyrate
Toney red. *See* D&C Red No. 17
Tonkalide. *See* γ-Hexalactone
Tosic acid. *See* p-Toluene sulfonic acid
Toxilic acid. *See* Maleic acid
Toxilic anhydride. *See* Maleic anhydride
TPG. *See* Tripropylene glycol
Tragacanth. *See* Tragacanth gum

Tragacanth gum
CAS 9000-65-1; EINECS 232-552-5
FEMA 3079
Synonyms: Gum tragacanth; Gum dragon; Tragacanth
Definition: Dried gummy exudate from *Astragalus gummifer*
Properties: Wh. powd., wh. to pale yel. translucent, horny pieces, odorless, mucilaginous taste; insol. in alcohol; strongly hydrophilic
Precaution: Combustible when exposed to heat or flame
Toxicology: LD50 (oral, rat) 16,400 mg/kg; mildly toxic by ingestion; mild allergen causing hay fever, dermatitis, GI distress, asthma; may cause intolerance; linked to liver damage in test animals; heated to decomp., emits acrid smoke and irritating fumes
Uses: Suspending agent, thickener, emulsifier; tablet excipient; used in nasal sol'ns., sublingual tablets, oral suspensions, ointments, medicinal emulsions, dentifrices
Usage level: 4.8-6.0% (oral liqs.); 0.42-100 mg (tablets)
Regulatory: FDA 21CFR §133.133, 133.134, 133.162, 133.178, 133.179, 150.141, 150.161, 184.1351, GRAS; FEMA GRAS; Japan approved; Europe listed; UK approved; FDA approved for orals; USP/NF, BP, Ph.Eur. compliance
Manuf./Distrib. (pharm. & food): Agrisales; Ashland; Bio-Botanica; Arthur Branwell; Chart; Cornelius; Florexco; Gumix Int'l.; Importers Service; Int'l. Ingreds.; Meer; MLG Enterprises; Penta Mfg.; Quest; Red Carnation; Rhone-Poulenc; Ruger; Spectrum Chem. Mfg.; Spice King; Thew Arnott; TIC Gums
Trade names: Gum Tragacanth Ribbons and Flakes; Powdered Gum Tragacanth BP; Powdered Gum Tragacanth T-150; Powdered Gum Tragacanth T-200; Powdered Gum Tragacanth T-300; Powdered Gum Tragacanth T-400; Powdered Gum Tragacanth T-500; Powdered Gum Tragacanth Type B-1 NF Premium; Powdered Gum Tragacanth Type B-12 NF Premium; Powdered Gum Tragacanth Type C-5 NF; Powdered Gum Tragacanth Type G-1 NF Premium; Powdered Gum Tragacanth Type G-2 NF Premium; Powdered Gum Tragacanth Type G-2S NF Premium; Powdered Gum Tragacanth Type M-3 NF Premium; Powdered Tragacanth Gum Type A/10; Powdered Tragacanth Gum Type E-1; Powdered Tragacanth Gum Type G-3; Powdered Tragacanth Gum Type L; Powdered Tragacanth Gum Type W; TIC Pretested® Tragacanth 440; Tragacanth Flake No. 27; Tragacanth Gum Ribbon No. 1

Triacetin
CAS 102-76-1; EINECS 203-051-9
FEMA 2007
Synonyms: Glyceryl triacetate; Acetin; Enzactin; 1,2,3-Propanetriol triacetate; Triacetyl glycerol; Triacetyl glycerin
Definition: Triester of glycerin and acetic acid
Empirical: $C_9H_{14}O_6$
Formula: $C_3H_5(OCOCH_3)_3$
Properties: Colorless oily liq., sl. fatty odor, bitter taste; sol. in water, alcohol, ether, other org. solvs.; sl. sol. in CS_2; m.w. 218.20; dens. 1.160 (20 C); m.p. -78 C; b.p. 258-260 C; flash pt. 300 F; ref. index 1.4307 (20 C)
Precaution: Combustible exposed to heat, flame, or powerful oxidizers
Toxicology: LD50 (oral, rat) 3000 mg/kg, (IV, mouse) 1600 ± 81 mg/kg; poison by ingestion; mod. toxic by IP, subcutaneous, IV routes; eye irritant; heated to decomp., emits acrid smoke and irritating fumes
Uses: Plasticizer, topical antifungal, syn. flavoring; used in orals, toothpaste
Regulatory: FDA 21CFR §175.300, 175.320, 181.22, 181.27, 184.1901, GRAS; FEMA GRAS; FDA approved for orals; USP/NF, BP compliance
Manuf./Distrib.: Aldrich; Eastman; MTM Spec. Chem. Ltd; Penta Mfg.; Spectrum Chem. Mfg.; Unichema; Yuki Gosei Kogyo
Manuf./Distrib. (pharm. & food): Aldrich; Britannia Natural Prods.; Eastman; Mallinckrodt; Ruger; Spectrum Chem. Mfg.; Unipex
Trade names: Eastman® Triacetin
Trade names containing: Chroma-Seal™ 859027; Chroma-Seal™ 889031

Triacetyl glycerin. *See* Triacetin
Triacetyl glycerol. *See* Triacetin
Tribasic calcium phosphate. *See* Calcium phosphate tribasic

Tribehenin
CAS 18641-57-1; 68334-28-1; EINECS 242-471-7
Synonyms: Glyceryl tribehenate; 1,2,3-Propanetriol tridocosanoate; Docosanoic acid, 1,2,3-propanetriyl ester
Definition: Triester of glycerin and behenic acid
Empirical: $C_{69}H_{134}O_6$
Uses: Excipient; emollient; lubricant for tablets/capsules; lipophilic agent for sustained-release formulations
Trade names: Compritol 888; Compritol 888 ATO; Pelemol® GTB; Syncrowax HR-C
Trade names containing: Compritol HD5 ATO

Tributyl acetyl citrate. *See* Acetyl tributyl citrate

Tributyl citrate
CAS 77-94-1; EINECS 201-071-2
Synonyms: TBC; 2-Hydroxy-1,2,3-propanetricarboxylic acid, tributyl ester; Butyl citrate
Definition: Triester of butyl alcohol and citric acid
Empirical: $C_{18}H_{32}O_7$
Formula: $C_3H_5O(COOC_4H_9)_3$
Properties: Colorless or pale yel., odorless; insol. in water; m.w. 360.45; dens. 1.042 (25/25 C); m.p. -20 C; b.p. 233.5 C (22.5 mm); flash pt. (COC) 315 F; ref. index 1.4453
Precaution: Combustible
Uses: Plasticizer for aq. pharmaceutical coatings; controlled sustained-release drugs
Regulatory: FDA 21CFR §175.105
Manuf./Distrib.: Morflex; Unitex
Trade names: TBC

Tributyl phosphite
CAS 102-85-2; EINECS 203-061-3
Synonyms: Tributyl (n) phosphite
Classification: Phosphorus deriv.
Empirical: $(C_4H_9O)_3P$
Formula: $(CH_3CH_2CH_2CH_2O)_3P$
Properties: Clear liq.; sol. in common org. solvs.; dec. in water; m.w. 250; dens. 0.910-0.940; b.p. 120 C (8 mm); flash pt. 121 C
Precaution: Combustible
Toxicology: Moderately toxic by ingestion; skin and eye irritant
Uses: Intermediate; reagent; scavenging agent
Manuf./Distrib.: Albright & Wilson; Janssen Chimica

Tributyl (n) phosphite

    Manuf./Distrib. (pharm. & food): Aldrich
    Trade names: TBP-HP

Tributyl (n) phosphite. *See* Tributyl phosphite

Tributyrin
    CAS 60-01-5; EINECS 200-451-5
    FEMA 2223
    Synonyms: Glyceryl tributyrate; Butyrin; Butanoic acid 1,2,3-propanetriyl ester
    Definition: Triester of glycerin and butyric acid
    Empirical: $C_{15}H_{26}O_6$
    Formula: $(C_3H_7COO)_3C_3H_5$
    Properties: Colorless oily liq., bitter taste; very sol. in alcohol, ether; insol. in water; m.w. 302.36; dens. 1.032
        (20/4 C); m.p. -75 C; b.p. 305-310 C (760 mm), 90C (15 mm); flash pt. 345 F; ref. index 1.4358 (20 C)
    Precaution: Combustible liq.
    Toxicology: Poison by IV route; mod. toxic by ingestion; experimental tumorigen; heated to decomp., emits
        acrid smoke and irritating fumes
    Uses: Synthetic flavoring agent; used in nutritional supplements
    Regulatory: FDA 21CFR §172.515, 184.1903, GRAS; FEMA GRAS
    Manuf./Distrib.: Aldrich
    Manuf./Distrib. (pharm. & food): Aldrich
    Trade names containing: Neobee® SL-140

Tricalcium citrate. *See* Calcium citrate
Tricalcium orthophosphate. *See* Calcium phosphate tribasic
Tricalcium phosphate. *See* Calcium phosphate tribasic

Tricaprylin
    CAS 538-23-8; EINECS 208-686-5
    Synonyms: Glyceryl tricaprylate; Caprylic acid, 1,2,3-propanetriyl ester; 1,2,3-Propanetriol trioctanoate
    Classification: Triester
    Definition: Triester of glycerin and caprylic acid
    Empirical: $C_{27}H_{50}O_6$
    Formula: $[CH_3(CH_2)_6COOCH_2]_2CHOCO(CH_2)_6CH_3$
    Properties: M.w. 470.70; dens. 0.954 (20/4 C); m.p. 9-10 C; b.p. 233 C (1 mm); ref. index 1.447
    Uses: Lubricant, carrier/vehicle
    Trade names: Captex® 8000

Tricarballylic acid-β-acetoxytributyl ester. *See* Acetyl triethyl citrate
β,β,β-Trichloro-t-butyl alcohol. *See* Chlorobutanol hemihydrate
Trichloro-t-butyl alcohol. *See* Chlorobutanol
Trichloroethene. *See* Trichloroethylene

Trichloroethylene
    CAS 79-01-6; EINECS 201-167-4
    UN No. 1710
    Synonyms: TCE; Trichloroethene; 1,1-Dichloro-2-chloroethylene; Ethinyl trichloride; 1-Chloro-2,2-
        dichloroethylene; Acetylene trichloride
    Classification: Aliphatic organic compd.
    Empirical: C_2HCl_3
    Formula: $CHCl:CCl_2$
    Properties: Colorless, photoreactive liq., chloroform odor; misc. with common org. solvs.; sl. sol. in water; m.w.
        131.40; dens. 1.456-1.462 (25/25 C); m.p. -84.8 C; b.p. 86.7 C (760 mm); ref. index 1.45560 (25 C)
    Precaution: High concs. of vapor in high-temp. air can be made to burn mildly under strong flame; light-
        sensitive; heated to decomp., emits toxic fumes of Cl⁻
    Toxicology: TLV 50 ppm (air); LD50 (oral, rat) 4.92 ml/kg; mildly toxic to humans by ingestion, inhalation;
        experimental carcinogen, tumorigen, teratogen, reproductive effects; human systemic effects, mutagenic
        data; eye, severe skin irritant; carcinogen in mice
    Uses: Analgesic and anesthetic prop. make it useful for short operations; mfg. of pharmaceuticals, org.
        chemicals
    Regulatory: FDA 21CFR §173.290; BP compliance
    Manuf./Distrib.: Asahi Glass; Ashland; Asahi-Penn; Elf Atochem N. Am.; General Chem.; Kanto; Spectrum
        Chem. Mfg.
    Manuf./Distrib. (pharm. & food): Aldrich; Ashland; Integra; Nickerson Chem. Ltd; PPG Industries; Ruger

Trichlorofluoromethane
    CAS 75-69-4; EINECS 200-892-3

Synonyms: Fluorocarbon-11; Fluorotrichloromethane; Trichloromonofluoromethane
Empirical: CCl_3F
Formula: Cl_3CF
Properties: Colorless volatile liq., nearly odorless; sol. in alcohol, ether; insol. in water; m.w. 137.4; dens. 1.494 (17.2 C); b.p. 23.7 C; f.p. -111 C
Toxicology: Poison by inhalation; moderately toxic by intraperitoneal route; TLV:CL 1000 ppm in air
Uses: Aerosol propellant; used in inhalants
Regulatory: FDA approved for inhalants; USP/NF, BP compliance
Manuf./Distrib.: Aldrich; Elf Atochem

2,4,4´-Trichloro-2´-hydroxydiphenyl ether. *See* Triclosan
Trichloromethane. *See* Chloroform
1,1,1-Trichloro-2-methyl-2-propanol. *See* Chlorobutanol
1,1,1-Trichloro-2-methyl-2-propanol hemihydrate. *See* Chlorobutanol hemihydrate
cis-N-[(Trichloromethyl) thio]-4-cyclohexene-1,2-dicarboximide. *See* Captan
N-Trichloromethylthio-4-cyclohexene-1,2-dicarboximide. *See* Captan
N-Trichloromethylthiotetrahydrophthalimide. *See* Captan
Trichloromonofluoromethane. *See* Trichlorofluoromethane
Trichlorostibine. *See* Antimony trichloride

Triclosan
　　CAS 3380-34-5; EINECS 222-182-2
　　Synonyms: 2,4,4´-Trichloro-2´-hydroxydiphenyl ether; 5-Chloro-2(2,4-dichlorophenoxy)phenol
　　Classification: Substituted organic ether
　　Empirical: $C_{12}H_7Cl_3O_2$
　　Toxicology: Can cause allergic dermatitis esp. when used in prods. for the feet
　　Uses: Broad spectrum bacteriostat for deodorant soaps, vaginal deodorant sprays, and other drug prods.

l-Tridecanecarboxylic acid. *See* Myristic acid
Tridecanol stearate. *See* Tridecyl stearate
Tridecen-2-al-1. *See* 2-Tridecenal

2-Tridecenal
　　CAS 7774-82-5
　　FEMA 3082
　　Synonyms: 3-Decylacrolein; Tridecen-2-al-1
　　Empirical: $C_{13}H_{24}O$
　　Properties: White or sl. yellowish liq.; oily, citrus odor; sol. in alcohol, most fixed oils; insol. in water; m.w. 196.33; dens. 0.8476; b.p. 232 C; ref. index 1.457-1.460
　　Uses: Citrus synthetic flavoring agent
　　Regulatory: FDA 21CFR §172.515; FEMA GRAS
　　Manuf./Distrib. (pharm. & food): Aldrich

Trideceth-10
　　CAS 24938-91-8 (generic); 78330-21-9
　　Synonyms: PEG-10 tridecyl ether; PEG 500 tridecyl ether; POE (10) tridecyl ether
　　Definition: PEG ether of tridecyl alcohol
　　Formula: $C_{13}H_{26}(OCH_2CH_2)_nOH$, avg. n = 10
　　Uses: Used in topicals
　　Regulatory: FDA approved for topicals

Trideceth-100
　　CAS 24938-91-8 (generic)
　　Synonyms: PEG-100 tridecyl ether; POE (100) tridecyl ether
　　Definition: PEG ether of tridecyl alcohol
　　Empirical: $C_{213}H_{427}O_{101}$
　　Formula: $C_{13}H_{26}(OCH_2CH_2)_nOH$, avg. n = 100
　　Uses: Emulsifier, wetting agent for pharmaceutical applics.

Trideceth-7 carboxylic acid
　　CAS 56388-96-6 (generic); 68412-55-5 (generic); 24938-91-8 (generic)
　　Synonyms: PEG-7 tridecyl ether carboxylic acid; POE (7) tridecyl ether carboxylic acid
　　Classification: Organic acid
　　Empirical: $C_{29}H_{58}O_{10}$
　　Formula: $C_{13}H_{27}(OCH_2CH_2)_nOCH_2COOH$, avg. n = 6
　　Uses: Detergent, wetting agent for medicated soaps
　　Trade names: Sandopan® DTC-Acid

Tridecyl neopentanoate

CAS 106436-39-9
Synonyms: Neopentanoic acid, tridecyl ester
Definition: Ester of tridecyl alcohol and neopentanoic acid
Empirical: $C_{18}H_{36}O_2$
Formula: $(CH_3)_3CCOOC_{13}H_{27}$
Properties: Liq., char. mild odor; sol. in min. oil, ethanol (> 95%), IPM, cyclomethicone; insol. in water; m.w. 284; sp.gr. 0.850-0.860; ref. index 1.4345-1.4365
Toxicology: LD50 (rat, oral) > 5 g/kg; minimal eye irritation; mild skin irritation
Uses: Emollient for topical pharmaceuticals; lubricant; aids gloss and spreading in pigmented prods.
Trade names: Ceraphyl® 55

Tridecyl stearate

CAS 31556-45-3; EINECS 250-696-7
Synonyms: Octadecanoic acid, tridecyl ester; Tridecanol stearate
Definition: Ester of tridecyl alcohol and stearic acid
Empirical: $C_{31}H_{62}O_2$
Formula: $CH_3(CH_2)_{16}COOC_{13}H_{27}$
Properties: M.w. 466.83
Uses: Emollient for creams and lotions
Trade names: Kemester® 5721

Trien. *See* Triethylenetetramine
Trientine. *See* Triethylenetetramine

Triethanolamine

CAS 102-71-6; EINECS 203-049-8
Synonyms: TEA; 2,2',2''-Nitrilotris(ethanol); Trolamine; Trihydroxytriethylamine; Tris (2-hydroxyethyl) amine
Classification: Aliphatic organic compd.; alkanolamine
Empirical: $C_6H_{15}NO_3$
Formula: $N(CH_2CH_2OH)_3$
Properties: Colorless to pale yel. visc. liq., sl. ammoniacal odor, very hygroscopic; misc. with water, alcohol; sol. in chloroform; sl. sol. in benzene, ether; m.w. 149.19; dens. 1.126; m.p. 21.2 C; b.p. 335 C; flash pt. (OC) 375 F; ref. index 1.4835
Precaution: Combustible when exposed to heat or flame; can react vigorously with oxidizing materials; light-sensitive
Toxicology: LD50 (oral, rat) 8 g/kg; mod. toxic by IP; mildly toxic by ingestion; experimental carcinogen; liver and kidney damage in animals from chronic exposure; human skin irritant; eye irritant; heated to decomp., emits toxic fumes of NO_x and CN.
Uses: Alkalizing agent, emulsifier, solubilizer for pharmaceuticals; used in rectals, topicals, vaginals
Regulatory: FDA 21CFR §173.315, 175.105, 175.300, 175.380, 175.390, 176.170, 176.180, 176.200, 176.210, 177.1210, 177.1680, 177.2260, 177.2600, 177.2800, 178.3120, 178.3910; FDA approved for orals, topicals, vaginals; USP/NF, BP compliance
Manuf./Distrib.: Aldrich; Hüls AG; Mitsui Toatsu; Nippon Shokubai; Occidental; Schweizerhall; Texaco; Union Carbide
Manuf./Distrib. (pharm. & food): Spectrum Chem. Mfg.
Trade names containing: Grillocin® AT Basis

Triethanolamine abietoyl hydrolyzed animal protein. *See* TEA-abietoyl hydrolyzed collagen
Triethanolamine alginate. *See* TEA-alginate
Triethanolamine lauryl sulfate. *See* TEA-lauryl sulfate
Triethanolamine stearate. *See* TEA-stearate
Triethanolammonium lauryl sulfate. *See* TEA-lauryl sulfate
Triethyl acetylcitrate. *See* Acetyl triethyl citrate

Triethyl citrate

CAS 77-93-0; EINECS 201-070-7
FEMA 3083
Synonyms: TEC; 2-Hydroxy-1,2,3-propanetricarboxylic acid, triethyl ester; Ethyl citrate
Definition: Triester of ethyl alchol and citric acid
Empirical: $C_{12}H_{20}O_7$
Formula: $C_3H_5O(COOC_2H_5)_3$
Properties: Colorless mobile oily liq., odorless, bitter taste; sol. 65 g/100 cc water; sol. 0.8g/100 cc oil; misc. with alcohol, ether; m.w. 276.32; dens. 1.136 (25 C); b.p. 294 C; flash pt. (COC) 303 F; ref. index 1.4420
Precaution: Combustible liq. when exposed to heat or flame

Toxicology: LD50 (oral, rat) 5900 mg/kg; mod. toxic by IP route; mildly toxic by ingestion, inh.; no known skin toxicity; heated to decomp., emits acrid smoke and irritating fumes
Uses: Sweet plum-like flavoring agent; plasticizer; deodorant active; used in orals
Regulatory: FDA 21CFR §175.300, 175.320, 181.22, 181.27, 182.1911, GRAS; FEMA GRAS; FDA approved for orals; USP/NF compliance
Manuf./Distrib.: Aldrich; Great Western; Morflex; Penta Mfg.; Unitex
Manuf./Distrib. (pharm. & food): Aldrich; H E Daniel; Morflex; Penta Mfg.; Sharon Labs
Trade names: Hydagen® C.A.T.; TEC
Trade names containing: Hydagen® DEO

Triethylene glycol dimethyl ether. *See* PEG-3 dimethyl ether
Triethylene glycol dodecyl ether. *See* Laureth-3

Triethylenetetramine
CAS 112-24-3; EINECS 203-950-6
UN No. 2259
Synonyms: TETA; N,N´-Bis(2-aminoethyl)-1,2-ethanediamine; Trien; Trientine
Empirical: $C_6H_{18}N_4$
Formula: $NH_2(C_2H_4NH)_2C_2H_4NH_2$
Properties: Moderately visc. ylsh. oily liq.; sol. in water, alcohol; m.w. 146.23; dens. 0.9818 (20/20 C); m.p. 12 C; b.p. 277.5 C; flash pt. (CC) 275 F; ref. index 1.4971 (20 C); pH 14
Precaution: DOT: Corrosive material; combustible
Toxicology: LD50 (rat, oral) 2.5 g/kg; strong irritant to tissue; skin burns, eye damage
Uses: Synthesis of pharmaceuticals; biomaterial used in topicals, slow-release and microencapsulation prods.
Manuf./Distrib.: Allchem Ind.; Ashland; Great Western; Rit-Chem; Sumitomo Seika Chem.; Texaco; Tosoh; Union Carbide
Manuf./Distrib. (pharm. & food): Aldrich

Triethyl phosphite
CAS 122-52-1; EINECS 204-552-5
UN No. 2323
Empirical: $C_6H_{15}O_3P$
Formula: $(C_2H_5O)_3P$
Properties: M.w. 166.16
Uses: Intermediate; reagent
Manuf./Distrib.: Akzo; Albright & Wilson; ICI Am.; Janssen Chimica
Trade names: TEP-HP

Triethyl phosphonoacetate
CAS 867-13-0
Uses: Intermediate
Manuf./Distrib.: Albright & Wilson
Manuf./Distrib. (pharm. & food): Aldrich
Trade names: TEPA

Triethyl phosphonoformate
Uses: Intermediate
Manuf./Distrib.: Albright & Wilson
Manuf./Distrib. (pharm. & food): Aldrich
Trade names: TEPF

Triflic acid. *See* Trifluoromethane sulfonic acid

Trifluoromethane sulfonic acid
CAS 1493-13-6; EINECS 216-087-5
UN No. 1760
Synonyms: Triflic acid
Classification: Aliphatic organic compd.
Empirical: CF_3HSO_3
Formula: CHF_3O_3S
Properties: Colorless to amber clear liq.; hygroscopic; sol. in water, alcohol; m.w. 150.08; dens. 1.708 (20/4 C); m.p. 40 C; b.p. 167-180 C; flash pt. none; ref. index 1.331 (20 C)
Precaution: Strong acid; violent reaction with acyl chlorides or aromatic hydrocarbons, evolving toxic hydrogen chloride gas
Toxicology: Corrosive irritant to skin, eyes, mucous membrane; heated to decomp., emits toxic fumes of F. and SO_x

Triglyceryl diisostearate

    Uses: Mfg. of pharmaceuticals
    Regulatory: FDA 21CFR §173.395
    Manuf./Distrib.: Aldrich; Amber Syn.; 3M; MTM Research; SAF Bulk; Schweizerhall
    Trade names: FC-24; Fluorad® FC-24

Triglyceryl diisostearate. *See* Polyglyceryl-3 diisostearate
Triglyceryl oleate. *See* Polyglyceryl-3 oleate
Triglyceryl stearate. *See* Polyglyceryl-3 stearate
Trihydrated alumina. *See* Aluminum hydroxide
1,2,3-Trihydroxybenzene. *See* Pyrogallol

1,3,5-Trihydroxybenzene
    CAS 108-73-6; 6099-90-7 (dihydrate); EINECS 203-611-2
    Synonyms: Phloroglucine; Phloroglucinol; s-Trihydroxybenzene
    Classification: Aromatic organic compd.
    Empirical: $C_6H_6O_3$
    Formula: $C_6H_3(OH)_3$ • 2HOH (dihydrate)
    Properties: Wh. to ylsh. cryst., odorless, sweet taste; sol. in alcohol, ether; sl. sol. in water; m.w. 126.12
      (anhyd.), 162.14 (dihydrate); m.p. 218-221 C (anhyd.), sublimes with dec.
    Precaution: Light-sensitive
    Toxicology: Moderately toxic by subcutaneous, intraperitoneal routes; ingestion may cause severe gas-
      trointestinal irritation, kidney and liver damage, circulatory collapse, and death
    Uses: Antioxidant in prep. of pharmaceuticals
    Regulatory: BP compliance
    Manuf./Distrib.: ISK Europe SA; Schweizerhall; Spectrum Chem. Mfg.
    Manuf./Distrib. (pharm. & food): Aldrich; Ishihara Sangyo; Ruger
    Trade names: Phloroglucinol

s-Trihydroxybenzene. *See* 1,3,5-Trihydroxybenzene
3,4,5-Trihydroxybenzoic acid. *See* Gallic acid
3,4,5-Trihydroxybenzoic acid, dodecyl ester. *See* Dodecyl gallate
3,4,5-Trihydroxybenzoic acid, n-propyl ester. *See* Propyl gallate
Trihydroxypropane glycerol. *See* Glycerin

Trihydroxystearin
    CAS 8001-78-3; 139-44-6
    Synonyms: Glyceryl tri(12-hydroxystearate); 12-Hydroxyoctadecanoic acid, 1,2,3-propanetriyl ester
    Definition: Triester of glycerin and hydroxystearic acid
    Empirical: $C_{57}H_{110}O_9$
    Uses: Used in topicals
    Regulatory: FDA approved for topicals

Trihydroxytriethylamine. *See* Triethanolamine

Triisopropanolamine
    CAS 122-20-3; EINECS 204-528-4
    Synonyms: TIPA; 1,1´,1´´-Nitrilotris-2-propanol; Tris(2-hydroxypropyl)amine
    Classification: Aliphatic amine
    Empirical: $C_9H_{21}NO_3$
    Formula: $N(CH_2CHOHCH_3)_3$
    Properties: White crystalline solid, hygroscopic; sol. in water; m.w. 191.27; dens. 0.9996 (50/20 C); m.p. 45
      C; b.p. 305 C; flash pt. (OC) 320 F
    Precaution: Combustible; corrosive
    Toxicology: No known toxicity; irritating to skin and eyes
    Uses: Emulsifying agent for pharmaceuticals
    Regulatory: FDA 21CFR §175.105, 176.200, 176.210
    Manuf./Distrib.: Aldrich; Ashland
    Trade names: TIPA 99

Triisopropyl phosphite
    CAS 116-17-6
    Uses: Intermediate
    Manuf./Distrib.: Albright & Wilson
    Manuf./Distrib. (pharm. & food): Aldrich
    Trade names: TIPP

Triisostearin PEG-6 esters
    Definition: Mixt. formed from the transesterification of triisostearin and PEG-6

Uses: Solv., amphiphilic agent for improving drug delivery; excipient
Trade names: Labrafil® Isostearique

Trilaneth-4 phosphate
Synonyms: PEG-4 lanolin ether triphosphate
Definition: Predominantly the triester of phosphoric acid and ethoxylated lanolin alcohols with avg. ethoxylation level of 4
Uses: Used in topicals
Regulatory: FDA approved for topicals
Trade names containing: Sedefos 75®

Trilaureth-4 phosphate
Definition: Triester of laureth-4 and phosphoric acid
Uses: Used in topicals
Regulatory: FDA approved for topicals

Trilaurin
CAS 538-24-9; EINECS 208-687-0
Synonyms: Glyceryl trilaurate; Glyceryl tridodecanoate; Lauric acid triglyceride; Dodecanoic acid, 1,2,3-propanetriyl ester; Glycerol trilaurate; 1,2,3-Propanetriol tridodecanoate
Definition: Triester of glycerin and lauric acid
Empirical: $C_{39}H_{74}O_6$
Properties: Wh. solid, sl. bay odor; sol. in ether, chloroform, petrol. ether; m.w. 639.01; m.p. 45-47 C
Toxicology: Mild irritant
Uses: Foaming agent; consistency regulator; emollient; tablet lubricant, binder, retarding agent
Regulatory: FDA 21CFR §177.2800
Trade names: Dynasan® 112; Lipo 320

Trimetaphosphate sodium. *See* Sodium trimetaphosphate
Trimethylacetyl chloride. *See* Pivaloyl chloride
(1S)-1,3,3-Trimethylbicyclo[2.2.1]heptan-2-ol. *See* Fenchyl alcohol
1,7,7-Trimethylbicyclo[2.2.1]heptan-2-ol acetate. *See* Bornyl acetate
1,7,7-Trimethylbicyclo[2.2.1] heptan-2-one. *See* Camphor
2,6,6-Trimethylbicyclo(3.1.1)-2-heptene. *See* α-Pinene
2,6,6-Trimethylbicyclo(3.1.1)-2-hept-2-ene. *See* α-Pinene
Trimethyl carbinol. *See* t-Butyl alcohol
2,6,6-Trimethyl-1 and 2-cyclohexen-1-carboxyaldehyde. *See* β-Cyclocitral
α,α,4-Trimethyl-3-cyclohexene-1-methanol. *See* α-Terpineol
4-(2,6,6-Trimethyl-2-cyclohexene-1-yl)-3-butene-2-one. *See* α-Ionone
1-(2,6,6-Trimethyl-2-cyclohexene-1-yl)-1,6-heptadiene-3-one. *See* Allyl α-ionone
3,3,5-Trimethyl-2-cyclohexen-1-one. *See* Isophorone
1,3,7-Trimethyl-2,6-dioxopurine. *See* Caffeine
N,N,N-Trimethyl-1-dodecanaminium chloride. *See* Laurtrimonium chloride

Trimethyldodecatrieneol
CAS 142-50-7 (cis); EINECS 205-540-2 (cis)
FEMA 2772
Synonyms: Nerolidol; 3,7,11-Trimethyl-1,6,10-dodecatrien-3-ol; Peruviol
Definition: Found in essential oils from many flowers
Empirical: $C_{15}H_{26}O$
Properties: M.w. 222.36; cis-: Liq.; dens. 0.876 (20/4 C); b.p. 70 C (0.1 mm); flash pt. 96 C; ref. index 1.4775; trans-: Liq.; b.p. 78 C (0.15 mm); ref. index 1.4792
Uses: Citrus, apple-like synthetic flavoring agent
Regulatory: FDA 21CFR §172.515; FEMA GRAS
Manuf./Distrib.: BASF
Manuf./Distrib. (pharm. & food): Aldrich; BASF

3,7,11-Trimethyl-1,6,10-dodecatrien-3-ol. *See* Trimethyldodecatrieneol
3,7,11-Trimethyl-2,6,10-dodecatrien-1-ol. *See* Farnesol
3,7,11-Trimethyl-2,6,10-dodecatrien-1-ol, acetate. *See* Farnesyl acetate
N,N,N-Trimethyl-1-hexadecanaminium bromide. *See* Cetrimonium bromide
3,5,5-Trimethylhexanoic acid, 3,5,5-trimethylhexyl ester. *See* Isononyl isononanoate
1,3,3-Trimethyl-2-norbornanol. *See* Fenchyl alcohol
1,3,3-Trimethyl-2-oxabicyclo[2.2.2]octane. *See* Eucalyptol
1,7,7-Trimethyl-3-(phenylmethylene)bicyclo[2.2.1]heptan-2-one. *See* 3-Benzylidene camphor

Trimethyl phosphite

Trimethyl phosphite
 CAS 121-45-9; EINECS 204-471-5
 UN No. 2329
 Classification: Aliphatic organic compd.
 Empirical: $(CH_3O)_3P$
 Properties: M.w. 124.1; m.p. -75 C; b.p. 111 C; flash pt. 54.4 C
 Toxicology: Hardly toxic
 Uses: Intermediate; reagent
 Manuf./Distrib.: Albright & Wilson
 Manuf./Distrib. (pharm. & food): Aldrich
 Trade names: TMP-HP

α-(Trimethylsilyl)-ω-methylpoly[oxy(dimethylsilylene)], mixt. with silicon dioxide. *See* Simethicone
N,N,N-Trimethyl-1-tetradecanaminium bromide. *See* Myrtrimonium bromide

Trimethyl thiazole
 CAS 13623-11-5
 FEMA 3325
 Synonyms: 2,4,5-Trimethylthiazole
 Classification: Thiazole
 Empirical: C_6H_9NS
 Properties: M.w. 127.21; dens. 1.013; b.p. 166-167 C (717.5 mm); flash pt. 56 C
 Uses: Chocolate flavoring agent
 Regulatory: FEMA GRAS
 Manuf./Distrib. (pharm. & food): Aldrich

2,4,5-Trimethylthiazole. *See* Trimethyl thiazole
5,7,8-Trimethyltocol. *See* D-α-Tocopherol
α,α,α´-**Trimethyltrimethyleneglycol.** *See* Hexylene glycol
1,3,7-Trimethylxanthine. *See* Caffeine

Trimyristin
 CAS 555-45-3; EINECS 209-099-7
 Synonyms: Glyceryl trimyristate; 1,2,3-Propanetriol tritetradecanoate; Myristin
 Definition: Triester of glycerin and myristic acid
 Empirical: $C_{45}H_{86}O_6$
 Properties: White to yellowish-gray solid; insol. in water; sol. in alcohol, benzene, chloroform, ether; m.w. 723.14; dens. 0.885 (60/4 C); m.p. 56-57 C; ref. index 1.4429 (60 C)
 Uses: Consistency regulator; tablet lubricant, binder, mold release, retarding agent
 Regulatory: FDA 21CFR §177.2800
 Trade names: Dynasan® 114

Trioctanoin
 CAS 7360-38-5; EINECS 230-896-0
 Synonyms: Glyceryl tri(2-ethylhexanoate); Glyceryl trioctanoate; Octanoic acid, 1,2,3-propanetriol ester
 Definition: Triester of glycerin and 2-ethylhexanoic acid
 Empirical: $C_{27}H_{50}O_6$
 Uses: Lubricant, emollient for pharmaceuticals; vehicle for vitamins, medicinals, nutritional prods.

Trioctyldodecyl citrate
 CAS 126121-35-5
 Synonyms: 2-Hydroxy-1,2,3-propanetricarboxylic acid, tris(2-octyldodecyl) ester
 Definition: Triester of octyldodecanol and citric acid
 Empirical: $C_{66}H_{128}O_7$
 Uses: Pigment wetting agent; emollient; used in pharmaceutical topicals
 Trade names: Pelemol® TGC

Trioctyldodecyl citrate dilinoleate
 Uses: Used in pharmaceutical topicals
 Trade names: Pelemol® C-150

Triolein
 CAS 122-32-7; 67701-30-8; EINECS 204-534-7; 266-948-4
 Synonyms: Glyceryl trioleate; Olein; 9-Octadecenoic acid, 1,2,3-propanetriyl ester
 Definition: Triester of glycerin and oleic acid
 Empirical: $C_{57}H_{104}O_6$
 Properties: Colorless to yellowish oily liq., tasteless, odorless; pract. insol. in water; sol. in chloroform, ether,

CCl_4; sl. sol. in alcohol; m.w. 885.40; dens. 0.915 (15/4 C); m.p. -4 to -5 C; b.p. 235-240 C (15 mm); ref. index 1.4676 (20 C)

Toxicology: No known toxicity

Uses: Lubricant, emollient, solubilizer, stabilizer; used in creams and oils; carbon source in antibiotic culture broths

Regulatory: FDA 21CFR §177.2800

Manuf./Distrib.: ABITEC; Witco/Oleo-Surf.

Trade names: Emerest® 2423; Hodag GTO; Sunyl® 80 ES

Triolein PEG-6 complex. *See* Triolein PEG-6 esters

Triolein PEG-6 esters

Synonyms: Triolein PEG-6 complex

Definition: Complex mixture formed from the transesterification of triolein and PEG-6

Uses: Excipient

Trade names: Labrafil® M 2735 CS

Trioxylmethylene. *See* Paraformaldehyde

Tripalmitin

CAS 555-44-2; EINECS 209-098-1

Synonyms: Glyceryl tripalmitate; Palmitin; Hexadecanoic acid, 1,2,3-propanetriyl ester

Definition: Triester of glycerin and palmitic acid

Empirical: $C_{51}H_{98}O_6$

Properties: White crystalline powd. or needles; sol. in ether, chloroform, benzene; pract. insol. in alcohol; insol. in water; m.w. 807.29; dens. 0.886 (80/4 C); m.p. 65.5 C; b.p. 310-320 C; ref. index 1.43807 (80 C); sapon. no. 208.5

Precaution: Combustible

Uses: Lubricant, mold release, binder, retarding agent for tablets; flow and consistency regulator

Regulatory: FDA 21CFR §177.2800

Trade names: Dynasan® 116

Trade names containing: Precirol ATO 5

Tripotassium citrate monohydrate. *See* Potassium citrate

Tripropylene glycol

CAS 24800-44-0; 13987-01-4

Synonyms: TPG

Formula: $HO(C_3H_6O)_2C_3H_6OH$

Properties: Colorless liq.; sol. in water, methanol, ether; dens. 1.019; b.p. 268 C; flash pt. 285 F; ref. index 1.442

Precaution: Combustible

Uses: Pharmaceutical intermediate

Manuf./Distrib.: Arco; Ashland; Coyne; Union Carbide

Manuf./Distrib. (pharm. & food): Aldrich

See also PPG-3...

Tris. *See* Tris (hydroxymethyl) aminomethane
Trisamine. *See* Tris (hydroxymethyl) aminomethane
Tris Buffer. *See* Tris (hydroxymethyl) aminomethane
Tris (2-hydroxyethyl) amine. *See* Triethanolamine

Tris (hydroxymethyl) aminomethane

CAS 77-86-1; EINECS 201-064-4

Synonyms: THAM; Tromethamine; Trometamol; Tris (hydroxymethyl) methylamine; Aminotrimethylol-methane; 2-Amino-2-(hydroxymethyl)-1,3-propanediol; Tris; Tris Buffer; Trisamine

Empirical: $C_4H_{11}NO_3$

Formula: $(CH_2OH)_3CNH_3$

Properties: Wh. cryst. gran. or powd., sl. char. odor; hygroscopic; sol. 80 g/100 cc water (20 C); sol. in low m.w. aliphatic alcohols; pract. insol. in chloroform, benzene, CCl_4; m.w. 121.14; m.p. 168-171 C; b.p. 219-220 C (10 mm); pH 10-11.5 (5%)

Precaution: Combustible

Toxicology: Irritant to skin and eyes

Uses: Pharmaceutical intermediate; solubilizer, stabilizer; buffering agent; used in injectables, orals, topicals, ophthalmics

Regulatory: FDA approved for injectables, orals, topicals

Manuf./Distrib.: Aldrich; ANGUS; Hampshire; Heico; Janssen Chimica; Monomer-Polymer & Dajac; Schweizerhall; Sigma; Spectrum Chem. Mfg.; Van Waters & Rogers

Tris (hydroxymethyl) methylamine

    Manuf./Distrib. (pharm. & food): Aldrich; Ruger; Spectrum Chem. Mfg.
    Trade names: Tris Amino® Conc.; Tris Amino® Crystals; Tris Amino® Molecular Biology Grade; Tris Amino®
    Ultra Pure Standard

Tris (hydroxymethyl) methylamine. *See* Tris (hydroxymethyl) aminomethane
Tris(2-hydroxypropyl)amine. *See* Triisopropanolamine
Trisodium-3-carboxy-5-hydroxy-1-p-sulfophenyl-4-p-sulfophenylazopyrazole. *See* FD&C Yellow No. 5

Trisodium citrate

    CAS 68-04-2 (anhyd.); 6858-44-2 (hydrate); 6132-04-3 (dihydrate); EINECS 200-675-3
    FEMA 3026
    Synonyms: Citric acid trisodium salt; Sodium citrate tertiary; Sodium citrate
    Empirical: $C_6H_5Na_3O_7$ (anhyd.), $C_6H_5Na_3O_7 \cdot 2H_2O$ (dihydrate)
    Formula: $HOC(COONa)(CH_2COONa)_2$ (anhyd.), $HOC(COONa)(CH_2COONa)_2 \cdot 2H_2O$ (dihydrate)
    Properties: Colorless cryst. or wh. cryst. powd., odorless, pleasant acid taste; hydrous form freely sol. in water,
    very sol. in boiling water, insol. in alcohol; m.w. 258.07 (anhyd.), 294.10 (dihydrate)
    Toxicology: LD50 (IP, rat) 1548 mg/kg, (IV, mouse) 170 mg/kg; poison by IV route; mod. toxic by IP route;
    heated to decomp., emits toxic fumes of Na_2O
    Uses: Buffering agent for pharmaceuticals; used in diuretics, expectorants, in treating dehydration and
    acidosis due to diarrhea
    Regulatory: FDA 21CFR §131.111, 131.138, 131.146, 131.160, 131.185, 133.112, 133.144, 133.169,
    133.173, 133.179, 150.141, 150.161, 175.300, 181.22, 181.29; USDA 9CFR §381.147; FEMA GRAS;
    Japan approved; BP compliance
    Manuf./Distrib.: ADM; Spectrum Chem. Mfg.
    Manuf./Distrib. (pharm. & food): Jungbunzlauer; Lohmann; Spectrum Chem. Mfg.

Trisodium edetate. *See* Trisodium EDTA

Trisodium EDTA

    CAS 150-38-9; EINECS 205-758-8
    Synonyms: Edetate trisodium; Trisodium edetate; Trisodium ethylenediamine tetraacetate; Trisodium
    hydrogen ethylene diaminetetraacetate
    Classification: Substituted amine
    Empirical: $C_{10}H_{16}N_2O_8 \cdot 3Na$
    Formula: $(NaOOCCH_2)_3NCH_2CH_2NCH_2COOH$
    Properties: Wh. powd.; sol. in water
    Uses: Chelating agent used in topicals
    Regulatory: FDA 21CFR §175.105, 176.170, 177.2800, 178.3910; FDA approved for topicals; BP compliance
    Manuf./Distrib.: Chemplex; Hampshire; Spectrum Chem. Mfg.; Surfactants Inc.

Trisodium ethylenediamine tetraacetate. *See* Trisodium EDTA

Trisodium HEDTA

    CAS 139-89-9; EINECS 205-381-9
    Synonyms: HEDTANa$_3$; N-[2-[Bis(carboxymethyl)amino]ethyl]-N-(2-hydroxyethyl)glycine, trisodium salt;
    Trisodium hydroxyethyl ethylenediaminetriacetate
    Classification: Substituted amine
    Empirical: $C_{10}H_{18}N_2O_7 \cdot 3Na$
    Formula: $(CH_2COONa)_3NCH_2CH_2NHOCH_2CH_2$
    Uses: Chelating agent; drug stabilization; heavy metal poisoning treatment; used in topicals
    Regulatory: FDA approved for topicals
    Trade names: Versenol 120

Trisodium hydrogen ethylene diaminetetraacetate. *See* Trisodium EDTA
Trisodium hydroxyethyl ethylenediaminetriacetate. *See* Trisodium HEDTA

Tristearin

    CAS 555-43-1; EINECS 209-097-6
    Synonyms: Glyceryl tristearate; Glyceryl monotristearate; Stearin; 1,2,3-Propanetriol trioctadecanoate;
    Octadecanoic acid, 1,2,3-propanetriyl ester
    Definition: Triester of glycerin and stearic acid
    Empirical: $C_{57}H_{110}O_6$
    Formula: $[CH_3(CH_2)_{16}COOCH_2]_2CHOCO(CH_2)_{16}CH_3$
    Properties: Colorless crystals or powd., odorless, tasteless; insol. in water; sol. in hot alcohol, benzene,
    chloroform, carbon disulfide; m.w. 891.45; dens. 0.943 (65 C); m.p. 71.6 C; ref. index 1.4385 (80 C)
    Precaution: Combustible
    Toxicology: No known toxicity; heated to decomp., emits acrid smoke and irritating fumes

Uses: Lubricant, mold release, binder, retarding agent in tablets; flow and consistency regulator; used in orals
Regulatory: FDA 21CFR §172.811, 177.2800; FDA approved for orals
Manuf./Distrib.: Spectrum Chem. Mfg.
Trade names: Dynasan® 118
Trade names containing: Precirol ATO 5

Triticum aestivum germ oil. *See* Wheat germ oil

Triundecanoin
CAS 13552-80-2; EINECS 236-935-8
Uses: Emollient, lubricant, moisturizer, visc. modifier for dermatological emulsions
Trade names: Captex® 8227

Trolamine. *See* Triethanolamine
Trolamine alkyl sulfate. *See* TEA alkyl sulfate
Trolamine lauryl sulfate. *See* TEA-lauryl sulfate
Trometamol. *See* Tris (hydroxymethyl) aminomethane
Tromethamine. *See* Tris (hydroxymethyl) aminomethane

Tromethamine magnesium aluminum silicate
Definition: Reaction prod. of tromethamine and magnesium aluminum silicate
Uses: Emulsion stabilizer, suspending agent
Trade names: Veegum® PRO

Trypsin
CAS 9002-07-7; EINECS 232-650-8
Classification: Enzyme
Properties: Wh. to ylsh. wh. cryst. or amorphous powd., odorless; hygroscopic (amorphous); sparingly sol. in water; pH 3-5.5 (1%)
Precaution: Protect from light
Toxicology: May cause hypersensitivity reactions
Uses: Proteolytic enzyme; used for protein digestion, in tissue culture, for debridement of wounds; for relief of edema and inflammation associated with infection or trauma and gastro-intestinal disorders; in orals, inhalants
Regulatory: FDA GRAS; Japan approved; USP, BP, Ph.Eur. compliance
Manuf./Distrib.: Am. Biorganics; Unibios SpA; U.S. Biochemical; Worthington Biochemical
Trade names: Trypsin 1:75; Trypsin 1:80; Trypsin 1:150

TSPP. *See* Tetrasodium pyrophosphate
Tuberyl alcohol. *See* Dihydrocarveol
Turkey-red oil. *See* Sulfated castor oil

Turpentine oil
CAS 8006-64-2
UN No. 1299
Synonyms: Purified gum spirits; Turpentine, purified; Turpentine, rectified
Definition: Volatile essential oil obtained by distillation and rectification from turpentine, an oleoresin obtained from *Pinus* spp., contg. pinene and diterpene
Empirical: $C_{10}H_{16}$
Properties: Colorless liq., penetrating odor; immisc. with water; dens. 0.860-0.875 (15 C); flash pt. (CC) 32-46 C; ref. index 1.463-1.483 (20 C)
Precaution: DOT: Flamm. liq.; mod. fire risk; protect from light
Toxicology: TLV 100 ppm in air; toxic by ingestion; irritating to skin and mucous membranes; can cause allergic reactions; CNS depressant; death due to respiratory failure
Uses: Solvent, rubefacient, diuretic; used in inhalants; liniments; preps. for respiratory tract disorders
Regulatory: FDA approved for inhalants; BP compliance
Manuf./Distrib.: Spectrum Chem. Mfg.

Turpentine, purified. *See* Turpentine oil
Turpentine, rectified. *See* Turpentine oil

Tyloxapol
CAS 25301-02-4
Synonyms: Phenol, 4-(1,1,3,3-tetramethylbutyl)-, polymer with formaldehyde and oxirane; p-(1,1,3,3-Tetramethylbutyl) phenol polymer with ethylene oxide and formaldehyde
Definition: An oxyethylated-t-octylphenolpolymethylene polymer
Properties: Amber thick liq., sl. aromatic odor; nonionic; slowly misc. with water; sol. in benzene, glac. acetic acid, toluene, CCl_4, chloroform, CS_2; cloud pt. 92-97 C flash pt. > 230 F; pH 4-7 (5%)

Ulmus campestris extract

Precaution: Prevent contact with metals
Toxicology: Low toxicity; may cause pharyngeal and tracheobronchial irritation, maculopapular rashes
Uses: Wetting agent, solubilizer; used in ophthalmics; can withstand autoclaving
Regulatory: FDA approved for ophthalmics; USP/NF compliance
Manuf./Distrib. (pharm. & food): Aldrich; Ruger

Ulmus campestris extract. *See* Elm bark extract

δ-Undecalactone
CAS 710-04-3
FEMA 3294
Synonyms: 5-Hydroxyundecanoic acid lactone
Empirical: $C_{11}H_{20}O_2$
Properties: M.w. 184.28; dens. 0.969; b.p. 152-155 C (10.5 mm); flash pt. > 230 F
Uses: Peach-like flavoring agent
Regulatory: FEMA GRAS
Manuf./Distrib. (pharm. & food): Aldrich

γ-Undecalactone
CAS 104-67-6
FEMA 3091
Synonyms: Peach aldehyde; γ-Undecyl lactone; γ-Heptyl butyrolactone; 5-Hydroxyundecanoic acid γ-lactone; Aldehyde C-14 pure
Classification: Heterocyclic compd.
Empirical: $C_{11}H_{20}O_2$
Properties: Colorless to sl. yel. liq., creamy peach-like odor; sol. in alcohol, most fixed oils, propylene glycol; insol. in glycerin, water; m.w. 184.28; dens. 0.943; b.p. 164-166 C (13 mm); flash pt. > 230 F; ref. index 1.430
Precaution: Combustible liq.
Toxicology: Heated to decomp., emits acrid smoke and irritating fumes
Uses: Peach-like synthetic flavoring agent
Regulatory: FDA 21CFR §172.515; FEMA GRAS
Manuf./Distrib.: Aldrich
Manuf./Distrib. (pharm. & food): Acme-Hardesty; Aldrich

Undecanal
CAS 112-44-7
FEMA 3092
Synonyms: Aldehyde C-11 undecyclic; n-Undecyl aldehyde; Undecylic aldehyde; Hendecanal
Empirical: $C_{11}H_{22}O$
Properties: Colorless to sl. yellow liq.; sweet, fatty, floral odor; sol. in most common organic solvents; insol. in water; m.w. 170.30; dens. 0.825; m.p. -4 C; b.p. 118-120 C (20 mm); flash pt. 96 C; ref. index 1.430-1.435
Toxicology: Tends to polymerize unless tightly sealed
Uses: Orange-like synthetic flavoring agent
Regulatory: FEMA GRAS
Manuf./Distrib. (pharm. & food): Aldrich

1-Undecanol. *See* Undecyl alcohol

2-Undecanone
CAS 112-12-9; EINECS 203-937-5
FEMA 3093
Synonyms: Methyl nonyl ketone
Empirical: $C_{11}H_{22}O$
Formula: $CH_3(CH_2)_8COCH_3$
Properties: Colorless to sl. yellowish liq.; rue odor; sweet peachy flavor; sol. in most organic solvents; insol. in water; m.w. 170.30; dens. 0.825 (20/4 C); m.p. 11-13 C; b.p. 231-232 C; flash pt. 89 C; ref. index 1.4280-1.4330 (20 C)
Uses: Citrus synthetic flavoring agent
Regulatory: FDA 21CFR §172.515; FEMA GRAS
Manuf./Distrib. (pharm. & food): Aldrich

9-Undecenal
FEMA 3094
Synonyms: Undecenoic aldehyde; Undecylenic aldehyde; Hendecen-9-al; Aldehyde C-11 Undecylenic; 9-

Undecen-1-al
Empirical: $C_{11}H_{20}O$
Properties: Colorless pale yel. oily liq., orange peel-like sweet odor, citrus flavor; sol. in alcohol; insol. in water; m.w. 168.28
Uses: Synthetic flavoring agent
Regulatory: FDA 21CFR §172.515; FEMA GRAS

9-Undecen-1-al. *See* 9-Undecenal

10-Undecenal
CAS 112-45-8
FEMA 3095
Synonyms: Aldehyde C-11 undecylenic; Hendecenal; Undecen-10-al; Undecylenaldehyde; Undecylenic aldehyde
Empirical: $C_{11}H_{20}O$
Properties: Colorless to lt. yel. liq., fatty rose odor on dilution; sol. in fixed oils, propylene glycol; insol. in water, glycerin; m.w. 168.31; dens. 0.840-0.850; b.p. 101-103 C; flash pt. 92 C; ref. index 1.441-1.447
Precaution: Combustible
Toxicology: Skin irritant; heated to decomp., emits acrid smoke and irritating fumes
Uses: Sweet synthetic flavoring agent
Regulatory: FDA 21CFR §172.515; FEMA GRAS
Manuf./Distrib. (pharm. & food): Aldrich

Undecen-10-al. *See* 10-Undecenal
Undecenoic acid. *See* Undecylenic acid
10-Undecenoic acid. *See* Undecylenic acid
11-Undecenoic acid. *See* Undecylenic acid
10-Undecenoic acid, calcium (2+) salt. *See* Calcium undecylenate
10-Undecenoic acid, sodium salt. *See* Sodium undecylenate
Undecenoic aldehyde. *See* 9-Undecenal

Undecyl alcohol
CAS 112-42-5; EINECS 203-970-5
FEMA 3097
Synonyms: Hendecanoic alcohol; 1-Hendecanol; Hendecyl alcohol; C-11 primary alcohol; 1-Undecanol; Alcohol C-11 undecylic
Classification: Aliphatic alcohol
Empirical: $C_{11}H_{24}O$
Formula: $CH_3(CH_2)_9CH_2OH$
Properties: Colorless liq., mild fatty-floral odor; sol. in water, alcohol 60%; m.w. 172.35; dens. 0.822 (35/4 C); m.p. 19 C; b.p. 131 C (15 mm); flash pt. 93.3 C; ref. index 1.4370-1.4430
Precaution: Combustible
Toxicology: LD50 (oral, rat) 3000 mg/kg; mod. toxic by ingestion; low acute inhalation toxicity; severely irritating to eyes; moderately irritating to skin; heated to decomp., emits acrid smoke and irritating fumes
Uses: Sweet, lemon-, lime-, or orange-like synthetic flavoring agent
Regulatory: FDA 21CFR §172.515; FEMA GRAS
Manuf./Distrib.: Aldrich
Manuf./Distrib. (pharm. & food): Aldrich

n-Undecyl aldehyde. *See* Undecanal
Undecylenaldehyde. *See* 10-Undecenal

Undecylenic acid
CAS 112-38-9; EINECS 203-965-8
FEMA 3247
Synonyms: 10-Undecenoic acid; Undecenoic acid; 11-Undecenoic acid
Classification: Aliphatic acid
Empirical: $C_{11}H_{20}O_2$
Formula: $CH_2=CH(CH_2)_8COOH$
Properties: Lt. colored liq., fruity-rosy odor; insol. in water; misc. with alcohol, chloroform, ether, benzene; m.w. 184.28; dens. 0.910-0.913 (25/25 C); m.p. 22 C; b.p. 137 C (2 mm); flash pt. 295 F
Precaution: Combustible
Uses: Sweet flavoring agent
Regulatory: FEMA GRAS; BP, Ph.Eur. compliance
Manuf./Distrib.: Elf Atochem; CasChem; Schweizerhall
Manuf./Distrib. (pharm. & food): Aldrich

Undecylenic aldehyde

Undecylenic aldehyde. *See* 9-Undecenal; 10-Undecenal
Undecylic aldehyde. *See* Undecanal
γ-Undecyl lactone. *See* γ-Undecalactone
Uranine. *See* D&C Yellow No. 8

Urea
CAS 57-13-6; EINECS 200-315-5
Synonyms: Carbamide; Carbonyldiamide; Carbamidic acid; Isourea
Classification: Organic compd.
Definition: Prod. of protein metabolism excreted from human urine
Empirical: CH_4N_2O
Formula: NH_2CONH_2
Properties: Colorless to wh. cryst. or powd., almost odorless; sl. ammonia odor on standing; sol. in water, boiling alcohol, benzene; sl. sol. in ether; insol. in chloroform; m.w. 60.06; dens. 1.335; m.p. 132.7 C; b.p. dec.
Precaution: Heated to decomp., emits toxic fumes of NO_x
Toxicology: LD50 (oral, rat) 14,300 mg/kg; mod. toxic by ingestion, IV, subcutaneous routes; experimental carcinogen, neoplastigen, reproductive effects; human reproductive effects by intraplacental route; human mutagenic data; human skin irritant
Uses: Diuretic; antiseptic; keratin softener for dry skin prods.; in ammoniated dentifrices; used in injectables, orals
Regulatory: FDA 21CFR §175.300, 177.1200, 184.1923, GRAS; BATF 27CFR §240.1051; FDA approved for injectables, orals; BP, Ph.Eur. compliance
Manuf./Distrib.: Air Prods.; Bio-Rad Labs; Chisso Am.; Elf Atochem SA; EM Industries; Heico; Mallinckrodt; Mitsui Toatsu; Nissan Chem. Ind.; Norsk Hydro AS; Occidental; Showa Denko
Manuf./Distrib. (pharm. & food): Aldrich; Heico; Mallinckrodt; Ruger; Spectrum Chem. Mfg.

Urea-(2,5-dioxo-4-imidazolidine). *See* Allantoin
Urea hydrogen peroxide. *See* Urea peroxide

Urea peroxide
CAS 124-43-6; EINECS 204-701-4
UN No. 1511
Synonyms: Hydrogen peroxide carbamide; Urea hydrogen peroxide; Carbamide peroxide
Empirical: $CH_4N_2O \cdot H_2O_2$
Properties: M.w. 94.07
Precaution: DOT: Oxidizer; moisture-sensitive; refrigerate
Uses: OTC active ingred. in U.S.; strong oxidizing agent; antiseptic in oral rinse prods.; for softening wax
Manuf./Distrib.: Spectrum Chem. Mfg.
Manuf./Distrib. (pharm. & food): Robeco

5-Ureidohydrantoin. *See* Allantoin
UV Absorber-3. *See* Octocrylene

Vanilla
CAS 8024-06-4
FEMA 3104
Synonyms: Protovanol; Vanilla flavor; Vanilla beans; Vanilla pods
Definition: Natural prod. obtained from cured full-grown unripe fruit of *Vanilla planifolia* or *V. tahitensis*
Uses: Natural flavoring agent
Regulatory: FDA 21CFR §163.111, 163.112, 163.113, 163.114, 163.117, 163.123, 163.130, 163.135, 163.140, 163.145, 163.150, 163.153, 163.155, 182.10, 182.20, GRAS; FEMA GRAS; Japan approved; USP compliance
Manuf./Distrib. (pharm. & food): Beck Flavors; Bell Flavors & Fragrances; Berk; Bush Boake Allen; C.A.L.-Pfizer; Consolidated Flavor; Diamalt; Eurovanillin; Frutarom; Givaudan-Roure; Haarmann & Reimer; IFF; V E Kohnstamm; Penta Mfg.; Pointing; Quest; Robertet; Spice King; Synthite

Vanilla beans. *See* Vanilla
Vanilla flavor. *See* Vanilla
Vanillal. *See* Ethyl vanillin
Vanillaldehyde. *See* Vanillin
Vanilla pods. *See* Vanilla
Vanillic aldehyde. *See* Vanillin

Vanillin

CAS 121-33-5; EINECS 204-465-2

FEMA 3107

Synonyms: 4-Hydroxy-m-anisaldehyde; 4-Hydroxy-3-methoxybenzaldehyde; Methylprotocatechuic aldehyde; Methylprotocatechualdehyde; Vanillaldehyde; Vanillic aldehyde

Classification: Substituted aromatic aldehyde

Definition: Methyl ether of protocatechuic aldehyde

Empirical: $C_8H_8O_3$

Formula: $(CH_3O)(OH)C_6H_3CHO$

Properties: White cryst. needles, pleasant vanilla odor and taste; sol. in 125 parts water, 20 parts glycerol, 2
parts 95% alcohol, chloroform, ether; m.w. 152.16; dens. 1.056; m.p. 80-81 C; b.p. 285 C

Precaution: Combustible; moisture- and light-sensitive

Toxicology: LD50 (oral, rat) 1580 mg/kg; moderately toxic by ingestion, intraperitoneal, subcutaneous,
intravenous routes; experimental reproductive effects; human mutagenic data; heated to decomp., emits
acrid smoke and irritating fumes

Uses: Medicinal excipient; aromatic, perfume, vanilla-like synthetic flavoring agent; used in orals, topicals

Regulatory: FDA 21CFR §135.110, 163.111, 163.112, 163.113, 163.114, 163.117, 163.123, 163.130,
163.135, 163.140, 163.145, 163.150, 163.153, 163.155, 182.60, GRAS; FEMA GRAS; Japan approved
as flavoring; FDA approved for orals, topicals; USP/NF, BP, Ph.Eur. compliance

Manuf./Distrib.: Aldrich; Penta Mfg.; Rhone-Poulenc Food Ingreds.; Schweizerhall; Trafford Chem. Ltd

Manuf./Distrib. (pharm. & food): Aldrich; Ashland; Beck Flavors; Chart; Diamalt; Eurovanillin; Forum;
Frutarom; Haarmann & Reimer; V E Kohnstamm; Mitsubishi; Penta Mfg.; Pointing; Polarome; Prova; Quest
Int'l.; Rhone-Poulenc Food; Rit-Chem; Ruger; Scanchem; Siber Hegner; Spectrum Chem. Mfg.; Spice King

Trade names: Unisweet VAN

Vanillin isobutyrate

CAS 20665-85-4

FEMA 3754

Synonyms: Vanillyl isobutyrate

Empirical: $C_{12}H_{14}O_4$

Properties: M.w. 222.24; dens. 1.120; flash pt. > 230 F

Uses: Vanilla-like flavoring agent

Regulatory: FEMA GRAS

Manuf./Distrib. (pharm. & food): Aldrich

Vanillin methyl ether. *See* Veratraldehyde
Vanillylacetone. *See* Zingerone

Vanillyl alcohol

CAS 498-00-0

FEMA 3737

Empirical: $C_8H_{10}O_3$

Properties: M.w. 154.17; m.p. 112-115 C

Uses: Sweet flavoring agent

Regulatory: FEMA GRAS

Manuf./Distrib. (pharm. & food): Aldrich

Vanillyl isobutyrate. *See* Vanillin isobutyrate
Vaseline. *See* Petrolatum
Vat blue 1. *See* CI 73000; D&C Blue No. 6
Vat blue 6. *See* CI 69825; D&C Blue No. 9
Vat red 1. *See* CI 73360; D&C Red No. 30
VC. *See* Vinyl chloride
Vegetable gum. *See* Dextrin

Vegetable oil

CAS 68956-68-3; 68938-35-2; EINECS 273-313-5

Synonyms: Oils, vegetable

Definition: Expressed oil of vegetable origin consisting primarily of triglycerides of fatty acids

Toxicology: May cause contact dermatitis

Uses: Filler; used in orals, topicals, suppositories

Regulatory: FDA approved for orals, topicals

Manuf./Distrib.: ABITEC; Arista Industries; Int'l. Flora Tech.; Lipo; Mendell; A.E. Staley Mfg.

Manuf./Distrib. (pharm. & food): ABITEC; Arista Industries; A.E. Staley Mfg.

Trade names containing: Annatto OS #2894; Canthaxanthin Beadlets 10%; Lipovol SES-S

Vegetable oil glyceride
　　CAS 97593-29-8
　　Synonyms: Vegetable oil monoglyceride
　　Trade names containing: Annatto OS #2922; Annatto OS #2923

Vegetable oil, hydrogenated. *See* Hydrogenated vegetable oil
Vegetable oil monoglyceride. *See* Vegetable oil glyceride
Vegetable pepsin. *See* Papain
Vegetable protein hydrolysate. *See* Hydrolyzed vegetable protein

Veratraldehyde
　　CAS 120-14-9; EINECS 204-373-2
　　FEMA 3109
　　Synonyms: 3,4-Dimethoxybenzaldehyde; Veratric aldehyde; Dimethyl ether protocatechualdehyde; Vanillin
　　　methyl ether; Protocatechualdehyde dimethyl ether; 3,4-Dimethoxybenzenecarbonal
　　Empirical: $C_9H_{10}O_3$
　　Properties: Need., vanilla bean odor; freely sol. in alcohol, ether; sl. sol. in hot water; m.w. 166.18; m.p. 41-
　　　44 C; b.p. 281 C (760 mm); flash pt. > 230 F
　　Precaution: Sol'ns. oxidize to veratric acid under influence of light
　　Toxicology: Skin irritant
　　Uses: Vanilla-like synthetic flavoring agent
　　Regulatory: FDA 21CFR §172.515; FEMA GRAS
　　Manuf./Distrib. (pharm. & food): Aldrich

Veratric aldehyde. *See* Veratraldehyde

Veratrole
　　CAS 91-16-7
　　Empirical: $C_8H_{10}O_2$
　　Properties: M.w. 138.17; dens. 1.084; m.p. 15 C; b.p. 205-207 C; flash pt. 189 F
　　Uses: Vanilla-like flavoring agent
　　Manuf./Distrib. (pharm. & food): Aldrich

(1S)-(-)-Verbenone
　　CAS 1196-01-6
　　Empirical: $C_{10}H_{14}O$
　　Properties: M.w. 150.22; dens. 0.974; b.p. 227-228 C; flash pt.185 F
　　Uses: Medicinal flavoring agent
　　Manuf./Distrib. (pharm. & food): Aldrich

Veridian. *See* Chromium hydroxide green
Vinegar acid. *See* Acetic acid; Acetic acid, glacial
Vinegar naphtha. *See* Ethyl acetate
Vinegar salts. *See* Calcium acetate
Vinyl alcohol polymer. *See* Polyvinyl alcohol
Vinylbenzene. *See* Styrene

Vinyl bromide
　　CAS 593-60-2
　　UN No. 1085 (inhibited)
　　Synonyms: Bromoethylene
　　Formula: CH_2CHBr
　　Properties: Gas; m.w. 106.96; dens. 1.51; m.p. -138 C; b.p. 15.6 C
　　Toxicology: Carcinogen; TLV 5 ppm in air
　　Uses: Pharmaceutical intermediate
　　Manuf./Distrib.: Albemarle
　　Manuf./Distrib. (pharm. & food): Aldrich
　　Trade names: Saytex® VBR

Vinyl carbinyl cinnamate. *See* Allyl cinnamate

Vinyl chloride
　　CAS 75-01-4; EINECS 200-831-0
　　UN No. 1086
　　Synonyms: VC; Chloroethene; Chloroethylene
　　Classification: Vinyl monomer; aliphatic organic compd.
　　Formula: $CH_2{:}CHCl$
　　Properties: Compressed gas, easily liquefied, ethereal odor; sol. in alcohol, ether; sl. sol. in water; dens. 0.9121

(liq., 20/20 C); f.p. -159.7 C; b.p. -13.9 C; flash pt. -77 C
Precaution: Explosive limits in air 4-22 by vol.
Toxicology: Extremely toxic; carcinogen; TLV:TWA 5 ppm in air; prohibited for use in aerosol sprays
Uses: Used in orals
Regulatory: FDA approved for orals
Manuf./Distrib.: PPG Ind.; Vista
Manuf./Distrib. (pharm. & food): Aldrich

p-Vinylguaiacol. *See* 2-Methoxy-4-vinylphenol
1-Vinyl-2-pyrrolidinone homopolymer. *See* Crospovidone
1-Vinyl-2-pyrrolidinone polymer. *See* PVP
Vinylpyrrolidone/dimethylaminoethyl methacrylate copolymer. *See* PVP/dimethylaminoethylmethacrylate copolymer
Vinylpyrrolidone/vinyl acetate copolymer. *See* PVP/VA copolymer
Virginian prune bark. *See* Wild cherry bark

Viscarin
CAS 8047-25-4
Uses: Used in orals, topicals
Regulatory: FDA approved for orals, topicals

Vital wheat gluten. *See* Wheat gluten
Vitamin A palmitate. *See* Retinyl palmitate
Vitamin B. *See* Niacinamide
Vitamin B$_1$ hydrochloride. *See* Thiamine HCl
Vitamin B$_1$ nitrate. *See* Thiamine nitrate
Vitamin B$_2$. *See* Riboflavin
Vitamin B$_2$ phosphate sodium. *See* Riboflavin-5´-phosphate sodium
Vitamin B$_3$. *See* Nicotinic acid
Vitamin B$_5$, calcium salt. *See* Calcium D-pantothenate

Vitamin B$_6$
Uses: Oil control agent for skin care prods.
Trade names: Pyridoxine Hydrochloride USP

Vitamin B$_6$ hydrochloride. *See* Pyridoxine HCl
Vitamin B$_{12}$. *See* Cyanocobalamin
Vitamin Bc. *See* Folic acid
Vitamin C. *See* L-Ascorbic acid
Vitamin C sodium salt. *See* Sodium ascorbate
Vitamin D$_3$. *See* Cholecalciferol
Vitamin E. *See* Tocopherol; D-α-Tocopherol; DL-α-Tocopherol
Vitamin E acetate. *See* Tocopheryl acetate; d-α-Tocopheryl acetate
Vitamin E nicotinate. *See* d-α-Tocopheryl nicotinate
Vitamin F. *See* Ethyl linoleate
Vitamin G. *See* Riboflavin
Vitamin H. *See* d-Biotin

Vitamin K$_1$
Synonyms: Phytonadione; Phytomenadione; Phylloquinone; Phytodione
Empirical: $C_{31}H_{46}O_2$
Properties: M.w. 450.68
Toxicology: No adverse human effects with prolonged ingestion
Uses: Component of enzyme systems associated with blood-clotting mechanism
Regulatory: BP compliance
Manuf./Distrib. (pharm. & food): Am. Roland
Trade names: Phytonadione USP No. 61749
Trade names containing: Dry Phytonadione 1% SD No. 61748

Vitamin L. *See* Anthranilic acid
Vitamin M. *See* Folic acid
Vulcan red R. *See* D&C Red No. 36

Vythene
CAS 1299-89-4
Uses: Used in orals
Regulatory: FDA approved for orals

Walnut extract

Walnut extract
  CAS 84012-43-1
  FEMA 3111
  Synonyms: Juglans regia extract; Juglans nigra extract; Walnut hull extract
  Definition: Extract of the husk and shells of the nut of *Juglans regia* or *J. nigra*
  Uses: Natural flavoring agent; functional adjuvant for skin care prods.; helps relieve effects of eczema; used in suntan oils, foot care, antiperspirants
  Regulatory: FDA 21CFR §172.510; FEMA GRAS
  Manuf./Distrib.: Bio-Botanica
  Trade names containing: Crodarom Nut A; Crodarom Nut O

Walnut hull extract. *See* Walnut extract

Walnut oil
  CAS 8024-09-7; 84604-00-2
  Definition: Oil derived from the nut meats of walnuts, *Juglans* spp.
  Properties: Iodine no. 145-155; sapon. no. 190; ref. index 1.4691 (40 C)
  Uses: Lubricant for topical pharmaceuticals, ointments
  Regulatory: FDA 21CFR §172.510, 175.300
  Manuf./Distrib.: Air Prods.; Arista Industries; Penta Mfg.; Tri-K
  Manuf./Distrib. (pharm. & food): Arista Industries; Penta Mfg.
  Trade names: EmCon Walnut

Waxes, microcrystalline. *See* Microcrystalline wax
Waxes, montan fatty acids. *See* Montan acid wax
West Indian bay leaf oil. *See* Bay oil
West Indian lemongrass oil. *See* Lemongrass oil West Indian

Wheat bran
  Uses: Natural fiber used in pharmaceuticals.
  Trade names: Stabilized Red Wheat Bran; Stabilized White Wheat Bran
  Trade names containing: Hony-Tab®; Mola-Tab®

Wheat germ oil
  CAS 8006-95-9
  Synonyms: Triticum aestivum germ oil
  Definition: Oil obtained by expression or extraction of wheat germ
  Properties: Lt. yel. oil; fat-sol.; sp.gr. 0.93-0.94; iodine no. 120-140; sapon.no. 179-194; ref. index 1.469-1.479
  Uses: Nutritional source, topical moisturizer and lubricant
  Manuf./Distrib.: Arista Industries; Croda; Penta Mfg.; Provital; Spectrum Chem. Mfg.; Tri-K
  Manuf./Distrib. (pharm. & food): ABITEC; Able Prods.; Am. Roland; Arista Industries; S Black; British Arkady; Cornelius; Henry Lamotte; Penta Mfg.; Quimdis; Spectrum Naturals; Viobin; Vitamins Inc.; Westhove
  Trade names: EmCon W; Super Refined® Wheat Germ Oil

Wheat gluten
  CAS 8002-80-0; EINECS 232-317-7
  Synonyms: Gluten; Vital wheat gluten; Devitalized wheat gluten
  Definition: Principal protein component of wheat; consists mainly of gliadin and glutenin
  Properties: Cream to lt. tan powd.; sol. in alkalies, alcohol
  Toxicology: No known toxicity; certain individuals may have gluten sensitivity or intolerance; ingestion may cause hives and angioedema; heated to decomp., emits acrid smoke and irritating fumes
  Uses: Tablet coating agent, film-former for microencapuslation, etc.; used in orals
  Regulatory: FDA 21CFR §184.1322, GRAS; FDA approved for orals
  Manuf./Distrib. (pharm. & food): Crespel & Deiters GmbH; Goorden

Wheat starch
  CAS 9005-25-8
  Definition: Natural material obtained from wheat, *Triticum aestivum*, contg. amylose and amylopectin
  Formula: $(C_6H_{10}O_5)_n$
  Properties: Lenticular or spherical gran.
  Toxicology: May cause allergic reactions such as red eyes or stuffy nose
  Uses: Used as a demulcent and emollient in dusting powds.
  Regulatory: FDA 21CFR §175.105, 178.3520, 182.70; BP, Ph.Eur. compliance
  Manuf./Distrib.: Spectrum Chem. Mfg.
  Manuf./Distrib. (pharm. & food): Ruger

White beeswax. *See* Beeswax, white

White caustic. *See* Sodium hydroxide
White charcoal. *See* Magnesium oxide
White copperas. *See* Zinc sulfate
White gelatin. *See* Gelatin
White mineral oil. *See* Mineral oil
White ozokerite wax. *See* Ceresin
White petrolatum. *See* Petrolatum
White shellac. *See* Shellac
White soft paraffin. *See* Petrolatum
White tea tree. *See* Cajeput oil
White vitriol. *See* Zinc sulfate
White wax. *See* Beeswax; Beeswax, white

Whole rice syrup
  Uses: Used in pharmaceutical tableting (throat lozenges, cough syrups)
  Trade names containing: FruitSource® Granular; FruitSource® Liquid Sweetener; FruitSource® Liquid
    Sweetener Plus

Whole wheat flour
  Uses: Ingred. in pharmaceutical tableting
  Trade names containing: Hony-Tab®; Mola-Tab®

Wild black cherry bark. *See* Wild cherry bark
Wild cherry. *See* Wild cherry bark

Wild cherry bark
  Synonyms: Virginian prune bark; Wild black cherry bark; Wild cherry
  Definition: Dried bark of the wild cherry, *Prunus serotina*
  Properties: Sl. odor, astringent aromatic bitter taste
  Uses: Natural flavoring agent; used in cough syrups

Wilkinite. *See* Bentonite
Wine ether. *See* Ethyl pelargonate

Wintergreen oil
  FEMA 3113
  Synonyms: Menthyl salicylate
  Definition: Oil derived from *Gaultheria procumbens*
  Toxicology: Strong irritant; ing. of sm. amts. may cause severe poisoning and death; very irritating to mucous
    membranes and skin; absorbed readily thru the skin
  Uses: Natural flavoring agent used in toothpaste and tooth powds.; aromatic, astringent, stimulant
  Regulatory: FEMA GRAS; Japan approved; BP compliance
  Manuf./Distrib. (pharm. & food): Virginia Dare
  See also Methyl salicylate

Witch hazel extract
  CAS 84696-19-5; 68916-39-2
  Synonyms: Hamamelis extract
  Definition: Extract containing hamamelitannin obtained from the twigs, bark, and leaves of *Hamamelis
    virginiana*
  Uses: Astringent in hemorrhoidal prods.
  Manuf./Distrib.: Bio-Botanica
  Trade names containing: Witch Hazel Lubrajel

Wood alcohol. *See* Methyl alcohol
Wood naphtha. *See* Methyl alcohol
Wood pulp, bleached. *See* Cellulose
Wood spirit. *See* Methyl alcohol
Wool fat. *See* Lanolin
Wool wax. *See* Lanolin
Wool wax alcohol. *See* Lanolin alcohol

Wormwood oil
  FEMA 3116
  Synonyms: Artemisia absinthium oil; Absinthium oil
  Definition: Volatile oil from leaves and tops of *Artemisia absinthium*, contg. thujyl alcohol and acetate, thujone,
    phellandrene, cadinene
  Properties: Brnsh.-green liq.; sol. in ether, 2 vols 80% aclohol; very sl. sol. in water; dens. 0.925-0.955 (15/

Xanthan

15 C); ref. index 1.460-1.4741 (20 C)

Precaution: Keep cool, well closed; protect from light

Toxicology: A narcotic poison in large or repeated doses, causing headache, trembling, and convulsions; ing. of the volatile oil may cause gastrointestinal symptoms, nervousness, stupor, coma, and death

Uses: Flavoring agent; tonic, stomachic, febrifuge, anthelmintic

Regulatory: FEMA GRAS

Xanthan. *See* Xanthan gum

Xanthan gum

CAS 11138-66-2; EINECS 234-394-2

Synonyms: Corn sugar gum; Xanthan

Classification: Polysaccharide gum

Definition: High m.w. hetero polysaccharide gum produced by a pure-culture fermentation of a carbohydrate with *Xanthomonas campestris*; contains D-glucose, D-mannose, and D-glucuronic acid and is prepared as the sodium, potassium, or calcium salt

Properties: Wh. to cream-colored powd., sl. organic odor, tasteless; very hygroscopic; sol. in hot or cold water; insol. in oils, most org. solvs.; visc. 600 cps min.

Toxicology: No known toxicity; heated to decomp., emits acrid smoke and irritating fumes

Uses: Thickener, suspending agent, stabilizer, emulsifier; used in orals, rectals, topicals

Regulatory: FDA 21CFR §133.124, 133.133, 133.134, 133.162, 133.178, 133.179, 172.695, 176.170; USDA 9CFR §318.7 (limitation 8%), 381.147; Japan, JCID, Europe, UK approvals; FDA approved for orals, rectals, topicals; USP/NF compliance

Manuf./Distrib.: Gumix Int'l.; Kelco Int'l; Meer

Manuf./Distrib. (pharm. & food): ADM; Aldrich; Am. Roland; D F Anstead; Calaga Food Ingreds.; Cornelius; Courtaulds; Ellis & Everard; G Fiske; Gumix Int'l.; Jungbunzlauer; Kelco Int'l.; Meer; Meyhall AG; Penta Mfg.; Rhone-Poulenc; Ruger; Sanofi; Spectrum Chem. Mfg.; Spice King; TIC Gums; Valmar; Zumbro

Trade names: Gumixan K; Gumixan KF; KELTROL®; KELTROL® 1000; KELTROL® BT; KELTROL® CR; KELTROL® F; KELTROL® GM; KELTROL® RD; KELTROL® SF; KELTROL® T; KELTROL® TF; Merecol® MS; Merezan® 8; Merezan® 20; Rhodigel®; Rhodigel® 23; Rhodigel® 200; Ticaxan® Regular

Trade names containing: Ches® 500

Xenon

CAS 7440-63-3

UN No. 2036, 2591 (refrig. liq.)

Classification: Element; noble gas

Empirical: Xe

Properties: Colorless gas or liq., odorless; at.no. 54; at.wt. 131.30; dens. 5.8971 (gas); liquefaction temp. -106.9 C; Liq.: dens. 1.987 (@ b.p.); b.p. -108 C (1 mm)

Uses: Used in inhalants, anesthesia

Regulatory: FDA approved for inhalants; BP compliance (Xe_{133} injection)

Manuf./Distrib.: Air Prods.; Electrochem Ltd; Liquid Air Corp.

Xylenol

CAS 1300-71-6

UN No. 2261

Synonyms: Dimethylphenol; Hydroxydimethylbenzene; Hydroxyxylene; Dimethylhydroxybenzene

Empirical: $C_8H_{10}O$

Formula: $(CH_3)_2C_6H_3OH$

Properties: M.w. 122.17; Commercial mixt.: wh. cryst. solid; sol. in most org. solvs.; sl. sol. in water; dens. 1.02-1.03 (15 C); m.p. 20-76 C; b.p. 203-225 C

Precaution: Combustible

Toxicology: Toxic by ingestion, skin absorption

Uses: Pharmaceuticals

Manuf./Distrib.: J.T. Baker; Coalite Chem. Div.; Crowley; Crowley Tar Prods.; Merichem

Manuf./Distrib. (pharm. & food): Aldrich

2,5-Xylenol

CAS 95-87-4

FEMA 3595

Empirical: $C_8H_{10}O$

Properties: M.w. 122.17; m.p. 72-76 C; b.p. 212 C

Uses: Medicinal flavoring agent
Regulatory: FEMA GRAS
Manuf./Distrib. (pharm. & food): Aldrich

2,6-Xylenol
CAS 576-26-1
FEMA 3249
Synonyms: 2,6-Dimethylphenol
Empirical: $C_8H_{10}O$
Properties: M.w. 122.17; m.p. 45-48 C; b.p. 203 C; flash pt. 173 F
Uses: Medicinal flavoring agent
Regulatory: FEMA GRAS
Manuf./Distrib. (pharm. & food): Aldrich

Xylit. *See* Xylitol
Xylite. *See* Xylitol

Xylitol
CAS 87-99-0; EINECS 201-788-0
Synonyms: Xylite; 1,2,3,4,5-Pentahydroxypentane; Xylit
Classification: Pentahydric alcohol
Empirical: $C_5H_{12}O_5$
Properties: Wh. cryst. or cryst. powd., sweet taste with cooling sensation; hygroscopic; sol. in water; sl. sol. in alcohol; m.w. 152.17; m.p. 92-96 C
Toxicology: LD50 (oral, mouse) 22 g/kg; mod. toxic by IV route; mildly toxic by ingestion; lg. doses may cause an osmotic diarrhea; heated to decomp., emits acrid smoke and irritating fumes
Uses: Sweetener; sugar substitute in medicine; used in lozenges
Regulatory: FDA 21CFR §172.395
Manuf./Distrib.: Am. Roland; Am. Xyrofin; Atomergic Chemetals; FR Benson; Cerestar Int'l.; Food Addit. & Ingreds.; Forum Chems.; Melida; Penta Mfg.; Roquette UK; Scanchem; Spectrum Chem. Mfg.; Xyrofin
Manuf./Distrib. (pharm. & food): Aldrich; Am. Roland; Am. Xyrofin; Atomergic Chemetals; F R Benson; Cerestar Int'l.; Food Addit. & Ingreds.; Forum Chems.; Int'l. Sourcing; Melida; Penta Mfg.; Roquette UK; Ruger; Scanchem; Xyrofin
Trade names: Xylitol C

Yeast
CAS 68876-77-7
Synonyms: Barm
Definition: Fungus with unicellular growth form; several types are: bakers' yeast, bakers' compressed yeast, active dry yeast, brewers' yeast
Properties: Ylsh-wh. viscid liq. or soft mass, flakes, or granules, consisting of cells and spores of *Saccharomyces cerevisiae*
Toxicology: No known toxicity
Uses: Dietary source of folic acid
Manuf./Distrib.: Champlain Industries; Gist-brocades Food Ingreds.
Manuf./Distrib. (pharm. & food): Aldrich; Allied Custom Gypsum; Am. Roland; Ashland; Bio Springer; Browning; Croxton & Garry; Euroma Food Ingreds.; Fermex; Food Additives & Ingreds.; Gist-brocades; Edw. Gittens; Hoechst AG; Integrated Ingreds.; Novo Nordisk; Provesta; Quest; Red Star
Trade names: Type B Torula Dried Yeast

Yeast protein hydrolysate. *See* Hydrolyzed yeast protein
Yellow beeswax. *See* Beeswax, yellow
Yellow oxide of mercury. *See* Mercury oxide (ic), red and yellow
Yellow pine rosin. *See* Rosin
Yellow precipitate. *See* Mercury oxide (ic), red and yellow
Yellow wax. *See* Beeswax; Beeswax, yellow

Ylang ylang oil
CAS 8006-81-3
FEMA 3119
Definition: Oil from flowers of *Cananga odorata*
Toxicology: Sensitizer
Uses: Natural flavoring for pharmaceuticals

Zea mays oil

Regulatory: FDA 21CFR §182.20; FEMA GRAS; Japan approved (ylang-ylang)
Manuf./Distrib. (pharm. & food): Pierre Chauvet

Zea mays oil. *See* Corn oil

Zein

CAS 9010-66-6; EINECS 232-722-9
Definition: Alcohol-sol. protein obtained from corn, *Zea mays;* component of corn gluten
Properties: Wh. to yel. powd., odorless; sol. in aq. alcohols, glycols, glycol ethers, furfuryl alcohol, tetrahydrofurfuryl alcohol, aq. alkaline sol'ns. with pH ≥ 11.5; insol. in water, acetone, all anhyd. alcohols except methanol; m.w. ≈ 38,000; dens. 1.226
Precaution: Combustible
Toxicology: No known toxicity; heated to decomp., emits acrid smoke and irritating fumes
Uses: Coating agent for pharmaceutical preps.; substitute for shellac; used in orals
Regulatory: FDA 21CFR §175.105, 184.1984, GRAS; Japan approved; FDA approved for orals; USP/NF compliance
Manuf./Distrib.: Aldrich; Spectrum Chem. Mfg.
Manuf./Distrib. (pharm. & food): Aldrich

Zeolite

CAS 1318-02-1
Definition: Hydrated alkali aluminum silicate
Uses: Deodorant
Trade names: Abscents® Deodorizing Powd.
See also Sodium silicoaluminate

Zinc

CAS 7440-66-6; EINECS 231-175-3
Classification: Metallic element
Empirical: Zn
Properties: Shining white metal; sol. in acids, alkalies; insol. in water; at.wt. 65.38; dens. 7.14; m.p. 419 C; b.p. 907 C
Uses: Ingred. in dental amalagam
Regulatory: BP compliance
Manuf./Distrib.: Aldrich; Cerac; Cuproquim; Ferro/Bedford; Pasminco Europe; U.S. Zinc; Zinc Corp. of Am.

Zinc acetate

CAS 557-34-6 (anhyd.); 5970-45-6 (dihydrate); EINECS 209-170-2
Classification: Aliphatic organic compd.
Definition: Zinc salt of acetic acid
Empirical: $C_4H_6O_4Zn \cdot 2H_2O$
Formula: $Zn(C_2H_3O_2)_2 \cdot 2H_2O$
Properties: Wh. cryst. lustrous plates, faint acetous odor, astringent taste; sl. efflorescent; sol. in water, boiling alcohol; sl. sol. in alcohol; m.w. 219.50 (dihydrate); dens. 1.735; loses $2H_2O$ @ 100 C; m.p. 200 C (dec.)
Uses: Dietary supplement; medicine (astringent); used in topicals, oral zinc supplements; for treatment of acne vulgaris, Wilson's disease
Regulatory: FDA approved for topicals; USP compliance
Manuf./Distrib.: Lohmann; Osaki Ind.; Nihon Kagaku Sangyo; Wako Pure Chem. Ind.
Manuf./Distrib. (pharm. & food): Aldrich; Integra; Mallinckrodt; Ruger; Spectrum Chem. Mfg.

Zinc chloride

CAS 7646-85-7; EINECS 231-592-0
UN No. 2331
Synonyms: Butter of zinc
Empirical: Cl_2Zn
Formula: $ZnCl_2$
Properties: Wh. cubic cryst., odorless; hygroscopic; deliq.; sol. in water, alcohol, glycerol, ether; m.w. 136.27; dens. 2.91 (25 C); m.p. 290 C; b.p. 732 C
Precaution: DOT: Corrosive material
Toxicology: TLV:TWA 1 mg/m^3 (air); poison by ingestion, intravenous, subcutaneous, intraperitoneal routes; corrosive irritant to skin, eyes, mucous membranes; causes burns
Uses: Coloring agent, antiseptic and astringent; used in parenterals, mouthwashes, dentifrices, deodorant, disinfectants

Regulatory: FDA 21CFR §182.70, 182.5985, 182.8985, 582.80, GRAS; FDA approved for parenterals; BP, Ph.Eur. compliance
Manuf./Distrib.: Aldrich; AlliedSignal; Blythe, William Ltd; Elf Atochem N. Am.; EM Industries; Hosoi Chem. Ind.; Kraft; Mallinckrodt; Nagai Chem. Ind.; Penta Mfg.; SAF Bulk; San Yuan; Spectrum Chem. Mfg.; Zaclon
Manuf./Distrib. (pharm. & food): Mallinckrodt; Ruger; Spectrum Chem. Mfg.

Zinc-eugenol cement
Definition: Zinc compounds and eugenol cement NF
Uses: Dental protective

Zinc gluconate
CAS 4468-02-4 (anhyd.); EINECS 224-736-9
Definition: Zinc salt of gluconic acid
Empirical: $C_{12}H_{22}O_{14}Zn$
Properties: Wh. gran. or cryst. powd.; sol. in water; very sl. sol. in alcohol; m.w. 455.7; pH 5.5-7.5 (1%)
Toxicology: Heated to decomp., emits toxic fumes of ZnO
Uses: Mineral source for pharmaceuticals
Regulatory: FDA 21CFR §182.5988, 182.8988, GRAS; Japan approved with limitations
Manuf./Distrib.: Akzo; Atomergic Chemetals; Lohmann
Manuf./Distrib. (pharm. & food): Am. Roland; Lohmann; Ruger; Spectrum Chem. Mfg.
Trade names: Gluconal® ZN

Zinc glycinate
Uses: Ingred. in antiperspirants
Trade names containing: Westchlor® A2Z 8106

Zinc-L-2-hydroxypropionate. *See* Zinc lactate

Zinc lactate
CAS 16039-53-5
Synonyms: Zinc-L-2-hydroxypropionate
Formula: $Zn(C_3H_5O_3)_2 \cdot 3H_2O$
Properties: Wh. powd.; m.w. 243 (anhyd.)
Uses: Dietary supplement
Manuf./Distrib.: Am. Ingreds.; Lohmann
Trade names: Puramex® ZN

Zinc octadecanoate. *See* Zinc stearate

Zinc oxide
CAS 1314-13-2; EINECS 215-222-5
Synonyms: Chinese white; Pigment white 4; CI 77947; Zinc white; Flowers of zinc
Classification: Inorganic oxide
Empirical: OZn
Formula: ZnO
Properties: White to gray amorphous powd. or crystals, odorless, bitter taste; sol. in dilute acetic or min. acids, alkalis; insol. in water, alcohol; m.w. 81.38; dens. 5.67; m.p. 1975 C; ref. index 2.0041-2.0203; pH 6.95 (Amer. process), 7.37 (French process)
Precaution: Heated to decomp., emits toxic fumes of ZnO
Toxicology: TLV/TWA 5 mg/m³; LD50 (IP, rat) 240 mg/kg; poison by IP route; fumes may cause metal fume fever with chills, fever, tightness in chest, cough, leukocytes; experimental teratogen; mutagenic data; skin/ eye irritant
Uses: Color additive for external pharmaceuticals; used in parenterals, rectals; dental cements; creamy wh. ointment used medicinally as an astringent, antiseptic, and protectant in skin treatments, hemorrhoidal prods.; sunscreen agent
Regulatory: FDA 21CFR §73.1991, 73.2991, 175.300, 177.1460, 182.5991, 182.8991, 582.80, GRAS; FDA approved for parenterals, rectals; BP, Ph.Eur. compliance
Manuf./Distrib.: Aceto; Am. Chemet; Asarco; Ashland; Bayer; Browning; R.E. Carroll; The Chemical Co.; Eagle Zinc; General Chem.; C.P. Hall; Harcros Durham; Landers-Segal Color; Lohmann; D.N. Lukens; Mallinckrodt; Nippon Chem. Ind.; Reade Advanced Materials; H.M. Royal; Royale Pigments & Chems.; Sachtleben Chemie GmbH; Sino-Am. Pigment Systems; Tamms Ind.; Toho Zinc; Van Waters & Rogers; Zinc Corp. of Am.; ZOCHEM
Manuf./Distrib. (pharm. & food): Aldrich; Avrachem; Integra; Ruger; Spectrum Chem. Mfg.
Trade names: USP-1; USP-2; Zinc Oxide USP 66
See also CI 77947

Zinc 2-pyridinethiol-1-oxide. *See* Zinc pyrithione

Zinc pyrithione

Zinc pyrithione

Zinc pyrithione
CAS 13463-41-7; EINECS 236-671-3
Synonyms: Bis[1-hydroxy-2(1H)-pyridinethinato-O,S]-(T-4) zinc; Zinc 2-pyridinethiol-1-oxide; Pyrithione zinc
Classification: Aromatic salt
Empirical: $C_{10}H_8N_2O_2S_2Zn$
Properties: M.w. 317.7
Precaution: Do not store with strong oxidizing agents
Toxicology: LD50 (rat, oral) 260 mg/kg; LD50 (rat, dermal) > 2 g/kg; poison by ingestion, intraperitoneal; irritating to skin and extremely irritating to eyes
Uses: Antimicrobial; used in topicals
Regulatory: FDA approved for topicals
Manuf./Distrib.: Allchem Ind.; Olin; Pyrion-Chemie GmbH; Ruetgers-Nease
Manuf./Distrib. (pharm. & food): Ruger

Zinc ricinoleate
CAS 13040-19-2; EINECS 235-911-4
Synonyms: 12-Hydroxy-9-octadecenoic acid, zinc salt; 9-Octadecenoic acid, 12-hydroxy-, zinc salt
Definition: Zinc salt of ricinoleic acid
Empirical: $C_{18}H_{34}O_3 \cdot {}^1\!/_2$ Zn
Formula: $[CH_3(CH_2)_5CHOHCH_2CH=CH(CH_2)_7COO]_2 \cdot Zn^{++}$
Properties: White powd., fatty acid odor; dens. 1.10 (25/25 C); m.p. 92-95 C
Precaution: Combustible
Uses: Ingred. in antiperspirants
Regulatory: FDA 21CFR §175.300
Trade names containing: Grillocin® AT Basis

Zinc soap. *See* Zinc stearate

Zinc stearate
CAS 557-05-1; EINECS 209-151-9
Synonyms: Zinc octadecanoate; Octadecanoic acid zinc salt; Zinc soap
Definition: Zinc salt of stearic acid
Empirical: $C_{36}H_{70}O_4Zn$
Formula: $Zn(C_{18}H_{35}O_2)_2$
Properties: White powd., faint char. odor; sol. in acids, common solvs. (hot); insol. in water, alcohol, ether; dec. by dilute acids; m.w. 632.33; dens. 1.095; m.p. 130 C
Precaution: Combustible
Toxicology: No known toxicity to skin; inh. of powd. may cause lung problems and produce death in infants from pneumonitis, with lesions resembling those caused by talc but more severe
Uses: Tablet/capsule lubricant; used in orals, tablet mfg., pharmaceutical powds. and ointments; protectant in diaper rash and prickly heat prods.
Regulatory: FDA 21CFR §175.105, 175.300, 176.170, 176.180, 176.200, 176.210, 177.1200, 177.1460, 177.1900, 177.2410, 177.2600, 178.2010, 178.3910, 182.5994, 182.8994, GRAS; FDA approved for orals; USP/NF, BP, Ph.Eur. compliance
Manuf./Distrib.: Aldrich; Allchem Ind.; Ferro/Grant; Lohmann; Magnesia GmbH; Mallinckrodt; Norac; Stave; Syn. Prods.
Manuf./Distrib. (pharm. & food): Aldrich; Integra; Mallinckrodt; Ruger; Spectrum Chem. Mfg.
Trade names: Cecavon ZN 70; Cecavon ZN 71; Cecavon ZN 72; Cecavon ZN 73; Cecavon ZN 735; Haro® Chem ZPR-2; Synpro® Zinc Stearate USP; Witco® Zinc Stearate U.S.P.-D

Zinc sulfate
CAS 7446-02-0; 7733-02-0 (anhyd.); 7446-19-7 (monohydrate); 7746-20-0 (heptahydrate); EINECS 231-793-3
Synonyms: Sulfuric acid zinc salt (1:1); White vitriol; White copperas; Zinc vitriol
Classification: Inorganic salt
Definition: Reaction prod. of sulfuric acid with zinc
Formula: $ZnSO_4$ (anhyd.), $ZnSO_4 \cdot H_2O$ (monohydrate), $ZnSO_4 \cdot 7H_2O$ (heptahydrate)
Properties: Colorless rhombic cryst. or cryst. powd., odorless; hygroscopic; efflorescent in dry air; sol. in water, glycerin; almost insol. in alcohol; m.w. 161.43 (anhyd.), 179.46 (monohydrate), 287.56 (hepathydrate); dens. 3.74 (15 C); m.p. dec. @ 740 C
Precaution: Heated to dec., emits toxic fumes of SO_x and ZnO
Toxicology: LD50 (oral, rat) 2949 mg/kg; poison by IP, subcutaneous, IV; mod. toxic by ing.; experimental tumorigen, teratogen, reproductive effects; human systemic effects, mutagenic data; eye irritant; allergen; irritating to skin and mucous membranes

Uses: Used in orals, eye lotions, astringents, styptics, gargle sprays, skin tonic; medicinally as an emetic
Regulatory: FDA 21CFR §182.90, 182.5997, 182.8997, 582.80, GRAS; Japan approved with limitations; FDA approved for orals; BP, Ph.Eur. compliance
Manuf./Distrib.: Aldrich; Lohmann; Mallinckrodt; Mitsui Mining & Smelting; Spectrum Chem. Mfg.; Toho Zinc
Manuf./Distrib. (pharm. & food): Integra; Mallinckrodt; Ruger; Spectrum Chem. Mfg.; Tomita Pharmaceutical; Wako Pure Chem. Ind.; Yoneyama Yakuhin Kogyo
Trade names: Zinc Sulfate Monohydrate CP Grade

Zinc vitriol. *See* Zinc sulfate
Zinc white. *See* Zinc oxide

Zingerone
CAS 122-48-5
FEMA 3124
Synonyms: 4-(4-Hydroxy-3-methoxyphenyl)-2-butanone; (4-Hydroxy-3-methoxyphenyl)ethyl methyl ketone; Vanillylacetone; Zingherone; Zingiberone
Empirical: $C_{11}H_{14}O_3$
Properties: Cryst.; sol. in ether, dil. alkalies; sparingly sol. in water, petroleum ether; m.w. 194.22; dens. 1.138-1.139; m.p. 40-41 C; b.p. 187-188 C (14 mm); ref. index 1.5440-1.5450
Uses: Sweet vanilla-like synthetic flavoring agent
Regulatory: FDA 21CFR §172.515; FEMA GRAS
Manuf./Distrib. (pharm. & food): Aldrich

Zingherone. *See* Zingerone
Zingiberone. *See* Zingerone

Part III
Functional
Cross-Reference

Functional Cross-Reference

Trade name and generic chemical additives from the first and second parts of this reference are grouped by broad functional areas derived from research and manufacturers' specifications

Absorbents • Sorbents

Trade names: Akorex B; Amerchol® BL; Amerchol® C; Amerchol® CAB; Amerchol® H-9; Anhydrous Lanolin USP Cosmetic Grade; Anhydrous Lanolin USP Pharmaceutical Grade; Anhydrous Lanolin USP Pharmaceutical Light Grade; Anhydrous Lanolin USP X-tra Deodorized; Argobase 125T; Argobase EU; Argobase EUC 2
Capmul® EMG; Capmul® GDL; Capmul® GMO; Capmul® GMS; Capmul® MCM; Capmul® MCMC8; Capmul® POE-L; Capmul® POE-S; Capmul® S; Caprol® 3GO; Caprol® 3GS; Caprol® 6G2O; Caprol® 6G2S; Caprol® 10G4O; Caprol® 10G10O; Caprol® ET; Caprol® PGE860; Captex® 200; Captex® 300; Captex® 350; Captex® 355; Captex® 810A; Captex® 810D; Clarity
Dehymuls® E
Emery® 1732; Emery® 1740
Imwitor® 742
Labrafil® M 2130 CS; Labrasol; Lexate® PX; Liquid Absorption Base Type A; Liquid Absorption Base Type T
Noveon® CA-1; Nymcel® ZSC
Orgasol 1002 D WHITE 5 COS; Orgasol 2002 D NAT COS; Orgasol 2002 EX D NAT COS; Orgasol 2002 UD NAT COS
Pre-Gel Amaranth Powd.; Protegin®; Protegin® W; Protegin® WX; Protegin® X; Pureco® 76; Pure-Dent® B810; Pure-Dent® B851; Pure-Dent® B852; Pure-Dent® B880; Pure-Dent® B890
Ritachol®; Ritahydrox; Ritawax
Softisan® 378; Softisan® 601; Solka-Floc® BW-100; Solka-Floc® BW-200; Solka-Floc® BW-2030; Solka-Floc® Fine Granular; Sta-Rx®; Super-Sat

Chemicals: Amaranth
Barium hydroxide lime
Cellulose
Diatomaceous earth
Food starch modified
Maltodextrin; Microcrystalline cellulose
Nylon-6; Nylon-12
Orange wax; Oryzanol
PEG-25 PABA
Soda lime; Sorbitol

Acidulants. *See pH control agents*

Adjuvants • Synergists

Trade names: Alpha W6 HP 0.6; Alpha W6 M1.8; Alpha W 6 Pharma Grade

Adjuvants *(cont'd.)*

Byco A; Byco C; Byco E; Byco O
CornSweet® Crystalline Fructose; Crodarom Nut A; Crodarom Nut O; Crodyne BY-19
DSS Granular; DSS Tablet Grade
Germall® 115; Glycyrrhetinic Acid Phytosome®
Incropol CS-20
Magnasweet®
Rehydragel® LV
Volpo S-2; Volpo S-10

Chemicals: Acacia
Caffeine; Citric acid monohydrate; Clove oil; Copper gluconate
Dioctyl sodium sulfosuccinate
Ethyl formate; Eugenol
Fumaric acid
Hydrolyzed gelatin
Propylene glycol alginate
Walnut extract

Adsorbents

Trade names: Cab-O-Sil® EH-5; Cab-O-Sil® H-5; Cab-O-Sil® L-90; Cab-O-Sil® LM-150; Cab-O-Sil® M-5; Cab-O-Sil® MS-55
Imwitor® 928; Imwitor® 988
Pharmasorb Colloidal Pharmaceutical Grade
Rederm® Gel; Rederm® Powd.; Rehydragel® CG; Rehydragel® HPA; Rehydragel® LV; Rehydragel® T
Witafrol® 7420

Chemicals: Aluminum hydroxide; Attapulgite
Bismuth subcarbonate; Bismuth subnitrate; Bismuth subsalicylate
Carbon, activated; Charcoal, activated
Kaolin
Pectin; Polycarbophil
Silica; Silica, hydrated; Starch

Aerosols. *See Propellants*

Air displacement aids

Chemicals: Carbon dioxide
Nitrogen

Alkalizing agents. *See pH control agents*

Antacids. *See pH control agents*

Anticaking agents • Free-flow agents • Glidants • Antitacking agents

Trade names: Act II 500 USP; Aerosil® 200; Aerosil® R972; Alphafil 500 USP; Alpine Talc USP BC 127; Altalc 200 USP; Altalc 300 USP; Altalc 400 USP; Altalc 500 USP; Avicel® PH-102; Avicel® PH-103; Avicel® PH-105

Anticaking agents *(cont'd.)*

Cab-O-Sil® EH-5; Cab-O-Sil® H-5; Cab-O-Sil® LM-150; Cab-O-Sil® M-5; Cab-O-Sil® MS-55; Cab-O-Sil® PTG; Candex®; Cecavon MG 51; Ceraphyl® 28; Ceraphyl® 31; Ceraphyl® 41; Ceraphyl® 45; Ceraphyl® 368; Ceraphyl® 375; Cremophor® S 9

Destab™ Calcium Carbonate 90; Destab™ Calcium Carbonate 95; Durkote Calcium Carbonate/ Starch, Acacia Gum; Durkote Ferrous Sulfate/Hydrog. Veg. Oil

Elcema® F150; Elcema® G250; Elcema® P100; Emdex® Plus

FK 500LS; Free-flowing KCl

Maltrin® M040; Miglyol® 812; Myvaplex® 600; Myvaplex® 600P NF

Petrac® Magnesium Stearate MG-20 NF; Purtalc USP

Sipernat® 22LS; Sipernat® 22S; Sorbelite™ C; Standamul® G-32/36; Supreme USP

Unisweet MAN

Chemicals: C12-15 alkyl lactate; Calcium silicate
Dioctylmalate
Isostearyl neopentanoate
Lauryl lactate
Magnesium carbonate; Magnesium stearate; D-Mannitol
PPG-2 myristyl ether propionate
Silica; Silica, hydrated
Talc

Anticoagulants

Trade names: SPL Heparin Ammonium; SPL Heparin Lithium; SPL Heparin Sodium USP

Chemicals: Citric acid; Citric acid monohydrate
Heparin ammonium; Heparin lithium; Heparin sodium

Antidandruff agents

Trade names: Elestab® HP 100
Lipacide SH Co 90; Lipacide SH K 90
Nipacide® PX-R
Oramix® L30
Proteol UCO

Antifoams • Defoaming agents

Trade names: Arlacel® 186
Crill 1; Crill 4
Dow Corning® 360 Medical Fluid; Dow Corning® Medical Antifoam; Dow Corning® Q7-2243 LVA, Simethicone USP; Dow Corning® Q7-2587 30% Simethicone Emulsion USP
Emery® Methyl Oleate
Fancol OA-95; Foam Blast 5, 7; Foam Blast 10; Foam Blast 100 Kosher; Foam Blast 106; Foam Blast 150 Kosher; Foamkill® 8G; Foamkill® 30 Series; Foamkill® 618 Series; Foamkill® 634 Series; Foamkill® 810F; Foamkill® 830; Foamkill® 830F; Foamkill® 836A; Foamkill® MS Conc.
Hodag Antifoam CO-350; Hodag Antifoam F-1; Hodag Antifoam F-2; Hodag Antifoam FD-62; Hodag Antifoam FD-82
Jeffox PPG-400; Jeffox PPG-2000
Macol® 1; Macol® 2; Macol® 2D; Macol® 2LF; Macol® 4; Macol® 10; Macol® 22; Macol® 27; Macol® 33; Macol® 40; Macol® 85; Mazu® DF 200SP
Prox-onic EP 1090-1
Silwet® L-7500; Silwet® L-7602; Sorgen 30; Sorgen 40; Sorgen 50; Sorgen 90
Wacker Silicone Antifoam Emulsion SE 9

Chemicals: Dimethicone; Dimethicone copolyol

Antifoams *(cont'd.)*

EO/PO block polymer or copolymer
Jojoba oil
Methyl oleate
PPG-400; PPG-2000; Propylene glycol alginate
Silica aerogel; Silicone; Silicone emulsions; Simethicone; Sorbitan sesquiol

Antigellants. *See Thickeners*

Anti-inflammatory agents • Antiphlogistic agents • Counter-irritants

Trade names: Aldo® PGHMS; Allantoin; Aloe-Moist™ A
Biophytex®
Co-Grhetinol
Drewmulse® POE-SML
Ethosperse® LA-12; Ethosperse® LA-23
Fancol CH
Hydagen® B
Monteine PCO
Nikkol Dipotassium Glycyrrhizinate; Nikkol Glycyrrhetinic Acid; Nikkol Glycyrrhizic Acid; Nikkol Stearyl Glycyrrhetinate
Orange Wax; Orange Wax, Deodorized
Polyplasdone® INF-10; 2-Pyrol®
Reishi Extract
Wickenol® 171

Chemicals: Allyl isothiocyanate; Amylase
Bisabolol; Butcherbroom extract
Cajeput oil; Calendula extract; Camphor; Capsicum oleoresin; Clove oil
Dipotassium glycyrrhizate
Glycyrrhetinic acid; Glycyrrhizic acid; Guaiacol
Hydrocotyl extract
Laureth-12; Laureth-23
Octyl hydroxystearate; Orange wax
Palmitoyl collagen amino acids; D-Panthenol; DL-Panthenol; PEG-60 almond glycerides; Petrolatum
Stearyl glycyrrhetinate

Antimicrobials

Trade names: Airaseptic Spray; Arquad® B-100
Bronopol; Bronopol-Boots® BP
Capmul® MCM; Capmul® MCMC8; Catigene® DC 100; Catinal MB-50A; Cloronine; Clorpactin; CPC; CPC Sumquat 6060; Crodasinic LS30; Crodasinic LS35; Crodex C
Elestab® HP 100; EmCon Tea Tree; Empigen® 5073; Empigen® 5089; Empigen® BAC50; Empigen® BAC50/BP; Empigen® BAC90; Ethyl Parasept® NF
Gardiquat 1450; Gardiquat 1480; Germaben® II; Germall® 115; Germall® II
Hexetidine 90; Hexetidine 99; Hyamine® 10X; Hyamine® 1622 50%; Hyamine® 1622 Crystals; Hyamine® 3500 50%
Igepal® CO-630 Special; Imwitor® 308; Imwitor® 312; Imwitor® 742
Lexgard® B; Lexgard® M; Lexgard® P; Lipacide C8CO; Lipacide SH Co 90; Lipacide SH K 90; LiquaPar® Oil; Lubraseptic Jelly
Myacide® SP
Nipabenzyl; Nipabutyl; Nipabutyl Potassium; Nipabutyl Sodium; Nipacide® PX-R; Nipacombin A; Nipacombin SK; Nipagin A; Nipagin A Potassium; Nipagin A Sodium; Nipagin M; Nipagin M Potassium; Nipagin M Sodium; Nipasept Sodium; Nipasol M; Nipasol M Potassium; Nipasol M Sodium; Nipastat

Antimicrobials *(cont'd.)*

Oramix® L30; Orange Wax, Deodorized; Ottasept®; Ottasept® Extra; Oxaban®-A; Oxaban®-E
Phenoleum; Phenoxetol; Phospholipid PTD; Phospholipid PTL; Phospholipid PTZ; Propyl
  Parasept® NF/FCC; Purasal® P/HQ 60; Purasal® P/USP 60; Purasal® S/HQ 60; PVP-Iodine
  17/12, 30/06
Quataphen; Querton 246
Rederm® Gel; Rederm® Powd.
Silvercide; Socci 7340; Spectradyne® G
Triamite
Uniphen P-23; Uniquart CPC
Vancide® 89 RE

Chemicals: Benzalkonium chloride; Benzethonium chloride; Benzoic acid; Benzyl alcohol; Benzylparaben;
  Boric acid; 2-Bromo-2-nitropropane-1,3-diol; Butylparaben
Calcium chloride; Calcium propionate; Calcium undecylenate; Capryloyl collagen amino acids;
  Captan; Cetalkonium chloride; Cetrimonium chloride; Cetylpyridinium chloride;
  Chlorhexidine diacetate; Chlorhexidine digluconate; Chloroacetamide; Chlorobutanol;
  Chlorobutanol hemihydrate; p-Chloro-m-cresol; Chloroxylenol; Cocohydroxyethyl PEG-
  imidazolinium chloride phosphate; Cocohydroxyethyl PEG-imidazolinium chloride phos-
  phate; m-Cresol
Dehydroacetic acid; Diazolidinyl urea; Dimethyl oxazolidine; Domiphen bromide
7-Ethyl bicyclooxazolidine; Ethylparaben
Formaldehyde
Glutaral
Hexachlorophene; Hexamidine diisethionate; Hexetidine; 8-Hydroxyquinoline sulfate
Imidazolidinyl urea
Lactic acid; Lauralkonium chloride; Lauramidopropyl PEG-dimonium chloride phosphate;
  Laurtrimonium chloride
Methenamine hippurate; Methylbenzethonium chloride; Methylchloroisothiazolinone; 1,2-
  Methylenedioxybenzene; Methylisothiazolinone; Methylparaben; Methyl salicylate;
  Myristalkonium chloride; Myrtrimonium bromide
Orange wax
Pentasodium pentetate; Phenethyl alcohol; Phenol; Phenoxyethanol; Phenylmercuric acetate;
  Phenylmercuric borate; Phenylmercuric nitrate; Potassium benzoate; Potassium butyl
  paraben; Potassium ethylparaben; Potassium lactate; Potassium methylparaben; Potassium
  propylparaben; Potassium sorbate; Propylparaben; Pyrogallol
Quaternium-14; Quaternium-15
Resorcinol
Silver; Sodium benzoate; Sodium butylparaben; Sodium dehydroacetate; Sodium ethylparaben;
  Sodium lactate; Sodium lauroyl sarcosinate; Sodium methylparaben; Sodium N-oleoyl
  sarcosinate; Sodium propionate; Sodium propylparaben; Sodium sulfite; Sodium/TEA-
  undecenoyl collagen amino acids; Sodium undecylenate; Sorbic acid; Squalane;
  Stearalkonium chloride; Succinic acid
Tall oil; Tea tree oil; α-Terpineol; Tetramethylthiuram disulfide; Thimerosal; Thymol; Triacetin;
  Triclosan
Zinc pyrithione

Antioxidants

Trade names: Ascorbic Acid USP/FCC, 100 Mesh; Ascorbic Acid USP, FCC Fine Gran. No. 6045655; Ascorbic
  Acid USP, FCC Fine Powd. No. 6045652; Ascorbic Acid USP, FCC Gran. No. 6045654;
  Ascorbic Acid USP, FCC Type S No. 6045660; Ascorbic Acid USP, FCC Ultra-Fine Powd No.
  6045653; Ascorbyl Palmitate NF, FCC No. 60412
24% Beta Carotene HS-E in Veg. Oil No. 65671; 30% Beta Carotene in Veg. Oil No. 65646
Calcium Ascorbate FCC No. 60475; CAO®-3; CAO®-3/Blend 29; Cavitron Cyclo-dextrin™;
  Copherol® 950LC; Copherol® 1250; Copherol® F-1300; Crystal® Crown LP
Gamma Oryzanol
Lysidone®
Mark® 5095
Orange Wax; Orange Wax, Deodorized; Oxynex® 2004; Oxynex® K; Oxynex® LM
PAG DLTDP; PAG DSTDP

Antioxidants *(cont'd.)*

Sodium Ascorbate USP, FCC Fine Powd. No. 6047708; Sodium Ascorbate USP, FCC Type AG No. 6047710

Tecquinol® USP Grade; Triamite; Tri-K Vitamin E Acetate; Turpinal® SL

Veltol®-Plus; Veltol®-Plus; Vitamin E Acetate USP Oil; Vitamin E USP Tocopherol; Vitamin E USP, FCC No. 60525; Vitamin E USP, FCC No. 60526; Vitinc® dl-alpha Tocopheryl Acetate USP XXII

Chemicals: L-Ascorbic acid; Ascorbyl palmitate

BHA; BHT; t-Butyl hydroquinone

Calcium ascorbate

Dilauryl thiodipropionate; Dimyristyl thiodipropionate; Distearyl thiodipropionate; Ditridecyl thiodipropionate; Dodecyl gallate

Erythorbic acid; Etidronic acid

Gallic acid

Hydroquinone; Hydroquinone monomethyl ether; Hypophosphorous acid

Lauryl/stearyl thiodipropionate; Lysine PCA

Maltol

Nordihydroguairetic acid

Octyl gallate; Orange wax; Oryzanol

Potassium bisulfite; Potassium metabisulfite; Propionic acid; Propyl gallate

Sodium ascorbate; Sodium bisulfite; Sodium formaldehyde sulfoxylate; Sodium metabisulfite; Sodium sulfite; Sodium thiosulfate anhydrous; Stannous chloride anhyd; Sulfur dioxide

Thioglycerin; Tocopherol; D-α-Tocopherol; DL-α-Tocopherol; Tocopheryl acetate; d-α-Tocopheryl acetate; dl-α-Tocopheryl acetate; 1,3,5-Trihydroxybenzene

Antiperspirants • Deodorants

Trade names: Chloracel® 40% Sol'n; Chloracel® Solid

Eudragit® L 100-55

Gardiquat 1450; Gardiquat 1480; Grillocin® AT Basis

Hyamine® 1622 50%; Hyamine® 1622 Crystals; Hydagen® C.A.T; Hydagen® DEO

Chemicals: Aluminum chloride basic; Aluminum chlorohydrate; Aluminum chlorohydrex PG; Aluminum diacetate; Aluminum sesquichloride; Aluminum sesquichlorohydrate; Aluminum zirconium octachlorohydrex GLY; Aluminum zirconium pentachlorohydrate; Aluminum zirconium pentachlorohydrex GLY; Aluminum zirconium tetrachlorohydrex GLY; Aluminum/zirconium trichlorohydrex GLY

Cinnamyl alcohol

Ferrous sulfate

Phenol

Sodium aluminum chlorohydroxy lactate

Thymol; Triclosan; Triethyl citrate

Zeolite

Antiphlogistic agents. *See Anti-inflammatory agents*

Antiseptics • Sterilizing agents

Trade names: Airaseptic Spray

Cloronine

Empigen® 5089; Empigen® BAC50; Empigen® BAC50/BP; Empigen® BAC90; Ethyl Ether USP/ACS

Guardian Protective Skin Cream

Iodasept

Lactic Acid 88% USP/FCC; Lipacide C8CO

Nipacide® PX-R

Ottasept® Extra

Antiseptics *(cont'd.)*

Pentonium 4Br40; Phenonip; Phenosept; Phenoxetol; Propylene Phenoxetol
Ringwell

Chemicals: Aluminum chloride anhydrous; Aluminum sulfate
Balsam Peru; Bay oil; Benzalkonium chloride; Benzethonium chloride; Benzoic acid; Benzyl alcohol; Bismuth subgallate; Boric acid
Cajeput oil; Capryloyl collagen amino acids; Cetalkonium chloride; Cetearyl alcohol; Cetrimonium bromide; Cetylpyridinium chloride; Chlorhexidine digluconate; Chlorobutanol
Diazolidinyl urea; Dichlorobenzyl alcohol; Domiphen bromide
Ethyl ether; Eucalyptol; Eucalyptus oil; Eugenol
Glutaral; Gum benzoin
Hexamidine diisethionate; Hexyl alcohol; Hydrogen peroxide
Iodine; Isopropyl alcohol
Menthol; Mercury oxide (ic), red and yellow; Methylbenzethonium chloride; Methylparaben; Methyl salicylate; Morpholine; Myrtrimonium bromide
Phenethyl alcohol; Phenol; Phenoxyisopropanol; Phenylmercuric acetate; Phenylmercuric nitrate; Potassium iodide; Potassium metabisulfite; PVP-iodine
Salicylic acid; Sodium hypochlorite; Sodium iodide; Sodium salicylate; Sodium sulfite; Storax
Terpene resin, natural; α-Terpineol
Urea; Urea peroxide
Zinc chloride; Zinc oxide

Antitacking agents *See Anticaking agents*

Aromatics. *See Fragrances*

Astringents

Trade names: Rederm® Powd.
USP-1; USP-2
Witch Hazel Lubrajel

Chemicals: Aluminum diacetate; Aluminum hydroxide; Aluminum sulfate; Amaranth
Bay oil; Benzyl alcohol; Bismuth subgallate
Cinnamon oil
Ferrous sulfate
Gallic acid
Logwood extract
Oleyl alcohol
Potassium alum dodecahydrate
Sambucus oil; Sodium chlorate; Stearyl alcohol; Sulfuric acid
Wintergreen oil; Witch hazel extract
Zinc acetate; Zinc chloride; Zinc oxide

Bases

Trade names: Alcolan®; Aloe-Moist™ A; Aloe Vera Gel 1X; Aloe Vera Gel 10X; Aloe Vera Gel 40X; Aloe Vera Gel Decolorized 1X; Aloe Vera Gel Decolorized 10X; Aloe Vera Gel Decolorized 40X; Amerchol® BL; Amerchol® C; Amerchol® H-9; Anhydrous Lanolin Grade 1; Anhydrous Lanolin Grade 2; Anhydrous Lanolin Superfine; Apifil®; Argobase 125T; Argobase EU; Argobase EUC 2
Carbowax® PEG 300; Carbowax® Sentry® PEG 300; Carbowax® Sentry® PEG 400; Carbowax® Sentry® PEG 540 Blend; Carbowax® Sentry® PEG 600; Carbowax® Sentry® PEG 900; Carbowax® Sentry® PEG 1000; Carbowax® Sentry® PEG 1450; Carbowax® Sentry® PEG 3350; Carbowax® Sentry® PEG 4600; Carbowax® Sentry® PEG 8000; Cire Lanol® CTO; Corona Lanolin; Coronet Lanolin; Cutina® GMS; Cutina® KD16

Bases (cont'd.)

Dehymuls® K; Dow E300 NF; Dow E400 NF; Dow E600 NF; Dow E900 NF; Dow E1000 NF; Dow E1450 NF; Dow E3350 NF; Dow E4500 NF; Dow E8000 NF; Drakeol® 6; Drakeol® 7; Dynasan® 112; Dynasan® 114

Edible Beef Gelatin; Emerwax® 1266; Emery® 1732; Emery® 1740; Estaram 299; Estaram A; Estaram H5; Estaram H15; Estaram H37; Estaram S55; Estaram S58; Estaram W25; Estaram W45

Galenol® 1618 AE; Galenol® 1618 CS; Galenol® 1618 DSN; Galenol® 1618 KS; Gelot 64®

Hydrokote® 95; Hydrokote® 97; Hydrokote® 102; Hydrokote® 108; Hydrokote® 112; Hydrokote® 118; Hydrolactol 70

Imwitor® 960 Flakes; Imwitor® 965

Kessco® 653

Lanesta P; Lanesta SA-30; Lanette® N; Lanette® O; Lanette® W; Lexate® PX; Lipo PE Base G-55; Lipo PE Base GP-55; Liquid Absorption Base Type A; Liquid Absorption Base Type T

Macol® 1; Macol® 2; Macol® 2D; Macol® 2LF; Macol® 4; Macol® 8; Macol® 10; Macol® 22; Macol® 27; Macol® 33; Macol® 40; Macol® 85; Massa Estarinum® 299; Massa Estarinum® A; Massa Estarinum® AB; Massa Estarinum® B; Massa Estarinum® BB; Massa Estarinum® BC; Massa Estarinum® BCF; Massa Estarinum® BD; Massa Estarinum® C; Massa Estarinum® D; Massa Estarinum® E; Mazawax® 163R; Monomuls® 90-25; Multiwax® 180-M; Multiwax® ML-445; Multiwax® W-445; Multiwax® W-835; Multiwax® X-145A

Narangrex Complex D; Narangrex Complex G; Neobee® 18; Nipacide® PX-R; Novata® 299; Novata® 3525; Novata® A; Novata® AB; Novata® B; Novata® BBC; Novata® BC; Novata® BCF; Novata® BD; Novata® C; Novata® D; Novata® E; Novata® PK

Ointment Base No. 3; Ointment Base No. 4; Ointment Base No. 6

Pelemol® CP; Penreco Amber; Penreco Blond; Penreco Cream; Penreco Lily; Penreco Regent; Penreco Royal; Penreco Snow; Penreco Super; Penreco Ultima; Pionier® BS-WO II; Pionier® KWH-soft; Pionier® MAA; Pionier® OEWA-II; Pionier® PLW; Pionier® WWH-N; Pionier® WWH-soft; Pluracol® E400 NF; Pluracol® E600 NF; Pluracol® E1450 NF; Polawax® GP200; Polyjel; Pomelex Complex D; Pomelex Complex G; Protegin®; Protegin® W; Protegin® WX; Protegin® X; Pureco® 100

Ritachol®

Sebase; Sedefos 75®; Softisan® 100; Softisan® 378; Softisan® 601; Softisan® 649; Sonojell® No. 4; Sonojell® No. 9; Standamul® 302; Standamul® 318; Standamul® 1414-E; Standamul® 7061; Standamul® 7063; Standamul® 7105; Standamul® CTA; Standamul® CTV; Standamul® G-32/36 Stearate; Sterol TE 200; Sugartab®; Superpolystate; Supoweiss A; Supoweiss B; Supoweiss B0; Supoweiss B10; Supoweiss B90; Supoweiss BV; Supoweiss C; Supoweiss C2; Supoweiss D; Sweetrex®

Tefose® 63; Tefose® 1500; Tefose® 2000; Tefose® 2561; Teric PEG 300; Teric PEG 400; Teric PEG 600; Teric PEG 1500; Teric PEG 3350; Teric PEG 4000; Teric PEG 6000; Teric PEG 8000; Terra-Dry™ FD Aloe Vera Powd. Decolorized FDD; Terra-Dry™ FD Aloe Vera Powd. Reg. FDR; Tesal; Texapon® SB-3; Trisynlane

Vaseline 335 G; Vaseline 7702; Vaseline 8332; Vaseline 10049 BL; Vaseline A

W.G.S. Cetyl Palmitate; Witepsol® E75; Witepsol® E76; Witepsol® E85; Witepsol® H5; Witepsol® H12; Witepsol® H15; Witepsol® H32; Witepsol® H35; Witepsol® H37; Witepsol® H175; Witepsol® H185; Witepsol® S51; Witepsol® S55; Witepsol® S58; Witepsol® W25; Witepsol® W31; Witepsol® W32; Witepsol® W35; Witepsol® W45

Chemicals:
Caprylic/capric/stearic triglyceride; Caprylic/capric triglyceride PEG-4 esters; Cetyl palmitate; Chloroxylenol; Cocamidopropyl betaine; Cocoglycerides; Coconut oil

Disodium laureth sulfosuccinate

EO/PO block polymer or copolymer

Glyceryl tricocoate; Glycol stearate; Glycol stearate SE

Hexyl laurate; Hydrogenated coco-glycerides

Lactose; Lanolin; Lanolin oil

D-Mannitol; Meglumine; Meroxapol 252; Meroxapol 311; Myreth-3 myristate

Octyldodecyl stearate

PEG-6; PEG-8; PEG-12; PEG-20; PEG-32; PEG-40; PEG-75; PEG-100; PEG-150; PEG-200; PEG-8M; PEG-8 beeswax; Petrolatum; Polyethylene glycol; Polyethylene glycol monomethyl ether

Rose water

Simethicone; Sodium cocoate; Soluble collagen; Squalane

Tetradecyleicosyl stearate

860

Binders

Trade names: Avicel® PH-101; Avicel® PH-102; Avicel® PH-103; Avicel® PH-105
Benecel® Methylcellulose; Britol®; Britol® 6NF; Britol® 7NF; Britol® 9NF; Britol® 20USP; Britol® 35USP; Britol® 50USP; Byco C; Byco E; Byco O
Capsulec 51-SB; Capsulec 51-UB; Capsulec 56-SB; Capsulec 56-UB; Capsulec 62-SB; Capsulec 62-UB; Carbowax® PEG 300; Carbowax® Sentry® PEG 300; Carbowax® Sentry® PEG 400; Carbowax® Sentry® PEG 540 Blend; Carbowax® Sentry® PEG 600; Carbowax® Sentry® PEG 900; Carbowax® Sentry® PEG 1000; Carbowax® Sentry® PEG 1450; Carbowax® Sentry® PEG 3350; Carbowax® Sentry® PEG 4600; Carbowax® Sentry® PEG 8000; Cekol® 30; Cekol® 150; Cekol® 300; Cekol® 700; Cekol® 2000; Cekol® 4000; Cekol® 10000; Cekol® 30000; Cekol® 50000; Cellogen HP; CMC Daicel 1150; CMC Daicel 1160; CMC Daicel 1220; CMC Daicel 1260; Compritol 888 ATO; Corn Po 4; Cozeen®
Dow Corning® 365 35% Dimethicone NF Emulsion
Emulmetik™ 970
Genu® Carrageenan; Genu® HM USP 100; Genu® HM USP L200; Genugel® Series; Genuvisco; Granular Gum Ghatti #1; Gum Tragacanth Ribbons and Flakes
Hectalite® 200; Hydrobrite 200PO; Hydrobrite 300PO; Hydrobrite 380PO; Hydrobrite 550PO
Imwitor® 191; Imwitor® 900
Karaya Gum #1 FCC; Kaydol® S; KELTROL®; KELTROL® F
Locust Bean Gum Type A-100; Locust Bean Gum Type A-250; Locust Bean Gum Type A-270; Luviform® FA 119
Magnabrite® F; Magnabrite® FS; Magnabrite® HS; Maltrin® M040; Maltrin® M100; Maltrin® M150; Maltrin® M180; Maltrin® M200; Maltrin® M250; Maltrin® M510; Maltrin® QD M500; Maltrin® QD M550; Maltrin® QD M600; Methocel® A4C Premium; Methocel® A4M Premium; Methocel® E4M Premium; Methocel® E50LV Premium; Methocel® K4M Premium; Methocel® K15M Premium; Methocel® K100LV Premium; Methocel® K100M Premium; Methocel® K Premium
Natrosol® 250; Natrosol® Hydroxyethylcellulose; Natrosol® Plus CS, Grade 330
Penreco Amber; Penreco Blond; Penreco Cream; Penreco Lily; Penreco Royal; Penreco Super; Plasdone® C-15; Plasdone® C-30; Polargel® HV; Polargel® NF; Polargel® T; Powdered Gum Karaya Superfine #1 FCC; Powdered Gum Karaya Superfine XXXX FCC; Powdered Gum Tragacanth BP; Powdered Gum Tragacanth Type B-1 NF Premium; Powdered Gum Tragacanth Type B-12 NF Premium; Powdered Gum Tragacanth Type C-5 NF; Powdered Gum Tragacanth Type G-1 NF Premium; Powdered Gum Tragacanth Type G-2 NF Premium; Powdered Gum Tragacanth Type G-2S NF Premium; Powdered Gum Tragacanth Type M-3 NF Premium; Powdered Tragacanth Gum Type A/10; Powdered Tragacanth Gum Type E-1; Powdered Tragacanth Gum Type G-3; Powdered Tragacanth Gum Type L; Powdered Tragacanth Gum Type W; Purity® 21
Rederm® Gel; Rederm® Powd.; Rehydragel® HPA; Rehydragel® LV; Rehydragel® T; Rhodasurf® PEG 300; Rhodasurf® PEG 600
Soageena®; Soageena® LX26; Softisan® 649; Solka-Floc® BW-100; Solka-Floc® BW-200; Solka-Floc® BW-2030; Solka-Floc® Fine Granular; Sol-U-Tein EA; Spray Dried Fish Gelatin; Spray Dried Fish Gelatin/Maltodextrin; Spray Dried Gum Arabic NF Type CSP; Spray Dried Gum Arabic NF/FCC CM; Spray Dried Gum Arabic NF/FCC CS (Low Bacteria); Spray Dried Gum Arabic NF/FCC CS-R; Spray Dried Hydrolysed Fish Gelatin; Starch 1500®; Starch 1500® LM
Ticalose® 15; Ticalose® 30; Ticalose® 150 R; Ticalose® 700 R; Ticalose® 2000 R; Ticalose® 5000 R; Ticaxan® Regular; Ticolv; Tragacanth Flake No. 27; Tragacanth Gum Ribbon No. 1; 28-1801; Tylose® MH Grades; Tylose® MHB
Volclay® NF-BC; Volclay NF-ID
Yelkin F; Yelkin G; Yelkin P

Chemicals: Albumen; Aluminum hydroxide
Carrageenan; Cellulose acetate trimellitate; Corn syrup solids
Hydrogenated cottonseed oil; Hydroxyethylcellulose; Hydroxypropylcellulose
PEG-14; PEG-32; PEG-100; PEG-150; PEG-200; Polyvinyl acetate (homopolymer)
Sodium bentonite; Sodium hectorite; Sucrose polystearate
Trimyristin; Tristearin

Bodying agents. *See Thickeners*

Buffers. *See pH control agents*

Bulking agents. *See Fillers*

Carriers • Vehicles

Trade names: A-641; Acconon W230; Aerosil® 200; Agar Agar NF Flake #1; Akoext SB; Akorex B; Aldo® MCT KFG; Aldo® TC; Aloe Vera Oil; Arlex

Basic Magnesium Carbonate USP Heavy Low Moisture; Basic Magnesium Carbonate USP Pregranular Heavy; Basic Magnesium Carbonate USP Pregranular Light; Britol®; Britol® 6NF; Britol® 7NF; Britol® 9NF; Britol® 20USP; Britol® 35USP; Britol® 50USP; Butyl Diglyme

Cab-O-Sil® EH-5; Cab-O-Sil® L-90; Cab-O-Sil® LM-150; Cab-O-Sil® M-5; Cab-O-Sil® MS-55; Cal-Carb® 4450; Cal-Carb® 4450 PG; Cal-Carb® 4457; Cal-Carb® 4462; Calgene CC-22; Calgene CC-22-S; Calgene CC-33; Calgene CC-33-F; Calgene CC-33-L; Calgene CC-33-S; Cal-Tab®; Candex® Plus; Capmul® MCM; Capmul® MCMC8; Captex® 200; Captex® 300; Captex® 350; Captex® 355; Captex® 800; Captex® 810A; Captex® 810D; Captex® 8000; Carbowax® PEG 300; Carbowax® Sentry® PEG 300; Carbowax® Sentry® PEG 400; Carbowax® Sentry® PEG 540 Blend; Carbowax® Sentry® PEG 600; Carbowax® Sentry® PEG 900; Carbowax® Sentry® PEG 1000; Carbowax® Sentry® PEG 1450; Carbowax® Sentry® PEG 3350; Carbowax® Sentry® PEG 4600; Carbowax® Sentry® PEG 8000; Ceraphyl® ICA; Cetiol®; Cetiol® A; Cetiol® V; Coconut Oil® 76; Coconut Oil® 92; Colored Nu-Pareil® PG 14/18; Colored Nu-Pareil® PG 16/20; Colored Nu-Pareil® PG 18/20; Colored Nu-Pareil® PG 20/25; Colored Nu-Pareil® PG 25/30; Colored Nu-Pareil® PG 30/35; Corn Po 4; Crodamol EO; Crodamol GTCC

Dow E300 NF; Dow E400 NF; Dow E600 NF; Dow E900 NF; Dow E1000 NF; Dow E1450 NF; Dow E3350 NF; Dow E4500 NF; Dow E8000 NF; Drakeol® 7; Dynacerin® 660

Eastman® OC; Edible Beef Gelatin; Emdex®; Emdex® Plus; Emvelop®; Epikuron™ 145; Epikuron™ 170; Epikuron™ 200; Estasan GT 8-40 3578; Estasan GT 8-60 3575; Estasan GT 8-60 3580; Estasan GT 8-65 3577; Estasan GT 8-70 3579; Ethoxylan® 1685; Ethoxylan® 1686; Eutanol® G; Eutanol® G16

Fancol SORB

Hony-Tab®; Hydrobrite 200PO

Imwitor® 308; Imwitor® 312; Imwitor® 742; Imwitor® 928; Imwitor® 988; Isopropylmyristat; Isopropylpalmitat

Karajel; Kaydol® S

Labrafil® M 1944 CS; Lanaetex CO; Lanesta P; Lanesta SA-30; Lexate® PX; Lexol® GT-855; Lexol® GT-865; Lexol® IPP; Lexol® IPP-A; Lexol® IPP-NF; Lexol® PG-800; Lexol® PG-865; Liposorb 70; Lipovol SES-S

Maltrin® QD M440; Maltrin® QD M500; Maltrin® QD M550; Maltrin® QD M600; Mazol® PGO-104; Miglyol® 810; Miglyol® 812; Miglyol® 840; Miglyol® 8810; Mola-Tab®; Monoglyme; Multiwax® 180-M; Multiwax® ML-445; Multiwax® W-445; Multiwax® W-835; Multiwax® X-145A

Neobee® 1053; Neobee® 1054; Neobee® 1062; Neobee® M-5; Neobee® M-20; Neobee® O; Nu-Core® 35/45; Nu-Core® 40/50; Nu-Core® 45/60; Nu-Pareil® PG 14/18; Nu-Pareil® PG 16/20; Nu-Pareil® PG 18/20; Nu-Pareil® PG 20/25; Nu-Pareil® PG 25/30; Nu-Pareil® PG 30/35; Nu-Tab®

Ointment Base No. 3; Ointment Base No. 4; Ointment Base No. 6; Orgasol 1002 D WHITE 5 COS; Orgasol 2002 D NAT COS; Orgasol 2002 EX D NAT COS; Orgasol 2002 UD NAT COS; Os-Tab™ 4455; Os-Tab™ 4455; Oyster Shell Powd. 4402

Penreco Amber; Penreco Blond; Penreco Cream; Penreco Lily; Penreco Regent; Penreco Royal; Penreco Snow; Penreco Super; Penreco Ultima; Perfecta® USP; Pharma-Carb®; Pharma-Gel™; Plasdone® K-25; Plasdone® K-29/32; Plasdone® K-90; Plasdone® K-90D; Plasdone® K-90M; Pluracol® E400 NF; Pluracol® E600 NF; Pluracol® E1450 NF; Pluronic® F68NF; Pluronic® F87NF; Pluronic® F108NF; Pluronic® F127NF; Pluronic® L44NF; Poly-G® 200; Powdered Agar Agar Bacteriological Grade; Powdered Agar Agar NF M-100 (Gracilaria); Powdered Agar Agar NF MK-60; Powdered Agar Agar NF MK-80-B; Powdered Agar Agar NF MK-80 (Bacteriological); Powdered Agar Agar NF S-100; Powdered Agar Agar NF S-100-B; Powdered Agar Agar NF S-150; Powdered Agar Agar NF S-150-B; Powdered

Carriers *(cont'd.)*

Agar Agar Type K-60; Powdered Agar Agar Type K-80; Powdered Agar Agar Type K-100; Powdered Agar Agar Type K-150; Propylene Glycol USP/FCC Ultra Grade; Protopet® Alba; Protopet® White 1S; Protopet® White 2L; Protopet® White 3C; Protopet® Yellow 2A; Pureco® 76; Pyrax® ABB; Pyrax® B

Rehydragel® CG; Ritawax AEO; Robane®

Sebase; Sesame Oil USP/NF 16; Simchin® Natural; Simchin® Refined; Softisan® 378; Standamul® 318; Standamul® 1414-E; Standamul® CTA; Standamul® CTV; Sunyl® 80; Sunyl® 90; Super Refined® Almond Oil; Super Refined® Corn Oil; Super Refined® Cottonseed Oil; Super Refined® Olive Oil; Super Refined® Peanut Oil; Super Refined® Safflower Oil; Super Refined® Sesame Oil; Super Refined® Soybean Oil USP; Super-Sat; Supraene®

Tetraglyme; TIC Pretested® Arabic FT-1 USP

Unichem ACETA; Unisweet 70; Unisweet 70/CONC; Unisweet CONC

Vivacel® 10

Witafrol® 7420

Chemicals: Acetyl methyl carbinol; Agar; Apricot kernel oil; Aromatic elixir USP/NF

Balsam tolu; Benzaldehyde; Butylene glycol; Butylene glycol dicaprylate/caprate

Caprylic/capric glycerides; Caprylic/capric/lauric triglyceride; Caprylic/capric/linoleic triglyceride; Caprylic/capric/stearic triglyceride; Caprylic/capric triglyceride; Castor oil; Cocoa butter; Coco caprylate/caprate; Corn oil; Corn syrup; Corn syrup solids; Cottonseed oil

Diethylene glycol dibutyl ether; Dimethyl isosorbide; Dimethyl sulfoxide; Distarch phosphate

Ethylene glycol dimethyl ether; Ethyl oleate

Gelatin; Glycerin; Glyceryl alginate; Glyceryl caprylate/caprate; Glyceryl cocoate; Glyceryl formal; Glyceryl laurate; Glyceryl myristate

Hydrogenated cottonseed oil

Isocetyl alcohol; Isomaltose; Isopropyl myristate; Isopropyl palmitate

Jojoba oil

Lanolin

Maltodextrin; Mineral oil; Myreth-3 myristate; Myristyl alcohol

Nylon-6; Nylon-12

Octyldodecanol; Oleyl erucate; Olive oil; Oxidized cellulose; Oyster shell powder

Peanut oil; PEG-4; PEG-4 dimethyl ether; Peppermint oil; Phosphatidylcholine; PPG-2 lanolin alcohol ether; Propylene glycol; Propylene glycol dicaprylate/dicaprate; Propylene glycol dioctanoate; Pyrophyllite

Safflower oil; Sarsaparilla; Sesame oil; Shea butter; Silica; Silica, hydrated; Sorbitol; Sorbitol sol'n; Soybean oil; Squalane; Squalene; Sugar spheres; Sunflower seed oil; Sweet almond oil; Syrup

Tricaprylin; Trioctanoin

Catalysts

Trade names: ChiroCLEC™-CR
Fascat® 9100; Fascat® 9102; Fascat® 9201
PeptiCLEC™-TR

Chemicals: Mercury acetate (ic)

Chelating agents • Sequestrants

Trade names: Briquest® ADPA-60AW
Cheelox® 80
Sequestrene® NA2; Sequestrene® NA2Ca
Turpinal® 4 NL; Turpinal® SL
Versene 100; Versene 100 EP; Versene 100 LS; Versene 100 SRG; Versene 100 XL; Versene 220; Versene Acid; Versene CA; Versene Diammonium EDTA; Versene NA; Versene Na$_2$; Versene Tetraammonium EDTA; Versenex 80; Versenol 120
Wayhib® S

Chemicals: Calcium citrate; Calcium disodium EDTA; β-Cyclodextrin

Chelating agents *(cont'd.)*

Diammonium EDTA; Disodium EDTA; Distarch phosphate
Edetic acid; Etidronic acid
D-Gluconic acid
Pentasodium pentetate; Potassium phosphate
Sodium citrate
Tetraammonium EDTA; Tetrahydroxypropyl ethylenediamine; Tetrasodium EDTA; Tetrasodium etidronate; Trisodium EDTA; Trisodium HEDTA

Coagulants

Trade names: Barquat® CT-29
Carsoquat® CT-429
Polyox® WSR Coagulant
Sol-U-Tein EA

Chemicals: Albumen
Cetrimonium chloride
Vitamin K_1

Coating agents

Trade names: AA USP; Akorex B; Altalc 200 USP; Altalc 300 USP
Byco C; Byco E; Byco O
C-A-P Enteric Coating Material; Cap-Shure® KCL-140-50; Cap-Shure® KCL-165-70; Carbowax® Sentry® PEG 300; Carbowax® Sentry® PEG 400; Carbowax® Sentry® PEG 540 Blend; Carbowax® Sentry® PEG 600; Carbowax® Sentry® PEG 900; Carbowax® Sentry® PEG 1000; Carbowax® Sentry® PEG 1450; Carbowax® Sentry® PEG 3350; Carbowax® Sentry® PEG 4600; Carbowax® Sentry® PEG 8000; C-A-T Enteric Coating Polymer; Chroma-Kote®; Chroma-Seal™ 859027; Chroma-Seal™ 889031; Chroma-Teric™; Chroma-Tone™; Chroma-Tone™ P; Cozeen®; Crodyne BY-19; Cutina® HR Powd.
Docusate Sodium USP; Dri-Klear™
Eudragit® RL 30 D; Eudragit® RS 30 D
Gelatin USP/NF, Type A; Granular Gum Ghatti #1
HPMCP 50; HPMCP 55; HPMCP 55S
Kollidon® 25, 30, 90; Kollidon® USP; Koster Keunen Carnauba; Koster Keunen Carnauba, Powd.; Koster Keunen Microcrystalline Waxes
Lamegin® EE Range
Maltrin® M100; Maltrin® M200; Maltrin® QD M440; Mono-Coat® E91
Opadry® Enteric; Opadry II®; Opaglos®; Opaseal®
Penreco Amber; Penreco Blond; Penreco Cream; Penreco Lily; Penreco Royal; Penreco Super; pHthalavin™; Plasdone® K-25; Plasdone® K-29/32; Plasdone® K-90; Plasdone® K-90D; Plasdone® K-90M; Pluronic® F68NF; Polyox® WSR 205; Polyox® WSR 301; Polyox® WSR 303; Polyox® WSR 308; Polyox® WSR 1105; Polyox® WSR 3333; Polyox® WSR N-10; Polyox® WSR N-12K; Polyox® WSR N-60K; Polyox® WSR N-80; Polyox® WSR N-750; Polyox® WSR N-3000; Polyox® WSR Coagulant; Polypro 5000® Pharmaceutical Grade; Polypro 15000® Pharmaceutical Grade; Powdered Gum Ghatti #1; Powdered Gum Ghatti #2; PVP/VA S-630
Rocoat® Niacinamide $33^1/_3$% No. 69907; Rocoat® Niacinamide $33^1/_3$% Type S No. 69909; Rocoat® Pyridoxine Hydrochloride $33^1/_3$% No. 60688; Rocoat® Riboflavin 25% No. 60289; Rocoat® Riboflavin $33^1/_3$ No. 60288; Rocoat® Thiamine Mononitrate $33^1/_3$% No. 60188
Sheerskin; Simchin® Natural; Simchin® Refined; SPL Heparin Ammonium; SPL Heparin Lithium; SPL Heparin Sodium USP; Surelease®; Sureteric™

Chemicals: Acetylated mono- and diglycerides of fatty acids; Ammonio methacrylate copolymer
Beeswax
Carboxymethylcellulose sodium; Carnauba; Cellulose acetate; Cellulose acetate phthalate; Cellulose acetate trimellitate; Coconut oil; Collodion
Ethylcellulose

Coating agents *(cont'd.)*

Gelatin; Glucose, liquid; Gum ghatti

Hydrogenated coconut oil; Hydrolyzed gelatin; Hydroxypropylcellulose; Hydroxypropyl methyl-cellulose; Hydroxypropyl methylcellulose phthalate

Jojoba oil

Maltodextrin; Methacrylic acid copolymer; Methylcellulose; Microcrystalline wax

Paraffin; PEG-6; PEG-8; PEG-12; PEG-20; PEG-32; PEG-40; PEG-75; PEG-100; PEG-150; PEG-200; PEG-2M; PEG-5M; PEG-7M; PEG-9M; PEG-14M; PEG-20M; PEG-23M; PEG-45M; PEG-90M; PEG-115M; Pharmaceutical glaze; Polyethylene glycol; Polyethylene oxide; Polylysine; Polyvinyl acetate phthalate; PVM/MA copolymer, butyl ester; PVP/VA copolymer

Shellac; Simethicone; Sucrose

Titanium dioxide

Wheat gluten

Zein

Colorants • Color enhancers • Dyes • Pigments

Trade names: Acid Proof Caramel Powd.; Alphafil 500 USP; Alpine Talc USP BC 127; Altalc 200 USP; Altalc 300 USP; Altalc 500 USP; Annatto OS #2894; Annatto OS #2922; Annatto OS #2923; Annatto Liq. #3968, Acid Proof; Annatto Powd. WS

Basic Magnesium Carbonate USP Heavy Low Moisture; Basic Magnesium Carbonate USP Pregranular Heavy; Basic Magnesium Carbonate USP Pregranular Light; B&C Caramel Powd.; 24% Beta Carotene HS-E in Veg. Oil No. 65671; 24% Beta Carotene Semi-Solid Suspension No. 65642; 30% Beta Carotene in Veg. Oil No. 65646; Bixin Crystal 95

Canthaxanthin Beadlets 10%; Caramel Color Double Strength; Caramel Color Single Strength; Carmacid R; Carmacid Y; Carmine AS; Carmine FG; Carmine PG; Carmine Powd. 272010, 272015, 272020; Carmine Powd. WS; Carmine XY/UF; Carminic Acid 90; Carmisol A; Carmisol NA; Cloisonné®; Cosmica®

Double Strength Acid Proof Caramel Colour; Duocrome®

Extramalt 10; Extramalt 35; Extramalt Dark; Extramalt Light

Flamenco® Interference Color Powds; Flamenco® White Pearl Powds

Gemtone®; Grape Skin Extract, 2X #3850; Grape Skin Extract, Double Strength; Grape Skin Extract, Powd. 282730; Grape Skin Extract, Single Strength

Hilton Davis Titanium Dioxide

Mearlmaid® AA; Mearlmaid® TR

Natural Liquid AP Carmine Colorant; Natural Red Beet Liq. 275280; Natural Red Beet Powd. 654200; Natural Soluble Carmine Powd.; Natural Soluble Powder AP Carmine Colorant; Natural Yellow Colour Q-500, Q-1000, Q-2000; Norbixin 40

Opacode®; Opacode® WB; Opadry®; Opadry II®; Opalux®; Opaspray®; Opatint®

Potassium Sodium Copper Chlorophyllin 033280; Powdered Caramel Color 986010; Powdered Caramel Color, Acid Proof; Powdered Caramel Colour Non-Ammoniated-All Natural T-717; Pure Malt Colorant A6000; Purtalc USP; Pyrax® ABB; Pyrax® B

Red Soluble Powd. Natural Colorant; Riboflavin USP, FCC 184045; Riboflavin USP, FCC Type S

Sicopharm®; Sicopharm® Iron Oxides; Single Strength Acid Proof Caramel Colour; Supreme USP

Timica®

Unibix AP (Acid Proof); Unibix CUS; Unibix ENC (Acid Proof); Unibix W; Unisweet Caramel

Zea Red

Chemicals: Alumina; Aluminum; Amaranth; Annatto; Annatto extract

Barley extract; Beet powder; Betanine; Bismuth oxychloride; Bronze powder

Calcium carbonate; Calendula extract; Canthaxanthine; Caramel; Carmine; Carotene; Chlorophyllin-copper complex; Chromium-cobalt-aluminum oxide; Chromium hydroxide green; Chromium oxide greens; CI 10316; CI 12085; CI 14700; CI 15510; CI 15850; CI 15985; CI 16035; CI 17200; CI 19140; CI 26100; CI 40800; CI 40850; CI 42053; CI 42090; CI 45350; CI 45380; CI 45410; CI 45425; CI 45430; CI 47000; CI 47005; CI 59040; CI 60725; CI 61565; CI 61570; CI 69825; CI 73000; CI 73015; CI 73360; CI 75120; CI 75130; CI 75170; CI 75470; CI 75810; CI 77000; CI 77002; CI 77163; CI 77220; CI 77288; CI 77289; CI 77400; CI 77489; CI 77491; CI 77492; CI 77499; CI 77510; CI 77947; Copper powder

D&C Blue No. 4; D&C Blue No. 6; D&C Blue No. 9; D&C Green No. 5; D&C Green No. 6; D&C

Colorants *(cont'd.)*

Green No. 8; D&C Orange No. 4; D&C Orange No. 5; D&C Orange No. 10; D&C Orange No. 11; D&C Orange No. 17; D&C Red No. 6; D&C Red No. 7; D&C Red No. 8; D&C Red No. 9; D&C Red No. 17; D&C Red No. 19; D&C Red No. 21; D&C Red No. 22; D&C Red No. 27; D&C Red No. 28; D&C Red No. 30; D&C Red No. 30 aluminum lake; D&C Red No. 31; D&C Red No. 33; D&C Red No. 34; D&C Red No. 36; D&C Red No. 37; D&C Red No. 39; D&C Violet No. 2; D&C Yellow No. 7; D&C Yellow No. 8; D&C Yellow No. 10; D&C Yellow No. 11; Dihydroxyacetone; Dipotassium glycyrrhizate

Ext. D&C Yellow No. 7

FD&C Blue No. 1; FD&C Blue No. 1 aluminum lake; FD&C Blue No. 2; FD&C Green No. 3; FD&C Red No. 3; FD&C Red No. 4; FD&C Red No. 40; FD&C Yellow No. 5; FD&C Yellow No. 6; Ferric ammonium ferrocyanide; Ferric ferrocyanide; Ferric oxide

D-Glucose anhyd; Grape skin extract; Guanine

Iron ammonium citrate; Iron (III) oxide hydrated; Iron oxides

Lavender oil; Logwood extract

Magnesium carbonate; Magnesium stearate; Magnesium trisilicate; Malt extract; Meadowfoam seed oil; Mica; Molasses

Norbixin

Pyrogallol; Pyrophyllite

Riboflavin

Talc; Tartrazine; Titanium dioxide

Zinc chloride; Zinc oxide

Color enhancers. *See Colorants*

Compatibilizers

Trade names: Aerosil® 300; Aerosil® 380; Aerosil® COK 84
Tebol™; Tebol™ 99

Complexing agents

Trade names: Gantrez® AN-119; Gantrez® AN-139; Gantrez® AN-139 BF; Gantrez® AN-149; Gantrez® AN-169
Noveon® AA-1
Polyplasdone® XL; Polyplasdone® XL-10

Chemicals: Disodium EDTA
Edetic acid
Gentisic acid ethanolamine
8-Hydroxyquinoline sulfate
PVM/MA copolymer

Conditioners • Softeners

Trade names: Abil® EM-90; Aldo® PGHMS; Amerchol L-101®; Amerchol® L-500; Amerlate® P; Aminoxid WS 35; Amonyl® 380 BA; Arquad® DM18B-90
Britol®; Britol® 7NF; Britol® 9NF; Britol® 20USP; Britol® 35USP; Britol® 50USP
Cosmowax J; Cosmowax K; Crodafos N-3 Acid; Croderol G7000
EmCon CO; EmCon Rice Bran; Emery® 1650; Emery® 1656; Emery® 1660; Emery® HP-2050; Emery® HP-2060; Eumulgin® B1; Eumulgin® B2
Fancol CB; Fancol CB Extra; Fancol LA; Fancol LAO; Fancor Lanwax; Fancorsil LIM 1; Fancorsil LIM 2; Fancorsil LIM 3; Fancorsil P
Glucam® P-20 Distearate
Hartolan; Hyaluronic Acid FCH; Hydrobrite 200PO; Hydroxylan
Lan-Aqua-Sol 50; Lan-Aqua-Sol 100; Laneto 50; Laneto 100; Laneto AWS; Lanotein AWS 30;

Conditioners *(cont'd.)*

Lantrol® HP-2074; Lipolan 31; Lipolan 31-20; Lipolan Distilled; Lipolan S; Liponic 70-NC; Liponic 76-NC; Liponic 83-NC

Modulan®

Nikkol BPS-5

Pelemol® OL; Perfecta® USP; Phospholipid PTD; Phospholipid PTL; Phospholipid PTZ; Propylene Glycol USP/FCC Ultra Grade; Protopet® Alba; Protopet® White 1S; Protopet® White 2L; Protopet® White 3C; Protopet® Yellow 2A

Ritachol® 2000

Solulan® PB-2; Solulan® PB-5; Solulan® PB-10; Solulan® PB-20; Sol-U-Tein EA; Span® 20; Span® 40; Span® 60; Span® 60K; Span® 65; Span® 65K; Span® 85; Super Refined® Shark Liver Oil; Super Solan Flaked; Super Sterol Ester

Vee Gee Pharmaceutical Gelatins; Vigilan

White Swan

Chemicals: C18-36 acid glycol ester; C18-36 acid triglyceride; Calcium stearate; Ceteareth-10; Ceteareth-14; Citric acid

DEA-oleth-3 phosphate; DEA-oleth-10 phosphate; Diazolidinyl urea; Dimethicone copolyol eicosanate

Hydrolyzed collagen

Imidazolidinyl urea; Isostearyl lactate

Lactic acid; Laneth-5; Laneth-15

Maleated soybean oil; Meadowfoam seed oil

Oleth-3 phosphate; Oleth-10 phosphate; Oleyl lactate; Olive oil

Peanut oil; PEG-7 hydrogenated castor oil; PEG-4 tallate; Phenoxyacetic acid; PPG-2 lanolin alcohol ether; PPG-10 lanolin alcohol ether; PPG-20 lanolin alcohol ether; PPG-20 methyl glucose ether distearate

Sesame oil; Stearic acid; Sweet almond oil

Urea; Urea peroxide

Consistency regulators. *See Thickeners*

Counter-irritants. *See Anti-inflammatory agents*

Crystal growth inhibitors

Trade names: Caprol® ET; Centrolex® F

Kollidon®

Lanfrax® 1776; Lanfrax® 1779; Liponic Sorbitol Sol'n. 70% USP; Liquid Fish Gelatin Conc.

Macol® 57; Maltrin® M040; Maltrin® M200

Spray Dried Fish Gelatin; Spray Dried Fish Gelatin/Maltodextrin; Spray Dried Hydrolysed Fish Gelatin

Chemicals: PPG-10 butanediol

Crystallization promoters

Trade names: Akolizer C; Akolizer P; Akolizer S

Chemicals: Hydrogenated cottonseed oil; Hydrogenated soybean oil

Defoaming agents. *See Antifoams*

Dehydrating agents. *See Desiccants*

Demulcents. *See Protective agents*

Denaturants

Chemicals: t-Butyl alcohol
Denatonium benzoate
Methyl isobutyl ketone
Sucrose octaacetate
α-Terpineol

Deodorants. *See Antiperspirants*

Deodorizing agents • Odor masking agents

Trade names: Abscents® Deodorizing Powd.; Airaseptic Spray; Alpha W6 HP 0.6; Alpha W6 M1.8; Alpha W 6
Pharma Grade
Beta W 7; Beta W7 HP 0.9; Beta W7 M1.8; Beta W7 P
Calgon® Type APA; Cavitron Cyclo-dextrin™; Cloronine; Clorpactin
Descote® Ascorbic Acid 60%; Descote® Niacinamide $33^{1}/_{3}$%; Descote® Pyridoxine
Hydrochloride $33^{1}/_{3}$%; Descote® Riboflavin $33^{1}/_{3}$%; Descote® Sodium Ascorbate 50%;
Descote® Thiamine Mononitrate $33^{1}/_{3}$%
Gamma W8; Gamma W8 HP0.6; Gamma W8 M1.8
Marinco® CL

Chemicals: Carbon, activated; Chlorophyllin-copper complex; Cyclodextrin; β-Cyclodextrin
Hydroxypropyl-α-cyclodextrin; Hydroxypropyl-β-cyclodextrin; Hydroxypropyl-γ-cyclodextrin; N-
Hydroxysuccinic acid
Lavender oil
Methyl-α-cyclodextrin; Methyl-β-cyclodextrin; Methyl-γ-cyclodextrin
Thymol

Desiccants • Drying agents • Dehydrating agents

Trade names: A.F.S

Chemicals: Acetic anhydride
Calcium chloride; Calcium sulfate; Calcium sulfate dihydrate; Capryloyl collagen amino acids
Nutmeg oil, expressed
Silicone emulsions

Detoxicants

Trade names: Plasdone® C-15; Plasdone® C-30; Plasdone® K-25; Plasdone® K-29/32; Plasdone® K-90;
Plasdone® K-90D; Plasdone® K-90M; Polyplasdone® INF-10; Polyplasdone® XL;
Polyplasdone® XL-10

Chemicals: L-Arginine

Dietary supplements. *See Nutrients*

Diluents

Trade names: Akorex B; Alphafil 500 USP; Altalc 200 USP; Altalc 300 USP; Altalc 400 USP; Altalc 500 USP

Diluents *(cont'd.)*

Captex® 300; Captex® 350; Captex® 355; Captex® 810A; Captex® 810D; Clarity; Calgene CC-22; Calgene CC-22-S; Calgene CC-33; Calgene CC-33-F; Calgene CC-33-L; Calgene CC-33-S

Maltrin® M510; Maltrin® QD M500

Neobee® 1053; Neobee® M-5; Neobee® M-20; Neobee® O

Pre-Gel Amaranth Powd.; Pureco® 76; Pyrax® ABB; Pyrax® B

Solka-Floc® BW-100; Solka-Floc® BW-200; Solka-Floc® BW-2030; Solka-Floc® Fine Granular

Chemicals: Albumin
Calcium carbonate
Hydrogenated soybean oil
Isopropyl alcohol
Nitrogen
Pyrophyllite
Sunflower seed oil

Dispersants

Trade names: Abil®-Wax 9814; Acconon 200-MS; Acconon 400-ML; Acconon 400-MO; Acconon 400-MS; Acconon CA-5; Acconon CA-8; Acconon CA-9; Acconon CA-15; Acconon CON; Acconon E; Acconon TGH; Acconon W230; Acritamer® 934; Acritamer® 934P; Acritamer® 940; Acritamer® 941; Adinol CT95; Aerosil® R812; Albrite® Dicalcium Phosphate Anhyd; Alcolec® Z-3; Aldosperse® MO-50 FG; Alkamuls® EL-620; Amerlate® W; Anhydrous Lanolin USP Cosmetic Grade; Anhydrous Lanolin USP Pharmaceutical Grade; Anhydrous Lanolin USP Pharmaceutical Light Grade; Anhydrous Lanolin USP X-tra Deodorized

Capmul® EMG; Capmul® MCM; Capmul® MCMC8; Capmul® POE-L; Capmul® POE-S; Caprol® 3GO; Caprol® 6G2O; Caprol® 10G10O; Caprol® PGE860; Carbowax® Sentry® PEG 300; Cekol® 150; Cekol® 700; Cekol® 10000; Ceraphyl® 791; Cerasynt® 303; Chroma-GDF™; Chroma-SRF™; Chroma-Teric™; Cithrol GML N/E; Corona Lanolin; Coronet Lanolin; Crill 1; Crill 4; Crill 43; Crill 45; Crill 50; Crillet 1; Crodalan AWS; Crodesta F-10; Crodesta F-50; Crodesta F-110; Crodesta F-160; Crodet L4; Crodet L8; Crodet L12; Crodet L24; Crodet L40; Crodet L100; Crodet S4; Crodet S8; Crodet S12; Crodet S24; Crodet S40; Crodet S100; Crovol A40; Crovol A70; Crovol M40; Crovol M70

Docusate Sodium USP; Drewmulse® 3-1-O; Drewmulse® 6-2-S; Drewmulse® 10-4-O; Drewmulse® 10-8-O; Drewmulse® 10-10-O; Drewmulse® 10-10-S; Drewmulse® 10K; Drewmulse® POE-SMO; Drewmulse® POE-SMS; Drewmulse® POE-STS; Drewmulse® SML; Drewmulse® SMO; Drewmulse® SMS; Drewmulse® STS; DSS Granular; DSS Tablet Grade; Dulectin; Dynacerin® 660

Eccowet® W-50; Eccowet® W-88; Emalex C-20; Emalex C-30; Emalex C-40; Emalex C-50; Emery® 1656; Emery® 1660; Emery® HP-2050; Emery® HP-2060; Empicol® 0185; Epikuron™ H; Ethoxylan® 1685; Ethoxylan® 1686; Eumulgin® PRT 36; Eumulgin® PRT 56; Eumulgin® PRT 200; Eutanol® G; Eutanol® G16

Fancol LA; Fancor IPL; Forlan C-24

Gantrez® AN-119; Gantrez® AN-139; Gantrez® AN-139 BF; Gantrez® AN-149; Gantrez® AN-169; Gantrez® ES-225; Gantrez® ES-335; Gantrez® ES-425; Gantrez® ES-435; Glycosperse® L-20; Glycosperse® O-5; Glycosperse® O-20; Glycosperse® O-20 FG; Glycosperse® O-20 KFG; Glycosperse® P-20; Glycosperse® S-20; Glycosperse® TO-20; Glycosperse® TS-20

Hartolan; Hydrobrite 200PO; Hydrobrite 300PO; Hydrobrite 380PO; Hydrobrite 550PO; Hydroxylan

Imwitor® 742; Imwitor® 900; Imwitor® 928; Imwitor® 988

Kaydol® S; Kessco® PEG 200 DL; Kessco® PEG 200 DO; Kessco® PEG 200 DS; Kessco® PEG 200 ML; Kessco® PEG 200 MO; Kessco® PEG 200 MS; Kessco® PEG 300 DL; Kessco® PEG 300 DO; Kessco® PEG 300 DS; Kessco® PEG 300 MO; Kessco® PEG 300 MS; Kessco® PEG 400 DL; Kessco® PEG 400 DO; Kessco® PEG 400 DS; Kessco® PEG 400 ML; Kessco® PEG 400 MS; Kessco® PEG 600 DL; Kessco® PEG 600 DO; Kessco® PEG 600 DS; Kessco® PEG 600 ML; Kessco® PEG 600 MO; Kessco® PEG 600 MS; Kessco® PEG 1000 DL; Kessco® PEG 1000 DO; Kessco® PEG 1000 DS; Kessco® PEG 1000 ML; Kessco® PEG 1000 MO; Kessco® PEG 1000 MS; Kessco® PEG 1540 DL; Kessco® PEG 1540 DO; Kessco® PEG 1540 DS; Kessco® PEG 1540 ML; Kessco® PEG 1540 MO;

Dispersants *(cont'd.)*

Kessco® PEG 1540 MS; Kessco® PEG 4000 DL; Kessco® PEG 4000 DO; Kessco® PEG 4000 DS; Kessco® PEG 4000 ML; Kessco® PEG 4000 MO; Kessco® PEG 4000 MS; Kessco® PEG 6000 DL; Kessco® PEG 6000 DO; Kessco® PEG 6000 DS; Kessco® PEG 6000 ML; Kessco® PEG 6000 MO; Kessco® PEG 6000 MS; Kollidon®

Lan-Aqua-Sol 50; Lan-Aqua-Sol 100; Lanfrax® 1779; Lanogel® 21; Lanogel® 31; Lanogel® 41; Lanogel® 61; Lantrol® HP-2074; Lecigran™ 5750; Lecigran™ 6750; Lecigran™ A; Lecigran™ C; Lecigran™ T

Macol® 1; Macol® 2; Macol® 2D; Macol® 2LF; Macol® 4; Macol® 8; Macol® 10; Macol® 22; Macol® 27; Macol® 33; Macol® 40; Macol® 85; Mapeg® 200 DL; Mapeg® 200 DO; Mapeg® 200 ML; Mapeg® 200 MO; Mapeg® 400 DL; Mapeg® 400 DO; Mapeg® 400 DOT; Mapeg® 400 DS; Mapeg® 400 ML; Mapeg® 400 MO; Mapeg® 400 MOT; Mapeg® 400 MS; Mapeg® 600 DO; Mapeg® 600 DOT; Mapeg® 600 DS; Mapeg® 600 MOT; Mapeg® 600 MS; Mapeg® 1000 MS; Mapeg® 6000 DS; Mapeg® EGDS; Mapeg® EGMS; Mapeg® S-40K; Methocel® A4C Premium; Methocel® A4M Premium; Methocel® A15LV Premium; Methocel® E3 Premium; Methocel® E4M Premium; Methocel® E6 Premium; Methocel® E15LV Premium; Methocel® E50LV Premium; Methocel® E50P; Methocel® K3 Premium; Methocel® K4M Premium; Methocel® K15M Premium; Methocel® K100LV Premium; Methocel® K100M Premium; Miglyol® 810; Miglyol® 812; Miglyol® 840; Miglyol® 8810; Monawet MO-70R; Monomuls® 60-10; Monomuls® 60-15; Monomuls® 60-20; Monomuls® 60-25; Monomuls® 60-25/2; Monomuls® 60-30; Monomuls® 60-35; Monomuls® 60-40; Monomuls® 60-45; Monomuls® 90-10; Monomuls® 90-15; Monomuls® 90-20; Monomuls® 90-25/2; Monomuls® 90-25/5; Monomuls® 90-30; Monomuls® 90-35; Monomuls® 90-40; Monomuls® 90-45; Myvatex® TL

Nikkol BC-23; Nikkol BC-25TX; Nikkol BC-30TX; Nikkol BC-40TX; Nikkol BPS-5; Nikkol DDP-2; Nikkol OTP-100S; Nikkol PBC-31; Nikkol PMS-1C; Nikkol PMS-1CSE; Nikkol TL-10, TL-10EX; Nikkol TO-10; Nikkol TS-10; Nikkol Decaglyn 1-IS; Nikkol Decaglyn 1-L; Nikkol Decaglyn 1-LN; Nikkol Decaglyn 1-M; Nikkol Decaglyn 1-O; Nikkol Decaglyn 1-S

OHlan®; Ovothin 170; Ovothin 180; Ovothin 200

Pecosil® PS-100; Pecosil® WDS-100; Pegosperse® 50 DS; Phosal® 50 PG; Phospholipid PTD; Phospholipid PTL; Phospholipid PTZ; Plasdone® C-15; Plasdone® C-30; Polyox® WSR 205; Polyox® WSR 301; Polyox® WSR 303; Polyox® WSR 308; Polyox® WSR 1105; Polyox® WSR 3333; Polyox® WSR N-10; Polyox® WSR N-12K; Polyox® WSR N-60K; Polyox® WSR N-80; Polyox® WSR N-750; Polyox® WSR N-3000; Polyox® WSR Coagulant

Rhodasurf® ON-870; Ritahydrox; Ritawax AEO

Silwet® L-77; Silwet® L-7500; Silwet® L-7602; Simulsol® 58; Simulsol® 78; Simulsol® 98; Simulsol® CS; Simulsol® P4; Simulsol® P23; Solulan® 25; Solulan® 97; Solulan® 98; Solulan® PB-2; Solulan® PB-5; Solulan® PB-10; Solulan® PB-20; Standamul® CTA; Standamul® CTV; Supralate® C; Synperonic PE/F127

Tagat® L2; Tagat® O2; Tagat® S2; Tetronic® 304; Texapon® K-12 Powd.; Texapon® K-1296 Powd.; Texapon® Z; Texapon® Z Highly Conc. Needles; Texapon® Z Highly Conc. Powder; T-Maz® 20; T-Maz® 28; T-Maz® 60K; T-Maz® 61; T-Maz® 65K; T-Maz® 80; T-Maz® 80K; T-Maz® 80KLM; T-Maz® 81; T-Maz® 81K; T-Maz® 85; Tylose® MH Grades; Tylose® MHB

Vee Gee Pharmaceutical Gelatins; Volpo CS-20

White Swan; Wickenol® 155; Wickenol® 156; Wickenol® 158; Wickenol® 159; Wickenol® 160; Wickenol® 161; Wickenol® 171; Witafrol® 7420

Yeoman

Chemicals: Alumina

Butylene glycol dicaprylate/caprate

Calcium phosphate dibasic; Carbomer; Carbomer 934; Carbomer 940; Carbomer 941; Cocohydroxyethyl PEG-imidazolinium chloride phosphate

Diethanolamine; Diethylaminoethyl stearate; Dimethicone copolyol; Dimethicone copolyol phosphate; Dioctyl adipate; Dioctyl succinate

EO/PO block polymer or copolymer

Glyceryl caprylate/caprate; Glyceryl cocoate; Glyceryl dilaurate; Glyceryl dilaurate SE; Glyceryl isostearate; Glyceryl mono shortening

Hexyl laurate; Hydrogenated lard glyceride; Hydrogenated lard glycerides; Hydrogenated palm glyceride; Hydrogenated palm glycerides; Hydrogenated soybean glycerides; Hydrogenated soy glyceride; Hydrogenated tallow glyceride; Hydrogenated tallow glycerides; Hydroxypropyl methylcellulose

Isocetyl alcohol; Isocetyl stearoyl stearate

Dispersants *(cont'd.)*

Laneth-5; Laneth-15; Lard glyceride; Lard glycerides; Lauramidopropyl PEG-dimonium chloride phosphate

Methylcellulose; Methyl hydroxyethylcellulose

Octoxynol-9; Octyl hydroxystearate; Octyl pelargonate; Octyl stearate; Oleyl erucate

Palm glyceride; Palm glycerides; PEG-2M; PEG-7M; PEG-9M; PEG-14M; PEG-20M; PEG-23M; PEG-45M; PEG-90M; PEG-115M; PEG-20 almond glycerides; PEG-60 almond glycerides; PEG-5 castor oil; PEG-8 castor oil; PEG-9 castor oil; PEG-15 castor oil; PEG-20 castor oil; PEG-30 castor oil; PEG-36 castor oil; PEG-40 castor oil; PEG-50 castor oil; PEG-56 castor oil; PEG-200 castor oil; PEG-20 corn glycerides; PEG-60 corn glycerides; PEG-4 dilaurate; PEG-6 dilaurate; PEG-8 dilaurate; PEG-12 dilaurate; PEG-20 dilaurate; PEG-32 dilaurate; PEG-75 dilaurate; PEG-150 dilaurate; PEG-4 dioleate; PEG-6 dioleate; PEG-8 dioleate; PEG-12 dioleate; PEG-20 dioleate; PEG-4 distearate; PEG-6 distearate; PEG-8 distearate; PEG-12 distearate; PEG-20 distearate; PEG-32 distearate; PEG-75 distearate; PEG-150 distearate; PEG-8 ditallate; PEG-12 ditallate; PEG-7 glyceryl cocoate; PEG-20 glyceryl laurate; PEG-20 glyceryl oleate; PEG-20 glyceryl stearate; PEG-27 lanolin; PEG-40 lanolin; PEG-70 lanolin; PEG-85 lanolin; PEG-4 laurate; PEG-6 laurate; PEG-8 laurate; PEG-12 laurate; PEG-20 laurate; PEG-32 laurate; PEG-75 laurate; PEG-150 laurate; PEG-4 oleate; PEG-6 oleate; PEG-8 oleate; PEG-12 oleate; PEG-20 oleate; PEG-32 oleate; PEG-75 oleate; PEG-150 oleate; PEG-300 oleate; PEG-5 phytosterol; PEG-10 phytosterol; PEG-15 phytosterol; PEG-20 phytosterol; PEG-25 phytosterol; PEG-30 phytosterol; PEG-10-PPG-10 glyceryl stearate; PEG-10 propylene glycol; PEG-80 sorbitan laurate; PEG-20 sorbitan tritallate; PEG-4 stearate; PEG-6 stearate; PEG-6-32 stearate; PEG-8 stearate; PEG-12 stearate; PEG-20 stearate; PEG-24 stearate; PEG-32 stearate; PEG-75 stearate; PEG-150 stearate; PEG-300 stearate; PEG-8 tallate; PEG-12 tallate; Phosphatidylcholine; Poloxamine 304; Poloxamine 504; Poloxamine 701; Poloxamine 702; Poloxamine 704; Poloxamine 707; Poloxamine 901; Poloxamine 904; Poloxamine 908; Poloxamine 1101; Poloxamine 1102; Poloxamine 1104; Poloxamine 1107; Poloxamine 1301; Poloxamine 1302; Poloxamine 1304; Poloxamine 1307; Poloxamine 1501; Poloxamine 1502; Poloxamine 1504; Poloxamine 1508; Polyethylene oxide; Polyglyceryl-10 decaoleate; Polyglyceryl-10 decastearate; Polyglyceryl-6 dioleate; Polyglyceryl-4 isostearate; Polyglyceryl-10 isostearate; Polyglyceryl-10 laurate; Polyglyceryl-10 linoleate; Polyglyceryl-10 myristate; Polyglyceryl-10 octaoleate; Polyglyceryl-3 oleate; Polyglyceryl-10 oleate; Polyglyceryl-3 stearate; Polyglyceryl-10 stearate; Polyglyceryl-10 tetraoleate; Polysorbate 80; Polysorbate 81; PPG-4 ceteth-1; PPG-4-ceteth-10; PPG-8-ceteth-1; PPG-2 lanolin alcohol ether; PPG-5 lanolin alcohol ether; PPG-3-laureth-9; PPG-15 stearyl ether; Propylene glycol myristate; Propylene glycol stearate; PVM/MA copolymer; PVP

Sodium methyl cocoyl taurate; Sorbitan tristearate; Steareth-20; Sucrose cocoate; Sucrose distearate; Sucrose stearate; Sunflower seed oil glyceride; Sunflower seed oil glycerides

Tallow glyceride; Tallow glycerides

Drying agents. *See Desiccants*

Dyes. *See Colorants*

Emollients

Trade names: AA USP; Abil® EM-90; Abil®-Wax 2434; Abil®-Wax 9801; Abil®-Wax 9814; A-C® 617, 617A; Acylan; Adol® 61 NF; Adol® 90 NF; Aethoxal® B; Akoext SB; Alcolan® 36W; Alcolan® 40; Aldo® PGHMS; Aldo® TC; Amerchol® 400; Amerchol® BL; Amerchol® C; Amerchol® CAB; Amerchol® H-9; Amerchol L-101®; Amerchol® L-500; Amerlate® P; Amerlate® W; Anhydrous Lanolin Grade 1; Anhydrous Lanolin Grade 2; Anhydrous Lanolin P.80; Anhydrous Lanolin P.95; Anhydrous Lanolin Superfine; Anhydrous Lanolin USP; Anhydrous Lanolin USP Cosmetic; Anhydrous Lanolin USP Cosmetic AA; Anhydrous Lanolin USP Cosmetic Grade; Anhydrous Lanolin USP Deodorized AAA; Anhydrous Lanolin USP Pharmaceutical; Anhydrous Lanolin USP Pharmaceutical; Anhydrous Lanolin USP Pharmaceutical Grade;

Emollients *(cont'd.)*

Anhydrous Lanolin USP Pharmaceutical Light Grade; Anhydrous Lanolin USP Superfine; Anhydrous Lanolin USP Ultrafine; Anhydrous Lanolin USP X-tra Deodorized; Aqualose L75; Aqualose L75/50; Argobase EU; Argobase EUC 2

Britol®; Brookswax™ G

Cachalot® S-56; Capmul® EMG; Capmul® GDL; Capmul® GMO; Capmul® GMS; Caprol® 3GO; Caprol® 6G2O; Caprol® 10G4O; Caprol® 10G10O; Captex® 200; Captex® 200-E6; Captex® 300; Captex® 350; Captex® 800; Captex® 810A; Captex® 810D; Captex® 8227; Carnation®; Castor Oil USP; Cegesoft® C 17; Ceraphyl® 28; Ceraphyl® 31; Ceraphyl® 45; Ceraphyl® 50; Ceraphyl® 55; Ceraphyl® 140; Ceraphyl® 140-A; Ceraphyl® 230; Ceraphyl® 368; Ceraphyl® 375; Ceraphyl® 424; Ceraphyl® 494; Ceraphyl® 791; Ceraphyl® 847; Ceraphyl® ICA; Cetina; Cetiol®; Cetiol® 868; Cetiol® A; Cetiol® B; Cetiol® HE; Cetiol® LC; Cetiol® MM; Cetiol® OE; Cetiol® S; Cetiol® SB45; Cetiol® SN; Cetiol® V; Cholesterol NF; Clearlan® 1650; Cobee 76; Corona PNL; Corona Lanolin; Coronet Lanolin; Cosmetic Lanolin; Cosmetic Lanolin Anhydrous USP; Cosmetol® X; Cremba; Crodalan 0477; Crodalan AWS; Crodalan LA; Crodamol CAP; Crodamol CSP; Crodamol GTCC; Crodamol MM; Crodamol PMP; Crodamol PTC; Crodamol PTIS; Crodamol SS; Crodamol W; Crodesta SL-40; Crovol A40; Crovol A70; Crovol M40; Crovol M70; Crystal® O; Crystal® Crown

Diamond Quality®; Dipsal; Distilled Lipolan; D.P.P.G; Drewmulse® POE-SML; Dynacerin® 660

Emery® 1650; Emery® 1656; Emery® 1660; Emery® 1732; Emery® 1740; Emery® 1747; Emery® HP-2050; Emery® HP-2060; Escalol® 557; Ethoxylan® 1685; Ethoxylan® 1686; Eumulgin® B1; Eumulgin® B2; Eutanol® G; Eutanol® G16

Fancol Acel; Fancol CAB; Fancol HL; Fancol Karite Extract; Fancol LA; Fancol LA-15; Fancol LAO; Fancor IPL; Fancor LFA; Fancor Lanwax; Fancorsil A; Fancorsil P; Fluilan; Fluilan AWS; Forlan C-24

Gastric Mucin N.N.R; Gloria®; Glucam® E-20 Distearate; Glucam® P-20 Distearate; Glycerine (Pharmaceutical)

Hartolan; Hydrokote® 175; Hydrokote® M; Hydroxylan; Hyfatol 16-98; Hyfatol 18-95; Hyfatol 18-98

Incrocas 35; Ivarlan™ Light

Kaydol®; Kemester® 1418; Kemester® 5721; Kemester® EGDL; Kemester® GDL; Kessco® 653; Kessco® PEG 200 DL; Kessco® PEG 200 DO; Kessco® PEG 200 DS; Kessco® PEG 200 ML; Kessco® PEG 200 MO; Kessco® PEG 200 MS; Kessco® PEG 300 DL; Kessco® PEG 300 DO; Kessco® PEG 300 DS; Kessco® PEG 300 MO; Kessco® PEG 300 MS; Kessco® PEG 400 DL; Kessco® PEG 400 DO; Kessco® PEG 400 DS; Kessco® PEG 400 ML; Kessco® PEG 400 MO; Kessco® PEG 400 MS; Kessco® PEG 600 DL; Kessco® PEG 600 DO; Kessco® PEG 600 DS; Kessco® PEG 600 ML; Kessco® PEG 600 MO; Kessco® PEG 1000 DL; Kessco® PEG 1000 DO; Kessco® PEG 1000 DS; Kessco® PEG 1000 ML; Kessco® PEG 1000 MO; Kessco® PEG 1000 MS; Kessco® PEG 1540 DL; Kessco® PEG 1540 DO; Kessco® PEG 1540 DS; Kessco® PEG 1540 ML; Kessco® PEG 1540 MO; Kessco® PEG 1540 MS; Kessco® PEG 4000 DL; Kessco® PEG 4000 DO; Kessco® PEG 4000 DS; Kessco® PEG 4000 ML; Kessco® PEG 4000 MO; Kessco® PEG 4000 MS; Kessco® PEG 6000 DL; Kessco® PEG 6000 DO; Kessco® PEG 6000 DS; Kessco® PEG 6000 ML; Kessco® PEG 6000 MO; Kessco® PEG 6000 MS; Kessco® Glyceryl Monostearate Pure; Klearol®; Koster Keunen Beeswax; Koster Keunen Synthetic Spermaceti

Lameform® TGI; Lanacet® 1705; Lanaetex CO; Lan-Aqua-Sol 50; Lan-Aqua-Sol 100; Lanesta P; Lanesta SA-30; Laneto 50; Laneto 100; Laneto 100-Flaked; Laneto AWS; Lanette® 14; Lanette® 16; Lanette® 18; Lanette® 18-22; Lanette® 18 DEO; Lanette® 22 Flakes; Lanette® O; Lanexol AWS; Lanfrax® 1776; Lanfrax® 1779; Lanogel® 21; Lanogel® 31; Lanogel® 41; Lanogel® 61; Lanolin Anhydrous USP; Lanolin Anhydrous USP; Lanolin Pharmaceutical; Lanolin U.S.P; Lanolin USP; Lanotein AWS 30; Lantrol® 1673; Lantrol® 1674; Lantrol® HP-2073; Lantrol® HP-2074; Lexate® PX; Lexemul® 515; Lexemul® AR; Lexemul® AS; Lexemul® CS-20; Lexemul® PEG-200 DL; Lexol® 60; Lexol® 3975; Lexol® EHP; Lexol® GT-865; Lexol® IPP; Lexol® IPP-A; Lexol® IPP-NF; Lexol® PG-800; Lipo 320; Lipocol; Lipolan 31; Lipolan 31-20; Lipolan Distilled; Lipolan S; Lipovol P; Lipovol SES; Lipovol SES-S; Liquid Absorption Base Type A; Liquid Absorption Base Type T; Luvitol® EHO

Mackol 18; Macol® 57; Macol® CA 30P; Mapeg® 200 DO; Mapeg® 200 ML; Mapeg® 400 DO; Mazawax® 163R; Mazol® 159; Mazol® GMS-D; Medilan™; Miglyol® 810; Miglyol® 818; Miglyol® 829; Miglyol® 840; Miglyol® 8810; MOD; M.O.D. WL 2949; Modulan®; Myritol® 318; Myritol® PC

Nacol® 14-98; Nacol® 16-95; Nacol® 16-98; Nacol® 18-98; Nacol® 20-95; Nacol® 22-97; Nacolox®; Nafol® C14-C22; Neobee® 1053; Neobee® 1054; Neobee® M-5; Nikkol BPS-5;

Emollients *(cont'd.)*

Nikkol Batyl Alcohol 100, EX; Nikkol Behenyl Alcohol 65, 80; Nikkol Chimyl Alcohol 100; Novol NF

OHlan®; Orange Wax; Orange Wax, Deodorized; Orzol®

Pecosil® DCU; Pecosil® WDS-100; Pegosperse® 50 DS; Pelemol® 89; Pelemol® BB; Pelemol® CL; Pelemol® CP; Pelemol® CR; Pelemol® DIPS; Pelemol® DO; Pelemol® EE; Pelemol® G7A; Pelemol® G45L; Pelemol® GTB; Pelemol® HAB; Pelemol® ICB; Pelemol® ICIS; Pelemol® ICS; Pelemol® IDO; Pelemol® IN-2; Pelemol® ISB; Pelemol® ISL; Pelemol® L2A; Pelemol® ML; Pelemol® MM; Pelemol® MS; Pelemol® ODM; Pelemol® OP; Pelemol® PTL; Pelemol® TGC; Penreco Amber; Penreco Blond; Penreco Cream; Penreco Lily; Penreco Regent; Penreco Royal; Penreco Snow; Penreco Super; Penreco Ultima; Pharmaceutical Lanolin; Phosal® NAT-50-PG; Polyaldo® DGHO; Pricerine 9088; Promulgen® D; Promulgen® G; Propylene Glycol USP/FCC Ultra Grade; Protegin®; Protegin® W; Protegin® WX; Protegin® X; Protol®; Protopet® Alba; Protopet® White 1S; Protopet® White 2L; Protopet® White 3C; Protopet® Yellow 2A; Pureco® 76

Rhodasurf® L-4; Rhodasurf® L-25; Rhodasurf® LA-12; RITA IPM; RITA IPP; Ritacetyl®; Ritachol®; Ritachol® 4000; Ritahydrox; Ritalan®; Ritalan® AWS; RITA Lanolin; Ritasol; Ritawax; Ritawax AEO; Ritawax ALA; Ritawax Super; Robane®; Ross Spermaceti Wax Substitute 573

Sebase; Simulsol® PS20; Softigen® 701; Softigen® 767; Softisan® 100; Softisan® 378; Softisan® 601; Softisan® 649; Solan; Solan 50; Solulan® 97; Solulan® 98; Solulan® PB-2; Solulan® PB-5; Solulan® PB-10; Solulan® PB-20; Sorba; Stamere® CK-S; Stamere® N-325; Stamere® N-350; Stamere® N-350 S; Stamere® NI; Standamul® 302; Standamul® 318; Standamul® 1414-E; Standamul® 7061; Standamul® 7063; Standamul® CTA; Standamul® CTV; Standamul® G-32/36; Standamul® G-32/36 Stearate; Standamul® HE; Steraffine; Sterotex®; Sunyl® 80; Sunyl® 90; Super Corona Lanolin; Superfine Lanolin; Super Refined® Cottonseed Oil; Super Refined® Olive Oil; Super Refined® Sesame Oil; Super-Sat; Super-Sat AWS-4; Super-Sat AWS-24; Super Solan Flaked; Super Sterol Ester; Supraene®; Syncrowax ERL-C; Syncrowax HGL-C; Syncrowax HR-C

Unihydag Wax-18

Vigilan; Vigilan AWS; Volpo 3; Volpo 5; Volpo 10; Volpo 20

Wecobee® FS; Wecobee® HTR; Wecobee® M; Wecobee® R Mono; Wecobee® S; Wecobee® SS; W.G.S. Cetyl Palmitate; W.G.S. Synaceti 116 NF/USP; White Swan; Wickenol® 142; Wickenol® 155; Wickenol® 156; Wickenol® 158; Wickenol® 159; Wickenol® 160; Wickenol® 161; Wickenol® 171

Yelkin F; Yelkin G; Yelkin P; Yeoman; York Krystal Kleer Castor Oil; York USP Castor Oil

Chemicals: Acetylated lanolin; Acetylated lanolin alcohol; Agar; Apricot kernel oil; Arachidyl alcohol; Arachidyl propionate; Avocado oil

Batyl alcohol; Behenyl alcohol; Behenyl behenate; Butylene glycol dicaprylate/caprate

C10-30 cholesterol/lanosterol esters; C12-15 alkyl lactate; C12-15 pareth-12; C18-36 acid glycol ester; C18-36 acid triglyceride; Caprylic/capric diglyceryl succinate; Caprylic/capric/ disuccinic triglyceride; Caprylic/capric/lauric triglyceride; Caprylic/capric/linoleic triglyceride; Caprylic/capric/stearic triglyceride; Caprylic/capric triglyceride; Castor oil; Ceteareth-10; Ceteareth-12; Ceteareth-14; Ceteareth-15; Ceteareth-20; Ceteareth-30; Cetearyl alcohol; Cetearyl isononanoate; Cetearyl octanoate; Cetearyl palmitate; Cetrimonium chloride; Cetyl alcohol; Cetyl dimethicone; Cetyl dimethicone copolyol; Cetyl esters; Cetyl glyceryl ether; Cetyl lactate; Cetyl palmitate; Cetyl ricinoleate; Cocoa butter; Coco caprylate/caprate; Coconut oil

Decyl oleate; Dibutyl adipate; Dihydroabietyl behenate; Diisopropyl adipate; Diisopropyl sebacate; Dimethicone copolyol eicosanate; Dimethicone copolyol undecylenate; Dioctyl adipate; Dioctyl calcium sulfosuccinate; Dioctyl cyclohexane; Dioctyl ether; Dioctylmalate; Dioctyl sodium sulfosuccinate; Dioctyl succinate; Dipropylene glycol salicylate

Glycereth-7 benzoate; Glycereth-5 lactate; Glycereth-7 triacetate; Glycerin; Glyceryl dilaurate; Glyceryl tricaprate/caprylate; Glyceryl triheptanoate; Glycol dilaurate

Hexyl laurate; Hybrid safflower oil; Hydrogenated coco-glycerides; Hydrogenated palm oil; Hydrogenated polyisobutene; Hydrogenated tallow glyceride lactate; Hydrogenated vegetable oil; Hydrolyzed collagen; Hydroxylated lanolin

Isobutyl stearate; Isocetyl behenate; Isocetyl isostearate; Isocetyl stearate; Isocetyl stearoyl stearate; Isodecyl oleate; Isononyl isononanoate; Isopropyl lanolate; Isopropyl laurate; Isopropyl myristate; Isopropyl palmitate; Isopropyl stearate; Isostearyl behenate; Isostearyl isostearate; Isostearyl lactate; Isostearyl neopentanoate

Emollients *(cont'd.)*

Laneth-5; Laneth-15; Lanolin; Lanolin acid; Lanolin oil; Lanolin wax; Lauramine oxide; Laureth-23; Laureth-2 acetate; Lauryl lactate; Lecithin; Linseed oil

Methyl gluceth-20 distearate; Myreth-3 myristate; Myristyl lactate; Myristyl myristate; Myristyl stearate

Neopentyl glycol dicaprylate/dicaprate

Octyldodecanol; 2-Octyldodecyl erucate; Octyldodecyl myristate; Octyldodecyl stearate; Octyldodecyl stearoyl stearate; Octyl hydroxystearate; Octyl isononanoate; Octyl palmitate; Octyl pelargonate; Octyl stearate; Oleth-3; Oleth-5; Oleth-25; Oleyl alcohol; Oleyl erucate; Oleyl oleate; Olive oil; Orange wax

PEG-20 almond glycerides; PEG-60 almond glycerides; PEG-6 caprylic/capric glycerides; PEG-20 corn glycerides; PEG-60 corn glycerides; PEG-6 dilaurate; PEG-8 dilaurate; PEG-12 dilaurate; PEG-20 dilaurate; PEG-32 dilaurate; PEG-75 dilaurate; PEG-150 dilaurate; PEG-4 dioleate; PEG-6 dioleate; PEG-12 dioleate; PEG-20 dioleate; PEG-32 dioleate; PEG-75 dioleate; PEG-150 dioleate; PEG-4 distearate; PEG-6 distearate; PEG-8 distearate; PEG-12 distearate; PEG-20 distearate; PEG-32 distearate; PEG-75 distearate; PEG-150 distearate; PEG-7 glyceryl cocoate; PEG-40 hydrogenated castor oil; PEG-60 hydrogenated castor oil; PEG-100 hydrogenated castor oil; PEG-20 hydrogenated lanolin; PEG-24 hydrogenated lanolin; PEG-27 lanolin; PEG-40 lanolin; PEG-60 lanolin; PEG-70 lanolin; PEG-75 lanolin; PEG-85 lanolin; PEG-4 laurate; PEG-6 laurate; PEG-12 laurate; PEG-20 laurate; PEG-32 laurate; PEG-75 laurate; PEG-150 laurate; PEG-4 oleate; PEG-6 oleate; PEG-12 oleate; PEG-20 oleate; PEG-32 oleate; PEG-75 oleate; PEG-150 oleate; PEG-5 phytosterol; PEG-10 phytosterol; PEG-15 phytosterol; PEG-20 phytosterol; PEG-25 phytosterol; PEG-30 phytosterol; PEG-6 propylene glycol dicaprylate/dicaprate; PEG-25 propylene glycol stearate; PEG-4 stearate; PEG-6 stearate; PEG-8 stearate; PEG-12 stearate; PEG-20 stearate; PEG-32 stearate; PEG-75 stearate; PEG-100 stearate; PEG-150 stearate; Pentaerythrityl tetracaprylate/caprate; Pentaerythrityl tetraisostearate; Pentaerythrityl tetralaurate; Petrolatum; Polyglyceryl-10 decaoleate; Polyglyceryl-3 diisostearate; Polyglyceryl-6 dioleate; Polyglyceryl-10 hexaoleate; PPG-10 butanediol; PPG-30 cetyl ether; PPG-2 lanolin alcohol ether; PPG-5 lanolin alcohol ether; PPG-10 lanolin alcohol ether; PPG-20 lanolin alcohol ether; PPG-5-laureth-5; PPG-20 methyl glucose ether distearate; PPG-2 myristyl ether propionate; PPG-12-PEG-50 lanolin; PPG-12-PEG-65 lanolin oil; PPG-15 stearyl ether; Propylene glycol dioctanoate; Propylene glycol dipelargonate; Propylene glycol laurate; Propylene glycol ricinoleate

Quaternium-22; Quaternium-26

Rice starch

Safflower oil; Sesame oil; Shea butter; Shea butter extract; Squalene; Starch glycerin; Stearoxy dimethicone; Stearyl alcohol; Stearyl heptanoate; Sunflower seed oil; Sweet almond oil

Tetradecyleicosanol; Tetradecyleicosyl stearate; Tribehenin; Tridecyl neopentanoate; Tridecyl stearate; Trilaurin; Trioctanoin; Trioctyldodecyl citrate; Triolein; Triundecanoin

Wheat starch

Emulsifiers

Trade names: Abil® EM-90; Abil® WE 09; Ablunol S-20; Ablunol S-40; Ablunol S-60; Ablunol S-80; Ablunol S-85; Ablunol T-20; Ablunol T-40; Ablunol T-60; Ablunol T-80; Accomid PK; Acconon 200-MS; Acconon 400-ML; Acconon 400-MO; Acconon 400-MS; Acconon 1300 MS; Acconon CA-5; Acconon CA-8; Acconon CA-9; Acconon CA-15; Acconon CON; Acconon E; Acconon SA-2; Acconon TGH; Acconon W230; Acritamer® 934; Acritamer® 934P; Acritamer® 940; Acritamer® 941; Agar Agar NF Flake #1; Albagel Premium USP 4444; Alcolan®; Alcolan® 36W; Alcolan® 40; Alcolec® Granules; Alcolec® Z-3; Aldo® MLD; Aldo® MO FG; Aldo® MR; Aldo® MS; Aldo® MS-20 KFG; Aldo® MSA; Aldo® MSC; Aldo® MSD; Aldo® PGHMS; Aldosperse® O-20 FG; Aldosperse® O-20 KFG; Algon LA 40; Algon LA 80; Algon OL 60; Algon OL 70; Algon ST 50; Algon ST 80; Algon ST 100; Algon ST 200; Algon ST 400; Algon ST 500; Algon ST 1000; Alkamuls® EL-620; Alkamuls® EL-719; Alkamuls® PSML-20; Alkamuls® PSMS-4; Amerchol® 400; Amerchol® BL; Amerchol® C; Amerchol® H-9; Amerchol L-101®; Amerchol® L-500; Amerlate® P; Amerlate® W; Aminoxid WS 35; Amonyl® 265 BA; Amonyl® 380 BA; Amphisol® K; Anhydrous Lanolin Grade 1; Anhydrous Lanolin Grade 2; Anhydrous Lanolin P.80; Anhydrous Lanolin P.95; Anhydrous Lanolin Superfine; Anhydrous Lanolin USP Cosmetic Grade; Anhydrous Lanolin USP Pharmaceutical Grade;

Emulsifiers *(cont'd.)*

Anhydrous Lanolin USP X-tra Deodorized; Aqualose L75; Aqualose L75/50; Argobase EU; Argobase EUC 2; Arlacel® 20; Arlacel® 40; Arlacel® 60; Arlacel® 80; Arlacel® 83; Armotan® MO; Arquad® DM18B-90; Asol

Bentonite USP BC 670; BFP 64 O; BFP 74E; Britex C; Britex C 100; Britex C 200; Britex CO 220; Britex CS 110; Britex CS 200 B; Britex CS 250; Britex L 20; Britex L 40; Britex L 100; Britex L 230; Britex O 20; Britex O 100; Britex O 200; Britex S 20; Britex S 100; Britex S 200

Cab-O-Sil® H-5; Cab-O-Sil® L-90; Cab-O-Sil® LM-150; Cab-O-Sil® M-5; Cab-O-Sil® MS-55; Capmul® EMG; Capmul® GDL; Capmul® GMO; Capmul® GMS; Capmul® MCM; Capmul® MCM-90; Capmul® MCMC8; Capmul® POE-L; Capmul® POE-S; Caprol® S; Caprol® 3GO; Caprol® 3GS; Caprol® 6G2O; Caprol® 6G2S; Caprol® 10G4O; Caprol® 10G10O; Caprol® PGE860; Capsulec 51-SB; Capsulec 51-UB; Capsulec 56-SB; Capsulec 56-UB; Capsulec 62-SB; Capsulec 62-UB; Captex® 200-E6; Carbopol® 907; Carbopol® 910; Carbopol® 934; Carbopol® 934P; Carbopol® 940; Carbopol® 941; Carbopol® 971P; Carbopol® 974P; Carbopol® 981; Carbopol® 1342; Carbopol® 2984; Carbopol® 5984; Carbopol® ETD 2050; Centrolex® P; Cerasynt® 303; Cerasynt® 840; Cerasynt® 945; Cerasynt® D; Cerasynt® GMS; Cerasynt® IP; Cerasynt® M; Cerasynt® MN; Cerasynt® PA; Cerasynt® Q; Cerasynt® SD; Cerasynt® WM; Cerex ELS 50; Cetomacrogol 1000 BP; Cetostearyl Alcohol NF; Ches® 500; Cholesterol NF; Cholesterol NF; Cithrol GML N/E; Cithrol GDS N/E; Cithrol GDS S/E; Cithrol GML N/E; Cithrol GMO N/E; Cithrol GMO S/E; Cithrol GMR N/E; Cithrol GMR S/E; Cithrol GMS Acid Stable; Cithrol GMS N/E; Cithrol GMS S/E; Cithrol PGML N/E; Cithrol PGML S/E; Cithrol PGMO N/E; Cithrol PGMR N/E; Cithrol PGMR S/E; Cithrol PGMS N/E; Cithrol PGMS S/E; Colloid 488T; Colloid 602; Corona PNL; Corona Lanolin; Coronet Lanolin; Cosmetic Lanolin; Cosmowax J; Cosmowax K; CPC; CPC Sumquat 6060; Creamjel; Cremba; Cremophor® A 11; Cremophor® A 25; Cremophor® EL; Cremophor® RH 40; Cremophor® RH 410; Cremophor® RH 455; Cremophor® S 9; Crill 1; Crill 3; Crill 4; Crill 6; Crill 35; Crill 43; Crill 45; Crill 50; Crillet 1; Crillet 2; Crillet 3; Crillet 4; Crillet 6; Crillet 11; Crillet 31; Crillet 35; Crillet 41; Crillet 45; Crodacol C-95NF; Crodacol S-95NF; Crodafos N-3 Acid; Crodalan 0477; Crodalan AWS; Crodesta F-10; Crodesta F-50; Crodesta F-110; Crodesta F-160; Crodet L4; Crodet L8; Crodet L12; Crodet L24; Crodet L40; Crodet L100; Crodet S4; Crodet S8; Crodet S12; Crodet S24; Crodet S40; Crodet S100; Crodex A; Crodex C; Crodex N; Croduret 50; Cromul EM 0685; Crossential Oleic; Crovol A40; Crovol A70; Crovol M40; Crovol M70; Cutina® FS 25 Flakes; Cutina® FS 45 Flakes; Cutina® KD16

Dehydag® Wax E; Dehydol® LS 2 DEO; Dehydol® LS 3 DEO; Dehydol® LS 4 DEO; Dehydol® PID 6; Dehydol® PIT 6; Dehymuls® E; Dehymuls® F; Dehymuls® FCE; Dehymuls® HRE 7; Dehymuls® SML; Dehymuls® SMO; Dehymuls® SMS; Dehymuls® SSO; Dimodan PM; Dimodan PV; DIPA Commercial Grade; DIPA Low Freeze Grade 85; DIPA Low Freeze Grade 90; DIPA NF Grade; Distilled Whole Coconut Oil 6226 6222; Docusate Sodium USP; Drewmulse® 3-1-O; Drewmulse® 6-2-S; Drewmulse® 10-4-O; Drewmulse® 10-8-O; Drewmulse® 10-10-O; Drewmulse® 10-10-S; Drewmulse® 10K; Drewmulse® 85K; Drewmulse® 200K; Drewmulse® 700K; Drewmulse® 900K; Drewmulse® 1128; Drewmulse® GMOK; Drewmulse® HM-100; Drewmulse® POE-SML; Drewmulse® POE-SMO; Drewmulse® POE-SMS; Drewmulse® POE-STS; Drewmulse® SML; Drewmulse® SMO; Drewmulse® SMS; Drewmulse® STS; Drewmulse® TP; Drewmulse® V; Drewmulse® V-SE; Drewpol® 3-1-O; Drewpol® 6-1-O; Drewpol® 10-4-O; Drewpol® 10-10-O; Dulectin; Dur-Em® 117; Dur-Em® 207-E

Eccowet® W-50; Eccowet® W-88; Emalex C-20; Emalex C-30; Emalex C-40; Emalex C-50; Emalex ET-2020; Emalex ET-8020; Emalex ET-8040; Emerest® 2423; Emerest® 2715; Emersol® 6313 NF; Emersol® 6332 NF; Emersol® 6333 NF; Emerwax® 1257; Emerwax® 1266; Emery® 1650; Emery® 1656; Emery® 1660; Emery® 1732; Emery® 1740; Emery® 1747; Emery® HP-2060; Empicol® 0185; Empicol® LXS95; Empiwax SK/BP; Emulgade® SE; Emulgator E 2149; Emulgator E 2155; Emulgator E 2568; Emulmetik™ 970; Emulsifier D-1; Emulsynt® 1055; Epikuron™ 145; Epikuron™ 170; Epikuron™ 200; Epikuron™ H; Espholip; Ethomeen® C/25; Ethosperse® G-26; Ethosperse® LA-4; Ethosperse® LA-12; Ethosperse® LA-23; Ethosperse® SL-20; Ethoxylan® 1685; Ethoxylan® 1686; Ethylan® C160; Ethylan® CF71; Ethylan® GEO8; Ethylan® GL20; Ethylan® GO80; Ethylan® GS60; Ethylan® GT85; Ethylan® L10; Eumulgin® B1; Eumulgin® B2; Eumulgin® B3; Eumulgin® HRE 40; Eumulgin® HRE 60; Eumulgin® O5; Eumulgin® O10; Eumulgin® PRT 36; Eumulgin® PRT 56; Eumulgin® PRT 200; Eumulgin® RO 35; Eumulgin® SML 20; Eumulgin® SMO 20; Eumulgin® SMS 20

Fancol CH; Fancol CO-30; Fancol HCO-25; Fancol LA; Fancol LA-15; Fancol LAO; Fancol VB; Fancor IPL; Fancor LFA; Forlan C-24; Forlanit® E

Emulsifiers *(cont'd.)*

G-1441; Geleol; Glucam® E-20 Distearate; Glycomul® L; Glycomul® O; Glycomul® P; Glycomul® S; Glycomul® SOC; Glycomul® TO; Glycomul® TS; Glycosperse® L-20; Glycosperse® O-5; Glycosperse® O-20; Glycosperse® P-20; Glycosperse® S-20; Glycosperse® TO-20; Glycosperse® TS-20; Granular Gum Ghatti #1; Gum Tragacanth Ribbons and Flakes

Hartolan; Hectabrite® AW; Hectabrite® DP; Hodag 20-L; Hodag 22-L; Hodag 40-L; Hodag 40-O; Hodag 40-R; Hodag 40-S; Hodag 42-L; Hodag 42-O; Hodag 42-S; Hodag 60-L; Hodag 60-S; Hodag 62-O; Hodag 100-S; Hodag 150-S; Hodag GML; Hodag GMO; Hodag GMO-D; Hodag GMR; Hodag GMR-D; Hodag GMS; Hodag GTO; Hodag PE-1803; Hodag PE-1810; Hydroxylan; Hyfatol 16-98; Hypan® SA100H; Hypan® SR150H; Hystrene® 1835; Hystrene® 3022; Hystrene® 4516; Hystrene® 5012; Hystrene® 5016 NF; Hystrene® 7022; Hystrene® 9016; Hystrene® 9022; Hystrene® 9512; Hystrene® 9718 NF

Igepal® CO-630 Special; Imwitor® 191; Imwitor® 312; Imwitor® 375; Imwitor® 742; Imwitor® 780 K; Imwitor® 900; Imwitor® 928; Imwitor® 960 Flakes; Imwitor® 965; Imwitor® 988; Incrocas 35; Incropol CS-20; Incroquat B65C; Incroquat Behenyl TMS; Industrene® 223

Karaya Gum #1 FCC; KELACID®; KELCOLOID® D; KELCOLOID® DH; KELCOLOID® DSF; KELCOLOID® HVF; KELCOLOID® LVF; KELCOLOID® S; KELTONE®; KELVIS®; Kemester® S40; Kemester® S65; Kessco® Glycerol Distearate 386F; Kessco® PEG 200 DL; Kessco® PEG 200 DO; Kessco® PEG 200 DS; Kessco® PEG 200 ML; Kessco® PEG 200 MO; Kessco® PEG 200 MS; Kessco® PEG 300 DL; Kessco® PEG 300 DO; Kessco® PEG 300 DS; Kessco® PEG 300 MO; Kessco® PEG 300 MS; Kessco® PEG 400 DL; Kessco® PEG 400 DO; Kessco® PEG 400 DS; Kessco® PEG 400 ML; Kessco® PEG 400 MO; Kessco® PEG 400 MS; Kessco® PEG 600 DL; Kessco® PEG 600 DO; Kessco® PEG 600 DS; Kessco® PEG 600 ML; Kessco® PEG 600 MO; Kessco® PEG 600 MS; Kessco® PEG 1000 DL; Kessco® PEG 1000 DO; Kessco® PEG 1000 DS; Kessco® PEG 1000 ML; Kessco® PEG 1000 MO; Kessco® PEG 1000 MS; Kessco® PEG 1540 DL; Kessco® PEG 1540 DO; Kessco® PEG 1540 DS; Kessco® PEG 1540 ML; Kessco® PEG 1540 MO; Kessco® PEG 1540 MS; Kessco® PEG 4000 DL; Kessco® PEG 4000 DO; Kessco® PEG 4000 DS; Kessco® PEG 4000 ML; Kessco® PEG 4000 MO; Kessco® PEG 4000 MS; Kessco® PEG 6000 DL; Kessco® PEG 6000 DO; Kessco® PEG 6000 DS; Kessco® PEG 6000 ML; Kessco® PEG 6000 MO; Kessco® PEG 6000 MS; Kessco PGMS; Kessco® Glyceryl Monostearate Pure; Korthix H-NF; Koster Keunen Beeswax; Koster Keunen Emulsifying Wax

Labrafac® CM10; Labrafac® Hydro; Labrafil® M 1944 CS; Labrafil® WL 2609 BS; Lameform® TGI; Lamegin® EE Range; Lamegin® GLP 10, 20; Lamegin® NSL; Lan-Aqua-Sol 50; Lan-Aqua-Sol 100; Lanbritol Wax N21; Laneto 50; Laneto 100; Laneto 100-Flaked; Laneto AWS; Lanette® E; Lanette® Wax SX, SXBP; Lanfrax® 1776; Lanfrax® 1779; Lanogel® 21; Lanogel® 31; Lanogel® 41; Lanogel® 61; Lantrol® HP-2073; Lantrol® HP-2074; Lecigran™ 5750; Lecigran™ 6750; Lecigran™ A; Lecigran™ C; Lecigran™ F; Lecigran™ M; Lecigran™ Super A; Lecigran™ T; Lexate® PX; Lexemul® 55G; Lexemul® 503; Lexemul® 515; Lexemul® AR; Lexemul® AS; Lexemul® CS-20; Lexemul® EGMS; Lexemul® PEG-200 DL; Lipocol; Lipolan 31; Lipolan 31-20; Lipolan Distilled; Locust Bean Gum Pharmaceutical Grade; Loralan-CH; Low I.V. Coconut Oil 6227, 6228

Macol® 1; Macol® 2; Macol® 4; Macol® 27; Macol® 124; Macol® 125; Macol® CPS; Maltrin® M700; Mapeg® 200 DL; Mapeg® 200 DO; Mapeg® 200 ML; Mapeg® 200 MO; Mapeg® 400 DL; Mapeg® 400 DO; Mapeg® 400 DOT; Mapeg® 400 DS; Mapeg® 400 ML; Mapeg® 400 MO; Mapeg® 400 MOT; Mapeg® 400 MS; Mapeg® 600 DO; Mapeg® 600 DOT; Mapeg® 600 DS; Mapeg® 600 MOT; Mapeg® 600 MS; Mapeg® 1000 MS; Mapeg® 6000 DS; Mapeg® EGDS; Mapeg® EGMS; Mapeg® S-40K; Mazamide® CMEA; Mazamide® L-5; Mazawax® 163R; Mazawax® 163SS; Mazol® 165C; Mazol® GMS-90; Mazol® GMS-D; Mazol® GMS-K; Mazol® PGO-31 K; Mazol® PGO-104; MEA Commercial Grade; MEA Low Freeze Grade; MEA Low Iron Grade; MEA Low Iron-Low Freeze Grade; MEA NF Grade; Medilan™; Methocel® A15C Premium; Methocel® A15-LV; Methocel® F4M Premium; Miranol® C2M Conc. NP; Monomuls® 60-10; Monomuls® 60-15; Monomuls® 60-20; Monomuls® 60-25; Monomuls® 60-25/2; Monomuls® 60-30; Monomuls® 60-35; Monomuls® 60-40; Monomuls® 60-45; Monomuls® 90-10; Monomuls® 90-15; Monomuls® 90-20; Monomuls® 90-25; Monomuls® 90-25/2; Monomuls® 90-25/5; Monomuls® 90-30; Monomuls® 90-35; Monomuls® 90-40; Monomuls® 90-O18; Monosteol; Montane® 20; Montane® 40; Montane® 60; Montane® 65; Montane® 80; Montane® 83; Montane® 85; Montane® 481; Montanol® 68; Montanox® 20; Montanox® 20 DF; Montanox® 40; Montanox® 40 DF; Montanox® 60; Montanox® 60 DF; Montanox® 65; Montanox® 80; Montanox® 80 DF; Montanox® 85; Monthyle; Myrj® 45; Myrj® 49; Myrj® 51; Myrj® 52; Myrj®

Emulsifiers *(cont'd.)*

52S; Myrj® 53; Myrj® 59

Nacol® 16-95; Naxolate™ WA-97; Naxolate™ WAG; Niaproof® Anionic Surfactant 4; Nikkol BC-5.5; Nikkol BC-7; Nikkol BC-10TX; Nikkol BC-15TX; Nikkol BC-20TX; Nikkol BC-23; Nikkol BC-25TX; Nikkol BC-30TX; Nikkol BC-40TX; Nikkol BEG-1630; Nikkol BPS-5; Nikkol CO-3; Nikkol DDP-2; Nikkol DGDO; Nikkol DGMO-C; Nikkol DGMS; Nikkol GBW-8; Nikkol GBW-25; Nikkol GBW-125; Nikkol GO-430; Nikkol GO-440; Nikkol GO-460; Nikkol HCO-5; Nikkol HCO-7.5; Nikkol HCO-10; Nikkol HCO-20; Nikkol HCO-30; Nikkol HCO-40; Nikkol HCO-40 Pharm; Nikkol HCO-50; Nikkol HCO-50 Pharm; Nikkol HCO-60; Nikkol HCO-60 Pharm; Nikkol HCO-80; Nikkol HCO-100; Nikkol MYS-1EX; Nikkol MYS-2; Nikkol MYS-4; Nikkol MYS-10; Nikkol MYS-25; Nikkol MYS-40; Nikkol MYS-45; Nikkol MYS-55; Nikkol PBC-31; Nikkol PMS-1C; Nikkol PMS-1CSE; Nikkol SI-10R; Nikkol SI-10T; Nikkol SI-15R; Nikkol SI-15T; Nikkol TDP-2; Nikkol TL-10, TL-10EX; Nikkol TO-10; Nikkol TO-30; Nikkol TO-106; Nikkol TS-10; Nikkol TS-30; Nikkol TS-106; Nikkol Batyl Alcohol 100, EX; Nikkol Chimyl Alcohol 100; Nikkol Decaglyn 1-IS; Nikkol Decaglyn 1-L; Nikkol Decaglyn 1-LN; Nikkol Decaglyn 1-M; Nikkol Decaglyn 1-O; Nikkol Decaglyn 1-S; Nikkol Decaglyn 2-O; Nikkol Decaglyn 2-S; Nissan Monogly M; Nissan Nonion CP-08R; Nissan Nonion DN-202; Nissan Nonion DN-203; Nissan Nonion DN-209; Nissan Nonion LP-20R, LP-20RS; Nissan Nonion LT-221; Nissan Nonion MP-30R; Nissan Nonion OP-80R; Nissan Nonion OP-83RAT; Nissan Nonion OP-85R; Nissan Nonion OT-221; Nissan Nonion PP-40R; Nissan Nonion PT-221; Nissan Nonion SP-60R; Nissan Nonion ST-221; Noramium MS 50

OHlan®; Olepal ISO; Ovothin™ 160; Ovothin 170; Ovothin 180; Ovothin 200

Pecosil® PS-100; Pecosil® PS-100K; Pecosil® WDS-100; Pemulen® TR-1; Pemulen® TR-2; Pharmaceutical Lanolin; Phosal® 50 PG; Phosal® 60 PG; Phosal® NAT-50-PG; PhosPho LCN-TS; Phospholipid PTD; Phospholipid PTL; Phospholipid PTZ; Phospholipon® 80; Phospholipon® 90; Phospholipon® 90 G; Phospholipon® 100, 100G; Phospholipon® CC; Phospholipon® MC; Phospholipon® PG Na; Phospholipon® SG Na; Plurol® Diisostearique; Plurol® Isostearique; Plurol® Oleique WL 1173; Pluronic® F68NF; Pluronic® F87NF; Pluronic® F108NF; Pluronic® F127NF; Pluronic® L44NF; Polawax®; Polawax® A31; Polawax® GP200; Polyaldo® DGHO; Polychol 5; Polychol 10; Polychol 15; Polychol 20; Polychol 40; Polystep® B-3; Powdered Agar Agar Bacteriological Grade; Powdered Agar Agar NF M-100 (Gracilaria); Powdered Agar Agar NF MK-60; Powdered Agar Agar NF MK-80-B; Powdered Agar Agar NF MK-80 (Bacteriological); Powdered Agar Agar NF S-100; Powdered Agar Agar NF S-100-B; Powdered Agar Agar NF S-150; Powdered Agar Agar NF S-150-B; Powdered Agar Agar Type K-60; Powdered Agar Agar Type K-80; Powdered Agar Agar Type K-100; Powdered Agar Agar Type K-150; Powdered Gum Ghatti #1; Powdered Gum Ghatti #2; Powdered Gum Karaya Superfine #1 FCC; Powdered Gum Karaya Superfine XXXX FCC; Powdered Gum Tragacanth BP; Powdered Gum Tragacanth T-150; Powdered Gum Tragacanth T-200; Powdered Gum Tragacanth T-300; Powdered Gum Tragacanth T-400; Powdered Gum Tragacanth T-500; Powdered Gum Tragacanth Type B-1 NF Premium; Powdered Gum Tragacanth Type B-12 NF Premium; Powdered Gum Tragacanth Type C-5 NF; Powdered Gum Tragacanth Type G-1 NF Premium; Powdered Gum Tragacanth Type G-2 NF Premium; Powdered Gum Tragacanth Type G-2S NF Premium; Powdered Gum Tragacanth Type M-3 NF Premium; Powdered Tragacanth Gum Type A/10; Powdered Tragacanth Gum Type E-1; Powdered Tragacanth Gum Type G-3; Powdered Tragacanth Gum Type L; Powdered Tragacanth Gum Type W; Premium Powdered Gum Ghatti G-1; Premium Spray Dried Gum Arabic; Promulgen® D; Promulgen® G; Protegin®; Protegin® W; Protegin® WX; Protegin® X; Prox-onic L 081-05; Prox-onic L 101-05; Prox-onic L 102-02; Prox-onic L 121-09; Prox-onic L 161-05; Prox-onic L 181-05; Prox-onic L 201-02; Prox-onic OA-1/020; Prox-onic OA-2/020; Prox-onic PEG-2000; Prox-onic PEG-10,000; Prox-onic PEG-20,000; Prox-onic PEG-35,000

Renex® 759; Rewopal® CSF 11; Rheodol AO-10; Rheodol AO-15; Rheodol AS-10; Rheodol MO-60; Rheodol MS-50, MS-60, SEM; Rheodol TW-L106, -L120; Rhodasurf® E-15; Rhodasurf® ON-870; Rhodasurf® ON-877; Ricinion; Ritachol®; Ritachol® 1000; Ritachol® 2000; Ritachol® 3000; Ritachol® 4000; Ritahydrox; Ritalan® AWS; RITA Lanolin; Ritawax; Ritawax AEO; Ritawax ALA; Ritawax Super; Ryoto Sugar Ester B-370; Ryoto Sugar Ester L-195; Ryoto Sugar Ester L-595; Ryoto Sugar Ester L-1570; Ryoto Sugar Ester L-1695; Ryoto Sugar Ester LN-195; Ryoto Sugar Ester LWA-1570; Ryoto Sugar Ester M-1695; Ryoto Sugar Ester O-170; Ryoto Sugar Ester O-1570; Ryoto Sugar Ester OWA-1570; Ryoto Sugar Ester P-1570; Ryoto Sugar Ester P-1570S; Ryoto Sugar Ester P-1670; Ryoto Sugar Ester S-170; Ryoto Sugar Ester S-170 Ac; Ryoto Sugar Ester S-270; Ryoto Sugar Ester S-370; Ryoto Sugar Ester S-370F; Ryoto Sugar Ester S-570; Ryoto Sugar Ester S-770; Ryoto Sugar Ester S-970; Ryoto

Emulsifiers *(cont'd.)*

Sugar Ester S-1170; Ryoto Sugar Ester S-1170S; Ryoto Sugar Ester S-1570; Ryoto Sugar Ester S-1670; Ryoto Sugar Ester S-1670S

Sarkosyl® L; Sarkosyl® LC; Seagel L; Sebase; Sellig R 3395; Sepigel 305; Silwet® L-7500; Silwet® L-7602; Simulsol® 58; Simulsol® 78; Simulsol® 98; Simulsol® 165; Simulsol® 989; Simulsol® 1292; Simulsol® 1293; Simulsol® 5719; Simulsol® 5817; Simulsol® CS; Simulsol® M 52; Simulsol® OL 50; Simulsol® P4; Simulsol® P23; S-Maz® 60K; Solulan® 25; Sorbilene ISM; Sorbilene L; Sorbilene L 4; Sorbilene LH; Sorbilene O; Sorbilene O 5; Sorbilene P; Sorbilene S; Sorbilene S 4; Sorbilene TO; Sorbilene TS; Sorbirol ISM; Sorbirol O; Sorbirol P; Sorbirol S; Sorbirol SQ; Sorbirol TO; Sorbirol TS; Sorbitol L; Sorgen 30; Sorgen 40; Sorgen 50; Sorgen 90; Sorgen TW80; Span® 20; Span® 40; Span® 60; Span® 60K; Span® 60 VS; Span® 65; Span® 65K; Span® 85; Split Coconut Oil 6254, 6255; Spray Dried Kordofan Gum Arabic; Standamul® 1414-E; Standamul® HE; Stearate 400 WL 817; Stearate 1500; Stearate 6000 WL 1644; Stripped Coconut Oil 6212, 6256; Sucro Ester 7; Sucro Ester 11; Sucro Ester 15; Sunyl® 80; Sunyl® 90; Super Corona Lanolin; Superfine Lanolin; Super Hartolan; Super-Sat AWS-4; Super-Sat AWS-24; Supralate® C; Syncrowax ERL-C; Syncrowax HGL-C; Syncrowax HR-C; Synperonic NP1; Synperonic NP2; Synperonic NP4; Synperonic NP5; Synperonic NP5.5; Synperonic NP6; Synperonic NP7; Synperonic NP8; Synperonic NP8.5; Synperonic NP8.75; Synperonic NP9; Synperonic NP9.5; Synperonic NP9.75; Synperonic NP10; Synperonic NP12; Synperonic NP13; Synperonic NP15; Synperonic NP17; Synperonic NP20; Synperonic NP25; Synperonic NP30; Synperonic NP30/70; Synperonic NP35; Synperonic NP40; Synperonic NP50; Synperonic OP3; Synperonic OP4.5; Synperonic OP6; Synperonic OP7.5; Synperonic OP8; Synperonic OP10; Synperonic OP10.5; Synperonic OP11; Synperonic OP12.5; Synperonic OP16; Synperonic OP16.5; Synperonic OP20; Synperonic OP25; Synperonic OP30; Synperonic OP40; Synperonic OP40/70; Synperonic PE/F127

Tagat® R40; Tagat® R60; Tagat® R63; Tegin®; Tegin® 4011; Tegin® 4480; Tegin® 4600 NSE; Tegin® M; Tegin® O; Tegin® P; Tegin® Spezial; Tego®-Betaine L-7; Tetronic® 304; Tewax TC 10; Tewax TC 65; Tewax TC 72; Tewax TC 80; Tewax TC 81; Tewax TC 82; Tewax TC 83; Ticaxan® Regular; TIC Pretested® Tragacanth 440; TIPA 99; T-Maz® 20; T-Maz® 28; T-Maz® 60K; T-Maz® 61; T-Maz® 65K; T-Maz® 80; T-Maz® 80K; T-Maz® 80KLM; T-Maz® 81; T-Maz® 81K; T-Maz® 85; Tragacanth Flake No. 27; Tragacanth Gum Ribbon No. 1; Tylose® MH Grades; Tylose® MHB

Uniquart CPC

Vifcoll CCN-40, CCN-40 Powd.; Vigilan; Vigilan AWS; Volpo 3; Volpo 5; Volpo 10; Volpo 20; Volpo CS-20; Volpo L23; Volpo S-2; Volpo S-10; Volpo S-20

Wayhib® S; White Swan; Witafrol® 7420; Witconol™ MST; Witco® Zinc Stearate U.S.P.-D

Yelkin F; Yelkin G; Yelkin P

Chemicals: Acacia; Acetylated lanolin; Acetylated mono- and diglycerides of fatty acids; Acrylates/C10-30 alkyl acrylate crosspolymer; Acrylic acid/acrylonitrogens copolymer; Agar; Albumen; Algin; Alginic acid; 2-Amino-1-butanol; 2-Amino-2-methyl-1,3-propanediol; Apricot kernel oil PEG-6 esters

Batyl alcohol; Beeswax; Behenalkonium chloride; Behenic acid; Bentonite

C12-13 pareth-23; C12-15 pareth-2 phosphate; C18-36 acid glycol ester; Calcium alginate; Calcium carrageenan; Calcium stearoyl lactylate; Carbomer; Carbomer 934; Carbomer 934P; Carbomer 940; Carbomer 941; Carrageenan; Carrageenan extract; Ceteareth-9; Ceteareth-11; Ceteareth-12; Ceteareth-16; Ceteareth-20; Ceteareth-25; Ceteareth-30; Ceteareth-33; Cetearyl alcohol; Cetearyl glucoside; Ceteth-2; Ceteth-5; Ceteth-6; Ceteth-7; Ceteth-10; Ceteth-12; Ceteth-15; Ceteth-16; Ceteth-20; Ceteth-23; Ceteth-24; Ceteth-25; Ceteth-30; Ceteth-40; Cetoleth-22; Cetrimonium chloride; Cetyl alcohol; Cetyl dimethicone copolyol; Cetyl glyceryl ether; Cholesterol; Choleth-24; Cocamide DEA; Cocamide MEA; Cocamidopropylamine oxide; Cocamidopropyl betaine; Coco-betaine; Cocohydroxyethyl PEG-imidazolinium chloride phosphate; Cocohydroxyethyl PEG-imidazolinium chloride phosphate; Coconut acid; Coconut oil; Cocoyl sarcosine; Corn oil PEG-8 esters

DEA-cetyl phosphate; DEA-oleth-3 phosphate; DEA-oleth-10 phosphate; Dextrin; 1,2-Dicaproyl-sn-glycero(3) phosphatidylcholine; Dicocoyl pentaerythrityl distearyl citrate; Diethanolamine; Diethylaminoethyl stearate; Dihydrogenated tallow phthalic acid amide; Diisopropanolamine; Dimethicone copolyol; Dimethicone copolyol phosphate; 1,2-Dimyristoyl-sn-glycero(3) phosphatidylcholine; Dioctyl sodium sulfosuccinate; Disodium cocoamphodiacetate

Emulsifying wax NF; Ethanolamine

Gelatin; Glycereth-26; Glyceryl caprylate; Glyceryl caprylate/caprate; Glyceryl citrate/lactate/

Emulsifiers *(cont'd.)*

linoleate/oleate; Glyceryl cocoate; Glyceryl dilaurate; Glyceryl dilaurate SE; Glyceryl dioleate; Glyceryl dioleate SE; Glyceryl distearate; Glyceryl distearate SE; Glyceryl isostearate; Glyceryl laurate; Glyceryl laurate SE; Glyceryl mono/dioleate; Glyceryl mono shortening; Glyceryl myristate; Glyceryl oleate; Glyceryl oleate SE; Glyceryl ricinoleate; Glyceryl ricinoleate SE; Glyceryl sorbitan oleo/stearate; Glyceryl stearate; Glyceryl stearate citrate; Glyceryl stearate SE; Glycol stearate; Glycol stearate SE; Guar gum; Gum ghatti

Hectorite; Hexyl laurate; Hydrogenated coconut acid; Hydrogenated lard glyceride; Hydrogenated lard glycerides; Hydrogenated menhaden acid; Hydrogenated palm glyceride; Hydrogenated palm glycerides; Hydrogenated soybean glycerides; Hydrogenated soy glyceride; Hydrogenated tallow glyceride; Hydrogenated tallow glyceride lactate; Hydrogenated tallow glycerides; Hydroxycetyl phosphate; Hydroxylated lanolin; Hydroxylated lecithin

Isoceteth-20; Isoceteth-30; Isopropanolamine; Isopropyl lanolate; Isopropyl palmitate; Isostearyl diglyceryl succinate

Karaya gum

Laneth-5; Laneth-10; Laneth-15; Laneth-16; Laneth-20; Laneth-40; Laneth-10 acetate; Lanolin; Lanolin acid; Lanolin alcohol; Lanolin wax; Lard glyceride; Lard glycerides; Lauramide DEA; Lauramidopropyl PEG-dimonium chloride phosphate; Laureth-2; Laureth-3; Laureth-4; Laureth-6; Laureth-7; Laureth-10; Laureth-12; Laureth-23; Lauric acid; Lauroyl sarcosine; Lecithin; Linoleic acid; Locust bean gum

Malt extract; Meroxapol 172; Meroxapol 174; Methylcellulose; Methyl gluceth-20 distearate; Methyl hydroxyethylcellulose; Mono- and diglycerides of fatty acids; Myreth-3 myristate; Myristamide DEA; Myristamide MEA

Nonoxynol-1; Nonoxynol-2; Nonoxynol-4; Nonoxynol-5; Nonoxynol-6; Nonoxynol-7; Nonoxynol-8; Nonoxynol-10; Nonoxynol-12; Nonoxynol-13; Nonoxynol-15; Nonoxynol-17; Nonoxynol-20; Nonoxynol-25; Nonoxynol-30; Nonoxynol-35; Nonoxynol-40; Nonoxynol-50

Octoxynol-3; Octoxynol-5; Octoxynol-6; Octoxynol-8; Octoxynol-9; Octoxynol-10; Octoxynol-11; Octoxynol-13; Octoxynol-16; Octoxynol-20; Octoxynol-25; Octoxynol-30; Octoxynol-40; Oleic acid; Oleth-2; Oleth-3; Oleth-5; Oleth-10; Oleth-12; Oleth-16; Oleth-20; Oleth-3 phosphate; Oleth-10 phosphate; Oleyl alcohol

Palm glyceride; Palm glycerides; Palmitic acid; Palm kernelamide DEA; Peanut oil; Pectin; PEG-10M; PEG-20M; PEG-35M; PEG-20 almond glycerides; PEG-60 almond glycerides; PEG-8 beeswax; PEG-3 castor oil; PEG-5 castor oil; PEG-8 castor oil; PEG-9 castor oil; PEG-15 castor oil; PEG-20 castor oil; PEG-30 castor oil; PEG-33 castor oil; PEG-35 castor oil; PEG-36 castor oil; PEG-40 castor oil; PEG-50 castor oil; PEG-56 castor oil; PEG-200 castor oil; PEG-15 cocamine; PEG-20 corn glycerides; PEG-60 corn glycerides; PEG-4 dilaurate; PEG-8 dilaurate; PEG-12 dilaurate; PEG-20 dilaurate; PEG-4 dioleate; PEG-8 dioleate; PEG-12 dioleate; PEG-4 distearate; PEG-12 distearate; PEG-150 distearate; PEG-8 ditallate; PEG-12 ditallate; PEG-7 glyceryl cocoate; PEG-12 glyceryl laurate; PEG-20 glyceryl laurate; PEG-20 glyceryl oleate; PEG-1 glyceryl sorbitan isostearate; PEG-5 glyceryl stearate; PEG-20 glyceryl stearate; PEG-5 hydrogenated castor oil; PEG-7 hydrogenated castor oil; PEG-10 hydrogenated castor oil; PEG-20 hydrogenated castor oil; PEG-25 hydrogenated castor oil; PEG-30 hydrogenated castor oil; PEG-40 hydrogenated castor oil; PEG-50 hydrogenated castor oil; PEG-60 hydrogenated castor oil; PEG-80 hydrogenated castor oil; PEG-100 hydrogenated castor oil; PEG-24 hydrogenated lanolin; PEG-6 isostearate; PEG-27 lanolin; PEG-40 lanolin; PEG-70 lanolin; PEG-75 lanolin; PEG-6 lauramide DEA; PEG-4 laurate; PEG-6 laurate; PEG-8 laurate; PEG-12 laurate; PEG-20 laurate; PEG-24 laurate; PEG-40 laurate; PEG-75 laurate; PEG-100 laurate; PEG-150 laurate; PEG-4 oleate; PEG-6 oleate; PEG-7 oleate; PEG-8 oleate; PEG-12 oleate; PEG-20 oleate; PEG-150 oleate; PEG-8 palmitostearate; PEG-150 palmitostearate; PEG-5 phytosterol; PEG-10 phytosterol; PEG-15 phytosterol; PEG-20 phytosterol; PEG-25 phytosterol; PEG-30 phytosterol; PEG-10-PPG-10 glyceryl stearate; PEG-10 propylene glycol; PEG-6 propylene glycol dicaprylate/dicaprate; PEG-8 ricinoleate; PEG-6 sorbitan beeswax; PEG-8 sorbitan beeswax; PEG-20 sorbitan beeswax; PEG-20 sorbitan isostearate; PEG-40 sorbitan lanolate; PEG-80 sorbitan laurate; PEG-6 sorbitan oleate; PEG-40 sorbitan oleate; PEG-6 sorbitan stearate; PEG-30 sorbitan tetraoleate; PEG-40 sorbitan tetraoleate; PEG-60 sorbitan tetraoleate; PEG-17 sorbitan trioleate; PEG-20 sorbitan tritallate; PEG-2 stearate; PEG-4 stearate; PEG-5 stearate; PEG-6 stearate; PEG-6-32 stearate; PEG-8 stearate; PEG-10 stearate; PEG-12 stearate; PEG-20 stearate; PEG-24 stearate; PEG-25 stearate; PEG-30 stearate; PEG-40 stearate; PEG-45 stearate; PEG-55 stearate; PEG-100 stearate; PEG-150 stearate; PEG-4 tallate; PEG-8 tallate; PEG-12 tallate; PEG-660 tallate; Pentaerythrityl tetralaurate; Phosphatidylcholine; Poloxamer 101; Poloxamer 105; Poloxamer 108; Poloxamer 123; Poloxamer

Emulsifiers *(cont'd.)*

124; Poloxamer 181; Poloxamer 182; Poloxamer 184; Poloxamer 185; Poloxamer 188; Poloxamer 217; Poloxamer 231; Poloxamer 234; Poloxamer 235; Poloxamer 237; Poloxamer 238; Poloxamer 282; Poloxamer 284; Poloxamer 288; Poloxamer 331; Poloxamer 333; Poloxamer 334; Poloxamer 335; Poloxamer 338; Poloxamer 401; Poloxamer 402; Poloxamer 403; Poloxamer 407; Poloxamine 304; Poloxamine 504; Poloxamine 701; Poloxamine 702; Poloxamine 704; Poloxamine 707; Poloxamine 901; Poloxamine 904; Poloxamine 908; Poloxamine 1101; Poloxamine 1102; Poloxamine 1104; Poloxamine 1107; Poloxamine 1301; Poloxamine 1302; Poloxamine 1304; Poloxamine 1307; Poloxamine 1501; Poloxamine 1502; Poloxamine 1504; Poloxamine 1508; Polyacrylic acid; Polyglyceryl-10 decaoleate; Polyglyceryl-10 decastearate; Polyglyceryl-2 dioleate; Polyglyceryl-6 dioleate; Polyglyceryl-10 dioleate; Polyglyceryl-6 distearate; Polyglyceryl-10 distearate; Polyglyceryl-10 hexaoleate; Polyglyceryl-6 isostearate; Polyglyceryl-10 isostearate; Polyglyceryl-10 laurate; Polyglyceryl-10 linoleate; Polyglyceryl-10 myristate; Polyglyceryl-10 octaoleate; Polyglyceryl-2 oleate; Polyglyceryl-3 oleate; Polyglyceryl-4 oleate; Polyglyceryl-6 oleate; Polyglyceryl-10 oleate; Polyglyceryl-2-PEG-4 stearate; Polyglyceryl-2 sesquiisostearate; Polyglyceryl-2 sesquioleate; Polyglyceryl-2 stearate; Polyglyceryl-3 stearate; Polyglyceryl-10 stearate; Polyglyceryl-10 tetraoleate; Polysorbate 20; Polysorbate 21; Polysorbate 40; Polysorbate 60; Polysorbate 61; Polysorbate 65; Polysorbate 80; Polysorbate 81; Polysorbate 85; Polyvinyl alcohol; Potassium cetyl phosphate; Potassium dimethicone copolyol phosphate; Potassium stearate; PPG-4 ceteth-1; PPG-4-ceteth-10; PPG-4-ceteth-20; PPG-8-ceteth-1; PPG-5 ceteth-10 phosphate; PPG-3-laureth-9; PPG-12-PEG-50 lanolin; PPG-12-PEG-65 lanolin oil; PPG-15 stearyl ether; Propylene glycol alginate; Propylene glycol diacetate; Propylene glycol laurate; Propylene glycol laurate SE; Propylene glycol oleate; Propylene glycol oleate SE; Propylene glycol palmito/stearate; Propylene glycol ricinoleate; Propylene glycol ricinoleate SE; Propylene glycol stearate; Propylene glycol stearate SE
Quaternium-26
Sodium borate; Sodium borate decahydrate; Sodium cetearyl sulfate; Sodium 1,2-dipalmitoyl-sn-glycero(3)phosphatidylcholine; Sodium 1,2-distearoyl-sn-glycero(3)phosphatidylcholine; Sodium glyceryl oleate phosphate; Sodium lauryl sulfate; Sodium methyl cocoyl taurate; Sodium myristyl sulfate; Sodium octyl sulfate; Sodium stearate; Sodium stearoyl lactylate; Sorbeth-20; Sorbitan caprylate; Sorbitan isostearate; Sorbitan laurate; Sorbitan myristate; Sorbitan oleate; Sorbitan palmitate; Sorbitan sesquiisostearate; Sorbitan sesquioleate; Sorbitan stearate; Sorbitan trioleate; Sorbitan tristearate; Stearalkonium chloride; Stearamide MEA-stearate; Stearamidoethyl diethylamine; Steareth-2; Steareth-7; Steareth-8; Steareth-10; Steareth-16; Steareth-20; Steareth-21; Steareth-100; Stearic acid; Stearyl alcohol; Sucrose cocoate; Sucrose dilaurate; Sucrose distearate; Sucrose laurate; Sucrose mono/disterarate; Sucrose myristate; Sucrose oleate; Sucrose palmitate; Sucrose polylaurate; Sucrose polylinoleate; Sucrose polyoleate; Sucrose polystearate; Sucrose stearate; Sucrose tetrastearate triacetate; Sucrose tribehenate; Sucrose tristearate; Sunflower seed oil; Sunflower seed oil glyceride; Sunflower seed oil glycerides
Tallow glyceride; Tallow glycerides; Tallowtrimonium chloride; TEA-lauryl sulfate; TEA-stearate; Tetrahydroxypropyl ethylenediamine; Tragacanth gum; Trideceth-100; Triethanolamine; Triisopropanolamine
Xanthan gum

Encapsulants

Trade names: A-C® 617, 617A
Cap-Shure® FF-165-60; Cap-Shure® KCL-140-50; Cap-Shure® KCL-165-70; Cavitron Cyclodextrin™; Croda 50 Bloom Gelatin; Croda 60 Bloom Alkaline Processed Gelatin; Croda 160 Bloom Limed Gelatin; Croda 190 Bloom Acid Ossein Gelatin; Croda 250 Bloom Acid Ossein Gelatin
Espholip
KELTONE® HV; KELTONE® LV
Phospholipon® 80; Phospholipon® 90; Phospholipon® 90 G; Phospholipon® 90 H; Polypro 5000® Pharmaceutical Grade; Polypro 15000® Pharmaceutical Grade
Ticalose® 15; Ticalose® 30

Chemicals: Pectin; Phosphatidylcholine

Enzymes

Trade names: Biodiastase 1000; Biodiastase Conc.; Bromelain 1:10; Bromelain Conc.
Cellulase 4000; Cellulase AP 3; Cellulase T-AP6; Cellulase Tr Conc.; Cellulase TRL; Diastase JP
Fungal Lactase 100,000; Fungal Protease 31,000; Fungal Protease 60,000; Fungal Protease 500,000; Fungal Protease Conc.
Hemi-Cellulase Amano 90
Lipase 8 Powd.; Lipase 16 Powd.; Lipase 24 Powd.; Lipase 30 Powd.
Pancreatic Lipase 250; Pancreatin 3X USP Powd.; Pancreatin 4X USP Powd.; Pancreatin 5X USP Powd.; Pancreatin 6X USP Powd.; Pancreatin 8X USP Powd.; Pancreatin USP Powd.; Pancrelipase USP; Papain 16,000; Papain 30,000; Papain Conc.; Pepsin 1:3000 NF XII Powd.; Pepsin 1:10,000 Powd. or Gran.; Pepsin 1:15,000 Powd.; Prolase® 300
SPL High Lipase Pancreatic Enzyme Conc. (PEC); SPL Undiluted Pancreatic Enzyme Conc. (PEC)
Trypsin 1:75; Trypsin 1:80; Trypsin 1:150
Yeast Lactase L-50,000

Chemicals: Glucose oxidase
Hemicellulase
Keratinase
Lipase
Protease
Trypsin

Excipients. *See Fillers*

Extenders. *See Fillers*

Fatting agents. *See Superfatting agents*

Fillers • Excipients • Bulking agents • Extenders • Inert ingredients

Trade names: Act II 500 USP; Aerosil® 200; A.F.S; Alphafil 500 USP; Altalc 200 USP; Altalc 300 USP; Altalc 400 USP; Aqualon® Cellulose Gum; Avicel® PH-102; Avicel® PH-103; Avicel® PH-105
Benecel® Hydroxypropyl Methylcellulose; Britol® 6NF; Britol® 7NF; Britol® 9NF; Britol® 20USP; Britol® 35USP; Britol® 50USP; Byco A; Byco C; Byco E; Byco O
Cab-O-Sil® TS-530; C-A-P Enteric Coating Material; Captex® 350; C-A-T Enteric Coating Polymer; Ceraphyl® ICA; CMC Daicel 1160; CMC Daicel 1220; CMC Daicel 1260; Compactrol®; Compritol 888; Compritol 888 ATO; Corn Po 4; Crodyne BY-19
Destab™
Eastman® CA; Eastman® CAB; Eastman® CAPr; Eastman® SAIB-SG; Edicol® ULV Series; Emcompress®; Estaram 299; Estaram A; Estaram H5; Estaram H15; Estaram H37; Estaram S55; Estaram S58; Estaram W25; Estaram W45; Ethyl Parasept® NF
Gelucire 33/01; Gelucire 35/10; Gelucire 37/02; Gelucire 42/12; Gelucire 44/14; Gelucire 46/07; Gelucire 48/09; Gelucire 50/02; Gelucire 50/13; Gelucire 53/10; Gelucire 62/05; Granular Gum Arabic NF/FCC C-4010; Gum Arabic NF/FCC Clean Amber Sorts
HPMCP 50; HPMCP 55; HPMCP 55S; Hydex® 100 Coarse Powd.; Hydex® 100 Coarse Powd. 35; Hydex® 100 Gran. 206; Hydex® 100 Powd. 60; Hydex® Tablet Grade; Hydrobrite 200PO; Hydrobrite 300PO; Hydrobrite 380PO; Hydrobrite 550PO
Imwitor® 742
Jerusalem Arthichoke Flour (JAF); Justfiber® CL-40-H; Justfiber® CL-60-H; Justfiber® CL-80-H
Kaydol® S; Keycel®; Klucel® 'F' Grades; Kollidon® 25, 30, 90; Kollidon® CL; Kollidon® CLM
Labrafil® Isostearique; Labrafil® M 1944 CS; Labrafil® M 2735 CS; Labrafil® WL 2609 BS; Labrasol; L.A.S; Lauroglycol; Locust Bean Gum Speckless Type D-200

Fillers *(cont'd.)*

Maltrin® M040; Maltrin® M100; Maltrin® M150; Maltrin® M180; Maltrin® M700; Maltrin® QD M440; Maltrin® QD M600; Methyl Parasept® NF/FCC; Micro-Cel® C; Miglyol® 812; Myvatex® TL

Ovucire WL 2558; Ovucire WL 2944

Peerless® No. 1; Peerless® No. 2; Peerless® No. 3; Peerless® No. 4; Pharma-Gel™; Phosal® 53 MCT; Pluracol® E400 NF; Pluracol® E600 NF; Pluracol® E1450 NF; Polyplasdone® XL; Polyplasdone® XL-10; Powdered Agar Agar Bacteriological Grade; Powdered Agar Agar Type K-60; Powdered Agar Agar Type K-80; Powdered Agar Agar Type K-100; Powdered Agar Agar Type K-150; Powdered Gum Arabic NF/FCC G-150; Powdered Gum Arabic NF/ FCC Superselect Type NB-4; Powdered Locust Bean Gum Type D-200; Powdered Locust Bean Gum Type D-300; Powdered Locust Bean Gum Type P-100; Powdered Locust Bean Gum Type PP-100; Precirol ATO 5; Propyl Parasept® NF/FCC; Protanal LF 10/60; Protanal LF 20/200; Protanal LF 200; Protanal SF; Protanal SF 120; Purity® 21

Ryoto Sugar Ester B-370; Ryoto Sugar Ester L-595; Ryoto Sugar Ester L-1570; Ryoto Sugar Ester L-1695; Ryoto Sugar Ester LWA-1570; Ryoto Sugar Ester M-1695; Ryoto Sugar Ester O-1570; Ryoto Sugar Ester OWA-1570; Ryoto Sugar Ester P-1570; Ryoto Sugar Ester P-1570S; Ryoto Sugar Ester P-1670; Ryoto Sugar Ester S-270; Ryoto Sugar Ester S-370; Ryoto Sugar Ester S-370F; Ryoto Sugar Ester S-570; Ryoto Sugar Ester S-770; Ryoto Sugar Ester S-970; Ryoto Sugar Ester S-1170; Ryoto Sugar Ester S-1170S; Ryoto Sugar Ester S-1570; Ryoto Sugar Ester S-1670; Ryoto Sugar Ester S-1670S

SB-30; Snowite® Oat Fiber; Softisan® 378; Solka-Floc®; Solka-Floc® BW-100; Solka-Floc® BW-200; Solka-Floc® BW-2030; Solka-Floc® Fine Granular; Sorbelite™ C; Sorbelite™ FG; Spray Dried Gum Arabic NF/FCC CM; Spray Dried Gum Arabic NF/FCC CS (Low Bacteria); Spray Dried Gum Arabic NF/FCC CS-R; Starch 1500®; Sta-Rx®; Supoweiss A; Supoweiss B; Supoweiss B0; Supoweiss B10; Supoweiss B90; Supoweiss BV; Supoweiss C; Supoweiss C2; Supoweiss D; Suppocire® A; Suppocire® AI; Suppocire® AIM; Suppocire® AIML; Suppocire® AIP; Suppocire® AIX; Suppocire® AM; Suppocire® AML; Suppocire® AP; Suppocire® AS2; Suppocire® AS2X; Suppocire® B; Suppocire® BM; Suppocire® BML; Suppocire® BP; Suppocire® BS2; Suppocire® BS2X; Suppocire® BT; Suppocire® C; Suppocire® CM; Suppocire® CP; Suppocire® CS2; Suppocire® CS2X; Suppocire® CT; Suppocire® D; Suppocire® DM; Suppocire® NA; Suppocire® NAIL; Suppocire® NAIX; Suppocire® NAL; Suppocire® NAX; Suppocire® NB; Suppocire® NBL; Suppocire® NBX; Suppocire® NC; Suppocire® ND; Supra A

Tullanox HM-100; Tullanox HM-150; Tullanox HM-250; 28-1801

Unisweet MAN

Vaseline 335 G; Vaseline 7702; Vaseline 8332; Vaseline 10049 BL; Vaseline A

Wacker HDK® H20; Wecobee® FS; Wecobee® M; Wecobee® SS

Chemicals: Agar; Albumin; Alcohol; Algin; Alumina trihydrate; Aluminum hydroxide

Beeswax

Calcium carbonate; Calcium phosphate dibasic dihydrate; Calcium polycarbophil; Calcium silicate; Calcium sulfate; Calcium sulfate dihydrate; Caprylic/capric/lauric triglyceride; Caprylic/capric/linoleic triglyceride; Caprylic/capric/stearic triglyceride; Carboxymethylcellulose sodium; Carrageenan; Cellulose acetate butyrate; Cellulose acetate phthalate; Cellulose acetate propionate; Cellulose acetate trimellitate; Cetyl alcohol; Cocoa butter; Coconut oil; Corn bran; Corn oil PEG-8 esters; Corn starch; Creatinine

Dextrates; Diacetylated monoglycerides

Edetic acid

D-Glucose anhyd; Glyceryl behenate

Hectorite; Hydroabietyl alcohol; Hydrolyzed gelatin; Hydroxypropyl methylcellulose phthalate

Isocetyl alcohol

Jerusalem artichoke flour

Karaya gum

Lactose; Lanolin; Locust bean gum

Maltodextrin; D-Mannitol; Methyl alcohol; Methylcellulose; Microcrystalline cellulose; Mineral oil

Peach kernel oil; PEG-4; PEG-6; PEG-8; PEG-9; PEG-12; PEG-14; PEG-16; PEG-20; PEG-32; PEG-40; PEG-60; PEG-75; PEG-100; PEG-150; PEG-200; Petrolatum; Polyethylene; Polypropylene; Polystyrene; Polyvinyl chloride

Rapeseed oil

Silica, hydrated; Starch; Starch glycerin; Sucrose acetate isobutyrate; Sucrose dilaurate; Sucrose laurate; Sucrose myristate; Sucrose oleate; Sucrose palmitate; Sucrose

Fillers *(cont'd.)*

polystearate; Sucrose stearate; Sucrose tribehenate; Sucrose tristearate
Talc; Tragacanth gum; Tribehenin; Triisostearin PEG-6 esters; Triolein PEG-6 esters
Vanillin; Vegetable oil
Wheat bran

Film-formers

Trade names: A-C® 617, 617A; Acylan; Alphafil 500 USP; Altalc 200 USP; Altalc 300 USP; Anhydrous Lanolin
USP Cosmetic; Anhydrous Lanolin USP Pharmaceutical; Anhydrous Lanolin USP Superfine;
Anhydrous Lanolin USP Ultrafine
Benecel® Methylcellulose; Byco A; Byco C; Byco E; Byco O
Cekol® 30; Cekol® 150; Cekol® 300; Cekol® 700; Cekol® 2000; Cekol® 4000; Cekol® 10000;
Cekol® 30000; Cekol® 50000; Colloid 488T; Colloid 602; Cozeen®; Crodyne BY-19
Dermacryl® 79
Fancol CH
Gantrez® AN-119; Gantrez® AN-139; Gantrez® AN-139 BF; Gantrez® AN-149; Gantrez® AN-
169; Gantrez® MS-955D; Gantrez® S-95; Gantrez® S-97; Gelatin USP/NF, Type A
KELGIN® XL; KELTONE® LV; Klucel® 'F' Grades
Lanfrax® 1776; Lanfrax® 1779; Lanotein AWS 30; Liquid Fish Gelatin Conc.
Maltrin® M040; Maltrin® M050; Maltrin® M180; MANUCOL DM; MANUCOL DMF; MANUCOL
LB; Methocel® A4C Premium; Methocel® A4M Premium; Methocel® A15LV Premium;
Methocel® E3 Premium; Methocel® E4M Premium; Methocel® E6 Premium; Methocel®
E15LV Premium; Methocel® E50LV Premium; Methocel® E50P; Methocel® K4M Premium;
Methocel® K15M Premium; Methocel® K100LV Premium; Methocel® K100M Premium
Natrosol® Plus CS, Grade 330
Pecogel® GC-310; Pecogel® H-12; Pecogel® H-115; Pecogel® H-1220; Pecogel® S-1120;
Pecosil® OS-100B; Plasdone® C-15; Plasdone® C-30; Plasdone® K-25; Plasdone® K-29/
32; Plasdone® K-90; Plasdone® K-90D; Plasdone® K-90M; PVP/VA E-335; PVP/VA E-535;
PVP/VA E-635; PVP/VA E-735; PVP/VA I-235; PVP/VA I-335; PVP/VA I-535; PVP/VA I-735;
PVP/VA S-630
Ritacetyl®; Ritasol
Sheerskin; Skin-Lite; Sobalg FD 100 Range; Sol-U-Tein EA; Spray Dried Fish Gelatin; Spray
Dried Fish Gelatin/Maltodextrin; Spray Dried Hydrolysed Fish Gelatin; Sureteric™
Ticolv
Vee Gee Pharmaceutical Gelatins

Chemicals: Acrylic acid/acrylonitrogens copolymer; Albumen; Algin
Calcium alginate; Carbomer; Carboxymethylmethylcellulose; Cellulose acetate phthalate; Cetyl
hydroxyethyl cellulose
Dimethicone propylethylenediamine behenate
Hydrolyzed gelatin
Lanolin wax
Polyethylene; Polyquaternium-1; Polyvinyl acetate (homopolymer); Polyvinyl acetate phthalate;
Propylene glycol alginate; PVM/MA copolymer; PVP/dimethiconylacrylate/polycarbamyl/
polyglycol ester; PVP/dimethylaminoethylmethacrylate copolymer; PVP/dimethylaminoethyl
methacrylate/polycarbamyl polyglycol ester; PVP/polycarbamyl polyglycol ester; PVP/VA
copolymer
Silicone emulsions
Wheat gluten

Filtering aids

Trade names: Hyflo Super-Cel

Chemicals: Cellulose
Diatomaceous earth
Microcrystalline cellulose
Phenylbenzimidazole sulfonic acid

Flavor enhancers. *See Flavors*

Flavor masking agents

Trade names: Alpha W6 HP 0.6; Alpha W6 M1.8; Alpha W 6 Pharma Grade
Beta W 7; Beta W7 HP 0.9; Beta W7 M1.8; Beta W7 P
Cap-Shure® FF-165-60; Cap-Shure® KCL-140-50; Cavitron Cyclo-dextrin™
Descote® Ascorbic Acid 60%; Descote® Citric Acid 50%; Descote® Copper Gluconate 20%; Descote® Ferrous Fumarate 60%; Descote® Ferrous Sulfate 60%; Descote® Niacinamide $33^1/_3$%; Descote® Pyridoxine Hydrochoride $33^1/_3$%; Descote® Riboflavin $33^1/_3$%; Descote® Sodium Ascorbate 50%; Descote® Thiamine Mononitrate $33^1/_3$%; Disodium Pamoate; Durkote Ferrous Fumarate/Hydrog. Veg. Oil; Durkote Ferrous Sulfate/Hydrog. Veg. Oil; Durkote Potassium Chloride/Hydrog. Veg. Oil; Durkote Vitamin B-1/Hydrog. Veg. Oil; Durkote Vitamin C/Hydrog. Veg. Oil
Eudragit® L 100-55; Extract of Whole Grapefruit
Gamma W8; Gamma W8 HP0.6; Gamma W8 M1.8; Granular Gum Arabic NF/FCC C-4010; Gum Arabic NF/FCC Clean Amber Sorts
Hony-Tab®
Magnasweet®; Mola-Tab®
Natural Prosweet™ Liq. #604; Natural Prosweet™ Powd. #875; Nu-Tab®
Powdered Gum Arabic NF/FCC G-150; Powdered Gum Arabic NF/FCC Superselect Type NB-4; Prosweet™ Liq.; Prosweet™ Powd.
Spray Dried Gum Arabic NF/FCC CM; Spray Dried Gum Arabic NF/FCC CS (Low Bacteria); Spray Dried Gum Arabic NF/FCC CS-R; Sugartab®; Surelease®

Chemicals: Acetylated hydrogenated vegetable oil glycerides
Cyclodextrin; β-Cyclodextrin
Disodium pamoate
Hydroxypropyl-α-cyclodextrin; Hydroxypropyl-β-cyclodextrin; Hydroxypropyl-γ-cyclodextrin; N-Hydroxysuccinic acid
Methyl-α-cyclodextrin; Methyl-β-cyclodextrin

Flavors • Flavor enhancers

Trade names: Citric Acid USP FCC Anhyd. Fine Gran. No. 69941; Citrid Acid USP FCC Anhyd. Gran. No. 69942; CornSweet® Crystalline Fructose
Emery® 912; Emery® 916; Emery® 917; Emery® 918; Eromenth®; Extract of Whole Grapefruit; Extramalt 10; Extramalt 35; Extramalt Dark; Extramalt Light
Hony-Tab®; HSC Aspartame
Isoamyl Alcohol 95%; Isoamyl Alcohol 99%
Magnasweet®; Mola-Tab®
Narangrex Complex G; Natural Prosweet™ Liq. #604; Natural Prosweet™ Powd. #875
alpha-Pinene P&F, FCC; beta-Pinene P&F; Pomelex Complex D; Pomelex Complex G; Prosweet™ Liq.; Prosweet™ Powd.; Purac® USP 88; Purasal® P/USP 60
Unamino GLUT; Unisweet EVAN; Unisweet VAN
Veltol®-Plus

Chemicals: Acacia; Acetal; Acetaldehyde; Acetaldehyde phenethyl propyl acetal; Acetanisole; Acetic acid; Acetisoeugenol; 2´-Acetonaphthone; Acetone; Acetophenone; Acetyl butyryl; Acetyl methyl carbinol; 3-Acetylpyridine; Acetyl tributyl citrate; Aconitic acid; Alfalfa; Alfalfa extract; Allyl anthranilate; Allyl butyrate; Allyl caproate; Allyl cinnamate; Allyl cyclohexaneacetate; Allyl cyclohexanebutyrate; Allyl cyclohexanehexanoate; Allyl cyclohexanepropionate; Allyl cyclohexanevalerate; Allyl heptanoate; Allyl α-ionone; Allyl isothiocyanate; Allyl isovalerate; Allyl nonanoate; Allyl octanoate; Allyl phenoxyacetate; Allyl phenylacetate; Allyl propionate; Allyl sorbate; Allyl tiglate; Allyl 10-undecenoate; Aloe extract; Althea extract; Ambrette seed oil; Amyl acetate; n-Amyl alcohol; Amyl butyrate; α-Amylcinnamaldehyde; α-Amylcinnamaldehyde dimethyl acetal; α-Amylcinnamyl alcohol; Amyl formate; Amyl octanoate; Amyl salicylate; Anethole; Angelica extract; p-Anisaldehyde; Anise; Anise oil; p-Anisic acid; Anisyl acetate; Anisyl alcohol; Anisyl formate; Anisyl phenylacetate; Anisyl

Flavors *(cont'd.)*

propionate
Balm mint; Balsam Peru; Balsam tolu; Barley extract; Bay oil; Benzaldehyde; Benzoin; Ben-zophenone; Benzyl acetate; Benzyl acetoacetate; Benzyl alcohol; Benzyl benzoate; Benzyl butyrate; Benzyl cinnamate; Benzyl ether; Benzylidene acetone; Benzyl isobutyrate; Benzyl isovalerate; Benzyl methoxyethyl acetal; Benzyl phenylacetate; Benzyl propionate; Benzylsalicylate; Bornyl acetate; Butan-3-one-2-yl butyrate; Butyl alcohol; n-Butylamine; Butyl anthranilate; Butyl butyrate; Butyl 2-decenoate; Butyl formate; Butyl heptanoate; Butyl hexanoate; Butyl isobutyrate; n-Butyl isovalerate; Butyl lactate; Butyl levulinate; Butylparaben; Butyl phenylacetate; n-Butyl propionate; Butyl stearate; Butyl valerate; n-Butyraldehyde; Butyrophenone

Caffeine; Cajeput oil; Camphor; Cananga oil; Capric acid; Caproic acid; Caprylic acid; Caprylic alcohol; Capsicum; Capsicum extract; Capsicum oleoresin; Caramel; Caraway oil; Car-boxymethylcellulose; Cardamom; Cardamom oil; Carveol; l-Carvone; Carvyl acetate; Carvyl propionate; Cascara extract; Cinnamal; Cinnamaldehyde ethylene glycol acetal; Cinnamic acid; Cinnamon oil; Cinnamyl alcohol; Cinnamyl butyrate; Cinnamyl isobutyrate; Cinnamyl phenylacetate; Cinnamyl propionate; Citral; Citral diethyl acetal; Citral dimethyl acetal; Citronellal; β-Citronellol; Citronellyl acetate; Citronellyl butyrate; Citronellyl formate; Citronellyl phenylacetate; Citronellyl propionate; Citronellyl valerate; Clove oil; Coriander oil; Corn syrup solids; m-Cresol; o-Cresol; p-Cresol; Cubeb oil; Cuminaldehyde; β-Cyclocitral; Cyclohexyl acetate; Cyclohexyl anthranilate; Cyclohexyl butyrate; Cyclohexylethyl acetate; Cyclohexyl formate; Cyclohexyl isovalerate; Cyclohexyl propionate; p-Cymene

trans-trans-2,4-Decadienal; Δ-Decalactone; γ-Decalactone; Decanal; 3-Decanone; cis-4-Decen-1-al; trans-2-Decenal; 3-Decen-2-one; Decyl acetate; n-Decyl alcohol; Decyl butyrate; Decyl propionate; Denatonium benzoate; 4,4-Dibutyl-γ-butyrolactone; Dicyclohexyl disul-fide; Diethylacetic acid; Diethyl malate; Diethyl maleate; Diethyl malonate; Diethyl sebacate; Diethyl tartrate; 2,5-Diethyltetrahydrofuran; Dihydrocarveol; d-Dihydrocarvone; Dihydrocarvyl acetate; Dihydrocoumarin; 3,4-Dihydroxybenzaldehyde; Diisobutyl ketone; Dill seed oil; Dillweed oil; m-Dimethoxybenzene; 2,4-Dimethylacetophenone; Dimethyl anthranilate; 2,4-Dimethylbenzaldehyde; α,α-Dimethylbenzyl isobutyrate; 2,6-Dimethyl-5-heptanal; 3,7-Dimethyl-1-octanol; α,α-Dimethylphenethyl butyrate; 2,3-Dimethylpyrazine; 2,5-Dimethylpyrazine; Dimethyl succinate; Dipotassium glycyrrhizate; Disodium guanylate; Disodium inosinate; δ-Dodecalactone; γ-Dodecalactone; 2-Dodecenal

Estragole; p-Ethoxybenzaldehyde; Ethyl acetate; Ethylacetoacetate; Ethyl 2-acetyl-3-phenylpropionate; Ethyl acrylate; Ethyl-p-anisate; Ethyl anthranilate; p-Ethylbenzaldehyde; Ethyl benzoate; α-Ethylbenzyl butyrate; 2-Ethylbutyl acetate; Ethyl butyrate; Ethyl caproate; Ethyl cinnamate; Ethyl cyclohexanepropionate; Ethyl decanoate; 2-Ethyl-3,5(6)-dimethylpyrazine; Ethylene brassylate; Ethyl formate; 2-Ethylfuran; Ethyl heptanoate; 2-Ethylhexanol; Ethyl isobutyrate; Ethyl isovalerate; Ethyl lactate; Ethyl laurate; Ethyl levulinate; Ethyl maltol; Ethyl 2-methylbutyrate; Ethyl methylphenylglycidate; Ethyl 3-(methylthio)propionate; Ethyl octanoate; Ethyl pelargonate; p-Ethylphenol; Ethyl phenylacetate; Ethyl-4-phenylbutyrate; Ethyl phenylglycidate; Ethyl-3-phenylpropionate; Ethyl propionate; Ethyl pyruvate; Ethyl salicylate; Ethyl sorbate; Ethyl tiglate; Ethyl undecanoate; Ethyl 10-undecenoate; Ethyl valerate; Ethyl vanillin; Eucalyptol; Eucalyptus oil; Eugenol

Farnesol; l-Fenchone; Fenchyl alcohol; Fennel; Fennel oil; Furfural; Furfuryl acetate; Furfuryl alcohol; Furfuryl butyrate

Gentian; Geraniol; Geranium oil; Geranyl acetate; Geranyl isobutyrate; Gluconolactone; L-Glutamic acid; Grape juice conc.; Guaiacol; Gum benzoin

Heliotropine; γ-Heptalactone; Heptanal; 3-Heptanone; 4-Heptanone; Heptyl acetate; Heptyl alcohol; Heptyl butyrate; Heptyl formate; γ-Hexalactone; 3-Hexanol; 3-Hexanone; 2-Hexenal; 2-Hexenol; trans-2-Hexenyl acetate; cis-3-Hexenyl 2-methylbutyrate; Hexyl acetate; 2-Hexyl-4-acetoxytetrahydrofuran; Hexyl alcohol; Hexyl-2-butenoate; Hexyl butyrate; Hexyl formate; Hexyl isobutyrate; Hexyl isovalerate; Hexyl 2-methylbutyrate; Hexyl octanoate; Hexyl propionate; Hydrocinnamaldehyde; Hydrocinnamic acid; Hydrolyzed vegetable pro-tein; p-Hydroxybenzaldehyde; Hydroxycitronellal; Hydroxycitronellol; 4-Hydroxy-2,5-dim-ethyl-3(2H)furanone; 4-(p-Hydroxyphenyl)-2-butanone; N-Hydroxysuccinic acid; Hyssop extract

α-Ionone; Isoamyl acetate; Isoamyl acetoacetate; Isoamyl alcohol; Isoamyl butyrate; Isoamyl formate; Isoamyl hexanoate; Isoamyl isobutyrate; Isoamyl isovalerate; Isoamyl nonanoate; Isoamyl propionate; Isobutyl acetate; Isobutyl acetoacetate; Isobutyl alcohol; Isobutyl-2-butenoate; Isobutyl butyrate; Isobutyl cinnamate; Isobutyl formate; Isobutyl hexanoate;

Flavors *(cont'd.)*

Isobutyl isobutyrate; α-Isobutylphenethyl alcohol; Isobutyl phenylacetate; Isoeugenol; Isoeugenyl benzyl ether; Isoeugenyl phenylacetate; Isophorone; Isopropyl acetate; Isopropyl alcohol; Isopropyl butyrate; Isopropyl cinnamate; Isopropyl formate; Isopropyl hexanoate; Isopropyl isobutyrate; Isopropyl isovalerate; o-Isopropylphenol; p-Isopropylphenol; p-Isopropylphenylacetaldehyde; Isopropyl phenylacetate; Isopropyl propionate; Isopropyl tiglate; Isopulegol; Isopulegyl acetate; Isoquinoline; Isovaleraldehyde

cis-Jasmone; Juniper oil

Kelp

Lauric aldehyde; Lauryl acetate; Lauryl alcohol; Lavender oil; Lemon extract; Lemongrass oil East Indian; Lemongrass oil West Indian; Lemon juice; Lemon oil; Levulinic acid; Licorice; Licorice extract; Lime oil; d-Limonene; Linalool; Linalyl acetate; Linalyl anthranilate; Linalyl butyrate; Linalyl cinnamate; Linalyl formate; Linalyl isovalerate; Linalyl propionate; Linden extract; 2,6-Lutidine

Mace oil; Maltol; Maltyl isobutyrate; Mandarin orange oil; Menthalactone; p-Mentha-8-thiol-3-one; Menthol; l-Menthone; dl-Menthyl acetate; Menthyl lactate; l-Menthyl lactate; o-Methoxybenzaldehyde; o-Methoxycinnamaldehyde; 2-Methoxy-4-methylphenol; 4-p-Methoxyphenyl-2-butanone; 1-(p-Methoxyphenyl)-2-propanone; 2-Methoxypyrazine; 2-Methoxy-4-vinylphenol; 4´-Methyl acetophenone; 2-Methylallyl butyrate; Methyl n-amyl ketone; Methyl anthranilate; Methyl benzoate; α-Methylbenzyl acetate; α-Methylbenzyl butyrate; 3-Methyl-2-buten-1-ol; 2-Methylbutyl acetate; 2-Methylbutyl isovalerate; 2-Methylbutyraldehyde; 2-Methylbutyric acid; Methyl caproate; Methyl caprylate; α-Methylcinnamaldehyde; Methyl cinnamate; 6-Methylcoumarin; 3-Methyl-2-cyclohexen-1-one; 1,2-Methylenedioxybenzene; Methyl 2-furoate; Methyl heptanoate; Methyl heptenone; Methyl hexyl ketone; Methyl isobutyl ketone; Methyl isobutyrate; Methyl isovalerate; Methyl laurate; Methyl 2-methylbutyrate; Methyl 3-methylthiopropionate; Methyl 4-methylvalerate; Methyl myristate; Methyl nonanoate; Methyl 2-nonynoate; 3-Methylpentanoic acid; 2-Methyl-2-pentenoic acid; 4-Methyl-1-phenyl-2-pentanone; Methyl 3-phenylpropionate; 2-Methylpropanal; Methyl propionate; Methyl propyl ketone; Methyl salicylate; Methyl valerate; Monoammonium glycyrrhizinate; MSG; Myrcene; Myristaldehyde; Myrtenol

d-Neomenthol; Neryl acetate; Neryl butyrate; Neryl isobutyrate; Neryl isovalerate; Neryl propionate; γ-Nonalactone; Nonanal; 2-Nonanol; 2-Nonanone; cis-6-Nonen-1-ol; Nonyl alcohol; Nutmeg oil; Nutmeg oil, expressed

γ-Octalactone; n-Octanal; Octyl acetate; 3-Octyl acetate; Octyl butyrate; Octyl formate; Octyl isovalerate; Orange oil; Orange tincture

Patchouli oil; Pentadecalactone; Pentyl 2-furyl ketone; Peppermint leaves; Peppermint oil; Peppermint spirit; Perillaldehyde; α-Phellandrene; Phenethyl alcohol; Phenethyl anthranilate; Phenethyl benzoate; Phenethyl butyrate; Phenethyl hexanoate; Phenethyl isobutyrate; Phenethyl isovalerate; Phenethyl 2-methylbutyrate; Phenoxyacetic acid; Phenoxyethyl isobutyrate; Phenylacetaldehyde; Phenylacetaldehyde 2,3-butylene glycol acetal; Phenylacetic acid; 2-Phenylethyl acetate; 5-Phenyl-1-pentanol; 1-Phenyl-1,2-propanedione; 2-Phenylpropyl butyrate; 2-Phenylpropyl isobutyrate; 3-Phenylpropyl isobutyrate; 3-Phenylpropyl isovalerate; Phenyl salicylate; Pineapple juice; α-Pinene; β-Pinene; Pine needle oil; Piperidine; d-Piperitone; Piperonyl acetate; Piperonyl isobutyrate; Potassium acetate; Potassium chloride; Propenylguaethol; Propyl acetate; n-Propyl alcohol; Propyl benzoate; Propylene carbonate; Propylene glycol alginate; Propyl formate; Propyl 2-furanacrylate; Propyl heptanoate; 3-Propylidenephthalide; Propyl isobutyrate; α-Propylphenethyl alcohol; 4-Propylphenol; Propyl phenylacetate; Propyl propionate; Propyl tiglate; Pulegone; Pyrazine; Pyridine; Pyruvaldehyde

Quassia; Quince seed

Resorcinol; Rhodinyl butyrate; Rosemary oil; Rose oil; Rose water

Sage; Sambucus oil; Sandalwood oil; Sarsaparilla; Senna extract; Serpentaria extract; Sodium chloride; Spearmint; Spearmint oil; Star anise; Styrene; Sweet almond oil

α-Terpinene; γ-Terpinene; α-Terpineol; Terpinyl formate; 4,5,6,7-Tetrahydro-3,6-dimethylbenzofuran; Tetrahydrofurfuryl butyrate; Tetrahydrofurfuryl propionate; 2,3,5,6-Tetramethylpyrazine; Theaspirane; Thyme; Thyme extract; Thyme oil; Thymol; p-Tolyl aldehyde; o-Tolyl isobutyrate; Triacetin; Tributyrin; 2-Tridecenal; Triethyl citrate; Trimethyldodecatrieneol; Trimethyl thiazole

δ-Undecalactone; γ-Undecalactone; Undecanal; 2-Undecanone; 9-Undecenal; 10-Undecenal; Undecyl alcohol; Undecylenic acid

Vanilla; Vanillin; Vanillin isobutyrate; Vanillyl alcohol; Veratraldehyde; Veratrole; (1S)-(-)-Verbenone

Flavors *(cont'd.)*

Walnut extract; Wild cherry bark; Wintergreen oil; Wormwood oil
2,5-Xylenol; 2,6-Xylenol
Ylang ylang oil
Zingerone

Foaming agents. *See Surfactants*

Fragrances • Perfumes • Aromatics

Chemicals: α-Amylcinnamaldehyde; Amyl salicylate; p-Anisaldehyde; Anisyl alcohol
Benzaldehyde; Benzophenone
Cardamom; Cinnamon oil; Cinnamyl alcohol; Citral; β-Citronellol; Coriander oil; Cubeb oil
Diethyl phthalate
Fennel oil
Menthol; Methyl anthranilate; 1,2-Methylenedioxybenzene; Methyl salicylate; MSG
Peppermint oil; Peppermint spirit; Phenethyl alcohol; Phenylacetaldehyde; Pine needle oil
Vanillin
Wintergreen oil

Free-flow agents. *See Anticaking agents*

Gelling agents • Hardeners • Stiffening agents

Trade names: Acritamer® 934; Acritamer® 934P; Acritamer® 940; Acritamer® 941; Agar-Agar; Agar Agar NF
Flake #1; Aquagel SP 399; Aquathik
Bone Gelatin Type B 200 Bloom
Cab-O-Sil®EH-5; Cab-O-Sil®H-5; Cab-O-Sil®L-90; Cab-O-Sil®LM-150; Cab-O-Sil®M-5; Cab-
O-Sil® MS-55; Carbopol® 1342; Carbopol® 1382; Carbopol® ETD 2020; Carbopol® ETD
2050; Cecavon ZN 70; Cecavon ZN 71; Cecavon ZN 72; Cecavon ZN 73; Cecavon ZN 735;
Cerasynt® 945; CM-80; Collagenite; Colloid 488T; Colloid 602; Crodafos N-3 Acid; Crodamol
CP; Crodamol CSP; Crodamol SS
Fancol HL-20; Fancol HL-24
Gelatin USP/NF, Type A; GELRITE®; Genu® Carrageenan; Genugel® Series; Genuvisco
Hydrine; Hypan® SA100H; Hypan® SR150H
KELACID®; KELCOSOL®; KELGIN® F; KELGIN® HV; KELGIN® LV; KELGIN® MV; KELGIN®
XL; KELMAR®; KELMAR® CR; KELMAR® Improved; KELSET®; KELTONE®; KELTONE®
HV; KELTONE® HVCR; KELTONE® LV; KELTONE® LVCR; KELTROL® CR; KELVIS®;
Koster Keunen Synthetic Spermaceti
Lutrol® F 127
Macol® 1; Macol® 2; Macol® 2D; Macol® 2LF; Macol® 4; Macol® 8; Macol® 10; Macol® 22;
Macol® 27; Macol® 33; Macol® 40; Macol® 85; Magnabrite® HS; MANUCOL DM;
MANUCOL DMF; MANUCOL LB; Methocel® A4C Premium; Methocel® A4M Premium;
Methocel® A15C Premium; Methocel® A15-LV; Methocel® A15LV Premium; Methocel® E3
Premium; Methocel® E4M Premium; Methocel® E6 Premium; Methocel® E15LV Premium;
Methocel® E50LV Premium; Methocel® E50P; Methocel® F4M Premium; Methocel® K4M
Premium; Methocel® K15M Premium; Methocel® K100LV Premium; Methocel® K100M
Premium; Mexpectin LA 100 Range; Mexpectin XSS 100 Range; Myverol® 18-99
Norgel
P-4 Pharmaceutical Gelatin; P-5 Pharmaceutical Gelatin; P-6 Pharmaceutical Gelatin; P-7
Pharmaceutical Gelatin; P-8 Pharmaceutical Gelatin; P-9 Pharmaceutical Gelatin; P-10
Pharmaceutical Gelatin; Plasdone® K-25; Plasdone® K-29/32; Plasdone® K-90; Plasdone®
K-90D; Plasdone® K-90M; Pluronic® F127NF; Polargel® NF; Polychol 5; Polychol 15;
Powdered Agar Agar Bacteriological Grade; Powdered Agar Agar NF M-100 (Gracilaria);
Powdered Agar Agar NF MK-60; Powdered Agar Agar NF MK-80-B; Powdered Agar Agar NF

Gelling agents *(cont'd.)*

MK-80 (Bacteriological); Powdered Agar Agar NF S-100; Powdered Agar Agar NF S-100-B; Powdered Agar Agar NF S-150; Powdered Agar Agar NF S-150-B; Powdered Agar Agar Type K-60; Powdered Agar Agar Type K-80; Powdered Agar Agar Type K-100; Powdered Agar Agar Type K-150; Powdered Aloe Vera (1:200) Food Grade; Promulgen® D; Promulgen® G; Protacid F 120; Protanal KF 200; Protanal KF 200 RBS; Protanal KF 200 S; Protanal LF 10/40; Protanal LF 10/60; Protanal LF 20/200; Protanal LF 120 M; Protanal LF 200; Protanal LF 200 M; Protanal LF 200 RB; Protanal LF 200 S; Protanal SF 120 RB; Protanal TA 250; Protanal TA 375; Protanal TFX 200

Red Reishi Mushroom Extract RREXTR; Rehydragel® CG; Rehydragel® HPA; Rehydragel® LV
Sepigel 305; Simulsol® 58; Simulsol® 78; Simulsol® 98; Simulsol® 165; Simulsol® CS; Simulsol® P4; Simulsol® P23; Soageena®; Sobalg FD 000 Range; Sobalg FD 100 Range; Sobalg FD 200 Range; Sobalg FD 300 Range; Sobalg FD 460; Sobalg FD 900 Range; Spermwax®; Superpolystate; Super-Sat AWS-4; Super-Sat AWS-24; Syncrowax HR-C
Vee Gee Pharmaceutical Gelatins; Volclay® NF-BC; Volclay NF-ID; Volpo CS-20

Chemicals: Acrylic acid/acrylonitrogens copolymer; Algin; Alkenyl succinic anhydride; Aluminum sulfate; Ammonium alginate
Beeswax; Beeswax, white; Beeswax, yellow
Calcium carboxymethyl cellulose; Carrageenan; Ceteareth-33; Cetearyl alcohol; Cetyl alcohol; Cetyl esters
DEA-oleth-3 phosphate; DEA-oleth-10 phosphate; Dextrin
Emulsifying wax NF; EO/PO block polymer or copolymer
Gellan gum; Glycol hydroxystearate
Hydrogenated castor oil
Oleth-3 phosphate; Oleth-10 phosphate
Paraffin; Paraformaldehyde; PEG-20 hydrogenated lanolin; Polyglyceryl-10 tetraoleate; Potassium alginate; PPG-5 ceteth-10 phosphate; Propylene glycol alginate
Rosin
Sodium bentonite; Sodium hyaluronate; Sodium stearate; Stearalkonium hectorite; Steareth-20; Stearyl alcohol
TEA-alginate

Glidants *See Anticaking agents*

Hardeners. *See Gelling agents*

Humectants

Trade names: A-641; Adeka Propylene Glycol (P); Amalty®; Amino Gluten MG; Arlex
Caprol® 6G2O; Caprol® 10G4O; Carbowax® PEG 300; Carbowax® Sentry® PEG 300; Carbowax® Sentry® PEG 400; Carbowax® Sentry® PEG 540 Blend; Carbowax® Sentry® PEG 600; Carbowax® Sentry® PEG 900; Carbowax® Sentry® PEG 1000; Carbowax® Sentry® PEG 1450; Carbowax® Sentry® PEG 3350; Carbowax® Sentry® PEG 4600; Carbowax® Sentry® PEG 8000; CornSweet® Crystalline Fructose; Croderol G7000
Emery® 912; Emery® 916; Emery® 917; Emery® 918; Ethosperse® G-26; Ethosperse® SL-20; Extramalt 10; Extramalt 35; Extramalt Dark; Extramalt Light
Fancol HL; Fancol LA; Fancol LAO; Fancol SORB; Fancol VB; Fancor Lanwax
Glycon® G 100; Glycon® G-300
Hydex® 100 Coarse Powd.; Hydex® 100 Coarse Powd. 35; Hydex® 100 Gran. 206; Hydex® 100 Powd. 60; Hydex® Tablet Grade; Hystar® 3375; Hystar® 4075; Hystar® 5875; Hystar® 6075; Hystar® CG; Hystar® HM-75; Hystar® TPF
Kemstrene® 96.0% USP; Kemstrene® 99.0%; Kemstrene® 99.7% USP
Lactic Acid 88% USP/FCC; Lanotein AWS 30; Liponic 70-NC; Liponic 76-NC; Liponic 83-NC; Liponic Sorbitol Sol'n. 70% USP; Liposorb 70
Macol® E-200; Macol® E-300; Macol® E-400; Macol® E-600; Maltrin® M040; Maltrin® M150
Non-Diastatic Malt Syrup #40600

Humectants *(cont'd.)*

Patlac® LA USP; Patlac® NAL; Pecosil® OS-100B; Pelemol® G7A; Pelemol® G45L; Pricerine 9088; Propylene Glycol USP/FCC Ultra Grade; Purac® PH 88; Purasal® P/HQ 60; Purasal® S/HQ 60

Ritapan D; Ritapan DL; Ritapan TA; Robane®

Solan 50; Star; Superol

Unisweet 70; Unisweet 70/CONC; Unisweet CONC; Unisweet MAN

Chemicals: Barley extract
Dimethicone propylethylenediamine behenate
Glycereth-26; Glycereth-5 lactate; Glycereth-7 triacetate; Glycerin
Hexylene glycol; Hydrogenated lanolin; Hydrogenated starch hydrolysate
Isopentyldiol
Lanolin wax
Malt extract; D-Mannitol
D-Panthenol; DL-Panthenol; Panthenyl triacetate; PEG-60 lanolin; Polyglyceryl-10 dioleate; Potassium lactate; Propylene glycol; Propylene glycol dioctanoate; Propylene glycol stearate
Quaternium-22
Sodium lactate; Sodium PCA; Sorbeth-20; Sorbitol

Inert ingredients. *See Fillers*

Intermediates

Trade names: AB®; Acconon 400-MO; AEPD®; AMPD
BLO®
Cumal
DECMP; Distilled Whole Coconut Oil 6226 6222; DMP; DPCP
Ebal; Epal® 16NF; Epal® 18NF
Fancol HL; Fancol LA
Hystrene® 1835; Hystrene® 3022; Hystrene® 5012
Ibbal; Industrene® 223; Isatin
Jeffox PPG-400; Jeffox PPG-2000
KELTROL® CR
Low I.V. Coconut Oil 6227, 6228
NEPD; Neustrene® 060; Neustrene® 064; NiPar S-10™; NiPar S-20™; NMP
PDCP; Philacid 1200; Phloroglucinol; PTAL; Purac® PH 88; Purasal® NH 70; Purasal® S/PF 60; Purasal® S Powd.; Purasolv® BL; Pyridine 1°; 2-Pyrol®
Quadrol®
Saytex® VBR; Split Coconut Oil 6254, 6255; Stripped Coconut Oil 6212, 6256
TBP-HP; TEPA; TEPF; TEP-HP; TIPMDP; TIPP; TMP-HP; Tris Amino® Molecular Biology Grade; Tris Amino® Ultra Pure Standard
Unichem ACETA; Unichem Levula
Velsicure®; Versene Acid

Chemicals: Acetonitrile; Acetophenone; Acetylacetone; Acetyl chloride; p-Aminobenzoic acid; 2-Amino-1-butanol; Aminoethylpiperazine; 2-Amino-2-ethyl-1,3-propanediol; 2-Amino-2-methyl-1,3-propanediol; Ammonium lactate; m-Anisidine; o-Anisidine; p-Anisidine; Arsenic trichloride
Benzoin; n-Butylamine; Butyl lactate; But-2-yne-1,4-diol; Butyrolactone; Butyronitrile
Chloroacetophenone; m-Chloroaniline; o-Chloroaniline; p-Chloroaniline; 2-Chloropyridine; Cuminaldehyde
Decene-1; Diallyl maleate; 2,3-Dibromo-1-propanol; p-Dichlorobenzene; 1,3-Dichloro-5,5-dimethyl hydantoin; Diethyl cyanomethylphosphonate; Diethyl toluene diamine; Dimethoxypropane; Dimethylolpropionic acid; Diphenyl chlorophosphate; N,N´-Diphenyl-p-phenylenediamine
Ethylacetoacetate; p-Ethylbenzaldehyde; Ethylene carbonate; Ethyl formate
p-Fluorophenol; Furan polymer
Hexamethyleneimine; Hydrogenated coconut acid; Hydrogenated lanolin; Hydrogenated menhaden acid; Hydrogenated menhaden oil; Hydrogenated soybean oil

Intermediates *(cont'd.)*

p-Isobutylbenzaldehyde

Lauric acid; Levulinic acid

Maleic acid; Malonic acid; 2-Mercaptoethanol; Methyl acetoacetate; Methyl anthranilate; Methyl butynol; 1,2-Methylenedioxybenzene; Methyl pentynol

2-Nitro-1-butanol; 2-Nitro-2-ethyl-1,3-propanediol; 5-Nitroisophthalic acid; 2-Nitro-2-methyl-1-propanol; Nitropropane; 2-Nitropropane

PEG-8 oleate; Phenoxyacetic acid; Phenyl dichlorophosphate; Phenyl glycidyl ether; N-Phenyl-p-phenylenediamine; α-Picoline; Pivaloyl chloride; Polyglyceryl-6 dioleate; Potassium thiocyanate; PPG-400; PPG-2000; Pyridine; Pyrogallol; 2-Pyrrolidone

Sodium lactate; Sodium thiocyanate; Squalene; Suberic acid

Tetrahydrofuran; Tetrahydroxypropyl ethylenediamine; Tetraisopropyl methylenediphosphonate; Thioglycerin; p-Toluene sulfonic acid; p-Tolyl aldehyde; Tributyl phosphite; Triethyl phosphite; Triethyl phosphonoacetate; Triethyl phosphonoformate; Triisopropyl phosphite; Trimethyl phosphite; Tripropylene glycol; Tris (hydroxymethyl) aminomethane

Vinyl bromide

Lubricants

Trade names: AA USP; Acconon 400-MO; Adol® 90 NF; Agar Agar NF Flake #1; Akoext SB; Akolizer C; Akolizer P; Akolizer S; Akorex B; Aldo® PGHMS; Alkamuls® EL-620; Alkamuls® PSML-20; Alkamuls® PSMS-4; Alphafil 500 USP; Alpine Talc USP BC 127; Altalc 200 USP; Altalc 300 USP; Altalc 400 USP; Amerlate® P; Amerlate® W

BBS; Benol®; Blandol®; Britol®; Britol® 6NF; Britol® 7NF; Britol® 9NF; Britol® 20USP; Britol® 35USP; Britol® 50USP

Candex®; Capmul® GMS; Caprol® 10G10O; Caprol® ET; Captex® 300; Captex® 355; Captex® 800; Captex® 8000; Captex® 8227; Carbopol® 907; Carbowax® PEG 300; Carbowax® Sentry® PEG 300; Carbowax® Sentry® PEG 400; Carbowax® Sentry® PEG 540 Blend; Carbowax® Sentry® PEG 600; Carbowax® Sentry® PEG 900; Carbowax® Sentry® PEG 1000; Carbowax® Sentry® PEG 1450; Carbowax® Sentry® PEG 3350; Carbowax® Sentry® PEG 4600; Carbowax® Sentry® PEG 8000; Carnation®; Cecavon ZN 70; Cecavon ZN 71; Cecavon ZN 72; Cecavon ZN 73; Cecavon ZN 735; Ceraphyl® 28; Ceraphyl® 31; Ceraphyl® 50; Ceraphyl® 55; Ceraphyl® 140; Ceraphyl® 494; Ceraphyl® 791; Ceraphyl® 847; Cetina; C-Flakes; Cithrol GDS N/E; Cithrol GDS S/E; Cithrol GML N/E; Cithrol GMO N/E; Cithrol GMO S/E; Cithrol GMR N/E; Cithrol GMR S/E; Cithrol GMS Acid Stable; Cithrol GMS N/E; Cithrol GMS S/E; Cithrol PGML N/E; Cithrol PGML S/E; Cithrol PGMO N/E; Cithrol PGMR N/E; Cithrol PGMR S/E; Cithrol PGMS N/E; Cithrol PGMS S/E; Clarity; Compritol 888; Compritol 888 ATO; Cosmetol® X; Cremophor® S 9; Crill 1; Crill 3; Crill 35; Crodamol CP; Crodamol CSP; Crodamol PTC; Crodamol PTIS; Crodamol SS; Crodasinic LS35; Crystal® O; Crystal® Crown; Crystosol USP 240; Crystosol USP 350; Cutina® HR Powd.

Diamond Quality®; Dimethicone L-45 Series; Distilled Lipolan; Dow Corning® 360 Medical Fluid; Dow Corning® 365 35% Dimethicone NF Emulsion; Drakeol® 5; Drakeol® 7; Drakeol® 9; Drakeol® 32; Drakeol® 34; Duratex; Dynacerin® 660; Dynasan® 112; Dynasan® 114; Dynasan® 116; Dynasan® 118

Eastman® OC; Emcocel® 50M; Emcocel® 90M; Emcocel® LM; EmCon W; EmCon Walnut; Emdex® Plus; Emerest® 2423; Emerest® 2715; Emersol® 6332 NF; Emery® 1650; Emery® 1660; Estasan GT 8-40 3578; Estasan GT 8-60 3575; Estasan GT 8-60 3580; Estasan GT 8-65 3577; Estasan GT 8-65 3581; Estasan GT 8-70 3579; Eutanol® G

Fancol ALA; Fancol ALA-10; Fancol CAB; Fancol CH; Fancol HL; Fancol LA; Fancor Lanwax

Gastric Mucin N.N.R; Gloria®; Glucam® E-20 Distearate

Hodag PEG 3350; Hodag PEG 8000; Hydrobrite 200PO; Hydrobrite 300PO; Hydrobrite 380PO; Hydrobrite 550PO; Hydrokote® 175; Hydrokote® M; Hystar® CG; Hystar® TPF; Hystrene® 4516; Hystrene® 5016 NF; Hystrene® 7022; Hystrene® 9016; Hystrene® 9022; Hystrene® 9512; Hystrene® 9718 NF

Imwitor® 191; Imwitor® 900; Imwitor® 928; Imwitor® 988; Incrocas 35

Kaydol®; Kaydol® S; KELGIN® MV; KELTOSE®

Lanaetex CO; Laneto 100-Flaked; Lanexol AWS; Lanolin Pharmaceutical; Lanolin USP; Lanotein AWS 30; Lantrol® HP-2073; Lexemul® 55G; Lexemul® PEG-200 DL; Lipex 109; Lipex 201; Lipex 202; Lipex 203; Lipex 401; Lipolan S; Liponic 70-NC; Liponic 76-NC; Liponic 83-NC; Lubragluv; Lubrajel® CG; Lubrajel® DV; Lubrajel® MS; Lubrajel® Oil; Lubrajel® RR;

Lubricants *(cont'd.)*

Lubrajel® TW; Lubrajel® WA; Lubritab®

Macol® 1; Mazamide® L-5; Mazol® GMS-K; Methocel® A4C Premium; Methocel® A4M Premium; Methocel® A15LV Premium; Methocel® E3 Premium; Methocel® E4M Premium; Methocel® E6 Premium; Methocel® E15LV Premium; Methocel® E50LV Premium; Methocel® E50P; Methocel® K4M Premium; Methocel® K15M Premium; Methocel® K100LV Premium; Methocel® K100M Premium; Miglyol® 810; Miglyol® 812; Miglyol® 840; Miglyol® 8810; Modulan®; Multiwax® 180-M; Multiwax® ML-445; Multiwax® W-445; Multiwax® W-835; Multiwax® X-145A; Myvaplex® 600; Myvaplex® 600P NF; Myvatex® TL

Neobee® 18

Orzol®

Pegosperse® 50 DS; Pelemol® G7B; Pelemol® IBS; Penreco Amber; Penreco Blond; Penreco Cream; Penreco Lily; Penreco Royal; Penreco Super; Perfecta® USP; Petrac® Magnesium Stearate MG-20 NF; Polyaldo® DGHO; Polyox® WSR 205; Polyox® WSR 301; Polyox® WSR 303; Polyox® WSR 308; Polyox® WSR 1105; Polyox® WSR 3333; Polyox® WSR N-10; Polyox® WSR N-12K; Polyox® WSR N-60K; Polyox® WSR N-80; Polyox® WSR N-750; Polyox® WSR N-3000; Polyox® WSR Coagulant; Powdered Agar Agar Bacteriological Grade; Powdered Agar Agar NF M-100 (Gracilaria); Powdered Agar Agar NF MK-60; Powdered Agar Agar NF MK-80-B; Powdered Agar Agar NF MK-80 (Bacteriological); Powdered Agar Agar NF S-100; Powdered Agar Agar NF S-100-B; Powdered Agar Agar NF S-150; Powdered Agar Agar NF S-150-B; Powdered Agar Agar Type K-60; Powdered Agar Agar Type K-80; Powdered Agar Agar Type K-100; Powdered Agar Agar Type K-150; Powdered Guar Gum Type A; Powdered Guar Gum Type AA; Powdered Guar Gum Type B; Powdered Guar Gum Type BB; Precirol ATO 5; Protol®; Protopet® Alba; Protopet® White 1S; Protopet® White 2L; Protopet® White 3C; Protopet® Yellow 2A; Protopet® Yellow 3C; Protopet® Yellow A; Pruv™; Pureco® 76; Pureco® 100; Pure-Dent® B700; Pure-Dent® B851; Pure-Dent® B852; Purtalc USP

Rhodasurf® PEG 300; Rhodasurf® PEG 600; Ritachol®; Ritalan®; Ritawax AEO; Ritawax ALA; Robane®; Ryoto Sugar Ester B-370; Ryoto Sugar Ester L-595; Ryoto Sugar Ester L-1570; Ryoto Sugar Ester L-1695; Ryoto Sugar Ester LWA-1570; Ryoto Sugar Ester M-1695; Ryoto Sugar Ester O-1570; Ryoto Sugar Ester OWA-1570; Ryoto Sugar Ester P-1570; Ryoto Sugar Ester P-1570S; Ryoto Sugar Ester P-1670; Ryoto Sugar Ester S-270; Ryoto Sugar Ester S-370; Ryoto Sugar Ester S-370F; Ryoto Sugar Ester S-570; Ryoto Sugar Ester S-770; Ryoto Sugar Ester S-970; Ryoto Sugar Ester S-1170; Ryoto Sugar Ester S-1170S; Ryoto Sugar Ester S-1570; Ryoto Sugar Ester S-1670; Ryoto Sugar Ester S-1670S

Sarkosyl® L; Sarkosyl® LC; Sebase; Silwet® L-7500; Sodium Benzoate BP88; Solulan® 25; Solulan® 97; Solulan® 98; Soluwax; Span® 20; Span® 40; Span® 60; Span® 60K; Span® 65; Span® 65K; Span® 85; Stamere® CK-S; Stamere® N-325; Stamere® N-350; Stamere® N-350 S; Stamere® NI; Standamul® G-32/36; Standamul® G-32/36 Stearate; Starch 1500®; Starch 1500® LM; Sterotex®; Sterotex® C; Sterotex® HM; Sterotex® K; Sterotex® NF; Superla® No. 5; Superla® No. 6; Superla® No. 7; Superla® No. 9; Superla® No. 10; Superla® No. 13; Superla® No. 18; Superla® No. 21; Superla® No. 31; Superla® No. 35; Super Refined® Olive Oil; Super Refined® Sesame Oil; Super Refined® Soybean Oil USP; Super Sterol Ester; Super White Protopet®; Supreme USP; Syncrowax ERL-C; Syncrowax HGL-C

Ticalose® 15; Ticalose® 30

Volpo 3; Volpo 5; Volpo 10; Volpo 20

Witafrol® 7420; Witco® Zinc Stearate U.S.P.-D

Chemicals: Acetylated lanolin; Aluminum orthophosphate; Apricot kernel oil; Arachidyl alcohol

Behenic acid; Butylene glycol dicaprylate/caprate

C10-30 cholesterol/lanosterol esters; C18-36 acid glycol ester; Calcium stearate; Canola oil; Castor oil; Cetyl lactate; Cocoyl sarcosine

Decyl oleate; Dioctyl calcium sulfosuccinate; Dioctyl sodium sulfosuccinate

Glycereth-26; Glycereth-7 benzoate; Glyceryl behenate; Glyceryl cocoate; Glyceryl dioleate; Glyceryl dioleate SE; Glyceryl distearate; Glyceryl distearate SE; Glyceryl laurate SE; Glyceryl oleate SE; Glyceryl polymethacrylate; Glyceryl ricinoleate SE

Hydrogenated castor oil; Hydrogenated coconut oil; Hydrogenated cottonseed oil; Hydrogenated lanolin; Hydrogenated menhaden acid; Hydrogenated palm oil; Hydrogenated soybean oil; Hydrogenated starch hydrolysate; Hydrogenated vegetable oil

Isocetyl stearate; Isocetyl stearoyl stearate; Isopropyl lanolate; Isopropyl laurate; Isopropyl myristate; Isopropyl stearate; Isostearyl isostearate; Isostearyl lactate

Jojoba oil

Lubricants *(cont'd.)*

Lanolin wax; Laureth-4; Lauric acid; Lauryl lactate

Magnesium stearate; Methyl gluceth-20 distearate; Microcrystalline cellulose; Microcrystalline wax; Mineral oil; Myristyl lactate

Octyldodecanol; Octyldodecyl stearoyl stearate; Octyl isononanoate; Oleth-3; Oleth-5; Oleyl alcohol; Oleyl erucate; Oleyl oleate; Olive oil; Oxidized cellulose

Palmitic acid; PEG-6; PEG-8; PEG-12; PEG-14; PEG-20; PEG-32; PEG-40; PEG-75; PEG-100; PEG-150; PEG-200; PEG-2M; PEG-5M; PEG-7M; PEG-9M; PEG-14M; PEG-20M; PEG-23M; PEG-45M; PEG-90M; PEG-115M; PEG-9 castor oil; PEG-15 castor oil; PEG-30 castor oil; PEG-4 dilaurate; PEG-8 dioleate; PEG-6 lauramide DEA; PEG-8 oleate; PEG-300 oleate; PEG-6-32 stearate; PEG-40 stearate; PEG-300 stearate; PEG-4 tallate; Pentaerythrityl tetracaprylate/caprate; Pentaerythrityl tetraisostearate; Polyacrylic acid; Polyethylene glycol; Polyethylene oxide; Polyglyceryl-10 decaoleate; Polyglyceryl-10 dioleate; Polyglyceryl-10 hexaoleate; Polyglyceryl-10 tetraoleate; Polysorbate 61; Polyvinyl alcohol; Potassium benzoate; PPG-400; PPG-2000; PPG-15 stearyl ether; Propylene glycol dioctanoate; Propylene glycol dipelargonate; Propylene glycol laurate; Propylene glycol laurate SE; Propylene glycol myristate; Propylene glycol oleate; Propylene glycol oleate SE; Propylene glycol ricinoleate; Propylene glycol ricinoleate SE; Propylene glycol stearate; Propylene glycol stearate SE

Sesame oil; Shea butter; Sodium N-oleoyl sarcosinate; Sodium stearyl fumarate; Sorbitan tristearate; Squalane; Stearic acid; Sucrose dilaurate; Sucrose laurate; Sucrose myristate; Sucrose oleate; Sucrose polystearate; Sucrose tribehenate; Sucrose tristearate

Talc; Tetradecyleicosyl stearate; Tribehenin; Tricaprylin; Tridecyl neopentanoate; Trilaurin; Trimyristin; Trioctanoin; Triolein; Tripalmitin; Tristearin; Triundecanoin

Walnut oil; Wheat germ oil

Zinc stearate

Mineral supplements. *See Nutrients*

Moisturizers

Trade names: Akoext SB; Akolizer C; Akolizer P; Akolizer S; Akorex B; Aloe-Moist™; Amerchol® 400; Amerchol® BL; Amerchol® C; Amerchol® CAB; Amerchol L-101®; Amerchol® L-500; Amerlate® P; Anhydrous Lanolin P.80; Anhydrous Lanolin P.95; Aqualose L75

BBS

Captex® 200; Captex® 200-E6; Captex® 300; Captex® 350; Captex® 800; Captex® 8227; Carbopol® 1342; Ceraphyl® GA-D; Cholesterol NF; Clarity; Copherol® 950LC; Copherol® 1250; Copherol® F-1300; Corona PNL; Corona Lanolin; Coronet Lanolin; Cosmetic Lanolin; Creamjel; Cremba; Croderol G7000

Dermajel; Dexpanthenol USP, FCC No. 63909

Emery® 912; Emery® 916; Emery® 917; Emery® 918; Emery® 1656; Emery® 1660; Emery® 1732; Emery® 1740; Emery® 1747; Emery® HP-2050; Emery® HP-2060

Fancol HL; Fancol LAO; Fancol VB; Fancor IPL; Forlan C-24

Glucam® E-20 Distearate; Glucam® P-20 Distearate; Glycyrrhetinic Acid Phytosome®; Guardian Protective Skin Cream

Hartolan; Hydrokote® 175; Hydrokote® M

Karajel; Koster Keunen Synthetic Spermaceti

Lanesta P; Lanesta SA-30; Laneto 50; Laneto 100; Laneto AWS; Lanfrax® 1779; Lanolin Pharmaceutical; Lantrol® HP-2074; Lexol® GT-865; Lexol® PG-800; Lipocol; Lipolan 31-20; Lipolan Distilled; Lubrajel® CG; Lubrajel® DV; Lubrajel® MS; Lubrajel® Oil; Lubrajel® TW; Lubrajel® WA; Lysidone®

Macol® CA 30P; Medilan™

Nasojel; Natipide® II PG; NCL-818; Noveon® AA-1

Orange Wax, Deodorized

DL-Panthenol USP, FCC No. 63915; Pharmaceutical Lanolin; Polypro 5000® Pharmaceutical Grade; Polypro 15000® Pharmaceutical Grade; Pureco® 100

Ritachol®; Ritalan®; Ritalan® AWS; RITA Lanolin; Ritawax AEO; Ritawax ALA; Ritawax Super; Robane®

Sebase; Softisan® 378; Standamul® 1414-E; Sterotex®; Super Corona Lanolin; Superfine

Moisturizers *(cont'd.)*

Lanolin; Super Refined® Wheat Germ Oil; Super Sterol Ester

Terra-Dry™ FD Aloe Vera Powd. Decolorized FDD; Terra-Dry™ FD Aloe Vera Powd. Reg. FDR; Terra-Spray® Spray Dried Aloe Vera Powd. Decolorized SDD; Terra-Spray® Spray Dried Aloe Vera Powd. Reg. SDR; Ticalose® 15; Ticalose® 30; Ticalose® 150 R; Ticalose® 700 R; Ticalose® 2000 R; Ticalose® 5000 R

Vigilan; Vitamin A Palmitate Type PIMO/BH No. 638280100; Vitamin A Palmitate USP, FCC Type P1.7 No. 262090000; Vitamin A Palmitate USP, FCC Type P1.7/BHT No. 63693

White Swan; Wickenol® 155; Wickenol® 156; Wickenol® 158; Wickenol® 159; Wickenol® 160; Wickenol® 161; Wickenol® 171

Chemicals: Aloe vera gel

Candelilla wax; Caprylic/capric/stearic triglyceride

Dioctyl adipate; Dioctyl succinate

Glyceryl alginate; Glyceryl polymethacrylate

Hydrogenated coconut oil; Hydrogenated cottonseed oil; Hydrogenated lecithin; Hydrogenated soybean oil

Isopentyldiol

Lysine PCA

Maleated soybean oil

Octyl hydroxystearate; Octyl pelargonate; Octyl stearate; Oleyl lactate; Orange wax

DL-Panthenol; PEG-4; PEG-16; PEG-60; PEG-5 hydrogenated castor oil; PEG-7 hydrogenated castor oil; PEG-10 hydrogenated castor oil; PEG-20 hydrogenated castor oil; PEG-30 hydrogenated castor oil; PEG-80 hydrogenated castor oil; PEG-100 hydrogenated castor oil; PEG-20 hydrogenated lanolin; PEG-6 propylene glycol dicaprylate/dicaprate; Polycarbophil; Polypropylene glycol; PPG-30 cetyl ether; Propylene glycol dioctanoate

Retinyl palmitate

Shea butter

Triundecanoin

Wheat germ oil

Neutralizers. *See pH control agents*

Nutrients • Dietary supplements • Mineral supplements

Trade names: A-641; Albrite® Dicalcium Phosphate Anhyd; Alcolec® Granules; Aloe Con WLG 200; Ascorbic Acid USP/FCC, 100 Mesh; Ascorbic Acid USP, FCC Fine Gran. No. 6045655; Ascorbic Acid USP, FCC Gran. No. 6045654; Ascorbic Acid USP, FCC Type S No. 6045660; Ascorbic Acid USP, FCC Ultra-Fine Powd No. 6045653; Ascorbyl Palmitate NF, FCC No. 60412

d-Biotin USP, FCC No. 63345; Bitrit-1™ (1% Biotin Trituration No. 65324)

Calcium Ascorbate FCC No. 60475; Calfos; Cap-Shure® FF-165-60; Coated Ascorbic Acid 97.5% No. 60482; Cozeen®; Crodamol GTCC; Cyanocobalamin USP Cryst. No. 69932

Desiccated Beef Liver Granular Undefatted; Desiccated Beef Liver Granular Defatted; Desiccated Beef Liver Powd.; Desiccated Beef Liver Powd. Defatted; Desiccated Hog Bile; Desiccated Ox Bile; Desiccated Pork Liver Powd.; Destab™; Dry Beta Carotene Beadlets 10% CWS No. 65633; Dry Beta Carotene Beadlets 10% No. 65661; Dry Vitamin A Palmitate Type 250-SD No. 65378; Dry Vitamin D$_3$ Beadlets Type 850 No. 652550401, 652550601; Dry Vitamin D$_3$ Type 100 CWS No. 65242; Dry Vitamin E Acetate 50% SD No. 65356; Dry Vitamin E Acetate 50% Type CWS/F No. 652530001; Durkote Calcium Carbonate/Starch, Acacia Gum; Durkote Ferrous Fumarate/Hydrog. Veg. Oil; Durkote Ferrous Sulfate/Hydrog. Veg. Oil; Durkote Vitamin B-1/Hydrog. Veg. Oil; Durkote Vitamin C/Hydrog. Veg. Oil

Extract of Hog Bile; Extract of Ox Bile NF XI; Extramalt 10; Extramalt 35; Extramalt Dark; Extramalt Light

Folic Acid 10% Trituration No. 69997; Folic Acid USP, FCC No. 20383; Freeze Dried Beef Liver Powd.; Freeze Dried Beef Liver Powd. Defatted; Freeze Dried Pork Liver Powd.

Gluconal® CA A; Gluconal® CA M; Gluconal® CA M B; Gluconal® CO; Gluconal® CU; Gluconal® FE; Gluconal® K; Gluconal® MG; Gluconal® MN; Gluconal® NA; Gluconal® ZN

Iron Bile Salts

Jerusalem Artichoke Flour (JAF)

Nutrients *(cont'd.)*

Liver Conc. Paste

Magnesium Hydroxide USP; Magnesium Hydroxide USP DC; Maltrin® M040; Maltrin® M050; Maltrin® M100; Maltrin® M150; Maltrin® M180; Marinco® CH; Marinco® CH-Granular; Marinco® CL; Marinco OH; Micro-White® 10 Codex; Micro-White® 25 Codex; Micro-White® 50 Codex; Micro-White® 100 Codex; Milk Calcium ND (Food Grade)

Neobee® 1053; Neobee® SL-110; Neobee® SL-120; Neobee® SL-130; Neobee® SL-140; Niacin USP, FCC Fine Granular No. 69901; Niacin USP, FCC No. 69902; Niacinamide Free Flowing No. 69914; Niacinamide USP, FCC No. 69905; Niacinamide USP, FCC Fine Granular No. 69916

d,l-Panthenol FCC Grade; Puracal® PG; Puracal® PP; Puracal® TG; Puramex® AL; Puramex® FE; Puramex® MG; Puramex® MN; Puramex® ZN; Pyridoxine Hydrochloride USP, FCC Fine Powd. No. 60650

Riboflavin USP, FCC No. 602940002; Riboflavin-5´-Phosphate Sodium USP, FCC No. 60296; Ritapan D; Ritapan DL; Ritapan TA; Rocoat® Riboflavin 25% No. 60289; Rocoat® Riboflavin $33^1/_3$ No. 60288; Rocoat® Thiamine Mononitrate $33^1/_3$% No. 60188

Safester A-75; Safester A 75 WS; Shiitake KS-2; Shiitake Mushroom Extract SHIEXT; Sodium Ascorbate USP, FCC Fine Gran. No. 6047709; Sodium Ascorbate USP, FCC Fine Powd. No. 6047708; Sodium Ascorbate USP, FCC Type AG No. 6047710; Soluble Liver Powd.; Soluble Trachea CS 16 Substance; Sunyl® 80; Sunyl® 90; Super Refined® Menhaden Oil; Super Refined® Soybean Oil USP; Super Refined® Wheat Germ Oil

Thiamine Hydrochloride USP, FCC Regular Type No. 601160; Thiamine Mononitrate USP, FCC Fine Powd. No. 601340; Type B Torula Dried Yeast

Vitacote® B12 1%; Vitamin A Palmitate Type 250-CWS No. 65312; Vitamin A Palmitate Type PIMO/BH No. 638280100; Vitamin A Palmitate USP, FCC Type P1.7 No. 262090000; Vitamin A Palmitate USP, FCC Type P1.7/BHT No. 63693; Vitamin A Palmitate USP, FCC Type P1.7/E No. 63699; Vitamin B_{12} 0.1% SD No. 65354; Vitamin B_{12} 1% Trituration No. 69992; Vitamin B_{12} 1% Trituration No. 69993; Vitamin B_{12} 1.0% SD No. 65305; Vitamin E Acetate USP Oil; Vitamin E USP Tocopherol; Vitamin E USP, FCC No. 60525; Vitamin E USP, FCC No. 60526; Vitinc® dl-alpha Tocopheryl Acetate USP XXII

Chemicals: Aluminum lactate; Amaranth; Ammonium phosphate
d-Biotin
Calcium ascorbate; Calcium borogluconate; Calcium citrate; Calcium gluceptate; Calcium gluconate; Calcium lactate; Calcium D-pantothenate; Calcium phosphate dibasic; Calcium phosphate dibasic dihydrate; Calcium phosphate tribasic; Calcium pyrophosphate; Cholecalciferol; Chondroitin sulfate; Cobalt gluconate; Cod liver oil; Copper gluconate; Cyanocobalamin
Ethyl linoleate
Ferric pyrophosphate; Ferrous fumarate; Ferrous gluconate; Ferrous lactate; Ferrous sulfate; Folic acid
D-Gluconic acid; Glycine
L-Histidine
Jerusalem artichoke flour
Kelp
Lecithin; Linolenic acid
Magnesium gluconate; Magnesium lactate; Magnesium oxide; Maltodextrin; Maltose; Manganese gluconate; Manganese lactate; Menhaden oil; DL-Methionine; L-Methionine
Niacinamide; Nicotinic acid
Octacosanol; Olive oil
D-Panthenol; DL-Panthenol; Panthenyl triacetate; Peanut oil; Phosphatidylcholine; Potassium chloride; Potassium D-gluconate; Potassium iodide; Pyridoxine HCl
Riboflavin; Riboflavin-5´-phosphate sodium
L-Serine; Sodium gluconate; Sunflower seed oil; Sweet almond oil
Tapioca starch; Thiamine HCl; Thiamine nitrate; Tocopherol; D-α-Tocopherol
Wheat germ oil
Yeast
Zinc acetate; Zinc gluconate; Zinc lactate

Odor masking agents. *See Deodorizing agents*

Opacifiers

Trade names: Alphafil 500 USP; Altalc 200 USP; Altalc 300 USP; Amerlate® P

Cecavon ZN 70; Cecavon ZN 71; Cecavon ZN 72; Cecavon ZN 73; Cecavon ZN 735; Cerasynt® PA; Cetostearyl Alcohol BP; Cetostearyl Alcohol NF; Cosmowax J; Cosmowax K; Cromul EM 0685

Drewmulse® 1128; Drewmulse® GMOK; Drewmulse® HM-100; Drewmulse® TP; Drewmulse® V; Drewmulse® V-SE

Fancor IPL

Geleol

Hilton Davis Titanium Dioxide; Hodag GML; Hodag GMO; Hodag GMO-D; Hodag GMR; Hodag GMR-D; Hodag GMS; Hodag GTO

Kemester® EGDS; Kemester® EGMS; Kessco® PEG 200 DL; Kessco® PEG 200 DO; Kessco® PEG 200 DS; Kessco® PEG 200 ML; Kessco® PEG 200 MO; Kessco® PEG 200 MS; Kessco® PEG 300 DL; Kessco® PEG 300 DO; Kessco® PEG 300 DS; Kessco® PEG 300 MO; Kessco® PEG 300 MS; Kessco® PEG 400 DL; Kessco® PEG 400 DO; Kessco® PEG 400 DS; Kessco® PEG 400 ML; Kessco® PEG 400 MO; Kessco® PEG 400 MS; Kessco® PEG 600 DL; Kessco® PEG 600 DO; Kessco® PEG 600 DS; Kessco® PEG 600 ML; Kessco® PEG 600 MO; Kessco® PEG 600 MS; Kessco® PEG 1000 DL; Kessco® PEG 1000 DO; Kessco® PEG 1000 DS; Kessco® PEG 1000 ML; Kessco® PEG 1000 MO; Kessco® PEG 1000 MS; Kessco® PEG 1540 DL; Kessco® PEG 1540 DO; Kessco® PEG 1540 DS; Kessco® PEG 1540 ML; Kessco® PEG 1540 MO; Kessco® PEG 1540 MS; Kessco® PEG 4000 DL; Kessco® PEG 4000 DO; Kessco® PEG 4000 DS; Kessco® PEG 4000 ML; Kessco® PEG 4000 MO; Kessco® PEG 4000 MS; Kessco® PEG 6000 DL; Kessco® PEG 6000 DO; Kessco® PEG 6000 DS; Kessco® PEG 6000 ML; Kessco® PEG 6000 MO; Kessco® PEG 6000 MS; Kessco PGMS; Kessco® Glyceryl Monostearate Pure

Lexemul® 55G; Lexemul® 503; Lexemul® 515; Lexemul® AR; Lexemul® AS

Maltrin® M050; Mapeg® EGDS; Mapeg® EGMS; Mazol® 165C; Monomuls® 60-10; Monomuls® 60-15; Monomuls® 60-20; Monomuls® 60-25; Monomuls® 60-25/2; Monomuls® 60-30; Monomuls® 60-35; Monomuls® 60-40; Monomuls® 60-45; Monomuls® 90-10; Monomuls® 90-15; Monomuls® 90-20; Monomuls® 90-25/2; Monomuls® 90-25/5; Monomuls® 90-30; Monomuls® 90-35; Monomuls® 90-40; Monomuls® 90-45

Nikkol MYS-1EX

Polawax®

Simulsol® 165; Solulan® 98; Standamul® G-32/36 Stearate; Syncrowax ERL-C; Syncrowax HGL-C; Syncrowax HR-C

Tegin® G

Chemicals: Behenic acid

Calcium carbonate; Cetyl alcohol; CI 77891

Glycol distearate

Hydrogenated tallow glycerides

Lard glycerides

Myristamide MEA

Palm glyceride; Palm glycerides; PEG-6 dilaurate; PEG-20 dilaurate; PEG-32 dilaurate; PEG-75 dilaurate; PEG-150 dilaurate; PEG-6 dioleate; PEG-20 dioleate; PEG-32 dioleate; PEG-75 dioleate; PEG-150 dioleate; PEG-6 distearate; PEG-8 distearate; PEG-20 distearate; PEG-32 distearate; PEG-75 distearate; PEG-32 laurate; PEG-32 oleate; PEG-75 oleate; PEG-300 oleate; PEG-32 stearate; PEG-75 stearate; Propylene glycol myristate; Propylene glycol stearate SE

Styrene/acrylates copolymer; Sucrose acetate isobutyrate; Sunflower seed oil glycerides

Titanium dioxide

Penetrating agents. *See Spreading agents*

Perfumes. *See Fragrances*

pH control agents • Acidulants • Alkalizing agents • Buffers • Neutralizers • Antacids

Trade names: AMP; AMP-95; AMPD
Basic Magnesium Carbonate USP Heavy; Basic Magnesium Carbonate USP Heavy Low Moisture; Basic Magnesium Carbonate USP Light; Basic Magnesium Carbonate USP Pregranular Heavy; Basic Magnesium Carbonate USP Pregranular Light
Destab™; Durkote Malic Acid/Maltodextrin
Lactic Acid 88% USP/FCC
Magnesium Hydroxide USP; Magnesium Hydroxide USP DC; Marinco® CH; Marinco® CH-Granular; Marinco® CL; Marinco H-USP; Marinco OH; Marinco OL
Patlac® NAL; Purac® USP 88
Sodium Bicarbonate USP No. 2 Fine Gran.; Sodium Citrate USP, FCC Dihydrate Gran. No. 69976; Sodium Citrate USP, FCC Dihydrate Fine Gran. No. 69975
Tris Amino® Conc.; Tris Amino® Crystals; Tris Amino® Molecular Biology Grade; Tris Amino® Ultra Pure Standard
Unichem ACETA

Chemicals: Acetic acid; Acetic acid, glacial; Acetic anhydride; Adipic acid; Albumin; Aluminum hydroxide; Aluminum orthophosphate; 2-Amino-2-methyl-1,3-propanediol; 2-Amino-2-methyl-1-propanol; Ammonia; Ammonium acetate; Ammonium carbonate; Ammonium hydroxide; Ammonium phosphate, dibasic
Boric acid
Calcium carbonate; Calcium citrate; Calcium gluconate; Calcium pyrophosphate; Citric acid; Citric acid monohydrate
Diethanolamine
Ethylenediamine
Gluconolactone; Glycine
Hydrochloric acid; N-Hydroxysuccinic acid
Lactic acid
Magnesium aluminum silicate; Magnesium carbonate; Magnesium oxide; Magnesium silicate
Nitric acid
Phosphoric acid; Potassium bicarbonate; Potassium citrate; Potassium hydroxide; Potassium metaphosphate; Potassium phosphate; Potassium phosphate dibasic; Propionic acid
Ricinoleic acid
Sodium acetate anhydrous; Sodium acetate trihydrate; Sodium bicarbonate; Sodium borate; Sodium borate decahydrate; Sodium carbonate; Sodium citrate; Sodium hydroxide; Sodium lactate; Sodium phosphate; Sodium phosphate dibasic anhydrous; Sodium phosphate dibasic heptahydrate; Succinic acid; Sulfuric acid
Tartaric acid; Triethanolamine; Tris (hydroxymethyl) aminomethane; Trisodium citrate

Pigments. *See Colorants*

Plasticizers

Trade names: Adeka Propylene Glycol (P); Admex® 760; Aldo® PGHMS; Amerchol® CAB; ATBC; ATEC
Carbowax® Sentry® PEG 300; Carbowax® Sentry® PEG 540 Blend; Carbowax® Sentry® PEG 600; Carbowax® Sentry® PEG 900; Carbowax® Sentry® PEG 1000; Carbowax® Sentry® PEG 1450; Carbowax® Sentry® PEG 3350; Carbowax® Sentry® PEG 4600; Carbowax® Sentry® PEG 8000; Crodamol CP; Crodamol CSP; Crovol A40; Crovol M40; Crovol M70
Dow E300 NF; Dow E400 NF; Dow E600 NF; Dow E900 NF; Dow E1000 NF; Dow E1450 NF; Dow E3350 NF; Dow E4500 NF; Dow E8000 NF
Eastman® Triacetin
Fancol HL; Fancol LA; Fancol LAO; Forlan C-24
Hartolan; Hodag 20-L; Hodag 22-L; Hodag 40-L; Hodag 40-O; Hodag 40-R; Hodag 40-S; Hodag 42-L; Hodag 42-O; Hodag 42-S; Hodag 60-L; Hodag 60-S; Hodag 62-O; Hodag 100-S; Hodag 150-S; Hodag PEG 300
Imwitor® 928; Imwitor® 988

Plasticizers *(cont'd.)*

Lamegin® GLP 10, 20; Laneto 100-Flaked; Liponic 70-NC; Liponic 76-NC; Liponic 83-NC
Mazol® GMS-K; Myvacet® 5-07; Myvacet® 7-07; Myvacet® 9-45
Ritalan®; Ritawax AEO; Ritawax ALA
Solan; Solulan® PB-2; Solulan® PB-5; Solulan® PB-10; Solulan® PB-20; Super Hartolan; Super-Sat; Super-Sat AWS-4; Super-Sat AWS-24; Super Solan Flaked; Super Sterol Ester
TBC; TEC
Vigilan AWS
Wickenol® 142; Witafrol® 7420

Chemicals: Acetylated hydrogenated cottonseed glyceride; Acetylated hydrogenated soybean oil glycerides; Acetylated hydrogenated vegetable oil glycerides; Acetyl tributyl citrate; Acetyl triethyl citrate
Carnauba; Castor oil; Cetearyl palmitate
Diacetylated monoglycerides; Dibutyl sebacate; Diethyl phthalate; Dipropylene glycol salicylate
Glycerin; Glyceryl cocoate; Glyceryl tricaprate/caprylate; Glyceryl triheptanoate
Hydrogenated lanolin; Hydrogenated tallow glyceride lactate
Mono- and di-acetylated monoglycerides
Octyldodecyl myristate
PEG-6; PEG-12; PEG-20; PEG-75; PEG-150; PEG-8 dilaurate; PEG-12 dioleate; PEG-60 lanolin; PEG-8 ricinoleate; PEG-20 stearate; Polybutene; Polyester adipate; Polyethylene glycol; Polyethylene glycol monomethyl ether; Polyglyceryl-10 tetraoleate; PPG-2 lanolin alcohol ether; PPG-5 lanolin alcohol ether; Propylene glycol
Sorbitol
Triacetin; Tributyl citrate; Triethyl citrate

Polymer membranes

Chemicals: Cellulose acetate; Cellulose acetate trimellitate
Glyceryl linoleate
Hydroxypropyl methylcellulose acetate succinate; Hydroxypropyl methylcellulose phthalate
Oxidized cellulose
Polycarbophil; Poly (DL-lactic acid)

Preservatives

Trade names: Adeka Propylene Glycol (P); Ascorbyl Palmitate NF, FCC No. 60412
Benzoic Acid U.S.P./F.C.C; Biopure® 100; Bronopol; Bronopol-Boots® BP; Butyl Parasept® NF
Calcium Ascorbate FCC No. 60475; Catigene® DC 100; CPC; CPC Sumquat 6060
Elestab® HP 100; Ethyl Parasept® NF
Germaben® II; Germall® 115; Germall® II
Hyamine® 1622 50%; Hyamine® 1622 Crystals
Lexgard® B; Lexgard® M; Lexgard® P; LiquaPar® Oil
Methyl Parasept® NF/FCC; Myacide® SP
Nipa ISDN; Nipa Benzocaine; Nipabenzyl; Nipabutyl; Nipabutyl Potassium; Nipabutyl Sodium; Nipacide® Potassium; Nipacide® Sodium; Nipacombin A; Nipacombin PK; Nipacombin SK; Nipagin A; Nipagin A Potassium; Nipagin A Sodium; Nipagin M; Nipagin M Potassium; Nipagin M Sodium; Nipaguard® BPX; Nipasept Potassium; Nipasept Sodium; Nipasol M; Nipasol M Potassium; Nipasol M Sodium; Nipastat
Ottasept® Extra
Phenonip; Phenoxetol; Propylene Glycol USP/FCC Ultra Grade; Propyl Parasept® NF/FCC; Purac® PH 88; Purac® USP 88; Purasal® P/HQ 60; Purasal® S/HQ 60
RSP 50-5 BZK; RSP 451-5 BZK
Sodium Ascorbate USP, FCC Fine Gran. No. 6047709; Sodium Ascorbate USP, FCC Fine Powd. No. 6047708; Sodium Ascorbate USP, FCC Type AG No. 6047710; Sodium Benzoate BP88
Teric PEG 400; Teric PEG 1500
Unicide U-13; Uniphen P-23; Uniquart CPC
Vancide® 89 RE

Chemicals: Ascorbyl palmitate

Preservatives (cont'd.)

Benzalkonium chloride; Benzethonium chloride; Benzoic acid; Benzoin; Benzyl alcohol; Benzyl benzoate; Benzylparaben; BHA; BHT; Boric acid; 2-Bromo-2-nitropropane-1,3-diol; Butylparaben

Calcium acetate; Calcium ascorbate; Calcium benzoate; Calcium disodium EDTA; Captan; Cetrimonium bromide; Cetylpyridinium chloride; Chloroacetamide; Chlorobutanol hemihydrate; p-Chloro-m-cresol; Chloroform; Chloroxylenol; m-Cresol

Dehydroacetic acid; Diazolidinyl urea; Dichlorobenzyl alcohol; Dilauryl thiodipropionate; Disodium EDTA; DMDM hydantoin

Edetic acid; Erythorbic acid

Formaldehyde

Glucose oxidase; Glycerin; Gum benzoin

Hexamidine diisethionate; Hydrochloric acid

Imidazolidinyl urea; Isobutylparaben; Isopropylparaben; Isosorbide dinitrate

Maleic acid; Maleic anhydride; Methenamine hippurate; Methylchloroisothiazolinone; Methylisothiazolinone; Methylparaben

Paraformaldehyde; Phenethyl alcohol; Phenol; Phenoxyethanol; Phenylmercuric acetate; Phenylmercuric borate; Phenylmercuric nitrate; Polyaminopropyl biguanide; Polyquaternium-1; Potassium benzoate; Potassium bisulfite; Potassium butyl paraben; Potassium ethylparaben; Potassium lactate; Potassium metabisulfite; Potassium methylparaben; Potassium propylparaben; Potassium sorbate; Propionic acid; Propyl gallate

Quaternium-15

Salicylic acid; Sodium ascorbate; Sodium benzoate; Sodium borate; Sodium borate decahydrate; Sodium butylparaben; Sodium chloride; Sodium dehydroacetate; Sodium ethylparaben; Sodium lactate; Sodium methylparaben; Sodium propionate; Sodium propylparaben; Sodium salicylate; Sodium sulfite; Sorbic acid; Sulfur dioxide

Tetrahydroxypropyl ethylenediamine; Thimerosal; Thioglycerin; Thymol; D-α-Tocopherol

Processing aids

Trade names:
Aerosil® 380; Aerosil® COK 84
Compritol 888 ATO; Corn Po 4
Docusate Calcium USP in Corn Oil NF Sol'n; Docusate Sodium USP in Polyethylene Glycol 400 NF; Durkote Calcium Carbonate/Starch, Acacia Gum
Empicol® LX; Empicol® LZ; Empilan® P7061; Empilan® P7062; Empilan® P7087
Softigen® 701
Tebol™ 99
Wacker Silicone Antifoam Emulsion SE 9

Chemicals:
Acacia; Ammonium phosphate, dibasic
t-Butyl alcohol; N,N-Butyl benzene sulfonamide; But-2-yne-1,4-diol
Carbon, activated; Chlorotrifluoromethane; Crotonic acid
Disodium EDTA; Distarch phosphate
Ethyl maltol
Hydrogenated castor oil
D-Mannitol; Metanilic acid
Polysorbate 80; Propylene glycol alginate; Pyrocatechol; 2-Pyrrolidone
Saccharin; Sodium 1,2-dimyristoyl-sn-glycero(3)phosphatidylcholine; Sodium 1,2-dipalmitoyl-sn-glycero(3)phosphatidylcholine; Sodium 1,2-distearoyl-sn-glycero(3)phosphatidylcholine
Thiophene; Thiophenol; Thiourea; Triethylenetetramine; Trifluoromethane sulfonic acid

Propellants • Aerosols

Chemicals:
Butane
Cryofluorane
Dichlorodifluoromethane; Dichlorotetrafluoroethane; Dichlorotetrafluoromethane
Isobutane
Nitrogen; Nitrous oxide
Propane
Trichlorofluoromethane

Protective agents • Soothing agents • Demulcents

Trade names: Albagel Premium USP 4444; Allantoin; Aloe-Moist™; Aloe-Moist™ A; Aloe Vera Gel Decolorized 1X; Aloe Vera Gel Decolorized 10X; Aloe Vera Gel Decolorized 40X
Benecel® Hydroxypropyl Methylcellulose; Bentonite USP BC 670; Britol® 6NF; Britol® 7NF; Britol® 9NF; Britol® 20USP; Britol® 35USP; Britol® 50USP
CMC Daicel 1150; CMC Daicel 1160; CMC Daicel 1220; CMC Daicel 1260; Copherol® 1250; Copherol® F-1300; Crodyne BY-19; Crovol M40; Crovol M70
Dermajel; Dow Corning® 360 Medical Fluid; DPCP
Fancol CB; Fancol CB Extra; Fancol CH
Glycyrrhetinic Acid Phytosome®; Granular Gum Arabic NF/FCC C-4010; Granular Gum Arabic Type A-1 NF Premium; Granular Gum Arabic Type A-2 NF Premium; Guardian Protective Skin Cream; Gum Arabic NF, Tech; Gum Arabic NF/FCC Clean Amber Sorts
Hydrobrite 200PO; Hydrobrite 300PO; Hydrobrite 380PO; Hydrobrite 550PO
Imwitor® 928; Imwitor® 988
Kaydol® S; Kelisema Natural Pure Shea Butter; Klucel® 'F' Grades; Korthix H-NF
Multiwax® 180-M; Multiwax® ML-445; Multiwax® W-445; Multiwax® W-835; Multiwax® X-145A
Natrosol® 250; Natrosol® Hydroxyethylcellulose
PDCP; Penreco Amber; Penreco Blond; Penreco Cream; Penreco Lily; Perfecta® USP; Plasdone® C-15; Plasdone® K-29/32; Plasdone® K-90; Plasdone® K-90D; Plasdone® K-90M; Pluronic® F68NF; Pluronic® F87NF; Pluronic® F108NF; Pluronic® F127NF; Pluronic® L44NF; Powdered Gum Arabic NF/FCC G-150; Powdered Gum Arabic NF/FCC Superselect Type NB-4; Powdered Gum Arabic Type B-100 NF Premium; Powdered Gum Arabic Type B-200 NF Premium; Protopet® Alba; Protopet® White 1S; Protopet® White 2L; Protopet® White 3C; Protopet® Yellow 2A
Spray Dried Gum Arabic NF/FCC CM; Spray Dried Gum Arabic NF/FCC CS (Low Bacteria); Spray Dried Gum Arabic NF/FCC CS-R; Spray Dried Gum Arabic Type A-180 NF Premium; Spray Dried Gum Arabic Type A-230 NF Extra; Spray Dried Hydrolysed Fish Gelatin; Supercol® Guar Gum; Super Refined® Shark Liver Oil; Supraene®
Tepescohuite AMI Watersoluble; Tepescohuite HG; Tepescohuite HS; Tepescohuite LS; Tylose® MH Grades; Tylose® MHB
Vee Gee Pharmaceutical Gelatins
Witafrol® 7420

Chemicals: Agar; Allantoin; Aloe vera gel; Aluminum silicate
Bentonite; Bismuth oxychloride; Bismuth subgallate; Bismuth subnitrate
Caramel; Carrageenan; Castor oil; Cocoa butter; Cod liver oil
Dimethicone; Dimethicone propylethylenediamine behenate; Dipotassium glycyrrhizate
Elm bark extract
Glyceryl cocoate; Guar gum; Gum benzoin
Hydrolyzed vegetable protein; Hydroxyethylcellulose; Hydroxypropylcellulose
Isopropyl alcohol
Jojoba oil
Karaya gum
Lanolin; Linseed oil
Magnesium hydroxide; Methyl hydroxyethylcellulose; Microcrystalline wax; Mimosa bark extract
Pectin; Potato starch; Propylene glycol; Pyrogallol
Quince seed
Rice starch
Shark liver oil; Shea butter; Squalene; Storax; Sweet almond oil
Tapioca starch
Wheat starch
Zinc oxide; Zinc stearate

Refatting agents. *See Superfatting agents*

Retarding agents

Trade names: CAO®-3/Blend 29; Cutina® HR Powd.

Retarding agents *(cont'd.)*

Dynasan® 112; Dynasan® 114; Dynasan® 116; Dynasan® 118
Hoechst Wax E Pharma
Imwitor® 900
Plasdone® K-25; Plasdone® K-29/32; Plasdone® K-90; Plasdone® K-90D; Plasdone® K-90M

Chemicals: Magnesium carbonate; Maleic acid; Montan acid wax
Trilaurin; Trimyristin; Tripalmitin; Tristearin

Rheology control agents. *See Thickeners*

Sequestrants. *See Chelating agents*

Softeners. *See Conditioners*

Solubilizers

Trade names: Abil®-Wax 9801; Accomid PK; Acconon 200-MS; Acconon 400-ML; Acconon 400-MO; Acconon 400-MS; Acconon CA-5; Acconon CA-8; Acconon CA-15; Acconon E; Acconon TGH; Acconon W230; Alcolec® Z-3; Aldo® MO FG; Aldo® MR; Aldo® MS-20 KFG; Aldo® MSD; Aldo® PGHMS; Aldosperse® MO-50 FG; Aldosperse® O-20 FG; Aldosperse® O-20 KFG; Alkamuls® EL-620; Alkamuls® PSML-20; Aloe Vera Oil; Alpha W6 HP 0.6; Alpha W6 M1.8; Alpha W 6 Pharma Grade; Aqualose L75
Brij® 700
Capmul® EMG; Capmul® GDL; Capmul® GMO; Capmul® MCM; Capmul® MCMC8; Capmul® POE-L; Capmul® POE-S; Caprol® 3GO; Caprol® 6G2O; Caprol® 10G4O; Caprol® 10G10O; Caprol® PGE860; Captex® 200; Captex® 300; Captex® 355; Captex® 810A; Captex® 810D; Cavitron Cyclo-dextrin™; Cegesoft® C 17; Ceraphyl® 45; Ceraphyl® 140-A; Ceraphyl® 230; Ceraphyl® 368; Cerex ELS 250; Cerex ELS 400; Cerex ELS 450; Cetiol® A; Cetiol® HE; Cholesterol NF; Cremba; Cremophor® EL; Cremophor® RH 40; Cremophor® RH 410; Cremophor® RH 455; Crill 3; Crill 4; Crill 6; Crillet 1; Crillet 2; Crillet 3; Crillet 4; Crillet 6; Crillet 11; Crillet 31; Crillet 35; Crillet 41; Crillet 45; Crodalan AWS; Crodet L4; Crodet L8; Crodet L12; Crodet L24; Crodet L40; Crodet L100; Crodet S4; Crodet S8; Crodet S12; Crodet S24; Crodet S40; Crodet S100; Croduret 50; Crossential Oleic; Crovol A40; Crovol A70; Crovol M40; Crovol M70
Dehydol® LS 2 DEO; Dehydol® LS 3 DEO; Dehydol® LS 4 DEO; Docusate Sodium USP; Drewmulse® 3-1-O; Drewmulse® 6-2-S; Drewmulse® 10-4-O; Drewmulse® 10-8-O; Drewmulse® 10-10-O; Drewmulse® 10-10-S; Drewmulse® POE-SML; Drewmulse® POE-SMO; Drewmulse® POE-STS; Drewmulse® SML; Drewmulse® SMO; Drewmulse® SMS; Drewmulse® STS; Drewpol® 10-4-O; Drewpol® 10-10-O; DSS Granular; DSS Tablet Grade; Dynacerin® 660
Eccowet® W-50; Eccowet® W-88; Emalex C-20; Emalex C-30; Emalex C-40; Emalex C-50; Emalex ET-2020; Emalex ET-8020; Emalex ET-8040; Emalex HC-40; Emersol® 6313 NF; Emersol® 6333 NF; Emery® 912; Emery® 916; Emery® 917; Emery® 918; Emulmetik™ 970; Escalol® 587; Ethylan® GEO8; Eumulgin® HRE 40; Eumulgin® HRE 60; Eumulgin® L; Eumulgin® PRT 36; Eumulgin® PRT 56; Eumulgin® PRT 200; Eumulgin® RO 35; Eumulgin® SML 20; Eumulgin® SMO 20; Eumulgin® SMS 20
Fancol HL-20; Fancol HL-24; Fluilan AWS; Forlan C-24
Glucam® E-10; Glucam® E-20; Glucam® P-10; Glucam® P-20; Glycosperse® L-20; Glycosperse® O-5; Glycosperse® O-20; Glycosperse® O-20 FG; Glycosperse® O-20 KFG; Glycosperse® P-20; Glycosperse® S-20; Glycosperse® TO-20; Glycosperse® TS-20
Igepal® CO-630 Special; Imwitor® 308; Imwitor® 312; Imwitor® 370; Imwitor® 742; Imwitor® 928; Imwitor® 988; Isofol® 12; Isofol® 14T; Isofol® 16; Isofol® 18E; Isofol® 18T; Isofol® 20; Isofol® 24; Isopropylpalmitat
Kessco® PEG 200 DL; Kessco® PEG 200 DO; Kessco® PEG 200 DS; Kessco® PEG 200 ML;

Solubilizers *(cont'd.)*

Kessco® PEG 200 MO; Kessco® PEG 200 MS; Kessco® PEG 300 DL; Kessco® PEG 300 DO; Kessco® PEG 300 DS; Kessco® PEG 300 MO; Kessco® PEG 300 MS; Kessco® PEG 400 DL; Kessco® PEG 400 DO; Kessco® PEG 400 DS; Kessco® PEG 400 ML; Kessco® PEG 400 MO; Kessco® PEG 400 MS; Kessco® PEG 600 DL; Kessco® PEG 600 DO; Kessco® PEG 600 DS; Kessco® PEG 600 ML; Kessco® PEG 600 MO; Kessco® PEG 600 MS; Kessco® PEG 1000 DL; Kessco® PEG 1000 DO; Kessco® PEG 1000 DS; Kessco® PEG 1000 ML; Kessco® PEG 1000 MO; Kessco® PEG 1000 MS; Kessco® PEG 1540 DL; Kessco® PEG 1540 DO; Kessco® PEG 1540 DS; Kessco® PEG 1540 ML; Kessco® PEG 1540 MO; Kessco® PEG 1540 MS; Kessco® PEG 4000 DL; Kessco® PEG 4000 DO; Kessco® PEG 4000 DS; Kessco® PEG 4000 ML; Kessco® PEG 4000 MO; Kessco® PEG 4000 MS; Kessco® PEG 6000 DL; Kessco® PEG 6000 DO; Kessco® PEG 6000 DS; Kessco® PEG 6000 ML; Kessco® PEG 6000 MO; Kessco® PEG 6000 MS; Kollidon®

Labrafac® CM10; Labrafac® Hydro; Labrafil® M 1944 CS; Labrafil® M 2125 CS; Labrafil® WL 2609 BS; Labrasol; Lan-Aqua-Sol 50; Lan-Aqua-Sol 100; Laneto 50; Laneto 100; Laneto 100-Flaked; Laneto AWS; Lanogel® 21; Lanogel® 31; Lanogel® 41; Lanogel® 61; Lexol® GT-855; Lexol® IPP; Lexol® IPP-A; Lexol® IPP-NF; Lexol® PG-865; Lipolan 31; Lipolan 31-20; Lipolan Distilled; Liquid Absorption Base Type A; Liquid Absorption Base Type T; Loralan-CH

Macol® 1; Macol® 2; Macol® 2D; Macol® 2LF; Macol® 4; Macol® 8; Macol® 10; Macol® 22; Macol® 27; Macol® 33; Macol® 40; Macol® 85; Maltrin® M700; Mazamide® C-2; Mazamide® L-5; Mazol® 159; Mazol® PGO-31 K; Mazol® PGO-104; Miglyol® 810; Miglyol® 812; Miglyol® 840; Miglyol® 8810; Miranol® C2M Conc. NP; Monawet MO-70R; Montanox® 20; Montanox® 20 DF; Montanox® 80; Montanox® 80 DF; Montanox® 85; Myritol® 318; Myverol® 18-99

Neobee® 18; Neobee® 1053; Neobee® 1054; Neobee® M-5; Neobee® M-20; Neobee® O; Nikkol BC-23; Nikkol BC-25TX; Nikkol BC-30TX; Nikkol BC-40TX; Nikkol BEG-1630; Nikkol BPS-5; Nikkol DOP-8N; Nikkol GO-430; Nikkol GO-440; Nikkol GO-460; Nikkol MYS-1EX; Nikkol MYS-2; Nikkol MYS-4; Nikkol MYS-10; Nikkol MYS-25; Nikkol MYS-40; Nikkol MYS-45; Nikkol MYS-55; Nikkol PBC-31; Nikkol TDP-2; Nikkol TL-10, TL-10EX; Nikkol TO-10; Nikkol TS-10; Nikkol TS-30; Nikkol TS-106; Nikkol Decaglyn 1-IS; Nikkol Decaglyn 1-L; Nikkol Decaglyn 1-LN; Nikkol Decaglyn 1-M; Nikkol Decaglyn 1-O; Nikkol Decaglyn 1-S; Novol NF

Oramix® CG 110-60; Oramix® L30

Pelemol® DIPS; Pelemol® G7A; Pharmasolve™; Phosal® 50 PG; Phosal® 53 MCT; Phosal® 75 SA; Phospholipid PTD; Phospholipid PTL; Phospholipid PTZ; Phospholipon® 90; Phospholipon® 90 G; Phospholipon® 100, 100G; Phospholipon® CC; Phospholipon® MC; Phospholipon® PG Na; Phospholipon® SG Na; Plasdone® C-15; Plasdone® C-30; Plasdone® K-25; Plasdone® K-29/32; Plasdone® K-90; Plasdone® K-90D; Plasdone® K-90M; Pluronic® F68NF; Pluronic® F87NF; Pluronic® F108NF; Pluronic® F127NF; Pluronic® L44NF; Polychol 5; Polychol 15; Prox-onic L 081-05; Prox-onic L 101-05; Prox-onic L 102-02; Prox-onic L 121-09; Prox-onic L 161-05; Prox-onic L 181-05; Prox-onic L 201-02; Prox-onic OA-1/020; Prox-onic OA-2/020; PVP/VA E-535; PVP/VA E-635; PVP/VA E-735; PVP/VA I-235; PVP/VA I-335; PVP/VA I-535; PVP/VA I-735; PVP/VA S-630; 2-Pyrol®

Renex® 759; Rewopal® CSF 11; Rhodasurf® ON-870; Rhodasurf® ON-877; RITA IPM; RITA IPP; Ritawax AEO; Ritawax ALA; Ritawax Super; Ryoto Sugar Ester B-370; Ryoto Sugar Ester L-595; Ryoto Sugar Ester L-1570; Ryoto Sugar Ester L-1695; Ryoto Sugar Ester LWA-1570; Ryoto Sugar Ester M-1695; Ryoto Sugar Ester O-1570; Ryoto Sugar Ester OWA-1570; Ryoto Sugar Ester P-1570; Ryoto Sugar Ester P-1570S; Ryoto Sugar Ester P-1670; Ryoto Sugar Ester S-270; Ryoto Sugar Ester S-370; Ryoto Sugar Ester S-370F; Ryoto Sugar Ester S-570; Ryoto Sugar Ester S-770; Ryoto Sugar Ester S-970; Ryoto Sugar Ester S-1170; Ryoto Sugar Ester S-1170S; Ryoto Sugar Ester S-1570; Ryoto Sugar Ester S-1670; Ryoto Sugar Ester S-1670S

Sellig R 3395; Simulsol® 58; Simulsol® 78; Simulsol® 98; Simulsol® 1292; Simulsol® 1293; Simulsol® 5719; Simulsol® 5817; Simulsol® CS; Simulsol® OL 50; Simulsol® P4; Simulsol® P23; Sobalg FD 000 Range; Sobalg FD 900 Range; Softigen® 767; Solan; Solimate; Solubilisant γ 2420; Solubilisant γ 2428; Solulan® 25; Sorbilene L; Sorbilene O; Sorgen TW80; Span® 60; Span® 60K; Span® 60 VS; Standamul® HE; Super Refined® Orange Roughy Oil; Super-Sat AWS-4; Super-Sat AWS-24; Super Solan Flaked; Synperonic NP1; Synperonic NP2; Synperonic NP4; Synperonic NP5; Synperonic NP5.5; Synperonic NP6; Synperonic NP7; Synperonic NP8; Synperonic NP8.5; Synperonic NP8.75; Synperonic NP9; Synperonic NP9.5; Synperonic NP9.75; Synperonic NP10; Synperonic NP12; Synperonic NP13; Synperonic NP15; Synperonic NP17; Synperonic NP20; Synperonic NP25; Synperonic NP30; Synperonic NP30/70; Synperonic NP35; Synperonic NP40; Synperonic

Solubilizers *(cont'd.)*

NP50; Synperonic OP3; Synperonic OP4.5; Synperonic OP6; Synperonic OP7.5; Synperonic OP8; Synperonic OP10; Synperonic OP10.5; Synperonic OP11; Synperonic OP12.5; Synperonic OP16; Synperonic OP16.5; Synperonic OP20; Synperonic OP25; Synperonic OP30; Synperonic OP40; Synperonic OP40/70

Tagat® L2; Tagat® O2; Tagat® R40; Tagat® R60; Tagat® R63; Tagat® S2; Tetronic® 304; T-Maz® 20; T-Maz® 28; T-Maz® 60K; T-Maz® 61; T-Maz® 65K; T-Maz® 80; T-Maz® 80K; T-Maz® 80KLM; T-Maz® 81; T-Maz® 81K; T-Maz® 85; Transcutol; Tris Amino® Conc.; Tris Amino® Molecular Biology Grade; Tris Amino® Ultra Pure Standard

Vigilan AWS; Volpo 3; Volpo 5; Volpo 10; Volpo 20; Volpo CS-20; Volpo L23

Wickenol® 171; Witafrol® 7420

Chemicals: Acacia

Benzalkonium chloride; Benzethonium chloride; Benzyl alcohol; Butylene glycol dicaprylate/caprate; 2-Butyl-1-octanol

C12-13 pareth-23; C12-15 pareth-2 phosphate; Caprylic/capric glycerides; Caprylic/capric triglyceride; Caprylyl/capryl glucoside; Ceteareth-11; Ceteareth-16; Ceteareth-20; Ceteareth-33; Cetyl dimethicone; Cetylpyridinium chloride; Cholesterol; Choleth-24; Cocamide DEA; Cocohydroxyethyl PEG-imidazolinium chloride phosphate; Cocohydroxy-ethyl PEG-imidazolinium chloride phosphate; Corn oil PEG-6 esters; Corn oil PEG-8 esters

Decyl dodecanol; 1,2-Dicaproyl-sn-glycero(3) phosphatidylcholine; Diethanolamine; Diisopropyl sebacate; Dimethyl sulfoxide; 1,2-Dimyristoyl-sn-glycero(3) phosphatidylcholine; Dioctylmalate; Dioctyl sodium sulfosuccinate; Disodium cocoamphodiacetate

Emulsifying wax NF; EO/PO block polymer or copolymer; Ethoxydiglycol

Glycereth-7 triacetate; Glycerin; Glyceryl caprylate; Glyceryl caprylate/caprate; Glyceryl cocoate; Glyceryl dilaurate; Glyceryl laurate; Glyceryl mono/dioleate; Glyceryl myristate; Glyceryl ricinoleate; Glyceryl stearate; Glyceryl stearate citrate; Glyceryl stearate SE; Glyceryl tricaprate/caprylate; Glyceryl triheptanoate; Glycol stearate

2-Hexyl-1-decanol; Hybrid safflower oil; Hydroxypropyl-β-cyclodextrin

Isoceteth-20; Isoceteth-30; Isodecyl oleate; Isostearyl lactate

Laneth-5; Laneth-15; Lanolin alcohol; Lauramidopropyl PEG-dimonium chloride phosphate; Laureth-2; Laureth-3; Laureth-4; Lecithin

Methyl gluceth-10; Methyl gluceth-20; N-Methyl-2-pyrrolidone; Myristyl lactate

Nonoxynol-1; Nonoxynol-2; Nonoxynol-4; Nonoxynol-5; Nonoxynol-6; Nonoxynol-7; Nonoxynol-8; Nonoxynol-9; Nonoxynol-10; Nonoxynol-12; Nonoxynol-13; Nonoxynol-15; Nonoxynol-17; Nonoxynol-20; Nonoxynol-25; Nonoxynol-30; Nonoxynol-35; Nonoxynol-40; Nonoxynol-50

Octoxynol-3; Octoxynol-5; Octoxynol-6; Octoxynol-8; Octoxynol-9; Octoxynol-10; Octoxynol-11; Octoxynol-13; Octoxynol-16; Octoxynol-20; Octoxynol-25; Octoxynol-30; Octoxynol-40; Octyldodecanol; Octyl hydroxystearate; Octyl palmitate; Octyl salicylate; Oleic acid; Oleth-3; Oleth-5; Oleth-10; Oleth-20; Oleyl alcohol; Oleyl erucate; Orange roughy oil

PEG-20 almond glycerides; PEG-60 almond glycerides; PEG-6 caprylic/capric glycerides; PEG-8 caprylic/capric glycerides; PEG-5 castor oil; PEG-8 castor oil; PEG-9 castor oil; PEG-15 castor oil; PEG-20 castor oil; PEG-30 castor oil; PEG-35 castor oil; PEG-36 castor oil; PEG-40 castor oil; PEG-50 castor oil; PEG-56 castor oil; PEG-200 castor oil; PEG-3 cocamide MEA; PEG-20 corn glycerides; PEG-60 corn glycerides; PEG-4 dilaurate; PEG-6 dilaurate; PEG-8 dilaurate; PEG-12 dilaurate; PEG-20 dilaurate; PEG-32 dilaurate; PEG-75 dilaurate; PEG-150 dilaurate; PEG-4 dioleate; PEG-6 dioleate; PEG-8 dioleate; PEG-12 dioleate; PEG-20 dioleate; PEG-32 dioleate; PEG-75 dioleate; PEG-150 dioleate; PEG-4 distearate; PEG-6 distearate; PEG-8 distearate; PEG-12 distearate; PEG-20 distearate; PEG-32 distearate; PEG-75 distearate; PEG-150 distearate; PEG-7 glyceryl cocoate; PEG-12 glyceryl laurate; PEG-20 glyceryl laurate; PEG-20 glyceryl oleate; PEG-20 glyceryl stearate; PEG-25 hydrogenated castor oil; PEG-40 hydrogenated castor oil; PEG-45 hydrogenated castor oil; PEG-50 hydrogenated castor oil; PEG-60 hydrogenated castor oil; PEG-100 hydrogenated castor oil; PEG-20 hydrogenated lanolin; PEG-24 hydrogenated lanolin; PEG-27 lanolin; PEG-30 lanolin; PEG-40 lanolin; PEG-60 lanolin; PEG-70 lanolin; PEG-75 lanolin; PEG-85 lanolin; PEG-6 lauramide DEA; PEG-4 laurate; PEG-6 laurate; PEG-8 laurate; PEG-12 laurate; PEG-20 laurate; PEG-32 laurate; PEG-75 laurate; PEG-150 laurate; PEG-4 oleate; PEG-6 oleate; PEG-8 oleate; PEG-12 oleate; PEG-20 oleate; PEG-32 oleate; PEG-75 oleate; PEG-150 oleate; PEG-5 phytosterol; PEG-10 phytosterol; PEG-15 phytosterol; PEG-20 phytosterol; PEG-25 phytosterol; PEG-30 phytosterol; PEG-10-PPG-10 glyceryl stearate; PEG-10 propylene glycol; PEG-80 sorbitan laurate; PEG-40 sorbitan oleate; PEG-6 sorbitan stearate; PEG-30 sorbitan tetraoleate; PEG-40 sorbitan tetraoleate; PEG-60 sorbitan tetraoleate; PEG-20

Solubilizers *(cont'd.)*

sorbitan tritallate; PEG-2 stearate; PEG-4 stearate; PEG-6 stearate; PEG-8 stearate; PEG-10 stearate; PEG-12 stearate; PEG-25 stearate; PEG-32 stearate; PEG-40 stearate; PEG-45 stearate; PEG-50 stearate; PEG-55 stearate; PEG-75 stearate; PEG-100 stearate; PEG-150 stearate; Poloxamer 101; Poloxamer 105; Poloxamer 108; Poloxamer 123; Poloxamer 181; Poloxamer 182; Poloxamer 185; Poloxamer 217; Poloxamer 231; Poloxamer 234; Poloxamer 235; Poloxamer 237; Poloxamer 238; Poloxamer 282; Poloxamer 284; Poloxamer 288; Poloxamer 331; Poloxamer 333; Poloxamer 334; Poloxamer 335; Poloxamer 338; Poloxamer 401; Poloxamer 402; Poloxamer 403; Poloxamer 407; Poloxamine 304; Poloxamine 504; Poloxamine 701; Poloxamine 702; Poloxamine 704; Poloxamine 707; Poloxamine 901; Poloxamine 904; Poloxamine 908; Poloxamine 1101; Poloxamine 1102; Poloxamine 1104; Poloxamine 1107; Poloxamine 1301; Poloxamine 1302; Poloxamine 1304; Poloxamine 1307; Poloxamine 1501; Poloxamine 1502; Poloxamine 1504; Poloxamine 1508; Polyglyceryl-10 decaoleate; Polyglyceryl-10 decastearate; Polyglyceryl-6 dioleate; Polyglyceryl-10 isostearate; Polyglyceryl-10 laurate; Polyglyceryl-10 linoleate; Polyglyceryl-10 myristate; Polyglyceryl-10 octaoleate; Polyglyceryl-3 oleate; Polyglyceryl-10 oleate; Polyglyceryl-3 stearate; Polyglyceryl-10 stearate; Polysorbate 20; Polysorbate 21; Polysorbate 40; Polysorbate 60; Polysorbate 61; Polysorbate 65; Polysorbate 80; Polysorbate 81; Polysorbate 85; PPG-2-ceteareth-9; PPG-4 ceteth-1; PPG-4-ceteth-10; PPG-4-ceteth-20; PPG-8-ceteth-1; PPG-3-laureth-9; PPG-10 methyl glucose ether; PPG-20 methyl glucose ether; PPG-12-PEG-50 lanolin; PPG-15 stearyl ether; Propylene glycol diacetate; Propylene glycol isoceteth; PVP/VA copolymer; 2-Pyrrolidone

Sodium dioleth-8 phosphate; Sodium 1,2-dipalmitoyl-sn-glycero(3)phosphatidylcholine; Sodium 1,2-distearoyl-sn-glycero(3)phosphatidylcholine; Sodium lauryl sulfate; Sodium stearate; Sodium xylenesulfonate; Sorbitan isostearate; Sorbitan laurate; Sorbitan oleate; Sorbitan palmitate; Sorbitan sesquioleate; Sorbitan stearate; Sorbitan trioleate; Sorbitan tristearate; Steareth-20; Stearic acid; Sucrose cocoate; Sucrose dilaurate; Sucrose distearate; Sucrose laurate; Sucrose myristate; Sucrose palmitate; Sucrose polystearate; Sucrose stearate; Sucrose tribehenate; Sucrose tristearate; 5-Sulfosalicylic acid

TEA-stearate; Triethanolamine; Triolein; Tris (hydroxymethyl) aminomethane; Tyloxapol

Solvents

Trade names: Adeka Propylene Glycol (P)

Capmul® MCM-90; Captex® 200; Captex® 300; Captex® 350; Captex® 810A; Captex® 810D; Carbowax® PEG 300; Carbowax® Sentry® PEG 300; Carbowax® Sentry® PEG 400; Carbowax® Sentry® PEG 540 Blend; Carbowax® Sentry® PEG 600; Carbowax® Sentry® PEG 900; Carbowax® Sentry® PEG 1000; Carbowax® Sentry® PEG 1450; Carbowax® Sentry® PEG 3350; Carbowax® Sentry® PEG 4600; Carbowax® Sentry® PEG 8000; Ceraphyl® 140; Ceraphyl® 140-A; Comperlan® COD; Corona Lanolin; Coronet Lanolin; Cosmetol® X; Crill 1; Crillet 6; Crodamol CAP; Crodamol GTCC; Crodamol PMP; Crystal® O; Crystal® Crown

Diamond Quality®; Diglyme; DMSO; Dow E300 NF; Dow E400 NF; Dow E600 NF; Dow E900 NF; Dow E1000 NF; Dow E1450 NF; Dow E3350 NF; Dow E4500 NF; Dow E8000 NF; Dynacerin® 660

Eastman® Triacetin; EmCon CO; EmCon Olive; EmCon Rice Bran; Emery® 912; Emery® 916; Emery® 917; Emery® 918; Estasan GT 8-40 3578; Estasan GT 8-60 3575; Estasan GT 8-60 3580; Estasan GT 8-65 3577; Estasan GT 8-65 3581; Ethyl Diglyme

Fancol CB; Fancol CB Extra; Fancorsil A; Filmex® A-2; Filmex® B; Filmex® C; Filmex® D-1; Filmex® D-2

Glucam® E-10; Glucam® E-20; Glucam® P-10; Glucam® P-20

High Purity MTBE

Imwitor® 742; Incrocas 35

Kemstrene® 96.0% USP; Kemstrene® 99.0%; Kemstrene® 99.7% USP

Labrafac® Hydro; Labrafac® LIPO; Labrafil® Isostearique; Labrasol; Lexol® 3975; Lexol® PG-800; Lexol® PG-865; Lipovol SES; Lipovol SES-S

Macol® 57; Miglyol® 810; Miglyol® 812; Miglyol® 840; Miglyol® 8810; Monoglyme; Myritol® 318; Myritol® PC

Neobee® 18; Neobee® 1054; Neobee® 1062; Neobee® M-5; Neobee® O; Novol NF

PD-23; PD-25; PD-28; Pecosil® DCU; Pelemol® G7A; Penreco Snow; Pharmasolve™;

Solvents *(cont'd.)*

Pluracol® E400 NF; Pluracol® E600 NF; Pluracol® E1450 NF; Propylene Glycol USP/FCC Ultra Grade; Punctilious® SDA 1-1; 2-Pyrol®

Ricinion; Ritawax AEO; Ritawax ALA

Sesame Oil USP/NF 16; Solimate; Soluphor® P; Stearate 400 WL 817; Stearate 1500; Stearate 6000 WL 1644; Super Refined® Almond Oil; Super Refined® Corn Oil; Super Refined® Cottonseed Oil; Super Refined® Olive Oil; Super Refined® Peanut Oil; Super Refined® Safflower Oil; Super Refined® Sesame Oil; Super Refined® Soybean Oil USP

Tebol™; Tebol™ 99; Tetraglyme; Transcutol; Triglyme

Wickenol® 158; Wickenol® 171

York Krystal Kleer Castor Oil; York USP Castor Oil

Chemicals: Acetone; Acetyl triethyl citrate; Alcohol; t-Amyl alcohol; Apricot kernel oil PEG-6 esters

Benzyl benzoate; Bornyl acetate; Butyl alcohol; t-Butyl alcohol; Butylene glycol; Butyrolactone

Caprylic/capric glycerides; Caprylic/capric/lauric triglyceride; Caprylic/capric/linoleic triglyceride; Castor oil; Chloroform; Collodion; Corn oil; Cottonseed oil

Diacetylated monoglycerides; Diethylene glycol dibutyl ether; Diethylene glycol dimethyl ether; Dimethicone copolyol undecylenate; Dimethyl isosorbide; Dimethyl sulfoxide; Dioctyl adipate; Dioctyl phthalate; 1,4-Dioxane

Ethoxydiglycol; Ethylene glycol dimethyl ether; Ethyl oleate

Glycereth-7 triacetate; Glycerin; Glyceryl caprylate/caprate; Glyceryl formal; Glycol

Hexylene glycol; Hybrid safflower oil; Hydrogenated castor oil

Isodecyl oleate; Isopropyl alcohol; Isopropyl myristate; Isostearyl lactate

Methyl alcohol; Methyl t-butyl ether; Methylene chloride; Methyl gluceth-10; Methyl gluceth-20; Methyl isobutyl ketone; N-Methyl-2-pyrrolidone; Mineral oil

Octyl hydroxystearate; Oleic acid; Olive oil

Peanut oil; PEG-4; PEG-6; PEG-8; PEG-9; PEG-12; PEG-14; PEG-16; PEG-20; PEG-75; PEG-150; PEG-33 castor oil; PEG-4 dilaurate; PEG-20 dilaurate; PEG-3 dimethyl ether; PEG-4 dimethyl ether; PEG-6 isostearate; PEG-8 palmitostearate; PEG-150 palmitostearate; PEG-20 sorbitan isostearate; 3-Pentanol; Phenethyl alcohol; β-Picoline; γ-Picoline; Polyethylene glycol; Polyethylene glycol monomethyl ether; Polyglyceryl-3 diisostearate; Polypropylene glycol; PPG-10 butanediol; PPG-10 methyl glucose ether; PPG-20 methyl glucose ether; PPG-15 stearyl ether; Propylene glycol; Propylene glycol alginate; Propylene glycol dicaprylate/dicaprate; Propylene glycol laurate; 2-Pyrrolidone

Rice bran oil

SDA alcohol 3A; Sesame oil; Sweet almond oil

α-Terpineol; Tetrahydrofuran; Tetrahydroxypropyl ethylenediamine; Triisostearin PEG-6 esters; Turpentine oil

Soothing agents. *See Protective agents*

Sorbents. *See Absorbents*

Spreading agents • Penetrating agents

Trade names: Abil®-Wax 2434; Abil®-Wax 9801; Abil®-Wax 9814; Amerchol® H-9; Amerchol L-101®; Amerlate® P

Capmul® MCM; Capmul® MCMC8; Captex® 200; Captex® 800; Cegesoft® C 24; Ceraphyl® 55; Ceraphyl® 375; Ceraphyl® 791; Cetiol® A; Cetiol® LC; Cetiol® OE; Cetiol® V; Crodalan LA; Crodamol CAP; Crodamol GTCC; Crodamol PMP; Crodasinic LS35; Crodex N

Eccowet® W-50; Eccowet® W-88; Estasan GT 8-40 3578; Estasan GT 8-60 3575; Estasan GT 8-60 3580; Estasan GT 8-65 3577; Estasan GT 8-65 3581; Estasan GT 8-70 3579; Eutanol® G; Eutanol® G16

Fancol Acel; Fancol Karite Extract; Fancol LAO; Fluilan

Hartolan

Imwitor® 928; Imwitor® 988; Isopropylmyristat

Kessco® PEG 200 DL; Kessco® PEG 200 DO; Kessco® PEG 200 DS; Kessco® PEG 200 ML;

Spreading agents *(cont'd.)*

Kessco® PEG 200 MO; Kessco® PEG 200 MS; Kessco® PEG 300 DL; Kessco® PEG 300 DO; Kessco® PEG 300 DS; Kessco® PEG 300 MO; Kessco® PEG 300 MS; Kessco® PEG 400 DL; Kessco® PEG 400 DO; Kessco® PEG 400 DS; Kessco® PEG 400 ML; Kessco® PEG 400 MO; Kessco® PEG 400 MS; Kessco® PEG 600 DL; Kessco® PEG 600 DO; Kessco® PEG 600 DS; Kessco® PEG 600 ML; Kessco® PEG 600 MO; Kessco® PEG 600 MS; Kessco® PEG 1000 DL; Kessco® PEG 1000 DO; Kessco® PEG 1000 DS; Kessco® PEG 1000 ML; Kessco® PEG 1000 MO; Kessco® PEG 1000 MS; Kessco® PEG 1540 DL; Kessco® PEG 1540 DO; Kessco® PEG 1540 DS; Kessco® PEG 1540 ML; Kessco® PEG 1540 MO; Kessco® PEG 1540 MS; Kessco® PEG 4000 DL; Kessco® PEG 4000 DO; Kessco® PEG 4000 DS; Kessco® PEG 4000 ML; Kessco® PEG 4000 MO; Kessco® PEG 4000 MS; Kessco® PEG 6000 DL; Kessco® PEG 6000 DO; Kessco® PEG 6000 DS; Kessco® PEG 6000 ML; Kessco® PEG 6000 MO; Kessco® PEG 6000 MS

Labrafil® M 2130 CS; Labrasol; Lipovol SES; Lipovol SES-S

Mapeg® 200 DL; Mapeg® 400 MO; Miglyol® 810; Miglyol® 812; Miglyol® 818; Miglyol® 8810; Monawet MO-70R; Monteine PCO; Myritol® 312; Myritol® 318; Myritol® PC

Natipide® II; Neobee® O; Niaproof® Anionic Surfactant 4; Niaproof® Anionic Surfactant 08; Novol NF

Phosal® 50 SA; Phosal® 75 SA; Propylene Glycol USP/FCC Ultra Grade

RITA IPM; RITA IPP; Ritacetyl®; Ritalan®; RITA Lanolin; Ritasol; Ritawax AEO; Ritawax ALA; Robane®

Silwet® L-77; Softisan® 100; Softisan® 133; Softisan® 134; Softisan® 138; Softisan® 142; Softisan® 154; Solulan® PB-2; Solulan® PB-5; Solulan® PB-10; Solulan® PB-20; Standamul® CTA; Standamul® CTV; Super Corona Lanolin; Super-Sat

Trisynlane

Veegum®; Veegum® HV; Vigilan

Witafrol® 7420

Chemicals: Butylene glycol dicaprylate/caprate
Cetyl dimethicone
Dimethyl sulfoxide; Dioctyl ether
Glyceryl caprylate/caprate; Glyceryl cocoate
Hexyl laurate
Isocetyl alcohol; Isocetyl stearoyl stearate; Isopropyl myristate; Isostearyl neopentanoate
Keratinase
Lanolin oil; Levomenol
Octyl palmitate
PEG-6 dilaurate; PEG-20 dilaurate; PEG-32 dilaurate; PEG-75 dilaurate; PEG-150 dilaurate; PEG-4 dioleate; PEG-6 dioleate; PEG-12 dioleate; PEG-20 dioleate; PEG-32 dioleate; PEG-75 dioleate; PEG-150 dioleate; PEG-4 distearate; PEG-6 distearate; PEG-8 distearate; PEG-12 distearate; PEG-20 distearate; PEG-32 distearate; PEG-75 distearate; PEG-150 distearate; PEG-4 laurate; PEG-6 laurate; PEG-20 laurate; PEG-32 laurate; PEG-75 laurate; PEG-150 laurate; PEG-4 oleate; PEG-6 oleate; PEG-12 oleate; PEG-20 oleate; PEG-32 oleate; PEG-75 oleate; PEG-150 oleate; PEG-4 stearate; PEG-6 stearate; PEG-6-32 stearate; PEG-12 stearate; PEG-32 stearate; PEG-75 stearate; PEG-150 stearate; PPG-2 lanolin alcohol ether; PPG-5 lanolin alcohol ether; PPG-2 myristyl ether propionate; PPG-12-PEG-65 lanolin oil; Propylene glycol dioctanoate; Propylene glycol stearate SE
Shea butter extract; Sodium myristyl sulfate; Sodium octyl sulfate; Sodium N-oleoyl sarcosinate; Stearoxy dimethicone
Tea tree oil; Tridecyl neopentanoate

Stabilizers

Trade names: Ablunol S-20; Ablunol S-40; Ablunol S-60; Ablunol S-80; Ablunol S-85; A-C® 617, 617A; Acritamer® 934; Acritamer® 934P; Acritamer® 940; Acritamer® 941; Activera™ 1-1FA (Filtered); Activera™ 104; Adol® 90 NF; Aerosil® 200; Aerosil® 300; Aerosil® COK 84; A.F.S.; Alcolec® Granules; Aldo® PGHMS; Alpha W6 HP 0.6; Alpha W6 M1.8; Alpha W 6 Pharma Grade; Amerchol® 400; Amerchol® BL; Amerchol® C; Amerchol® CAB; Amerchol® H-9; Amerchol L-101®; Amerchol® L-500; Amerlate® P; Aminoxid WS 35; Amphisol®; Amphisol® K; Anhydrous Lanolin USP Cosmetic Grade; Anhydrous Lanolin USP Pharmaceutical Grade; Anhydrous Lanolin USP Pharmaceutical Light Grade; Anhydrous Lanolin USP X-tra Deodor-

Stabilizers *(cont'd.)*

ized; Apifil®; Argobase EU; Argobase EUC 2

Baco AF; Beta W 7; Beta W7 HP 0.9; Beta W7 M1.8; Beta W7 P; BLO®; Bone Gelatin Type B 200 Bloom; Butyl Diglyme; Byco C; Byco E; Byco O

Cab-O-Sil® EH-5; Cab-O-Sil® H-5; Cab-O-Sil® L-90; Cab-O-Sil® LM-150; Cab-O-Sil® M-5; Cab-O-Sil® MS-55; CAO®-3; Carbopol® 1342; Carbopol® 1382; Carbopol® 2984; Carbopol® 5984; Carbopol® ETD 2001; Carbopol® ETD 2020; Carbopol® ETD 2050; Cekol® 150; Cekol® 300; Cekol® 700; Cekol® 2000; Cekol® 4000; Cekol® 10000; Cekol® 30000; Cekol® 50000; Cellogen HP; Cerasynt® 840; Cetostearyl Alcohol BP; Cetostearyl Alcohol NF; Cholesterol NF; Cholesterol NF; CI-100; Cithrol GDS N/E; Cithrol GDS S/E; Cithrol GML N/E; Cithrol GMO N/E; Cithrol GMO S/E; Cithrol GMR N/E; Cithrol GMR S/E; Cithrol GMS Acid Stable; Cithrol GMS N/E; Cithrol GMS S/E; Cithrol PGML N/E; Cithrol PGML S/E; Cithrol PGMO N/E; Cithrol PGMR N/E; Cithrol PGMR S/E; Cithrol PGMS N/E; Cithrol PGMS S/E; CMC Daicel 1150; CMC Daicel 1160; CMC Daicel 1220; CMC Daicel 1260; Compritol 888; Cosmowax J; Cosmowax K; Cremophor® S 9; Crill 3; Crill 4; Crodacol C-95NF; Crodacol S-95NF; Crodamol CAP; Crodamol GTCC; Crodamol PMP; Crodamol SS; Cutina® MD

Drewmulse® 10K; Drewmulse® 1128; Drewmulse® GMOK; Drewmulse® HM-100; Drewmulse® TP; Drewmulse® V; Drewmulse® V-SE; Dulectin; Durkote Malic Acid/Maltodextrin; Durkote Vitamin B-1/Hydrog. Veg. Oil; Durkote Vitamin C/Hydrog. Veg. Oil

Eastman® SAIB-SG; Edible Beef Gelatin; Emerest® 2715; Emulgator E 2155; Emulgator E 2568; Emulsynt® 1055; Epikuron™ 145; Ethosperse® LA-23

Fancol LA; Fancol LAO; Fancol OA-95; Fancol VB; Fancor IPL; Fancor LFA; Forlan C-24

Gamma W8; Gamma W8 M1.8; Gantrez® AN-119; Gantrez® AN-139; Gantrez® AN-139 BF; Gantrez® AN-149; Gantrez® AN-169; Gantrez® ES-225; Gantrez® ES-335; Gantrez® ES-425; Gantrez® ES-435; Gantrez® MS-955D; Gantrez® S-95; Gantrez® S-97; Gelatin USP/NF, Type A; Gelot 64®; Gelucire 33/01; Gelucire 35/10; Gelucire 37/02; Gelucire 42/12; Gelucire 46/07; Gelucire 48/09; Gelucire 50/13; Gelucire 53/10; Gelucire 62/05; Genu® Carrageenan; Genu® HM USP 100; Genu® HM USP L200; Genu® Pectins; Genu® Pectin (citrus) type USP/100; Genu® Pectin (citrus) type USP/200; Genu® Pectin (citrus) type USP-H; Genu® Pectin (citrus) type USP-L/200; Genugel® Series; Genuvisco; Granular Gum Arabic Type A-1 NF Premium; Granular Gum Arabic Type A-2 NF Premium; Granular Gum Ghatti #1; Gum Arabic NF/FCC Clean Amber Sorts; Gumixan K; Gumixan KF; Gum Tragacanth Ribbons and Flakes

Haro® Chem ALMD-2; Haro® Chem CPR-2; Haro® Chem MF-2; Haro® Chem NG; Haro® Chem ZPR-2; Hartolan; Hectabrite® DP; Hodag GML; Hodag GMO; Hodag GMO-D; Hodag GMR; Hodag GMR-D; Hodag GMS; Hodag GTO; Hydrine; Hydroxylan; Hystrene® 5016 NF

Imwitor® 191; Imwitor® 900

Karaya Gum #1 FCC; KELACID®; KELCOLOID® D; KELCOLOID® DH; KELCOLOID® DSF; KELCOLOID® HVF; KELCOLOID® LVF; KELCOLOID® S; KELCOSOL®; KELGIN® F; KELGIN® HV; KELGIN® LV; KELGIN® MV; KELGIN® XL; KELSET®; KELTONE®; KELTONE® HV; KELTONE® LV; KELTROL®; KELTROL® 1000; KELTROL® BT; KELTROL® F; KELTROL® GM; KELTROL® RD; KELTROL® SF; KELTROL® TF; KELVIS®; Kimiloid HV; Kimiloid NLS-K; Kimitsu Algin I-3; Kimitsu Algin I-7; Kimitsu Algin IS; Klucel® 'F' Grades; Kollidon®; Kollidon® 12PF, 17PF; Kollidon® 25, 30, 90; Kollidon® CL

Laneto 50; Laneto 100; Laneto AWS; Lanexol AWS; Lanfrax® 1779; Lanogel® 21; Lanogel® 31; Lanogel® 41; Lanogel® 61; Lanolin Pharmaceutical; Lanolin USP; Lecigran™ 5750; Lecigran™ 6750; Lecigran™ A; Lecigran™ C; Lecigran™ F; Lecigran™ M; Lecigran™ T; Lexemul® 503; Lexemul® 515; Lexemul® AR; Lexemul® AS; Lexemul® EGMS; Lipolan 31-20; Lipolan Distilled; Liponic Sorbitol Sol'n. 70% USP; Liquid Fish Gelatin Conc.; Locust Bean Gum Type A-100; Locust Bean Gum Type A-250; Locust Bean Gum Type A-270; Locust Bean Gum Pharmaceutical Grade; Locust Bean Gum Speckless Type D-200; Luviform® FA 119

Magnabrite® F; Magnabrite® HV; Magnabrite® K; Magnabrite® S; Magnasweet®; MANUCOL DM; MANUCOL DMF; MANUCOL LB; Mazamide® C-2; Mazamide® CMEA; Mazamide® L-5; Merecol® MS; Methocel® A4C Premium; Methocel® A4M Premium; Methocel® A15C Premium; Methocel® A15-LV; Methocel® A15LV Premium; Methocel® E3 Premium; Methocel® E4M Premium; Methocel® E6 Premium; Methocel® E15LV Premium; Methocel® E50LV Premium; Methocel® E50P; Methocel® F4M Premium; Methocel® K3 Premium; Methocel® K4M Premium; Methocel® K15M Premium; Methocel® K100LV Premium; Methocel® K100M Premium; Mexpectin LA 100 Range; Mexpectin LC 700 Range; Mexpectin XSS 100 Range; Miglyol 840 Gel B; Miglyol® Gel B; Miglyol® Gel T; Monomuls® 60-10; Monomuls® 60-15; Monomuls® 60-20; Monomuls® 60-25; Monomuls® 60-25/2; Monomuls® 60-30; Monomuls® 60-35; Monomuls® 60-40; Monomuls® 60-45; Monomuls®

Stabilizers *(cont'd.)*

90-10; Monomuls® 90-15; Monomuls® 90-20; Monomuls® 90-25/2; Monomuls® 90-25/5; Monomuls® 90-30; Monomuls® 90-35; Monomuls® 90-40; Monomuls® 90-45; Monomuls® 90-O18; Monosteol; Monthyle

Natrosol® 250; Natrosol® Hydroxyethylcellulose; Natrosol® Plus CS, Grade 330; Nikkol DDP-2; Nikkol GBW-25; Nikkol GBW-125; Nikkol PMS-1C; Nikkol PMS-1CSE; Nikkol Behenyl Alcohol 65, 80; Novol NF

OHlan®; Optigel CF, CG, CK, CL; Oxynex® K

Patlac® NAL; Petrac® Magnesium Stearate MG-20 NF; Phosal® NAT-50-PG; Pionier® NP 37; Plasdone® C-15; Plasdone® C-30; Plasdone® K-25; Plasdone® K-29/32; Plasdone® K-90; Plasdone® K-90D; Plasdone® K-90M; Polawax®; Polyplasdone® XL; Polyplasdone® XL-10; Powdered Agar Agar NF M-100 (Gracilaria); Powdered Agar Agar NF MK-60; Powdered Agar Agar NF MK-80-B; Powdered Agar Agar NF MK-80 (Bacteriological); Powdered Agar Agar NF S-100; Powdered Agar Agar NF S-100-B; Powdered Agar Agar NF S-150; Powdered Agar Agar NF S-150-B; Powdered Guar Gum Type A; Powdered Guar Gum Type AA; Powdered Guar Gum Type B; Powdered Guar Gum Type BB; Powdered Gum Arabic NF/FCC G-150; Powdered Gum Arabic NF/FCC Superselect Type NB-4; Powdered Gum Arabic Type B-200 NF Premium; Powdered Gum Ghatti #1; Powdered Gum Ghatti #2; Powdered Gum Karaya Superfine #1 FCC; Powdered Gum Karaya Superfine XXXX FCC; Powdered Gum Tragacanth BP; Powdered Gum Tragacanth Type B-1 NF Premium; Powdered Gum Tragacanth Type B-12 NF Premium; Powdered Gum Tragacanth Type C-5 NF; Powdered Gum Tragacanth Type G-1 NF Premium; Powdered Gum Tragacanth Type G-2 NF Premium; Powdered Gum Tragacanth Type G-2S NF Premium; Powdered Gum Tragacanth Type M-3 NF Premium; Precirol ATO 5; Premium Powdered Gum Ghatti G-1; Promulgen® D; Promulgen® G; Protanal LF 10/60; Protanal LF 20/200; Protanal LF 200; Protanal SF; Protanal SF 120; PVP/VA E-535; PVP/VA E-635; PVP/VA E-735; PVP/VA I-235; PVP/VA I-335; PVP/VA I-535; PVP/VA I-735; PVP/VA S-630

Rhodasurf® ON-870; Rhodigel®; Rhodigel® 23; Ritachol®; Ritahydrox; Ritawax; Ritawax Super; Ryoto Sugar Ester B-370; Ryoto Sugar Ester L-595; Ryoto Sugar Ester L-1570; Ryoto Sugar Ester L-1695; Ryoto Sugar Ester LWA-1570; Ryoto Sugar Ester M-1695; Ryoto Sugar Ester O-1570; Ryoto Sugar Ester OWA-1570; Ryoto Sugar Ester P-1570; Ryoto Sugar Ester P-1570S; Ryoto Sugar Ester P-1670; Ryoto Sugar Ester S-270; Ryoto Sugar Ester S-370; Ryoto Sugar Ester S-370F; Ryoto Sugar Ester S-570; Ryoto Sugar Ester S-770; Ryoto Sugar Ester S-970; Ryoto Sugar Ester S-1170; Ryoto Sugar Ester S-1170S; Ryoto Sugar Ester S-1570; Ryoto Sugar Ester S-1670; Ryoto Sugar Ester S-1670S

Sarkosyl® L; Sarkosyl® LC; Seagel L; Sebase; Sepigel 305; Simulsol® 58; Simulsol® 78; Simulsol® 98; Simulsol® 165; Simulsol® CS; Simulsol® P4; Simulsol® P23; Soageena®; Sobalg FD 100 Range; Softisan® 378; Softisan® 649; Solan 50; Solka-Floc® BW-100; Solka-Floc® BW-200; Solka-Floc® BW-2030; Solka-Floc® Fine Granular; Span® 20; Span® 40; Span® 60; Span® 60K; Span® 65; Span® 65K; Span® 85; Spray Dried Fish Gelatin; Spray Dried Fish Gelatin/Maltodextrin; Spray Dried Gum Arabic NF/FCC CM; Spray Dried Gum Arabic NF/FCC CS (Low Bacteria); Spray Dried Gum Arabic NF/FCC CS-R; Spray Dried Gum Arabic Type A-180 NF Premium; Spray Dried Gum Arabic Type A-230 NF Extra; Spray Dried Hydrolysed Fish Gelatin; Spray Dried Kordofan Gum Arabic; Standamul® G-32/36; Standamul® G-32/36 Stearate; Supercol® Guar Gum; Super Hartolan; Syncrowax ERL-C; Syncrowax HGL-C; Syncrowax HR-C

Tegin® 90 NSE; Tegin® 4100 NSE; Tegin® 4480; Tego®-Betaine L-7; Tetraglyme; Tetronic® 304; Thiovanol®; Ticalose® 75; Ticalose® 100; Ticalose® 1200; Ticalose® 2500; Ticalose® 4000; Ticalose® 4500; Ticaxan® Regular; TIC Pretested® CMC PH-2500; T-Maz® 20; T-Maz® 28; T-Maz® 60K; T-Maz® 61; T-Maz® 65K; T-Maz® 80; T-Maz® 80K; T-Maz® 80KLM; T-Maz® 81; T-Maz® 81K; T-Maz® 85; Tris Amino® Ultra Pure Standard; Turpinal® 4 NL; Turpinal® SL; Tylose® MH Grades

Unifilter U-41; Unipabol U-17; Unisol S-22

Vee Gee Pharmaceutical Gelatins; Veegum®; Veegum® HV; Veegum® K; Veegum® PRO; Versene 100; Versene 100 EP; Versene 100 LS; Versene 100 SRG; Versene 100 XL; Versene 220; Versene Acid; Versene CA; Versene Diammonium EDTA; Versene NA; Versene Tetraammonium EDTA; Versenex 80; Versenol 120

Chemicals: Acacia; Agar; Algin; Aloe extract; Alumina trihydrate; p-Aminobenzoic acid; Ammonium alginate Benzophenone-4; 3-Benzylidene camphor; Butyrolactone

C18-36 acid glycol ester; Calcium alginate; Calcium carboxymethyl cellulose; Calcium carrageenan; Calcium saccharate; Calcium/sodium PVM/MA copolymer; Caprylic/capric/stearic

Stabilizers *(cont'd.)*

triglyceride; Carboxymethylmethylcellulose; Carrageenan; Ceteareth-33; Ceteth-20; Cetyl hydroxyethyl cellulose; Cocamide MEA; Cocamidopropyl betaine; Cocoyl sarcosine; Crospovidone; Cyclodextrin; β-Cyclodextrin

DEA-cetyl phosphate; Diammonium EDTA; Diethylene glycol dibutyl ether; Disodium cocoamphodiacetate

Ethylenediamine

Glyceryl dioleate; Glyceryl dioleate SE; Glyceryl distearate; Glyceryl distearate SE; Glyceryl laurate; Glyceryl laurate SE; Glyceryl mono shortening; Glyceryl oleate SE; Glyceryl ricinoleate; Glyceryl ricinoleate SE; Guar gum; Gum ghatti

Hectorite; Hydrogenated lard glyceride; Hydrogenated lard glycerides; Hydrogenated palm glyceride; Hydrogenated palm glycerides; Hydrogenated soybean glycerides; Hydrogenated soy glyceride; Hydrogenated tallow glyceride; Hydrogenated tallow glycerides; Hydrolyzed gelatin; Hydrotalcite; Hydroxyethylcellulose; Hydroxylated lanolin; Hydroxypropylcellulose; Hydroxypropyl-α-cyclodextrin; Hydroxypropyl-β-cyclodextrin; Hydroxypropyl-γ-cyclodextrin

Isopropyl lanolate

Karaya gum

Laneth-5; Laneth-15; Lanolin acid; Lard glyceride; Lard glycerides; Laureth-23; Lecithin; Locust bean gum

Magnesium aluminum silicate; Magnesium stearate; Maltose; D-Mannitol; Methylcellulose; Methyl-α-cyclodextrin; Methyl-β-cyclodextrin; Methyl-γ-cyclodextrin

Oleth-20; Oleyl alcohol

Palm glyceride; Palm glycerides; PEG-8 beeswax; PEG-3 cocamide MEA; PEG-4 dimethyl ether; PEG-20 hydrogenated lanolin; PEG-27 lanolin; PEG-40 lanolin; PEG-60 lanolin; PEG-85 lanolin; PEG-6 lauramide DEA; PEG-25 PABA; PEG-6 sorbitan beeswax; PEG-20 sorbitan beeswax; PEG-80 sorbitan laurate; PEG-20 sorbitan tritallate; PEG-20 stearate; PEG-40 stearate; Pentasodium pentetate; Poloxamer 105; Poloxamer 123; Poloxamer 181; Poloxamer 188; Poloxamer 237; Poloxamer 238; Poloxamer 288; Poloxamer 331; Poloxamer 407; Poloxamine 304; Poloxamine 504; Poloxamine 701; Poloxamine 702; Poloxamine 704; Poloxamine 707; Poloxamine 901; Poloxamine 904; Poloxamine 908; Poloxamine 1101; Poloxamine 1102; Poloxamine 1104; Poloxamine 1107; Poloxamine 1301; Poloxamine 1302; Poloxamine 1304; Poloxamine 1307; Poloxamine 1501; Poloxamine 1502; Poloxamine 1504; Poloxamine 1508; Polyacrylic acid; Polyvinyl acetate (homopolymer); Potassium cetyl phosphate; PPG-2 myristyl ether propionate; Propylene glycol; Propylene glycol alginate; Propylene glycol laurate; Propylene glycol laurate SE; Propylene glycol oleate; Propylene glycol oleate SE; Propylene glycol palmito/stearate; Propylene glycol ricinoleate; Propylene glycol ricinoleate SE; Propylene glycol stearate SE; PVM/MA copolymer; PVP/VA copolymer

Shellac; Silica; Sodium bisulfite; Sorbitan tristearate; Steareth-20; Sucrose acetate isobutyrate; Sucrose dilaurate; Sucrose laurate; Sucrose myristate; Sucrose palmitate; Sucrose polystearate; Sucrose tribehenate; Sucrose tristearate; Sunflower seed oil glyceride; Sunflower seed oil glycerides

Tallow glyceride; Tallow glycerides; Tetraammonium EDTA; Tetradecyleicosyl stearate; Tetrasodium EDTA; Tetrasodium etidronate; Thioglycerin; Triolein; Tris (hydroxymethyl) aminomethane; Trisodium HEDTA; Tromethamine magnesium aluminum silicate

Xanthan gum

Sterilizing agents. *See Antiseptics*

Stiffening agents. *See Gelling agents*

Superfatting agents • Fatting agents • Refatting agents

Trade names: Aethoxal® B

Cetiol® 868; Cetiol® HE; Cetiol® LC; Cetiol® S; Cetiol® SB45; Cobee 76; Corona PNL; Coronet Lanolin; Cosmetic Lanolin; Crodalan 0477; Crodalan AWS; Cutina® KD16

Superfatting agents *(cont'd.)*

Emulmetik™ 970
Fancol Acel; Fancol CAB; Fancol HL-20; Fancol HL-24; Fancol LA; Fancor IPL; Fluilan
Hartolan; Hydrophilol ISO
Imwitor® 928; Imwitor® 988; Iso Isotearyle WL 3196
Labrafac® LIPO; Labrafac® Lipophile WL 1349; Lafil WL 3254; Lanacet® 1705; Lan-Aqua-Sol
   50; Lan-Aqua-Sol 100; Lanexol AWS
Monomuls® 90-O18; Myritol® 312
Nikkol GO-430; Nikkol GO-440; Nikkol GO-460; Novol NF
Pharmaceutical Lanolin
Ritacetyl®; Ritahydrox
Softigen® 701; Softigen® 767; Solan; Solan 50; Standamul® HE; Super Corona Lanolin;
   Superfine Lanolin; Super Solan Flaked
Wickenol® 171; Witafrol® 7420

Chemicals: Coco caprylate/caprate
Dioctyl cyclohexane
Lanolin oil
Octyl stearate
PEG-6 caprylic/capric glycerides; PEG-7 glyceryl cocoate; PEG-20 hydrogenated lanolin; PEG-
   60 lanolin; PEG-70 lanolin; PEG-75 lanolin; PEG-30 sorbitan tetraoleate; PEG-40 sorbitan
   tetraoleate; PEG-60 sorbitan tetraoleate; Polyglyceryl isostearostearate; PPG-5-laureth-5;
   Propylene glycol isostearate

Surfactants • Foaming agents

Trade names: Acconon 200-MS; Acconon 400-ML; Acconon 400-MS; Acconon 1300 MS; Acconon CA-5;
   Acconon CA-8; Acconon CA-9; Acconon CA-15; Acconon SA-2; Acconon TGH; Acconon
   W230; Aldo® MSC; Amonyl® 265 BA; Amonyl® 380 BA; Amonyl® 440 NI; Antarox® L-72;
   Arlacel® 85
Calgene CC-22; Calgene CC-22-S; Calgene CC-33; Calgene CC-33-F; Calgene CC-33-L;
   Calgene CC-33-S; Captex® 200-E6; Crodafos N-3 Acid; Crodasinic LS30; Crodasinic LS35;
   Crodesta F-10
Dehyton® AB-30; Docusate Calcium USP in Corn Oil NF Sol'n; Docusate Sodium USP; Docusate
   Sodium USP in Polyethylene Glycol 400 NF; DSS Granular; DSS Tablet Grade; Dulectin
Emalex GMS-10SE; Emalex GMS-15SE; Emalex GMS-20SE; Emalex GMS-25SE; Emalex
   GMS-45RT; Emalex GMS-50; Emalex GMS-55FD; Emalex GMS-195; Emalex GMS-A;
   Emalex GMS-ASE; Emalex GMS-B; Emalex GMS-P; Emalex GWIS-100; Empicol® 0303;
   Empicol® 0303VA; Empicol® LX100; Empicol® LXV100; Empicol® LXV/D; Empicol® LZ/D;
   Empicol® LZV/D
Fancol CO-30; Fancol LAO
G-1441
Hamposyl® L-30; Hodag PE-1820
Imwitor® 308; Imwitor® 928; Imwitor® 988; Incrocas 35
Labrafac® CM10; Labrafil® M 2125 CS; Labrasol; L.A.S; Lexate® PX; Lexemul® 55G; Lipacide
   SH Co 90; Lipacide SH K 90; Liquid Absorption Base Type A; Liquid Absorption Base Type
   T
Niaproof® Anionic Surfactant 4; Niaproof® Anionic Surfactant 08; Nikkol Dipotassium
   Glycyrrhizinate; Nikkol Glycyrrhizic Acid
Oramix® CG 110-60; Oramix® NS 10
Patlac® LA USP; PhosPho LCN-TS; Plurol® Isostearique; Plurol® Oleique WL 1173; Pluronic®
   F68NF; Pluronic® F87NF; Pluronic® F108NF; Pluronic® L44NF
Renex® PEG 300; Renex® PEG 400; Renex® PEG 600; Renex® PEG 1000; Renex® PEG
   1500FL; Renex® PEG 4000FL; Renex® PEG 6000FL; Renex® PEG 8000FL
Sandopan® LA-8-HC; Sellig R 3395; Silwet® L-77; Silwet® L-720; Silwet® L-7500; Silwet® L-
   7602; Solan 50; Sunyl® 80; Sunyl® 90
Tego®-Betaine L-7; Tego®-Betaine L-10 S; Tego®-Betaine ZF; Texapon® K-12 USP; Texapon®
   K-1296 Needles; Texapon® K-1296 USP; Transcutol
Witafrol® 7420

Chemicals: Ammonium laureth sulfate; Ammonium lauryl sulfate

Surfactants (cont'd.)

Caprylyl/capryl glucoside; Cetalkonium chloride; Cetrimonium bromide; Cetyl alcohol; Cetyl dimethicone copolyol; Cocamide DEA; Cocamide MEA; Cocamidopropylamine oxide; Cocamidopropyl betaine; Coco-betaine; Cocoyl sarcosine; Corn oil PEG-6 esters

DEA-lauryl sulfate; DEA-oleth-3 phosphate; DEA-oleth-10 phosphate; Decyl glucoside; Dimethicone copolyol; Dioctyl calcium sulfosuccinate; Disodium lauryl sulfosuccinate

Ethoxydiglycol

Glyceryl cocoate; Glyceryl dioleate; Glyceryl isostearate; Glyceryl palmitate; Glycol distearate; Glycyrrhizic acid

Hydrogen peroxide

Isoceteth-20

Lauramidopropyl betaine; Lauramine oxide; Lecithin

Magnesium lauryl sulfate; Meroxapol 105; Meroxapol 251; Meroxapol 252; Meroxapol 254; Meroxapol 258; Meroxapol 311; Monoammonium glycyrrhizinate

Nonoxynol-4; Nonoxynol-9; Nonoxynol-30

Oleth-3 phosphate; Oleth-10 phosphate; Oleth-20 phosphate

PEG-8 caprylic/capric glycerides; PEG-3 cocamide MEA; PEG-6 dilaurate; PEG-32 dilaurate; PEG-75 dilaurate; PEG-150 dilaurate; PEG-6 dioleate; PEG-20 dioleate; PEG-32 dioleate; PEG-75 dioleate; PEG-150 dioleate; PEG-6 distearate; PEG-8 distearate; PEG-20 distearate; PEG-32 distearate; PEG-75 distearate; PEG-6 lauramide DEA; PEG-32 laurate; PEG-32 oleate; PEG-75 oleate; PEG-6 propylene glycol dicaprylate/dicaprate; PEG-32 stearate; PEG-75 stearate; PEG-100 stearate; Poloxamer 101; Poloxamer 124; Poloxamer 188; Poloxamer 331; Poloxamer 407; Polyglyceryl-6 isostearate; Polysorbate 80; Polysorbate 85; PPG-5 ceteth-10 phosphate; PPG-3-laureth-9; Propylene glycol stearate

Quaternium-22; Quaternium-26

Sodium cetearyl sulfate; Sodium dodecylbenzenesulfonate; Sodium laureth-5 carboxylate; Sodium lauroyl sarcosinate; Sodium methyl cocoyl taurate; Sodium/TEA-undecenoyl collagen amino acids; Sorbitan laurate; Sorbitan oleate; Sorbitan palmitate; Sorbitan stearate; Sorbitan trioleate; Sorbitan tristearate; Steareth-2; Steareth-10; Steareth-16; Steareth-21; Stearyl alcohol; Sulfated castor oil

TEA-lauryl sulfate; Trideceth-7 carboxylic acid; Trilaurin

Suspending agents

Trade names: Acritamer® 934; Acritamer® 934P; Acritamer® 940; Acritamer® 941; Aerosil® R812; Agar Agar NF Flake #1; Albagel Premium USP 4444; Aldo® MCT KFG; Aqualon® Cellulose Gum

Benecel® Hydroxypropyl Methylcellulose; Benecel® Methylcellulose; Bentonite USP BC 670

Cab-O-Sil® EH-5; Cab-O-Sil® H-5; Cab-O-Sil® L-90; Cab-O-Sil® LM-150; Cab-O-Sil® M-5; Cab-O-Sil® MS-55; Carbopol® 907; Carbopol® 910; Carbopol® 934; Carbopol® 934P; Carbopol® 940; Carbopol® 971P; Carbopol® 974P; Carbopol® 2984; Carbopol® 5984; Carbopol® ETD 2001; Centrolex® P; CMC Daicel 1150; CMC Daicel 1160; CMC Daicel 1220; CMC Daicel 1260; Colloid 488T; Colloid 602; Crystal® Crown LP

Dow E300 NF; Dow E400 NF; Dow E600 NF; Dow E900 NF; Dow E1000 NF; Dow E1450 NF; Dow E3350 NF; Dow E4500 NF; Dow E8000 NF

Genu® Carrageenan; Genu® Pectins; Genugel® Series; Genuvisco; Gumixan K; Gumixan KF; Gum Tragacanth Ribbons and Flakes

Hectabrite® AW; Hectabrite® DP; Hectalite® 200

Imwitor® 191; Imwitor® 900; Imwitor® 965; Incroquat Behenyl TMS

KELMAR®; KELMAR® CR; KELMAR® Improved; KELTONE® HVCR; KELTONE® LVCR; KELTROL®; KELTROL® BT; KELTROL® CR; KELTROL® GM; KELTROL® SF; KELTROL® TF; KELVIS®; Klucel® 'F' Grades; Koraid PSM; Korthix H-NF

Lecigran™ F; Lecigran™ M; Locust Bean Gum Type A-100; Locust Bean Gum Type A-250; Locust Bean Gum Type A-270

Magnabrite® F; Magnabrite® FS; Magnabrite® HS; Magnabrite® HV; Magnabrite® K; Magnabrite® S; MANUCOL DM; MANUCOL DMF; MANUCOL LB; Methocel® A4C Premium; Methocel® A4M Premium; Methocel® A15LV Premium; Methocel® E3 Premium; Methocel® E4M Premium; Methocel® E6 Premium; Methocel® E15LV Premium; Methocel® E50LV Premium; Methocel® E50P; Methocel® K15M Premium; Methocel® K100LV Premium; Methocel® K100M Premium; Miglyol® 810; Miglyol® 812; Miglyol® 840; Miglyol® 8810

Natrosol® 250; Natrosol® Hydroxyethylcellulose; Natrosol® Plus CS, Grade 330

Suspending agents *(cont'd.)*

Plasdone® C-15; Plasdone® C-30; Plasdone® K-25; Plasdone® K-29/32; Plasdone® K-90; Plasdone® K-90D; Plasdone® K-90M; Plurol® Oleique WL 1173; Polargel® HV; Polargel® NF; Polargel® T; Polawax®; Polyox® WSR 205; Polyox® WSR 301; Polyox® WSR 303; Polyox® WSR 308; Polyox® WSR 1105; Polyox® WSR 3333; Polyox® WSR N-10; Polyox® WSR N-12K; Polyox® WSR N-60K; Polyox® WSR N-80; Polyox® WSR N-750; Polyox® WSR N-3000; Polyox® WSR Coagulant; Powdered Agar Agar Bacteriological Grade; Powdered Agar Agar NF M-100 (Gracilaria); Powdered Agar Agar NF MK-60; Powdered Agar Agar NF MK-80-B; Powdered Agar Agar NF MK-80 (Bacteriological); Powdered Agar Agar NF S-100; Powdered Agar Agar NF S-100-B; Powdered Agar Agar NF S-150; Powdered Agar Agar NF S-150-B; Powdered Agar Agar Type K-60; Powdered Agar Agar Type K-80; Powdered Agar Agar Type K-100; Powdered Agar Agar Type K-150; Powdered Gum Arabic Type B-100 NF Premium; Powdered Gum Arabic Type B-200 NF Premium; Powdered Gum Tragacanth BP; Powdered Gum Tragacanth Type B-1 NF Premium; Powdered Gum Tragacanth Type B-12 NF Premium; Powdered Gum Tragacanth Type C-5 NF; Powdered Gum Tragacanth Type G-1 NF Premium; Powdered Gum Tragacanth Type G-2 NF Premium; Powdered Gum Tragacanth Type G-2S NF Premium; Powdered Gum Tragacanth Type M-3 NF Premium; Powdered Tragacanth Gum Type A/10; Powdered Tragacanth Gum Type E-1; Powdered Tragacanth Gum Type G-3; Powdered Tragacanth Gum Type L; Powdered Tragacanth Gum Type W

Rhodigel®; Rhodigel® 23; Rhodigel® 200

Soageena®; Spray Dried Gum Arabic Type A-180 NF Premium; Spray Dried Gum Arabic Type A-230 NF Extra; Stepanol® WA-100; Stepan TAB®-2; Suspengel Elite; Suspengel Micro; Suspengel Ultra; Syncrowax ERL-C; Syncrowax HGL-C; Syncrowax HR-C; Synpro® Aluminum Monostearate NF; Synpro® Aluminum Stearate USP

Ticalose® 150 R; Ticalose® 700 R; Ticalose® 1200; Ticalose® 2000 R; Ticalose® 2500; Ticalose® 4000; Ticalose® 4500; Ticalose® 5000 R; Ticaxan® Regular; T-Maz® 20; T-Maz® 60K; T-Maz® 61; T-Maz® 65K; T-Maz® 80; T-Maz® 80KLM; T-Maz® 81; T-Maz® 81K; T-Maz® 85; Tragacanth Flake No. 27; Tragacanth Gum Ribbon No. 1

Veegum® PRO; Volclay® NF-BC; Volclay® NF-ID

Sweeteners • Sweetness regulators

Trade names: A-641; Amalty®; Arlex

Candex®; Clintose® A; Clintose® L; CornSweet® Crystalline Fructose; 42/43 Corn Syrup

Extramalt 10; Extramalt 35; Extramalt Dark; Extramalt Light; Fancol SORB

Finmalt L; Fructofin® C; FruitSource® Granular; FruitSource® Liquid Sweetener; FruitSource® Liquid Sweetener Plus

Glycerine (Pharmaceutical)

HSC Aspartame; Hystar® 3375; Hystar® 4075

Jungbunzlauer GS 7097

Lactitol MC; Liponic 70-NC; Liponic 76-NC; Liposorb 70

Magnasweet®; Maltrin® M200; Maltrin® M510; Maltrin® QD M500

Natural Prosweet™ Liq. #604; Natural Prosweet™ Powd. #875; Non-Diastatic Malt Syrup #40600

Prosweet™ Liq.; Prosweet™ Powd.

Sorbelite™ C; Sorbelite™ FG; Sugartab®; Sweetrex®; Syncal® CAS; Syncal® GS; Syncal® GSD; Syncal® S; Syncal® SDI; Syncal® SDS; Syncal® US

Unisweet 70; Unisweet 70/CONC; Unisweet CALSAC; Unisweet CONC; Unisweet EVAN; Unisweet MAN; Unisweet SAC; Unisweet SOSAC; Unisweet VAN

Veltol®-Plus; Veltol®-Plus

Xylitol C

Chemicals: Acesulfame potassium; Acetophenone; Acetyl butyryl; 3-Acetylpyridine; Acetyl tributyl citrate; L-Arabinose; Aspartame

Butyl lactate

Calcium saccharin; Caramel; Carvyl propionate; Corn syrup

Dextrates

Fructose

D-Galactose; D-Glucose anhyd; D-Glucose monohydrate

Honey

Invert sugar; Isomalt; Isophorone

Sweeteners *(cont'd.)*

Lactitol monohydrate; Lactose

Malt extract; Maltitol; Maltose; D-Mannitol; 3-Methylpentanoic acid; 4-Methyl-1-phenyl-2-pentanone; Methyl salicylate; Molasses; Myrcene

Neryl acetate; Neryl butyrate; Neryl isobutyrate; Neryl isovalerate

Phenethyl butyrate; 2-Phenylpropyl butyrate; Piperidine

Rhamnose

Saccharin; Saccharin sodium; Sorbitol; Sorbitol sol'n; Sucrose; Sugar, compressible; Sugar, confectioner's; Sugar spheres; Syrup

Xylitol

Sweetness regulators. *See Sweeteners*

Synergists. *See Adjuvants*

Tablet binders

Trade names: Alginic Acid FCC; Altalc 200 USP; Aqualon® Cellulose Gum

Byco A

Cab-O-Sil® EH-5; Cab-O-Sil® H-5; Cab-O-Sil® L-90; Cab-O-Sil® LM-150; Cab-O-Sil® M-5; Cab-O-Sil MS-55; C-A-P Enteric Coating Material; Carbowax® Sentry® PEG 300; Carbowax® Sentry® PEG 400; Carbowax® Sentry® PEG 540 Blend; Carbowax® Sentry® PEG 600; Carbowax® Sentry® PEG 900; Carbowax® Sentry® PEG 1000; Carbowax® Sentry® PEG 1450; Carbowax® Sentry® PEG 3350; Carbowax® Sentry® PEG 4600; Carbowax® Sentry® PEG 8000; C-A-T Enteric Coating Polymer; Cekol® 30; Compritol 888 ATO; Crodyne BY-19

Destab™; Dynasan® 112; Dynasan® 114; Dynasan® 116; Dynasan® 118

Edible Beef Gelatin; Edicol®; Edicol® P; Emcocel® 50M; Emcocel® 90M; Emcocel® LM; Emvelop®; Ethocel Standard Premium

Granular Gum Arabic NF/FCC C-4010; Granular Gum Arabic Type A-1 NF Premium; Granular Gum Arabic Type A-2 NF Premium; Granular Gum Ghatti #1; Gum Arabic NF/FCC Clean Amber Sorts

Hodag PEG 3350; Hodag PEG 8000; HPMCP 50; HPMCP 55; HPMCP 55S; Hydex® 100 Coarse Powd.; Hydex® 100 Coarse Powd. 35; Hydex® 100 Gran. 206; Hydex® 100 Powd. 60; Hydex® Tablet Grade

Justfiber® CL-60-H; Justfiber® CL-80-H

KELCOSOL®; KELTOSE®; Klucel® 'F' Grades; Kollidon®; Kollidon® 25, 30, 90; Kollidon® USP

Lubritab®

Magnabrite® F; Magnabrite® FS; Maltrin® M150; Maltrin® M180; Maltrin® M200; Maltrin® M250; Maltrin® M510; Maltrin® QD M500; Maltrin® QD M550; Maltrin® QD M600; Methocel® A15LV Premium; Methocel® A Premium; Methocel® E3 Premium; Methocel® E5P; Methocel® E6 Premium; Methocel® E15LV Premium; Methocel® E50P; Methocel® E Premium

Noveon® AA-1

Pharma-Gel™; Plasdone® K-25; Plasdone® K-29/32; Plasdone® K-90; Plasdone® K-90D; Plasdone® K-90M; Polyplasdone® XL; Polyplasdone® XL-10; Powdered Guar Gum Type A; Powdered Guar Gum Type AA; Powdered Guar Gum Type B; Powdered Guar Gum Type BB; Powdered Gum Arabic NF/FCC G-150; Powdered Gum Arabic NF/FCC Superselect Type NB-4; Powdered Gum Arabic Type B-100 NF Premium; Powdered Gum Arabic Type B-200 NF Premium; Powdered Gum Ghatti #1; Powdered Gum Ghatti #2; Powdered Gum Guar NF Type 80 Mesh B/T; Powdered Gum Guar Type 140 Mesh B/T; Powdered Gum Guar Type ECM; Powdered Gum Guar Type M; Powdered Gum Guar Type MM FCC; Powdered Gum Guar Type MM (HV); Powdered Gum Guar Type MMM $^{1}/_{2}$; Powdered Gum Guar Type MMW; Precirol ATO 5; Premium Spray Dried Gum Arabic; Protanal LF 10/60; Protanal LF 20/200; Protanal LF 200; Protanal SF; Protanal SF 120; Pure-Dent® B700; Pure-Dent® B810; Pure-Dent® B880; Pure-Dent® B890; PVP/VA E-535; PVP/VA E-635; PVP/VA E-735; PVP/VA I-235; PVP/VA I-335; PVP/VA I-535; PVP/VA I-735; PVP/VA S-630

Tablet binders *(cont'd.)*

Ryoto Sugar Ester B-370; Ryoto Sugar Ester L-595; Ryoto Sugar Ester L-1570; Ryoto Sugar Ester L-1695; Ryoto Sugar Ester LWA-1570; Ryoto Sugar Ester M-1695; Ryoto Sugar Ester O-1570; Ryoto Sugar Ester OWA-1570; Ryoto Sugar Ester P-1570; Ryoto Sugar Ester P-1570S; Ryoto Sugar Ester P-1670; Ryoto Sugar Ester S-270; Ryoto Sugar Ester S-370; Ryoto Sugar Ester S-370F; Ryoto Sugar Ester S-570; Ryoto Sugar Ester S-770; Ryoto Sugar Ester S-970; Ryoto Sugar Ester S-1170; Ryoto Sugar Ester S-1170S; Ryoto Sugar Ester S-1570; Ryoto Sugar Ester S-1670; Ryoto Sugar Ester S-1670S

Spray Dried Gum Arabic NF Type CSP; Spray Dried Gum Arabic NF/FCC CM; Spray Dried Gum Arabic NF/FCC CS (Low Bacteria); Spray Dried Gum Arabic NF/FCC CS-R; Spray Dried Gum Arabic Type A-180 NF Premium; Spray Dried Gum Arabic Type A-230 NF Extra; Staform P; Stamere® CK-S; Stamere® N-325; Stamere® N-350; Stamere® N-350 S; Stamere® NI; Sta-Rx®; Sunyl® 80; Sunyl® 90; Supercol® Guar Gum; Sweetrex®

Teric PEG 300; Teric PEG 400; Teric PEG 600; Teric PEG 800; Teric PEG 4000; Teric PEG 6000; Teric PEG 8000

Vee Gee Pharmaceutical Gelatins; Veegum®; Veegum® HV; Vivacel® 10; Vivacel® 12; Vivacel® 20; Vivacel® 101; Vivacel® 102; Vivacel® 103; Vivacel® 105; Vivacel® 112; Vivacel® 200

Chemicals: Algin; Alginic acid; Amaranth
Carboxymethylcellulose sodium; Corn starch, pregelatinized
Dextrin
Ethylcellulose
Food starch modified
Gelatin; Glucose, liquid; Glyceryl behenate; Glyceryl di/tripalmitostearate; Guar gum; Gum ghatti
Hydrolyzed gelatin; Hydrotalcite; Hydroxypropyl methylcellulose
Lecithin
Magnesium aluminum silicate; Maltodextrin; Methylcellulose; Microcrystalline cellulose
PEG-20; PEG-40; PEG-75; PEG-8M; Polycarbophil; Polyvinylpolypyrrolidone; PVP; PVP/VA copolymer
Silica; Starch; Starch, pregelatinized; Sucrose dilaurate; Sucrose laurate; Sucrose myristate; Sucrose oleate; Sucrose palmitate; Sucrose stearate; Sucrose tribehenate; Sucrose tristearate; Sunflower seed oil; Syrup
Trilaurin

Tablet diluents

Trade names: Arlex
Fancol SORB
Liposorb 70
Maltrin® M150; Maltrin® QD M500
Nu-Tab®
Pure-Dent® B700; Pure-Dent® B810; Pure-Dent® B880; Pure-Dent® B890
Sta-Rx®; Sunyl® 80; Sunyl® 90
Terra Alba 114836
Unisweet 70; Unisweet 70/CONC; Unisweet CONC; Unisweet L; Unisweet Lactose; Unisweet MAN

Chemicals: Amaranth
Calcium phosphate dibasic; Calcium phosphate dibasic dihydrate; Calcium phosphate tribasic; Calcium sulfate; Calcium sulfate dihydrate; Cellulose; Corn starch, pregelatinized
Dextrates
Food starch modified; Fructose
D-Glucose anhyd; Glucose, liquid
Kaolin
Lactose; Lactose monohydrate
Maltodextrin; D-Mannitol; Microcrystalline cellulose
Sorbitol; Starch; Starch, pregelatinized; Sucrose; Sugar, compressible; Sugar, confectioner's; Sugar spheres
Tapioca starch

Tablet disintegrants

Trade names: Ac-Di-Sol®; Aerosil® 200; Aerosil® 300; Aerosil® 380; Aerosil® COK 84; Akolizer C; Akolizer P; Akolizer S; Alcolec® Granules; Alginic Acid FCC; Amberlite® IRP-88; Asol; ATBC; ATEC; Avicel® PH-101; Avicel® PH-102; Avicel® PH-103; Avicel® PH-105
BBS
Cab-O-Sil® EH-5; Cab-O-Sil® H-5; Cab-O-Sil® L-90; Cab-O-Sil® LM-150; Cab-O-Sil® M-5; Cab-O-Sil® MS-55; Cal-Carb® 4462; Cap-Shure® FF-165-60; Cap-Shure® KCL-140-50; Cap-Shure® KCL-165-70; Carbopol® 934P; Chroma-GDF™; Chroma-SRF™; Compritol 888; Compritol 888 ATO
Disodium Pamoate; Duratex; Durkote Ferrous Fumarate/Hydrog. Veg. Oil; Durkote Ferrous Sulfate/Hydrog. Veg. Oil; Durkote Vitamin B-1/Hydrog. Veg. Oil; Durkote Vitamin C/Hydrog. Veg. Oil
Eastman® CA; Eastman® OC; Edible Beef Gelatin; Edicol®; Edicol® ULV Series; Elcema® G250; Elcema® P100; Emcocel® 50M; Emcocel® 90M; Emcocel® LM; Emcosoy®; Emdex® Plus; Empicol® 0185; Emvelop®; Ethocel Medium Premium; Eudragit® NE 30 D; Eudragit® RL 30 D; Eudragit® RS 30 D; Explotab®
Gantrez® AN-119; Gantrez® ES-225; Gantrez® ES-335; Gantrez® ES-425; Gantrez® ES-435; Gantrez® MS-955D; Gantrez® S-95; Gantrez® S-97; Gelucire 44/14; Gelucire 50/02
Hydrokote® 95; Hydrokote® 102; Hydrokote® 108; Hydrokote® 112; Hydrokote® 118; Hydrokote® 175; Hydrokote® M
Imwitor® 742
KELACID®; KELCOSOL®; KELTOSE®; Kimitsu Acid; Kollidon® CL; Kollidon® CLM
Magnabrite® F; Magnabrite® FS; Methocel® A Premium; Methocel® E4M Premium; Methocel® E10MP CR; Methocel® E Premium; Methocel® F Premium; Methocel® J Premium; Methocel® K4M Premium; Methocel® K15M Premium; Methocel® K100LV Premium; Methocel® K100M Premium; Methocel® K Premium; Myvacet® 5-07; Myvacet® 7-07; Myvaplex® 600; Myvaplex® 600P NF; Myverol® 18-92; Myverol® 18-99
Nymcel® ZSB-10; Nymcel® ZSB-16; Nymcel® ZSC; Nymcel® ZSD-16; Nymcel® ZSX
Opadry® Enteric; Opaseal®
Pharma-Gel™; pHthalavin™; Plasvita® TSM; Polargel® HV; Polyox® WSR 205; Polyox® WSR 301; Polyox® WSR 303; Polyox® WSR 308; Polyox® WSR 1105; Polyox® WSR 3333; Polyox® WSR N-10; Polyox® WSR N-12K; Polyox® WSR N-60K; Polyox® WSR N-80; Polyox® WSR N-750; Polyox® WSR N-3000; Polyox® WSR Coagulant; Polyplasdone® XL; Polyplasdone® XL-10; Powdered Agar Agar Bacteriological Grade; Powdered Agar Agar Type K-60; Powdered Agar Agar Type K-80; Powdered Agar Agar Type K-100; Powdered Agar Agar Type K-150; Powdered Guar Gum Type A; Powdered Guar Gum Type AA; Powdered Guar Gum Type B; Powdered Guar Gum Type BB; Pre-Gel Amaranth Powd.; Primojel®; Protacid F 120; Protanal LF 10/60; Protanal LF 20/200; Protanal LF 120 M; Protanal LF 200; Protanal LF 200 M; Protanal LF 200 RB; Protanal SF; Protanal SF 120; Protanal SF 120 RB; Protanal TFX 200; Pure-Dent® B700; Pure-Dent® B810; Pure-Dent® B880; Pure-Dent® B890; Purity® 21
Ryoto Sugar Ester B-370; Ryoto Sugar Ester L-595; Ryoto Sugar Ester L-1570; Ryoto Sugar Ester L-1695; Ryoto Sugar Ester LWA-1570; Ryoto Sugar Ester M-1695; Ryoto Sugar Ester O-1570; Ryoto Sugar Ester OWA-1570; Ryoto Sugar Ester P-1570; Ryoto Sugar Ester P-1570S; Ryoto Sugar Ester P-1670; Ryoto Sugar Ester S-270; Ryoto Sugar Ester S-370; Ryoto Sugar Ester S-370F; Ryoto Sugar Ester S-570; Ryoto Sugar Ester S-770; Ryoto Sugar Ester S-970; Ryoto Sugar Ester S-1170; Ryoto Sugar Ester S-1170S; Ryoto Sugar Ester S-1570; Ryoto Sugar Ester S-1670S
Satialgine™ H8; Soageena® WX87; Solka-Floc® BW-100; Solka-Floc® BW-200; Solka-Floc® BW-2030; Solka-Floc® Fine Granular; Starch 1500®; Starch 1500® LM; Sta-Rx®; Sterotex®; Sterotex® K; Suppocire® AIP; Suppocire® AP; Suppocire® BP; Suppocire® CP; Surelease®; Sureteric™
TBC; TEC; 28-1801
Veegum®; Veegum® HV

Chemicals: Agar; Alginic acid; Amaranth
Calcium carboxymethyl cellulose; Cellulose; Corn starch; Corn starch, pregelatinized; Croscarmellose sodium; Crospovidone
Dextrin
Food starch modified
Magnesium aluminum silicate; Methylene casein; Microcrystalline cellulose

Tablet disintegrants *(cont'd.)*

Polacrilin potassium; Polyvinylpolypyrrolidone
Silica; Sodium starch glycolate; Soy flour; Starch; Starch, pregelatinized; Sucrose dilaurate; Sucrose laurate; Sucrose myristate; Sucrose oleate; Sucrose palmitate; Sucrose polystearate; Sucrose stearate; Sucrose tribehenate; Sucrose tristearate
Tapioca starch

Thickeners • Viscosity control agents • Consistency regulators • Bodying agents • Rheology control agents • Antigellants

Trade names: Ablunol S-20; Ablunol S-40; Ablunol S-60; Ablunol S-80; Ablunol S-85; A-C® 7, 7A; A-C® 617, 617A; Accomid PK; Acconon 200-MS; Acconon 400-ML; Acconon 400-MO; Acconon 400-MS; Acconon 1300 MS; Acconon CA-5; Acconon CA-8; Acconon CON; Acconon TGH; Acritamer® 934; Acritamer® 934P; Acritamer® 940; Acritamer® 941; Aerosil® 200; Aerosil® 300; Aerosil® COK 84; A.F.S; Akoext SB; Akolizer C; Akolizer P; Akolizer S; Albagel Premium USP 4444; Aldo® PGHMS; Alkamuls® PSML-20; Amonyl® 265 BA; Amonyl® 380 BA; Aqualon® Cellulose Gum; Arlypon® F
Benecel® Methylcellulose
Cab-O-Sil® EH-5; Cab-O-Sil® H-5; Cab-O-Sil® HS-5; Cab-O-Sil® L-90; Cab-O-Sil® LM-150; Cab-O-Sil® M-5; Cab-O-Sil® MS-55; Cab-O-Sil® PTG; Cab-O-Sil® TS-530; Capmul® GMS; Capmul® S; Caprol® 3GS; Caprol® 6G2S; Caprol® PGE860; Captex® 300; Captex® 355; Captex® 8227; Carbopol® 907; Carbopol® 910; Carbopol® 934; Carbopol® 934P; Carbopol® 940; Carbopol® 941; Carbopol® 971P; Carbopol® 974P; Carbopol® 980; Carbopol® 981; Carbopol® 1342; Carbopol® 1382; Carbopol® 2984; Carbopol® 5984; Carbopol® ETD 2001; Carbopol® ETD 2020; Carbopol® ETD 2050; Carbowax® Sentry® PEG 300; Cekol® 30; Cekol® 150; Cekol® 300; Cekol® 700; Cekol® 2000; Cekol® 4000; Cekol® 10000; Cekol® 30000; Cekol® 50000; Ceraphyl® 424; Cerasynt® 840; Cerasynt® 945; Cerasynt® GMS; Cerasynt® MN; Cetiol® SB45; Cetostearyl Alcohol BP; Cetostearyl Alcohol NF; CI-90; CI-100; CM-80; CMC Daicel 1150; CMC Daicel 1160; CMC Daicel 1220; CMC Daicel 1260; Comperlan® COD; Cosmowax J; Cosmowax K; Crill 1; Crodacol C-95NF; Crodacol S-95NF; Crodafos N-3 Acid; Crodamol CP; Crodamol CSP; Crodamol SS; Crodyne BY-19; Cutina® CP; Cutina® FS 25 Flakes; Cutina® FS 45 Flakes; Cutina® GMS; Cutina® MD
Dehydag® Wax 14; Dehydag® Wax 16; Dehydag® Wax 18; Dehydag® Wax 22 (Lanette); Dehydag® Wax O; Drewmulse® 1128; Drewmulse® GMOK; Drewmulse® HM-100; Drewmulse® POE-SMO; Drewmulse® POE-SMS; Drewmulse® POE-STS; Drewmulse® SML; Drewmulse® SMO; Drewmulse® SMS; Drewmulse® STS; Drewmulse® TP; Drewmulse® V; Drewmulse® V-SE; Dynasan® 112; Dynasan® 114; Dynasan® 116; Dynasan® 118
Edicol®; Emerest® 2715; Emery® 912; Emery® 916; Emery® 917; Emery® 918; Ethosperse® LA-23; Eumulgin® B1; Eumulgin® B2
Fancol LA; Forlan C-24
Gantrez® AN-119; Gantrez® AN-139; Gantrez® AN-139 BF; Gantrez® AN-149; Gantrez® AN-169; Gantrez® ES-225; Gantrez® ES-335; Gantrez® ES-425; Gantrez® ES-435; Gantrez® MS-955D; Gantrez® S-95; Gantrez® S-97; Geleol; Genu® Carrageenan; Genu® Pectins; Genu® Pectin (citrus) type USP/100; Genu® Pectin (citrus) type USP/200; Genu® Pectin (citrus) type USP-H; Genu® Pectin (citrus) type USP-L/200; Genugel® Series; Genuvisco; Glycon® G 100; Glycon® G-300; Granular Gum Arabic Type A-1 NF Premium; Granular Gum Arabic Type A-2 NF Premium; Gum Arabic NF/FCC Clean Amber Sorts; Gum Arabic, Purified, Spray-Dried No. 1834; Gumixan K; Gumixan KF; Gum Tragacanth Ribbons and Flakes
Hectabrite® AW; Hectabrite® DP; Hectalite® 200; Hi-Sil® T-600; Hyaluronic Acid FCH; Hydex® 100 Coarse Powd.; Hydex® 100 Coarse Powd. 35; Hydex® 100 Gran. 206; Hydex® 100 Powd. 60; Hydex® Tablet Grade; Hydrine; Hydrokote® 175; Hydrokote® M; Hypan® SA100H; Hypan® SR150H; Hystar® 3375; Hystar® 4075; Hystar® 5875; Hystar® 6075; Hystar® HM-75
Imwitor® 191; Imwitor® 370; Imwitor® 900; Imwitor® 928; Imwitor® 988
KELCOLOID® HVF; KELCOSOL®; KELGIN® F; KELGIN® HV; KELGIN® LV; KELGIN® MV; KELGIN® XL; KELMAR®; KELMAR® CR; KELMAR® Improved; KELTONE® HV; KELTONE® HVCR; KELTONE® LV; KELTONE® LVCR; KELTROL®; KELTROL® 1000; KELTROL® BT; KELTROL® CR; KELTROL® F; KELTROL® GM; KELTROL® RD;

Thickeners *(cont'd.)*

KELTROL® SF; KELTROL® TF; Kemester® EGDS; Kemester® EGMS; Kessco® 653; Kessco® PEG 200 DL; Kessco® PEG 200 DO; Kessco® PEG 200 DS; Kessco® PEG 200 ML; Kessco® PEG 200 MO; Kessco® PEG 200 MS; Kessco® PEG 300 DL; Kessco® PEG 300 DO; Kessco® PEG 300 DS; Kessco® PEG 300 MO; Kessco® PEG 300 MS; Kessco® PEG 400 DL; Kessco® PEG 400 DO; Kessco® PEG 400 DS; Kessco® PEG 400 ML; Kessco® PEG 400 MO; Kessco® PEG 400 MS; Kessco® PEG 600 DL; Kessco® PEG 600 DO; Kessco® PEG 600 DS; Kessco® PEG 600 ML; Kessco® PEG 600 MO; Kessco® PEG 600 MS; Kessco® PEG 1000 DL; Kessco® PEG 1000 DO; Kessco® PEG 1000 DS; Kessco® PEG 1000 ML; Kessco® PEG 1000 MO; Kessco® PEG 1000 MS; Kessco® PEG 1540 DL; Kessco® PEG 1540 DO; Kessco® PEG 1540 DS; Kessco® PEG 1540 ML; Kessco® PEG 1540 MO; Kessco® PEG 1540 MS; Kessco® PEG 4000 DL; Kessco® PEG 4000 DO; Kessco® PEG 4000 DS; Kessco® PEG 4000 ML; Kessco® PEG 4000 MO; Kessco® PEG 4000 MS; Kessco® PEG 6000 DL; Kessco® PEG 6000 DO; Kessco® PEG 6000 DS; Kessco® PEG 6000 ML; Kessco® PEG 6000 MO; Kessco® PEG 6000 MS; Kessco® Glyceryl Monostearate Pure; Kimiloid HV; Kimiloid NLS-K; Kimitsu Algin I-3; Kimitsu Algin I-7; Kimitsu Algin IS; Klucel® 'F' Grades; Kollidon® 25, 30, 90; Kollidon® USP; Korthix H-NF; Koster Keunen Beeswax; Koster Keunen Ceresine; Koster Keunen Emulsifying Wax; Koster Keunen Ozokerite; Koster Keunen Synthetic Spermaceti

Lanette® 14; Lanette® 16; Lanette® 18; Lanette® 18-22; Lanette® 18 DEO; Lanette® 22 Flakes; Lanette® N; Lanette® O; Lanette® W; Laponite® D; Lexemul® 503; Lexemul® 515; Lexemul® EGMS; Lipoxol® 200 MED; Lipoxol® 300 MED; Lipoxol® 400 MED; Lipoxol® 550 MED; Lipoxol® 600 MED; Lipoxol® 800 MED; Lipoxol® 1000 MED; Lipoxol® 1550 MED; Lipoxol® 2000 MED; Lipoxol® 3000 MED; Lipoxol® 4000 MED; Lipoxol® 6000 MED; Locust Bean Gum Type A-100; Locust Bean Gum Type A-250; Locust Bean Gum Type A-270; Locust Bean Gum Speckless Type D-200; Lutrol® F 127

Magnabrite® HV; Maltrin® M040; Maltrin® M050; Maltrin® M150; Maltrin® M200; MANUCOL DM; MANUCOL DMF; MANUCOL LB; Mapeg® EGDS; Mapeg® EGMS; Mazamide® CMEA; Mazawax® 163R; Mazol® 165C; Mazol® GMS-K; Methocel® A4C Premium; Methocel® A4M Premium; Methocel® A15C Premium; Methocel® A15-LV; Methocel® A15LV Premium; Methocel® E3 Premium; Methocel® E4M Premium; Methocel® E6 Premium; Methocel® E15LV Premium; Methocel® E50LV Premium; Methocel® E50P; Methocel® F4M Premium; Methocel® K4M Premium; Methocel® K15M Premium; Methocel® K100LV Premium; Methocel® K100M Premium; Mexpectin LC 700 Range; Miglyol® 840 Gel B; Miglyol® Gel B; Miglyol® Gel T; Monomuls® 90-O18; Monthyle

Nacol® 14-98; Nacol® 16-98; Nacol® 18-98; Nacol® 20-95; Nacol® 22-97; Nacolox®; Nafol® C14-C22; Natrosol® 250; Natrosol® Hydroxyethylcellulose; Natrosol® Plus CS, Grade 330; Nikkol BPS-5; Nikkol Batyl Alcohol 100, EX; Nikkol Chimyl Alcohol 100; Novata® 299; Novata® AB; Novata® B; Novata® BBC; Novata® BC; Novata® BCF; Novata® BD; Novata® C; Novata® D; Novata® E; Noveon® AA-1

Pelemol® BB; Pelemol® CP; Pelemol® MS; Phospholipid PTD; Phospholipid PTL; Phospholipid PTZ; Pionier® NP 37; Polargel® HV; Polargel® NF; Polargel® T; Polawax®; Polychol 10; Polychol 15; Polychol 20; Polychol 40; Powdered Guar Gum Type A; Powdered Guar Gum Type AA; Powdered Guar Gum Type B; Powdered Guar Gum Type BB; Powdered Gum Arabic NF/FCC G-150; Powdered Gum Arabic NF/FCC Superselect Type NB-4; Powdered Gum Arabic Type B-200 NF Premium; Powdered Gum Tragacanth BP; Powdered Gum Tragacanth T-150; Powdered Gum Tragacanth T-200; Powdered Gum Tragacanth T-300; Powdered Gum Tragacanth T-400; Powdered Gum Tragacanth T-500; Powdered Gum Tragacanth Type B-1 NF Premium; Powdered Gum Tragacanth Type B-12 NF Premium; Powdered Gum Tragacanth Type C-5 NF; Powdered Gum Tragacanth Type G-1 NF Premium; Powdered Gum Tragacanth Type G-2 NF Premium; Powdered Gum Tragacanth Type G-2S NF Premium; Powdered Gum Tragacanth Type M-3 NF Premium; Powdered Locust Bean Gum Type D-200; Powdered Locust Bean Gum Type D-300; Powdered Locust Bean Gum Type P-100; Powdered Locust Bean Gum Type PP-100; Powdered Tragacanth Gum Type A/10; Powdered Tragacanth Gum Type E-1; Powdered Tragacanth Gum Type G-3; Powdered Tragacanth Gum Type L; Powdered Tragacanth Gum Type W; Protanal LF 10/60; Protanal LF 20/200; Protanal LF 200; Protanal SF; Protanal SF 120; PVP/VA E-535; PVP/VA E-635; PVP/VA E-735; PVP/VA I-235; PVP/VA I-335; PVP/VA I-535; PVP/VA I-735; PVP/VA S-630

Rehydragel® CG; Rhodigel®; Rhodigel® 23; Ritachol® 4000; Ritahydrox; Ritawax; Ross Ceresine Wax; Ross Spermaceti Wax Substitute 573

Sebase; Sepigel 305; Sident® 15; Sident® 22LS; Sident® 22S; Simulsol® PS20; Sipernat®

Thickeners *(cont'd.)*

22LS; Soageena®; Soageena® LX7; Softisan® 100; Softisan® 133; Softisan® 134; Softisan® 138; Softisan® 142; Softisan® 154; Solan; Solan 50; Soluwax; Span® 20; Span® 40; Span® 60; Span® 60K; Span® 65; Span® 65K; Span® 85; Spermwax®; Spray Dried Gum Arabic NF/FCC CM; Spray Dried Gum Arabic NF/FCC CS (Low Bacteria); Spray Dried Gum Arabic NF/FCC CS-R; Spray Dried Gum Arabic Type A-180 NF Premium; Spray Dried Gum Arabic Type A-230 NF Extra; Standamul 1616; Stepanol® AM; Stepanol® AM-V; Stepanol® WAC; Stepanol® WA Extra; Stepanol® WA Paste; Stepanol® WAQ; Stepanol® WA Special; Sterotex®; Supercol Guar Gum; Super Hartolan; Super-Sat AWS-4; Super-Sat AWS-24; Suspengel Elite; Suspengel Micro; Suspengel Ultra; Syncrowax HGL-C; Synpro® Aluminum Monostearate NF; Synpro® Aluminum Stearate USP

Tego®-Betaine L-7; Tego®-Betaine ZF; Tetronic® 304; Ticalose® 15; Ticalose® 30; Ticalose® 75; Ticalose® 100; Ticalose® 150 R; Ticalose® 700 R; Ticalose® 750; Ticalose® 1200; Ticalose® 2000 R; Ticalose® 2500; Ticalose® 4000; Ticalose® 4500; Ticalose® 5000 R; Ticaxan® Regular; Ticolv; TIC Pretested® CMC 2500 S; TIC Pretested® CMC PH-2500; Tixosil 331; Tixosil 333, 343; Tixosil 375; T-Maz® 20; T-Maz® 28; T-Maz® 60K; T-Maz® 61; T-Maz® 65K; T-Maz® 80; T-Maz® 80K; T-Maz® 80KLM; T-Maz® 81; T-Maz® 81K; T-Maz® 85; Tragacanth Flake No. 27; Tragacanth Gum Ribbon No. 1; Tullanox HM-100; Tullanox HM-150; Tullanox HM-250; T-Wax; Tylose® C, CB Series; Tylose® MH Grades; Tylose® MHB

Veegum®; Veegum® HV; Veegum® K

Wacker HDK® H20; Wacker HDK® N20; Wacker HDK® V15; W.G.S. Cetyl Palmitate; W.G.S. Synaceti 116 NF/USP; Witafrol® 7420

Chemicals: Acrylamide/sodium acrylate copolymer; Acrylates/C10-30 alkyl acrylate crosspolymer; Acrylic acid/acrylonitrogens copolymer; Algin; Alginic acid; Aloe extract; Aluminum silicate; Aluminum stearate; Ammonium alginate; Ammonium lauryl sulfate; Arachidyl alcohol; Attapulgite

Batyl alcohol; Behenyl alcohol; Behenyl behenate; Bentonite; Bentonite magma

C18-36 acid triglyceride; Calcium alginate; Calcium carboxymethyl cellulose; Calcium carrageenan; Calcium chloride; Calcium gluconate; Calcium/sodium PVM/MA copolymer; Carbomer; Carbomer 910; Carbomer 934; Carbomer 934P; Carbomer 940; Carbomer 941; Carbomer 1342; Carboxymethylcellulose sodium; Carboxymethylmethylcellulose; Carrageenan; Cellulose; Ceresin; Ceteareth-12; Cetearyl alcohol; Cetyl alcohol; Cetyl esters; Cetyl glyceryl ether; Cetyl hydroxyethyl cellulose; Cetyl palmitate; Choleth-24; Cocamide DEA; Cocamide MEA; Coco-betaine; Cocohydroxyethyl PEG-imidazolinium chloride phosphate; Cocohydroxyethyl PEG-imidazolinium chloride phosphate; Corn starch

DEA-oleth-3 phosphate; DEA-oleth-10 phosphate; Dextran; Dextrin; Distearyldimonium chloride

Glyceryl cocoate; Glyceryl stearate citrate; Glycol distearate; Glycol stearate SE; Guar gum

Hectorite; Hydrogenated coco-glycerides; Hydrogenated cottonseed oil; Hydrogenated palm oil; Hydrogenated soybean oil; Hydroxyethylcellulose; Hydroxypropylcellulose; Hydroxypropyl methylcellulose

Isostearyl lactate

Karaya gum

Laneth-10; Laneth-20; Laneth-40; Lauramidopropyl PEG-dimonium chloride phosphate; Lauramine oxide; Laureth-2; Laureth-23; Locust bean gum

Magnesium aluminum silicate; Maltodextrin; D-Mannitol; Methylcellulose; Methyl hydroxyethylcellulose; Microcrystalline cellulose; Milk protein; Myreth-3 myristate; Myristamide MEA; Myristyl alcohol; Myristyl stearate

Ozokerite

Palm kernelamide DEA; Pectin; PEG-4; PEG-16; PEG-60; PEG-5 castor oil; PEG-8 castor oil; PEG-9 castor oil; PEG-15 castor oil; PEG-4 dilaurate; PEG-6 dilaurate; PEG-8 dilaurate; PEG-12 dilaurate; PEG-20 dilaurate; PEG-32 dilaurate; PEG-75 dilaurate; PEG-150 dilaurate; PEG-4 dioleate; PEG-6 dioleate; PEG-12 dioleate; PEG-20 dioleate; PEG-32 dioleate; PEG-75 dioleate; PEG-150 dioleate; PEG-4 distearate; PEG-6 distearate; PEG-8 distearate; PEG-12 distearate; PEG-20 distearate; PEG-32 distearate; PEG-75 distearate; PEG-150 distearate; PEG-60 lanolin; PEG-4 laurate; PEG-6 laurate; PEG-12 laurate; PEG-20 laurate; PEG-32 laurate; PEG-75 laurate; PEG-150 laurate; PEG-4 oleate; PEG-6 oleate; PEG-8 oleate; PEG-12 oleate; PEG-20 oleate; PEG-32 oleate; PEG-75 oleate; PEG-150 oleate; PEG-5 phytosterol; PEG-10 phytosterol; PEG-15 phytosterol; PEG-20 phytosterol; PEG-25 phytosterol; PEG-30 phytosterol; PEG-10-PPG-10 glyceryl stearate; PEG-10 propylene glycol; PEG-25 propylene glycol stearate; PEG-120 propylene glycol stearate; PEG-80 sorbitan laurate; PEG-20 sorbitan tritallate; PEG-2 stearate; PEG-4 stearate; PEG-6 stearate; PEG-8 stearate; PEG-20 stearate; PEG-32 stearate; PEG-40 stearate; PEG-75 stearate;

Thickeners *(cont'd.)*

PEG-150 stearate; PEG-300 stearate; Poloxamine 304; Poloxamine 504; Poloxamine 701; Poloxamine 702; Poloxamine 704; Poloxamine 707; Poloxamine 901; Poloxamine 904; Poloxamine 908; Poloxamine 1101; Poloxamine 1102; Poloxamine 1104; Poloxamine 1107; Poloxamine 1301; Poloxamine 1302; Poloxamine 1304; Poloxamine 1307; Poloxamine 1501; Poloxamine 1502; Poloxamine 1504; Poloxamine 1508; Polyacrylic acid; Polycarbophil; Polyethylene; Polyethylene wax; Polyglyceryl-3 diisostearate; Polyglyceryl-6 distearate; Polyglyceryl-3 stearate; Polysorbate 81; Polyvinyl acetate phthalate; Polyvinyl alcohol; Potassium alginate; PPG-3-laureth-9; PPG-15 stearyl ether; Propylene glycol alginate; PVM/MA copolymer; PVP; PVP/VA copolymer
SD alcohol 40; SD alcohol 40-B; Shea butter; Silica; Silica, hydrated; Sodium hectorite; Sodium magnesium silicate; Sorbitan tristearate; Stearalkonium hectorite; Sucrose stearate
Tragacanth gum; Trilaurin; Trimyristin; Tripalmitin; Tristearin; Triundecanoin
Xanthan gum

Tonicity agents

Trade names: Pricerine 9088
Unisweet MAN

Chemicals: D-Glucose anhyd; D-Glucose monohydrate; Glycerin
D-Mannitol
Potassium chloride
Sodium chloride
Zinc sulfate

UV absorbers

Trade names: Abil® WE 09
Dipsal
Gamma Oryzanol
Orange Wax, Deodorized
Spectra-Sorb® UV 9; Syntase® 62
Zinc Oxide USP 66

Chemicals: p-Aminobenzoic acid
Benzophenone-3; Benzophenone-4; 3-Benzylidene camphor
Dipropylene glycol salicylate
Menthyl anthranilate; Methyl salicylate
Octocrylene; Octyl dimethyl PABA; Octyl methoxycinnamate; Octyl salicylate; Orange wax; Oryzanol
PEG-25 PABA; Phenylbenzimidazole sulfonic acid
Titanium dioxide
Zinc oxide

Vehicles. *See Carriers*

Viscosity control agents. *See Thickeners*

Water repelling agents

Trade names: A-C® 617, 617A; Acylan
Britol®; Britol® 6NF; Britol® 7NF; Britol® 9NF; Britol® 20USP; Britol® 35USP; Britol® 50USP
Cecavon ZN 70; Cecavon ZN 71; Cecavon ZN 72; Cecavon ZN 73; Cecavon ZN 735; Crodamol

Water repelling agents *(cont'd.)*

CAP; Crodamol W
Dow Corning® 360 Medical Fluid; Durkote Vitamin C/Hydrog. Veg. Oil
Fancor Lanwax
Hydrobrite 200PO; Hydrobrite 300PO; Hydrobrite 380PO; Hydrobrite 550PO
Kaydol® S
Monteine PCO
Pecogel® GC-310; Pecogel® GC-1110; Pecogel® H-12; Pecogel® H-115; Pecogel® H-1220;
    Pecogel® S-1120; Pelemol® ISB; Pelemol® ML; Petrac® Magnesium Stearate MG-20 NF;
    Protopet® Alba; Protopet® White 1S; Protopet® White 2L; Protopet® White 3C; Protopet®
    Yellow 2A
Sheerskin; Skin-Lite

Chemicals: Acetylated lanolin
Cetearyl octanoate; Cyclomethicone
Dimethicone
Hydrogenated tallow
Isostearyl behenate
Palmitoyl collagen amino acids; Paraformaldehyde; β-Pinene
Silicone emulsions; Simethicone; Stearyl heptanoate

Wetting agents

Trade names: Accomid PK; Acconon CA-9; Acconon CA-15; Acconon TGH; Acconon W230; Adinol CT95;
    Alcolec® Granules; Alcolec® Z-3; Alkamuls® EL-620; Amerlate® W; Aminoxid WS 35
Brij® 700
Capmul® EMG; Capmul® POE-L; Capmul® POE-S; Caprol® 3GO; Caprol® 6G2O; Caprol®
    10G4O; Caprol® PGE860; Cerasynt® 303; Cithrol GDS N/E; Cithrol GDS S/E; Cithrol GML
    N/E; Cithrol GMO N/E; Cithrol GMO S/E; Cithrol GMR N/E; Cithrol GMR S/E; Cithrol GMS Acid
    Stable; Cithrol GMS N/E; Cithrol GMS S/E; Cithrol PGML N/E; Cithrol PGML S/E; Cithrol
    PGMO N/E; Cithrol PGMR N/E; Cithrol PGMR S/E; Cithrol PGMS N/E; Cithrol PGMS S/E;
    Corona Lanolin; Coronet Lanolin; Cosmetol® X; Crill 1; Crill 4; Crill 43; Crill 45; Crill 50; Crillet
    1; Crillet 2; Crillet 3; Crillet 4; Crillet 6; Crillet 11; Crillet 31; Crillet 35; Crillet 41; Crillet 45;
    Crodalan AWS; Crodalan LA; Crodasinic LS30; Crodasinic LS35; Crodesta F-10; Crodesta
    F-50; Crodesta F-110; Crodesta F-160; Crodet L4; Crodet L8; Crodet L12; Crodet L24; Crodet
    L40; Crodet L100; Crodet S4; Crodet S8; Crodet S12; Crodet S24; Crodet S40; Crodet S100;
    Crodex N; Crovol A40; Crovol M40; Crovol M70; Crystal® O; Crystal® Crown; Crystal® Crown
    LP
Dehydol® PID 6; Dehydol® PIT 6; Diamond Quality®; Docusate Sodium USP; Drewmulse®
    POE-SMO; Drewmulse® POE-SMS; Drewmulse® POE-STS; Drewmulse® SML;
    Drewmulse® SMO; Drewmulse® SMS; Drewmulse® STS; DSS Granular; DSS Tablet Grade
Eccowet® W-50; Eccowet® W-88; Emulmetik™ 970; Epikuron™ 145
Fancor IPL
Hodag 20-L; Hodag 22-L; Hodag 40-L; Hodag 40-O; Hodag 40-R; Hodag 40-S; Hodag 42-L;
    Hodag 42-O; Hodag 42-S; Hodag 60-L; Hodag 60-S; Hodag 62-O; Hodag 100-S; Hodag 150-
    S; Hydroxylan
Incrocas 35
Kessco® PEG 200 DL; Kessco® PEG 200 DO; Kessco® PEG 200 DS; Kessco® PEG 200 ML;
    Kessco® PEG 200 MO; Kessco® PEG 200 MS; Kessco® PEG 300 DL; Kessco® PEG 300
    DO; Kessco® PEG 300 DS; Kessco® PEG 300 MO; Kessco® PEG 300 MS; Kessco® PEG
    400 DL; Kessco® PEG 400 DO; Kessco® PEG 400 DS; Kessco® PEG 400 ML; Kessco® PEG
    400 MO; Kessco® PEG 400 MS; Kessco® PEG 600 DL; Kessco® PEG 600 DO; Kessco®
    PEG 600 DS; Kessco® PEG 600 ML; Kessco® PEG 600 MO; Kessco® PEG 600 MS;
    Kessco® PEG 1000 DL; Kessco® PEG 1000 DO; Kessco® PEG 1000 DS; Kessco® PEG
    1000 ML; Kessco® PEG 1000 MO; Kessco® PEG 1000 MS; Kessco® PEG 1540 DL;
    Kessco® PEG 1540 DO; Kessco® PEG 1540 DS; Kessco® PEG 1540 ML; Kessco® PEG
    1540 MO; Kessco® PEG 1540 MS; Kessco® PEG 4000 DL; Kessco® PEG 4000 DO;
    Kessco® PEG 4000 DS; Kessco® PEG 4000 ML; Kessco® PEG 4000 MO; Kessco® PEG
    4000 MS; Kessco® PEG 6000 DL; Kessco® PEG 6000 DS; Kessco® PEG 6000 ML; Kessco®
    PEG 6000 MO; Kessco® PEG 6000 MS
Labrasol; Lan-Aqua-Sol 50; Lan-Aqua-Sol 100; Lanette® E; Lanogel® 21; Lanogel® 31;

Wetting agents *(cont'd.)*

Lanogel® 41; Lanogel® 61; Lipacide SH Co 90; Lipacide SH K 90

Macol® 1; Macol® 2; Macol® 2D; Macol® 2LF; Macol® 4; Macol® 8; Macol® 10; Macol® 22; Macol® 27; Macol® 33; Macol® 40; Macol® 85; Monawet MO-70R

Naxolate™ WA-97; Naxolate™ WAG; Niaproof® Anionic Surfactant 4; Niaproof® Anionic Surfactant 08; Nikkol OTP-100S

OHlan®; Orange Wax, Deodorized

Pecosil® PS-100; Pecosil® WDS-100; Pelemol® TGC; Phospholipid PTD; Phospholipid PTL; Phospholipid PTZ; Prox-onic L 081-05; Prox-onic L 101-05; Prox-onic L 102-02; Prox-onic L 121-09; Prox-onic L 161-05; Prox-onic L 181-05; Prox-onic L 201-02; Prox-onic PEG-2000; Prox-onic PEG-10,000; Prox-onic PEG-20,000; Prox-onic PEG-35,000

Rhodasurf® ON-870; Ritahydrox

Sandopan® DTC-Acid; Sarkosyl® L; Sarkosyl® LC; Silwet® L-77; Simulsol® 58; Simulsol® 78; Simulsol® 98; Simulsol® CS; Simulsol® P4; Simulsol® P23; Softigen® 767; Stepanol® WA-100; Supralate® C

Tetronic® 304; Texapon® K-12 Powd.; Texapon® K-1296 Powd.; Texapon® Z; Texapon® Z Highly Conc. Needles; Texapon® Z Highly Conc. Powder; T-Maz® 20; T-Maz® 28; T-Maz® 60K; T-Maz® 61; T-Maz® 65K; T-Maz® 80; T-Maz® 80K; T-Maz® 80KLM; T-Maz® 81; T-Maz® 81K; T-Maz® 85

Vigilan AWS; Volpo CS-20

Wickenol® 155; Wickenol® 156; Wickenol® 158; Wickenol® 159; Wickenol® 160; Wickenol® 161; Wickenol® 171

Yelkin F; Yelkin G; Yelkin P

Chemicals: Benzalkonium chloride; Benzethonium chloride

Ceteareth-20; Cetylpyridinium chloride; Cocohydroxyethyl PEG-imidazolinium chloride phosphate

Dimethicone copolyol phosphate; Dioctyl sodium sulfosuccinate; Dioctyl succinate

EO/PO block polymer or copolymer

Glyceryl dioleate SE; Glyceryl distearate; Glyceryl distearate SE; Glyceryl laurate SE; Glyceryl oleate SE; Glyceryl ricinoleate SE

Laneth-5; Laneth-15; Lauramidopropyl PEG-dimonium chloride phosphate; Laureth-6; Lecithin

Meroxapol 172; Meroxapol 174

Nonoxynol-9; Nonoxynol-10

Octoxynol-9; Octyl hydroxystearate; Octyl pelargonate; Octyl stearate; Oleth-10

Palm kernelamide DEA; PEG-10M; PEG-20M; PEG-35M; PEG-20 almond glycerides; PEG-60 almond glycerides; PEG-6 caprylic/capric glycerides; PEG-30 castor oil; PEG-35 castor oil; PEG-20 corn glycerides; PEG-60 corn glycerides; PEG-6 dilaurate; PEG-8 dilaurate; PEG-20 dilaurate; PEG-32 dilaurate; PEG-75 dilaurate; PEG-150 dilaurate; PEG-4 dioleate; PEG-6 dioleate; PEG-8 dioleate; PEG-12 dioleate; PEG-20 dioleate; PEG-32 dioleate; PEG-75 dioleate; PEG-150 dioleate; PEG-4 distearate; PEG-6 distearate; PEG-8 distearate; PEG-12 distearate; PEG-20 distearate; PEG-32 distearate; PEG-75 distearate; PEG-20 glyceryl stearate; PEG-40 hydrogenated castor oil; PEG-27 lanolin; PEG-40 lanolin; PEG-85 lanolin; PEG-4 laurate; PEG-6 laurate; PEG-12 laurate; PEG-20 laurate; PEG-32 laurate; PEG-75 laurate; PEG-150 laurate; PEG-4 oleate; PEG-6 oleate; PEG-12 oleate; PEG-20 oleate; PEG-32 oleate; PEG-75 oleate; PEG-150 oleate; PEG-300 oleate; PEG-10-PPG-10 glyceryl stearate; PEG-8 ricinoleate; PEG-20 sorbitan isostearate; PEG-80 sorbitan laurate; PEG-20 sorbitan tritallate; PEG-4 stearate; PEG-6 stearate; PEG-12 stearate; PEG-20 stearate; PEG-24 stearate; PEG-32 stearate; PEG-40 stearate; PEG-50 stearate; PEG-55 stearate; PEG-75 stearate; PEG-150 stearate; PEG-300 stearate; PEG-4 tallate; Poloxamer 101; Poloxamer 105; Poloxamer 108; Poloxamer 123; Poloxamer 124; Poloxamer 181; Poloxamer 182; Poloxamer 184; Poloxamer 185; Poloxamer 188; Poloxamer 217; Poloxamer 231; Poloxamer 234; Poloxamer 235; Poloxamer 237; Poloxamer 238; Poloxamer 282; Poloxamer 284; Poloxamer 288; Poloxamer 331; Poloxamer 333; Poloxamer 334; Poloxamer 335; Poloxamer 338; Poloxamer 401; Poloxamer 402; Poloxamer 403; Poloxamer 407; Poloxamine 304; Poloxamine 504; Poloxamine 701; Poloxamine 702; Poloxamine 704; Poloxamine 707; Poloxamine 901; Poloxamine 904; Poloxamine 908; Poloxamine 1101; Poloxamine 1102; Poloxamine 1104; Poloxamine 1107; Poloxamine 1301; Poloxamine 1302; Poloxamine 1304; Poloxamine 1307; Poloxamine 1501; Poloxamine 1502; Poloxamine 1504; Poloxamine 1508; Polyglyceryl-6 dioleate; Polysorbate 20; Polysorbate 21; Polysorbate 40; Polysorbate 60; Polysorbate 65; Polysorbate 80; Polysorbate 81; Propylene glycol laurate SE; Propylene glycol myristate; Propylene glycol oleate; Propylene glycol oleate SE;

Wetting agents *(cont'd.)*

Propylene glycol ricinoleate; Propylene glycol ricinoleate SE; Propylene glycol stearate SE
Sodium cetearyl sulfate; Sodium lauroyl sarcosinate; Sodium lauryl sulfate; Sodium myristyl sulfate; Sodium octyl sulfate; Sodium N-oleoyl sarcosinate; Sorbitan isostearate; Sorbitan laurate; Sorbitan oleate; Sorbitan palmitate; Sorbitan stearate; Sorbitan tristearate; Steareth-20; Sucrose cocoate; Sucrose distearate; Sucrose stearate
Trideceth-100; Trideceth-7 carboxylic acid; Trioctyldodecyl citrate; Tyloxapol

Part IV
Manufacturers Directory

Manufacturers Directory

Aarbor Int'l. Corp.

9434 Maltby Rd., Brighton, MI 48116 USA (Tel.: 313-220-0080; Telefax: 313-220-0088)

Aarhus

Aarhus Oliefabrik A/S, Postboks 50, Bruunsgade 27, DK-8100 Aarhus C Denmark (Tel.: 86-12 60 00; Telefax: 86-183839; Telex: 64341)

Aarhus Inc., 131 Marsh St., PO Box 4240, Newark, NJ 07114 USA (Tel.: 201-344-1300; Telefax: 201-344-9049)

Abco Industries Ltd.

200 Railroad St., PO Box 335, Roebuck, SC 29376 USA (Tel.: 803-576-6821; 800-476-4476; Telefax: 803-576-9378; Telex: 628 17731)

ABITEC Corp., Subsid. of Associated British Foods (ABF)

525 W. First Ave., PO Box 569, Columbus, OH 43216-0569 USA (Tel.: 614-299-3131; 800-848-1340; Telefax: 614-299-8279; Telex: 245494 capctyprdcol)

Able Products Ltd.

Tame St., Stalybridge, Cheshire, SK15 1QW UK (Tel.: 44 161 343 1772; Telefax: 44 161 343 1169; Telex: 667014)

AB Technology Limited

Salthouse Rd, Brackmills, Northampton, Northamptonshire, NN4 0EX UK (Tel.: 44 1604 768999; Telefax: 44 1604 701503; Telex: 311848)

Accurate Chemical & Scientific Corp.

300 Shames Dr., Westbury, NY 11590 USA (Tel.: 516-333-2221; 800-645-6264; Telefax: 516-997-4948; Telex: 4972582)

Aceto

Aceto Chemical Co., Inc., 1 Hollow Lane, Suite 201, Lake Success, NY 11042-1215 USA (Tel.: 516-627-6000; Telefax: 516-627-6000; Telex: FTCC 824609)

Pfaltz & Bauer Inc., Research chemicals subsidiary of Aceto Corp., 172 E. Aurora St., Waterbury, CT 06708 USA (Tel.: 203-574-0075; 800-225-5172; Telefax: 203-574-3181; Telex: 996471)

AC Industries, Inc., Sattva Chemical Co. Div.

5 Landmark Sq., Suite 308, Stamford, CT 06901 USA (Tel.: 203-348-8002; 800-736-7893; Telefax: 203-348-3666; Telex: 6819048 SATVA UW)

Acme-Hardesty Co., Div. of Jacob Stern & Sons, Inc.

626 Fox Pavilion, Jenkintown, PA 19046-0831 USA (Tel.: 215-885-3610; 800-223-7054; Telefax: 215-886-2309)

Active Organics, Inc.

11230 Grader St., Dallas, TX 75238 USA (Tel.: 214-348-2015; 800-541-1478; Telefax: 214-348-1557)

Adams Food Ingredients Ltd.

Prince St., Leek, Staffordshire, ST13 6DB UK (Tel.: 44 1538 399686; Telex: 36134)

Adeka Fine Chemical. *See under* Asahi Denka Kogyo

ADM

ADM Corn Processing, Div. Archer Daniels Midland Co., Box 1470, Decatur, IL 62525 USA (Tel.: 217-424-5200; 800-323-0735; Telefax: 217-424-5978)

ADM Ethanol Sales, Div. Archer Daniels Midland Co., Box 1470, Decatur, IL 62525 USA (Tel.: 217-424-5200; Telefax: 217-424-5978)

ADM Lecithin, Div. Archer Daniels Midland Co., 4666 Faries Pkwy., Box 1470, Decatur, IL 62525 USA (Tel.: 217-424-5898; 800-637-5843; Telefax: 217-424-4119; Telex: 190021)

Advance Coatings, Inc.

Depot Rd., Westminster, MA 01473 USA (Tel.: 508-874-5921; Telefax: 508-874-2788)

Advanced Sweeteners Ltd.

53 The Green, West Cornforth, Ferry Hill, Co. Durham, DL17 9JH UK (Tel.: 44 1740 54955; Telex: 537681)

Agrisales Ltd.

Royal Oak House, 45A Porchester Rd., London, W2 5DP UK (Tel.: 44 171 221 1275; Telefax: 44 171 792 9014; Telex: 266910)

Air Liquide Hellas SA

26-28 Asklipiou St, GR-10679 Athens, Greece (Tel.: 30 1-360 84 11; Telefax: 30 1-362-54 31; Telex: 216444)

Air Products and Chemicals

Air Products and Chemicals, Inc., 7201 Hamilton Blvd., Allentown, PA 18195-1501 USA (Tel.: 215-481-4911; 800-345-3148; Telefax: 215-481-5900; Telex: 847416)

Air Products Nederland B.V., Kanaalweg 15, PO Box 3193, 3502 GD Utrecht The Netherlands (Tel.: 31-30-857100; Telefax: 31-30 857111)

Air Products Japan, Inc., Shuwa No. 2 Kamiyacho Bldg., 3-18-19, Toranomon, Minato-ku, Tokyo, 105 Japan (Tel.: (81)(3)3432-7046; Telefax: (81)(3)3432-7048)

Aisan Chemical Co., Ltd.

32, Ooyada, Ooya-cho, Inazawa-shi, Aichi, 492 Japan (Tel.: (0587) 36-0121; Telefax: (0587) 36-1139; Telex: 04427746 AISAN J)

Ajinomoto

Ajinomoto Co., Inc., 15-1, Kyobashi 1-chome, Chuo-ku, Tokyo, 104 Japan (Tel.: (03) 5250-8111; Telex: J22690)

Ajinomoto USA, Inc., Glenpointe Centre West, 500 Frank W. Burr Blvd., Teaneck, NJ 07666-6894 USA (Tel.: 201-488-1212; Telefax: 201-488-6282; Telex: 275425 (AJNJ))

Akcros

Akcros Chemicals, Lankro House, PO Box 1, Eccles, Manchester, M30 0BH UK (Tel.: 44 161 789 7300; Telefax: 44 161 788 7886; Telex: 587135)

Akcros Chemicals France S.A., Zone Industrielle BP 40, 441220 St Laurent-Nouan France (Tel.: 33 54 87 73 89; Telefax: 33 54 87 79 40; Telex: 750679 Tinstab)

Akcros Chemicals GmbH & Co. KG, Chemiewerk Greiz-Dolau, Liebigstrasse 7, 07973 Greiz Germany (Tel.: 49 36 61 780; Telefax: 49 36 61 782 02; Telex: 331141)

Akcros Chemicals Iberica S.L., Autovia Castelldefels Km. 4,65, 08820 El Prat De Llobregat, Barcelona Spain (Tel.: 34 3 4785 755; Telefax: 34 3 4780 888; Telex: 16152 Akrcos dk)

Akcros Chemicals Italia Srl, Via Cristina Belgioioso 13/15, 20021 Baranzate DiBollate (MI) Italy (Tel.: 39 2 38200484; Telefax: 39 2 38200443)

Akcros Chemicals Nordic ApS, Naverland 2, 8. floor, DK-2600 Glostrup-Copenhagen Denmark (Tel.: 45 4344 4201; Telefax: 45 4344 4203; Telex: 16152 Akrcos dk)

Akcros Chemicals v.o.f., Haagen House, PO Box 44, 6040 AA Roermond The Netherlands (Tel.: 31 4750-91777; Telefax: 31 4750-17489; Telex: 58021 haro nl)

Akcros Chemicals America, 500 Jersey Ave., PO Box 638, New Brunswick, NJ 08903 USA (Tel.: 908-247-2202; 800-500-7890; Telefax: 908-247-2287)

Akcros Chemicals, Taiwan Branch, Room 1408, 145h Fl. No. 96, Chung Shan N. Rd., Sec. 2, Taipei 10449, Taiwan, R.O.C. (Tel.: 886 2 562 6922; Telefax: 886 2 536 5287; Telex: 15185)

Akcros Chemicals (Asia Pacific) Pte Ltd., 7500A Beach Rd., 15-309 The Plaza, Singapore 0719 (Tel.: 65 292 1966; Telefax: 65 292 9665; Telex: RS 23241 AKCROS)

Akrochem Chemical Co.

255 Fountain St., Akron, OH 44304 USA (Tel.: 216-535-2108; 800-321-2260; Telefax: 216-535-8947)

Akzo

Akzo Nobel België NV/SA, 13 Marnix Ave., 1050 Bruxelles Belgium (Tel.: 2-518 04 07; Telefax: 02 518 05 05; Telex: 62 664)

Akzo Nobel Chemicals, 300 S. Riverside Plaza, Chicago, IL 60606 USA (Tel.: 312-906-7500; 800-828-7929; Telefax: 312-906-7633; Telex: 25-3233)

Akzo Salt Co., Abington Executive Park, Clarks Summit, PA 18411 USA (Tel.: 717-587-5131; Telefax: 717-586-7792; Telex: 756470)

Akzo Nobel Chemicals Ltd., 1 City Center Dr., Suite 320, Mississauga, Ontario, L53 IM2 Canada (Tel.: 905-273-5959; Telefax: 905-273-7339)

Akzo Nobel Chemicals Ltd., 1-5, Queens Road, Hersham, Walton-on-Thames, Surrey, KT12 5NL UK (Tel.: 44 1932 247891; Telefax: 44 1932-231204; Telex: 21997)

Akzo Nobel Chemicals bv, Postbus 247, Stationsstraat 48, 3800 AE Amersfoort The Netherlands (Tel.: 31-33-67 67 67; Telefax: 31-33-67 61 00; Telex: 79322)

Akzo Salt Europe, PO Box 247, 3800 AE Amersfoort The Netherlands (Tel.: 31 33 676767; Telefax: 31 33 676132; Telex: 79322)

Akzo Chemicals SpA, 80 Via E Vismara, 20020 Arese (Milano) Italy (Tel.: (02) 9356251; Telefax: (02 9380816; Telex: 332526)

Akzo Nobel Chemicals GmbH, Postfach 100132, Phillippstrasse 27, 52301 Düren Germany (Tel.: 2421-49201; Telefax: 2421-492487; Telex: 833911)

Akzo Chemie GmbH, Postfach 100132, Duren Germany (Tel.: 49 2421-492261; Telefax: 49 2421-595380)

Akzo Nobel Chemicals Ltd., 6 Grand Ave., PO Box 80, Camellia, NSW, 2150 Australia (Tel.: (02) 6384555; Telefax: (02) 6384681; Telex: AA 21562)

Akzo Nobel K.K., Godo Kaikan Bldg., 3-27 Kioi-cho, Chiyoda-ku, Tokyo, 102 Japan (Tel.: (03)5275-6300; Telefax: (03)3222-0465; Telex: J24262)

Eka Nobel Ltd., Div. of Eka Nobel AB, Unit 304 Worle Pkwy., Summer Lane, Worle, Weston-Super-Mare, Avon, BS22 OWA UK (Tel.: 44 1934 522244; Telefax: 44 1934 522577; Telex: 444351)

Eka Nobel AB, Div. of Nobel Industrier Sverige AB, S-445 80 Bohus, Sweden (Tel.: 46-31-58 70 00; Telefax: 46-31-98 17 74; Telex: 2435 EKÅGBGS)

Alba International Inc.

508 Clearwater Dr., N. Aurora, IL 60542 USA (Tel.: 708-897-4200; 800-669-9333; Telefax: 708-377-5330)

Alban Muller Int'l.

212, rue de Rosny, 93102 Montreuil France (Tel.: 1-48-58-30-25; Telefax: 1-48-58-03-71; Telex: 236030 F)

Albemarle

Albemarle Corp., 451 Florida St., Baton Rouge, LA 70801 USA (Tel.: 504-388-7040; 800-535-3030; Telefax: 504-388-7686; Telex: 586441, 586431)

Albemarle SA, Div. of Albemarle Corp., 523 Ave. Louise, Box 19, B-1050 Brussels Belgium (Tel.: 2-642-4411; Telefax: 2-648-0560; Telex: 22549)

Albemarle Asia Pacific Co., #13-06 PUB Bldg., Devonshire Wing, 111 Somerset Rd., Singapore 0923 Singapore (Tel.: 65-732-6286; Telefax: 65-737-4123)

Albemarle Japan Corporation, Shiroyama Hills 19F, 4-3-1, Toranomon, Minato-ku, Tokyo, 105 Japan (Tel.: 81-3-5401-2901; Telefax: 81-3-5401-3368)

Albright & Wilson

Albright & Wilson Ltd., European & Corporate Hdqtrs., PO Box 3, 210-222 Hagley Rd. West, Oldbury, Warley, West Midlands, B68 0NN UK (Tel.: 44 121 429-4942; Telefax: 44 121-420-5151; Telex: 336291)

Albright & Wilson Americas Inc., PO Box 26229, Richmond, VA 23260-6229 USA (Tel.: 804-550-4300; 800-446-3700; Telefax: 804-550-4385)

Albright & Wilson Saint Mihiel SA, B.P. 19 Han-Sur-Meuse, 55300 Saint-Mihiel France (Tel.: 33 29 91 73 00; Telefax: 33 29 91 73 99; Telex: 961058)

Albright & Wilson Am. (Canada), PO Box 2220, St. John's, Newfoundland, A1C 6E6 Canada (Tel.: 709-753-0838; Telefax: 709-753-5353)

Albright & Wilson Castiglione Srl, Via Cavour 50, Casella Postale No. 142, I-46043 Castiglione delle Stiviere, (Mantova) Italy (Tel.: 39-376-6371; Telefax: 39-376 637323; Telex: 300432)

Albright & Wilson GmbH, City Center, Frankfurter Strasse 181, 63263 Ne-Isenburg Germany (Tel.: 49-6102 27051; Telefax: 49-6102 25286; Telex: 4032069)

Albright & Wilson (Australia) Limited, PO Box 20, Yarraville, Victoria, 3013 Australia (Tel.: 61 3-688-7777; Telefax: 61 3-688-7788)

Albright & Wilson Asia Pacific Pte Ltd., 6 Jalan Besut, Jurong Industrial Estate, Singapore 2261 (Tel.: 011-65-261-2151; Telefax: 011-65-265-1941; Telex: 37007)

Albright & Wilson Ltd. Japan, No. 2 Okamotoya Bldg. 6 Fl., 1-24, Toranomon 1-chome, Minato-ku, Tokyo, 105 Japan (Tel.: (03) 3508 9461; Telefax: (03) 3591 0733; Telex: 2226721)

Alcan Chemicals, Div. of Alcan Aluminum Corp

3690 Orange Place, Suite 400, Cleveland, OH 44122-4438 USA (Tel.: 216-765-2550; 800-321-3864; Telefax: 216-765-2570; Telex: 135069)

Alcoa Industrial Chemicals Div.

4701 Alcoa Rd., PO Box 300, Bauxite, AR, 72011 USA (Tel.: 501-776-4987; 800-643-8771; Telefax: 501-776-4592; Telex: 536447)

Alco Chemical Corp, Div. of National Starch & Chem.

909 Mueller Dr., PO Box 5401, Chattanooga, TN 37406 USA (Tel.: 615-629-1405; 800-251-1080; Telefax: 615-698-8723; Telex: 755002)

Aldrich

Aldrich Chemical Co., Inc., 1001 W. St. Paul Ave., Milwaukee, WI 53233 USA (Tel.: 414-273-3850; 800-558-9160; Telefax: 414-273-4979; Telex: 26843 ALDRICH MI)

Aldrich Flavors & Fragrances, 1101 W. St. Paul Ave., Milwaukee, WI 53233 USA (Tel.: 414-273-3850; 800-227-4563; Telefax: 414-273-5793; Telex: 910-262-3052)

Aldrich Chemical Co. Ltd., The Old Brickyard, New Rd., Gillingham, Dorset, SP8 4JL UK (Tel.: 44 1747 822211; 0800-71 71 81; Telefax: 44 1747 823779; Telex: 417238)

Sigma-Aldrich NV/SA, K. Cardijnplei 8, B-2880 Bornem Belgium (Tel.: 038991301; Telefax: 038991311)

Aldrich-Chimie S.a.r.l., BP 701, 38297 Saint Quentin Fallavier, Cedex France (Tel.: 74822800; Telefax: 74956808; Telex: 308215 Aldrich F)

Aldrich Chemical, Unit 2, 10 Anella Ave., Castle Hill, NSW, 2154 Australia (Tel.: 028999977; Telefax: 028999742)

Aldrich Japan Inc., Kyodo Bldg., Shinkanda, 10 Kanda-Mikura-cho, Chiyoda-ku, Tokyo, 101 Japan (Tel.: (03)3258 0155; Telefax: (03)3258 0157)

Alemark Chemicals

1177 High Ridge Rd., Stamford, CT 06905 USA (Tel.: 203-966-7410; Telefax: 203-966-4276)

Alfa Chem

1661 N. Spur Dr., Central Islip, NY 11722-4325 USA (Tel.: 516-277-7681; Telefax: 516-277-7681; Telex: 6504811992)

Allan Chemical Corp.

PO Box 1837, Fort Lee, NJ 07024-8337 USA (Tel.: 201-592-8122; Telefax: 201-592-9298; Telex: 170991)

Allchem Industries Inc.

4001 Newberry Rd, Suite E-3, Gainesville, FL 32607 USA (Tel.: 904-378-9696; Telefax: 904-338-0400; Telex: 509540 ALLCHEM UD)

All Chemie Ltd.

1429 John St., Fort Lee, NJ 07024 USA (Tel.: 201-947-7776; Telefax: 201-947-3343)

Allchem International Ltd.

Broadway House, 21 Broadway, Maidenhead, Berkshire, SL6 1JE UK (Tel.: 44 1628 776666; Telefax: 44 1628 776591)

Allied Colloids Inc.

2301 Wilroy Rd., PO Box 820, Suffolk, VA 23439-0820 USA (Tel.: 804-538-3700; Telefax: 804-538-0204)

Allied Custom Gypsum Inc.

PO Box 69, Lindsay, OK 73052 USA (Tel.: 405-756-9565; Telefax: 405-756-3443)

AlliedSignal

AlliedSignal Inc., PO Box 1053, 101 Columbia Rd., Morristown, NJ 07960 USA (Tel.: 201-455-2000; 800-526-0717; Telefax: 201-455-3198; Telex: 136410)

AlliedSignal Inc./Performance Additives, PO Box 1039, 101 Columbia Rd., Morristown, NJ 07962-1039 USA (Tel.: 201-455-2145; 800-222-0094; Telefax: 201-455-6154; Telex: 990433)

AlliedSignal Europe NV, Haasrode Research Park, Grauwmeer 1, B-3001 Heverlee (Leuven) Belgium (Tel.: 32-16-39 12 33; Telefax: 32-16-40 03 77)

Altus Biologics Inc.

40 Allston St., Cambridge, MA 02139-4211 USA (Tel.: 617-499-0500; Telefax: 617-499-2480)

AluChem Inc.

One Landy Lane, Reading, OH 45215 USA (Tel.: 513-733-8519; Telefax: 513-733-0608; Telex: 298252 ALUC UR)

Amano

Amano Enzyme USA Co. Ltd., Rt. 2, Box 1475, Troy, VA 22974 USA (Tel.: 804-589-8278; 800-446-7652; Telefax: 804-589-8270)

Amano International Enzyme Co., 1157 North Main St., Lombard, IL 60148 USA (Tel.: 708-953-1891; 800-446-7652; Telefax: 708-953-1895; Telex: 822438)

Amano Pharmaceutical Co., Ltd., 2-7, Nishiki 1-chome, Naka-ku, Nagoya, 460 Japan (Tel.: (052) 211-3032; Telefax: (052) 211-3054; Telex: BIOAMANO 59805)

Amber Synthetics, Amsyn Inc.

1177 High Ridge Rd., Stamford, CT 06905 USA (Tel.: 203-972-7401; Telefax: 203-966-4276)

Amcan Ingredients International

5 Square Channaleilles, 78510 Le Chesnay France (Tel.: 33 3955 5260; Telefax: 33 3954 7268)

Amerchol

Amerchol Corp., Div. of United-Guardian, Inc., PO Box 4051, 136 Talmadge Rd., Edison, NJ 08818-4051 USA (Tel.: 908-248-6000; 800-367-3534; Telefax: 908-287-4186; Telex: 833472)

Amerchol, D.F. Anstead Ltd., Victoria House, Radford Way, Billericay, Essex, CM12 0DE UK (Tel.: 44 1277 630063; Telefax: 44 1277 631356; Telex: 851-99410 ANSTED G)

Amerchol Europe, Havenstraat 86, B-1800 Vilvoorde Belgium (Tel.: 2-252-4012; Telefax: 2-252-4909; Telex: 846-69105 AMRCHL B)

American Biorganics, Inc.

2236 Liberty Dr, Niagara Falls, NY 14304 USA (Tel.: 716-283-1434; 800-648-6689; Telefax: 716-283-1570; Telex: 926074)

American Bio-Synthetics Corp.

710 W. National Ave., Milwaukee, WI 53204 USA (Tel.: 414-384-7017; Telefax: 414-384-1369)

American Casein Co.

109 Elbow Lane, Burlington, NJ 08016 USA (Tel.: 609-387-3130; Telefax: 609-387-7204; Telex: 843368)

American Chemet Corp.

400 Lake Cook Rd., Deerfield, IL 60015 USA (Tel.: 708-948-0800; Telefax: 708-948-0811; Telex: 72-4301)

American Colloid Co.

1500 W. Shure Dr., Arlington Hts., IL 60004-1434 USA (Tel.: 708-392-4600; Telefax: 708-506-6199; Telex: 4330321)

American Cyanamid/Corporate Headquarters, Subsid. of American Home Products

One Cyanamid Plaza, Wayne, NJ 07470 USA (Tel.: 201-831-2000; Telefax: 201-831-2637)

American Dairy Products Institute

130 N. Franklin St., Chicago, IL 60606 USA (Tel.: 312-782-4888; Telefax: 312-782-5299)

American Fruit Processors

10725 Sutter Ave., PO Box 331060, Pacolma, CA 91333-1060 USA (Tel.: 818-899-9574; Telefax: 818-899-6042)

American Ingredients

American Ingredients Co., 3947 Broadway, Kansas City, MO 64111 USA (Tel.: 800-669-4092)

American Ingredients Co./Patco Polymer Additives Div., 3947 Broadway, Kansas City, MO 64111 USA (Tel.: 816-561-9050; 800-669-2250; Telefax: 816-561-0422)

American International Chemical, Inc.

17 Strathmore Rd, Natick, MA 01760 USA (Tel.: 508-655-5805; 800-238-0001; Telefax: 508-655-0927; Telex: 948342)

American Laboratories Inc.

4410 South 102 St., Omaha, NE 68127 USA (Tel.: 402-339-2494; 800-445-5989; Telefax: 402-339-0801; Telex: 3735593 CACOMA)

American Lecithin. *See under* Rhone-Poulenc

American Maize Products Co./Amaizo

1100 Indianapolis Blvd., Hammond, IN 46320-1094 USA (Tel.: 219-659-2000; 800-348-9896; Telefax: 219-473-6601)

American Norit Co., Inc. *See* Norit America

American Roland Chemical Corp.

222 Sherwood Ave., Farmingdale, NY 11735-1718 USA (Tel.: 516-694-9090; Telefax: 516-694-9177; Telex: 232771)

American Xyrofin. *See under* Xyrofin

Amoco

Amoco Chemical Co., 200 East Randolph Dr., Mail code 4106, Chicago, IL 60601 USA (Tel.: 312-856-3092; 800-621-4567; Telefax: 312-856-4151; Telex: 25-3731)

Amoco Petroleum Products, 1515 W. 22nd St., Suite 800, Oak Brook, IL 60521 USA (Tel.: 708-571-7100)

Amoco Oil Co., Lubricants Div., 2021 Spring Rd., Oak Brook, IL 60562-1857 USA (Tel.: 708-571-7100; Telefax: 708-571-7174)

AMRESCO

30175 Solon Ind. Pkwy., Solon, OH 44139 USA (Tel.: 216-349-1313; 800-829-2802; Telefax: 216-349-1182; Telex: 985582)

Andeno BV

Grubbenvorsterweg 8, 5928 NX, Venlo-Holland The Netherlands (Tel.: 077-899-555; Telefax: 077-299300; Telex: 58310)

Andrulex Trading Ltd.

Unit 34, Saffron Court, Southfields Industrial Estate, Laindon, Basildon, Essex, SS15 6SS UK (Tel.: 44 1268 416441; Telefax: 44 1268 541639; Telex: 99339 RULEX G)

Anedco, Inc.

10429 Koenig Rd., Houston, TX 77034 USA (Tel.: 713-484-3900; Telefax: 713-484-3931)

Anglia Speciality Oils

King George Dock, Kingston-upon-Hull, North Humberside, HU9 5PX UK (Tel.: 44 1482 701271; Telefax: 44 1482-709447; Telex: 592136)

ANGUS

ANGUS Chemical Co., 1500 E. Lake Cook Rd., Buffalo Grove, IL 60089-6556 USA (Tel.: 708-215-8600; 800-362-2580; Telefax: 708-215-8626; Telex: 275422 ANGUS UR)

ANGUS Chemie GmbH, Unit 7, Rotunda Business Centre, Thorncliffe Park Estate, Chapeltown, Sheffield, S30 4PH UK (Tel.: 44 1742 571322; Telefax: 44 1742 571336)

ANGUS Chemie GmbH, Huyssenallee 5, 45128 Essen Germany (Tel.: (49) 201-233531; Telefax: (49)201-238661; Telex: 8571563 ANGE D)

ANGUS Chemie GmbH, Le Bonaparte, Centre d'Affaires, Paris Nord, 93153 Le Blanc Mesnil France (Tel.: (33)1-48-65-73-40; Telefax: (33)1-48-65-73-20; Telex: ANGUS 232089 F)

ANGUS Chemical (Singapore) Pte. Ltd., 150 Beach Rd., #17-01 Gateway West, Singapore 0718 (Tel.: (65) 293-1738; Telefax: (65) 293-3307)

D.F. Anstead Ltd. *See* Ellis & Everard

Aqualon

Aqualon Co, A Hercules Inc. Co, 1313 North Market St., Wilmington, DE 19899-8740 USA (Tel.: 302-594-5000; 800-345-8104; Telefax: 302-594-6660; Telex: 4761123)

Aqualon France, 3 Rue Eugene & Armand, Peugeot, 92500 Rueil-Malmaison France (Tel.: 33 1 4751 2919; Telefax: 33 1 4777 0614; Telex: 6314244)

Aqualon UK Ltd., Genesis Centre, Garret & Field, Birchwood, Warnington, Cheshire, WA3 7BH UK (Tel.: 44 1925 830077; Telefax: 44 1925 830112; Telex: 626219)

Aquatec Quimica SA

Av. Paulista no. 37-12° andar, 01311-000 Sao Paulo-SP Brazil (Tel.: 55 11-284-4188; Telefax: 55 11-288-4431; Telex: 1121312)

Arakawa

Arakawa Chemical Industries Ltd., 3-7, Hiranomachi 1-chome, Chuo-ku, Osaka, 541 Japan (Tel.: (06) 209-8581; Telefax: (06) 209-8542; Telex: 5222296 ARKOSA J)

Arakawa Chemical (USA) Inc., 625 N. Michigan Ave., Suite 1700, Chicago, IL 60611 USA (Tel.: 312-642-1750; Telefax: 312-642-0089; Telex: 26-5514)

ARCO

ARCO Chemical/Headquarters, Research & Engineering Center, 3801 West Chester Pike, Newtown Sq., PA 19073-2387 USA (Tel.: 610-359-2000; 800-345-0252; Telefax: 610-359-2841)

ARCO Chemical Canada Inc., 100 Consilium Pl., Suite 306, Scarborough, Ontario, M1H 3E3 Canada (Tel.: 416-296-9864)

ARCO Chemical Pan American, Inc., Paseo de la Reforma, 390 Decimo Piso, 06600 Mexico City Mexico (Tel.: 905-514-6833)

ARCO Chemical Europe Inc., Bridge Ave., Maidenhead, Berkshire, SL6 1YP UK (Tel.: 44 1628 775000; Telex: 847436)

ARCO Chemical Asia/Pacific Ltd., Toranomon 37 Mori Bldg., 5th Floor, 5-1 Toranomon 3-Chome, Minato-Ku, Tokyo, 105 Japan

ARCO Chemical Japan, Inc., Hamacho Center Bldg., 2-31-1 Nihonbashi, Hama-cho, Chuo-ku, Tokyo, 103 Japan (Tel.: (03) 5641-4500; Telefax: (03) 5641-4550)

Arenol Chemical Corp.

189 Meister Ave., Somerville, NJ 08876 USA (Tel.: 908-526-5900; Telefax: 908-526-9688)

M. Argueso & Co., Inc.

441 Waverly Ave., PO Box E, Mamaroneck, NY 10543 USA (Tel.: 914-698-8500; Telefax: 914-698-0325)

Arista Industries, Inc.

1082 Post Rd., Darien, CT 06820 USA (Tel.: 203-655-0881; 800-255-6457; Telefax: 203-656-0328; Telex: 996493)

Aristech Chemical Corp.

600 Grant St., Room 1028, Pittsburgh, PA 15230-0250 USA (Tel.: 412-433-7700; 800-526-4032; Telefax: 412-433-1816; Telex: 6503608865)

Arizona Chemical Co, Div. of International Paper

1001 E. Business Hwy. 98, Panama City, FL 32401-3633 USA (Tel.: 904-785-6700; 800-526-5294; Telefax: 904-785-2203; Telex: 441695)

Arla Foods AB

PO Box 47, S-59521 Mjolby, Sweden (Tel.: 46 142 89000; Telefax: 46 142 10485; Telex: 8155024)

Asada Chemical Industry Co., Ltd.

180, Miya, Shikama-ku, Himeji-shi, Hyogo, 672 Japan (Tel.: (0792) 35-1911; Telefax: (0792) 35-1915)

Asahi Chemical Industry Co., Ltd.

Hibiya Mitsui Bldg., 1-2, Yuraku-cho 1-chome, Chiyoda-ku, Tokyo, 100 Japan (Tel.: (03) 3507-2730; Telefax: (03) 3507-2495; Telex: 222-3518 BEMBRGJ)

Asahi Denka Kogyo

Asahi Denka Kogyo K.K., Furukawa Bldg. 2-8, Nihonbashi Muro-machi 2-chome Chuo-ku, Tokyo, 103 Japan (Tel.: (03) 5255-9002; Telefax: (03) 3270-2463; Telex: 222-2407 TOKADK)

Adeka Fine Chemical Co., Ltd., Subsid. of Asahi Denka Kogyo, Yoko Bldg., 4-5, Hongo 1-chome, Bunkyo-ku, Tokyo, 113 Japan (Tel.: (03) 5689-8681; Telefax: (03) 5689-8680)

Asahi Glass Co Ltd

Chiyoda Bldg, 1-2, Marunouchi 2-chome, Chiyoda-ku, Tokyo, 100 Japan (Tel.: (03) 3218-5555; Telex: J24616 ASAGLAS)

Asahi-Penn Chemical Co. Ltd., Joint venture of Asahi Glass Co Ltd./PPG Industries Inc.

13-3, Nihonbashi Kobuna-cho, Chuo-ku, Tokyo, 103 Japan (Tel.: (03) 3662-0520; Telefax: (03) 3662-0596)

Asarco Inc.

180 Maiden Lane, New York, NY 10038 USA (Tel.: 212-510-2000; Telex: ITT 420585)

Ash Grove Cement Co.

8900 Indian Creek Pkwy., Overland Park, KS 66225 USA (Tel.: 913-451-8900)

Ashland

Ashland Chemical Inc./Industrial Chemicals & Solvents, PO Box 2219, Columbus, OH 43216 USA (Tel.: 614-889-3333; Telefax: 614-889-3465)

Ashland Chemical Inc./Fine Ingredients Group, PO Box 2219, Columbus, OH 43216 USA (Tel.: 614-889-4530; Telefax: 614-889-3465)

Astor Wax Corp.

200 Piedmont Ct., Doraville, GA 30340 USA (Tel.: 404-448-8083; Telefax: 404-840-0954)

Atochem. *See under* Elf Atochem

Atomergic Chemetals Corp.

222 Sherwood Ave., Farmingdale, NY 11735-1718 USA (Tel.: 516-694-9000; Telefax: 516-694-9177; Telex: 6852289)

Auschem SpA

Via Cavriana, 14, 20134 Milano Italy (Tel.: 0039-2-70140259; Telefax: 0039-2-70140374; Telex: 312093 AUSCHEM 1)

Austin Chemical Co. Inc.

1565 Barclay Blvd., Buffalo Grove, IL 60089 USA (Tel.: 708-520-9600; Telefax: 708-520-9160; Telex: 280342)

Avebe

Avebe America Inc., 4 Independence Way, Princeton, NJ 08540 USA (Tel.: 609-520-1400; Telefax: 609-520-1473; Telex: 0820713)

Avebe BV, Avebeweg 1, 9607 PT Foxhol The Netherlands (Tel.: 31 5980-42234; Telefax: 5980-97892; Telex: 53018)

Avebe UK Ltd., Thornton Hall, Thornton Curtis, Ulceby, South Humberside, DN39 6XD UK (Tel.: 44 1469 32222; Telefax: 44 1469-31488)

Avrachem AG

PO Box 51, Gartenstrasse 12, CH-6340 Baar 1 Switzerland (Tel.: 41 42 318 355; Telefax: 41 42 310 250; Telex: 864-996)

Aztec Peroxides, Inc., Div. of Laporte Organics

One Northwind Plaza, 7600 W. Tidwell, Suite 500, Houston, TX 77040 USA (Tel.: 713-895-2015; 800-231-2702; Telefax: 713-895-2040)

BA Chemicals Ltd., Div. of Alcan

Chalfont Park, Gerrards Cross, Buckinghamshire, SL9 0QB UK (Tel.: 44 1753-887373; Telefax: 44 1753-889602; Telex: 847343)

J.T. Baker, Inc.

600 North Broad St., Phillipsburg, NJ 08865 USA (Tel.: 908-859-2151)

Balchem Corp.

PO Box 175, Slate Hill, NY 10973 USA (Tel.: 914-355-2861; Telefax: 914-355-6314)

Barium & Chemicals Inc.

County Road 44, PO Box 218, Steubenville, OH 43952 USA (Tel.: 614-282-9776; Telefax: 614-282-9161)

Barker Industries, Inc.

2841 Old Steele Creek Rd., Charlotte, NC 28208 USA (Tel.: 704-391-1023; Telefax: 704-393-0464)

Barnet Products Corp.

560 Sylvan Ave., Englewood Cliffs, NJ 07632 USA (Tel.: 201-569-6622; Telefax: 201-569-8847)

Barrington Chemical Corp.

540 W. Boston Post Rd., Mamaroneck, NY 10543 USA (Tel.: 914-833-1283; Telefax: 914-833-1765)

Bartek Ingredients Inc.

2490 Bloor St. West, Suite 401, Toronto, Ontario, M6S 1R4 Canada (Tel.: 416-763-1100; 800-537-7287 (USA); Telefax: 416-763-1155; Telex: 061-8498)

BASF

BASF AG, Carl-Bosch Str. 38, 67056 Ludwigshafen Germany (Tel.: 0621-60-99739; Telefax: 0621-60-93344; Telex: 62157120BASF)

BASF Corp., 3000 Continental Dr. North, Mount Olive, NJ 07828-1234 USA (Tel.: 201-426-2600; 800-367-9861)

BASF Fine Chemicals/BASF K&F Corp., 100 Cherry Hill Rd., Parsippany, NJ 07054 USA (Tel.: 201-316-3928)

BASF Canada Ltd., PO Box 430, Montreal, Quebec, H4L 4V8 Canada

BASF plc, PO Box 4, Earl Road, Cheadle Hulme, Cheadle, Cheshire, SK8 6QG UK (Tel.: 44 161 485-6222; Telefax: 44 161-486-0891; Telex: 669211 BASFCH G)

BASF Belgium S.A., Ave. Hamoir-laan 14, B-1180 Brussels Belgium (Tel.: 32 2 373 21 11; Telefax: 32 2 375 10 42)

BASF Espanola S.A., Paseo de Gracia, 99 E-08008, Barcelona Spain (Tel.: 34 3488 1010; Telefax: 34 3488 2020; Telex: 97923 BASF B E)

BASF France & Co. Cie, 140, Rue Jules Guesde, BP 8T F-92303 Levallois-Perret, Cedex France (Tel.: 33 47 30 55 00; Telefax: 33 47 57 5104; Telex: 610132 BASF F)

BASF India, Ltd., Maybaker House, S.K. Ahire Marg., PO Box 19108, Bombay, 400 025 India

BASF Japan Ltd., 3-3, Kioi-cho, Chiyoda-ku, Tokyo, 102 Japan (Tel.: (03) 3238-2300; Telex: 222-2130 BASFTK)

Bayer

Bayer AG, Bayerwerk, D-5090 Leverkusen Germany (Tel.: 49 (214)30-1; Telefax: 49 (214)30 6 51 36; Telex: 85103-0 byd)

Bayer Antwerpen NV, Div. of Bayer AG, Haven 507, Scheldelaan 420, B-2040 Antwerp Belgium (Tel.: 32-3540 3011; Telefax: 32-3541 6936; Telex: 71175 BAYANT B)

Bayer Inc./Fibers, Organics & Rubber, Bldg. 14, Mobay Rd., Pittsburgh, PA 15205-9741 USA (Tel.: 412-777-2000; 800-662-2927; Telefax: 412-777-7840; Telex: 1561261)

Beck Flavors

411 E. Gano, PO Box 22509, St. Louis, MO 63147 USA (Tel.: 314-436-3133; 800-851-8100; Telefax: 314-436-1049)

Bell Flavors & Fragrances, Inc.

500 Academy Dr., Northbrook, IL 60062 USA (Tel.: 708-291-8300; 800-323-4387; Telefax: 708-291-1217; Telex: 910-686-0653)

F.R. Benson & Partners Ltd.

Crossroads House, 165 The Parade, High St., Watford, Hertfordshire, WD1 1NJ UK (Tel.: 44 1923 240560; Telefax: 44 1923 240569)

Berje Inc.

5 Lawrence St., Bloomfield, NJ 07003 USA (Tel.: 201-748-8980; Telefax: 201-680-9618; Telex: 475-4165A)

Berk Natural Products Ltd.

PO Box 56, Priestley Rd., Basingstoke, Hampshire, RG24 9PU UK (Tel.: 44 1256 29292; Telefax: 44 1256 64711; Telex: 858371)

Bernel Chemical Co., Inc.

174 Grand Ave., Englewood, NJ 07631 USA (Tel.: 201-569-8934; Telefax: 201-569-1741)

Berol Nobel

Berol Nobel AB, S-44485 Stenungsund, Sweden (Tel.: 46 303 85000; Telefax: 46 303 84659; Telex: 10513 benobl s)

Berol Nobel Ltd., Div. of Berol Nobel AB, 23 Grosvenor Road, St. Albans, Hertfordshire, AL1 3AW UK (Tel.: 44 1727 841421; Telefax: 44 1727-841529; Telex: 23242 BEROL G)

Berol Nobel Inc., Meritt 8 Corporate Park, 99 Hawley Lane, Stratford, CT 06497 USA (Tel.: 203-378-0500; Telefax: 203-378-5960)

Bestoval Products Co. Ltd.

49 Ridge Hill, London, NW11 UK (Tel.: 44 181 455 3020)

Biddle Sawyer Corp.

2 Penn Plaza, New York, NY 10121 USA (Tel.: 212-736-1580; Telefax: 212-239-1089; Telex: 427471BSCE)

Bio-Botanica, Inc.

75 Commerce Dr., Hauppauge, NY 11788 USA (Tel.: 516-231-5522; 800-645-5720; Telefax: 516-231-7332)

Bioengineering AG

Sagenrainstrasse 7, 8636 Wald Switzerland (Tel.: 41 55 938 111; Telefax: 41 55 954 964; Telex: 375977)

Bio-Rad Laboratories

85A Marcus Dr., Melville, NY 11747 USA (Tel.: 800-4-BIORAD; Telefax: 516-756-2594; Telex: 71-3720184)

Bio Springer/Fould Springer

103 Rue Jean Jaures, 94701 Maisons Alfort France (Tel.: 33 1 4977 1846; Telefax: 33 1 4977 0358; Telex: 264067)

S. Black (Import & Export) Ltd.

The Colonnade, High St., Cheshunt, Waltham Cross, Hertfordshire, EN8 0DJ UK (Tel.: 44 1992 30751; Telefax: 44 1992 22838; Telex: 894085)

Blossom Farm Products Co.

12 Rt. 17 N, Paramus, NJ 07652 USA (Tel.: 201-587-1818; 800-729-1818; Telefax: 201-526-0310; Telex: 13-0489)

Blythe, William Ltd., Div. of Holliday Chemical Holdings plc

Holland Bank Works, Bridge St., Church, Accrington, Lancashire, BB5 4PD UK (Tel.: 44 1254 872872; Telefax: 44 1254 872000; Telex: 63142 BLYCO G)

BOC Gases

The Priestley Centre, The Surrey Research Park, Guildford, Surrey, GU2 5XY UK (Tel.: 44-1483-579857; Telefax: 44-1483-505211; Telex: 858078)

Boehringer Ingelheim

Boehringer Ingelheim KG, Binger Strasse 173, Postfach 200, D-6507 Ingelheim Germany (Tel.: 49-6132 773666; Telefax: 49-6132-773755; Telex: 79122 BI W)

Henley Div., B.I. Chemicals, Inc., Div. of Boehringer Ingelheim, 50 Chestnut Ridge Rd., Montvale, NJ 07645 USA (Tel.: 201-307-0422; 800-635-3558; Telefax: 201-307-0424; Telex: 232210 HNLY UR)

Boehringer Mannheim GmbH

Postfach 310120, Sandhofer Strasse 116, W-6800 Mannheim 31 Germany (Tel.: 49 621-7591; Telefax: 49 621-7592; Telex: 463193 BM D)

Boliden Intertrade Inc.

3379 Peachtree Rd. NE, Suite 300, Atlanta, GA 30326 USA (Tel.: 404-239-6700; 800-241-1912; Telefax: 404-239-6701; Telex: 981036)

Booths Raglan Works

Methey Rd., Whitwood Mere, Castleford, West Yorkshire, WF10 1NX UK (Tel.: 44 1977 518515; Telefax: 44 1977 519167)

Boots

Boots Chemicals, D110 Main Office, Beeston, Nottingham, Nottinghamshire, NG2 3AA UK (Tel.: 44 1159 591648; Telefax: 44 1159 593715)

Boots Microcheck, Nottingham, Nottinghamshire, NG2 3AA UK (Tel.: 44 1602 595504; Telefax: 1602 595508)

Boots Pharmaceuticals, Subsidiary of Boots Company plc, Suite 200, 300 Tri-State International Center, Lincolnshire, IL 60069-4415 USA (Tel.: 708-405-7400; Telefax: 708-405-7505)

BP Chemicals

BP Chemicals Ltd., Britannic House, 6th Flr., 1 Finsbury Circus, London, EC2M 7BA UK (Tel.: 44 171 496 4867; Telefax: 44 171 496 4898; Telex: 266883 BPCLBH G)

BP Chemicals Inc., 4440 Warrensville Center Rd., Warrensville Hts., OH 44128 USA (Tel.: 216-586-6455; 800-272-4367; Telefax: 216-586-3838; Telex: 6873120, 6873119)

Bradleys (Hart's Mill Ltd.)

Mill Lane, Aldington, Ashford, Kent, TN25 7AJ UK (Tel.: 44 1233 720768; Telefax: 44 1233 720007)

Bradshaw-Praeger. *See* William Vinsser & Co., Inc.

Brand-Nu Laboratories, Inc.

PO Box 895, 30 Maynard St., Meriden, CT 06450 USA (Tel.: 203-235-7989; 800-243-3768; Telefax: 203-235-7163)

Arthur Branwell & Co. Ltd.

Bronte House, 58-62 High St., Epping, Essex, CM16 4AE UK (Tel.: 44 1992 577333; Telefax: 44 1992 575043; Telex: 817158)

Bretagne Chimie Fine SA

Boisel, F-56140 Pleucadeuc France (Tel.: 33 97 26 91 21; Telefax: 33 97 26 90 46; Telex: 951084 BCFF)

BritAg Industries Ltd.

Waterfront House, Skeldergate Bridge, York, North Yorkshire, YO1 1DR UK (Tel.: 44 1904 611800; Telefax: 44 1904 627473; Telex: 57827 BRITAG G)

Britannia Natural Proucts Ltd.

Unit 5, Woodlands Business Park, Rougham Ind. Estate, Rougham, Suffolk, IP30 9ND UK (Tel.: 44 1359 71461; Telefax: 44 1359 71672)

British Arkady

British Arkady Co. Ltd., Arkady Soya Mills, Skerton Rd., Old Trafford, Manchester, Lancashire, M16 0NJ UK (Tel.: 44 161 872 7161; Telefax: 44 161 873 8083; Telex: 668488)

British Arkady Group, 62/70 rue Ivan Tourgueneff, 78380 Bougival France (Tel.: 33 1 3969 7070; Telefax: 33 1 3918 4610; Telex: 689413)

British Bakels Ltd.

238 Bath Road, Slough, Berkshire, SL1 4DU UK (Tel.: 44 1753 526261; Telefax: 44 1753 825455; Telex: 848115)

British Pepper & Spice Co. Ltd.

Rhosili Rd., Brackmills, Northampton, Northamptonshire, NN4 0LD UK (Tel.: 44 1604 766461; Telefax: 44 1604 763156; Telex: 312472)

British Traders & Shippers Ltd., Div. of Linton Park plc

6-7 Merrielands Crescent, Dagenham, Essex, RM9 6SL UK (Tel.: 44 181 595 4211; Telefax: 44 181-593 0933; Telex: 897438 SHIPEX G)

British Wax Refining Co Ltd.

29 St John's Rd, Redhill, Surrey, RH1 6DT UK (Tel.: 44 1737 761242; Telefax: 44 1737 761472)

Bronson & Jacobs Pty. Ltd.

288 Burns Bay Rd., Lane Cove, NSW, 2066 Australia (Tel.: 61 2 427 0066; Telefax: 61 2 428 2845)

Brooks Industries Inc.

70 Tyler Place, South Plainfield, NJ 07080 USA (Tel.: 908-561-5200; Telefax: 908-561-9174)

Brotherton Specialty Products Ltd.

Calder Vale Rd, Wakefield, West Yorkshire, WF1 5PH UK (Tel.: 44 1924 371919; Telefax: 44 1924 290408; Telex: 556320 BROKEM G)

Brown Chemical Co., Inc./Industrial and Fine Chems.

302 W. Oakland Ave., Oakland, NJ 07436-0785 USA (Tel.: 201-337-0900)

M. Brown & Sons, Inc.

118 S. Center St., Bremen, IN 46506 USA (Tel.: 219-546-3565; 800-648-1123; Telefax: 219-546-3563, 276424)

Browne & Dureau Int'l. Ltd.

Suite 502, Henry Lawson Centre, Birkenhead Point, Drummoyne, NSW, 2047 Australia (Tel.: 61 2 819 7933; Telefax: 61 2 819 6262; Telex: AA 120406)

Browning Chemical Corp./Food Ingredients Div.

707 West Chester Ave., White Plains, NY 10604 USA (Tel.: 914-686-0300; Telefax: 914-686-0310)

Robert Bryce & Co.

1a Queen St., Auburn, NSW, 2144 Australia (Tel.: 61 2 646 1777; Telefax: 61 2 646 2904; Telex: 31486)

Buckton Scott Ltd.

Black Horse House, Bentalls, Pipps Hill Estate, Basildon, Essex, SS14 3BX UK (Tel.: 44 1268 531308; Telefax: 44 1268 531316; Telex: 995923)

Bunge Foods

725 N. Kinzie Ave., Bradley, IL 60915 USA (Tel.: 815-937-8129; 800-828-0800; Telefax: 815-939-4289)

Burgess Pigment Co.

PO Box 349, Sandersville, GA 31082 USA (Tel.: 912-552-2544; 800-841-8999; Telefax: 912-552-1772; Telex: 804523)

Burlington Bio-Medical Corp.

222 Sherwood Ave., Farmingdale, NY 11735-1718 USA (Tel.: 516-694-9000; Telefax: 516-694-9177; Telex: 6852289)

Bush Boake Allen

Bush Boake Allen Inc., 7 Mercedes Dr., Montvale, NJ 07645 USA (Tel.: 201-391-9870; Telefax: 201-391-0860; Telex: 98224)

Bush Boake Allen Ltd./GMB Proteins, Blackhorse Lane, Walthamstow, London, E17 5QP UK (Tel.: 44 181 531-4211; Telefax: 44 181-27 2360; Telex: 897808)

Byk-Chemie

Byk Chemie GmbH, Div. of Altana Industrie Aktien und Anlagen AG, Abelstrasse 14, 4230 Wesel Germany (Tel.: 011-49-281-6700; Telefax: 011-49-281-65735; Telex: 812772)

Byk-Chemie USA, 524 S. Cherry St., PO Box 5670, Wallingford, CT 06492-7656 USA (Tel.: 203-265-2086; Telefax: 203-284-9158; Telex: 643378)

Byk-Chemie Japan KK, Sunshine 6 Bldg., 2-29-12, Shiba, Minato-Ku, Tokyo, 105 Japan (Tel.: 81-3-3256-5409; Telefax: 81-3-3256-5420)

Byrton Dairy Products Inc.

28354 N. Ballard Dr., Lake Forest, IL 60045 USA (Tel.: 708-367-8300; Telefax: 708-367-8332)

Cabot

Cabot Corp./Cab-O-Sil® Div., PO Box 188, Tuscola, IL 61953-0188 USA (Tel.: 217-253-3370; 800-222-6745; Telefax: 217-253-4334; Telex: 910-663-2542)

Cabot Brasil Industriai E Comercio Ltda., Rua Beira Rio 57, 12° andar, Sao Paulo, SP 04548-906 Brazil (Tel.: 55 11 820-2711; Telefax: 55 11 820-9193)

Cabot Carbon Ltd./Cab-O-Sil Div., Div. of Cabot Corp, Barry Site, Sully Moors Rd., Sully, S. Glamorgan, CF6 2XP UK (Tel.: 44 1446-736999; Telefax: 44 1446-737123)

Cabot GmbH/Cab-O-Sil® Div., Postfach 90 11 20, Josef-Bautz-Strasse 15, D-63457 Hanau Germany (Tel.: 49 6181 5 05-150; Telefax: 49 6181 5 05-201; Telex: 4184134 CAB D)

Cabot Pacific Asia Carbon Black Div. (PACBD), 6th Fl., RHB 1, 424 Jalan Tun Razak, 50400 Kuala Lumpur, Malaysia (Tel.: (60) 3-984-9730; Telefax: (60) 3-983-9749)

Cairn Foods Ltd.

Cairn House, Elgiva Lane, Chesham, Buckinghamshire, HP5 2JD UK (Tel.: 44 1494 786066; Telefax: 44 1494 791816; Telex: 837075)

Calaga Food Ingredients

28B Westgate, Grantham, Lincolnshire, NG31 6LX UK (Tel.: 44 1476 590252; Telefax: 44 1476 73436)

Calgene Chemical Inc.

7247 North Central Park Ave., Skokie, IL 60076-4093 USA (Tel.: 708-675-3950; 800-432-7187; Telefax: 708-675-3013; Telex: 72-4417)

Calgon

Calgon Corp., PO Box 717, Pittsburgh, PA 15230-0717 USA (Tel.: 412-787-6700; 800-648-9005; Telefax: 4412-787-6713; Telex: 671183CCC)

Calgon Carbon Corp., PO Box 717, Pittsburgh, PA 15230-0717 USA (Tel.: 412-787-6700; 800-422-7266; Telefax: 412-787-6676; Telex: 6711837 CCC)

C.A.L.-Pfizer. *See under* Pfizer

Cambridge Industries Co. of America

7-33 Amsterdam St., Newark, NJ 07105 USA (Tel.: 201-465-4565; Telefax: 201-465-7713)

Caminiti Foti & Co. S.r.l.

Via Calatafimi 2, 98023 Furci Siculo (ME) Italy (Tel.: 39 942 791596; Telefax: 39 942 793832; Telex: 980158)

Canada Packers. *See* CanAmera Foods

Canadian Harvest

Canadian Harvest Process, 2 Barrie Blvd., St. Thomas, Ontario, N5P 4B9 Canada (Tel.: 519-633-5030; Telefax: 519-633-3718)

Canadian Harvest USA, 1001 S. Cleveland St., PO Box 272, Cambridge, MN 55008 USA (Tel.: 612-689-5800; Telefax: 612-689-5949)

CanAmera Foods

30 Weston Rd., Toronto, Ontario, M6N 3P4 Canada (Tel.: 416-761-4172; Telefax: 416-761-4452)

Canbro Inc.

29 E. Park St., Valleyfield, Quebec, J6S 1P8 Canada (Tel.: 514-866-8514)

Captree Chemical Corp.

32 B Nancy St., West Babylon, NY 11704 USA (Tel.: 516-491-7400; 800-899-2725; Telefax: 516-491-7130)

Carbonic Industries Corp.

3700 Crestwood Pkwy., Suite 200, Deluth, GA 30136-5583 USA (Tel.: 800-241-5882; Telefax: 404-717-2222)

Cardolite Corp.

500 Doremus Ave., Newark, NJ 07105-4805 USA (Tel.: 201-344-5015; 800-322-7365; Telefax: 201-344-1197; Telex: 325446)

Cargill

Cargill, Inc., Box 5630, Minneapolis, MN 55440 USA (Tel.: 612-475-6478; Telex: CGL MPS 290625)

Cargill, Knowle Hill Park, Fairmile Lane, Cobham, Surrey, KT11 2PD UK (Tel.: 44 1932 861175; Telefax: 44 1932 861286)

Carrageenan Company

3830 S. Teakwood St., Santa Ana, CA 92707 USA (Tel.: 714-751-1521; Telefax: 714-850-9865)

R.E. Carroll, Inc.

1570 N. Olden Ave., PO Box 139, Trenton, NJ 08638 USA (Tel.: 609-695-6211; 800-257-9365; Telefax: 609-695-0102)

CasChem Inc.

40 Ave. A, Bayonne, NJ 07002 USA (Tel.: 201-858-7900; 800-CASCHEM; Telefax: 201-437-2728; Telex: 710-729-4466)

Catalysts & Chemicals Industries Co., Ltd., Joint venture of Asahi Glass Co. Ltd./JGC Corp.

Nippon Bldg., 6-2, Ohte-machi 2-chome, Chiyoda-ku, Tokyo, 100 Japan (Tel.: (03) 3270-6086; Telefax: (03) 3246-0617; Telex: 2223480 PETCATJ)

Catomance Ltd.

96 Bridge Rd East, Welwyn Garden City, Hertfordshire, AL7 1JW UK (Tel.: 44 1707 324373; Telefax: 44 1707 372191; Telex: 267418 CATAC G)

Ceca SA. *See under* Elf Atochem

Celite

Celite Corp., PO Box 519, Lompoc, CA 93438-0519 USA (Tel.: 805-735-7791; 800-348-8062; Telefax: 805-735-5699; Telex: 62776493 ESL UD)

Celite Corp. (Canada), 295 The West Mall, Etobicoke, Ontario, M9C 4Z7 Canada (Tel.: 416-626-8175; Telefax: 416-626-8235)

Celite (UK) Ltd., Livingston Rd., Hessle, North Humberside, HU13 OEG UK (Tel.: 44 1482 64 52 65; Telefax: 44 1482 64 11 76; Telex: 592160)

Celite France, 9 rue du Colonel-de-Rochebrune B.P. 240, 92504 Rueil-Malmaison Cedex France (Tel.: (14)749-0560; Telefax: (1) 47 08 30 25; Telex: Celite 631969 F)

Celite Italiana srl, Viale Pasubio No. 6, I-20154 Milano Italy (Tel.: 39 2 654531; Telefax: 39 2 29005439; Telex: 311136 MANVII)

Celite Pacific, 2nd Floor, Shui On Centre, 8 Harbor Road Hong Kong (Tel.: 582 5609; Telefax: 802 4275)

Celtic Chemicals Ltd.

Gas Works Industrial Estate, Victoria Rd, Port Talbot, West Glamorgan, SA12 6DB, Wales UK (Tel.: 44 1639 886236; Telefax: 44 1639 893147; Telex: 94013871 CCPT G)

CE Minerals, Div. Combustion Engrg.

901 E. Eighth Ave., King of Prussia, PA 19406 USA (Tel.: 215-265-6880; Telefax: 215-337-7163)

Central Soya

Central Soya Co., Inc./Chemurgy Div., PO Box 2507, Fort Wayne, IN 46801-2507 USA (Tel.: 219-425-5432; 800-348-0960; Telefax: 219-425-5301; Telex: 49609682)

Central Soya Aarhus A/S, Skansevej 2, PO Box 380, DK-8100 Aarhus C Denmark (Tel.: 45 89 31 21 11; Telefax: 45 89 31 21 12; Telex: 64348)

Cerac, Inc.

PO Box 1178, 407 N. 13th St., Milwaukee, WI 53201 USA (Tel.: 414-289-9800; Telefax: 414-289-9805; Telex: RCA 286122)

Cerestar

Cerestar UK Ltd., Trafford Park Rd, Trafford Park, Manchester, M17 1PA UK (Tel.: 44 161 872 5959; Telefax: 44 161-848 9034; Telex: 667022)

Cerestar International Sales, Ave. Louise 149, Bte 13, B-1050 Brussels Belgium (Tel.: 32 2 535 1711; Telefax: 32 2 537 8554; Telex: 22648)

Cham Foods (Israel) Ltd.

PO Box 299, 38102 Hadera Israel (Tel.: 972 6334755; Telefax: 972 6336194; Telex: 471794)

Champlain Industries Inc.

PO Box 3055, 25 Styertowne Rd., Clifton, NJ 07012 USA (Tel.: 201-778-4900; 800-222-4904; Telefax: 201-778-0094; Telex: 3725769)

Charabot SA

BP 68, 10 Ave. Y-E Baudoin, 06332 Grasse Cedex France (Tel.: 33 93 09 33 33; Telefax: 33 93 93 33 03; Telex: 470822)

Charkit Chemical Corp.

PO Box 1725, 330 Post Rd., Darien, CT 06820 USA (Tel.: 203-655-3400; Telefax: 203-655-8643; Telex: 6819184)

Chart Corporation Inc.

787 E. 27th St., Paterson, NJ 07504 USA (Tel.: 201-345-5554; Telefax: 201-345-2139)

Pierre Chauvet

Pierre Chauvet S.A., 83440 Seillans France (Tel.: 94 76 96 03; Telefax: 94 76 96 16)

Pierre Chauvet, Inc., 3 Reuten Dr., Closter, NJ 07624 USA (Tel.: 201-784-9300; Telefax: 201-784-0604)

Cheil Foods & Chemicals

Cheil Foods & Chemicals Inc., Samsung House, 3 Riverbank Way, Great West Rd., Brentford, Middlesex, TW8 9RE UK (Tel.: 44 181 862 9334; Telefax: 44 181 862 0094; Telex: 258237)

Cheil Foods & Chemicals Inc., 105 Challenger Rd., 4th Floor, Ridgefield Park, NJ 07660-0511 USA (Tel.: 201-229-6037; Telefax: 201-229-6040; Telex: 219176)

Chemcentral Corp

7050 W. 71 St., PO Box 730, Bedford Park, IL 60499-0730 USA (Tel.: 708-594-7000; 800-331-6174; Telefax: 708-594-6328)

Chemcolloids Ltd.

Tunstall Rd., Bosley, Macclesfield, Cheshire, SK11 0PE UK (Tel.: 44 1260 223284; Telefax: 44 1260 223589; Telex: 668002)

ChemDesign Corp., A Bayer Company

99 Development Rd., Fitchburg, MA 01420 USA (Tel.: 508-345-9999; Telefax: 508-342-9769)

The Chemical Co

PO Box 436, 19B Narragansett Ave, Jamestown, RI 02835 USA (Tel.: 401-423-3100; Telefax: 401-423-3102)

Chemie Linz

Chemie Linz GmbH, Div. of Chemie Holding AG, Postfach 296, St Peter-Strasse 25, A-4021 Linz Austria (Tel.: 43-732-59160; Telefax: 43-732-3800; Telex: 221324)

Chemie Linz UK Ltd., Div. of Chemie Linz GmbH, 12 The Green, Richmond, Surrey, TW9 1PX UK (Tel.: 44 181 948 6966; Telefax: 44 181-332 2516; Telex: 924941)

Chemie Linz North America, Inc., 65 Challenger Rd, Ridgefield Park, NJ 07660 USA (Tel.: 201-641-6410; Telefax: 201-641-2323; Telex: 853211 Chemie Linz)

Chemisphere

Chemisphere Corp., 2101 Clifton Ave., St. Louis, MO 63139 USA (Tel.: 314-644-1300; Telefax: 314-644-1425)

Chemisphere Ltd., 38 King St., Chester, Cheshire, CH1 2AH UK (Tel.: 44 1244 320878; Telefax: 44 1244 320858; Telex: 61398 CHEMSPR G)

ChemMark Development Inc.

70 Tyler Place, South Plainfield, NJ 07080 USA (Tel.: 908-561-5200; Telefax: 908-561-9174)

Chem-Materials Co.

16600 Sprague Rd., Cleveland, OH 44130-6318 USA (Tel.: 216-243-5590; Telefax: 216-243-1940)

Chemplex Chemicals, Inc.

201 Route 17, Suite 300, Rutherford, NJ 07070 USA (Tel.: 201-935-8903; Telefax: 201-935-9051)

Chemron Corp.

PO Box 2299, Paso Robles, CA 93447 USA (Tel.: 805-239-1550; Telefax: 805-239-8551; Telex: 501532)

Chem-Trend

Chem-Trend Inc., 1445 W. McPherson Park Dr., PO Box 860, Howell, MI 48844-0860 USA (Tel.: 517-546-4520; 800-727-7730; Telefax: 517-546-6875)

Chem-Trend A/S, Smedeland 14, Postboks 1384, DK-2600 Glostrup Denmark (Tel.: 45-42 45 6711; Telefax: 45-43 63 03 50; Telex: 33187 CMTREND DK)

Chevron Chemical Co.

PO Box 3766, Houston, TX 77253 USA (Tel.: 713-754-2000; 800-231-3260; Telex: 762799)

Chisso

Chisso Corp., Tokyo Bldg., 7-3, Marunouchi 2-chome, Chiyoda-ku, Tokyo, 100 Japan (Tel.: (03) 3284-8411; Telefax: (03) 3284-8412; Telex: 02225212 CHISSO J)

Chisso Petrochemical Corp., Subsid. of Chisso Corp., Tokyo Bldg., 7-3 Marunouchi 2-chome, Chiyoda-ku, Tokyo, 100 Japan (Tel.: (03) 3284-8411; Telefax: (03) 3284-8412; Telex: 02225212 CHISSO J)

Chisso America Inc., 1185 Ave of the Americas, New York, NY 10036 USA (Tel.: 212-302-0500; Telefax: 212-302-0643; Telex: WU 147029 CHISSO NYK)

Charles B. Chrystal Co. Inc.

30 Vesey St., New York, NY 10007 USA (Tel.: 212-227-2151; Telefax: 212-233-7916; Telex: 420803 CBCC)

Church & Dwight Co. Inc./Specialty Prods. Div.

Box CN5297, 469 N. Harrison St., Princeton, NJ 08543-5297 USA (Tel.: 609-497-7116; 800-221-0453; Telefax: 609-497-7176; Telex: 752226)

Ciba-Geigy

Ciba-Geigy Corp., 540 White Plains Rd., Tarrytown, NY 101591 USA (Tel.: 914-785-2000; 800-431-1874)

Ciba-Geigy Corp./Dyestuffs & Chemicals Div., PO Box 18300, 410 Swing Rd., Greensboro, NC 27419 USA (Tel.: 919-632-2011; 800-334-9481; Telefax: 919-632-7008; Telex: 131411)

Ciba Pharmaceutical Co., 556 Morris Ave., Summit, NJ 07901 USA (Tel.: 800-742-2422)

Ciba-Geigy plc, Hulley Rd., Maccles Field, Cheshire, SK10 2NX UK (Tel.: 44 1625 421933; Telefax: 44 1625 619637; Telex: 667336)

Ciba-Geigy AG, CH-4002, Basel Switzerland (Tel.: 41-61 696 7329; Telefax: 41-61 696 6322; Telex: 963962)

Cimbar Performance Minerals

25 Old River Rd. S.E., PO Box 250, Cartersville, GA 30120 USA (Tel.: 404-387-0319; 800-852-6868; Telefax: 404-386-6785)

Classic Flavors & Fragrances

125 E. 23rd St., Suite 400, New York, NY 10010 USA (Tel.: 212-777-0004; Telefax: 212-353-0404)

W.A. Cleary Chemical Corp.

Southview Industrial Park, 178 Route #522 Suite A, Dayton, NJ 08810 USA (Tel.: 908-329-8399; 800-524-1662; Telefax: 908-274-0894)

Climax Performance

Climax Performance Materials Corp./Corporate Headquarters, PO Box 22015, Tempe, AZ 85285-2015 USA

Climax Performance Materials, Div. of Amax, Inc., 7666 West 63 St., Chicago, IL 60501 USA (Tel.: 708-458-8450; 800-323-3231; Telefax: 708-458-0286)

Clofine Dairy & Food Products Inc.

1407 New Rd., Linwood, NJ 08221 USA (Tel.: 609-653-1000; Telefax: 609-653-0127)

CNC International, Limited Partnership

PO Box 3000, 20 Privilege St., Woonsocket, RI 02895 USA (Tel.: 401-769-6100; Telefax: 401-769-4509)

Coalite Chemicals Div.

PO Box 152, Buttermilk Lane, Bolsover, Chesterfield, Derbyshire, S44 6AZ UK (Tel.: 44 1246 826816; Telefax: 44 1246 240309; Telex: 547624)

Coastal Chem Inc.

PO Box 1287, Cheyenne, WY, 82003 USA (Tel.: 307-633-2200; 800-443-2754; Telefax: 800-832-7601)

Colloides Naturels International

4 rue Frederic Passy, 92200 Neuilly sur Seine France (Tel.: 33 1 47 47 1850; Telefax: 33 1 47 471891)

Colombus Foods Co.

800 N. Albany Ave., Chicago, IL 60622 USA (Tel.: 312-265-6500; Telefax: 312-265-6985)

Colorcon

Colorcon, Div. of Berwind Pharmaceutical Services, Inc., 415 Moyer Blvd., West Point, PA 19486 USA (Tel.: 215-699-7733; Telefax: 215-661-2605)

Colorcon P.R., Inc., PO Box 979, Punta Santiago, 00661 PR(Tel.: 809-852-3815; Telefax: 809-852-0030)

Colorcon Ltd., Murray Road, St Paul's Cray, Orpington, Kent, BR5 3QY UK (Tel.: 44 1689 838301; Telefax: 44 1689-878342; Telex: 896271 COLOUR G)

Colorcon GmbH, Hauptstrasse 5, 61462 Königstein Germany (Tel.: 49 6174-93890; Telefax: 49 6174-23698; Telex: 410668 COLO D)

Colorcon s.a.r.l., Bureaux de la Jonchère, 62-70 rue Yvan Tourgueneff, 78380 Bougival France (Tel.: 33 1 30 82 15 82; Telefax: 33 1 30 82 78 79; Telex: 698786 COLOUR F)

Colorcon S.r.l., Via Disciplini 18, 20123 Milano Italy (Tel.: 39 2 8052222; Telefax: 39 2 861229; Telex: 328408 COLOUR I)

Colorcon (Japan) Ltd., Asahi Bldg., 2-61-15 Itabashi, Itabashi-ku, Tokyo, 173 Japan (Tel.: 81 3 5248 0581; Telefax: 81 3-5248 0547; Telex: 2523489 COLOUR J)

Cometals Inc., Subsid. of Commercial Metals Co.

1 Penn Plaza, New York, NY 10119 USA (Tel.: 212-760-1200; Telefax: 212-564-7915; Telex: 424087)

Commodity Services Int'l. Inc.

114B N. West St., PO Box 1876, Easton, MD 21601 USA (Tel.: 410-820-8880; Telefax: 410-820-8890; Telex: 898099 CSI MD)

Complex Quimica SA

PO Box 544, Monterrey, NL Mexico (64000 Mexico (Tel.: 011(528)336-2577; Telefax: 011 (528)336-3650)

Conap, Inc.

1405 Buffalo St., Olean, NY 14760 USA (Tel.: 716-372-9650; Telefax: 716-372-1594)

Condea

Condea Chemie GmbH, Überseering 40, 2000 Hamburg 60 Germany (Tel.: 40 6375-0; Telefax: 40 6375 3595; Telex: 215166 conh d)

Condea Chimie Sarl, 125 Rue de Saussure, B.P. 89-11, 75813 Paris Cedex 17 France (Tel.: 01-47 662424; Telefax: 01-47662425; Telex: 650386 condea f)

Condea Vista Japan Inc., PO Box 110, Kasumigaseki Bldg., 25th Floor, Chiyoda-ku, Tokyo, 110 Japan (Tel.: 3593-0611; Telefax: 3593-0615; Telex: J 29368 VISTACHM)

Condor Corp.

Executive Center, 560 Sylvan Ave., Englewood Cliffs, NJ 07632-3193 USA (Tel.: 201-567-3337; 800-321-3005; Telefax: 201-567-6489)

Consolidated Flavor Corp.

231 Rock Industrial Dr., Bridgeton, MO 63044 USA (Tel.: 314-291-5444; 800-422-5444; Telefax: 314-291-3289)

Cookson Specialty Additives

1000 Wayside Rd., Cleveland, OH 44110 USA (Tel.: 216-531-6010; 800-321-4236; Telefax: 216-486-6638)

Copenhagen Pectin

Copenhagen Pectin A/S, Div. of Hercules Inc., DK-4623 Lille Skensved Denmark (Tel.: 45 53 66 9210; Telefax: 45 53 66 9446; Telex: 43572 GENU DK)

Pomosin GmbH, Div. of Copenhagen Pectin A/S, Postfach 7, Von-Herwarth-Strasse, W-2443 Grobenbrode Germany (Tel.: 49 4367-8051; Telefax: 49 4367-692; Telex: 436710)

Cornelius Chemical Group Ltd.

St. James's House, 27-43 Eastern Road, Romford, Essex, RM1 3NN UK (Tel.: 44 1708 722300; Telefax: 44 1708 768204; Telex: 885589 CORNEL G)

Corn Products/Unit of CPC Int'l.

6500 Archer Rd., Summit-Argo, IL 60501 USA (Tel.: 708-563-2400; 800-443-2746; Telefax: 708-563-6878)

Courtaulds

Courtaulds plc, Patents Dept, PO Box 111, 72 Lockhurst Lane, Coventry, West Midlands, CV6 5RS UK (Tel.: 44 1203 688771; Telefax: 44 1203-583837)

Courtaulds Chemicals, Nelson Acetate Works, Caton Rd., Lancaster, Lancashire, LA1 3PF UK (Tel.: 44 1524 66111; Telefax: 44 1524 846384)

Courtaulds Water Soluble Polymers, Div. of Courtaulds plc, P O Box 5, Spondon, Derbyshire, DE21 7BP UK (Tel.: 44 1332 661422; Telefax: 44 1332-661078; Telex: 32771)

Cox Chemicals Ltd.

Overley Hill, Wellington, Telford, Shropshire, TF6 5HD UK (Tel.: 44 1952 86333; Telefax: 44 1952 86207)

Coyne Chemical

3015 State Rd., Croydon, PA 19021 USA (Tel.: 215-785-3000; Telefax: 215-785-1585)

CPS Chemical Co Inc.

PO Box 162, Old Bridge, NJ 08857 USA (Tel.: 908-607-2700; Telefax: 908-607-2562; Telex: 844532-CPSOLDB)

Cray Valley

Cedex 101, F92970 Paris la Défense France (Tel.: 33 1 41 35 68 10; Telefax: 33 1 41 35 61 43; Telex: 615 289)

Crescent Bronze Powder Co., Inc.

3400 N. Avondale Ave., Chicago, IL 60618-5432 USA (Tel.: 312-539-2441; 800-445-6810; Telefax: 312-539-1131)

Crespel & Deiters GmbH

Groner Allee 76, D-4530 Ibbenburen Germany (Tel.: 49 5451 5000-0; Telefax: 49 5451 5000-60; Telex: 94545)

CR Minerals Corp.

14142 Denver W. Pkwy., Suite 250, Golden, CO 80401 USA (Tel.: 303-278-1706; 800-527-7315; Telefax: 303-279-3772)

Croda

Croda International plc, Cowick Hall, Snaith, Goole, North Humberside, DN14 9AA UK (Tel.: 44 1405 860551; Telefax: 44 1405 860205)

Croda Chemicals Ltd., Div. of Croda International plc, Cowick Hall, Snaith, Goole, North Humberside, DN14 9AA UK (Tel.: 44 1405 860551; Telefax: 44 1405 860205; Telex: 57601)

Croda Surfactants Ltd., Cowick Hall, Snaith, Goole, North Humberside, DN14 9AA UK (Tel.: 44 1405 860551; Telefax: 44 1405 860205; Telex: 57601)

Croda Colloids Ltd., Foundry Lane, Ditton Widnes, Cheshire, WA8 8UB UK (Tel.: 44 151 423 3441; Telefax: 44 151 423 3205; Telex: 629586)

Croda Food Products Ltd., Div. of Croda International plc, Cowick Hall, Snaith, Goole, North Humberside, DN14 9AA UK (Tel.: 44 1405 860551; Telefax: 44 1405 860205; Telex: 57601)

Croda Inc., 7 Century Dr., Parsippany, NJ 07054-4698 USA (Tel.: 201-644-4900; Telefax: 201-644-9222)

Croda Canada Ltd., 78 Tisdale Ave., Toronto, Ontario, M4A 1Y7 Canada (Tel.: 416-751-3571; Telefax: 416-751-9611)

Croda Singapore PTE Ltd., 20 Chia Ping Rd., S-2261 Singapore (Tel.: 65 261 3008; Telefax: 65 261 2825; Telex: 38943)

Croda Japan KK, Aceman Bldg., 1-10, Tokui-cho 1-chome, Chuo-ku, Osaka, 540 Japan (Tel.: (06) 942-1791; Telefax: (06) 942-1790; Telex: 5233117)

The O.C. Lugo Co., Inc., U.S. representative for Croda Colloids Ltd., 42 Burd St., Nyack, NY 10960 USA (Tel.: 914-353-7711; Telefax: 914-353-7702)

Crompton & Knowles

Crompton & Knowles Corp./Dyes & Chems. Div., PO Box 33188, Charlotte, NC 28233 USA (Tel.: 704-372-5890; 800-438-4122; Telefax: 704-372-1522)

Crompton & Knowles Corp./Ingredient Technology Div., 1595 MacArthur Blvd., Mahwah, NJ 07430 USA (Tel.: 201-818-1200; 800-343-4860; Telefax: 201-818-2173)

Crompton & Knowles Tertre SA, Div. of Crompton & Knowles Corp, 141 ave de la Reine, B-1210 Brussels Belgium (Tel.: 32-216 2045; Telefax: 32-242 84 83; Telex: 57 288 ATSATRB)

Crosfield Chemicals, Inc.

101 Ingalls Ave., Joliet, IL 60435 USA (Tel.: 815-727-3651; 800-727-3651; Telefax: 815-727-5312)

Crowley

Crowley Chemical Co., 261 Madison Ave., New York, NY 10016 USA (Tel.: 212-682-1200; 800-424-9300; Telefax: 212-953-3487; Telex: 12-7662)

Crowley Tar Products Co., Inc., 261 Madison Ave., New York, NY 10016 USA (Tel.: 212-682-1200)

Croxton & Garry Ltd.

Curtis Rd. Industrial Estate, Dorking, Surrey, RH4 1XA UK (Tel.: 44 1306 886688; Telefax: 44 1306-887780; Telex: 859567/8 cand g)

CRS Co.

4940 Viking Dr., Minneapolis, MN 55435 USA (Tel.: 612-893-1610; Telefax: 612-893-9028)

Crucible Chemical Co. Inc.

PO Box 6786, Donaldson Center, Greenville, SC 29606 USA (Tel.: 803-277-1284; 800-845-8873; Telefax: 803-299-1192)

Crystal, Inc./H & S Chemical, A Huntington Company

970 E. Tipton St., Huntington, IN 46750 USA (Tel.: 219-356-7073; Telefax: 219-358-9154)

CSR Food Ingredients

Bowman St., Pyrmont, NSW, 2009 Australia (Tel.: 61 2 692 7685; Telefax: 61 2 552 1712)

C&T Refinery Inc.

2000 W. Broad St., Richmond, VA 23220 USA (Tel.: 804-359-5786; Telefax: 804-359-5514)

Cuproquim Corp.

PO Box 171357, Memphis, TN 38187-1357 USA (Tel.: 901-537-7257; Telefax: 901-685-8372)

CVC Specialty Chemicals, Inc.

600 Deer Rd., Cherry Hill, NJ 08034 USA (Tel.: 609-354-0040; Telefax: 609-354-6226)

Cytec

Cytec Industries Inc., A Business Unit of American Cyanamid Co., Five Garret Mountain Plaza, West Paterson, NJ 07424 USA (Tel.: 800-253-4078; Telefax: 908-862-9312; Telex: 130400)

Cytec de Argentina S.A., Charcas 5051, EP 1425, Buenos Aires, Argentina (Tel.: 541-772-4031; Telefax: 541-953-6619)

Cytec Industries UK Ltd., Bowling Park Dr., Bradford, West Yorkshire, BD4 7TT UK (Tel.: 44 1274 733891; Telefax: 44-1274 734770; Telex: 51295)

Cytec Industries BV, Coolsingel 139, 3012 AG Rotterdam The Netherlands (Tel.: 31-10 2248400; Telefax: 31-10 4136788; Telex: 23554)

Cytec Australia Ltd., 5 Gibbon Rd., Baulkham Hills, NSW, 2153 Australia (Tel.: 612-624-9223; Telefax: 612-838-9985; Telex: 70879 CYANAMI AA)

Cytec Japan Ltd., No. 30 Kowa Bldg., 4th Floor, 4-5 Roppongi 2-chome, Minato-ku, Tokyo, 106 Japan (Tel.: 813-3586-9716; Telefax: 813-3586-9710; Telex: 22439 CYANAMID J)

Daicel

Daicel Chemical Industries, Ltd., Toranomon Mitsui Bldg., 8-1 Kasumigaseki, 3-Chome, Chiyoda-ku, Tokyo, 100 Japan (Tel.: (03)507-3203; Telefax: (03)507-3198; Telex: 2224632 DAICEL J)

Daicel (USA) Inc., Subsid. of Diacel Chem. Industries, Ltd., One Parker Plaza, 400 Kelby St., Fort Lee, NJ 07024 USA (Tel.: 201-461-4466; Telefax: 201-461-2776)

Daicel (Europa) GmbH, Subsid. of Daicel Chem. Industries Ltd., Ost St. 22, 4000 Düsseldorf 1 Germany (Tel.: (211)369848; Telefax: (211)364429; Telex: (41)8588042 DCELD)

Daicel-Hüls Ltd., Joint venture of Daicel Chem. Industries, Ltd./Hüls AG

1-19-5, Toranomon, Minato-ku, Tokyo, 105 Japan (Tel.: (03) 3592-6333; Telefax: (03) 3592-6338; Telex: 222-7385 DAHU J)

Daihachi Chemical Industry Co., Ltd.

Sanyo Nissei Kawaramachi Bldg., 2-7, Kawaramachi 2-chome, Chuo-ku, Osaka, 541 Japan (Tel.: (06) 201-1455; Telefax: (06) 201-1458)

Dai-ichi Kogyo Seiyaku Co., Ltd.

New Kyoto Center Bldg., 614, Higashishiokoji-cho, Shimokyo-ku, Kyoto, 600 Japan (Tel.: (075) 343-1656; Telefax: (075) 343-5006)

Daiichi Pharmaceutical Co. Ltd.

14-10, Nihonbashi 3-Chome, Chuo-ku, Tokyo, 103 Japan (Tel.: (03) 3272-0611; Telefax: (03) 3276-0694; Telex: J22729)

Dainippon Pharmaceutical Co. Ltd.

2-6-8, Dosho-machi, Chuo-ku, Osaka, 541 Japan (Tel.: (06) 203-5321; Telefax: (06) 203-6581)

Daito Chemical Industries, Ltd.

Mitsui No. 2 Bldg., 4-4-20, Nihonbashi Hongoku-cho, Chuo-ku, Tokyo, 103 Japan (Tel.: (03) 3279-6431; Telefax: (03) 3231-0503)

Daiwa Chemical Co., Ltd. (Daiwa Kasei K.K.)

20-19, Takadono 2-chome, Asahi-ku, Osaka, 535 Japan (Tel.: (06) 922-1978; Telefax: (06) 925-3425)

H.E. Daniel Ltd.

Longfield Rd., Tunbridge Wells, Kent, TN2 3EY UK (Tel.: 44 1892 511444; Telefax: 44 1892 510013; Telex: 957103)

De Choix Speciality Foods Co., Div. of Amazon Coffee & Tea Co.

58-25 52nd Ave., Woodside, NY 11377 USA (Tel.: 718-507-8080)

The Degen Co.

200 Kellogg St., PO Box 5240, Jersey City, NJ 07305 USA (Tel.: 201-432-1192; Telefax: 201-432-8483; Telex: 325999 DEGEN CO)

Degussa

Degussa AG, Postfach 110533, Frankfurt Germany (Tel.: +49 69-21801; Telefax: +49 69-2183218; Telex: 415200-25 dwd)

Degussa Ltd., Div. of Degussa AG, Earl Rd, Stanley Green, Handforth, Wilmslow, Cheshire, SK9 3RL UK (Tel.: 44 161 486 6211; Telefax: 44 161-485 6445; Telex: 51665053 DGMCHR G)

Degussa Corp., Wholly owned subsid. of Degussa AG, 65 Challenger Rd., Ridgefield Park, NJ 07660 USA (Tel.: 201-641-6100; 800-237-6745; Telefax: 201-807-3182; Telex: 221420 degus ur)

Jan Dekker BV

Postbus 10, NL-1520 AA Wormerveer The Netherlands (Tel.: 31-75-2782 78; Telefax: 31-75-21 38 83; Telex: 19273)

J.W.S. Delavau Co. Inc.

2140 Germantown Ave., Philadelphia, PA 19122 USA (Tel.: 215-235-1100; Telefax: 215-235-2202)

Dena GmbH & Co. KG

Fleher Dieich 3, W-4000 Dusseldorf Germany (Tel.: 49 211 15 52 15; Telefax: 49 211 15 60 75; Telex: 8581367)

Deutsche Nichimen GmbH

Wehrhahn Center, D4000 Dusseldorf Germany (Tel.: 49 211 3551 (278); Telefax: 49 211 362492; Telex: 466240)

The Dial Corp., A Greyhound Dial Co.

2000 Aucutt Rd., Montgomery, IL 60538 USA (Tel.: 708-892-4381; 800-323-5385)

Diamalt GmbH

Georg-Reismuller-Strasse 32, Munchen Germany (Tel.: 49 89-81060; Telefax: 49 89-8106513; Telex: 525316)

Dietary Foods Ltd.

Cumberland House, Brook St., Soham, Ely, Cambridgeshire, CB7 5BA UK (Tel.: 44 1353 720791; Telefax: 44 1353 721705; Telex: 817612)

DMV International

NCB-Laan 80, 5462 GE Veghel The Netherlands (Tel.: 31 4130 72222; Telefax: 31 4130 43695; Telex: 74650)

Dover Chemical Corp., Subsid. of ICC Industries Inc.

3676 Davis Rd. N.W., PO Box 40, Dover, OH 44622 USA (Tel.: 216-343-7711; 800-321-8805/6; Telefax: 216-364-1579; Telex: 983466)

Dow

Dow Chemical U.S.A., 2020 Willard H. Dow Center, Midland, MI 48674 USA (Tel.: 517-636-1000; 800-441-4DOW; Telex: 227455)

Dow Chemical Canada Inc., 1086 Modeland Rd., PO Box 1012, Sarnia, Ontario, N7T 7K7 Canada (Tel.: 519-339-3131)

Dow Chemical Europe S.A., Bachtobelstrasse 3, CH-8810 Horgen Switzerland (Tel.: 1-728-2111; Telefax: 1-728-2935; Telex: 826940)

Dow Europe SA, Bachtobelstrasse 3, CH-8810 Horgen Switzerland (Tel.: 41-1-728-2111; Telefax: 41-1-728-2935; Telex: 826940)

Dow Chemical Co Ltd., Div. of The Dow Chemical Co, Lakeside House, Stockley Park, Uxbridge, Middlesex, UB10 1BE UK (Tel.: 44 181 848-8688; Telefax: 44 181-848-5400; Telex: 934626)

Dow Chemical Pacific ltd., 39th Floor, Sun Hung Kai Centre, 30 Harbour Rd., Wanchai, PO Box 711 Hong Kong

Dowa Mining Co., Ltd., Joint venture of Dainippon Ink & Chemicals, Inc. and Hercules Inc.

Daiichi Tekko Bldg.; 8-2 Marunouchi 1-chome, Chiyoda-ku, Tokyo, 100 Japan (Tel.: (03) 3201-1062; Telefax: (03) 3201-1297; Telex: J26928)

Dow Corning

Dow Corning Corp., Box 0994, Midland, MI 48686-0994 USA (Tel.: 517-496-4000; Telefax: 517-496-4586)

Dow Corning Ltd., Div. of Dow Corning Corp, Kings Court, 185 Kings Rd, Reading, Berkshire, RG1 4EX UK (Tel.: 44 1734 507251; Telefax: 44 1734-575051)

Dow Corning France SA, Div. of Dow Corning Corp, BP 203, European Health Care Center, 300 route des Cretes, F-06904 Sophio Antipoles Cedex France (Tel.: 33 92 94 40 00; Telefax: 78 62 78 98; Telex: 300537)

Dow Corning Kabushiki Kaisha, Subsid. Dow Corning Corp., 507-1, Kishi Yamakita-cho, Ashigarakami-gun, Kanagawa, 258-01 Japan (Tel.: (0465) 76-3108; Telefax: (0465) 75-1064)

Dragoco

Dragoco Gerberding & Co. GmbH, D37601 Holzminden Germany (Tel.: 49 5531 970; Telefax: 49 5531 971391; Telex: 965336)

Dragoco Inc., 10 Gordon Dr., Totowa, NJ 07512 USA (Tel.: 201-256-3850; Telefax: 201-256-6420; Telex: 130449)

Dragoco (GB) Ltd., Lady Lane Ind. Estate, Hadleigh, Ipswich, Suffolk, IP7 6AX UK (Tel.: 44 1473 822011; Telefax: 44 1473 824323; Telex: 98426)

Dragoco Australia Pty. Ltd., 168 South Creek Rd., Dee Why West, NSW, 2099 Australia (Tel.: 61 2 982 7800; Telefax: 61 2 981 2536)

Dragoco Japan Ltd., Subsid. of Dragoco Gerberding & Co. GmbH, 4-34-12, Higashi-yamada, Kohoku-ku, Yokohama, 223 Japan (Tel.: (045) 592-4661; Telefax: (045) 592-4887; Telex: DRANP J 2524306)

Dry Branch Kaolin

Rt. 1, Box 468D, Dry Branch, GA 31020 USA (Tel.: 912-750-3500; 800-DBK-CLAY; Telefax: 912-746-0217)

DSM

DSM NV, Postbus 6500, NL 6401, JH Heerlen The Netherlands (Tel.: 45-78 81 11; Telefax: 45-74 06 80; Telex: 56018)

DSM United Kingdom Ltd., Div. of DSM NV, Kingfisher House, Kingfisher Walk, Redditch, Worcestershire, B97 4EZ UK (Tel.: 44 1527 68254; Telefax: 44 1527-68-949; Telex: 339861)

DSM Chemicals North America, Inc., 4751 Best Road, Ste 140, Atlanta, GA 30337 USA (Tel.: 404-766-3179; 800-825-4376; Telefax: 404-766-3540)

DSM Japan K.K., 7F., Shin Kokusai Bldg., 4-1, Marunouchi 3-chome, Chiyoda-ku, Tokyo, 100 Japan (Tel.: (03) 3217-8941; Telefax: (03) 3201-5074)

DuPont

DuPont Chemicals, 1007 Market St., Wilmington, DE 19898 USA (Tel.: 800-441-7515)

DuPont Chemicals, 15305 Brandwine Bldg., Wilmington, DE 19801 USA (Tel.: 800-441-9493; Telefax: 302-774-7230)

DuPont Canada Inc., PO Box 26, Toronto Bank Tower, Toronto, Ontario, M5K 1B6 Canada (Tel.: 416-362-5621)

DuPont S.A. de C.V., Apartado Postal 5819, 06500 Mexico D.F. Mexico (Tel.: 52-5-250-9033; Telefax: 52-5-250-9033)

DuPont (UK) Ltd., Div. of E I Du Pont de Nemours & Co, Wedgewood Way, Stevenage, Hertsfordshire, SG1 4QN UK (Tel.: 44 1438 734026; Telefax: 44 1438 734379; Telex: 825591 DUPONT G)

DuPont de Nemours (France) S.A., 137 rue de L'Université, F-75334 Paris France (Tel.: 33-45 50 65 50; Telefax: 33-47 53 09 65; Telex: 206772)

DuPont (Australia) Ltd., Northside Gardens, 168 Walker St., PO Box 930, North Sydney, NSW, 2060 Australia (Tel.: (02) 923-6111)

DuPont Asia Pacific, Ltd., 1122 New World Office Bldg., East Wing, Salisbury Rd., Kowloon Hong Kong (Tel.: 852-734-5345; Telefax: 852-724-4458)

Dutch Protein & Services BV

Sir Rowland Hillstraat 3, PO Box 6181, 4000 JT Tiel The Netherlands (Tel.: 31 3440 23400; Telefax: 31 3440 24784)

DynaGel Inc.

Wentworth Ave. & Plummer St., Calumet City, IL 60409 USA (Tel.: 708-891-8400; Telefax: 708-891-8432; Telex: 211666)

Dynaloy, Inc.

7 Great Meadow Lane, Hanover, NJ 07936 USA (Tel.: 201-887-9270; Telefax: 201-887-3678; Telex: 642033)

Eagle-Picher Industries, Inc./Chemicals Dept

PO Box 550, C & Porter Sts., Joplin, MO 64801 USA (Tel.: 417-623-8000; Telefax: 417-782-1923; Telex: 9102508335)

Eagle Zinc Co.

30 Rockefeller Plaza, New York, NY 10112 USA (Tel.: 212-582-0420; Telefax: 212-582-3412)

Eastern Color & Chemical Co.

35 Livingston St., PO Box 6161, Providence, RI 02904 USA (Tel.: 401-331-9000; Telefax: 401-331-2155)

Eastman

Eastman Chemical Products, Inc., PO Box 431, Kingsport, TN 37662 USA (Tel.: 423-229-2318; 800-EASTMAN; Telefax: 423-229-1196; Telex: 6715569)

Eastman Chemical International AG, Hertizentrum 6, 3263 Zug Switzerland (Tel.: 41 42 23 25 25; Telefax: 41 42 21 12 52; Telex: 868 824)

Eastman Chemical International Ltd., 11 Spring St., Chatswood, NSW, 2067 Australia (Tel.: 61 2 411 3399; Telefax: 61 2 411 6430)

ECC International

ECC International, 5775 Peachtree-Dunwoody Rd. NE, Suite 200G, Atlanta, GA 30342 USA (Tel.: 404-303-4415; 800-843-3222; Telefax: 404-303-4384; Telex: 6827225)

ECC International Ltd., Div. of ECC Group plc, John Keay House, St. Austell, Cornwall, PL25 4DJ UK (Tel.: 44 1726 74482; Telefax: 44 1726 623019; Telex: 45526 ECCSAU G)

ECC International SA, Div. of ECC Group plc, 2 rue du Canal, B-4551 Lixhe Belgium (Tel.: 32-41 79 98 11; Telefax: 32-41 79 82 79)

ECC Japan Ltd., Div. of ECC International, 1-5-11, Shiba, Minato-ku, Tokyo, 105 Japan (Tel.: (03) 5443-3144; Telefax: (03) 5443-3137; Telex: J28915)

Eisai

Eisai Co., Ltd., 6-10, Koishikawa 4-chome, Bunkyo-ku, Tokyo, 112-88 Japan (Tel.: (03) 3817-5015; Telefax: (03) 3811-3305; Telex: J 28859 EISAI TOK J)

Eisai USA, Inc., Glenpointe Centre East, 300 Frank W. Burr Blvd., Teaneck, NJ 07666-6741 USA (Tel.: 201-692-0999; Telefax: 201-692-1972)

Eka Nobel. *See under* Akzo Nobel

Electrochem Ltd.

Unit 11, Newfield Industrial Estate, Tunstall, Stoke-on-Trent, Staffordshire, ST6 5PD UK (Tel.: 44 1782 822 058; Telefax: 44 1782 822 350; Telex: 848668 GASKEM G)

Elf Atochem

Elf Atochem S.A., 4, cours Michelet, La Défense 10, F-92091 Paris Cedex 42 France (Tel.: 49-00-8080; Telefax: 49-00-7447; Telex: 611922 ATO F)

Elf Atochem North America Inc., Headquarters, 2000 Market St., Philadelphia, PA 19103-3222 USA (Tel.: 215-419-7000; 800-225-7788; Telefax: 215-419-7591)

Elf Atochem North America Inc./Organic Chemicals, 2000 Market St., Philadelpha, PA 19103-3222 USA (Tel.: 215-419-7000; 800-628-4453; Telefax: 215-419-7875)

Elf Atochem North America Inc./Wire Mill Products Dept., 43 James St., Homer, NY 13077 USA (Tel.: 607-749-2652)

Elf Atochem Canada, PO Box 278, Oakville, Ontario, L6J 5A3 Canada (Tel.: 905-827-9841; Telefax: 905-827-7913)

Elf Atochem UK Ltd., Colthrop Lane, Thatcham, Newbury, Berkshire, RG13 4LW UK (Tel.: 44 1635 870000; Telefax: 44 1635-861212; Telex: 847689 ATOKEM G)

Ceca SA, Div. of Elf Atochem, 22, place de l'Iris, La Défense 2, Cedex 54, 92062 Paris-La Défense France (Tel.: 147-96-9090; Telefax: 147-96-9234; Telex: 611444 ckd)

Ellis & Everard

Ellis & Everard (UK) Ltd., 46 Peckover St., Bradford, West Yorkshire, BD1 5BD UK (Tel.: 44 1274 377000; Telefax: 44 1274 377001)

Ellis & Everard Food & Personal Care, Caspian House, East Parade, Bradford, West Yorkshire, BD1 5EP UK (Tel.: 44 1274 377000; Telefax: 44 1274 377001; Telex: 517464)

EM Industries, Inc./Fine Chems. Div.

5 Skyline Drive, Hawthorne, NY 10532 USA (Tel.: 914-592-4350; Telefax: 914-592-9469)

Emkay Chemical Co.

319-325 Second St., PO Box 42, Elizabeth, NJ 07206 USA (Tel.: 908-352-7053; Telefax: 908-352-6398)

EMS-Dottikon AG

CH-5605 Dottikon Switzerland (Tel.: 41-57-26 11 55; Telefax: 41-57-24 21 20)

Enco Products (London) Ltd.

71-75 Fortess Rd., London, NW5 1AU UK (Tel.: 44 171 485 2217; Telex: 28241)

Engelhard

Engelhard Corp., 101 Wood Ave. South, CN 770, Iselin, NJ 08830-0770 USA (Tel.: 908-205-5000; 800-631-9505; Telefax: 908-906-0337; Telex: 219984 ENGL UR)

Engelhard Canada Limited, 195 Riviera Dr., Markham, Ontario, L3R 5J6 Canada (Tel.: 905-940-4020; Telefax: 905-940-4470)

Engelhard Ltd., Chancery House, St. Nicholas Way, Sutton, Surrey, SM1 1JB UK (Tel.: 44-181-643-8080; Telefax: 44-181-643-6063)

Engelhard SA, 4 Rue de Beaubourg, 75004 Paris France (Tel.: 33-1-44-611000; Telefax: 33-1-44-611192)

Engelhard GmbH, Lise Meitner Strasse 7, 63303 Dreieich Germany (Tel.: 49-6103-9345-0; Telefax: 49-6103-34787)

Engelhard s.r.l., Via Ronchi, 17, 20134 Milan Italy (Tel.: 39-2-264-251; Telefax: 39-2-215-4602)

Engelhard Corp. (Japan), 9th Fl. Toranomon 3-Chome, Annex, 7-12 Toranomon 3-Chome, Minato-ku, Tokyo, 105 Japan

Engelhard (Hong Kong) Ltd., Block B2, 6/F, Eldex Industrial Bldg., 21 Ma Tau Wei Road, Hunghom, Kowloon Hong Kong (Tel.: 852-2365-0302; Telefax: 852-2765-6406)

Engelhard Australia Pty. Ltd., 10-12 Prospect St., Box Hill 3128, Victoria Australia (Tel.: 61-3-899-6330; Telefax: 61-3-899-6360)

EniChem

EniChem Elastomeri Srl, Strada 3, Palazzo B1, Milanofiori, I-20090 Assago, Milan Italy (Tel.: 39 2 5201; Telefax: 39 2 52026077; Telex: 310246)

EniChem Elastomers Ltd., Div. of EniChem Elastomeri Srl, Charleston Rd, Hardley, Hythe, Southampton, Hamsphire, SO4 6YY UK (Tel.: 44 1703 894919; Telefax: 44 1703 894334; Telex: 47519)

EniChem America, Inc., 1211 Ave. of the Americas, New York, NY 10036 USA (Tel.: 212-382-6521; Telefax: 212-382-6584; Telex: 6801159 ENICHEM)

EniChem Synthesis SpA, Via Medici del Vascello 40, 20138 Milano Italy (Tel.: 02 5203 9218; Telefax: 02 5203 9450; Telex: 310246)

EPI Bretagne

41 rue des Hauts Chemins, F22360 Langueux France (Tel.: 33 96 627660; Telefax: 33 96 727335)

Esprit Chemical Co.

800 Hingham St., Suite 207S, Rockland, MA 02370 USA (Tel.: 617-878-5555; 800-2-ESPRIT; Telefax: 617-871-5431; Telex: 951346)

Euroma Food Ingredients

PO Box 4, 8190 AA Wapenveld The Netherlands (Tel.: 31 5206 73550; Telefax: 31 5206 73195)

Eurovanillin

Postfach 330, N-1701 Sarpsborg Norway (Tel.: 47 9 118000; Telefax: 47 9 118640)

Evans Chemetics. *See* Hampshire Chemical Corp.

Expansia SA

BP 6, F-30390 Aramon France (Tel.: 33 66 57 01 01; Telefax: 33 66 57 01 48; Telex: 480191)

Exxon

Exxon Chemical Co., PO Box 3272, Houston, TX 77253-3272 USA (Tel.: 713-870-6000; 800-526-0749; Telefax: 713-870-6661; Telex: 794588)

Exxon Chemical Geopolymers Ltd., Div. of Exxon Corp, PO Box 122, 4600 Parkway, Solent Business Park, Whiteley, Fareham, Hampshire, PO15 7AZ UK (Tel.: 44 1489 884400; Telefax: 44 1489 884403; Telex: 47437)

Exxon Chemical Europe Inc., 280 Vorstlaan, Bld du Souverain, B-1160 Bruxelles Belgium (Tel.: 32-2-674-41 11; Telefax: 32-2-674 41 29)

Fabrichem Inc.

211 Sigwin Dr., Fairfield, CT 0006430 USA (Tel.: 203-259-5512; Telefax: 203-254-7886)

Faesy & Besthoff, Inc.

143 River Rd., Edgewater, NJ 07020-0029 USA (Tel.: 201-945-6200; Telefax: 201-945-6145)

Fairmount Chemical Co., Inc.

117 Blanchard St., Newark, NJ 07105 USA (Tel.: 201-344-5790; 800-872-9999; Telefax: 201-690-5298; Telex: 138905)

Fanning Corp., The

2450 W. Hubbard St., Chicago, IL 60612-1408 USA (Tel.: 312-563-1234; Telefax: 312-563-0087)

Farbest Brands

160 Summit Ave., Montvale, NJ 07645 USA (Tel.: 201-573-4900; Telefax: 201-573-0404)

Farleyway Chemicals Ltd.

Ham Lane, Kingswinford, West Midlands, DY6 7JU UK (Tel.: 44 1384 400 222; Telefax: 44 1384 400 020; Telex: 339528 FAR G)

FAR Research, Inc.

2210 Wilitelmina Ct., Palm Bay, FL 32905 USA (Tel.: 407-723-6160; Telefax: 407-723-8753)

The Feldspar Corp.

One West Pack Square, Suite 700, Asheville, NC 28801 USA (Tel.: 704-254-7400; Telefax: 704-255-4909)

Fermex

Fermex International Ltd., E3 Blackpole Trading Estate, (East), Worcester, Worcestershire, WR3 8SG UK (Tel.: 44 1905 755811; Telefax: 44 1905 754145)

Fermex Australia Pty. Ltd., 1 Ferndell St., Granville, NSW, 2142 Australia (Tel.: 61 2 632 2222; Telefax: 61 2 632 1784)

Ferro

Ferro Corp./World Headquarters, 1000 Lakeside Ave., Cleveland, OH 44114-1183 USA (Tel.: 216-641-8580; Telefax: 216-696-6958; Telex: 98-0165)

Ferro Corp./Bedford Chemical Div., 7050 Krick Rd., Bedford, OH 44146 USA (Tel.: 216-641-8580; 800-321-9946; Telefax: 216-439-7686; Telex: 98-165)

Ferro Corp./Grant Chemical Div., PO Box 263, Baton Rouge, LA 70821 USA (Tel.: 504-654-6801; Telefax: 504-654-3268; Telex: 980165)

Ferro Corp./Keil Chemical Div., 3000 Sheffield Ave., Hammond, IN 46320 USA (Tel.: 219-931-2630; 800-628-9079; Telefax: 219-931-0895; Telex: 725484)

Ferro Corp./Transelco Div., Box 217, Penn Yan, NY 14527 USA (Tel.: 315-536-3357; Telefax: 315-536-8091; Telex: 97 8373)

Ferrosan A/S, Div. of Novo Nordisk A/S

Sydmarken 1-5, DK-2860 Soborg Denmark (Tel.: 45 1-6921 11; Telex: 16383 FERRO DK)

Fina Chemicals, Div. of Petrofina SA

Nijverheldsstraat, 52 Rue de l'Industrie, B-1040 Brussels Belgium (Tel.: 32 2-288 9132; Telefax: 32-2-288-3322; Telex: 21 556 PFINA B)

Finetex Inc.

418 Falmouth Ave., PO Box 216, Elmwood Park, NJ 07407 USA (Tel.: 201-797-4686; Telefax: 201-797-6558; Telex: 710-988-2239)

Firmenich, Inc.

PO Box 5880, Princeton, NJ 08543-5880 USA (Tel.: 609-452-1000; 800-257-9591; Telefax: 609-921-0719; Telex: 21-99-15)

First Chemical Corp.

PO Box 1427, Pascagoula, MS, 39568-1427 USA (Tel.: 601-762-0870; 800-828-7940; Telefax: 601-762-5213; Telex: 510-990-3361)

G. Fiske & Co Ltd.

64 Sheen Rd., Richmond, Surrey, TW9 1UF UK (Tel.: 44 181 948 5811; Telefax: 44 181-948 7059; Telex: 925878)

Flavors of North America Inc.

525 Randy Rd., Carol Stream, IL 60188 USA (Tel.: 708-462-1414; Telefax: 708-462-8855)

Florexco Inc.

25 Central Park West, Suite 4M, New York, NY 10023 USA (Tel.: 212-586-7588; Telefax: 212-246-7317)

Florida Food Prods., Inc./Aloe Div.

2231 W. Hwy. 44, PO Box 1300, Eustis, FL 32727-1300 USA (Tel.: 904-357-4141; 800-874-2331; Telefax: 904-483-3192)

Florida Treatt. *See under* Treatt

Fluka

Fluka Chemical Corp, 980 South Second St., Ronkonkoma, NY 11779 USA (Tel.: 516-467-0980; 800-FLUKA-US; Telefax: 800-441-8841; Telex: 96-7807)

Fluka Sarl, BP 1114, 68052 Mulhouse Cedex France (Tel.: 89 61 87 47; Telex: 881236 F)

Fluka Chemie AG, Industriestrasse 25, CH-9470 Buchs Switzerland (Tel.: 41-85 60275; Telefax: 41-85 65449; Telex: 855 282)

Fluka Chemicals, The Old Brickyard, New Road, Gillingham, Dorset, SP8 4JL UK (Tel.: 44 1747 823097; Telefax: 44 1747 824596; Telex: 417238)

FMC

FMC Corp./Chemical Products Group, 1735 Market St., Philadelphia, PA 19103 USA (Tel.: 215-299-6000; 800-346-5101; Telefax: 215-299-5999; Telex: 685-1326)

FMC Corp./Food Ingredients Div., 1735 Market St., Philadelphia, PA 19103 USA (Tel.: 800-346-5101; Telefax: 215-299-6291; Telex: 6851326 FMC PHA)

FMC Corp/Pharmaceutical and Bioscience Div., 1735 Market St., Philadelphia, PA 19103 USA (Tel.: 215-299-6000; Telefax: 215-299-6821)

FMC Corp. Canada, 11475 Cote de Liesse Rd., Dorval, Quebec, H9P 1B3 Canada

FMC Corp (UK) Ltd./Process Additives Div., Tenax Rd., Trafford Park, Manchester, Lancaster, M17 1WT UK (Tel.: 44 161 872 2323; Telefax: 44 161 873 3177; Telex: 666177)

FMC Corp. N.V., Ave. Louise 480-B9, Brussels 1050 Belgium (Tel.: 322-645 5511; Telefax: 322-640 6350)

FMC International S.A., 4th Floor, Interbank Bldg., 111 Paseo de Roxas, Makati, Metro Manila Phillippines (Tel.: (632) 817 5546; Telefax: (632) 818 1485)

Focus Chemical.

875 Greenland Rd., Orchard Park, Suite B9, Portsmouth, NH 03801 USA (Tel.: 603-430-9802)

Folexco Inc.

150 Domorah Dr., Montgomeryville, PA 18936 USA (Tel.: 215-628-8895; Telefax: 215-628-8651)

Food Additives & Ingredients Inc.

222 Sherwood Ave., Farmingdale, NY 117535 USA (Tel.: 516-694-9090; Telefax: 516-694-9177; Telex: 6852289)

Food Ingredients Technology Ltd.

Cunningham House, Westfield Lane, Kenton, Harrow, Middlesex, HA3 9ED UK (Tel.: 44 181 907 7278; Telefax: 44 181 909 1053; Telex: 8811603)

Foodtech Ltd.

73/75 High St., Hornsey, London, N8 7QW UK (Tel.: 44 181 348 4545; Telefax: 44 181 348 2313; Telex: 24124)

The Foote & Jenkins Corp.

1420 Crestmont Ave., Camden, NJ 08103 USA (Tel.: 609-966-0700; Telefax: 609-966-6132)

Formula One

222 Kensal Rd., London, W10 5BN UK (Tel.: 44 181 969 6807; Telefax: 44 181 969 5337)

Forrester Wood Co. Ltd.

Hawksley Ind. Estate, Heron St., Hollinwood, Oldham, Lancashire, OL8 4UJ UK (Tel.: 44 161 620 4124; Telefax: 44 161 627 1050)

Forum Chemicals Ltd.

Forum House, 41-51 Brighton Rd., Redhill, Surrey, RH1 6YS UK (Tel.: 44 1737 773711; Telefax: 44 1737 773116; Telex: 939065)

Franklin Industrial Minerals

Franklin Industrial Minerals, 612 Tenth Ave. North, Nashville, TN 37203 USA (Tel.: 615-259-4222; Telefax: 615-726-2693)

Franklin Industrial Minerals, 821 Tilton Bridge Rd., S.E., Dalton, GA 30721 USA (Tel.: 404-277-3740; Telefax: 404-277-9827)

Frigova Produce Ltd.

31 Tooley St., London, SE1 2RY UK (Tel.: 44 171 407 7701; Telefax: 44 171 407 6476; Telex: 888464)

Frutarom

Frutarom Ltd., 25 Hashaish St., PO Box 10067, Haifa, 26110 Israel (Tel.: 972 4 462 462; Telefax: 972 4 722 517; Telex: 45125 FRUT IL)

Frutarom USA Inc., 9500 Railroad Ave., N. Bergen, NJ 07047-1422 USA (Tel.: 201-861-7760; Telefax: 201-861-8040)

Frutarom (UK) Ltd., Northbridge Works, Northbridge Rd., Berkhamsted, Hertsfordshire, HP4 1EF UK (Tel.: 44 1442 876611; Telefax: 44 1442 876204)

Fry's Metals Ltd., Div. of Cookson Group plc

Tandem House, Beddington Farm Rd, Croydon, Greater London, CR9 4BT UK (Tel.: 44 181 665 6666; Telefax: 44 181-665 6196; Telex: 265732)

Fuji Chemical Industry Co., Ltd.

1570 Nakanoshima, Wakayami-shi, Wakayama, 640 Japan (Tel.: (0734) 23-1247; Telefax: (0734) 31-3005)

Fujisawa Pharmaceutical Co., Ltd.

3-4-7, Dosho-machi, Chuo-ku, Osaka, 541 Japan (Tel.: (06) 202-1141; Telefax: (06) 222-4988)

Fuji Titanium Industry Co., Ltd.

3-6-32, Nakanoshima, Kita-ku, Osaka, 530 Japan (Tel.: (06) 441-6856; Telefax: (06) 441-6855)

H.B. Fuller Co.

3530 Lexington Ave. North, St. Paul, MN 55126-8076 USA (Tel.: 612-481-1816; 800-468-6358; Telefax: 612-481-1863)

Furukawa Co., Ltd.

6-1, Marunouchi 2-chome, Chiyoda-ku, Tokyo, 100 Japan (Tel.: (03) 3212-6561; Telefax: (03) 3287-0696; Telex: 02225614 FURUKOJ)

Fushimi Pharmaceutical Co., Ltd.

1676, Nakatsu-cho, Marugame-shi, Kagawa, 763 Japan (Tel.: (0877) 22-6231; Telefax: (0877) 22-6235)

Gallard-Schlesinger Industries, Inc.

584 Mineola Ave., Carle Place, NY 11514-1712 USA (Tel.: 516-333-5600; Telefax: 516-333-5628; Telex: 6852390 (WUI))

Garuda International Inc.

PO Box 5155, Santa Cruz, CA 95063 USA (Tel.: 408-462-6341; Telefax: 408-462-6355; Telex: 296614 Garuda UR)

Gattefosse

Gattefosse SA, 36 Chemin de Genas, BP 603, F 69804 Saint Priest France (Tel.: 72 22 98 00; Telefax: 78 90 45 67; Telex: 340 240 F)

Gattefosse Corp., 372 Kinderkamack Rd., Westwood, NJ 07675 USA (Tel.: 201-358-1700; Telefax: 201-358-4050)

Gaylord Chemical Co.

PO Box 1209, 106 Galeria Blvd., Slidell, LA 70459-1209 USA (Tel.: 504-649-5464; 800-426-6620; Telefax: 504-649-0068; Telex: 901 4748663)

GCA Chemical Corp.

916 West 13th St., Bradenton, FL 34205 USA (Tel.: 813-748-6090; Telefax: 813-748-0194)

Gelatine Products Ltd.

Sutton Weaver, Runcorn, Cheshire, WA7 3EH UK (Tel.: 44 1928 716444; Telefax: 44 1928 718325; Telex: 629303)

Gelest Inc.

612 William Leigh Dr., Tullytown, PA 19007-6308 USA (Tel.: 215-547-1015; Telefax: 215-547-2484)

Geltech, Inc.

1 Progress Blvd., #8, Alachua, FL 32615 USA (Tel.: 904-462-2358; 800-323-6595; Telefax: 904-462-2993)

General Chemical Corp.

90 East Halsey Rd., Parsippany, NJ 07054-0373 USA (Tel.: 201-515-0900; 800-631-8050; Telefax: 201-515-2468; Telex: 139-450 GEN-CHEMPAPY)

General Electric

General Electric Co./Silicone Products Div., 260 Hudson River Rd., Waterford, NY 12188 USA (Tel.: 518-237-3330; 800-255-8886; Telefax: 518-233-3931)

GE Silicones Europe, Postbus 117, Plasticslaan 1, NL-4600 AC Bergen op Zoom The Netherlands (Tel.: 31-1640-32291; Telefax: 31-1640-32708; Telex: 78421)

GE Silicones, Div. of GE Plastics Ltd., Old Hall Rd., Sale, Manchester, M33 2HG UK (Tel.: 44 161 905 5000; Telefax: 44 161-905 5022)

General Latex & Chemical Corp.

67 High St., N. Bellerica, MA 01862 USA (Tel.: 508-663-3485; Telefax: 508-663-3488)

Generichem Corp.

85 Main St., PO Box 369, Little Falls, NJ 07424 USA (Tel.: 201-256-9266; Telefax: 201-256-0069; Telex: 510-601-6431)

Genesee Polymers Corp.

G-5251 Fenton Rd., PO Box 7047, Flint, MI 48507-0047 USA (Tel.: 810-238-4966; Telefax: 810-767-3016)

Genstar Stone Products Co.

Executive Plaza IV, 11350 McCormick Rd., Hunt Valley, MD 21031 USA (Tel.: 410-527-4000; Telefax: 410-527-4535)

Georgia Gulf Corp./PVC Div.

PO Box 629, Plaquemine, LA 70765-0629 USA (Tel.: 504-685-1200; 800-PVC-VYCM)

Georgia Marble Co.

1201 Roberts Blvd., Bldg. 100, Kennesaw, GA 30144-3619 USA (Tel.: 404-421-6500, Telefax 404-421-6507)

Georgia-Pacific

Georgia-Pacific Chemical Div., 1754 Thorne Rd., Tacoma, WA 98421 USA (Tel.: 206-572-8181; Telefax: 206-572-4721)

Georgia-Pacific Resins Inc., 2883 Miller Rd, Decatur, GA 30035 USA (Tel.: 404-593-6895; Telefax: 404-593-6801; Telex: 804600)

GFS Chemicals, Inc.

PO Box 245, Powell, OH 43065 USA (Tel.: 614-881-5501; 800-858-9682; Telefax: 614-881-5989; Telex: 981282 GFS CHEM UD)

Gist-brocades

Gist-brocades Food Ingredients, Inc., 2200 Renaissance Blvd., Suite 150, King of Prussia, PA 19406 USA (Tel.: 215-272-4040; 800-662-4478; Telefax: 215-272-5695; Telex: 216902)

Gist-brocades, 8720 Red Oak Blvd., Suite 401, Charlotte, NC 28217 USA (Tel.: 704-527-9000; 800-438-1361; Telefax: 704-527-8184)

Gist-brocades, 1 Wateringseweg, PO Box 1, Delft 2600 MA The Netherlands (Tel.: 31 15 794046; Telefax: 31 15 794020; Telex: 38103)

Gist-brocades Savoury BV, PO Box 1195, Zaandam 1500 AD The Netherlands (Tel.: 31 75 700041; Telefax: 31 75 161559; Telex: 19115)

Gist-brocades SpA, Via Milano 42, I-27045 Casteggio Italy (Tel.: 39-383-8931; Telefax: 39-383-805397; Telex: 321197 VINAL I)

Edward Gittens Ltd.

Firwood Works, Firwood Fold, Off Thicketford Rd., Bolton, Lancastershire, BL2 3AG UK (Tel.: 44 1204 309091; Telefax: 44 1204 309119; Telex: 38103)

Giulini Corp.

105 East Union Ave., Bound Brook, NJ 08805 USA (Tel.: 908-469-6504; Telefax: 908-469-8418; Telex: 700179)

Givaudan

Givaudan-Roure SA, 5 Chemin de la Perfumiere, CH-1214 Vernier-Geneva Switzerland (Tel.: 22-780 91 11; Telefax: 22-780 91 50)

Givaudan Iberica SA, Plá d'en Batlle, Sant Celoni, E-08470 Barcelona Spain (Tel.: 34 3-867 06 00; Telefax: 34 3-867 03 19; Telex: 94000)

Givaudan-Roure Corp., 1775 Windsor Rd., Teaneck, NJ 07666 USA (Tel.: 201-833-7500; Telefax: 201-833-8165; Telex: 219259 givc ur)

Glucona

Postbus 247, NL-3800 AE Amersfoort The Netherlands (Tel.: 31 33 67 67 67; Telefax: 31 33 67 61 85; Telex: 79322 AKZO NV)

GMI Products Inc.

2525 Davie Rd., Suite 330, Davie, FL 33317 USA (Tel.: 305-999-9373; Telefax: 305-474-0989)

Goldschmidt

Goldschmidt AG, Th., Goldschmidtstrasse 100, Postfach 101461, D-4300 Essen 1 Germany (Tel.: 0201-173-01; Telefax: 201-173-2160; Telex: 857170)

Goldschmidt Ltd., Subsid. of Goldschmidt AG, Tego House, Victoria Road, Ruislip, Middlesex, HA4 0YL UK (Tel.: 44 181 422 7788; Telefax: 44 181-864 8159; Telex: 923146)

Goldschmidt Chemical Corp., 914 E. Randolph Rd., PO Box 1299, Hopewell, VA 23860 USA (Tel.: 804-541-8658; 800-446-1809; Telefax: 804-541-8689; Telex: 710-958-1350)

Goldschmidt Canada, 2150 Winston Park Dr., Unit 201, Oakville, Ontario, L6H 5V1 Canada (Tel.: 905-829-2233; Telefax: 905-829-2575)

Tego Chemie Service Dept., Div. of Goldschmidt, PO Box 1299, 914 E. Randolph Rd., Hopewell, VA 23860 USA (Tel.: 804-541-8658; 800-446-1809; Telefax: 804-541-2783)

Good Food Inc.

W. Main St., PO Box 160, Honey Brook, PA 19344 USA (Tel.: 610-273-3776; Telefax: 610-273-2087)

BFGoodrich

BFGoodrich Co.Specialty Chemicals, 9911 Brecksville Rd., Brecksville, OH 44141-3247 USA (Tel.: 216-447-5000; 800-331-1144; Telefax: 216-447-5720; Telex: 4996831)

Goodrich Canada, 125 Northfield Dr. West, Waterloo, Ontario, N2L 6K4 Canada (Tel.: 519-888-3330; Telefax: 519-888-3337)

BFGoodrich Chemical (UK) Ltd., The Lawn, 100 Lampton Road, Hounslow, Middlesex, TW3 4EB UK (Tel.: 44 181 570 4700; Telefax: 44 181-570 0850)

BFGoodrich Chemical Europe, 742 Rue de Verdun, B-1130 Brussels Belgium (Tel.: 32-2-247-1911; Telefax: 32-2-247-1991)

BFGoodrich Chemical (Deutschland) GmbH, Goerlitzer Str. 1, D-41460 Neuss 1 Germany (Tel.: 49-2131-18050; Telefax: 49-2131-180530)

BFGoodrich Chemical (Italia) Srl, Viale Gian Galeazzo 25/27, 20136 Milano Italy (Tel.: 39-2-5830-6961; Telefax: 39-2-5831-0390)

BFGoodrich Chemical Ltd., 14 Queens Rd., Melbourne, Victoria, 3004 Australia (Tel.: 61-3-267-6488; Telefax: 61-3-820-1094)

BFGoodrich Chemical (Far East) Ltd., 2208 Fortress Tower, 250 Kings Rd. Hong Kong (Tel.: 852-508-1021; Telefax: 852-512-2241)

Goodyear

Goodyear Tire & Rubber Co./The Chemical Div., 1485 E. Archwood Ave., Akron, OH 44316 USA (Tel.: 216-796-8295; Telefax: 216-796-3199; Telex: 640550 Gdyr)

Goodyear Chemicals Europe, 14 Ave. des Tropiques, Z.A. de Courtaboeuf, 91952 Les Ulis Cedex France (Tel.: 33-1-69-29-28-15; Telefax: 33-1-69-29-27-04; Telex: 602895F)

Goorden NV

Melkerijstraat 1, 2900 Schoten Belgium (Tel.: 32 33 243835; Telefax: 32 33 243838)

Graden Chemical Co., Inc.

426 Bryan St., Havertown, PA 19083 USA (Tel.: 215-449-3808)

Grain Processing Corp.

1600 Oregon St., Muscatine, IA 52761 USA (Tel.: 319-264-4265; Telefax: 319-264-4289; Telex: 46-8497)

Great Lakes

Great Lakes Chemical Corp., PO Box 2200, W. Lafayette, IN 47906-0200 USA (Tel.: 317-497-6100; 800-621-9521; Telefax: 317-497-6234)

Great Lakes Chemical Corp., Rua Itapaiuna 1800-Casa 56, Morumbi, Sao Paulo SP 05707-001 Brazil (Tel.: 55-11-844-6486; Telefax: 55-11-844-6787)

Great Lakes Chemical (Europe) Ltd., P O Box 44, Oil Sites Road, Ellesmere Port, South Wirral, L65 4GD UK (Tel.: 44 151 356 8489; Telefax: 44 151-356 8490)

Great Lakes-QO Chemicals, Inc., Industrieweg 12, Haven 391, B-2030 Antwerp Belgium (Tel.: 32-3-541-2165; Telefax: 32-3-541-6503)

Great Lakes Chemical Corp./Japan, LaVie Sakuragicho Bldg., 5-26-3, Sakuragicho, Nishi-Ku, Yokohama, 220 Japan (Tel.: 81-45-212-9541; Telefax: 81-45-212-9539)

Great Western Chemical Co.

808 SW 15th Ave., Portland, OR 97205 USA (Tel.: 503-228-2600; Telefax: 503-221-5752; Telex: 910-464-4733)

K & K Greeff Chemicals Ltd., Div. of Beijer Industries AB

Suffolk House, George Streeet, Croydon, Greater London, CR9 3QL UK (Tel.: 44 181 686 0544; Telefax: 44 181 686 4792; Telex: 28386)

R.W. Greeff & Co Inc.

777 West Putnam Ave, Greenwich, CT 06830 USA (Tel.: 203-532-2900; Telefax: 203-532-2980; Telex: 996609)

Grefco Inc.

3435 W. Lomita Blvd., Torrance, CA 90509 USA (Tel.: 310-517-0700; Telefax: 310-517-0794; Telex: 664266)

Grillo-Werke AG

Sparte Chemie, Postfach 11 02 65, Weseler Strasse 1, D-4100 Duisburg 11 Germany (Tel.: 49-203-55571; Telefax: 49-203-5557440; Telex: 8 551 525 gllo d)

R.I.T.A., U.S. distributor, 1725 Kilkenny Court, PO Box 585, Woodstock, IL 60098 USA (Tel.: 815-337-2500; 800-426-7759; Telefax: 815-337-2522; Telex: 72-2438)

Grindsted

Grindsted Products A/S, Edwin Rahrs Vej 38, DK-8220 Brabrand Denmark (Tel.: 45 86-25-3366; Telefax: 45 86-25-1077; Telex: 64177 gvdan dk)

Grindsted Products, Ltd., Northern Way, Bury St Edmunds, Suffolk, IP32 6NP UK (Tel.: 44 1284 769631; Telefax: 44 1284 760839; Telex: 81203)

Grindsted Products GmbH, Roberts-Bosch Strasse 20-24, D-25451 Quickborn Germany (Tel.: 4106/70960; Telefax: 4106/709666; Telex: 2180684 gpd d)

Grinsted France S.A.R.L., Parc D'Activités de Pissaloup, Ave. Jean D'Alembert, F-78190 Trappes France (Tel.: (1) 30 66 08 08; Telefax: (1) 30 66 75 08; Telex: 696064 f grindt)

Grindsted Products, Inc., 201 Industrial Pkwy., PO Box 26, Industrial Airport, KS 66031 USA (Tel.: 913-764-8100; 800-255-6837; Telefax: 913-764-5407; Telex: 4-37295)

Grindsted Products, Inc., 10 Carlson Court, Suite 580, Rexdale, Ontario, M9W 6L2 Canada (Tel.: 416-674-7340; Telefax: 416-674-7378)

Grindsted de México, S.A. de C.V., Cerrada de las Granjas 623, Col. Jagüey, Delegación Azcapotzalco, 02300 México, D.F. Mexico (Tel.: (5) 352 9102; Telefax: (5) 561 3285)

Grindsted do Brazil, Indústria e Comércio Ltda., Rodovia Regisé Bittencourt, KM 275,5, 06818-900 Embú S.P. Brazil (Tel.: (11) 494-3899; Telefax: (11) 494-3823; Telex: 1171854 gpbr br)

Grünau GmbH, Chemische Fabrik, A Henkel Group Co.

Postfach 1063, Robert-Hansen-Strasse 1, D-89251 Jllertissen Germany (Tel.: (07303)13-706; Telefax: (07303)13203; Telex: 719114 gruea-d)

Guardian Laboratories, Div. of United-Guardian, Inc.

PO Box 2500, Smithtown, NY 11787 USA (Tel.: 516-273-0900; 800-645-5566; Telefax: 516-273-0858; Telex: 497-4275 GCCHAVP)

Gumix International Inc.

2160 N. Central Rd., Fort Lee, NJ 07024-7552 USA (Tel.: 201-947-6300; 800-2GU-MIX2; Telefax: 201-947-9265; Telex: 134227)

Gum Technology

PO Box 356, Sta. A, Flushing, NY 11358 USA (Tel.: 914-278-4599; Telefax: 718-961-7297)

Haarmann & Reimer

Haarmann & Reimer GmbH, Postfach 1253, Rumohrtalstrasse 1, Holzminden Germany (Tel.: 49 5531 900; Telefax: 49 5531 901649; Telex: 965 330 HARM D)

Haarmann & Reimer Ltd., Fieldhouse Lane, Marlow, Buckinghamshire, SL7 1NA UK (Tel.: 44 1628 472051; Telefax: 44 1628 890795; Telex: 848 859)

Haarmann & Reimer Ltd./Food Ingredients Business Group, Div. of Bayer UK Ltd., Denison Rd, Selby, North Yorkshire, YO8 8EF UK (Tel.: 44 1757 703691; Telefax: 44 1757 701468; Telex: 57852)

Haarmann & Reimer Corp., PO Box 175, 70 Diamond Road, Springfield, NJ 07081 USA (Tel.: 201-4912-5707; 800-422-1559; Telefax: 201-912-0499; Telex: 219134 HAR UR)

Haarmann & Reimer Corp./Food Ingreds. Div., 1127 Myrtle St., PO Box 932, Elkhart, IN 46515 USA (Tel.: 219-264-8716; 800-348-7414; Telefax: 219-262-6747)

Haarmann & Reimer Australia Pty. Ltd., 9 Garling Rd., Marayong, NSW, 2148 Australia (Tel.: 61 2 671 3444; Telefax: 61 2 621 8086)

C.P. Hall Co.

7300 South Central Ave., Chicago, IL 60638-0428 USA (Tel.: 708-594-6000; 800-321-8242; Telefax: 708-458-0428)

Howard Hall, Div. of R.W. Greeff & Co. Inc.

777 West Putnam Ave., Greenwich, CT 06830 USA (Tel.: 203-532-2900; Telefax: 203-532-2980; Telex: 681 9012)

Hamari Chemicals Ltd.

1-4-29, Kunijima, Higashi Yodogawa-ku, Osaka, 533 Japan (Tel.: (06) 323-9027)

Hammill & Gillespie Inc.

154 S. Livingston Ave., PO Box 104, Livingston, NJ 07039 USA (Tel.: 201-994-3650; Telefax: 201-994-3847; Telex: 139114)

Hampshire Chemical Corp.

55 Hayden Ave., Lexington, MA 02173 USA (Tel.: 617-861-9700; Telefax: 617-861-9700; Telex: 200076 GRLX UR)

Handy & Harman

555 Theodore Fremd Ave., Rye, NY 10580-1437 USA (Tel.: 914-921-5200; Telefax: 914-925-4498; Telex: 126288)

Hansen & Rosenthal KG

Heilholtkamp 11, 2000 Hamburg 60 Germany (Tel.: 040-5130930; Telefax: 040-51309340; Telex: 211902 hur)

Chr. Hansen's Lab

Chr. Hansen's Lab Inc., 9015 W. Maple St., Milwaukee, WI 53214 USA (Tel.: 414-476-3630; 800-558-0802; Telefax: 414-259-9399)

Chr. Hansen's Laboratorium Danmark A/S, 10-12 Boge AlleDK-2970 Horsholm Denmark (Tel.: 45 45 76 76 76; Telefax: 45 45 76 08 48; Telex: 19184)

Chr. Hansen's Lab (Aust), 3/7-9 Newcastle Rd., Bayswater, Victoria, 3153 Australia (Tel.: 61 3 720 8022; Telefax: 61 3 720 7801)

Harcros

Harcros Durham Chemicals, Div. of Harcros Chemicals UK Ltd., Birtley, Chester-le-Street, Co. Durham, DH3 1QX UK (Tel.: 44 1914 102361; Telefax: 44 1914 106005; Telex: 53618 DURHAM G)

Harcros Chemicals Inc./Organics Div., 5200 Speaker Rd., PO Box 2930, Kansas City, KS 66106-1095 USA (Tel.: 913-321-3131; Telefax: 913-621-7718; Telex: 477266)

Hardman Inc., A Harcros Chemical Group Co.

600 Cortlandt St., Belleville, NJ 07109 USA (Tel.: 201-751-3000; Telefax: 201-751-8407; Telex: TWX: 710-995-4940)

Hardwicke Chemical Inc.

2114 Larry Jeffers Rd., Elgin, SC 29045 USA (Tel.: 803-438-3471; Telefax: 803-438-4497; Telex: 810-671-1814)

Keith Harris & Co. Ltd.

7 Sefton Rd., Pennant Hills, PO Box 147, Thornleigh, NSW, 2120 Australia (Tel.: 61 2 484 1341; Telefax: 61 2 481 8145; Telex: 26214)

Harrisons Trading Co. Inc.

303 South Broadway, Tarrytown, NY 10591 USA (Tel.: 914-332-4600; Telefax: 914-332-8575; Telex: 427906)

Hart Chemicals Ltd.

256 Victoria Rd. South, Guelph, Ontario, N1H 6K8 Canada (Tel.: 519-824-3280; Telefax: 519-824-0755; Telex: 06956537)

Hart Products Corp.

173 Sussex St., Jersey City, NJ 07302 USA (Tel.: 201-433-6632)

Harwick Chemical Corp.

60 S. Seiberling St., PO Box 9360, Akron, OH 44305-0360 USA (Tel.: 216-798-9300; Telefax: 216-798-0214; Telex: TWX: 810-431-2126)

T. Hasegawa Co., Ltd.

4-4-14, Nihonbashi Hon-cho, Chuo-ku, Tokyo, 103 Japan (Tel.: (03) 3241-1151; Telefax: (03) 3278-8075)

Hatco Corp.

1020 King George Post Rd., Fords, NJ 08863-0601 USA (Tel.: 908-738-1000; Telefax: 908-738-9385; Telex: 84-4545)

A.C. Hatrick Chemicals Pty Ltd.

49-61 Stephen Road, Botany Bay, Botany, NSW, 2019 Australia (Tel.: 61 2 666-9331; Telefax: 61 2 666 3872)

Hayashi Pure Chemical Industries Co., Ltd.

2-14, Dosho-machi 2-chome, Chuo-ku, Osaka, 541 Japan (Tel.: (06) 231-0841; Telefax: (06) 222-1035)

Hays Chemicals Distribution Ltd.

Rawdon House, Green Lane, Yeadon, Leeds, West Yorkshire, LS19 7XX UK (Tel.: 44 1132 505811; Telefax: 44 1132 508776; Telex: 55329)

Heico Chemicals, Inc., A Cambrex Co.

Route 611, PO Box 160, Delaware Water Gap, PA 18327-0160 USA (Tel.: 717-420-3900; 800-34-HEICO; Telefax: 717-421-9012)

Helianthus S.A.

PO Box 133, Lima, 9, Peru (Tel.: 511 467 3680; Telefax: 511 467 3777)

Henkel

Henkel KGaA, Henkelstrasse 67, D-40191 Düsseldorf Germany (Tel.: 49-211-797-3300; Telefax: 49-211-798-9638; Telex: 858170)

Henkel KGaA/Cospha, Postfach 101100, D-40191, Düsseldorf Germany (Tel.: 49-211-797-0; Telefax: 49-211-798-7696; Telex: 85817-0)

Henkel Ltd., Div. of Henkel KG, Henkel House, 292-308 Southbury Road, Enfield, Middlesex, EN1 1TS UK (Tel.: 44 181 804 3343; Telefax: 44 181 443 2777; Telex: 922708 HENKEL G)

Henkel (Ireland) Ltd., Western Industrial Estate, Naas Road, Dublin, 12, Ireland (Tel.: 35 31 4 505 622; Telefax: 35 31 4 503 649)

Henkel France SA, Div. of Henkel KG, BP 309, 150 rue Gallieni, F-92102 Boulogne Billancourt France (Tel.: 33-46 84 90 00; Telefax: 33-46 84 90 90; Telex: 633177 HENKEL F)

Henkel Belgium SA, Div. of Henkel KG, 66 ave du Port, Havenlaan 65, 1210 Brussels Belgium (Tel.: 32-423 17 11; Telefax: 32-428 34 67; Telex: 21294 HENKEL B)

Henkel Chimica SpA, Via Scalabrini 24, 22073 Fino Mornasco (Co) Italy (Tel.: 3931 88 42 01; Telefax: 3931 88 43 60)

Henkel South Africa, PO Box 3933, Johannesburg, 2000, South Africa (Tel.: 27 11 864-4950; Telefax: 27 11 864 7888; Telex: 4-29310)

Pulcra SA, Pasaje Mariner no. 9, 08025 Barcelona Spain (Tel.: 34 3 290 47 63; Telefax: 34 3 290 48 79)

Henkel Corp./Coatings & Inks Div., 300 Brookside Ave., Ambler, PA 19002-3498 USA (Tel.: 215-628-1000; 800-445-2207)

Henkel Corp./Cospha, 300 Brookside Ave., Ambler, PA 19002 USA (Tel.: 215-628-1476; 800-531-0815; Telefax: 215-628-1450; Telex: 125854)

Henkel Corp./Fine Chemicals Div., 5325 South 9th Ave., La Grange, IL 60525-3602 USA (Tel.: 708-579-6150; 800-328-6199; Telefax: 708-579-6152; Telex: 4330913 HNKC UI)

Henkel Corp./Functional Products, 300 Brookside Ave., Ambler, PA 19002 USA (Tel.: 215-628-1583; 800-654-7588; Telefax: 215-628-1155)

Henkel Australia Pty. Ltd., 1 Clyde St., Silverwater, NSW, 2141 Australia (Tel.: 61 2 748 4355; Telefax: 61 2 748 3863; Telex: AA 25058)

Henkel Corp./Organic Products Div., 300 Brookside Ave., Ambler, PA 19022 USA (Tel.: 215-628-1000; 800-922-0605; Telefax: 215-628-1200; Telex: 6851092 amchm uw)

Henkel Corp./Textile Chemicals, 11709 Fruehauf Dr., Charlotte, NC 28273-6507 USA (Tel.: 800-634-2436; Telefax: 704-587-3804)

Henkel Canada Ltd., 2290 Argentia Rd., Mississauga, Ontario, L5N 6H9 Canada (Tel.: 416-542-7588; 800-668-6023; Telefax: 416-542-7566)

Henkel Argentina S.A., Carabelas 2398, 1870 Avellaneda, Casilla de Correo 3496, AR-1000 Buenos Aires, Argentina (Tel.: 541 2042056; Telefax: 541 205 33 60; Telex: 22475 hen ar)

Henkel S.A. Indústrias Químicas, Avenida das Nacoes, Unidas 10.989, CEP 04578 Sao Paulo, SP Brazil (Tel.: 55 11 828 2340; Telefax: 55 11 828 2326; Telex: 038-1138417 hbiq br)

Henkel Mexicana S.A. de C.V., Calz. de la Viga S/N, Fracc. Los Laureles en Tulpetlac, Ecatepec de Morelos, C.P. 55090 Mexico (Tel.: 525 787-1899; Telefax: 525 729-9804; Telex: 1762295 henk me)

Henkel Corp./Emery Group, 11501 Northlake Dr., Cincinnati, OH 45249 USA (Tel.: 513-530-7300; 800-543-7370; Telefax: 513-530-7581; Telex: 4333016)

Henley. *See under* Boehringer Ingelheim

Henry Lamotte. *See under* Lamotte

Herbstreith & Fox KG/Pektin-Fabrik Neuenbürg

PO Box 1261, D-75302 Neuenbürg Germany (Tel.: 49 7082 7913-0; Telefax: 49 7082 20281; Telex: 7245019)

Hercules

Hercules Inc., Hercules Plaza-6205SW, Wilmington, DE 19894 USA (Tel.: 302-594-5000; 800-247-4372; Telefax: 302-594-5400; Telex: 835-479)

Hercules Ltd., Div. of Hercules Inc., 31 London Road, Reigate, Surrey, RH2 9YA UK (Tel.: 44 1737 242434; Telefax: 44 1737-224288; Telex: 25803)

Hercules BV, 8 Veraartlaan, NL-2288GM Rijswijk The Netherlands (Tel.: 31-70-150-000; Telefax: 31-70-3989893; Telex: 31172)

Hershey Import Co. Inc.

700 E. Lincoln Ave., Rahway, NJ 07065 USA (Tel.: 201-388-9000)

Heterene Chemical Co., Inc.

PO Box 247, 795 Vreeland Ave., Paterson, NJ 07543 USA (Tel.: 201-278-2000; Telefax: 201-278-7512; Telex: 883358)

Hickson Danchem Corp.

1975 Richmond Blvd., PO Box 400, Danville, VA 24540 USA (Tel.: 804-797-8105; Telefax: 804-799-2814; Telex: 940103 WU PUBTLXBSN)

Hickson Manro Ltd.

Bridge St., Stalybridge, Cheshire, SK15 1PH UK (Tel.: 44 161 338-5511; Telefax: 44 161-303-2991; Telex: 668442)

Hilton Davis Chemical Co., A Freedom Chemical Co.

2235 Langdon Farm Rd., Cincinnati, OH 45237 USA (Tel.: 513-841-4000; 800-477-1022; Telefax: 800-477-4565)

Hitox Corp. of America

PO Box 2544, Corpus Christi, TX 78403 USA (Tel.: 512-882-5175; Telefax: 512-882-6948)

Hoechst

Hoechst AG, Postfach 800320, D-65926 Frankfurt am Main Germany (Tel.: 49 69 305-5753; Telefax: 49 69 316700; Telex: 41234-0 HOD)

Hoechst Chemicals (UK) Ltd., Div. of Hoechst AG, Hoechst House, Salisbury Rd., Hounslow, Middlesex, TW4 6JH UK (Tel.: 44 181 570 7712; Telefax: 44 181-577 1854; Telex: 22284)

Hoechst Celanese/Int'l. Headqtrs., 26 Main St., Chatham, NJ 07928 USA (Tel.: 201-635-2600; 800-235-2637; Telefax: 201-635-4330; Telex: 136346)

Hoechst Celanese/Bulk Pharmaceuticals & Intermediates Div., 1601 West LBJ Freeway, PO Box 819005, Dallas, TX 75381-9005 USA (Tel.: 214-277-4783; Telefax: 214-277-3858)

Hoechst Celanese/Colorants & Surfactants Div., 5200 77 Center Dr., Charlotte, NC 28217 USA (Tel.: 704-599-4000; 800-255-6189; Telefax: 704-559-6323)

Hoechst Celanese/Fine Chemicals Div.. 5200 77 Center Dr., Charlotte, NC 28201-1026 USA (Tel.: 800-242-6222 x6183; Telefax: 704-559-6153)

Hoechst Canada Inc., Div. of Hoechst AG, 800 Blvd Rene Levesque O, Montreal, Quebec, PQH38121 Canada (Tel.: 514-871-5511)

Hoechst Japan Limited/Chemicals Dept., New Hoechst Bldg., 10-16, Akasaka 8-chome, Minato-ku, Tokyo, 107 Japan (Tel.: (03) 3479-5118; Telefax: (03) 3479-6715)

Hoechst-Roussel Pharmaceuticals Inc., Route 202-206 North, P.O. Box 2500, Somerville, NJ 08876-1258 USA (Tel.: 201-231-2000; 800-451-4455)

Hoffmann-La Roche

Hoffmann-La Roche Inc., 340 Kingsland St., Nutley, NJ 07110 USA (Tel.: 201-909-8332; 800-526-0189; Telefax: 201-909-8414)

Hoffmann-La Roche SA, Grenzacherstrasse 124, CH-4002 Basle Switzerland (Tel.: 41 61-688 1111; Telefax: 41 61 688 6590; Telex: 962292 HLR CH)

Holland Sweetener

Holland Sweetener Co. VoF, Joint venture between DSM and TOSOH Corp., PO Box 1201, 6201 BE Maastricht The Netherlands (Tel.: 31 43 21 2228; Telefax: 31 43 21 6633; Telex: 56384)

Holland Sweetener North America, Inc., 1100 Circle 75 Parkway, Suite 690, Atlanta, GA 30339-3097 USA (Tel.: 404-956-8443; 800-757-9648; Telefax: 404-956-7102)

Honeywill & Stein Ltd., Div. of BP Chemicals Ltd.

Times House, Throwley Way, Sutton, Surrey, SM1 4AF UK (Tel.: 44 181 770 7090; Telefax: 44 181-770 7295; Telex: 946560 BPCLGH G)

Honig Chemical and Processing Corp.

414 Wilson Ave., Newark, NJ 07105 USA (Tel.: 201-344-0881)

The Honjo Chemical Corp.

Shin-Osaka Daiichi Seimei Bldg., 3-5-24, Miyahara, Yodogawa-ku, Osaka, 532 Japan (Tel.: (06) 399-2331; Telefax: (06) 399-2345)

Hormel Foods Corp.

1 Hormel Place, Austin, MN 55912-3680 USA (Tel.: 507-437-5608; Telefax: 507-437-5120)

Hosoi Chemical Industry Co., Ltd.

3-16, Nihonbashi Muromachi 2-chome, Chuo-ku, Tokyo, 103 Japan (Tel.: (03) 3270-3601; Telefax: (03) 3279-5863)

J.M. Huber

J.M. Huber Corp./Chemicals Div., PO Box 310, 907 Revolution St., Havre de Grace, MD 21078 USA (Tel.: 410-939-3500; Telefax: 410-939-7313)

J.M. Huber Corp./Engineered Minerals, 4940 Peachtree Industrial Blvd., Suite 340, Norcross, GA 30071 USA (Tel.: 404-441-1301; Telefax: 404-368-9908)

Solem Europe, Subsid. of J.M. Huber, PO Box 3142, Planetwenweg 39, 2130 KC Hoofddorp The Netherlands (Tel.: 31(0) 2503-43052; Telefax: 31(0) 2503-43452)

Hüls

Hüls AG, Postfach 1320, D-4370 Marl 1 Germany (Tel.: 49 2365-49-1; Telefax: 49-2365-49-2000; Telex: 829211 HSD)

Hüls AG/Troisdorf Works, PO Box 1347, 5210 Troisdorf Germany (Tel.: 49 2241 85 4321; Telefax: 49 2241 85 4319)

Hüls (UK) Ltd., Featherstone Rd., Wolverton Mill South, Milton Keynes, Buckinghamshire, MK12 5TB UK (Tel.: 44 908 226 444; Telefax: 44 908 224950; Telex: 826500)

Hüls France SA, Div. of Hüls AG, 49-51 Quai de Dion Bouton, F-92815 Puteaux Cedex France (Tel.: 33 49 06 50 00; Telefax: 1 47 73 97 65; Telex: 611868 huels f)

Hüls Japan Ltd., Mita Kokusai Bldg., 4-28, Mita 1-cho, Minato-ku, Tokyo, 108 Japan (Tel.: (03) 3455 1981; Telefax: (03) 3453 3233; Telex: 2422288 huels jp j)

Hüls America Inc., PO Box 365, 80 Centennial Ave., Piscataway, NJ 08855-0456 USA (Tel.: 908-980-6800; 800-631-5275; Telefax: 908-980-6970; Telex: 4754585 Huls UI)

Hüls America Inc., Turner Place, PO Box 365, Piscataway, NJ 08855-0365 USA (Tel.: 908-981-5377; Telefax: 908-981-5497; Telex: 219875)

Hüls America Inc./Chemicals Div., Petrarch Systems, 80 Centennial Ave., PO Box 456, Piscataway, NJ 08855-0456 USA (Tel.: 908-980-6984; Telefax: 908-980-6970)

Hüls Canada, Inc., 235 Orenda Rd., Brampton, Ontario, L6T 1E6 Canada (Tel.: 416-451-3810; Telefax: 416-451-4469; Telex: 0697557)

Hüls de Mexico, S.A. de C.V., San Francisco 657 A, Desp. 8 B, Col. Del Valle, C.P. 03100 Mexico Mexico (Tel.: 011 (525) 523-4299; Telefax: 011(525)543-7257)

Humphrey Chemical Co Inc., A Cambrex Co.

45 Devine St., North Haven, CT 06473-0325 USA (Tel.: 203-230-4945; 800-652-3456; Telefax: 203-287-9197; Telex: 994487)

Hunt Chemicals Inc.

530 Permalume Pl. NW, Atlanta, GA 30318 USA (Tel.: 404-352-1418; Telefax: 404-352-0395)

Huntington Laboratories, Inc.

970 East Tipton St., Huntington, IN 46750 USA (Tel.: 219-356-8100; 800-537-5724; Telefax: 219-356-6485)

Huntsman Chemical Corp.

2000 Eagle Gate Tower, Salt Lake City, UT, 84111 USA (Tel.: 801-532-5200; 800-421-2411; Telefax: 801-536-1581)

N.I. Ibrahim Co.

8 Falaki St., Alexandria Egypt (Tel.: 20 3 4833923; Telex: 54317)

ICC Industries Inc.

720 Fifth Ave., New York, NY 10019 USA (Tel.: 212-903-1732; Telefax: 212-903-1726; Telex: CCI 7607944)

ICI

ICI plc, Imperial Chemical House, 9 Millbank, London, SW11 3JS UK (Tel.: 44 171 834 4444; Telefax: 44 171 834 2040; Telex: 21324)

ICI Surfactants Ltd. (UK), PO Box 90, Wilton, Middlesbrough, Cleveland, TS90 8JE UK (Tel.: 44 1642 454144; Telefax: 44 1642 437374; Telex: 587461)

ICI Americas, Inc., Subsidiary of ICI plc, PO Box 15391, Wilmington, DE 19850 USA (Tel.: 302-887-3000; 800-441-7780; Telefax: 302-887-4320; Telex: 62032112)

ICI Pharma, Wilmington, DE 19897 USA (Tel.: 302-886-2231)

ICI Polyurethanes Group, 286 Mantua Grove Rd., West Deptford, NJ 08066-1732 USA (Tel.: 609-423-8300; 800-257-5547; Telefax: 609-423-8580; Telex: 4945649)

ICI Specialty Chemicals, Concord Pike & New Murphy Rd., Wilmington, DE 19897 USA (Tel.: 302-886-3000; 800-822-8215; Telefax: 302-886-2972)

ICI Surfactants Americas, Concord Plaza, 3411 Silverside Rd., PO Box 15391, Wilmington, DE 19850 USA (Tel.: 302-886-3000; 800-822-8215; Telefax: 302-887-3525; Telex: 4945649)

ICI Atkemix Inc., Div. of ICI, PO Box 1085, 70 Market St., Brantford, Ontario, N3T 5T2 Canada (Tel.: 519-756-6181; Telefax: 519-758-8140)

ICI Australia Operations Pty. Ltd./ICI Surfactants Australia, ICI House, 1 Nicholson St., Melbourne, 300 Australia (Tel.: 3-665-7111; Telefax: 61-03-665-7009; Telex: 30192)

ICI Belgium SA, Div. of ICI plc, Everslaan 45, B-3078 Everberg Belgium (Tel.: 2-758 92 11; Telefax: 2-759 77 22; Telex: 21332 ICIEVB B)

ICI Surfactants, Everslaan 45, B-3078 Everberg Belgium (Tel.: 02-758-9361; Telefax: 02-758-9686; Telex: 26151 ICIEVB B)

ICI Deutsche GmbH, Postfach 500728, Emil-von-Behring-Strasse 2, W-6000 Frankfurt am Main Germany (Tel.: 49-69-5801-00; Telefax: 49-69-5801234; Telex: 416974 ICI D)

ICI Surfactants (Australia), Newscom St., Ascot Vale, Victoria, 3032 Australia (Tel.: (03) 2836411; Telefax: (03) 2725353)

ICI Surfactants Asia Pacific (ICI (China) Ltd.), PO Box 107, 1, Pacific Pl., 14th Floor, HK-88 Queensway Hong Kong (Tel.: 8434888; Telefax: 8685282; Telex: 73248)

IFF, International Flavours & Fragrances

International Flavours & Fragrances Ltd., Duddery Hill, Haverhill, Suffolk, CB9 8LG UK (Tel.: 44 1440 704488; Telefax: 44 1440 62199; Telex: 818881 IFFGB G)

International Flavors & Fragrances, 1515 Hwy 36, Union Beach, NJ 07735 USA (Tel.: 908-264-4500; Telefax: 908-888-2595; Telex: 275284)

IGI

85 Old Eagle School Rd., Wayne, PA 19087 USA (Tel.: 215-687-9030; 800-852-6537)

Igreca

Rue de Bourg de Paille, 49070 Beaucouze France (Tel.: 33 41 482312; Telefax: 33 41 483158; Telex: 720345)

Ikeda Corp.

New Tokyo Bldg., 3-1-Marunouchi, 3-Chome, Chiyoda-ku, Tokyo, 100 Japan (Tel.: 81 (03) 3212-8791; Telefax: 81 (03) 3215-5069; Telex: J26370)

Ikoma Fine Chemical Co., Ltd.

8-9-30, Ebie, Fukushima-ku, Osaka, 553 Japan (Tel.: (06) 451-2116/7; Telefax: (06) 454-8746)

IMC/Americhem

5129 Unruh Ave., Philadelphia, PA 19135-2990 USA (Tel.: 215-335-0990; 800-220-6800; Telefax: 215-624-3420; Telex: 244417)

IMC Fertilizer, Inc.

501 E. Lange St., Mundelein, IL 60060 USA (Tel.: 708-949-3700; 800-323-5523)

Importers Service Corp.

233 Suydam Ave., Jersey City, NJ 07304-3399 USA (Tel.: 201-332-6970; Telefax: 201-332-4152)

Indena Gruppo Inverni Della Beffa

Via Ripamonti, 99, 20141 Milano Italy (Tel.: (02) 574961; Telefax: (02) 57404620; Telex: 312535 Idebef I)

Indspec

Indspec Chemical Corp., 411 Seventh Ave., Suite 300, Pittsburgh, PA 15219 USA (Tel.: 412-765-1200; Telefax: 412-765-0439; Telex: 199187 Indspec)

Indspec Chemical Corp./European Sales, Gebouw de Goudsesingel, Kipstraat 8-10, 3011 RT Rotterdam The Netherlands (Tel.: 10-4-120-122; Telex: 21253 Indsp NL)

Induchem AG

Lagerstrasse 14, CH-8600 Dübendorf 1 Switzerland (Tel.: 1/820-11 61; Telefax: 1/820 21 13; Telex: 828-455)

Industrial Proteins Ltd.

405 Lordship Lane, London, SE22 8JN UK (Tel.: 44 181 693 9067; Telefax: 44 181 299 3977; Telex: 898181)

Industrias Quimicas del Valles SA

Avenida Rafael de Casanova 81, Mollet del Vallés, E-08100 Barcelona Spain (Tel.: 34-3-570 56 96; Telefax: 34-3-593 80 11; Telex: 52170)

Inolex Chemical Co.

Jackson & Swanson Sts., Philadelphia, PA 19148-3497 USA (Tel.: 215-271-0800; 800-521-9891; Telefax: 215-289-9065; Telex: 834617)

Integra Chemical Co.

710 Thomas Ave. SW, Renton, WA 98055 USA (Tel.: 206-277-9244; Telefax: 206-277-9246)

Integrated Ingredients

1420 Harbor Bay Pkwy., Suite 210, Alameda, CA 94501 USA (Tel.: 510-748-6362; Telefax: 510-748-6375)

International Flora Technologies, Inc./FloraTech Am.

2295 S. Coconino Dr., Apache Junction, AZ 85220 USA (Tel.: 602-983-7909; Telefax: 602-982-4183)

International Ingredients Co.

City South Business Park, Unit 14, 16-34 Dunning Ave., Rosebery, NSW, 2018 Australia (Tel.: 61 2 663 3999; Telefax: 61 2 633 3933)

International Sourcing Inc.

121 Pleasant Ave., Upper Saddle River, NJ 07458 USA (Tel.: 201-934-8900; 800-772-7672; Telefax: 201-934-8291; Telex: 697-2957 INSOURC)

Ishihara Sangyo Kaisha, Ltd.

3-15, Edobori 1-chome, Nishi-ku, Osaka, 550 Japan (Tel.: (06) 444-1451; Telefax: (06) 445-7798; Telex: 5622-774)

ISK Europe SA, Div. of Ishihara Sangyo Kaisha Ltd.

Tour ITT, 480 avenue Louise, B-1050 Brussels Belgium (Tel.: 32 2-646 34 90; Telefax: 32 2-648 34 72; Telex: 23362 ISK B)

ISP

ISP, International Specialty Products, World Headquarters, 1361 Alps Rd., Wayne, NJ 07470-3688 USA (Tel.: 201-628-4000; 800-522-4423; Telefax: 201-628-4117; Telex: 219264)

ISP (Canada) Inc., 1075 The Queensway East, Box 1740, Station B, Mississauga, Ontario, L4Y 4C1 Canada (Tel.: 905-277-0381; Telefax: 905-272-0552; Telex: 06961186)

ISP Europe, 40 Alan Turing Rd., Surrey Research Park, Guildford, Surrey, GU2 5YF UK (Tel.: 44 1483 301757; Telefax: 44 1483 302175; Telex: 859142)

ISP Global Technologies Deutschland GmbH, Rudolf-Diesel-Strasse 25, Postfach 1380, 5020 Frechen Germany (Tel.: 02234 105-0; Telefax: 02234 105-211; Telex: 889931)

ISP (Österreich) GmbH, Belvederegasse 18/1, A-1040 Wien Vienna Austria (Tel.: 43 1 504-76-21; Telefax: 43 1 505-89-44; Telex: 133990)

ISP (Australasia) Pty. Ltd., 73-75 Derby St., Silverwater, N.S.W., 2141 Australia (Tel.: Sydney (02) 648-5177; Telefax: (02) 647-1608; Telex: 73711)

ISP Asia Pacific Pte. Ltd., 200 Cantonment Rd., Hex 06-07 Southpoint, 0208 Singapore (Tel.: (65) 2249406; Telefax: (65) 2260853; Telex: 25071)

ISP (Japan) Ltd., Shinkawa Iwade Bldg. 8F, 26-9, Shinkawa 1-Chome, Chuo-Ku, Tokyo, 104 Japan (Tel.: (03) 3555-1571; Telefax: (03) 3555-1660; Telex: J23568)

ISP Van Dyk, Inc., Member of the ISP Group, Main & William Sts., Belleville, NJ 07109 USA (Tel.: 201-450-7722; Telefax: 201-751-2047; Telex: 710-995-4928)

Itochu Specialty Chemicals Inc.

350 Fifth Ave., Suite 5822, New York, NY 10118 USA (Tel.: 212-629-2660; Telex: 12297 C ITOH NYK)

Iwata Koryo. *See under* SCM

James River Corp.

Fourth & Adams St., Camas, WA 98607 USA (Tel.: 206-834-8134; Telefax: 206-834-8278; Telex: 152845)

Jan Dekker. *See under* Dekker

Janssen

Janssen Biotech N.V., Lammerdries 55, B-2250 Olen Belgium (Tel.: 014 22 40 15; Telefax: 014 23 15 33; Telex: 72404 janbio)

Janssen Chimica, Div. of Janssen Pharmaceutica, Janssen Pharmaceuticalaan 3, B-2440 Geel Belgium (Tel.: 14-60 42 00; Telefax: 14-60 42 20; Telex: 34103)

Janssen Chimica, Div. of Janssen Pharmaceutica, 755 Jersey Ave., New Brunswick, NJ 08901 USA (Tel.: 908-214-1300; 800-772-8786; Telefax: 908-220-6553; Telex: 182395 BIOSPECT)

Spectrum Chemical Mfg Corp, distributor, 14422 S. San Pedro St, Gardena, CA 90248 USA (Tel.: 310-516-8000; 800-772-8786; Telefax: 310-516-9843; Telex: 182395 BIOSPECT)

Jarchem Industries Inc.

414 Wilson Ave., Newark, NJ 07105 USA (Tel.: 201-344-0600; Telefax: 201-344-5743; Telex: 362-660)

Johnson-Matthey

Johnson Matthey plc, Orchard Rd, Royston, Hertfordshire, SG8 5HE UK (Tel.: 44 1763 253000; Telefax: 44 1763 253649)

Johnson Matthey SA, Div. of Johnson Matthey plc, BP 50240, 13 rue de la Perdrix, F-95956 Roissy CDG Cedex France (Tel.: 33 1 48 17 21 99; Telefax: 33 1 48 63 27 02; Telex: 230195 JMATT AF)

Johnson Matthey Inc., 2003 Nolte Dr., West Deptford, NJ 08066 USA (Tel.: 800-444-8544)

Jonas Chemical Corp./Specialty Chemical Div.

1682 59th St., Brooklyn, NY 11204 USA (Tel.: 718-236-1666; Telefax: 718-236-2248; Telex: 423616)

Jonk BV, Div. of Witco

Postbus 5, Wezelstraat 12, NL-1540 AA Koog a/d Zaan The Netherlands (Tel.: 31-75-283 854; Telefax: 731-5-210 811; Telex: 19270)

Jungbunzlauer

Jungbunzlauer International AG, St. Alban-Vorstadt 90, CH-4002 Basel Switzerland (Tel.: 41 61 295 51 00; Telefax: 41 61 295 51 08; Telex: 964963 jubu ch)

Jungbunzlauer Inc., 75 Wells Ave., Newton Centre, MA 02159-3214 USA (Tel.: 617-969-0900; 800-828-0062; Telefax: 617-964-2921)

Junsei Chemical Co., Ltd.

4-16, Nihonbashi Honcho 4-chome, Chuo-ku, Tokyo, 103 Japan (Tel.: (03) 3270-5414; Telefax: (03) 3270-5685)

Juzen Chemical Co., Ltd.

1-10, Kiba-machi, Toyama-shi, Toyama, 930 Japan (Tel.: (0764) 33-3111; Telefax: (0764) 32-1165)

Kalama Chemical, Inc.

1110 Bank of California Center, Seattle, WA 98164 USA (Tel.: 206-682-7890; 800-742-6147; Telefax: 206-682-1907; Telex: 910-444-2294)

Kanto Chemical Co., Inc.

2-8, Nihonbashi Hon-cho 3-chome, Chuo-ku, Tokyo, 103 Japan (Tel.: (03) 3279-1751; Telefax: (03) 3279-5560; Telex: 2223446 CICA J)

Kanto Denka Kogyo Co., Ltd.

New Tokyo Kaijo Bldg., 2-1, Marunouchi 1-chome, Chiyoda-ku, Tokyo, 100 Japan (Tel.: (03) 3216-4561; Telefax: (03) 3216-4581)

Kao Corp.

14-10, Nihonbashi, Kayabacho 1-chome, Chuo-ku, Tokyo, 103 Japan (Tel.: (03) 3660-7111; Telefax: (03) 3660-7965; Telex: KAOTYO A J24816)

Kao Corp. S.A.

Puig dels Tudons, 10, 08210 Barbera Del Valles, Barcelona Spain (Tel.: 3-729-0000; Telefax: 3-718-9829; Telex: 59749)

Kaopolite, Inc.

2444 Morris Ave., Union, NJ 07083 USA (Tel.: 908-789-0609; Telefax: 908-851-2974)

Katayama Chemical Industries Co., Ltd.

2-5-10, Dosho-machi, Chuo-ku, Osaka, 541 Japan (Tel.: (06) 203-3441)

Kato Worldwide Ltd.

One Bradford Rd., Mt. Vernon, NY 10553 USA (Tel.: 914-664-6200; Telefax: 914-664-0413)

Kawaguchi Chemical Industry Co., Ltd.

Yamada Bldg., 8-4, Uchikanda 2-chome, Chiyoda-ku, Tokyo, 101 Japan (Tel.: (03) 3254-8481; Telefax: (03) 3254-8497; Telex: Tokyo 222-3386)

Kelco

Kelco, A Unit of Monsanto Co., 8355 Aero Drive, PO Box 23576, San Diego, CA 92123-1718 USA (Tel.: 619-292-4900; 800-535-2656; Telefax: 619-467-6520; Telex: 695454)

Kelco Speciality Colloids, Ltd., 385 The West Mall, Suite 255, Etobicoke, Ontario, M9C 1E7 Canada (Tel.: 416-620-6770; Telefax: 416-622-4130)

Kelco International Ltd., Westminster Tower, 3 Albert Embankment, London, SE1 7RZ UK (Tel.: 44 171 735-0333; Telefax: 44 171-735-1363; Telex: 23815 KAILIL G)

Kelco International GmbH, Neuer Wall 63, D-20354 Hamburg 36 Germany (Tel.: 49 40 37 35 91; Telefax: 49 40 36 57 47)

Kelco International S.A., Les Mercuriales, 40 Rue Jean Jaures, 93176 Bagnolet Cedex France (Tel.: 33 1 49 72 28 00; Telefax: 33 1 43 62 80 38)

Kelco International Ltd., c/o MSD Japan Co., Ltd., Seventh Floor, Kowa Bldg. No. 16 Annex, 9-20 Akasaka 1-Chome, Minato-Ku, Tokyo, 107 Japan (Tel.: 81 33 586 2840; Telefax: 81 33 586 2889)

Kelco Speciality Colloids (S) Pte. Ltd., 16A Science Park Dr., #02-03 The Pascal, Singapore Science Park, Singapore 0511 (Tel.: 65 774-5200; Telefax: 65 774 5300)

Kelco International Ltd., 54-68 Ferndell St., South Granville, Sydney, NSW 2142 Australia (Tel.: 61 2 795-9777; Telefax: 61 2 795-9957)

Kelisema Srl

Via Urago 13/B, 22038 Tavernerio/Como Italy (Tel.: 031-427746; Telefax: 031-427745)

Kemira Kemi

Kemira Kemi AB, Div. of Kemira Oy, Box 902, Industrigatan 83, S-251 09 Helsingborg, Sweden (Tel.: 46-42-17 10 00; Telefax: 46-42-14 06 35; Telex: 72185 KEMWATS S)

Kemira Kemi (UK) Ltd., Div. of Kemira Oy, Orm House, 2 Hookstone Park, Harrogate, North Yorkshire, HG2 8QT UK (Tel.: 44 1423 885005; Telefax: 44 1423 885939; Telex: 57215 KEMFOS G)

Kenrich Petrochemicals, Inc.

140 E. 22nd St., PO Box 32, Bayonne, NJ 07002-0032 USA (Tel.: 201-823-9000; 800-LICA KPI; Telefax: 201-823-0691; Telex: 125023)

Kerr-McGee Chemical Corp.

Kerr-McGee Ctr., PO Box 25861, Oklahoma City, OK 73125 USA (Tel.: 405-270-1313; 800-654-3911; Telefax: 405-270-3123; Telex: 747-128)

Kerry Foods Ltd.

Kerry House, Hillingdon Hill, Uxbridge, Middlesex, UB10 0JH UK (Tel.: 44 181 842 1121; Telefax: 44 181 895 74119; Telex: 9413175)

Key Polymer Corp.

One Jacob's Way, Lawrence Ind. Park, Lawrence, MA 01842 USA (Tel.: 508-683-9411; Telefax: 508-686-7729; Telex: 940 103)

Kimitsu Chemical Industries Co., Ltd., Distrib. by Unipex

15-4 Uchikanda, 2-Chome, Chiyoda-ku, Tokyo, 101 Japan (Tel.: (03) 3252-8708; Telefax: (03) 3252-8704)

Kincaid Enterprises, Inc.

PO Box 549, Plant Rd., Nitro, WV 25143 USA (Tel.: 304-755-3377; Telefax: 304-755-4547; Telex: 3791803-KEINC)

Kingfood Australia Pty. Ltd.

73 Porters Rd., Kenthurst, NSW, 2156 Australia (Tel.: 61 2 654 2555; Telefax: 61 2 654 2587)

Kishida Chemical Co., Ltd.

1-6-9, Dosho-machi, Chuo-ku, Osaka, 541 Japan (Tel.: (06) 202-0451; Telefax: (06) 226-0670)

Kishimoto Sangyo Co., Ltd.

3-3-7, Fushimi-machi, Chuo-ku, Osaka, 541 Japan (Tel.: (06) 203-5651; Telefax: (06) 222-5218)

KMG Minerals, Inc.

PO Box 729, 1433 Grover Rd., Kings Mountain, NC 28086 USA (Tel.: 704-739-1321; 800-443-MICA; Telefax: 704-739-7888; Telex: 703063)

Knoll

Knoll AG, Div. of BASF AG, Postfach 210805, W-6700 Ludwigshafen Germany (Tel.: 49 621-5890; Telefax: 49 621-5892950; Telex: 464823)

Knoll AG, Div. of BASF AG, Oristalstrasse 65, CH-4410 Liestal Switzerland (Tel.: 41 061-925 0505; Telefax: 41 061-91 2563; Telex: 966000 KNL CH)

Koch Chemicals Ltd.

2 Marshgate Drive, Hertford, Hertfordshire, SG13 7JY UK (Tel.: 44 1992 553781; Telefax: 44 1992 586961; Telex: 817136 KOCHEM G)

Koei Chemical Co., Ltd., Subsid. of Sumitomo Chem. Co. Ltd.

Sumkia Fudosan Yokobori Bldg., 6-17, Koraibashi 4-chome, Chuo-ku, Osaka, 541 Japan (Tel.: (06) 204-1515; Telefax: (06) 204-1510; Telex: 522-7415 KOEI J)

V&E Kohnstamm Inc.

Bldg. #10-Bush Terminal, 882 Third Ave., Brooklyn, NY 11232 USA (Tel.: 718-788-6320; Telefax: 718-768-3978; Telex: 425707)

Konishi Co., Ltd.

6-10, Dosho-machi 1-chome, Chuo-ku, Osaka, 541 Japan (Tel.: (06) 228-2915; Telefax: (06) 228-2986; Telex: 5222219 KONISI J)

Konishi Chemical Ind. Co., Ltd.

3-4-77, Kazaika, Wakayama-shi, Wakayama, 641 Japan (Tel.: (0734) 25-0331; Telefax: (0734) 25-6116)

Koriyama Kasei Co., Ltd.

13-10, Nihonbashi Kobuna-cho, Chuo-ku, Tokyo, 103 Japan (Tel.: (03) 3249-3021; Telefax: (03) 3249-3023)

Koster Keunen, Inc.

1021 Echo Lake Rd., Watertown, CT 06795 USA (Tel.: 203-945-3333; Telefax: 203-945-0330)

Koster Keunen Holland BV

Postbus 53, 5530 AB Bladel The Netherlands (Tel.: 4977-2929; Telex: 51422 KOKEU NL)

Koyo Chemical Co., Ltd.

Iidabashi, Hitown-Bldg., 2-28, Shimomiyabi-cho, Shinjuku-ku, Tokyo, 162 Japan (Tel.: (03) 3268-1717; Telefax: (03) 3268-1723)

Kraeber GmbH & Co

Hochallee 80, W-2000 Hamburg 13 Germany (Tel.: 49-40-4450613; Telefax: 49-40-455163; Telex: 17403443)

Kraft Chemical Co.

61975 N. Hawthorne, Melrose Park, IL 60160 USA (Tel.: 708-345-5200; Telefax: 708-345-4005; Telex: 654268 KRAFT)

W. Kündig & Cie AG

Postfach 6784, Stampfenbachstrasse 38, CH-8023 Zurich 1 Switzerland (Tel.: 41 1 361 6144; Telefax: 41 1 362 8414; Telex: 815855 WKU CH)

Kuraray Co. Ltd.

Shin Hankyu Bldg., 1-12-39, Umeda, Kita-ku, Osaka, 530 Japan (Tel.: (06) 348-2111; Telefax: (06) 348-2189; Telex: 222-2272 Kurart J)

Kyowa

Kyowa Chemical Industry Co., Ltd., 305, Yashima-Nishimachi, Takamatsu-shi, Kagawa, 761-01 Japan (Tel.: 0877-47-2500; Telefax: 0877-47-4208; Telex: 5822220)

Kyowa America Corp., 385 Clinton, Costa Mesa, CA 92626 USA (Tel.: 714-641-0411; Telefax: 714-540-5849)

Laboratoires Sérobiologiques

Laboratoires Sérobiologiques S.A., 3, Rue de Seichamps, F-54420 Pulnoy France (Tel.: 83 29 08 02; Telefax: 83 29 18 04; Telex: LABSERO 961 008 F)

Laboratoires Sérobiologiques, Inc., 161 Chambers Brook Rd., Somerville, NJ 08876 USA (Tel.: 908-218-0330; Telefax: 908-218-0333; Telex: 709485 LABSEBIO)

Laevosan GmbH

Postfach 316, Estermannstrasse 17, A-4021 Linz Austria (Tel.: 43 732-7651; Telefax: 43 732-2782833; Telex: 21803 LAEV A)

Lake States, Div. of Rhinelander Paper Co. Inc.

515 W. Davenport St., Rhinelander, WI 54501 USA (Tel.: 715-369-4356; Telefax: 715-369-4141)

LaMonde Ltd.

500 S. Jefferson St., Placentia, CA 92670 USA (Tel.: 714-993-7700)

Henry Lamotte Import/Export

Auf dem Dreieck 3, 2800 Bremen Germany (Tel.: 49 421 547060; Telefax: 49 421 5470699; Telex: 244144)

Lanaetex Products, Inc.

151-157 Third Ave., PO Box 52 Station A, Elizabeth, NJ 07206 USA (Tel.: 908-351-9700; Telefax: 908-351-8753; Telex: 3792268 TLAP1)

Landers-Segal Color Co. Inc. (LANSCO)

90 Dayton Ave., Passaic, NJ 07055 USA (Tel.: 201-779-5001; Telefax: 201-779-8948; Telex: 6971185)

Land O'Lakes/Food Ingredients Div.

PO Box 116, Minneapolis, MN 55440 USA (Tel.: 612-481-2064)

Langley Smith & Co Ltd.

36 Spital Square, London, E1 6DY UK (Tel.: 44 171 247 7473; Telefax: 44 171-375 1470; Telex: 883013)

LaRoche Industries Inc.

1100 Johnson Ferry Rd. NE, Atlanta, GA 30342 USA (Tel.: 404-851-0300; Telefax: 404-851-0476)

Laserson SA

BP 57, Zone Industrielle, 91151 Etampes Cedex France (Tel.: 64 94 31 24; Telefax: 64 94 98 97; Telex: 601532 LASAROM)

Lenape Chemical

210 E. High St., Bound Brook, NJ 08805 USA (Tel.: 908-469-7310)

Lenzing AG

Abt. P84, A-4860 Lenzing Austria (Tel.: 43 7672-701-0; Telefax: 43 7672-74817; Telex: 26606 lenfa a)

Leverton-Clarke Ltd.

Unit 16, Sherrington Way, Lister Rd Industrial Estate, Basingstoke, Hampshire, RG22 4DQ UK (Tel.: 44 1256 810393; Telefax: 44 1256 479324; Telex: 858558 LEVCOS G)

Lipo Chemicals, Inc.

207 19th Ave., Paterson, NJ 07504 USA (Tel.: 201-345-8600; Telefax: 201-345-8365; Telex: 130117)

Liquid Air Corp.

2121 North California Blvd., Suite 350, Walnut Creek, CA 94596 USA (Tel.: 510-977-6500; Telefax: 510-746-6306; Telex: ITT 470020)

LNP Engineering Plastics Inc.

475 Creamery Way, Exton, PA 19341 USA (Tel.: 610-363-4500; 800-854-8774; Telefax: 610-363-4749; Telex: 4973041)

Lohmann Chemicals, Dr. Paul Lohmann GmbH KG

PO Box 1220, D-31857 Emmerthal Germany (Tel.: 49 5155 63-0; Telefax: 49 5155 63-118; Telex: 92858 lohma d)

Lonza

Lonza Ltd., Münchensteinerstrasse 38, Basle Switzerland (Tel.: 061-316 81 11; Telefax: 061-316 83 01; Telex: 965960 lon ch)

Lonza AG, A member of the A-L Alusuisse-Lonza Group, Münchensteinerstrasse 38, CH-4002 Basle Switzerland (Tel.: 61-316 8111; Telefax: 61-316 8733; Telex: 965960 lon ch)

Lonza SpA, Via Vittor Pisani, 31, I-20124 Milan Italy (Tel.: (02) 66 99 91; Telefax: (02) 66 98 76 30; Telex: 312431 ftalmi i)

Lonza (UK) Ltd., Imperial House, Lypiatt Road, Cheltenham, Gloucestershire, GL50 2QJ UK (Tel.: 44 1242 513211; Telefax: 44 1242 222294; Telex: 43152)

Lonza France SARL, Div. of Alusuisse, 55, rue Aristide Briand, F-92309 Levallois-Perret Cedex France (Tel.: 1/40 89 99 25; Telefax: 1/40 89 99 21; Telex: 613647)

Lonza Inc., 17-17 Route 208, Fair Lawn, NJ 07410 USA (Tel.: 201-794-2400; 800-777-1875 (tech.); Telefax: 201-703-2028; Telex: 4754539 LONZAF)

Lonza Japan Ltd., Kyowa Shinkawa Bldg., 8th Fl., 20-8, Shinkawa 2-chome, Chuo-ku, Tokyo, 104 Japan (Tel.: (03) 5566-0612; Telefax: (03) 5566-0619)

Lowenstein Dyes & Cosmetics Inc.

420 Morgan Ave., Brooklyn, NY 11222 USA (Tel.: 718-388-5410; Telefax: 718-387-3806)

LSI/Liquid Sugars, Div. of LSI Inc.

1285 66th St., PO Box 96, Oakland, CA 94604-0096 USA (Tel.: 510-420-7149; 800-227-1577; Telefax: 510-420-7103)

Lubrizol

Lubrizol Corp., 29400 Lakeland Blvd., Wickliffe, OH 44092 USA (Tel.: 216-943-4200; Telefax: 216-943-5337; Telex: 4332033)

Lubrizol France SA, 25 quai de France, F-76100 Rouen France (Tel.: 33-35 72 04 09; Telex: 180641 LUZOFRA F)

Lubrizol Japan Ltd., 3-5-1, Toranomon, Minato-ku, Tokyo, 105 Japan (Tel.: (03) 5041-4170; Telefax: (03) 5401-4178; Telex: 26814)

Lucas Meyer. *See under* Meyer

Lucta SA

Km 12, Carretera Masnou-Granollers, Montornés del Vallés, E-08170 Barcelona Spain (Tel.: 34 3-845 93 00; Telex: 52485 LUCTA E)

O.C. Lugo. *See under* Croda

D.N. Lukens Inc.

15 Old Flanders Rd., Westboro, MA 01581 USA (Tel.: 508-366-1300; 800-3-LUKENS; Telefax: 508-366-0771)

Luzenac

Luzenac America, Inc., 9000 E. Nichols Ave., Suite 200, Englewood, CO 80112 USA (Tel.: 303-643-0400; 800-325-0299; Telefax: 303-643-0444)

Luzenac, Inc., 1075 North Service Rd. W., Suite 14, Oakville, Ontario, L6M 2G2 Canada (Tel.: 416-825-3930; Telefax: 416-825-3932)

MacAndrews & Forbes Co. *See* Mafco Worldwide Corp.

MacFarlan Smith Ltd.

Wheatfield Road, Midlothian, Edinburgh, EH11 2QA, Scotland UK (Tel.: 44 131-337 2434; Telefax: 44 131-337 9813; Telex: 727271 MSEDI G)

Dr. Madis Laboratories Inc.

375 Huyler St., PO Box 2247, South Hackensack, NJ 07606 USA (Tel.: 201-440-5000; Telefax: 201-342-8000; Telex: 134-200)

Mafco Worldwide Corp.

3rd St. & Jefferson Ave., Camden, NJ 08104 USA (Tel.: 609-964-8840; Telefax: 609-964-6029; Telex: 845337)

Magie Bros. Oil, Div. Pennzoil Products Co.

9101 Fullerton Ave., Franklin Park, IL 60131 USA (Tel.: 708-455-4500; 800-MAGIE 47; Telefax: 708-455-0383)

Magnablend, Inc.

I-35E Sterrett Rd., Exit 406, Waxahachie, TX 75165 USA (Tel.: 214-223-2068; Telefax: 214-576-8721)

Magnesia GmbH

Postfach 2168, Kurt-Höbold-Strasse 6, W-2120 Lüneburg Germany (Tel.: 49-4131-52011-14; Telefax: 49-4131-53050; Telex: 2182159)

Mallinckrodt

Mallinckrodt, Inc./Drug and Fine Chemicals Div., Mallinkdrodt & 2nd Street, PO Box 5439, St Louis, MO 63147 USA (Tel.: 314-895-2000; 800-325-8888; Telefax: 314-539-1251)

Mallinckrodt Specialty Chemicals, 16305 Swingley Ridge Dr., Chesterfield, MO 63017 USA (Tel.: 314-895-2000; 800-325-7155; Telefax: 314-530-2562)

Mallinckrodt Specialty Chemicals Europe GmbH, Postfach 1268, Industriestrasse 19-21, W-6110 Dieburg Germany (Tel.: 49-6071-20040; Telefax: 49-6071-200444; Telex: 4191823 MCD D)

Malt Products Corp.

PO Box 739, Maywood, NJ 07607 USA (Tel.: 800-526-0180; Telefax: 201-845-0028)

Manac Incorporated

Fukuyama Chamber of Commerce & Industry Bldg., 10-1, Nishi-Machi 2-chome, Fukuyama-shi, Hiroshima, 720 Japan (Tel.: (0849) 26-0433; Telefax: (0849) 26-0441)

George Mann & Co., Inc.

PO Box 9066, Harborside Blvd., Providence, RI 02940-9066 USA (Tel.: 401-781-5600; Telefax: 401-941-0830)

Mantrose-Haeuser Co.

500 Post Road East, Westport, CT 06880 USA (Tel.: 203-454-1800; 800-344-4229; Telefax: 203-227-0558)

Marcel Trading Corp.

926 Araneta Ave., Quezon City, Philippines (Tel.: (632) 712-2631; Telefax: (632) 712-1989)

Mar-Gel Food Products Ltd.

Sudpre House, Worplesdon Rd., Guildford, Surrey, GU3 3RB UK (Tel.: 44 1483 233001; Telex: 859244)

Marine Colloids, Div. of FMC Corp.

1735 Market St., Philadelphia, PA 19103 USA (Tel.: 215-299-6199)

Marine Magnesium Co.

995 Beaver Grade Rd., Coraopolis, PA 15108 USA (Tel.: 412-264-0200; Telefax: 412-264-9020)

Mariovilla SpA

Casella Postale 70, I-28013 Gattico Italy (Tel.: 39 322-88001; Telefax: 39 322-880022; Telex: 223338 MAVILL I)

Martin Marietta Magnesia Specialties

PO Box 15470, Baltimore, MD 21220-0470 USA (Tel.: 410-780-5500; 800-648-7400; Telefax: 410-780-5777; Telex: 710-862-2630)

Maruzen Chemicals Co., Ltd.

4-7, Dosho-machi 2-chome, Chuo-ku, Osaka, 541 Japan (Tel.: (06) 206-5616; Telefax: (06) 206-5607; Telex: J63545)

Maruzen Fine Chemicals Inc., Div. of Maruzen Kasei Co Ltd.

525 Yale Ave, Pitman, NJ 08071 USA (Tel.: 609-589-4042; Telefax: 609-582-8894; Telex: 333812 MARFINE)

Mason Chemical Co

721 West Algonquin Rd., Arlington Heights, IL 60005 USA (Tel.: 708-290-1621; 800-362-1855; Telefax: 708-290-1625)

Matsutani Chem. Ind. Co., Ltd.

5-3, Kita-itami, Itami-shi, Hyogo, 664 Japan (Tel.: (0727) 71-2001; Telefax: (0727) 70-4680)

Maybrook Inc.

570 Broadway, PO Box 68, Lawrence, MA 01842 USA (Tel.: 508-682-1853; Telefax: 508-682-2544)

McIntyre Chemical Co., Ltd.

1000 Governors Hwy., University Park, IL 60466 USA (Tel.: 708-534-6200; Telefax: 708-534-6216)

MD Foods

Skanderborgvej 277, DK-8260 Viby J Denmark (Tel.: 45 86 281000; Telefax: 45 86 281838; Telex: 68799)

Mearl

Mearl Corp., PO Box 3030, 320 Old Briarcliff Rd., Briarcliff Manor, NY 10510 USA (Tel.: 914-923-8500; Telefax: 914-923-9594; Telex: 421841)

Mearl International BV, Emrikweg 18, 2031 BT Haarlem The Netherlands (Tel.: 31-23-318058; Telefax: 31-23-315365; Telex: 41492 MRLN)

Mearl Corp. Japan, Room No. 802, Mido-Suji Urban-Life Bldg., 4-3 Minami Semba 4-Chome Chuo-ku, Osaka, 542 Japan (Tel.: (06) 281-1560; Telefax: (06) 281 1291)

Meer Corp.

PO Box 9006, 9500 Railroad Ave., N. Bergen, NJ 07047-1206 USA (Tel.: 201-861-9500; Telefax: 201-861-9267; Telex: 219130)

Meggle GmbH

Postfach 40, Megglestrasse 6-12, W-8090 Wasserburg 2 Germany (Tel.: 49 8071-730; Telefax: 49 8071-73444; Telex: 525137)

MEI (Magnesium Elektron Inc.)

500 Point Breeze Rd., Flemington, NJ 08822 USA (Tel.: 908-782-5800; 800-366-9596; Telefax: 908-782-7768)

Melida SpA

Synthesis, Via Medici del Vascello 40, I-20138 Milano Italy (Tel.: 39 2 520 39339; Telefax: 39 2 520 39385; Telex: 310246 EN I)

Mendell

Edward Mendell Co., Inc., A Penwest Company, 2981 Rt. 22, Patterson, NY 12563-9970 USA (Tel.: 914-878-3414; 800-431-2457; Telefax: 914-878-3484; Telex: 4971034)

Mendell Company, Church House, 48 Church St., Reigate, Surrey, RH1 6YS UK (Tel.: 44-1737-222 323)

Mendell GmbH, Postfach 1207, 25430 Uetersen Germany (Tel.: 49 4122 92530)

Mendell Oy, Maitotie 4, 15560 Nastola Finland (Tel.: 358 18 6112290)

Mercian Corp.

5-8, Kyobashi 1-chome, Chuo-ku, Tokyo, 104 Japan (Tel.: (03) 3231-3917; Telefax: (03) 3276-0151; Telex: 2522761 SROKJ)

Merck

E. Merck, Postfach 4119, Frankfurter Strasse 250, D-6100 Darmstadt 1 Germany (Tel.: 06151-72-0; Telefax: 06151-72-2000; Telex: 419328-0 em d)

Merck Ltd., Div. of Merck AG, Merck House, Poole, Dorset, BH12 4NN UK (Tel.: 44 1202 669700; Telefax: 44 1202 665599; Telex: 41186 TETRA G)

Merck & Co Inc., PO Box 4, West Point, PA 19486-0004 USA (Tel.: 800-672-6372)

Merck & Co., Inc./Merck Chemical Div., PO Box 2000, Rahway, NJ 07065-0900 USA (Tel.: 908-594-4000; Telefax: 908-594-5431; Telex: 138825)

Merck Pty. Ltd., 207 Colchester Rd., Kilsyth, Victoria, 3137 Australia (Tel.: 61 3 728 5855; Telefax: 61 3 728 1351)

Merck Japan Ltd., Arco Tower, 8-1, Shimomeguro 1-chome, Meguro-ku, Tokyo, 153 Japan (Tel.: (03) 5434-4700; Telefax: (03) 5434-4705; Telex: MJTKO J 2226868)

Merichem Co.

4800 Texas Commerce Tower, Houston, TX 77002 USA (Tel.: 713-224-3030; 800-231-3030; Telefax: 713-224-4403)

Metallgesellschaft AG

Postfach 10 15 01, Reuterweg 14, D-6000 Frankfurt am Main 1 Germany (Tel.: 49-69-159-0; Telefax: 49-69-159-2125; Telex: 41225)

Metsä-Serla

Metsä-Serla Chemicals Oy, PO Box 500, 44101 Aänekoski Finland (Tel.: 358 45 518 311; Telefax: 358 45 518 3333; Telex: 228291 aanek fi)

Metsä-Serla Chemicals BV, PO Box 31, Winselingseweg 12, 6500 AA Nijmegen The Netherlands (Tel.: 31 24 377 2182; Telefax: 31 24 378 8160; Telex: 48071 metsa nl)

Metsä-Serla Chemicals Ltd., St. George House, Station Approach, Cheam, Surrey, SM2 7AT UK (Tel.: 44 181 642 9560; Telefax: 44 181 642 9560; Telex: 927842 fincem g)

Metsä-Serla Chemicals Inc., Suite 260, 3000 Corporate Center Dr., Morrow, GA 30260 USA (Tel.: 404-960-9967; Telefax: 404-960-1267)

Lucas Meyer

Lucas Meyer GmbH & Co., Postfach 261665, D-2000 Hamburg 26 Germany (Tel.: 49-40-789-550; Telefax: 49-40-789-8329; Telex: 2163220 MYER D)

Lucas Meyer (UK) Ltd., Unit 46, Deeside Ind. Park, First Ave., Deeside, Clwyd, CH5 2NU, Wales UK (Tel.: 44 1244 281168; Telefax: 44 1244 281169)

Lucas Meyer Inc., 765 E. Pythian Ave., Decatur, IL 62526 USA (Tel.: 217-875-3660; 800-769-3660; Telefax: 217-877-5046)

Meyhall Chemical AG

Sonnenwiesenstrasse 18, PO Box 862, CH-8280 Kreuzlingen Switzerland (Tel.: 41 72 747576; Telefax: 41 72 752181; Telex: 882222 MHAL CH)

M. Michel & Co., Inc.

90 Broad St., New York, NY 10004 USA (Tel.: 212-344-3878; Telefax: 212-344-3880; Telex: 421468)

Mid-America Food Sales Ltd.

3701 Commercial Ave., Suite 11B, Northbrook, IL 60062 USA (Tel.: 708-480-0720; Telefax: 708-480-9392)

Midori Kagaku Co. Ltd.

4F No. 10 Nohagi Bldg., 2-27-8 Minami-Ikebukuro, Toshima-ku, Tokyo, 171 Japan (Tel.: 81 (03) 3980 8808; Telefax: 81 (03) 3980 8805; Telex: 2324039)

Mikuni Pharmaceutical Industrial Co., Ltd.

2-35, Kamisu-cho, Toyonaka-shi, Osaka, 561 Japan (Tel.: (06) 333-5971; Telefax: (06) 333-3387)

Miljac Inc.

280 Elm St., New Canaan, CT 06840 USA (Tel.: 203-966-8777; Telefax: 203-966-3577)

Minerals Technologies, Inc., Specialty Minerals Subsid.

405 Lexington Ave., New York, NY 10174 USA (Tel.: 212-878-1919; Telefax: 212-878-1903)

Mirachem Srl

Via Guido Rossa 12, I-40111 Bologna Italy (Tel.: 39-51-73 71 11; Telefax: 39-51-73 64 40; Telex: 510011)

Mitsubishi Gas

Mitsubishi Gas Chemical Co., Inc., Mitsubishi Bldg., 2-5-2, Marunouchi, Chiyoda-ku, Tokyo, 100 Japan (Tel.: (03) 3283-5000; Telefax: (03) 3287-0844; Telex: 222-2624 MGCHO J)

Mitsubishi Gas Chemical Co., Inc., 520 Madison Ave., 9th Floor, New York, NY 10022 USA (Tel.: 212-752-4620; Telefax: 212-758-4012; Telex: 649545 MGC UR NYK)

Mitsubishi International Corp./Fine Chemicals Dept.

520 Madison Ave., New York, NY 10022-4223 USA (Tel.: 212-605-2193; 800-442-6266; Telefax: 212-605-1704)

Mitsubishi Kasei

Mitsubishi Kasei Corp., Mitsubishi Bldg., 5-2, Marunouchi 2-chome, Chiyoda-ku, Tokyo, 100 Japan (Tel.: (03) 3283-6254; Telex: BISICH J 24901)

Mitsubishi Kasei Foods Corp., Ichikawa Bldg., 13-3, Ginza 5-chome, Chuo-ku, Tokyo, 104 Japan (Tel.: (03) 3542-6525; Telefax: (03) 3545-4860; Telex: BISICHJ 24901 AH.MFC)

Mitsubishi Kasei Foods Corp., Jitsugyo Bldg., 1-3-9, Ginza, Chuo-ku, Tokyo, 104 Japan (Tel.: (03) 3563-1570; Telefax: (03) 3563-1513; Telex: BISICH J24901)

Mitsubishi Kasei America, Inc., 81 Main St., Suite 401, White Plains, NY 10601 USA (Tel.: 914-286-3600; Telefax: 914-681-0760; Telex: 233570 MCI UR)

Mitsubishi Materials Corp.

1-5-1, Ohte-machi, Chiyoda-ku, Tokyo, 100 Japan (Tel.: (03) 5252-5200; Telefax: (03) 5252-5270/1)

Mitsubishi Petrochemical Co., Ltd.

Mitsubishi Bldg., 5-2, Marunouchi 2-chome, Chiyoda-ku, Tokyo, 100 Japan (Tel.: (03) 3283-5700; Telefax: (03) 3283-5472; Telex: 222-3172)

Mitsui Mining & Smelting Co., Ltd.

Mitsui Bldg., 1-1, Nihonbashi Muro-machi 2-chome, Chuo-ku, Tokyo, 103 Japan (Tel.: (03) 3246-8080; Telefax: (03) 3246-8247; Telex: J28512 MITUIKIN)

Mitsui Petrochemical

Mitsui Petrochemical Industries, Ltd., Kasumigaseki Bldg., 2-5, Kasumigaseki 3-chome, Chiyoda-ku, Tokyo, 100 Japan (Tel.: (03) 3580-3616; Telefax: (03) 3593-0028; Telex: J22984 MIPECA)

Mitsui Petrochemicals (America) Ltd., 250 Park Ave., Suite 950, New York, NY 10017 USA (Tel.: 212-682-2366; Telefax: 212-490-6694; Telex: 7105814089)

Mitsui Toatsu

Mitsui Toatsu Chemicals, Inc., Kasumigaseki Bldg., 2-5, Kasumigaseki 3-chome, Chiyoda-ku, Tokyo, 100 Japan (Tel.: (03) 3592-4111; Telefax: (03) 3592-4267; Telex: 2223622 MTCHEM J)

Mitsui Toatsu Chemicals, Inc., NY Office, Two Grand Central Tower Bldg., 34th Fl., 140 E. 45 St., New York, NY 10017 USA (Tel.: 212-867-6330; Telefax: 212-867-6315; Telex: 127057 MTC NYK)

Mitsui Toatsu Chemicals, Inc., London Office, 13 Charles II St., London, SW1Y 4QU UK (Tel.: 44 171 976-1180; Telefax: 44 171-976-1185; Telex: 8953938 MITOL G)

MLG Enterprises Ltd.

PO Box 52568, Turtle Creek P.O., 1801 Lakeshore Road West, Mississauga, Ontario, L5J 4S6 Canada (Tel.: 905-569-3330; Telefax: 905-569-2133; Telex: 06982341)

Mobil Chemical Co

PO Box 3029, Edison, NJ 08818-3029 USA (Tel.: 908-321-6000)

Molycorp, Inc., A Unocal Co.

709 Westchester Ave., White Plains, NY 10604 USA (Tel.: 914-997-8880; Telefax: 914-997-8898)

Mona Industries Inc.

PO Box 425, 76 E. 24th St., Paterson, NJ 07544 USA (Tel.: 201-345-8220; 800-553-6662; Telefax: 201-345-3527; Telex: 130308)

Monomer-Polymer & Dajac Labs, Inc.

1675 Bustleton Pike, Feasterville, PA 19053 USA (Tel.: 215-364-1155; Telefax: 215-364-1583)

Monsanto

Monsanto Chemical Co., 800 N. Lindbergh Blvd., St. Louis, MO 63167 USA (Tel.: 314-694-1000; 800-325-4330; Telefax: 314-694-7625; Telex: 650 397 7820)

Monsanto Europe SA, Ave. de Tervuren 270-272, B-1150 Brussels Belgium (Tel.: 32-761-41-11; Telefax: 32-761-40-40; Telex: 62927 Mesab)

Monsanto Japan Ltd., 1-12-32, Akasaka, Minato-ku, Tokyo, 107 Japan (Tel.: (03) 5562-2600; Telefax: (03) 5562-2601; Telex: J22614)

Montedipe SpA

Via Rosellini 15-17, I-20124 Milan Italy (Tel.: 39 2-63331; Telefax: 39 2-63338943; Telex: 310679)

Moore Fine Foods Ltd.

Hainton House, Hainton Sq., Grimsby, South Humberside, DN32 9AQ UK (Tel.: 44 1472 240704; Telefax: 44 1472 250075; Telex: 56261)

Morflex

Morflex, Inc., 2110 High Point Rd., Greensboro, NC 27403 USA (Tel.: 910-292-1781; Telefax: 910-854-4058; Telex: 910240 7846)

Reilly Chemicals S.A., Rue Defacqz 115, Bte 19, B-1050 Bruxelles Belgium (Tel.: 32-2-537-1299; Telefax: 32-2 537 1208)

Morton International

Morton International Inc., 100 North Riverside Plaza, Chicago, IL 60606-1598 USA (Tel.: 312-807-2562; Telefax: 312-807-2899; Telex: 25-4433)

Morton International, Inc./Plastics Additives, 150 Andover St., Danvers, MA 01923 USA (Tel.: 508-774-3100; Telefax: 508-750-9511)

Morton International Ltd./Specialty Chem., Ind. Chem. & Addit., 7900-A Taschereau Blvd., Suite 106, Brossard, Quebec, J4X 1C2 Canada (Tel.: 514-466-7764; Telefax: 514-466-7771)

Morton International Ltd., Westward House, 155-157 Staines Rd., Hounslow, Middlesex, TW3 3JB UK (Tel.: 44 181 570 7766; Telefax: 44 181-570 6943; Telex: 262002)

Morton International SA, Chaussee de la Hulpe 130, Boite 5, B-1050 Brussels Belgium (Tel.: 32-2-790211; Telefax: 32-2-790250; Telex: 23708)

Morton Salt, 100 North Riverside Plaza, Chicago, IL 60606-1597 USA (Tel.: 312-807-2562; Telefax: 312-807-2228; Telex: 25-4433)

Mosselman NV

80 Boulevard Industriel, B-1070 Brussels Belgium (Tel.: 32-2-524 18 78; Telefax: 32-2-5200158; Telex: 23533 MOSS B)

MTM Research Chemicals, Inc.

PO Box 1000, Windham, NH 03087 USA (Tel.: 603-889-3306; 800-238-2324; Telefax: 603-889-3326)

MTM Speciality Chemicals Ltd., Div. of MTM plc

Station Rd, Cheddleton, Leek, Staffordshire, ST13 7EF UK (Tel.: 44 1538 361302; Telefax: 44 1538 361330; Telex: 367443)

Multi-Kem Corp.

553 Broad Ave., PO Box 538, Ridgefield, NJ 07657-0538 USA (Tel.: 201-941-4520; 800-462-4425; Telefax: 201-941-5239; Telex: 134 611 multikem)

Mykroy/Mycalex Ceramics

125 Clifton Blvd., Clifton, NJ 07011 USA (Tel.: 201-779-8866; Telefax: 201-779-2013)

Nagai Chemical Industrial Co., Ltd. (Nagai Seiyakusho K.K.)

3-27-15, Chikko-shinmachi, Sakai-shi, Osaka, 592 Japan (Tel.: (0722) 44-2321; Telefax: (0722) 44-2818)

Napp Technologies, Inc.

199 Main St., PO Box 900, Lodi, NJ 07644 USA (Tel.: 201-773-3900; Telefax: 201-773-2010; Telex: 13-4649)

National Casein Co.

601 W. 80 St., Chicago, IL 60620 USA (Tel.: 312-846-7300; Telefax: 312-487-5709; Telex: 910-221-2582)

National Chemical Co.

600 W. 52 St., Chicago, IL 60609 USA (Tel.: 312-924-3700; 800-525-3750; Telefax: 312-924-7760)

National Cottonseed Products Assn.

PO Box 172267, Memphis, TN 38187 USA (Tel.: 901-682-0880; Telefax: 901-682-2856)

National Starch & Chemical

National Starch & Chemical Corp., Box 6500, 10 Finderne Ave., Bridgewater, NJ 08807-3300 USA (Tel.: 908-685-5000; 800-726-0450; Telefax: 908-685-5005; Telex: 710-480-9240)

National Starch & Chemical Ltd., Prestbury Court, Greencourts Business Park, 333 Styal Rd., Manchester, M22 5LW UK (Tel.: 44 161 435 3200; Telefax: 44 161 435 3300)

National Starch & Chemical (Asia), 107 Neythal Rd., Jurong, S-2262 Singapore (Tel.: 65 2615528; Telefax: 65 264 1870; Telex: 55445)

Natrochem, Inc.

PO Box 1205, Exley Ave., Savannah, GA 31498 USA (Tel.: 912-236-4464; Telefax: 912-236-1919)

Nattermann Phospholipid. *See under* Rhone-Poulenc

Natural Oils International, Inc.

12350 Montague St., Unit C & D, Pacoima, CA 91331 USA (Tel.: 818-897-0536; Telefax: 818-896-4277; Telex: 371-0352)

Naturex

BP 152, F84147 Montfavet Cedex France (Tel.: 33 90 239689; Telefax: 33 90 239684)

Nepera, Inc., A Cambrex Co.

Route 17, Harriman, NY 10926 USA (Tel.: 914-782-1202; Telefax: 914-782-2418; Telex: 510-249-4847)

Neste Chemicals UK Ltd., Div. of Neste Oy

Neste House, Water Lane, Wilmslow, Cheshire, SK9 5AR UK (Tel.: 44 1625 537390; Telefax: 44 1625 535218; Telex: 668398)

New England Spice Co. Inc.

60 Clayton St., Drawer B, Dorchester, MA 01211 USA (Tel.: 617-825-7900)

New Japan Chemical Co., Ltd.

1-8, Bingo-machi 2-chome, Chuo-ku, Osaka, 541 Japan (Tel.: (06) 202-0621; Telefax: (06) 222-0062; Telex: 522-4703)

New Zealand Milk Prods., Inc.

3637 Westwind Blvd., Santa Rosa, CA 95403 USA (Tel.: 707-524-6600; 800-336-1269; Telefax: 707-524-6666)

Niacet Corp.

PO Box 258, 400 47th St., Niagara Falls, NY 14304 USA (Tel.: 716-285-1474; 800-828-1207; Telefax: 716-285-1497; Telex: 6730170)

Nichia Chemical Industries, Ltd. (Nichia Kagaku Kogyo K.K.)

PO Box 6, Anan, Tokushima, 774 Japan (Tel.: (0884) 22-2311; Telefax: (0884) 23-1802; Telex: 5867790 NICHIA J)

Nichirin Chemical Industries Ltd.

4-320, Senzo, Itami-shi, Hyogo, 664 Japan (Tel.: (0727) 81-0771; Telefax: (0727) 81-3596)

Nickerson Chemicals Ltd., Div. of Nickerson Investments Ltd.

Mill St East, Dewsbury, West Yorkshire, WF12 9BQ UK (Tel.: 44 1924 453886; Telefax: 44 1924 458995)

Nihon Emulsion Co., Ltd.

5-32-7, Koenji Minami, Suginami-ku, Tokyo, 166 Japan (Tel.: (03) 3314-3211; Telefax: (03) 3312-7207; Telex: 2322358 EMALEX J)

Nihon Kagaku Sangyo Co., Ltd.

20-5, Shitaya 2-chome, Taito-ku, Tokyo, 110 Japan (Tel.: (03) 3876-3131; Telefax: (03) 3876-3278; Telex: J 28318 NIKKASAN)

Nikko Chemicals Co., Ltd.

4-8, Nihonbashi, Bakuro-cho 1-chome, Chuo-ku, Tokyo, 103 Japan (Tel.: (03) 3662-0371; Telefax: (03) 3664-8620; Telex: 2522744 NIKKOL J)

Nipa Hardwicke Inc.

3411 Silverside Rd., 104 Hagley Bldg., Wilmington, DE 19810 USA (Tel.: 302-478-1522; Telefax: 302-478-4097; Telex: 905030)

Nipa Laboratories Ltd., Div. of BTP plc

Llanwit Fardre, Pontypridd, Mid Glamorgan, CF38 2SN, Wales UK (Tel.: 44 1443 205311; Telefax: 44 1443-207746; Telex: 497111)

Nippoh Chemicals Co., Ltd.

3-3-3, Nihonbashi Muro-machi, Chuo-ku, Tokyo, 103 Japan (Tel.: (03) 3270-5341; Telefax: (03) 3246-0346)

Nippon Aerosil Co., Ltd.

Aoyama Tower Bldg., 2-24-15, Minami-aoyama, Minato-ku, Tokyo, 107 Japan (Tel.: (03) 3402-5121; Telefax: (03) 3402-4289)

Nippon Carbide Industries Co., Inc.

New Tokyo Bldg., 3-1, Marunouchi 3-chome, Chiyoda-ku, Tokyo, 100 Japan (Tel.: (03) 3240-8600; Telefax: (03) 3287-2884; Telex: 222-2664 CARBID J)

Nippon Chemical Industrial Co., Ltd.

2-6-10, Iwamoto-cho, Chiyoda-ku, Tokyo, 101 Japan (Tel.: (03) 3862-4730; Telefax: (03) 3762-4705; Telex: 262-2161 JCIHOA)

Nippon Denko Co., Ltd.

11-8, Ginza 2-chome, Chuo-ku, Tokyo, 104 Japan (Tel.: (03) 3546-9331; Telefax: (03) 3542-3690; Telex: 2522209 NDKTOK J)

Nippon Fine Chemical Co., Ltd.

Nippon Seika Bldg., 4-9, Bingomachi 2-chome, Chuo-ku, Osaka, 541 Japan (Tel.: (06) 231-4781; Telefax: (06) 231-4787)

Nippon Kayaku Co., Ltd.

Tokyo Fujimi Bldg., 1-11-2, Fujimi, Chiyoda-ku, Tokyo, 102 Japan (Tel.: (03) 3237-5111; Telefax: (03) 3237-5091)

Nippon Nyukazai Co., Ltd., Subsid. of Sankyo Co., Ltd.

Yoshizawa Bldg., 9-19, Ginza 3-chome, Chuo-ku, Tokyo, 104 Japan (Tel.: (03) 3543-8571; Telefax: (03) 3546-3174)

Nippon Oils & Fats Co., Ltd. (NOF Corp.)

Yurakucho Bldg., 10-1, Yarakucho 1-chome Chiyoda-Ku, Tokyo, 100 Japan (Tel.: (03) 3283-7295; Telefax: (03) 3283-7178; Telex: 222-2041 NIPOIL J)

Nippon Petrochemicals Co., Ltd.

Saiwai Bldg., 3-1, Uchisaiwaicho 1-chome, Chiyoda-ku, Tokyo, 100 Japan (Tel.: (03) 3501-7313; Telefax: (03) 3501-7630; Telex: 2226966 NIPPEC J)

Nippon Rikagakuyakuhin Co., Ltd.

2-12, Nihonbashi-Honcho 4-chome, Chuo-ku, Tokyo, 103 Japan (Tel.: (03) 3241-3557; Telefax: (03) 3242-3345; Telex: 2223651 NITIRJ J)

Nippon Sanso Corp.

1-16-7, Nishi-shinbashi, Minato-ku, Tokyo, 105 Japan (Tel.: (03) 3581-8200; Telefax: (03) 3580-9425)

Nippon Shokubai Co., Ltd.

Kogin Bldg., 1-1, Koraibashi 4-chome, Chuo-ku, Osaka, 541 Japan (Tel.: (06) 223-9111; Telefax: (06) 201-3716; Telex: 522-5243 NSKKOJ)

Nippon Silica Industrial Co., Ltd.

Toso-Kyobashi Bldg., 2-4, Kyobashi 3-chome, Chuo-ku, Tokyo, 104 Japan (Tel.: (03) 3273-1641; Telefax: (03) 5255-6647)

Nippon Soda Co., Ltd.

Shin Ohtemachi Bldg., 2-1, Ohte-machi 2-chome, Chioyda-ku, Tokyo, 101 Japan (Tel.: (03) 3245-6054; Telefax: (03) 3242-2882)

Nippon Starch Chemical Co., Ltd.

2-2-7, Kawara-machi, Chuo-ku, Osaka, 541 Japan (Tel.: (06) 231-1326; Telefax: (06) 226-0325)

Nippon Synthetic Chemical Industry Co., Ltd.

Higashiumeda Bldg., 9-6, Nozaki-cho, Kita-ku, Osaka, 530 Japan (Tel.: (06) 314-1962; Telefax: (06) 312-5601)

Nippon Zeon Co., Ltd.

Furukawa Sogo Bldg., 2-6-1, Marunouchi, Chiyoda-ku, Tokyo, 100 Japan (Tel.: (03) 3216-2335; Telefax: (03) 3216-0501; Telex: 222-4001)

Nissan Chemical Industries, Ltd.

Kowa-Hitotsubashi Bldg., 3-7-1, Kanda-Nishiki-cho, Chiyoda-ku, Tokyo, 101 Japan (Tel.: (03) 3296-8111; Telefax: (03) 3296-8360; Telex: 222-3071)

Nisso Petrochemical Industries Co., Ltd., Joint venture of Nippon Soda Co., Ltd. and Teijin Ltd.

Seisho Nihonbashi Bldg., 12-2, Nihonbashi Ohdenma-cho, Chuo-ku, Tokyo, 103 Japan (Tel.: (03) 3664-1991; Telefax: (03) 3664-1990; Telex: 222-5337 J)

Nitta Gelatin Inc.

8-12, Honmachi 1-chome, Chuo-ku, Osaka, 541 Japan (Tel.: (06) 266-1911; Telefax: (06) 266-1900; Telex: 522-2882 NITTAO J)

Noah Chemical Div., Div. of Noah Technologies Corp

7001 Fairgrounds Pkwy, San Antonio, TX 78238 USA (Tel.: 512-680-9000; Telefax: 512-521-3323)

NOF Corp.

4-20-3, Ebisu, Sibuya-ku, Tokyo, 150 Japan (Tel.: (03) 5424-6600; Telefax: (03) 5424-6800; Telex: 222-2041 NIPOIL J)

Norac

Norac Co., Inc., 169 Kennedy Dr., Lodi, NJ 07644-0230 USA (Tel.: 201-779-4981)

Norac Co., Inc., PO Box 577, 405 S. Motor Ave., Azusa, CA 91702-0706 USA (Tel.: 818-334-2908; Telefax: 818-334-3512)

Norba (UK) Ltd.

Chiltern Lodge, Windsor Lane, Little Kingshill, Great Missenden, Buckinghamshire, HP16 0DL UK (Tel.: 44 10944-494 865004; Telefax: 44 10944-494 868734)

Nordmann Rassmann GmbH & Co.

Kajen 2, D2000 Hamburg 11 Germany (Tel.: 49 40 36 87307; Telefax: 49 40 36 87414; Telex: 212087)

Norit America

1050 Crown Pointe Pkwy., Suite 1500, Atlanta, GA 30338 USA (Tel.: 404-512-4610; 800-641-9245; Telefax: 404-512-4622)

Norman, Fox & Co.

5511 S. Boyle Ave., PO Box 58727, Vernon, CA 90058 USA (Tel.: 213-583-0016; 800-632-1777; Telefax: 213-583-9769)

Norsk Hydro AS

Bygdoyalle 2, N 0240 Oslo 2 Norway (Tel.: 472 243 2100; Telefax: 472 243 2725; Telex: 78350 HYDRO N)

North Western Bakers Ltd.

74 Roman Way Ind. Estate, Longridge Rd., Preston, Lancashire, PR2 5BE UK (Tel.: 44 1772 651616; Telefax: 44 1772 655003)

Norton Chemical Process Products

PO Box 350, Akron, OH 44309 USA (Tel.: 216-677-7216; Telefax: 216-677-7245; Telex: 433-8012)

Novarina Srl

Via Pinerolo 35, I-10060 Bibiana Italy (Tel.: 39 121-55724; Telex: 211591 NOVAR I)

Novo Nordisk A/S, Bioindustrial Group

Novo Allé, DK-2880 Bagsvaerd Denmark (Tel.: 45 4444-8888; Telefax: 45 4444-5918; Telex: 37173)

NutraSweet AG

Innere Guterstrasse 2-4, 6304 Zug Switzerland (Tel.: 41 42 226622; Telefax: 41 42 214246; Telex: 862339)

Nu-World Amaranth Inc.

PO Box 2202, Naperville, IL 60567 USA (Tel.: 708-369-6819; Telefax: 708-369-6851)

Nyco Minerals, Inc., A Canadian Pacific Ltd. Co.

124 Mountain View Dr., Willsboro, NY 12996-0368 USA (Tel.: 518-963-4262; Telefax: 518-963-4187; Telex: 957014)

Obron Atlantic Corp.

830 E. Erie St., Painesville, OH 44077 USA (Tel.: 216-354-0600; 800-556-1111; Telefax: 216-354-6224; Telex: 428904 Powders)

Occidental Chemical Corp.

5005 LBJ Freeway, Dallas, TX 75244 USA (Tel.: 214-404-3800; 800-752-5151; Telefax: 214-404-3669; Telex: 229835)

Ogawa & Co. Ltd., AVRI Companies Inc.

1080 Essex Ave., Richmond, CA 94801 USA (Tel.: 510-233-0633; Telefax: 510-233-0636)

O'Laughlin Industries Co. Ltd.

20th Floor, Jubilee Centre, 18 Fenwick St., Wanchai Hong Kong (Tel.: 852 527 1031; Telefax: 852 529 0231; Telex: 76724)

Olin Corp.

120 Long Ridge Rd., PO Box 1355, Stamford, CT 06904 USA (Tel.: 203-271-3036; 800-243-9171; Telefax: 203-271-4060; Telex: 420202)

The Ore & Chem. Corp.

520 Madison Ave., New York, NY 10022 USA (Tel.: 212-715-5232; Telefax: 212-486-2742; Telex: ITT 422681)

Original Bradford Soap Works Inc.

PO Box 1007, West Warwick, RI 02893 USA (Tel.: 401-821-2141; Telefax: 401-821-5960; Telex: 952 240)

Osaka Organic Chemical Ind. Co., Ltd.

Shin Toyama Bldg., 1-7-20, Azuchi-machi, Chuo-ku, Osaka, 541 Japan (Tel.: (06) 264-5071; Telefax: (06) 264-1675)

Osaki Industry Co., Ltd.

89, Kami, Sakai-shi, Osaka, 593 Japan (Tel.: (0722) 72-1453; Telefax: (0722) 74-6980)

Osi Specialties

OSi Specialties, Inc., 39 Old Ridgebury Rd., Danbury, CT 06810-5121 USA (Tel.: 203-794-4300; 800-523-2862)

OSi Specialties, Inc./Customer Service Center, PO Box 38002, S. Charleston, WV 25303-3802 USA (Tel.: 800-523-5862; Telefax: 304-747-3397)

OSi Specialties Canada, Inc., 1210 Sheppard Ave. East, Suite 210, Box 38, Willowdale, Ontario, M2K 1E3 Canada (Tel.: 416-490-0466)

OSi Specialties do Brasil Ltda., Rua Dr. Eduardo De Souza, Aranha 153, Sao Paulo, 04530 Brazil (Tel.: 55-11-828-1104)

OSi Specialties S.A., 7 Rue de Pre-Bouvier, Meyrin, CH-1217 Geneva Switzerland (Tel.: 41-22-989-2111)

OSi Specialties Singapore PTE, Ltd., 22-01 Treasury Bldg., 8 Shenton Way, 0106 Singapore (Tel.: 65-322-9922)

Osram Sylvania Inc.

100 Endicott St., Danvers, MA 01923 USA (Tel.: 508-777-1900)

Otsuka Chemical Co., Ltd.

2-27, Ote-dori 3-chome, Chuo-ku, Osaka, 540 Japan (Tel.: (06) 946-6231; Telefax: (06) 946-0860; Telex: J63586 JPOTSUKA)

Ouchi Shinko Chemical Industrial Co., Ltd.

7-4, Nihonbashi Kobune-cho, Chuo-ku, Tokyo, 103 Japan (Tel.: (03) 3662-6451; Telefax: (03) 3661-1762; Telex: 2522671 NOUCHI J)

Outokumpu Oy

PO Box 280, SF-02101 Espoo Finland (Tel.: 358-4211; Telefax: 358-4213888; Telex: 124441 OKHI SF)

Oxiteno S/A Industria E Comercio

Av. Brigedeiro Luiz Antonio 1343, 7 andar, Sao Paulo SP, 01350-900 Brazil (Tel.: (55-11)283 6118; Telefax: (55-11)2893533; Telex: (55-11) TLX 31727)

OxyChem. *See* Occidental

Pacific Foods Inc.

21612 88th Ave. S., Kent, WA 98031 USA (Tel.: 206-395-9400; Telefax 206-395-3330)

Particle Dynamics Inc.

2503 S. Hanley Rd., St. Louis, MO 63144 USA (Tel.: 314-968-2376; 800-452-4682; Telefax: 314-968-5208; Telex: 434182)

Pasminco Europe Ltd./ISC Alloys Div., Div. of Pasminco Ltd.

Alloys House, PO Box 36, Willenhall Lane, Bloxwich, Walsall, West Midlands, WS3 2XW UK (Tel.: 44 1922 408444; Telefax: 44 1922-710043; Telex: 338270)

Passaic Color & Chemical Co.

28-36 Paterson St., Paterson, NJ 07501 USA (Tel.: 201-279-0400; Telefax: 201-279-8561; Telex: 820907 PASDYE UD)

PCR, Inc.

PO Box 1466, Gainesville, FL 32602 USA (Tel.: 904-376-8246; 800-331-6313; Telefax: 904-371-6246)

Pelron Corp.

7847 W. 47 St., Lyons, IL 60534 USA (Tel.: 708-442-9100; Telefax: 708-442-0213)

Penreco, Div. of Pennzoil Prods. Co.

138 Petrolia St., Box 1, Karns City, PA 16041 USA (Tel.: 412-756-0110; 800-245-3952; Telefax: 412-756-1050; Telex: 1561596)

Penta Manufacturing Co.

50 Okner Parkway, Livingston, NJ 07039 USA (Tel.: 201-740-2300; Telefax: 201-740-1839; Telex: 219472 PENT UR)

Pentagon Chemicals Ltd.

Northside, Workington, Cumbria, CA14 1JJ UK (Tel.: 44 1900 604371; Telefax: 44 1900 66943; Telex: 64353 PENTA G)

Penwest Foods Co.

11011 E. Peakview Ave., Englewood, CO 80111-6800 USA (Tel.: 303-649-1900; Telefax: 303-649-1700)

Peter Whiting (Ingredients). *See* Whiting, Peter (Chemicals) Ltd.

Pfaltz & Bauer. *See under* Aceto

Pfanstiehl Laboratories, Inc.

1219 Glen Rock Ave., PO Box 439, Waukegan, IL 60085 USA (Tel.: 708-623-0370; 800-383-0126; Telefax: 708-623-9173; Telex: 25 3672 PFANLAB)

Pfister Chem, Inc.

Linden Ave, Ridgefield, NJ 07657 USA (Tel.: 201-945-5400 x 208; Telefax: 201-945-0159; Telex: 130295)

Pfizer

Pfizer International, 235 East 42nd Street, New York, NY 10017 USA (Tel.: 212-573-2323)

Pfizer Food Science Group, 235 E. 42nd St., New York, NY 10017 USA (Tel.: 212-573-2323/2548; 800-TECK-SRV; Telefax: 212-573-1166)

C.A.L.-Pfizer/Flavor & Fragrance Prod. Group, 230 Brighton Rd., Clifton, NJ 07012 USA (Tel.: 201-470-7892; 800-245-4495; Telefax: 201-470-7895)

Pfizer Canada, PO Box 800, Point Claire/Dorval, Montreal, Quebec, H9R 4V2 Canada (Tel.: 514-695-0500)

Pfizer Europe/Africa/Middle East, 10 Dover Rd., Sandwich, Kent, CT13 0BN UK (Tel.: 44 1304 615518; Telefax: 44 1304 615529; Telex: 966555)

Pfizer SA, Principe de Vergara 109, E-28002 Madrid Spain (Tel.: 1-262 11 00; Telex: 42732 PRIZ E)

C.A.L. Pfizer, 27, Ave. Saint-Lorette, 06130 Grasse France (Tel.: 33 93 36 08 69; Telefax: 33 93 36 81 73)

Pfizer Asia/Australia, PO Box 57, West Ryde, NSW, 2114 Australia (Tel.: 61-2-858-9500)

Pfizer K.K., 3-22 Toranomon 2-chome, Minato-ku, Tokyo, 105 Japan (Tel.: (03) 3503-0441; Telefax: (03) 3503-0447)

Pharmacia Biotech AB

Rapsagatan 7, S-751 82 Uppsala, Sweden (Tel.: 46 18-165 109; Telefax: 46 18 101 403; Telex: 76027 PHARMUP S)

Phibrochem, Div. of Philipp Bros Chemicals Inc.

One Parker Plaza, Fort Lee, NJ 07090 USA (Tel.: 201-944-6020; 800-223-0434; Telefax: 201-944-6245)

Phillips Chemical Co., Div. of Phillips Petroleum Co

PO Box 968, Borger, TX 79008 USA (Tel.: 806-274-5236; 800-858-4327; Telefax: 806-274-5230)

Phoenix Chemical, Inc.

322 Courtyard Dr., Somerville, NJ 08876 USA (Tel.: 908-707-0232; Telefax: 908-707-0186)

Phytone Ltd.

Unit 2B, Boardman Ind. Estate, Hearthcote Rd., Swadlincote, Derbyshire, DE11 9DL UK (Tel.: 44 1283 550338; Telefax: 44 1283 550714)

J.W. Pike Ltd.

Unit 4 Eley Rd., Eley Estate, Edmonton, London, N18 3BH UK (Tel.: 44 181 807 9924; Telefax: 44 181 803 9972)

AJ & JO Pilar, Inc.

145 Chapel St., Newark, NJ 07105-4198 USA (Tel.: 201-589-3808; Telefax: 201-589-0836)

Pilot Chemical Co.

11756 Burke St., Santa Fe Springs, CA 90670 USA (Tel.: 213-723-0036; Telefax: 213-945-1877; Telex: 4991200 PILOT)

Plastics & Chemicals, Inc.

PO Box 306, Cedar Grove, NJ 07009 USA (Tel.: 908-221-0002; Telefax: 908-221-1097; Telex: 219744)

PMC

PMC Specialties Group, Inc., Div. of PMC, Inc., 20525 Center Ridge Road, Rocky River, OH 44116 USA (Tel.: 216-356-0700; 800-543-2466; Telefax: 216-356-2787; Telex: 4332035)

PMC Specialties Group, Inc., Div. of PMC, Inc., 501 Murray Rd., Cincinnati, OH 45217 USA (Tel.: 513-242-3300; 800-543-2466; Telefax: 513-482-7353; Telex: 5106000948)

PMC Specialities International Ltd., Div. of PMC Specialities Group, 65B Wigmore Street, London, W1H 9LG UK (Tel.: 44 171 935-4058; Telefax: 44 171-935 9895; Telex: 24358 PMCS G)

PMP Fermentation Products, Inc.

Columbia Center III, 9525 W. Bryn Mawr Ave., Suite 725, Rosemont, IL 60018 USA (Tel.: 708-928-0050; 800-558-1031; Telefax 708-928-0065)

Pointing Ltd.

Princess Way, Prudhoe, Northumberland, NE42 6NJ UK (Tel.: 44 1661 832621; Telefax: 44 1661-835650; Telex: 537036 POINTX G)

Polarome Mfg. Co. Inc.

200 Theodore Conrad Dr., Jersey City, NJ 07305 USA (Tel.: 201-309-4500; Telefax: 201-433-0638; Telex: RCA 233 176)

Poly Research Corp.

125 Corporate Dr., Holtsville, NY 11742 USA (Tel.: 516-758-0460; Telefax: 516-758-0471)

Polysat Inc.

7240 State Rd., Philadelphia, PA 19135 USA (Tel.: 215-332-7700; 800-858-2828; Telefax: 215-332-9997; Telex: 831869)

Polysciences

Polysciences Inc., 400 Valley Road, Warrington, PA 18976-2590 USA (Tel.: 215-343-6484; 800-523-2575; Telefax: 800-343-3291; Telex: 510-665-8542)

Polysciences, Europe GmbH, Postfach 1130, D-69208 Eppelheim Germany (Tel.: (49) 6221-765767; Telefax: (49) 6221-764620)

Polyurethane Corp. of America

PO Box 8, Everett, MA 02149 USA (Tel.: 617-389-7889)

Polyurethane Specialties Co. Inc.

624 Schuyler Ave., Lyndhurst, NJ 07071 USA (Tel.: 201-438-2325; Telefax: 201-507-1367)

Pomosin GmbH. *See under* Copenhagen Pectin

PPG

PPG Industries, Inc., One PPG Place, Pittsburgh, PA 15272 USA (Tel.: 412-434-3131; 800-CHEM-PPG; Telefax: 412-434-2891; Telex: 86 6570)

PPG Industries, Inc./Chemicals Group, One PPG Place, 34 North, Pittsburgh, PA 15272 USA (Tel.: 412-434-3131; Telefax: 412-434-2891)

PPG Industries, Inc./Specialty Chemicals, 3938 Porett Dr., Gurnee, IL 60031 USA (Tel.: 708-244-3410; 800-323-0856; Telefax: 708-244-9633; Telex: 25-3310)

PPG Canada Inc./Specialty Chem., 2 Robert Speck Pkwy., Suite 900, Mississauga, Ontario, L4Z 1H8 Canada (Tel.: 905-848-2500; Telefax: 905-848-2185; Telex: 38906960351canbizmis)

PPG Industrial do Brazil Ltda., Edificio Grande Avenida, Paulista Ave. 1754, Suite 153, 01310 Sao Paulo Brazil (Tel.: 55-011-284-0433; Telefax: 55-011-289-2105; Telex: 011-39104 PPGB BR)

PPG-Mazer Mexico, S.A. de C.V., Av. Presidente Juarex No. 1978, Tlalnepantla, Edo., C.P. 54090 Mexico (Tel.: 52-5-397-8222; Telefax: 52-5-398-5133)

PPG Industries (UK) Ltd./Specialty Chem., Carrington Business Park, Carrington, Urmston, Manchester, M31 4DD UK (Tel.: 44 161 777-9203; Telefax: 44 161-777-9064; Telex: 851-94014896 mazu g)

PPG Industries (France) SA, BP 377, Écluse Folien, F-59307 Valenciennes France (Tel.: 33-27 14 46 00; Telefax: 33-27 29 36 34)

PPG Ouvrie S.A., 64, rue Faldherbe, B.P. 127, 59811 Lesquin Cedex France (Tel.: 33-2087-0510; Telefax: 33-2087-5631; Telex: 131419 F)

PPG Industries Taiwan, Ltd., Suite 601, Worldwide House, No. 131, Ming East Rd., Sec. 3, Taipei, 105, Taiwan, R.O.C. (Tel.: 886-2-514-8052; Telefax: 886-2-514-7957; Telex: 10985 PPGTWN)

PQ Corp.

PO Box 840, Valley Forge, PA 19482 USA (Tel.: 610-651-4200; 800-944-7411; Telefax: 610-251-9118; Telex: 476 1129 PQCO VAF)

Premier Services Corp.

7251 Engle Rd., Suite 415, Middleburg Hts., OH 44130 USA (Tel.: 216-234-4600; 800-227-4287; Telefax: 216-234-5772)

J.L. Priestley & Co. Ltd.

Station Rd., Heckington, Sleaford, Lincolnshire, NG34 9NF UK (Tel.: 44 1529 60751; Telefax: 44 1529 60630; Telex: 377189)

Primachem Inc.

12 Greenwoods Rd., Old Tappan, NJ 07675 USA (Tel.: 201-784-3434; Telefax: 201-784-7997; Telex: 175094 PRIMA)

Procter & Gamble

Procter & Gamble Co/Chemicals Div., PO Box 599, Cincinnati, OH 45201 USA (Tel.: 513-983-2026; 800-543-1580; Telefax: 513-983-1436; Telex: 21-4185, P&GCIN)

Procter & Gamble Inc. Canada, 4711 Yonge St., PO Box 355, Station A, Toronto, Ontario, M5W 1C5 Canada (Tel.: 416-730-4064; Telefax: 416-730-4122)

Procter & Gamble Ltd./Europe Div., PO Box 9, 27 Uxbridge Rd., Hayes, Middlesex, UB4 0JD UK (Tel.: 44 181 242 2300; Telefax: 44 181 561 5287; Telex: 936310)

Produits Roche

52 boulevard du Parc, F92521 Neuilly sur Seine Cedex France (Tel.: 33 46 405000; Telefax: 33 46 405282; Telex: 610788 PROROCHE)

Pronova

Pronova Biopolymer A/S, Tomtegt. 36, Postboks 494, N-3002 Drammen Norway (Tel.: 47-32-83 73 00; Telefax: 47-32-83 34 88; Telex: 76594 prota n)

Pronova Biopolymer Ltd., PO Box 8, Alton, Hampshire, GU34 1YL UK (Tel.: 44 1420 82503; Telefax: 44 1420 83360)

Pronova Biopolymer GmbH, Gutenbergring 1-5, 22848 Norderstedt Germany (Tel.: (040) 523 5098; Telefax: (040) 523 1420; Telex: 213619 pronb d)

Pronova Biopolymer, Inc., 135 Commerce Way, Suite 201, Portsmouth, NH 03801 USA (Tel.: 603-433-1231; 800-223-9030; Telefax: 603-433-1348)

Pronova Biopolymer Asia Ltd., Unit 1401-02 14/F Shun Kwong, Commercial Bldg., 8 Des Voeux Rd. W. Hong Kong (Tel.: 852-517 3028; Telefax: 852 517 3198)

Protameen Chemicals, Inc.

375 Minnisink Rd., PO Box 166, Totowa, NJ 07511 USA (Tel.: 201-256-4374; Telefax: 201-256-6764; Telex: 130125)

Protein Technologies

Protein Technologies International, One Checkerboard Square, St. Louis, MO 63164 USA (Tel.: 314-982-1983; 800-325-7108; Telefax: 314-982-5057)

Protein Technologies International/Polymer Prods. Group, 14T, One Checkerboard Square, St. Louis, MO 63164 USA (Tel.: 314-982-3831; 800-325-7137; Telefax: 314-982-1190; Telex: 44 7240 KAL PRO STL)

Protein Technologies International, Subsid. of Ralston Purina Co., Excelsiorlaan 13, B-1930 Zaventem Belgium (Tel.: 32 2 720 9544; Telefax: 32 2 720 6755; Telex: 64388)

Protex SA

B.P. 177, 6 rue Barbès, 92305 Levallois-Paris France (Tel.: 33 1-47-57-74-00; Telefax: 33 1-47-57-1271; Telex: 620987)

Prova SA

46 rue Colmet Lepinay, 931000 Montreuil France (Tel.: 33 1 42 873676; Telefax: 33 1 42 871013; Telex: 212513)

Provesta Corp.

15 Phillips Bldg., Bartlesville, OK 74004 USA (Tel.: 918-661-5281; Telefax: 918-662-2208)

Provital

Centro Industrial Santiaga, Talleres 6, no. 15, Apartado Correos 78, Barcelona Spain (Tel.: 93-718-80-12; Telefax: 93-718-38-30; Telex: 98476 DITT E)

Pulcra S.A. *See under* Henkel

Punda Mercantile Inc.

310 Victoria Ave., Montreal, Quebec, H3Z 2M9 Canada (Tel.: 514-489-7278)

Purac

Purac Biochem, Postbus 21, Arkelsedijk 46, NL-4200 AA Gorinchem The Netherlands (Tel.: 1830-41799; Telefax: 1830-22741; Telex: 23615 CCA NL)

Purac Biochem (UK), 50-54 St. Paul's Square, Birmingham, West Midlands, B3 1QS UK (Tel.: 44 121 236 1828; Telefax: 44 121 236 1401)

Purac America, Inc., 111 Barclay Blvd., Suite 280, Lincolnshire Corporate Center, Lincolnshire, IL 60069 USA (Tel.: 708-634-6330; Telefax: 708-634-1992; Telex: 280231 PURACINC ARHT)

Purac Far East PTE Ltd., 09-02 Cecil Court, 138 Cecil St., S-0106 Singapore (Tel.: 65 220 6022; Telefax: 65 222 1707; Telex: 23463)

Pure Malt Products Ltd.

Victoria Bridge, Haddington, East Lothian, EH41 4BD, Scotland UK (Tel.: 44 162 082 4696; Telefax: 44 162 082 2018; Telex: 728158)

Pyrion-Chemie

Pyrion-Chemie GmbH, Geulenstr. 94, Neuss Germany (Tel.: 49-2101-591025; Telefax: 49-2101-593624; Telex: 8517459)

Pyrion-Chemie GmbH, Represented in U.S. by Ruetgers-Nease Corp., 201 Struble Rd., State College, PA 16801 USA (Tel.: 814-231-9261; 800-458-3434; Telefax: 814-238-4235)

QO Chemicals

QO Chemicals, Inc., Subsid. of Great Lakes Chem. Corp., PO Box 2500, West Lafayette, IN 47906 USA (Tel.: 317-497-6300; 800-621-9521; Telefax: 317-497-6287; Telex: 446968 QOC UD)

QO Chemicals Inc., Industriepark, B-2440 Geel Belgium (Tel.: 32-58 9572; Telefax: 32-580896; Telex: 34827)

Qualcepts Nutrients Inc.

4940 Viking Dr., Minneapolis, MN 55435 USA (Tel.: 612-893-9976)

Quantum Chemical Corp./USI Div.

11500 Northlake Dr., PO Box 429550, Cincinnati, OH 45249 USA (Tel.: 513-530-6500; 800-323-4905; Telefax: 513-530-6119; Telex: 155116)

Quest International

Quest International, Postbus 2, 1400 CA Bussum The Netherlands (Tel.: 31 2159-99111; Telefax: 31 2159-46067; Telex: 43050 QSTN NL)

Quest International (UK) Ltd., Bromborough Port, Wirral, Merseyside, L62 4SU UK (Tel.: 44 151 645 2060; Telefax: 44 151 645 6975; Telex: 627173)

Quest International Fragrances USA, Inc., 400 International Dr., Mt. Olive, NJ 07828 USA (Tel.: 201-691-7100; Telefax: 201-691-7100; Telex: 6714933)

Quimdis

24 Ave. de Gresillons, 92601 Asnieres France (Tel.: 33 1 47 902580; Telefax: 33 1 47 339096; Telex: 614450)

Ragus Sugars

193 Bedford Ave., Slough, Berkshire, SL1 4RT UK (Tel.: 44 1753 575353; Telefax: 44 1753 691514)

Rasa Industries, Ltd.

Yaesu Dai Bldg., 1-1, Kyobashi 1-chome, Chuo-ku, Tokyo, 104 Japan (Tel.: (03) 3278-3801; Telefax: (03) 3281-6697; Telex: 2225818 RASAKOJ)

Raschig

Raschig AG, Mundenheimer Strasse 100, D-6700 Ludwigshafen/Rhine Germany (Tel.: (0621)56180; Telefax: 0621-532885; Telex: 464 877 ralu d)

Raschig Corp., 5000 Old Osborne Tpke., Box 7656, Richmond, VA 23231 USA (Tel.: 804-222-9516; Telefax: 804-226-1569)

Reade Advanced Materials

PO Box 15039, Riverside, RI 02915-0039 USA (Tel.: 401-433-7000; Telefax: 401-433-7001)

Red Carnation Gums Ltd.

St. John Lyon House, 5 High Timber St., Upper Thames St., London, EC4V 3PA UK (Tel.: 44 171 236 8560; Telefax: 44 171 489 8427; Telex: 8956136 EMULS G)

Red Star Specialty Products

433 E. Michigan St., Milwaukee, WI 53202 USA (Tel.: 414-347-3936; Telefax: 414-347-3912)

Reedy International Corp.

25 East Front St., Suite 200, Keyport, NJ 07735 USA (Tel.: 908-264-1777; Telefax: 908-264-1189)

Regency Mowbray Co. Ltd.

Regency House, Hixon Ind. Estate, Hixon, Staffordshire, ST18 0PY UK (Tel.: 44 1889 270554; Telefax: 44 1889 270927)

Reheis

Reheis Inc., PO Box 609, 235 Snyder Ave., Berkeley Heights, NJ 07922 USA (Tel.: 908-464-1500; Telefax: 908-464-8094; Telex: 219463 RCCA UR)

Reheis Ireland, Div. of Reheis Inc., Kilbarrack Rd., Dublin, 5, Irish Republic (Tel.: 353-1-322621; Telefax: 353-1-392205; Telex: 32532 REHI EI)

Reichhold Chemicals, Inc./Corporate Headquarters

PO Box 13582, Research Triangle Park, NC 27709 USA (Tel.: 919-990-7500; 800-448-3482; Telefax: 919-990-7711)

Reilly Chemicals. *See under* Morflex

Reilly Industries Inc.

151 N. Delaware St., Suite 1510, Indianapolis, IN 46204 USA (Tel.: 317-638-7531; Telefax: 317-248-6413; Telex: 27 404)

Reilly-Whiteman Inc.

801 Washington St., Conshohocken, PA 19428 USA (Tel.: 215-828-3800; 800-533-4514; Telefax: 215-834-7855; Telex: 5106608845)

J. Rettenmaier & Sohne GmbH & Co.

Faserstoffwerke, D-73494 Rosenberg/Holzmühle Germany (Tel.: 49 7967 1520; Telefax: 49 7967 6111; Telex: 74728)

Rewo Chemische Werke GmbH. *See under* Witco

Rhone-Poulenc

Rhone-Poulenc SA, 25 quai Paul Doumer, 92408 Courbevoie Cedex France (Tel.: 33 1 47 68 12 34; Telex: 610500)

Rhone-Poulenc Chimie, Div. of Rhone-Poulenc SA, 25 Quai Paul Doumer, F-92408 Courbevoie Cedex France (Tel.: 47 68 1234; Telefax: 47 68 23 00; Telex: 610500)

Rhone-Poulenc Santé SA, Div. of Rhone-Poulenc SA, 18 ave d'Alsace, F-92400 Courbevoie Cedex 29 France (Tel.: 47 68 12 34; Telex: 610500 RHONE F)

Rhone-Poulenc Surfactants & Specialties (Europe), Les Miroirs-Defense 3, 18 ave. d'Alsace, Cedex 29, 92097 Paris, LaDefense France (Tel.: (33-1) 4768 1234; Telefax: (33-1) 4768 0900)

Rhone-Poulenc, Inc., CN7500, Prospect Plain Rd., Cranbury, NJ 08512-7500 USA (Tel.: 609-860-4000; Telefax: 609-860-0466)

Rhone-Poulenc Basic Chemical Co., One Corporate Dr., Box 881, Shelton, CT 06484 USA (Tel.: 800-642-4200; Telefax: 203-925-3627)

Rhone-Poulenc Food Ingredients, CN 7500, Prospect Plains Rd., Cranbury, NJ 08512 USA (Tel.: 609-860-4600; 800-253-5052)

Rhone-Poulenc Rorer Pharmaceuticals Inc., 500 Arcola Road, Collegeville, PA 19426-0107 USA (Tel.: 610-454-8000)

Rhone-Poulenc, Inc./Performance Resins & Coatings, 1525 Church St. Ext., Marietta, GA 30060 USA (Tel.: 404-422-1250; Telefax: 404-427-0874; Telex: 542-112)

Rhone-Poulenc, Inc./Specialty Chemicals, CN 7500, Prospect Plains Rd., Cranbury, NJ 08512-7500 USA (Tel.: 609-860-4000; 800-922-2189; Telefax: 609-860-0466)

Rhone-Poulenc, Inc./Surfactants & Specialty Chemicals, CN 7500, Prospect Plains Rd., Cranberry, NJ 08512-7500 USA (Tel.: 609-860-4000; 800-922-2189; Telefax: 609-860-0459)

Rhone-Poulenc, Inc./Water Treatment Chemicals, One Gatehall Dr., Parsippany, NJ 07054 USA (Tel.: 201-292-2900; 800-848-7659; Telefax: 201-292-5295)

Rhone-Poulenc Surfactants & Specialties Canada, 3265 Wolfdale Rd., Mississauga, Ontario, L5C 1V8 Canada (Tel.: 905-270-5534; Telefax: 905-270-5816)

Rhone-Poulenc Chemicals Ltd., Div. of Rhone-Poulenc SA, Staveley, Chesterfield, Derbyshire, S43 2PB UK (Tel.: 44 1246 277251; Telefax: 44 1246-280090; Telex: 577425 STAVEX G)

Rhone-Poulenc Rorer Ltd., Div. of Rhone-Poulenc SA, Rainham Rd South, Dagenham, Essex, RM10 7XS UK (Tel.: 44 181 592 3060; Telefax: 44 181-593 2140; Telex: 28691 MBDAGN G)

Rhone-Poulenc Surfactants & Specialties (Asia Pacific), 27 06/07 The Concourse, 300 Beach Road, Singapore 0719 (Tel.: (65) 291 1921; Telefax: (65) 296 6044)

Nattermann Phospholipid GmbH, Div. of Rhone-Poulenc Rorer, PO Box 350120, Nattermannallee 1, D-5000 Cologne 30 Germany (Tel.: 49 221-509-2267; Telefax: 49 221-509-2816; Telex: 8882663)

American Lecithin Co., Div. of Rhone-Poulenc Rorer/Nattermann, 115 Hurley Rd. Unit 2B, Oxford, CT 06478 USA (Tel.: 203-262-7100; Telefax: 203-262-7101)

Riceland Foods, Inc.

PO Box 8201, Little Rock, AR, 72221 USA (Tel.: 501-225-0936; Telefax: 501-225-9179)

Richman Chemical, Inc.

768 N. Bethlehem Pike, Lower Gwynedd, PA 19002 USA (Tel.: 215-628-2946; Telefax: 215-628-4262)

Riken Vitamin Oil Co., Ltd.

TDC Bldg., 9-18, Misaki-Cho 2-chome, Chiyoda-Ku, Tokyo, 101 Japan (Tel.: 81 (03) 5275 5130; Telefax: 81 (03) 5275 2905; Telex: 2322783)

R.I.T.A. Corp.

1725 Kilkenny Court, PO Box 585, Woodstock, IL 60098 USA (Tel.: 815-337-2500; 800-426-7759; Telefax: 815-337-2522; Telex: 72-2438)

Rit-Chem Co. Inc.

109 Wheeler Ave., PO Box 435, Pleasantville, NY 10570 USA (Tel.: 914-769-9110; Telefax: 914-769-1408; Telex: 229 639 RTCH)

Robeco Chemicals Inc.

99 Park Ave., New York, NY 10016 USA (Tel.: 212-986-6410; Telefax: 212-986-6419; Telex: 23-3053 A (RCA))

Robertet & Cie

36 ave. Sidi Brahim, BP 100, 06333 Grasse Cedex France (Tel.: 33 93 40 3366; Telefax: 33 93 70 6809; Telex: 470863)

Roche Vitamins & Fine Chemicals, Div. of Hoffman-La Roche Inc.

340 Kingsland St., Nutley, NJ 07110-1199 USA (Tel.: 201-235-5000; Telefax: 201-535-7606)

Roeper GmbH & Co., CE

Hans-Duncker-Str. 13, D2050 Hamburg 80 Germany (Tel.: 49 40 7341030; Telefax: 49 40 73410335; Telex: 211079 HARZE D)

Rohm and Haas

Rohm and Haas Co., 100 Independence Mall West, Philadelphia, PA 19106-2399 USA (Tel.: 215-592-3000; 800-323-4165; Telefax: 215-592-6909; Telex: 845-247)

Rohm & Haas Europe, 185 rue de Bercy, 75579 Paris, Cedex 12 France (Tel.: 011-33-1 40 02 50 00; Telefax: 011-33-1 43 45 28 19)

Rohm & Haas (UK) Ltd., Lennig House, 2 Mason's Avenue, Croydon, Greater London, CR9 3NB UK (Tel.: 44 181 686-8844; Telefax: 44 181-686 8329; Telex: 917266)

Rohm & Haas Pacific Region, 391B Orchard Road #16-05/07, 0 Ngee Ann City, 0923 Singapore (Tel.: 011-65-735-0855; Telefax: 011-65-735-0877)

Röhm Pharma GmbH

Weiterstadt Germany

Rohm Tech Inc., A Company of the Hüls Group

195 Canal St., Malden, MA 02148 USA (Tel.: 617-321-6984; 800-666-7646; Telefax: 617-322-0358; Telex: 200721 Rohm UR)

Rona, Div. of EM Industries, Inc.

5 Skyline Dr., Hawthorne, NY 10532 USA (Tel.: 914-592-4660; Telefax: 914-592-9469; Telex: 17-8993)

Ronsheim & Moore Ltd., Div. of Hickson & Welch Ltd.

Wheldon Road, Castleford, West Yorkshire, WF10 2JT UK (Tel.: 44 1977 556565; Telefax: 44 1977-518058; Telex: 55378)

Roquette (UK) Ltd.

Pantiles House, 2 Nevill St., Tunbridge Wells, Kent, TN2 5TT UK (Tel.: 44 1892 540188; Telefax: 44 1892-510872; Telex: 957558 G)

Rorer. *See* Rhone-Poulenc Rorer

Ross Chemical, Inc.

303 Dale Dr., PO Box 458, Fountain Inn, SC 29644 USA (Tel.: 803-862-4474; 800-521-8246; Telefax: 803-862-2912)

Frank B. Ross Co., Inc.

22 Halladay St., PO Box 4085, Jersey City, NJ 07304-0085 USA (Tel.: 201-433-4512; Telefax: 201-332-3555)

Ross & Rowe Lecithin. *See* ADM Lecithin

Rottapharm SpA

Via Valosa di Sopra 9, I-20052 Monza Italy (Tel.: 39-73901; Telefax: 39-747806; Telex: 331661 ROTTA I)

Rotuba Extruders, Inc.

1401 Park Ave. S., Linden, NJ 07036 USA (Tel.: 908-486-1000; Telefax: 908-486-0874)

Roussel Uclaf, Fine Chemicals, Div. of Hoechst AG

Tour Roussel Hoechst, F-92080 Paris la Defense France (Tel.: 33 40 81 48 84; Telefax: 33 40 90 00 32; Telex: 610884 UCLAF F)

H.M. Royal, Inc.

689 Pennington Ave., PO Box 28, Trenton, NJ 08601 USA (Tel.: 609-396-9176; Telefax: 609-396-3185)

Royale Pigments & Chems.

12 Rte. 17N, Suite 309, Paramus, NJ 07652 USA (Tel.: 201-845-4666; Telefax: 201-845-0719)

Royce Associates, ALP

207 Ave. L, Newark, NJ 07105 USA (Tel.: 201-465-3932; Telefax: 201-279-8561; Telex: 820-907 PASDYE US)

RTD Chemical Corp.

1500 Rt. 517, Hackettstown, NJ 07840 USA (Tel.: 908-852-6128; Telefax: 908-852-1335)

Ruetgers-Nease Chemical Co., Inc., Subsid. of Rütgerswerke AG

201 Struble Rd., State College, PA 16801 USA (Tel.: 814-238-2424; Telefax: 814-238-1567)

Ruger Chemical Co. Inc.

85 Cordier St., Irvington, NJ 07111 USA (Tel.: 201-926-0331; 800-631-7844; Telefax: 201-926-4921)

W. Ruitenberg & ZN BV

Postbus 44, 3800 AA Amersfoort The Netherlands (Tel.: 31 33 621364; Telefax: 31 33 633548; Telex: 79153)

Sachtleben Chemie

Sachtleben Chemie GmbH, Dr Rudolph-Sachtleben-Str. 4, 47198 Duisburg Germany (Tel.: 02066-22-2640; Telefax: 02066-22 2650; Telex: 855202 sc d)

Sachtleben Chemie GmbH, UK Sales Office, Huntingdon House, Princess St., Bolton, BL1 1EJ UK (Tel.: 44 1204 363634; Telefax: 44 1204 36 11 44)

SAF Bulk Chemicals

PO Box 14508, St. Louis, MO 63178 USA (Tel.: 800-336-9719; Telefax: 800-368-4661)

Sakai Chemical Industry Co., Ltd.

1-1-23, Ebisuno-cho Nishi, Sakai-shi, Osaka, 590 Japan (Tel.: (0722) 23-4111; Telefax: (0722) 23-8355)

L.A. Salomon Inc.

150 River Rd., Suite A-4, Montville, NJ 07045 USA (Tel.: 201-335-8300; Telefax: 201-335-1236; Telex: 96-1470)

Samson Chem. Co.

8915 Sorenson Ave., PO Box 2163, Santa Fe Springs, CA 90670 USA (Tel.: 310-945-9188; Telefax: 310-698-7571)

Sandoz (now known as Clariant Corp.)

Sandoz Chemicals Corp., 4000 Monroe Rd., Charlotte, NC 28205 USA (Tel.: 704-331-7234; 800-631-8077; Telefax: 704-372-1064; Telex: 704-216-922)

Sandoz, 608 5th Avenue, New York, NY 10020 USA (Tel.: 212-307 1122)

Sandoz Nutrition, 5320 West 23rd St., Minneapolis, MN 55416 USA (Tel.: 612-925-2100; Telefax: 612-593-2087)

Sandoz Pharmaceuticals, Div. of Sandoz Inc., Route 10, East Hanover, NJ 07936 USA (Tel.: 201-503-7500)

Sandoz Chemicals (UK) Ltd., Div. of Sandoz AG, Calverley Lane, Horsforth, Leeds, West Yorkshire, LS18 4RP UK (Tel.: 44 1132 584646; Telefax: 44 1132 591232; Telex: 557114)

Sandoz Products Ltd./Pharmaceuticals Div., Div. of Sandoz AG, Frimley Business Park, Frimley, Camberley, Surrey, GU16 5SG UK (Tel.: 44 1276 692255; Telefax: 44 1276 692508)

Sandoz Huningue SA, Rte de Bâle, F-68330 Huningue France (Tel.: 33-89-696000; Telefax: 33-89-696195; Telex: 881355 SANUSA F)

Sandoz K.K., Kobe Chamber of Commerce & Ind. Bldg., 6-1, Minatojima Nakamachi, Chuo-ku, Kobe, 650 Japan (Tel.: (078) 303-5850; Telefax: (078) 303-5896; Telex: 05624139 SANDOZ J)

San-Ei Gen F.F.I., Inc.

1-4-9, Hirano-machi, Chuo-ku, Osaka, 541 Japan (Tel.: (06) 202-3751; Telefax: (06) 202-3770)

Sanken Chemical Co., Ltd.

4-6-17, Koraibashi, Chuo-ku, Osaka, 541 Japan (Tel.: (06) 223-1407; Telefax: (06) 222-2973)

Sanko Kagaku K.K.

2-18-29, Jyuhachijyo, Yodogawa-ku, Osaka, 532 Japan (Tel.: (06) 391-1971)

Sankyo Organic Chemicals Co., Ltd.

788, Kuji, Takatsu-ku, Kawasaki, 213 Japan (Tel.: (044) 822-8151; Telefax: (044) 833-6208)

Sanofi Bio-Industries

66 ave. Marceau, 75008 Paris France (Tel.: 33 1 40 73 20 80; Telefax: 33 1 40 73 28 27)

Sanwa Chemical Co., Ltd., Subsid. of Nippon Carbide Ind. Co.

Ito Bldg., 8, Kanda, Nishiki-cho 1-chome, Chiyoda-ku, Tokyo, 101 Japan (Tel.: (03) 3293-8771; Telefax: (03) 3233-2218)

Sanwa Kagaku Kogyo K.K.

1-9-1, Marunouchi, Chiyoda-ku, Tokyo, 100 Japan (Tel.: (03) 3214-3766; Telefax: (03) 3214-3765)

San Yuan Chemical Co., Ltd.

PO Box 26-1134, Taipei, Taiwan, R.O.C. (Tel.: 86286630343; Telefax: 86287770155)

SAPA

23 rue de la Fraternite, BP 30, 95460 Ezanville France (Tel.: 33 1 39 91 9300; Telefax: 33 1 39 91 1926; Telex: 606040)

Sartomer Co.

Oaklands Corp. Center, 468 Thomas Jones Way, Exton, PA 19341 USA (Tel.: 215-363-4100; 800-345-8247; Telefax: 215-363-4140; Telex: 173071)

ScanChem UK Ltd.

16 Jordangate, Macclesfield, Cheshire, SK10 1EW UK (Tel.: 44 1625 511222; Telefax: 44 1625 511391)

Scheel Corp.

38 Franklin St., Brooklyn, NY 11222 USA (Tel.: 609-395-1100; Telefax: 609-395-5525)

Scher Chemicals, Inc.

Industrial West & Styertowne Rd., PO Box 4317, Clifton, NJ 07012 USA (Tel.: 201-471-1300; Telefax: 201-471-3783; Telex: 642643 Scherclif)

Schweizerhall Inc.

10 Corporate Place South, Piscataway, NJ 08854 USA (Tel.: 908-981-8200; 800-243-6564; Telefax: 908-981-8282; Telex: 4754581 SUSA)

Scientific Adsorbents

PO Box 80998, Atlanta, GA 30366-0998 USA (Tel.: 404-455-1140; 800-4-ADSORB; Telefax: 404-455-7502)

Scientific Protein Laboratories, Div. of Viobin Corp.

PO Box 158, 700 E. Main St., Waunakee, WI 53597 USA (Tel.: 608-849-5944; 800-334-4SPL; Telefax: 608-849-4053; Telex: 26-5479)

SCI Natural Ingredients

4 Kings Rd., Reading, Berkshire, RG1 3AA UK (Tel.: 44 1734 580247; Telefax: 44 1734 589580; Telex: 847746)

SCM

SCM Chemicals, 7 St. Paul St., Suite 1010, Baltimore, MD 21202 USA (Tel.: 410-783-1120; 800-638-3234; Telefax: 410-783-1087/9)

SCM Glidco Organics, PO Box 389, Jacksonville, FL 32201 USA (Tel.: 904-768-5800; 800-231-6728; Telefax: 904-768-2200; Telex: 441763)

SCM Glidco Organics, 210 Summit Ave., Montvale, NJ 07645-1526 USA (Tel.: 201-391-3040; Telefax: 201-391-3284)

N.V. SCM Europe S.A., 141 Rue Saint Lambert, 1200 Brussels Belgium (Tel.: 32-2-771-2110; Telefax: 32-2-771-4902)

Iwata Koryo, 1230-3, Kuden-cho, Sakae-Ku, Yokohama, Kangawa Pref. Japan (Tel.: 81-45-891-8418; Telefax: 81-45-895-3063)

SCM Metal Products, Inc., 2601 Weck Dr., PO Box 12166, Research Triangle Park, NC 27709-2166 USA (Tel.: 919-544-8090; Telefax: 919-544-7996; Telex: 196 072)

Scott Bader Co. Ltd.

Wollaston, Wellingborough, Northamptonshire, NN8 7RL UK (Tel.: 44 1933 663100; Telefax: 44 1933-663474; Telex: 31387 S BADER G)

Scott Specialty Gases

6141 Easton Rd., Plumsteadville, PA 18949 USA (Tel.: 215-766-8861; Telefax: 215-766-0320)

Seah International

PO Box 275, 62204 Boulogne sur Mer France (Tel.: 33 21 32 2929; Telefax: 33 21 32 2828; Telex: 110900)

Sea-Land Chemical Co.

795 Sharon Dr., Westlake, OH 44145 USA (Tel.: 216-871-7887; Telefax: 216-871-7949)

John L Seaton & Co Ltd.

Bankside, Hull, North Humberside, HU5 1RR UK (Tel.: 44 1482 41345; Telefax: 44 1482 447157; Telex: 592207)

Seefast (Europe) Ltd.

59 Lampton Rd., Hounslaw, TW3 4DH UK (Tel.: 081-5770033; Telefax: 081-5706376)

Seegott Inc.

5400 Naiman Pkwy., Solon, OH 44139 USA (Tel.: 216-248-5400; 800-321-2865; Telefax: 216-248-3451)

Seeler Industries Inc.

2000 N. Broadway, Joliet, IL 60435 USA (Tel.: 815-740-2640; 800-336-2422; Telefax: 815-740-6469)

Sefcol (Sales) Ltd.

Whitehouse Ind. Estate, Runcorn, Cheshire, WA7 3BJ UK (Tel.: 44 1928 713121; Telefax: 44 1928 712827)

Seiko Chemical Co., Ltd.

Hiranuma Bldg., 6, Kanda Tsukasa-cho 2-chome, Chioyda-ku, Tokyo, 101 Japan (Tel.: (03) 3254-2771; Telefax: (03) 3258-1431; Telex: SKK J27140)

Seimi Chemical Co., Ltd.

2-10, Chigasaki 3-chome, Chigasaki-shi, Kanagawa, 253 Japan (Tel.: (0467) 82-4131; Telefax: (0467) 86-2767)

Seppic

Seppic, Div. of L'Air Liquide, 75 Quai d'Orsay, F-75321 Paris Cedex 07 France (Tel.: 40 62 55 55; Telefax: 40 62 52 53; Telex: 202901 SEPPI F)

Seppic Inc., Subsid. of Seppic France, 30 Two Bridges Rd., Suite 225, Fairfield, NJ 07004 USA (Tel.: 201-882-5597; Telefax: 201-882-5178)

Servo Delden B.V.

Postbus 1, NL-7490 AA Delden The Netherlands (Tel.: 5407-63535; Telefax: 5407-64125; Telex: 44347)

Sharon Laboratories Israel

Industrial Zone Ad Halom, Ashdod 77106 Israel

Sheffield Bronze Paint Corp.

17814 Waterloo Rd., Cleveland, OH 44119 USA (Tel.: 216-481-8330)

Shell

Shell Chemical Co., One Shell Plaza, Room 1671, Houston, TX 77002 USA (Tel.: 713-241-6161; 800-872-7435; Telefax: 713-241-4043; Telex: 762248)

Shell Chemical Co., 4868 Blazer Memorial Pkwy., PO Box 1227, Dublin, OH 43017 USA (Tel.: 614-793-7700; Telefax: 614-793-7711)

Pecten Chemicals, Inc., representing for Int'l. sales, One Shell Plaza, Houston, TX 77252-9932 USA (Tel.: 713-241-6161; Telefax: 713-241-4044)

Shell Chemicals Ireland Ltd., Gratton House, 68-72 Lower Mount Street, Dublin, Irish Republic (Tel.: 1-785177; Telefax: 1-767489; Telex: 93450)

Shell Chimie SA, BP 319, 23-25 ave de Republique, 7539 Paris Cedex 08, F-92506 Rueil-Malmaison France (Tel.: 47 52 27 00; Telefax: 47 52 28 02; Telex: 632051 SHELL F)

Shin-Etsu Chemical Co., Ltd.

Asahi Tokai Bldg., 6-1, Ohtemachi 2-chome, Chiyoda-ku, Tokyo, 100 Japan (Tel.: 81 (03) 3246 5011; Telefax: 81 (03) 3246 5350; Telex: SHINCHEM J-24790)

Showa Denko K.K.

13-9, Shiba-Daimon 1-chome, Minato-ku, Tokyo, 105 Japan (Tel.: (03) 5470-3533; Telefax: (03) 3436-2625; Telex: J26232)

Siber Hegner Ltd., Div. of Siber Hegner & Co Ltd.

County House, 221-241 Beckenham Road, Beckenham, Kent, BR3 4UF UK (Tel.: 44 181 659 2345; Telefax: 44 181-659 1292; Telex: 946651)

Sigma/Aldrich. *See under* Aldrich

Simonis BV

Postbus 33, Conradstraat 38, NL-3000 AA Rotterdam The Netherlands (Tel.: 31 10-411 32 00; Telefax: 31 10-413 56 27; Telex: 22418)

Sino-American Pigment Systems Inc.

5801 Christie Ave., Suite 575, Emeryville, CA 94608-1933 USA (Tel.: 510-653-9931; 800-536-9932; Telefax: 510-653-7501)

SKW Chemicals Inc.

1509 Johnson Ferry Rd., Marietta, GA 30062 USA (Tel.: 404-971-1317; Telefax: 404-971-4306)

Sloss Industries Corp.

PO Box 5327, Birmingham, AL 35207 USA (Tel.: 205-808-7909; Telefax: 205-808-7885)

Smith Lime Flour Co.

60-70 Central Ave., S. Kearny, NJ 07032 USA (Tel.: 201-344-1700; Telefax: 201-690-5936)

Werner G Smith, Inc.

1730 Train Ave., Cleveland, OH 44113 USA (Tel.: 216-861-3676; 800-535-8343; Telefax: 216-861-3680)

SNIA (UK) Ltd.

36 Broadway, St. Jame's, London, SW1H 0BH UK (Tel.: 44 171 222 8696; Telefax: 44 171 222 8705; Telex: 23377)

SNPE Chimie

12, quai Henri-IV, 75181 Paris Cedex 4 France (Tel.: 48 04 66 66; Telefax: 48 04 69 89; Telex: 220 380 SNPE F)

Société Chimique Roche

BP 170, Boulevard d'Alsace, F-68305 Saint Louis France (Tel.: 33 89 69 00 20; Telefax: 33 89 69 85 05; Telex: 881528 ROCHE F)

Soda Aromatic

Soda Aromatic Co., Ltd., 15-9, Nihonbashi Honcho 4-chome, Chuo-ku, Tokyo, 103 Japan (Tel.: (03) 3666-0553; Telefax: (03) 3666-2913; Telex: SODAROMA J27930)

Soda Aromatic USA Inc., The Chrysler Bldg., Suite 4920, 405 Lexington Ave., New York, NY 10174 USA (Tel.: 212-557-2071; Telefax: 212-856-9502)

Solabia

29 Rue Delizy, 93500 Pantin France (Tel.: 148 91 02 32; Telefax: 148 91 18 77; Telex: 230 827 BIOSOR)

Soluol Chemical Co.

Green Hill & Market Sts., PO Box 112, W. Warwick, RI 02893 USA (Tel.: 401-821-8100; Telefax: 401-823-6673)

Solvay

Solvay SA, 33 rue du Prince Albert, B-1050 Brussels Belgium (Tel.: 32-509-6111; Telefax: 32-509-6617; Telex: 21337 SOLV B)

Solvay Deutschland GmbH, Postfach 220, W-3000 Hannover-1 Germany (Tel.: 511-857-0; Telefax: 511-282126; Telex: 922-755)

Solvay Duphar BV, Postbus 900, Bldg. WWO, Room B1066, 1380 DA Weesp The Netherlands (Tel.: 31 2940-77000; Telefax: 31 2940-15401; Telex: 14232)

Solvay Enzymes, Inc., PO Box 4859, 1230 Randolph St., Elkhart, IN 46514 USA (Tel.: 219-523-3700; 800-487-4704; Telefax: 219-523-3800)

Solvay Minerals, Inc., Subsidiary of Solvay America Inc., 3333 Richmond Ave., PO Box 27328, Houston, TX 77227-7328 USA (Tel.: 713-525-6800; Telefax: 713-525-7804)

Solvay Polymers Inc., Subsidiary of Solvay America Inc., 3333 Richmond Ave., PO Box 27328, Houston, TX 77227-7328 USA (Tel.: 713-525-4000; 800-231-6313; Telefax: 713-522-7890; Telex: 166307)

Southern Clay Prods.

1212 Church St., PO Box 44, Gonzales, TX 78629 USA (Tel.: 210-672-2891; 800-324-2891; Telefax: 210-672-3650)

Soya Mainz

Dammweg 2, PO Box 3767, D6500 Mainz Germany (Tel.: 49 6131 895-0; Telefax: 49 6131 834104; Telex: 4187761)

SPCI

58 rue du Landy, F93121 Paris France (Tel.: 33 1 4933 3115; Telefax: 33 1 4243 8223)

Specialty Chem Products Corp.

Two Stanton St., Marinette, WI 54143 USA (Tel.: 715-735-9033; Telefax: 715-735-5304; Telex: 887445)

Specialty Minerals Inc., Subsid. of Minerals Technologies Inc.

640 N. 13th St., Easton, PA 18042 USA (Tel.: 610-250-3000; Telefax: 610-250-3344)

Spectrum Chemical Mfg. Corp.

14422 S. San Pedro St., Gardena, CA 90248 USA (Tel.: 310-516-8000; 800-772-8786; Telefax: 800-525-2299; Telex: 182395)

Spectrum Naturals

133 Copeland St., Pentaluma, CA 94952 USA (Tel.: 707-778-8900; Telefax: 707-765-1026)

Spice King Corp.

6009 Washington Blvd., Culver City, CA 90232-7488 USA (Tel.: 213-836-7770; Telefax: 213-836-6454; Telex: 664350)

A.E. Staley Manufacturing Co., Subsid. of Tate & Lyle PLC

2200 E. Eldorado St., PO Box 151, Decatur, IL 62525 USA (Tel.: 217-423-4411; 800-258-7536; Telefax: 217-421-2881)

StanChem, Inc.

401 Berlin St., East Berlin, CT 06023 USA (Tel.: 203-828-0571; Telefax: 203-828-3297)

Stanchem, A Business Unit of HCI Inc.

43 Jutland Rd., Etobicoke, Ontario, M8Z 2G3 Canada (Tel.: 416-259-8231; Telefax: 416-259-5333)

Stan Chem International Ltd.

4 Kings Rd, Reading, Berkshire, RG1 3AA UK (Tel.: 44 1734 580247; Telefax: 44 1734 589580; Telex: 847746)

Stepan

Stepan Co, 22 West Frontage Rd., Northfield, IL 60093 USA (Tel.: 708-446-7500; 800-745-7837; Telefax: 708-501-2100; Telex: 910-992-1437)

Stepan/Food Ingredients Dept., 100 West Hunter Ave., Maywood, NJ 07607 USA (Tel.: 201-845-3030; 800-523-3614; Telefax: 201-845-6754; Telex: 710-990-5170)

Stepan Canada, 90 Matheson Blvd. W., Suite 201, Mississauga, Ontario, L5R 3P3 Canada (Tel.: 416-507-1631; Telefax: 416-507-1633)

Stepan Europe, BP127, 38340 Voreppe France (Tel.: 33-76-50-51-00; Telefax: 33-7656-7165; Telex: 320511 F)

Stern-France SARL

40 ave. Gustave Eiffel, F37100 Tours France (Tel.: 33 47 490970; Telefax: 33 47 546633)

Stevenson Cooper

PO Box 38349, 1039 West Venango St., Philadelphia, PA 19140 USA (Tel.: 215-223-2600; Telefax: 215-223-3597)

Strahl & Pitsch, Inc.

PO Box 1098, 230 Great E. Neck Rd., W. Babylon, NY 11704 USA (Tel.: 516-587-9000; Telefax: 516-587-9120; Telex: 221636 STRALUR)

Suchema AG

Haupstrasse 15, CH-8251 Kaltenbach Switzerland (Tel.: 41 54-41 12 65; Telefax: 41 54-41 32 34; Telex: 897170 BGK CH)

Süd-Chemie

Süd-Chemie AG, Postfach 200154, Munich 2 Germany (Tel.: 49 89-5110 0; Telefax: 49 89 5110375; Telex: 523872 SCMU D)

Süd-Chemie Rheologicals, Lenbachplatz 6, D-80333 München Germany (Tel.: 49 89-51 10-0; Telefax: 49 89 51 10-412)

Sumikin Chemical Co., Ltd.

No. 2 DIC Bldg., 16-2, Soto-Kanda 2-chome, Chiyoda-ku, Tokyo, 101 Japan (Tel.: (03) 3258-3171; Telefax: (03) 3258-3179)

Sumisho Plaschem Co., Ltd.

1-1-8, Toranomon, Minato-ku, Tokyo, 105 Japan (Tel.: (03) 3502-1350; Telefax: (03) 3595-2924)

Sumitomo Chemical Co., Ltd.

New Sumitomo Bldg., 5-33, Kitahama 4-chome, Chuo-ku, Osaka, 541 Japan (Tel.: (06) 220-3272; Telefax: (06) 220-3345; Telex: 63823 SUMIKAJ)

Sumitomo Metal Mining Co., Ltd.

5-11-3, Shinbashi, Minato-ku, Tokyo, 105 Japan (Tel.: (03) 3436-7701; Telefax: (03) 3436-7734)

Sumitomo Pharmaceuticals Co., Ltd., Subsid. of Sumitomo Chemical Co., Ltd.

2-2-8, Doshomachi, Chuo-ku, Osaka, 541 Japan (Tel.: (06) 229-5775; Telefax: (06) 202-7370; Telex: 522-2115 SUMYAK J)

Sumitomo Seika Chemicals Co., Ltd.

Sumitomo Bldg., No. 2, 4-7-28, Kitahama, Chuo-ku, Osaka, 541 Japan (Tel.: (06) 220-8508; Telefax: (06) 220-8541)

Sunette Brand Sweetener

25 Worlds Fair Dr., Somerset, NJ 08873 USA (Tel.: 908-271-7220; Telefax: 908-271-7235)

Sunnyside

225 Carpenter Ave., Wheeling, IL 60090 USA (Tel.: 312-541-5700; 800-323-8611)

Surco Products, Inc.

PO Box 777, Eighth & Pine Aves., Braddock, PA 15104 USA (Tel.: 412-351-7700; 800-556-0111; Telefax: 412-351-7701)

Surfactants, Inc.

260 Ryan St., S. Plainfield, NJ 07080 USA (Tel.: 908-755-3300; Telefax: 755-0592)

Sutton Laboratories, Inc., Member of the ISP Inc. Group

116 Summit Ave., PO Box 837, Chatham, NJ 07928-0837 USA (Tel.: 201-635-1551; Telefax: 201-635-4964; Telex: 710-999-5607)

SVO Enterprises, Business Unit of The Lubrizol Corp.

35585-B Curtis Blvd., Eastlake, OH 44095 USA (Tel.: 216-975-2802; 800-292-4786; Telefax: 216-942-1045; Telex: 4938879 AGCEAKE)

Sweeteners Plus Inc.

3239 Rochester Rd., Lakeville, NY 14480 USA (Tel.: 716-346-2318; Telefax: 716-346-2310)

SWS Oilchemicals BV

Raadhuisstraat 84, NL-2101 HJ Heemstede The Netherlands (Tel.: 31 23-28 39 52; Telefax: 31 23-29 46 81)

Sybron

Sybron Chemicals Inc., PO Box 125, Hwy. 29, Wellford, SC 29385 USA (Tel.: 803-439-6333; 800-677-3500; Telefax: 803-439-1612)

Sybron Chemie Nederland BV, Postbus 46, NL-6710 BA Ede The Netherlands (Tel.: 31-8380-70911; Telefax: 31-8380-30236; Telex: 37249)

Synthetic Products Co., Subsid. of Cookson America Inc.

1000 Wayside Rd., Cleveland, OH 44110 USA (Tel.: 216-531-6010; 800-321-4236; Telefax: 216-486-6638)

Synthite Industrial Chemicals Ltd.

Kadayiruppu, 632 311 Kolenchery India (Tel.: 91 484 354616; Telefax: 91 484 370405; Telex: 8856593)

Taiwan Surfactant Corp.

No. 106, 8-1 Floor, Sec. 2, Chung An E. Rd., Taipei, Taiwan, R.O.C. (Tel.: 886-2-507-9155; Telefax: 886-2-507-7011; Telex: 27568 surfact)

Takasago International

Takasago International Corp., 19-22, Takanawa 3-chome, Minato-ku, Tokyo, 108 Japan (Tel.: (03) 3442-1211; Telefax: (03) 3442-1285; Telex: TAKAS A J32508)

Takasago International Corp., 11 Volvo Dr., Rockleigh, NJ 07647 USA (Tel.: 201-767-9001; Telefax: 201-767-8062; Telex: 685-3936)

Takeda

Takeda Chemical Industries, Ltd., 1-1, Dosho-machi 4-chome, Chuo-ku, Osaka, 541 Japan (Tel.: (06) 204-2111; Telefax: (06) 204-2880; Telex: TAKEDA J63404)

Takeda USA, Inc., 8 Corporate Dr., Orangeburg, NY 10962-2614 USA (Tel.: 914-365-2080; 800-825-3328; Telefax: 914-365-2786; Telex: 421149)

Takeda Europe GmbH, Domstrasse 17, 20095 Hamburg Germany (Tel.: 49 40 329050; Telefax: 49 40 327506; Telex: 2161408)

Tamms Industries Co.

Rt. 72 West, Kirkland, IL 60146 USA (Tel.: 815-522-3394)

Tanabe USA, Inc.

PO Box 85132, San Diego, CA 92186 USA (Tel.: 619-571-8410; 800-7-TANABE; Telefax: 619-571-3476)

Tanabe Seiyaku Co., Ltd.

2-10, Dosho-machi 3-chome, Chuo-ku, Osaka, 541 Japan (Tel.: (06) 205-5555; Telefax: (06) 222-5262; Telex: J63659 TANAGO A)

Tateyama Kasei Co., Ltd.

3766, Tobari, Kosugi-cho, Imizu-gun, Toyama, 939-03 Japan (Tel.: (0766) 56-2366; Telefax: (0766) 56-6414)

Technical Chemicals & Products, Inc.

3341 SW 15th St., Pompano Beach, FL 33069 USA (Tel.: 305-979-0400; Telefax: 305-979-0009)

Tego Chemie. *See under* Goldschmidt

Teknor Apex Co.

505 Central Ave., Pawtucket, RI 02861 USA (Tel.: 401-725-8000; 800-554-9893; Telefax: 401-724-6250; Telex: 927530)

Terry Laboratories, Inc.

390 Wickham Rd. N., Suite F, Melbourne, FL 32935-8647 USA (Tel.: 407-259-1630; 800-367-2563; Telefax: 407-242-0625)

Tesco

Hansaalee 177 c, 4000 Dusseldorf 11 Germany (Tel.: 49 211 596150; Telefax: 49 211 5961530)

Texaco

Texaco Chemical Co, PO Box 27707, Houston, TX 77227-7707 USA (Tel.: 713-961-3711; 800-231-3107; Telefax: 713-235-6437; Telex: 227-031 TEX UR)

Texaco Ltd., Div. of Texaco Chemical Europe, 195 Knightsbridge Green, London, SW7 1RU UK (Tel.: 44 171 581 5500; Telefax: 44 171-581 9163; Telex: 8956681 TEXACO G)

Texaco France S.A., 5, rue Bellini, Tour Arago, F-92806 Puteaux Cedex France (Tel.: 33-1-47-17 26 02; Telefax: 33-1-47 76 30 50)

Texaco Chemical Deutschland GmbH, Baumwall 5, 2000 Hamburg 11 Germany (Tel.: 49-40-37670147; Telefax: 49 40 37282 9)

Texaco Olie Matschappij BV, Weena 170, NL-3012 CR Rotterdam The Netherlands (Tel.: 31-614471; Telex: 31542)

Texasgulf Inc.

3101 Glenwood Ave., PO Box 30321, Raleigh, NC 27622-0321 USA (Tel.: 919-881-2700; Telefax: 919-881-2847; Telex: 6844904)

Texas Petrochemicals Corp.

8707 Katy Frwy., Suite 300, Houston, TX 77024 USA (Tel.: 713-461-3322; Telefax: 713-461-1029; Telex: TWX 510-891-7831)

Thew Arnott & Co. Ltd.

Newman Works, 270 London Rd., Wallington, Surrey, SM6 7DJ UK (Tel.: 44 181 669 3131; Telefax: 44 181 669 7747; Telex: 46601)

Thiele Kaolin Co.

Box 1056, Sandersville, GA 31082 USA (Tel.: 912-552-3951; Telefax: 912-552-4131)

Thor

Thor Chemicals, Inc., Brook House, 37 North Ave., Norwalk, CT 06851 USA (Tel.: 203-846-8613; Telefax: 203-846-4810; Telex: 888630)

Thor Chemicals (UK) Ltd., Cowley House, Earl Road, Cheadle Hulme, Cheshire, SK8 6QP UK (Tel.: 44 161 486-1051; Telefax: 44 161-488-4125; Telex: 666679 THORUK G)

3M

3M Co/Industrial Chem. Prods. Div., 3M Center Bldg. 223-6S-04, St. Paul, MN 55144-1000 USA (Tel.: 612-736-1394; 800-541-6752)

3M Pharmaceuticals, Bldg 275-3W-01, 3M Center, St Paul, MN 55133-3275 USA (Tel.: 612-736-4930; 800-562-0255)

3M Canada Inc., PO Box 5757 Terminal A, 1840 Oxford St. East, London, Ontario, N6A 4T1 Canada (Tel.: 519-451-2500)

3M Europe/Performance Polymers and Additives, PO Box 100422, D-4040 Neuss 1 Germany (Tel.: 2101-142414)

3V Inc.

1500 Harbor Blvd., Weehawken, NJ 07087 USA (Tel.: 201-865-3600; 800-441-5156; Telefax: 201-865-1892)

Thymly Products Inc.

1332 Colora Rd., PO Box 65, Colora, MD 21917 USA (Tel.: 410-658-4820; Telefax: 410-658-4824)

TIC Gums, Inc.

4609 Richlynn Dr., Belcamp, MD 21017-1227 USA (Tel.: 410-273-7300; 800-221-3953; Telefax: 410-273-6469; Telex: 221049)

Tioxide Americas Inc.

Esplanade at Locust Point, 2001 Butterfield Rd., Suite 601, Downers Grove, IL 60515 (Tel.: 708-663-4900; Telefax: 708-663-4902

Titan Kogyo Kabushiki Kaisha (Titan Kogyo K.K.)

1978, Kogushi, Ube-shi, Yamaguchi, 755 Japan (Tel.: (0836) 31-4156; Telefax: (0836) 31-5148)

Todd's Ltd.

4413 Northeast 14th St., Box 4821, Des Moines, IA 50306 USA (Tel.: 515-266-2276; Telefax: 515-266-1669)

Toho Chemical Industry Co., Ltd.

No. 1-1-5, Shintomi, Nihonbashi, Chuo-ku, Tokyo, 104 Japan (Tel.: (81-3) 3555 3731; Telefax: (81-3) 3555 3755; Telex: 252-2332 TOHO K J)

Toho Zinc Co., Ltd.

Asahi Bldg., 12-2, Nihonbashi 3-chome, Chuo-ku, Tokyo, 103 Japan (Tel.: (03) 3272-5611; Telefax: (03) 3271-0070; Telex: 222-3725 TOHO ZN)

Tokuyama Petrochemical Co., Ltd.

4980, Kasei-cho, Shin-Nanyo-shi, Yamaguchi, 746 Japan (Tel.: (0834) 62-4121; Telefax: (0834) 62-3545)

Tokyo Kasei Kogyo Co., Ltd.

1-13, Nihonbashi-Honcho 3-chome, Chuo-ku, Tokyo, 103 Japan (Tel.: (03) 3808-2821; Telefax: (03) 3808-2827; Telex: 2223592 ASACEM J)

Tomita Pharmaceutical Co., Ltd.

85-1, Aza Maruyama, Akinokami, Seto-machi, Naruto-shi, Tokushima, 771-03 Japan (Tel.: (0886) 88-0511; Telefax: (0886) 88-0565)

Tomiyama Pure Chemical Industries, Ltd.

Nikko Bldg., 5-7, Nihonbashi-Honcho 2-chome, Chuo-ku, Tokyo, 103 Japan (Tel.: (03) 3242-5141; Telefax: (03) 3242-3166; Telex: TOMYPURE J 23635)

Toray Fine Chemicals Co., Ltd.

273, Katsube-cho, Moriyama-shi, Shiga, 524 Japan (Tel.: (0775) 83-2570; Telefax: (0775) 83-3312)

Toray Thiokol Co., Ltd.

Toray Bldg., 1-8-1, Mihama, Urayasu-shi, Chiba, 279 Japan (Tel.: (0473) 50-6151; Telefax: (0473) 50-6091)

Tosoh

Tosoh Corp., 7-7 Akasaka 1-chome, Minato-ku, Tokyo, 107 Japan (Tel.: (03) 3585-9891; Telefax: (03) 3582-8120; Telex: J24475tosoh)

Tosoh USA Inc., 1100 Circle 75 Pkwy., Suite 600, Atlanta, GA 30339 USA (Tel.: 404-956-1100; Telefax: 404-956-7368; Telex: 542272 tosoh atl)

Tosoh Europe BV, World Trade Centre Amsterdam, Tower C, Floor 13, Strawinskylaan 1351, 1077 XX Amsterdam The Netherlands (Tel.: 020-644026, 020-623412; Telex: 18573tosoh nl)

Total Petroleum Inc.

East Superior St., Alma, MI 48801 USA (Tel.: 517-463-9630; 800-292-9033; Telefax: 517-463-9623)

Tournay Bio-Industries

CD 17 Zone Industrielle, 02990 Fontenoy France (Tel.: 33 23 293222; Telefax: 33 26 500285; Telex: 140839)

Towa Chemical Industry Co., Ltd.

1-2, Ohte-machi 2-chome, Chiyoda-ku, Tokyo, 100 Japan (Tel.: (03) 3243-0045; Telefax: (03) 3242-7407)

Toyo Kasei Kogyo Co., Ltd.

Shindai Bldg., 1-2-6, Dojimahama, Kita-ku, Osaka, 530 Japan (Tel.: (06) 346-6707; Telefax: (06) 341-6715)

Toyotama Perfumery Co., Ltd.

Kyodo Bldg. (Showa), 3-8, Nihonbashi Honcho 1-chome, Chuo-ku, Tokyo, 103 Japan (Tel.: (03) 3270-5511; Telefax: (03) 3279-6947; Telex: J 23403)

TR-AMC Chemicals

PO Box 296, Hudson Ave., Ridgefield, NJ 07657 USA (Tel.: 201-941-7706; Telefax: 201-941-7702; Telex: 130594)

Transol Chemicals (UK) Ltd., Div. of Transol Chemicals Int'l. BV

Caledonian House, Tatton St, Knutsford, Cheshire, WA16 6AG UK (Tel.: 44 1565 650386; Telefax: 44 1565 653255)

Treasure Island Food Co.

1672 Funston, San Francisco, CA 94122 USA (Tel.: 415-665-3553; Telefax: 415-665-3553)

Treatt

Florida Treatt, PO Box 215, Haines City, FL 33845 USA (Tel.: 813-421-4708; 800-866-7704; Telefax: 813-422-5930)

R.C. Treatt & Co. Ltd., Northern Way, Bury St Edmunds, Suffolk, IP32 6NL UK (Tel.: 44 1284 702500; Telefax: 44 1284 752888; Telex: 81583)

Tricon Colors Inc.

16 Leliarts Ln., Elmwood Park, NJ 07407-3291 USA (Tel.: 201-794-3800; Telefax: 201-797-4660; Telex: 4991537 TRICN)

Tri-K Industries, Inc.

27 Bland St., PO Box 312, Emerson, NJ 07630 USA (Tel.: 201-261-2800; 800-526-0372; Telefax: 201-261-1432; Telex: 215085 TRIK UR)

Tropic Agro Products Ltd.

3 Mountington Park Close off Donnington Rd., Kenton, Harrow, Middlesex, HA3 0NW UK (Tel.: 44 181 907 9428; Telefax: 44 181 909 1661; Telex: 261507)

Tulco, Inc.

9 Bishop Rd., Ayer, MA 01432 USA (Tel.: 508-772-4412; Telefax: 508-772-1751)

Ube Industries, Ltd.

UBE Bldg., 2-3-11, Higashi-shinagawa, Shinagawa-ku, Tokyo, 140 Japan (Tel.: (03) 5460-3311; Telefax: (03) 5460-3388; Telex: 2224645)

UCB SA/Chemical Sector

33 rue d'Anderlecht, B-1620 Drogenbos Belgium (Tel.: 322-3714923; Telefax: 322-3714924; Telex: 22342 UCBOS B)

UCIB/Usines Chimiques D'Ivry-La-Bataille

Route D'Oulins, 28260 Anet France (Tel.: (33) 37 62 82 00; Telefax: (33) 37 41 91 32)

UCIB/Distrib. by SST Corp.

635 Brighton Rd., PO Box 1649, Clifton, NJ 07015 USA (Tel.: 201-473-4300; Telefax: 201-473-4326; Telex: RCA 219149)

Ueno Fine Chemicals Industry, Ltd.

2-4-8 Koraibashi, Chuo-ku, Osaka, 541 Japan (Tel.: (06) 203-0761; Telefax: (06) 222-2413; Telex: J63638 UENOFCI)

Ultra Additives, Inc.

460 Straight St., Paterson, NJ 07501 USA (Tel.: 201-279-1306; 800-524-0055; Telefax: 201-279-0602)

Unger Fabrikker AS

PO Boks 254, N-1601 Fredrikstad Norway (Tel.: 47-9693 20020; Telefax: 47-9693 23775; Telex: 76382 UNGER N)

Ungerer & Co.

4 Bridgewater Lane, PO Box U, Lincoln Park, NJ 07035 USA (Tel.: 201-628-0600; Telefax: 201-628-0251; Telex: 4754267)

Unibios SpA

Via S Pellico 3, I-28069 Trecate Italy (Tel.: 39 321-73261; Telefax: 39 321-76816; Telex: 200329 UBS I)

Unichema

Unichema International, Part of the Unilever Speciality Chemicals Group, Postbus 2, 2800 AA Gouda The Netherlands (Tel.: 31-0-1820-42911; Telefax: 31-0-1820-42250; Telex: 20661)

Unichema Chemicals Ltd., Div. of Unichema International, Bebington, Wirral, Merseyside, L62 4UF UK (Tel.: 44 151 645-2020; Telefax: 44 151-645-9197; Telex: 629408)

Unichema Chemie GmbH, Postfach 100963, D-4240 Emmerich Germany (Tel.: 49 0 2822-720; Telefax: 49 0 2822-72276; Telex: 8125113)

Unichema France SA, 148 Boulevard Haussemann, 75008 Paris France (Tel.: 33 1 44 95 08 40; Telefax: 33 1 42563188; Telex: 643217)

Unichema North America, 4650 S. Racine Ave., Chicago, IL 60609 USA (Tel.: 312-376-9000; 800-833-2864; Telefax: 312-376-0095; Telex: 176068)

Unichema Japan, Sankei Bldg. 7F 708, 4-9, Umeda 2-chome, Kita-ku, Osaka, 530 Japan (Tel.: 81 6341-7221; Telefax: 81 6341-7725)

Unichema Australia Pty. Ltd., 164 Ingles St., Port Melbourne, Victoria, 3207 Australia (Tel.: 61-3 647-9311; Telefax: 61-3 645 3001; Telex: 30130)

Unilait France

24 Blvd de l'Hopital, 87005 Paris France (Tel.: 33 1 45354744; Telefax: 33 1 47072591; Telex: 206903)

Unimin

Unimin Corp., 258 Elm St., New Canaan, CT 06840 USA (Tel.: 203-966-8880; 800-243-9004; Telefax: 203-966-3453; Telex: 99-6355)

Unimin Canada Ltd., RR #4, PO Box 2000, Havelock, Ontario, K0L 1Z0 Canada (Tel.: 705-877-2210; 800-363-4140; Telefax: 705-877-3343)

Union Camp

Union Camp Corp./Chem. Prods. Div., 1600 Valley Rd., Wayne, NJ 07470 USA (Tel.: 201-628-2375; 800-628-9220; Telefax: 201-628-2840; Telex: 130735)

Union Camp Chemicals Ltd., Vigo Lane, Chester-le-Street, Co. Durham, DH3 2RB UK (Tel.: 44-91-410-2631; Telefax: 44-91-410-9391; Telex: 851 53163)

Union Carbide

Union Carbide Corp., 39 Old Ridgebury Rd., Danbury, CT 06817-0001 USA (Tel.: 203-794-2000; 800-568-4000; Telefax: 203-794-3133)

Union Carbide Corp./Industrial Chemicals, 39 Old Ridgebury Road, Danbury, CT 06817-0001 USA (Tel.: 203-794-5300; Telefax: 203-794-2381; Telex: 126019 MYKA)

Union Carbide Corp./Specialty Chemicals, 39 Old Ridgebury Road, Danbury, CT 06817-0001 USA (Tel.: 203-794-5300)

Union Carbide Canada Ltd., 7400 Blvd des Galleries, d'Anjou, Quebec, H1M 3M2 Canada (Tel.: 514-493-2610; Telefax: 514-493-2619)

Union Carbide (UK) Ltd./Chemicals & Plastics, 93-95 High Street, Rickmansworth, Hertfordshire, WD3 1RB UK (Tel.: 44 1923 720 366; Telefax: 44 1923-896721)

Union Carbide Chemicals & Plastics Europe S.A., 15 Chemin Louis-Dunant, CH-1211 Geneve 20 Switzerland (Tel.: 41-22-739-6111; Telefax: 41-22-739-6527; Telex: 419207 UNC CH)

Union Derivan SA

Av. Meridiana 133, Barcelona E-08026 Spain (Tel.: 343-2322113; Telefax: 343-2323951; Telex: 98204 UNDER E)

Unipex

30 Rue du Fort, PO Box 150, 92504 Rueil Malmaison Cedex France (Tel.: 33 1 4732 9293; Telefax: 33 1 4749 0235; Telex: 634022)

Uniroyal Chemical Co Inc./World Headquarters

Benson Road, Middlebury, CT 06749 USA (Tel.: 203-573-2000; 800-243-3024; Telefax: 203-573-2489; Telex: 6710383 uniroyal)

United Catalysts Inc., Süd-Chemie Rheologicals Group

PO Box 32370, Louisville, KY 40232 USA (Tel.: 502-634-7500; 800-468-7210; Telefax: 502-634-7727; Telex: 204190, 204239)

United Coconut Chemicals, Inc./Cocochem

UCPB Bldg., 17th Fl., Makat Ave., Makati, Metro Manila, Philippines (Tel.: 818-8361; Telefax: (00632) 817-2251; Telex: 66928 COCOCHEM PN)

United-Guardian

United-Guardian, Inc., 230 Marcus Blvd, PO Box 2500, Smithtown, NY 11787 USA (Tel.: 516-273-0900; 800-645-5566; Telefax: 516-273-0858)

Guardian Chemical, A Div. of United Guardian Inc., 230 Marcus Blvd, PO Box 2500, Smithtown, NY 11787 USA (Tel.: 516-273-0900; 800-645-5566; Telefax: 516-273-0858)

United Mineral & Chemical Corp.

1100 Valley Brook Ave., Lyndhurst, NJ 07071-3608 USA (Tel.: 201-507-3300; 800-777-0505; Telefax: 201-507-1506; Telex: 6505113226)

United States Bronze Powders, Inc.

PO Box 31, Rte. 202, Flemington, NJ 08822 USA (Tel.: 908-782-5454; Telefax: 908-782-3489; Telex: 833488)

Unitex Chemical Corp.

PO Box 16344, 520 Broome Rd., Greensboro, NC 27406 USA (Tel.: 910-378-0965; Telefax: 910-272-4312)

Universal Flavors International Inc., A Universal Foods Co.

5600 West Raymond St., Indianapolis, IN 46241 USA (Tel.: 317-243-3521; Telefax: 317-248-1753)

Universal Preserv-A-Chem Inc./UPI

297 North 7th St., Brooklyn, NY 11211 USA (Tel.: 718-782-7429)

UOP

UOP, 25 E. Algonquin Rd., Des Plaines, IL 60017-5017 USA (Tel.: 708-391-2395; 800-348-0832; Telex: 25-3285)

UOP Molecular Sieves, Old Saw Mill River Rd., Tarrytown, NY 10591 USA (Tel.: 914-347-4600)

UOP Ltd., Liongate, Ladymeade, Guildford, Surrey, GU1 1AT UK (Tel.: 44 1483 304848; Telefax: 44 1483-304863; Telex: 858051 UOPINT G)

UOP GmbH, Steinhof 39, W-4006 Erkrath Germany (Tel.: 211-24903-23; Telefax: 211-249109)

U.S. Biochemical Corp

PO Box 22400, Cleveland, OH 44122 USA (Tel.: 216-765-5000; 800-321-9322; Telefax: 216-464-5075; Telex: 980718)

U.S. Borax Inc.

26877 Tourney Rd., Valencia, CA 91355-1847 USA (Tel.: 805-287-5400; 800-729-2672; Telefax: 805-287-5455; Telex: 371-6120)

U.S. Gypsum Co

125 S. Franklin St., Chicago, IL 60606 USA (Tel.: 312-606-4018)

U.S. Petrochemical Industries, Inc.

675 Galleria Financial Ctr., 5075 Westheimer Rd., Houston, TX 77056 USA (Tel.: 713-871-1951; Telefax: 713-871-1963; Telex: 402814)

U.S. Synthetics Co.

PO Box 2236, Danbury, CT 06813 USA (Tel.: 203-270-0187; Telefax: 203-790-6407; Telex: 4972481 mbe tam)

U.S. Zinc Corp.

6020 Esperson St., PO Box 611, Houston, TX 77001 USA (Tel.: 713-926-1705; Telefax: 713-924-4824; Telex: 3785919)

Valmar

ZI de St Mitre, PO Box 539, 13400 Aubagne le Charrel France (Tel.: 33 42 849292; Telefax: 33 42 841079; Telex: 430570)

Vamo-Fuji Specialities

Kuhlmannlaan 36, 9042 Gent Belgium (Tel.: 32 91 430202; Telefax: 32 91 430256; Telex: 11033)

Vamo Mills NV (Group Vandemoortele)

Prins Albertlaan 12, 8870 Izegem Belgium (Tel.: 32 51 332211; Telefax: 32 51 311965; Telex: 81622)

Vandemoortele Professional NV Vamix

Ottergemsesteenweg 806, B-9000 Gent Belgium (Tel.: 32 91 401711; Telefax: 32 91 227264; Telex: 12561)

Van Den Bergh Foods Co.

2200 Cabot Dr., Lisle, IL 60532 USA (Tel.: 708-505-5300; 800-949-7344; Telefax: 708-955-5497)

R.T. Vanderbilt Co Inc.

30 Winfield St, PO Box 5150, Norwalk, CT 06856 USA (Tel.: 203-853-1400; 800-243-6064; Telefax: 203-853-1452; Telex: 6813581 RTVAN)

Vanguard Chem. Int'l.

Nationsbank Tower, 101 E. Park Blvd., Plano, TX 75074 USA (Tel.: 214-423-1120; Telefax: 214-423-1291; Telex: 49 75044)

Van Waters & Rogers Inc., Subsid. of Univar Corp

6100 Carillon Point, Kirkland, WA 98033 USA (Tel.: 206-889-3400; 800-234-4588; Telefax: 206-889-4133)

Veckridge Chemical Co. Inc.

60-70 Central Ave., Kearny, NJ 07032 USA (Tel.: 201-344-1818; Telefax: 201-690-5936)

Veitsiluoto Oy/Forest Chemicals Industry

PO Box 196, SF-90101 Oulu 10 Finland (Tel.: 358-81-316 3111; Telefax: 358-81-378 5755; Telex: 32125 oulpk sf)

Velsicol

Velsicol Chemical Corp, 10400 W Higgins Road, Rosemont, IL 60018 USA (Tel.: 708-298-9000; 800-843-7759; Telefax: 708-298-9014; Telex: 3730755)

Velsicol Chemical Ltd., Worting House, Basingstoke, Hampshire, RG23 8PY UK (Tel.: 44 1256 817640; Telefax: 44 1256 817744; Telex: 9312131051 VC G)

Verdugt BV

Postbus 60, Papesteeg 91, NL-4000 AB Tiel The Netherlands (Tel.: 31-3440-15224; Telefax: 31-3440-11475; Telex: 47200)

Vicente Trapani SA

Casilla de Correo 247, 4000 Tucuman, Argentina (Tel.: 54 81 617154; Telefax: 54 81 311381; Telex: 61189)

William Vinsser & Co., Inc.

3248-62 W. 47th Place, Chicago, IL 60632 USA (Tel.: 312-523-2050; Telefax: 312-523-6093)

Viobin Corp., Subsid. of American Home Prods.

PO Box 158, Waunakee, WI 53597 USA (Tel.: 608-849-5944; Telefax: 608-849-4053; Telex: 26-5479)

Virginia Dare

Virginia Dare Extract Co., Inc., 882 Third Ave., Brooklyn, NY 11232 USA (Tel.: 718-788-1776; 800-847-4500; Telefax: 718-768-3978; Telex: 425707DARE UI)

Virginia Dare Flavors Inc., 882 Third Ave., Brooklyn, NY 11232 USA (Tel.: 800-847-4500; Telefax: 718-768-3978; Telex: 425707)

Vista Chemical Co.

900 Threadneedle, PO Box 19029, Houston, TX 77224-9029 USA (Tel.: 713-588-3000; 800-231-8216; Telefax: 713-588-3236; Telex: 794557)

Vitamins, Inc.

200 E. Randolph Dr., Chicago, IL 60601 USA (Tel.: 312-861-0700; Telefax: 312-861-0708; Telex: 25 4717)

Volclay Ltd., Div. of American Colloid Co

Birkenhead Rd, Wallasey, Merseyside, L44 7BU UK (Tel.: 44 151 638 0967; Telefax: 44 151-630 2764; Telex: 627029)

Vrymeer Commodities, A Ronstadt Group Company

PO Box 545, 36W171 Indian Mound Rd., St. Charles, IL 60174-0545 USA (Tel.: 708-377-2584; Telefax: 708-377-5521)

Vulcan Chemicals, Div. of Vulcan Materials Co.

One Metroplex Dr., Birmingham, AL 35209 USA (Tel.: 205-877-3000; 800-633-8280; Telefax: 205-877-3448; Telex: 59-6108)

VYN-AC Inc.

PO Box 788, Ormond Beach, FL 32175-0788 USA (Tel.: 800-342-8475, #567)

Vyse Gelatin Co.

5010 N. Rose St., Schiller Park, IL 60176 USA (Tel.: 708-678-4780; Telefax: 708-628-0329)

Wacker

Wacker-Chemie GmbH, Div. S, Hanns-Seidel-Platz 4, D-81737 München Germany (Tel.: (089) 62 79 01; Telefax: (089) 62791771; Telex: 5291210)

Wacker Chemicals (USA) Inc., 535 Connecticut Ave., Norwalk, CT 06854 USA (Tel.: 203-866-9400; Telefax: 203-866-9427; Telex: 643 444)

Wacker Silicones Corp., Subsid. of Wacker-Chemie, 3301 Sutton Rd., Adrian, MI 49221-9397 USA (Tel.: 517-264-8500; 800-248-0063; Telefax: 517-264-8246; Telex: 510-450-2700 sadrnud)

Waitaki Int'l. Biosciences

Distributed by Tri-K Industries

Wako Pure Chemical Industries Ltd.

1,2-Doshomachi 3-Chome, Chuo-ku, Osaka, 541 Japan (Tel.: (06) 203-3741; Telefax: (06) 222-1203; Telex: 65188 wakoos j)

Walton Pharmaceuticals Ltd.

Bowes House, Bowes Rd, Walton-on-Thames, Surrey, KT12 3HS UK (Tel.: 44 1932 245585; Telefax: 44 1932 253461; Telex: 928306 WPHARM G)

Wander Ltd.

Station Rd., King's Langley, Hertfordshire, WD4 8LJ UK (Tel.: 44 1923 266122; Telefax: 44 1923 260038; Telex: 922747)

Warner-Jenkinson

Warner-Jenkinson Co., 2526 Baldwin St., St. Louis, MO 63106 USA (Tel.: 314-889-7600; 800-325-8110; Telefax: 314-658-7318; Telex: 44 7184)

Warner-Jenkinson Europe Ltd., Oldmeadow Rd., King's Lynn, Norfolk, PE30 4LA UK (Tel.: 44 1553 763236; Telefax: 44 1553 766891; Telex: 817144)

Warner-Jenkinson Netherlands, Kleine Koppel 39-40, PO Box 1493, 3800 BL Amersfoort The Netherlands (Tel.: 31 33 673411; Telefax: 31 33 650002; Telex: 70924)

Weiders Farmasøytiske A/S

Postboks 9113, Gronland, N-0133 Oslo Norway (Tel.: 47 2-20 54 15; Telefax: 47 22-36 40 52; Telex: 78151 WEIFA N)

Welch, Holme & Clark Co. Inc.

7 Ave. L, Newark, NJ 07105 USA (Tel.: 201-465-1200; Telefax: 201-465-7332)

Welding GmbH & Co.

Grosse Theaterstr. 50, 200 Hamburg 36 Germany (Tel.: 49 40 359080; Telefax: 49 40 403870)

Wensleydale Foods

Mawson House, The Bridge, Aiskew, Bedale, North Yorkshire, DL8 1AW UK (Tel.: 44 1677 424881; Telefax: 44 1677 424588)

Westbrook Lanolin Co., A Div. of Woolcombers (Holdings) Ltd.

Argonaut Works, Laisterdyke, Bradford, West Yorkshire, BD4 8AU UK (Tel.: 44 1274 663331; Telefax: 44 1274-667665; Telex: 51502)

Westbrook Lanolin SA Belge

4-6 Rue Beribou, B-4800 Verviers Belgium (Tel.: 32 87 336121; Telefax: 32 87 316552)

Westco Chemicals, Inc.

11312 Hartland St., North Hollywood, CA 91605 USA (Tel.: 213-877-0077; Telefax: 818-766-7170; Telex: 673150)

Westhove

39 rue Loucheur, BP 73, 62510 Arques France (Tel.: 33 21 38 3316; Telefax: 33 21 98 4437; Telex: 130889)

Westin Inc./Feaster Foods Div.

4727 Center St., Omaha, NE 68106 USA (Tel.: 402-533-3363; Telefax: 402-553-1932)

Westlake Plastics Co.

PO Box 127, W. Lenni Rd., Lenni, PA 19052 USA (Tel.: 215-459-1000; Telefax: 215-459-1084; Telex: 83-5406)

Westvaco Corp., Chemical Div.

PO Box 70848, Charleston Hts., SC 29415-0848 USA (Tel.: 803-740-2300; Telefax: 803-740-2329; Telex: 4611159)

Westwood Chemical Corp.

46 Tower Dr., Middletown, NY 10940 USA (Tel.: 914-692-6721; Telefax: 914-695-1906)

Whitfield Chemicals Ltd.

23 Albert St, Newcastle, Staffordshire, ST5 1JP UK (Tel.: 44 1782 711777; Telefax: 44 1782 717290; Telex: 367165)

Whiting, Peter (Chemicals) Ltd.

5 Lord Napier Place, Upper Mall, London, W6 9UB UK (Tel.: 44 181 741 4025; Telefax: 44 181-741 1737; Telex: 8814670 WHICHEM G)

Whittaker, Clark & Daniels

1000 Coolidge St., South Plainfield, NJ 07080 USA (Tel.: 800-732-0562; Telefax: 800-833-8139; Telex: 221478)

Wilbur-Ellis Co.

PO Box 1286, Fresno, CA 93715 USA (Tel.: 209-442-1220; Telefax: 209-442-4089)

Wilke International Inc.

1375 N. Winchester, Olathe, KS 66061 USA (Tel.: 913-78-5544; 800-779-5545; Telefax: 913-780-5574)

Witco

Witco Corp/Oleochemicals/Surfactants Group, One American Lane, Greenwich, CT 06831-2559 USA (Tel.: 203-552-3382; 800-494-8287; Telefax: 203-552-2893)

Witco Corp., PO Box 125, Memphis, TN 38101-0125 USA (Tel.: 901-684-7000; 800-238-9150; Telefax: 901-761-1851; Telex: 53-298)

Witco Corp/Household, Industrial, Personal Care, One American Lane, Greenwich, CT 06831-2559 USA (Tel.: 800-494-8673; Telefax: 203-552-2878)

Witco Corp/Lubricants Group Golden Bear Prods., 10100 Santa Monica Blvd., Suite 1470, Los Angeles, CA 90067-4183 USA (Tel.: 310-277-4511; Telefax: 310-201-0383)

Witco Corp/Petroleum Specialties Group, One American Lane, Greenwich, CT 06831-2559 USA (Tel.: 203-552-3446; 800-494-8673; Telefax: 203-552-2878)

Witco Corp/Polymer Additives Group, One American Lane, Greenwich, CT 06831-2559 USA (Tel.: 203-552-3294; 800-494-8737; Telefax: 203-552-2010)

Witco Canada Ltd., 2 Lansing Sq., Suite 1200, Willowdale, Ontario, M2J 4Z4 Canada (Tel.: 416-497-9991)

Witco BV, 1 Canalside, Lowesmoor Wharf, Worcester, Worcestershire, WR1 2RS UK (Tel.: 44 1905 21521; Telefax: 44 1905-611593)

Witco Corp/Petroleum Specialties Group-Europe, PO Box 5, 1540 AA Koog aan de Zaan The Netherlands (Tel.: 31 175 283854; Telefax: 31 75 210811)

Rewo Chemische Werke GmbH, Postfach 1160, 36392 Steinau an der Strasse, Max Wolf Strasse 7, Industriegebiet West, W-6497 Steinau Germany (Tel.: 06663-540; Telefax: 06663-54-129; Telex: 493589)

Witco Corp/Petroleum Specialties Group-Asia, 396 Alexandra Rd., #06-04 BP Tower, Singapore 0511 (Tel.: 65 274 3878; Telefax: 65 274 8693)

Alfred L. Wolff GmbH & Co.

Grosse Baeckerstrasse 13, D20095 Hamburg Germany (Tel.: 49 40 362971; Telefax: 49 40 363912; Telex: 211778)

World Trade Service Singapore

142 Killiney Rd., PT 08-148, Devonshire Court, Singapore 0923

E.H. Worlee GmbH & Co.

Grusonstrasse 22, 2000 Hamburg 74 Germany (Tel.: 49 40 733 33-0; Telefax: 49 40 733 332 90; Telex: 212384)

Worthington Biochemical Corp.

Halls Mill Rd, Freehold, NJ 07728 USA (Tel.: 908-462-3838; 800-445-9603; Telefax: 800-368-3108; Telex: 3715614)

Wyckoff Chemical Co., Inc.

1421 Kalamazoo St., South Haven, MI 49090 USA (Tel.: 616-637-8474; Telefax: 616-637-8410)

Wynmouth Lehr Ltd.

Kemp House, 158 City Rd., London, EC1V 2PA UK (Tel.: 44 171 253 5871; Telex: 28293)

Xyrofin

Xyrofin (UK) Ltd., A Cultor Company, 41-51 Brighton Rd., Redhill, Surrey, RH1 6YS UK (Tel.: 44 1737 773732; Telefax: 44 1737 773117; Telex: 938830 XYFIN G)

Xyrofin France SA, 33 Ave. Friedland, 75008 Paris France (Tel.: 33 1 4 053 0909; Telefax: 33 1 4 440 4283)

Xyrofin GmbH, Buchenring 53, D-22359 Hamburg Germany (Tel.: 49 40 603 1239; Telefax: 49 40 603 0387)

American Xyrofin Inc., 1101 Perimeter Dr., Suite 475, Schaumburg, IL 60173 USA (Tel.: 708-413-8200; Telefax: 708-413-8282)

Xyrofin Far East KK, 4F Towa Kanda-Nishikicho Bldg., 3-4 Kanda-Nishikicho, Chiyoda-ku, Tokyo, 101 Japan (Tel.: 81 3 3295 4011; Telefax: 81 3 3295 5299)

Yamamoto Chemicals, Inc.

1-43, Yumizoe-machi Minami, Yao-shi, Osaka, 581 Japan (Tel.: (0729) 49-4561; Telefax: 0729) 49-5479)

Yanagishima Pharmaceutical Co., Ltd.

2-5-5, Nihonbashi Muro-machi, Chuo-ku, Tokyo, 103 Japan (Tel.: (03) 3241-4584; Telefax: (03) 3241-0309)

Yoneyama Chemical Industries, Ltd.

Takahashi Bldg., Higashi-kan, 5-2-18, Nishitenma, Kita-ku, Osaka, 530 Japan (Tel.: (06) 363-0824; Telefax: (06) 365-9982)

Yoneyama Yakuhin Kogyo Co., Ltd.

2-3-11, Dosho-machi, Chuo-ku, Osaka, 541 Japan (Tel.: (06) 231-3555/8; Telefax: (06) 223-1093)

Yoshitomi Pharmaceutical Industries, Ltd.

Hirano-machi Showa Bldg.; 2-6-9, Hiranomachi, Chuo-ku, Osaka, 541 Japan (Tel.: (06) 201-1694; Telefax: (06) 229-0258; Telex: 5225370)

Jesse S. Young Co., Inc.

520 Westfield Ave., Elizabeth, NJ 07208 USA (Tel.: 908-351-0140; Telefax: 908-351-8837)

Yuki Gosei Kogyo Co., Ltd.

Hirakawa-cho CH Bldg., 2-3-24, Hirakawa-cho, Chiyoda-ku, Tokyo, 102 Japan (Tel.: (03) 5275-5067; Telefax: (03) 5275-5079)

Zaclon Inc.

2981 Independence Rd., Cleveland, OH 44115 USA (Tel.: 216-271-1717; 800-356-7327; Telefax: 216-271-1911)

Zeeland Chemicals, Inc., A Cambrex Co.

215 N. Centennial St., Zeeland, MI 49464 USA (Tel.: 616-772-2193; 800-223-0453; Telefax: 616-772-7344; Telex: 226375)

Zeneca Resins

730 Main St., Wilmington, MA 01887 USA (Tel.: 508-658-6600; 800-225-0947; Telefax: 508-657-7978)

Zeochem

1314 S. 12 St., PO Box 35940, Louisville, KY 40232 USA (Tel.: 502-634-7600; Telefax: 502-634-8133; Telex: 204190, 204239)

Zinc Corp. of America

300 Frankfort Rd., Monaca, PA 15061 USA (Tel.: 412-774-1020; 800-962-7500; Telefax: 412-773-2217; Telex: 510-462-1899)

Zinchem, Inc., Subsid. of William Zinsser & Co., Inc.

173 Belmont Dr., Somerset, NJ 08875 USA (Tel.: 908-469-8100; Telefax: 908-469-4539)

Zircar Products Inc.

110 N. Main St., PO Box 458, Florida, NY 10921 USA (Tel.: 914-651-4481; Telefax: 914-651-3192; Telex: 996608)

ZOCHEM, Div. of Hudson Bay Mining & Smelting Co., Ltd.

1 Tilbury Court, PO Box 1120, Brampton, Ontario, L6V 2LB Canada (Tel.: 905-453-4100; Telefax: 905-453-2920)

Zohar Detergent Factory

PO Box 11 300, Tel-Aviv, 61 112 Israel (Tel.: 03-528-7236; Telefax: 03-5287239; Telex: 33557 zohar il)

Zumbro Inc.

c/o Garuda Int'l. Inc., PO Box 5155, Santa Cruz, CA 95063 USA (Tel.: 408-462-6341; Telefax: 408-462-6355; Telex: 296614)

Appendices

Cas Number-to-Trade Name
Cross-Reference

CAS	Trade name	CAS	Trade name	CAS	Trade name
50-21-5	Patlac® LA USP	56-81-5	Emery® 917	64-02-8	Versene 100 EP
50-21-5	Purac® PH 88	56-81-5	Emery® 918	64-02-8	Versene 100 LS
50-21-5	Purac® USP 88	56-81-5	Glycerine (Pharmaceu-	64-02-8	Versene 100 SRG
50-21-5	Lactic Acid 88% USP/		tical)	64-02-8	Versene 100 XL
	FCC	56-81-5	Glycon® G 100	64-02-8	Versene 220
50-70-4	A-641	56-81-5	Glycon® G-300	64-17-5	Punctilious® SDA 1-1
50-70-4	Arlex	56-81-5	Kemstrene® 96.0%	64-19-7	Unichem ACETA
50-70-4	Fancol SORB		USP	65-85-0	Benzoic Acid U.S.P./
50-70-4	Hydex® 100 Coarse	56-81-5	Kemstrene® 99.0%		F.C.C
	Powd.	56-81-5	Kemstrene® 99.7%	67-03-8	Thiamine Hydrochloride
50-70-4	Hydex® 100 Coarse		USP		USP, FCC Regular
	Powd. 35	56-81-5	Natural Glycerine USP		Type No. 601160
50-70-4	Hydex® 100 Gran. 206		96%	67-68-5	DMSO
50-70-4	Hydex® 100 Powd. 60	56-81-5	Natural Glycerine USP	68-04-2	Sodium Citrate USP,
50-70-4	Hydex® Tablet Grade		99%		FCC Dihydrate Fine
50-70-4	Liponic 70-NC	56-81-5	Natural Glycerine USP		Gran. No. 69975
50-70-4	Liponic 76-NC		99.5%	68-19-9	Vitacote® B12 1%
50-70-4	Liponic 83-NC.	56-81-5	Pricerine 9088	68-19-9	Cyanocobalamin USP
50-70-4	Liponic Sorbitol Sol'n.	56-81-5	Star		Cryst. No. 69932
	70% USP	56-81-5	Superol	69-65-8	Unisweet MAN
50-70-4	Liposorb 70	56-86-0	Unamino GLUT	71-36-3	Nacol® 4-99
50-70-4	Sorbelite™ C	57-10-3	Hystrene® 9016	72-17-3	Patlac® NAL
50-70-4	Sorbelite™ FG	57-11-4	Emersol® 6332 NF	72-17-3	Purasal® S/HQ 60
50-70-4	Unisweet 70	57-11-4	Hystrene® 4516	72-17-3	Purasal® S/PF 60
50-70-4	Unisweet 70/CONC	57-11-4	Hystrene® 5016 NF	72-17-3	Purasal® S Powd.
50-70-4	Unisweet CONC	57-11-4	Hystrene® 9718 NF	75-52-5	NM™
50-81-7	Ascorbic Acid USP/	57-55-6	Adeka Propylene	75-65-0	Tebol™
	FCC, 100 Mesh		Glycol (P)	75-65-0	Tebol™ 99
50-81-7	Ascorbic Acid USP,	57-55-6	Propylene Glycol USP/	76-39-1	NMP
	FCC Fine Gran. No.		FCC Ultra Grade	77-86-1	Tris Amino® Molecular
	6045655	57-88-5	Cholesterol NF		Biology Grade
50-81-7	Ascorbic Acid USP,	57-88-5	Fancol CH	77-86-1	Tris Amino® Ultra Pure
	FCC Fine Powd. No.	57-88-5	Loralan-CH		Standard
	6045652	58-56-0	Pyridoxine Hydrochlo-	77-86-1	Tris Amino® Conc.
50-81-7	Ascorbic Acid USP,		ride USP, FCC Fine	77-86-1	Tris Amino® Crystals
	FCC Gran. No.		Powd. No. 60650	77-89-4	ATEC
	6045654	58-85-5	d-Biotin USP, FCC No.	77-90-7	ATBC
50-81-7	Ascorbic Acid USP,		63345	77-92-9	Citric Acid Anhyd. USP/
	FCC Type S No.	58-95-7	Copherol® 1250		FCC
	6045660	59-02-9	Copherol® F-1300	77-92-9	Citric Acid USP FCC
50-81-7	Ascorbic Acid USP,	59-30-3	Folic Acid USP, FCC		Anhyd. Fine Gran. No.
	FCC Ultra-Fine Powd		No. 20383		69941
	No. 6045653	59-67-6	Niacin USP, FCC Fine	77-92-9	Citric Acid USP FCC
50-81-7	Descote® Ascorbic		Granular No. 69901		Anhyd. Gran. No.
	Acid 60%	59-67-6	Niacin USP, FCC No.		69942
50-99-7	Candex®		69902	77-92-9	Descote® Citric Acid
50-99-7	Emdex®	60-00-4	Versene Acid		50%
51-05-8	Unicaine-B	60-29-7	Ethyl Ether USP/ACS	77-93-0	Hydagen® C.A.T
52-51-7	Bronopol	60-33-3	Crossential LS	77-93-0	TEC
52-51-7	Bronopol-Boots® BP	62-33-9	Versene CA	77-94-1	TBC
56-81-5	Croderol GA7000	63-42-3	Unisweet L	78-70-6	Linalool 95
56-81-5	Emery® 912	63-42-3	Unisweet Lactose	79-24-3	NE™
56-81-5	Emery® 916	64-02-8	Versene 100	79-46-9	NiPar S-20™

CAS	Trade name	CAS	Trade name	CAS	Trade name
79-81-2	Vitamin A Palmitate Type PIMO/BH No. 638280100	111-03-5	Cithrol GMO N/E	122-19-0	Arquad® DM18B-90
		111-03-5	Monomuls® 90-O18	122-20-3	TIPA 99
		111-27-3	Nacol® 6-98	122-32-7	Emerest® 2423
79-81-2	Vitamin A Palmitate USP, FCC Type P1.7 No. 262090000	111-60-4	Cerasynt® IP	122-32-7	Hodag GTO
		111-60-4	Cerasynt® M	122-52-1	TEP-HP
		111-60-4	Kemester® EGMS	122-99-6	Phenoxetol
79-81-2	Vitamin A Palmitate USP, FCC Type P1.7/E No. 63699	111-60-4	Lexemul® EGMS	123-03-5	CPC
		111-60-4	Mapeg® EGMS	123-03-5	CPC Sumquat 6060
		111-60-4	Monthyle	123-03-5	Uniquart CPC
81-07-2	Syncal® SDI	111-87-5	Nacol® 8-97	123-28-4	PAG DLTDP
81-07-2	Unisweet SAC	111-87-5	Nacol® 8-99	123-31-9	Tecquinol® USP Grade
81-13-0	Ritapan D	111-90-0	Transcutol	123-51-3	Isoamyl Alcohol 95%
83-88-5	Riboflavin USP, FCC 184045	111-96-6	Diglyme	123-51-3	Isoamyl Alcohol 99%
		112-00-5	Empigen® 5089	123-76-2	Unichem Levula
83-88-5	Riboflavin USP, FCC No. 602940002	112-02-7	Barquat® CT-29	123-94-4	Aldo® MS
		112-02-7	Carsoquat® CT-429	123-94-4	Aldo® MSA
83-88-5	Riboflavin USP, FCC Type S	112-30-1	Cachalot® DE-10	123-94-4	Drewmulse® 200K
		112-30-1	Nacol® 10-97	123-94-4	Drewmulse® 900K
87-99-0	Xylitol C	112-30-1	Nacol® 10-99	124-68-5	AMP
88-04-0	Nipacide® PX-R	112-49-2	Triglyme	124-68-5	AMP-95
88-04-0	Ottasept®	112-53-8	Cachalot® L-90	126-13-6	Eastman® SAIB-SG
88-04-0	Ottasept® Extra	112-53-8	Nacol® 12-96	126-92-1	Niaproof® Anionic Surfactant 08
94-13-3	Nipasol M	112-53-8	Nacol® 12-99		
94-13-3	Propyl Parasept® NF/ FCC	112-53-8	Unihydag Wax 12	128-37-0	CAO®-3
		112-72-1	Dehydag® Wax 14	128-37-0	CAO®-3/Blend 29
94-13-3	Lexgard® P	112-72-1	Lanette® 14	128-44-9	Syncal® GS
94-18-8	Nipabenzyl	112-72-1	Nacol® 14-95	128-44-9	Syncal® GSD
94-26-8	Butyl Parasept® NF	112-72-1	Nacol® 14-98	128-44-9	Syncal® S
94-26-8	Lexgard® B	112-72-1	Unihydag Wax-14	128-44-9	Syncal® SDS
94-26-8	Nipabutyl	112-73-2	Butyl Diglyme	128-44-9	Syncal® US
96-20-8	AB®	112-73-2	Ethyl Diglyme	128-44-9	Unisweet SOSAC
96-27-5	Thiovanol®	112-80-1	Crossential Oleic	130-40-5	Riboflavin-5´-
96-48-0	BLO®	112-80-1	Emersol® 6313 NF		Phosphate Sodium
97-59-6	Allantoin	112-80-1	Emersol® 6321 NF		USP, FCC No. 60296
97-78-9	Sarkosyl® L	112-80-1	Emersol® 6333 NF	131-57-7	Escalol® 567
98-92-0	Niacinamide USP, FCC No. 69905	112-85-6	Hystrene® 7022	131-57-7	Spectra-Sorb® UV 9
		112-85-6	Hystrene® 9022	131-57-7	Syntase® 62
98-92-0	Niacinamide USP, FCC Fine Granular No. 69916	112-92-5	Adol® 61 NF	133-06-2	Vancide® 89 RE
		112-92-5	Cachalot® S-56	134-03-2	Descote® Sodium Ascorbate 50%
		112-92-5	Crodacol S-95NF		
99-76-3	Lexgard® M	112-92-5	Dehydag® Wax 18	134-03-2	Sodium Ascorbate USP, FCC Fine Gran. No. 6047709
99-76-3	Methyl Parasept® NF/ FCC	112-92-5	Epal® 18NF		
		112-92-5	Hyfatol 18-95		
99-76-3	Nipagin M	112-92-5	Hyfatol 18-98	134-03-2	Sodium Ascorbate USP, FCC Fine Powd. No. 6047708
102-60-3	Quadrol®	112-92-5	Lanette® 18		
102-76-1	Eastman® Triacetin	112-92-5	Lanette® 18 DEO		
102-85-2	TBP-HP	112-92-5	Mackol 18	134-03-2	Sodium Ascorbate USP, FCC Type AG No. 6047710
103-23-1	Wickenol® 158	112-92-5	Nacol® 18-94		
104-15-4	Eltesol® TSX	112-92-5	Nacol® 18-98		
104-15-4	Eltesol® TSX/A	112-92-5	Steraffine	137-08-6	Calcium Pantothenate USP, FCC Type SD No. 63924
104-15-4	Eltesol® TSX/SF	112-92-5	Unihydag Wax-18		
104-87-0	PTAL	115-69-5	AMPD		
105-99-7	Cetiol® B	115-70-8	AEPD®	137-16-6	Crodasinic LS30
106-11-6	Nikkol MYS-2	116-17-6	TIPP	137-16-6	Crodasinic LS35
108-03-2	NiPar S-10™	118-60-5	Escalol® 587	137-16-6	Hamposyl® L-30
110-27-0	Isopropylmyristat	118-71-8	Veltol®	137-16-6	Oramix® L30
110-27-0	RITA IPM	119-61-9	Velsicure®	137-66-6	Ascorbyl Palmitate NF, FCC No. 60412
110-71-4	Monoglyme	120-47-8	Ethyl Parasept® NF		
110-86-1	Pyridine 1°	120-47-8	Nipagin A	138-22-7	Purasolv® BL
110-97-4	DIPA Commercial Grade	120-51-4	Unichem BZBN	139-07-1	Catinal MB-50A
		120-80-9	Catechol XP	139-08-2	Catigene® DC 100
110-97-4	DIPA Low Freeze Grade 85	121-32-4	Unisweet EVAN	139-33-3	Sequestrene® NA2
		121-33-5	Unisweet VAN	139-33-3	Versene NA
110-97-4	DIPA Low Freeze Grade 90	121-45-9	TMP-HP	139-33-3	Versene Na2
		121-54-0	Hyamine® 1622 50%	139-88-8	Niaproof® Anionic Surfactant 4
110-97-4	DIPA NF Grade	121-54-0	Hyamine® 1622 Crystals		
111-01-3	Robane®			139-89-9	Versenol 120
111-02-4	Supraene®	122-03-2	Cumal	139-96-8	Stepanol® WAT

CAS	Trade name	CAS	Trade name	CAS	Trade name
140-01-2	Cheelox® 80	151-21-3	Texapon® K-1296	593-60-2	Saytex® VBR
140-01-2	Versenex 80		Needles	597-09-1	NEPD
141-01-5	Descote® Ferrous	151-21-3	Texapon® K-1296	616-45-5	2-Pyrol®
	Fumarate 60%		Powd.	624-04-4	Kemester® EGDL
141-08-2	Aldo® MR	151-21-3	Texapon® K-1296 USP	627-83-8	Kemester® EGDS
141-08-2	Cithrol GMR N/E	151-21-3	Texapon® Z	627-83-8	Mapeg® EGDS
141-08-2	Hodag GMR	151-21-3	Zoharpon LAS	627-83-8	Pegosperse® 50 DS
141-08-2	Hodag GMR-D	151-21-3	Zoharpon LAS Spray	629-70-9	Pelemol® CA
141-08-2	Rilanit GMRO		Dried	629-82-3	Cetiol® OE
141-08-2	Softigen® 701	299-27-4	Gluconal® K	629-96-9	Nacol® 20-95
141-43-5	MEA Commercial	299-28-5	Gluconal® CA A	646-13-9	Pelemol® IBS
	Grade	299-28-5	Gluconal® CA M	659-40-5	Elestab® HP 100
141-43-5	MEA Low Freeze	299-29-6	Gluconal® FE	661-19-8	Cachalot® Behenyl
	Grade	300-92-5	Haro® Chem ALMD-2		Alcohol BE-22
141-43-5	MEA Low Iron Grade	463-40-1	Crossential ALA	661-19-8	Dehydag® Wax 22
141-43-5	MEA Low Iron-Low	471-53-4	Nikkol Glycyrrhetinic		(Lanette)
	Freeze Grade		Acid	661-19-8	Lanette® 22 Flakes
141-43-5	MEA NF Grade	506-26-3	Crossential GLA	661-19-8	Nacol® 22-97
141-94-6	Hexetidine 90	515-69-5	Hydagen® B	661-19-8	Nikkol Behenyl Alcohol
141-94-6	Hexetidine 99	515-98-0	Purasal® NH 70		65, 80
142-18-7	Cithrol GML N/E	527-07-1	Gluconal® NA	661-19-8	Unihydag Wax 22
142-18-7	Hodag GML	527-09-3	Descote® Copper	693-36-7	PAG DSTDP
142-18-7	Imwitor® 312		Gluconate 20%	770-12-7	PDCP
142-55-2	Cithrol PGML N/E	527-09-3	Gluconal® CU	814-80-2	Puracal® PG
142-55-2	Lauroglycol	532-32-1	Sodium Benzoate	814-80-2	Puracal® PP
142-91-6	Isopropylpalmitat		BP88	814-80-2	Puracal® TG
142-91-6	Lexol® IPP	532-43-4	Thiamine Mononitrate	816-94-4	Phospholipon® SC
142-91-6	Lexol® IPP-A		USP, FCC Fine Powd.	822-16-2	Haro® Chem NG
142-91-6	Lexol® IPP-NF		No. 601340	867-13-0	TEPA
142-91-6	RITA IPP	538-23-8	Captex® 8000	872-50-4	Pharmasolve™
143-00-0	Stepanol® DEA	538-24-9	Dynasan® 112	900-28-6	Granular Gum Ghatti
143-07-7	Hystrene® 9512	538-24-9	Lipo 320		#1
143-07-7	Philacid 1200	540-10-3	Crodamol CP	900-28-6	Powdered Gum Ghatti
143-28-2	Adol® 90 NF	540-10-3	Cutina® CP		#1
143-28-2	Fancol OA-95	540-10-3	Kessco® 653	900-28-6	Powdered Gum Ghatti
143-28-2	Novol NF	540-10-3	Kessco CP		#2
144-55-8	Sodium Bicarbonate	540-10-3	Pelemol® CP	900-28-6	Premium Powdered
	USP No. 1 Powd.	540-10-3	Precifac ATO		Gum Ghatti G-1
144-55-8	Sodium Bicarbonate	540-10-3	Standamul® 1616	900-28-6	Staform P
	USP No. 2 Fine Gran	540-10-3	W.G.S. Cetyl Palmitate	915-67-3	Amaranth Oil
144-55-8	Sodium Bicarbonate	544-35-4	Safester A-75	915-67-3	Pre-Gel Amaranth
	USP No. 3 Extra Fine	544-62-7	Nikkol Batyl Alcohol		Powd.
	Powd.		100, EX	996-31-6	Purasal® P/HQ 60
144-55-8	Sodium Bicarbonate	546-93-0	Marinco® CH	996-31-6	Purasal® P/USP 60
	USP No. 5 Coarse	546-93-0	Unichem MC	1119-97-7	Pentonium 4Br40
	Gran	546-93-0	Unichem MGC	1302-78-9	Albagel Premium USP
150-13-0	4-Aminobenzoic Acid,	555-43-1	Dynasan® 118		4444
	Pure, No. 102	555-44-2	Dynasan® 116	1302-78-9	Bentonite USP BC 670
151-21-3	Empicol® 0185	555-45-3	Dynasan® 114	1302-78-9	Korthix H-NF
151-21-3	Empicol® LX100	557-04-0	Cecavon MG 51	1302-78-9	Polargel® HV
151-21-3	Empicol® LXS95	557-04-0	Haro® Chem MF-2	1302-78-9	Polargel® NF
151-21-3	Empicol® LXV100	557-04-0	Petrac® Magnesium	1302-78-9	Polargel® T
151-21-3	Empicol® LXV/D		Stearate MG-20 NF	1305-62-0	Calcium Hydroxide
151-21-3	Naxolate™ WA-97	557-04-0	Synpro® Magnesium		USP 802
151-21-3	Naxolate™ WAG		Stearate NF	1309-42-8	Hydro-Magma
151-21-3	Polystep® B-3	557-05-1	Cecavon ZN 70	1309-42-8	Magnesium Hydroxide
151-21-3	Stepanol® ME Dry	557-05-1	Cecavon ZN 71		Fluid 25
151-21-3	Stepanol® WA-100	557-05-1	Cecavon ZN 72	1309-42-8	Magnesium Hydroxide
151-21-3	Stepanol® WAC	557-05-1	Cecavon ZN 73		HD
151-21-3	Stepanol® WA Extra	557-05-1	Cecavon ZN 735	1309-42-8	Magnesium Hydroxide
151-21-3	Stepanol® WA Paste	557-05-1	Haro® Chem ZPR-2		Paste
151-21-3	Stepanol® WAQ	557-05-1	Synpro® Zinc Stearate	1309-42-8	Magnesium Hydroxide
151-21-3	Stepanol® WA Special		USP		Powd.
151-21-3	Supralate® C	557-05-1	Witco® Zinc Stearate	1309-42-8	Magnesium Hydroxide
151-21-3	Texapon® K-12		U.S.P.-D		USP
	Needles	577-11-7	Nikkol OTP-100S	1309-42-8	Magnesium Hydroxide
151-21-3	Texapon® K-12 Powd.	585-88-6	Amalty®		USP DC
151-21-3	Texapon® K-12 USP	585-88-6	Finmalt L	1309-42-8	Marinco H-USP

CAS	Trade name	CAS	Trade name	CAS	Trade name
1309-48-4	Magnesium Oxide USP 30 Light	1332-58-7	Peerless® No. 4	1393-63-1	Annatto Powd. WS
1309-48-4	Magnesium Oxide USP 60 Light	1333-39-7	Eltesol® PSA 65	1405-86-3	Nikkol Glycyrrhizic Acid
		1337-76-4	Pharmasorb Colloidal Pharmaceutical Grade	1406-70-8	Vitamin E Acetate USP Oil
1309-48-4	Magnesium Oxide USP 90 Light	1338-39-2	Ablunol S-20	1406-70-8	Vitamin E USP, FCC No. 60525
1309-48-4	Magnesium Oxide USP Heavy	1338-39-2	Crill 1		
		1338-39-2	Drewmulse® SML	1406-70-8	Vitamin E USP, FCC No. 60526
1309-48-4	Marinco OH	1338-39-2	Ethylan® GL20		
1309-48-4	Marinco OL	1338-39-2	Glycomul® L	1406-70-8	Vitinc® dl-alpha Tocopheryl Acetate USP XXII
1314-13-2	USP-1	1338-39-2	Montane® 20		
1314-13-2	USP-2	1338-39-2	Nissan Nonion LP-20R, LP-20RS	1407-03-0	Magnasweet®
1314-13-2	Zinc Oxide USP 66			1493-13-6	FC-24
1317-65-3	Micro-White® 10 Codex	1338-39-2	Sorbitol L	1493-13-6	Fluorad® FC-24
		1338-39-2	Sorgen 90	1592-23-0	Haro® Chem CPR-2
1317-65-3	Micro-White® 25 Codex	1338-39-2	Span® 20	1592-23-0	Synpro® Calcium Stearate NF
1317-65-3	Micro-White® 50 Codex	1338-41-6	Ablunol S-60		
		1338-41-6	Arlacel® 60	1634-04-4	High Purity MTBE
1317-65-3	Micro-White® 100 Codex	1338-41-6	Capmul® S	1643-20-5	Empigen® OB
		1338-41-6	Crill 3	1777-82-8	Myacide® SP
1318-02-1	Abscents® Deodorizing Powd.	1338-41-6	Dehymuls® SMS	2235-54-3	Stepanol® AM
		1338-41-6	Drewmulse® SMS	2235-54-3	Stepanol® AM-V
1323-03-1	Cegesoft® C 17	1338-41-6	Ethylan® GS60	2277-28-3	Myverol® 18-92
1323-03-1	Ceraphyl® 50	1338-41-6	Glycomul® S	2425-77-6	Isofol® 16
1323-03-1	Pelemol® ML	1338-41-6	Kemester® S60	2524-64-3	DPCP
1323-39-3	Nikkol PMS-1C	1338-41-6	Montane® 60	2537-48-6	DECMP
1323-39-3	Aldo® PGHMS	1338-41-6	Nissan Nonion SP-60R	2644-64-6	Phospholipon® PC
1323-39-3	Cerasynt® PA	1338-41-6	Rheodol AS-10	2695-37-6	Spinomar NaSS
1323-39-3	Cithrol PGMS N/E	1338-41-6	S-Maz® 60K	2778-96-3	Ritachol® SS
1323-39-3	Drewmulse® 10K	1338-41-6	Sorbirol S	2809-21-4	Turpinal® SL
1323-39-3	Kessco PGMS	1338-41-6	Sorgen 50	2915-57-3	Wickenol® 159
1323-83-7	Kessco® Glycerol Distearate 386F	1338-41-6	Span® 60	3055-96-7	Dehydol® PID 6
		1338-41-6	Span® 60K	3097-08-3	Stepanol® MG
1327-36-2	Kaopolite® 1147	1338-41-6	Span® 60 VS	3151-59-5	Unifluorid H 101
1327-36-2	Kaopolite® SF	1338-43-8	Ablunol S-80	3179-81-5	Cerasynt® 303
1327-36-2	Suspengel Elite	1338-43-8	Arlacel® 80	3234-85-3	Ceraphyl® 424
1327-36-2	Suspengel Micro	1338-43-8	Armotan® MO	3234-85-3	Cetiol® MM
1327-36-2	Suspengel Ultra	1338-43-8	Crill 4	3234-85-3	Crodamol MM
1327-41-9	Reach® 101	1338-43-8	Crill 50	3234-85-3	Pelemol® MM
1327-41-9	Reach® 103	1338-43-8	Dehymuls® SMO	3436-44-0	Phospholipon® CC
1327-41-9	Reach® 301	1338-43-8	Drewmulse® SMO	3598-16-1	Niacet Sodium Phenoxy Acetate
1327-41-9	Reach® 301 Sol'n.	1338-43-8	Ethylan® GO80		
1327-41-9	Reach® 501	1338-43-8	Glycomul® O	3632-91-5	Gluconal® MG
1327-41-9	Reach® 501 Sol'n.	1338-43-8	Kemester® S80	3687-46-5	Cetiol® V
1327-41-9	Ritachlor 50%	1338-43-8	Montane® 80	3687-46-5	Pelemol® DO
1327-41-9	Westchlor® 200	1338-43-8	Nissan Nonion OP-80R	3687-46-5	Standamul® CTV
1327-41-9	Westchlor® 200 Custom Powd. 10	1338-43-8	Rheodol AO-10	3794-83-0	Turpinal® 4 NL
		1338-43-8	Sorbirol O	3913-02-8	Isofol® 12
1327-41-9	Westchlor® 200 Impalpable	1338-43-8	Sorgen 40	4070-80-8	Pruv™
		1344-95-2	Micro-Cel® C	4169-04-4	Propylene Phenoxetol
1327-41-9	Westchlor® DM 200 Impalpable	1390-65-4	Carmacid Y	4468-02-4	Gluconal® ZN
		1390-65-4	Carmine FG	4748-78-1	Ebal
1327-41-9	Chlorhydrol® 50% Sol'n	1390-65-4	Carmine PG	4767-03-7	DMPA®
		1390-65-4	Carmine Powd. 272010, 272015, 272020	4940-11-8	Veltol®-Plus
1327-41-9	Chlorhydrol® Granular			5026-62-0	Nipagin M Sodium
1327-41-9	Chlorhydrol®, Impalpable	1390-65-4	Carmine Powd. WS	5274-68-0	Simulsol® P4
		1390-65-4	Carmine XY/UF	5333-42-6	Eutanol® G
1327-41-9	Chlorhydrol® Powd.	1390-65-4	Carmisol A	5333-42-6	Isofol® 20
1327-41-9	Macrospherical® 95	1390-65-4	Carmisol NA	5466-77-3	Escalol® 557
1327-41-9	Micro-Dry®	1390-65-4	Natural Liquid AP Carmine Colorant	5743-27-1	Calcium Ascorbate FCC No. 60475
1327-41-9	Micro-Dry® Super-ultrafine	1390-65-4	Natural Liquid Carmine Colorant (Type 100, 50, and Simple)	5743-34-0	Gluconal® CA M B
				5905-52-2	Puramex® FE
1327-41-9	Micro-Dry® Ultrafine			6197-30-4	Escalol® 597
1330-80-9	Cithrol PGMO N/E	1390-65-4	Natural Soluble Carmine Powd.	6283-92-7	Ceraphyl® 31
1332-58-7	Peerless® No. 1			6485-34-3	Syncal® CAS
1332-58-7	Peerless® No. 2	1390-65-4	Natural Soluble Powder AP Carmine Colorant	6485-34-3	Unisweet CALSAC
1332-58-7	Peerless® No. 3			6485-39-8	Gluconal® MN

CAS	Trade name	CAS	Trade name	CAS	Trade name
6818-37-7	Unifluorid D 401		Soybean Oil USP		A6000
6938-94-9	Ceraphyl® 230	8001-23-8	Neobee® 18	8002-48-0	Pure Malt Colorant
7047-84-9	Synpro® Aluminum Monostearate NF	8001-23-8	Super Refined® Safflower Oil	8002-48-0	A6001
7047-84-9	Synpro® Aluminum Stearate USP	8001-25-0	EmCon Olive	8002-48-0	Extramalt Dark
		8001-25-0	Super Refined® Olive Oil	8002-50-4	Neobee® SL-120
7446-19-7	Zinc Sulfate Monohydrate CP Grade	8001-29-4	Super Refined® Cottonseed Oil	8002-50-4	Super Refined® Menhaden Oil
7447-40-7	Controlled Particle Size KCl	8001-30-7	Lipex 104	8002-74-2	Koster Keunen Paraffin Wax
7447-40-7	Free-flowing KCl	8001-30-7	Super Refined® Corn Oil	8006-54-0	Anhydrous Lanolin Grade 1
7447-40-7	Standard KCl	8001-31-8	Cobee 76	8006-54-0	Anhydrous Lanolin Grade 2
7447-40-7	Superfine KCl	8001-31-8	Coconut Oil® 76	8006-54-0	Anhydrous Lanolin P.80
7447-40-7	Wholecut KCl	8001-31-8	Coconut Oil® 92		
7491-02-3	Pelemol® DIPS	8001-31-8	Pureco® 76	8006-54-0	Anhydrous Lanolin P.95
7491-14-7	Dipsal	8001-39-6	Ross Japan Wax	8006-54-0	Anhydrous Lanolin Superfine
7585-39-9	Beta W7	8001-75-0	Koster Keunen Ceresine		
7585-39-9	Beta W7 P			8006-54-0	Anhydrous Lanolin USP
7585-39-9	Cavitron Cyclo-dextrin.™	8001-75-0	Ross Ceresine Wax	8006-54-0	Anhydrous Lanolin USP Cosmetic
7631-86-9	Hyflo Super-Cel	8001-78-3	Castorwax® MP-70		
7631-86-9	Tixosil 311	8001-78-3	Castorwax® NF	8006-54-0	Anhydrous Lanolin USP Cosmetic AA
7647-14-5	Sterling® Purified USP Salt	8001-78-3	Cutina® HR Powd.	8006-54-0	Anhydrous Lanolin USP Cosmetic Grade
		8001-78-3	Ross Castor Wax		
7651-02-7	Lipamine SPA	8001-78-3	Unitina HR	8006-54-0	Anhydrous Lanolin USP Deodorized AAA
7659-95-2	Natural Red Beet Liq. 275280	8001-79-4	AA USP	8006-54-0	Anhydrous Lanolin USP Pharmaceutical
		8001-79-4	Castor Oil USP		
7695-91-2	Tri-K Vitamin E Acetate	8001-79-4	Cosmetok® X	8006-54-0	Anhydrous Lanolin USP Pharmaceutical Grade
7720-78-7	Descote® Ferrous Sulfate 60%	8001-79-4	Crystal® Crown	8006-54-0	Anhydrous Lanolin USP Pharmaceutical Light Grade
		8001-79-4	Crystal® Crown LP		
7722-76-1	Albrite® Monoammo-nium Phosphate Food Grade	8001-79-4	Crystal® O		
		8001-79-4	Diamond Quality®	8006-54-0	Anhydrous Lanolin USP Superfine
		8001-79-4	EmCon CO		
7722-84-1	Albone® 35 CG	8001-79-4	Lanaetex CO	8006-54-0	Anhydrous Lanolin USP Ultrafine
7722-84-1	Albone® 50 CG	8001-79-4	York Krystal Kleer Castor Oil	8006-54-0	Anhydrous Lanolin USP X-tra Deodorized
7722-84-1	Albone® 70CG				
7722-84-1	Ringwell	8001-79-4	York USP Castor Oil	8006-54-0	Clearlan® 1650
7747-35-5	Oxaban®-E	8002-03-7	Super Refined® Peanut Oil	8006-54-0	Corona Lanolin
7757-93-9	Albrite® Dicalcium Phosphate Anhyd			8006-54-0	Coronet Lanolin
		8002-23-1	W.G.S. Synaceti 116 NF/USP	8006-54-0	Cosmetic Lanolin
7757-93-9	Anhydrous Emcom-press®	8002-31-1	Fancol CB	8006-54-0	Cosmetic Lanolin Anhydrous USP
7758-87-4	Calfos	8002-31-1	Fancol CB Extra		
7778-18-9	Terra Alba 114836	8002-43-5	Alcolec® Granules	8006-54-0	Emery® 1650
7783-28-0	Albrite® Diammonium Phosphate Food Grade	8002-43-5	Asol	8006-54-0	Emery® 1656
		8002-43-5	Capcithin™	8006-54-0	Emery® 1660
7785-26-4	alpha-Pinene P&F, FCC	8002-43-5	Capsulec 51-SB	8006-54-0	Emery® HP-2050
		8002-43-5	Capsulec 51-UB	8006-54-0	Emery® HP-2060
7789-77-7	Emcompress®	8002-43-5	Capsulec 56-SB	8006-54-0	Fluilan
8001-21-6	GTO 80	8002-43-5	Capsulec 56-UB	8006-54-0	Ivarlan™ Light
8001-21-6	GTO 90	8002-43-5	Capsulec 62-SB	8006-54-0	Lanolin Anhydrous USP
8001-21-6	GTO 90E	8002-43-5	Capsulec 62-UB		
8001-21-6	Neobee® SL-130	8002-43-5	Centrolex® F	8006-54-0	Lanolin Pharmaceutical
8001-21-6	NS-20	8002-43-5	Centrolex® P	8006-54-0	Lanolin U.S.P.
8001-21-6	Sunyl® 80	8002-43-5	Dulectin	8006-54-0	Lanolin USP
8001-21-6	Sunyl® 80 RBD	8002-43-5	Emulmetik™ 970	8006-54-0	Lantrol® HP-2073
8001-21-6	Sunyl® 80 RBD ES	8002-43-5	Lecigran™ 5750	8006-54-0	Medilan™
8001-21-6	Sunyl® 80 RBWD	8002-43-5	Lecigran™ 6750	8006-54-0	Pharmaceutical Lanolin
8001-21-6	Sunyl® 80 RBWD ES	8002-43-5	Lecigran™ A	8006-54-0	RITA Lanolin
8001-21-6	Sunyl® 90	8002-43-5	Lecigran™ F	8006-54-0	Sorba
8001-21-6	Sunyl® 90 RBD	8002-43-5	Lecigran™ M	8006-54-0	Super Corona Lanolin
8001-21-6	Sunyl® 90 RBWD	8002-43-5	PhosPho F-97	8006-54-0	Superfine Lanolin
8001-21-6	Sunyl® 90E RBWD	8002-43-5	PhosPho LCN-TS		
8001-21-6	Sunyl® 90E RBWD ES 1016	8002-43-5	PhosPho T-20		
		8002-43-5	Phospholipon® 80		
8001-21-6	Sunyl® HS 500	8002-48-0	Non-Diastatic Malt Syrup #40600		
8001-22-7	Neobee® SL-110				
8001-22-7	Super Refined®	8002-48-0	Pure Malt Colorant		

CAS	Trade name	CAS	Trade name	CAS	Trade name
8006-54-0	White Swan		Powd.	9000-01-5	Gum Arabic, Purified,
8006-54-0	Yeoman	8028-89-5	B&C Caramel Powd.		Spray-Dried No. 1834
8006-95-9	EmCon W	8028-89-5	Caramel Color Double	9000-01-5	Natural Arabic Type
8006-95-9	Super Refined® Wheat		Strength		Gum Purified, Spray-
	Germ Oil	8028-89-5	Caramel Color Single		Dried
8007-43-0	Arlacel® 83		Strength	9000-01-5	Powdered Gum Arabic
8007-43-0	Crill 43	8028-89-5	Double Strength Acid		NF/FCC G-150
8007-43-0	Dehymuls® SSO		Proof Caramel Colour	9000-01-5	Powdered Gum Arabic
8007-43-0	Glycomul® SOC	8028-89-5	Powdered Caramel		NF/FCC Superselect
8007-43-0	Montane® 83		Color 986010		Type NB-4
8007-43-0	Nissan Nonion OP-	8028-89-5	Powdered Caramel	9000-01-5	Powdered Gum Arabic
	83RAT		Color, Acid Proof		Type B-100 NF
8007-43-0	Rheodol AO-15	8028-89-5	Powdered Caramel		Premium
8007-43-0	Sorbirol SQ		Colour Non-	9000-01-5	Powdered Gum Arabic
8007-43-0	Sorgen 30		Ammoniated-All Natural		Type B-200 NF
8007-69-0	Super Refined®		T-717		Premium
	Almond Oil	8028-89-5	Single Strength Acid	9000-01-5	Premium Spray Dried
8008-74-0	Lipovol SES		Proof Caramel Colour		Gum Arabic
8008-74-0	Sesame Oil USP/NF 16	8028-89-5	Unisweet Caramel	9000-01-5	Spray Dried Gum
8008-74-0	Super Refined®	8029-43-4	42/43 Corn Syrup		Arabic NF/FCC CM
	Sesame Oil	8029-43-4	Jungbunzlauer GS	9000-01-5	Spray Dried Gum
8009-03-8	Mineral Jelly No. 14		7097		Arabic NF/FCC CS
8009-03-8	Mineral Jelly No. 17	8029-76-3	Alcolec® Z-3		(Low Bacteria)
8009-03-8	Ointment Base No. 3	8030-12-4	Special Fat 168T	9000-01-5	Spray Dried Gum
8009-03-8	Ointment Base No. 4	8030-76-0	Yelkin F		Arabic NF/FCC CS-R
8009-03-8	Ointment Base No. 6	8030-76-0	Yelkin G	9000-01-5	Spray Dried Gum
8009-03-8	Penreco Amber	8030-76-0	Yelkin P		Arabic NF Type CSP
8009-03-8	Penreco Blond	8030-78-2	Noramium MS 50	9000-01-5	Spray Dried Gum
8009-03-8	Penreco Cream	8031-44-5	Distilled Lipolan		Arabic Type A-180 NF
8009-03-8	Penreco Lily	8031-44-5	Fancol HL		Premium
8009-03-8	Penreco Regent	8031-44-5	Lipolan Distilled	9000-01-5	Spray Dried Gum
8009-03-8	Penreco Royal	8031-44-5	Lipolan S		Arabic Type A-230 NF
8009-03-8	Penreco Snow	8031-44-5	Super-Sat		Extra
8009-03-8	Penreco Super	8036-77-9	G-1441	9000-01-5	Spray Dried Gum Talha
8009-03-8	Penreco Ultima	8038-43-5	Vigilan		(Acacia)
8015-67-6	Bixin Crystal 95	8038-93-5	Chloracel® 40% Sol'n	9000-01-5	Spray Dried Gum Talha
8015-67-6	Natural Yellow Colour	8038-93-5	Chloracel® Solid		(Acacia) Special
	Q-500, Q-1000, Q-2000	8039-09-6	Lan-Aqua-Sol 50	9000-01-5	Spray Dried Kordofan
8015-67-6	Norbixin 40	8039-09-6	Lan-Aqua-Sol 100		Gum Arabic
8015-67-6	Unibix W	8039-09-6	Laneto 50	9000-01-5	TIC Pretested® Arabic
8015-86-9	Koster Keunen	8040-05-9	Monomuls® 90-15		FT-1 USP
	Carnauba	8042-47-5	Drakeol® 5	9000-07-1	Aquagel SP 399
8015-86-9	Koster Keunen	8042-47-5	Drakeol® 6	9000-07-1	CI-100
	Carnauba, Powd.	8042-47-5	Drakeol® 7	9000-07-1	CM-80
8015-86-9	Ross Carnauba Wax	8042-47-5	Drakeol® 9	9000-07-1	Cracked Bleached Irish
8016-70-4	Akolizer S	8042-47-5	Drakeol® 13		Moss
8016-70-4	Sterotex® HM	8042-47-5	Drakeol® 19	9000-07-1	Genu® Carrageenan
8021-55-4	Koster Keunen	8042-47-5	Drakeol® 21	9000-07-1	Genugel® Series
	Ozokerite	8042-47-5	Drakeol® 32	9000-07-1	Genuvisco
8024-09-7	EmCon Walnut	8042-47-5	Drakeol® 34	9000-07-1	Soageena®
8027-32-5	Fonoline® White	8042-47-5	Drakeol® 35	9000-07-1	Soageena® LX7
8027-32-5	Fonoline® Yellow	8050-81-5	Hodag Antifoam F-1	9000-07-1	Soageena® LX26
8027-32-5	Perfecta® USP	8050-81-5	Mazu® DF 200SP	9000-07-1	Soageena® WX87
8027-32-5	Protopet® Alba	8050-81-5	Wacker Silicone	9000-07-1	Stamere® CK-S
8027-32-5	Protopet® White 1S		Antifoam Emulsion SE	9000-07-1	Stamere® N-325
8027-32-5	Protopet® White 2L		9	9000-07-1	Stamere® N-350
8027-32-5	Protopet® White 3C	8051-15-8	Nikkol GBW-25	9000-07-1	Stamere® N-350 S
8027-32-5	Protopet® Yellow 2A	8051-73-8	Nikkol GBW-125	9000-07-1	Stamere® NI
8027-32-5	Protopet® Yellow 3C	8067-32-1	Precirol WL 2155 ATO	9000-30-0	Edicol®
8027-32-5	Protopet® Yellow A	9000-01-5	Granular Gum Arabic	9000-30-0	Edicol® P
8027-32-5	Super White Fonoline®		NF/FCC C-4010	9000-30-0	Edicol® ULV Series
8027-32-5	Super White Protopet®	9000-01-5	Granular Gum Arabic	9000-30-0	Powdered Gum Guar
8027-32-5	Fancol LA		Type A-1 NF Premium		NF Type 80 Mesh B/T
8027-33-6	Hartolan	9000-01-5	Granular Gum Arabic	9000-30-0	Powdered Guar Gum
8027-33-6	Ritawax		Type A-2 NF Premium		Type A
8027-33-6	Ritawax Super	9000-01-5	Gum Arabic NF, Tech	9000-30-0	Powdered Guar Gum
8027-33-6	Super Hartolan	9000-01-5	Gum Arabic NF/FCC		Type AA
8028-89-5	Acid Proof Caramel		Clean Amber Sorts	9000-30-0	Powdered Guar Gum

CAS	Trade name	CAS	Trade name	CAS	Trade name
	Type B	9000-65-1	Powdered Gum Tragacanth Type C-5 NF	9000-70-8	P-4 Pharmaceutical Gelatin
9000-30-0	Powdered Guar Gum Type BB			9000-70-8	P-5 Pharmaceutical Gelatin
9000-30-0	Powdered Gum Guar Type 140 Mesh B/T	9000-65-1	Powdered Gum Tragacanth Type G-1 NF Premium	9000-70-8	P-6 Pharmaceutical Gelatin
9000-30-0	Powdered Gum Guar Type ECM	9000-65-1	Powdered Gum Tragacanth Type G-2 NF Premium	9000-70-8	P-7 Pharmaceutical Gelatin
9000-30-0	Powdered Gum Guar Type M			9000-70-8	P-8 Pharmaceutical Gelatin
9000-30-0	Powdered Gum Guar Type MM FCC	9000-65-1	Powdered Gum Tragacanth Type G-2S NF Premium	9000-70-8	P-9 Pharmaceutical Gelatin
9000-30-0	Powdered Gum Guar Type MM (HV)	9000-65-1	Powdered Gum Tragacanth Type M-3 NF Premium	9000-70-8	P-10 Pharmaceutical Gelatin
9000-30-0	Powdered Gum Guar Type MMM $^1/_2$			9000-70-8	Spray Dried Fish Gelatin
9000-30-0	Powdered Gum Guar Type MMW	9000-65-1	Powdered Tragacanth Gum Type A/10	9000-70-8	Spray Dried Hydrolysed Fish Gelatin
9000-30-0	Supercol® Guar Gum	9000-65-1	Powdered Tragacanth Gum Type E-1	9000-70-8	Vee Gee Pharmaceuti-
9000-30-0	Ticolv	9000-65-1	Powdered Tragacanth Gum Type G-3		cal Gelatins
9000-36-6	Karaya Gum #1 FCC			9000-92-4	Biodiastase 1000
9000-36-6	Powdered Gum Karaya Superfine #1 FCC	9000-65-1	Powdered Tragacanth Gum Type L	9000-92-4	Biodiastase Conc.
9000-36-6	Powdered Gum Karaya Superfine XXXX FCC	9000-65-1	Powdered Tragacanth Gum Type W	9000-92-4	Diastase JP
				9001-62-1	Lipase 8 Powd.
9000-36-6	Premium Powdered Gum Karaya No. 1	9000-65-1	TIC Pretested® Tragacanth 440	9001-62-1	Lipase 16 Powd.
9000-36-6	Premium Powdered Gum Karaya No. 1 Special	9000-65-1	Tragacanth Flake No. 27	9001-62-1	Lipase 24 Powd.
				9001-62-1	Lipase 30 Powd.
9000-40-2	Locust Bean Gum Type A-100	9000-65-1	Tragacanth Gum Ribbon No. 1	9001-62-1	Pancreatic Lipase 250
				9001-75-6	Pepsin 1:3000 NF XII Powd.
9000-40-2	Locust Bean Gum Type A-250	9000-69-5	Genu® HM USP 100		
		9000-69-5	Genu® HM USP L200	9001-75-6	Pepsin 1:10,000 Powd. or Gran
9000-40-2	Locust Bean Gum Type A-270	9000-69-5	Genu® Pectins		
9000-40-2	Locust Bean Gum Pharmaceutical Grade	9000-69-5	Genu® Pectin (citrus) type USP/100	9001-75-6	Pepsin 1:15,000 Powd.
				9002-07-7	Trypsin 1:75
9000-40-2	Locust Bean Gum Speckless Type D-200	9000-69-5	Genu® Pectin (citrus) type USP/200	9002-07-7	Trypsin 1:80
				9002-07-7	Trypsin 1:150
9000-40-2	Powdered Locust Bean Gum Type D-200	9000-69-5	Genu® Pectin (citrus) type USP-H	9002-18-0	Agar-Agar
				9002-18-0	Agar Agar NF Flake #1
9000-40-2	Powdered Locust Bean Gum Type D-300	9000-69-5	Genu® Pectin (citrus) type USP-L/200	9002-18-0	Powdered Agar Agar Bacteriological Grade
9000-40-2	Powdered Locust Bean Gum Type P-100	9000-69-5	Mexpectin LA 100 Range	9002-18-0	Powdered Agar Agar NF M-100 (Gracilaria)
9000-40-2	Powdered Locust Bean Gum Type PP-100	9000-69-5	Mexpectin LC 700 Range	9002-18-0	Powdered Agar Agar NF MK-60
9000-40-2	Seagel L	9000-69-5	Mexpectin XSS 100 Range	9002-18-0	Powdered Agar Agar NF MK-80-B
9000-65-1	Gum Tragacanth Ribbons and Flakes	9000-70-8	Bone Gelatin Type B 200 Bloom	9002-18-0	Powdered Agar Agar NF MK-80 (Bacterio- logical)
9000-65-1	Powdered Gum Tragacanth BP	9000-70-8	Croda 50 Bloom Gelatin	9002-18-0	Powdered Agar Agar NF S-100
9000-65-1	Powdered Gum Tragacanth T-150	9000-70-8	Croda 60 Bloom Alkaline Processed Gelatin	9002-18-0	Powdered Agar Agar NF S-100-B
9000-65-1	Powdered Gum Tragacanth T-200	9000-70-8	Croda 160 Bloom Limed Gelatin	9002-18-0	Powdered Agar Agar NF S-150
9000-65-1	Powdered Gum Tragacanth T-300	9000-70-8	Croda 190 Bloom Acid Ossein Gelatin	9002-18-0	Powdered Agar Agar NF S-150-B
9000-65-1	Powdered Gum Tragacanth T-400	9000-70-8	Croda 250 Bloom Acid Ossein Gelatin	9002-18-0	Powdered Agar Agar Type K-60
9000-65-1	Powdered Gum Tragacanth T-500	9000-70-8	Crodyne BY-19	9002-18-0	Powdered Agar Agar Type K-80
		9000-70-8	Edible Beef Gelatin		
9000-65-1	Powdered Gum Tragacanth Type B-1 NF Premium	9000-70-8	Gelatin USP/NF, Type A	9002-18-0	Powdered Agar Agar Type K-100
		9000-70-8	Gelatin XF	9002-18-0	Powdered Agar Agar Type K-150
9000-65-1	Powdered Gum Tragacanth Type B-12 NF Premium	9000-70-8	Liquid Fish Gelatin Conc.	9002-18-0	TIC Pretested® Gum Agar Agar 100 FCC/NF Powd.

CAS	Trade name	CAS	Trade name	CAS	Trade name
9002-88-4	A-C® 7, 7A		Gum	9004-39-1	Eastman® CAPr
9002-88-4	A-C® 617, 617A	9004-32-4	Cekol® 30	9004-57-3	Ethocel Medium
9002-92-0	Britex L 20	9004-32-4	Cekol® 150		Premium
9002-92-0	Britex L 40	9004-32-4	Cekol® 300	9004-57-3	Ethocel Standard
9002-92-0	Britex L 100	9004-32-4	Cekol® 700		Premium
9002-92-0	Britex L 230	9004-32-4	Cekol® 2000	9004-57-3	Surelease®
9002-92-0	Ethosperse® LA-4	9004-32-4	Cekol® 4000	9004-62-0	Natrosol® 250
9002-92-0	Ethosperse® LA-12	9004-32-4	Cekol® 10000	9004-62-0	Natrosol® Hydroxy-
9002-92-0	Ethosperse® LA-23	9004-32-4	Cekol® 30000		ethylcellulose
9002-92-0	Rhodasurf® L-25	9004-32-4	Cekol® 50000	9004-64-2	Klucel® 'F' Grades
9002-92-0	Simulsol® P23	9004-32-4	Cellogen HP	9004-65-3	Benecel® Hydroxy-
9002-92-0	Volpo L23	9004-32-4	CMC Daicel 1150		propyl Methylcellulose
9002-93-1	Renex® 759	9004-32-4	CMC Daicel 1160	9004-65-3	Methocel® E3 Premium
9002-93-1	Synperonic OP3	9004-32-4	CMC Daicel 1220	9004-65-3	Methocel® E4M
9002-93-1	Synperonic OP4.5	9004-32-4	CMC Daicel 1260		Premium
9002-93-1	Synperonic OP6	9004-32-4	Nymcel® ZSB-10	9004-65-3	Methocel® E5P
9002-93-1	Synperonic OP7.5	9004-32-4	Nymcel® ZSB-16	9004-65-3	Methocel® E6 Premium
9002-93-1	Synperonic OP8	9004-32-4	Nymcel® ZSD-16	9004-65-3	Methocel® E10MP CR
9002-93-1	Synperonic OP10	9004-32-4	Ticalose® 15	9004-65-3	Methocel® E15LV
9002-93-1	Synperonic OP10.5	9004-32-4	Ticalose® 30		Premium
9002-93-1	Synperonic OP11	9004-32-4	Ticalose® 75	9004-65-3	Methocel® E50LV
9002-93-1	Synperonic OP12.5	9004-32-4	Ticalose® 100		Premium
9002-93-1	Synperonic OP16	9004-32-4	Ticalose® 150 R	9004-65-3	Methocel® E50P
9002-93-1	Synperonic OP16.5	9004-32-4	Ticalose® 700 R	9004-65-3	Methocel® E Premium
9002-93-1	Synperonic OP20	9004-32-4	Ticalose® 750	9004-65-3	Methocel® F4M
9002-93-1	Synperonic OP25	9004-32-4	Ticalose® 1200		Premium
9002-93-1	Synperonic OP30	9004-32-4	Ticalose® 2000 R	9004-65-3	Methocel® F Premium
9002-93-1	Synperonic OP40	9004-32-4	Ticalose® 2500	9004-65-3	Methocel® J Premium
9002-93-1	Synperonic OP40/70	9004-32-4	Ticalose® 4000	9004-65-3	Methocel® K3 Premium
9003-01-4	Carbopol® 907	9004-32-4	Ticalose® 4500	9004-65-3	Methocel® K4M
9003-01-4	Lubrajel® Oil	9004-32-4	Ticalose® 5000 R		Premium
9003-01-4	Lubrajel® WA	9004-32-4	TIC Pretested® CMC	9004-65-3	Methocel® K15M
9003-01-4	Noveon® AA-1		2500 S		Premium
9003-11-6	Empilan® P7061	9004-32-4	TIC Pretested® CMC	9004-65-3	Methocel® K100LV
9003-11-6	Empilan® P7062		PH-2500		Premium
9003-11-6	Empilan® P7087	9004-32-4	Tylose® C, CB Series	9004-65-3	Methocel® K100M
9003-11-6	Macol® 1	9004-34-6	Avicel® PH-101		Premium
9003-11-6	Macol® 2	9004-34-6	Avicel® PH-102	9004-65-3	Methocel® K Premium
9003-11-6	Macol® 4	9004-34-6	Avicel® PH-103	9004-67-5	Benecel® Methylcellu-
9003-11-6	Macol® 8	9004-34-6	Avicel® PH-105		lose
9003-11-6	Macol® 27	9004-34-6	Elcema® F150	9004-67-5	Methocel® A4C
9003-11-6	Macol® 33	9004-34-6	Elcema® G250		Premium
9003-11-6	Macol® 40	9004-34-6	Elcema® P100	9004-67-5	Methocel® A4M
9003-11-6	Macol® 85	9004-34-6	Emcocel® 50M		Premium
9003-11-6	Nikkol GO-440	9004-34-6	Emcocel® 90M	9004-67-5	Methocel® A15C
9003-11-6	Pluronic® F68NF	9004-34-6	Emcocel® LM		Premium
9003-11-6	Pluronic® F87NF	9004-34-6	Justfiber® CL-40-H	9004-67-5	Methocel® A15-LV
9003-11-6	Pluronic® F108NF	9004-34-6	Keycel®	9004-67-5	Methocel® A15LV
9003-11-6	Pluronic® F127NF	9004-34-6	Solka-Floc®		Premium
9003-11-6	Pluronic® L44NF	9004-34-6	Solka-Floc® BW-40	9004-67-5	Methocel® A Premium
9003-11-6	Synperonic PE/F127	9004-34-6	Solka-Floc® BW-100	9004-81-3	Acconon 400-ML
9003-39-8	Plasdone® C-15	9004-34-6	Solka-Floc® BW-200	9004-81-3	Algon LA 40
9003-39-8	Plasdone® C-30	9004-34-6	Solka-Floc® BW-2030	9004-81-3	Algon LA 80
9003-39-8	Plasdone® K-25	9004-34-6	Solka-Floc® Fine	9004-81-3	Crodet L4
9003-39-8	Plasdone® K-29/32		Granular	9004-81-3	Crodet L8
9003-39-8	Plasdone® K-90	9004-34-6	Vivacel® 10	9004-81-3	Crodet L12
9003-39-8	Plasdone® K-90D	9004-34-6	Vivacel® 12	9004-81-3	Crodet L24
9003-39-8	Plasdone® K-90M	9004-34-6	Vivacel® 20	9004-81-3	Crodet L40
9003-39-8	Polyplasdone® INF-10	9004-34-6	Vivacel® 101	9004-81-3	Crodet L100
9003-39-8	Polyplasdone® XL	9004-34-6	Vivacel® 102	9004-81-3	Ethylan® L10
9003-39-8	Polyplasdone® XL-10	9004-34-6	Vivacel® 103	9004-81-3	Hodag 20-L
9003-39-8	Iodasept	9004-34-6	Vivacel® 105	9004-81-3	Hodag 40-L
9003-39-8	Kollidon®	9004-34-6	Vivacel® 112	9004-81-3	Hodag 60-L
9003-39-8	Kollidon® CL	9004-34-6	Vivacel® 200	9004-81-3	Kessco® PEG 200 ML
9003-39-8	Kollidon® USP	9004-35-7	Eastman® CA	9004-81-3	Kessco® PEG 300 ML
9003-97-8	Noveon® CA-1	9004-36-8	Eastman® CAB	9004-81-3	Kessco® PEG 400 ML
9003-97-8	Noveon® CA-2	9004-38-0	C-A-P Enteric Coating	9004-81-3	Kessco® PEG 600 ML
9004-32-4	Aqualon® Cellulose		Material	9004-81-3	Kessco® PEG 1000 ML

CAS	Trade name	CAS	Trade name	CAS	Trade name
9004-81-3	Kessco® PEG 1540 ML	9004-99-3	Crodet S40	9005-07-6	Kessco® PEG 600 DO
9004-81-3	Kessco® PEG 4000 ML	9004-99-3	Crodet S100	9005-07-6	Kessco® PEG 1000 DO
9004-81-3	Kessco® PEG 6000 ML	9004-99-3	Emerest® 2715	9005-07-6	Kessco® PEG 1540 DO
9004-81-3	Mapeg® 200 ML	9004-99-3	Hodag 40-S	9005-07-6	Kessco® PEG 4000 DO
9004-81-3	Mapeg® 400 ML	9004-99-3	Hodag 60-S	9005-07-6	Kessco® PEG 6000 DO
9004-94-3	Acconon 1300 MS	9004-99-3	Hodag 100-S	9005-07-6	Mapeg® 200 DO
9004-95-9	Britex C	9004-99-3	Hodag 150-S	9005-07-6	Mapeg® 400 DO.
9004-95-9	Britex C 100	9004-99-3	Hydrine	9005-07-6	Mapeg® 600 DO
9004-95-9	Britex C 200	9004-99-3	Kessco® PEG 200 MS	9005-08-7	Hodag 42-S
9004-95-9	Cetomacrogol 1000 BP	9004-99-3	Kessco® PEG 300 MS	9005-08-7	Kessco® PEG 200 DS
9004-95-9	Nikkol BC-5.5	9004-99-3	Kessco® PEG 400 MS	9005-08-7	Kessco® PEG 300 DS
9004-95-9	Nikkol BC-7	9004-99-3	Kessco® PEG 600 MS	9005-08-7	Kessco® PEG 400 DS
9004-95-9	Nikkol BC-10TX	9004-99-3	Kessco® PEG 1000 MS	9005-08-7	Kessco® PEG 600 DS
9004-95-9	Nikkol BC-15TX	9004-99-3	Kessco® PEG 1540 MS	9005-08-7	Kessco® PEG 1000 DS
9004-95-9	Nikkol BC-20TX			9005-08-7	Kessco® PEG 1540 DS
9004-95-9	Nikkol BC-23	9004-99-3	Kessco® PEG 4000 MS	9005-08-7	Kessco® PEG 4000 DS
9004-95-9	Nikkol BC-25TX			9005-08-7	Kessco® PEG 6000 DS
9004-95-9	Nikkol BC-30TX	9004-99-3	Kessco® PEG 6000 MS	9005-08-7	Mapeg® 400 DS
9004-95-9	Nikkol BC-40TX			9005-08-7	Mapeg® 600 DS
9004-95-9	Simulsol® 58	9004-99-3	Mapeg® 400 MS	9005-08-7	Mapeg® 6000 DS
9004-96-0	Acconon 400-MO	9004-99-3	Mapeg® 600 MS	9005-25-8	Pharma-Gel™
9004-96-0	Algon OL 60	9004-99-3	Mapeg® 1000 MS	9005-25-8	Pure-Dent® B700
9004-96-0	Algon OL 70	9004-99-3	Mapeg® S-40K	9005-25-8	Pure-Dent® B810
9004-96-0	Hodag 40-O	9004-99-3	Myrj® 45	9005-25-8	Pure-Dent® B812
9004-96-0	Kessco® PEG 200 MO	9004-99-3	Myrj® 49	9005-25-8	Pure-Dent® B815
9004-96-0	Kessco® PEG 300 MO	9004-99-3	Myrj® 51	9005-25-8	Pure-Dent® B816
9004-96-0	Kessco® PEG 400 MO	9004-99-3	Myrj® 52	9005-25-8	Pure-Dent® B852
9004-96-0	Kessco® PEG 600 MO	9004-99-3	Myrj® 52S	9005-25-8	Pure-Dent® B880
9004-96-0	Kessco® PEG 1000 MO	9004-99-3	Myrj® 53	9005-25-8	Pure Food Starch Bleached 142-A
9004-96-0	Kessco® PEG 1540 MO	9004-99-3	Myrj® 59	9005-25-8	Purity® 21
9004-96-0	Kessco® PEG 4000 MO	9004-99-3	Nikkol MYS-4	9005-25-8	Starch 1500®
9004-96-0	Kessco® PEG 6000 MO	9004-99-3	Nikkol MYS-10	9005-25-8	Starch 1500® LM
9004-96-0	Mapeg® 200 MO	9004-99-3	Nikkol MYS-25	9005-25-8	Sta-Rx®
9004-96-0	Mapeg® 400 MO	9004-99-3	Nikkol MYS-40	9005-25-8	28-1801
9004-97-1	Hodag 40-R	9004-99-3	Nikkol MYS-45	9005-32-7	Alginic Acid FCC
9004-98-2	Britex O 20	9004-99-3	Nikkol MYS-55	9005-32-7	KELACID®
9004-98-2	Britex O 100	9004-99-3	Simulsol® M 52	9005-32-7	Kimitsu Acid
9004-98-2	Britex O 200	9004-99-3	Superpolystate	9005-32-7	Protacid F 120
9004-98-2	Eumulgin® O5	9004-99-3	Tefose® 1500	9005-32-7	Satialgine™ H8
9004-98-2	Eumulgin® O10	9005-00-9	Acconon SA-2	9005-32-7	Sobalg FD 000 Range
9004-98-2	Prox-onic OA-1/020	9005-00-9	Brij® 700	9005-34-9	Sobalg FD 300 Range
9004-98-2	Prox-onic OA-2/020	9005-00-9	Britex S 20	9005-35-0	Protanal TFX 200
9004-98-2	Rhodasurf® ON-870	9005-00-9	Britex S 100	9005-35-0	Sobalg FD 460
9004-98-2	Rhodasurf® ON-877	9005-00-9	Britex S 200	9005-36-1	KELMAR®
9004-98-2	Simulsol® 98	9005-00-9	Simulsol® 78	9005-36-1	KELMAR® CR
9004-98-2	Volpo 3	9005-00-9	Tewax TC 72.	9005-36-1	KELMAR® Improved
9004-98-2	Volpo 5	9005-00-9	Volpo S-2	9005-36-1	Protanal KF 200
9004-98-2	Volpo 10	9005-00-9	Volpo S-10	9005-36-1	Protanal KF 200 RBS
9004-98-2	Volpo 20	9005-00-9	Volpo S-20	9005-36-1	Protanal KF 200 S
9004-99-3	Acconon 200-MS	9005-02-1	Hodag 22-L	9005-36-1	Sobalg FD 200 Range
9004-99-3	Acconon 400-MS	9005-02-1	Hodag 42-L	9005-37-2	Colloid 602
9004-99-3	Algon ST 50	9005-02-1	Kessco® PEG 200 DL	9005-37-2	KELCOLOID® D
9004-99-3	Algon ST 80	9005-02-1	Kessco® PEG 300 DL	9005-37-2	KELCOLOID® DH
9004-99-3	Algon ST 100	9005-02-1	Kessco® PEG 400 DL	9005-37-2	KELCOLOID® DSF
9004-99-3	Algon ST 200	9005-02-1	Kessco® PEG 600 DL	9005-37-2	KELCOLOID® HVF
9004-99-3	Algon ST 400	9005-02-1	Kessco® PEG 1000 DL	9005-37-2	KELCOLOID® LVF
9004-99-3	Algon ST 500	9005-02-1	Kessco® PEG 1540 DL	9005-37-2	KELCOLOID® S
9004-99-3	Algon ST 1000	9005-02-1	Kessco® PEG 4000 DL	9005-37-2	Kimiloid HV
9004-99-3	Cerasynt® 840	9005-02-1	Kessco® PEG 6000 DL	9005-37-2	Kimiloid NLS-K
9004-99-3	Cremophor® S 9	9005-02-1	Lexemul® PEG-200 DL	9005-38-3	Colloid 488T
9004-99-3	Crodet S4	9005-02-1	Mapeg® 200 DL	9005-38-3	KELCOSOL®
9004-99-3	Crodet S8	9005-02-1	Mapeg® 400 DL	9005-38-3	KELGIN® F
9004-99-3	Crodet S12	9005-07-6	Hodag 42-O	9005-38-3	KELGIN® HV
9004-99-3	Crodet S24	9005-07-6	Hodag 62-O		
		9005-07-6	Kessco® PEG 200 DO		
		9005-07-6	Kessco® PEG 300 DO		
		9005-07-6	Kessco® PEG 400 DO		

CAS	Trade name	CAS	Trade name	CAS	Trade name
9005-38-3	KELGIN® LV	9005-65-6	Montanox® 80 DF	9014-01-1	Fungal Protease
9005-38-3	KELGIN® MV	9005-65-6	Nikkol TO-10		60,000
9005-38-3	KELGIN® XL	9005-65-6	Nikkol TO-106	9014-01-1	Fungal Protease
9005-38-3	KELSET®	9005-65-6	Sorbilene O		500,000
9005-38-3	KELTONE®	9005-65-6	Sorbilene O 5	9014-01-1	Fungal Protease Conc.
9005-38-3	KELTONE® HV	9005-65-6	Sorgen TW80	9014-01-1	Papain 16,000
9005-38-3	KELTONE® HVCR	9005-65-6	T-Maz® 80	9014-01-1	Papain 30,000
9005-38-3	KELTONE® LV	9005-65-6	T-Maz® 80K	9014-01-1	Papain Conc.
9005-38-3	KELTONE® LVCR	9005-65-6	T-Maz® 80KLM	9014-01-1	Prolase® 300
9005-38-3	KELVIS®	9005-65-6	T-Maz® 81	9016-45-9	Igepal® CO-630
9005-38-3	Kimitsu Algin I-3	9005-65-6	T-Maz® 81K		Special
9005-38-3	Kimitsu Algin I-7	9005-66-7	Crillet 2	9016-45-9	Synperonic NP4
9005-38-3	Kimitsu Algin IS	9005-66-7	Glycosperse® P-20	9016-45-9	Synperonic NP5
9005-38-3	MANUCOL DM	9005-66-7	Montanox® 40	9016-45-9	Synperonic NP5.5
9005-38-3	MANUCOL DMF	9005-66-7	Montanox® 40 DF	9016-45-9	Synperonic NP6
9005-38-3	MANUCOL LB	9005-66-7	Sorbilene P	9016-45-9	Synperonic NP7
9005-38-3	MANUCOL LKX	9005-67-8	Alkamuls® PSMS-4	9016-45-9	Synperonic NP8
9005-38-3	Pronova™ UP MVG	9005-67-8	Capmul® POE-S	9016-45-9	Synperonic NP8.5
9005-38-3	Pronova™ P MVG	9005-67-8	Crillet 3	9016-45-9	Synperonic NP8.75
9005-38-3	Pronova™ LVG	9005-67-8	Crillet 31	9016-45-9	Synperonic NP9
9005-38-3	Pronova™ P LVG	9005-67-8	Drewmulse® POE-	9016-45-9	Synperonic NP9.5
9005-38-3	Pronova™ LVM		SMS	9016-45-9	Synperonic NP9.75
9005-38-3	Pronova™ MVG	9005-67-8	Eumulgin® SMS 20	9016-45-9	Synperonic NP10
9005-38-3	Pronova™ MVM	9005-67-8	Glycosperse® S-20	9016-45-9	Synperonic NP12
9005-38-3	Protanal LF 5/60.	9005-67-8	Montanox® 60	9016-45-9	Synperonic NP13
9005-38-3	Protanal LF 10/40	9005-67-8	Montanox® 60 DF	9016-45-9	Synperonic NP15
9005-38-3	Protanal LF 10/60	9005-67-8	Nikkol TS-10	9016-45-9	Synperonic NP17
9005-38-3	Protanal LF 20/200	9005-67-8	Nikkol TS-106	9016-45-9	Synperonic NP20
9005-38-3	Protanal LF 120 M	9005-67-8	Sorbilene S	9016-45-9	Synperonic NP25
9005-38-3	Protanal LF 200	9005-67-8	Sorbilene S 4	9016-45-9	Synperonic NP30
9005-38-3	Protanal LF 200 M	9005-67-8	T-Maz® 60K	9016-45-9	Synperonic NP30/70
9005-38-3	Protanal LF 200 RB	9005-67-8	T-Maz® 61	9016-45-9	Synperonic NP35
9005-38-3	Protanal LF 200 S	9005-70-3	Crillet 45	9016-45-9	Synperonic NP40
9005-38-3	Protanal LFR 5/60	9005-70-3	Glycosperse® TO-20	9016-45-9	Synperonic NP50
9005-38-3	Protanal SF	9005-70-3	Montanox® 85	9025-56-3	Hemi-Cellulase Amano
9005-38-3	Protanal SF 120	9005-70-3	Nikkol TO-30		90
9005-38-3	Protanal SF 120 RB	9005-70-3	Sorbilene TO	9032-42-2	Tylose® MH Grades
9005-38-3	Sobalg FD 100 Range	9005-70-3	T-Maz® 85	9032-42-2	Tylose® MHB
9005-64-5	Alkamuls® PSML-20	9005-71-4	Crillet 35	9035-85-2	Macol® CA 30P
9005-64-5	Capmul® POE-L	9005-71-4	Drewmulse® POE-STS	9041-08-1	SPL Heparin Sodium
9005-64-5	Crillet 1	9005-71-4	Glycosperse® TS-20		USP
9005-64-5	Crillet 11	9005-71-4	Montanox® 65	9045-22-1	SPL Heparin Lithium
9005-64-5	Drewmulse® POE-SML	9005-71-4	Nikkol TS-30	9050-30-0	Nymcel® ZSC
9005-64-5	Emalex ET-2020	9005-71-4	Sorbilene TS	9050-36-6	Maltrin® M040
9005-64-5	Eumulgin® SML 20	9005-71-4	T-Maz® 65K	9050-36-6	Maltrin® M050
9005-64-5	Glycosperse® L-20	9006-50-2	Sol-U-Tein EA	9050-36-6	Maltrin® M100
9005-64-5	Montanox® 20	9007-28-7	Soluble Trachea CS 16	9050-36-6	Maltrin® M150
9005-64-5	Montanox® 20 DF		Substance	9050-36-6	Maltrin® M180
9005-64-5	Nikkol TL-10, TL-10EX	9007-34-5	Collagenite	9050-36-6	Maltrin® M510
9005-64-5	Nissan Nonion LT-221	9007-48-1	Caprol® 3GO	9050-36-6	Maltrin® M700
9005-64-5	Sorbilene L	9007-48-1	Caprol® 6G2O	9050-36-6	Maltrin® QD M440
9005-64-5	Sorbilene L 4	9007-48-1	Caprol® PGE860	9050-36-6	Maltrin® QD M500
9005-64-5	Sorbilene LH	9007-48-1	Drewmulse® 3-1-O	9050-36-6	Maltrin® QD M550
9005-64-5	T-Maz® 20	9007-48-1	Drewpol® 3-1-O	9050-36-6	Maltrin® QD M580
9005-64-5	T-Maz® 28	9007-48-1	Drewpol® 6-1-O	9063-38-1	Explotab®
9005-65-6	Crillet 4	9007-48-1	Mazol® PGO-31 K	9063-38-1	Primojel®
9005-65-6	Crillet 41	9007-48-1	Nikkol DGMO-C	9067-32-7	Hyaluronic Acid FCH
9005-65-6	Drewmulse® POE-	9007-48-1	Nikkol Decaglyn 1-O	9067-32-7	Kelisema Sodium
	SMO	9011-16-9	Gantrez® AN-139		Hyaluronate Bio
9005-65-6	Emalex ET-8020	9011-16-9	Gantrez® AN-139 BF	9067-32-7	Pronova™
9005-65-6	Ethylan® GEO8	9011-16-9	Luviform® FA 119	9102-54-8	Cellulase AP 3
9005-65-6	Eumulgin® SMO 20	9012-54-8	Cellulase 4000	9102-54-8	Cellulase T-AP6
9005-65-6	Glycosperse® O-5	9012-54-8	Cellulase Tr Conc.	9174-23-9	Imwitor® 375
9005-65-6	Glycosperse® O-20	9012-54-8	Cellulase TRL	10016-20-3	Alpha W6 Pharma
9005-65-6	Glycosperse® O-20 FG	9014-01-1	Bromelain 1:10		Grade
9005-65-6	Glycosperse® O-20	9014-01-1	Bromelain Conc.	10101-41-4	Compactrol®
	KFG	9014-01-1	Fungal Protease	10401-55-5	Pelemol® CR
9005-65-6	Montanox® 80		31,000	11006-31-1	Potassium Sodium

CAS	Trade name	CAS	Trade name	CAS	Trade name
	Copper Chlorophyllin 033280	14807-96-6	Supreme USP	25085-02-3	Pionier® NP 37
11042-64-1	Gamma Oryzanol	14807-96-6	Ultrafino	25086-89-9	PVP/VA S-630
11094-60-3	Caprol® 10G10O	15087-24-8	Unisol S-22	25155-18-4	Hyamine® 10X
11094-60-3	Drewmulse® 10-10-O	16039-53-5	Puramex® ZN	25168-73-4	Crodesta F-160
11094-60-3	Drewpol® 10-10-O	16039-56-8	Puramex® MN	25168-73-4	Ryoto Sugar Ester S-1170
11097-68-0	Westchlor® 170	16485-10-2	d,l-Panthenol FCC Grade	25168-73-4	Ryoto Sugar Ester S-1170S
11099-07-3	Mazol® GMS-K	16485-10-2	DL-Panthenol USP, FCC No. 63915	25168-73-4	Ryoto Sugar Ester S-1570
11111-34-5	Tetronic® 304			25168-73-4	Ryoto Sugar Ester S-1670
11138-66-2	Gumixan K	16485-10-2	Ritapan DL		
11138-66-2	Gumixan KF.	17465-86-0	Gamma W8.	25168-73-4	Ryoto Sugar Ester S-1670S
11138-66-2	KELTROL®	17661-50-6	Kemester® 1418	25231-21-4	Acconon E
11138-66-2	KELTROL® 1000	17661-50-6	Pelemol® MS	25322-68-3	Carbowax® PEG 300
11138-66-2	KELTROL® BT	17661-50-6	Spermwax®	25322-68-3	Carbowax® Sentry® PEG 300
11138-66-2	KELTROL® CR	17671-27-1	Pelemol® BB		
11138-66-2	KELTROL® F	17673-56-2	Dynacerin® 660	25322-68-3	Carbowax® Sentry® PEG 400
11138-66-2	KELTROL® GM	18172-67-3	beta-Pinene P&F		
11138-66-2	KELTROL® RD	18194-24-6	Phospholipon® MC	25322-68-3	Carbowax® Sentry® PEG 600
11138-66-2	KELTROL® SF	18285-71-7	Phospholipon® LC		
11138-66-2	KELTROL® T	18472-51-0	Spectradyne® G	25322-68-3	Carbowax® Sentry® PEG 900
11138-66-2	KELTROL® TF	18641-57-1	Syncrowax HR-C		
11138-66-2	Merecol® MS	18641-57-1	Compritol 888	25322-68-3	Carbowax® Sentry® PEG 1000
11138-66-2	Merezan® 8	18641-57-1	Compritol 888 ATO		
11138-66-2	Merezan® 20	18917-91-4	Puramex® AL	25322-68-3	Carbowax® Sentry® PEG 1450
11138-66-2	Rhodigel®	18917-93-6	Puramex® MG		
11138-66-2	Rhodigel® 23	19035-79-1	Amphisol® K	25322-68-3	Carbowax® Sentry® PEG 3350
11138-66-2	Rhodigel® 200	20824-56-0	Versene Diammonium EDTA		
11138-66-2	Ticaxan® Regular			25322-68-3	Carbowax® Sentry® PEG 4600
11660-95-3	TIPMDP	20834-06-4	Pelemol® ICLA		
12173-47-6	Hectabrite® AW	21245-02-3	Escalol® 507	25322-68-3	Carbowax® Sentry® PEG 8000
12173-47-6	Hectabrite® DP	21645-51-2	Baco AF		
12199-37-0	Magnabrite® F	21645-51-2	F-500®	25322-68-3	Dow E300 NF
12199-37-0	Magnabrite® FS	21645-51-2	F-500® Low Sodium	25322-68-3	Dow E400 NF
12199-37-0	Magnabrite® HS	21645-51-2	F-1000®	25322-68-3	Dow E600 NF
12199-37-0	Magnabrite® HV	21645-51-2	F-1500™	25322-68-3	Dow E900 NF
12199-37-0	Magnabrite® K	21645-51-2	F-1500™ Reductionized	25322-68-3	Dow E1000 NF
12199-37-0	Magnabrite® S			25322-68-3	Dow E1450 NF
12199-37-0	Veegum®	21645-51-2	F-2000®	25322-68-3	Dow E3350 NF
12199-37-0	Veegum® HV	21645-51-2	F-2100®	25322-68-3	Dow E4500 NF
12199-37-0	Veegum® K	21645-51-2	F-2200®	25322-68-3	Dow E8000 NF
12269-78-2	Pyrax® ABB	21645-51-2	F-2300™	25322-68-3	Hodag PEG 200
12269-78-2	Pyrax® B	21645-51-2	F-4400™	25322-68-3	Hodag PEG 300
12694-22-3	Nikkol DGMS	21645-51-2	Hydral® 710	25322-68-3	Hodag PEG 400
12764-60-2	Nikkol Decaglyn 2-S	21645-51-2	Liquigel®	25322-68-3	Hodag PEG 600
12804-12-8	Pelemol® G7B	21645-51-2	Liquigel® D4	25322-68-3	Hodag PEG 1000
13057-50-6	Pelemol® PTL	21645-51-2	Liquigel® HO	25322-68-3	Hodag PEG 1450
13463-67-7	Hilton Davis Titanium Dioxide	21645-51-2	R-1000™	25322-68-3	Hodag PEG 3350
		21645-51-2	Rederm® Gel	25322-68-3	Hodag PEG 8000
13552-80-2	Captex® 8227	21645-51-2	Rederm® Powd.	25322-68-3	Lipoxol® 200 MED
13832-70-7	Co-Grhetinol	21645-51-2	Rehydragel® CG	25322-68-3	Lipoxol® 300 MED
13832-70-7	Nikkol Stearyl Glycyrrhetinate	21645-51-2	Rehydragel® HPA	25322-68-3	Lipoxol® 400 MED
		21645-51-2	Rehydragel® LV	25322-68-3	Lipoxol® 600 MED
14351-40-7	Cerasynt® D	21645-51-2	Rehydragel® T	25322-68-3	Lipoxol® 800 MED
14807-96-6	Act II 500 USP	21645-51-2	SB-30	25322-68-3	Lipoxol® 1000 MED
14807-96-6	Alphafil 500 USP	22766-82-1	Standamul® 7063	25322-68-3	Lipoxol® 1550 MED
14807-96-6	Alpine Talc USP BC 127	22766-83-2	Isofol® 20 Myristat	25322-68-3	Lipoxol® 2000 MED
		22766-83-2	Pelemol® ODM	25322-68-3	Lipoxol® 3000 MED
14807-96-6	Altalc 200 USP	22801-45-2	Isofol® 20 Oleat	25322-68-3	Lipoxol® 4000 MED
14807-96-6	Altalc 300 USP	22839-47-0	HSC Aspartame	25322-68-3	Lipoxol® 6000 MED
14807-96-6	Altalc 400 USP	24938-91-8	Dehydol® PIT 6	25322-68-3	Macol® E-200
14807-96-6	Altalc 500 USP	25038-54-4	Orgasol 1002 D WHITE 5 COS	25322-68-3	Macol® E-300
14807-96-6	Brillante			25322-68-3	Macol® E-400
14807-96-6	Dover 50 A	25038-74-8	Orgasol 2002 D NAT COS	25322-68-3	Macol® E-600
14807-96-6	Purtalc USP			25322-68-3	Pluracol® E400 NF
14807-96-6	SteriLine 200	25038-74-8	Orgasol 2002 EX D NAT COS	25322-68-3	Pluracol® E600 NF
14807-96-6	Supra A				
14807-96-6	Supra EF A	25038-74-8	Orgasol 2002 UD NAT COS		
14807-96-6	Suprafino A				

CAS	Trade name	CAS	Trade name	CAS	Trade name
25322-68-3	Pluracol® E1450 NF	26266-58-0	Nissan Nonion OP-85R	34424-98-1	Drewmulse® 10-4-O
25322-68-3	Poly-G® 200	26266-58-0	Sorbirol TO	34424-98-1	Drewpok® 10-4-O
25322-68-3	Polyox® WSR 205	26266-58-0	Span® 85	34424-98-1	Mazol® PGO-104
25322-68-3	Polyox® WSR 301	26402-22-2	Capmul® MCMC8	35274-05-6	Ceraphyl® 28
25322-68-3	Polyox® WSR 303	26402-26-6	Imwitor® 308	35274-05-6	Pelemol® CL
25322-68-3	Polyox® WSR 308	26402-26-6	Imwitor® 742	35285-68-8	Nipagin A Sodium
25322-68-3	Polyox® WSR 1105	26402-26-6	Imwitor® 988	35285-69-9	Nipasol M Sodium
25322-68-3	Polyox® WSR 3333	26402-26-6	Witafrol® 7420	36311-34-9	Ceraphyl® ICA
25322-68-3	Polyox® WSR N-10	26402-31-3	Cithrol PGMR N/E	36311-34-9	Eutanol® G16
25322-68-3	Polyox® WSR N-12K	26446-38-8	Ryoto Sugar Ester P-1570	36457-19-9	Nipagin A Potassium
25322-68-3	Polyox® WSR N-60K			36457-20-2	Nipabutyl Sodium
25322-68-3	Polyox® WSR N-80	26446-38-8	Ryoto Sugar Ester P-1570S	36653-82-4	Crodacol C-95NF
25322-68-3	Polyox® WSR N-750			36653-82-4	Dehydag® Wax 16
25322-68-3	Polyox® WSR N-3000	26446-38-8	Ryoto Sugar Ester P-1670	36653-82-4	Epal® 16NF
25322-68-3	Polyox® WSR Coagulant			36653-82-4	Hyfatol 16-98
		26446-38-8	Sucro Ester 15	36653-82-4	Lanette® 16
25322-68-3	Prox-onic PEG-2000	26657-96-5	Emalex GMS-P	36653-82-4	Nacol® 16-95
25322-68-3	Prox-onic PEG-10,000	26658-19-5	Crill 35	36653-82-4	Nacol® 16-98
25322-68-3	Prox-onic PEG-20,000	26658-19-5	Drewmulse® STS	37349-34-1	Caprol® 3GS
25322-68-3	Prox-onic PEG-35,000	26658-19-5	Glycomul® TS	37349-34-1	Drewmulse® 3-1-S
25322-68-3	Renex® PEG 300	26658-19-5	Kemester® S65	38566-94-8	Nipabutyl Potassium
25322-68-3	Renex® PEG 400	26658-19-5	Montane® 65	39175-72-9	Imwitor® 370
25322-68-3	Renex® PEG 600	26658-19-5	Sorbirol TS	39236-46-9	Biopure® 100
25322-68-3	Renex® PEG 1000	26658-19-5	Span® 65	39236-46-9	Germall® 115
25322-68-3	Renex® PEG 1500FL	26658-19-5	Span® 65K	39236-46-9	Unicide U-13
25322-68-3	Renex® PEG 4000FL	27195-16-0	Crodesta F-10	39464-69-2	Crodafos N-3 Acid
25322-68-3	Renex® PEG 6000FL	27195-16-0	Crodesta F-50	39464-69-2	Hodag PE-1803
25322-68-3	Rhodasurf® PEG 300	27195-16-0	Ryoto Sugar Ester S-570	39464-69-2	Hodag PE-1810
25322-68-3	Rhodasurf® PEG 600			39464-69-2	Hodag PE-1820
25322-68-3	Teric PEG 300	27195-16-0	Ryoto Sugar Ester S-770	39529-26-5	Drewmulse® 10-10-S
25322-68-3	Teric PEG 400			41395-83-9	D.P.P.G
25322-68-3	Teric PEG 600	27195-16-0	Ryoto Sugar Ester S-970	41669-30-1	Iso Isotearyle WL 3196
25322-68-3	Teric PEG 800			42131-25-9	Pelemol® IN-2
25322-68-3	Teric PEG 4000	27195-16-0	Sucro Ester 7.	42131-28-2	Pelemol® ISL
25322-68-3	Teric PEG 6000	27215-38-9	Aldo® MLD	42175-36-0	Pelemol® OL
25322-68-3	Teric PEG 8000	27306-78-1	Silwet® L-77	42233-07-8	Pelemol® LB
25339-09-7	Ceraphyl® 494	27638-00-2	Capmul® GDL	51158-08-8	Tagat® S2
25339-09-7	Pelemol® ICS	27638-00-2	Kemester® GDL	51158-08-8	Tewax TC 83
25339-09-7	Standamul® 7061	28319-77-9	GPC	51192-09-7	Tagat® O2
25339-99-5	Ryoto Sugar Ester L-1570	29383-26-4	Wickenol® 171	51200-87-4	Oxaban®-A
		29806-73-3	Cegesoft® C 24	51248-32-9	Tagat® L2
25339-99-5	Ryoto Sugar Ester L-1695	29806-73-3	Ceraphyl® 368	52229-50-2	Gantrez® AN-119
		29806-73-3	Lexol® EHP	52229-50-2	Gantrez® AN-149
25339-99-5	Ryoto Sugar Ester LWA-1570	29806-73-3	Pelemol® OP	52229-50-2	Gantrez® AN-169
		29806-73-3	Wickenol® 155	52504-24-2	Softigen® 767
25383-99-7	Lamegin® NSL	30657-38-6	Lysidone®	53124-00-8	Pure-Dent® B890
25496-72-4	Aldo® MO FG	31556-45-3	Kemester® 5721	53320-86-8	Laponite® D
25496-72-4	Capmul® GMO	31566-31-1	Aldo® MSC	53694-15-8	Ethosperse® SL-20
25496-72-4	Hodag GMO	31566-31-1	Capmul® GMS	54392-26-6	Nikkol SI-10R
25496-72-4	Tegin® O	31566-31-1	Cithrol GMS Acid Stable	54392-26-6	Nikkol SI-10T
25655-41-8	PVP-Iodine 17/12, 30/06			54392-26-6	Nikkol SI-15T
		31566-31-1	Cithrol GMS N/E	54392-26-6	Sorbirol ISM
26112-07-2	Nipagin M Potassium	31566-31-1	Cithrol GMS S/E	54549-25-6	Oramix® NS 10
26266-57-9	Ablunol S-40	31566-31-1	Geleol	55963-33-2	Corn Po 4
26266-57-9	Arlacel® 40	31566-31-1	Hodag GMS	56002-14-3	Olepal ISO
26266-57-9	Glycomul® P	31566-31-1	Imwitor® 191	56235-92-8	Ceraphyl® 45
26266-57-9	Kemester® S40	31566-31-1	Tegin® 4011	56519-71-1	Captex® 800
26266-57-9	Montane® 40	31566-31-1	Tegin® 4100 NSE	56519-71-2	Lexol® PG-800
26266-57-9	Nissan Nonion PP-40R	31694-55-0	Ethosperse® G-26	57569-76-3	Pelemol® G7A
26266-57-9	Sorbirol P	32289-26-2	Pelemol® L2A	58958-60-4	Ceraphyl® 375
26266-57-9	Span® 40	33939-64-9	Sandopan® LA-8-HC	59231-34-4	Ceraphyl® 140
26266-58-0	Ablunol S-85	33940-99-7	Nikkol Decaglyn 2-O	59231-34-4	Ceraphyl® 140-A
26266-58-0	Arlacel® 85	34316-64-8	Cetiol® A	59231-34-4	Pelemol® IDO
26266-58-0	Crill 45	34316-64-8	Standamul® CTA	59587-44-9	Wickenol® 160
26266-58-0	Ethylan® GT85	34362-27-1	Isofol® 16 Laurat	59686-68-9	Standamul® 1414-E
26266-58-0	Glycomul® TO	34406-66-1	Nikkol Decaglyn 1-L	60800-63-7	SPL Heparin Ammonium
26266-58-0	Kemester® S85	34424-97-0	Drewmulse® 6-2-S		
26266-58-0	Montane® 85	34424-98-1	Caprol® 10G4O	60842-32-2	Aerosik® R972

CAS	Trade name	CAS	Trade name	CAS	Trade name
61693-41-2	Amphisol®	61791-12-6	Acconon CA-9	65381-09-1	Captex® 355
61725-93-7	Caprol® 6G2S	61791-12-6	Acconon CA-15	65381-09-1	Estasan GT 8-40 3578
61788-40-7	Hypan® SA100H	61791-12-6	Alkamuls® EL-620	65381-09-1	Estasan GT 8-60 3575
61788-48-5	Acylan	61791-12-6	Alkamuls® EL-719	65381-09-1	Estasan GT 8-60 3580
61788-48-5	Fancol Acel	61791-12-6	Cremophor® EL	65381-09-1	Estasan GT 8-65 3577
61788-48-5	Lanacet® 1705	61791-12-6	Emalex C-20	65381-09-1	Estasan GT 8-65 3581
61788-48-5	Modulan®	61791-12-6	Emalex C-30	65381-09-1	Estasan GT 8-70 3579
61788-48-5	Ritacetyl®	61791-12-6	Emalex C-40	65381-09-1	Labrafac® LIPO
61788-78-1	Noramium MSH 50	61791-12-6	Emalex C-50	65381-09-1	Labrafac® Lipophile
61788-85-0	Cerex ELS 50	61791-12-6	Eumulgin® PRT 36		WL 1349
61788-85-0	Cerex ELS 250	61791-12-6	Eumulgin® PRT 56	65381-09-1	Lexol® GT-855
61788-85-0	Cerex ELS 400	61791-12-6	Eumulgin® PRT 200	65381-09-1	Lexol® GT-865
61788-85-0	Cerex ELS 450	61791-12-6	Eumulgin® RO 35	65381-09-1	Miglyol® 810
61788-85-0	Cremophor® RH 40	61791-12-6	Fancol CO-30	65381-09-1	Miglyol® 812
61788-85-0	Cremophor® RH 410	61791-12-6	Incrocas 35	65381-09-1	Neobee® 1053
61788-85-0	Croduret 50	61791-12-6	Nikkol CO-3	65381-09-1	Neobee® M-5
61788-85-0	Dehymuls® HRE 7	61791-12-6	Ricinion	65381-09-1	Neobee® O
61788-85-0	Emalex HC-40	61791-12-6	Sellig R 3395	65381-09-1	Standamul® 318
61788-85-0	Eumulgin® HRE 40	61791-12-6	Servirox OEG 45	65381-09-1	Standamul® 7105
61788-85-0	Eumulgin® HRE 60	61791-12-6	Servirox OEG 55	66009-41-4	Crodamol W
61788-85-0	Fancol HCO-25	61791-12-6	Servirox OEG 65	66082-42-6	Lameform® TGI
61788-85-0	Nikkol HCO-5	61791-12-6	Servirox OEG 90/50	66082-42-6	Plurol® Diisostearique
61788-85-0	Nikkol HCO-7.5	61791-12-6	Simulsol® 5817	66085-00-5	Imwitor® 780 K
61788-85-0	Nikkol HCO-10	61791-12-6	Simulsol® OL 50	66794-58-9	Crillet 6
61788-85-0	Nikkol HCO-20	61791-14-8	Ethomeen® C/25	66794-58-9	Sorbilene ISM
61788-85-0	Nikkol HCO-30	61791-20-6	Fancol LA-15	67700-98-5	Empigen® 5073
61788-85-0	Nikkol HCO-40	61791-20-6	Polychol 5	67701-26-2	Hydrokote® 175
61788-85-0	Nikkol HCO-40 Pharm	61791-20-6	Polychol 10	67701-26-2	Novata® 299
61788-85-0	Nikkol HCO-50	61791-20-6	Polychol 15	67701-26-2	Novata® A
61788-85-0	Nikkol HCO-50 Pharm	61791-20-6	Polychol 20	67701-26-2	Novata® AB
61788-85-0	Nikkol HCO-60	61791-20-6	Polychol 40	67701-26-2	Novata® B
61788-85-0	Nikkol HCO-60 Pharm	61791-31-9	Comperlan® COD	67701-26-2	Novata® BBC
61788-85-0	Nikkol HCO-80	61791-42-2	Adinol CT95	67701-26-2	Novata® BC
61788-85-0	Nikkol HCO-100	61849-72-7	Glucam® P-10	67701-26-2	Novata® BCF
61788-85-0	Simulsol® 989	61849-72-7	Glucam® P-20	67701-26-2	Novata® BD
61788-85-0	Simulsol® 1292	62386-95-2	Gantrez® MS-955D	67701-26-2	Novata® C
61788-85-0	Simulsol® 1293	63231-60-7	Multiwax® 180-M	67701-26-2	Novata® D
61788-85-0	Tagat® R40	63231-60-7	Multiwax® ML-445	67701-26-2	Novata® E
61788-85-0	Tagat® R60	63231-60-7	Multiwax® W-445	67701-27-3	Koster Keunen
61789-05-7	Imwitor® 928	63231-60-7	Multiwax® W-835		Synthetic Japan Wax
61789-09-1	Monomuls® 90-25	63231-60-7	Multiwax® X-145A	67701-27-3	Monomuls® 60-20
61789-10-4	Monomuls® 90-10	63393-93-1	Amerlate® P	67701-27-3	Neustrene® 060
61789-13-7	Monomuls® 90-20	63393-93-1	Amerlate® W	67701-28-4	Captex® 810A
61789-40-0	Dehyton® K	63393-93-1	Fancor IPL	67701-28-4	Captex® 810D
61789-40-0	Tego®-Betaine L-7	63393-93-1	Lanesta P	67701-28-4	Miglyol® 818
61789-40-0	Tego®-Betaine ZF	63393-93-1	Lanesta SA-30	67701-33-1	Cutina® GMS
61789-75-1	Noramium S 75	63393-93-1	Ritasol	67762-27-0	Lanette® O
61789-91-1	Simchin® Natural	64365-11-3	Calgon® Type 114A	67762-27-0	Laurex® CS/D
61789-91-1	Simchin® Refined		AWD	67784-82-1	Caprol® ET
61790-81-6	Aqualose L75	64365-11-3	Calgon® Type ADP	67784-87-6	Monomuls® 90-35
61790-81-6	Aqualose L75/50	64365-11-3	Calgon® Type APA	68002-71-1	Neustrene® 064
61790-81-6	Ethoxylan® 1685	64365-11-3	Calgon® Type BL®	68002-97-1	Rhodasurf® L-4
61790-81-6	Ethoxylan® 1686	64365-11-3	Calgon® Type CAL®	68131-37-3	Maltrin® M200
61790-81-6	Laneto 100	64365-11-3	Calgon® Type CPG®	68131-37-3	Maltrin® M250
61790-81-6	Laneto 100-Flaked	64365-11-3	Calgon® Type CPG®	68131-37-3	Maltrin® QD M600
61790-81-6	Lanogel® 21		LF	68131-39-5	Rhodasurf® E
61790-81-6	Lanogel® 31	64365-11-3	Calgon® Type OL®	68140-00-1	Mazamide® CMEA
61790-81-6	Lanogel® 41	64365-11-3	Calgon® Type PWA®	68155-09-9	Aminoxid WS 35
61790-81-6	Lanogel® 61	64365-11-3	Calgon® Type RB®	68155-12-2	Accomid PK
61790-81-6	Solan	64365-11-3	Calgon® Type RC®	68171-38-0	Hydrophilol ISO
61790-81-6	Solan 50	64365-11-3	Calgon® Type SGL®	68201-48-9	Monomuls® 60-45
61790-81-6	Super Solan Flaked	64742-42-3	Koster Keunen	68201-49-0	Fancor Lanwax
61791-00-2	Mapeg® 400 MOT		Microcrystalline Waxes	68201-49-0	Lanfrax® 1776
61791-00-2	Mapeg® 600 MOT	65381-09-1	Calgene CC-33	68201-49-0	Lanfrax® 1779
61791-01-3	Mapeg® 400 DOT	65381-09-1	Calgene CC-33-F	68239-42-9	Glucam® E-10
61791-01-3	Mapeg® 600 DOT	65381-09-1	Calgene CC-33-L	68239-43-0	Glucam® E-20
61791-12-6	Acconon CA-5	65381-09-1	Calgene CC-33-S	68308-54-3	Monomuls® 60-25
61791-12-6	Acconon CA-8	65381-09-1	Captex® 300	68334-00-9	Akolizer C

CAS	Trade name	CAS	Trade name	CAS	Trade name
68334-00-9	C-Flakes	68439-49-6	Volpo CS-20	68991-68-4	Captex® 350
68334-00-9	Duratex	68439-50-9	Arlypon® F	69275-02-1	Isofol® 16 Palmitat
68334-00-9	Emvelop®	68439-50-9	Dehydol® LS 2 DEO	71010-52-1	GELRITE®
68334-00-9	Lipex 109	68439-50-9	Dehydol® LS 3 DEO	71566-49-9	Pelemol® 89
68334-00-9	Lubritab®	68439-50-9	Dehydol® LS 4 DEO	71902-01-7	Crill 6
68334-00-9	Sterotex®	68439-51-0	Aethoxal® B	71957-08-9	Gluconal® CO
68334-00-9	Sterotex® NF	68439-53-2	Solulan® PB-2	72869-69-3	Lipovol P
68334-28-1	Hydrokote® 95	68439-53-2	Solulan® PB-5	73296-89-6	Tensopol USP 94
68334-28-1	Hydrokote® 97	68439-53-2	Solulan® PB-10	73296-89-6	Tensopol USP 97
68334-28-1	Hydrokote® 102	68439-53-2	Solulan® PB-20	73398-61-5	Aldo® MCT KFG
68334-28-1	Hydrokote® 108	68440-66-4	Silwet® L-7500	73398-61-5	Myritol® 312
68334-28-1	Hydrokote® 112	68441-68-9	Crodamol PTC	73398-61-5	Myritol® 318
68334-28-1	Hydrokote® 118	68458-58-8	Fluilan AWS	74665-14-8	Eltesol® PA 65
68334-28-1	Hydrokote® M	68458-58-8	Ritalan® AWS	74811-65-7	Nymcel® ZSX
68334-28-1	Lipex 401	68458-58-8	Vigilan AWS	76009-37-5	Plurol® Oleique WL
68334-28-1	Pelemol® GTB	68458-88-8	Laneto AWS		1173
68334-28-1	Pureco® 100	68458-88-8	Lanexol AWS	78491-02-8	Germall® II
68334-28-1	Special Fat 42/44	68476-03-9	Hoechst Wax E	79777-30-3	Nikkol Decaglyn 1-S
68334-28-1	Wecobee® FS		Pharma	81025-04-9	Lactitol MC
68334-28-1	Wecobee® R Mono	68513-95-1	Emcosoy®	82708-25-6	Lipacide SH Co 90
68334-28-1	Wecobee® S	68514-74-9	Akolizer P	82708-26-7	Lipacide SH K 90
68334-28-1	Wecobee® SS	68515-73-1	Oramix® CG 110-60	83682-78-4	Phospholipid PTD
68391-01-5	Arquad® B-100	68553-81-1	EmCon Rice Bran	84930-16-5	Nipasol M Potassium
68410-45-7	Byco A	68554-53-0	Abil®-Wax 2434	85341-79-3	Crodamol CSP
68410-45-7	Byco C	68554-65-4	Silwet® L-720	85536-07-8	Labrasol
68410-45-7	Byco E	68583-51-7	Captex® 200	85536-07-8	L.A.S
68410-45-7	Byco O	68583-51-7	Myritol® PC	85536-08-9	Labrafac® CM10
68410-45-7	Polypro 5000®	68583-51-7	Neobee® M-20	85536-08-9	Labrafil® M 2125 CS
	Pharmaceutical Grade	68585-47-7	Empicol® 0303	85666-92-8	Imwitor® 900
68410-45-7	Polypro 15000®	68585-47-7	Empicol® 0303VA	85666-92-8	Imwitor® 960 Flakes
	Pharmaceutical Grade	68585-47-7	Empicol® LX	86418-55-5	Cerasynt® MN
68411-97-2	Sarkosyl® LC	68647-73-4	EmCon Tea Tree	86418-55-5	Tegin® G
68424-43-1	Fancor LFA	68648-27-1	Fancol HL-20	87390-32-7	Nikkol Decaglyn 1-M
68424-59-9	Fancol Karite Extract.	68648-27-1	Fancol HL-24	90052-75-8	Ceraphyl® 847
68424-60-2	Cetiol® SB45	68648-27-1	Lipolan 31	91031-48-0	Cetiol® 868
68424-60-2	Kelisema Natural Pure	68648-27-1	Lipolan 31-20	91031-88-8	Crodesta SL-40
	Shea Butter	68648-27-1	Super-Sat AWS-4	91052-08-3	Syncrowax HGL-C
68424-60-2	Lipex 102	68648-27-1	Super-Sat AWS-24	92777-70-9	Isofol® 16 Caprylat
68424-60-2	Lipex 202	68648-66-8	Ceraphyl® GA-D	94035-02-6	Beta W7 HP 0.9
68424-66-8	Hydroxylan	68650-39-5	Miranol® C2M Conc.	94035-02-6	Encapsin HPB
68424-66-8	OHlan®		NP	94247-28-6	Pelemol® ICB
68424-66-8	Ritahydrox	68783-63-1	Acconon TGH	94278-07-6	Isofol® 16 Oleat
68424-85-1	Hyamine® 3500 50%	68797-35-3	Nikkol Dipotassium	97026-94-0	Koster Keunen
68424-85-1	Querton 246		Glycyrrhizinate		Substitute Beeswax
68424-94-2	Amonyl® 265 BA	68876-77-7	Type B Torula Dried	97069-99-0	Emerwax® 1257
68424-94-2	Dehyton® AB-30		Yeast	97069-99-0	Koster Keunen
68425-17-2	Hystar® 3375	68909-20-6	Aerosil® R812		Emulsifying Wax
68425-17-2	Hystar® 4075	68920-66-1	Britex CO 220	97069-99-0	Polawax®
68425-17-2	Hystar® 5875	68938-15-8	Hystrene® 5012	97069-99-0	Polawax® A31
68425-17-2	Hystar® 6075	68938-15-8	Industrene® 223	97069-99-0	T-Wax
68425-17-2	Hystar® CG	68938-37-4	Wecobee® HTR	97281-47-5	Phospholipon® 90
68425-17-2	Hystar® HM-75	68938-37-4	Wecobee® M	97281-47-5	Phospholipon® 90 G
68425-17-2	Hystar® TPF	68938-54-5	Silwet® L-7602	97281-47-5	Phospholipon® 100,
68439-49-6	Acconon W230	68955-19-1	Empicol® LZ		100G
68439-49-6	Britex CS 110	68955-19-1	Empicol® LZ/D	97281-48-6	Phospholipon® 90 H
68439-49-6	Britex CS 200 B	68955-19-1	Empicol® LZV/D	97281-48-6	Phospholipon® 100 H
68439-49-6	Britex CS 250	68955-19-1	Texapon® Z Highly	97338-28-8	Ceraphyl® 791
68439-49-6	Cremophor® A 11		Conc. Needles	97488-91-0	Labrafil® M 1944 CS
68439-49-6	Cremophor® A 25	68955-19-1	Texapon® Z Highly	98073-10-0	Glucam® E-20
68439-49-6	Emulgator E 2568		Conc. Powder		Distearate
68439-49-6	Eumulgin® B1	68955-20-4	Dehydag® Wax E	98133-47-2	Ritapan TA
68439-49-6	Eumulgin® B2	68955-20-4	Lanette® E	99241-24-4	Alpha W6 HP 0.6
68439-49-6	Eumulgin® B3	68989-00-4	Empigen® BAC50/BP	99241-25-5	Encapsin HPG
68439-49-6	Incropol CS-20	68989-52-6	Lipacide C8CO	99241-25-5	Gamma W8 HP0.6
68439-49-6	Rewopal® CSF 11	68990-06-7	Lamegin® GLP 10, 20	103819-46-1	Labrafil® M 1980 CS
68439-49-6	Rhodasurf® E-15	68990-63-6	Super Refined® Shark	106392-12-5	Lutrol® F 127
68439-49-6	Simulsol® CS		Liver Oil	106436-39-9	Ceraphyl® 55
68439-49-6	Tewax TC 10	68990-82-9	Paramount B	112926-00-8	Sident® 22S

CAS NUMBER-TO-TRADE NAME CROSS-REFERENCE

CAS	Trade name	CAS	Trade name	CAS	Trade name
112926-00-8	Sipernat® 22S	116870-31-6	Phospholipon® PG Na	136097-97-7	Koster Keunen
112945-52-5	Aerosil® 200	125804-16-2	Pelemol® ISB		Synthetic Spermaceti
112945-52-5	Aerosil® 300	125804-19-5	Pelemol® ICO	136505-00-5	Hypan® SR150H
112945-52-5	Aerosil® 380	125804-28-6	Pelemol® G45L	144514-51-2	Orange Wax
112945-52-5	Cab-O-Sil® EH-5	126121-35-5	Pelemol® TGC	144514-51-2	Orange Wax,
112945-52-5	Cab-O-Sil® H-5	126928-07-2	Plurol® Isostearique		Deodorized
112945-52-5	Cab-O-Sil® HS-5	127036-29-7	Pelemol® HAB	150522-09-1	Pecosil® PS-100K
112945-52-5	Cab-O-Sil® L-90	127733-92-0	Stepan TAB®-2	157479-50-0	Fancorsil LIM 1
112945-52-5	Cab-O-Sil® LM-150	129521-59-1	Monomuls® 60-30	157479-51-1	Fancorsil LIM 2
112945-52-5	Cab-O-Sil® M-5	132207-31-9	Pecosil® PS-100	157479-51-1	Fancorsil LIM 3
112945-52-5	Cab-O-Sil® MS-55	132207-31-9	Pecosil® WDS-100	159100-33-1	Pecosil® DCU
112945-52-5	Cab-O-Sil® PTG	132208-25-4	Pelemol® EE	977026-99-5	Akoext SB
113010-52-9	Unipabol U-17	133448-12-1	Pecosil® OS-100B	977059-83-8	Pelemol® CCT
116870-30-5	Phospholipon® MG Na	133738-23-5	Nikkol Decaglyn 1-IS		

Cas Number-to-Chemical Cross-Reference

CAS	Chemical	CAS	Chemical	CAS	Chemical
50-00-0	Formaldehyde	60-29-7	Ethyl ether	75-65-0	t-Butyl alcohol
50-01-1	Guanidine hydrochloride	60-33-3	Linoleic acid	75-69-4	Trichlorofluoromethane
		60-80-0	Antipyrine	75-71-8	Dichlorodifluoromethane
50-21-5	Lactic acid	62-33-9	Calcium disodium EDTA (anhyd.)	75-72-9	Chlorotrifluoromethane
50-70-4	Sorbitol				
50-70-4	Sorbitol sol'n.	62-38-2	Phenylmercuric acetate	75-75-2	Methanesulfonic acid
50-81-7	L-Ascorbic acid	62-54-4	Calcium acetate (anhyd.)	75-85-4	t-Amyl alcohol
50-99-7	D-Glucose (anhyd.)			76-14-2	Cryofluorane
51-05-8	Benzocaine	62-56-6	Thiourea	76-14-2	Dichlorotetrafluoroethane
52-51-7	2-Bromo-2-nitropropane-1,3-diol	63-42-3	Lactose		
		63-68-3	L-Methionine	76-22-2	DL-Camphor
52-89-1	Cysteine hydrochloride anhydrous	64-02-8	Tetrasodium EDTA	76-39-1	2-Nitro-2-methyl-1-propanol
		64-17-5	Alcohol		
52-90-4	L-Cysteine	64-19-7	Acetic acid	76-49-3	Bornyl acetate
54-21-7	Sodium salicylate	64-19-7	Acetic acid, glacial	77-04-3	Pyrithyldione
54-28-4	(+)-γ-Tocopherol	65-85-0	Benzoic acid	77-75-8	Methyl pentynol
54-64-8	Thimerosal	67-03-8	Thiamine HCl	77-76-9	Dimethoxypropane
55-68-5	Phenylmercuric nitrate	67-56-1	Methyl alcohol	77-83-8	Ethyl methylphenylglycidate
56-40-6	Glycine	67-63-0	Isopropyl alcohol		
56-45-1	L-Serine	67-64-1	Acetone	77-86-1	Tris (hydroxymethyl) aminomethane
56-65-5	Adenosine triphosphate	67-66-3	Chloroform		
56-81-5	Glycerin	67-68-5	Dimethyl sulfoxide	77-89-4	Acetyl triethyl citrate
56-84-8	L-Aspartic acid	67-97-0	Cholecalciferol	77-90-7	Acetyl tributyl citrate
56-86-0	L-Glutamic acid	68-04-2	Trisodium citrate (anhyd.)	77-92-9	Citric acid (anhyd.)
56-87-1	L-Lysine			77-93-0	Triethyl citrate
56-95-1	Chlorhexidine diacetate	68-19-9	Cyanocobalamin	77-94-1	Tributyl citrate
57-06-7	Allyl isothiocyanate	69-65-8	D-Mannitol	78-36-4	Linalyl butyrate
57-09-0	Cetrimonium bromide	69-72-7	Salicylic acid	78-59-1	Isophorone
57-10-3	Palmitic acid	69-79-4	Maltose	78-70-6	Linalool
57-11-4	Stearic acid	70-18-8	Glutathione	78-83-1	Isobutyl alcohol
57-13-6	Urea	70-30-4	Hexachlorophene	78-84-2	2-Methylpropanal
57-15-8	Chlorobutanol (anhyd.)	71-00-1	L-Histidine	78-96-6	Isopropanolamine
57-48-7	D-Fructose	71-23-8	n-Propyl alcohol	78-98-8	Pyruvaldehyde
57-50-1	Sucrose	71-36-3	Butyl alcohol	79-01-6	Trichloroethylene
57-55-6	Propylene glycol	71-41-0	n-Amyl alcohol	79-07-2	Chloroacetamide
57-88-5	Cholesterol	72-17-3	Sodium lactate	79-09-4	Propionic acid
58-08-2	Caffeine	72-48-0	Sulfated castor oil	79-24-3	Nitroethane
58-56-0	Pyridoxine HCl	73-40-5	CI 75170	79-33-4	L-Lactic acid
58-85-5	d-Biotin	73-40-5	Guanine	79-41-4	Methacrylic acid
58-93-5	Hydrochlorothiazide	74-31-7	N,N′-Diphenyl-p-phenylenediamine	79-46-9	2-Nitropropane
58-95-7	d-α-Tocopheryl acetate			79-63-0	Lanosterol
59-02-9	d-α Tocopherol	74-79-3	L-Arginine	79-78-7	Allyl α-ionone
59-23-4	D-Galactose	74-98-6	Propane	79-81-2	Retinyl palmitate
59-30-3	Folic acid	75-01-4	Vinyl chloride	80-56-8	α-Pinene
59-46-1	Procaine	75-05-8	Acetonitrile	81-07-2	Saccharin
59-50-7	p-Chloro-m-cresol	75-07-0	Acetaldehyde	81-13-0	D-Panthenol
59-51-8	DL-Methionine	75-09-2	Methylene chloride	81-48-1	CI 60725
59-67-6	Nicotinic acid	75-21-8	Ethylene oxide	81-48-1	D&C Violet No. 2
60-00-4	Edetic acid	75-28-5	Isobutane	81-88-9	D&C Red No. 19
60-01-5	Tributyrin	75-36-5	Acetyl chloride	83-88-5	Riboflavin
60-12-8	Phenethyl alcohol	75-43-4	Dichlorofluoromethane	84-66-2	Diethyl phthalate
60-24-2	2-Mercaptoethanol	75-52-5	5-Nitroisophthalic acid	84-74-2	Dibutyl phthalate
60-27-5	Creatinine	75-52-5	Nitromethane	85-86-9	CI 26100

CAS	Chemical	CAS	Chemical	CAS	Chemical
85-86-9	D&C Red No. 17	97-87-0	Butyl isobutyrate	104-87-0	p-Tolyl aldehyde
85-91-6	Dimethyl anthranilate	98-00-0	Furfuryl alcohol	104-94-9	p-Anisidine
87-20-7	Amyl salicylate	98-01-1	Furfural	105-13-5	Anisyl alcohol
87-25-2	Ethyl anthranilate	98-55-5	α-Terpineol	105-21-5	γ-Heptalactone
87-33-2	Isosorbide dinitrate	98-67-9	Phenol sulfonic acid	105-34-0	Methyl cyanoacetate
87-66-1	Pyrogallol	98-86-2	Acetophenone	105-37-3	Ethyl propionate
87-69-4	L-Tartaric acid	98-92-0	Niacinamide	105-43-1	3-Methylpentanoic acid
87-91-2	Diethyl tartrate	99-26-3	Bismuth subgallate	105-45-3	Methyl acetoacetate
87-99-0	Xylitol	99-48-9	Carveol	105-53-3	Diethyl malonate
88-04-0	Chloroxylenol	99-76-3	Methylparaben	105-54-4	Ethyl butyrate
88-09-5	Diethylacetic acid	99-83-2	α-Phellandrene	105-57-7	Acetal
88-14-2	2-Furoic acid	99-85-4	γ-Terpinene	105-68-0	Isoamyl propionate
88-69-7	o-Isopropylphenol	99-86-5	α-Terpinene	105-79-3	Isobutyl hexanoate
89-49-6	Isopulegyl acetate	99-87-6	p-Cymene	105-85-1	Citronellyl formate
89-65-6	Erythorbic acid	99-89-8	p-Isopropylphenol	105-87-3	Geranyl acetate
89-74-7	2,4-Dimethylaceto-	100-06-1	Acetanisole	105-93-3	Ethylene brassylate
	phenone	100-09-4	p-Anisic acid	105-99-7	Dibutyl adipate
89-78-1	Menthol	100-37-8	Diethylaminoethanol	106-02-5	Pentadecalactone
89-82-7	Pulegone	100-42-5	Styrene	106-07-0	PEG-4 stearate
89-83-8	Thymol	100-51-6	Benzyl alcohol	106-11-6	PEG-2 stearate
90-04-0	o-Anisidine	100-52-7	Benzaldehyde	106-21-8	3,7-Dimethyl-1-octanol
90-05-1	Guaiacol	101-39-3	α-Methylcinnamal-	106-22-9	β-Citronellol
90-80-2	Gluconolactone		dehyde	106-23-0	Citronellal
91-16-7	Veratrole	101-54-2	N-Phenyl-p-	106-24-1	Geraniol
91-63-4	Quinaldine		phenylenediamine	106-27-4	Isoamyl butyrate
91-87-2	α-Amylcinnamalde-	101-97-3	Ethyl phenylacetate	106-30-9	Ethyl heptanoate
	hyde dimethyl acetal	102-08-9	N,N´-Diphenylthiourea	106-32-1	Ethyl octanoate
92-48-8	6-Methylcoumarin	102-60-3	Tetrahydroxypropyl	106-33-2	Ethyl laurate
93-08-3	2´-Acetonaphthone		ethylenediamine	106-35-4	3-Heptanone
93-29-8	Acetisoeugenol	102-71-6	Triethanolamine	106-36-5	Propyl propionate
93-51-6	2-Methoxy-4-	102-76-1	Triacetin	106-44-5	p-Cresol
	methylphenol	102-85-2	Tributyl phosphite	106-46-7	p-Dichlorobenzene
93-58-3	Methyl benzoate	102-98-7	Phenylmercuric borate	106-47-8	p-Chloroaniline
93-82-5	Stearamide DEA	103-23-1	Dioctyl adipate	106-65-0	Dimethyl succinate
93-89-0	Ethyl benzoate	103-25-3	Methyl 3-phenyl-	106-70-7	Methyl caproate
93-92-5	α-Methylbenzyl acetate		propionate	106-72-9	2,6-Dimethyl-5-
94-13-3	Propylparaben	103-26-4	Methyl cinnamate		heptenal
94-18-8	Benzylparaben	103-28-6	Benzyl isobutyrate	106-73-0	Methyl heptanoate
94-26-8	Butylparaben	103-36-6	Ethyl cinnamate	106-97-8	Butane
94-30-4	Ethyl-p-anisate	103-37-7	Benzyl butyrate	107-15-3	Ethylenediamine
94-36-0	Benzoyl peroxide	103-38-8	Benzyl isovalerate		(anhyd.)
94-47-3	Phenethyl benzoate	103-41-3	Benzyl cinnamate	107-21-1	Glycol
94-86-0	Propenylguaethol	103-45-7	2-Phenylethyl acetate	107-35-7	Taurine
95-48-7	o-Cresol	103-48-0	Phenethyl isobutyrate	107-41-5	Hexylene glycol
95-51-2	o-Chloroaniline	103-50-4	Benzyl ether	107-64-2	Distearyldimonium
95-87-4	2,5-Xylenol	103-52-6	Phenethyl butyrate		chloride
96-13-9	2,3-Dibromo-1-	103-56-0	Cinnamyl propionate	107-74-4	Hydroxycitronellol
	propanol	103-58-2	3-Phenylpropyl	107-75-5	Hydroxycitronellal
96-17-3	2-Methylbutyraldehyde		isobutyrate	107-87-9	Methyl propyl ketone
96-20-8	2-Amino-1-butanol	103-59-3	Cinnamyl isobutyrate	107-88-0	Butylene glycol
96-26-4	Dihydroxyacetone	103-60-6	Phenoxyethyl	107-97-1	Sarcosine
96-27-5	Thioglycerin		isobutyrate	108-01-0	Dimethylethanolamine
96-33-3	Methyl acrylate	103-61-7	Cinnamyl butyrate	108-03-2	Nitropropane
	(monomer)	103-82-2	Phenylacetic acid	108-10-1	Methyl isobutyl ketone
96-48-0	Butyrolactone	104-01-8	p-Methoxyphenylacetic	108-21-4	Isopropyl acetate
96-49-1	Ethylene carbonate		acid	108-24-7	Acetic anhydride
97-05-2	5-Sulfosalicylic acid	104-15-4	p-Toluene sulfonic acid	108-30-5	Succinic anhydride
97-42-7	Carvyl acetate	104-20-1	4-p-Methoxyphenyl-2-	108-31-6	Maleic anhydride
97-45-0	Carvyl propionate		butanone	108-32-7	Propylene carbonate
97-53-0	Eugenol	104-21-2	Anisyl acetate	108-39-4	m-Cresol
97-54-1	Isoeugenol	104-46-1	Anethole	108-42-9	m-Chloroaniline
97-59-6	Allantoin	104-50-7	γ-Octalactone	108-46-3	Resorcinol
97-62-1	Ethyl isobutyrate	104-53-0	Hydrocinnamaldehyde	108-48-5	2,6-Lutidine
97-64-3	Ethyl lactate	104-54-1	Cinnamyl alcohol	108-64-5	Ethyl isovalerate
97-67-6	N-Hydroxysuccinic acid	104-55-2	Cinnamal	108-73-6	1,3,5-Trihydroxy-
	(L)	104-61-0	γ-Nonalactone		benzene
97-78-9	Lauroyl sarcosine	104-67-6	γ-Undecalactone	108-83-8	Diisobutyl ketone
97-85-8	Isobutyl isobutyrate	104-76-7	2-Ethylhexanol	108-89-4	γ-Picoline

CAS	Chemical	CAS	Chemical	CAS	Chemical
108-95-2	Phenol	112-23-2	Heptyl formate	122-40-7	α-Amylcinnamal-dehyde
108-98-5	Thiophenol	112-24-3	Triethylenetetramine		
108-99-6	β-Picoline	112-30-1	n-Decyl alcohol	122-43-0	Butyl phenylacetate
109-02-4	p-Methyl morpholine	112-31-2	Decanal	122-48-5	Zingerone
109-06-8	α-Picoline	112-32-3	Octyl formate	122-52-1	Triethyl phosphite
109-09-1	2-Chloropyridine	112-38-9	Undecylenic acid	122-57-6	Benzylidene acetone
109-19-3	n-Butyl isovalerate	112-42-5	Undecyl alcohol	122-59-8	Phenoxyacetic acid
109-21-7	Butyl butyrate	112-44-7	Undecanal	122-60-1	Phenyl glycidyl ether
109-43-3	Dibutyl sebacate	112-45-8	10-Undecenal	122-63-4	Benzyl propionate
109-60-4	Propyl acetate	112-49-2	PEG-3 dimethyl ether	122-67-8	Isobutyl cinnamate
109-73-9	n-Butylamine	112-53-8	Lauryl alcohol	122-78-1	Phenylacetaldehyde
109-74-0	Butyronitrile	112-54-9	Lauric aldehyde	122-84-9	1-(p-Methoxyphenyl)-2-propanone
109-89-7	Diethylamine	112-60-7	PEG-4		
109-94-4	Ethyl formate	112-61-8	Methyl stearate	122-91-8	Anisyl formate
109-99-9	Tetrahydrofuran	112-62-9	Methyl oleate	122-99-6	Phenoxyethanol
110-00-9	Furan polymer	112-66-3	Lauryl acetate	123-03-5	Cetylpyridinium chloride (anhyd.)
110-02-1	Thiophene	112-72-1	Myristyl alcohol		
110-15-6	Succinic acid	112-73-2	Diethylene glycol dibutyl ether	123-08-0	p-Hydroxybenzalde-hyde
110-16-7	Maleic acid				
110-17-8	Fumaric acid	112-80-1	Oleic acid	123-11-5	p-Anisaldehyde
110-19-0	Isobutyl acetate	112-85-6	Behenic acid	123-19-3	4-Heptanone
110-27-0	Isopropyl myristate	112-92-5	Stearyl alcohol	123-28-4	Dilauryl thiodipropionate
110-38-3	Ethyl decanoate	115-19-5	Methyl butynol		
110-39-4	Octyl butyrate	115-69-5	2-Amino-2-methyl-1,3-propanediol	123-29-5	Ethyl pelargonate
110-40-7	Diethyl sebacate			123-31-9	Hydroquinone
110-43-0	Methyl n-amyl ketone	115-70-8	2-Amino-2-ethyl-1,3-propanediol	123-32-0	2,5-Dimethylpyrazine
110-44-1	Sorbic acid			123-35-3	Myrcene
110-45-2	Isoamyl formate	115-95-7	Linalyl acetate	123-51-3	Isoamyl alcohol
110-58-7	Pentylamine	115-99-1	Linalyl formate	123-54-6	Acetylacetone
110-65-6	But-2-yne-1,4-diol	116-17-6	Triisopropyl phosphite	123-66-0	Ethyl caproate
110-71-4	Ethylene glycol dimethyl ether	117-81-7	Dioctyl phthalate	123-68-2	Allyl caproate
		117-84-0	Dioctyl phthalate	123-72-8	n-Butyraldehyde
110-74-7	Propyl formate	117-96-4	Diatrizoic acid	123-76-2	Levulinic acid
110-82-7	Cyclohexane	118-52-5	1,3-Dichloro-5,5-dimethyl hydantoin	123-91-1	1,4-Dioxane
110-85-0	Piperazine			123-92-2	Isoamyl acetate
110-86-1	Pyridine	118-55-8	Phenyl salicylate	123-94-4	Glyceryl stearate
110-89-4	Piperidine	118-58-1	Benzylsalicylate	123-95-5	Butyl stearate
110-91-8	Morpholine	118-60-5	Octyl salicylate	124-04-9	Adipic acid
110-93-0	Methyl heptenone	118-61-6	Ethyl salicylate	124-07-2	Caprylic acid
110-97-4	Diisopropanolamine	118-71-8	Maltol	124-10-7	Methyl myristate
111-01-3	Squalane	118-92-3	Anthranilic acid	124-13-0	n-Octanal
111-02-4	Squalene	119-36-8	Methyl salicylate	124-19-6	Nonanal
111-03-5	Glyceryl oleate	119-53-9	Benzoin	124-25-4	Myristaldehyde
111-03-5	Glyceryl oleate SE	119-61-9	Benzophenone	124-29-8	Cetyl alcohol
111-11-5	Methyl caprylate	119-65-3	Isoquinoline	124-38-9	Carbon dioxide
111-13-7	Methyl hexyl ketone	119-84-6	Dihydrocoumarin	124-43-6	Urea peroxide
111-27-3	Hexyl alcohol	120-14-9	Veratraldehyde	124-68-5	2-Amino-2-methyl-1-propanol
111-30-8	Glutaral	120-24-1	Isoeugenyl phenyl-acetate		
111-42-2	Diethanolamine			126-13-6	Sucrose acetate isobutyrate
111-49-9	Hexamethyleneimine	120-40-1	Lauramide DEA		
111-60-4	Glycol stearate	120-47-8	Ethylparaben	126-14-7	Sucrose octaacetate
111-62-6	Ethyl oleate	120-51-4	Benzyl benzoate	126-92-1	Sodium octyl sulfate
111-70-6	Heptyl alcohol	120-57-0	Heliotropine	127-08-2	Potassium acetate
111-71-7	Heptanal	120-80-9	Pyrocatechol	127-09-3	Sodium acetate anhydrous
111-80-8	Methyl 2-nonynoate	121-32-4	Ethyl vanillin		
111-82-0	Methyl laurate	121-33-5	Vanillin	127-41-3	α-Ionone
111-87-5	Caprylic alcohol	121-39-1	Ethyl phenylglycidate	127-91-3	β-Pinene
111-90-0	Ethoxydiglycol	121-45-9	Trimethyl phosphite	128-37-0	BHT
111-96-6	Diethylene glycol dimethyl ether	121-47-1	Metanilic acid	128-44-9	Saccharin sodium (anhyd.)
		121-54-0	Benzethonium chloride		
112-00-5	Laurtrimonium chloride	121-79-9	Propyl gallate	128-80-3	CI 61565
112-02-7	Cetrimonium chloride	122-00-9	4′-Methyl aceto-phenone	128-80-3	D&C Green No. 6
112-06-1	Heptyl acetate			130-20-1	CI 69825
112-10-7	Isopropyl stearate	122-03-2	Cuminaldehyde	130-20-1	D&C Blue No. 9
112-12-9	2-Undecanone	122-18-9	Cetalkonium chloride	130-40-5	Riboflavin-5′-phosphate sodium
112-14-1	Octyl acetate	122-19-0	Stearalkonium chloride		
112-17-4	Decyl acetate	122-20-3	Triisopropanolamine	131-57-7	Benzophenone-3
112-18-5	Dimethyl lauramine	122-32-7	Triolein	133-06-2	Captan

CAS NUMBER-TO-CHEMICAL CROSS-REFERENCE

CAS	Chemical	CAS	Chemical	CAS	Chemical
133-17-5	Iodohippurate sodium	143-08-8	Nonyl alcohol		acid
133-18-6	Phenethyl anthranilate	143-28-2	Oleyl alcohol	501-52-0	Hydrocinnamic acid
133-37-9	DL-α-Tartaric acid	144-39-8	Linalyl propionate	504-53-0	Stearone
134-03-2	Sodium ascorbate	144-55-8	Sodium bicarbonate	505-48-6	Suberic acid
134-09-8	Menthyl anthranilate	147-14-8	Copper phthalocyanine	506-26-3	γ-Linolenic acid
134-20-3	Methyl anthranilate		blue	506-87-6	Ammonium carbonate
134-31-6	8-Hydroxyquinoline	147-71-7	D-Tartaric acid	513-86-0	Acetyl methyl carbinol
	sulfate	147-73-9	m-Tartaric acid	514-78-3	Canthaxanthine
135-02-4	o-Methoxybenz-	148-24-3	8-Hydroxyquinoline	514-78-3	CI 40850
	aldehyde	148-65-2	Chlorothen	515-00-4	Myrtenol
137-08-6	Calcium D-pantothen-	149-44-0	Sodium formaldehyde	515-69-5	Bisabolol
	ate		sulfoxylate	515-98-0	Ammonium lactate
137-16-6	Sodium lauroyl	149-91-7	Gallic acid	518-40-1	D&C Orange No. 10
	sarcosinate	150-13-0	p-Aminobenzoic acid	518-47-8	CI 45350
137-26-8	Tetramethylthiuram	150-38-9	Trisodium EDTA	518-47-8	D&C Yellow No. 8
	disulfide	150-76-5	Hydroquinone	520-45-6	Dehydroacetic acid
137-40-6	Sodium propionate		monomethyl ether	526-83-0	L-Tartaric acid
	(anhyd.)	150-84-5	Citronellyl acetate	526-95-4	D-Gluconic acid
137-58-6	Lidocaine	150-90-3	Sodium succinate	527-07-1	Sodium gluconate
137-66-6	Ascorbyl palmitate		(hexahydrate)	527-09-3	Copper gluconate
138-15-8	L-Glutamic acid	151-10-0	m-Dimethoxybenzene	530-26-7	D-Mannose
	hydrochloride	151-21-3	Sodium lauryl sulfate	532-27-4	Chloroacetophenone
138-22-7	Butyl lactate	151-41-7	Lauryl sulfate	532-32-1	Sodium benzoate
138-86-3	dl-Limonene	274-09-9	1,2-Methylenedioxy-	532-43-4	Thiamine nitrate
139-07-1	Lauralkonium chloride		benzene	536-90-3	m-Anisidine
139-08-2	Myristalkonium chloride	290-37-9	Pyrazine	537-55-3	Acetyltyrosine
139-33-3	Disodium EDTA	298-14-6	Potassium bicarbonate	538-23-8	Tricaprylin
	(anhyd.)	299-27-4	Potassium D-gluconate	538-24-9	Trilaurin
139-44-6	Trihydroxystearin	299-28-5	Calcium gluconate	538-71-6	Domiphen bromide
139-85-5	3,4-Dihydroxybenzal-		(anhyd.)	539-82-2	Ethyl valerate
	dehyde	299-29-6	Ferrous gluconate	539-88-8	Ethyl levulinate
139-88-8	Sodium myristyl sulfate		(anhyd.)	539-90-2	Isobutyl butyrate
139-89-9	Trisodium HEDTA	300-92-5	Aluminum distearate	540-10-3	Cetyl palmitate
139-96-8	TEA-lauryl sulfate	302-95-4	Sodium desoxycholate	540-18-1	Amyl butyrate
140-01-2	Pentasodium pentetate	304-59-6	Potassium sodium	540-72-7	Sodium thiocyanate
140-10-3	Cinnamic acid		tartrate anhyd.	540-92-1	Acetone sodium
140-11-4	Benzyl acetate	326-61-4	Piperonyl acetate		bisulfite
140-26-1	Phenethyl isovalerate	333-18-6	Ethylenediamine	542-55-2	Isobutyl formate
140-31-8	Aminoethylpiperazine		dihydrochloride	544-35-4	Ethyl linoleate
140-67-0	Estragole	333-20-0	Potassium thiocyanate	544-62-7	Batyl alcohol
140-88-5	Ethyl acrylate	334-48-5	Capric acid	544-63-8	Myristic acid
141-01-5	Ferrous fumarate	350-03-8	3-Acetylpyridine	546-93-0	Magnesium carbonate
141-05-9	Diethyl maleate	367-51-1	Sodium thioglycolate		(anhyd.)
141-08-2	Glyceryl ricinoleate	371-41-5	p-Fluorophenol	547-63-7	Methyl isobutyrate
141-12-8	Neryl acetate	409-02-9	Methyl heptenone	548-26-5	CI 45380
141-16-2	Citronellyl butyrate	432-25-7	β-Cyclocitral	548-26-5	D&C Red No. 22
141-22-0	Ricinoleic acid	440-58-6	Iodamide	552-89-6	o-Nitrobenzaldehyde
141-43-5	Ethanolamine	461-58-5	Dicyandiamide	554-12-1	Methyl propionate
141-78-6	Ethyl acetate	463-40-1	Linolenic acid	555-06-6	Sodium aminobenzoate
141-82-2	Malonic acid	464-49-3	D-Camphor	555-16-8	p-Nitrobenzaldehyde
141-94-6	Hexetidine	470-82-6	Eucalyptol	555-43-1	Tristearin
141-97-9	Ethylacetoacetate	471-34-1	Calcium carbonate	555-44-2	Tripalmitin
142-03-0	Aluminum diacetate	471-34-1	CI 77220	555-45-3	Trimyristin
142-18-7	Glyceryl laurate	471-53-4	Glycyrrhetinic acid	556-24-1	Methyl isovalerate
142-19-8	Allyl heptanoate	482-89-3	CI 73000	556-82-1	3-Methyl-2-buten-1-ol
142-20-1	PEG-4 distearate	482-89-3	D&C Blue No. 6	557-04-0	Magnesium stearate
142-31-4	Sodium octyl sulfate	488-10-8	cis-Jasmone	557-05-1	Zinc stearate
142-47-2	MSG	490-79-9	Gentisic acid	557-34-6	Zinc acetate (anhyd.)
142-50-7	Trimethyldodeca-	492-62-6	D-Glucose	557-61-9	Octacosanol
	trieneol (cis)	494-90-6	4,5,6,7-Tetrahydro-3,6-	576-26-1	2,6-Xylenol
142-55-2	Propylene glycol		dimethylbenzofuran	577-11-7	Dioctyl sodium
	laurate	495-40-9	Butyrophenone		sulfosuccinate
142-58-5	Myristamide MEA	497-19-8	Sodium carbonate	579-07-7	1-Phenyl-1,2-
142-62-1	Caproic acid		(anhyd.)		propanedione
142-91-6	Isopropyl palmitate	498-00-0	Vanillyl alcohol	582-25-2	Potassium benzoate
142-92-7	Hexyl acetate	499-12-7	Aconitic acid		(anhyd.)
143-00-0	DEA-lauryl sulfate	499-40-1	Isomaltose	584-02-1	3-Pentanol
143-07-7	Lauric acid	500-38-9	Nordihydroguaiaretic	584-08-7	Potassium carbonate

CAS	Chemical	CAS	Chemical	CAS	Chemical
585-88-6	Maltitol	706-14-9	γ-Decalactone	1308-38-9	Chromium oxide
589-38-8	3-Hexanone	710-04-3	δ-Undecalactone		greens
589-66-2	Isobutyl-2-butenoate	713-95-1	δ-Dodecalactone	1308-38-9	CI 77288
589-68-4	Glyceryl myristate	770-12-7	Phenyl dichloro-	1309-37-1	CI 77491
590-00-1	Potassium sorbate		phosphate	1309-37-1	CI 77499
590-01-2	n-Butyl propionate	771-03-9	Dehydroacetic acid	1309-37-1	Ferric oxide (anhyd.)
590-86-3	Isovaleraldehyde	813-94-5	Calcium citrate (anhyd.)	1309-37-1	Iron oxides (Fe$_2$O$_3$)
591-68-4	Butyl valerate	814-80-2	Calcium lactate	1309-42-8	Magnesium hydroxide
592-84-7	Butyl formate		(anhyd.)		(anhyd.)
593-29-3	Potassium stearate	815-85-0	Stannous tartrate	1309-48-4	Magnesium oxide
593-60-2	Vinyl bromide	816-94-4	1,2-Distearoyl-sn-	1310-58-3	Potassium hydroxide
596-03-2	D&C Orange No. 5		glycero(3) phosphati-	1310-73-2	Sodium hydroxide
597-09-1	2-Nitro-2-ethyl-1,3-		dylcholine	1314-13-2	CI 77947
	propanediol	821-55-6	2-Nonanone	1314-13-2	Zinc oxide
598-82-3	DL-Lactic acid	822-16-2	Sodium stearate	1317-61-9	CI 77499
600-07-7	2-Methylbutyric acid	824-35-1	Calcium salicylate	1317-61-9	Iron oxides (Fe$_3$O$_4$)
606-17-7	Iodipamide	846-70-8	CI 10316	1317-65-3	Calcium carbonate
609-31-4	2-Nitro-1-butanol	846-70-8	Ext. D&C Yellow No. 7	1317-80-2	Titanium dioxide
611-13-2	Methyl 2-furoate	860-22-0	CI 73015	1318-02-1	Sodium silicoaluminate
616-45-5	2-Pyrrolidone	860-22-0	FD&C Blue No. 2	1318-02-1	Zeolite
617-35-6	Ethyl pyruvate	866-84-2	Potassium citrate	1323-03-1	Myristyl lactate
617-48-1	N-Hydroxysuccinic acid		(anhyd.)	1323-38-2	Castor oil
	(DL)	867-13-0	Triethyl phosphono-	1323-39-3	Propylene glycol
618-88-2	5-Nitroisophthalic acid		acetate		stearate
620-79-1	Ethyl 2-acetyl-3-	867-56-1	Sodium L-lactate	1323-83-7	Glyceryl distearate
	phenylpropionate	868-14-4	Potassium acid tartrate	1327-36-2	Aluminum silicate
621-82-9	Cinnamic acid	868-18-8	Sodium tartrate	1327-41-9	Aluminum chloride
622-45-7	Cyclohexyl acetate		(anhyd.)		basic
623-17-6	Furfuryl acetate	868-57-5	Methyl 2-methyl-	1327-41-9	Aluminum chloro-
623-21-2	Furfuryl butyrate		butyrate		hydrate
623-37-0	3-Hexanol	872-05-9	Decene-1	1327-43-1	Magnesium aluminum
623-84-7	Propylene glycol	872-50-4	N-Methyl-2-pyrrolidone		silicate
	diacetate	900-28-6	Gum ghatti	1330-43-4	Sodium borate (anhyd.)
624-04-4	Glycol dilaurate	915-67-3	Amaranth	1330-80-9	Propylene glycol oleate
624-24-8	Methyl valerate	928-80-3	3-Decanone	1332-58-7	Kaolin
626-11-9	Diethyl malate	928-95-0	2-Hexenol	1332-73-6	CI 77002
626-82-4	Butyl hexanoate	996-31-6	Potassium lactate	1332-98-5	Iron ammonium citrate
627-83-8	Glycol distearate	999-21-3	Diallyl maleate	1333-00-2	Iron ammonium citrate
627-90-7	Ethyl undecanoate	999-40-6	Neryl butyrate	1333-39-7	Phenol sulfonic acid
628-63-7	Amyl acetate	999-97-3	Hexamethyldisilazane	1333-89-7	Hydroabietyl alcohol
628-99-9	2-Nonanol	1034-01-1	Octyl gallate	1334-78-7	p-Tolyl aldehyde
629-33-4	Hexyl formate	1066-33-7	Ammonium bicarbonate	1335-72-4	Sodium laureth sulfate
629-70-9	Cetyl acetate	1069-55-2	Bucrylate	1336-21-6	Ammonium hydroxide
629-82-3	Dioctyl ether	1117-55-1	Hexyl octanoate	1337-33-3	Stearyl citrate
629-96-9	Arachidyl alcohol	1118-27-0	Linalyl isovalerate	1337-76-4	Attapulgite
631-61-8	Ammonium acetate	1119-97-7	Myrtrimonium bromide	1338-39-2	Sorbitan laurate
633-96-5	CI 15510	1124-11-4	2,3,5,6-Tetramethyl-	1338-41-6	Sorbitan stearate
633-96-5	D&C Orange No. 4		pyrazine	1338-43-8	Sorbitan oleate
636-61-3	N-Hydroxysuccinic acid	1166-52-5	Dodecyl gallate	1343-88-0	Magnesium silicate
	(+)	1185-57-5	Iron ammonium citrate	1343-98-2	Silica, hydrated (silicic
637-65-0	Tetrahydrofurfuryl		(green)		acid)
	propionate	1185-57-6	Iron ammonium citrate	1344-00-9	Sodium silicoaluminate
638-11-9	Isopropyl butyrate		(brown)	1344-28-1	Alumina
638-49-3	Amyl formate	1191-50-0	Sodium myristyl sulfate	1344-95-2	Calcium silicate
644-49-5	Propyl isobutyrate	1193-18-6	3-Methyl-2-cyclohexen-	1345-25-1	CI 77489
645-56-7	4-Propylphenol		1-one	1345-25-1	CI 77499
646-13-9	Isobutyl stearate	1196-01-6	(1S)-(-)-Verbenone	1345-25-1	Iron oxides (FeO)
659-40-5	Hexamidine	1260-17-9	CI 75470	1369-66-3	Dioctyl sodium
	diisethionate	1299-89-4	Vythene		sulfosuccinate
659-70-1	Isoamyl isovalerate	1300-71-6	Xylenol	1390-65-4	Carmine
661-19-8	Behenyl alcohol	1300-72-7	Sodium xylene-	1393-63-1	Annatto
692-86-4	Ethyl 10-undecenoate		sulfonate	1393-63-1	CI 75120
693-36-7	Distearyl thiodipro-	1302-78-9	Bentonite	1401-55-4	Tannic acid
	pionate	1303-96-4	Sodium borate	1405-86-3	Glycyrrhizic acid
695-06-7	γ-Hexalactone		decahydrate	1406-18-4	Tocopherol
705-73-7	α-Propylphenethyl	1304-85-4	Bismuth subnitrate	1406-70-8	Tocopheryl acetate
	alcohol	1305-62-0	Calcium hydroxide	1407-03-0	Monoammonium
705-86-2	Δ-Decalactone	1305-78-8	Calcium oxide		glycyrrhizinate

CAS	Chemical	CAS	Chemical	CAS	Chemical
1490-04-6	Menthol	2644-64-6	1,2-Dipalmitoyl-sn-glycero(3) phosphatidylcholine	3913-71-1	trans-2-Decenal
1493-13-6	Trifluoromethane sulfonic acid			3915-83-1	Neryl isovalerate
				3959-43-3	Sorbitol sol'n.
1504-74-1	o-Methoxycinnamaldehyde	2650-18-2	D&C Blue No. 4	4065-45-6	Benzophenone-4
		2650-18-2	FD&C Blue No. 1	4070-80-8	Sodium stearyl fumarate
1551-44-6	Cyclohexyl butyrate	2682-20-4	Methylisothiazolinone		
1592-23-0	Calcium stearate	2695-37-6	Sodium p-styrene-sulfonate	4075-81-4	Calcium propionate (anhyd.)
1600-27-7	Mercury acetate (ic)				
1632-73-1	Fenchyl alcohol	2705-87-5	Allyl cyclohexane-propionate	4080-31-3	Quaternium-15
1634-04-4	Methyl t-butyl ether			4169-04-4	Phenoxyisopropanol
1643-20-5	Lauramine oxide	2778-96-3	Stearyl stearate	4180-23-8	Anethole (E isomer)
1731-84-6	Methyl nonanoate	2783-94-0	CI 15985	4191-73-5	Isopropylparaben
1733-25-1	Isopropyl tiglate	2783-94-0	FD&C Yellow No. 6	4230-97-1	Allyl octanoate
1777-82-8	Dichlorobenzyl alcohol	2809-21-4	Etidronic acid	4247-02-3	Isobutylparaben
1797-74-6	Allyl phenylacetate	2814-77-9	CI 12085	4254-14-2	(-)-Propylene glycol
1847-58-1	Sodium lauryl sulfoacetate	2814-77-9	D&C Red No. 36	4254-15-3	(+)-Propylene glycol
		2835-39-4	Allyl isovalerate	4254-16-4	(±)-Propylene glycol
1866-31-5	Allyl cinnamate	2915-57-3	Dioctyl succinate	4292-10-8	Lauramidopropyl betaine
1934-21-0	CI 19140	2917-94-4	Sodium octoxynol-2 ethane sulfonate		
1934-21-0	FD&C Yellow No. 5			4403-90-1	CI 61570
1934-21-0	Tartrazine	3051-35-2	PEG vegetable oil	4403-90-1	D&C Green No. 5
1948-33-0	t-Butyl hydroquinone	3055-93-4	Laureth-2	4418-26-2	Sodium dehydroacetate
1984-06-1	Sodium caprylate	3055-94-5	Laureth-3	4468-02-4	Zinc gluconate (anhyd.)
1984-15-2	Medronic acid	3055-96-7	Laureth-6	4478-97-1	Ceteth-5
2021-28-5	Ethyl-3-phenyl-propionate	3055-97-8	Laureth-7	4548-53-2	CI 14700
		3056-00-6	Laureth-12	4548-53-2	FD&C Red No. 4
2050-01-3	Isoamyl isobutyrate	3088-31-1	Sodium laureth sulfate	4568-28-9	TEA-stearate
2051-78-7	Allyl butyrate	3097-08-3	Magnesium lauryl sulfate	4584-46-7	Dimethylaminoethyl chloride hydrochloride
2052-15-5	Butyl levulinate				
2090-05-3	Calcium benzoate	3149-28-8	2-Methoxypyrazine	4602-84-0	Farnesol
2092-56-0	D&C Red No. 8	3151-59-5	Cetylamine hydro-fluoride	4606-15-9	Propyl phenylacetate
2153-26-6	Terpinyl formate			4691-65-0	Disodium inosinate (anhyd.)
2198-61-0	Isoamyl hexanoate	3179-81-5	Diethylaminoethyl stearate		
2216-51-5	(-)-Menthol			4740-78-7	Glyceryl formal
2216-52-6	d-Neomenthol	3208-16-0	2-Ethylfuran	4748-78-1	p-Ethylbenzaldehyde
2235-54-3	Ammonium lauryl sulfate	3234-85-3	Myristyl myristate	4767-03-7	Dimethylolpropionic acid
		3282-30-2	Pivaloyl chloride		
2277-28-3	Glyceryl linoleate	3380-34-5	Triclosan	4861-85-2	Isopropyl phenylacetate
2305-05-7	γ-Dodecalactone	3386-18-3	PEG-9	4864-61-3	3-Octyl acetate
2315-62-0	Octoxynol-3	3398-33-2	Sodium undecylenate	4940-11-8	Ethyl maltol
2315-64-2	Octoxynol-5	3436-44-0	1,2-Dicaproyl-sn-glycero(3) phosphatidylcholine	5026-62-0	Sodium methylparaben
2315-66-4	Octoxynol-10			5117-19-1	PEG-8
2315-67-5	Octoxynol-1	3458-28-4	D-Mannose	5160-02-1	D&C Red No. 9
2315-68-6	Propyl benzoate	3460-44-4	α-Methylbenzyl butyrate	5168-91-2	Ceteth-6
2321-07-5	D&C Yellow No. 7			5274-61-3	Ceteth-2
2321-07-5	Fluorescein	3468-63-1	D&C Orange No. 17	5274-65-7	Oleth-2
2345-24-6	Neryl isobutyrate	3567-66-6	CI 17200	5274-66-8	Oleth-3
2349-07-7	Hexyl isobutyrate	3567-66-6	D&C Red No. 33	5274-68-0	Laureth-4
2353-45-9	CI 42053	3598-16-1	Sodium phenoxy acetate	5281-04-9	D&C Red No. 7
2353-45-9	FD&C Green No. 3			5306-85-4	Dimethyl isosorbide
2370-64-1	PEG-6 laurate	3615-41-6	Rhamnose	5333-42-6	Octyldodecanol
2379-74-0	CI 73360	3622-84-2	N,N-Butyl benzene sulfonamide	5349-62-2	4-Methyl-1-phenyl-2-pentanone
2379-74-0	D&C Red No. 30	3632-91-5	Magnesium gluconate (anhyd.)		
2396-84-1	Ethyl sorbate			5353-27-5	Oleth-5
2412-80-8	Methyl 4-methylvalerate	3658-77-3	4-Hydroxy-2,5-dimethyl-3(2H)furanone	5392-40-5	Citral
2425-77-6	2-Hexyl-1-decanol			5396-89-4	Benzyl acetoacetate
2445-76-3	Hexyl propionate	3687-45-4	Oleyl oleate	5452-07-3	3-Phenylpropyl isovalerate
2445-77-4	2-Methylbutyl isovalerate	3687-46-5	Decyl oleate		
		3724-65-0	Crotonic acid	5454-09-1	Decyl butyrate
2497-18-9	trans-2-Hexenyl acetate	3734-33-6	Denatonium benzoate (anhyd.)	5454-19-3	Decyl propionate
2524-64-3	Diphenyl chloro-phosphate			5454-28-4	Butyl heptanoate
		3794-83-0	Tetrasodium etidronate	5461-08-5	Piperonyl isobutyrate
2537-48-6	Diethyl cyanomethyl-phosphonate	3844-45-9	CI 42090	5466-77-3	Octyl methoxy-cinnamate
		3844-45-9	FD&C Blue No. 1		
2550-40-5	Dicyclohexyl disulfide	3848-24-6	Acetyl butyryl	5471-51-2	4-(p-Hydroxyphenyl)-2-butanone
2568-33-4	Isopentyldiol	3913-02-8	2-Butyl-1-octanol		
2615-15-8	PEG-6			5550-12-9	Disodium guanylate (anhyd.)
2639-63-6	Hexyl butyrate				

CAS	Chemical	CAS	Chemical	CAS	Chemical
5743-26-0	Calcium acetate (monohydrate)	6358-69-6	D&C Green No. 8	7446-70-0	Aluminum chloride anhydrous
5743-27-1	Calcium ascorbate	6363-07-5	D&C Red No. 37	7447-40-7	Potassium chloride
5743-28-2	Calcium ascorbate (dihydrate)	6363-53-7	Maltose (monohydrate)	7452-79-1	Ethyl 2-methylbutyrate
		6365-83-9	Herbacol	7487-88-9	Magnesium sulfate anhyd.
5743-34-0	Calcium borogluconate	6371-55-7	D&C Red No. 39		
5785-44-4	Calcium citrate (tetrahyrate)	6371-76-2	D&C Red No. 31	7490-88-2	Diethylaminoethyl stearamide phosphate
		6371-85-3	D&C Blue No. 4		
5793-88-4	Calcium saccharate (anhyd.)	6381-59-5	Potassium sodium tartrate tetrahydrate	7491-02-3	Diisopropyl sebacate
5793-89-5	Calcium saccharate (tetrahydrate)	6381-91-5	Calcium saccharin (hydrate)	7491-05-2	Tallowtrimonium chloride
5793-94-2	Calcium stearoyl lactylate	6381-92-6	Disodium EDTA (dihydrate)	7491-14-7	Dipropylene glycol salicylate
5837-78-5	Ethyl tiglate	6417-83-0	D&C Red No. 34	7491-35-2	Gentisic acid ethanolamine
5856-63-3	2-Amino-1-butanol	6440-58-0	DMDM hydantoin		
5858-81-1	CI 15850	6485-34-3	Calcium saccharin (anhyd.)	7492-66-2	Citral diethyl acetal
5858-81-1	D&C Red No. 6			7493-57-4	Acetaldehyde phenethyl propyl acetal
5870-93-9	Heptyl butyrate	6485-39-8	Manganese gluconate		
5892-10-4	Bismuth subcarbonate	6485-40-1	l-Carvone	7493-71-2	Allyl tiglate
5905-52-2	Ferrous lactate	6540-99-4	Laureth-10	7493-72-3	Allyl nonanoate
5910-89-4	2,3-Dimethylpyrazine	6700-17-0	Sodium propionate (hydrate)	7493-74-5	Allyl phenoxyacetate
5938-38-5	Sorbitan oleate			7540-53-6	Citronellyl valerate
5949-29-1	Citric acid monohydrate	6728-26-3	2-Hexenal	7545-23-5	Myristamide DEA
5959-89-7	Sorbitan laurate	6732-80-8	Sodium 1,2-dimyristoyl-sn-glycero(3)phospha-tidylcholine	7546-12-5	Sodium bisulfate acetone
5965-83-3	5-Sulfosalicylic acid (dihydrate)			7549-33-9	Anisyl propionate
		6780-13-8	Ethylenediamine (monohydrate)	7549-37-3	Citral dimethyl acetal
5968-11-6	Sodium carbonate (monohydrate)			7553-56-2	Iodine
		6790-09-6	PEG-12	7558-79-4	Sodium phosphate dibasic anhydrous
5970-45-6	Zinc acetate (dihydrate)	6818-37-7	Stearyl trihydroxyethyl propylenediamine dihydrofluoride		
5989-27-5	d-Limonene			7558-80-7	Sodium phosphate (anhyd.)
5995-86-8	Gallic acid (monohydrate)	6858-44-2	Trisodium citrate (hydrate)	7585-39-9	β-Cyclodextrin
5996-10-1	D-Glucose monohydrate	6915-15-7	N-Hydroxysuccinic acid (±)	7631-86-9	Diatomaceous earth
				7631-86-9	Silica aerogel
6001-64-5	Chlorobutanol (hemihydrate)	6916-74-1	Glyceryl behenate	7631-86-9	Silica (colloidal)
		6938-94-9	Diisopropyl adipate	7631-90-5	Sodium bisulfite
6001-64-5	Chlorobutanol hemihydrate	7047-84-9	Aluminum stearate	7631-99-4	Sodium nitrate
		7048-04-6	Cysteine hydrochloride monohydrate	7632-00-0	Sodium nitrite
6004-24-6	Cetylpyridinium chloride (monohydrate)			7646-85-7	Zinc chloride
		7235-40-7	Carotene	7647-01-0	Hydrochloric acid
6035-47-8	Sodium formaldehyde sulfoxylate (dihydrate)	7235-40-7	CI 40800	7647-14-5	Sodium chloride
		7235-40-7	CI 75130	7651-02-7	Stearamidopropyl dimethylamine
6047-12-7	Ferrous gluconate	7311-27-5	Nonoxynol-4		
6067-86-0	Diatomaceous earth	7360-38-5	Trioctanoin	7659-95-2	Betanine
6099-90-7	1,3,5-Trihydroxyben-zene (dihydrate)	7384-98-7	Propylene glycol dioctanoate	7660-25-5	Fructose
				7664-38-2	Phosphoric acid
6100-05-6	Potassium citrate (monohydrate)	7429-90-5	Aluminum	7664-41-7	Ammonia
		7429-90-5	CI 77000	7664-93-9	Sulfuric acid
6100-16-9	Potassium sodium tartrate tetrahydrate	7439-93-2	Lithium	7681-11-0	Potassium iodide
		7439-97-6	Mercury	7681-38-1	Sodium bisulfate
6119-70-6	Quinine sulfate dihydrate	7440-21-3	Silicon	7681-52-9	Sodium hypochlorite
		7440-22-4	Silver	7681-57-4	Sodium metabisulfite
6131-90-4	Sodium acetate trihydrate	7440-31-5	Tin	7681-82-5	Sodium iodide
		7440-44-0	Carbon, activated	7695-91-2	dl-α-Tocopheryl acetate
6132-02-1	Sodium carbonate (decahydrate)	7440-50-8	Bronze powder		
		7440-50-8	CI 77400	7697-37-2	Nitric acid
6132-04-3	Trisodium citrate (dihydrate)	7440-50-8	Copper	7704-34-9	Sulfur
		7440-50-8	Copper powder	7720-78-7	Ferrous sulfate (anhyd.)
6155-57-3	Saccharin sodium (dihydrate)	7440-57-5	Gold	7722-76-1	Ammonium phosphate
		7440-63-3	Xenon	7722-84-1	Hydrogen peroxide
6197-30-4	Octocrylene	7440-66-6	Zinc	7722-88-5	Tetrasodium pyrophosphate
6222-35-1	Cyclohexyl propionate	7440-69-9	Bismuth		
6283-92-7	Lauryl lactate	7446-02-0	Zinc sulfate	7727-21-1	Potassium persulfate
6284-40-8	Meglumine	7446-09-5	Sulfur dioxide	7727-37-9	Nitrogen
6290-37-5	Phenethyl hexanoate	7446-19-7	Zinc sulfate (monohydrate)	7727-43-7	Barium sulfate
6303-21-5	Hypophosphorous acid			7727-73-3	Sodium sulfate (decahydrate)
6358-69-6	CI 59040				

CAS	Chemical	CAS	Chemical	CAS	Chemical
7733-02-0	Zinc sulfate (anhyd.)	8000-25-7	Rosemary oil	8007-80-5	Cinnamon oil
7746-20-0	Zinc sulfate (heptahydrate)	8000-26-8	Pine needle oil	8008-26-2	Lime oil
		8000-28-0	Lavender oil	8008-31-9	Mandarin orange oil
7747-35-5	7-Ethyl bicyclo-oxazolidine	8000-34-8	Clove oil	8008-45-5	Nutmeg oil
		8000-41-7	α-Terpineol	8008-52-4	Coriander oil
7756-96-9	Butyl anthranilate	8000-42-8	Caraway oil	8008-56-8	Lemon extract
7757-82-6	Sodium sulfate (anhyd.)	8000-46-2	Geranium oil	8008-56-8	Lemon oil
7757-83-7	Sodium sulfite	8000-48-4	Eucalyptus oil	8008-57-9	Orange oil
7757-93-9	Calcium phosphate dibasic	8000-66-6	Cardamom oil	8008-74-0	Sesame oil
		8000-73-5	Ammonium carbonate	8008-79-5	Spearmint oil
7758-02-3	Potassium bromide	8001-01-0	Rose oil	8009-03-8	Petrolatum NF
7758-11-4	Potassium phosphate dibasic	8001-21-6	Sunflower seed oil	8011-89-0	Balsam tolu
		8001-22-7	Soybean oil	8012-89-3	Beeswax, yellow
7758-23-8	Calcium phosphate monobasic anhydrous	8001-23-8	Safflower oil	8012-91-7	Juniper oil
		8001-25-0	Olive oil	8012-95-1	Mineral oil
7758-87-4	Calcium phosphate tribasic	8001-26-1	Linseed oil	8012-99-5	Cherry juice
		8001-29-4	Cottonseed oil	8013-17-0	Invert sugar
7758-98-7	Cupric sulfate anhyd.	8001-30-7	Corn oil	8015-67-6	Annatto extract
7758-99-8	Cupric sulfate pentahydrate	8001-31-8	Coconut oil	8015-86-9	Carnauba
		8001-39-6	Japan wax	8015-95-0	Carrageenan extract
7764-50-3	d-Dihydrocarvone	8001-54-5	Benzalkonium chloride	8016-06-6	Dill seed oil
7772-98-7	Sodium thiosulfate anhydrous	8001-69-2	Cod liver oil	8016-42-0	Balsam Peru
		8001-75-0	Ceresin	8016-70-4	Hydrogenated soybean oil
7772-99-8	Stannous chloride anhyd.	8001-78-3	Hydrogenated castor oil		
		8001-78-3	Trihydroxystearin	8020-83-5	Mineral oil (white)
7773-03-7	Potassium bisulfite	8001-79-4	Castor oil	8020-84-6	Lanolin (hydrate)
7774-44-9	Cyclohexyl isovalerate	8001-80-7	Carmine solution	8021-55-4	Ozokerite
7774-82-5	2-Tridecenal	8002-03-7	Peanut oil	8022-93-3	Carmine
7775-09-9	Sodium chlorate	8002-13-9	Canola oil	8023-62-9	Storax
7775-14-6	Sodium dithionite (anhyd.)	8002-13-9	Rapeseed oil	8023-77-6	Capsicum oleoresin
		8002-23-1	Cetyl esters	8023-79-8	Palm kernel oil
7778-18-9	Calcium sulfate (anhyd.)	8002-26-4	Tall oil	8023-98-1	Peach kernel oil
		8002-31-1	Cocoa butter	8024-06-4	Vanilla
7778-77-0	Potassium phosphate	8002-33-3	Sulfated castor oil	8024-09-7	Walnut oil
7778-87-2	Propyl heptanoate	8002-43-5	Lecithin	8024-32-6	Avocado oil
7779-70-6	Isoamyl nonanoate	8002-48-0	Malt extract	8024-48-4	Casanthranol
7779-75-1	Isobutyl acetoacetate	8002-50-4	Menhaden oil	8027-32-5	Petrolatum USP
7782-63-0	Ferrous sulfate (heptahydrate)	8002-74-2	Paraffin	8027-33-6	Lanolin alcohol
		8002-75-3	Palm oil	8027-47-2	Syrup
7782-85-6	Sodium phosphate dibasic heptahydrate	8002-80-0	Wheat gluten	8027-56-3	Glucose, liquid
		8003-05-2	Phenylmercuric nitrate	8028-66-8	Honey
7782-99-2	Sulfurous acid	8003-22-3	CI 47000	8028-77-1	Isotonic sodium chloride sol'n.
7783-28-0	Ammonium phosphate, dibasic	8003-22-3	D&C Yellow No. 11		
		8004-92-0	CI 47005	8028-89-5	Caramel
7783-47-3	Stannous fluoride (anhyd.)	8004-92-0	D&C Yellow No. 10	8029-43-4	Corn syrup
		8005-44-5	Cetearyl alcohol	8029-76-3	Hydroxylated lecithin
7784-24-9	Potassium alum dodecahydrate	8006-28-8	Soda lime	8029-76-3	Lecithin
		8006-40-4	Beeswax (white)	8029-92-3	Diacetylated monoglycerides
7784-30-7	Aluminum orthophos-phate	8006-44-8	Candelilla wax		
		8006-54-0	Lanolin oil	8030-00-0	Peppermint spirit
7784-34-1	Arsenic trichloride	8006-54-0	Lanolin (anhyd.)	8030-12-4	Hydrogenated tallow
7785-26-4	(-)-α-Pinene	8006-64-2	Turpentine oil	8030-76-0	Lecithin
7785-70-8	(+)-α-Pinene	8006-75-5	Dillweed oil	8030-78-2	Tallowtrimonium chloride
7785-84-4	Sodium trimeta-phosphate	8006-78-8	Bay oil		
		8006-81-3	Ylang ylang oil	8031-44-5	Hydrogenated lanolin
7786-30-3	Magnesium chloride	8006-84-6	Fennel oil	8033-29-2	Hydrogenated palm oil
7786-58-5	Octyl isovalerate	8006-87-9	Sandalwood oil	8036-54-2	Sodium alkyl sulfate
7786-61-0	2-Methoxy-4-vinylphenol	8006-90-4	Peppermint oil	8036-77-9	PEG-40 sorbitan lanolate
		8006-95-9	Wheat germ oil		
7786-67-6	Isopulegol	8007-00-9	Balsam Peru	8037-14-7	Coconut acid
7787-20-4	l-Fenchone	8007-01-0	Rose oil	8038-43-5	Lanolin oil
7787-59-9	Bismuth oxychloride	8007-02-1	Lemongrass oil West Indian	8038-93-5	Sodium aluminum chlorohydroxy lactate
7787-59-9	CI 77163				
7789-77-7	Calcium phosphate dibasic dihydrate	8007-12-3	Nutmeg oil, expressed	8039-09-6	PEG-75 lanolin
		8007-43-0	Sorbitan sesquioleate	8040-05-9	Hydrogenated lard glyceride
7790-53-6	Potassium metaphos-phate	8007-46-3	Thyme oil		
		8007-69-0	Sweet almond oil	8041-63-2	Hydrocarbon 40
7790-76-3	Calcium pyrophosphate	8007-70-3	Anise oil	8042-47-5	Mineral oil

CAS	Chemical	CAS	Chemical	CAS	Chemical
8046-19-3	Storax	9002-93-1	Octoxynol-40	9004-38-0	Cellulose acetate
8047-25-4	Viscarin	9003-01-4	Carbomer		phthalate
8049-66-9	Jelene	9003-01-4	Carbomer 910	9004-39-1	Cellulose acetate
8049-97-6	Melanin	9003-01-4	Carbomer 934		propionate
8050-09-7	Rosin	9003-01-4	Carbomer 934P	9004-53-9	Dextrin
8050-62-2	Polyox	9003-01-4	Carbomer 940	9004-54-0	Dextran
8050-81-5	Simethicone	9003-01-4	Carbomer 941	9004-57-3	Ethylcellulose
8051-15-8	PEG-6 sorbitan	9003-01-4	Polyacrylic acid	9004-61-9	Hyaluronic acid
	beeswax	9003-01-4	Polycarbophil	9004-62-0	Hydroxyethylcellulose
8051-30-7	Cocamide DEA	9003-05-8	Polyacrylamide	9004-64-2	Hydroxypropylcellulose
8051-52-3	PEG-15 cocamine	9003-07-0	Polypropylene	9004-65-3	Hydroxypropyl
8051-73-8	PEG-20 sorbitan	9003-11-6	Meroxapol 105		methylcellulose
	beeswax	9003-11-6	Meroxapol 172	9004-67-5	Methylcellulose
8051-81-8	PEG-27 lanolin	9003-11-6	Meroxapol 174	9004-70-0	Collodion
8051-82-9	PEG-40 lanolin	9003-11-6	Meroxapol 251	9004-70-0	Nitrocellulose
8052-10-6	Rosin	9003-11-6	Meroxapol 252	9004-74-4	Polyethylene glycol
8052-48-0	Sodium tallowate	9003-11-6	Meroxapol 254		monomethyl ether
8063-08-9	Microcrystalline wax	9003-11-6	Meroxapol 258	9004-81-3	PEG-4 laurate
8067-32-1	Glyceryl di/tripalmito-	9003-11-6	Meroxapol 311	9004-81-3	PEG-6 laurate
	stearate	9003-11-6	PEG-40 sorbitan	9004-81-3	PEG-8 laurate
8067-32-1	Glyceryl di/tristearate		tetraoleate	9004-81-3	PEG-12 laurate
9000-01-5	Acacia	9003-11-6	Poloxamer 101	9004-81-3	PEG-20 laurate
9000-05-9	Gum benzoin	9003-11-6	Poloxamer 105	9004-81-3	PEG-24 laurate
9000-07-1	Carrageenan	9003-11-6	Poloxamer 108	9004-81-3	PEG-32 laurate
9000-11-7	Carboxymethylcellulose	9003-11-6	Poloxamer 123	9004-81-3	PEG-40 laurate
9000-30-0	Guar gum	9003-11-6	Poloxamer 124	9004-81-3	PEG-75 laurate
9000-36-6	Karaya gum	9003-11-6	Poloxamer 181	9004-81-3	PEG-100 laurate
9000-40-2	Locust bean gum	9003-11-6	Poloxamer 182	9004-81-3	PEG-150 laurate
9000-59-3	Shellac	9003-11-6	Poloxamer 184	9004-82-4	Sodium laureth sulfate
9000-64-0	Balsam tolu	9003-11-6	Poloxamer 185	9004-87-9	Octoxynol-1
9000-65-1	Tragacanth gum	9003-11-6	Poloxamer 188	9004-87-9	Octoxynol-3
9000-69-5	Pectin	9003-11-6	Poloxamer 217	9004-87-9	Octoxynol-5
9000-70-8	Gelatin	9003-11-6	Poloxamer 231	9004-87-9	Octoxynol-8
9000-71-9	Casein	9003-11-6	Poloxamer 234	9004-87-9	Octoxynol-9
9000-71-9	Milk protein	9003-11-6	Poloxamer 235	9004-87-9	Octoxynol-10
9000-92-4	Amylase	9003-11-6	Poloxamer 237	9004-87-9	Octoxynol-11
9001-05-2	Catalase	9003-11-6	Poloxamer 238	9004-87-9	Octoxynol-13
9001-37-0	Glucose oxidase	9003-11-6	Poloxamer 282	9004-87-9	Octoxynol-16
9001-62-1	Lipase	9003-11-6	Poloxamer 284	9004-87-9	Octoxynol-20
9001-73-4	Papain	9003-11-6	Poloxamer 288	9004-87-9	Octoxynol-25
9001-75-6	Pepsin	9003-11-6	Poloxamer 331	9004-87-9	Octoxynol-30
9002-07-7	Trypsin	9003-11-6	Poloxamer 333	9004-87-9	Octoxynol-40
9002-18-0	Agar	9003-11-6	Poloxamer 334	9004-94-3	PPG-3-laureth-9
9002-86-2	Polyvinyl chloride	9003-11-6	Poloxamer 335	9004-95-9	Ceteth-2
9002-88-4	Polyethylene	9003-11-6	Poloxamer 338	9004-95-9	Ceteth-5
9002-88-4	Polyethylene wax	9003-11-6	Poloxamer 401	9004-95-9	Ceteth-6
9002-89-5	Polyvinyl alcohol	9003-11-6	Poloxamer 402	9004-95-9	Ceteth-7
	(super and fully	9003-11-6	Poloxamer 403	9004-95-9	Ceteth-10
	hydrolyzed)	9003-11-6	Poloxamer 407	9004-95-9	Ceteth-12
9002-92-0	C12-13 pareth-23	9003-20-7	Polyvinyl acetate	9004-95-9	Ceteth-15
9002-92-0	Laureth-2		(homopolymer)	9004-95-9	Ceteth-16
9002-92-0	Laureth-3	9003-27-4	Polyisobutene	9004-95-9	Ceteth-20
9002-92-0	Laureth-7	9003-28-5	Polybutene	9004-95-9	Ceteth-23
9002-92-0	Laureth-10	9003-39-8	Crospovidone	9004-95-9	Ceteth-24
9002-92-0	Laureth-12	9003-39-8	Polyvinylpolypyrroli-	9004-95-9	Ceteth-25
9002-92-0	Laureth-23		done	9004-95-9	Ceteth-30
9002-93-1	Octoxynol-1	9003-39-8	PVP	9004-95-9	Ceteth-40
9002-93-1	Octoxynol-3	9003-53-6	Polystyrene	9004-96-0	PEG-400
9002-93-1	Octoxynol-5	9003-74-1	Terpene resin, natural	9004-96-0	PEG-4 oleate
9002-93-1	Octoxynol-8	9003-97-8	Calcium polycarbophil	9004-96-0	PEG-6 oleate
9002-93-1	Octoxynol-9	9004-32-4	Carboxymethylcellulose	9004-96-0	PEG-7 oleate
9002-93-1	Octoxynol-10		sodium	9004-96-0	PEG-8 oleate
9002-93-1	Octoxynol-11	9004-34-6	Cellulose	9004-96-0	PEG-12 oleate
9002-93-1	Octoxynol-13	9004-34-6	Microcrystalline	9004-96-0	PEG-20 oleate
9002-93-1	Octoxynol-16		cellulose	9004-96-0	PEG-32 oleate
9002-93-1	Octoxynol-20	9004-35-7	Cellulose acetate	9004-96-0	PEG-75 oleate
9002-93-1	Octoxynol-25	9004-36-8	Cellulose acetate	9004-96-0	PEG-150 oleate
9002-93-1	Octoxynol-30		butyrate	9004-97-1	PEG-8 ricinoleate

CAS	Chemical	CAS	Chemical	CAS	Chemical
9004-98-2	Oleth-2	9005-32-7	Alginic acid	9025-56-3	Hemicellulase
9004-98-2	Oleth-3	9005-34-9	Ammonium alginate	9032-42-2	Methyl hydroxyethyl-
9004-98-2	Oleth-5	9005-35-0	Calcium alginate		cellulose
9004-98-2	Oleth-10	9005-36-1	Potassium alginate	9035-85-2	PPG-30 cetyl ether
9004-98-2	Oleth-12	9005-37-2	Propylene glycol	9036-19-5	Octoxynol-1
9004-98-2	Oleth-16		alginate	9036-19-5	Octoxynol-3
9004-98-2	Oleth-20	9005-38-3	Algin	9036-19-5	Octoxynol-5
9004-98-2	Oleth-25	9005-64-5	PEG-80 sorbitan	9036-19-5	Octoxynol-8
9004-99-3	PEG-2 stearate		laurate	9036-19-5	Octoxynol-9
9004-99-3	PEG-4 stearate	9005-64-5	Polysorbate 20	9036-19-5	Octoxynol-10
9004-99-3	PEG-5 stearate	9005-64-5	Polysorbate 21	9036-19-5	Octoxynol-11
9004-99-3	PEG-6 stearate	9005-65-5	Polysorbate 81	9036-19-5	Octoxynol-13
9004-99-3	PEG-6-32 stearate	9005-65-6	PEG-6 sorbitan oleate	9036-19-5	Octoxynol-16
9004-99-3	PEG-8 stearate	9005-65-6	Polysorbate 80	9036-19-5	Octoxynol-20
9004-99-3	PEG-10 stearate	9005-66-7	Polysorbate 40	9036-19-5	Octoxynol-25
9004-99-3	PEG-12 stearate	9005-67-8	PEG-6 sorbitan	9036-19-5	Octoxynol-30
9004-99-3	PEG-20 stearate		stearate	9036-19-5	Octoxynol-40
9004-99-3	PEG-24 stearate	9005-67-8	Polysorbate 60	9038-95-3	PPG-12-buteth-16
9004-99-3	PEG-25 stearate	9005-67-8	Polysorbate 61	9041-08-1	Heparin sodium
9004-99-3	PEG-30 stearate	9005-70-3	PEG-17 sorbitan	9045-22-1	Heparin lithium
9004-99-3	PEG-32 stearate		trioleate	9049-05-2	Calcium carrageenan
9004-99-3	PEG-40 stearate	9005-70-3	Polysorbate 85	9050-04-8	Calcium carboxymethyl
9004-99-3	PEG-45 stearate	9005-71-4	Polysorbate 65		cellulose
9004-99-3	PEG-50 stearate	9005-84-9	Starch	9050-36-6	Maltodextrin
9004-99-3	PEG-55 stearate	9006-50-2	Albumen	9062-04-8	Propylene glycol
9004-99-3	PEG-75 stearate	9006-65-9	Dimethicone		dicaprylate/dicaprate
9004-99-3	PEG-100 stearate	9007-16-3	Carbomer	9063-38-1	Sodium starch glycolate
9004-99-3	PEG-150 stearate	9007-16-3	Carbomer 934	9065-63-8	PPG-12-buteth-16
9005-00-9	Ceteareth-20	9007-17-4	Carbomer	9067-32-7	Sodium hyaluronate
9005-00-9	Steareth-2	9007-17-4	Carbomer 940	9087-53-0	PPG-4 ceteth-1
9005-00-9	Steareth-7	9007-20-9	Carbomer	9087-53-0	PPG-4-ceteth-10
9005-00-9	Steareth-8	9007-28-7	Chondroitin sulfate	9087-53-0	PPG-4-ceteth-20
9005-00-9	Steareth-10	9007-34-5	Collagen	9087-53-0	PPG-8-ceteth-1
9005-00-9	Steareth-16	9007-34-5	Soluble collagen	9106-45-9	Nonoxynol-15
9005-00-9	Steareth-20	9007-48-1	Polyglyceryl-6 dioleate	9174-23-9	Glyceryl citrate/lactate/
9005-00-9	Steareth-21	9007-48-1	Polyglyceryl-2 oleate		linoleate/oleate
9005-00-9	Steareth-25	9007-48-1	Polyglyceryl-3 oleate	10016-20-3	α-Cyclodextrin
9005-00-9	Steareth-100	9007-48-1	Polyglyceryl-4 oleate	10024-97-2	Nitrous oxide
9005-02-1	PEG-4 dilaurate	9007-48-1	Polyglyceryl-6 oleate	10025-87-3	Phosphorus
9005-02-1	PEG-6 dilaurate	9007-48-1	Polyglyceryl-10 oleate		oxychloride
9005-02-1	PEG-8 dilaurate	9009-48-1	Polyglyceryl-10 dioleate	10025-91-9	Antimony trichloride
9005-02-1	PEG-12 dilaurate	9009-65-8	Protamine sulfate	10031-43-3	Copper nitrate (ic)
9005-02-1	PEG-20 dilaurate	9010-43-9	Octoxynol-9	10031-82-0	p-Ethoxybenzaldehyde
9005-02-1	PEG-32 dilaurate	9010-66-6	Zein	10031-87-5	2-Ethylbutyl acetate
9005-02-1	PEG-75 dilaurate	9010-79-1	Polypropylene	10032-13-0	Hexyl isovalerate
9005-02-1	PEG-150 dilaurate		(nucleated)	10032-15-2	Hexyl 2-methylbutyrate
9005-07-6	PEG-4 dioleate	9010-85-9	Isobutylene/isoprene	10034-76-1	Calcium sulfate
9005-07-6	PEG-6 dioleate		copolymer		hemihydrate
9005-07-6	PEG-8 dioleate	9011-16-9	PVM/MA copolymer	10034-85-2	Hydriodic acid
9005-07-6	PEG-12 dioleate	9012-54-8	Cellulase	10035-04-8	Calcium chloride
9005-07-6	PEG-20 dioleate	9014-01-1	Protease		(dihydrate)
9005-07-6	PEG-32 dioleate	9015-54-7	Hydrolyzed collagen	10039-26-6	Lactose monohydrate
9005-07-6	PEG-75 dioleate	9016-00-6	Dimethicone	10043-01-3	Aluminum sulfate
9005-07-6	PEG-150 dioleate	9016-45-9	Nonoxynol-2		(anhyd.)
9005-08-7	PEG-4 distearate	9016-45-9	Nonoxynol-4	10043-35-3	Boric acid
9005-08-7	PEG-6 distearate	9016-45-9	Nonoxynol-5	10043-52-4	Calcium chloride
9005-08-7	PEG-8 distearate	9016-45-9	Nonoxynol-6		(anhyd.)
9005-08-7	PEG-12 distearate	9016-45-9	Nonoxynol-7	10049-21-5	Sodium phosphate
9005-08-7	PEG-20 distearate	9016-45-9	Nonoxynol-8		(monohydrate)
9005-08-7	PEG-32 distearate	9016-45-9	Nonoxynol-9	10058-44-3	Ferric pyrophosphate
9005-08-7	PEG-75 distearate	9016-45-9	Nonoxynol-10		(anhyd.)
9005-08-7	PEG-150 distearate	9016-45-9	Nonoxynol-12	10094-36-7	Ethyl cyclohexane-
9005-25-8	Corn starch	9016-45-9	Nonoxynol-13		propionate
9005-25-8	Potato starch	9016-45-9	Nonoxynol-20	10094-41-4	cis-3-Hexenyl 2-
9005-25-8	Rice starch	9016-45-9	Nonoxynol-30		methylbutyrate
9005-25-8	Starch	9016-45-9	Nonoxynol-40	10101-39-0	Calcium silicate
9005-25-8	Tapioca starch	9016-45-9	Nonoxynol-50	10101-41-4	Calcium sulfate
9005-25-8	Wheat starch	9025-41-6	Keratinase		dihydrate

CAS	Chemical
10108-24-4	PEG-4 laurate
10108-25-5	PEG-4 oleate
10108-28-8	PEG-6 stearate
10124-56-8	Sodium hexameta-phosphate
10191-41-0	DL-α-Tocopherol
10233-13-3	Isopropyl laurate
10326-41-7	D-Lactic acid
10361-29-2	Ammonium carbonate
10401-55-5	Cetyl ricinoleate
10519-33-2	3-Decen-2-one
10521-91-2	5-Phenyl-1-pentanol
10595-72-9	Ditridecyl thiodipropionate
11006-34-1	Chlorophyllin-copper complex
11006-34-1	CI 75810
11042-64-1	Oryzanol
11094-60-3	Polyglyceryl-10 decaoleate
11097-68-0	Aluminum sesqui-chlorohydrate
11099-07-3	Glyceryl stearate
11099-07-3	Glyceryl stearate SE
11111-34-5	Poloxamine 304
11111-34-5	Poloxamine 504
11111-34-5	Poloxamine 701
11111-34-5	Poloxamine 702
11111-34-5	Poloxamine 704
11111-34-5	Poloxamine 707
11111-34-5	Poloxamine 901
11111-34-5	Poloxamine 904
11111-34-5	Poloxamine 908
11111-34-5	Poloxamine 1101
11111-34-5	Poloxamine 1102
11111-34-5	Poloxamine 1104
11111-34-5	Poloxamine 1107
11111-34-5	Poloxamine 1301
11111-34-5	Poloxamine 1302
11111-34-5	Poloxamine 1304
11111-34-5	Poloxamine 1307
11111-34-5	Poloxamine 1501
11111-34-5	Poloxamine 1502
11111-34-5	Poloxamine 1504
11111-34-5	Poloxamine 1508
11138-66-2	Xanthan gum
11660-95-3	Tetraisopropyl methylenediphosphonate
12001-26-2	Mica
12001-31-9	Quaternium-18 hectorite
12001-99-9	Chromium hydroxide green
12001-99-9	CI 77289
12042-91-0	Aluminum chlorohy-drate (dihydrate)
12058-66-1	Sodium stannate
12111-24-9	Pentetate calcium trisodium
12141-46-7	Aluminum silicate
12167-74-7	Calcium phosphate tribasic
12173-47-6	Hectorite
12182-82-0	Chromium hydroxide green
12199-37-0	Magnesium aluminum silicate
12230-71-6	Barium hydroxide lime
	(octahydrate)
12240-15-2	Ferric ammonium ferrocyanide
12263-40-0	Bismuth subgallate
12269-78-2	Pyrophyllite
12389-15-0	Ferrous gluconate
12691-60-0	Stearalkonium hectorite
12694-22-3	Polyglyceryl-2 stearate
12764-60-2	Polyglyceryl-10 distearate
12765-39-8	Sodium methyl cocoyl taurate
12804-12-8	Glycereth-7 benzoate
13007-85-7	Gluceptate sodium
13040-19-2	Zinc ricinoleate
13057-50-6	Pentaerythrityl tetralaurate
13149-83-2	Ceteth-12
13149-86-5	Steareth-10
13150-00-0	Sodium laureth sulfate
13192-12-6	Disodium lauryl sulfosuccinate
13327-56-5	Ethyl 3-(methylthio) propionate
13341-72-5	Menthalactone
13463-41-7	Zinc pyrithione
13463-67-7	CI 77891
13463-67-7	Titanium dioxide
13472-35-0	Sodium phosphate (dihydrate)
13473-26-2	D&C Red No. 27
13494-80-9	Tellurium
13532-18-8	Methyl 3-methylthio-propionate
13552-80-2	Triundecanoin
13623-11-5	Trimethyl thiazole
13699-48-4	1,2-Dimyristoyl-sn-glycero(3) phosphati-dylcholine
13832-70-7	Stearyl glycyrrhetinate
13987-01-4	Tripropylene glycol
14007-07-9	Chlorhexidine digluconate
14038-43-8	CI 77510
14038-43-8	Ferric ferrocyanide
14073-97-3	l-Menthone
14332-09-3	Hypophosphorous acid
14351-40-7	Stearamide MEA-stearate
14360-50-0	Pentyl 2-furyl ketone
14471-10-9	Cinnamal
14409-72-4	Nonoxynol-9
14504-95-1	Aluminum silicate
14529-40-9	Ceteth-10
14807-96-6	Talc
14882-18-9	Bismuth subsalicylate
14987-04-3	Magnesium trisilicate (anhyd.)
15086-94-9	D&C Red No. 21
15087-24-8	3-Benzylidene camphor
15356-60-2	(+)-Menthol
15356-70-4	(±)-Menthol
15578-26-4	Stannous pyrophos-phate
15716-30-0	PEG-25 PABA
15763-02-7	Dioctyl malate
15764-16-6	2,4-Dimethylbenzal-dehyde
15792-67-3	FD&C Blue No. 1 aluminum lake
15826-16-1	Sodium laureth sulfate
16039-53-5	Zinc lactate
16039-56-8	Manganese lactate
16057-43-5	Steareth-2
16291-96-6	Charcoal, activated
16409-44-2	Geranyl acetate
16409-45-3	dl-Menthyl acetate
16423-68-0	CI 45430
16423-68-0	FD&C Red No. 3
16485-10-2	DL-Panthenol
16545-54-3	Dimyristyl thiodipro-pionate
16731-55-8	Potassium metabisulfite
16841-14-8	Behenalkonium chloride
16889-14-8	Stearamidoethyl diethylamine
16957-70-3	2-Methyl-2-pentenoic acid
17140-60-2	Calcium gluceptate
17194-00-2	Barium hydroxide lime (anhyd.)
17369-59-4	3-Propylidenephthalide
17372-87-1	CI 45380
17372-87-1	D&C Red No. 22
17465-86-0	γ-Cyclodextrin
17661-50-6	Cetyl esters
17661-50-6	Myristyl stearate
17671-27-1	Behenyl behenate
17673-56-2	Oleyl erucate
17699-09-1	Dihydrocarveol
17927-65-0	Aluminum sulfate (hydrate)
18016-24-5	Calcium gluconate (monohydrate)
18031-40-8	Perillaldehyde
18172-67-3	β-Pinene
18194-24-6	1,2-Dimyristoyl-sn-glycero(3) phosphati-dylcholine
18285-71-7	1,2-Dilauroyl-sn-glycero(3) phospho-choline
18472-51-0	Chlorhexidine digluconate
18472-87-2	CI 45410
18472-87-2	D&C Red No. 28
18641-57-1	Tribehenin
18917-91-4	Aluminum lactate
18917-93-6	Magnesium lactate
18996-35-5	Sodium citrate
19035-79-1	Potassium cetyl phosphate
19040-44-9	Disodium lauryl sulfosuccinate
19089-92-0	Hexyl-2-butenoate
20344-49-4	CI 77492
20344-49-4	Iron (III) oxide hydrated
20636-48-0	Nonoxynol-5
20665-85-4	Vanillin isobutyrate
20777-49-5	Dihydrocarvyl acetate
20824-56-0	Diammonium EDTA
20834-06-4	Isocetyl laurate
21245-02-3	Octyl dimethyl PABA
21645-51-2	Alumina trihydrate
21645-51-2	Aluminum hydroxide

CAS	Chemical	CAS	Chemical	CAS	Chemical
21662-09-9	cis-4-Decen-1-al	25322-68-3	PEG-14M	27176-97-2	Nonoxynol-4
21722-83-8	Cyclohexylethyl acetate	25322-68-3	PEG-20M	27176-99-4	Octoxynol-5
21908-53-2	Mercury oxide (ic), red	25322-68-3	PEG-23M	27177-01-1	Nonoxynoı-6
	and yellow	25322-68-3	PEG-35M	27177-05-5	Nonoxynol-6
22047-49-0	Octyl stearate	25322-68-3	PEG-45M	27177-05-5	Nonoxynol-7
22242-53-1	Ferrous citrate	25322-68-3	PEG-90M	27177-05-5	Nonoxynol-8
22500-92-1	Sorbic acid	25322-68-3	PEG-115M	27177-07-7	Octoxynol-10
22766-82-1	Octyldodecyl stearate	25322-68-3	Polyethylene glycol	27177-08-8	Nonoxynol-10
22766-83-2	Octyldodecyl myristate	25322-69-4	Polypropylene glycol	27194-74-7	Propylene glycol
22839-47-0	Aspartame	25339-09-7	Isocetyl stearate		laurate
23089-26-1	Levomenol	25339-99-5	Sucrose laurate	27195-16-0	Sucrose distearate
23383-11-1	Ferrous citrate (anhyd.)	25383-99-7	Sodium stearoyl	27215-38-9	Glyceryl laurate SE
23389-33-5	Magnesium carbonate		lactylate	27321-72-8	Polyglyceryl-3 stearate
	(hydrate)	25496-72-4	Glyceryl mono/dioleate	27321-96-6	Choleth-24
23411-34-9	Calcium disodium	25496-72-4	Glyceryl oleate	27479-28-3	Quaternium-14
	EDTA	25496-72-4	Glyceryl oleate SE	27503-81-7	Phenylbenzimidazole
24634-61-5	Potassium sorbate	25637-84-7	Glyceryl dioleate		sulfonic acid
24800-44-0	Tripropylene glycol	25655-41-8	PVP-iodine	27638-00-2	Glyceryl dilaurate
24817-51-4	Phenethyl 2-	25681-89-4	Medronate disodium	27942-26-3	Nonoxynol-10
	methylbutyrate	25869-00-5	Ferric ammonium	27986-36-3	Nonoxynol-1
24871-34-9	Oleth-10		ferrocyanide	28319-77-9	Glycerophosphocholine
24936-97-8	Polybutilate	25928-94-3	Epoxy resin	28874-51-3	Sodium PCA
24937-16-4	Nylon-12	25956-17-6	CI 16035	29039-00-7	Calcium glucepate
24937-78-8	Ethylene/VA copolymer	25956-17-6	FD&C Red No. 40		(dihydrate)
24938-91-8	Trideceth-10	26027-38-3	Nonoxynol-1	29059-24-3	Propylene glycol
24938-91-8	Trideceth-100	26027-38-3	Nonoxynol-2		myristate
24938-91-8	Trideceth-7 carboxylic	26027-38-3	Nonoxynol-4	29383-26-4	Octyl hydroxystearate
	acid	26027-38-3	Nonoxynol-5	29548-30-9	Farnesyl acetate
24991-55-7	PEG-3 dimethyl ether	26027-38-3	Nonoxynol-6	29590-42-9	Isooctyl acrylate
24991-55-7	PEG-4 dimethyl ether	26027-38-3	Nonoxynol-7	29710-25-6	Octyl hydroxystearate
25013-16-5	BHA	26027-38-3	Nonoxynol-8	29806-73-3	Octyl palmitate
25038-54-4	Nylon-6	26027-38-3	Nonoxynol-9	30233-64-8	Glyceryl behenate
25038-74-8	Nylon-12	26027-38-3	Nonoxynol-10	30245-51-3	Sodium thiomalate
25085-02-3	Acrylamide/sodium	26027-38-3	Nonoxynol-12	30525-89-4	Paraformaldehyde
	acrylate copolymer	26027-38-3	Nonoxynol-13	30581-59-0	PVP/dimethylamino-
25086-89-9	PVP/VA copolymer	26027-38-3	Nonoxynol-15		ethylmethacrylate
25152-84-5	trans-trans-2,4-	26027-38-3	Nonoxynol-20		copolymer
	Decadienal	26027-38-3	Nonoxynol-30	30657-38-6	Lysine PCA
25155-18-4	Methylbenzethonium	26027-38-3	Nonoxynol-40	31394-71-5	PPG-26 oleate
	chloride	26027-38-3	Nonoxynol-50	31556-45-3	Tridecyl stearate
25155-30-0	Sodium dodecylben-	26112-07-2	Potassium methyl-	31566-31-1	Glyceryl stearate
	zenesulfonate		paraben	31566-31-1	Glyceryl stearate SE
25168-73-4	Sucrose stearate	26172-55-4	Methylchloroiso-	31694-55-0	Glycereth-26
25190-05-0	Oleth-16		thiazolinone	31791-00-2	PEG-40 stearate
25231-21-4	PPG-15 stearyl ether	26264-02-8	Nonoxynol-5	32057-14-0	Glyceryl isostearate
25301-02-4	Tyloxapol	26266-57-9	Sorbitan palmitate	32289-26-2	Laureth-2 acetate
25322-68-3	PEG-4	26266-58-0	Sorbitan trioleate	32440-50-9	PVP/hexadecene
25322-68-3	PEG-6	26266-77-3	Hydroabietyl alcohol		copolymer
25322-68-3	PEG-8	26399-02-0	Octyl stearate	32612-48-9	Ammonium laureth
25322-68-3	PEG-9	26402-26-6	Caprylic/capric		sulfate
25322-68-3	PEG-12		glycerides	33239-19-9	D&C Orange No. 11
25322-68-3	PEG-14	26402-26-6	Glyceryl caprylate	33907-46-9	Glycol hydroxystearate
25322-68-3	PEG-16	26402-31-3	Propylene glycol	33939-64-9	Sodium laureth-5
25322-68-3	PEG-20		ricinoleate		carboxylate
25322-68-3	PEG-32	26446-38-8	Sucrose palmitate	33940-98-6	Polyglyceryl-3 oleate
25322-68-3	PEG-40	26447-10-9	Ammonium xylene-	33940-99-7	Polyglyceryl-10 dioleate
25322-68-3	PEG-60		sulfonate	34316-64-8	Hexyl laurate
25322-68-3	PEG-75	26571-11-9	Nonoxynol-8	34406-66-1	Polyglyceryl-10 laurate
25322-68-3	PEG-100	26571-11-9	Nonoxynol-9	34424-97-0	Polyglyceryl-6
25322-68-3	PEG-150	26657-96-5	Glyceryl palmitate		distearate
25322-68-3	PEG-200	26658-19-5	Sorbitan tristearate	34424-98-1	Polyglyceryl-10
25322-68-3	PEG-350	26838-05-1	Disodium lauryl		tetraoleate
25322-68-3	PEG-2M		sulfosuccinate	35179-86-3	PEG-8 laurate
25322-68-3	PEG-5M	26855-43-6	Polyglyceryl-3 stearate	35274-05-6	Cetyl lactate
25322-68-3	PEG-7M	27083-27-8	Polyaminopropyl	35285-68-8	Sodium ethylparaben
25322-68-3	PEG-8M		biguanide	35285-69-9	Sodium propylparaben
25322-68-3	PEG-9M	27176-93-8	Nonoxynol-2	35854-86-5	cis-6-Nonen-1-ol
25322-68-3	PEG-10M	27176-94-9	Octoxynol-3	36311-34-9	Isocetyl alcohol

CAS	Chemical	CAS	Chemical	CAS	Chemical
36409-57-1	Disodium lauryl sulfosuccinate	42175-36-0	Oleyl lactate	56388-96-6	Trideceth-7 carboxylic acid
36431-72-8	Theaspirane	42233-07-8	Lauryl behenate	56519-71-1	Propylene glycol dioctanoate
36438-54-7	o-Tolyl isobutyrate	49553-76-6	Polyglyceryl-2 oleate		
36457-19-9	Potassium ethyl-paraben	50643-20-4	PPG-5 ceteth-10 phosphate	57307-99-0	PEG-8 caprylic/capric glycerides
36457-20-2	Sodium butylparaben	50935-57-4	PVM/MA copolymer, ethyl ester	57569-76-3	Glycereth-7 triacetate
36653-82-4	Cetyl alcohol	51158-08-8	PEG-5 glyceryl stearate	57576-09-7	Isopulegyl acetate
37200-49-0	Polysorbate 80	51158-08-8	PEG-20 glyceryl stearate	58450-52-5	Disodium laureth sulfosuccinate
37205-87-1	Nonoxynol-1				
37205-87-1	Nonoxynol-2	51192-09-7	PEG-20 glyceryl oleate	58450-52-5	Octyldodecyl stearoyl stearate
37205-87-1	Nonoxynol-4	51200-87-4	Dimethyl oxazolidine		
37205-87-1	Nonoxynol-5	51229-78-8	Quaternium-15	58748-27-9	Propylene glycol dicaprylate/dicaprate
37205-87-1	Nonoxynol-6	51248-32-9	PEG-12 glyceryl laurate		
37205-87-1	Nonoxynol-7	51248-32-9	PEG-20 glyceryl laurate	58855-63-3	DEA-oleth-3 phosphate
37205-87-1	Nonoxynol-8	51812-80-7	Quaternium-22	58855-63-3	DEA-oleth-10 phosphate
37205-87-1	Nonoxynol-9	52229-50-2	PVM/MA copolymer		
37205-87-1	Nonoxynol-10	52504-24-2	PEG-6 caprylic/capric glycerides	58958-60-4	Isostearyl neopen-tanoate
37205-87-1	Nonoxynol-12				
37205-87-1	Nonoxynol-13	52688-97-0	PEG-4 dioleate	58969-27-0	Sodium cocoyl isethionate
37205-87-1	Nonoxynol-15	52688-97-0	PEG-6 dioleate		
37205-87-1	Nonoxynol-20	52688-97-0	PEG-8 dioleate	59017-64-0	Ioxaglic acid
37205-87-1	Nonoxynol-30	52688-97-0	PEG-12 dioleate	59070-56-3	PEG-12 glyceryl laurate
37205-87-1	Nonoxynol-40	52688-97-0	PEG-20 dioleate	59070-56-3	PEG-20 glyceryl laurate
37205-87-1	Nonoxynol-50	52688-97-0	PEG-32 dioleate	59130-70-7	Cetearyl octanoate
37220-82-9	Glyceryl oleate	52688-97-0	PEG-75 dioleate	59160-29-1	Lidofenin
37244-96-5	Nepheline syenite	52688-97-0	PEG-150 dioleate	59186-41-3	Sodium cetearyl sulfate
37307-56-5	D&C Blue No. 4	52668-97-0	PEG-4 distearate	59231-34-4	Decyl oleate
37310-95-5	Glyceryl polymeth-acrylate	52668-97-0	PEG-6 distearate	59231-34-4	Isodecyl oleate
		52668-97-0	PEG-8 distearate	59259-38-0	Menthyl lactate
37311-01-6	PPG-4 ceteth-1	52668-97-0	PEG-12 distearate	59587-44-9	Octyl pelargonate
37311-01-6	PPG-4-ceteth-10	52668-97-0	PEG-20 distearate	59599-55-2	Myreth-3 myristate
37311-01-6	PPG-4-ceteth-20	52668-97-0	PEG-32 distearate	59686-68-9	Myreth-3 myristate
37311-01-6	PPG-8-ceteth-1	52668-97-0	PEG-75 distearate	60219-68-3	Polyglyceryl-2 dioleate
37318-14-2	PEG-8 laurate	52668-97-0	PEG-150 distearate	60344-26-5	PEG-6 oleate
37349-34-1	Polyglyceryl-3 stearate	52725-64-1	Lauramide DEA	60676-86-0	Silica
38462-22-5	p-Mentha-8-thiol-3-one	53026-57-6	FD&C Blue No. 1 aluminum lake	60800-63-7	Heparin ammonium
38566-94-8	Potassium butyl paraben			61332-02-3	Glyceryl isostearate
		53124-00-8	Food starch modified	61597-98-6	l-Menthyl lactate
38577-97-8	D&C Orange No. 10	53200-28-5	PVM/MA copolymer, butyl ester	61692-83-9	Propyl tiglate
38975-03-0	Sodium laureth-5 carboxylate	53320-86-8	Sodium magnesium silicate	61693-08-1	Hydrogenated polyisobutene
39175-72-9	Glyceryl stearate citrate			61693-41-2	DEA-cetyl phosphate
39236-46-9	Imidazolidinyl urea	53496-15-4	2-Methylbutyl acetate	61725-93-7	Polyglyceryl-6 distearate
39354-45-5	Disodium laureth sulfosuccinate	53597-25-4	Protamine sulfate		
		53637-25-5	Poloxamer 181	61788-40-7	Acrylic acid/ acrylonitrogens copolymer
39365-88-3	Sulfurated potash	53694-15-8	Sorbeth-20		
39394-76-5	Polacrilin potassium	54018-18-7	PVM/MA copolymer, butyl ester	61788-47-4	Coconut acid
39409-82-0	Magnesium carbonate (basic)	54077-45-1	PVM/MA copolymer, isopropyl ester	61788-48-5	Acetylated lanolin
				61788-49-6	Acetylated lanolin alcohol
39464-69-2	Oleth-3 phosphate	54392-26-6	Sorbitan isostearate		
39464-69-2	Oleth-10 phosphate	54549-25-6	Decyl glucoside	61788-78-1	Hydrogenated tallowtrimonium chloride
39464-69-2	Oleth-20 phosphate	54571-67-4	Sodium PCA		
39529-26-5	Polyglyceryl-10 decastearate	54578-88-0	PVM/MA copolymer, isopropyl ester	61788-85-0	PEG-5 hydrogenated castor oil
40754-59-4	Disodium laureth sulfosuccinate	54578-90-4	PVM/MA copolymer, ethyl ester	61788-85-0	PEG-7 hydrogenated castor oil
41372-22-9	Calcium lactate (monohydrate, trihydrate)	54578-91-5	PVM/MA copolymer, butyl ester	61788-85-0	PEG-10 hydrogenated castor oil
		55031-15-7	2-Ethyl-3,5(6)-dimethylpyrazine	61788-85-0	PEG-20 hydrogenated castor oil
41395-83-9	Propylene glycol dipelargonate				
41669-30-1	Isostearyl isostearate	55589-62-3	Acesulfame potassium	61788-85-0	PEG-25 hydrogenated castor oil
42016-08-0	Disodium laureth sulfosuccinate	55963-33-2	Distarch phosphate	61788-85-0	PEG-30 hydrogenated castor oil
		56002-14-3	PEG-6 isostearate		
42131-25-9	Isononyl isononanoate	56091-51-1	PVM/MA copolymer, isopropyl ester	61788-85-0	PEG-40 hydrogenated
42131-28-2	Isostearyl lactate				
42173-90-0	Octoxynol-9	56235-92-8	Dioctyl malate		

CAS	Chemical	CAS	Chemical	CAS	Chemical
	castor oil	61791-20-6	Laneth-40		ethyl ester
61788-85-0	PEG-45 hydrogenated castor oil	61791-31-9	Cocamide DEA	67762-19-0	Ammonium laureth sulfate
61788-85-0	PEG-50 hydrogenated castor oil	61791-32-0	Disodium cocoampho-diacetate	67762-27-0	Cetearyl alcohol
		61791-42-2	Sodium methyl cocoyl taurate	67762-38-3	Methyl oleate
61788-85-0	PEG-60 hydrogenated castor oil			67762-40-7	Methyl laurate
61788-85-0	PEG-80 hydrogenated castor oil	61849-72-7	PPG-10 methyl glucose ether	67762-96-3	Dimethicone copolyol
				67784-82-1	Hydrogenated vegetable oil
61788-85-0	PEG-100 hydrogenated castor oil	61849-72-7	PPG-20 methyl glucose ether	67784-82-1	Polyglyceryl-10 oleate
61789-05-7	Glyceryl cocoate	62386-95-2	Calcium/sodium PVM/MA copolymer	67784-87-6	Hydrogenated palm glyceride
61789-08-0	Hydrogenated soy glyceride	63148-55-0	Dimethicone copolyol	67923-87-9	Sodium octoxynol-2 ethane sulfonate
61789-09-1	Hydrogenated tallow glyceride	63148-62-9	Dimethicone		
		63231-60-7	Microcrystalline wax	67965-56-4	Polyglyceryl-2 dioleate
		63393-93-1	Isopropyl lanolate	68002-61-9	Tallowtrimonium chloride
61789-10-4	Lard glyceride	63690-56-2	Calcium lactate (pentahydrate)		
61789-13-7	Tallow glyceride			68002-71-1	Hydrogenated soybean oil
61789-30-8	Potassium cocoate	64044-51-5	Lactose monohydrate		
61789-31-9	Sodium cocoate	64365-11-3	Carbon, activated	68002-71-1	Hydrogenated soy glyceride
61789-32-0	Sodium cocoyl isethionate	64365-23-7	Dimethicone copolyol	68002-72-2	Hydrogenated menhaden oil
		64742-42-3	Microcrystalline wax		
61789-40-0	Cocamidopropyl betaine	64742-48-9	C13-14 isoparaffin	68002-97-1	Laureth-2
		65071-98-9	Laneth-10 acetate	68002-97-1	Laureth-3
61789-71-7	Benzalkonium chloride	65072-00-6	Hydrolyzed milk protein	68002-97-1	Laureth-4
61789-75-1	Tallowalkonium chloride	65072-01-7	Corn gluten amino acids	68037-74-1	Dimethicone (branched)
61789-91-1	Jojoba oil	65381-09-1	Caprylic/capric triglyceride	68081-81-2	Sodium dodecylben-zenesulfonate
61790-37-2	Tallow acid				
61790-81-6	PEG-27 lanolin	65416-14-0	Maltyl isobutyrate	68081-96-9	Ammonium lauryl sulfate
61790-81-6	PEG-30 lanolin	65591-14-2	Arachidyl propionate		
61790-81-6	PEG-40 lanolin	65717-97-7	Disofenin	68081-97-0	Magnesium lauryl sulfate
61790-81-6	PEG-60 lanolin	65813-53-8	2-Phenylpropyl isobutyrate		
61790-81-6	PEG-70 lanolin			68131-37-3	Corn syrup solids
61790-81-6	PEG-75 lanolin	65996-61-4	Cellulose	68131-39-5	C12-15 pareth-12
61790-81-6	PEG-85 lanolin	65996-62-5	Food starch modified	68140-00-1	Cocamide MEA
61790-86-1	Polysorbate 80	65996-63-6	Food starch modified	68153-76-4	PEG-20 glyceryl stearate
61790-95-2	Polyglyceryl-3 stearate	66009-41-4	Stearyl heptanoate		
61791-00-2	PEG-4 tallate	66082-42-6	Polyglyceryl-3 diisostearate	68155-09-9	Cocamidopropylamine oxide
61791-00-2	PEG-8 tallate				
61791-00-2	PEG-12 tallate	66085-00-5	Glyceryl isostearate	68155-12-2	Palm kernelamide DEA
61791-01-3	PEG-8 ditallate	66085-00-5	Isostearyl diglyceryl succinate	68171-38-0	Propylene glycol isostearate
61791-01-3	PEG-12 ditallate				
61791-12-6	PEG-3 castor oil	66105-29-1	PEG-7 glyceryl cocoate	68201-46-7	PEG-7 glyceryl cocoate
61791-12-6	PEG-5 castor oil	66146-84-7	Steareth-7	68201-48-9	Hydrogenated soybean glycerides
61791-12-6	PEG-8 castor oil	66794-58-9	PEG-20 sorbitan isostearate		
61791-12-6	PEG-9 castor oil			68201-49-0	Lanolin wax
61791-12-6	PEG-15 castor oil	67700-98-5	Dimethyl lauramine	68239-42-9	Methyl gluceth-10
61791-12-6	PEG-17 castor oil	67701-05-7	Coconut acid	68239-43-0	Methyl gluceth-20
61791-12-6	PEG-20 castor oil	67701-06-8	Tallow acid	68308-54-3	Hydrogenated tallow glycerides
61791-12-6	PEG-26 castor oil	67701-26-2	Cocoglycerides		
61791-12-6	PEG-30 castor oil	67701-26-2	Hydrogenated vegetable oil	68334-00-9	Hydrogenated cottonseed oil
61791-12-6	PEG-32 castor oil				
61791-12-6	PEG-33 castor oil	67701-27-3	Hydrogenated tallow glycerides	68334-00-9	Hydrogenated vegetable oil
61791-12-6	PEG-35 castor oil				
61791-12-6	PEG-36 castor oil	67701-27-3	Japan wax	68334-28-1	Hydrogenated coconut oil
61791-12-6	PEG-40 castor oil	67701-27-3	Tallow glycerides		
61791-12-6	PEG-50 castor oil	67701-28-4	Caprylic/capric/linoleic triglyceride	68334-28-1	Hydrogenated vegetable oil
61791-12-6	PEG-56 castor oil				
61791-12-6	PEG-180 castor oil	67701-28-4	Caprylic/capric/oleic triglyceride	68334-28-1	Tribehenin
61791-12-6	PEG-200 castor oil			68391-01-5	Benzalkonium chloride
61791-14-8	PEG-15 cocamine	67701-30-8	Triolein	68410-45-7	Hydrolyzed gelatin
61791-20-6	Laneth-5	67701-32-0	Mono- and diglycerides of fatty acids	68411-57-4	Disodium cocoampho-dipropionate
61791-20-6	Laneth-10				
61791-20-6	Laneth-15	67701-33-1	Glyceryl myristate	68411-97-2	Cocoyl sarcosine
61791-20-6	Laneth-16	67701-33-1	Mono- and diglycerides of fatty acids	68412-55-5	Trideceth-7 carboxylic acid
61791-20-6	Laneth-20				
61791-20-6	Laneth-25	67724-93-0	PVM/MA copolymer,		

CAS	Chemical	CAS	Chemical	CAS	Chemical
68424-43-1	Lanolin acid		lanolin		dicaprylate/dicaprate
68424-59-9	Shea butter extract	68648-66-8	Maleated soybean oil	70802-40-3	PEG-8 stearate
68424-60-2	Shea butter	68650-39-5	Disodium cocoampho-	70851-07-9	Cocamidopropyl
68424-66-8	Hydroxylated lanolin		diacetate		betaine
68424-85-1	Benzalkonium chloride	68783-63-1	PEG-10-PPG-10	71010-52-1	Gellan gum
68424-94-2	CI 45425		glyceryl stearate	71011-27-3	Quaternium-18
68424-94-2	Coco-betaine	68797-35-3	Dipotassium		hectorite
68425-17-2	Hydrogenated starch		glycyrrhizate	71012-10-7	Polyglyceryl-4 oleate
	hydrolysate	68855-54-9	Diatomaceous earth	71243-51-1	Synthetic beeswax
68439-49-6	Ceteareth-7	68876-77-7	Yeast	71566-49-9	Octyl isononanoate
68439-49-6	Ceteareth-9	68889-49-6	PEG-20 glyceryl oleate	71902-01-7	Sorbitan isostearate
68439-49-6	Ceteareth-10	68891-38-3	Sodium laureth sulfate	71957-08-9	Cobalt gluconate
68439-49-6	Ceteareth-11	68910-41-5	Disodium cocoampho-	72869-62-6	Sorbitan tristearate
68439-49-6	Ceteareth-12		dipropionate	72869-69-3	Apricot kernel oil
68439-49-6	Ceteareth-14	68915-31-1	Sodium hexameta-	73049-62-4	Juniper oil
68439-49-6	Ceteareth-15		phosphate	73049-73-7	Hydrolyzed protein
68439-49-6	Ceteareth-16	68916-39-2	Witch hazel extract	73398-61-5	Caprylic/capric
68439-49-6	Ceteareth-20	68916-55-2	Sambucus oil		triglyceride
68439-49-6	Ceteareth-25	68916-88-1	Lemon juice	73807-15-5	Palm kernelamide DEA
68439-49-6	Ceteareth-30	68916-91-6	Licorice	74623-31-7	PPG-12-buteth-16
68439-49-6	Ceteareth-33	68918-77-4	TEA-abietoyl	74665-14-8	Phenol sulfonic acid
68439-50-9	Laureth-2		hydrolyzed collagen	74811-65-7	Croscarmellose sodium
68439-50-9	Laureth-3	68919-40-4	Disodium cocoampho-	76009-37-5	Polyglyceryl-6 dioleate
68439-50-9	Laureth-4		dipropionate	76050-42-5	Carbomer
68439-51-0	PPG-5-laureth-5	68920-66-1	Cetoleth-22	77465-45-3	Melanin
68439-53-2	PPG-2 lanolin alcohol	68921-42-6	FD&C Blue No. 1	78330-21-9	Trideceth-10
	ether		aluminum lake	78491-02-8	Diazolidinyl urea
68439-53-2	PPG-5 lanolin alcohol	68937-10-0	Hydrogenated	79665-92-2	Polyglyceryl-6 oleate
	ether		polyisobutene	79665-93-3	Polyglyceryl-10 oleate
68439-53-2	PPG-10 lanolin alcohol	68937-85-9	Coconut acid	79777-30-3	Polyglyceryl-10
	ether	68938-15-8	Hydrogenated coconut		stearate
68439-53-2	PPG-20 lanolin alcohol		acid	80866-83-7	2-Phenylpropyl butyrate
	ether	68938-35-2	Vegetable oil	81025-04-9	Lactitol monohydrate
68439-57-6	Sodium C14-16 olefin	68938-37-4	Hydrogenated	81646-13-1	Behentrimonium
	sulfonate		vegetable oil		methosulfate
68441-68-9	Pentaerythrityl	68953-64-0	Quaternium-26	82970-95-4	Quaternium-22
	tetracaprylate/caprate	68955-19-1	Sodium lauryl sulfate	83138-08-3	Cocamidopropyl
68458-58-8	PPG-12-PEG-65	68955-20-4	Sodium cetearyl sulfate		betaine
	lanolin oil	68956-68-3	Vegetable oil	83138-08-3	Disodium cocoampho-
68458-88-8	PPG-12-PEG-50	68988-72-7	Propylene glycol		dipropionate
	lanolin		dicaprylate/dicaprate	83682-78-4	Lauramidopropyl PEG-
68476-03-9	Montan acid wax	68989-00-4	Benzalkonium chloride		dimonium chloride
68476-78-8	Molasses	68989-52-6	Capryloyl collagen		phosphate
68479-98-1	Diethyl toluene diamine		amino acids	83826-43-1	Octyldodecyl myristate
68513-95-1	Soy flour	68990-06-7	Hydrogenated tallow	84012-28-2	Orange extract
68514-74-9	Hydrogenated palm oil		glyceride lactate	84012-38-4	Butcherbroom extract
68515-73-1	Caprylyl/capryl	68990-53-4	Mono- and diglycerides	84012-43-1	Walnut extract
	glucoside		of fatty acids	84082-36-0	Alfalfa extract
68518-54-7	Polyquaternium-1	68990-55-6	Acetylated mono- and	84603-93-0	Rose oil
68526-79-4	Hexyl alcohol		diglycerides of fatty	84604-00-2	Walnut oil
68526-85-2	n-Decyl alcohol		acids	84625-29-6	Capsicum extract
68526-86-3	Lauryl alcohol	68990-58-9	Acetylated mono- and	84650-19-1	Laneth-15
68553-11-7	PEG-20 glyceryl		diglycerides of fatty	84650-55-5	Cascara extract
	stearate		acids	84696-19-5	Witch hazel extract
68553-81-1	Rice bran oil	68990-63-6	Shark liver oil	84696-21-9	Hydrocotyl extract
68554-53-0	Stearoxy dimethicone	68990-82-9	Hydrogenated palm	84696-35-5	Mandarin orange oil
68583-51-7	Propylene glycol		kernel oil	84696-37-7	Rice bran oil
	dicaprylate/dicaprate	68991-68-4	Caprylic/capric/lauric	84753-08-2	Dioctyl cyclohexane
68585-34-2	Sodium laureth sulfate		triglyceride	84775-41-7	Angelica extract
68585-44-4	DEA-lauryl sulfate	69005-67-8	Sorbitan stearate	84775-44-0	Serpentaria extract
68585-47-7	Sodium lauryl sulfate	69226-96-6	Pentaerythrityl	84775-66-6	Licorice extract
68603-42-9	Cocamide DEA		tetracaprylate/caprate	84776-23-8	Calendula extract
68604-71-7	Disodium cocoampho-	69430-24-6	Cyclomethicone	84776-24-9	Hydrocotyl extract
	dipropionate	70321-63-0	Lanolin oil	84929-31-7	Lemon extract
68647-73-4	Tea tree oil	70356-09-1	Butyl methoxy	84929-31-7	Lemon oil
68648-27-1	PEG-20 hydrogenated		dibenzoyl methane	84929-51-1	Thyme extract
	lanolin	70592-80-2	Lauramine oxide	84929-52-2	Linden extract
68648-27-1	PEG-24 hydrogenated	70693-32-2	Neopentyl glycol	84930-16-5	Potassium propyl-

CAS	Chemical	CAS	Chemical	CAS	Chemical
	paraben		isostearate	113010-52-9	PEG-25 PABA
85049-36-1	Ethyl oleate	92128-87-5	Hydrogenated lecithin	116870-30-5	Sodium 1,2-dimyristoyl-
85085-71-8	Senna extract	92345-48-7	Tetrahydrofurfuryl		sn-glycero(3)phospha-
85116-97-8	PEG-2 stearate		butyrate		tidylcholine
85117-50-6	Sodium dodecylben-	92666-21-2	Isoeugenyl benzyl ether	116870-31-6	Sodium 1,2-dipalmitoyl-
	zenesulfonate	92797-39-2	Hydrolyzed milk protein		sn-glycero(3)phospha-
85186-88-5	Sorbitan trioleate	93572-53-3	Hydrogenated		tidylcholine
85251-77-0	Glyceryl stearate		menhaden oil	120962-03-0	Canola oil
85341-79-3	Cetearyl palmitate	94035-02-6	Hydroxypropyl-β-	125804-13-9	Glycereth-5 lactate
85404-84-8	Polyglyceryl-3		cyclodextrin	125804-16-2	Isostearyl behenate
	diisostearate	94247-28-6	Isocetyl behenate	125804-19-5	Isocetyl octanoate
85409-09-2	Caprylic/capric	94349-67-4	Barley extract	125804-28-6	Glycereth-5 lactate
	triglyceride	94891-33-5	Stearalkonium hectorite	126121-35-5	Trioctyldodecyl citrate
85409-22-9	Benzalkonium chloride	97026-94-0	Synthetic beeswax	126928-07-2	Polyglyceryl-6
85409-25-2	Coco-betaine	97069-99-0	Emulsifying wax NF		isostearate
85507-69-3	Aloe extract	97281-23-7	Glycol stearate	127036-29-7	Dihydroabietyl
85536-04-5	Stearyl stearate	97281-47-5	Lecithin		behenate
85536-08-9	Corn oil PEG-6 esters	97281-47-5	Phosphatidylcholine	127733-92-0	Dihydrogenated tallow
85536-08-9	PEG-8 caprylic/capric	97281-48-6	Hydrogenated lecithin		phthalic acid amide
	glycerides	97338-28-8	Isocetyl stearoyl	129521-59-1	Palm glycerides
85586-21-6	Methyl stearate		stearate	132207-30-8	Dimethicone
85666-92-8	Glyceryl stearate	97488-91-0	Apricot kernel oil PEG-		propylethylenediamine
85666-92-8	Glyceryl stearate SE		6 esters		behenate
85736-49-8	PEG-12 dioleate	97593-29-8	Hydrogenated palm	132207-31-9	Dimethicone copolyol
85865-69-6	Isobutyl stearate		glyceride		phosphate
86398-53-0	Denatonium benzoate	97593-29-8	Lard glyceride	132208-25-4	2-Octyldodecyl erucate
	(monohydrate)	97593-29-8	Vegetable oil glyceride	133448-12-1	Dimethicone
86418-55-5	Glycol stearate SE	97676-23-8	Licorice extract		propylethylenediamine
86438-35-9	Disodium cocoampho-	97676-24-9	Althea extract		behenate
	dipropionate	98073-10-0	Methyl gluceth-20	133738-23-5	Polyglyceryl-10
86438-78-0	Lauramidopropyl		distearate		isostearate
	betaine	98133-47-2	Panthenyl triacetate	134141-38-1	PEG-4 dioleate
86438-79-1	Cocamidopropyl	99241-24-4	Hydroxypropyl-α-	136097-97-7	Cetyl esters
	betaine		cyclodextrin	136505-00-5	Acrylic acid/
86438-79-1	Disodium cocoampho-	99241-25-5	Hydroxypropyl-γ-		acrylonitrogens
	dipropionate		cyclodextrin		copolymer
87390-32-7	Polyglyceryl-10	100085-40-3	Fish glycerides	136505-01-6	Acrylic acid/
	myristate	100182-46-5	Dioctyl cyclohexane		acrylonitrogens
88103-59-7	2-Octyldodecyl erucate	100209-45-8	Hydrolyzed vegetable		copolymer
89957-89-1	Beet powder		protein	144514-51-2	Orange wax
89998-01-6	Cucumber extract	100684-36-4	Hydrolyzed yeast	150522-09-1	Potassium dimethicone
90045-79-7	Horse chestnut extract		protein		copolyol phosphate
90052-75-8	Octyldodecyl stearoyl	103819-46-1	Olive oil PEG-6 esters	157479-50-0	Dimethicone copolyol
	stearate	106392-12-5	EO/PO block polymer		eicosanate
91031-48-0	Octyl stearate		or copolymer	157479-51-1	Dimethicone copolyol
91031-88-6	Sucrose cocoate	106436-39-9	Tridecyl neopentanoate		eicosanate
91052-08-3	C18-36 acid triglyceride	112926-00-8	Silica, hydrated	159100-33-1	Dimethicone copolyol
91744-38-6	Glyceryl stearate citrate	112926-00-8	Silica aerogel		undecylenate
91824-88-3	Polyglyceryl-4	112945-52-5	Silica (fumed)	977026-99-5	Shea butter

EINECS Number-to-Trade Name Cross-Reference

EINECS	Trade name	EINECS	Trade name	EINECS	Trade name
200-018-0	Patlac® LA USP	200-289-5	Glycon® G-300	200-599-2	Unisweet Lactose
200-061-5	A-641	200-289-5	Kemstrene® 96.0%	200-618-2	Benzoic Acid U.S.P./
200-061-5	Arlex		USP		F.C.C
200-061-5	Fancol SORB	200-289-5	Kemstrene® 99.0%	200-641-8	Thiamine Hydrochloride
200-061-5	Hydex® 100 Coarse	200-289-5	Kemstrene® 99.7%		USP, FCC Regular
	Powd.		USP		Type No. 601160
200-061-5	Hydex® 100 Coarse	200-289-5	Natural Glycerine USP	200-664-3	DMSO
	Powd. 35		96%	200-675-3	Sodium Citrate USP,
200-061-5	Hydex® 100 Gran. 206	200-289-5	Natural Glycerine USP		FCC Dihydrate Fine
200-061-5	Hydex® 100 Powd. 60		99%		Gran. No. 69975
200-061-5	Hydex® Tablet Grade	200-289-5	Natural Glycerine USP	200-680-0	Cyanocobalamin USP
200-061-5	Liponic 70-NC		99.5%		Cryst. No. 69932
200-061-5	Liponic 76-NC	200-289-5	Pricerine 9088	200-680-0	Vitacote® B12 1%
200-061-5	Liponic 83-NC	200-289-5	Star	200-711-8	Unisweet MAN
200-061-5	Liponic Sorbitol Sol'n.	200-289-5	Superol	200-751-6	Nacol® 4-99
	70% USP	200-293-7	Unamino GLUT	200-772-0	Purasal® S/HQ 60
200-061-5	Liposorb 70	200-312-9	Hystrene® 9016	200-772-0	Purasal® S/PF 60
200-061-5	Sorbelite™ C	200-313-4	Emersol® 6332 NF	200-772-0	Purasal® S Powd.
200-061-5	Sorbelite™ FG	200-313-4	Hystrene® 4516	200-772-0	Patlac® NAL
200-061-5	Unisweet 70	200-313-4	Hystrene® 5016 NF	200-815-3	A-C® 7, 7A
200-061-5	Unisweet 70/CONC.	200-313-4	Hystrene® 9718 NF	200-815-3	A-C® 617, 617A
200-061-5	Unisweet CONC.	200-338-0	Adeka Propylene	200-876-6	NM™
200-066-2	Ascorbic Acid USP/		Glycol (P)	200-889-7	Tebol™
	FCC, 100 Mesh	200-338-0	Propylene Glycol USP/	200-889-7	Tebol™ 99
200-066-2	Ascorbic Acid USP,		FCC Ultra Grade	201-064-4	Tris Amino® Conc.
	FCC Fine Gran. No.	200-353-2	Cholesterol NF	201-064-4	Tris Amino® Crystals
	6045655	200-353-2	Fancol CH	201-064-4	Tris Amino® Molecular
200-066-2	Ascorbic Acid USP,	200-353-2	Loralan-CH		Biology Grade
	FCC Fine Powd. No.	200-386-2	Pyridoxine Hydrochlo-	201-064-4	Tris Amino® Ultra Pure
	6045652		ride USP, FCC Fine		Standard
200-066-2	Ascorbic Acid USP,		Powd. No. 60650	201-066-5	ATEC
	FCC Gran. No.	200-399-3	d-Biotin USP, FCC No.	201-067-0	ATBC
	6045654		63345	201-069-1	Citric Acid Anhyd. USP/
200-066-2	Ascorbic Acid USP,	200-412-2	Copherol® F-1300		FCC
	FCC Type S No.	200-419-0	Folic Acid USP, FCC	201-069-1	Citric Acid USP FCC
	6045660		No. 20383		Anhyd. Fine Gran. No.
200-066-2	Ascorbic Acid USP,	200-441-0	Niacin USP, FCC Fine		69941
	FCC Ultra-Fine Powd		Granular No. 69901	201-069-1	Citric Acid USP FCC
	No. 6045653	200-441-0	Niacin USP, FCC No.		Anhyd. Gran. No.
200-066-2	Descote® Ascorbic		69902		69942
	Acid 60%	200-449-4	Versene Acid	201-069-1	Descote® Citric Acid
200-075-1	Candex®	200-467-2	Ethyl Ether USP/ACS		50%
200-075-1	Emdex®	200-470-9	Crossential LS	201-070-7	Hydagen® C.A.T
200-143-0	Bronopol	200-529-9	Versene CA	201-070-7	TEC
200-143-0	Bronopol-Boots® BP	200-559-2	Unisweet L	201-071-2	TBC
200-289-5	Croderol GA7000	200-573-9	Versene 100	201-134-4	Linalool 95
200-289-5	Emery® 912	200-573-9	Versene 100 EP	201-188-9	NE™
200-289-5	Emery® 916	200-573-9	Versene 100 LS	201-209-1	NiPar S-20™
200-289-5	Emery® 917	200-573-9	Versene 100 SRG	201-228-5	Vitamin A Palmitate
200-289-5	Emery® 918	200-573-9	Versene 100 XL		Type PIMO/BH No.
200-289-5	Glycerine (Pharmaceu-	200-573-9	Versene 220		638280100
	tical)	200-578-6	Punctilious® SDA 1-1	201-228-5	Vitamin A Palmitate
200-289-5	Glycon® G 100	200-580-7	Unichem ACETA		USP, FCC Type P1.7/E

EINECS	Trade name	EINECS	Trade name	EINECS	Trade name
	No. 63699	203-820-9	DIPA Commercial	204-402-9	Unichem BZBN
201-228-5	Vitamin A Palmitate		Grade	204-408-2	Descote® Copper
	USP, FCC Type P1.7	203-820-9	DIPA Low Freeze		Gluconate 20%
	No. 262090000		Grade 85	204-427-5	Catechol XP
201-321-0	Syncal® SDI	203-820-9	DIPA Low Freeze	204-464-7	Uniswet EVAN
201-321-0	Uniswet SAC		Grade 90	204-465-2	Uniswet VAN
201-327-3	Ritapan D	203-820-9	DIPA NF Grade	204-471-5	TMP-HP
201-507-1	Riboflavin USP, FCC	203-825-6	Robane®	204-479-9	Hyamine® 1622 50%
	184045	203-826-1	Supraene®	204-479-9	Hyamine® 1622
201-507-1	Riboflavin USP, FCC	203-852-3	Nacol® 6-98		Crystals
	No. 602940002	203-886-9	Cerasynt® IP	204-516-9	Cumal
201-507-1	Riboflavin USP, FCC	203-886-9	Cerasynt® M	204-527-9	Arquad® DM18B-90
	Type S	203-886-9	Kemester® EGMS	204-528-4	TIPA 99
201-788-0	Xylitol C	203-886-9	Lexemul® EGMS	204-534-7	Emerest® 2423
201-793-8	Nipacide® PX-R	203-886-9	Mapeg® EGMS	204-534-7	Hodag GTO
201-793-8	Ottasept®	203-886-9	Monthyle	204-552-5	TEP-HP
201-793-8	Ottasept® Extra	203-917-6	Nacol® 8-97	204-589-7	Phenoxetol
201-800-4	Iodasept	203-917-6	Nacol® 8-99	204-593-9	CPC
201-800-4	Kollidon®	203-919-7	Transcutol	204-593-9	CPC Sumquat 6060
201-800-4	Kollidon® USP	203-924-4	Diglyme	204-593-9	Uniquart CPC
201-800-4	Plasdone® C-15	203-927-0	Empigen® 5089	204-614-1	PAG DLTDP
201-800-4	Plasdone® C-30	203-928-6	Barquat® CT-29	204-617-8	Tecquinol® USP Grade
201-800-4	Plasdone® K-25	203-928-6	Carsoquat® CT-429	204-633-5	Isoamyl Alcohol 95%
201-800-4	Plasdone® K-29/32	203-956-9	Cachalot® DE-10	204-633-5	Isoamyl Alcohol 99%
201-800-4	Plasdone® K-90	203-956-9	Nacol® 10-97	204-648-7	2-Pyrol®
201-800-4	Plasdone® K-90D	203-956-9	Nacol® 10-99	204-649-2	Unichem Levula
201-800-4	Plasdone® K-90M	203-982-0	Cachalot® L-90	204-709-8	AMP
202-307-7	Lexgard® P	203-982-0	Nacol® 12-96	204-709-8	AMP-95
202-307-7	Nipasol M	203-982-0	Nacol® 12-99	204-771-6	Eastman® SAIB-SG
202-307-7	Propyl Parasept® NF/	203-982-0	Unihydag Wax 12	204-812-8	Niaproof® Anionic
	FCC	203-989-9	Hodag PEG 200		Surfactant 08
202-311-9	Nipabenzyl	203-989-9	Lipoxol® 200 MED	204-881-4	CAO®-3
202-318-7	Butyl Parasept® NF	203-989-9	Macol® E-200	204-881-4	CAO®-3/Blend 29
202-318-7	Lexgard® B	203-989-9	Poly-G® 200	204-886-1	Syncal® GS
202-318-7	Nipabutyl	204-000-3	Dehydag® Wax 14	204-886-1	Syncal® GSD
202-488-2	AB®	204-000-3	Lanette® 14	204-886-1	Syncal® S
202-495-0	Thiovanol®	204-000-3	Nacol® 14-95	204-886-1	Syncal® SDS
202-509-5	BLO®	204-000-3	Nacol® 14-98	204-886-1	Syncal® US
202-592-8	Allantoin	204-000-3	Unihydag Wax-14	204-886-1	Unisweet SOSAC
202-608-3	Sarkosyl® L	204-001-9	Butyl Diglyme	204-988-6	Riboflavin-5´-
202-713-4	Niacinamide USP, FCC	204-001-9	Ethyl Diglyme		Phosphate Sodium
	Fine Granular No.	204-007-1	Crossential Oleic		USP, FCC No. 60296
	69916	204-007-1	Emersol® 6313 NF	205-031-5	Escalol® 567
202-713-4	Niacinamide USP, FCC	204-007-1	Emersol® 6321 NF	205-031-5	Spectra-Sorb® UV 9
	No. 69905	204-007-1	Emersol® 6333 NF	205-031-5	Syntase® 62
202-785-7	Lexgard® M	204-010-8	Hystrene® 7022	205-087-0	Vancide® 89 RE
202-785-7	Methyl Parasept® NF/	204-010-8	Hystrene® 9022	205-126-1	Descote® Sodium
	FCC	204-017-6	Adol® 61 NF		Ascorbate 50%
202-785-7	Nipagin M	204-017-6	Cachalot® S-56	205-126-1	Sodium Ascorbate
203-041-4	Quadrol®	204-017-6	Crodacol S-95NF		USP, FCC Fine Gran.
203-051-9	Eastman® Triacetin	204-017-6	Dehydag® Wax 18		No. 6047709
203-061-3	TBP-HP	204-017-6	Epal® 18NF	205-126-1	Sodium Ascorbate
203-090-1	Wickenol® 158	204-017-6	Hyfatol 18-95		USP, FCC Fine Powd.
203-180-0	Eltesol® TSX	204-017-6	Hyfatol 18-98		No. 6047708
203-180-0	Eltesol® TSX/A	204-017-6	Lanette® 18	205-126-1	Sodium Ascorbate
203-180-0	Eltesol® TSX/SF	204-017-6	Lanette® 18 DEO		USP, FCC Type AG
203-246-9	PTAL	204-017-6	Mackol 18		No. 6047710
203-350-4	Cetiol® B	204-017-6	Nacol® 18-94	205-278-9	Calcium Pantothenate
203-358-8	Acconon 200-MS	204-017-6	Nacol® 18-98		USP, FCC Type SD
203-358-8	Crodet S4	204-017-6	Steraffine		No. 63924
203-358-8	Kessco® PEG 200 MS	204-017-6	Unihydag Wax-18	205-281-5	Crodasinic LS30
203-358-8	Nikkol MYS-4	204-100-0	AMPD	205-281-5	Crodasinic LS35
203-363-5	Hydrine	204-101-2	AEPD®	205-281-5	Hamposyl® L-30
203-363-5	Nikkol MYS-2	204-263-4	Escalol® 587	205-281-5	Oramix® L30
203-544-9	NiPar S-10™	204-271-8	Veltol®	205-305-4	Ascorbyl Palmitate NF,
203-751-4	Isopropylmyristat	204-337-6	Velsicure®		FCC No. 60412
203-751-4	RITA IPM	204-399-4	Ethyl Parasept® NF	205-351-5	Catinal MB-50A
203-809-9	Pyridine 1°	204-399-4	Nipagin A	205-352-0	Catigene® DC 100

EINECS	Trade name	EINECS	Trade name	EINECS	Trade name
215-171-9	Magnesium Oxide USP Heavy	215-665-4	Drewmulse® SMO	220-476-5	Ritachol® SS
215-171-9	Marinco OH	215-665-4	Ethylan® GO80	220-552-8	Turpinal® SL
215-171-9	Marinco OL	215-665-4	Glycomul® O	220-836-1	Wickenol® 159
215-222-5	USP-1	215-665-4	Kemester® S80	221-279-7	Arlypon® F
215-222-5	USP-2	215-665-4	Montane® 80	221-279-7	Britex L 20
215-222-5	Zinc Oxide USP 66	215-665-4	Nissan Nonion OP-80R	221-279-7	Dehydol® LS 2 DEO
215-350-1	Cegesoft® C 17	215-665-4	Rheodol AO-10	221-280-2	Dehydol® LS 3 DEO
215-350-1	Ceraphyl® 50	215-665-4	Sorbirol O	221-282-3	Dehydol® PID 6
215-350-1	Pelemol® ML	215-665-4	Sorgen 40	221-286-5	Ethosperse® LA-12
215-354-3	Aldo® PGHMS	215-665-4	Sorgen TW80	221-450-6	Stepanol® MG
215-354-3	Cerasynt® PA	215-683-2	FK 500LS	221-588-7	Unifluorid H 101
215-354-3	Cithrol PGMS N/E	215-683-2	Sipernat® 22LS	221-662-9	Cerasynt® 303
215-354-3	Kessco PGMS	215-683-2	Sipernat® 22S	221-787-9	Ceraphyl® 424
215-354-3	Nikkol PMS-1C	215-683-2	Tixosil 311	221-787-9	Cetiol® MM
215-359-0	Kessco® Glycerol Distearate 386F	215-683-2	Tixosil 321	221-787-9	Crodamol MM
		215-683-2	Tixosil 331	221-787-9	Pelemol® MM
215-475-1	Kaopolite® 1147	215-683-2	Tixosil 333, 343	222-848-2	Gluconal® MG
215-475-1	Kaopolite® SF	215-683-2	Tixosil 375	222-981-6	Ceraphyl® 140
215-475-1	Suspengel Elite	215-683-2	Tullanox HM-100	222-981-6	Cetiol® V
215-475-1	Suspengel Micro	215-683-2	Tullanox HM-150	222-981-6	Pelemol® DO
215-475-1	Suspengel Ultra	215-683-2	Tullanox HM-250	222-981-6	Standamul® CTV
215-477-2	Chlorhydrol® 50% Sol'n	215-710-8	Micro-Cel® C	223-267-7	Turpinal® 4 NL
		215-724-4	Carmacid Y	223-470-0	Isofol® 12
215-477-2	Chlorhydrol® Granular	215-724-4	Carmine FG	224-027-4	Propylene Phenoxetol
215-477-2	Chlorhydrol®, Impalpable	215-724-4	Carmine PG	224-292-6	Tego®-Betaine L-10 S
		215-724-4	Carmine Powd. 272010, 272015, 272020	224-736-9	Gluconal® ZN
215-477-2	Chlorhydrol® Powd.			225-268-8	Ebal
215-477-2	Macrospherical® 95			225-714-1	Nipagin M Sodium
215-477-2	Micro-Dry®	215-724-4	Carmine Powd. WS	225-856-4	Carbowax® Sentry® PEG 400
215-477-2	Micro-Dry® Super-ultrafine	215-724-4	Carmine XY/UF		
		215-724-4	Carminic Acid 90	225-856-4	Dow E400 NF
215-477-2	Micro-Dry® Ultrafine	215-724-4	Carmisol A	225-856-4	Hodag PEG 400
215-477-2	Reach® 101	215-724-4	Carmisol NA	225-856-4	Lipoxol® 400 MED
215-477-2	Reach® 103	215-724-4	Natural Liquid AP Carmine Colorant	225-856-4	Macol® E-400
215-477-2	Reach® 301			225-856-4	Pluracol® E400 NF
215-477-2	Reach® 301 Sol'n	215-724-4	Natural Liquid Carmine Colorant (Type 100, 50, and Simple)	225-856-4	Renex® PEG 400
215-477-2	Reach® 501			225-856-4	Teric PEG 400
215-477-2	Reach® 501 Sol'n	215-724-4	Natural Soluble Carmine Powd.	226-097-1	Britex L 40
215-477-2	Ritachlor 50%			226-097-1	Dehydol® LS 4 DEO
215-477-2	Westchlor® 200	215-724-4	Natural Soluble Powder AP Carmine Colorant	226-097-1	Ethosperse® LA-4
215-549-3	Cithrol PGMO N/E			226-097-1	Rhodasurf® L-4
215-663-3	Montane® 20	215-735-4	Annatto Powd. WS	226-097-1	Simulsol® P4
215-663-3	Sorgen 90	215-785-7	Nikkol Glycyrrhizic Acid	226-242-9	Eutanol® G
215-664-9	Ablunol S-60	216-087-5	FC-24	226-242-9	Isofol® 20
215-664-9	Arlacel® 60	216-087-5	Fluorad® FC-24	226-775-7	Escalol® 557
215-664-9	Capmul® S	216-472-8	Haro® Chem CPR-2	227-608-0	Puramex® FE
215-664-9	Crill 3	216-472-8	Synpro® Calcium Stearate NF	228-250-8	Escalol® 597
215-664-9	Dehymuls® SMS			228-504-8	Ceraphyl® 31
215-664-9	Drewmulse® SMS	216-653-1	High Purity MTBE	229-349-9	Syncal® CAS
215-664-9	Ethylan® GS60	216-700-6	Empigen® OB	229-349-9	Unisweet CALSAC
215-664-9	Glycomul® S	217-210-5	Myacide® SP	229-350-4	Gluconal® MN
215-664-9	Kemester® S60	218-793-9	Stepanol® AM	229-859-1	Carbowax® Sentry® PEG 600
215-664-9	Montane® 60	218-793-9	Stepanol® AM-V.		
215-664-9	Nissan Nonion SP-60R	218-901-4	Myverol® 18-92	229-859-1	Dow E600 NF
215-664-9	Rheodol AS-10	219-136-9	Kessco® PEG 300 ML	229-859-1	Hodag PEG 600
215-664-9	S-Maz® 60K	219-370-1	Isofol® 16	229-859-1	Lipoxol® 600 MED
215-664-9	Sorbirol S	220-045-1	Carbowax® PEG 300	229-859-1	Macol® E-600
215-664-9	Sorgen 50	220-045-1	Carbowax® Sentry® PEG 300	229-859-1	Pluracol® E600 NF
215-664-9	Span® 60			229-859-1	Renex® PEG 600
215-664-9	Span® 60K	220-045-1	Dow E300 NF	229-859-1	Teric PEG 600
215-664-9	Span® 60 VS	220-045-1	Hodag PEG 300	230-325-5	Synpro® Aluminum Monostearate NF
215-665-4	Ablunol S-80	220-045-1	Lipoxol® 300 MED		
215-665-4	Arlacel® 80	220-045-1	Macol® E-300	230-325-5	Synpro® Aluminum Stearate USP
215-665-4	Armotan® MO	220-045-1	Renex® PEG 300		
215-665-4	Crill 4	220-045-1	Rhodasurf® PEG 300	231-153-3	Calgon® Type 114A AWD
215-665-4	Crill 50	220-045-1	Teric PEG 300		
215-665-4	Dehymuls® SMO	220-266-3	Spinomar NaSS	231-153-3	Calgon® Type ADP
				231-153-3	Calgon® Type APA

EINECS	Trade name	EINECS	Trade name	EINECS	Trade name
231-153-3	Calgon® Type BL®		Phosphate Anhyd	232-307-2	Alcolec® Granules
231-153-3	Calgon® Type CAL®	231-826-1	Anhydrous	232-307-2	Asol
231-153-3	Calgon® Type CPG®		Emcompress®	232-307-2	Capcithin™
231-153-3	Calgon® Type CPG®	231-826-1	Emcompress®	232-307-2	Capsulec 51-SB
	LF	231-840-8	Calfos	232-307-2	Capsulec 51-UB
231-153-3	Calgon® Type OL®	231-900-3	Compactrol®	232-307-2	Capsulec 56-SB
231-153-3	Calgon® Type PWA®	231-900-3	Terra Alba 114836	232-307-2	Capsulec 56-UB
231-153-3	Calgon® Type RB®	231-987-8	Albrite® Diammonium	232-307-2	Capsulec 62-SB
231-153-3	Calgon® Type RC®		Phosphate Food Grade	232-307-2	Capsulec 62-UB
231-153-3	Calgon® Type SGL®	232-077-3	alpha-Pinene P&F,	232-307-2	Centrolex® F
231-211-8	Controlled Particle Size		FCC	232-307-2	Centrolex® P
	KCl	232-273-9	GTO 80	232-307-2	Dulectin
231-211-8	Free-flowing KCl	232-273-9	GTO 90	232-307-2	Emulmetik™ 970
231-211-8	Standard KCl	232-273-9	GTO 90E	232-307-2	Lecigran™ 5750
231-211-8	Superfine KCl	232-273-9	Neobee® SL-130	232-307-2	Lecigran™ 6750
231-211-8	Wholecut KCl	232-273-9	NS-20	232-307-2	Lecigran™ A
231-306-4	Pelemol® DIPS	232-273-9	Sunyl® 80	232-307-2	Lecigran™ F
231-493-2	Beta W7	232-273-9	Sunyl® 80 RBD	232-307-2	Lecigran™ M
231-493-2	Beta W7 P	232-273-9	Sunyl® 80 RBD ES	232-307-2	PhosPho F-97
231-493-2	Cavitron Cyclo-	232-273-9	Sunyl® 80 RBWD	232-307-2	PhosPho LCN-TS
	dextrin.™	232-273-9	Sunyl® 80 RBWD ES	232-307-2	Phospholipon® 80
231-545-4	Aerosil® 200	232-273-9	Sunyl® 90	232-307-2	Phospholipon® 90
231-545-4	Aerosil® 300	232-273-9	Sunyl® 90 RBD	232-307-2	Phospholipon® 90 G
231-545-4	Aerosil® 380	232-273-9	Sunyl® 90 RBWD	232-307-2	Phospholipon® 100,
231-545-4	Aerosil® R812	232-273-9	Sunyl® 90E RBWD		100G
231-545-4	Aerosil® R972	232-273-9	Sunyl® 90E RBWD ES	232-307-2	Yelkin F
231-545-4	A.F.S		1016	232-307-2	Yelkin G
231-545-4	Cab-O-Sil® EH-5	232-273-9	Sunyl® HS 500	232-307-2	Yelkin P
231-545-4	Cab-O-Sil® H-5	232-274-4	Neobee® SL-110	232-310-9	Extramalt Dark
231-545-4	Cab-O-Sil® HS-5	232-274-4	Super Refined®	232-310-9	Non-Diastatic Malt
231-545-4	Cab-O-Sil® L-90		Soybean Oil USP		Syrup #40600
231-545-4	Cab-O-Sil® LM-150	232-276-5	Neobee® 18	232-310-9	Pure Malt Colorant
231-545-4	Cab-O-Sil® M-5	232-276-5	Super Refined®		A6000
231-545-4	Cab-O-Sil® MS-55		Safflower Oil	232-310-9	Pure Malt Colorant
231-545-4	Cab-O-Sil® PTG	232-277-0	EmCon Olive		A6001
231-545-4	Hi-Sil® T-600	232-277-0	Super Refined® Olive	232-311-4	Neobee® SL-120
231-545-4	Hyflo Super-Cel		Oil	232-311-4	Super Refined®
231-545-4	Koraid PSM	232-280-7	Super Refined®		Menhaden Oil
231-545-4	Sident® 15		Cottonseed Oil	232-315-6	Koster Keunen Paraffin
231-545-4	Sident® 22LS	232-281-2	Lipex 104		Wax
231-545-4	Sident® 22S	232-281-2	Super Refined® Corn	232-348-6	Anhydrous Lanolin
231-545-4	Wacker HDK® H20		Oil		Grade 1
231-545-4	Wacker HDK® N20	232-282-8	Cobee 76	232-348-6	Anhydrous Lanolin
231-545-4	Wacker HDK® V15	232-282-8	Coconut Oil® 76		Grade 2
231-598-3	Sterling® Purified USP	232-282-8	Coconut Oil® 92	232-348-6	Anhydrous Lanolin
	Salt	232-282-8	Pureco® 76		P.80
231-609-1	Lipamine SPA	232-290-1	Koster Keunen	232-348-6	Anhydrous Lanolin
231-710-0	Tri-K Vitamin E Acetate		Ceresine		P.95
231-710-0	Vitamin E Acetate USP	232-290-1	Ross Ceresine Wax	232-348-6	Anhydrous Lanolin
	Oil	232-292-2	Castorwax® MP-70		Superfine
231-710-0	Vitamin E USP, FCC	232-292-2	Castorwax® NF	232-348-6	Anhydrous Lanolin
	No. 60525	232-292-2	Cutina® HR Powd.		USP
231-710-0	Vitamin E USP, FCC	232-292-2	Ross Castor Wax	232-348-6	Anhydrous Lanolin
	No. 60526	232-292-2	Unitina HR		USP Cosmetic
231-710-0	Vitinc® dl-alpha	232-293-8	AA USP	232-348-6	Anhydrous Lanolin
	Tocopheryl Acetate	232-293-8	Castor Oil USP		USP Cosmetic AA
	USP XXII	232-293-8	Cosmetol® X	232-348-6	Anhydrous Lanolin
231-764-5	Albrite®	232-293-8	Crystal® O		USP Cosmetic Grade
	Monoammonium	232-293-8	Crystal® Crown	232-348-6	Anhydrous Lanolin
	Phosphate Food Grade	232-293-8	Crystal® Crown LP		USP Deodorized AAA
231-765-0	Albone® 35 CG	232-293-8	Diamond Quality®	232-348-6	Anhydrous Lanolin
231-765-0	Albone® 50 CG	232-293-8	EmCon CO		USP Pharmaceutical
231-765-0	Albone® 70CG	232-293-8	Lanaetex CO	232-348-6	Anhydrous Lanolin
231-765-0	Ringwell	232-293-8	York Krystal Kleer		USP Pharmaceutical
231-793-3	Zinc Sulfate		Castor Oil	232-348-6	Anhydrous Lanolin
	Monohydrate CP Grade	232-293-8	York USP Castor Oil		USP Pharmaceutical
231-810-4	Oxaban®-E	232-296-4	Super Refined® Peanut		Grade
231-826-1	Albrite® Dicalcium		Oil	232-348-6	Anhydrous Lanolin

EINECS NUMBER-TO-TRADE NAME CROSS-REFERENCE

EINECS	Trade name	EINECS	Trade name	EINECS	Trade name
	USP Pharmaceutical Light Grade	232-373-2	Protopet® White 3C		NF/FCC G-150
232-348-6	Anhydrous Lanolin USP Superfine	232-373-2	Protopet® Yellow 2A	232-519-5	Powdered Gum Arabic NF/FCC Superselect
232-348-6	Anhydrous Lanolin USP Ultrafine	232-373-2	Protopet® Yellow 3C		Type NB-4
		232-373-2	Protopet® Yellow A	232-519-5	Powdered Gum Arabic Type B-100 NF
232-348-6	Anhydrous Lanolin USP X-tra Deodorized	232-373-2	Sonojell® No. 4		Premium
		232-373-2	Sonojell® No. 9	232-519-5	Powdered Gum Arabic Type B-200 NF
232-348-6	Clearlan® 1650	232-373-2	Super White Fonoline®		Premium
232-348-6	Corona PNL	232-373-2	Super White Protopet®	232-519-5	Premium Spray Dried Gum Arabic
232-348-6	Corona Lanolin	232-399-4	Koster Keunen Carnauba		
232-348-6	Coronet Lanolin	232-399-4	Koster Keunen Carnauba, Powd.	232-519-5	Spray Dried Gum Arabic NF/FCC CM
232-348-6	Cosmetic Lanolin			232-519-5	Spray Dried Gum Arabic NF/FCC CS (Low Bacteria)
232-348-6	Cosmetic Lanolin Anhydrous USP	232-399-4	Ross Carnauba Wax		
232-348-6	Emery® 1650	232-410-2	Akolizer S	232-519-5	Spray Dried Gum Arabic NF/FCC CS-R
232-348-6	Emery® 1656	232-410-2	Clarity		
232-348-6	Emery® 1660	232-410-2	Neustrene® 064	232-519-5	Spray Dried Gum Arabic NF Type CSP
232-348-6	Emery® HP-2050	232-410-2	Sterotex® HM		
232-348-6	Emery® HP-2060	232-430-1	Fancol LA	232-519-5	Spray Dried Gum Arabic Type A-180 NF
232-348-6	Ivarlan™ Light	232-430-1	Hartolan		Premium
232-348-6	Lanolin Anhydrous USP	232-430-1	Ritawax	232-519-5	Spray Dried Gum Arabic Type A-230 NF
		232-430-1	Ritawax Super		Extra
232-348-6	Lanolin Pharmaceutical	232-430-1	Super Hartolan	232-519-5	Spray Dried Gum Talha (Acacia)
232-348-6	Lanolin USP	232-435-9	Acid Proof Caramel Powd.		
232-348-6	Medilan™	232-435-9	B&C Caramel Powd.	232-519-5	Spray Dried Gum Talha (Acacia) Special
232-348-6	Pharmaceutical Lanolin	232-435-9	Caramel Color Double Strength	232-519-5	Spray Dried Kordofan Gum Arabic
232-348-6	RITA Lanolin	232-435-9	Caramel Color Single Strength	232-519-5	TIC Pretested® Arabic FT-1 USP
232-348-6	Sorba			232-524-2	Aquagel SP 399
232-348-6	Super Corona Lanolin	232-435-9	Double Strength Acid Proof Caramel Colour	232-524-2	CI-100
232-348-6	Superfine Lanolin	232-435-9	Powdered Caramel Color 986010	232-524-2	CM-80
232-348-6	White Swan			232-524-2	Cracked Bleached Irish Moss
232-348-6	Yeoman	232-435-9	Powdered Caramel Color, Acid Proof	232-524-2	Genu® Carrageenan
232-360-1	Arlacel® 83	232-435-9	Powdered Caramel Colour Non-Ammoniated-All Natural T-717	232-524-2	Genugel® Series
232-360-1	Crill 43			232-524-2	Genuvisco
232-360-1	Dehymuls® SSO			232-524-2	Soageena®
232-360-1	Glycomul® SOC			232-524-2	Soageena® LX7
232-360-1	Montane® 83	232-435-9	Single Strength Acid Proof Caramel Colour	232-524-2	Soageena® LX26
232-360-1	Nissan Nonion OP-83RAT	232-435-9	Unisweet Caramel	232-524-2	Soageena® WX87
232-360-1	Rheodol AO-15	232-436-4	42/43 Corn Syrup	232-524-2	Stamere® CK-S
232-360-1	Sorbirol SQ	232-436-4	Jungbunzlauer GS 7097	232-524-2	Stamere® N-325
232-360-1	Sorgen 30			232-524-2	Stamere® N-350
232-370-6	Lipovol SES	232-440-6	Alcolec® Z-3	232-524-2	Stamere® N-350 S
232-370-6	Sesame Oil USP/NF 16	232-442-7	Special Fat 168T	232-524-2	Stamere® NI
232-370-6	Super Refined® Sesame Oil	232-447-4	Noramium MS 50	232-536-8	Edicol®
		232-452-1	Distilled Lipolan	232-536-8	Edicol® P
232-373-2	Fonoline® White	232-452-1	Fancol HL	232-536-8	Edicol® ULV Series
232-373-2	Fonoline® Yellow	232-452-1	Lipolan S	232-536-8	Powdered Guar Gum Type A
232-373-2	Mineral Jelly No. 10	232-452-1	Lipolan Distilled		
232-373-2	Mineral Jelly No. 14	232-452-1	Super-Sat	232-536-8	Powdered Guar Gum Type AA
232-373-2	Mineral Jelly No. 17	232-519-5	Granular Gum Arabic NF/FCC C-4010	232-536-8	Powdered Guar Gum Type B
232-373-2	Ointment Base No. 3				
232-373-2	Ointment Base No. 4	232-519-5	Granular Gum Arabic Type A-1 NF Premium	232-536-8	Powdered Guar Gum Type BB
232-373-2	Ointment Base No. 6	232-519-5	Granular Gum Arabic Type A-2 NF Premium	232-536-8	Powdered Gum Guar NF Type 80 Mesh B/T
232-373-2	Penreco Amber				
232-373-2	Penreco Blond	232-519-5	Gum Arabic NF/FCC Clean Amber Sorts	232-536-8	Powdered Gum Guar Type 140 Mesh B/T
232-373-2	Penreco Cream				
232-373-2	Penreco Lily	232-519-5	Gum Arabic NF, Tech	232-536-8	Powdered Gum Guar
232-373-2	Penreco Regent	232-519-5	Gum Arabic, Purified, Spray-Dried No. 1834		
232-373-2	Penreco Royal				
232-373-2	Penreco Snow	232-519-5	Natural Arabic Type Gum Purified, Spray-Dried		
232-373-2	Penreco Super				
232-373-2	Penreco Ultima				
232-373-2	Perfecta® USP	232-519-5	Powdered Gum Arabic		
232-373-2	Protopet® Alba				
232-373-2	Protopet® White 1S				
232-373-2	Protopet® White 2L				

EINECS	Trade name	EINECS	Trade name	EINECS	Trade name
	Type ECM	232-552-5	Powdered Gum Tragacanth Type G-2 NF Premium	232-554-6	P-7 Pharmaceutical Gelatin
232-536-8	Powdered Gum Guar Type M			232-554-6	P-8 Pharmaceutical Gelatin
232-536-8	Powdered Gum Guar Type MM FCC	232-552-5	Powdered Gum Tragacanth Type G-2S NF Premium	232-554-6	P-9 Pharmaceutical Gelatin
232-536-8	Powdered Gum Guar Type MM (HV)	232-552-5	Powdered Gum Tragacanth Type M-3 NF Premium	232-554-6	P-10 Pharmaceutical Gelatin
232-536-8	Powdered Gum Guar Type MMM 1/2	232-552-5	Powdered Tragacanth Gum Type A/10	232-554-6	Spray Dried Fish Gelatin
232-536-8	Powdered Gum Guar Type MMW	232-552-5	Powdered Tragacanth Gum Type E-1	232-554-6	Spray Dried Hydrolysed Fish Gelatin
232-536-8	Supercol® Guar Gum	232-552-5	Powdered Tragacanth Gum Type G-3	232-554-6	Vee Gee Pharmaceutical Gelatins
232-536-8	Ticolv			232-567-7	Biodiastase 1000
232-539-4	Karaya Gum #1 FCC	232-552-5	Powdered Tragacanth Gum Type L	232-567-7	Biodiastase Conc.
232-539-4	Powdered Gum Karaya Superfine #1 FCC	232-552-5	Powdered Tragacanth Gum Type W	232-567-7	Diastase JP
232-539-4	Powdered Gum Karaya Superfine XXXX FCC	232-552-5	TIC Pretested® Tragacanth 440	232-619-9	Lipase 8 Powd.
				232-619-9	Lipase 16 Powd.
232-539-4	Premium Powdered Gum Karaya No. 1	232-552-5	Tragacanth Flake No. 27	232-619-9	Lipase 24 Powd.
232-539-4	Premium Powdered Gum Karaya No. 1 Special	232-552-5	Tragacanth Gum Ribbon No. 1	232-619-9	Lipase 30 Powd.
				232-619-9	Pancreatic Lipase 250
232-541-5	Locust Bean Gum Pharmaceutical Grade	232-553-0	Genu® HM USP 100	232-629-3	Pepsin 1:3000 NF XII Powd.
232-541-5	Locust Bean Gum Speckless Type D-200	232-553-0	Genu® HM USP L200	232-629-3	Pepsin 1:10,000 Powd. or Gran.
232-541-5	Locust Bean Gum Type A-100	232-553-0	Genu® Pectin (citrus) type USP/100	232-629-3	Pepsin 1:15,000 Powd.
232-541-5	Locust Bean Gum Type A-250	232-553-0	Genu® Pectin (citrus) type USP/200	232-650-8	Trypsin 1:75
				232-650-8	Trypsin 1:80
232-541-5	Locust Bean Gum Type A-270	232-553-0	Genu® Pectin (citrus) type USP-H	232-650-8	Trypsin 1:150
				232-658-1	Agar-Agar
232-541-5	Powdered Locust Bean Gum Type D-200	232-553-0	Genu® Pectin (citrus) type USP-L/200	232-658-1	Agar Agar NF Flake #1
232-541-5	Powdered Locust Bean Gum Type D-300	232-553-0	Genu® Pectins	232-658-1	Powdered Agar Agar Bacteriological Grade
232-541-5	Powdered Locust Bean Gum Type P-100	232-553-0	Mexpectin LA 100 Range	232-658-1	Powdered Agar Agar NF M-100 (Gracilaria)
232-541-5	Powdered Locust Bean Gum Type PP-100	232-553-0	Mexpectin LC 700 Range	232-658-1	Powdered Agar Agar NF MK-60
232-541-5	Seagel L	232-553-0	Mexpectin XSS 100 Range	232-658-1	Powdered Agar Agar NF MK-80-B
232-552-5	Gum Tragacanth Ribbons and Flakes	232-554-6	Bone Gelatin Type B 200 Bloom.	232-658-1	Powdered Agar Agar NF MK-80 (Bacteriological)
232-552-5	Powdered Gum Tragacanth BP	232-554-6	Croda 50 Bloom Gelatin	232-658-1	Powdered Agar Agar NF S-100
232-552-5	Powdered Gum Tragacanth T-150	232-554-6	Croda 60 Bloom Alkaline Processed Gelatin	232-658-1	Powdered Agar Agar NF S-100-B
232-552-5	Powdered Gum Tragacanth T-200	232-554-6	Croda 160 Bloom Limed Gelatin	232-658-1	Powdered Agar Agar NF S-150
232-552-5	Powdered Gum Tragacanth T-300	232-554-6	Croda 190 Bloom Acid Ossein Gelatin	232-658-1	Powdered Agar Agar NF S-150-B
232-552-5	Powdered Gum Tragacanth T-400	232-554-6	Croda 250 Bloom Acid Ossein Gelatin	232-658-1	Powdered Agar Agar Type K-60
232-552-5	Powdered Gum Tragacanth T-500	232-554-6	Crodyne BY-19	232-658-1	Powdered Agar Agar Type K-80
		232-554-6	Edible Beef Gelatin		
232-552-5	Powdered Gum Tragacanth Type B-1 NF Premium	232-554-6	Gelatin USP/NF, Type A	232-658-1	Powdered Agar Agar Type K-100
232-552-5	Powdered Gum Tragacanth Type B-12 NF Premium	232-554-6	Gelatin XF	232-658-1	Powdered Agar Agar Type K-150
		232-554-6	Liquid Fish Gelatin Conc.	232-658-1	TIC Pretested® Gum Agar Agar 100 FCC/NF Powd.
232-552-5	Powdered Gum Tragacanth Type C-5 NF	232-554-6	P-4 Pharmaceutical Gelatin	232-674-9	Elcema® F150
		232-554-6	P-5 Pharmaceutical Gelatin	232-674-9	Elcema® G250
232-552-5	Powdered Gum Tragacanth Type G-1 NF Premium	232-554-6	P-6 Pharmaceutical Gelatin	232-674-9	Elcema® P100
				232-674-9	Justfiber® CL-40-H
				232-674-9	Justfiber® CL-60-H
				232-674-9	Justfiber® CL-80-H

EINECS	Trade name	EINECS	Trade name	EINECS	Trade name
232-674-9	Keycel®	233-293-0	Mapeg® 200 MO	241-640-2	Pelemol® MS
232-674-9	Solka-Floc®	233-864-4	Pelemol® CR	241-640-2	Ritaceti
232-674-9	Solka-Floc® BW-40	234-242-5	Potassium Sodium	241-640-2	Ross Spermaceti Wax
232-674-9	Solka-Floc® BW-100		Copper Chlorophyllin		Substitute 573
232-674-9	Solka-Floc® BW-200		033280	241-640-2	Spermwax®
232-674-9	Solka-Floc® BW-2030	234-316-7	Caprol® 10G10O	241-640-2	W.G.S. Synaceti 116
232-674-9	Solka-Floc® Fine	234-316-7	Drewmulse® 10-10-O		NF/USP
	Granular	234-316-7	Drewpol® 10-10-O	241-646-5	Pelemol® BB
232-679-6	Pharma-Gel™	234-325-6	Imwitor® 900	241-654-9	Dynacerin® 660
232-679-6	Pure-Dent® B700	234-394-2	Gumixan K	242-060-2	beta-Pinene P&F
232-679-6	Pure-Dent® B810	234-394-2	Gumixan KF	242-354-0	Spectradyne® G
232-679-6	Pure-Dent® B812	234-394-2	KELTROL®	242-471-7	Compritol 888
232-679-6	Pure-Dent® B815	234-394-2	KELTROL® 1000	242-471-7	Compritol 888 ATO
232-679-6	Pure-Dent® B816	234-394-2	KELTROL® BT	242-471-7	Pelemol® GTB
232-679-6	Pure-Dent® B852	234-394-2	KELTROL® CR	242-471-7	Syncrowax HR-C
232-679-6	Pure-Dent® B880	234-394-2	KELTROL® F	242-769-1	Amphisol® K
232-679-6	Pure Food Starch	234-394-2	KELTROL® GM	244-063-4	Versene Diammonium
	Bleached 142-A	234-394-2	KELTROL® RD		EDTA
232-679-6	Purity® 21	234-394-2	KELTROL® SF	244-289-3	Escalol® 507
232-679-6	Starch 1500®	234-394-2	KELTROL® T	244-492-7	F-500®
232-679-6	Starch 1500® LM	234-394-2	KELTROL® TF	244-492-7	F-500® Low Sodium
232-679-6	Sta-Rx®	234-394-2	Merecol® MS	244-492-7	F-1000®
232-679-6	28-1801	234-394-2	Merezan® 8	244-492-7	F-1500™
232-680-1	Alginic Acid FCC	234-394-2	Merezan® 20	244-492-7	F-1500™
232-680-1	KELACID®	234-394-2	Rhodigel®		Reductionized
232-680-1	Kimitsu Acid	234-394-2	Rhodigel® 23	244-492-7	F-2000®
232-680-1	Protacid F 120	234-394-2	Rhodigel® 200	244-492-7	F-2100®
232-680-1	Satialgine™ H8	234-394-2	Ticaxan® Regular	244-492-7	F-2200®
232-680-1	Sobalg FD 000 Range	235-340-0	Hectabrite® AW	244-492-7	F-2300™
232-681-7	SPL Heparin	235-340-0	Hectabrite® DP	244-492-7	F-4400™
	Ammonium	235-374-6	Magnabrite® F	244-492-7	Liquigel®
232-681-7	SPL Heparin Lithium	235-374-6	Magnabrite® FS	244-492-7	Liquigel® D4
232-681-7	SPL Heparin Sodium	235-374-6	Magnabrite® HS	244-492-7	Liquigel® HO
	USP	235-374-6	Magnabrite® HV	244-492-7	R-1000™
232-697-4	Collagenite	235-374-6	Magnabrite® K	244-492-7	Rederm® Gel
232-734-4	Cellulase 4000	235-374-6	Magnabrite® S	244-492-7	Rederm® Powd.
232-734-4	Cellulase AP 3	235-374-6	Veegum®	244-492-7	Rehydragel® CG
232-734-4	Cellulase T-AP6	235-374-6	Veegum® HV	244-492-7	Rehydragel® HPA
232-734-4	Cellulase Tr Conc.	235-374-6	Veegum® K	244-492-7	Rehydragel® LV
232-734-4	Cellulase TRL	235-777-7	Nikkol DGMS	244-492-7	Rehydragel® T.
232-752-2	Bromelain 1:10	235-946-5	Pelemol® PTL	245-204-2	Standamul® 7063
232-752-2	Bromelain Conc.	236-675-5	Hilton Davis Titanium	245-205-8	Isofol® 20 Myristat
232-752-2	Fungal Protease		Dioxide	245-228-3	Isofol® 20 Oleat
	31,000	236-935-8	Captex® 8227	245-261-3	HSC Aspartame
232-752-2	Fungal Protease	238-310-5	Cerasynt® D	246-675-7	Hyamine® 10X
	60,000	238-877-9	Act II 500 USP	246-705-9	Crodesta F-160
232-752-2	Fungal Protease	238-877-9	Alphafil 500 USP	246-705-9	Ryoto Sugar Ester S-
	500,000	238-877-9	Alpine Talc USP BC		1170
232-752-2	Fungal Protease Conc.		127	246-705-9	Ryoto Sugar Ester S-
232-752-2	Papain 16,000	238-877-9	Altalc 200 USP		1170S
232-752-2	Papain 30,000	238-877-9	Altalc 300 USP	246-705-9	Ryoto Sugar Ester S-
232-752-2	Papain Conc.	238-877-9	Altalc 400 USP		1570
232-752-2	Prolase® 300	238-877-9	Altalc 500 USP	246-705-9	Ryoto Sugar Ester S-
232-936-2	Sol-U-Tein EA	238-877-9	Brillante		1670
232-940-4	Maltrin® M040	238-877-9	Dover 50 A	246-705-9	Ryoto Sugar Ester S-
232-940-4	Maltrin® M050	238-877-9	Purtalc USP		1670S
232-940-4	Maltrin® M100	238-877-9	SteriLine 200	246-868-6	Ceraphyl® 494
232-940-4	Maltrin® M150	238-877-9	Supra A	246-868-6	Pelemol® ICS
232-940-4	Maltrin® M180	238-877-9	Supra EF A	246-868-6	Standamul® 7061
232-940-4	Maltrin® M510	238-877-9	Suprafino A	246-873-3	Ryoto Sugar Ester L-
232-940-4	Maltrin® M700	238-877-9	Supreme USP		1570
232-940-4	Maltrin® QD M440	238-877-9	Ultrafino	246-873-3	Ryoto Sugar Ester L-
232-940-4	Maltrin® QD M500	239-139-9	Unisol S-22		1695
232-940-4	Maltrin® QD M550	241-482-4	Gamma W8	246-873-3	Ryoto Sugar Ester
232-940-4	Maltrin® QD M580	241-640-2	Crodamol SS		LWA-1570
233-007-4	Alpha W6 Pharma	241-640-2	Kemester® 1418	246-929-7	Lamegin® NSL
	Grade	241-640-2	Koster Keunen	247-464-2	Nipagin M Potassium
233-293-0	Kessco® PEG 200 MO		Synthetic Spermaceti	247-568-8	Ablunol S-40

EINECS	Trade name	EINECS	Trade name	EINECS	Trade name
269-820-6	Wecobee® FS	270-664-6	Hoechst Wax E	275-117-5	GELRITE®
269-820-6	Wecobee® HTR		Pharma	275-286-5	Lipobee 102
269-820-6	Wecobee® M	271-397-8	EmCon Rice Bran	275-637-2	Pelemol® 89
269-820-6	Wecobee® R Mono	271-557-7	Empicol® 0303	277-962-5	Eltesol® PA 65
269-820-6	Wecobee® S	271-557-7	Empicol® 0303VA	278-928-2	Germall® II
269-820-6	Wecobee® SS	272-043-5	Miranol® C2M Conc.	283-854-9	Cetiol® S
270-082-2	Byco A		NP	284-283-8	Lipex 401
270-082-2	Byco C	272-296-1	Nikkol Dipotassium	284-283-8	Pureco® 100
270-082-2	Byco E		Glycyrrhizinate	284-283-8	Special Fat 42/44
270-082-2	Byco O	273-257-1	Empicol® LZ/D	288-459-5	Hodag 62-O
270-082-2	Polypro 5000®	273-257-1	Empicol® LZV/D	288-459-5	Kessco® PEG 600 DO
	Pharmaceutical Grade	273-544-1	Empigen® BAC50/BP	288-459-5	Mapeg® 600 DO.
270-082-2	Polypro 15000®	273-576-6	Lamegin® GLP 10, 20	289-991-0	Ceraphyl® 847
	Pharmaceutical Grade	273-616-2	Super Refined® Shark	291-548-1	Lameform® TGI
270-156-4	Sarkosyl® LC		Liver Oil	291-548-1	Plurol® Diisostearique
270-302-7	Fancor LFA	273-942-5	Isofol® 16 Palmitat	296-473-8	Peerless® No. 1
270-315-8	Hydroxylan	274-559-6	Fluilan	296-473-8	Peerless® No. 2
270-315-8	OHlan®	274-559-6	Lantrol® 1673	296-473-8	Peerless® No. 3
270-315-8	Ritahydrox	274-559-6	Lantrol® 1674	296-473-8	Peerless® No. 4
270-325-2	Querton 246	274-559-6	Lantrol® HP-2073	298-104-6	Isofol® 16 Caprylat
270-329-4	Amonyl® 265 BA	274-559-6	Lantrol® HP-2074	304-205-9	Pelemol® ICB
270-329-4	Dehyton® AB-30	274-559-6	Ritalan®	304-693-3	Isofol® 16 Oleat
270-474-3	Crodamol PTC	274-559-6	Vigilan	306-549-5	Phospholipon® 100 H

EINECS Number-to-Chemical Cross-Reference

EINECS	Chemical	EINECS	Chemical	EINECS	Chemical
200-001-8	Formaldehyde	200-466-7	Creatinine	200-892-3	Trichlorofluoromethane
200-001-8	Paraformaldehyde	200-467-2	Ethyl ether	200-893-9	Dichlorodifluoromethane
200-002-3	Guanidine hydrochloride	200-470-9	Linoleic acid	200-894-4	Chlorotrifluoromethane
200-018-0	Lactic acid	200-486-6	Antipyrine	200-898-6	Methanesulfonic acid
200-061-5	Sorbitol	200-529-9	Calcium disodium EDTA	200-908-9	t-Amyl alcohol
200-066-2	L-Ascorbic acid	200-532-5	Phenylmercuric acetate	201-055-5	Methyl pentynol
200-075-1	D-Glucose anhyd.	200-540-9	Calcium acetate	201-056-0	Dimethoxypropane
200-075-1	D-Glucose monohydrate	200-543-5	Thiourea	201-064-4	Tris (hydroxymethyl)
200-143-0	2-Bromo-2-nitropropane-1,3-diol	200-559-2	Lactose		aminomethane
		200-559-2	Lactose monohydrate	201-066-5	Acetyl triethyl citrate
200-157-7	Cysteine hydrochloride anhydrous	200-562-9	L-Methionine	201-067-0	Acetyl tributyl citrate
		200-573-9	Tetrasodium EDTA	201-069-1	Citric acid
200-157-7	Cysteine hydrochloride monohydrate	200-578-6	Alcohol	201-070-7	Triethyl citrate
		200-580-7	Acetic acid	201-071-2	Tributyl citrate
200-158-2	L-Cysteine	200-580-7	Acetic acid, glacial	201-126-0	Isophorone
200-198-0	Sodium salicylate	200-618-2	Benzoic acid	201-134-4	Linalool
200-201-5	(+)-γ-Tocopherol	200-641-8	Thiamine HCl	201-148-0	Isobutyl alcohol
200-210-4	Thimerosal	200-659-6	Methyl alcohol	201-149-6	2-Methylpropanal
200-272-2	Glycine	200-661-7	Isopropyl alcohol	201-162-7	Isopropanolamine
200-274-3	L-Serine	200-662-2	Acetone	201-164-8	Pyruvaldehyde
200-283-2	Adenosine triphosphate	200-663-8	Chloroform	201-167-4	Trichloroethylene
200-289-5	Glycerin	200-664-3	Dimethyl sulfoxide	201-174-2	Chloroacetamide
200-291-6	L-Aspartic acid	200-673-2	Cholecalciferol	201-176-3	Propionic acid
200-293-7	L-Glutamic acid	200-675-3	Trisodium citrate	201-178-4	Carboxymethylcellulose
200-294-2	L-Lysine	200-680-0	Cyanocobalamin		sodium
200-302-4	Chlorhexidine diacetate	200-711-8	D-Mannitol	201-188-9	Nitroethane
200-309-2	Allyl isothiocyanate	200-712-3	Salicylic acid	201-204-4	Methacrylic acid
200-311-3	Cetrimonium bromide	200-716-5	Maltose	201-209-1	2-Nitropropane
200-312-9	Palmitic acid	200-725-4	Glutathione	201-214-9	Lanosterol
200-313-4	Stearic acid	200-745-3	L-Histidine	201-228-5	Retinyl palmitate
200-315-5	Urea	200-746-9	n-Propyl alcohol	201-296-2	L-Lactic acid
200-317-6	Chlorobutanol	200-751-6	Butyl alcohol	201-321-0	Saccharin
200-317-6	Chlorobutanol hemihydrate	200-752-1	n-Amyl alcohol	201-327-3	D-Panthenol
		200-772-0	Sodium lactate	201-353-5	CI 60725
200-333-3	D-Fructose	200-799-8	CI 75170	201-353-5	D&C Violet No. 2
200-334-9	Sucrose	200-799-8	Guanine	201-507-1	Riboflavin
200-338-0	Polypropylene glycol	200-806-4	N,N´-Diphenyl-p-phenylenediamine	201-550-6	Diethyl phthalate
200-338-0	Propylene glycol			201-557-4	Dibutyl phthalate
200-353-2	Cholesterol	200-811-1	L-Arginine	201-642-6	Dimethyl anthranilate
200-362-1	Caffeine	200-815-3	Polyethylene	201-735-1	Ethyl anthranilate
200-386-2	Pyridoxine HCl	200-815-3	Polyethylene wax	201-762-9	Pyrogallol
200-399-3	d-Biotin	200-827-9	Propane	201-766-0	L-Tartaric acid
200-412-2	D-α-Tocopherol	200-831-0	Vinyl chloride	201-783-3	Diethyl tartrate
200-412-2	Tocopherol	200-835-2	Acetonitrile	201-788-0	Xylitol
200-416-4	D-Galactose	200-836-8	Acetaldehyde	201-793-8	Chloroxylenol
200-419-0	Folic acid	200-838-9	Methylene chloride	201-796-4	Diethylacetic acid
200-431-6	p-Chloro-m-cresol	200-849-9	Ethylene oxide	201-800-4	PVP
200-432-1	DL-Methionine	200-849-9	Polysorbate 80	201-803-0	2-Furoic acid
200-441-0	Nicotinic acid	200-857-2	Isobutane	201-852-8	o-Isopropylphenol
200-449-4	Edetic acid	200-865-6	Acetyl chloride	201-928-0	Erythorbic acid
200-451-8	Tributyrin	200-876-6	5-Nitroisophthalic acid	201-935-9	2,4-Dimethylaceto-
200-456-2	Phenethyl alcohol	200-876-6	Nitromethane		phenone
200-464-6	2-Mercaptoethanol	200-889-7	t-Butyl alcohol	201-939-0	Menthol

EINECS	Chemical	EINECS	Chemical	EINECS	Chemical
201-943-2	Pulegone	203-213-9	Cinnamal	203-672-5	Dibutyl sebacate
201-944-8	Thymol	203-219-1	γ-Nonalactone	203-686-1	Propyl acetate
201-963-1	o-Anisidine	203-234-3	2-Ethylhexanol	203-699-2	n-Butylamine
201-964-7	Guaiacol	203-246-9	p-Tolyl aldehyde	203-700-6	Butyronitrile
202-016-5	Gluconolactone	203-254-2	p-Anisidine	203-716-3	Diethylamine
202-085-1	Quinaldine	203-273-6	Anisyl alcohol	203-721-0	Ethyl formate
202-216-2	2´-Acetonaphthone	203-288-8	Methyl cyanoacetate	203-726-8	Tetrahydrofuran
202-252-9	2-Methoxy-4-methyl-phenol	203-291-4	Ethyl propionate	203-729-4	Thiophene
		203-299-8	Methyl acetoacetate	203-740-4	Succinic acid
202-259-7	Methyl benzoate	203-305-9	Diethyl malonate	203-742-5	Maleic acid
202-280-1	Stearamide DEA	203-306-4	Ethyl butyrate	203-743-0	Fumaric acid
202-284-3	Ethyl benzoate	203-310-6	Acetal	203-745-1	Isobutyl acetate
202-307-7	Propylparaben	203-341-5	Geranyl acetate	203-751-4	Isopropyl myristate
202-311-9	Benzylparaben	203-347-8	Ethylene brassylate	203-761-9	Ethyl decanoate
202-318-7	Butylparaben	203-350-4	Dibutyl adipate	203-764-5	Diethyl sebacate
202-327-6	Benzoyl peroxide	203-354-6	Pentadecalactone	203-767-1	Methyl n-amyl ketone
202-423-8	o-Cresol	203-358-8	PEG-4 stearate	203-768-7	Sorbic acid
202-480-9	2,3-Dibromo-1-propanol	203-363-5	PEG-2 stearate	203-780-2	Pentylamine
202-485-6	2-Methylbutyraldehyde	203-374-5	3,7-Dimethyl-1-octanol	203-788-6	But-2-yne-1,4-diol
202-488-2	2-Amino-1-butanol	203-375-0	β-Citronellol	203-798-0	Propyl formate
202-494-5	Dihydroxyacetone	203-376-6	Citronellal	203-806-2	Cyclohexane
202-495-0	Thioglycerin	203-377-1	Geraniol	203-808-3	Piperazine
202-500-6	Methyl acrylate (monomer)	203-382-9	Ethyl heptanoate	203-809-9	Pyridine
		203-385-5	Ethyl octanoate	203-813-0	Piperidine
202-509-5	Butyrolactone	203-386-0	Ethyl laurate	203-815-1	Morpholine
202-510-0	Ethylene carbonate	203-388-1	3-Heptanone	203-816-7	Methyl heptenone
202-555-6	5-Sulfosalicylic acid	203-389-7	Propyl propionate	203-820-9	Diisopropanolamine
202-589-1	Eugenol	203-398-6	p-Cresol	203-825-6	Squalane
202-589-1	Isoeugenol	203-400-5	p-Dichlorobenzene	203-826-1	Squalene
202-592-8	Allantoin	203-401-0	p-Chloroaniline	203-827-7	Glyceryl oleate
202-595-4	Ethyl isobutyrate	203-419-9	Dimethyl succinate	203-835-0	Methyl caprylate
202-601-5	N-Hydroxysuccinic acid	203-425-1	Methyl caproate	203-837-1	Methyl hexyl ketone
202-608-3	Lauroyl sarcosine	203-428-8	Methyl heptanoate	203-852-3	Hexyl alcohol
202-612-5	Isobutyl isobutyrate	203-448-7	Butane	203-856-5	Glutaral
202-626-1	Furfuryl alcohol	203-468-6	Ethylenediamine	203-868-0	Diethanolamine
202-627-7	Furfural	203-473-3	Glycol	203-875-9	Hexamethyleneimine
202-691-6	Phenol sulfonic acid	203-473-3	Polyethylene glycol	203-886-9	Glycol stearate
202-708-7	Acetophenone	203-483-8	Taurine	203-889-5	Ethyl oleate
202-713-4	Niacinamide	203-489-0	Hexylene glycol	203-897-9	Heptyl alcohol
202-785-7	Methylparaben	203-508-2	Distearyldimonium chloride	203-898-4	Heptanal
202-794-6	γ-Terpinene			203-911-3	Methyl laurate
202-796-7	p-Cymene	203-518-7	Hydroxycitronellal	203-917-6	Caprylic alcohol
202-845-2	Diethylaminoethanol	203-528-1	Methyl propyl ketone	203-919-7	Ethoxydiglycol
202-851-5	Styrene	203-529-7	Butylene glycol	203-924-4	Diethylene glycol dimethyl ether
202-859-9	Benzyl alcohol	203-538-6	Sarcosine		
202-860-4	Benzaldehyde	203-542-8	Dimethylethanolamine	203-927-0	Laurtrimonium chloride
202-951-9	N-Phenyl-p-phenylene-diamine	203-544-9	Nitropropane	203-928-6	Cetrimonium chloride
		203-550-1	Methyl isobutyl ketone	203-934-9	Isopropyl stearate
202-993-8	Ethyl phenylacetate	203-561-1	Isopropyl acetate	203-937-5	2-Undecanone
203-004-2	N,N´-Diphenylthiourea	203-564-8	Acetic anhydride	203-942-2	Decyl acetate
203-041-4	Tetrahydroxypropyl ethylenediamine	203-570-0	Succinic anhydride	203-943-8	Dimethyl lauramine
		203-571-6	Maleic anhydride	203-950-6	Triethylenetetramine
203-049-8	Triethanolamine	203-572-1	Propylene carbonate	203-956-9	n-Decyl alcohol
203-051-9	Triacetin	203-577-9	m-Cresol	203-957-4	Decanal
203-061-3	Tributyl phosphite	203-581-0	m-Chloroaniline	203-965-8	Undecylenic acid
203-090-1	Dioctyl adipate	203-585-2	Resorcinol	203-970-5	Undecyl alcohol
203-093-8	Methyl cinnamate	203-587-3	2,6-Lutidine	203-982-0	Lauryl alcohol
203-104-6	Ethyl cinnamate	203-602-3	Ethyl isovalerate	203-983-6	Lauric aldehyde
203-109-3	Benzyl cinnamate	203-611-2	1,3,5-Trihydroxybenzene	203-989-9	PEG-4
203-113-5	2-Phenylethyl acetate	203-620-1	Diisobutyl ketone	203-990-4	Methyl stearate
203-118-2	Benzyl ether	203-626-4	γ-Picoline	203-992-5	Methyl oleate
203-148-6	Phenylacetic acid	203-632-7	Phenol	204-000-3	Myristyl alcohol
203-166-4	p-Methoxyphenylacetic acid	203-635-3	Thiophenol	204-001-9	Diethylene glycol dibutyl ether
		203-636-9	β-Picoline		
203-180-0	p-Toluene sulfonic acid	203-640-0	p-Methyl morpholine	204-007-1	Oleic acid
203-205-5	Anethole	203-643-7	α-Picoline	204-010-8	Behenic acid
203-211-8	Hydrocinnamaldehyde	203-646-3	2-Chloropyridine	204-017-6	Stearyl alcohol
203-212-3	Cinnamyl alcohol	203-656-8	Butyl butyrate	204-070-5	Methyl butynol

EINECS	Chemical
204-100-7	2-Amino-2-methyl-1,3-propanediol
204-101-2	2-Amino-2-ethyl-1,3-propanediol
204-116-4	Linalyl acetate
204-211-0	Dioctyl phthalate
204-259-2	Phenyl salicylate
204-262-9	Benzylsalicylate
204-263-4	Octyl salicylate
204-265-5	Ethyl salicylate
204-271-8	Maltol
204-287-5	Anthranilic acid
204-317-7	Methyl salicylate
204-331-3	Benzoin
204-337-6	Benzophenone
204-341-8	Isoquinoline
204-354-9	Dihydrocoumarin
204-373-2	Veratraldehyde
204-393-1	Lauramide DEA
204-399-4	Ethylparaben
204-402-9	Benzyl benzoate
204-409-7	Heliotropine
204-427-5	Pyrocatechol
204-442-7	BHA
204-464-7	Ethyl vanillin
204-465-2	Vanillin
204-471-5	Trimethyl phosphite
204-473-6	Metanilic acid
204-479-9	Benzalkonium chloride
204-479-9	Benzethonium chloride
204-498-2	Propyl gallate
204-514-8	4´-Methyl acetophenone
204-516-9	Cuminaldehyde
204-526-3	Cetalkonium chloride
204-527-9	Stearalkonium chloride
204-528-4	Triisopropanolamine
204-534-7	Triolein
204-552-5	Triethyl phosphite
204-555-1	Benzylidene acetone
204-556-7	Phenoxyacetic acid
204-557-2	Phenyl glycidyl ether
204-574-5	Phenylacetaldehyde
204-589-7	Phenoxyethanol
204-593-9	Cetylpyridinium chloride
204-599-1	p-Hydroxybenzaldehyde
204-602-6	p-Anisaldehyde
204-608-9	4-Heptanone
204-614-1	Dilauryl thiodipropionate
204-615-7	Ethyl pelargonate
204-617-8	Hydroquinone
204-618-3	2,5-Dimethylpyrazine
204-633-5	Isoamyl alcohol
204-634-0	Acetylacetone
204-640-3	Ethyl caproate
204-642-4	Allyl caproate
204-646-6	n-Butyraldehyde
204-648-7	2-Pyrrolidone
204-649-2	Levulinic acid
204-661-8	1,4-Dioxane
204-662-3	Isoamyl acetate
204-664-4	Glyceryl stearate
204-666-5	Butyl stearate
204-673-3	Adipic acid
204-677-5	Caprylic acid
204-680-1	Methyl myristate
204-683-8	n-Octanal
204-688-5	Nonanal
204-692-7	Myristaldehyde

EINECS	Chemical
204-696-9	Carbon dioxide
204-701-4	Urea peroxide
204-709-8	2-Amino-2-methyl-1-propanol
204-771-6	Sucrose acetate isobutyrate
204-772-1	Sucrose octaacetate
204-812-8	Sodium octyl sulfate
204-822-2	Potassium acetate
204-823-8	Sodium acetate anhydrous
204-823-8	Sodium acetate trihydrate
204-841-6	α-Ionone
204-881-4	BHT
204-886-1	Saccharin sodium
204-909-5	CI 61565
204-909-5	D&C Green No. 6
204-988-6	Riboflavin-5´-phosphate sodium
205-031-5	Benzophenone-3
205-087-0	Captan
205-105-7	DL-Tartaric acid
205-126-1	Sodium ascorbate
205-129-8	Menthyl anthranilate
205-132-4	Methyl anthranilate
205-171-7	o-Methoxybenzaldehyde
205-278-9	Calcium D-pantothenate
205-281-5	Sodium lauroyl sarcosinate
205-286-2	Tetramethylthiuram disulfide
205-290-4	Sodium propionate
205-305-4	Ascorbyl palmitate
205-315-9	L-Glutamic acid hydrochloride
205-341-0	dl-Limonene
205-351-5	Lauralkonium chloride
205-352-0	Myristalkonium chloride
205-358-3	Disodium EDTA
205-381-9	Trisodium HEDTA
205-388-7	TEA-lauryl sulfate
205-391-3	Pentasodium pentetate
205-398-1	Cinnamic acid
205-399-7	Benzyl acetate
205-411-0	Aminoethylpiperazine
205-438-8	Ethyl acrylate
205-447-7	Ferrous fumarate
205-455-0	Glyceryl ricinoleate
205-459-2	Neryl acetate
205-470-2	Ricinoleic acid
205-483-3	Ethanolamine
205-500-4	Ethyl acetate
205-503-0	Malonic acid
205-513-5	Hexetidine
205-516-1	Ethylacetoacetate
205-526-6	Glyceryl laurate
205-538-1	MSG
205-540-2	cis-Trimethyldodeca-trieneol
205-542-3	Propylene glycol laurate
205-546-5	Myristamide MEA
205-550-7	Caproic acid
205-571-1	Isopropyl palmitate
205-572-7	Hexyl acetate
205-577-4	DEA-lauryl sulfate
205-582-1	Lauric acid
205-583-7	Nonyl alcohol
205-597-3	Oleyl alcohol

EINECS	Chemical
205-633-8	Sodium bicarbonate
205-685-1	Copper phthalocyanine blue
205-695-6	D-Tartaric acid
205-696-1	m-Tartaric acid
205-698-2	Potassium sodium tartrate tetrahydrate
205-711-1	8-Hydroxyquinoline
205-749-9	Gallic acid
205-753-0	p-Aminobenzoic acid
205-758-8	Trisodium EDTA
205-769-8	Hydroquinone monomethyl ether
205-775-0	Citronellyl acetate
205-783-4	m-Dimethoxybenzene
205-788-1	Sodium lauryl sulfate
206-059-0	Potassium bicarbonate
206-074-2	Potassium D-gluconate
206-075-8	Calcium gluconate
206-076-3	Ferrous gluconate
206-101-8	Aluminum distearate
206-132-7	Sodium desoxycholate
206-156-8	Potassium sodium tartrate anhyd.
206-156-8	Potassium sodium tartrate tetrahydrate
206-369-6	Ethylenediamine dihydrochloride
206-370-1	Potassium thiocyanate
206-376-4	Capric acid
206-696-4	Sodium thioglycolate
206-736-0	p-Fluorophenol
207-312-8	Dicyandiamide
207-334-8	Linolenic acid
207-355-2	Camphor
207-431-5	Eucalyptol
207-439-9	Calcium carbonate
207-439-9	CI 77220
207-444-6	Glycyrrhetinic acid
207-586-9	CI 73000
207-718-5	Gentisic acid
207-757-8	D-Glucose anhyd.
207-838-8	Sodium carbonate
207-903-0	Nordihydroguairetic acid
207-924-5	Hydrocinnamic acid
207-993-1	Stearone
208-010-9	Suberic acid
208-174-1	Acetyl methyl carbinol
208-187-2	Canthaxanthine
208-187-2	CI 40850
208-205-9	Bisabolol
208-253-0	CI 45350
208-253-0	D&C Yellow No. 8
208-293-9	Dehydroacetic acid
208-401-4	D-Gluconic acid
208-407-7	Sodium gluconate
208-408-2	Copper gluconate
208-534-8	Sodium benzoate
208-537-4	Thiamine nitrate
208-651-4	m-Anisidine
208-671-3	Acetyltyrosine
208-686-5	Tricaprylin
208-687-0	Trilaurin
208-702-0	Domiphen bromide
208-726-1	Ethyl valerate
208-728-2	Ethyl levulinate
208-736-6	Cetyl palmitate
208-739-2	Amyl butyrate

EINECS	Chemical	EINECS	Chemical	EINECS	Chemical
208-750-2	Polyvinyl chloride	213-191-2	2-Hexenol	217-210-5	Dichlorobenzyl alcohol
208-754-4	Sodium thiocyanate	213-631-3	Potassium lactate	217-431-7	Sodium lauryl
208-868-4	Ethyl linoleate	213-658-0	Diallyl maleate		sulfoacetate
208-874-7	Batyl alcohol	213-668-5	Hexamethyldisilazane	217-699-5	CI 19140
208-875-2	Myristic acid	213-853-0	Octyl gallate	217-699-5	FD&C Yellow No. 5
208-915-9	Magnesium carbonate	213-911-5	Ammonium bicarbonate	217-699-5	Tartrazine
208-929-5	Methyl isobutyrate	214-291-9	Myrtrimonium bromide	217-752-2	t-Butyl hydroquinone
208-953-6	D&C Red No. 22	214-620-6	Dodecyl gallate	217-850-5	Sodium caprylate
209-025-3	o-Nitrobenzaldehyde	214-686-6	Iron ammonium citrate	217-966-6	Ethyl-3-phenylpropionate
209-060-4	Methyl propionate	214-737-2	Sodium myristyl sulfate	218-080-2	Amyl salicylate
209-084-5	p-Nitrobenzaldehyde	215-090-9	Sodium xylenesulfonate	218-235-4	Calcium benzoate
209-097-6	Tristearin	215-108-5	Bentonite	218-691-4	d-Neomenthol
209-098-1	Tripalmitin	215-136-8	Bismuth subnitrate	218-793-9	Ammonium lauryl sulfate
209-099-7	Trimyristin	215-137-3	Calcium hydroxide	218-901-4	Glyceryl linoleate
209-117-3	Methyl isovalerate	215-138-9	Calcium oxide	219-031-8	D&C Yellow No. 7
209-141-4	3-Methyl-2-buten-1-ol	215-160-9	Chromium oxide greens	219-031-8	Fluorescein
209-150-3	Magnesium stearate	215-160-9	CI 77288	219-091-5	CI 42053
209-151-9	Zinc stearate	215-168-2	CI 77491	219-091-5	FD&C Green No. 3
209-170-2	Zinc acetate	215-168-2	Ferric oxide	219-136-9	PEG-6 laurate
209-183-3	Polyvinyl alcohol	215-168-2	Iron oxides (Fe_2O_3)	219-163-6	CI 73360
209-406-4	Dioctyl sodium	215-170-3	Magnesium hydroxide	219-163-6	D&C Red No. 30
	sulfosuccinate	215-171-9	Magnesium oxide	219-370-1	2-Hexyl-1-decanol
209-481-3	Potassium benzoate	215-181-3	Potassium hydroxide	220-045-1	PEG-6
209-526-7	3-Pentanol	215-185-5	Carboxymethylcellulose	220-120-9	Saccharin
209-529-3	Potassium carbonate		sodium	220-239-6	Methylisothiazolinone
209-567-0	Maltitol	215-185-5	Sodium hydroxide	220-266-3	Sodium p-styrene-
209-691-5	Isovaleraldehyde	215-222-5	CI 77947		sulfonate
209-772-5	Butyl formate	215-222-5	Zinc oxide	220-476-5	Stearyl stearate
209-786-1	Potassium stearate	215-277-5	Iron oxides	220-491-7	CI 15985
209-876-6	D&C Orange No. 5	215-350-1	Myristyl lactate	220-491-7	FD&C Yellow No. 6
209-954-4	DL-Lactic acid	215-354-3	Propylene glycol stearate	220-552-8	Etidronic acid
209-982-7	2-Methylbutyric acid	215-359-0	Glyceryl distearate	220-562-2	CI 12085
210-511-2	Ethyl pyruvate	215-475-1	Aluminum silicate	220-562-2	D&C Red No. 36
210-736-6	Cyclohexyl acetate	215-477-2	Aluminum chlorohydrate	220-836-1	Dioctyl succinate
210-817-6	Propylene glycol	215-540-4	Sodium borate	220-851-3	Sodium octoxynol-2
	diacetate	215-540-4	Sodium borate		ethane sulfonate
210-827-0	Glycol dilaurate		decahydrate	221-279-7	Laureth-2
210-838-0	Methyl valerate	215-549-3	Propylene glycol oleate	221-280-2	Laureth-3
211-014-3	Glycol distearate	215-573-4	CI 77002	221-282-3	Laureth-6
211-047-3	Amyl acetate	215-587-0	Phenol sulfonic acid	221-283-9	Laureth-7
211-103-7	Cetyl acetate	215-647-6	Ammonium hydroxide	221-286-5	Laureth-12
211-119-4	Arachidyl alcohol	215-654-4	Stearyl citrate	221-416-0	Sodium laureth sulfate
211-162-9	Ammonium acetate	215-663-3	Sorbitan laurate	221-450-6	Magnesium lauryl sulfate
211-199-0	CI 15510	215-664-9	Sorbitan stearate	221-588-7	Cetylamine hydrofluoride
211-199-0	D&C Orange No. 4	215-665-4	Polysorbate 80	221-662-9	Diethylaminoethyl
211-466-1	Isobutyl stearate	215-665-4	Sorbitan oleate		stearate
211-533-5	Hexamidine diisethionate	215-681-1	Magnesium silicate	221-787-9	Myristyl myristate
211-546-6	Behenyl alcohol	215-683-2	Silica, hydrated	221-838-5	Copper nitrate (ic)
211-750-5	Distearyl thiodipropionate	215-684-8	Sodium silicoaluminate	221-921-6	Pivaloyl chloride
211-889-1	Δ-Decalactone	215-691-6	Alumina	222-182-2	Triclosan
212-227-4	Dehydroacetic acid	215-710-8	Calcium silicate	222-206-1	PEG-9
212-359-2	Quinine sulfate dihydrate	215-721-8	CI 77489	222-264-8	Sodium undecylenate
212-391-7	Calcium citrate	215-721-8	Iron oxides (FeO)	222-656-9	CI 17200
212-406-7	Calcium lactate	215-724-4	Carmine	222-656-9	D&C Red No. 33
212-480-0	2-Nonanone	215-724-4	CI 75470	222-823-6	N,N-Butyl benzene
212-490-5	Sodium stearate	215-735-4	Annatto		sulfonamide
212-690-2	CI 10316	215-735-4	CI 75120	222-848-2	Magnesium gluconate
212-690-2	Ext. D&C Yellow No. 7	215-753-2	Tannic acid	222-980-4	Oleyl oleate
212-728-8	CI 73015	215-785-7	Glycyrrhizic acid	222-981-6	Decyl oleate
212-728-8	FD&C Blue No. 2	215-798-8	Tocopherol	223-095-2	Denatonium benzoate
212-755-5	Potassium citrate	216-087-5	Trifluoromethane sulfonic	223-267-7	Tetrasodium etidronate
212-762-3	Sodium L-lactate		acid	223-339-8	FD&C Blue No. 1
212-769-1	Potassium acid tartrate	216-472-8	Calcium stearate	223-350-8	Acetyl butyryl
212-773-3	Sodium tartrate	216-491-1	Mercury acetate (ic)	223-470-0	2-Butyl-1-octanol
212-778-0	Methyl 2-methylbutyrate	216-639-5	Fenchyl alcohol	223-472-1	trans-2-Decenal
212-819-0	Decene-1	216-653-1	Methyl t-butyl ether	223-772-2	Benzophenone-4
212-828-1	N-Methyl-2-pyrrolidone	216-700-6	Lauramine oxide	223-795-8	Calcium propionate
213-022-2	Amaranth	217-052-7	Methyl nonanoate	223-805-0	Quaternium-15

EINECS	Chemical	EINECS	Chemical	EINECS	Chemical
232-541-5	Locust bean gum	235-374-6	Magnesium aluminum silicate	246-705-9	Sucrose stearate
232-549-9	Shellac			246-868-6	Isocetyl stearate
232-550-4	Balsam tolu	235-777-7	Polyglyceryl-2 stearate	246-873-3	Sucrose laurate
232-552-5	Tragacanth gum	235-911-9	Zinc ricinoleate	246-929-7	Sodium stearoyl lactylate
232-553-0	Pectin	235-946-5	Pentaerythrityl tetralaurate	247-144-2	Glyceryl dioleate
232-554-6	Gelatin			247-464-2	Potassium methyl-paraben
232-555-1	Casein	236-149-5	Disodium lauryl sulfosuccinate		
232-555-1	Milk protein			247-500-7	Methylchloroiso-thiazolinone
232-567-7	Amylase	236-671-3	Zinc pyrithione		
232-577-1	Catalase	236-675-5	CI 77891	247-555-7	Nonoxynol-5
232-601-0	Glucose oxidase	236-675-5	Titanium dioxide	247-568-8	Sorbitan palmitate
232-619-9	Lipase	236-747-6	D&C Red No. 27	247-569-3	Sorbitan trioleate
232-627-2	Papain	236-813-4	Tellurium	247-574-0	Hydroabietyl alcohol
232-629-3	Pepsin	236-883-6	Methyl 3-methylthiopro-pionate	247-655-0	Octyl stearate
232-650-8	Trypsin			247-668-1	Glyceryl caprylate
232-658-1	Agar	236-935-8	Triundecanoin	247-669-7	Propylene glycol ricinoleate
232-674-9	Cellulose	237-875-5	CI 77510		
232-675-4	Dextrin	237-875-5	Ferric ferrocyanide	247-706-7	Sucrose palmitate
232-677-5	Dextran	238-310-5	Stearamide MEA-stearate	247-710-9	Ammonium xylene-sulfonate
232-678-0	Hyaluronic acid	238-877-9	Talc		
232-679-6	Corn starch	239-076-7	Magnesium trisilicate	247-816-5	Nonoxynol-8
232-680-1	Alginic acid	239-138-3	D&C Red No. 21	247-887-2	Glyceryl palmitate
232-681-7	Heparin ammonium	239-139-9	3-Benzylidene camphor	247-891-4	Sorbitan tristearate
232-681-7	Heparin lithium	239-635-5	Stannous pyrophosphate	248-030-5	Disodium lauryl sulfosuccinate
232-681-7	Heparin sodium	240-458-0	Geranyl acetate		
232-686-4	Starch	240-474-8	CI 45430	248-291-5	Nonoxynol-2
232-697-4	Collagen	240-474-8	FD&C Red No. 3	248-292-0	Nonoxynol-7
232-697-4	Soluble collagen	240-613-2	Dimyristyl thiodipro-pionate	248-293-6	Nonoxynol-8
232-722-9	Zein			248-294-1	Nonoxynol-10
232-734-4	Cellulase	240-795-3	Potassium metabisulfite	248-317-5	Sucrose distearate
232-752-2	Protease	240-865-3	Behenalkonium chloride	248-403-2	Polyglyceryl-3 stearate
232-936-2	Albumen	240-924-3	Stearamidoethyl diethylamine	248-486-5	Quaternium-14
232-940-4	Maltodextrin			248-586-9	Glyceryl dilaurate
233-007-4	α-Cyclodextrin	240-980-2	CI 69825	248-586-9	Glyceryl dilaurate SE
233-032-0	Nitrous oxide	240-980-2	D&C Blue No. 9	248-762-5	Nonoxynol-1
233-046-7	Phosphorus oxychloride	241-409-6	CI 45380	249-277-1	Sodium PCA
233-047-2	Antimony trichloride	241-482-4	γ-Cyclodextrin	249-395-3	Propylene glycol myristate
233-093-3	p-Ethoxybenzaldehyde	241-640-2	Cetyl esters		
233-109-9	Hydriodic acid	241-640-2	Myristyl stearate	249-689-1	Farnesyl acetate
233-135-0	Aluminum sulfate	241-646-5	Behenyl behenate	249-862-1	Octyl palmitate
233-139-2	Boric acid	241-654-9	Oleyl erucate	250-097-0	Glyceryl behenate
233-140-8	Calcium chloride	242-060-2	(-)-β-Pinene	250-275-8	Lysine PCA
233-141-3	Potassium alum dodecahydrate	242-354-0	Chlorhexidine digluconate	250-696-7	Tridecyl stearate
				250-705-4	Glyceryl stearate
233-190-0	Ferric pyrophosphate	242-355-6	CI 45410	251-419-2	D&C Orange No. 11
233-293-0	PEG-4 oleate	242-355-6	D&C Red No. 28	251-732-4	Glycol hydroxystearate
233-343-1	Sodium hexametaphos-phate	242-471-7	Tribehenin	251-932-1	Hexyl laurate
		242-734-6	Sodium citrate	252-011-7	Polyglyceryl-10 tetraoleate
233-466-0	DL-α-Tocopherol	242-769-1	Potassium cetyl phosphate		
233-560-1	Isopropyl laurate			252-478-7	Cetyl lactate
233-713-2	D-Lactic acid	244-029-9	Dihydrocarvyl acetate	252-487-6	Sodium ethylparaben
233-786-0	Ammonium carbonate	244-063-4	Diammonium EDTA	252-488-1	Sodium propylparaben
233-864-4	Cetyl ricinoleate	244-289-3	Octyl dimethyl PABA	252-964-9	Isocetyl alcohol
234-059-0	3-Decen-2-one	244-492-7	Aluminum hydroxide	253-149-0	Cetyl alcohol
234-206-9	Ditridecyl thiodipropionate	244-654-7	Mercury oxide (ic), red and yellow	253-407-2	Glyceryl oleate
234-242-5	Chlorophyllin-copper complex			253-458-0	PEG-8 laurate
		244-754-0	Octyl stearate	254-372-6	Imidazolidinyl urea
234-242-5	CI 75810	245-204-2	Octyldodecyl stearate	254-495-5	Polyglyceryl-10 decastearate
234-316-7	Polyglyceryl-10 decaoleate	245-261-3	Aspartame		
		245-625-1	Ferrous citrate	255-062-3	Disodium laureth sulfosuccinate
234-325-6	Glyceryl stearate	246-376-1	Potassium sorbate		
234-394-2	Xanthan gum	246-563-8	BHA	255-350-9	Propylene glycol dipelargonate
234-406-6	Quaternium-18 hectorite	246-668-9	trans-trans-2,4-Decadienal		
235-030-5	Sodium stannate			255-485-3	Isostearyl isostearate
235-192-7	Magnesium carbonate (basic)	246-675-7	Methylbenzethonium chloride	255-674-0	Isostearyl lactate
				257-048-2	Dimethyl oxazolidine
235-253-8	Aluminum silicate	246-680-4	Sodium dodecylbenzene-sulfonate	257-440-3	Quaternium-22
235-340-0	Hectorite			258-476-2	Sodium magnesium

EINECS	Chemical	EINECS	Chemical	EINECS	Chemical
	silicate	268-770-2	Cocamide MEA	275-117-5	Gellan gum
259-218-1	Decyl glucoside	268-938-5	Cocamidopropylamine	275-286-5	Synthetic beeswax
260-070-5	Dioctyl malate		oxide	275-637-2	Octyl isononanoate
261-521-9	Isostearyl neopentanoate	269-027-5	Propylene glycol	276-638-0	Tannic acid
261-619-1	Cetearyl octanoate		isostearate	276-951-2	Sorbitan tristearate
261-673-6	Isodecyl oleate	269-220-4	Lanolin wax	277-962-5	Phenol sulfonic acid
261-678-3	Menthyl lactate	269-658-6	Hydrogenated tallow	278-928-2	Diazolidinyl urea
261-819-9	Octyl pelargonate		glycerides	281-984-0	Alfalfa extract
262-710-9	Glyceryl isostearate	269-804-9	Hydrogenated cottonseed	283-854-9	Dioctyl cyclohexane
262-978-7	Coconut acid		oil	283-871-1	Angelica extract
262-979-2	Acetylated lanolin	269-820-6	Hydrogenated vegetable	283-873-2	Serpentaria extract
262-980-8	Acetylated lanolin alcohol		oil	283-949-5	Calendula extract
263-005-9	Hydrogenated	269-919-4	Benzalkonium chloride	284-283-8	Hydrogenated coconut oil
	tallowtrimonium chloride	270-082-2	Hydrolyzed gelatin	284-635-0	Cinnamon oil extract
263-027-9	Glyceryl cocoate	270-131-8	Disodium cocoamphodi-	285-206-0	Ethyl oleate
263-031-0	Hydrogenated tallow		propionate	285-550-1	PEG-2 stearate
	glyceride	270-156-4	Cocoyl sarcosine	286-074-7	Sorbitan trioleate
263-032-6	Lard glyceride	270-302-7	Lanolin acid	286-476-2	Barley extract
263-035-2	Tallow glyceride	270-315-8	Hydroxylated lanolin	286-490-9	Glyceryl stearate
263-049-9	Potassium cocoate	270-325-2	Benzalkonium chloride	287-089-1	Benzalkonium chloride
263-050-4	Sodium cocoate	270-329-4	Coco-betaine	287-484-9	Stearyl stearate
263-052-5	Sodium cocoyl	270-407-8	Sodium C14-16 olefin	287-824-6	Methyl stearate
	isethionate		sulfonate	288-459-5	PEG-12 dioleate
263-058-8	Cocamidopropyl betaine	270-474-3	Pentaerythrityl	288-668-1	Isobutyl stearate
263-080-8	Benzalkonium chloride		tetracaprylate/caprate	288-920-0	Capsicum extract
263-085-5	Tallowalkonium chloride	270-664-6	Montan acid wax	288-921-6	Caraway oil extract
263-129-3	Tallow acid	271-397-8	Rice bran oil	288-922-1	Cardamom oil extract
263-163-9	Cocamide DEA	271-557-7	Sodium lauryl sulfate	289-561-2	Annatto (tree) extract
264-038-1	Microcrystalline wax	272-043-5	Disodium cocoampho-	289-610-8	Beet powder
264-119-1	Isopropyl lanolate		diacetate	289-752-0	Lemongrass oil extract,
264-520-1	Octoxynol-1	272-296-1	Dipotassium glycyrrhizate		West Indian
265-134-6	Ozokerite	272-897-9	Disodium cocoamphodi-	289-991-0	Octyldodecyl stearoyl
265-363-1	Hydrolyzed milk protein		propionate		stearate
265-724-3	Caprylic/capric	273-222-0	Quaternium-26	291-548-1	Polyglyceryl-3
	triglyceride	273-257-1	Sodium lauryl sulfate		diisostearate
265-839-9	Arachidyl propionate	273-313-5	Vegetable oil	295-635-5	Hydrolyzed collagen
265-995-8	Carboxymethylcellulose	273-544-1	Benzalkonium chloride	295-786-7	Hydrogenated lecithin
	sodium	273-576-6	Hydrogenated tallow	296-473-8	Kaolin
266-124-4	Glyceryl isostearate		glyceride lactate	297-599-6	Capsicum (C. annuum
266-922-2	Dimethyl lauramine	273-616-2	Shark liver oil		extract)
266-948-4	Triolein	274-559-6	Lanolin oil	304-205-9	Isocetyl behenate
267-008-6	Cetearyl alcohol	274-581-6	Butyl methoxy dibenzoyl	305-181-2	Aloe extract
267-015-4	Methyl oleate		methane	306-522-8	Glycol stearate
267-791-4	Sodium octoxynol-2	274-923-4	Cocamidopropyl betaine	306-549-5	Hydrogenated lecithin
	ethane sulfonate				

FEMA Number-to-Chemical
Cross-Reference

FEMA	Chemical	FEMA	Chemical	FEMA	Chemical
2001	Acacia	2075	Isoamyl hexanoate	2194	Butyl 2-decenoate
2002	Acetal	2078	Isoamyl nonanoate	2196	Butyl formate
2003	Acetaldehyde	2079	Amyl octanoate	2197	Isobutyl formate
2004	Acetaldehyde phenethyl	2082	Isoamyl propionate	2199	Butyl heptanoate
	propyl acetal	2084	Amyl salicylate	2201	Butyl hexanoate
2005	Acetanisole	2085	Isoamyl isovalerate	2202	Isobutyl hexanoate
2006	Acetic acid	2086	Anethole	2203	Butylparaben
2006	Acetic acid, glacial	2087	Angelica extract	2205	Butyl lactate
2007	Triacetin	2093	Anise	2207	Butyl levulinate
2008	Acetyl methyl carbinol	2094	Anise oil	2208	α-Isobutylphenethyl alcohol
2009	Acetophenone	2095	Star anise	2209	Butyl phenylacetate
2010	Aconitic acid	2098	Anisyl acetate	2210	Isobutyl phenylacetate
2011	Adipic acid	2099	Anisyl alcohol	2211	n-Butyl propionate
2012	Agar	2101	Anisyl formate	2214	Butyl stearate
2013	Alfalfa extract	2102	Anisyl propionate	2217	Butyl valerate
2015	Algin	2103	Annatto extract	2218	n-Butyl isovalerate
2015	Ammonium alginate	2104	Annatto	2219	n-Butyraldehyde
2015	Calcium alginate	2105	Apricot kernel oil	2220	2-Methylpropanal
2020	Allyl anthranilate	2109	L-Ascorbic acid	2223	Tributyrin
2021	Allyl butyrate	2111	Balm mint	2224	Caffeine
2022	Allyl cinnamate	2116	Balsam Peru	2225	Cajeput oil
2023	Allyl cyclohexaneacetate	2122	Bay oil	2228	Calcium acetate
2024	Allyl cyclohexanebutyrate	2126	Beeswax (white)	2230	D-Camphor
2025	Allyl cyclohexanehexanoate	2127	Benzaldehyde	2232	Cananga oil
2026	Allyl cyclohexanepropionate	2131	Benzoic acid	2233	Capsicum extract
2027	Allyl cyclohexanevalerate	2132	Benzoin	2235	Caramel
2031	Allyl heptanoate	2133	Gum benzoin	2238	Caraway oil
2032	Allyl caproate	2134	Benzophenone	2239	Carboxymethylcellulose
2033	Allyl α-ionone	2135	Benzyl acetate	2240	Cardamom
2034	Allyl isothiocyanate	2136	Benzyl acetoacetate	2241	Cardamom oil
2036	Allyl nonanoate	2137	Benzyl alcohol	2242	Carmine
2037	Allyl octanoate	2138	Benzyl benzoate	2247	Carveol
2038	Allyl phenoxyacetate	2140	Benzyl butyrate	2249	l-Carvone
2039	Allyl phenylacetate	2141	Benzyl isobutyrate	2250	Carvyl acetate
2040	Allyl propionate	2142	Benzyl cinnamate	2251	Carvyl propionate
2041	Allyl sorbate	2148	Benzyl methoxyethyl acetal	2253	Cascara extract
2043	Allyl tiglate	2149	Benzyl phenylacetate	2256	Cinnamon oil
2044	Allyl 10-undecenoate	2150	Benzyl propionate	2263	Castor oil
2045	Allyl isovalerate	2151	Benzylsalicylate	2266	Capsicum
2047	Aloe extract	2152	Benzyl isovalerate	2286	Cinnamal
2048	Althea extract	2159	Bornyl acetate	2287	Cinnamaldehyde ethylene
2051	Ambrette seed oil	2175	Isobutyl acetate		glycol acetal
2055	Isoamyl acetate	2177	Isobutyl acetoacetate	2288	Cinnamic acid
2056	n-Amyl alcohol	2178	Butyl alcohol	2294	Cinnamyl alcohol
2057	Isoamyl alcohol	2179	Isobutyl alcohol	2296	Cinnamyl butyrate
2059	Amyl butyrate	2181	Butyl anthranilate	2297	Cinnamyl isobutyrate
2060	Isoamyl butyrate	2183	BHA	2300	Cinnamyl phenylacetate
2061	α-Amylcinnamaldehyde	2184	BHT	2301	Cinnamyl propionate
2062	α-Amylcinnamaldehyde	2186	Butyl butyrate	2303	Citral
	dimethyl acetal	2187	Isobutyl butyrate	2304	Citral diethyl acetal
2065	α-Amylcinnamyl alcohol	2188	Butyl isobutyrate	2305	Citral dimethyl acetal
2068	Amyl formate	2189	Isobutyl isobutyrate	2306	Citric acid
2069	Isoamyl formate	2193	Isobutyl cinnamate	2306	Citric acid monohydrate

FEMA	Chemical	FEMA	Chemical	FEMA	Chemical
2307	Citronellal	2422	Ethyl benzoate	2548	Heptyl alcohol
2309	β-Citronellol	2424	α-Ethylbenzyl butyrate	2549	Heptyl butyrate
2311	Citronellyl acetate	2425	2-Ethylbutyl acetate	2552	Heptyl formate
2312	Citronellyl butyrate	2427	Ethyl butyrate	2554	Cetyl alcohol
2314	Citronellyl formate	2428	Ethyl isobutyrate	2556	γ-Hexalactone
2315	Citronellyl phenylacetate	2429	Diethylacetic acid	2558	Acetyl butyryl
2316	Citronellyl propionate	2430	Ethyl cinnamate	2559	Caproic acid
2317	Citronellyl valerate	2431	Ethyl cyclohexane-	2560	2-Hexenal
2323	Clove oil (bud)		propionate	2562	2-Hexenol
2325	Clove oil (leaf)	2432	Ethyl decanoate	2564	trans-2-Hexenyl acetate
2328	Clove oil (stem)	2433	Ethylene oxide	2565	Hexyl acetate
2334	Coriander oil	2434	Ethyl formate	2566	2-Hexyl-4-acetoxytetra-
2337	p-Cresol	2437	Ethyl heptanoate		hydrofuran
2339	Cubeb oil	2439	Ethyl caproate	2567	Hexyl alcohol
2341	Cuminaldehyde	2440	Ethyl lactate	2568	Hexyl butyrate
2348	Cyclohexylethyl acetate	2441	Ethyl laurate	2570	Hexyl formate
2349	Cyclohexyl acetate	2442	Ethyl levulinate	2575	Hexyl octanoate
2350	Cyclohexyl anthranilate	2443	Ethyl 2-methylbutyrate	2576	Hexyl propionate
2351	Cyclohexyl butyrate	2444	Ethyl methylphenylglycidate	2583	Hydroxycitronellal
2353	Cyclohexyl formate	2447	Ethyl pelargonate	2586	Hydroxycitronellol
2354	Cyclohexyl propionate	2449	Ethyl octanoate	2588	4-(p-Hydroxyphenyl)-2-
2355	Cyclohexyl isovalerate	2450	Ethyl oleate		butanone
2356	p-Cymene	2452	Ethyl phenylacetate	2590	Hyssop extract
2360	γ-Decalactone	2453	Ethyl-4-phenylbutyrate	2594	α-Ionone
2361	Δ-Decalactone	2454	Ethyl phenylglycidate	2596	Carrageenan extract
2362	Decanal	2455	Ethyl-3-phenylpropionate	2604	Juniper oil
2364	Capric acid	2456	Ethyl propionate	2605	Karaya gum
2365	n-Decyl alcohol	2457	Ethyl pyruvate	2606	Kelp
2366	trans-2-Decenal	2458	Ethyl salicylate	2611	Lactic acid
2367	Decyl acetate	2459	Ethyl sorbate	2614	Lauric acid
2368	Decyl butyrate	2460	Ethyl tiglate	2615	Lauric aldehyde
2369	Decyl propionate	2461	Ethyl 10-undecenoate	2616	Lauryl acetate
2371	Benzyl ether	2462	Ethyl valerate	2617	Lauryl alcohol
2372	4,4-Dibutyl-γ-butyrolactone	2463	Ethyl isovalerate	2622	Lavender oil
2373	Dibutyl sebacate	2464	Ethyl vanillin	2623	Lemon extract
2374	Diethyl malate	2465	Eucalyptol	2624	Lemongrass oil East Indian
2375	Diethyl malonate	2466	Eucalyptus oil	2624	Lemongrass oil West Indian
2376	Diethyl sebacate	2467	Eugenol	2625	Lemon oil
2378	Diethyl tartrate	2468	Isoeugenol	2627	Levulinic acid
2379	Dihydrocarveol	2470	Acetisoeugenol	2628	Licorice extract
2380	Dihydrocarvyl acetate	2477	Isoeugenyl phenylacetate	2631	Lime oil
2381	Dihydrocoumarin	2478	Farnesol	2633	d-Limonene
2383	Dill seed oil	2480	Fenchyl alcohol	2635	Linalool
2385	m-Dimethoxybenzene	2481	Fennel	2636	Linalyl acetate
2387	2,4-Dimethylacetophenone	2482	Fennel (sweet)	2637	Linalyl anthranilate
2388	α,α-Dimethylbenzyl	2483	Fennel oil	2639	Linalyl butyrate
	isobutyrate	2488	Fumaric acid	2641	Linalyl cinnamate
2389	2,6-Dimethyl-5-heptenal	2489	Furfural	2642	Linalyl formate
2391	3,7-Dimethyl-1-octanol	2490	Furfuryl acetate	2645	Linalyl propionate
2394	α,α-Dimethylphenethyl	2491	Furfuryl alcohol	2646	Linalyl isovalerate
	butyrate	2507	Geraniol	2648	Locust bean gum
2396	Dimethyl succinate	2508	Geranium oil	2653	Mace oil
2398	Sodium phosphate dibasic	2509	Geranyl acetate	2655	N-Hydroxysuccinic acid
	anhydrous	2513	Geranyl isobutyrate	2656	Maltol
2400	γ-Dodecalactone	2519	Gum ghatti	2657	Mandarin orange oil
2401	δ-Dodecalactone	2525	Glycerin	2665	Menthol
2402	2-Dodecenal	2526	Glyceryl oleate	2666	d-Neomenthol
2410	Erythorbic acid	2527	Glyceryl stearate	2667	l-Menthone
2411	Estragole	2528	Monoammonium	2668	dl-Menthyl acetate
2413	p-Ethoxybenzaldehyde		glycyrrhizinate	2670	p-Anisaldehyde
2414	Ethyl acetate	2532	Guaiacol	2671	2-Methoxy-4-methylphenol
2415	Ethylacetoacetate	2537	Guar gum	2672	4-p-Methoxyphenyl-2-
2416	Ethyl 2-acetyl-3-	2539	γ-Heptalactone		butanone
	phenylpropionate	2540	Heptanal	2674	1-(p-Methoxyphenyl)-2-
2418	Ethyl acrylate	2544	Methyl n-amyl ketone		propanone
2419	Alcohol	2545	3-Heptanone	2675	2-Methoxy-4-vinylphenol
2420	Ethyl-p-anisate	2546	4-Heptanone	2677	4'-Methyl acetophenone
2421	Ethyl anthranilate	2547	Heptyl acetate	2678	2-Methylallyl butyrate

FEMA	Chemical	FEMA	Chemical	FEMA	Chemical
2682	Methyl anthranilate	2848	Peppermint oil	2965	Isopulegyl acetate
2683	Methyl benzoate	2856	α-Phellandrene	2966	Pyridine
2684	α-Methylbenzyl acetate	2857	2-Phenylethyl acetate	2969	Pyruvaldehyde
2686	α-Methylbenzyl butyrate	2858	Phenethyl alcohol	2977	Quinine sulfate dihydrate
2691	2-Methylbutyraldehyde	2859	Phenethyl anthranilate	2978	Isoquinoline
2692	Isovaleraldehyde	2860	Phenethyl benzoate	2982	Rhodinyl butyrate
2694	Methyl isobutyrate	2861	Phenethyl butyrate	2989	Rose oil
2695	2-Methylbutyric acid	2862	Phenethyl isobutyrate	2992	Rosemary oil
2696	Methylcellulose	2871	Phenethyl isovalerate	2993	Rose water
2697	α-Methylcinnamaldehyde	2872	Phenoxyacetic acid	2997	Saccharin sodium
2698	Methyl cinnamate	2873	Phenoxyethyl isobutyrate	3000	Sage
2699	6-Methylcoumarin	2874	Phenylacetaldehyde	3005	Sandalwood oil
2703	Methyl 2-furoate	2875	Phenylacetaldehyde 2,3-	3024	Sodium acetate anhydrous
2705	Methyl heptanoate		butylene glycol acetal	3025	Sodium benzoate
2707	Methyl heptenone	2878	Phenylacetic acid	3026	Trisodium citrate
2708	Methyl caproate	2881	Benzylidene acetone	3027	Sodium hexameta-
2710	Methylparaben	2887	Hydrocinnamaldehyde		phosphate
2715	Methyl laurate	2889	Hydrocinnamic acid	3028	Sorbitan stearate
2718	Dimethyl anthranilate	2891	2-Phenylpropyl butyrate	3029	Sorbitol
2719	Methyl 2-methylbutyrate	2892	2-Phenylpropyl isobutyrate	3029	Sorbitol sol'n.
2720	Methyl 3-methylthio-	2893	3-Phenylpropyl isobutyrate	3032	Spearmint oil
	propionate	2899	3-Phenylpropyl isovalerate	3035	Stearic acid
2721	Methyl 4-methylvalerate	2900	Phosphoric acid	3036	Storax
2722	Methyl myristate	2902	α-Pinene	3038	Sucrose octaacetate
2723	2'-Acetonaphthone	2903	β-Pinene	3039	Sulfur dioxide
2724	Methyl nonanoate	2905	Pine needle oil	3042	Tannic acid
2726	Methyl 2-nonynoate	2908	Piperidine	3044	Tartaric acid
2728	Methyl caprylate	2910	d-Piperitone	3045	α-Terpineol
2731	Methyl isobutyl ketone	2911	Heliotropine	3052	Terpinyl formate
2740	4-Methyl-1-phenyl-2-	2912	Piperonyl acetate	3057	Tetrahydrofurfuryl butyrate
	pentanone	2913	Piperonyl isobutyrate	3058	Tetrahydrofurfuryl
2741	Methyl 3-phenylpropionate	2915	Polysorbate 20		propionate
2742	Methyl propionate	2916	Polysorbate 60	3064	Thyme oil
2745	Methyl salicylate	2917	Polysorbate 80	3066	Thymol
2752	Methyl valerate	2920	Potassium acetate	3070	Balsam tolu
2753	Methyl isovalerate	2921	Potassium sorbate	3079	Tragacanth gum
2756	MSG	2922	Propenylguaethol	3080	Acetyl tributyl citrate
2762	Myrcene	2924	Propionic acid	3081	Calcium phosphate tribasic
2763	Myristaldehyde	2925	Propyl acetate	3082	2-Tridecenal
2764	Myristic acid	2926	Isopropyl acetate	3083	Triethyl citrate
2772	Trimethyldodecatrieneol	2928	n-Propyl alcohol	3088	Quinine sulfate dihydrate
2773	Neryl acetate	2929	Isopropyl alcohol	3091	γ-Undecalactone
2774	Neryl butyrate	2931	Propyl benzoate	3092	Undecanal
2775	Neryl isobutyrate	2935	Isopropyl butyrate	3093	2-Undecanone
2777	Neryl propionate	2936	Propyl isobutyrate	3094	9-Undecenal
2778	Neryl isovalerate	2937	Isopropyl isobutyrate	3095	10-Undecenal
2779	Nitrous oxide	2939	Isopropyl cinnamate	3097	Undecyl alcohol
2781	γ-Nonalactone	2940	Propylene glycol	3104	Vanilla
2782	Nonanal	2941	Propylene glycol alginate	3107	Vanillin
2785	2-Nonanone	2942	Propylene glycol stearate	3109	Veratraldehyde
2789	Nonyl alcohol	2943	Propyl formate	3111	Walnut extract
2793	Nutmeg oil	2944	Isopropyl formate	3113	Wintergreen oil
2796	γ-Octalactone	2945	Propyl 2-furanacrylate	3116	Wormwood oil
2797	n-Octanal	2947	Propyl gallate	3119	Ylang ylang oil
2799	Caprylic acid	2948	Propyl heptanoate	3124	Zingerone
2800	Caprylic alcohol	2950	Isopropyl hexanoate	3130	n-Butylamine
2802	Methyl hexyl ketone	2951	Propylparaben	3135	trans-trans-2,4-Decadienal
2806	Octyl acetate	2952	3-Propylidenephthalide	3149	2-Ethyl-3,5(6)-dimethyl-
2807	Octyl butyrate	2953	α-Propylphenethyl alcohol		pyrazine
2809	Octyl formate	2954	p-Isopropylphenylacet-	3151	2-Ethylhexanol
2814	Octyl isovalerate		aldehyde	3172	Hexyl isobutyrate
2815	Oleic acid	2955	Propyl phenylacetate	3174	4-Hydroxy-2,5-dimethyl-
2821	Orange oil	2956	Isopropyl phenylacetate		3(2H)furanone
2832	Palmitic acid	2958	Propyl propionate	3177	p-Mentha-8-thiol-3-one
2838	Patchouli oil	2959	Isopropyl propionate	3181	o-Methoxycinnamaldehyde
2840	Pentadecalactone	2961	Isopropyl isovalerate	3195	2-Methyl-2-pentenoic acid
2842	Methyl propyl ketone	2962	Isopulegol	3196	cis-Jasmone
2847	Peppermint leaves	2963	Pulegone	3216	Paraffin

FEMA	Chemical	FEMA	Chemical	FEMA	Chemical
3221	Phenethyl hexanoate	3351	3-Hexanol	3556	Isopropyl myristate
3223	Phenol	3354	Hexyl-2-butenoate	3557	Perillaldehyde
3226	1-Phenyl-1,2-propanedione	3360	3-Methyl-2-cyclohexen-1-one	3558	α-Terpinene
3229	Isopropyl tiglate			3559	γ-Terpinene
3233	Styrene	3418	Pentyl 2-furyl ketone	3565	d-Dihydrocarvone
3235	4,5,6,7-Tetrahydro-3,6-dimethylbenzofuran	3424	3-Acetylpyridine	3583	3-Octyl acetate
		3427	2,4-Dimethylbenzaldehyde	3589	Resorcinol
3237	2,3,5,6-Tetramethyl-pyrazine	3432	Isobutyl-2-butenoate	3595	2,5-Xylenol
		3437	3-Methylpentanoic acid	3616	Thiophenol
3247	Undecylenic acid	3439	Myrtenol	3618	5-Phenyl-1-pentanol
3249	2,6-Xylenol	3448	Dicyclohexyl disulfide	3632	Phenethyl 2-methylbutyrate
3255	L-Arabinose	3461	o-Isopropylphenol	3639	β-Cyclocitral
3263	L-Cysteine	3462	Maltyl isobutyrate	3644	2-Methylbutyl acetate
3264	cis-4-Decen-1-al	3465	cis-6-Nonen-1-ol	3647	3-Methyl-2-buten-1-ol
3271	2,3-Dimethylpyrazine	3479	Candelilla wax	3649	4-Propylphenol
3272	2,5-Dimethylpyrazine	3480	o-Cresol	3656	L-Aspartic acid
3277	Sodium succinate	3487	Ethyl maltol	3668	Disodium guanylate
3285	L-Glutamic acid	3492	Ethyl undecanoate	3669	Disodium inosinate
3287	Glycine	3497	cis-3-Hexenyl 2-methylbutyrate	3673	2-Ethylfuran
3290	3-Hexanone			3694	L-Histidine
3291	Butyrolactone	3499	Hexyl 2-methylbutyrate	3698	Isoeugenyl benzyl ether
3294	δ-Undecalactone	3500	Hexyl isovalerate	3730	Rhamnose
3301	DL-Methionine	3506	2-Methylbutyl isovalerate	3737	Vanillyl alcohol
3302	2-Methoxypyrazine	3507	Isoamyl isobutyrate	3740	Anisyl phenylacetate
3315	2-Nonanol	3530	m-Cresol	3743	2,5-Diethyltetrahydrofuran
3322	Thiamine HCl	3532	3-Decen-2-one	3748	l-Menthyl lactate
3325	Trimethyl thiazole	3537	Diisobutyl ketone	3753	o-Tolyl isobutyrate
3326	Acetone	3540	2,6-Lutidine	3754	Vanillin isobutyrate
3332	Butan-3-one-2-yl butyrate	3543	Ethylene brassylate	3756	p-Ethylbenzaldehyde
3343	Ethyl 3-(methylthio)pro-pionate	3551	Isoamyl acetoacetate	3764	Menthalactone
		3553	Isophorone	3774	Theaspirane

Chemicals in Compliance with Pharmaceutical Standards

Inactive Ingredient Guide Chemicals

This table lists the chemicals listed in the most recently published *Inactive Ingredient Guide* (October 1993).

The *Inactive Ingredient Guide* contains all inactive ingredients present in approved drug products or conditionally approved drug products currently marketed for human use. The Guide is compiled by the Division of Drug Information Resources (DDIR). It provides CDER/CBER Reviewers with information on inactive ingredients in products which have been approved by the Agency. Once an active ingredient appears in a currently approved drug product for a particular route of administration, the inactive ingredient would not usually be considered new and may require a less extensive review.

Acacia
Acacia mucilage
Acetate
Acetic acid
Acetic acid, glacial
Acetyl tributyl citrate
Acetylated monoglycerides
Acetylcysteine
A380
Aerosil-200
Agar
Air
Albumin aggregated
Albumin colloidal
Albumin human
Albumin microsphere human serum
Alcohol
Alcohol, dehydrated
Alcohol, denatured
Alcohol, diluted
Alginic acid
Alkyl ammonium sulfonic acid betaine
Alkyl aryl sodium sulfonate
Allantoin
Althea
Alum, potassium
Aluminum acetate
Aluminum hydroxide
Aluminum hydroxide-sucrose powder, hydrated
Aluminum hydroxide gel
Aluminum hydroxide gel F 500
Aluminum hydroxide gel F 5000
Aluminum oxide
Aluminum polyester
Aluminum silicate
Aluminum starch octenylsuccinate

Aluminum stearate
Aluminum sulfate
Alzamer-50
Amberlite
Amberlite XE-88
Amerchol L101
Amerchol-CAB
Ammonia
Ammonia solution
Ammonium acetate
Ammonium calcium alginate
Ammonium chloride
Ammonium hydroxide
Ammonium salt of C-12-C-15 linear pirmary alcohol
    ethoxylate
Ammonium sulfate
Ammonyx
Amphoteric-2
Amphoteric-9
Anethole
Anhidrisorb 85/70
Anise extract
Anise oil
Anise, star
Antifoam
Antifoam DC
Antipyrine
Aquacoat
Aquacoat ECD
Aquaphor
Arginine
Arlatone 289
Ascorbic acid
Ascorbyl palmitate
Aspartame
Aspartic acid

Balsam Canada
Balsam, fir
Barium sulfate
Beeswax
Beeswax, synthetic
Bentonite
Benzaldehyde
Benzalkonium chloride
Benzenesulfonic acid solution
Benzethonium chloride
Benzoic acid
Benzoin
Benzyl alcohol
Benzyl benzoate
Benzyl chloride
Beta-naphthol
Bismuth subcarbonate
Boric acid
Buffer, acetic acid-sodium acetate
Buffer, citric acid-sodium citrate
Butane
Butyl alcohol, tertiary
Butyl stearate
Butylated hydroxyanisole
Butylated hydroxytoluene
Butyl paraben
Caffeine
Calcium
Calcium acetate
Calcium ascorbate
Calcium carbonate, precipitated
Calcium chloride
Calcium gluceptate
Calcium hydroxide
Calcium lactate
Calcium phosphate
Calcium phosphate dibasic dihydrate-sucrose
    agglomerate
Calcium phosphate dibasic
Calcium phosphate, dibasic, dihydrate
Calcium phosphate tribasic
Calcium pyrophosphate
Calcium silicate
Calcium stearate
Calcium sulfate
Calcium sulfate dihydrate
Calcium sulfate, anhydrous
Caldiamide sodium
Calteridol calcium
Candelilla wax
Canola oil
Caprylic/capric diglyceryl succinate
Caprylic/capric triglyceride
Capsicum oleoresin
Caramel
Carbomer
Carbomer 934
Carbomer 934P
Carbomer 940

Carbomer 941
Carbon dioxide
Carboxy vinyl copolymer
Carboxymethyl starch
Carboxymethylamylopectin sodium
Carboxymethylcellulose
Carboxymethylcellulose calcium
Carboxymethylcellulose sodium
Carboxypolymethylene
Cardamom
Carmine
Carmine solution
Carnauba wax
Carnauba yellow wax
Carrageenan
Carrageenan salt
Castor oil
Castor oil hydrogenated
Cellulose
Cellulose acetate
Cellulose acetate phthalate
Cellulose microcrystalline/carboxymethylcellulose
    sodium
Cellulose microcrystalline, aqueous
Cellulose, microcrystalline
Cellulose, oxidized
Cellulosic polymers
Cerasynt-SE
Ceteareth
Ceteareth-15
Ceteareth-20
Ceteareth-30
Cetearyl alcohol
Cetearyl alcohol/ceteareth-20
Ceteth-10
Ceteth-2
Ceteth-20
Cetrimonium chloride
Cetyl alcohol
Cetyl esters wax
Cetyl palmitate
Cetylpyridinium chloride
Cherry
Cherry juice
Chlorobutanol
Chlorobutanol hemihydrate
Chlorobutanol, anhydrous
Chlorocresol
Chloroxylenol
Chlorpheniramine maleate
Cholesterol
Choleth
Cinnamaldehyde
Cinnamon
Cinnamon oil
Citric acid
Citric acid, anhydrous
Citric acid, hydrous
Clove oil

Cocamide diethanolamine
Cocamide ether sulfate
Cocamine oxide
Cocoa bean
Cocoa butter
Cocoa butter (Pond's type 520A)
Cocoamphocarboxyglycinate
Coconut oil
Coconut oil, hydrogenated
Coloring suspension
Confectioners glaze
Coriander oil
Corn oil
Corn syrup
Cottonseed oil
Cottonseed oil, hydrogenated
Cream base
Creatine
Creatinine
Cresol
Cresol, M-
Croscarmellose sodium
Crospovidone
Cupric sulfate
Cyclomethicone
Cysteine
Cysteine hydrochloride
DC Antifoam AF Trituration 1% on Sucrose
Dehydroacetic acid
Dehymuls E
Denatonium benzoate
Desoxycholic acid
Dextrates
Dextrin
Dextrins modified
Dextrose
Dextrose solution
Dextrose, anhydrous
Di-Pac (97% Sucrose-3% Modified Dextrins)
Diacetylated monoglycerides
Diatrizoic acid
Diazolidinyl urea
Dibutyl phthalate
Dibutyl sebacate
Dichlorodifluoromethane
Dichlorofluoromethane
Dichlorotetrafluoroethane
Dicyclohexyl-carbodiimide
Diethanolamine
Diethyl phthalate
Diethyl sebacate
Diethylamine
Diglycerides
Diglycol stearate
Dihydroxyaluminum sodium carbonate
Diisopropanolamine
Diisopropyl adipate
Diisopropylbenzothiazyl-2-sulfenamide
Dimethicone

Dimethicone 350
Dimethyldioctadecylammonium bentonite
Dioctyl phthalate
Disodium edisylate
Disodium monooleamide sulfasuccinate
Disofenin
Docusate
Docusate sodium
Docusate sodium/sodium benzoate
Dry Flo
Duro-Tak 280-2516
Dusting powder
Dye beige P-1437
Dye black
Dye black LB-442
Dye blue
Dye blue #1
Dye blue #2 beadlets
Dye brown
Dye brown lake
Dye brown LB-292
Dye brown LB-464
Dye caramel
Dye caramel acid proof 100
Dye DC blue #2 lake
Dye DC blue #6
Dye DC green #3 lake
Dye DC green #5
Dye DC red #19
Dye DC red #21 lake
Dye DC red #22
Dye DC red #27
Dye DC red #27 aluminum lake
Dye DC red #28
Dye DC red # 3 lake
Dye DC red #30
Dye DC red #30 aluminum lake
Dye DC red #30 lake
Dye DC red #33
Dye DC red #33 lake
Dye DC red #36
Dye DC red #39
Dye DC red #4 lake
Dye DC red $40 lake
Dye DC red #6
Dye DC red #6 lake
Dye DC red #7
Dye DC red #7 calcium lake
Dye DC red #7 lake
Dye DC red lake
Dye DC violet #2 lake
Dye DC yellow
Dye DC yellow #10
Dye DC yellow #10 aluminum lake
Dye DC yellow #10 HT lake
Dye DC yellow #10 lake
Dye DC yellow #5 lake
Dye DC yellow #6
Dye DC yellow #6 lake

Dye FDC blue #1
Dye FDC blue #1 aluminum lake
Dye FDC blue #1 H.T. aluminum lake
Dye FDC blue #1 lake
Dye FDC blue #10
Dye FDC blue #2
Dye FDC blue #2 aluminum lake
Dye FDC green #3
Dye FDC green #6
Dye FDC green LB-3323
Dye FDC red #27 Al lake
Dye FDC red #28
Dye FDC red #3
Dye FDC red #3 lake
Dye FDC red #3-aluminum lake
Dye FDC red #30 aluminum lake
Dye FDC red #33
Dye FDC red #40
Dye FDC red #40 lake
Dye FDC red #7 aluminum lake
Dye FDC yellow #10
Dye FDC yellow #10 lake
Dye FDC yellow #5-aluminum lake
Dye FDC yellow #6
Dye FDC yellow #6 HT lake
Dye FDC yellow #6-aluminum lake
Dye green
Dye green LB-482
Dye green PMS-579
Dye green PR-1333
Dye lavender
Dye mint green
Dye orange
Dye pink
Dye purple LB-562
Dye red
Dye red cotolene-P
Dye rich yellow 062
Dye tetrarome orange
Dye white coateric YPA-6-7089
Dye white cotolene-P
Dye white TC-1032
Dye yellow
Dye yellow LB 9706
Dye yellow ochre
Edamine
Edetate calcium disodium
Edetate disodium
Edetate disodium, anhydrous
Edetate sodium
Edetic acid
Egg yolk phosphatides
Entsufon sodium
Ether
Ethyl acetate
Ethyl hexanediol
Ethyl maltol
Ethyl vanillin
Ethylcellulose

Ethylene glycol
Ethylene glycol monoethyl ether
Ethylene vinyl acetate copolymer
Ethylenediamine dihydrochloride
Ethylparaben
Ethylparaben sodium
Eucalyptol
Eucalyptus oil
Eudragit E 100
Eudragit E 30 D
Eudragit L 100
Eudragit RL 100
Eudragit RS 100
Exametazime
Fat, edible
Fatty acid esters, saturated
Fatty acid pentaerythritol ester
Fatty alcohol citrate
Ferric oxide
Ferric oxide, red
Ferrosoferric oxide
Fermenich 51.226/T
Flavor
Flavor, anise
Flavor apple
Flavor apricot
Flavor apricot peach
Flavor apricot 24829
Flavor aromalok 182608
Flavor aromalok 262453
Flavor banana
Flavor banana SA84
Flavor banana 71507
Flavor banana 74546
Flavor berry citrus blend 9756
Flavor berry cream
Flavor bitterness modifier 15555
Flavor black cherry
Flavor black currant
Flavor blood orange
Flavor blood orange 51.226T
Flavor blueberry
Flavor bubble gum
Flavor butter vanilla
Flavor buttermint toffee
Flavor buttermint 24020
Flavor butterscotch
Flavor butterscotch F-1785
Flavor candied sugar 510155U
Flavor caramel
Flavor caramel fritzsche
Flavor cheri-beri PFC-8573
Flavor cheri-beri PFC-8580
Flavor cherry
Flavor cherry burgundy 11650
Flavor cherry E.P. modified 151
Flavor cherry EP-3699
Flavor cherry F-232
Flavor cherry FMC 8513

Flavor cherry H&R pharma 004
Flavor cherry IFF 13530912
Flavor cherry mint
Flavor cherry N-2755
Flavor cherry R-6556
Flavor cherry raspberry
Flavor cherry vanilla compound A77487
Flavor cherry WL-1093
Flavor cherry WL-18022
Flavor cherry 11539
Flavor cherry 181612
Flavor cherry 3321
Flavor cherry 338614
Flavor cherry 349
Flavor cherry 500910U
Flavor cherry 594 S.D.
Flavor cherry-anise PFC 9758
Flavor chocolate
Flavor chocolate cream
Flavor citrus
Flavor citrus mint
Flavor citrus-vanilla
Flavor cocoa
Flavor coconut custard
Flavor cola FMC 15740
Flavor cough syrup 110257
Flavor cream
Flavor creme de menthe
Flavor creme de menthe 14677
Flavor creme de vanilla 28156
Flavor curacao 50.397A
Flavor custard
Flavor DF-119
Flavor DF-1530
Flavor E-472
Flavor enhancer
Flavor essence fritzbro orange
Flavor essense lemon terpeneless
Flavor essense orange terpeneless
Flavor F-5397A
Flavor felton 6-R-9
Flavor fig
Flavor fritzsche
Flavor fritzsche 21028-D
Flavor fritzsche 46215
Flavor fritzsche 75021
Flavor fruit gum 912
Flavor fruit mint 75588
Flavor fruit punch
Flavor fruit punch #28140
Flavor fruit punch #716
Flavor fruit punch 14761FM
Flavor fruit 01-10428
Flavor fruit 84.6422
Flavor fruits
Flavor grape
Flavor grape nectar PFC 8599
Flavor grape 13403873
Flavor grapefruit

Flavor guarana
Flavor guarana FMC-15417
Flavor haverstroo ZD 49284
Flavor herb alpine
Flavor kola
Flavor lemon
Flavor lemon cream
Flavor lemon lime
Flavor lemon mint fritzsche 54369
Flavor lemon vanilla
Flavor lemon 812
Flavor licorice
Flavor lime
Flavor Mafco-magnasweet 180
Flavor maque tree 377 (bush)
Flavor masking 35321
Flavor MCP lemon duramone 4409A
Flavor MCP lime duramone 6419
Flavor mint
Flavor orange
Flavor orange #7679
Flavor orange banana
Flavor orange banana WL-18093
Flavor orange I-1805
Flavor orange juice
Flavor orange natural & artificial
Flavor orange P-5614
Flavor orange sour (blood orange)
Flavor orange terpeneless
Flavor orange 13334
Flavor orange-lemon terpeneless
Flavor orbit serene 20340
Flavor passion fruit
Flavor peach
Flavor peach mint fritzsche 106109
Flavor peach pineapple
Flavor peach pineapple FMC 14258
Flavor peach 13503584
Flavor peppermint
Flavor peppermint K373
Flavor peppermint stick FMC 16170
Flavor peppermint 517
Flavor peppermint, natural spraylene
Flavor pineapple
Flavor pineapple N-2566
Flavor pineapple 182661
Flavor pineapple-coconut
Flavor punch 610962U
Flavor raspberry
Flavor raspberry F-1840
Flavor raspberry F-6887-S
Flavor raspberry PFC-8407
Flavor raspberry polak 5000064
Flavor raspberry 252085
Flavor raspberry 28106
Flavor raspberry 954
Flavor refrachessment FD-8027D
Flavor rhodia pharmaceutical #RF 451
Flavor root beer

Flavor sherry
Flavor spearmint
Flavor strawberry
Flavor strawberry F-5665
Flavor strawberry F-5930-A
Flavor strawberry guarana 586.997/AP05.51
Flavor strawberry microseal
Flavor strawberry PFC-9626
Flavor strawberry WL-16650
Flavor strawberry 133.5655
Flavor strawberry 14953
Flavor strawberry 52312/AP
Flavor strawberry 55058
Flavor strawberry 5951
Flavor sweet
Flavor sweet tone 28837
Flavor tangerine
Flavor tangerine fritzsche 51465
Flavor tetrarome
Flavor TPF 135
Flavor TPF 143
Flavor tropical fruit punch N&A 50432
Flavor tutti frutti
Flavor tutti frutti P-5400
Flavor tutti frutti 24093FM
Flavor vanilla
Flavor vanilla banana
Flavor vanilla creme
Flavor vanilla P-1160
Flavor veralock bubble gum
Flavor wild cherry
Flavor wild cherry K-321
Flavor wild cherry NV-101-1489
Flavor wild cherry PFC-14783
Flavor wild cherry 695047U
Flavor wildcherry 7598
Flavor wintergreen
Flavor wintergreen PFC 8421
Flavor 57000 IU
Flavor 57820/A
Flour
Fluorochlorohydrocarbons
Formaldehyde solution
Fragrance bouquet rel essence 9200
Fragrance bouquet 10328
Fragrance chemoderm 6411
Fragrance cream #73457
Fragrance felton 066M
Fragrance gardenia
Fragrance Givaudan ESS 9090/1C
Fragrance H-6540
Fragrance P O FL-147
Fragrance PA 52805
Fragrance pera derm D
Fragrance RBD-9819
Fragrance spicy metholated eugenol
Fragrance ungerer honeysuckle K 2771
Fragrance ungerer N5195
Fragrance unspecified

Fragrance 91-122
Fructose
Fumaric acid
Galactose, D-
Gamma-cyclodextrin
Gelatin
Gelatin 200 bloom
Gentisic acid
Gentisic acid ethanolamide
Ginger fluid extract
Gluceptate sodium
Gluconolactone
Glucose, liquid
Glutamic acid hydrochloride
Glutamic acid, DL-
Gluten
Glycerin
Glyceryl behenate
Glyceryl distearate
Glyceryl monostearate
Glyceryl oleate
Glyceryl oleate/propylene glycol
Glyceryl palmitate
Glyceryl palmito-stearate
Glyceryl ricinoleate
Glyceryl stearate SE
Glyceryl stearate-stearamidoethyl diethylamine
Glyceryl stearate-PEG stearate
Glyceryl stearate/PEG-100 stearate
Glyceryl stearate/PEG-40 stearate
Glyceryl tribehenate
Glycine
Glycol stearate
Glycyrrhiza
Glycyrrhizin, ammoniated
Guanidine hydrochloride
Guar gum
Gum base, chewing
Gum rosin
Gum, natural
Herbacol
Hexylene glycol
High fructose corn syrup
Hydrocarbon gel, plasticized
Hydrochloric acid
Hydrochloric acid, diluted
Hydrogen peroxide
Hydroxyethyl cellulose
Hydroxymethyl cellulose
Hydroxypropyl cellulose
Hydroxypropyl methylcellulose
Hydroxypropyl methylcellulose phthalate
Hydroxypropyl methylcellulose 2208
Hydroxypropyl methylcellulose 2906
Hydroxypropyl methylcellulose 2910
Imidazolidinyl urea
Imidurea
Ink black
Ink black A-10450

Ink black A-10509
Ink black A-1057
Ink black imprinting FGE-1386
Ink blue black A-9371
Ink edible
Ink edible black
Ink edible blue
Ink edible brown
Ink edible gray
Ink edible red A-8032
Ink edible white
Ink fine black 2202C
Ink fine black 2212
Ink green
Ink pink imprinting SB-1003
Ink red A-8032
Ink red S-1-9005
Ink white
Ink white A-8154
Ink white 21-K
Invert sugar
Invert syrup, medium
Iodine
Iofetamine hydrochloride
Irish moss extract
Iron oxide
Iron oxide, brown
Iron oxide, red-brown
Iron oxide, yellow
Isobutane
Isoceteth-20
Isooctylacrylate
Isopropyl alcohol
Isopropyl isostearate
Isopropyl myristate
Isopropyl palmitate
Isopropyl stearate
Isostearic acid
Isostearyl alcohol
Isotonic sodium chloride solution
Jelene
Kaolin
Karion 83 (D-sorbitol content 19-25%)
Kathon CG
Lac resin
Lactate
Lactic acid
Lactic acid, DL-
Lactobionic acid
Lactose
Lactose monohydrate
Lactose monohydrate, alpha
Lactose, anhydrous
Lactose, hydrous
Lanolin
Lanolin alcohols
Lanolin alcohols, acetylated
Lanolin cholesterols
Lanolin nonionic derivatives

Lanolin oil
Lanolin, anhydrous
Lanolin, hydrogenated
Lauramine oxide
Laurdimonium hydrolyzed animal collagen
Laureth sulfate
Laureth 23
Laureth 4
Lauric diethanolamide
Lauric myristic diethanolamide
Lauryl sulfate
Lavender
Lecithin
Lecithin, soy bean
Lemon essence 5-9738
Lemon oil
Lidofenin
Lime oil, distilled
Limonene, DL-
Linear alcohol ethylene oxide adduct
Locust bean gum
Lubritab
Lysine
Magnesium aluminum silicate
Magnesium carbonate
Magnesium chloride
Magnesium hydroxide
Magnesium nitrate
Magnesium oxide
Magnesium silicate
Magnesium stearate
Magnesium sulfate
Magnesium sulfate, anhydrous
Magnesium trisilicate
Maleic acid
Malic acid, DL-
Malic acid, L-
Maltodextrin
Maltol
Maltose
Mannitol
Mannose, D-
Mebrofenin
Medical antifoam emulsion C
Medical antifoam A-F emulsion
Medronate disodium
Medronic acid
Meglumine
Menthol
Menthol, L-
Metaphosphoric acid
Methacrylic acid copolymer
Methanesulfonic acid
Methionine
Methyl acrylate-methyl methacrylate
Methyl boronic acid
Methyl gluceth-120 dioleate
Methyl hydroxyethyl cellulose
Methyl salicylate

Methyl stearate
Methylated spirits
Methylcellulose
Methylcellulose 400
Methylchloroisothiazolinone
Methylisothiazolinone
Methylparaben
Methylparaben sodium
Microcrystalline wax
Milk
Mineral oil
Mineral oil, light
Mistron spray talc
Monoglyceride citrate
Monoglycerides
Mullein leaf
Multisterol extract
Muscatel wine
Myristic acid
Myristyl alcohol
Myristyl lactate
Myristyl-gamma-picolinium chloride
N-Decyl-methyl sulfoxide
N-2-Hydroxyethylpiperazine N´-2´-ethanesulphonic
    acid
N-3-Chloroallyl-methenamine chloride
N,N-Bis(2-hydroxyethyl)stearamide
N,N-Dimethyl lauramine oxide
N,N-Dimethylacetamide
Neutral oil
Nioxime
Nitric acid
Non-pareil seed
Nonoxynol
Nonoxynol-15
Nutmeg oil, expressed
Oatmeal
Octadecene-1/maleic acid copolymer
Octoxynol
Octoxynol-1
Octoxynol-40
Octoxynol-9
Octyldodecanol
Oil cream soda
Oleic acid
Oleth-10/oleth-5
Oleth-2
Oleth-20
Oleth-3 phosphate
Oleyl oleate
Olive oil
Opacoat NA2203
Opacoat NA4108 (blue)
Opacode S-1-1666 (red)
Opacode S-1-4157
Opacode S-1-4160 (blue)
Opacode S-1-4172 (blue)
Opacode S-1-4172M (blue)
Opacode S-1-7077

Opacode S-1-7078
Opacode S-1-7085 (white)
Opacode S-1-800HV (black)
Opacode S-1-8025 (black)
Opacode S-1-8081 (black)
Opacode S-1-8090 (black)
Opacode S-1-8092 (black)
Opacode S-1-8095
Opacode S-1-8100-HV (black)
Opacode S-1-8106 (black)
Opacode S-1-8114 (black)
Opacode S-1-8115 (black)
Opacode S-1-9009 (brown)
Opadry
Opadry (clear)
Opadry (white)
Opadry Y-1-1518 (pink)
Opadry Y-1-2102 (yellow)
Opadry Y-1-2132 (yellow)
Opadry Y-1-2605 (beige)
Opadry Y-1-3211 (green)
Opadry Y-1-4205 (blue)
Opadry Y-1-4234 (blue)
Opadry Y-1-7000 (white)
Opadry Y-1-7000B (white)
Opadry Y-5-1244 (pink)
Opadry Y-5-1727 (red)
Opadry Y-5-2028 (yellow)
Opadry Y-5-2312 (yellow)
Opadry Y-5-2360 (orange)
Opadry Y-5-2450 (orange)
Opadry Y-5-2451 (orange)
Opadry Y-5-2646 (beige)
Opadry Y-5-3140 (green)
Opadry Y-5-4129 (blue)
Opadry Y-5-4287 (blue)
Opadry Y-5-7058 (white)
Opadry Y-5-7068 (white)
Opadry Y-5-7072 (white)
Opadry Y-5-7411 (purple)
Opadry Y-5-8050 (black)
Opadry Y-5-9006 (brown)
Opadry YS-1-1252 (pink)
Opadry YS-1-1288 (pink)
Opadry YS-1-1510 (pink)
Opadry YS-1-1528 (pink)
Opadry YS-1-1724 (red)
Opadry YS-1-1847 (red)
Opadry YS-1-2122 (yellow)
Opadry YS-1-2134 (yellow)
Opadry YS-1-2136 (yellow)
Opadry YS-1-2167 (yellow)
Opadry YS-1-2465
Opadry YS-1-2522 (orange)
Opadry YS-1-2526 (orange)
Opadry YS-1-2527 (orange)
Opadry YS-1-2534
Opadry YS-1-2546 (orange)
Opadry YS-1-2558 (orange)

Opadry YS-1-2563 (orange)
Opadry YS-1-2604 (beige)
Opadry YS-1-2612 (beige)
Opadry YS-1-2635 (tan)
Opadry YS-1-2669 (rust)
Opadry YS-1-3105 (green)
Opadry YS-1-3130 (green)
Opadry YS-1-3146 (green)
Opadry YS-1-3166 (green)
Opadry YS-1-4112 (blue)
Opadry YS-1-4215
Opadry YS-1-4216
Opadry YS-1-4221 (blue)
Opadry YS-1-4229 (blue)
Opadry YS-1-4710
Opadry YS-1-6312 (yellow)
Opadry YS-1-7002 (white)
Opadry YS-1-7003 (white)
Opadry YS-1-7006 (clear)
Opadry YS-1-7507 (grey)
Opadry YS-1-7552 (grey)
Opadry YS-1-83450 (beige)
Opadry YS-1-8619 (orange)
Opadry YS-1-89193 (clear)
Opadry YS-1-9012 (brown)
Opadry YS-2-7013 (clear)
Opadry YS-3-7011 (clear)
Opadry YS-3-7031 (clear)
Opadry YS-5-2170 (yellow)
Opadry YS-5-2370 (orange)
Opadry YS-5-3116 (green)
Opadry YS-5-7068
Opaglos clear
Opalux AS 1537 (pink)
Opalux AS 1589 (pink)
Opalux AS 2006 (yellow)
Opalux AS 2167 (yellow)
Opalux AS 2236
Opalux AS 2269 (yellow)
Opalux AS 2324 (orange)
Opalux AS 2336 (orange)
Opalux AS 2413
Opalux AS 2498 (orange)
Opalux AS 2512
Opalux AS 2676 salmon (jasper red)
Opalux AS 2754
Opalux AS 3287
Opalux AS 3348-C (green)
Opalux AS 3376
Opalux AS 3391 (green)
Opalux AS 4208-A (blue)
Opalux AS 4270 (blue)
Opalux AS 4800 (lavender)
Opalux AS 4854 (lavender)
Opalux AS 4855 (purple)
Opalux AS 5178 (green)
Opalux AS 5203 (green)
Opalux AS 5212 (green)
Opalux AS 7000-B

Opalux AS 7000-P (white)
Opalux AS 7535 (gray)
Opalux AS 8050-L (black)
Opalux AS AS 9010 (brown)
Opalux AS red
Opalux red
Opaque blue 605
Opaque burrgandy
Opaque gray
Opaque green
Opaque green 1664
Opaque maroon 6 dar
Opaque orange
Opaque peach
Opaque pink BK
Opaque pink 0439
Opaque red
Opaque Swedish orange
Opaque white
Opaque yellow
Opaseal
Opaspray
Opaspray coral
Opaspray green
Opaspray K-1-1230 (pink)
Opaspray K-1-1279
Opaspray K-1-1289 (pink)
Opaspray K-1-1413 (pink)
Opaspray K-1-1414 (pink)
Opaspray K-1-1455 (pink)
Opaspray K-1-1460
Opaspray K-1-1563 (pink)
Opaspray K-1-1573 (lavender)
Opaspray K-1-1584
Opaspray K-1-2013 (yellow)
Opaspray K-1-2088
Opaspray K-1-2216-A (yellow)
Opaspray K-1-2227 (yellow)
Opaspray K-1-2228 (yellow)
Opaspray K-1-2240 (yellow)
Opaspray K-1-2275 (yellow)
Opaspray K-1-2301 (peach)
Opaspray K-1-2304 (orange)
Opaspray K-1-2314 (orange)
Opaspray K-1-2327 (orange)
Opaspray K-1-2330 (orange)
Opaspray K-1-2335 (orange)
Opaspray K-1-2410 (orange)
Opaspray K-1-2430
Opaspray K-1-2441 (orange)
Opaspray K-1-2473
Opaspray K-1-2492
Opaspray K-1-2533 (orange)
Opaspray K-1-2568 (orange)
Opaspray K-1-2588 (orange)
Opaspray K-1-2621 (brown)
Opaspray K-1-2626 (orange)
Opaspray K-1-2656 (beige)
Opaspray K-1-2670 (tan)

Opaspray K-1-2685
Opaspray K-1-3000
Opaspray K-1-3142 (green)
Opaspray K-1-3147
Opaspray K-1-3148 (green)
Opaspray K-1-3173 (green)
Opaspray K-1-3178 (green)
Opaspray K-1-3220 (green)
Opaspray K-1-3300-A (green)
Opaspray K-1-3300-C (green)
Opaspray K-1-4136 (blue)
Opaspray K-1-4210-A
Opaspray K-1-4214
Opaspray K-1-4227
Opaspray K-1-4235 (blue)
Opaspray K-1-4728
Opaspray K-1-4743 (lavender)
Opaspray K-1-4748 (purple)
Opaspray K-1-4786
Opaspray K-1-5024 (red)
Opaspray K-1-7000 (white)
Opaspray K-1-70008 (white)
Opaspray K-1-9027 (brown)
Opaspray K-1-9039-L (brown)
Opaspray K-1-9080 (brown)
Opaspray K-1-9112 (brown)
Opaspray L-2113
Opaspray L-3305 (green)
Opaspray L-3306 (green)
Opaspray L-7000 (white)
Opaspray M-1-711B (white)
Opaspray M-1-7111-B
Opaspray M-1-7120 (white)
Opaspray M-1-7301 (white)
Opaspray M-1-8429 (yellow)
Opaspray WD-1270 (pink)
Orange juice
Orange juice, synthetic
Orange oil
Orange oil, terpeneless
Oxidronate sodium
Oxyquinoline
Palm kernel oil
Palm oil-soybean oil, hydrogenated
Palm oil, hydrogenated
Palmitamine oxide
Parabens
Paraffin
Parmacoat 606
Peanut oil
Pectin
PEG glycolysed glycerides
PEG vegetable oil
Peglicol-5-oleate
Pegoxol 7 stearate
Pentaerythritol cocoate
Pentetate calcium trisodium
Pentetate pentasodium
Pentetic acid

Peppermint
Peppermint oil
Perfume E-1991
Perfume GD 5604
Perfume Tana 90/42, SCBA
Perfume 25677
Perfumes
Petrolatum
Petrolatum, white
Pharma-Sweet 24052
Pharmaceutical glaze
Phenol
Phenol, liquefied
Phenylethyl alcohol
Phenylmercuric acetate
Phenylmercuric nitrate
Phosphate buffer
Phospolipid
Phosphoric acid
Pine needle oil
Piperazine
Plastibase-50W
Plusweet
Polacrilin
Polacrilin potassium
Polistirex
Poloxamer
Poloxamer 188
Poloxamer 331
Poloxamer 407
Polyester
Polyethylene
Polyethylene glycol
Polyethylene glycol t-dodecylthioether
Polyethylene glycol 1000
Polyethylene glycol 1450
Polyethylene glycol 1500
Polyethylene glycol 1540
Polyethylene glycol 20,000
Polyethylene glycol 200
Polyethylene glycol 300
Polyethylene glycol 3350
Polyethylene glycol 3500
Polyethylene glycol 400
Polyethylene glycol 4000
Polyethylene glycol 600
Polyethylene glycol 6000
Polyethylene glycol 8000
Polyethylene glycol 900
Polyethylene oxide
Polyethylene terephthalates
Polyglactin
Polyglucose K
Polyglyceryl-10 tetralinoleate
Polyisobutylene
Polyisobutylene 1,200,000
Polymers
Polyoxyethylene-polyoxypropylene 1800
Polyoxyethylene alcohols

Polyoxyethylene fatty acid esters
Polyoxyethylene propylene
Polyoxyethylene sorbitan monoisostearate
Polyoxyl castor oil
Polyoxyl distearate
Polyoxyl lanolin
Polyoxyl stearate
Polyoxyl 50 stearate
Polyoxyl 100 glyceryl stearate
Polyoxyl 100 stearate
Polyoxyl 15 cocamine
Polyoxyl 150 distearate
Polyoxyl 2 stearate
Polyoxyl 20 stearate
Polyoxyl 35 castor oil
Polyoxyl 40 castor oil
Polyoxyl 40 stearate
Polyoxyl 50 stearate
Polyoxyl 75 lanolin
Polyoxyl 8 stearate
Polyoxypropylene 15 stearyl ether
Polyoxypropylene 26 oleate
Polypropylene
Polypropylene glycol
Polysaccharide
Polysorbate
Polysorbate 20
Polysorbate 40
Polysorbate 60
Polysorbate 80
Polysorbate 85
Polyurethane
Polyvinyl acetate
Polyvinyl acetate phthalate
Polyvinyl alcohol
Polyvinylacetal
Polyvinylpyridine
Polyvinylpyrrolidone ethylcellulose
Poppy seed oil
Potassium acetate
Potassium carbonate
Potassium chloride
Potassium citrate
Potassium hydroxide
Potassium metabisulfite
Potassium phosphate, dibasic
Potassium phosphate, monobasic
Potassium polacrilin
Potassium sorbate
Povidone
Povidone K29-32
Povidone K30
Povidone K90
Promalgen Type G
Promulgen D
Promulgen G
Propane
Propenyl guaethol
Propyl gallate

Propylene carbonate
Propylene glycol
Propylene glycol alginate
Propylene glycol diacetate
Propylene glycol monostearate
Propylparaben
Propylparaben sodium
Prosweet
Protamine sulfate
Protein hydrolysate
Quartinium 15
Quaternium-15
Quso-G 32
Rosin
Saccharin
Saccharin calcium
Saccharin sodium
Saccharin sodium anhydrous
Satialgine H
Sea Spen
Sesame oil
Shellac
Shellac P.V.P. Solution No. 4
Silastic Brand Medical Grade Tubing
Silastic Medical Adhesive, Silicone Type A
Silica gel
Silica, diatomaceous
Silicon
Silicon dioxide
Silicone
Silicone emulsion
Silicone/polyester film strip
Simethicone
Simethicone emulsion
Simethicone MDX4-4036
Soap
Soap, potassium
Soap, eiderdown
Sodium acetate
Sodium acetate, anhydrous
Sodium alginate
Sodium alkyl sulfate
Sodium aluminosilicate
Sodium aminobenzoate
Sodium ascorbate
Sodium benzoate
Sodium bicarbonate
Sodium bisulfate
Sodium bisulfite
Sodium borate
Sodium carbonate
Sodium carbonate hydrate
Sodium carragenate
Sodium cellulose
Sodium chlorate
Sodium chloride
Sodium chloride injection, bacteriostatic
Sodium citrate
Sodium citrate anhydrous

Sodium citrate dihydrate
Sodium citrate in solution
Sodium desoxycholate
Sodium dithionite
Sodium dodecylbenzenesulfonate
Sodium formaldehyde sulfoxylate
Sodium gluconate
Sodium hexametaphosphate
Sodium hydroxide
Sodium hypochlorite
Sodium iodide
Sodium L-cysteinate hydrochloride
Sodium L-lactate
Sodium lactate
Sodium laureth sulfate
Sodium laureth-5 sulfate
Sodium lauryl sulfate
Sodium lauryl sulfoacetate
Sodium metabisulfite
Sodium N-lauroyl sarcosinate
Sodium nitrate
Sodium phosphate
Sodium phosphate dihydrate
Sodium phosphate, dibasic
Sodium phosphate, dibasic, anhydrous
Sodium phosphate, dibasic, dihydrate
Sodium phosphate, dried
Sodium phosphate, monobasic
Sodium phosphate, monobasic, monohydrate
Sodium propionate
Sodium pyrophosphate
Sodium pyrrolidone carboxylate
Sodium starch glycolate
Sodium stearyl fumarate
Sodium succinate
Sodium sulfate
Sodium sulfate, anhydrous
Sodium sulfite
Sodium tartrate
Sodium thioglycolate
Sodium thiosulfate
Sodium thiosulfate, anhydrous
Sodium trimetaphosphate
Solulan
Sorbic acid
Sorbitan monolaurate
Sorbitan monooleate
Sorbitan monopalmitate
Sorbitan monostearate
Sorbitan sesquioleate
Sorbitan solution
Sorbitan trioleate
Sorbitol
Sorbitol solution
Soybean oil
Soybean oil, hydrogenated
Spearmint oil
Spermaceti
Squalane

Stannous chloride
Stannous chloride, anhydrous
Stannous fluoride
Stannous tartrate
Starch
Starch 1500
Starch 1551
Starch, corn
Starch, potato
Starch, pregelatinized
Starch, pregelatinized corn
Starch, pregelatinized tapioca
Starch, rice
Starch, wheat
Stear-O-Wet C
Stear-O-Wet M
Stearalkonium chloride
Stearalkonium hectorite/propylene carbonate
Stearamidoethyl diethylamine
Steareth
Steareth-10
Steareth-100
Steareth-2
Steareth-21
Stearic acid
Steartrimonium hydrolized animal protein
Stearyl alcohol
Stearyl citrate
Succimer
Succinic acid
Sucrose
Sucrose polyesters
Sucrose syrup
Sugar compressible
Sugar confectioner's
Sugar fruit fine
Sugar liquid type #0
Sugar non-pareil seeds
Sugar/starch insert granules
Sugars (unidentified)
Sulfuric acid
Sulfurous acid
Suppocire
Synchron oral carrier
Tagatose
Talc
Tall oil
Tallow glycerides
Tapioca food starch
Tartaric acid
Tartaric acid, DL-
Tartrazine
Tenox
Terpene resin
Terpineol, alpha
Tetrakis(1-isocyano-2-methoxy-2-methyl-propane)-
    copper(I) TE
Thiazoximic acid
Thimerosal

Thioglycerol
Thymol
Timing solution clear N-7
Titanium dioxide
Tocopherols
Tolu
Tragacanth
Triacetin
Trichloromonofluoromethane
Trideceth 10
Triethyl citrate
Triglyceride, synthetic
Triglycerides, unspecified length
Trihydroxy stearin
Trilaneth-4 phosphate
Trilaureth 4 phosphate
Trimyristin
Tristearin
Trithiazoximic acid
Triton X-200 sodium salt of alkylauryl polyether
    sulfonate
Trolamine
Trolamine lauryl sulfate
Tromethamine
Tyloxapol
Unspecified ingredient
Urea
Vanillin
Vegetable oil

Vegetable oils, hydrogenated
Vegetable shortening
Vinyl acetate-crotonic acid copolymer
Vinyl chloride
Viprostol
Viscarin
Vitamin E
Water for injection, bacteriostatic
Wax blend
Wax, Dehydag SX
Wax, emulsifying
Wax, white
Wax, yellow
Wecobee FS
Witepsol E-85
Witepsol W-35
Wool wax alcohol ointment
Xanthan gum
Zarzarol
Zein
Zinc acetate
Zinc chloride
Zinc oxide
Zinc stearate
Zinc sulfate
1-Aminocyclohexanecarboxylic acid, C-11
1,2,6-Hexanetriol
1,3-Dimethylol-5,5-dimethyl-hydantoin
2-Amino-2-methyl-1-propanol

Permanently Listed Color Additives

2-Ethyl-hexanoic acid
2-Naphtholene sulfonate sodium salt
Algae meal, dried
Alumina
Aluminum powder
Annatto
Annatto extract
Beet juice
Beet, dehydrated
Beet powder
Benzamide,N,N'-(9,10-dihydro-9,10-dioxo-1,5-
    anthracenediyl)bis-
Benzenetriol,2-[2,5-diethoxy-4[(4-methylphenyl)thio-
    phenyl]]
Beta-apo-8'-caroteneal
Beta carotene, natural & synthetic
Bismuth citrate
Bismuth oxychloride
Bixin
Bronze powder
Calcium carbonate
Canthaxanthin
Caramel
Carbazole violet
Carmine

Carmine-carotene
Carrot oil
Chlorophyllin-copper complex
Chlorophyllin-copper complex, oil soluble
Chromium hydroxide, green
Chromium oxide greens
Chromium-cobalt-aluminum oxide
CI vat orange 1
Citrus red #2
Cochineal extract
Copper metallic powder
Corn endosperm oil
Cottonseed flour, toasted, partially defatted & cooked
Dihydroxyacetone
Dinaphtho[2,3-A:2'3'-I]naphth(2'3':6,7) indolo(2,3-
    C)carbazole-5,10,15,17,22,24-hexone,14,23-di-
    hydro
Disodium EDTA-copper
Dye caramel
Dye DC blue #4
Dye DC blue #6
Dye DC blue #9
Dye DC brown #1
Dye DC green #5
Dye DC green #6

Dye DC green #8
Dye DC orange #10
Dye DC orange #11
Dye DC orange #4
Dye DC orange #5
Dye DC red #17
Dye DC red #21
Dye DC red #22
Dye DC red #27
Dye DC red #28
Dye DC red #30
Dye DC red #31
Dye DC red #33
Dye DC red #34
Dye DC red #36
Dye DC red #39
Dye DC red #6
Dye DC red #7
Dye DC violet #2
Dye DC yellow #10
Dye DC yellow #11
Dye DC yellow #7
Dye DC yellow #8
Dye Ext DC violet #2
Dye Ext DC yellow #7
Dye Ext DC lakes
Dye FDC blue #1
Dye FDC blue #2
Dye FDC green #3
Dye FDC red #3
Dye FDC red #40
Dye FDC yellow #10
Dye FDC yellow #5
Dye FDC yellow #6
Dye FDC yellow #7
Ferric ammonium citrate
Ferric ammonium ferrocyanide (iron blue)
Ferrous gluconate
Fruit juice
Grape color extract
Grape skin extract (enocianina)
Guanine (pearl essence)
Guatazulene (azulene)
Henna
Iron oxides
Iron oxide, synthetic

Lead acetate
Manganese violet-methyl umbilliferone
Mica
Norbixin
Orange B
Paprika & paprika oleoresin
Phthalocyaninato-2-copper
Phthalocyanine green
Poly(hydroxyethylmethacrylate)-dye copolymers
Pyrogallol
Pyrophyllite
Pyrophyllite aluminum silicate
Reactive blue #19
Riboflavin
Safferon (crocus sativa L.)
Silver
Tagetes metal & extract (Aztec marigold)
Talc
Titanium dioxide
Tumeric & tumeric oleoresin
Ultramarine green
Ultramarine pink
Ultramarine red
Ultramarine violet
Vegetable juice
Xanthophyll
Zinc oxide
4-[2,4-Dimethylphenyl)azol-2,4-dihydro-5-methyl-2-
  phenyl-3H-pyrazol-3-one
5,9,14,18-Anthrazine
9,10-Anthracenedione,1,4-bis[2-methylphenyl)amino]
6-Ethoxy-2-(6-ethoxy-3-oxo-benzo[b] thein-2-(3H)-
  ylidene) benzo[b] thiophen-3-(2H)-one
1,4-Bis[4-(2-methacryloxyethyl)phenlamino]-
  anthraquinone
16,23-Dihydrodinaphtho[2,3-a:2′,3′-I]napth[2′3′:6,7-
  indolo [2,3-C]carbazole-5,10,15,17,22,24-hexone
N,N′-(9,10-Dihydro-9,10-dioxo-1,5-anthracenediyl)
  bisbenzamide
7,16-Dichloro-6,15-dihydro-5,9,14,18-anthrazine-
  tetrone
16,17-Dimethoxydinaptho(1,2,3-CD:3′,2′,1′-
  IM)perylene-5,10-dione
2-[[2,5-Diethoxy-4-[(4-methylphenyl)thiol]phenyl]azo]-
  1,3,5-benzenetriol
1,4-Bis[(2-methylphenyl)amino]-9,10-anthracene-
  dione

Provisionally Listed Color Additives

Dinaphtho[1,2,3-CD:3′,2′,1′]M-perylene-5,10-
  dione,16,17-dimethoxy
Dye DC blue #2 lake
Dye DC green #3 lake
Dye DC red #21 lake
Dye DC red #27 Al lake
Dye DC red #30 Al lake

Dye DC red #30 lake
Dye DC red #33 lake
Dye DC red #6 lake
Dye DC red #7 Ca lake
Dye DC red #7 lake
Dye DC red #8
Dye DC violet #2 lake
Dye DC yellow #10 Al lake
Dye DC yellow #10 HT lake

Dye DC yellow #10 lake
Dye DC yellow #5 lake
Dye DC yellow #6
Dye DC yellow #6 lake
Dye FDC blue #1 Al lake
Dye FDC blue #1 HT Al lake

Dye FDC blue #1 lake
Dye FDC blue #2
Dye FDC red #33
Dye FDC red #40 lake
Dye FDC yellow #10 lake

Delisted Color Additives

Dye FDC yellow #5 Al lake
Dye FDC yellow #6
Alkanet (alkanna)
Alloxan
Aluminum benzoate
Aluminum hydroxide
Aluminum stearate
B-Methyl-umbelliferone
Barium sulfate
Bentonite
Bone black
Butter yellow
Calcium carbonate
Calcium silicate
Calcium stearate
Calcium sulfate
Carbon black (channel)
Carminic acid
Charcoal
Charcoal (NFXI)
Chlorophyll
Chlorophyll copper complex
Cobaltous aluminate (cobalt blue)
Cochineal
Cornstarch
Cudbear
Curcumin
Dye DC black #1
Dye DC blue #1 lake
Dye DC blue #3
Dye DC blue #5
Dye DC blue #6
Dye DC blue #7
Dye DC blue #8
Dye DC green #1 lake
Dye DC green #4
Dye DC green #7
Dye DC orange #12
Dye DC orange #13
Dye DC orange #14
Dye DC orange #15
Dye DC orange #16
Dye DC orange #17
Dye DC orange #3
Dye DC orange #6
Dye DC orange #7
Dye DC orange #8
Dye DC orange #9
Dye DC red #10
Dye DC red #11

Dye DC red #12
Dye DC red #13
Dye DC red #14
Dye DC red #15
Dye DC red #16
Dye DC red #18
Dye DC red #19
Dye DC red #2
Dye DC red #2 lake
Dye DC red #20
Dye DC red #23
Dye DC red #24
Dye DC red #25
Dye DC red #26
Dye DC red #29
Dye DC red # 3
Dye DC red #35
Dye DC red #37
Dye DC red #38
Dye DC red #4
Dye DC red #5
Dye DC red #6
Dye DC red #7
Dye DC red #8
Dye DC red #9
Dye DC violet #1
Dye DC yellow #1
Dye DC yellow #2
Dye DC yellow #3
Dye DC yellow #4
Dye DC yellow #5
Dye DC yellow #6
Dye DC yellow #8
Dye DC yellow #9
Dye Ext DC black #1
Dye Ext DC blue #1
Dye Ext DC blue #2
Dye Ext DC blue #3
Dye Ext DC blue #4
Dye Ext DC blue #5
Dye Ext DC green #1
Dye Ext DC orange #1
Dye Ext DC orange #2
Dye Ext DC orange #3
Dye Ext DC orange #4
Dye Ext DC red #1
Dye Ext DC red #2
Dye Ext DC red #3
Dye Ext DC red #8
Dye Ext DC red #10

Dye Ext DC red #11
Dye Ext DC red #13
Dye Ext DC red #14
Dye Ext DC red #15
Dye Ext DC yellow #1
Dye Ext DC yellow #5
Dye Ext DC yellow #6
Dye Ext DC yellow #9
Dye Ext DC yellow #10
Dye FDC blue #8
Dye FDC green #1
Dye FDC green #1 lake
Dye FDC green #2
Dye FDC orange #1
Dye FDC orange #2
Dye FDC red #1
Dye FDC red #2
Dye FDC red #2 Al lake
Dye FDC red #3
Dye FDC red #3 Al lake
Dye FDC red #3 lake
Dye FDC red #4
Dye FDC red #9
Dye FDC red #32
Dye FDC violet #1
Dye FDC violet #1 lake
Dye FDC yellow #1
Dye FDC yellow #2
Dye FDC yellow #3
Dye FDC yellow #4
Dye logwood black
Ferric chloride
Ferric hydroxide
Ferrous sulfate

Fuller's earth
Fustic
Gloss white
Gold
Graphite
Kaolin
Keiselguhr (diatomite)
Lapis lazuli (lazurite)
Lithium stearate
Lithopone
Logwood, chips & extract
Logwood (gluewood, campeche wood)
Magnesium aluminum silicate
Magnesium carbonate
Magnesium oxide
Magnesium stearate
Magneisum trisilicate
Metallic salts
Potassium ferrocyanide
Safflower (American saffron)
Saffron oleoresin
Sienna
Silicic acid
Silicon dioxide
Tin oxide
Ultramarine blue
Umber
Vegetable substances
Vermiculite
Zinc carbonate
Zinc stearate
Zirconium oxide
Zirconium silicate
4-Methyl-7-diethylaminocoumarin (MDAC)

USP/NF Chemicals

The following chemicals that appear in this reference are listed in the United States Pharmacopeia/National Formulary (USP 23/NF 18, 1995).

Acacia
Acetic acid
Acetic acid, glacial
Acetone
Agar
Alcohol
Algin
Alginic acid
Aluminum stearate
Aluminum sulfate
Ammonio methacrylate copolymer
Ammonium carbonate
Ammonium hydroxide
Ammonium phosphate, dibasic
t-Amyl alcohol
Anethole
Apricot kernel oil
Aromatic elixir USP/NF
L-Ascorbic acid
Ascorbyl palmitate
Aspartame
Attapulgite
Barium hydroxide lime
Beeswax
Bentonite
Bentonite magma
Benzaldehyde
Benzalkonium chloride
Benzethonium chloride
Benzoic acid
Benzyl alcohol
Benzyl benzoate
BHA
BHT
Boric acid
Butane
Butyl alcohol
Butylparaben
Calcium carbonate
Calcium carboxymethyl cellulose
Calcium chloride
Calcium phosphate dibasic
Calcium phosphate dibasic dihydrate
Calcium phosphate tribasic

Calcium saccharate
Calcium saccharin
Calcium silicate
Calcium stearate
Calcium sulfate
Calcium sulfate dihydrate
Caramel
Carbomer 910
Carbomer 934
Carbomer 934P
Carbomer 940
Carbomer 941
Carbomer 1342
Carbon dioxide
Carboxymethylcellulose sodium
Carnauba
Carrageenan
Castor oil
Cellulose
Cellulose acetate
Cellulose acetate phthalate
Ceteareth-20
Cetearyl alcohol
Cetyl alcohol
Cetyl esters
Cetylpyridinium chloride
Charcoal, activated
Chlorobutanol
Chlorobutanol hemihydrate
p-Chloro-m-cresol
Cholesterol
Citric acid
Citric acid monohydrate
Cocoa butter
Corn oil
Cottonseed oil
Creatinine
m-Cresol
Croscarmellose sodium
Crospovidone
β-Cyclodextrin
Cyclomethicone
Dehydroacetic acid
Denatonium benzoate

Dextrates
Dextrin
Diacetylated monoglycerides
Diatomaceous earth
Dibutyl sebacate
Dichlorodifluoromethane
Dichlorotetrafluoroethane
Diethanolamine
Diethyl phthalate
Diisopropanolamine
Dimethicone
Dioctyl sodium sulfosuccinate
Disodium EDTA
Edetic acid
Emulsifying wax NF
Ethanolamine
Ethyl acetate
Ethylcellulose
Ethylenediamine
Ethylparaben
Ethyl vanillin
Ferric oxide
Ferrous fumarate
Fructose
Fumaric acid
Gelatin
Gentisic acid ethanolamide
D-Glucose anhyd.
Glucose, liquid
D-Glucose monohydrate
Glyceryl behenate
Glyceryl stearate
Gutta percha
Heparin sodium
Hexachlorophene
Hexylene glycol
Hydrochloric acid
Hydrogenated castor oil
Hydrogenated vegetable oil
Hydroxyethylcellulose
Hydroxypropylcellulose
Hydroxypropyl methylcellulose
Hydroxypropyl methylcellulose phthalate
8-Hydroxyquinoline sulfate
N-Hydroxysuccinic acid
Hypophosphorous acid
Isobutane
Isopropyl alcohol
Isopropyl myristate
Isopropyl palmitate
Kaolin
Lactic acid
Lactose
Lactose monohydrate
Lanolin
Lanolin alcohol
Lecithin
Magnesium aluminum silicate
Magnesium silicate
Magnesium stearate
D-Mannitol
Meglumine

Menthol
Methacrylic acid copolymer
Methyl alcohol
Methylbenzethonium chloride
Methylcellulose
Methylene chloride
Methyl isobutyl ketone
Methylparaben
Methyl salicylate
Microcrystalline cellulose
Microcrystalline wax
Mineral oil
Mono- and di-acetylated monoglycerides
Mono- and diglycerides of fatty acids
MSG
Myristyl alcohol
Nitric acid
Nitrogen
Nonoxynol-9
Nonoxynol-10
Octyldodecanol
Oleic acid
Oleth-10
Oleyl alcohol
Olive oil
Paraffin
Peanut oil
Pectin
PEG-6
PEG-8
PEG-12
PEG-20
PEG-75
PEG-35 castor oil
PEG-40 hydrogenated castor oil
PEG-40 stearate
PEG-50 stearate
PEG-55 stearate
Peppermint oil
Peppermint spirit
Petrolatum
Pharmaceutical glaze
Phenethyl alcohol
Phenol
Phenylmercuric acetate
Phenylmercuric nitrate
Phosphoric acid
Polacrilin potassium
Poloxamer 101
Polyethylene glycol
Polysorbate 20
Polysorbate 40
Polysorbate 60
Polysorbate 80
Polyvinyl acetate phthalate
Polyvinyl alcohol
Potassium benzoate
Potassium chloride
Potassium citrate
Potassium hydroxide
Potassium metabisulfite
Potassium metaphosphate

Potassium phosphate
Potassium sorbate
Propane
Propionic acid
Propylene glycol
Propylene glycol alginate
Propylene glycol diacetate
Propylene glycol stearate
Propyl gallate
Propylparaben
PVP
PVP-iodine
Rose oil
Rose water
Saccharin
Saccharin sodium
Safflower oil
Sesame oil
Shellac
Silica
Silicone emulsions
Simethicone
Soda lime
Sodium acetate anhydrous
Sodium benzoate
Sodium bicarbonate
Sodium borate
Sodium carbonate
Sodium citrate
Sodium dehydroacetate
Sodium formaldehyde sulfoxylate
Sodium hydroxide
Sodium iodide
Sodium lactate
Sodium lauryl sulfate
Sodium metabisulfite
Sodium methylparaben
Sodium phosphate
Sodium phosphate dibasic anhydrous
Sodium phosphate dibasic heptahydrate
Sodium propionate
Sodium propylparaben
Sodium starch glycolate
Sodium stearate
Sodium stearyl fumarate

Sodium thiosulfate anhydrous
Sorbic acid
Sorbitan laurate
Sorbitan oleate
Sorbitan palmitate
Sorbitan stearate
Sorbitol
Sorbitol sol'n.
Soybean oil
Squalane
Stannous fluoride
Starch
Starch, pregelatinized
Stearic acid
Stearyl alcohol
Sucrose
Sucrose octaacetate
Sugar, compressible
Sugar, confectioner's
Sugar spheres
Sulfurated potash
Sulfur dioxide
Sulfuric acid
Sweet almond oil
Syrup
Talc
Tartaric acid
Thimerosal
Thioglycerin
Thymol
Titanium dioxide
Tocopherol
Tragacanth gum
Triacetin
Trichlorofluoromethane
Triethanolamine
Triethyl citrate
Trypsin
Tyloxapol
Vanilla
Vanillin
Xanthan gum
Zein
Zinc acetate
Zinc stearate

BP Chemicals

The following chemicals that appear in this reference are listed in the British Pharmacopoeia (1993).

Acacia
Acetic acid
Acetic acid, glacial
Acetone
Acetonitrile
Acetylacetone
Agar
Albumin
Alcohol
Algin
Alginic acid
Alumina
Alumina trihydrate
Aluminum
Aluminum chloride anhydrous
Aluminum hydroxide
Aluminum sulfate
Amaranth
p-Aminobenzoic acid
2-Amino-1-butanol
Ammonia
Ammonium acetate
Ammonium bicarbonate
Ammonium carbonate
Amyl acetate
n-Amyl alcohol
Anethole
p-Anisaldehyde
Anise
Anise oil
Anthranilic acid
Antimony trichloride
L-Arabinose
L-Arginine
L-Ascorbic acid
Ascorbyl palmitate
L-Aspartic acid
Attapulgite
Balsam Peru
Barium sulfate
Beeswax
Beeswax, white
Beeswax, yellow
Bentonite

Benzaldehyde
Benzalkonium chloride
Benzocaine
Benzoic acid
Benzoin
Benzophenone
Benzoyl peroxide
Benzyl alcohol
Benzyl benzoate
Benzyl cinnamate
Benzylparaben
BHA
BHT
Bismuth subcarbonate
Boric acid
2-Bromo-2-nitropropane-1,3-diol
Butyl alcohol
n-Butylamine
Butylparaben
Caffeine
Calcium acetate
Calcium carbonate
Calcium carboxymethyl cellulose
Calcium chloride
Calcium gluconate
Calcium hydroxide
Calcium lactate
Calcium D-pantothenate
Calcium phosphate dibasic
Calcium stearate
Calcium sulfate dihydrate
Calcium sulfate hemihydrate
Caprylic acid
Caraway oil
Carbomer
Carbon dioxide
Carboxymethylcellulose
Carboxymethylcellulose sodium
Cardamom
Cardamom oil
Carnauba
Casein
Castor oil
Cellulose

CHEMICALS IN COMPLIANCE WITH PHARMACEUTICAL STANDARDS—BP

Cellulose acetate
Cellulose acetate phthalate
Cetearyl alcohol
Ceteth-20
Cetrimonium bromide
Cetyl alcohol
Cetylpyridinium chloride
Charcoal, activated
Chlorhexidine diacetate
Chlorhexidine digluconate
p-Chloroaniline
Chlorobutanol
Chlorobutanol hemihydrate
p-Chloro-m-cresol
Chloroform
Chloroxylenol
Cholecalciferol
Cholesterol
Cinnamal
Cinnamic acid
Cinnamon oil
Citral
Citric acid
Citric acid monohydrate
Clove oil
Cocoa butter
Coconut oil
Cod liver oil
Collagen
Collodion
Copper
Coriander oil
Corn oil
Corn starch
Corn starch, pregelatinized
m-Cresol
o-Cresol
Crospovidone
Cyanocobalamin
Cyclohexane
L-Cysteine
Cysteine hydrochloride anhydrous
Diatomaceous earth
Diatrizoic acid
Dibutyl phthalate
Dichlorodifluoromethane
Dichlorotetrafluoroethane
Dicyandiamide
Diethanolamine
Diethylamine
Diethyl phthalate
Dill seed oil
Dimethicone
Dimethyl sulfoxide
Dioctyl phthalate
Dioctyl sodium sulfosuccinate
1,4-Dioxane
Disodium EDTA
Dodecyl gallate
Domiphen bromide
Ethanolamine
Ethyl acetate

Ethyl acrylate
Ethyl benzoate
Ethylcellulose
Ethyl cinnamate
Ethylenediamine
Ethylene glycol dimethyl ether
Ethylene oxide
Ethylparaben
Eucalyptus oil
Eugenol
Ferrous gluconate
Ferrous sulfate
Fluorescein
Folic acid
Formaldehyde
Fructose
Fumaric acid
D-Galactose
Gallic acid
Gelatin
Gentian
Geraniol
D-Glucose anhyd.
D-Glucose monohydrate
L-Glutamic acid
Glutaral
Glycerin
Glyceryl stearate
Glycine
Glycol
Glycyrrhetinic acid
Gold
Guaiacol
Guanine
Gum benzoin
Heparin sodium
Hexachlorophene
Hexamethyldisilazane
L-Histidine
Honey
Hydriodic acid
Hydrochloric acid
Hydrochlorothiazide
Hydrogen peroxide
Hydrolyzed gelatin
Hydroquinone
Hydrotalcite
p-Hydroxybenzaldehyde
Hydroxyethylcellulose
Hydroxypropylcellulose
8-Hydroxyquinoline
N-Hydroxysuccinic acid
Hypophosphorous acid
Invert sugar
Iodine
Iodipamide
Isobutyl acetate
Isopropyl alcohol
Isopropyl myristate
Isopropyl palmitate
Isosorbide dinitrate
Kaolin

Karaya gum
Lactic acid
Lactose
Lactose monohydrate
Lanolin
Lauryl alcohol
Lemon oil
Licorice
Linalool
Linseed oil
Lipase
Lithium
L-Lysine
Magaldrate
Magnesium aluminum silicate
Magnesium carbonate
Magnesium chloride
Magnesium hydroxide
Magnesium oxide
Magnesium stearate
Magnesium sulfate anhyd.
Magnesium trisilicate
Maleic acid
Maleic anhydride
D-Mannitol
D-Mannose
Meglumine
Menthol
dl-Menthyl acetate
Mercury
Mercury acetate (ic)
Mercury oxide (ic), red and yellow
Methanesulfonic acid
DL-Methionine
L-Methionine
Methyl alcohol
Methylcellulose
Methyl hydroxyethylcellulose
Methyl laurate
Methyl myristate
Methyl oleate
Methylparaben
Methyl salicylate
Methyl stearate
Microcrystalline cellulose
Mineral oil
Morpholine
Niacinamide
Nicotinic acid
Nitric acid
o-Nitrobenzaldehyde
Nitroethane
Nitrogen
Nitromethane
Nitrous oxide
Nutmeg oil
Nylon-6
Octyl gallate
Oleic acid
Olive oil
Orange oil
Oxidized cellulose

Palmitic acid
Palm kernel oil
Paraffin
Peanut oil
PEG-6
PEG-8
PEG-20
PEG-32
PEG-4M
PEG-20M
Peppermint leaves
Peppermint oil
Peppermint spirit
Pepsin
Petrolatum
Phenol
Phenoxyacetic acid
Phenoxyethanol
Phenylmercuric borate
Phenylmercuric nitrate
Phosphoric acid
Poloxamer 188
Polyacrylamide
Polypropylene
Polysorbate 20
Polysorbate 60
Polysorbate 80
Potassium acetate
Potassium alum dodecahydrate
Potassium bromide
Potassium carbonate
Potassium chloride
Potassium citrate
Potassium hydroxide
Potassium iodide
Potassium persulfate
Potassium phosphate
Potassium sodium tartrate anhyd.
Potassium sorbate
Potassium thiocyanate
Potato starch
n-Propyl alcohol
Propylene glycol
Propyl gallate
Propylparaben
Protamine sulfate
PVP
PVP-iodine
Pyridine
Pyridoxine HCl
Pyrocatechol
Pyrogallol
Quinine sulfate dihydrate
Rapeseed oil
Riboflavin
Riboflavin-5´-phosphate sodium
Rice starch
Saccharin
Saccharin sodium
Salicylic acid
Senna extract
L-Serine

Sesame oil
Silica
Silica aerogel
Soda lime
Sodium acetate anhydrous
Sodium ascorbate
Sodium benzoate
Sodium bicarbonate
Sodium borate
Sodium borate decahydrate
Sodium butylparaben
Sodium carbonate
Sodium cetearyl sulfate
Sodium chloride
Sodium citrate
Sodium desoxycholate
Sodium dithionite
Sodium hydroxide
Sodium hypochlorite
Sodium iodide
Sodium lactate
Sodium lauryl sulfate
Sodium metabisulfite
Sodium methylparaben
Sodium nitrate
Sodium nitrite
Sodium octyl sulfate
Sodium phosphate
Sodium phosphate dibasic anhydrous
Sodium propylparaben
Sodium salicylate
Sodium starch glycolate
Sodium sulfate
Sodium sulfite
Sodium tartrate
Sodium thioglycolate
Sodium thiosulfate anhydrous
Sorbic acid
Sorbitan laurate
Sorbitan oleate
Sorbitan stearate
Sorbitol
Sorbitol sol'n.
Soybean oil
Spearmint oil
Squalane
Starch
Stearic acid

Stearyl alcohol
Sucrose
5-Sulfosalicylic acid
Sulfur dioxide
Sulfuric acid
Sulfurous acid
Sunflower seed oil
Sweet almond oil
Syrup
Talc
Tannic acid
Tapioca starch
Tartaric acid
α-Terpineol
Tetrahydrofuran
Thiamine HCl
Thiamine nitrate
Thimerosal
Thiourea
Thymol
Tin
Titanium dioxide
Tocopherol
Tocopheryl acetate
p-Toluene sulfonic acid
Tragacanth gum
Triacetin
Trichloroethylene
Trichlorofluoromethane
Triethanolamine
1,3,5-Trihydroxybenzene
Trisodium citrate
Trisodium EDTA
Trypsin
Turpentine oil
Undecylenic acid
Urea
Vanillin
Vitamin K_1
Wheat starch
Wintergreen oil
Xenon
Zinc
Zinc chloride
Zinc oxide
Zinc stearate
Zinc sulfate

Eur.Ph. Chemicals

The following chemicals that appear in this reference are listed in the European Pharmacopoeia.

Acacia
Acetic acid, glacial
Agar
Alcohol
Algin
Alginic acid
Aluminum sulfate
Anise
L-Arginine
L-Ascorbic acid
Ascorbyl palmitate
L-Aspartic acid
Balsam Peru
Beeswax
Beeswax, white
Beeswax, yellow
Bentonite
Benzalkonium chloride
Benzocaine
Benzoic acid
Benzoyl peroxide
Benzyl alcohol
Benzyl benzoate
BHT
Bismuth subcarbonate
Boric acid
Caffeine
Calcium carbonate
Calcium carboxymethyl cellulose
Calcium chloride
Calcium gluconate
Calcium lactate
Calcium D-pantothenate
Calcium phosphate dibasic
Calcium stearate
Carbon dioxide
Carboxymethylcellulose sodium
Carnauba
Castor oil
Cellulose
Cellulose acetate
Cellulose acetate phthalate
Cetearyl alcohol
Cetrimonium bromide

Cetyl alcohol
Cetylpyridinium chloride
Charcoal, activated
Chlorhexidine diacetate
Chlorhexidine digluconate
Chlorobutanol
Chlorobutanol hemihydrate
Cholecalciferol
Citric acid
Citric acid monohydrate
Corn starch
Crospovidone
Cyanocobalamin
Cysteine hydrochloride anhydrous
Diatrizoic acid
Dibutyl phthalate
Dimethicone
Dimethyl sulfoxide
Disodium EDTA
Ethyl acetate
Ethylcellulose
Ethylenediamine
Eucalyptus oil
Ferrous gluconate
Ferrous sulfate
Folic acid
Fructose
Gelatin
Gentian
D-Glucose monohydrate
Glyceryl stearate
Glycine
Heparin sodium
L-Histidine
Hydrochloric acid
Hydrochlorothiazide
Hydroxyethylcellulose
Hydroxypropylcellulose
Hydroxypropyl methylcellulose phthalate
Iodine
Isopropyl myristate
Isopropyl palmitate
Lactic acid
Lactose

Lactose monohydrate
Lanolin
Lemon oil
Licorice
Magnesium carbonate
Magnesium chloride
Magnesium hydroxide
Magnesium oxide
Magnesium stearate
Magnesium sulfate anhyd.
Magnesium trisilicate
Maleic acid
D-Mannitol
DL-Methionine
Methylcellulose
Methylparaben
Methyl salicylate
Microcrystalline cellulose
Mineral oil
Niacinamide
Nicotinic acid
Nitrous oxide
Octyl gallate
Olive oil
PEG-8
PEG-20
Peppermint leaves
Peppermint oil
Pepsin
Phenol
Phenoxyethanol
Phenylmercuric borate
Phenylmercuric nitrate
Phosphoric acid
Polysorbate 20
Polysorbate 60
Polysorbate 80
Potassium alum dodecahydrate
Potassium bromide
Potassium chloride
Potassium citrate
Potassium iodide
Potassium phosphate
Potassium sorbate
Potato starch
Propylene glycol
Propylparaben

Protamine sulfate
PVP
Quinine sulfate dihydrate
Riboflavin
Riboflavin-5´-phosphate sodium
Saccharin sodium
Salicylic acid
Sesame oil
Silica
Sodium acetate anhydrous
Sodium benzoate
Sodium bicarbonate
Sodium borate decahydrate
Sodium carbonate
Sodium cetearyl sulfate
Sodium chloride
Sodium citrate
Sodium hydroxide
Sodium iodide
Sodium lauryl sulfate
Sodium phosphate dibasic anhydrous
Sodium salicylate
Sodium sulfate
Sodium sulfite
Sodium thiosulfate anhydrous
Sorbic acid
Sorbitol
Stearyl alcohol
Sucrose
Talc
Tartaric acid
Thiamine HCl
Thiamine nitrate
Thymol
Titanium dioxide
Tocopherol
Tocopheryl acetate
Tragacanth gum
Trypsin
Undecylenic acid
Urea
Vanillin
Wheat starch
Zinc chloride
Zinc oxide
Zinc stearate
Zinc sulfate

Glossary

absorbent. A substance that can 'take up' another substance by capillary, osmotic, chemical, or solvent action.

acetylated. Any organic compound that has been heated with acetic anhydride or acetyl chloride to remove its water. Acetylated lanolins are used in hand creams and lotions. Acetic anhydride produces irritation and necrosis of tissues in the vapor state and carries a warning against contact with skin and eyes.

acid. A compound that may be either organic or inorganic and is characterized by the following properties: gives up (donates) protons to other substances; has a hydrogen ion as its positive radical in solution; contains hydrogen atoms that are replaceable by positive components; reacts with a base to form a salt and water; has a pH less than 7.0.

acidity regulator. A substance that stabilizes the acidity of pharmaceuticals.

acidulant. Any of a number of acids added to pharmaceuticals to aid in preservation, to chelate metals, and to modify taste.

adhesive. Any substance, organic or inorganic, natural or synthetic, that is capable of bonding other substances together by attachment.

adjuvant. Subsidiary ingredient or additive in a mixture that contributes to the effectiveness of the primary ingredient.

adsorbate. A powdered flavor that is made by coating a liquid flavoring onto the surface of a powdered carrier such as corn starch, salt, or maltodextrin.

adsorbent. A solid or liquid that can 'take up' on its surface, by chemical or physical forces, the molecules of gases, liquids, or dissolved substances when it is in contact with these molecules.

aerosol. A suspension of ultramicroscopic solid or liquid particles in air or gas.

alkali. One of a class of chemical compounds that combines with acids to form salts. In water solution, alkalis are bitter; turn litmus blue, and have a pH above 7.0.

alkaloid. A vegetable substance with an organic nitrogen base capable of combining with acids to form crystalline salts. Chemical alkaloids end in -ine, such as betaine from beets, caffeine from coffee beans, and cocaine from the leaves of the coca plant.

alkyl. Meaning 'from alcohol,' usually derived from alkane. Any of a series of saturated hydrocarbons, e.g., methane. The introduction of one or more alkyls into a compound makes the product more soluble.

allergen. A substance that induces allergy, by acting in the manner of an antigen on coming into contact with body tissues by inhalation, ingestion, or skin adsorption. The allergen causes a specific reagin to be formed in the bloodstream.

allergic contact dermatitis. Skin rash caused by direct contact with a substance to which the skin is sensitive. Symptoms include a red rash, swelling, and intense itching.

allergic reaction. An adverse immune response following repeated contact with otherwise harmless substances such as pollens, molds, foods, cosmetics, and drugs.

allergy. Hypersensitivity to particular substances, often resulting in cough, sneezing, headaches, rashes, or nausea.

amines. A class of organic compounds derived from ammonia.

amphoteric. A material that can display both acid and basic properties.

anaphylaxis. A hypersensitive reaction to an allergen, (as to foreign proteins or drugs) that is marked by a tendency to intense systemic reaction and that results from specific sensitization following one or more usually parenteral contacts with a sensitizing agent.

angioedema. A condition characterized by patches of swelling on the skin, mucous membranes, and sometimes viscera, and believed to be an expression of an allergy.

anhydride. A residue resulting from water being removed from a compound.

anhydrous. A substance containing no water.

anionic surfactants. A class of synthetic compounds used as emulsifiers; an anion is a negatively charged ion that is 'surface active'.

anodyne. A substance that soothes, calms, or allays pain.

antacid. A substance that counteracts acidity.

anthelmintic. A substance that expels or destroys parasitic worms.

anti-inflammatory agent. A substance used to prevent redness, heat, and swelling as a result of infection or injury.

anticaking agent. An additive used to prevent or inhibit caking of dry material and thus maintain a free-flowing condition; often used in food and pharmaceutical products that tend to be hygroscopic.

anticoagulant. A substance that hinders the clotting of blood.

antidandruff agent. A substance that is used to mitigate the formation of white or grayish greasy scales forming on and spread from skin surfaces especially of the scalp.

antifoaming agent. A substance used to reduce or prevent foaming due to proteins, gases, or nitrogenous materials that interfere with the manufacture of the product, e.g., silicones.

antigen. Any substance that provokes an immune response when introduced into the body.

antimicrobial agent. A substance that acts to destroy or inhibit the activity of microorganisms.

antioxidant. A substance that retards oxidation, deterioration, rancidity, and gum formation in organic substances.

antiperspirant. Any substance having a mild astringent action that tends to reduce the size of skin pores and thus restrain the passage of moisture on local body areas, thus retarding the flow of perspiration. An example is aluminum chlorohydrate; classified by FDA as drugs not cosmetics.

antiphlogistic agent. A substance used to counteract inflammation.

antipruritic. A substance used to counteract itching.

antiseptic. A substance that prevents or arrests the growth or action of microorganisms on living tissue.

antispasmodic. A substance used to prevent or relieve spasms or convulsions.

antitacking agent. A substance used to prevent stickiness.

antiurolitic. Preventive for urinary calculus (stones).

aromatic. A fragrant, usually pleasant, spicy, slightly pungent.

astringent. A clear liquid containing mostly alcohol, but with small amounts of other ingredients such as boric acid, alum, menthol, and/or camphor. Provides a refreshed skin feel and a tightened feeling from the evaporation of the ingredients.

azo dyes. Broad series of synthetic dyes having double-bonded nitrogens as the chromophore group. The following are azo dyes: Tartrazine, Yellow 2G, Sunset Yellow FCF, Carmoisine, Amaranth, Ponceau 4R, Red 2G, Brown FK, Chocolate Brown HT, Black PN, Pigment rubine.

balm. Usually a soothing ointment or application.

balsam. The natural exudate from a tree or plant.

base. The usually inactive ingredient of a preparation serving as the vehicle for the active medicinal principle as in the fatty base of an ointment.

binder. A substance that gives a mixture uniform adhesion, solidification, and consistency; absorbs moisture at high temperatures; e.g., tragacanth gum, glycerin, sorbitol.

bioavailability. Amount of a drug that is absorbed from an administered dosage form at a certain rate by the body.

bioequivalency. Term used in pharmaceuticals to show that two drugs work in the same way, as in a branded or generic product.

bodying agent. A viscosity or consistency-giving substance.

buccal. By mouth.

buffer. A mixture of compounds that, when added to a solution, protects it from any substantial change in pH. Such mixtures are usually in solution form and contain either a weak acid and its related salt or a mixture of two acid salts.

bulking agent. Any innocuous, inert substance used to increase mass.

capsule. A gelatin or gelatin-like container used for enclosing medicine.

carcinogen. Cancer-causing agent; any substance that causes the development of cancerous growths in living tissues.

carminative. A substance that expels gas from the alimentary canal.

carrier. A usually inactive substance used in association with an active substance especially in aiding the application of the active substance.

catalyst. Any substance that notably affects the rate of chemical reaction without being consumed or undergoing change.

cathartic. A substance used to cleanse the bowels.

CFR (Code of Federal Register). Code of federal regulations, that is a codification of the general and permanent rules published in the Federal Register by the executive department and agencies of the federal government.

chelating agent. Substances used to remove ions from solutions and soils, e.g., EDTA (ethylenediaminetetraacetic acid).

citrus oil. The essential oil obtained from the peel of a citrus fruit such as lemon, lime, or orange.

clarifying agent. A substance that aids in the removal of small particles that cloud liquids.

coagulant. A substance capable of removing colloidal material. Coagulants are used in precipitating solids or semisolids from solution, e.g., casein from milk.

coating. A film or thin layer of material that is applied to a base material called the substrate.

color, certified. Synthetic colorants certified by the FDA for safety and purity for use in foods and pharmaceuticals. May be either a dye (soluble) or a lake (insoluble).

color, natural. Any of several colors that occur naturally in plant and animal tissues.

colorant. Any substance that imparts color to another material or mixture; broadly classified as either pigments or dyes.

compatibilizer. A substance that will allow other substances to exist in close and permanent proximity to each other for an indefinite time.

complexing agent. A molecule, atom, or ion that is attached to the central atom of a coordination compound, chelate, or other complex

conditioner. A substance added to a material or other product that improves its physical state.

consistency regulator. A substance that regulates the degree of firmness, density, viscosity or resistance to movement or separation of constituent particles.

counter-irritant. An agent applied locally to produce superficial inflammation with the object of removing inflammation in deeper adjacent parts of the body.

D&C. Colors, dyes, and pigments considered safe in drugs and cosmetics when applied locally to mucous membranes or when given orally.

decolorizing agent. Any material that removes color by a physical or chemical reaction. Also refers to bleaches involving a chemical reaction for removing color.

defoaming agent. A substance that reduces or inhibits foam formation due to proteins, gases, or nitrogenous materials that may interfere with processing.

dehydrating agent. A substance that removes chemically combined water or water of hydration.

Delaney amendment. Part of a 1958 law requested by the Food and Drug Administration and written by Congressman James Delaney. The law stated that food and chemical manufacturers had to test additives before marketing them and submitting results to the FDA. The amendment specifically states that 'no additive may be permitted in any amount if the tests show that it produces cancer when fed to man or animals or by other appropriate tests.'

delayed hypersensitivity. Manifested primarily as contact dermatitis due to drugs.

demulcent. Substance usually of mucilaginous or oily character capable of soothing an inflamed or abraded mucous membrane or protecting it from irritation, e.g., tragacanth, acacia, flaxseed.

denaturant. A poisonous or unpleasant substance added to alcoholic products to make them undrinkable; also a substance that changes another substance's natural qualities or characteristics.

dental. Of or relating to teeth.

dentifrice. A powder, paste, or liquid for cleaning the teeth.

deodorants. Substances that control perspiration odors by inhibiting the growth of microorganisms that produce the malodors. *See also* Antiperspirants.

desiccant. A hygroscopic substance such as activated alumina, calcium chloride, silica gel, or zinc chloride that adsorbs water vapor from the air and can be used to maintain a dry atmosphere in drug containers.

diaper rash (ammonia dermatitis). Skin irritation caused by urine and feces or by soap and detergents left in diapers. Produces red, spotty, sore, moist skin.

diaphoretic. A substance that increases perspiration.

diluent. Any component of a color additive mixture that is not itself a color additive and has been intentionally added to facilitate the uses of the mixture.

direct compression. Process by which ingredients are blended and compressed directly into the tablet without a granulating process.

disaccharide. Carbohydrates that are formed when monosaccharide units condense, with the elimination of water.

dispersing agent. A surface active agent added to a suspending medium to provide uniform and maximum separation of extremely fine, solid particles, often of colloidal size.

dispersion. A two-phase system where one phase consists of finely divided particles (often in the colloidal size range) distributed throughout a bulk substance, the particles being the disperse or internal phase, and the bulk substance being the continuous or external phase.

distillate. The volatile material recovered by condensing the vapors of an extract or press.

distilled oil. An essential oil obtained by the distillation of the portion of a botanical material, e.g. peel, leaves, stem, containing the essential oil.

diuretic. A substance that promotes water elimination from the body via kidney function; any substance that increases or stimulates the flow of urine, e.g., beer, coffee.

drug. By definition from the FDA, a drug is a substance "intended for use in the diagnosis, cure, mitigation, prevention, or treatment of disease, or to affect the structure or function of the body".

dry granulation. Process by which ingredients are blended and compressed on tablet presses.

drying agent. Substances with the ability to absorb moisture.

efficacy. The power of a drug to produce an effect.

elixir. Sweetened, aromatic preparation that contains variable percentages of alcohol and are used either for their medicinal ingredients or in their prescriptions for their flavoring quality.

emollient. Relaxing, soothing agent used to soften the skin or internally used to soothe an irritated surface.

emulsifier. A substance that prevents the separation of immiscible substances in an emulsion; helps to distribute evenly one substance in another; used to improve texture, homogeneity, consistency, and stability.

emulsion. A liquid flavoring that is a mixture of essential oils, gum acacia and/or other gums or modified food starch in water. This is a means of utilizing the flavoring properties of an essential oil in a water-based food or pharmaceutical product; an emulsion may contain added color.

encapsulant. That which surrounds, encases, or protects, such as a capsule.

enhancer. A substance used to make greater, intensify or heighten; a flavor enhancer increases the flavor of a food without contributing any taste of its own.

enzyme. An organic catalyst for metabolic reactions.

escharotic. Caustic substance producing an eschar, a hard crust or scab.

essence oil. The oil recovered from the distillate that is obtained during the concentration of citrus juices.

essential oil. The active flavoring principles of certain botanicals such as roots, stems, leaves, and buds of spices and herbs, seeds, flowers, citrus fruit skins, and barks of certain trees. The oil is found in small sacs that are distributed throughout the plant structure concerned and normally, the oil bears close resemblance to the parent plant.

European Economic Community. *See* European Union.

European Union (EU). A federation of European countries, formerly known as the European Economic Community (EEC), organized to promote economic growth and trade; member countries are Belgium, Denmark, France, Germany, Great Britain, Greece, Ireland, Italy, Luxembourg, The Netherlands, Portugal, and Spain.

excipient. A natural, inert, and somewhat tacky material used in the pharmaceutical industry as a binder in tablets, filler, etc.

Ext. D&C. Colorants not certifiable for use in oral products but considered safe for use in externally applied products; specifically excludes colorants that may have oral toxicity.

extender. A substance added to a product in the capacity of a diluent or modifier.

extract (flavoring). An alcohol or alcohol-water solution containing a flavoring ingredient; less potent than essential oils.

extract-solid. A viscous or semisolid material obtained by first extracting the botanical material with a water-ethanol solvent and then removing the solvent almost completely. This is a liquid extract that has been concentrated.

FD&C. Colors certifiable for use in coloring foods, drugs, and cosmetics.

febrifuge. A substance that mitigates or removes fever.

fiber. A fundamental form of solid characterized by relatively high tenacity and an extremely high ratio of length to diameter.

filler. A substance added to another substance to increase bulk or weight; a material used for filling cracks or pores in another substance, such as a tablet or caplet.

fixative. A substance used to reduce the overall volatility of flavoring agents.

flavor adjuncts. Substances that are added to a flavor but are not an essential part of it; e.g., antioxidants, carriers, emulsifiers, and solvents.

flavor enhancer. A substance that will magnify, modify, or supplement the natural or original flavor, taste, or aroma of a pharmaceutical without the substance contributing significantly to that flavor.

flavor, artificial. A flavor not found in nature.

flavor, natural. A flavor derived from a natural animal or plant product.

flavoring agent. A substance added to food or pharmaceuticals to give it a specific taste; an extract or essence that imparts its flavor to food.

foam inhibitor. A food additive that prevents the formation of foam in foods during processing.

foaming agent. A substance that regulates the amount of air in a product.

Food and Drug Administration (FDA). The federal agency responsible for enforcement of the Federal Food, Drug, and Cosmetic Act.

fungicide. Any substance that kills or inhibits the growth of fungi.

gelling agent. A substance that forms stiff gels when added to water; used in food and pharmaceutical products for its thickening and water-binding properties.

generally regarded as safe (GRAS). An FDA term for a group of chemicals that by current knowledge are safe to use in food and pharmaceuticals.

gluten. Protein, found primarily in wheat, yet also in other cereal grains.

granuloma. An inflammatory tumor or growth composed of granulation tissue.

gum. A sticky substance issuing from certain trees; this substance is used for stiffening or adhesive purposes.

hematopoietic. An organic system of the body consisting of the blood and the structures that function in its production.

humectant. A liquid that absorbs moisture from the air and thus maintains constant humidity in a closed container, e.g., glycerol.

hydrate. A crystalline product made up of salts and closely associated water molecules.

hydrogenation. Any reaction of hydrogen with an organic compound. It may occur as either direct addition of hydrogen to the double bonds of unsaturated molecules, resulting in a saturated product, or it may cause rupture of the bonds of organic compounds, with subsequent reaction of hydrogen with the molecular fragments.

hygroscopic. Descriptive of a liquid or solid material that picks up atmospheric water vapor and thus acts as a drying agent.

implant. Something placed inside of tissue such as a graft, a small container, or a radioactive material for the treatment of cancer, or a pellet containing hormones to be gradually absorbed.

inert. A term used to indicate chemical inactivity in an element or a compound. Ingredients added to mixtures chiefly for bulk and weight purposes are said to be inert.

intermediate. An organic compound, either cyclic or acyclic, that may be considered a stepping stone between the parent substance and the final product.

intramuscular. Within a muscle.

intraperitoneal. Within the peritoneal cavity.

intravenous. Being within or entering by way of the veins.

isolate. An aromatic compound consisting of one ingredient isolated from a natural raw material such as menthol from peppermint oil or citral from lemongrass oil.

lake. Any of a large group of organic pigments that are composed essentially of a soluble dye rendered insoluble by the absorption on or chemical combination with an inorganic carrier.

leavening agent. A substance that is added to food or pharmaceuticals in order to achieve the following: to produce or stimulate the production of carbon dioxide; to cause fermentation.

laxative. A substance that encourages or induces a bowel movement.

Lethal Dose Fifty (LD50). A calculated dose of a material that is expected to cause the death of 50% of an entire defined experimental animal population. It is determined from the exposure to the material by any route other than inhalation of a significant number from that population.

lipotropic. Tending to prevent abnormal deposition of fats.

liquid flavoring. A flavoring in liquid form that may or may not contain a solvent.

lubricant. A material used in topicals or tablets that adds slipperiness and reduces friction, thus making it easier to apply to the skin or swallow.

lymphadenopathy. Chronically swollen lymph nodes

monosaccharide. the simplest carbohydrate consisting of one unit of water per carbon atom; monosaccharides have the general formula $C_6H_{12}O_6$, e.g., glucose.

mutagen. A chemical or physical agent that interacts with DNA and causes a mutation.

mutation. A sudden, random, permanent, genetic change; a genetic change within cells that changes its characteristics.

nebulizer. To reduce a medicinal solution to a fine spray.

neutralizer. A substance that changes the acid-alkaline balance.

oleoresin. The solid, semisolid, or heavy viscous fluid or residue obtained by solvent extraction or percolation of plant matter. Oleoresins are stronger in flavor than essential (volatile) oils and are often used to add heat to a product; also, they have very distinctive odors.

ophthalmic. Pertaining to the eyes.

oral. Of or relating to the mouth.

organoleptic. A test of food product evaluated by a sense perception (hearing, sight, smell, taste, or touch).

organs of elimination. Describes the kidneys, liver, and gastrointestinal tract.

otic. Pertaining to the ear.

oxidizing agent. An agent that causes removal of electrons; an element that gains electrons and is reduced.

parenteral. Injected or for injection subcutaneously, intramuscularly, or intravenously, e.g., glucose , saline solution.

peritoneal. Relating to the smooth, transparent serous membrane that lines the cavity of the abdomen.

pH. Symbol for the negative logarithm of the effective hydrogen-ion concentration or hydrogen-ion activity in gram equivalents per liter and used for convenience in expressing both acidity and alkalinity in a scale of 0 to 14 (acidity to alkalinity) with 7 representing neutrality as in pure water.

pharmaceutical additive, unintentional. Chemical substances found in pharmaceuticals as a result of environmental or accidental contamination.

pharmaceutical, direct (intentional). Any substance added purposely to a drug or pharmaceutical for technological purposes such as preserving the pharmaceutical from bacterial deterioration, protecting it from oxidative changes, and improving its organoleptic characteristics, or texture.

pharmaceutical. A broad term that includes not only all types of drugs and medicinal and curative products but also ancillary products such as tonics, dietary supplements, vitamins, deodorants, and the like.

pigment. A natural or synthetic inorganic or organic substance that imparts a color (including black or white) to other materials.

plasticizer. A chemical substance added to a resin to impart flexibility, workability, or distensibility.

pneumonitis. A disease characterized by inflammation of the lungs.

potentiator. Substance that imparts flavor to a much greater extent than an enhancer. The most important of these are the 5´-nucleotides, that are approved by the FDA. Potentiators do not add any taste of their own, but intensify the taste response to substances already present in the food.

powdered flavoring. A flavor that is produced either by spray-drying, adsorption, agglomeration, dry-blending, or other such process.

preservative. Substance, either natural or synthetic, that protects pharmaceuticals against spoilage, discoloration, or decay; used to retard or prevent microbial or chemical spoilage.

propellant. A liquified gas with a vapor pressure greater than 14.7 lb/in^2 at 105 F.

pulmonary. Of or affecting the lungs

pulse therapy. Intervals of low levels between 'spikes" of high levels of a drug in the bloodstream.

pungent. Describes an astringent or acrid, sharp odor or flavor.

purgative. A substance that is used to cleanse or wash away impurities.

rancid. Having a rank smell; smelling or tasting like stale fat.

rectal. Of or relating to the rectum.

reducing agent. Substance that loses electrons and is oxidized.

refrigerant. A medicine or application used to allay fever or its symptoms.

rheology control agent. A substance that affects the flow of a liquid.

rubefacient. A substance for external application that produces redness of the skin.

sedative. A drug that allays irritability, nervousness or excitement.

sequestrant. Chemical compound that reacts with metal to form a complex, thus minimizing the effect of the metal. *See also* chelating agent.

solubilizer. Agent that increases the amount of a substance that will dissolve in another substance.

solvent. Substance capable of dissolving another substance (solute) to form a uniformly dispersed mixture (solution) at the molecular or ionic size level; solvents are either polar or nonpolar.

sorbent. That which can absorb or adsorb, or a combination of the two.

stabilizer. A pharmaceutical additive that thickens, prevents separation, prevents flavor deterioration, retards oxidation by increasing the viscosity, and gives a smoother product; also prevents evaporation and deterioration of volatile flavor.

steady-state blood level. Maintaining a constant level of a drug in the blood stream during therapy.

sterilizing agent. A substance that destroys bacteria and other infectious organisms.

stiffening agent. A substance that aids in the hardening or thickening of another substance.

stimulant. Any agent or drug that temporarily increases action of any organ of the body.

stomachic. A substance that excites action in the stomach.

styptic. A substance that acts as an astringent or inhibits the oozing of blood.

subcutaneous. Beneath the skin; injected beneath the skin.

sublingual. Situated or occurring under the tongue.

suppository. Semirigid plastic designed to deliver a unit dose to a body cavity; it either melts at body temperature or dissolves in the fluids of the body cavity into which they are inserted.

surfactant. Any compound that reduces surface tension when dissolved in water or a water solution, or reduces interfacial tension between two liquids or between a liquid and a solid.

suspending agent. Substance that causes particles to mix, but remain undissolved in a liquid or solid.

suspension. System in which very small particles are more or less uniformly dispersed in a liquid or gaseous medium.

sweetening agent. A sweet tasting substance used in foods and pharmaceuticals; may be either natural or synthetic; usually having much greater sweetness intensity than sugar (sucrose), but without the caloric value, e.g., saccharin, aspartame.

sympathomimetic. Simulating sympathetic nervous action in physiological effect,

synergist. A substance which when used with another substance produces an effect that is more than additive.

synovitis. Inflammation of a synovial membrane, usually with pain and swelling of the body's joints.

syrup. An aqueous solution of sugar, usually sucrose, commonly used as a vehicle due to its taste and favorable viscosity properties; also used as demulcent.

teratogen. Any substance that affects normal development, often causing developmental anomalies; ionizing radiation may have this effect.

thickener. A substance used to impart body, improve the consistency or texture of a pharmaceutical, or to stabilize an emulsion; works by absorbing water.

tincture. Alcoholic solutions of medications

tonicity agent. A substance which invigorates, restores, freshens, or stimulates.

topical. "Applied to the skin".

troche. A medicinal tablet or lozenge usually of circular or oval form, e.g., one used as a demulcent for soreness or irritation of the throat.

urticaria. A transient skin eruption characterized by itching red or pale smooth, slightly raised patches and caused by irritation of the gastrointestinal, pulmonary, or urinary mucous membranes or from contact with an external agent and found in individuals with a peculiar sensitivity.

uv absorber. A substance which absorbs radiant energy.

vaginal. Of or relating to the vagina, the canal that leads out from the uterus

vehicle. An inert substance such as a liquid or syrup in a medicinal compound through which an active agent is administered or by which other ingredients are held together.

viscosity control agent. A substance that controls the internal resistance to flow exhibited by a fluid.

volatile oil. A substance that will evaporate quickly; responsible for the aroma, odor, and flavor found in the aqueous distillation of organic compounds of flavorings or pure spices.

wet granulation. Powdered drug and diluent are blended with a dispersion of the binder excipient (e.g., gelatin) to a consistency that can be screened to, e.g., 840-1800 µm (10-20 mesh). The coarse granules are dried on trays in hot-air ovens or fluid-bed dryers.

wetting agent. A surface active agent that, when added to water causes it to penetrate more easily into, or to spread over the surface of, another material by reducing the surface tension of the water.

World Health Organization (WHO). A branch of the United Nations concerned with international health problems. Its interests are in maintenance of nutrition, wholesomeness of foods, and consumer health.

Bibliography

Aldrich Catalog Handbook of Fine Chemicals 1994-1995. Milwaukee, WI: Aldrich Chemical Co., Inc., 1994.

Aldrich Flavors & Fragrances 1995. Milwaukee, WI: Aldrich Chemical Co., Inc., 1995.

Aleung. *Encyclopedia of Common Natural Ingredients used in Foods, Drugs, and Cosmetics.* New York: Noyes Publications, 1990.

Braun, David. *Over the Counter Pharmaceutical Formulations.* New York: Noyes Publications, 1992.

British Pharmacopoeia 1993, Volume I. London: HMSO, 1993

British Pharmacopoeia 1993, Addendum 1994. London: HMSO, 1994.

British Pharmacopoeia 1993, Addendum 1995. London: HMSO, 1995.

Budavari, Susan, editor. *The Merck Index: An Encyclopedia of Chemicals, Drugs, and Biologicals.* 11th edition. Rahway, NJ: Merck & Co, 1989.

Chaffee, Francis H., M.D. and Guy A. Settipane, M.D. "Asthma Caused by FD&C Approved Dyes." *Journal of Allergy* vol. 40, no. 2 (August 1967): 65-72.

Chernomorsky, Simon. "Quantitative Procedure for Chlorophyllin Copper Complex." *Journal of AOAC International* vol. 77, no. 3 (1994): 756-757.

Code of Federal Regulations: Food and Drugs, Title 21, Parts 170-199. Washington, DC: U.S. Government Printing Office, 1993.

Commission of the European Communities. *EINECS, European Inventory of Existing Commercial Chemical Substances, Vol. IV.* Luxembourg: Office for Official Publications of the European Communities, 1987.

Feigal, R.J., M.E. Jensen, and C.A. Mensing. "Dental Caries Potential of Liquid Medications." *Pediatrics* vol. 68 (1981): 416-419.

Fluka Chemika-Biochemika 1995/96. Buchs, Switzerland: Fluka Chemie AG, 1995.

Food and Drug Administration. *Inactive Ingredient Guide.* Washington, DC: Freedom of Information Office, October, 1993.

Gennaro, Alfonso. *Remington's Pharmaceutical Sciences.* 17th edition. Easton, PA: Mack Publishing Company, 1985.

Handbook of Nonprescription Drugs. 10th edition. Washington, DC: American Pharmaceutical Association, 1995.

Handbook of Pharmaceutical Excipients. 2nd edition. Washington, DC: American Pharmaceutical Association and RPSGB, 1994.

Heikes, David L. and John C. Craun. "Rapid Multiresidue Procedure for the Determination of Pesticides in Anhydrous Lanolin and Lanolin-Containing Pharmaceutical Preparations Utilizing Gel Permeation Chromatography Cleanup with Gas Chromatographic and Mass Spectrometric Techiques." *J. Agric. Food Chem.* vol. 40 (1992): 1586-1590.

Hilton, Alan K. and Patrick B. Deasy. "Use of Hydroxypropyl Methylcellulose Acetate Succinate in an Enteric Polymer Matrix To Design Controlled-Release Tablets of Amoxicillin Trihydrate." *Journal of Pharmaceutical Sciences*, vol. 82, no. 7 (July 1993): 737-743.

Hogue, David R., Joseph A. Zimmardi, and Kirit A. Shah. "High-Performance Liquid Chromatographic Analysis of Docusate Sodium in Soft Gelatin Capsules." *Journal of Pharmaceutical Sciences* vol. 81, no. 4 (April 1992): 359.

Hughes, Christopher C. *The Additives Guide.* New York: John Wiley and Sons, 1987.

Kim, Cherng-Ju and Ping I. Lee. "Composite Poly(vinyl alcohol) Beads for Controlled Drug Delivery." *Pharmaceutical Research* vol. 9, no. 1 (1992): 10-16.

Kumar, Ashir, Rick D. Rawlings, and Dana C. Beaman. "The Mystery Ingredients: Sweeteners, Flavorings, Dyes, and Preservatives in Analgesic/Antipyretic, Antihistamine/Decongestant, Cough and Cold, Antidiahreeal, and Liquid Theophylline Preparations." *Pediatrics.* vol. 101, no. 5 (1992).

Lewis, Richard J., Sr. *Hawley's Condensed Chemical Dictionary.* 12th edition. New York: Van Nostrand Reinhold, 1993.

Mazumder, Ramendra N, S.K. Nath, H. Ashraf, F.C. Patra, and A.N. Alam. "Oral Rehydration Solution Containing Trisodium Citrate for Treating Severe Diarrhoea: Controlled Clinical Trial." *BMJ* vol. 302 (January 1991): 88-89.

Nakagami, Hiroaki. "Solid Dispersions of Indomethacin and Griseofulvin in Non-porous Fumed Silicon Dioxide, Prepared by Melting." *Chem. Pharm. Bull.* vol. 39, no. 9 (September 1991): 2417-2421.

Napke, Edward. "Excipients, Adverse Drug Reactions and Patients' Rights." *Can. Med. Assoc. J.* vol. 151, no. 5 (1994): 529-533.

Oliva, Alexis, Honorio Armas, and José B. Fariña. "HPLC Determination of Polyethylene Glycol 400 in Urine: Oligomeric Profile in Healthy and Celiac Disease Subjects." *Clinical Chemistry* vol. 40, no. 8 (1994): 1571-1574.

Omelczuk, Marcelo O. and James W. McGinity. "The Influence of Polymer Glass Transition Temperature and Molecular Weight on Drug Release from Tablets Containing Poly(DL-lactic Acid)." *Pharmaceutical Research* vol. 9, no. 1 (1992): 26.

Physicians Desk Reference. 49th edition. Montvale, NJ: Medical Economics Data Production Co., 1995.

Physicians Desk Reference for Non-prescription Drugs. 16th edition. Montvale, NJ: Medical Economics Data Production Co., 1995.

Porzio, Michael. "Formation and Stability of Citric Acid-Sodium Citrate Solid Solutions." *Journal of Food Science* vol. 59, no. 6 (1994): 1341.

Reynolds, James. E.F., editor. *Martindale: The Extra Pharmacopoeia,* Thirtieth edition. London: The Pharmaceutical Press, 1993

Sastry, N.V., J.-M. Séquaris, and M.J. Schwuger. "Adsorption of Polyacrylic Acid and Sodium Dodecylbenzene-sulfonate on Kaolinite." *Journal of Colloid and Interface Science* vol. 171 (1995): 224-233.

Smolinske, Susan C. *Handbook of Food, Drug, and Cosmetic Excipients.* Boca Raton, FL: CRC Press, 1992.

USP 23/NF18: The United States Pharmacopeia/The National Formulary. Rockville, MD: The United States Pharmacopeial Convention, Inc., 1994.

Varia, Sailesh A., Marilia M. Faustino, Ajit B. Thakur, Charles S. Clow, and Abu T.M. Serajuddin. "Optimization of Cosolvent Concentration and Excipient Composition in a Topical Corticosteroid Solution." *Journal of Pharmaceutical Sciences.* vol. 80, no. 9 (September 1991): 872-875.

Weiner, Murray and Leonard Bernstein. *Adverse Reactions to Drug Formulation Agents: A Handbook of Excipients.* New York: Marcel Dekker, Inc., 1989.

Winter, Ruth. *A Consumer's Dictionary of Cosmetic Ingredients.* New York: Crown Trade Paperbacks, 1994.

Yalkowsky, Samuel H., Elizabeth Davis, and Terry Clark. "Stabilization of Aspartame by Polyethylene Glycol 400." *Journal of Pharmaceutical Sciences* vol. 82, no. 9 (September 1993): 978.